Chambers & Par
Directory o

CW00434758

THE LEGAL
PROFESSION
1995-96

MICHAEL CHAMBERS
Managing Editor

SIXTH EDITION

Also available on CD-ROM

Chambers & Partners Publishing
74 Long Lane, London EC1A 9ET
Tel: (0171) 606 2266

Published by Chambers & Partners Publishing
(a division of Orbach & Chambers Ltd)
74 Long Lane, London EC1A 9ET

Tel: (0171) 606 2266 Fax: (0171) 600 3191

Chambers & Partners
(Legal Recruitment): (0171) 606 9371 (Fax: 606 1793)

Copyright © Michael Chambers and Orbach & Chambers Ltd 1995
ISBN: 0-85514-105-0

Managing Editor: *Michael Chambers, barrister-at-law*

Editor: *Pauline Lyle-Smith BA LLB; solicitor, NSW and England & Wales;
attorney, NY*

Research Assistants: *Patricia Harding, barrister; Christine Henson, barrister;
Carolyn Boey LLB; John Rollason, solicitor; Adrian Murtagh, solicitor;
John Whitehead, solicitor; Abhijeet Mukherjee, barrister; Matthew Illingworth
LLB; James Dennis LLB; Mark Pollard, solicitor; Adrian Kent, barrister;
Jessima Powell, solicitor; Nicholas Graham, solicitor*

Production Editor: *Reena SenGupta*

Production Assistants: *Janis Witicki; Elaine Kitcher; Julie Garner; Richard Beavan
LLB; Gordon McBain, solicitor; Sheela Pai, solicitor; Andrew Ashmore LLM;
David Geen; Neda Sharifi, barrister; Mary Pendrill*

Database Management: *Alan Kitcher*

Cover and Page Design: *Richard Stead*

Printed in England by BPC

Acknowledgements:
We are grateful to the thousands of lawyers who assisted our research team in identifying
leading practitioners in all the main areas of law. We are also indebted to the many clients
who recommended law firms and to Chambers & Partners' recruitment consultants whose
knowledge of solicitors and law firms throughout the country was invaluable.

INNOVATIONS

The directory has changed this year. Greater emphasis is placed on leading individuals. We continue to publish our 'specialist lists' recommending law firms and sets of chambers. But now, for the first time, these lists include profiles of individual practitioners – solicitors and barristers – who have been recommended most frequently to our researchers.

Editorial policy is to identify leading practitioners on merit: it is not possible to buy a place in our biographical lists. ***Inclusion of a profile in this directory is based solely on expertise and reputation.***

Another innovation is the ranking of law-firms, chambers, and individuals, based on the findings of our ten-strong editorial team (mainly solicitors and barristers). Enormous effort has been invested in this exercise, and we are confident about the results. However, mistakes and misjudgements are inevitable, and if readers would bring them to our attention we should be very grateful. *They will be rectified when the lists are revised next year on the basis of fresh research and information.*

This edition of the directory is also being published on CD-ROM, which allows rapid search, retrieval, and cross-referencing. To provide access to the directory in all parts of the world, the CD-ROM version is being made available through the Internet.

Michael Chambers

CONTENTS *Solicitors*

CHAMBERS & PARTNERS'
DIRECTORY OF THE LEGAL PROFESSION

Solicitors' Editorial

SURVIVING THE RECESSION

DURING the worst days of 1992, when no end to the recession was in sight, the question at many partnership meetings was one of basic survival. "We didn't have a crystal ball on the meeting table," says managing partner, Michael Johns, of Nicholson Graham & Jones. "Believe me, at this point in the recession there was panic." Simon Olswang, senior partner of Olswangs, agrees: "Fear," he says, "gripped the profession." There were many who expected a wave of law-firm insolvencies. The banks, too, became anxious, faced for the first time by the prospect of having to support firms which they had always regarded as totally secure.

In the event, the worst did not happen. In fact, most law-firms did surprisingly well. The graph on this page shows how the recession affected the growth and decline of firms in London. It is based on figures for the number of solicitors employed – partners and assistants – figures supplied by the firms themselves and published in this directory in 1991 and 1994. (The league tables starting on page 957 show the number of solicitors in the larger firms in -London and the regions for each year, 1992 to 1995.)

Most striking is the difference between Group Two, which suffered an overall decline, a fall in numbers of 2 per cent, and Group Three, which succeeded in growing by 15 per cent. The decline of the Group Two firms in what was the worst recession for the legal profession in living memory is hardly surprising; what calls for an explanation is the remarkable achievement of the firms in Group Three.

Group Two consists of about 20 firms lying just below the top nine City firms. They had between 100 and 250 partners plus assistants. As a group, they suffered most from the recession, although several of them did extremely well (Ashurst Morris Crisp, for instance, which expanded by 35 per cent; Wilde Sapte, up 22 per cent; and Berwin Leighton, up 18 per cent). The high

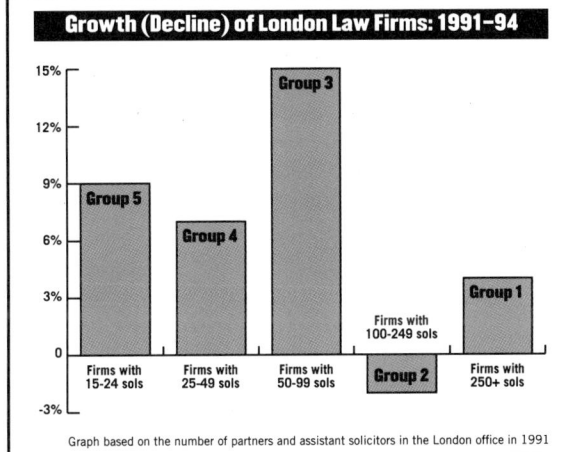

Growth (Decline) of London Law Firms: 1991–94

Graph based on the number of partners and assistant solicitors in the London office in 1991

achievers were the exception, however. More representative were firms such as Macfarlanes, Titmuss Sainer, Stephenson Harwood, and Lawrence Graham, whose numbers either remained static or fell during this period. The worst case was Turner Kenneth Brown, which declined by 38 per cent. It had a total of 117 solicitors in 1991; three years later the number was reduced to 72.

By contrast, the Group Three firms – with 50 to 100 partners and assistants – did remarkably well: firms such as Davies Arnold Cooper (which grew by 35 per cent), Travers Smith Braithwaite (up 32 per cent), Watson Farley & Williams (up 36 per cent), and Reynolds Porter Chamberlain (up 34 per cent). There is scarcely a firm in this group that declined in size: only three, in fact, out of a total of 29.

What was it about these Group Three firms that enabled them to expand during the recessionary years? Conventional wisdom predicted that firms of this size would decline. "In the late 1980s everybody was writing off medium-sized firms like ours, saying that unless we grew or merged we would die," says Tim Anderson, partner at Reynolds Porter Chamberlain. "In fact, during the recession financial growth in our firm has been 15 per cent a year."

It could be argued that many of these firms were niche practices handling recession-proof work, and in many cases this was certainly true: Davies Arnold Cooper, for instance, Hill Taylor Dickinson, and Berrymans. But other firms in this group were far from being recession-proof, and they too expanded. Travers Smith Braithwaite, for example, sustained a downturn in its non-contentious corporate practice.

The common factor shared by these Group Three firms was their size. They were not full-service firms with little room for manoeuvre. They were small enough to be flexible, to adapt rapidly to the onset of the recession, to re-focus their practices on the right niche areas;

they were small enough to act quickly. "I am sure in the larger firms it was difficult to have our kind of flexibility," says Michael Johns, of Nicholson Graham & Jones (which grew by 14 per cent). "When the partnership base is broader, it's more difficult to steer the ship on a new course."

Being smaller, however, would have been a disadvantage if it had meant that they lacked experience of top quality work, or that they did not have enough specialist lawyers. What distinguished the Group Three firms was that they were still large enough to hold their own against the Group Two firms above them. They were able to retain their clients against a head-on assault from the larger firms which were cutting their charges, low-balling, and competing for the same work, the same clientele. The so-called 'flight to quality' did not damage them. In their specialist areas, old and new, they were able to expand.

This article is based on 'The Recession in Retrospect', a 14-page survey by Michael Chambers and Patrick Wilkins, published in the July 1995 issue of *Commercial Lawyer*.

ADMINISTRATIVE & PUBLIC LAW

THE greatest part of administrative law work consists of judicial review. The last few years have seen an explosion of judicial review cases as the courts have considerably widened the range of bodies susceptible to judicial review. Bodies which may currently be subject to judicial review range from the Bank of England (*ex p. Datafin*), to University Visitors (*R v. Hull University ex parte Page*) through to the Jockey Club of Great Britain.

Solicitors who deal with judicial review work range as widely as the bodies reviewable. So, for example, judicial reviews involving immigration matters may be handled by small legal aid firms, whilst large commercial firms may deal with judicial review cases involving financial regulatory bodies. There is a tendency for strong litigious firms to be most prominent in this area.

It is worth noting that this area of practice is better known for high profile barristers rather than solicitors.

LONDON

The wide range of scenarios where judicial review may be available as a remedy is reflected in the diversity of the firms established as leaders in this area.

LEADING FIRMS – LONDON	
NABARRO NATHANSON	SHARPE PRITCHARD
BINDMAN & PARTNERS	EVERSHEDS
HERBERT SMITH	

For example, *Sharpe Pritchard*, well known for their parliamentary and public law work, have a very good reputation for administrative law. The firm carries out judicial review work for public and local authorities and professional clients. Trevor Griffiths carries out judicial review, statutory and planning appeal work, as well as local government reorganisation and compulsory competitive tendering challenges.

Nabarro Nathanson are also considered leaders in this field. David Hawkins, a partner in the planning department, has considerable experience advising local authorities on their powers and duties, including advice on the setting up of companies by authorities, equal opportunity policies and tendering procedures. The firm also acts for central govern-

ment, for education and health authorities and for overseas governments. It has acted in judicial review proceedings for British Coal on pit closures and for a university in an appeal to the House of Lords. It was also involved in judicial review proceedings on London Transport fares.

Eversheds handle judicial review proceedings for its public sector client base. John Glasson, a partner in the firm's public sector group, is highly regarded.

A firm which has developed an expertise in this area from its high profile work in civil liberties and environmental matters is *Bindman & Partners*. The firm acted in R v. Secretary of State for the Environment *ex parte* Friends of the Earth concerning water quality standards. Partner Stephen Grosz is known for his work acting for pressure groups and individuals in civil liberties and environmental cases. He was involved in the Pergau Dam Inquiry acting for the World Development movement. Geoffrey Bindman is also highly regarded in this area.

At the opposite end of the spectrum is *Herbert Smith*, whose experience in judicial review derives from its dealings with contentious matters in finance and business. The firm successfully represented the partners of PriceWaterhouse in a recent leading case on the subject of a stay of professional disciplinary proceedings. The firm has also acted on judicial review matters for the House of Fraser and Fayed Brothers. John Sissons who is on the Advisory Board of the Commercial Judicial Review Bulletin, is currently involved in judicial review proceedings on behalf of the Commissioner of Inland Revenue of Hong Kong.

HIGHLY REGARDED – LONDON	
ANTHONY GOLD, LERMAN & MUIRHEAD	T.V. EDWARDS
LEIGH DAY & CO	SCOTT-MONCRIEFF, HARBOUR & SINCLAIR
SIMMONS & SIMMONS	SLAUGHTER AND MAY
WINCKWORTH & PEMBERTON	
ASHURST MORRIS CRISP	BATES, WELLS & BRAITHWAITE
DENTON HALL	FRESHFIELDS
GOULDENS	LAWRENCE GRAHAM
LOVELL WHITE DURRANT	STEEL & SHAMASH
WILDE SAPTE	
CLIFFORD CHANCE	GREGORY, ROWCLIFFE & MILNERS

LEADING INDIVIDUALS – LONDON		
Geoffrey Bindman *Bindman & Partners*	**Martyn Day** *Leigh Day & Co*	**John Glasson** *Eversheds*
Trevor Griffiths *Sharpe Pritchard*	**Stephen Grosz** *Bindman & Partners*	**David Hawkins** *Nabarro Nathanson*
John D. Sissons *Herbert Smith*	**Richard Stein** *Leigh Day & Co*	
Richard Grandison *Slaughter and May*	**Robin Levett** *Anthony Gold, Lerman & Muirhead*	**Lucy Scott-Moncrieff** *Scott-Moncrieff, Harbour & Sinclair*
David Wilson *Simmons & Simmons*		

UP AND COMING
Deborah Gellner *T.V. Edwards*

The firms mentioned above are generally regarded to be leaders in the field although a number of other firms have also undertaken high profile judicial review work. For example *Leigh Day & Co.* has undertaken judicial review, arising mainly out of its work in environmental matters. Partners Martyn Day and Richard Stein are well regarded. Lucy Scott-Moncrieff of *Scott-Moncrieff, Harbour & Sinclair* undertakes judicial law work arising in connection with her mental health practice.

An up and coming lawyer is Deborah Gellner, an assistant at *T.V. Edwards*. She handles judicial work in connection with homelessness and immigration, and has acted in several judicial reviews which have reached the House of Lords.

SOUTH EAST

Matthew Knight of *Knights* acted for Quantock Hunt in its successful bid to overturn a hunting ban by Somerset County Council. *Pitmans* acted in Jones v. Sec. of State for Wales.

HIGHLY REGARDED – SOUTH EAST

GRIFFITH SMITH *Brighton*	KNIGHTS *Tunbridge Wells*
PITMANS *Reading*	

LEADING INDIVIDUALS – SOUTH EAST

Matthew Knight *Knights*

SOUTH WEST & WALES

Bevan Ashford has developed an expertise for administrative and public law acting for health authorities, local authorities and government agencies. In Exeter, *Stephens & Scown* has undertaken judicial review cases. Peter Smith, who advises on environmental law, recently handled a judicial review case in the House of Lords which considered the construction of the Environmental Protection Act 1990 and its application to county councils.

HIGHLY REGARDED – SOUTH WEST & WALES

BEVAN ASHFORD *Bristol*	EDWARDS GELDARD *Cardiff*
EVERSHEDS *Cardiff*	MORGAN BRUCE *Cardiff*
STEPHENS & SCOWN *Exeter*	
HUGH JAMES JONES & JENKINS *Cardiff*	

In Cardiff, *Eversheds* advise on public body powers and judicial review and are heavily involved in public sector work generally. Partner Eric Evans has experience in challenging the decisions of public bodies. A former solicitor in local government, his experience covers highways, health authorities, local government, compulsory purchase, quangos and planning.

Edwards Geldard represents public sector and quasi-governmental bodies as well as local authorities. It undertakes a wide range of work from planning issues to land assembly schemes, including compulsory purchase orders and infrastructure projects. It has also been involved in the promotion of private bills. Partner Huw Williams has been involved in proceedings concerning 'Cardiff Bay Barrage Project'. He also advises various arts organisations, including the Welsh Arts Council, on constitutional matters.

Morgan Bruce also has experience in this field and undertakes work for local and public authorities. Alun Cole advises a wide range of public bodies on the scope and effective use of their powers. He has been involved in drafting codes of practice for a major development agency.

LEADING INDIVIDUALS – SOUTH WEST & WALES

Alun B. Cole *Morgan Bruce*
Eric C. Evans *Eversheds*
Peter Smith *Stephens & Scown*
Huw R.C. Williams *Edwards Geldard*

MIDLANDS

Shakespeares has experience in this field particularly through its education law practice. *Wragge & Co* were also recommended in this context. *Martineau Johnson* has been recommended for health authority work.

Pinsent Curtis acts for NHS trusts, the Black Country Development Corporation and other public sector clients. It advises on the extent of their powers and duties, and has acted in judicial review proceedings.

HIGHLY REGARDED – MIDLANDS

MARTINEAU JOHNSON *Birmingham*	SHAKESPEARES *Birmingham*
WRAGGE & CO *Birmingham*	
PINSENT CURTIS *Birmingham*	TYNDALLWOODS *Birmingham*
BROWNE JACOBSON *Nottingham*	FREETH CARTWRIGHT HUNT DICKINS *Nottingham*

Tyndallwoods has been involved in a number of high profile judicial reviews. For example they acted for two of the applicants in R v.Ministry of Defence, *ex parte* Smith which considered whether the MOD were justified in banning homosexuals from serving in the armed forces.

EAST ANGLIA

Few firms in East Anglia claim to be specialists in administrative and public law, although all firms listed below have experience of judicial review.

HIGHLY REGARDED – EAST ANGLIA

BIRKETTS *Ipswich*	GOTELEE & GOLDSMITH *Ipswich*
HUNT & COOMBS *Peterborough*	

NORTH

Nabarro Nathanson in Doncaster were recommended for their expertise in administrative law. *Eversheds* in Leeds, which has a public sector unit, enjoys a good reputation for its expertise in this field.

LEADING FIRMS – NORTH

EVERSHEDS, LEEDS *Leeds*	**NABARRO NATHANSON** *Doncaster*

HIGHLY REGARDED – NORTH

ADDLESHAW SONS & LATHAM *Manchester*	**LACE MAWER** *Manchester*
PINSENT CURTIS	
IRWIN MITCHELL *Sheffield*	**OXLEY & COWARD** *Rotherham*

NORTHERN IRELAND

In Belfast, *Cleaver Fulton & Rankin* undertake judicial review and local government work, as do *Madden & Finucane, Carson & McDowell* and *Elliot Duffy Garrett*. In Newtownards, *JW Russel & Co* also practise in this area.

HIGHLY REGARDED – NORTHERN IRELAND

CARSON & McDOWELL *Belfast*	**CLEAVER FULTON & RANKIN** *Belfast*
ELLIOTT DUFFY GARRETT *Belfast*	**MADDEN & FINUCANE** *Belfast*
J.W. RUSSELL & CO *Newtonards*	

LEADERS IN ADMINISTRATIVE/PUBLIC LAW

LONDON

Bindman, Geoffrey
See under Civil Liberties.

Day, Martyn
See under Environmental Law.

Gellner, Deborah
T.V. Edwards, London (0171) 791 1050. Qualified 1989. Assistant 1989. Civil Department. Specialises in housing law. Born 10.2.1961.

Glasson, John
Eversheds, London (0171) 919 4500. Partner in International Private Client, Public Sector and Education Groups.
Specialisation: Main areas of practice are trusts, public sector and education law. Speaker and writer on international trusts including editorship of the encyclopedia 'International Trust Laws'. Member of the firm's public sector and education law teams. Acted in the winding up of the affairs of the Inner London Education Authority. Speaker in education law.
Prof. Membership: ELAS, STEP.
Career: Qualified in 1962, having joined *Jaques & Lewis* (now Eversheds) in 1959. Became a Partner in 1966.
Personal: Born 7th February 1936. Educated at Wellington School 1949-54, then Fitzwilliam College (formerly Fitzwilliam House), Cambridge 1956-59.

Grandison, Richard
See under Litigation (Commercial).

Griffiths, Trevor
Sharpe Pritchard, London (0171) 405 4600. Qualified 1984. Partner 1987. Specialises in judicial review, statutory and planning appeals. Born 6.12.1957.

Grosz, Stephen
Bindman & Partners, London (0171) 833 4433. Partner in Public Law and Litigation Department.
Specialisation: Specialises in public and administrative law handling applicant work on behalf of pressure groups and individuals in civil liberties and environmental cases including European Community law. Also handles respondent work on behalf of the Law Society and the Solicitors Complaints Bureau. Major clients include Friends of the Earth, the World Development Movement (the Pergau Dam case) and Amnesty International. Frequently writes articles on public law.
Prof. Membership: Administrative Law Bar Association, United Kingdom Environmental Law Association, Solicitors European Group, Executive Committee of Public Law Project and Govenor of British Institute of Human Rights.
Career: Qualified in 1978. Entire career spent at *Bindman & Partners*. Partner since 1981.
Personal: Born April 1953. Graduate in Law from Cambridge University and European Law from Université Libre de Bruxelles. Lives in London.

Hawkins, David
See under Planning.

Levett, Robin
Anthony Gold, Lerman & Muirhead, London (0171) 378 8005.

Scott-Moncrieff, Lucy
See under Health Authority.

Sissons, John D.
Herbert Smith, London (0171) 374 8000. Partner in Commercial Litigation Department.
Specialisation: Deals with all types of general commercial litigation acting for, amongst others, major publicly quoted companies, banks, regulatory authorities and firms of accountants. In particular he deals with contentious regulatory matters (including judicial review, disciplinary proceedings and commercial crime) and intellectual property (concentrating on trade mark issues).
Career: Qualified 1980. Partner at *Herbert Smith* since 1987.

Stein, Richard
Leigh Day & Co, London (0171) 242 1775. Qualified 1994. Solicitor. Specialises in judicial review of environmental regulators, government departments, etc.

Wilson, David
Simmons & Simmons, London (0171) 628 2020. Partner in Litigation Department.
Specialisation: Handles commercial litigation including insolvency, professional liability and judicial review.
Career: Qualified with *Simmons & Simmons* in 1987. Now a Partner with *Simmons & Simmons*.
Personal: Born 30th July 1963. Educated at Forest School, Southampton University and the College of Law. Leisure interests include opera and polo. Lives in London.

REGIONS

Cole, Alun B.
Morgan Bruce, Cardiff (01222) 385385. Qualified 1977. Partner 1993. Public Law Unit. Handles public law and commercial work for public bodies. Born 9.6.1951.

Evans, Eric C.
See under Planning.

Knight, Matthew
See under Defamation.

Smith, Peter
Stephens & Scown, Exeter (01392) 210700. Qualified 1980. Associate. Specialisation is the EPA 1990 as it relates to waste disposal privatisation by county councils.

Williams, Huw R.C.
See under Planning.

ADVERTISING & MARKETING

INCLUDED in this section are two kinds of 'advertising and marketing' lawyer.

First, those who practise 'pure' advertising and marketing law, namely legal clearance of copy, campaign advice, compliance with the ITC codes, the ASA's advertising and sales promotion codes and relevant provisions of the Trade Marks Act 1994, copyright and branding issues, consumer protection and contractual relations with the media and outside suppliers.

Second, corporate lawyers whose company/commercial expertise is specifically tailored to the needs of advertising and marketing agencies. Some litigators also fall into this second category.

LONDON

The two most highly recommended firms in London are *Lewis Silkin* and *Macfarlanes*.

LEADING FIRMS – LONDON

LEWIS SILKIN	MACFARLANES
THE SIMKINS PARTNERSHIP	
OLSWANG	

Stephen Groom of *Lewis Silkin* is regarded as the best advertising and marketing lawyer in the UK for advertising-related IP litigation, libel and industry regulations. Although he continues to practise in this area, he is also moving into

HIGHLY REGARDED – LONDON

BEACHCROFT STANLEYS	BRECHER & CO
CAMERON MARKBY HEWITT	CLIFFORD CHANCE
DENTON HALL	EVERSHEDS
FIELD FISHER WATERHOUSE	GARRETT & CO
HARBOTTLE & LEWIS	LAWRENCE GRAHAM
LOVELL WHITE DURRANT	MANCHES & CO
NABARRO NATHANSON	OSBORNE CLARKE
SIMMONS & SIMMONS	SLAUGHTER AND MAY
STEPHENS INNOCENT	TOWNLEYS

non-contentious work. Roger Alexander of the same firm is also highly recommended, dealing with employment issues relating to acquisitions and disposals by PR, advertising and marketing agencies.

As lawyers to Saatchi & Saatchi plc, *Macfarlanes* has recently illustrated the diverse talents required in an advertising and marketing practice. Jeremy Courtenay-Stamp and William King cover the 'pure' advertising side (see above), Robert Sutton has been busy with corporate issues, whilst Andrew Millmore has been involved in the Saatchi litigation.

The Simkins Partnership follows close behind, mainly on the strength of Charles Swan's outstanding reputation. Head of the firm's advertising group, he is a 'pure' advertising lawyer. Vanessa Hall-Smith is recommended as one of the best assistants in this sector.

Olswang is highly regarded in the market-place and, without having any 'pure' advertising lawyers, it has solid experience of all aspects of the industry. The arrival of Geraldine Proudler from *Lovell White Durrant* will further strengthen its expertise in copy-related work.

Other highly recommended firms include *Beachcroft Stanleys, Clifford Chance* and *Lawrence Graham,* whose ex-*Macfarlanes* lawyer Andrew Dobson is recommended in this field.

REGIONS

Although legal advice in relation to advertising and marketing is largely within the domain of the London practitioner, two firms in the provinces are acknowledged to have specialists who are able to provide a range of services.

HIGHLY REGARDED – REGIONS

GARRETT & CO *Leeds*	LESTER ALDRIDGE *Bournemouth*

In the South West, *Lester Aldridge* advises the financial services industry on all aspects of advertising and marketing law. Clients include one of the top ten building societies and a number of other nationally known companies.

In the North East of England, Mark Hill has been highly recommended for his expertise in the area. Having formerly

LEADING INDIVIDUALS – REGIONS

Mark Hill *Garrett & Co*

practised from the offices of *Simpson Curtis*, he has recently moved to *Garrett & Co,* which hopes to heighten its profile in the field.

LEADING INDIVIDUALS – LONDON

Roger Alexander *Lewis Silkin*	D. Jeremy Courtenay-Stamp *Macfarlanes*	Andrew Charles Dobson *Lawrence Graham*
Stephen Groom *Lewis Silkin*	William L. King *Macfarlanes*	Charles Swan *The Simkins Partnership*
Richard S. Bagehot *Field Fisher Waterhouse*	Timothy D. Birt *Osborne Clarke*	Vanessa Hall-Smith *The Simkins Partnership*
Andrew Inglis *Nabarro Nathanson*	John (Willie) H.R. Manners *Macfarlanes*	Andrew L. Millmore *Macfarlanes*
Geraldine Proudler *Olswang*	Robert H. Sutton *Macfarlanes*	Richard Thomas *Clifford Chance*
Peter Watts *Lovell White Durrant*	Ian Yonge *Manches & Co*	

UP AND COMING

Duncan Hope *Lawrence Graham*	Rafi Azim-Khan *Lewis Silkin*

LONDON

Alexander, Roger
Lewis Silkin, London (0171) 227 8000.
Qualified 1965. Partner 1965. Corporate Department. Employment work is also covered.

Bagehot, Richard S.
See under Sports Law.

Birt, Timothy D.
See under Company/Commercial.

Courtenay-Stamp, D. Jeremy
Macfarlanes, London (0171) 831 9222.
Partner in Company, Commercial and Banking Department.

Specialisation: Specialises in advertising and marketing. Acting for 5 of the top 20 advertising agencies, as well as a number of other above, below and through the line agencies. Has written articles and lectured extensively on this subject. Also advises on all aspects of commercial and intellectual property.

Prof. Memberships: City of London Law Society. Member of Commercial Law sub-committee.

Career: Qualified in 1986 while with *Macfarlanes*. Became a Partner in 1992.

Dobson, Andrew Charles
Lawrence Graham, London (0171) 379 0000. Partner in Litigation Department.

Specialisation: Specialises in all types of commercial dispute resolution, including brand protection and intellectual property. Also deals with arbitration and alternative dispute resolution involving international cross border disputes of all types. Was involved in the RHM Foods v. Bovril passing off case, Abercorn v. Compaq Computers (retention of title) and New Bullas Trading (Fixed charge on book debts).

Career: With *Macfarlanes* 1978-86. Qualified in 1980. Partner at *Knapp Fisher* 1986-87. Joined *Lawrence Graham* as a Partner in 1987.

Personal: Born 20th February 1956. Educated at Oundle School 1969-74 and St. Catharine's College, Cambridge 1974-77. Self-confessed sporting couch potato. Lives in Wandsworth.

Groom, Stephen
Lewis Silkin, London (0171) 227 8000.
Qualified 1975. Partner 1986. Litigation Department. Extensive experience in marketing services sector, in advertising law.

Hall-Smith, Vanessa
The Simkins Partnership, London (0171) 631 1050. Qualified 1993. Qualified 1993. Associate 1994. Advertising Department. Also handles immigration work.

Hope, Duncan
Lawrence Graham, London (0171) 379 0000. Solicitor in Company Commercial Department.

Specialisation: Principal area of practice is advertising and commercial law. Work includes advising on sales promotion mechanics including competitions and prize draws, promotional offers and British Codes of Advertising and Sales Promotion. Other areas of work are terms of trade, private company and business acquisitions and disposals, MBO's and MBI's. Acted in the management buy-out of the Colourcare photoprocessing business from London International Group plc (June 1994) and the disposal of the European mail order photoprocessing business of Colourcare (January 1995).

Career: Qualified in 1991. Articled (1989-91) at *Blyth Dutton* who merged with *Lawrence Graham* in February 1991.

Personal: Born 8th June 1964. Educated at Kimbolton School 1972-82 and the University of Surrey 1984-88 (BSc Hons in Russian and Soviet Studies with Law). Practitioner of close-up magic and plays tenor saxophone in a big band. Lives in Bromley.

Inglis, Andrew
Nabarro Nathanson, London (0171) 493 9933.

Azim-Khan, Rafi
Lewis Silkin, London (0171) 227 8000.
Qualified 1993. Solicitor. Intellectual Property and Advertising & Marketing Services Groups. Covers all aspects of advertising law.

King, William L.
Macfarlanes, London (0171) 831 9222.
Partner in Company, Commercial and Banking Department.

Specialisation: Media and entertainment industries, including film and television production, financing and distribution, advertising and sales promotion, merchandising copyright characters, trademark licensing and computer software licensing and development contracts. Author of a major review of the law affecting direct marketing. A member of the Government's advisory committee, The Standing Advisory Committee on Industrial Property. Was a member of the Institute of Practitioners in Advertising's Working Party on Moral Rights and put forward submissions on privacy law. Has lectured abroad on subsidies for film and TV production and distribution, on liability arising out of advertising campaigns and advertising codes for lawyers. Lectures regularly on copyright, design right and a variety of topics relevant to the press and the advertising industry.

Prof. Membership: City of London Solicitors' Company, Law Society.

Career: Qualified in 1974 while with *Macfarlanes*. Became a Partner in 1979.

Manners, John (Willie) H.R.
Macfarlanes, London (0171) 831 9222.
Qualified 1980. Partner 1987. Litigation Department. Main practice areas are property, employment and general commercial litigation.

Millmore, Andy L.
Macfarlanes, London (0171) 831 9222.
Qualified 1985. Partner 1990. Litigation Department. Specialises in advertising and marketing and its overlap with contentious intellectual property.

Proudler, Geraldine
See under Defamation.

Sutton, Robert H.
Macfarlanes, London (0171) 831 9222.
Qualified 1979. Partner 1983. Company, Commercial and Banking Department. Specialises in mergers and acquisitions, corporate finance, securities law and takeovers.

Swan, Charles
The Simkins Partnership, London (0171) 631 1050. Partner in Advertising and Marketing Department.

Specialisation: Main area of practice is advertising law, covering copy clearance, contracts, disputes, intellectual property and general advice to advertisers, their agencies and trade associations. Other area of expertise is copyright law, especially in relation to photographers, photo libraries and multimedia. Author of Butterworth's 'Encyclopaedia of Forms and Precedents' (Advertising title), co-author of 'The ABC of UK Photographic Copyright', contributor to the IPA's 'Some suggested Provisions for Use in Agency/Client Agreements' and monthly legal and regulatory bulletin, and author of numerous articles in International Media Law and trade journals. Frequent speaker at advertising, publishing and photographic trade seminars.

Career: Qualified 1983. Articled at *Woodham Smith* 1981-83 before moving to the *Speechly Bircham* litigation department. Joined *The Simkins Partnership* in 1985 and became a Partner in 1990. General Secretary of Advertising Law International.

Personal: Born 1956. Attended Cambridge University 1975-78. Leisure interests include hill walking.

Thomas, Richard
See under Parliamentary & Public Affairs.

Watts, Peter
Lovell White Durrant, London (0171) 236 0066. Qualified 1989. Corporate and Commercial Department. Specialises in sponsorship.

Yonge, Ian
Manches & Co, London (0171) 404 4433.
Partner in Commercial Department.

Specialisation: Principal area of practice is advertising and marketing law. Emphasis on advising on copy and contracts for above and below the line with a speciality in financial advertising. Also handles employment law matters. Contributes articles to specialist journals and is currently working on a book on advertising law aimed at the lay reader. Lectures on financial advertising and regularly presents in-house client seminars.

Prof. Membership: Law Society.

Career: Joined *Rubinstein Callingham Polden & Gale* in 1967, qualified in 1971 and became a Partner in 1980.

Personal: Born 18th January 1946. Attended Ealing Grammar 1959-64. Leisure pursuits include gardening, travel and reading. Lives in Haslemere.

REGIONS

Hill, Mark

Garrett & Co, Leeds (0113) 244 1954. Senior Solicitor in Intellectual Property Department and head of Marketing and Advertising Unit.

Specialisation: Main areas of practice are intellectual property and marketing and advertising. Experience covers all aspects of marketing and advertising work including: The drafting of contracts between clients and agents; branding and trade marks (including full registered trade mark prosecution service); sales promotion and advertising clearance (including under relevant legal controls and self regulatory codes of practice); comparative advertising clearance and litigation/disputes; all related intellectual property work including copyright, trade marks, passing off (unregistered trade marks), reputations (including libel), personalities and characters; Trading Standards issues (including labelling, trade descriptions and price indications); direct marketing, direct mail etc; anti-counterfeiting; sponsorship; character and personality merchandising; and full litigation service covering all aspects of the sector.

Recent experience includes: A major dispute relating to a comparative advertisement in the home improvements sector; advising on arrangements for the sponsorship of one of the UK's premier ice hockey teams by a large UK brewery; advising one of the UK's top FMCG brand owners on compliance with relevant labelling legislation; and advising a major UK retail chain on a high profile sales promotion to be run through its stores. Addressed major advertising law seminars in 1992, 1994 and 1995 and has been interviewed and quoted in the press including in the specialist marketing press.

EDITORIAL POLICY

Our policy is to identify leading practitioners entirely on merit. It is not possible to buy a place in our biographical lists: inclusion is based on a practitioner's expertise and professional reputation. The same applies to the lists of recommended law-firms and sets of chambers.

Enormous effort has been invested by our ten-strong research team (mainly solicitors and barristers) in canvassing recommendations and identifying leaders. We are confident in the overall accuracy of the results. However, mistakes and omissions are inevitable, and if readers have any suggestions regarding listings or rankings we should be very pleased to hear from them.

The lists will be revised on the basis of fresh research every year.

AGRICULTURE & BLOODSTOCK

LONDON

Clients of the London firms with expertise in agriculture work tend to be estate-owners wishing to invest in agriculture property. *Withers, Farrer & Co* and *Macfarlanes* are among the few London firms with a strong reputation in this field.

LEADING FIRMS – LONDON – AGRICULTURE	
FARRER & CO	MACFARLANES
WITHERS	

Withers advise on the acquisition and disposal of farms and farm businesses, rural land ownership and occupation, farm partnerships, share farm agreements, Common Agricultural Policy (CAP) and Agriculture Holdings Act legislation. *Farrer & Co*'s expertise covers common land and rural estate work. They have been the solicitors to the Duchy of Lancaster since 1991.

HIGHLY REGARDED – LONDON – AGRICULTURE	
CAMPBELL HOOPER	PAYNE HICKS BEACH
LEE & PEMBERTONS	
ALEXANDERS EASTON KINCH	DAWSON & CO
MAY, MAY & MERRIMANS	TITMUSS SAINER DECHERT
TROWERS & HAMLINS	

Macfarlanes act primarily for institutional investors, private estate landlords and farmers in agricultural land sales and agricultural holdings issues. It advises the five leading firms of land agents on the Agricultural Tenancies Bill. The firm also advised British Telecom on their entitlement to milk quotas on one of their farms. Another major transaction handled was the sale of Warwick Castle Park (a listed park and estate).

Also well regarded are *Campbell Hooper, Lee & Pembertons* and *Payne Hicks Beach*. The range of work undertaken by *Lee & Pembertons* includes advising on tenancies, the Agricultural Holdings Act, milk quotas, the granting of wayleaves, easements and mining leases, the sale/purchase of farms, forestry and landed estates.

Leading agricultural practitioners include Annabel Brenton *(Withers)*, Ivor Dicker *(Farrer & Co)* and John Moore *(Macfarlanes)*.

LEADING INDIVIDUALS – LONDON – AGRICULTURE
Annabel L. Brenton *Withers*
Ivor J. Dicker *Farrer & Co*
John E. Moore *Macfarlanes*
A.G.B. Cuppage *Campbell Hooper*
Damian Greenish *Lee & Pembertons*
John H. Hornby *Macfarlanes*
Christopher.R. Jessel *Farrer & Co*

SOUTH EAST

Brachers, Thomas Eggar Verrall Bowles and *White & Bowker* are among the leaders in this field. *Brachers* in Maidstone is legal advisor to the National Farmers Union (NFU) in Kent and East Sussex. *Thomas Eggar Verrall Bowles* has recently expanded its agricultural practice in Horsham. The above mentioned firms also undertake cases under the NFU legal assistance scheme.

Also highly respected is *Cole and Cole* where Chris Findley, previously an agricultural partner of *Thomas Mallam & Reeve,* comes highly recommended. The firm has considerable expertise in handling property transactions, landlord and tenant, trust and tax planning and EC legislation on milk and beef quotas.

LEADING FIRMS – SOUTH EAST – AGRICULTURE	
BRACHERS *Maidstone*	THOMAS EGGAR VERRALL BOWLES *Chichester, Horsham*
WHITE & BOWKER *Winchester*	
COLE and COLE *Oxford*	

Other well-established agricultural practices include *Furley Page Fielding & Barton, Hallett & Co, Stanley Tee & Co* and *Pryce & Co.*

HIGHLY REGARDED – SOUTH EAST – AGRICULTURE	
FURLEY PAGE FIELDING & BARTON *Canterbury*	HALLETT & CO *Ashford*
PRYCE & CO *Abingdon*	STANLEY TEE & CO *Bishop's Stortford*
CRIPPS HARRIES HALL *Tunbridge Wells*	HORWOOD & JAMES *Aylesbury*
BUSS MURTON *Tunbridge Wells*	HENMANS *Oxford*
HERBERT MALLAM GOWERS *Oxford*	LAMPORT BASSITT *Southampton*
LINNELLS *Oxford*	PARROTT & COALES *Aylesbury*
PENNINGTONS *Basingstoke*	SHARMAN & TRETHEWY *Bedford*
SPARLING BENHAM & BROUGH *Colchester*	

Stanley Tee & Co specialises in tax planning, tenancies, alternative land use and farm management agreements. *Hallett & Co* advises on share farming agreements, tied cottages, quotas and subsidies, applications and appeals for farmers, and agricultural holdings legislation. The firm also acts for the Ashford Farmers' Union and has a specialist who is a member of the Game Conservancy and the NFU.

LEADING INDIVIDUALS – SOUTH EAST – AGRICULTURE
R.J. Douglas Allan *Thomas Eggar Verrall Bowles*
C.D. Findley *Cole and Cole*
Douglas G. Horner *Brachers*
John R. Steel *White & Bowker*

Leading agricultural specialists include Douglas Allen *(Thomas Eggar Verrall Bowles)*, Christopher Findley *(Cole and Cole)*, Douglas Horner *(Brachers)* and John Steel *(White & Bowker)*.

BLOODSTOCK AND EQUINE LAW

Cripps Harries Hall is one of the few practices specialising in equine law. It acts for a wide range of professional and

amateur equestrian clients and equine organisations including the British Equestrian Federation, British Equestrian Olympic Fund and the British Equestrian Insurance Brokers Ltd. Its expertise covers the sale/purchase of riding establishments, equestrian loan agreements, disputes arising from the sale/purchase of horses, the holding of equestrian events and negligence claims against veterinary surgeons. Christopher Hall is highly regarded in this area of practice.

Consistently recommended for its bloodstock expertise is the Newbury firm of *Matthew McCloy & Partners*. Matthew McCloy is among the few practitioners with a recognised specialism in this field.

SOUTH WEST

Burges Salmon has a formidable national reputation, particularly in the field of contentious agricultural matters. It handles its own litigious work, including advocacy, and often receives instructions on contentious issues from other law firms. Its team, consisting of former barristers, has con-

siderable expertise in *inter alia,* agricultural holdings law and tax issues, tenancies, CAP, farming partnerships disputes, mixed user cases and agricultural banking. Its clients include the National Trust, Church Commissioners, Crown Estate Commissioners and the landed gentry. The firm recently represented Cricket St. Thomas in their £14m acquisition of the milk retailing and processing business of Devon Dairy. It was also involved in a ECJ quota damage case involving 400-600 farms in UK.

Other prominent firms include *Clarke Willmott & Clarke, Stephens & Scown, Thrings & Long* and *Wilsons*. *Clarke Willmott & Clarke* has a long tradition in support of the farming community in Somerset through its extensive network of offices, with an emphasis on tenancies, milk quotas and subsidies disputes. *Stephens & Scown* is the appointed NFU representative in Devon and advises on *inter alia,* CAP, tenancy law, tax planning, milk quota regulations and the development of agricultural land.

Thrings & Long serves landowners and the farming community in Avon, Gloucestershire, Wiltshire and Somerset, particularly in connection with quotas, agricultural land tribunal work, boundary disputes and tax planning. *Wilsons'* team of five partners represents some 240,000 acres of agricultural land and acts for around 50 agricultural estates. Its clients, which include a duke and four earls, are based in Wiltshire, Dorset, Yorkshire, Wales and Norfolk. The firm has recently expanded its agriculture team with the recruitment of two agricultural partners from *Fladgate Fielder*.

Leading individuals with national reputations include James Buxton, Andrew Densham, William Neville and Peter Williams, who are all from *Burges Salmon*.

BLOODSTOCK

Townsends, one of the few firms with expertise in this field, advises on all aspects of law and documentation affecting the racing industry. This includes training agreements, syndicates, purchase and sale of training and breeding establishments, letting of training properties, litigation, tax and tribunal matters. Its bloodstock clients are primarily from Lambourn, Wantage and Marlborough.

WALES

Edward Harris & Son has an excellent reputation in common land work and also handles a fair amount of manor law matters. The firm advises the Duke of Beaufort in respect of his 40,000-50,000 acres of common land.

Also highly regarded is *Jonathan Stephens & Co* particularly in the field of common land, rights of common and alternative land use. Also handled are milk and sheep quotas, agricultural tribunal work, tenancies and fish farming problems.

Other consistently recommended firms include *Margraves* (which has dealt with over 30 agricultural arbitrations on behalf of the Welsh Water Authority), *Ungoed Thomas & King* and *Price & Son* (acting primarily for farmers and handling a substantial amount of local NFU work).

HIGHLY REGARDED – WALES – AGRICULTURE		
MARGRAVES *Llandrindod Wells*	**PRICE & SON** *Haverfordwest*
UNGOED THOMAS & KING *Carmarthen*	
GABB & CO *Abergavenny*	**GREATHEAD & WHITELOCK** *Pembroke*
HUGH JAMES JONES & JENKINS *Cardiff*	

Recommended leading specialists include Edward Harris (*Edward Harris & Son*) and Jonathan Stephens (*Jonathan Stephens & Co*).

LEADING INDIVIDUALS – WALES – AGRICULTURE
Edward K. Harris *Edward Harris & Son*
Jonathan Stephens *Jonathan Stephens & Co*
David Hill *Price & Son*

MIDLANDS

The niche agricultural practice of *Arnold Thomson* has an excellent reputation. It handles the full range of agricultural matters including farm ownership, taxation, tenancies, tribunal and arbitration hearings, development work, quotas and livestock premia.

LEADING FIRMS – MIDLANDS – AGRICULTURE	
ARNOLD THOMSON *Towcester*	
ROYTHORNE & CO *Spalding*	**SHAKESPEARES** *Birmingham*
WRIGHT HASSALL & CO *Leamington Spa*	

Roythorne & Co, Shakespeares and *Wright Hassall & Co* are also highly respected in this field. *Roythorne & Co's* work includes CAP, agricultural tax planning and litigation. *Shakespeares'* expertise encompasses landlord and tenant problems, agricultural land sales, options on farmland and farm buildings, tax planning, farming partnerships and EC interpretation of CAP reforms. The firm has additionally advised the Hungarian Ministry of Agriculture and the Postgraduate Institute at Budapest on agricultural land holding, restructuring and privatisation, agricultural financing and EC interpretation.

A fair amount of *Wright Hassall & Co's* agriculture work is in connection with advice to agricultural bodies such as the NFU and the CRCSE.

Other well regarded practices include the Northampton branch of *Hewitson Becke + Shaw* (known particularly for its work for landed estates and major country landowners), *Lanyon Bowdler, Martineau Johnson* and *Morton Fisher*. *Hewitson Becke + Shaw* has significant expertise in tax plan-

ning, landlord and tenant, succession, quotas and mineral exploitation matters. The firm, additionally, has an agricultural law research department. *Lanyon Bowdler* has a substantial farm sales, milk quotas and agricultural trust workload whilst *Morton Fisher* is one of the few firms with a strong expertise in contentious matters.

HIGHLY REGARDED – MIDLANDS – AGRICULTURE	
HEWITSON BECKE + SHAW *Northampton*	**LANYON BOWDLER** *Shrewsbury*
MARTINEAU JOHNSON *Birmingham*	**MORTON FISHER** *Worcester*
BRETHERTONS *Rugby*	**CHATTERTONS** *Horncastle*
GABB & CO *Hereford*	**R. GWYNNE & SONS** *Wellington*
KNIGHT & SONS *Newcastle-under-Lyme*	**MANBY & STEWARD** *Wolverhampton*
RUSSELL & HALLMARK *Worcester*	**TALLENTS GODFREY** *Newark-on-Trent*
THURSFIELDS *Kidderminster*	**WACE MORGAN** *Shrewsbury*
WILKIN CHAPMAN *Cleethorpes*	

Leading individuals include James Arnold (*Arnold Thomson*), Nigel Davis (*Shakespeares*), Robin Ogg (*Wright Hassall & Co*), Graham Smith (*Roythorne & Co*) and Michael Thomson (*Arnold Thomson*).

LEADING INDIVIDUALS – MIDLANDS – AGRICULTURE
James R.M. Arnold *Arnold Thomson*
Michael Thomson *Arnold Thomson*
Nigel R. Davis *Shakespeares*
Robin S. Ogg *Wright Hassall & Co*
Graham C.H. Smith *Roythorne & Co*
Ian Barnett *Hewitson Becke + Shaw*
A.J. Plummer *Roythorne & Co*
James S. C. Quinn *Morton Fisher*
Jeanette L. Sharpe *Roythorne & Co*

EAST ANGLIA

Mills & Reeve has consistently been recommended as one of the market leaders, particularly for non-contentious matters. Its work covers farm tenancies and partnerships, share farming, milk quotas and farm taxation. The firm is also among a handful of practices with expertise in contentious work.

LEADING FIRMS – EAST ANGLIA – AGRICULTURE	
MILLS & REEVE *Norwich*	
HOWES PERCIVAL *Ipswich*	**TAYLOR VINTERS** *Cambridge*

Howes Percival and *Taylor Vinters* are also highly regarded. In addition to handling cases challenging and defending agricultural institutions and government bodies, *Howes Percival* advises on joint ventures, agricultural holdings disputes and representative actions on behalf of farmers. It is also known for its expertise in European agricultural matters. *Taylor Vinters'* practice covers landed estates, sales/purchases of farms, quotas, farming partnerships, crop loss claims, EC regulations and tenancies including Agricultural Holdings Act.

Other firms with well-established agricultural practices include *Bankes Ashton*, *Eversheds* (Ipswich and Norwich), *Hewitson Becke + Shaw* and *Rustons & Lloyd*. *Bankes Ashton*, based in Bury St. Edmunds, handles contract farming, tax planning, agricultural holdings and farm conveyancing.

HIGHLY REGARDED – EAST ANGLIA – AGRICULTURE	
HEWITSON BECKE + SHAW *Cambridge*	RUSTONS & LLOYD *Newmarket*
BANKES ASHTON *Bury St. Edmunds*	EVERSHEDS *Norwich*
BIRKETTS *Ipswich*	GREENE & GREENE *Bury St. Edmunds*
GREENWOODS *Peterborough*	HOOD VORES & ALLWOOD *Dereham*
LEEDS DAY *Sandy*	PALMER WHEELDON *Cambridge*
PRETTYS *Ipswich*	SPARLING BENHAM & BROUGH

Eversheds (Ipswich and Norwich) acts for around 400 farming and agricultural businesses in the Eastern region. Its expertise covers agricultural partnership disputes, EC quotas and regulations, finance, landlord and tenant, litigation (especially crop and livestock claims) and a high volume of land deals. Following the *Willcox & Co* merger in 1993, the firm also has an increasing involvement with non residents' interests in UK farming operations.

Hewitson Becke + Shaw's unit handles all agricultural land matters such as landlord and tenant, succession, AICS forms, beef herd premium and other quotas. It is one of the rare firms providing a farming audit for issues such as development, letting of surplus farm buildings and abstraction licenses.

Rustons & Lloyd has for many years been heavily involved with agricultural produce suppliers, including those of Marks & Spencer, and has over this time represented all the major Fen farmers.

LEADING INDIVIDUALS – EAST ANGLIA – AGRICULTURE	
W.D.W. Barr *Mills & Reeve*	
Richard Barker *Howes Percival*	
Penelope A.H. Elliott *Mills & Reeve*	
Adrian Horwood-Smart *Taylor Vinters*	
J.R. Barclay *Mills & Reeve*	
Jeanette A. Dennis *Taylor Vinters*	
Jeremy Heal *Howes Percival*	

Richard Barker (*Howes Percival*), William Barr (*Mills & Reeve*), Penelope Elliott (*Mills & Reeve*), Jeremy Heal (*Howes Percival*) and Adrian Horwood-Smart (*Taylor Vinters*) are among the leading specialists in this field.

BLOODSTOCK (EAST ANGLIA)

Most leading bloodstock specialists are centred in Newmarket. Among the few firms specialising in this field, *Rustons & Lloyd,* which has over 30 years of experience, and *Taylor Vinters* with a separate bloodstock department at its Newmarket office, are pre-eminent.

LEADING FIRMS – EAST ANGLIA – BLOODSTOCK	
RUSTONS & LLOYD *Newmarket*	TAYLOR VINTERS *Cambridge*
EDMONDSON HALL *Newmarket*	

Rustons & Lloyd continues to be heavily involved in advising and drafting syndication agreements, having first pioneered the concept of the syndication of thoroughbred stallions. It is also experienced in stud farm rating, bloodstock valuations, foal sharing agreements, insurance claims and bloodstock litigation. Owen Tebbs, a partner, is the Rating and Taxation advisor to the Thoroughbred Breeders Association

HIGHLY REGARDED – EAST ANGLIA – BLOODSTOCK
HEWITSON BECKE + SHAW *Newmarket*

Taylor Vinters advises the professionals in racing, particularly breeders, jockeys, trainers and bloodstock agents. The breadth of its knowledge covers syndication of stallions, doping cases, racing rules, tax, general common law and bloodstock litigation. It also handles appearances before the Disciplinary Committee of the Jockey Club.

LEADING INDIVIDUALS – EAST ANGLIA – BLOODSTOCK
Jeremy Richardson *Taylor Vinters*
Owen E. Tebbs *Rustons & Lloyd*
Mark A. Edmondson *Edmondson Hall*
Anna Hall *Edmondson Hall*

Also strongly recommended is the niche practice of *Edmonson Hall* (with a 65 % bloodstock workload), established in June 1994. They act for leading clients in the racing and breeding industry including overseas owners, bloodstock agents, trainers and jockeys (who are ranked within the top five in the country), studs, trade associations and racing charities. Work handled include the sale of race horses, foal share agreements, jockey club inquiries, stallion syndications, tax advice and arbitration referrals from the Thoroughbred Breeders Association.

Bloodstock expertise is also to be found in the Newmarket branch of *Hewitson Becke + Shaw*. It advises on all aspects of bloodstock law with a particular emphasis on property transactions and general litigation.

Jeremy Richardson (*Taylor Vinters*) and Owen Tebbs (*Rustons & Lloyd*) are among the leading bloodstock specialists.

NORTH WEST

Cartmell Shepherd has consistently been recognised as one of the leading firms. Its expertise covers quotas, agricultural land tribunals, arbitrations, landlord and tenant matters, and EU agricultural issues. It is also one of the few practices with expertise in contentious property matters. The highly respected *Oglethorpe Sturton & Gillibrand* has over 20 years experience in general agricultural work including tax planning, conveyancing, quotas and common land law. It has, additionally, handled a number of Commons Enquiries.

LEADING FIRMS – NORTH WEST – AGRICULTURE
CARTMELL SHEPHERD *Carlisle*
OGLETHORPE STURTON & GILLIBRAND *Lancaster*

Also well-regarded is *Walker Smith & Way*. It handles forestry matters as well as general agricultural work including agricultural land tribunals, arbitrations, milk quotas and farming

HIGHLY REGARDED – NORTH WEST – AGRICULTURE	
WALKER SMITH & WAY *Chester*	
COBBETT LEAK ALMOND *Manchester*	**MASON & MOORE DUTTON** *Chester*
BIRCH CULLIMORE *Chester*	**BUTCHER & BARLOW** *Bury*
GREENWOOD KYLE *Kendal*	**SENIOR CALVELEY & HARDY** *Lytham*

partnership disputes. Their clients include Staffordshire County Council and Bolesworth Estates Co Ltd. Other recommended firms include *Cobbett Leak Almond* and *Mason & Moore Dutton*. The former handles a fair amount of farmers' union work, whilst the latter advises on tenancies, tax planning and EC related issues.

Leading specialists in this field include Timothy Cartmell (*Cartmell Shepherd*) and Martin Gillibrand (*Oglethorpe Sturton & Gillibrand*).

LEADING INDIVIDUALS – NORTH WEST – AGRICULTURE
Timothy H. Cartmell *Cartmell Shepherd*
R. Martin Gillibrand *Oglethorpe Sturton & Gillibrand*
Peter Collins *Walker Smith & Way*

NORTH EAST

Dickinson Dees has an excellent reputation and is viewed as one of the leaders in agricultural law. Its practice encompasses all aspects of agricultural land ownership and land management, with particular reference to tenancies, CAP and exploitation of mineral rights. The firm additionally has recognised expertise in contentious matters.

LEADING FIRMS – NORTH EAST – AGRICULTURE
DICKINSON DEES *Newcastle upon Tyne*
WARD HADAWAY *Newcastle upon Tyne*

Ward Hadaway has also been consistently mentioned for its expertise in the non-contentious field. It has represented farmers, landowners and rural institutions in areas such as agricultural holdings, tenancies, partnerships, milk quotas, land use and tax planning.

HIGHLY REGARDED – NORTH EAST – AGRICULTURE	
BOOTH & CO. *Leeds*	**LATIMER HINKS** *Darlington*
ANDREW M. JACKSON & CO *Hull*	**EVERSHEDS** *Leeds*
ROLLIT FARRELL & BLADON *Hull*	
DENISON TILL *York*	**DIBB LUPTON BROOMHEAD** *Bradford*
EVERSHEDS *Newcastle upon Tyne*	**FORD AND WARREN** *Leeds*
HEPTONSTALLS *Goole*	**OAKLEYS** *Malton*
PINSENT CURTIS	**WILKIN CHAPMAN** *Grimsby*
WILKINSON MAUGHAN *Newcastle-upon-Tyne*	

Also recommended are *Andrew M. Jackson & Co*, *Booth & Co*, *Latimer Hinks* and *Rollit Farrell & Bladon*. The first of these acts for the landed gentry and farmers. *Booth & Co* deals primarily with landed estates and private landowners, and has represented a 14 member tenant syndicate in the acquisition of the Saltmarsh Estate (Humberside). *Latimer Hinks* handles all aspects, including landlord and tenant and quotas. *Rollit Farrell & Bladon* specialises in agricultural tenancies, tax planning, share and contract farming and milk quotas.

Eversheds (Leeds) has also developed a sound practice advising farmers and landowners on tenancies, share farming and management agreements, the sale and purchase of agricultural land (including options), quotas, mineral leases and the management of sporting rights. The firm acts for a number of larger estates in North Yorkshire and the Dales such as Darley, Cholmley, Mexborough and Tempest.

LEADING INDIVIDUALS – NORTH EAST – AGRICULTURE
R. Hume M. Hargreave *Dickinson Dees*
Christopher Hewitt *Ward Hadaway*
Alastair Morrison *Latimer Hinks*
James F. Stone *Booth & Co.*

Both Hume Hargreave (*Dickinson Dees*) and Christopher Hewitt (*Ward Hadaway*) are among the leading specialists in this field.

SCOTLAND

Edinburgh firms specialising in this field continue to maintain their traditional links with landed estates and large landowners, particularly those with strong private client portfolios.

LEADING FIRMS – SCOTLAND – AGRICULTURE	
CONNELL & CONNELL WS *Edinburgh*	
BRODIES WS *Edinburgh*	**W & J BURNESS WS** *Edinburgh*
THORNTONS WS *Dundee*	**TURNBULL, SIMSON & STURROCK** *Jedburgh*
ANDERSON STRATHERN *Edinburgh*	**DUNDAS & WILSON CS** *Edinburgh*

The Edinburgh firm of *Connell & Connell WS* has an outstanding reputation in this field, covering farm sales, landlord and tenant, quotas and partnerships. Other leading Edinburgh firms include *Brodies WS* and *W & J Burness WS*. The former's agricultural team handles tax planning, quotas, arbitration and agricultural tenancies including tenancy disputes. *W & J Burness WS'* expertise extends to taxation, agricultural tribunals and rural property matters where it advises proprietors of landed estates with let farms. Sales and purchases handled include the Grantully, Glenmoriston and Dagliesh Forest estates.

The Edinburgh based firms of *Anderson Strathern* and *Dundas & Wilson CS* have also been highly recommended. The former has over 20 years' experience in all aspects of agricultural tenancies, arbitrations and rural property matters. *Dundas & Wilson CS'* expertise covers agricultural land sales and leases, farming partnerships, quotas, forestry, minerals and all aspects of rural property law. During the past 12 months, the firm has acted in the sale/purchase of over 120,000 acres of farm/rural property with an aggregate value in excess of £22 million.

HIGHLY REGARDED – SCOTLAND – AGRICULTURE	
GRIGOR & YOUNG *Elgin*	McLEAN & STEWART *Dunblane*
McMILLAN KILPATRICK S.S.C. *Ayr*	STEWART & WATSON *Turriff*
ADAM COCHRAN *Aberdeen*	BURNETT & REID *Aberdeen*
PAULL & WILLIAMSONS *Aberdeen*	TODS MURRAY WS *Edinburgh*
BLACKADDER REID JOHNSTON *Dundee*	CONDIES *Perth*
GILLESPIE MACANDREW *Edinburgh*	KETCHEN & STEVENS WS *Edinburgh*
LINDSAYS WS *Edinburgh*	MACLAY MURRAY & SPENS *Glasgow*
McCASH & HUNTER *Perth*	MILLER HENDRY *Perth*
MUNRO & NOBLE *Inverness*	MURRAY BEITH & MURRAY *Edinburgh*
SHEPHERD & WEDDERBURN *Edinburgh*	

Moving out of Edinburgh, the leading provincial practices in agricultural matters are *Thorntons WS* and *Turnbull Simson & Sturrock*. David Laird of *Thorntons WS*, an accredited specialist is also on the Secretary of State's Panel of Agricultural Arbiters. Areas handled by *Turnbull, Simson & Sturrock* include the Agricultural Holdings Acts, farm sales, quotas, arbitrations and agricultural tax planning.

LEADING INDIVIDUALS – SCOTLAND – AGRICULTURE
Donald G. Rennie O.B.E. *Connell & Connell WS*
Alasdair G. Fox *Anderson Strathern*
Michael N.C. Gascoigne *Brodies WS*
I. Denbeigh Kirkpatrick *Turnbull, Simson & Sturrock*
David L. Laird *Thorntons WS*
Malcolm G. Strang Steel *W & J Burness WS*
David P. Sturrock *Turnbull, Simson & Sturrock*
Robert C. Turcan *Dundas & Wilson CS*
George Alpine *Paull & Williamsons*
Nicholas C. Kilpatrick *McMillan Kilpatrick S.S.C.*
James G.G. Lees *McLean & Stewart*
James McIldowie *McLean & Stewart*
William P. Mennie *Grigor & Young*
Thomas Nicol *Stewart & Watson*
Jonathan M. Robertson *Dundas & Wilson CS*

Also well regarded are *Grigor & Young, McLean & Stewart* (based in Dunblane), *McMillan Kilpatrick SSC,* specialising in agricultural sales, leases, woodlands, farming partnerships, quota sales and servitudes, and *Stewart & Watson*. These firms all have accredited agricultural law specialists. *Tods Murray WS's* expertise extends to forestry work and the acquisition, lease and disposal of rural property. The firm acts for large landowners, farmers, tenants and conservation bodies including RSPB and the Woodlands Trust. In Aberdeen, the recommended firms include *Adam Cochran, Burnett & Reid* and *Paull & Williamsons*.

Among the numerous agricultural practitioners, Alasdair Fox (*Anderson Strathern*), Michael Gascoigne (*Brodies WS*), Denbeigh Kirkpatrick (*Turnbull, Simson & Sturrock*), David Laird (*Thorntons WS*), David Sturrock (*Turnbull Stimson Sturrock*), Donald Rennie (*Connell & Connell WS*), Malcolm Strang Steel (*W & J Burness WS*) and Robert Turcan (*Dundas & Wilson CS*) are among the leading individuals in this field.

CROFTING LAW

Crofting law is becoming increasingly significant: it concerns 40% of Scotland's land, particularly the Highlands. The leaders in this field include *Anderson MacArthur & Co, MacArthur Stewart* and *Macleod & MacCallum*. They advise on all aspects of crofting law including the crofter's statutory right to purchase and the right to pass on tenancy.

LEADING FIRMS – SCOTLAND – CROFTING	
ANDERSON MACARTHUR & CO *Stornaway*	MACARTHUR STEWART *Fort William*
MACLEOD & MACCALLUM *Inverness*	

Another firm with strong crofting expertise is *Brodies WS*. The firm handles crofting litigation as well as advising on the resumption and the sale and purchase of crofts.

HIGHLY REGARDED – SCOTLAND – CROFTING
BRODIES WS *Edinburgh*

Leading individuals include Derek Flyn (*Macleod & MacCallum*), Simon Fraser (*Anderson MacArthur & Co*) and Duncan MacPhee (*MacArthur Stewart*). All three are among the few Law Society accredited specialists in crofting law.

LEADING INDIVIDUALS – SCOTLAND – CROFTING
Derek T. Flyn *Macleod & MacCallum*
Simon Fraser *Anderson MacArthur*
Duncan MacPhee *MacArthur Stewart*

LEADERS IN AGRICULTURE

LONDON

Brenton, Annabel L.
Withers, London (0171) 936 1000. Head of Property Department.

Specialisation: Principal area of work covers agricultural estates including acquisition and disposal of farms and farm businesses, advice on rural land ownership and occupation, farm partnership and share farm agreements, farm business tenancies, diversification, CAP and Agricultural Holdings legislation. Acts for many well-known landed estates. Addresses seminars regularly.

Prof. Membership: Law Society, Agricultural Law Association.

Career: Qualified in 1984 while at *Withers* and became a Partner in 1988. Head of Property Department.

Personal: Born 17th October 1958. Attended King's College, London 1977-80, then took a BCL at Oxford University, 1981. Leisure pursuits include gardening. Lives in Hadlow, Kent.

Cuppage, A.G.B.
Campbell Hooper, London (0171) 222 9070. Qualified 1973. Partner 1993. Private Client Department. Main areas of practice are agriculture, estate and tax planning and charities.

Dicker, Ivor John
Farrer & Co, London (0171) 242 2022. Partner in Property Department.

Specialisation: Covers all aspects of property work, but particularly agricultural work, acting for large landowners investing in agricultural and commercial property. Solicitor to the Duchy of Lancaster. Advisory Editor to certain volumes of 'Butterworth's Encyclopedia of Forms & Precedents'.

Prof. Membership: Agricultural Law Association.

Career: Qualified in 1978 and became a Partner in 1979. Solicitor to the Duchy of Lancaster since May 1991.

Personal: Born 12th January 1936. Lives in Horley, Surrey.

Greenish, Damian
Lee & Pembertons, London (0171) 589 1114. Partner and Head of Property Department.

Specialisation: Advises the owners of landed estates on their property portfolios. Acted in Barribal v. Everett and numerous other cases.

Prof. Membership: CLA.

Career: Qualified in 1979, having joined *Lee & Pembertons* in 1974. Became a Partner in 1980.

Personal: Born 20th December 1950. Attended Harrow 1964-69, then the University of Warwick 1969-72. Leisure interests include cricket, shooting and fishing. Lives in London.

Hornby, John H.
Macfarlanes, London (0171) 831 9222. Qualified 1980. Partner 1987. Property Department. Specialises in commercial property, related to the leisure industry and agricultural law.

Jessel, Christopher.R.
Farrer & Co, London (0171) 242 2022. Partner in Property Department.

Specialisation: Main area of practice covers rural estates, agriculture and manors. Acts on farms, common land and real estate work generally including development sales with trust and personal advice. Also covers charity and constitutional work, establishing and advising charities on parliamentary and administrative law. Author of numerous articles in professional and investment magazines. Lectures extensively in London and elsewhere.

Prof. Membership: Law Society.

Career: Joined *Farrer & Co* in 1967. Qualified in 1970. Became a Partner in 1979.

Personal: Born 16th March 1945. Attended Bryanston School 1958-63, Balliol College, Oxford 1964-67. Leisure interests include archaeology. Lives in Guildford.

Moore, John E.
Macfarlanes, London (0171) 831 9222. Qualified 1970. Partner 1979. Property Department. Specialises in agricultural law. Work includes disposals and acquisitions, landlord and tenant, healthcare. Also does commercial property law, covering investment and development work for private and public sector clients.

REGIONS

Allan, R.J. Douglas
Thomas Eggar Verrall Bowles, Horsham (01403) 269241. Qualified 1977. Partner 1979. Commercial Property Department. Main area of practice is agriculture, including property and tenancy work.

Alpine, George
Paull & Williamsons, Aberdeen (01224) 621621. Qualified 1968. Partner 1978. Private Client Department. Work includes agriculture, trusts, executries and financial management.

Arnold, James R.M.
Arnold Thomson, Towcester (01327) 350266. Qualified 1960. Partner 1990. Also taxation, tenancies, tribunals and arbitrations.

Barclay, J.R.
Mills & Reeve, Norwich +44 (0) 1603 660155. Senior Partner. Partner in Tax Planning Department.

Specialisation: Work mainly covers taxation and estate planning advice for owners of large landed estates and family companies. Qualified in 1971.

Barker, Richard
Howes Percival, Ipswich (01473) 611211. Partner in Agriculture Department.

Specialisation: Principal area of practice covers agricultural holdings, joint ventures, quotas. Other main area of work involves town and country planning in rural areas. Frequently visits the EC Commission (principally DG VI and DG XI) on a wide range of agricultural related matters. Handles cases challenging and defending agricultural institutions and government bodies. Involved in representative actions on behalf of groups of farmers. Major clients include the Meat and Livestock Commission and the Agricultural Development and Advisory Panel on Milk Quotas and Joint Ventures. Articles on joint ventures, rural planning and European issues for a number of agricultural magazines. Lectures frequently on a national basis. Charge-out rates are £100-122.50.

Prof. Membership: Law Society, Agricultural Law Association, Country Landowners, Member CLA Suffolk Branch Committee and the legal and Parliamentary Committee. Council Member of the Suffolk Agricultural Association, Chairman Suffolk Professional European Committee. Member of the Show Committee Wensleydale Agricultural Association. Member of Solicitors European Group

Career: Qualified in 1969. Partner with *Gotelee & Goldsmith* in Ipswich 1970-88, then joined *Howes Percival* as Head of Agriculture.

Personal: Born 7th September 1944. Attended Ipswich School and is now a Governor. Member of the Management Committee. Chairman of the Old Boys Club. Leisure pursuits include mountaineering, walking, gardening and Wordsworth. Lives in Ipswich.

Barnett, Ian
Hewitson Becke + Shaw, Northampton (01604) 233233. Qualified 1961. Partner 1968. Agricultural Property Division. Also deals with landed estates, commercial property and charities.

Barr, W.D.W.
Mills & Reeve, Cambridge (01223) 64422. Partner in Agriculture Department.

Specialisation: Work covers farm tenancies and partnerships, share farming, quotas and farm taxation. Co-author of 'Farm Tenancies'. Lectures frequently and contributes articles to Solicitors Journal.

Prof. Membership: Law Society, Agricultural Law Association, USA Agricultural Law Association.

Buxton, James Anthony Fowell

Burges Salmon, Bristol (0117) 939 2000. Qualified 1984. Partner 1984. Agriculture and Property Litigation Department. Principal area of practice is agricultural holdings and milk quotas. Also handles professional negligence. Born 14.3.1948.

Cartmell, Timothy Henry

Cartmell Shepherd, Carlisle (01228) 31561. Partner in Agriculture Department.

Specialisation: Work covers agricultural quotas, Landlord & Tenant matters, Agricultural Land Tribunal work, arbitrations and litigation in the Courts. Also farming legal matters generally, partnerships and private client work.

Personal: Glenalmond College 1961-66, Christ's College, Cambridge 1966-69. Articled with *Walker Martineau* in London 1970-72.

Cheal, Jonathan C.

Thrings & Long, Bath (01225) 448494. Qualified 1976. Partner 1989. Agriculture Department.

Collins, Peter

Walker Smith & Way, Chester (01244) 321111. Qualified 1968. Partner 1973. Head of Agricultural Department. Handles cases before the Agricultural Land Tribunals and Agricultural Arbitrators.

Davis, Nigel R.

Shakespeares, Birmingham (0121) 632 4199. Partner and Head of Agricultural Law Unit.

Specialisation: Handles all aspects of agricultural law. Particular expertise in landlord and tenant problems, arbitration and tribunal hearings, creation and dissolution of farming partnerships, and EC interpretation with particular reference to CAP reform generally and milk and livestock quota regimes specifically. Has advised Hungarian Ministry of Agriculture and Postgraduate Institute at Eotvos Lorand University, Budapest, on agricultural land holding, restructuring privatisation and EC interpretation. Anticipates undertaking similar work in St. Petersburg in 1995/6. Author of various articles on agricultural law and EC impact on agriculture. Considerable experience of lecturing and presenting seminars.

Prof. Membership: Founder Member of and now consultant to AgriLaw Group of Legal Practices, Agricultural Law Association (Member of Committee and Parliamentary Sub-Committee), Solicitors European Group, British Institute of International & Comparative Law, British Hungarian Law Association, Country Landowners Association, National Farmers' Union.

Career: Qualified in 1975. With *Wedlake Bell* 1972-76. Solicitor and then Partner with *Holland Rigby & Williams* 1976-85. Partner & Head of Agricultural Law Department at *Flint Bishop & Barnett* 1985-94. Joined *Shakespeares* as Partner and Head of Agricultural Law Unit in May 1994.

Personal: Born 30th November 1949. Educated at Tudor Grange Grammar School, Solihull and Fitzwilliam College, Cambridge. Secretary of the Midland Shires Aberdeen Angus Club. Vice-Chairman of the Jacob Sheep Society. Interests include the emergence and development of former U.S.S.R and Central and Eastern European countries, most sports, farming (Pedigree Aberdeen Angus cattle and Derbyshire Gritstone and Jacob sheep) and exhibiting and judging cattle and sheep. Lives in Turnditch, Belper, Derbyshire.

Dennis, Jeanette A.

Taylor Vinters, Cambridge (01223) 423444. Senior Solicitor in Agriculture Department. Secretary to AgriLaw.

Specialisation: Principal area of practice is agriculture. Work includes sales and purchases of farms and land, tenancies (including Agricultural Holdings Act 1986, Agricultural Tenancies Act 1995 and short term business leases), crop loss claims and financial arrangements for farmers. Author of articles in several periodicals. Regular Local BBC radio contributor. Charge-out rate is 95 per hour.

Prof. Membership: Cambridge Young Solicitors, Cambridge Law Society.

Career: Joined *Taylor Vinters* in 1988 and qualified in 1990. Has specialised in agricultural law since qualification.

Personal: Born 5th October 1965. Graduated from Hull University in 1987 (LL.B). Lives in Cambridge.

Densham, H. Andrew C.

Burges Salmon, Bristol (0117) 939 2000. Qualified 1965. Partner 1970. Senior Partner 1991. Agricultural Property (Litigation) Department. Specialises in agricultural holdings and EC Common Agricultural Policy problems. Born 30.11.1940.

Edmondson, Mark Andrew

Edmondson Hall, Newmarket (01638) 560 556. Founding Partner and Head of Litigation.

Specialisation: Handles a variety of matters relating to the transfer of racehorses, veterinary negligence, building disputes, personal injury, debt recovery, libel, employment and insolvency, mostly equine related. Firm also handles family & criminal work. Clients include racehorse trainers, owners, breeders, jockeys, bloodstock agents, shipping companies, stud farmers and racing charities.

Prof. Membership: Law Society, Thoroughbred Breeders Association (firm member).

Career: Qualified in 1991. Also has wide pre-qualification experience, having been in the law since 1982. Founded *Edmondson Hall* in 1994.

Personal: Born 2nd February 1963. Educated at Trent Polytecnic (LL.B 1988). Enjoys all sports. Lives in Newmarket.

Elliott, Penelope A.H.

Mills & Reeve, Cambridge + 44(0)1223

364422. Qualified 1985. Partner 1988. Agricultural Department. Handles all areas of agricultural law. Clients include landed estate owners, Oxbridge colleges and pension funds. Regular lecturer.

Findley, C.D.

Cole and Cole, Oxford (01865) 791122.

Specialisation: Farm Business Tenancy at Law and Landlord and Tenant Problems under Agricultural Holdings Act 1986 including succession applications and rent arbitrations. Advising the Tenant Farmers Association on farm tenancy reform and on the drafting and amendment of the Agricultural Tenancies Act 1995. Advising land agents, farmers and landowners regarding drafting of new farm business tenancies. Particular expertise in acting for farmers and landowners on planning matters including options for sale of development land and realisation of development potential of farmland and buildings. Advising on tax planning and the creation and dissolution of farming partnerships and companies.

Prof. Membership: Agricultural Law Association (member of Committee and Parliamentary Sub-Committee), Country Landowners Association (member of Oxfordshire Committee), National Farmers Union Tenant Farmers Association.

Career: Qualified in 1979 with *Boyce Evans & Sheppard* 1972-1980. Subsequently partner and Head of Agricultural Law Department at Thomas Mallam Oxford 1983-1993. Joined *Cole and Cole* as partner and Department Head of Agricultural Law Department.

FitzGerald, Peter Robin

See under Trusts & PTx.

Flyn, Derek T.

Macleod & MacCallum, Inverness (01463) 239393. Partner 1978. General Practice. Main area of practice is crofting law.

Fox, Alasdair G.

Anderson Strathern WS, Edinburgh (0131) 220 2345.

Specialisation: Partner in the Rural Property Department with over twenty five years experience of all aspects of rural property law. Particular expertise in the areas of agricultural landlord and tenant law and agricultural arbitrations (acting principally for arbiters but also for parties). Practice also covers advice to major estate proprietors, purchase and sale of rural estates, farms, salmon fishings, country houses, forestry and other heritable rights.

Prof. Membership: Society of Writers to H.M. Signet; Law Society of Scotland's Agricultural Law Committee.

Career: Qualified in 1969. Partner at Anderson Strathern WS since 1972. Accredited by the Law Society of Scotland as a specialist in agricultural law 1993.

Personal: Educated at Lime House School, Carlisle 1954-59, Fettes College, Edinburgh 1959-64 and at the University of Edinburgh 1964-67. Leisure pursuits include sailing, skiing, shooting and fishing. Born 1st January 1946. Lives in Edinburgh.

Fraser, Simon
Anderson MacArthur & Co, Stornoway (01851) 703356. Qualified 1981. Partner specialising in crofting law.

Gascoigne, Michael N.C.
Brodies WS, Edinburgh (0131) 228 3777. Partner in Rural Property Department.

Specialisation: Principal area of practice is agricultural law. Work includes documentation for agricultural tenancies, arbitration and litigation in relation to agricultural tenancy disputes, tax planning for farmers and agricultural quotas advice. Also experienced in crofting law, including documentation in relation to assignation, resumption, sale and purchase of crofts and litigation of crofting disputes. Lecturer on agricultural law for the Law Society of Scotland's Legal Update Courses.

Prof. Membership: Law Society of Scotland, W.S. Society, Crofting Law Group.

Career: Qualified in 1972. Legal assistant with *Brodie Cuthbertson & Watson WS* 1972-73. Partner of *Brodies WS* since 1974.

Personal: Born 1st February 1949. Educated at Blairmore School, Aberdeenshire 1957-62, Fettes College, Edinburgh 1962-67 and Aberdeen University (LL.B) 1967-70. Leisure pursuits include motorsport, stalking and gardening. Director of several motorsport administration companies. Lives in Aberlady, East Lothian.

Gillibrand, R. Martin
Oglethorpe Sturton & Gillibrand, Lancaster (01524) 67171. Partner in Agriculture Department.

Specialisation: Has over 20 years experience in general agricultural work, including agricultural tax planning and conveyancing, quotas, and law relating to common land. Also handles tax, probate and industrial conveyancing. Clerk to the General Tax Commissioners. Has handled a number of Commons Enquiries and general upland negotiations. Has addressed numerous Moorland seminars.

Prof. Membership: Agriculture Law Association, Secretary of Moorland Association.

Career: Qualified in 1972. Joined *Oglethorpe Sturton & Gillibrand* in 1972, becoming a Partner in 1973.

Personal: Born 9th October 1946. Attended Shrewsbury School 1960-65 and Pembroke College, Cambridge 1965-68. Secretary of the Moorland Association. Leisure interests include gardening and shooting. Lives in Tatham, near Lancaster.

Hall, Christopher
Cripps Harries Hall, Tunbridge Wells

(01892) 515121. Qualified 1962. Partner 1964. Private Client Department. Main areas of practice are field sports, equestrian and agriculture. Acts for the British Equestrian Federation, British Field Sports Society and many private clients involved in equestrian matters. Born 9.3.1936.

Hall, Anna
Edmondson Hall, Newmarket (01638) 560556. Partner in Bloodstock Department.

Specialisation: Acts for all sectors of bloodstock/racing industry. Acts on jockey club inquiries. Advises major racing charities, leading owners, trainers and studs.

Prof. Membership: Cambridge Law Society (Committee Member).

Career: Qualified in 1989 while at *Taylor Vinters* (Cambridge and Newmarket). Remained there until 1994 when setting up *Edmondson Hall.*

Personal: Born 26th July 1960. Leisure activities include racing and skiing. Lives in Newmarket.

Hargreave, R.Hume M.
Dickinson Dees, Newcastle upon Tyne (0191) 261 1911. Qualified 1971. Partner 1974. Property Department (Agricultural Law Unit). Main area of practice is agriculture, encompassing all aspects of land ownership and management, with particular reference to agricultural tenancies and CAP issues. Born 24.9.1940.

Harris, Edward Kynan
Edward Harris & Son, Swansea (01792) 652007. Qualified 1964. Senior Partner 1988. Practice covers the Law of Commons and the Manorial System, together with other specialised land law and agricultural law. Also countryside law, town and country planning and agricultural tenancies.

Heal, Jeremy
Howes Percival, Norwich (01603) 762103. Qualified 1967. Partner 1989. Other main area of practice is joint ventures and development consortia.

Hewitt, Christopher
Ward Hadaway, Newcastle upon Tyne (0191) 261 2651. Partner in Property Department.

Specialisation: Main emphasis on agricultural holdings, quotas, partnerships business and property law, land use and planning. Has handled a wide range of cases for farmers, landowners and rural institutions. Has spoken at conferences with the CLA, RICS and many other on agricultural law. Regular contributor to local press.

Prof. Membership: Law Society, Country Landowners Association, Agricultural Law Association.

Career: Qualified in 1971, Partner in 1987 upon joining *Ward Hadaway.*

Personal: Born 16th September 1947. Attended Sedbergh School and the University

of Newcastle-upon-Tyne. Leisure interests include music, opera and horse riding. Lives in Consett, County Durham.

Hill, David
Price & Son, Haverfordwest (01437) 765331. Qualified 1979. Partner specialising in agricultural law.

Horner, Douglas G.
Brachers, Maidstone (01622) 690691. Qualified 1969. Partner 1972. Main areas of practice are agricultural law, town planning and environmental.

Horwood-Smart, Adrian
Taylor Vinters, Cambridge (01223) 423444. Partner in Agriculture Department.

Specialisation: Principal area of practice is agriculture. Work includes landlord and tenant, contracting and management agreements, other joint farming operations, partnership arrangements, quota and set-aside transactions and the land law aspects of landed estates and farms. Regularly lectures at seminars and conferences. Charge-out rate is 135 per hour.

Prof. Membership: Law Society, Agricultural Law Association, Notaries Society.

Career: Qualified in 1977. At *Waltons & Morse* 1977-79 before joining *Taylor Vinters.* Became a Partner in 1983.

Personal: Born 25th September 1953. Educated at Marlborough College. Lives in Newmarket.

Kilpatrick, Nicholas C.
McMillan Kilpatrick S.S.C., Ayr Tel (01292) 264696 Fax (01292) 610647. Partner.

Specialisation: Main area of practice is agricultural law. Work includes buying and selling of farms, woodlands, fishings and shootings, agricultural leases, farming partnerships, quota sales and leases, wayleaves and servitudes, compulsory purchases, farm tax planning, wills and administration of farmers' estates. Also handles all general legal matters and estate agency including conveyancing, estate and trust administration, taxation, planning law and general assistance to personal and business clients. Member of Law Society's Agricultural Law Panel.

Prof. Membership: Law Society of Scotland, Society of Writers to the Signet, Law Agents Society, Associate of Scottish Agricultural Arbiters Association, NFU and SLF.

Career: Qualified in 1977. Worked at *Brodies WS* of Edinburgh 1974-77. Joined *McMillan Kilpatrick* in 1977, becoming a Partner in 1978.

Personal: Born 1953. School Governor; Vestry of local Church; Honorary Secretary and Treasurer of local charity, Company Secretary of Local Enterprise Trust, Secretary of local art gallery, married with three children.

Kirkpatrick, I. Denbeigh

Turnbull, Simson & Sturrock WS, Jedburgh (01835) 862391. Qualified 1965. Partner 1967. Principal area of practice is agriculture, including the purchase, sale and leasing of agricultural holdings and related matters. Born 15.12.1940.

Laird, David L.

Thorntons WS, Forfar (01307) 466886. Qualified 1971. Consultant 1995. Former Senior Partner. Private Client/Agriculture Department.

Lees, James G.G.

McLean & Stewart, Dunblane (01786) 823217. Qualified 1971. Partner handling all types of agricultural work.

MacPhee, Duncan

MacArthur Stewart, Fort William (01397) 702455. Qualified 1972. Partner 1981. Commercial and Domestic Conveyancing Departments.

McCloy, Matthew

Matthew McCloy & Partners, Newbury (01635) 551515. Senior Partner specialising in bloodstock and equine law.

Specialisation: Handles all aspects of legal work relating to bloodstock (i.e. racehorses) and horses generally including litigation, commercial, disciplinary tribunals, sales and purchases, breeding, ownership, etc. Also deals with sports, media and sponsorship law. Covers sports disciplinary and sponsorship work (including drug related cases), television rights (negotiation and contract) and sponsorship (negotiation and contract). Important cases handled include Naughton v. O'Callaghan and R v. The Jockey Club ex parte His Highness the Aga Khan. Clients include various bodies in racing e.g. The Jockey's Association, Federation of Bloodstocks Agents, breeding societies, etc. Also acts for the World Professional Billiards and Snooker Association and other sports bodies. Has had various articles published in magazines and newspapers, has appeared on television many times and given a number of lectures (e.g. Asian Racing Conference in Manila, 1993). Charge-out rate is £150 per hour.

Prof. Membership: Law Society.

Career: Qualified in 1974. Member of the Horseracing Advisory Council 1982-93. Society of International Thoroughbred Auctioneers since 1980 and the International Cataloguing Standards Committee since 1982. Member of the Racing Development Committee since 1992 and Director of the British Horseracing Board from 1995.

Personal: Born 7th May 1948. Educated at Radley College 1962-68 and Sandhurst 1968-70. Leisure interests include riding, fishing, shooting and gardening. Lives in Newbury.

McIldowie, James

McLean & Stewart, Dunblane (01786) 823217. Senior Partner specialising in agri-

cultural law and Inheritance tax.

sp; Accredited Expert in agricultural law, recognised by the Law Society of Scotland. Important cases include Cormack v. McIldowie's Executor [1974]. Acted for Bett Brothers, Dundee, in the development of 250 houses at Dunblane and is currently acting in relation to a gold mine being operated by Fynegold Exploration Limited (for the owner of the land which is part of Cononish farm, Tyndrum - £20 million transaction). Has many farming clients of substance throughout Scotland. Firm also has a full agency with the Halifax Building Society. Author of articles on agricultural law. Lecturer at seminars and conferences to students and the farming community. Individual charge-out rate around £80 per hour, depending on circumstances.

Career: Qualified in 1962. Appointed Partner at *McLean & Stewart* in 1963. Now Senior Partner. Honorary Sheriff since 1986.

Personal: Born 24th September 1937. Educated at Morrison's Academy, Crieff and Edinburgh University (MA, LL.B). Recreations include golf, music, theatre and all sports. Lives in Dunblane, Perthshire.

Mennie, William P.

Grigor & Young, Elgin (01343) 544077. Qualified 1960. Partner 1964. Main areas of practice are commercial and agricultural, including the malt distilling industry and environmental matters. Also handles executries and trusts. Born 11.10.1937.

Morrison, Alastair

Latimer Hinks, Darlington (01325) 381600. Partner in Commercial Property Department.

Specialisation: Main area of practice is agricultural and commercial property working for landlords and tenants on all aspects including quota work.

Prof. Membership: Agricultural Law Association (Chairman of Parliamentary Sub-Committee).

Career: Qualified 1986. Worked at *Macfarlanes* 1984-91, then *Eversheds Hepworth & Chadwick* 1991-93. Joined *Latimer Hinks* in 1993.

Neville, William J.

Burges Salmon, Bristol (0117) 939 2000. Qualified 1979. Partner 1988. Agricultural Department. Main areas of practice are common agricultural policy and agricultural holdings law. Born 6.9.1955.

Nicol, Thomas

Stewart & Watson, Turriff (01888) 563773. Qualified 1972. Partner 1975. Main area of practice is agricultural law, covering farm sale and purchase, leases and rent arbitrations. Also inheritance tax planning. Born 23.1.1949.

Ogg, Robin Stuart

Wright Hassall & Co, Leamington Spa

(01926) 886688. Qualified 1968. Partner with over 20 years experience as an agricultural law specialist.

Plummer, A.J.

Roythorne & Co, Spalding (01775) 724141. Partner in Litigation Department.

Specialisation: Main areas of practice are Landlord and Tenant litigation, particularly relating to Agricultural holdings, contentious trust matters, employment law, professional indemnity litigation. Speaker at AgriLaw seminars and other professional conferences.

Prof. Membership: ALA

Career: Qualified in 1979. Joined *Roythorne & Co* in 1976.

Quinn, James Stephen Christopher

Morton Fisher, Worcester (01905) 610410. Partner in Business Division.

Specialisation: Principal field of activity relates to Agricultural matters, including landlord and tenant issues, agreements and disputes, tribunal and arbitration work, general estate advice and quota work. Also advises on commercial property matters, including sales and purchases and commercial and agricultural estate development. Acted in Williamson v. Thompson [1980] AC 854 and McCarthy v. Bence [1990] 1 EGLR 1. Acts for landed estates and the farming community in Hereford and Worcester and Shropshire. Has spoken extensively at conferences and seminars.

Prof. Membership: Member Law Society; Agricultural Law Association; LawNet Agriculture Unit.

Career: Qualified in 1964. Joined *Morton Fisher* and became a Partner in 1964.

Personal: Born 11th July 1939. LI.BBirmingham University 1960. Leisure interests include golf, computing, caravanning and family. Is a Board Member Princes Youth Business Trust (Hereford & Worcester Region), and a member Lord Chancellor's Advisory Committee (Hereford & Worcester). Lives in Malvern.

Rennie O.B.E., Donald G.

Connell & Connell WS, Edinburgh (0131) 556 2993. Partner.

Specialisation: Main area of practice is agriculture. Handles all aspects including purchasing and selling farms, landlord and tenant quotas, professional negligence claims, and partnerships. Author of articles on the valuation of agricultural leases and succession to agricultural tenancies. Has lectured extensively at seminars organised by the Law Society of Scotland, RICS and Agricultural Law Association.

Prof. Membership: Agricultural Law Association, Scottish Lawyers' European Group, Society of Trust and Estate Practitioners.

Career: Qualified in 1972. Joined *Connell & Connell WS* in 1976, becoming a Partner in 1977. Secretary of the Scottish Agricultural Arbiters' Association since 1989; External

Examiner in Agricultural Law at Edinburgh University since 1994; Secretary of the Joint Committee of Professional Bodies on the Valuation of Agricultural Leases

Personal: Born 25th April 1947. Attended Aberdeen University (MA 1968, LLB 1970). Lives in Edinburgh.

Richardson, Jeremy

Taylor Vinters, Cambridge (01223) 423444. Partner in Bloodstock Department.

Specialisation: Provides legal services to the professionals in racing, particularly trainers, jockeys, breeders and bloodstock agents. Has thirty years' knowledge of the industry covering general common law, tax, bloodstock litigation, Syndication of Stallions charity law, employment, and conduct of inquiries at the Jockey Club involving Rules of Racing. Also specialist on Inland Revenue (Enquiry Branch) investigations. Has acted in a number of celebrated racing cases. Author of numerous articles; speaks widely, including in USA.

Personal: Born 1944. Governor of Riddlesworth Hall School. Leisure interests include racing, cricket, sailing, riding, golf, reading and television. Lives in Newmarket.

Robertson, Jonathan M.

Dundas & Wilson CS, Edinburgh (0131) 228 8000. Qualified 1986. Partner 1990. Private Client Department. Main area of practice is rural property and agricultural law. Also handles planning and environmental law. Born 25.1.1960.

Sharpe, Jeanette L.

Roythorne & Co, Spalding (01775) 724141. Partner in Conveyancing Department.

Specialisation: Main areas of practice are agricultural and commercial conveyancing, tenancy and insolvency work and environmental matters.

Prof. Membership: UKELA

Career: Qualified in 1975. Practised in the West Midlands before joining Roythorne & Co in 1988.

Personal: Attended Kesteven and Grantham Girls' School and the University of Birmingham.

Smith, Graham C.H.

Roythorne & Co, Spalding (01775) 724141. Partner in Private Client Department.

Specialisation: Main area of practice is agricultural law, including tax planning, wills and trusts, pensions, partnership and company affairs, succession planning, contracting and management agreements, CAP aspects and general advice. Author of in-house booklets 'CAP Rules; Land transfers and other problems' and 'Valuation of Agricultural Tenancies'. Contributed to 'Land; Rights and Liabilities' and assisted with 'Notes on Insolvency and Agriculture'. Founder member of AgriLaw. Speaker at AgriLaw seminars, various accountants' and surveyors' conferences and for Central Law

Training on Agricultural Law.

Prof. Membership: Agricultural Law Association, Country Landowners Association, Lincolnshire Agricultural Society, East of England Agricultural Society, Notaries Society, Association of Pension Lawyers.

Career: Qualified in 1974, having joined *Roythorne & Co.* in 1972. Notary Public 1990.

Personal: Born 19th May 1949. Attended Oundle School, then Selwyn College, Cambridge, gaining an MA and LLB. Lives in Spalding, Lincs.

Steel, John R.

White & Bowker, Winchester (01962) 844440. Qualified 1975. Partner 1977. Agriculture & Environment Team. Main areas of practice are environmental and agricultural. Born 9.5.1949.

Stephens, Jonathan

Jonathan Stephens & Co, Usk (01291) 673344. Qualified 1971. Sole Practitioner. Specialises in agricultural law, mainly in relation to family farms.

Stone, James F.

Booth & Co., Leeds (0113) 283 2000. Qualified 1981. Partner 1988. Commercial Property Department. Main areas of practice are agriculture, commercial property and property tax. Born 9.7.1957.

Strang Steel, Malcolm G.

W & J Burness WS, Edinburgh (0131) 226 2561. Partner in Private Client Department. Managing Partner.

Specialisation: Handles mainly rural property matters, including landlord and tenant, acting for proprietors of a number of landed estates with let farms. Also taxation in relation to the above. Has acted as clerk in agricultural arbitrations and in the purchase and sale of landed estates, including Grantully, Glenmoriston and Dalgliesh Forest. Also in timeshare sales of fishings at Grantully, Taymount and Carron. Has lectured on several occasions to Law Society of Scotland PQLE seminars on agricultural law and sporting law.

Prof. Membership: Agricultural Law Association, Scottish Agricultural Arbiters Association, Securities Institute.

Career: Qualified in 1972, joining *W & J Burness WS* the same year. Became Partner in 1973. Member of the Council of Law Society of Scotland 1984-90. Convener of Agricultural Law Committee of Law Society of Scotland since 1988. Member of Law and Parliamentary and Taxation Committees of Scottish Landowners Federation.

Personal: Born 24th November 1946. Educated at Eton College 1959-65, Trinity College, Cambridge 1965-68 and Edinburgh University 1968-70. Chairman of the Scottish Dyslexia Trust. Leisure pursuits include shooting, fishing, skiing, tennis and reading. Lives in Kinross.

Sturrock, David P.

Turnbull, Simson & Sturrock WS, Jedburgh (01835) 862391. Managing Partner.

Specialisation: Main area of practice is agricultural law. Handles all aspects of land ownership, Agricultural Holdings (Scotland) Acts, quotas and arbitrations. Also handles wills, succession and inheritance tax planning. Has addressed a variety of Conferences and Seminars.

Prof. Membership: Law Society of Scotland; Accredited by Law Society of Scotland as a Specialist in Agricultural Law; Writer to the Signet; Notary Public.

Career: Qualified in 1966. Joined *Turnbull, Simson & Sturrock* in 1966, becoming a Partner in 1968 and Managing Partner in 1990.

Personal: Born 16th March 1943. Attended Rugby School 1956-61 and Edinburgh University 1961-65. Lives in Jedburgh.

Tebbs, Owen E.

Rustons & Lloyd, Newmarket (01638) 661221. Qualified 1969. Senior Partner. Bloodstock specialist. Particular experience of stud farm rating having taken the leading case on the subject to the House of Lords on behalf of the Thoroughbred Breeders Association (for whom he acts as rating and taxation adviser). Member of the Taxation Committee of the British Horseracing Board.

Thomson, Michael

Arnold Thomson, Towcester (01327) 350266. Partner specialising in agriculture.

Specialisation: Main area of work covers agricultural property, development work, tenancies, quotas and livestock premia. Regularly addresses farming and professional audiences.

Prof. Membership: Agricultural Law Association, Country Landowners Association, National Farmers Union.

Career: Qualified 1981. Co-founder of *Arnold Thomson* in 1990.

Personal: Born July 1954. Attended Wrekin College 1967-71, then University College, London 1972-76. Leisure pursuits include shooting, golf and cricket. Lives in Blakesley, Northants.

Turcan, Robert C.

Dundas & Wilson CS, Edinburgh (0131) 228 8000. Qualified 1972. Partner 1973. Head of Private Client Department. Main area of practice is in private client asset protection, acting as adviser to landowners and substantial farmers. Also deals with conveyancing and agricultural law. Born 28.5.1947.

Williams, Peter Rhys

Burges Salmon, Bristol (0117) 939 2000. Qualified 1982. Partner 1987. Agricultural and Property Litigation Department. Main area of practice is agricultural work. General property litigation is also covered.

ALTERNATIVE DISPUTE RESOLUTION

ALTERNATIVE Dispute Resolution (ADR) was originally an American concept and was first introduced to the UK in 1989 by Richard Schiffer, the founder of ADR Group. Its central concept is the facilitation of out-of-court settlements by a neutral third party (a mediator) and the preservation of business relationships between disputing parties. Whilst few claim ADR will replace litigation, it already has a track record in this country that suggests its use in tandem with litigation could become very popular, as parties wary of the heavy cost of litigation turn to ADR for a quicker, cheaper way of resolving disputes.

London-based CEDR, the Centre for Dispute Resolution, was founded in 1990 and is now seen as the UK's principal ADR organisation because of its high-profile membership and the size of the settlements it mediates. Bristol-based ADR Group dominates the regions and boasts a larger membership of law firms, although these firms, and the settlements they produce, are smaller.

A requirement for disputing parties to consider ADR has now been incorporated into pre-trial checklists in the Queen's Bench and Chancery Divisions of the High Court following a Practice Direction by the Lord Chief Justice.

LONDON

HIGHLY REGARDED – LONDON

BERWIN LEIGHTON	CLIFFORD CHANCE
HOWARD KENNEDY	LEWIS SILKIN
MASONS	
CAMERON MARKBY HEWITT	GLOVERS
HERBERT SMITH	INCE & CO.
LOVELL WHITE DURRANT	NABARRO NATHANSON
PENNINGTONS	PINSENT CURTIS
SIMMONS & SIMMONS	STEPHENSON HARWOOD
WILMER CUTLER & PICKERING	

LEADING INDIVIDUALS – LONDON

Eileen Carroll	Howard Kennedy
David Miles	Glovers
Edward. Sibley	Berwin Leighton
Tony Willis	Clifford Chance
John Beechey	Clifford Chance
Henry J. Brown	Penningtons
Anthony Bunch	Masons
Arthur Marriott	Wilmer Cutler & Pickering
Mark Roe	Masons

REGIONS

HIGHLY REGARDED – REGIONS

DAVIES AND PARTNERS	Gloucester	JACKSONS	Middlesbrough
KNIGHT & SONS	Newcastle-under-Lyme	MORGAN BRUCE	Cardiff
VEALE WASBROUGH	Bristol		
ALSOP WILKINSON	Liverpool	ANDREW M. JACKSON	Hull
BARLOWS	Guildford	BEVAN ASHFORD	Bristol
BIRKETT LONG		BOND PEARCE	Plymouth
CRUTES	Newcastle-upon-Tyne	DIBB LUPTON BROOMHEAD	Birmingham
EDGE & ELLISON	Birmingham	EDWARDS GELDARD	Cardiff
FIELD SEYMOUR PARKES	Reading	FOSTER BAXTER COOKSEY	Wolverhampton
FREETH CARTWRIGHT HUNT DICKINS	Nottingham	GIRLINGS	Canterbury
HUMPHRIES KIRK	Wareham	LINNELLS	Oxford
McGRIGOR DONALD	Glasgow	MORTON FRASER MILLIGAN	Edinburgh
PUTSMANS	Birmingham	ROYTHORNE & CO	Spalding
SIMPSON & MARWICK WS	Edinburgh	WALKER SMITH & WAY	Chester
WARD GETHIN	King's Lynn	WHITE & BOWKER	Winchester

LEADING INDIVIDUALS – REGIONS

G. Leonard R. Mair	Morton Fraser Milligan
M.J. Winkworth-Smith	Dibb Lupton Broomhead

LEADERS IN ALTERNATIVE DISPUTE RESOLUTION

LONDON

Beechey, John
See under Arbitration.

Brown, Henry J.
Penningtons, London (0171) 457 3000. Consultant in Commercial and Family Departments.

Specialisation: Principal area of practice is ADR and general commercial matters including intellectual property, especially in the publishing sector, and partnerships (creation and termination). Other main area of practice is mediation and traditional family/ matrimonial work. Trained as a mediator in New York (1985). Member of pilot family mediation scheme 'Solicitors in Mediation' and related Law Society Working Party (1985-89). Mediation Consultant to City Disputes Panel on its establishment (1994). Member of Law Society ADR Working Party. Member of British Academy of Experts Committee on Language of ADR (1993). Author of Law Society's Report on ADR (1991), co-author of Brown & Marriott 'ADR Principles and Practice' (Sweet & Maxwell, 1993). Has also had articles on ADR published in several journals. Has conducted training courses and workshops for the Family Mediators Association, Centre for Dispute Resolution and College of Law and addressed a number of conferences. External Examiner in commercial law, family law and other subjects at The College of Law, Guildford and London for the LPC. Charge-out rate is around £180-£200 per hour (£120 per hour for family mediation).

Prof. Membership: Law Society, Solicitors Family Law Association, Family Mediators Association (Founder Member, 1988), Centre For Dispute Resolution, Mediation UK,

Academy of Family Mediators (US), Society of Professionals in Dispute Resolution (US), Immigration Law Practitioners' Association, Clarity.

Career: Qualified in South Africa, 1962. Partner *Frank Bernadt & Joffe*, Cape Town, S. Africa 1962-71. Articled at *Courts & Co*, London W1 1971-75. Qualified in England & Wales 1975. Established *Simanowitz & Brown* in 1975. Partner, following merger, at *Birkbeck Montagu's* 1980-91. Partner (again following merger) at *Penningtons* 1991-94. Consultant from 1994.

Personal: Born 29th May 1939. Educated at the University of Cape Town (Diploma in Law, 1959) and the University of South Africa (part-time) (BA, 1967). Certificate in the Fundamentals of Psychotherapy and Counselling (Regents College, 1994). Accredited Mediator (CEDR) and Family Mediator (FMA). Interests include reading, writing, walking and music. Lives in London.

Bunch, Anthony
See under Construction & Civil Engineering.

Carroll, Eileen
Howard Kennedy, London (0171) 636 1616. Partner in International Department.

Specialisation: Principal area of practice is international arbitration and resolution of international disputes.
Has 15 years' experience, advising a number of overseas clients, particularly US clients, on international disputes. Active user of dispute resolution techniques. Frequently advises drafting of international contracts. Spearheaded the setting up of the Centre for Dispute Resolution in London. Has also advised multinationals in negotiation with Lloyd's Insurance Market. Accredited mediator.

Marriott, Arthur
See under Arbitration.

Miles, David
See under Construction & Civil Engineering.

Roe, Mark
Masons, London (0171) 490 4000. Mark Row @ Masons.Con. Partner specialising in dispute resolution in the Construction and Information Technology Industries.

Specialisation: Information Technology with particular regard to project management and implementation of software. Also expert in resolution of disputes in the building and civil engineering industries both in the UK and abroad. Has advised upon the resolution of disputes by mediation and mini-trial/structured settlement, arbitration and mediation and acted successfully as a mediator. Author of articles of ADR, speaks regularly on ADR, project management and construction law matters.

Prof. Membership: ORSA Committee Member, Director of CEDR, Accredited Mediator.

Career: Qualified 1981. Joined Masons in 1981. Partner of Masons since 1985.

Personal: Born 30th May 1955. Attended the John Fisher School 1965-73, Baillol College, Oxford 1974-77. Leisure interests include rugby, tennis, cycling, skiing, theatre and furniture, jewelry and textiles of the arts and crafts movement. Lives in Central London.

Sibley, Edward.
Berwin Leighton, London (0171) 623 3144. Partner in Litigation Department.

Specialisation: Principal area of practice is international civil litigation, including insurance and re-insurance disputes and international civil fraud. Also handles domestic civil litigation in the same areas and in professional negligence, fraud and property related areas. Acted in CTI v. Oceanus, ICIC (O) v. Adham and Others and Eagle Trust v. Savory Milln. Clients include a major supplier of computer software packages and bureau services, one of the leading booksellers in the U.K., a number of public property companies and a major firm of accountants. Has written 'The European Community 1992 and Beyond' and addressed conferences world-wide on issues relating to the conflict of laws and comparative law.

Prof. Membership: Member of Court and Litigation Sub-Committee CIty of London Law Society; National Committee Union Internationale des Avocats; American Bar Association; International Bar Association; The Law Society and the New York State Bar.

Career: Qualified in 1965. Articled with *Clifford Turner* 1961-64 and joined *Berwin & Co.* upon qualification. Became a partner in 1968. Thereafter became a founder Partner *Berwin Leighton* in 1970 and Managing Partner 1984-86. Also admitted New York State Bar 1985 and Founder Member and Director of the Centre for European Dispute Resolution 1989; CEDR appointed Mediator 1992.

Personal: Born 21st July 1935. Educated at Rhymney Grammar School and University of Wales 1958-61 (First Class Honours and Sir Samuel Evans Prize for the best student of the year). College of Law, Lancaster Gate 1964. Is a member of the Appeals Committee Youth Clubs UK and of the Appeals Committee of the Friends of the British Theatre. Is a Governor of Daiglen School.

Willis, Tony
See under Litigation (Commercial).

Mair, G. Leonard R.
See under Family/Matrimonial.

Winkworth-Smith, M.J.
Dibb Lupton Broomhead, Leeds (0113) 243 9301. Qualified 1970. Partner 1972. Commercial Litigation Department. Specialises in engineering litigation and ADR.

INTERNATIONAL SECTION

The international section lists foreign law firms based in London. It also lists the foreign connections of English law firms: their branch offices overseas and the foreign languages spoken at their UK offices. The section is located just before the main solicitors' A-Z.

ARBITRATION

LONDON

London remains one of the 'big five' centres of international commercial arbitration in Europe along with Vienna, Stockholm, Geneva and the European leader, Paris, which is home to the International Chamber of Commerce and has the highest case turnover. Naturally, the principal English firms in this field are those with operations in both London and Paris, which enables them to do battle with strong American competition.

LEADING FIRMS

FRESHFIELDS
CLIFFORD CHANCE
ALLEN & OVERY

Freshfields may have suffered the double loss of Martin Hunter and Alan Redfern to the Bar in the last two years, but it is still the leading UK firm, albeit by a closer margin than before. Paris-based head of department Jan Paulsson is the leading arbitration lawyer working for a British firm. His team dealt with 27 new cases in 1994, a high figure and one that any firm in the world would struggle to eclipse. They act for a wide variety of international corporate clients. The highly-rated Nigel Rawding runs the London operation with an excellent young team that includes Philip Croall.

Hard on their heels come *Clifford Chance*, exemplifying the emergence of young talent to replace the 'old guard' of arbitration. Its outstanding arbitration practitioner is John Beechey, who leads a young team (including Audley Sheppard and Robert Lambert) that aims to compete on an equal footing with the strong American competition.

Allen & Overy is the other large City leader in arbitration, with Judith Gill (London) and David Sutton (Paris) its pre-eminent practitioners.

Coudert Brothers remains amongst the leaders in this field, largely due to the outstanding reputation of Laurence Craig in Paris. Similarly, *Wilmer Cutler & Pickering*'s reputation rests largely on Arthur Marriott, who is also an experienced university lecturer on this subject.

Firms with a construction or insurance-based clientele will always need a good team of arbitration lawyers. Hence the likes of *Masons* (with the highly regarded Phillip Capper) and *McKenna & Co* are included for their construction arbitration expertise, whilst *Clyde & Co, Norton Rose* (with

HIGHLY REGARDED

COUDERT BROTHERS	WILMER CUTLER & PICKERING
CLYDE & CO	DEBEVOISE & PLIMPTON
HERBERT SMITH	INCE & CO.
MASONS	McKENNA & CO
NORTON ROSE	WHITE & CASE
BARLOW LYDE & GILBERT	S J BERWIN & CO
DENTON HALL	DIBB LUPTON BROOMHEAD
EVERSHEDS	FRERE CHOLMELEY BISCHOFF
HAMMOND SUDDARDS	HOLMAN, FENWICK & WILLAN
LANE & PARTNERS	LINKLATERS & PAINES
LOVELL WHITE DURRANT	MIDDLETON POTTS
RICHARDS BUTLER	ROWE & MAW
SIMMONS & SIMMONS	SINCLAIR ROCHE & TEMPERLEY
TAYLOR JOYNSON GARRETT	

Michael Lee), and *Ince & Co* all have well-known insurance practices. *Herbert Smith,* with Lawrence Collins, is noted for its general commercial arbitration work which supplements its renowned litigation practice. This will undoubtedly be further strengthened by the recent move of Dr Julian Lew from *Coudert Brothers*.

LEADING INDIVIDUALS

John Beechey *Clifford Chance*	Jan Paulsson *Freshfields*	
Julian Lew *Herbert Smith*	Arthur Marriott *Wilmer Cutler & Pickering*	
John Bishop *Masons*	Stephen Bond *White & Case*	Anthony Bunch *Masons*
Phillip Capper *Masons*	Andrew J.C. Clark *Allen & Overy*	Lawrence A. Collins *Herbert Smith*
William Laurence Craig *Coudert Brothers*	Judith Gill *Allen & Overy*	Martin Harman *Masons*
David Jones-Parry *Clifford Chance*	Terence M. Lane *Lane & Partners*	Michael J.A. Lee *Norton Rose*
David L. Mackie *Allen & Overy*	Robin Neill *Clifford Chance*	Nigel K. Rawding *Freshfields*
David W. Rivkin *Debevoise & Plimpton*	Christopher Seppala *White & Case*	David St. John Sutton *Allen & Overy*
Nicholas E. Valner *Frere Cholmeley Bischoff*	Bob Van Mehren *Debevoise & Plimpton*	Gary B. Born *Wilmer Cutler & Pickering*
Philip M. Croall *Freshfields*		

UP AND COMING

Robert Lambert *Clifford Chance*	Sophie Nappart *Norton Rose*	Audley W. Sheppard *Clifford Chance*

LONDON

Beechey, John
Clifford Chance, London (0171) 600 1000. Partner. Handles international commercial arbitration, ADR and construction law.

Bishop, John
See under Construction & Civil Engineering.

Bond, Stephen
White & Case, London (00) 331 4260 3405.

Born, Gary B.
Wilmer Cutler & Pickering, London (0171) 839 4466. Qualified 1983. Managing Partner 1990. International Arbitration/ Litigation Department.

Bunch, Anthony
See under Construction & Civil Engineering.

Capper, Phillip
Masons, London (0171) 490 4000. Partner 1991. Specialises in engineering, transportation. Born 25 January 1952.

Clark, Andrew J.C.
Allen & Overy, London (0171) 330 3000. Qualified 1980. Partner in Litigation Department. Born 29.04.1955.

Collins, Lawrence A.
See under Litigation (Commercial).

Craig, William Laurence
Coudert Brothers, London (0171) 248 3000. Partner in Arbitration and Litigation Department. Also at Coudert Freres, Paris (331) 43 59 0160.

Specialisation: International commercial law practice in Paris since 1964, specialising in international arbitration since 1970. Has acted as counsel in nearly 100 International Chamber of Commerce arbitrations, including numerous disputes involving states and state agencies (also arbitration involving states before the International Centre for the Settlement of Investment Disputes). Acted as arbitrator (party-appointed, sole arbitrator or chairman) in 15 ICC arbirations and in numerous AAA and ad hoc arbitrations. Has represented parties in oil concession, production sharing, and operating and exploration agreements. Also agreements for the joint development of natural resources, and long term commodity purchase agreements. Has undertaken contract negotiations and dispute resolution in Brazil, Egypt, Kuwait, Qatar, Lebanon, Algeria, Iraq, Iran, Phillipines, Saudi Arabia and Libya. Co-author, 'International Chamber of Commerce Arbitration' (2nd Ed., 1990). Author of articles in numerous professional publications including *Harvard Law Review*, *Arbitration International* and the *Yearbook of Commercial Arbitration*.

Career: Admitted to Bars of New York 1958, District of Columbia 1960, US Supreme Court 1963. Admitted in Paris as Conseil Juridique 1972 and as Avocat 1992. Partner at *Coudert Freres*, Paris since 1964. Member, NATO Appeal Board 1972-76. Member, ICC Court of Arbitration 1976-84.

Personal: Born 17th September 1933. Educated at Williams College, Williamstown, Mass., Harvard Law School (Juris Doctor cum laude, 1957) and the University of Paris (Docteur en droit de l'Universite). Lives in Paris, France.

Croall, Philip. M.
Freshfields, London (0171) 936 4000. Partner specialising in Arbitration and Commercial Litigation.

Specialisation: Considerable practice in international commercial arbitration. Handles all aspects of arbitration work including advising as to contractual provisions for arbitration and Alternative Dispute Resolution, advising as to appropriate arbitration rules and procedures, and conducting arbitration under rules of the key arbitration institutions such as the International Chamber of Commerce, the London Court of International Arbitration and the UNCITRAL Rules.
Joint author of "Arbitration and Alternative Dispute Resolution" in "The Encyclopaedia of Forms and Precedents" Fifth Edition 1995 re-issue, Butterworths Publishers. Regular speaker at seminars and writer of articles on international commercial arbitration. Other areas of spaecialisation include all kinds of commercial litigation including banking, securities, pharmaceuticals and professional negligence cases.

Prof. Membership: Associate of the Chartered Institute of Arbitrators.

Career: Qualified in 1985 having completed Articles at Freshfields. Worked in Freshfields Hong Kong office from 1987 to 1990. Partner at Freshfields 1992.

Personal: Born 22 August 1959. Attended Stockport Grammar School 1971-1978, Emmanuel College, Cambridge 1978-1982. M.A Cantab (First Class Honours), LLM. Cantab (First Class Honours). Married with three children.

Gill, Judith
Allen & Overy, London (0171) 330 3000. Qualified 1985. Partner 1992. Litigation Department.

Harman, Martin
Masons, London (0171) 490 4000. Partner and Head of Construction Department.

Specialisation: Main area of practice is engineering and construction, covering contentious (litigation, arbitration and mediation) and non-contentious (drafting construction and related contracts) work. Particular focus upon international projects.

Advising various international entities, both governmental and private, upon the privitisation of major infrastructure projects and in that capacity, advising upon contract procurement strategy and drafting of project documentation. Has undertaken international arbitrations in Hong Kong, Singapore, Egypt, Kuwait, Yemen, Pakistan and India, with particular emphasis upon ICC arbitrations. Author of various articles on International arbitration. Lectures widely for various international conference organisers.

Prof. Membership: Faculty of Building, International Bar Association, Law Society of Hong Kong.

Career: Qualified in 1971. Joined *Masons* in 1975, becoming a Partner in 1976. Admitted in Hong Kong 1983; first resident Partner at *Masons* in Hong Kong 1983. Head of Construction Department of *Masons*.

Personal: Born 24th December 1946. Attended Brighton College, Brighton 1960-65, then Bristol University 1966-69. Leisure interests include tennis, walking, golf, reading and music. Lives in London.

Jones-Parry, David
Clifford Chance, London (0171) 600 1000. Partner. Principal area of practice is commercial and financial litigation .

Lambert, Robert
Clifford Chance, London (0171) 600 1000. Appears as counsel at arbitration hearings.

Lane, Terence M.
Lane & Partners, London (0171) 242 2626. Founding Partner and Senior Partner in Charge of Arbitration and Construction.

Specialisation: Main area of practice is arbitration, with emphasis on construction disputes. Since 1954 has advised on major construction contracts in Saudi Arabia, Kuwait, Abu Dhabi, Libya, Iraq, Iran, Oman, Algeria, Egypt, Tanzania, Botswana, Malawi, Zambia, Mauritius, Indonesia, the Bahamas, Pakistan, Malaysia, South Korea and Singapore. Has acted as Chairman of the ICC Arbitration Tribunal appointed to determine disputes involving major oil refinery in Saudi Arabia. Also handles intellectual property work, particularly licensing. Has acted in numerous international arbitrations, mainly as Counsel for the Contractor, involving claims against Government agencies and ministries and private (non-governmental) employers. Author of 'English Law of International Licensing Agreements', 'English Law of Trade Secrets and Confidence Agreements', 'Businessman's Guide to the Antitrust Provisions of the Rome Treaty', 'Legal Implications of British Entry to the Common Market' and 'Licensing in Eastern Europe'. Has wide experience of giving addresses and papers to organisations such as the International Management Association throughout Europe and the USA.

Prof. Membership: Fellow of the Chartered Institute of Arbitrators, Member of the International Bar Association, Member of the International Fiscal Association, Member of the Institute of Trade Mark Agents.

Career: Qualified in 1953. Founding Partner of *Lane & Partners* in 1974. Also Partner of *Marks & Murase* in New York. Served in the Royal Artillery 1940-46, seconded to the Indian Army as Major; and HM Colonial Administrative Service, District Commissioner and Judge, Chunya District, Tanganyika Territory (Tanzania) 1946-49.

Personal: Born 5th October 1918. Attended London University BA (Hons) (Modern History); Indiana University, USA (Constitutional Law) and College of Law, London. Freeman of the City of London, Liveryman of the Worshipful Company of Arbitrators. Lives in Rake, Liss, Hants.

Lee, Michael J.A.
See under Litigation (Commercial).

Lew, Julian
Herbert Smith, London (0171) 374 8000. (Bar) 1981 (Solicitor) 1985 (Attorney-at-Law, New York). Partner in Arbitration/Litigation Department.

Specialisation: Main area of practice is international commercial arbitration, acting as an adviser and representing clients in different forms of arbitrations: concerning all kinds of international contracts, particularly investments, distribution, intellectual property licenses and joint ventures. Has also been appointed as an arbitrator in ICC, LCIA, AAA, Ad hoc and other arbitrations. Editor of Applicable Law in International Commercial Arbitration(1978), Editor of International Trade: Law and Practice (1985), Contemporary Problems in International Commercial Arbitration (1985), The Immunity of Arbitrators (1990) and Enforcement of Foreign Judgements (1994). Head of the School of International Arbitration at the Centre for Commercial Law Studies at Queen Mary & Westfield College, University of London; Chairman of the Chartered Institute of Arbitrators Law Reform Working party, and Chairman of the ICC Working Party on Intellectual Property Disputes in Arbitration.

Prof. Memberships: British Institute of International and Comparative Law, London Court of International Arbitration, Chartered Institute of Arbitrators, American Society of International Law, American Bar Association, Swiss Arbitration Association, French Arbitration Committee, Hong Kong International Arbitration Centre, Arbitral Centre of the Federal Economic Chamber, Vienna. Partner at *SJ Berwin & Co.* 1986-1992, joined *Coudert Brothers* in 1992, and joined Herbert Smith in 1995.

Personal: Born 3rd February 1948. Took an LLB (Hons) London, 1969; Academy of International Law, the Hague, 1970-71; and Doctorat special en droit international, Université Catholique de Louvain, Belgium, 1977. Lives in Pinner, Middlesex.

Mackie, David L.
See under Litigation (Commercial).

Marriott, Arthur
Wilmer Cutler & Pickering, London (0171) 839 4466. Qualified 1966. Partner. Work also includes mediation.

Nappart, Sophie
Norton Rose, London (0171) 283 6000. Qualified 1987. (Quebec). Lawyer in Paris Office. Main area of practice is international commercial disputes.

Neill, Robin
Clifford Chance, London (0171) 600 1000. Partner. Principal area of work is international engineering and construction disputes.

Paulsson, Jan
Freshfields, London (Paris Office) Int+ 33 1 44564456. Partner in Litigation/Arbitration Department.

Specialisation: Main area of practice is international arbitration. Has acted as counsel or arbitrator in some 200 arbitral proceedings conducted in the major venues of Europe and the United States, mostly under the rules of the ICC, but also notably under those of the LCIA, UNCITRAL, the Stockholm Institute, as well as in ad hoc arbitrations governed directly by national laws. Author of numerous publications, among them 'International Chamber of Commerce Arbitration', the 'France' section in Encyclopaedia of International Commercial Litigation and articles in a wide range of professional publications in English and French. Frequent speaker on subjects relating to the resolution of international disputes.

Prof. Membership: London Court of International Arbitration, W.I.P.O. Consultative Commission, International Olympic Committee's Tribunal Arbitral du Sport.

Career: Qualified in 1977. Became a Partner in 1984 at *Coudert Frères*. Joined *Freshfields*, in Paris, as a Partner in 1989.

Personal: Born 5th November 1949. Attended Harvard University, Yale Law School and University of Paris. Editor of Arbitration International. Lives in Paris.

Rawding, Nigel K.
Freshfields, London (0171) 936 4000. Partner in International Arbitration Group of Litigation Department.

Specialisation: Principal area of practice is international arbitration representing clients in major commercial disputes involving litigation, international arbitration and ADR procedures. International arbitration experience includes ad hoc, International Chamber of Commerce (ICC) and London Court of International Arbitration (LCIA) cases. Co-author of The *Freshfields* Guide to Arbitration and ADR (Kluwer, 1992). Regular contributor to arbitration journals and conference speaker on subjects relating to the resolution of international disputes.

Prof. Membership: ICC United Kingdom, Chartered Institute of Arbitrators, LCIA.

Career: Joined *Freshfields* as an Articled Clerk in 1982. Qualified 1984. Seconded to Hong Kong Office 1986-89 and became a Partner in 1991.

Personal: Born 17th November 1958. Attended Manchester Grammar School and Sidney Sussex College, Cambridge. Lives in London.

Rivkin, David W.
Debevoise & Plimpton, London New York (001) 212 909 6000. Qualified 1982. Partner, 1988. Litigation Department. Specialises in international arbitration.

Seppala, Christopher
White & Case, London (00) 331 4260 3405.

Sheppard, Audley W.
Clifford Chance, London (0171) 600 1000. Partner 1995. International Commercial Arbitration Group. Also advises on public international law issues.

Sutton, David St. John
Allen & Overy, London Paris (00) 33 1 49 53 06 37. Qualified 1967. Partner 1971. Litigation Department. Also litigation and alternative dispute resolution.

Valner, Nicholas E.
Frere Cholmeley Bischoff, London (0171) 615 8000. Partner in Litigation Department and Head of Department.

Specialisation: Work includes civil engineering and construction arbitrations, banking disputes, fraud recovery through civil action, royalty and copyright disputes in the music business, insurance policy disputes, Gaming Act proceedings and property investment disputes. Has acted in many arbitrations and Court cases, including Apple Corps v. Apple Computers, Apple Corps v. EMI Records, Polygram v. Royal Reinsurance, Greencap v. Bride Hall, Steerpike (Overseas) Ltd v. Coutts Bank; and leading US/ Libya bank cases. Lectured at IBA. Chaired numerous conferences and seminars on arbitration law for Chartered Institute of Arbitrators. Has given numerous lectures on jurisdiction for the British Institute of International and Comparative Law.

Prof. Membership: International Bar Association, Chartered Institute of Arbitrators.

Career: Qualified 1979, having joined *Frere Cholmeley Bischoff* in 1977. Became a Partner in 1985. Head of Litigation Department 1995.

Personal: Born 14th September 1953. Attended Stonyhurst College 1967-73, then Oxford University 1973-76. Leisure interests include fishing, gardening, reading. Lives near Woking Surrey.

Van Mehren, Bob
Debevoise & Plimpton, London (001) 212 909 6000.

ASSET FINANCE & LEASING

THIS section concentrates on those firms with small, medium or large ticket leasing expertise, as well as those with general equipment, plant, vehicle and property asset finance capabilities. Firms and individuals with expertise in asset finance relating to aviation or shipping appear in the lists for those two subjects. Those firms with expertise in project finance are dealt with in the 'Major, Projects and Infrastructure' specialist list.

Small ticket work finances the basic equipment used in offices and factories. Deals at the top end of this range can be worth up to around £100,000. In the medium ticket range deals can be worth up to tens of millions. Big ticket work tends to be categorised by the complexity of the transactions rather than the sums involved.

LONDON

Wilde Sapte and *Watson Farley & Williams* emerge as pre-eminent in this area. *Wilde Sapte* has an excellent reputation in all aspects of asset finance and leasing, and has been particularly recommended for its big and medium ticket work.

LEADING FIRMS – LONDON	
WATSON, FARLEY & WILLIAMS	WILDE SAPTE
BERWIN LEIGHTON	CLIFFORD CHANCE
FRESHFIELDS	SLAUGHTER AND MAY
ALLEN & OVERY	BEAUMONT AND SON
HARRIS ROSENBLATT & KRAMER	LINKLATERS & PAINES
NORTON ROSE	SINCLAIR ROCHE & TEMPERLEY

Adrian Miles, who heads the strong department, is highly regarded for his sophisticated and large value transactions, especially in UK and cross-border asset finance. *Watson Farley & Williams* also has a well developed practice in this area, and James Watters at the firm has particular expertise in his medium and small ticket work, and has been involved in numerous international middle ticket deals.

Other firms with considerable expertise include *Freshfields*, *Clifford Chance*, *Berwin Leighton* and *Slaughter and May*. *Freshfields*, which has a well regarded team dealing with big, medium and small ticket work, are especially renowned in the field for their tax-based, cross-border financing and leasing work. Simon Hall at the firm has an established reputation for equipment leasing and tax-based work. The bulk of his work is largely international. Clive Carpenter at *Clifford Chance* has been particularly highly recommended to us. The firm's strength lies in the big and medium ticket categories, with specific expertise in loan financing and securitisation.

Berwin Leighton is also active in the field, with a leading reputation in property lending, house, club and fully syndicated loans, as well as an acknowledged capability in small ticket work. Hugh Homan at the firm has been recommended for his expertise with regard to asset finance work. Tom Kinnersley at *Slaughter and May* also enjoys a strong reputation, and the firm has considerable expertise in the international market, and at the larger end of the asset finance range.

Linklaters & Paines, *Allen & Overy*, *Norton Rose* and *Sinclair Roche & Temperley* also enjoy formidable reputations for the quality of their practices in this area. Ronald Gibbs emerges as the leading specialist in the team at *Linklaters & Paines,* which undertakes substantial amounts of both international and domestic asset finance work.

HIGHLY REGARDED – LONDON	
CAMERON MARKBY HEWITT	HERBERT SMITH
LOVELL WHITE DURRANT	MASONS
BOODLE HATFIELD	BRECHER & CO
FORSYTE SAUNDERS KERMAN	GOULDENS
LAWRENCE GRAHAM	NICHOLSON GRAHAM & JONES
THEODORE GODDARD	WALKER MARTINEAU
WEDLAKE BELL	

At *Norton Rose*, the team has a depth of experience in all aspects, and has been involved in many of the innovative structures which have developed in the asset finance sector during the last 20 years. Within this well regarded department, David Crane has been especially recommended to us.

LEADING INDIVIDUALS – LONDON		
Clive Carpenter *Clifford Chance*	**David Roger Crane** *Norton Rose*	**Stephen Finch** *Harris Rosenblatt & Kramer*
Ronald W. Gibbs *Linklaters & Paines*	**Simon A.D. Hall** *Freshfields*	**Hugh Homan** *Berwin Leighton*
T.A. Kinnersley *Slaughter and May*	**Adrian S. Miles** *Wilde Sapte*	**James A.D. Watters** *Watson Farley & Williams*
Mary Patricia Bonar *Wilde Sapte*	**A.D. Collins** *Wilde Sapte*	**Alan M. Crookes** *Norton Rose*
Neil Cuthbert *Watson Farley & Williams*	**Kevin J. Dean** *Sinclair Roche & Temperley*	**James A M Edmunds** *Beaumont and Son*
Elisabeth Gaunt *Wilde Sapte*	**Geoff Haley** *S J Berwin & Co*	**Thomas Stephen Lyon** *Berwin Leighton*
A.J. Morris *Sinclair Roche & Temperley*	**Dennis Rosenthal** *Forsyte Saunders Kerman*	**Mark Stewart** *Clifford Chance*
Dawood (David) Syed *Watson Farley & Williams*	**Peter Geoffrey Thorne** *Norton Rose*	**Martin A. Watson** *Watson Farley & Williams*
Geoffrey White *Clifford Chance*		

Cameron Markby Hewitt act for a wide range of clients in this area including banks and finance lessors, corporate lessees, public authorities, housing associations, charities, pension funds and universities.

Herbert Smith, Lovell White Durrant and *Masons* are also well known in the field.

Amongst those firms undertaking small ticket work, *Beaumont & Son* and *Harris Rosenblatt & Kramer* have been highly recommended, the latter firm also enjoying a strong reputation for consumer credit, HP and vehicle finance. Stephen Finch, who heads the department is particularly well thought of by his peers.

Within this area of law, in-house lawyers play a significant role. Foremost amongst those recommended to us was Dennis Hopkins at *Lombard North Central PLC*, who is head of legal services and has an excellent reputation for small, medium and big ticket work.

SOUTH EAST

Only a few firms in the South East handle this type of work. *Coole & Haddock* are well known for their small and medium ticket work, largely with regard to industrial plant and

HIGHLY REGARDED – SOUTH EAST		
COOLE & HADDOCK *Worthing*		PITMANS *Reading*
THOMAS EGGAR VERRALL BOWLES *Chichester*		

equipment leasing. *Thomas Eggar Verrall Bowles* also handles a wide range of work, with particular capability in the small and medium ticket sectors. In Reading, *Pitmans*, act for several asset finance and leasing companies.

SOUTH WEST

Lester Aldridge, has established a strong national reputation in this specialist area, and is renowned for its expertise in relation to small and medium ticket transactions for UK banks and independent finance houses. The firm is considered

HIGHLY REGARDED – SOUTH WEST
LESTER ALDRIDGE *Bournemouth*

to have one of the leading Banking and Asset Finance Units in the country, which includes specialist litigators and a computerised recovery of goods service. Janet Gregory has been highlighted in the team for her considerable expertise in the field. The firm, which acts for a wide range of lenders and trade associations, also offers a bulk asset finance debt collecting service.

LEADING INDIVIDUALS – SOUTH WEST
Janet Gregory *Lester Aldridge*

MIDLANDS

Asset finance and leasing is a highly specialised area of law which in the Midlands usually only comprises a small part of a firm's banking practice. *Edge & Ellison*, however, has a dedicated team of practitioners who handle all aspects of asset

HIGHLY REGARDED – MIDLANDS	
EDGE & ELLISON *Birmingham*	SHAKESPEARES *Birmingham*

leasing work, advising clients who operate in the equipment leasing, hire purchase and finance sectors. Clients include major clearing banks, leasing companies and financial institutions. Angela Davis at the firm has been recommended for her expertise.

Shakespeares also has a reputation for handling small ticket work, and Michael Cronin at the firm is well regarded.

LEADING INDIVIDUALS – MIDLANDS
Michael Cronin *Shakespeares*
Angela C. Davis *Edge & Ellison*

NORTH

Recommended for its asset finance work, *Bermans* has a well established clientele based throughout the UK in the small and middle ticket lease sectors. Its team is also experienced in the drafting of lease documentation and resolution of litigation disputes. *Berg & Co* has a strong practice in commercial leasing and consumer credit, and service private companies of many types, particularly in the sales aid, textile and freight sectors. Peter Woolf has been recommended to us for his expertise.

HIGHLY REGARDED – NORTH		
BERG & CO *Manchester*		BERMANS *Liverpool*
BOOTH & CO. *Leeds*		EVERSHEDS *Leeds*
PINSENT CURTIS *Leeds*		

In Leeds, *Booth & Co*, *Pinsent Curtis* and *Eversheds* all have active practices in this specialised area. *Booth & Co* has specialists undertaking small and medium ticket asset finance, whilst *Pinsent Curtis* are known for representing leasing companies and trade associations.

LEADING INDIVIDUALS – NORTH
Peter Graham Woolf *Berg & Co*

Eversheds is one of the few firms outside London who undertake 'big ticket' tax-based finance leasing transactions, and has an excellent reputation for its tax-based financing work. The team is particularly strong in tax advantaged finance for 'non-specialist' assets, such as land and rolling stock.

SCOTLAND

Morton Fraser & Milligan continue to undertake a substantial amount of asset finance work, and its partner, Bruce Wood who has been highly recommended for his expertise,

is the author of the only Scottish publication on equipment leasing. Clients of the firm include banks and financial companies.

Macdonalds remain active in representing several equipment and plant leasing companies, whilst *McGrigor Donald* and *Dickson Minto* both have considerable experience in asset finance work. Also well regarded is *McClure Naismith Anderson & Gardiner* which has a reputation in asset finance, especially in relation to consumer credit work.

LEADERS IN ASSET FINANCE & LEASING

LONDON

Bonar, Mary Patricia
Wilde Sapte, London (0171) 246 7000. Partner in Banking Department.

Specialisation: Head of Major Projects Group and Rail Group. Main areas of practice are project finance, leasing and rail privatisation. Has handled both road and rail infrastructure projects, power projects, cross border leasing transactions and vesting and franchising of passenger train operating companies. Clients include major banks and their leasing subsidiaries, British Railways Board and major corporate sponsors (projects). She is currently leading the *Wilde Sapte* team acting for British Rail in vesting and franchising three of the Train Operating Companies and has been handling track access negotiation with Railtrack. Speaker at conferences on project finance and rail privatisations.

Prof. Membership: Liveryman, City of London Solicitors Company; Women Solicitors Association.

Career: LLB. Admitted in 1971. Solicitor and Partner (from 1973) at *Gamlens* in Lincolns Inn 1971-89. Joined *Wilde Sapte* as a Partner in 1989.

Personal: Born 28th July 1947. Educated at St Bernard's Convent High School, Westcliff, Essex 1958-65, University College, London 1965-68 and The College of Law, Lancaster Gate 1970-71. Princes Youth Trust Business Adviser. Lives in the City of London.

Carpenter, Clive
Clifford Chance, London (0171) 600 1000. Partner 1994. Banking. Main areas of practice are aircraft, ship, rolling stock and other asset financing, tax and leveraged leasing, project finance and transportation asset securitisation. Born 2.10.1955.

Collins, A.D.
Wilde Sapte, London (0171) 246 7000.

Crane, David Roger
Norton Rose, London (0171) 283 6000.

Qualified 1975. Partner 1985. Banking Department. Specialises in project finance, equipment leasing and public sector finance. Also handles general commercial work. Born 28.10.1949.

Crookes, Alan M.
Norton Rose, London (0171) 283 6000. Qualified 1981. Partner 1988. Corporate and Financial Department. Principal area of practice is asset finance.

Cuthbert, Neil
Watson Farley & Williams, London (0171) 814 8000. Partner in Banking Department.

Specialisation: Handles all aspects of banking with particular expertise in asset or project related financings, including oil and gas, hotel and leisure, telecommunications and infrastructure. Author of 'Longmans Property Finance Precedents' and 'Longmans Practical Lending and Security Precedents'.

Prof. Membership: International Bar Association.

Career: Qualified in 1979. Worked at *Allen & Overy* 1977-81, then the Royal Bank of Canada 1981-85. Joined *Watson Farley & Williams* as a Partner in 1985.

Personal: Born 15th January 1954. Attended University of Exeter 1973-76. Lives in Hampshire.

Dean, Kevin J.
See under Company/Commercial.

Edmunds, James A M
Beaumont and Son, London (0171) 481 3100. Qualified 1988. Partner in the Commercial Department.

Finch, Stephen
Harris Rosenblatt & Kramer, London (0171) 242 3254. Partner in charge of Banking and Finance Department.

Specialisation: Since 1978 has advised lending institutions on all legal aspects of their activities, both consumer and commercial

lending. Served on the Legislation Committee of the Finance Houses Association whilst Company Solicitor at Citibank. Current work includes providing advice on asset finance and leasing arrangements including offshore and tax based leasing and securitisations, providing advice on the Consumer Credit Act 1974, banking related litigation matters and advice on the Financial Services Act and Insolvency Act. Examiner for the Finance and Leasing Association Diploma examination. Wide lecturing experience with particular emphasis on Consumer Credit Act.

Gaunt, Elisabeth
Wilde Sapte, London (0171) 246 7000.

Gibbs, Ronald W.
Linklaters & Paines, London (0171) 606 7080.

Haley, Geoff
See under Construction & Civil Engineering.

Hall, Simon A.D.
Freshfields, London (0171) 936 4000. Head of Finance Department.

Specialisation: Main areas of practice are asset and aircraft finance, and banking and project finance. Editor and co-author of 'Aircraft Financing' (Euromoney 2nd edition, 1993); co-author of 'Leasing Finance' (Euromoney 2nd edition, 1990). Active speaker.

Prof. Membership: Law Society, City of London Solicitors Company, American Bar Association.

Career: Qualified 1979 after joining *Freshfields* in 1977. Became a Partner in 1985.

Personal: Born 6th February 1955. Leisure interests include shooting and fishing. Lives near Colchester.

Homan, Hugh
Berwin Leighton, London (0171) 623 3144. Qualified 1970. Partner 1975. Corporate Finance Department. Main area of practice is asset finance, equipment leasing and securitisation. Born 26.6.1945.

Kinnersley, T.A.
Slaughter and May, London (0171) 600 1200. Qualified 1972. Partner 1980. Commercial Department. Handles asset finance and leasing, banking and general company and commercial work.

Lyon, Thomas Stephen
Berwin Leighton, London (0171) 623 3144. Qualified 1965. Partner 1970. Corporate Department. Also handles corporate tax and banking work.

Miles, Adrian S.
Wilde Sapte, London (0171) 246 7000. Partner in Banking Department.

Specialisation: Departmental Manager. Main area of practice is UK and cross-border asset finance, acting for UK and foreign banks in international financing transactions and cross-border structured finance transactions. Also handles aviation, leasing and project finance, acting for financing parties in sophisticated and large value transactions in the UK and internationally.

Career: Qualified in 1972. Joined *Wilde Sapte* and became a Partner in 1976.

Personal: Born 16th November 1947. Educated at Rutlish School, Merton 1959-66 and Queen Mary College, London University 1966-69. Recreations include classical music, opera and chess. Lives in Chislehurst, Kent.

Morris, A.J.
Sinclair Roche & Temperley, London (0171) 638 9044. Partner in ship finance transactions. Born 10.12.1935.

Rosenthal, Dennis
Forsyte Saunders Kerman, London (0171) 637 8566.

Specialisation: Advising lending institutions including banks, finance companies, building societies and trade associations, including the Consumer Credit Trade Association and CIFAS, on all aspects of their activities including lending and leasing documentation, financial services, sale and purchase of receivables, and company and commercial law generally. Settled standard agreement forms of the Consumer Credit Trade Association for some 15 years and has been responsible for the standard documentation of numerous institutions. Has devised and settled innovative products in relation to credit cards, savings and loans, leasing and security. Advises on related subjects including advertising law, insurance, fraud, money laundering and Data Protection Act issues. Assistant Editor of Goode: Consumer Credit Legislation and author of Guide to Consumer Credit Law & Practice (Butterworths 1994).

Prof. Membership: South African Attorney and Solicitor of the Supreme Court of Judicature, England.

Stewart, Mark
See under Banking.

Syed, Dawood (David)
Watson Farley & Williams, London +33 (1) 45 63 15 15 (Paris office). Partner specialising in asset finance and leasing.

Specialisation: Work covers French domestic asset and real estate leasing, cross-border tax leasing (aircraft, railcars and equipment) and off-balance sheet asset finance. Also handles project agreements and financing. Author of various publications; lecturer at the University of Tours, France.

Prof. Membership: Ordre des Avocats a la Cour de Paris, Association Francaise des Avocats Conseils d'Enterprises, International Bar Association.

Career: Admitted as Avocat 1992 (France)- formerly Conseil Juridique. Counsel with the Legal Department of Regie Nationale des Usines Renault 1986-90, Associate with *Baker & McKenzie* (Paris) 1990-91, becoming a Partner in 1991. Moved to *Watson Farley & Williams* as a Partner in 1992.

Personal: Born 3rd March 1964. Attended Exeter (LLM Hons), Universite de Rheims (Licence en droit felicitations du jury). Leisure interests include horseriding and diving.

Thorne, Peter Geoffrey
Norton Rose, London (0171) 283 6000. Qualified 1971. Partner 1977. Corporate and Financial Department (Banking Group). Principal area of work is asset finance in aviation field; also covers financing of shipping and other assets. Born 2.6.1948.

Watson, Martin A.
Watson Farley & Williams, London (0171) 814 8000. Partner in Shipping Department.

Specialisation: Main area of practice is ship finance, covering international finance, commercial leasing, banking, asset finance and corporate restructuring.

Career: Founding Partner of *Watson, Farley & Williams* 1982. Admitted 1984.

Personal: Educated at St. Catherine's College, Cambridge (BA).

Watters, James A.D.
Watson Farley & Williams, London (0171) 814 8000. Partner in Asset Finance Group.

Specialisation: Principal area of practice is asset finance. Work includes the provision of asset finance in the UK and elsewhere by leasing, loan, receivable discounting and other facilities, and the sale and purchase of leasing companies and lease portfolios. Frequent lecturer and co-ordinator of annual conference on 'Law and Leasing'.

Career: Qualified in September 1972. Partner at *Watson Farley & Williams* since May 1992.

Personal: Born 16th March 1948. Educated at KCS Wimbledon 1961-65 and Pembroke College, Oxford 1966-69. Lives in London.

White, Geoffrey
See under Aviation.

Cronin, Michael
Shakespeares, Birmingham (0121) 632 4199. Consultant in Commercial Department.

Specialisation: Principal area of work is Consumer Credit and Data Protection advice and drafting together with Asset Financing/Leasing. Obtained OBE for services to Consumer Credit.

Prof. Membership: Law Society.

Career: Qualified in 1957. Principal and then Group Solicitor to Forward Trust Limited 1959-1992. Chairman Crowther Legislation Committee, Finance Houses Association 1976-87, Chairman Legal Committee Finance Houses Association 1987-1992, Consumer Credit Committee and legal affairs committee, European Federation of Finance Houses, Brussels 1977-1992. Became a Consultant at Shakespeares in 1992.

Personal: Born 24th April 1932. Educated St Mary's College, Middlesbrough and Birmingham University. Lives in Balsall Common, Coventry.

Davis, Angela C.
Edge & Ellison, Birmingham (0121) 200 2001. Head of Asset Finance Group.

Specialisation: Principal area of practice, all legal aspects of Asset Finance, Leasing and Consumer Credit with particular expertise on the contentious side and with experience of mediation in the finance sector. Responsible for two leading Court of Appeal decisions; RoyScot Trust plc v. Rogerson and RoyScot Trust plc v. Ismail on damages and indemnities respectively.

Prof. Membership: Law Society, Birmingham Law Society and Associate of the Chartered Institute of Arbitrators.

Career: Qualified in 1982. Joined *Edge & Ellison*, becoming a Partner in 1990.

Personal: Born 4 March 1958. Attended West Kirby Grammer School for Girls, Wirral 1969-1976. Durham University 1976-79. Leisure interests include antique maps, reading, hockey and Everton FC.

Gregory, Janet
Lester Aldridge, Bournemouth (01202) 786161. Partner in Banking and Finance.

Specialisation: Head of Banking and Finance Department. Principal area of practice is asset finance and consumer credit. Undertakes all aspects of non-contentious asset finance in the small to medium ticket range and consumer credit for finance houses, banks, building societies and other financial institutions. Deals with the drafting of standard documentation, transactional work, sale and purchase of receivables and compliance advice in connection with marketing and advertising material. Acted in negotiating sale and purchase of receivables books for major financial institutions. Negotiated the stocking finance agreement for the Leyland Daf Trucks Dealers' Association. Has lectured to trading standards departments on advertisements regulations and carried out legal training for non-lawyers in finance institutions. Has written articles on financial advertising, asset finance and consumer credit topics for various journals and is a member of the Consumer Credit Sub-Committee of the Law Society.

Prof. Membership: Law Society.

Career: Qualified in 1977. Senior Solicitor with *Lombard North Central plc* 1979-89. Partner with *Saunders Sobell Leigh & Dobin 1989-92. Joined Lester Aldridge* as a Partner in 1993. Member of the Board of Examiners for the Finance Houses Association Diploma Examination 1982-89.

Personal: Born 18th October 1952. Educated at Merchant Taylors Girls' School, Liverpool 1964-71 and University College, London 1971-74. Recreations include theatre, reading and playing the saxophone. Lives in Bournemouth, Dorset.

Wood, R. Bruce

Morton Fraser Milligan WS, Edinburgh (0131) 556 8444. Partner and Head of Corporate Division.

Specialisation: Main areas of practice are asset and project finance and leasing, banking and debt factoring. Acts for Scottish finance companies throughout the UK and for English-based (and foreign-based) finance companies in Scotland: large, medium and small ticket work. Also handles general corporate work. Author of 'Location: Leasing and Hire of Moveables' in the Laws of Scotland, 'Leasing of Moveables' in Journal of the Law Society, 'Die Floating Charge Als Kreditsichereit Im Schottischen Recht'. Has lectured widely at legal seminars on, inter alia, leasing of moveables, joint ventures, Consumer Credit Act, banking practices in Scotland, corporate law in Scotland, the globalisation of law firms and the practice of law.

Prof. Membership: Law Society of Scotland, WS Society, Association of Pension Lawyers.

Career: Qualified 1976. Joined *Morton Fraser Milligan WS* in 1974, becoming a Partner in 1977 and Head of Corporate Division in 1991. Lecturer in Conveyancing at Edinburgh University 1979-89; Convenor of Conveyancing Teachers of the Scottish Universities in the Diploma in Legal Practice 1986-89. World Chairman of Interlaw 1989-91. Member of the Law Society working party on security over moveables and of the International Relations Committee of the Law Society. Member of the CBI Companies Committee.

Personal: Born 2nd October 1951. Holds an LLB (1st class Hons, Edinburgh 1973) and an LLM (UC Berkeley, 1974). Leisure interests include hill-walking and golf. Lives near Penicuik.

Woolf, Peter Graham

Berg & Co, Manchester (0161) 833 9211. Qualified 1976. Partner 1984. Litigation and Matrimonial Department. Specialises in consumer/corporate leasing litigation and matrimonial finance.

INDEXES TO PROFILES

Solicitors' Profiles The index to leading solicitors profiled in the specialist lists is located immediately after the section containing in-house lawyers' profiles. This index also includes heads of company legal departments.

Barristers' Profiles Leading barristers' profiles are indexed within the main Barristers' Index located at the end of the directory. Names of profiled barristers are set in bold type.

AVIATION

THE aviation field can be divided into the following: Regulatory / Competition, Insurance / Re-insurance, Finance / Leasing, General commercial advice. Some firms are associated with individual categories; few deal with all of the above.

This is a field with an emphasis on work being done by in-house lawyers. Foremost amongst those being recommended was Ross Marland of the *British Aviation Group*.

LONDON

Beaumont & Son emerge as the market leaders in this field, with expertise in all areas of aviation law. The firm, a niche

LEADING FIRMS – LONDON – AVIATION	
BEAUMONT AND SON	
FRERE CHOLMELEY BISCHOFF	LANE & PARTNERS
NORTON ROSE	WILDE SAPTE
BARLOW LYDE & GILBERT	CLIFFORD CHANCE
FRESHFIELDS	HARBOTTLE & LEWIS
INCE & CO.	LINKLATERS & PAINES
LOVELL WHITE DURRANT	

practice specialising in aviation insurance and accident litigation, has more specialists than any other firms devoted to this work. Sean Gates, manager of the aviation department, is highly regarded for his expertise in aviation catastrophe management, liability insurance and claims. Also recommended at the firm are Dennis Kilbride, Neil McGilchrist, David Clark, Timothy Unmack and David Willcox, creating a formidable team.

Other firms with excellent reputations include *Wilde Sapte*, *Norton Rose*, *Lane & Partners* and *Frere Cholmeley Bischoff*.

Wilde Sapte is especially well regarded in finance and regulatory matters. Within the large department, Hugh O'Donovan has an established reputation for international regulation work, and for EC and competition law, airline and airport

operations, aircraft leasing and airport financing. Colin Thaine is one of the foremost aviation finance specialists recommended to us, representing a wide range of financiers, banks and airlines.

Norton Rose are also highly regarded in all aspects of aviation law. Trevor Soames at the firm is well regarded for his expertise in competition and regulatory work and represents a variety of national and international airlines. Patrick Farrell has been recommended for his litigation work on behalf of airlines, travel agents and tour operators. Also well regarded at the firm are John Cook for competition work and Peter Thorne and Paul Giles for aviation finance.

Lane & Partners are particularly well-known for their regulatory work. Richard Venables, a leading specialist at the firm, has an excellent reputation in this field, for competition law and for general commercial work on behalf of airlines.

John Balfour, head of aviation at *Frere Cholmeley Bischoff* is known for his broad experience handling accident litigation, regulatory work, general commercial, leasing and finance work. The firm has a particularly strong reputation in aviation insurance and regulatory work. Peter Martin has also been recommended to us for his experience in the field.

HIGHLY REGARDED – LONDON	
CAMERON MARKBY HEWITT	DAVIES ARNOLD COOPER
JARVIS & BANNISTER	WATSON, FARLEY & WILLIAMS
ALLEN & OVERY	BRECHER & CO
CLYDE & CO	FIELD FISHER WATERHOUSE
HAMMOND SUDDARDS	LAWRENCE JONES
McKENNA & CO	RICHARDS BUTLER
ROWE & MAW	SLAUGHTER AND MAY
STRINGER SAUL	THEODORE GODDARD

Other highly respected firms include *Barlow Lyde & Gilbert, Harbottle & Lewis, Freshfields, Clifford Chance, Linklaters & Paines, Ince & Co* and *Lovell White Durrant*.

At *Barlow Lyde & Gilbert*, Ian Awford has an excellent reputation, and acts for insurers and air carriers, handling passenger and cargo claims, aerospace product liability, air traffic control and ground handling problems. Nicholas Hughes at the firm has also been recommended.

LEADING INDIVIDUALS – LONDON – AVIATION					
Ian Awford	*Barlow Lyde & Gilbert*	John M. Balfour	*Frere Cholmeley Bischoff*	Patrick Farrell	*Norton Rose*
Sean Gates	*Beaumont and Son*	Colin M. Howes	*Harbottle & Lewis*	Peter Martin	*Frere Cholmeley Bischoff*
Hugh O'Donovan	*Wilde Sapte*	Richard Venables	*Lane & Partners*		
Frances A.J. Butler-Sloss	*Harbottle & Lewis*	Simon Chamberlain	*Field Fisher Waterhouse*	David N. Clark	*Beaumont and Son*
C. John Cook	*Norton Rose*	Colin Franke	*Clyde & Co*	Nicholas M.L. Hughes	*Barlow Lyde & Gilbert*
D.A. Kilbride	*Beaumont and Son*	Neil R. McGilchrist	*Beaumont and Son*	M.W.T. Nott	*Rowe & Maw*
David Reynolds	*Clyde & Co*	Tim Scorer	*Jarvis & Bannister*	Dermot Scully	*Harbottle & Lewis*
Trevor I. Soames	*Norton Rose*	Gerrard Tyrrell	*Harbottle & Lewis*	T.S.B. Unmack	*Beaumont and Son*
David J. Willcox	*Beaumont and Son*				

Harbottle & Lewis continue to be active in the field, strengthening its reputation through its representation of Virgin Atlantic. Colin Howes, who is particularly well regarded, is principally known for his regulatory work. He also deals with finance and general commercial work. Other specialists at the firm include Gerrard Tyrrell, Frances Butler-Sloss and Dermot Scully.

LEADING FIRMS – LONDON – AVIATION FINANCE	
CLIFFORD CHANCE	FRESHFIELDS
NORTON ROSE	
ALLEN & OVERY	LOVELL WHITE DURRANT
SLAUGHTER AND MAY	WILDE SAPTE
BRECHER & CO	WATSON, FARLEY & WILLIAMS

Freshfields are well known for their work in aircraft finance, acting for manufacturers, lenders, lessors and lessees. *Clifford Chance* enjoy a strong international aviation practice, dealing with aircraft finance, route licensing and competition law as well as aviation liabilities and insurance. Their clients in this field include financiers, airlines and manufacturers. *Linklaters & Paines* are well regarded for their regu-

latory work: they advise British Airways, DHL and South African Airways. They also carry out aviation project finance work.

Ince & Co are well-known for accident investigations, official inquiries, insurance-based work, and the EU law relating to aviation. *Lovell White Durrant* has recently gained three aviation finance specialists from *Sinclair Roche & Temperley* including department head Robin Hallam, thereby strengthening *Lovell White Durrant's* activity in this field. *Cameron Markby Hewitt* have expertise in aircraft finance, air carriage, disaster, insolvency, insurance and regulatory matters. *Davies Arnold Cooper* provide a comprehensive service to the sector, specialising in insurance- related aspects. *Jarvis & Bannister* are also known for their insurance-based work and have particular expertise in disaster cases.

Watson Farley & Williams advise on aircraft financing, secured lending, tax-based, tax-leveraged and FSC leasing, the sale and purchase of aircraft, operating leases, aviation regulation and other associated transactions. Geoffrey Williams is a specialist in the field.

Firms and individuals who have been particularly recommended for aviation finance expertise are listed in a separate table.

LEADING INDIVIDUALS – LONDON – AVIATION FINANCE		
Bob Charlton *Clifford Chance*	Paul A. Giles *Norton Rose*	Simon A.D. Hall *Freshfields*
A. Littlejohns *Freshfields*	Peter Geoffrey Thorne *Norton Rose*	Geoffrey White *Clifford Chance*
Anne Williamson *Clifford Chance*		
Austen Hall *Brecher & Co*	Robin Hallam *Lovell White Durrant*	Peter Jolliffe *Slaughter and May*
Julia A. Salt *Allen & Overy*	Colin Thaine *Wilde Sapte*	Geoffrey C. Williams *Watson Farley & Williams*

SOUTH EAST

In the South East, *Dallas Brett* is the leading firm, with expertise in aircraft finance and leasing, the regulation and operation of civil air transport, air charter contracts and conditions of carriage. Glenvil Smith, at the firm, has been recommended for his expertise in these areas.

HIGHLY REGARDED – SOUTH EAST	
DALLAS BRETT *Oxford*	LAWFORD & CO *Nottingham*

Lawford & Co. also have a recognised capability in the field, specialising in air accident investigation work.

LEADING INDIVIDUALS – SOUTH EAST
Glenvil Smith *Dallas Brett*

SOUTH WEST

Two firms emerge in the region for expertise in aviation.

HIGHLY REGARDED – SOUTH WEST	
CARTWRIGHTS *Bristol*	STEELE RAYMOND *Bournemouth*

Steele Raymond, where John Andrews has a reputation for work across the aviation spectrum, has particular strength in regulatory and general commercial work. *Cartwrights* has

specialist skills for regional airports relating to the Civil Aviation Act 1982, the Airports Act 1986, the Air Navigation Order and associated legislation.

LEADING INDIVIDUALS – SOUTH WEST
John I. Andrews *Steele Raymond*

MIDLANDS

In Birmingham, *Eversheds* has considerable experience in general commercial work in the aviation sector. *Keely Smith & Jobson,* in Lichfield, handle contentious and non-contentious work in relation to light aircraft for private individuals and syndicates.

HIGHLY REGARDED – MIDLANDS	
EVERSHEDS *Birmingham*	KEELY SMITH & JOBSON *Lichfield*

EAST ANGLIA

Hansell Stevenson is known for handling regulatory, licensing and general commercial advice. Clients include a major UK airline and general aviation companies.

HIGHLY REGARDED – EAST ANGLIA
HANSELL STEVENSON *Norwich*

NORTH WEST

Elliott & Co, in Manchester, is particularly well regarded for its financing and leasing side, and the deputy senior partner, Katherine Mellor, has an excellent reputation in this area.

HIGHLY REGARDED – NORTH WEST

ELLIOTT & CO *Manchester*

LEADING INDIVIDUALS – NORTH WEST

Katherine M. Mellor *Elliott & Co*

SCOTLAND

Aircraft finance is a rather limited area of practice in Scotland, and firms' expertise tends to be concentrated on specialist aviation litigation advice.

Shepherd & Wedderburn WS and *Simpson & Marwick WS* are well regarded for their disaster litigation and inquiries work. Both firms have advised and represented most of the defenders and government agencies involved in the several air disasters (both fixed-wing and helicopter), which have occurred in Scotland over the last 16 years. Hugh Donald and Peter Anderson, at the above mentioned firms respectively, are highly regarded for this work.

HIGHLY REGARDED – SCOTLAND

MACLAY MURRAY & SPENS *Glasgow*	**SHEPHERD & WEDDERBURN** *Edinburgh*
SIMPSON & MARWICK WS *Edinburgh*	

Maclay Murray & Spens has been recommended for its litigation expertise, and has recently represented the underwriters insured in a Glasgow helicopter crash. Richard Clark at the firm is well regarded for his expertise.

LEADING INDIVIDUALS – SCOTLAND

M. Peter Anderson *Simpson & Marwick WS*
Richard A.F. Clark *Maclay Murray & Spens*
Hugh R. Donald *Shepherd & Wedderburn*

LEADERS IN AVIATION

LONDON

Awford, Ian
Barlow Lyde & Gilbert, London (0171) 247 2277. Partner in Aviation Department.

Specialisation: Main area of practice is aviation law, including law relating to commercial uses of outer space. Also handles insurance law, litigation and arbitration. Has acted in many major air disasters including BA/ Inex Andria, Zagreb mid-air 1976; Tenerife 1967; Dan Air in Tenerife; Avianca in Madrid; Saudia L1011 and British Airtours in Manchester. Author of various publications on legal issues concerning carriage by air, aerospace, products liability and the law relating to outer space.

Prof. Membership: International Institute of Space Law of the International Astronautics Federation; International Forum of Travel and Tourism Advocates; International Society of Air Safety Investigators; European Society of Air Safety Investigators; City of London Law Society (Shipping and Aviation Sub-Committee); International Associate of the American Bar Association; Air Law Group of the Royal Aeronautical Society; European Centre for Space Law; Air Law Working Party at the International Chamber of Commerce; Product Liability Advisory Council; International Association of Defence Counsel.

Career: Qualified in 1967, and in Hong Kong in 1988. Joined *Barlow Lyde & Gilbert* in 1969, becoming a Partner in 1973. Chairman of the Outer Space Committee of the International Bar Association: Section of Business Law 1987-90; Aerospace Law Committee, Inter Pacific Bar Association since 1990.

Personal: Born 15th April 1941. Attended Wellingborough School, Northants, then Sheffield University. Leisure interests include skiing, theatre, opera, ballet and painting. Lives in London.

Balfour, John M.
Frere Cholmeley Bischoff, London (0171) 615 8000. Partner and Head of Aviation Group.

Specialisation: Practice includes regulation, EC, and CAA work; accidents, liability and insurance; sale, purchase and leasing and other commercial arrangements; and international issues. Author of 'Air Law and the European Community' and 'Butterworths' European Law Service: Air Transport' and of many articles on aviation in the professional press. Lectures extremely widely; recent engagements include conferences and courses organised by IATA, the Institute of Economic Affairs, the European Institute of Public Administration, McGill University, the EC Commission and Russian Ministry of Transport and Avmark.

Prof Membership: Royal Aeronautical Society (Chairman, Air Law Group), European Air Law Association (Treasurer) and Solicitors European Group.

Career: Qualified 1979, having joined *Frere Cholmeley Bischoff* in 1977. Became a Partner in 1986 and Head of the Aviation Group in 1993.

Butler-Sloss, Frances A.J.
Harbottle & Lewis, London (0171) 629 7633. Partner in Aviation Group.

Specialisation: Handles exclusively aviation work, advising airlines and other aviation companies on international regulations, aero-political issues, competition law, commercial arrangements, airline business, aircraft/ engine leasing and travel matters.

Personal: Born 13th October 1959.

Chamberlain, Simon
Field Fisher Waterhouse, London (0171) 481 4841.

Specialisation: Partner in the Aviation, Travel & Tourism Department specialising in commercial, corporate and regulatory work within the aviation and travel industries.

Career: Qualified in 1977. Richards Butler &Co. 1973-81. British Airways Plc 1981-1990. Rowe & Maw 1990-1994. Partner at Field Fisher Waterhouse since 1994.

Personal: Educated at Downside School. Born 8th August 1953. Lives in East Sussex.

Charlton, Bob
Clifford Chance, London (0171) 600 1000. Partner 1987. Banking Department. Main area of practice is asset based finance. Also handles project finance and general banking work. Born 15.3.1957.

Clark, David N.
Beaumont and Son, London (0171) 481 3100. Qualified 1977. Partner 1990. Aviation Department. Work includes aerospace, litigation insurance and personal injury work for defendants. Born 8.3.1952.

Cook, C. John
See under European Community & Competition.

Farrell, Patrick
Norton Rose, London (0171) 283 6000. Qualified 1983. Partner 1989. Commercial Litigation Department. Main areas of practice are aviation and litigation. Acts for airlines, tour operators, financiers and insurers. Born 20.11.1957.

Franke, Colin

Clyde & Co, London (0171) 623 1244.
Qualified 1975. Partner 1979. Litigation Department. Main area of practice is aviation; also handles marine and insurance work. Born 2.1.1950.

Gates, Sean

Beaumont and Son, London (0171) 481 3100. Qualified 1972. Partner 1978. Head of Aviation Department. Principal areas of practice include aviation catastrophe management, liability, insurance and claims and defamation. Vice Chariman Air Law Group, Royal Aeronautical Society. Arbitrator with Cour Internationale d'Arbitrage Aerien et Spatial. Born 4.2.1949.

Giles, Paul A.

Norton Rose, London (0171) 283 6000.
Qualified 1974. Partner 1988. Banking Department. Transportation specialist. Work includes aircraft and rolling stock cross border tax transactions and aircraft sale and purchase. Born 9.4.1948

Hall, Simon A.D.

See under Asset Finance & Leasing.

Hall, Austen

Brecher & Co, London (0171) 493 5141. Partner in Banking and Asset Finance Department.

Specialisation: Work includes asset finance (especially aviation and shipping work), general banking, equipment leasing, secured lending and trade finance. Also handles public and private company law work. Author of numerous articles, for example on aviation and aviation insurance matters.

Prof. Membership: Law Society, Westminster Law Society.

Career: Qualified in 1986 with *Norton Rose*. Worked at *Wilde Sapte* 1987-91 and then *Berwin Leighton* 1991-93. Moved to *Brecher & Co.* as a Partner in 1993.

Personal: Born 23rd September 1960. Attended Dr Challoners Grammar School 1972-79, University of Southampton 1979-82, College of Law 1982-83 and University of Southampton (LLM) 1983-84. Leisure interests include flying (private pilot) and tennis. Lives in Bucks.

Hallam, Robin

Lovell White Durrant, London (0171) 236 0066. Partner in Banking Group; Aviation Finance. All aspects of aviation finance, particularly acting for banks and financiers. Born 21.11.53.

Howes, Colin M.

See under Company/Commercial.

Hughes, Nicholas M.L.

Barlow Lyde & Gilbert, London (0171) 247 2277. Qualified 1981. Partner 1984. Aerospace Department. Practice covers insurance and reinsurance and liability law. Born 10.10.1955.

Jolliffe, Peter

Slaughter and May, London (0171) 600 1200. Qualified 1981. Partner specialising in aircraft financing, banking and financing other types of equipment.

Kilbride, D.A.

Beaumont and Son, London (0171) 481 3100. Qualified 1979. Partner 1982. Aviation Department. Also handles aerospace and transport law, and litigation insurance work. Born 29.7.1948.

Littlejohns, A.

Freshfields, London (0171) 936 4000.

Martin, Peter

Frere Cholmeley Bischoff, London (0171) 615 8000. Consultant to Aviation Department.

Specialisation: Work covers air law including aviation insurance, international relations, regulation and financing. Active figure in civil aviation since 1961. Extensive experience in legal aspects of airworthiness, aircraft operations and licensing, bilateral and multilateral air services agreement negotiations, aircraft accident inquiry, product liability litigation and Lloyd's. Co-ordinating editor of Shawcross & Beaumont: Air Law since 1975. Visiting Professor in Aerospace Law, University College London. Co-editor 'Aviation' volume of Halsbury's Laws of England. Writer of numerous articles on air law subjects in aeronautical and legal journals. Frequent guest lecturer. Honorary legal adviser: Royal Aeronautical Society, British Helicopter Advisory Board, Museum of Army Flying.

Prof. Membership: Fellow of the Royal Aeronautical Society, Fellow of the Royal Geographical Society and Member of Finance and General Purposes Committee.

Career: Articled with *Allen & Overy* 1956-59. Partner at *Beaumont & Son* 1961-81, then joined *Frere Cholmeley* as Head of Aviation Department. Became Consultant *Frere Cholmeley Bischoff* in 1993 on retirement as Partner

Personal: Born 9th May 1934. Attended University College London. Director of Equitable Life Assurance Society; Sterling Underwriting Agencies Limited at Lloyd's, Permanent Insurance Co Ltd. Finsbury Underwriting Investment Trust plc. Trustee: Research into Ageing. Member of Management Committee Citizens Advice Bureau/ Royal Courts of Justice. Lives in London.

McGilchrist, Neil R.

Beaumont and Son, London (0171) 481 3100. Qualified 1969. Partner 1982. Aviation Department. Work includes reinsurance, aerospace and litigation insurance work. Born 8.12.1946.

Nott, M.W.T.

Rowe & Maw, London (0171) 248 4282.
Qualified 1971.

O'Donovan, Hugh

Wilde Sapte, London (0171) 246 7000.
Partner in Banking Department and Aviation Industry Group.

Specialisation: Main area of practice is aviation, covering international aviation regulation, commercial agreements in aviation, EC and competition law, airline and airport operations, aircraft leasing and airport financing. Also covers general transport work, particularly regulation and commercial aspects of the rail industry, travel agents and tour operators. Contributing editor of Sweet & Maxwell's Encyclopaedia of Competition Law (and author of Air Transport chapter). Regular speaker at various conferences and seminars on aviation-related topics.

Prof. Memberships: Law Society, International Bar Association, Royal Aeronautical Society.

Career: Called to the Bar in 1975. Practised as a barrister before joining *Knapp Fishers* in 1985. Left for *Richards Butler* in 1987 (Partner 1989). Presently with *Wilde Sapte* after joining as a partner in 1991.

Personal: Born 19th August 1952. Attended Royal Grammar School, Guildford 1963-69 then Balliol College, Oxford 1970-73. Leisure pursuits include golf, skiing, flying and rugby coaching. Lives in Witley, Surrey.

Reynolds, David

Clyde & Co, London (0171) 623 1244.
Qualified 1979. Partner 1981. Main areas of practice are aviation, principally cargo claims; and energy and environmental law. Born 23.6.1953.

Salt, Julia A.

Allen & Overy, London (0171) 330 3000.
Qualified 1980. Partner 1985. Banking Department. Broad financing practice, including aircraft securitisation and telecommunications.

Scorer, Tim

Jarvis & Bannister, London (0171) 242 3413.

Scully, Dermot

Harbottle & Lewis, London (0171) 629 7633.

Specialisation: Senior Associate in the Aviation Group specialising in regulatory, finance and general commercial work. Practice includes advising airlines, banks, maintenance contractors and other aviation businesses on leasing, regulatory work, competition, debt financing and general commercial matters.

Soames, Trevor I.

See under European Community & Competition.

Thaine, Colin

Wilde Sapte, London (0171) 246 7000.

Thorne, Peter Geoffrey
See under Asset Finance & Leasing.

Tyrrell, Gerrard
Harbottle & Lewis, London (0171) 629 7633. Qualified 1981. Partner 1984. Litigation Department. Main area of practice is commercial litigation. Works in aviation, media and entertainment industries.

Unmack, T.S.B.
Beaumont and Son, London (0171) 481 3100. Qualified 1965. Partner 1968. Senior Partner. Main areas of practice are aerospace, non-contentious insurance and reinsurance, and litigation insurance. Born 5.8.1937.

Venables, Richard
Lane & Partners, London (0171) 242 2626. Partner in Aviation and Travel Department.

Specialisation: Principal area of work is aviation law advising British and foreign airlines on regulatory matters including CAA licensing, European competition law and all other matters affecting airlines' commercial operations. Other main area of work is advising UK-based tour operators, particularly on Air Travel Organisers' Licensing, UK and European legal developments and contractual matters. Acted for a group of British charter airlines re foreign registered aircraft and scheduled airlines in a European Commission complaint about Computerised Reservation Systems. Contributor of articles to trade publications. Spoke at Aviation Law Association of Australia and New Zealand, 1993, and regularly addresses conferences.

Prof. Membership: Chartered Institute of Transport, Royal Aeronautical Society, European Air Law Association.

Career: Qualified in 1971 while with *Gregory, Rowcliffe & Co.*, then joined *Norton Rose* in 1973. Moved to *Booth & Co.* in Leeds 1975-76, then returned to *Norton Rose* 1976-82. Joined *Lane & Partners* in 1982 and became a Partner in 1983.

Personal: Born 6th December 1946. Attended Uppingham School 1960-65, then Keble College, Oxford 1965-68. Leisure pursuits include golf, walking, tennis and family activities. Lives in Hampton, Middlesex.

White, Geoffrey
Clifford Chance, London (0171) 600 1000. Partner. Principal area of practice is asset/project financing and leasing.

Willcox, David J.
Beaumont and Son, London (0171) 481 3100. Qualified 1981. Partner 1990. Aviation Department. Work includes aerospace, commercial litigation and litigation insurance. Born 25.3.1957.

Williams, Geoffrey C.
Watson Farley & Williams, London (0171) 814 8000. Partner in banking and asset finance department.

Specialisation: Main area of work is aviation law. Also advises on asset and project finance including shipping and banking. Clients include banks and finance lessors, operating lessors, owners and operators, brokers and packagers, manufacturers.

Prof. Membership: Law Society

Career: Partner *Norton Rose Botterell & Roche* 1974-1982. Partner *Watson Farley & Williams* 1982 to date.

Personal: Lives London W1. BA; LLB 1966.

Williamson, Anne
Clifford Chance, London (0171) 600 1000. Partner. Specialises in Asset Finance.

Anderson, M.Peter
See under Litigation (Commercial).

Andrews, John I.
Steele Raymond, Wimborne (01202) 885211. Qualified 1980. Partner 1983. Litigation/Commercial Department. Main areas of practice are civil aviation and airport operation. Born 24.2.1956.

Clark, Richard A.F.
Maclay Murray & Spens, Glasgow (0141) 248 5011. Qualified 1973. Partner. Commercial Litigation Department. Specialist fields include aviation, shipping, environmental and product liability law. Born 19.9.1949.

Donald, Hugh R.
See under Medical Negligence.

Mellor, Katherine M.
Elliott & Company, Manchester (0161) 834 9933. Qualified 1975. Deputy Senior Partner. Specialises in aircraft leasing, takeovers and mergers.

Smith, Glenvil
Dallas Brett, Oxford (01865) 791990. fax:(01865) 791772

Specialisation: Aviation Law, travel and tourism, in particular aircraft financing and leasing, asset value and deficiency guarantees, export credit support, sale and purchase agreements, maintenance agreements, aircrew contracts, 'dry' and 'wet' aircraft leases, air transport licences and permits, air operators' certificates, registration and certification of aircraft, air charter and brokerage agreements, conditions of carriage, air travel organisers' licences, bonding requirements and tour operators' trading terms and conditions. Clients include UK and overseas airlines, tour operators and travel agents, aviation brokers and maintenance organisations.

Prof. Membership: Law Society, International Bar Association (Member of the Aeronautical Law Committee).

Career: Qualified 1976. Articles *Norton Rose* 1973-75. In-house counsel with Spectra Travel 1976-79, Crown Agents 1979-82 and Dan-Air Services Limited 1982-86. Joined *Dallas Brett* as partner in 1986, became consultant in 1991.

Personal: Born 1949. Educated Shrewsbury School and Trinity College, Cambridge.

BANKING

LONDON

The banking sector in London is dominated by two firms, *Clifford Chance* and *Allen & Overy*. In terms of sheer size, and numbers of transactions undertaken, the former must take precedence with something approaching 200 lawyers working in this area. However, in qualitative terms there is probably little now to choose between the firms, with *Allen & Overy* having traditionally enjoyed a very high profile and reputation in virtually all areas of 'pure' banking.

LEADING FIRMS – LONDON	
ALLEN & OVERY	CLIFFORD CHANCE
FRESHFIELDS	LINKLATERS & PAINES
NORTON ROSE	SLAUGHTER AND MAY
CAMERON MARKBY HEWITT	LOVELL WHITE DURRANT
WILDE SAPTE	

In the next band we would list *Linklaters & Paines* (where Haydn Puleston Jones has been most frequently recommended, John Tucker is developing a strong reputation and Christopher Style is highly regarded in the area of banking litigation), *Freshfields* (where David Ereira and Edward Evans have excellent reputations), *Slaughter and May* and *Norton Rose*. All of these firms have been active on a wide range of high-quality, high-value banking transactions. *Linklaters & Paines*, for example, has acted on a range of major syndicated credits for Citibank, CS First Boston, Lloyds and Sumitomo Bank. *Freshfields*, as well as acting for the Bank of England, has also been involved in a number of high-profile financings including the US $2.3 billion facilities arranged in connection with the Shell/Montedison joint venture and the FF7.65 billion facilities provided by Société Générale and NatWest to Commercial Union in connection with the acquisition of Groupe Victoire.

The growing trend amongst major corporates to self-syndicate or generate bilateral or 'club' deals, often dictating terms to banks keen to lend, has been one area of activity resulting in continued banking work for the leading players including *Slaughter and May,* whose blue-chip corporate client base is still second to none in quality. The firm is also known for its work on behalf of merchant and investment banks such as J.P. Morgan for whom it acted when the bank arranged a $250 million syndicated loan facility to the Alliance & Leicester Building Society.

Norton Rose has developed its practice in the area of cable TV and telecommunications financings where its client Toronto Dominion Bank has been active, and the firm may be benefiting from some increased Midland Bank work as a result of the long-standing Hong Kong Shanghai Bank connection. On the syndicated financing side the firm recently advised the Kingdom of Sweden in a £6 billion facility, and on the structured debt side, acted for the banks making available a £2 billion facility for Trafalgar House in its bid for Northern Electric.

Also highly rated are *Cameron Markby Hewitt, Wilde Sapte* and *Lovell White Durrant.*

At *Cameron Markby Hewitt* banking accounts for 20% of the firm's work-load and is one of its five core areas. The firm acts for more than 80 UK and international banks and is engaged in all the traditional banking areas. The firm is particularly active in the Italian banking market and is one of the leading players in the Italian export credit field. The firm is also heavily involved in the distressed debt market, representing buyers and sellers and major English and foreign banks. Banking regulation continues as a growth area, as does advising building societies. Among recent transactions the firm was involved in the UK's first public securitisation of a commercial mortgage book, selling and exchanging

LEADING INDIVIDUALS – LONDON		
Haydn Puleston Jones *Linklaters & Paines*		
Michael Bray *Clifford Chance*	Michael G. Duncan *Allen & Overy*	David Philip Ereira *Freshfields*
Edward T.H. Evans *Freshfields*	Anthony R. Humphrey *Allen & Overy*	David H. Morley *Allen & Overy*
Stuart Popham *Clifford Chance*	Mark Stewart *Clifford Chance*	Christopher J.D. Style *Linklaters & Paines*
Graham D. Vinter *Allen & Overy*	Philip Wood *Allen & Overy*	
Maurice Allen *Clifford Chance*	Andrew G. Balfour *Slaughter and May*	Mark Campbell *Clifford Chance*
Armel Cates *Clifford Chance*	Ruth M. Fox *Slaughter and May*	Jonathan Horsfall Turner *Allen & Overy*
Alan Inglis *Clifford Chance*	James Johnson *Wilde Sapte*	A.C. Keal *Allen & Overy*
Michael Mathews *Clifford Chance*	Neil C. Morrison *McGrigor Donald*	Stephen R.P. Mostyn-Williams *Ashursts*
Chris Oakley *Clifford Chance*	Richard Pettit *Clifford Chance*	Brian Rutherford *Dundas & Wilson CS*
Peter F. Schulz *Allen & Overy*	George E.S. Seligman *Slaughter and May*	Richard Slater *Slaughter and May*
Malcolm Sweeting *Clifford Chance*	John T. Tucker *Linklaters & Paines*	Carol Wakefield *Osborne Clarke*
Martin A. Watson *Watson Farley & Williams*	Geoffrey. L. Wynne *Watson Farley & Williams*	P.M. Hall *Norton Rose*

UP AND COMING		
Lee Cullinane *Clifford Chance*	K. Ian Hodgson *Slaughter and May*	Sean Pierce *Linklaters & Paines*

Latin American debt assets and a publicly quoted Italian receivables securitisation programme.

Wilde Sapte claims banking law as its principal speciality, with the firm fielding 28 specialist partners engaged in banking matters. Recent rapid international expansion has led to the opening of offices in Tokyo and Hong Kong.

HIGHLY REGARDED – LONDON	
ASHURST MORRIS CRISP	HERBERT SMITH
SIMMONS & SIMMONS	STEPHENSON HARWOOD
ALSOP WILKINSON	DENTON HALL
LAWRENCE GRAHAM	MACFARLANES
McKENNA & CO	NABARRO NATHANSON
OSBORNE CLARKE	TAYLOR JOYNSON GARRETT
THEODORE GODDARD	TRAVERS SMITH BRAITHWAITE
WATSON, FARLEY & WILLIAMS	
BERWIN LEIGHTON	DIBB LUPTON BROOMHEAD
DUNDAS & WILSON CS	FIELD FISHER WATERHOUSE
GOULDENS	MACKENZIE MILLS
McGRIGOR DONALD	MIDDLETON POTTS
SIDLEY & AUSTIN	

Lovell White Durrant has historically had close links with Barclays Bank, although the practice now encompasses virtually all aspects of 'pure' banking work and advice to borrowers and lenders. Recently the banking team were engaged in the high profile acquisition of the Barings Group on behalf of ING.

Banking and capital markets work accounts for 10% of *Simmons & Simmons'* total work-load. The firm concentrates on core areas of practice including secured and unsecured lending, capital markets, particularly eurobonds and international equity offerings and securitisation and structured finance. The firm recently advised Goldman Sachs International as lead manager of two complex public securitisation issues by the National Home Loans Corporation plc. The banking team was also heavily involved in providing advice to the controlling shareholders of the Pedro Domecq wine and spirits group in the Allied-Lyons takeover.

Stephenson Harwood's Banking Group comprises teams focusing on lending, project and trade finance, capital markets, regulation and insolvency. Currently, the Group is especially active in loan syndications and club deals in the Scandanavian and Indian markets, structured trade finance in Central and Eastern Europe and the Far East, project finance (particularly in the renewable energy industry), and the acquisition and disposal of mortgage portfolios. The structuring and documentation of equity-linked derivative products (OTC and listed) is a major growth area for the Group.

Herbert Smith's general banking work is carried out within its International Finance and Banking Group. Although the bulk of its work is for the borrower, the firm does have major bank clients which instruct it from time to time, such as The Chase Manhattan Bank, UBS, Forward Trust and Kleinwort Benson. The firm advised Eurotunnel on all the banking aspects of its 1994 refinancing and rights issues; House of Fraser on its flotation and new syndicated facility; and

BSkyB on the banking aspects of its proposed flotation and new £400 million facility.

Despite having only four specialist banking and international finance partners, *Ashurst Morris Crisp* has an excellent reputation for its banking capability, which accounts for 10% of its work-load. The firm's clients include Bankers Trust, Morgan Stanley, NM Rothschild, Sumitomo Trust & Banking Co, Swiss Bank Corporation and Union Bank of Switzerland. The firm was engaged in advising on the first Euro-market financed leveraged buy-out in Portugal, using a proprietary structure created by the firm; the first use of 'B' notes in a cross-border LBO; the first Hong Kong residential mortgage securitisation and the new flexible participation facility launched in the London syndicated sterling market in January 1995.

SOUTH EAST

There is only a limited amount of 'pure' banking activity amongst firms in the South East. However, a number of firms do have experience in certain general areas such as secured lending and banking litigation. *Adams & Remers, Cripps Harries Hall* and *Shoosmiths & Harrison's* Reading office

HIGHLY REGARDED – SOUTH EAST		
ADAMS & REMERS *Lewes*	CRIPPS HARRIES HALL *Tunbridge Wells*	
SHOOSMITHS & HARRISON *Reading*		
BOYES TURNER & BURROWS *Reading*	DONNE MILEHAM & HADDOCK *Brighton*	
MOORE & BLATCH *Southampton*	RAWLISON & BUTLER *Crawley*	

all act for regional offices of one or other of the major clearing banks, principally in the area of banking litigation. *Boyes Turner & Burrows, Donne Mileham & Haddock, Moore & Blatch* and *Rawlison & Butler* are also active in debt collection, realisations and recovery work for banks.

SOUTH WEST

Although a number of firms in the region act for banks on a regular basis, the leading firm now is probably *Osborne Clarke* which benefits from its long-standing relationships with Nat-West and Lloyds Bank, acting as their regional representative.

LEADING FIRMS – SOUTH WEST	
BOND PEARCE *Plymouth*	BURGES SALMON *Bristol*
OSBORNE CLARKE *Bristol*	

The firm's specialist team which acts on a full range of commercial lending, acquisition finance, corporate recovery and banking litigation, has been strengthened in the last year by the arrival of Margaret Childs (ex-Bank of America) as Head of Corporate Banking and Carol Wakefield, ex-head of litigation at Lloyds Bank, who is based in the London office.

Both *Burges Salmon* and *Bond Pearce* have notable banking practices, the latter acting for regional offices of two of the UK clearing banks and also advising City-based institutions and London branches of overseas banks on trade and receivables, financings and regulatory matters. *Burges Salmon,* where both Guy Stobart and Sandra Rosser have been recommended, has made considerable efforts to build its practice in this area and has gained some notable clients such as Bank of Scotland, UCB and the agricultural finance arm of National Westminster Bank.

Cameron Markby Hewitt is, of course, a recognised banking firm although it is not perceived as having greatly extended its areas of activity in the region beyond servicing its major client Lloyds Bank, for which purpose the Bristol office was established five years ago.

HIGHLY REGARDED – SOUTH WEST

CAMERON MARKBY HEWITT *Bristol*	LESTER ALDRIDGE *Bournemouth*
LYONS DAVIDSON *Bristol*	WANSBROUGHS WILLEY HARGRAVE *Bristol*
EVERSHEDS *Bristol*	FOOT & BOWDEN *Plymouth*
TOZERS *Exeter*	

Lyons Davidson and *Wansbroughs Willey Hargrave* have traditionally done some banking work, although predominantly on the insolvency and banking litigation side. *Lester Aldridge* in Bournemouth has heightened its profile with the appointment of Graham Jeffries (formerly of McKenna & Co) who practises exclusively in non-contentious banking work.

The takeover of *Holt Phillips* by *Eversheds Phillips & Buck* (as it was known) resulted in the acquisition of a Bristol office already active in litigation work for banking and finance clients. *Eversheds* now operates its Cardiff and Bristol offices as an integrated unit. Their strength in banking generally indicates a clear potential for expansion at the Bristol arm of the practice.

LEADING INDIVIDUALS – SOUTH WEST

Margaret E. Childs *Osborne Clarke*	
Graham Jeffries *Lester Aldridge*	
Sandra Rosser *Burges Salmon*	
Guy W. Stobart *Burges Salmon*	
Victor Tettmar *Bond Pearce*	

WALES

Although the three major commercial practices in Cardiff all deal with aspects of banking, *Eversheds* is clearly pre-eminent in this area. They act not only in a local or regional capacity but as head office solicitors to a number of banks and

LEADING FIRMS – WALES

EVERSHEDS *Cardiff*

EDWARDS GELDARD *Cardiff*	MORGAN BRUCE *Cardiff*

financial institutions based both in Wales and elsewhere. On the litigation side, Kevin Doolan is well thought of and heads the overall banking and finance department. In the non-contentious department, the firm has been involved in a wide range of transactional and documentation matters including

HIGHLY REGARDED – WALES

BEVAN ASHFORD *Cardiff*

the launch of a new banking product for a major insurance company, a £50 million acquisition finance facility and the sale of a mortgage and loan portfolio on behalf of Chartered Trust plc (an area in which Philip Vaughan is recognised as having a special expertise).

LEADING INDIVIDUALS – WALES

Kevin J. Doolan *Eversheds*
Philip D. Vaughan *Eversheds*

Edwards Geldard acts regionally for Barclays Bank in a wide range of matters and *Morgan Bruce* are continually strengthening their banking expertise in both contentious and non-contentious work. *Bevan Ashford* have traditionally been associated with local debt collection litigation on behalf of Midland Bank.

MIDLANDS

Banking expertise is located primarily in Birmingham where *Wragge & Co* and *Pinsent Curtis* dominate the field. These firms continue to handle relatively sophisticated banking work which has historically been the province of the London City firms. *Wragge & Co* has long acted as regional solicitors for Lloyds Bank and has recently been appointed (jointly with *Pinsent Curtis*) to the panel of another UK clearer. The firm advises on a range of banking matters as well as commercial lending, and undertakes banking litigation. The firm also handles acquisition financings, with deals being concluded on behalf of Midland Bank, Standard Chartered and, in connection with the MBO of Leyland DAF Vans, the Royal Bank of Scotland. Notable members of the team are Richard Haywood and Julian Pallett, who has recently taken over as head of the banking section.

LEADING FIRMS – MIDLANDS

PINSENT CURTIS *Birmingham*	WRAGGE & CO *Birmingham*
EDGE & ELLISON *Birmingham*	EVERSHEDS *Birmingham*
GATELEY WAREING *Birmingham*	MARTINEAU JOHNSON *Birmingham*
FREETH CARTWRIGHT HUNT DICKINS *Nottingham*	SHOOSMITHS & HARRISON *Northampton*

In common with other firms operating in this sector, *Pinsent Curtis* has experienced a reduction in insolvency based work, although the firm has experienced high levels of activity in acquisition financings, mortgage and loan portfolio transfers and project finance.

LEADING INDIVIDUALS – MIDLANDS

Richard Haywood *Wragge & Co*
Julian C. Pallett *Wragge & Co*
Ian C. Reaves *Edge & Ellison*
David J. Cooke *Pinsent Curtis*
Pat Johnstone *Eversheds*
John Temple *Shoosmiths & Harrison*
G. Patrick A.S. Twist *Pinsent Curtis*

Eversheds (Birmingham) has historically benefited from its long-standing (but no longer exclusive) relationship with National Westminster Bank whilst *Edge & Ellison, Martineau Johnson* and *Gateley Wareing* also have recognised banking capability.

In the East Midlands *Shoosmiths & Harrison*, where John Temple is highly regarded, is well-known for banking work.

EAST ANGLIA

Banking expertise in the region is shared principally between two firms. *Eversheds* has a general commercial banking practice and acts as regional solicitor for one of the UK clearing banks. *Mills & Reeve's* major banking client is Barclays Bank

LEADING FIRMS – EAST ANGLIA	
EVERSHEDS *Norwich*	**MILLS & REEVE** *Norwich*

and although historically prominent in litigation and recovery work, they have also become increasingly active in the areas of commercial lending, securities and asset financing. Notable individuals are Andrew Croome at *Eversheds* and Edward Callaghan and John Lapraik at *Mills & Reeve.*

HIGHLY REGARDED – EAST ANGLIA
LEATHES PRIOR *Norwich*

In addition, *Leathes Prior* is recognised as having some banking expertise, although principally in the area of insolvency, recovery and litigation.

LEADING INDIVIDUALS – EAST ANGLIA
Edward J. Callaghan *Mills & Reeve*
Andrew Croome *Eversheds*
J.D. Lapraik *Mills & Reeve*

NORTH WEST

Manchester is undoubtedly the centre for the region's banking work although some expertise is provided in Liverpool. *Addleshaw Sons & Latham* enjoys a pre-eminent reputation in the field. The whole spectrum of banking work including structured finance and syndicated loans, acquisition and buy-out finance, corporate recovery and litigation work is handled by the firm where Shaun Rearden and Stephen Clark enjoy excellent reputations. *Addleshaw Sons & Latham's* position has been further strengthened by the addition of the highly recommended Cate Wood, formerly at *Davies Arnold Cooper.*

LEADING FIRMS – NORTH WEST	
ADDLESHAW SONS & LATHAM *Manchester*	
CHAFFE STREET *Manchester*	**SLATER HEELIS** *Manchester*
COBBETT LEAK ALMOND *Manchester*	**DAVIES WALLIS FOYSTER** *Liverpool*
DIBB LUPTON BROOMHEAD *Manchester*	**HAMMOND SUDDARDS** *Manchester*

Chaffe Street has a niche banking practice with a prominence and reputation out of proportion to their overall size. The firm acts for over 30 national and international banks and financial institutions. Christopher Lumsden has been particularly recommended.

HIGHLY REGARDED – NORTH WEST	
ALSOP WILKINSON *Liverpool*	**EVERSHEDS** *Manchester*
GARRETT & CO	**HALLIWELL LANDAU** *Manchester*
BERMANS *Liverpool*	**VAUDREYS** *Manchester*

Slater Heelis is also well-known for its banking work and Mark Warburton enjoys a strong reputation in the field. The firm has long acted for National Westminster Bank and expects to consolidate its position in this respect following the regional restructuring which has taken place within the Bank.

Both *Dibb Lupton Broomhead* and *Hammond Suddards* have been making efforts to raise their profiles and compete more effectively in the sector. Together with *Cobbett Leak Almond* and *Davies Wallis Foyster* they are mentioned most frequently as having a general banking capability.

Personnel movements have been a feature in the region this year with *Alsop Wilkinson* suffering a high-profile loss when its Manchester head of banking, Susan Molloy, moved to the newly established office of *Garrett & Co.*

Eversheds has also benefited from their extensive corporate client base to act on financings and may also benefit from some consolidation and cross-fertilisation between their Manchester and Leeds offices. *Halliwell Landau* has a good reputation, especially in the property financing area with Raymond McDaid receiving particular mention.

LEADING INDIVIDUALS – NORTH WEST
Christopher G.M. Lumsden *Chaffe Street*
Susan Molloy *Garrett & Co*
Shaun Rearden *Addleshaw Sons & Latham*
M.C. Warburton *Slater Heelis*
Cate Wood *Addleshaw Sons & Latham*
Edward Tjorn Bootland *Davies Wallis Foyster*
Stephen P. Clark *Addleshaw Sons & Latham*
Nigel A. Dale *Hammond Suddards*
Nicholas Henry Fisher *Dibb Lupton Broomhead*
Raymond McDaid *Halliwell Landau*
J.P. Orrell *Slater Heelis*
John Whatnall *Halliwell Landau*

NORTH EAST

The leading banking firm in the region is *Booth & Co* where Mark Chidley has a particularly strong reputation. Well-known as solicitors to Yorkshire Bank, the firm has achieved a 40% increase in turnover in non-contentious banking areas and generally expanded the size of their specialist team who are now responsible for more than 10% of the firm's overall turnover. Over the year, the firm has been involved in high-profile acquisition and buy-out debt financings, housing association financings and mortgage portfolio acquisitions, having an aggregate value of over £2.2 billion.

LEADING FIRMS – NORTH EAST	
BOOTH & CO. *Leeds*	
EVERSHEDS *Leeds*	HAMMOND SUDDARDS *Leeds*
WALKER MORRIS *Leeds*	
DIBB LUPTON BROOMHEAD *Bradford*	DICKINSON DEES *Newcastle upon Tyne*
PINSENT CURTIS	

Eversheds (Leeds) has also experienced an increase in corporate banking activity throughout the year and acts frequently for the Bank of Scotland, notably on acquisition and MBO financing, and at least one other UK clearing bank on a regional basis. Stephen Hopkins is particularly well-regarded.

HIGHLY REGARDED – NORTH EAST	
GARRETT & CO *Leeds*	ROBERT MUCKLE *Newcastle-upon-Tyne*
WANSBROUGHS WILLEY HARGRAVE *Leeds*	WARD HADAWAY *Newcastle upon Tyne*

Hammond Suddards, and in particular Patrick Mitchell, enjoys a sound reputation, especially in the field of acquisition finance (in relation to which they have acted, not only for bank lenders, but also for the providers of mezzanine and other subordinated debt).

LEADING INDIVIDUALS – NORTH EAST
Mark A. Chidley *Booth & Co.*
Stephen Martyn Hopkins *Eversheds*
Karen Jarvis *Garrett & Co*
J. Patrick Mitchell *Hammond Suddards*
J.H. Finnigan *Eversheds*
Ian M. Gilbert *Walker Morris*
Andrew W. Gosnay *Pinsent Curtis*
Chris Harker *Dickinson Dees*
R.G. Sanderson *Dickinson Dees*
Michael F. Taylor *Walker Morris*
H.B. Welch *Robert Muckle*
Catherine Mary Wood *Robert Muckle*

Walker Morris, where Ian Gilbert and Michael Taylor have been recommended, acts for a significant number of banks and has been involved in various syndicated loan facilities, the acquisition of a £110 million receivables and mortgage book from Refuge Assurance and the negotiation of a £40 million loan facility from First National Bank of Chicago.

Pinsent Curtis has traditionally maintained a broad national banking client base and has this year been involved in debt issues such as the $120 million US private placement for FKI plc, high-value syndicated loan transactions and a significant amount of property-related financing in the education sector. However, the strength of its banking team has been adversely affected by the losses of Catherine Baxan-

dall, who moved in-house to Spring Ram and, perhaps more seriously, the highly regarded Karen Jarvis who is now with *Garrett & Co.*

In Newcastle, *Dickinson Dees* remains the market leader, supplying an all-round high-quality service to a range of banks and building societies on a local and regional basis. The focus of their practice is tending to move from receivership and insolvency work towards increasing levels of lending and securitisation transactions and swaps and options work. *Robert Muckle* has also succeeded in building a practice incorporating general work for a number of the English and Scottish clearers and increasing activity in corporate recovery, intensive care, re-structuring and re-financing. Notable individuals include Chris Harker and Gordon Sanderson at *Dickinson Dees* and Hugh Welch and, in the litigation field, Catherine Wood at *Robert Muckle.*

SCOTLAND

Until recently there has been little tradition of specialist banking expertise in Scotland. This is changing with the emergence of a select group of firms and individuals with 'pure' banking expertise. The leading firms in this sector are clearly *Dundas & Wilson CS* and *McGrigor Donald.*

LEADING FIRMS – SCOTLAND	
DUNDAS & WILSON CS *Edinburgh*	McGRIGOR DONALD *Glasgow*
W & J BURNESS WS *Edinburgh*	DICKSON MINTO WS *Edinburgh*
SHEPHERD & WEDDERBURN *Edinburgh*	

Dundas & Wilson CS is engaged mainly on high-value and complex transactions in areas not restricted to commercial secured lending. For instance, the firm acted for The Royal Bank of Scotland in the outsourcing of their cheque and credit clearing operations to EDS Corp in the US, the first such transaction by a UK clearer. Throughout the year the firm acted in over 90 banking transactions with an aggregate value of over £90 billion. The practice is strengthened by the addition of Brian Rutherford (ex Charterhouse Bank) in London, whilst in Scotland Michael Stoneham's reputation is pre-eminent.

HIGHLY REGARDED – SCOTLAND	
BIGGART BAILLIE & GIFFORD *Glasgow*	MACLAY MURRAY & SPENS *Glasgow*
DORMAN JEFFREY & CO *Glasgow*	McCLURE NAISMITH ANDERSON & GARDINER *Glasgow*
TODS MURRAY WS *Edinburgh*	

McGrigor Donald has also taken steps to supplement its strong position in Scotland by attempting to develop a London operation where Neil Morrison is highly recommended.

Probably the next most active firms in the field are *W & J Burness WS, Dickson Minto WS,* who are particularly noted for their corporate client base and acquisition finance ability, and *Shepherd & Wedderburn WS* who carry out general commercial lending work for at least two UK clearers.

Michael P. Stoneham	*Dundas & Wilson CS*
Ian J.G. Lyall	*McGrigor Donald*
Iain M.C. Meiklejohn	*Shepherd & Wedderburn*
Andrew F. Sleigh	*W & J Burness WS*
Graham M. Burnside	*Tods Murray WS*
J. Fraser M. Hardie	*Biggart Baillie & Gifford*
Bruce W. Minto	*Dickson Minto WS*
Hamish A. Patrick	*Tods Murray WS*
W.W. Campbell Smith	*Biggart Baillie & Gifford*

UP AND COMING

Colin McHale	*Dickson Minto WS*
Colin B. McKay	*Biggart Baillie & Gifford*

Also worthy of mention are *Maclay Murray & Spens*, who are recognised for general banking, and *Biggart Baillie & Gifford* who represented the lead banks, Royal Bank of Scotland and Clydesdale Bank, in connection with the Scottish coal industry privatisation.

NORTHERN IRELAND

The leading banking firms in Northern Ireland are all based in Belfast. *L'Estrange & Brett* is pre-eminent in general banking matters and also in asset/ project finance work, while *Cleaver Fulton & Rankin* carries out multi-national work in this area, especially acting for foreign banks investing in Northern Ireland. The firms included below deal, some-

HIGHLY REGARDED – NORTHERN IRELAND

CARSON & McDOWELL *Belfast*	**CLEAVER FULTON & RANKIN** *Belfast*
ELLIOTT DUFFY GARRETT *Belfast*	**L'ESTRANGE & BRETT** *Belfast*
MILLS SELIG *Belfast*	**TUGHAN & CO** *Belfast*

NORMAN WILSON & CO

times on an agency basis, with a broad variety of work on behalf of the major domestic and foreign banks. Those firms which are mainly involved in debt recovery or repossession may be found in the Debt Collection or Litigation (Property) Lists. *Norman Wilson & Co* acts for the Bank of Ireland.

LEADING INDIVIDUALS – NORTHERN IRELAND

R. William C. McCann	*Mills Selig*

LEADERS IN BANKING

LONDON

Allen, Maurice
Clifford Chance, London (0171) 600 1000. Banking work ranges from structured finance to syndicated lending.

Balfour, Andrew G.
Slaughter and May, London (0171) 600 1200. Qualified 1981. Also handles capital markets, including Eurobonds, structured finance, GDRs and ADRs.

Bray, Michael
Clifford Chance, London (0171) 600 1000, Milan (0039) 2 7600 8040. Partner 1976. Banking Department. Practice covers project finance, aircraft finance, corporate restructurings, tax structured finance and general banking. Born 27.3.1947.

Campbell, Mark
Clifford Chance, London (0171) 600 1000.

Cates, Armel
Clifford Chance, London (0171) 600 1000.

Cullinane, Lee
Clifford Chance, London (0171) 600 1000.

Duncan, Michael G.
Allen & Overy, London (0171) 330 3000. Qualified 1981. Partner 1987. Banking Department. Specialises in international finance, acting primarily for leading international banks but also for several borrowers. Born 9.9.1957.

Ereira, David Philip
Freshfields, London (0171) 936 4000. Qualified 1981. Partner in Finance Department. Responsible for co-ordination of Freshfields' banking and property finance practices.

Evans, Edward T.H.
Freshfields, London (0171) 936 4000. Qualified 1980. Partner 1986. Finance Department. Main area of practice is banking, particularly asset and project finance. Also handles energy law. Born 12.12. 1954.

Fox, Ruth M.
Slaughter and May, London (0171) 600 1200. Qualified 1979. Partner specialising in banking and building society law. Also has capital markets expertise.

Hall, P.M.
Norton Rose, London (0171) 283 6000. Qualified 1987.

Hodgson, K. Ian
Slaughter and May, London (0171) 600 1200. Qualified 1986.

Horsfall Turner, Jonathan
See under Major Projects.

Humphrey, Anthony R.
Allen & Overy, London (0171) 330 3000. Qualified 1973. Partner 1981. Main area of practice is structured finance work, including debt/equity swaps, project finance and multi-tiered finance and corporate finance.

Inglis, Alan
Clifford Chance, London (0171) 600 1000. Partner. Principal area of practice is corporate restructuring and structured finance.

Johnson, James
Wilde Sapte, London (0171) 246 7000.

Keal, A.C.
Allen & Overy, London (0171) 330 3000. Qualified 1976.

Mathews, Michael
Clifford Chance, London (0171) 600 1000. Partner. Principal area of practice is banking and tax-based finance.

Morley, David H.
Allen & Overy, London (0171) 330 3000. Qualified 1982. Partner 1988. Banking Department. Specialises in international finance, acting primarily for international banks, leasing companies and building societies. Has special expertise in the syndicated loans market. Born 21.9.1956.

Morrison, Neil C.
McGrigor Donald, London (0171) 329 3299.

Mostyn-Williams, Stephen R.P.
Ashurst Morris Crisp, London (0171) 638 1111. Qualified 1981. Partner 1991.

Banking and International Finance Department. Main area of practice is structured finance.

Oakley, Chris
See under Capital Markets & Securitisation.

Pettit, Richard
Clifford Chance, London (0171) 600 1000.

Pierce, Sean
Linklaters & Paines, London (0171) 606 7080.

Popham, Stuart
Clifford Chance, London (0171) 600 1000. Partner. Principal area of practice is banking law.

Puleston Jones, Haydn
Linklaters & Paines, London (0171) 606 7080. Qualified 1973. Partner 1979. Head of Banking with extensive experience of acting for arrangers, borrowers and banks on syndicated and bilateral, secured and unsecured credits, structured financings, corporate recoveries and derivative related work.

Rutherford, Brian
Dundas & Wilson CS, London (0171) 256 9191.

Schulz, Peter F.
Allen & Overy, London (0171) 330 3000. Qualified 1981. Partner 1989. Banking Department. Specialises in banking and international finance.

Seligman, George E.S.
See under Capital Markets & Securitisation.

Slater, Richard
Slaughter and May, London (0171) 600 1200. Qualified 1972. Partner 1979. Commercial and Financial Department. Principal area of work covers capital markets, and project finance.

Stewart, Mark
Clifford Chance, London (0171) 600 1000. Partner. Principal areas of practice are general corporate banking, acquisition finance and corporate restructuring. Also handles asset/project financing and leasing.

Style, Christopher J.D.
See under Litigation (Commercial).

Sweeting, Malcolm
Clifford Chance, London (0171) 600 1000. Partner. Main area of practice is banking.

Tucker, John T.
Linklaters & Paines, London (0171) 606 7080.

Vinter, Graham D.
Allen & Overy, London (0171) 330 3000. Qualified 1982. Partner 1988. Project Finance Department. Wide experience in projects and project financing, including energy and infrastructure projects in the UK and abroad. Born 4.3.1956.

Wakefield, Carol
Osborne Clarke, London (0171) 600 0155.

Watson, Martin A.
See under Asset Finance & Leasing.

Wood, Philip
Allen & Overy, London (0171) 330 3000. Qualified 1970. Partner in Banking Department. Born 20.8.1942.

Wynne, Geoffrey.L.
Watson Farley & Williams, London (0171) 814 8000. Partner in Banking Department.

Specialisation: Handles all aspects of banking, corporate and international finance, asset and project finance, trade finance, syndicated lending, equipment leasing, insolvency and financial restructuring, bankruptcy, leveraged and management buy-outs. Joint editor, "Credit and Finance Law"; contributor "Longman's Banking Precedents"; editor "Butterworths Banking Law Handbook" (in preparation). Member of Law Society Committee on Banking.

Prof. Membership: International Bar Association, Law Society.

Career: Qualified 1975; assistant solicitor at *Slaughter & May*; 1975-1979; assistant general counsel international Royal Bank of Canada 1979-1985; 1985, Partner, *Watson, Farley & Williams*.

Personal: Born 1950. Attended Christ Church Oxford (1972 BA). Lives in London.

REGIONS

Bootland, Edward Tjorn
See under Litigation (Commercial).

Burnside, Graham M.
Tods Murray WS, Edinburgh (0131) 226 4771. Qualified 1978. Partner 1984. Corporate and Commercial Department. Main area of practice is refinancing, securitisation, and secured lending.

Callaghan, Edward J.
See under Litigation (Commercial).

Chidley, Mark A.
Booth & Co., Leeds (0113) 283 2000. Partner in Banking Group.

Specialisation: Work covers acquisitions, buy-out/buy-in finance, general banking law and venture capital. Also handles general

company/commercial work.

Prof. Membership: IBA.

Career: Qualified in 1979. Articled at *Slaughter and May* 1977-79. Joined *Booth & Co.* in 1982, becoming a Partner in 1984.

Personal: Born 24th March 1955. Attended Ardingly College, Haywards Heath, Sussex 1968-73; then Southampton University 1973-76. Leisure interests include spending time at home and 60s/70s sports cars. Lives near York.

Childs, M.E.
Osborne Clarke, Bristol (0117) 923 0220.

Clark, Stephen P.
Addleshaw Sons & Latham, Manchester (0161) 832 5994. Qualified 1987.

Cooke, David J.
Pinsent Curtis, Birmingham (0121) 200 1050. Qualified 1981. Partner 1983. Licensed Insolvency Practitioner. Work includes lending, security, restructurings, work outs, receiverships and administration. Also handles corporate finance. Born 23.8.1956.

Croome, Andrew
Eversheds, Norwich (01603) 272727. Qualified 1978. Partner 1982. Company Department. Main areas of practice are company and banking work. Covers a wide range of work for lenders and borrowers. Born 22.6.1954.

Dale, Nigel A.
Hammond Suddards, Manchester (0161) 834 2222.

Doolan, Kevin J.
Eversheds, Cardiff (01222) 471147. Partner in Banking Department.

Specialisation: Head of Banking and Finance Department responsible for over one hundred staff, who provide a wide range of advice to banks, building societies, centralised lenders, insurance companies and finance houses. Handles a high volume of cases involving recoveries, claims against professional advisers and property lending, for clients based throughout the UK. Author of articles published in Mortgage Finance Gazette on commercial and residential lending. Regular conference speaker on bank lending.

Prof. Membership: Member of the Institute of Credit Management, Chartered Institute of Bankers, Strategic Planning Society.

Career: Qualified in 1979. Joined *Eversheds* in 1977, becoming a Partner in 1981. Appointed to Urban Investment Grants Panel 1989 by Secretary of State for Wales. Member of Board of Management of *Eversheds Phillips & Buck.*

Personal: Born 14th November 1953. Attended University of Wales. Leisure interests include golf, skiing and computer programming. Lives in Cardiff and Thornbury.

Finnigan, J.H.
Eversheds, Leeds (0113) 243 0391.

Fisher, Nicholas Henry
Dibb Lupton Broomhead, Manchester (0161) 839 2266.

Gilbert, Ian M.
See under Company/Commercial.

Gosnay, Andrew W.
Pinsent Curtis, Leeds (0113) 244 5000. Partner and Head of Banking Department.

Specialisation: Mainstream banking, asset finance, leasing, property project finance and debt issues. Acted for FKI Plc in US$120m private placing by US subsidiary. Acted in £42m Private Finance Initiative Project financing for the New Royal Armouries Museum Project. Handled banking facilities for Holliday Chemical Holdings' acquisition of Reckitt's Colours International for £52m.

Career: Qualified in 1985. Worked at *Cameron Markby Hewitt* 1983-86. Joined *Simpson Curtis* in 1986, becoming an Associate Partner in 1988 and a Partner in 1990.

Personal: Born 21st February 1961. Attended Uppingham School 1974-79, then Newcastle University 1979-82 and College of Law 1982-83. Leisure interests include walking, skiing, travel and theatre. Lives in York.

Hardie, J. Fraser M.
Biggart Baillie & Gifford, Edinburgh (0131) 226 5541. Qualified 1983. Partner 1989. Property Department. Specialises in acting for lenders in relation to commercial property.

Harker, Chris
Dickinson Dees, Newcastle upon Tyne (0191) 261 1911. Qualified 1978. Partner 1981. Company and Commercial Department. Main areas of practice are banking and commercial lending and venture capital. Born 25.1.1954.

Haywood, Richard
Wragge & Co, Birmingham (0121) 233 1000. Qualified 1980. Partner 1986. Group leader of Corporate Group, specialising in corporate finance work. Born 8.11.1955.

Hopkins, Stephen Martyn
See under Corporate Finance.

Jarvis, Karen
Garrett & Co, Leeds (0113) 244 1954.

Jeffries, Graham
Lester Aldridge, Bournemouth (01202) 786161.

Johnstone, Pat
Eversheds, Birmingham (0121) 233 2001. Qualified 1986. Partner in banking. Special-

ises in investment banking, venture capital, security matters. Born 17.3.1955.

Lapraik, J.D.
Mills & Reeve, Norwich +44 (0) 1603 660155.

Lumsden, Christopher G.M.
Chaffe Street, Manchester (0161) 236 5800. Qualified 1977. Partner 1990. Banking Department. Main area of practice is banking and covers a comprehensive range of work. Also experienced in ship and aircraft financing and corporate acquisitions and disposals.

Lyall, Ian J.G.
McGrigor Donald, Glasgow (0141) 248 6677.

McCann, R. William C.
See under Corporate Finance.

McHale, Colin
Dickson Minto WS, Edinburgh (0131) 225 4455.

McKay, Colin B.
Biggart Baillie & Gifford, Glasgow (0141) 228 8000.

Meiklejohn, Iain M.C.
See under Company/Commercial.

Minto, Bruce W.
See under Company/Commercial.

Mitchell, J. Patrick
Hammond Suddards, Leeds (0113) 234 3500. Partner and Head of Banking in Corporate Department.

Specialisation: Work includes acquisition finance, syndicated lending and restructuring. Acted in the Funding of Royal Armouries, Quadromatic, GB Glass, Lotus, and other buy outs. Has undertaken Housing Association Lending for various building societies.

Career: Qualified 1981 with *Cameron Markby*. Worked for Robert Holmes, a Court's company Bell Group before joining *Hammond Suddards* in 1987. Became a Partner in 1989.

Personal: Born 24th February 1957. Attended Ardingley College, Haywards Heath, and Magdalen College, Oxford. Leisure interests include running, riding, football and sport generally. Lives in Harrogate.

Molloy, Susan
Garrett & Co, Manchester (0161) 228 0707.

McDaid, Raymond
Halliwell Landau, Manchester (0161) 835 3003.

Orrell, J.P.
Slater Heelis, Manchester (0161) 228 3781.

Pallett, Julian C.
Wragge & Co, Birmingham (0121) 233 1000. Qualified 1983.

Patrick, Hamish A.
Tods Murray WS, Edinburgh (0131) 226 4771. Qualified 1989. Partner 1992. Corporate and Commercial Department. Principal area of practice is debt finance, including conventional banking work.

Rearden, Shaun
Addleshaw Sons & Latham, Manchester (0161) 832 5994. Partner in Banking & Insolvency Department.

Specialisation: Main area of practice is banking. Emphasis on facility (including syndicated facilities) and security documentation, finance for acquisitions and MBOs, project finance, and asset finance. Other area of work is regulatory, covering consumer credit, financial services and data protection. Edits the *Addleshaws Sons & Latham* Banking and Finance Newsletter. Regular presenter at seminars.

Prof. Memberships: Law Society.

Career: Qualified in 1979, while at *Rutherfords* in Liverpool. Was in-house solicitor at Littlewoods 1980-82, then Manager of Legal Department at North West Securities plc to 1986. In-house legal advisor at the Co-Operative Bank plc in Manchester 1986-89 before joining *Davies Wallis Foyster* as a Partner. Joined *Addleshaw Sons & Latham* in 1990.

Personal: Born 10th April 1954. Attended West Park Grammar School 1965-72, then King's College, London 1972-75. Leisure pursuits include rugby, beer and sunshine. Lives in Wilmslow.

Reaves, Ian C.
Edge & Ellison, Birmingham (0121) 200 2001. Joint Head of Banking and Insolvency Department.

Specialisation: Main area of practice is banking and finance. Also Lead Partner for a number of the firm's substantial retail clients, operating in areas as diverse as convenience retailing, computer retailing and the retailing of wines and spirits. Has also worked in the corporate finance, franchising, public company, intellectual property and commercial conveyancing fields. Heavily involved in the development of the firm's London office.

Prof. Membership: Law Society.

Career: Qualified in 1975. Joined *Edge & Ellison* in 1973. Was involved in setting up the firm's Insolvency Department 1978-80 and became a Partner in 1981. Member of the firm's Main Board and its Marketing Directorate.

Personal: Attended Trent Polytechnic 1969-72 and College of Law, Guildford 1972-73. Leisure interests include tennis and music. Lives in Birmingham.

Rosser, Sandra
Burges Salmon, Bristol (0117) 939 2000.

Sanderson, R.G.
Dickinson Dees, Newcastle upon Tyne (0191) 261 1911.

Sleigh, Andrew F.
See under Insolvency.

Smith, W.W. Campbell
See under Company/Commercial.

Stobart, Guy W.
See under Insolvency.

Stoneham, Michael P.
Dundas & Wilson CS, Edinburgh (0131) 228 8000. Qualified 1980. Partner since 1987 in the Banking and Capital Markets Unit. Specialises in corporate banking including buy out finance and asset/project finance, acquisition finance, bilateral and syndicated finance, public sector and private finance initiatives, building society finance, and Scottish security structures. Regularly addresses conferences on subject of banking and security law. Has written a number of articles on North Sea oil and gas financing. Born 12.1.1955.

Taylor, Michael F.
Walker Morris, Leeds (0113) 283 2500.

Temple, John
Shoosmiths & Harrison, Northampton

(01604) 29977. Qualified 1977. Partner 1986. Acts for lenders in commercial lending, Housing Associations and Development Funding.

Tettmar, Victor
See under Insolvency.

Twist, G. Patrick A.S.
Pinsent Curtis, Birmingham (0121) 200 1050. Qualified 1981. Partner 1989. Corporate Department. Work includes asset finance and corporate finance.

Vaughan, Philip D.
Eversheds, Cardiff (01222) 471147. Qualified 1984. Partner. Specialist in banking and insolvency work. Born 14.12.1958.

Warburton, M.C.
Slater Heelis, Manchester (0161) 228 3781.

Welch, H.B.
Robert Muckle, Newcastle-upon-Tyne (0191) 232 4402.

Whatnall, John
See under Corporate Finance.

Wood, Cate
Addleshaw Sons & Latham, Manchester (0161) 832 5994. Qualified 1982. Partner

1993. Corporate Department. Head of Banking and Insolvency Unit. Handles a wide range of banking and insolvency matters, acting for banks, financial institutions and insolvency practitioners. Born 18.8.1958.

Wood, Catherine Mary
See under Insolvency.

EDITORIAL POLICY

Our policy is to identify leading practitioners entirely on merit. It is not possible to buy a place in our biographical lists: inclusion is based on a practitioner's expertise and professional reputation. The same applies to the lists of recommended law-firms and sets of chambers.

Enormous effort has been invested by our ten-strong research team (mainly solicitors and barristers) in canvassing recommendations and identifying leaders. We are confident in the overall accuracy of the results. However, mistakes and omissions are inevitable, and if readers have any suggestions regarding listings or rankings we should be very pleased to hear from them.

The lists will be revised on the basis of fresh research every year.

BUILDING SOCIETIES

LONDON

Building societies work undertaken by London firms falls into two main categories: commercial/corporate issues including M&A, conversions, flotations, wholesale funding, mortgage portfolio transactions and securitisations

LEADING FIRMS – LONDON – CORPORATE & REGULATORY	
ALLEN & OVERY	DENTON HALL
LINKLATERS & PAINES	SLAUGHTER AND MAY
CLIFFORD CHANCE	SIMMONS & SIMMONS

(areas favoured by the larger City firms), and specialised litigation matters such as fraud, professional negligence and contested repossession proceedings. Some of the larger City firms do offer advice on regulatory matters although the bulk of such work is handled by in-house lawyers.

One of the leading firms handling conversions/M&A/ flotations for building societies is *Allen & Overy*. The firm has experience in wholesale funding by means of debt issues, PIBS and debt convertible, mortgage portfolio sales/ purchases, M&A, swaps, project financing, consumer lending schemes and mortgage securitisation. It recently advised Bristol & West Building Society on the securitisation of commercial mortgages worth £150m. This was the first such transaction in the UK.

Also highly respected are *Denton Hall, Linklaters & Paines* and *Slaughter and May*. The first has a particular specialisation in treasury and funding activities of building societies including derivatives, syndicated borrowings and capital market issues. It has also handled mortgage fraud investigations and intellectual property matters for major building societies. Bradford & Bingley is one of their long-standing clients for whom the firm undertakes wholesale funding transactions, planning matters and general building society law advice.

Linklaters & Paines advised Halifax in the merger with Leeds Permanent. *Slaughter and May* has particular expertise in the conversion of building societies into broader-based institutions and their reconstruction and amalgamation. It also advises on capital markets, PIBS issues, the development of equity-linked saving schemes and regulatory issues. The firm advised Cheltenham & Gloucester in the Lloyds Bank bid for the society. Other clients include Abbey National.

LEADING FIRMS – LONDON – SPECIALISED LITIGATION
CHURCH ADAMS TATHAM
HAMLIN SLOWE

Other firms active in this type of work include *Clifford Chance* and *Simmons & Simmons* (particularly strong in mortgage portfolio acquisitions). *Clifford Chance's* expertise covers financing and fund arrangements, M&A, tax advice and regulatory issues. Work undertaken by *Simmons & Simmons* includes advising on prospective securitisations, commercial lending, review of loan and security documentation and mortgage portfolio acquisitions and disposals. Recently, the firm has been involved in a number of capital market transactions for building societies, acting for the lead manager.

Church Adams Tatham & Co continues to maintain its excellent reputation in litigation matters for building societies, especially professional negligence, fraud and mortgage repossessions in the High Court. The firm acts for four of the largest building societies and its team includes two specialists (including leading practitioner, Tom McKeown), who undertake solely building societies work.

HIGHLY REGARDED – LONDON	
CAMERON MARKBY HEWITT	FRESHFIELDS
HERBERT SMITH	LEWIS SILKIN
McKENNA & CO	PINSENT CURTIS
ROSLING KING	TROWERS & HAMLINS

Also strongly recommended for litigious work is *Hamlin Slowe*, particularly in relation to professional negligence, the recovery of shortfall losses following repossessions and mortgage actions (includes undue influence, forged documents of title, relief from forfeiture and squatters' actions). Within the last six months, the firm has handled substantial recoveries on behalf of building societies and centralised lenders against solicitors and valuers with an aggregate value in excess of £2.5 m.

LEADING INDIVIDUALS – LONDON – CORPORATE & REGULATORY	
Peter R.J. Holland	Allen & Overy
Ed Marlow	Denton Hall
Jonathan Beastall	Clifford Chance
Nicholas Jordan	Clifford Chance

LEADING INDIVIDUALS – LONDON – SPECIALISED LITIGATION	
R.H. Brown	Hamlin Slowe
Tom W. McKeown	Church Adams Tatham

Peter Holland (*Allen & Overy*), Ed Marlow (*Denton Hall*) and Tom McKeown (*Church Adams Tatham & Co*) are among the leading practitioners in this field.

SOUTH WEST & WALES

The firms mentioned here are those with recognised expertise in building societies work but there are no clear market leaders. Most building societies are located in the North and Midlands which accounts for the heavy concentration of such work there.

Burges Salmon, Lester Aldridge, Osborne Clarke, Veale Wasbrough and *Wansbroughs Willey Hargrave* are among the few firms with sound expertise in this area of practice. Work undertaken by *Burges Salmon* includes regulatory issues, litigation and secured lending including drafting of standard security documentation. *Lester Aldridge* advises a major building society on all its consumer credit and mortgage advertising requirements.

HIGHLY REGARDED – SOUTH WEST & WALES

BURGES SALMON *Bristol*	**EVERSHEDS** *Cardiff*
HUGH JAMES JONES & JENKINS *Cardiff*	**LESTER ALDRIDGE** *Bournemouth*
OSBORNE CLARKE *Bristol*	**VEALE WASBROUGH** *Bristol*
WANSBROUGHS WILLEY HARGRAVE *Bristol*	
BOND PEARCE *Plymouth*	

Osborne Clarke's forte is in litigious work, especially fraud and professional negligence. Its clients include Bristol & West Building Society and Stroud & Swindon. *Veale Wasbrough's* team consisting of 4 partners, acts for building societies on all aspects including recovery and professional negligence claims.

Work handled by *Wansbroughs Willey Hargrave,* which acts for Bristol & West amongst others, includes fraud claims, secured lending, property/planning and project development. The firm also acted for a major building society on the reorganisation of its business. Also notable in this field is *Bond Pearce* which handles primarily commercial lending, recovery and security documentation.

Welsh firms active in this field include *Eversheds* in Cardiff and *Hugh James Jones & Jenkins.* The former advises three of the top ten societies and are head office lawyers for a major society. The team handles primarily litigation and debt recovery work. The latter undertakes mortgage arrears, repossessions and secured lending for one of the top five building societies.

MIDLANDS

Pinsent Curtis, with the transfer of highly recommended Steven Clifford (13 years' experience within the industry) from its London office to the Birmingham branch, now shares the leading position with *Shoosmiths & Harrison.*

LEADING FIRMS – MIDLANDS

PINSENT CURTIS *Birmingham*	**SHOOSMITHS & HARRISON** *Northampton*

The former advises on regulatory issues, lending documentation (including a number of syndicated loans to housing

HIGHLY REGARDED – MIDLANDS

EVERSHEDS *Birmingham*	**EVERSHEDS, NOTTINGHAM**
WRAGGE & CO *Birmingham*	
EDGE & ELLISON *Birmingham*	**REES PAGE** *Wolverhampton*

associations), subordinated debt, swap contracts, wholesale funding and hedging, bid defence and mortgage book acqui-

sitions. It additionally advised West Bromwich Building Society on its first mortgage book acquisition involving a £85m portfolio acquired from AXA Equity & Law. Other clients include Bradford & Bingley on BES issues, Birmingham Midshires and Stroud & Swindon.

Shoosmiths & Harrison's expertise covers commercial lending , finance, complex recoveries and fraud. Its team is headed by leading specialist John Thorpe who has over 20 years' experience in this field.

Also strongly recommended are *Eversheds (Birmingham and Nottingham)* and *Wragge & Co.* The former's team includes John Young, founder member of BSA's panel of specialists, and advises over 25 societies on mergers, acquisitions, treasury issues and the Building Societies Act. *Wragge & Co's* expertise covers commercial lending, debt recovery and treasury matters.

LEADING INDIVIDUALS – MIDLANDS

Steven Clifford *Pinsent Curtis*
John Thorpe *Shoosmiths & Harrison*
John D.C. Young *Eversheds*

Leading individuals include Steven Clifford (*Pinsent Curtis*) previously head of Woolwich's legal services, and John Thorpe (*Shoosmiths & Harrison*).

NORTH

Booth & Co continues to maintain its national reputation for building society work. In the last 12 months it has advised 35 of the 77 building societies based in England and Wales including eight in the top ten. The firm has a particular strength in mortgage portfolio acquisitions, the aggregate value of which in the past year exceeded £2.2 billion. It also handles volume recoveries, syndicate arrangements, commercial lending, fund raising for treasury operations and specialised litigation. Current litigation matters include advising on negative equity borrowers and defending home income plans litigation.

LEADING FIRMS – NORTH

BOOTH & CO. *Leeds*

Another leader in this area is *Dibb Lupton Broomhead.* It advises a majority of the top ten building societies particularly on commercial lending, litigation (including fraud and professional negligence) and recovery matters. The recruitment of Frank Kraus, previously Nationwide Anglia's chief solicitor, to *Dibb Lupton Broomhead's* Building Society Group has further strengthened its presence in this field. The firm's specialisation has also been extended to include capital market and PIBS issues, and constitutional and practice matters.

Other firms strong in this field include *Eversheds* in Leeds, *Hammond Suddards, Pinsent Curtis* and *Walker Morris.*

Eversheds has carried out work for seven societies over the last 12 months, including four of the top ten. The team recently recruited an employment lawyer from Alliance & Leicester and a financial services specialist from SIB. The firm advises on syndicated loan structures and lending, compliance issues (in relation to the sale of pension schemes), repossessions, professional negligence, fraud and employment matters. Also handled are the acquisition of mortgage portfolios and the amendment of mortgage procedures and documentation (to comply with the consumer credit deregulation).

HIGHLY REGARDED – NORTH	
EVERSHEDS *Leeds*	HAMMOND SUDDARDS *Leeds*
PINSENT CURTIS	WALKER MORRIS *Leeds*

COBBETT LEAK ALMOND *Manchester*	EVERSHEDS, NEWCASTLE *Newcastle*

Hammond Suddards' work includes advice on treasury, commercial lending, M&As, purchase of mortgage books and documentation issues. *Pinsent Curtis* has experience in advising on wholesale funding, treasury management, swaps, derivatives and commercial lending including project/development finance and syndicated loans.

LEADING INDIVIDUALS – NORTH
G. Adam Bennett *Booth & Co.*
Andrew Geoffrey Chappell *Dibb Lupton Broomhead*
Frank Kraus *Dibb Lupton Broomhead*

UP AND COMING
Richard Papworth *Booth & Co.*

Walker Morris is currently acting for eight of the top twenty societies including three of the top four. It provides advice on the Building Societies Act and a wide range of commercial issues including professional negligence and fraud claims, wholesale funding, mortgage indemnity guarantee disputes, capital market transactions and secured lending. The firm recently advised Leeds & Holbeck Building Society in its £110m mortgage book acquisition and in respect of a £230m revolving credit facility. It also advises Halifax Building Society in relation to loans to housing associations (aggregate value is in excess of £100m).

Individuals consistently recommended as leaders in this area include Adam Bennett (*Booth & Co*) who is the founder

member of the BSA panel of specialists, Andrew Chappell (*Dibb Lupton Broomhead*) and Frank Kraus (*Dibb Lupton Broomhead*).

SCOTLAND

The majority of building societies in Scotland have strong in-house legal departments and tend to use law firms on an ad hoc basis. *Dundas & Wilson CS* is active in this field due to its strong banking expertise. The firm acted for Halifax Building Society in the provision of public sector finance to Bield Housing Association (£3m) and to Pentland Housing Association (£2.6m).

Other firms offering specialised services to building societies include *Bonar Mackenzie WS, Boyds, Brechin Robb, Ketchen & Stevens WS, Lindsays WS* and *Mitchells Robertson*. The type of work handled by all these firms includes the preparation and revision of security documentation and repossession. *Brechin Robb's* team with two specialists partners also advises on consumer credit matters.

HIGHLY REGARDED – SCOTLAND	
DUNDAS & WILSON CS *Edinburgh*	
BONAR MACKENZIE WS *Edinburgh*	BOYDS *Glasgow*
BRECHIN ROBB *Glasgow*	KETCHEN & STEVENS WS *Edinburgh*
LINDSAYS WS *Edinburgh*	MITCHELLS ROBERTON *Glasgow*

NORTHERN IRELAND

Carson & McDowell, Cleaver Fulton & Rankin and *O'Reilly Stewart* (5% of total workload) are steadily developing a strong expertise in general building society law. Work handled includes repossession and the preparation/revision of security documentation.

HIGHLY REGARDED – NORTHERN IRELAND	
CARSON & McDOWELL *Belfast*	CLEAVER FULTON & RANKIN *Belfast*
O'REILLY STEWART *Belfast*	

LEADERS IN BUILDING SOCIETIES

LONDON

Beastall, Jonathan
Clifford Chance, London (0171) 600 1000. Partner. Principal area of practice is corporate law, including mergers and acquisitions, flotations, secondary issues and MBOs. Also handles building society matters.

Brown, R.H.
Hamlin Slowe, London (0171) 629 1209. Qualified 1964. Partner 1967. Secured Lend-

ing Litigation Department. Principal area of practice covers mortgage litigation and professional negligence cases. Born 6.12.1937.

Holland, Peter R.J.
See under Corporate Finance.

Jordan, Nicholas
Clifford Chance, London (0171) 600 1000. Partner. Principal area of practice is building societies. Also handles insurance law and fiscal disputes generally.

Marlow, Ed
Denton Hall, London (0171) 242 1212. Partner in Banking and Financial Markets Group. Company and Commercial Department.

Specialisation: Main areas of practice cover all aspects of building society and banking work. Includes advice on funding and Treasury activities, including PIBs, capital markets and hedging, bilateral and syndicated borrowings, commercial lending and general building society law including mergers and conversions. Also experienced in limited recourse (project) finance, including energy, cable TV and telephony. Acted for Building Societies Association in amendments to model rules to provide for PIBs. Regular speaker at conferences on lending techniques.

Prof. Memberships: Law Society, City of London Solicitors Company, Freeman of City of London.

Career: Qualified in 1980 with *Herbert Oppenheimer Nathan Vandyk*. Moved to Heron Corporation plc in 1987. Joined *Denton Hall* in 1988. Partner 1989.

Personal: Born 18th December 1954. Attended Christ's College, Cambridge 1974-77.

McKeown, Tom W.

Church Adams Tatham & Co, London (0171) 242 0841. Qualified 1974. Partner 1979. Litigation Department. Mainly acts on behalf of mortgage lenders in claims arising from fraud, including claims for professional negligence and enforcement of securities. Born 26.9.1949.

REGIONS

Bennett, G. Adam

Booth & Co., Leeds (0113) 283 2000. Partner in Banking Department.

Specialisation: Main area of practice is building society law: founder member of Building Societies Association panel of specialists. Partner responsible for *Booth & Co.*'s Building Societies Unit, which acts for 15 of the top 20 building societies and 35 societies out of the total 77 in England and Wales. Specialises in corporate and regulatory matters for societies: acquisitions, mergers, powers, subsidiaries, the Building Societies Act 1986, directors, purchasing mortgage books and treasury work. Editor of Building Societies Law section of Halsbury's Laws of England. Author of a number of articles for Mortgage Finance Gazette and regular conference speaker.

Prof. Membership: Law Society.

Career: Qualified 1985, having joined *Booth & Co.* in 1983. Partner in 1991.

Personal: Born 10th February 1961. Attended Jordanthorpe School, Sheffield; then Christ's College, Cambridge 1979-82. Leisure interests include swimming, rugby, family and reading. Lives in Cawthorne, South Yorkshire.

Chappell, Andrew Geoffrey

Dibb Lupton Broomhead, Leeds (0113) 243 9301. Head of Building Society Group.

Specialisation: Principal area of practice is as head of the firm's Building Societies Group which advises societies on a wide range of issues including secured lending, commercial and corporate matters, recoveries and litigation including claims against Third parties.

Prof. Membership: Steering Committee of Leeds Financial Services Initiative.

Career: Qualified 1979 and joined *Dibb Lupton Broomhead*. Became Partner in 1983, Head of Litigation Division in 1990, Head of Building Societies Group 1995.

Personal: Born 17th August 1954. M.A. Oxon (1976). Leisure pursuits include sport, wine and philately. Lives in Leeds.

Clifford, Steven

Pinsent Curtis, Birmingham (0121) 200 1050. Partner.

Specialisation: Main area of practice is building societies. Provides advice on a range of regulatory, banking and lending issues. Also advises banks and other financial institutions in relation to debt and funding issues.

Career: Qualified in 1978. Woolwich Building Society 1978-91. Pinsent Curtis 1991.

Personal: Born 19th June 1954.

Kraus, Frank

Dibb Lupton Broomhead, Leeds (0113) 241 2654. Full-time consultant with the firm's Building Societies Group based in Leeds.

Specialisation: Regulatory and corporate aspects of Building Societies work, including mergers and acquisitions, wholesale funding including PIBS, mortgage book transfers and securitisation. Typically projects would be undertaken in conjunction with Banking and Company/Commerical departments. The firm is now a "top ten" law firm in England and Wales with a reservoir of expertise in the areas referred to above.

Prof. Membership: Former chairman of both Law Society's Commerce and Industry Group and Building Societies Association Legal Advisory Panel.

Career: Private practice after some 15 years as head of Nationwide Building Society's Legal Services, latterly as Group Secretary (1976 to 1991).

Papworth, Richard

Booth & Co., Leeds (0113) 283 2000. Partner in Banking Department.

Specialisation: Corporate banking specialist. Main areas of work are housing association finance (including local authority stock transfer funding), building society treasury work, acquisition finance, property finance, syndicated lending, work-outs and restructurings. Has acted on numerous large scale local authority stock transfers including recent lead fundings for Bradford & Bingley and Northern Rock Building Societies. Acted for Portman Building Society on the first ever syndicated loan by a building society.

Career: Qualified in 1989 while at *Travers Smith Braithwaite*. Joined *Booth & Co.* in 1991, becoming a Partner in 1995.

Personal: Born 25th December 1964. Educated at King Edward VI School, Louth 1979-83, Christ Church, Oxford 1983-86 and The College of Law, Guildford 1986-87. Leisure interests include golf, fitness, outdoor pursuits and football. Lives in Harrogate.

Thorpe, John

Shoosmiths & Harrison, Northampton (01604) 29977. Qualified 1963. Partner 1966. Senior Partner 1989. Main area of practice is building societies work, with 23 years experience in this field. Born 17.10.1939.

Young, John D.C.

Eversheds, Nottingham (0115) 950 6201. Partner in Corporate Department.

Specialisation: Main area of practice is building societies law. Founder member of Building Societies Association's panel of specialists. Chairman of *Eversheds* National Building Societies Team, which acts for over 25 societies. Specialist in mergers, acquisitions, treasury work and the Building Societies Act 1986. Also handles general corporate law including acquisitions and disposals and employee share schemes.

Career: Qualified in 1973. With *Eversheds* (or one if its predecessors, *Wells & Hind*) throughout career, apart form a period with *Linklaters & Paines* (1977-79). Became a Partner in 1980.

Personal: Born 27th March 1948. Attended Nottingham High School, then University College, Oxford 1966-69 (MA, Jurisprudence).

CAPITAL MARKETS & DERIVATIVES

LONDON

THE distinction between this capital markets list and the lists for of corporate finance, banking, and project, property and asset finance is not always clear cut. Each area of practice is concerned with raising finance through the issue of a variety of instruments comprising debt and/or equity.

LEADING FIRMS – INTERNATIONAL DEBT ISSUES	
ALLEN & OVERY	LINKLATERS & PAINES
CLIFFORD CHANCE	FRESHFIELDS
SIMMONS & SIMMONS	SLAUGHTER AND MAY

For this edition we have taken the Capital Markets field to include the issuing of debt and/or equity in the international markets (so that domestic issues of both debt and/or equity are included under Corporate Finance), 'structured finance' involving the pioneering of novel financing structures, including securitisation and the repackaging of existing instruments, and derivatives, including swaps, options and futures. Property, and project and asset finance, which some may regard as forms of structured finance are covered in other sections.

LEADING FIRMS – SECURITISATION & REPACKAGINGS	
ALLEN & OVERY	CLIFFORD CHANCE
FRESHFIELDS	LINKLATERS & PAINES
LOVELL WHITE DURRANT	SIMMONS & SIMMONS
SLAUGHTER AND MAY	

It is not always possible to maintain a rigid distinction between these categories since there is inevitably overlap, both in the personnel carrying out the work and the nature of the business itself. Obviously, elements of derivatives can be involved in almost any form of financing although, as in the case of 'securitisation', we have attempted to identify those firms recognised for a particular expertise in the area as a separate specialist topic.

Furthermore, although the capital markets field expanded in the 1980s and London is regarded by many as the foremost centre for international debt issues, the number of banks obtaining mandates for lead manager roles has contracted and therefore opportunities for new entrants among legal advisers are limited. There are probably only a dozen or so firms engaged in any material amount of true capital markets business.

LEADING FIRMS – LONDON – DERIVATIVES	
ALLEN & OVERY	CLIFFORD CHANCE
FRESHFIELDS	LINKLATERS & PAINES
NORTON ROSE	SIMMONS & SIMMONS
SLAUGHTER AND MAY	

Developments in this field include global depositary receipts (GDR's) (which provide a mechanism to permit trading in securities unfettered by imperfections in the relevant domestic market), convertible banks, and equity warrants. The leaders in this particular field are *Linklaters & Paines* and *Allen & Overy*.

Overall in the capital markets field the leading firms are *Linklaters & Paines, Allen & Overy, Clifford Chance, Freshfields, Slaughter and May* and *Simmons & Simmons*, although their strengths are in different areas, obviously influenced in part by their differing client bases. *Linklaters & Paines* has a huge, well entrenched international finance practice and is seen as the leader in capital markets. Terence Kyle and Andrew Carmichael are most frequently mentioned, together with Caird Forbes-Cockell and David Barnard in New York.

LEADING INDIVIDUALS – LONDON		
David M. Barnard *Linklaters & Paines*	Andrew J. Carmichael *Linklaters & Paines*	Caird Forbes-Cockell *Linklaters & Paines*
David T. Frank *Slaughter and May*	J. Terence Kyle *Linklaters & Paines*	Robert Palache *Clifford Chance*
Richard H. Sykes *Allen & Overy*		
Rupert. R.S. Beaumont *Slaughter and May*	Paul H.D. Bedford *Allen & Overy*	Jane Borrows *Simmons & Simmons*
A. Lachlan Burn *Linklaters & Paines*	Charles E.M. Clark *Linklaters & Paines*	John W. Davies *Simmons & Simmons*
D.R. Dickinson *Simmons & Simmons*	David Dunnigan *Clifford Chance*	Nicholas W. Eastwell *Linklaters & Paines*
Stephen R.R. Edlmann *Linklaters & Paines*	Ian.M Falconer *Freshfields*	Simon A. Haddock *Allen & Overy*
Stephen Hood *Clifford Chance*	David Hudd *Lovell White Durrant*	N.D. Johnson *Allen & Overy*
Mark A. Kalderon *Freshfields*	Alan J. Karter *Simmons & Simmons*	Richard Kendall *Ashurst Morris Crisp*
David S. Krischer *Allen & Overy*	Paul Monk *Allen & Overy*	Alan G. Murray-Jones *Lovell White Durrant*
Alan M. Newton *Freshfields*	Chris Oakley *Clifford Chance*	J.A.E. Pitkin *Freshfields*
Colin Potter *Clifford Chance*	Marke Raines *Allen & Overy*	S.M. Revell *Freshfields*
James J. Rice *Linklaters & Paines*	Stephen Roith *Clifford Chance*	John Russell *Simmons & Simmons*
George E.S. Seligman *Slaughter and May*	Richard Slater *Slaughter and May*	Christopher R. Smith *Slaughter and May*
Gilles Thieffrey *Norton Rose*	David Trott *Freshfields*	Mark R. Welling *Allen & Overy*
Boyan S. Wells *Allen & Overy*	John Woodhall *Clifford Chance*	

Allen & Overy represent the most significant competition to *Linklaters & Paines* with a notable presence in the area of medium term note (MTN) programmes and a strong all round capital markets practice. Richard Sykes and Mark Welling are both highly recommended. Both firms regularly act for governments and major international financial institutions. *Linklaters & Paines*, *Clifford Chance* and *Allen & Overy* have recruited US-qualified securities lawyers for their capi-

tal markets practices. This relatively recent development has come about in response to the pressure on major firms to compete on a level playing field with the US firms in relation to international issues where a part of the securities offered are sold in the US under Rule 144 A.

Freshfields, *Slaughter and May* and *Simmons and Simmons* are also involved, though to a materially lesser extent, in capital markets business.

LEADERS IN CAPITAL MARKETS & DERIVATIVES

LONDON

Barnard, David M.
Linklaters & Paines, London (0171) 606 7080. Qualified 1976. Joined *Linklaters & Paines* in 1973. Handles international financing transactions, particularly capital markets. Specialises in Latin American financings but has experience throughout the world. Also handles English corporate law, particularly M&A, compliance and banking.

Beaumont, Rupert. R.S.
Slaughter and May, London (0171) 600 1200. Qualified 1968. Partner since 1974. Emphasis on bank and finance.

Bedford, Paul H.D.
Allen & Overy, London (0171) 330 3000. Qualified 1982. Partner 1988. ICM Department. Extensive experience in securitisation transactions.

Borrows, Jane
Simmons & Simmons, London (0171) 628 2020. Partner in Banking and Capital Markets Department.

Specialisation: Main area of practice is securitisation and structured finance, including domestic and cross-border securitisation and other structured finance transactions. Also handles general banking and capital markets transactions such as secured lending and bond issues. Author of articles and speaker at conferences on securitisation and off-balance sheet finance.

Prof. Membership: Law Society, International Bar Association.

Career: Qualified in 1981. Sloan Fellow of London Business School 1986. Joined *Simmons & Simmons* in 1988 (following CS first Boston), becoming a Partner in 1989.

Personal: Attended Queen Mary, University of London, 1974-77 (LLB Hons). Lives in London.

Burn, A. Lachlan
Linklaters & Paines, London (0171) 606 7080. Qualified 1976. Joined 1974. International Finance (Capital Markets) Department.

Carmichael, Andrew J.
Linklaters & Paines, London (0171) 606 7080. Qualified 1981. Joined 1979. International finance: capital markets and UK corporate fund raising. Work includes inter-

national debt, equity related debt and equity issues, derivatives and warrants, synthetic and repackaged securities, and medium term note and debt issuance programmes.

Clark, Charles E.M.
Linklaters & Paines, London (0171) 606 7080.

Davies, John W.
Simmons & Simmons, London (0171) 628 2020. Qualified 1980. Partner 1989. Banking and Capital Markets Department. Acts for banks and corporate trustees.

Dickinson, D.R.
Simmons & Simmons, London (0171) 628 2020. Partner in Banking and Capital Markets Department.

Specialisation: Main area of practice is capital markets. Has gained a wide range of experience since 1978, including Eurobonds, international equities, securitisation issues and derivatives. Other area is international lending: experienced in syndicated and other bank lending, both secured and unsecured.

Prof. Membership: Securities Institute, Inter Pacific Bar Association, Law Society.

Career: Qualified 1974. Solicitor and Partner at *Blyth Dutton Hollway* 1974-78, moving to *Linklaters & Paines* in 1978. Director Legal Services, Union Bank of Switzerland (Securities) Ltd 1984-88. Joined *Simmons & Simmons* as a Partner in 1988.

Personal: Born 13th December 1950. Lives in Woldingham.

Dunnigan, David
Clifford Chance, London (0171) 600 1000. Partner in the Securities Group. Eurobonds.

Eastwell, Nicholas W.
Linklaters & Paines, London (0171) 606 7080. Qualified 1983. Partner 1989. International Finance, Capital Markets and Banking.

Edlmann, Stephen R.R.
Linklaters & Paines, London (0171) 606 7080. Qualified 1979. Partner 1985. Main area of practice is international finance.

Falconer, Ian.M
Freshfields, London (0171) 936 4000. Qualified 1983. Partner 1990. Finance Department. Securitisation and tax issues.

Forbes-Cockell, Caird
Linklaters & Paines, London $I(New York 00 1 (212) 751 1000)$N. Qualified 1981. Joined 1979. Main areas of practice are international finance, covering capital markets and banking (most recently in Latin America); and structured finance, acting on secured, credit enhanced or asset-backed transactions.

Frank, David T.
Slaughter and May, London (0171) 600 1200. Qualified 1979. Joined 1977. Partner and head of capital markets practice. Extensive eurobond and international equity experience with issuers in the UK and around the world. Also handles corporate and banking work with a number of listed plc clients and is active in the venture capital and project financing areas.

Haddock, Simon A.
Allen & Overy, London (Hong Kong) (00) 852 2840 1282. Qualified 1986. Partner 1992. International Capital Markets Department.

Hood, Stephen
Clifford Chance, London (0171) 600 1000. Partner in the New York office. Principal area of practice involves banking and international securities work.

Hudd, David
Lovell White Durrant, London (0171) 236 0066. Qualified 1983. Partner 1994. Capital Markets and Corporate Finance Group.

Johnson, N.D.
Allen & Overy, London (0171) 330 3000. Qualified 1978.

Kalderon, Mark A.
Freshfields, London (0171) 936 4000. Qualified 1983. Partner 1990. Finance Department. Main area of practice is capital markets.

Karter, Alan J.
Simmons & Simmons, London (0171) 628 2020. Partner in Corporate Department.

Specialisation: Principal area of practice is corporate and structured finance including securitisation and venture capital. Other main area of work involves advising financial institutions including banks, building societies and insurance companies. Addresses conferences on securitisation and investment advertisements.

Prof. Membership: Law Society, Law Society of Scotland.

Career: Qualified 1979 (Scotland). Joined *Simmons & Simmons* in 1987 and became a Partner in 1988.

Personal: Born 12th January 1955. Attended University of Edinburgh 1974-77. Lives in London.

Kendall, Richard
Ashurst Morris Crisp, London (0171) 638 1111. Qualified 1985. Partner 1994. Banking and Finance Department.

Krischer, David S.
Allen & Overy, London (0171) 330 3000. Qualified 1992. Partner 1992. International Capital Markets Department. Securitisation.

Kyle, J. Terence
Linklaters & Paines, London (0171) 606 7080. Qualified 1972. Joined 1970. International Finance: Capital Markets and Banking. Work includes securities for debt, equity-related debt and equity; repackaging; warrants; debt issuance programmes; and syndicated lending.

Monk, Paul
Allen & Overy, London (0171) 330 3000. Qualified 1974. Partner.

Murray-Jones, Alan G.
Lovell White Durrant, London (0171) 236 0066.

Newton, Alan M.
Freshfields, London (0171) 936 4000. Partner 1989. Finance Department.

Specialisation: Practice involves all aspects of capital markets work, including public and private debt and equity issues, MTN programmes, structured placements, securitisations, covered warrants, index-linked issues, the development of a broad range of OTC derivative products and related regulatory work. Member of *Freshfields'* Capital Markets Group and Head of its Derivatives Unit. Advised the Bank of England in connection with the UK Government ECU Treasury Bill and Treasury Note Programmes, the ECU2.75Bn 9 1/8% Bonds (due 2001), the DM5.5m 7 1/8th Bonds (due 1997) and the US$3bn 7 1/4% Bonds (due 2002). Involved in the development of a number of innovative securitisation transactions, including the first UK mortgage-backed transaction for The Mortgage Corporation (TMC1); the first fixed rate dual company structure (HMC 101); the first securitisation of lease and dealer finance receivables (originated by Leyland DAF) and the first commercial mortgage and public building society securitisation (Bristol & West). Also a member of Freshfield's Building Societies Group and advises on building society regulation mergers and transfers. Regularly lectures on a wide variety of capital markets topics. Participates in ISDA working groups on derivatives related mat-

ters. Member of the Editorial Board of the Journal of Derivatives Use, Trading and Regulation.

Prof. Membership: City of London Solicitors' Company.

Career: Qualified in 1982 with *Freshfields*, having joined in 1980. Seconded to New York office 1986-88. Became a Partner in 1989.

Personal: Born 4th January 1957. Attended Exeter College, Oxford 1975-79 (MA, BCL). Leisure interests include sailing and opera. Lives in London.

Oakley, Chris
Clifford Chance, London (0171) 600 1000. Partner. Principal area of work is capital markets and securitisation.

Palache, Robert
Clifford Chance, London (0171) 600 1000. Partner. Principal area of practice is capital markets and securitisation.

Pitkin, J.A.E.
Freshfields, London (0171) 936 4000.

Potter, Colin
Clifford Chance, London (0171) 600 1000. Partner. Principal area of practice is capital markets and securitisation work.

Raines, Marke
Allen & Overy, London (0171) 330 3000. Solicitor, International Capital Markets Department. Principal area is securitisation.

Revell, S.M.
Freshfields, London (0171) 936 4000.

Rice, James J.
Linklaters & Paines, London (0171) 606 7080. Qualified 1982. Joined 1980. International finance, securitisation and banking.

Roith, Stephen
Clifford Chance, London (0171) 600 1000. Partner, Head of Latin America practice group. Principal area of practice is capital markets and structured finance.

Russell, John
Simmons & Simmons, London (0171) 628 2020. Partner in Banking and Capital Markets Department.

Specialisation: Capital markets work includes international equity offerings, eurobonds, derivative issues, structured finance, MTN programmes, commercial paper programmes and securities buy-backs. Banking work includes swaps, repos, project finance and syndicated loans. Has particular experience of India and the Nordic countries. Transactions including $100 million GDR and Warrant Issues for ITC and SIV Industries Limited; GDR issues for Great Eastern Shipping Limited, DCW Limited and Sanghi Polyesters Limited; $1000 million Medium Term Note Programme for SmithKline Beecham plc; $2500 million Sires repackag-

ing MTN programme, involving the issue of a wide range of derivative securities backed by swaps and options; $3000 million bilateral facilities for BAT Industries plc; £100 million Convertible Captial Bond for rescue of Brent Walker; structuring of share offerings for shipping funds.

Career: Qualified in 1977, and in Hong Kong in 1981. Worked with *Linklaters & Paines* 1975-85 and *Merrill Lynch* 1985-88. Joined *Simmons & Simmons* in 1988 as a Partner.

Personal: Born 1.6.1953. Attended Southampton University. Lives in Berkhamsted.

Seligman, George E.S.
Slaughter and May, London (0171) 600 1200. Qualified 1977. Partner since 1984. Specialises in securitisations.

Slater, Richard
See under Banking.

Smith, Christopher R.
Slaughter and May, London (0171) 600 1200. Qualified 1980. Joined 1978. Partner specialising in banking and finance.

Sykes, Richard H.
Allen & Overy, London (0171) 330 3000. Qualified 1969. Partner 1974. Head of the International Capital Markets Department.

Thieffrey, Gilles
Norton Rose, London (0171) 283 6000. Partner and head of the Capital Markets Department. Former head of Capital Markets Legal, Banque National de Paris.

Trott, David
Freshfields, London (0171) 936 4000. Assistant Solicitor in Finance Department.

Specialisation: Deals with banking and finance with a particular emphasis on asset securitisation, building societies and banking law. Has lectured at a number of conferences on asset securitisation and building societies. Author of various articles for Butterworths Journal of International Banking and Finance Law and Journal of International Banking Law.

Career: Qualified in 1988.

Personal: Born in 1963. Attended Durham University.

Welling, Mark R.
Allen & Overy, London (0171) 330 3000. Qualified 1981. Partner 1987. International Capital Markets Department.

Wells, Boyan S.
Allen & Overy, London (0171) 330 3000. Qualified 1981. Partner 1987. International Capital Markets and Derivatives Department.

Woodhall, John
Clifford Chance, London (0171) 600 1000. Partner in the Hong Kong office. Principal area of work is capital markets and securitisation.

CHARITIES

THE effect of recent legislation continues to make itself felt in this area. Under the Charities Acts 1992 and 1993, Charities have become subject to far more stringent regulations covering most aspects of charity administration, from fund-raising to the disposal of property and the preparation of accounts.

As a result of this greater accountability, litigation has risen sharply. The proceedings currently pending concerning investment by Imperial Cancer Research in the tobacco industry are an instance of this. Charities are also having to pay more attention to health and safety. Educational establishments, for example, are becoming aware of the need for adequate insurance to cover the risk of student injuries on their premises.

LONDON

Several firms are highly regarded in the field including *Bates Wells & Braithwaite, Farrer & Co, Winckworth & Pemberton, Allen & Overy* and *Paisner & Co.* Stephen Lloyd, Fiona Middleton and Andrew Phillips of *Bates, Wells and Braithwaite* are well-known for all aspects of charity law, and the

LEADING FIRMS – LONDON

ALLEN & OVERY	BATES, WELLS & BRAITHWAITE
FARRER & CO	PAISNER & CO
WINCKWORTH & PEMBERTON	
BIRCHAM	HEMPSONS
MACFARLANES	NORTON ROSE

latter is author of 'Charitable Status: A Practical Handbook'. At *Farrer & Co*, Judith Hill is an experienced practitioner whose work includes the establishment of charities, constitutional issues and trading companies. She is a contributor to 'Trust Law International', 'The Charity Law and Practice Review' and 'Charity World Bulletin'.

Peter Mimpriss of *Allen & Overy* has a strong reputation and acts for several major charities including museums, galleries, universities, art centres and statutory bodies. He is Chairman of the Charity Law Association, formerly the Association of Charity Lawyers, which now has over 300 hundred members and includes other professionals in the field. *Paisner & Co* also enjoys an established reputation and has

a strong department led by Martin Paisner and Anne-Marie Piper who is Secretary of the Charity Law Association.

Other firms which enjoy excellent reputations in this field include *Hempsons, Norton Rose, Macfarlanes* and *Bircham & Co. Hempsons,* where Michael Stewart is well regarded, provides a full service to charities acting in both contentious cases and advisory matters. At *Norton Rose*, Michael Macfadyen and Catriona Syed act for a number of institutions across the charitable spectrum including English Heritage. Simon Weil of *Bircham & Co* has gained national acclaim for heritage property work, in addition to representing a number of charities throughout the UK. *Macfarlanes,* also well regarded, advises on formation and administration for public and private charities including breach of trust, tax and commercial activity.

Also notable for charity work is *Payne Hicks Beach* which has particular expertise in undertaking charitable work for museums and private foundations. Graham Brown is the leading specialist at the firm.

Sinclair Taylor & Martin has a specialism in legal work for charities, covering all aspects of non-contentious charity law. James Sinclair Taylor, who heads the group, has a particularly strong reputation. *Lovell White Durrant,* where Robert Meakin and Vanessa Reburn are well known, offer advice across the whole field, and Robert Meakin is particularly highly regarded for his experience of investigation of charities, having been a legal advisor to the Charity Commission.

HIGHLY REGARDED – LONDON

CHARLES RUSSELL	DENTON HALL
FIELD FISHER WATERHOUSE	GOODMAN DERRICK
HARBOTTLE & LEWIS	LEE BOLTON & LEE
LEE & PEMBERTONS	LOVELL WHITE DURRANT
PAYNE HICKS BEACH	RADCLIFFES CROSSMAN BLOCK
SINCLAIR TAYLOR & MARTIN	SPEECHLY BIRCHAM
TROWERS & HAMLINS	WITHAM WELD
WITHERS	
ALSOP WILKINSON	BRISTOWS COOKE & CARPMAEL
CAMERON MARKBY HEWITT	CROSSMAN BLOCK
EDWIN COE	ELLIS WOOD
GREGORY, ROWCLIFFE & MILNERS	HUNTERS
NABARRO NATHANSON	VIZARDS

Also highly regarded in the field are Michael Carpenter at *Withers* and Jean Dollimore at *Trowers & Hamlins.*

LEADING INDIVIDUALS – LONDON

Graham Stephen Brown *Payne Hicks Beach*	**Judith L. Hill** *Farrer & Co*	**Stephen T. Lloyd** *Bates, Wells & Braithwaite*
Michael R. Macfadyen *Norton Rose*	**Fiona Middleton** *Bates, Wells & Braithwaite*	**Peter Mimpriss** *Allen & Overy*
Martin D. Paisner *Paisner & Co*	**Andrew Phillips** *Bates, Wells & Braithwaite*	**Anne-Marie Piper** *Paisner & Co*
Michael S.E. Carpenter *Withers*	**J.D. Dollimore** *Trowers & Hamlins*	**Robert Meakin** *Lovell White Durrant*
Vanessa Reburn *Lovell White Durrant*	**James Sinclair Taylor** *Sinclair Taylor & Martin*	**Michael Stewart** *Hempsons*
M. Catriona Syed *Norton Rose*	**S.P. Weil** *Bircham*	

SOUTH EAST

There are many accomplished firms and individuals across the South East. In particular, Kenneth Brooks at *Brook Street des Roches* is well-regarded. He acts for Oxfam, educational, religious, wildlife and grant-making charities, as well as Merton College, Oxford, and the Oxford Union Society. *Morrell, Peel & Gamlen* is especially well-known for acting on behalf of educational charities, and Alan Poulter has been highly recommended at the firm. Also well regarded are *Thomson, Snell & Passmore* and *Winckworth & Pemberton* where John Rees has an established reputation.

HIGHLY REGARDED – SOUTH EAST	
BROOKSTREET DES ROCHES *Witney*	MORRELL PEEL & GAMLEN *Oxford*
NABARRO NATHANSON	THOMSON SNELL & PASSMORE *Tunbridge Wells*
WINCKWORTH & PEMBERTON *Chelmsford*	
BARLOWS *Guildford*	CHARLES LUCAS & MARSHALL *Newbury*
CRIPPS HARRIES HALL *Tunbridge Wells*	DONNE MILEHAM & HADDOCK *Brighton*
ELLISON & CO *Colchester*	FURLEY PAGE FIELDING & BARTON *Canterbury*
GRIFFITH SMITH *Brighton*	ILIFFES BOOTH BENNETT *Uxbridge*
LINNELLS *Oxford*	THOMAS EGGAR VERRALL BOWLES *Chichester*

Jonathan Burchfield at *Nabarro Nathanson* (incorporating *Turner Kenneth Brown*) in Reading has substantial experience in the field. He has contributed to 'Charity Appeals: the Complete Guide to Success.' *Griffith Smith,* which has particular expertise in disability and educational charities, and *Thomas Eggar Verrall Bowles* are also well-regarded.

LEADING INDIVIDUALS – SOUTH EAST
Kenneth Brooks *BrookStreet des Roches*
J.R. Burchfield *Nabarro Nathanson*
A.G. Poulter *Morrell Peel & Gamlen*
John Rees *Winckworth & Pemberton*

SOUTH WEST & WALES

Stone King & Wardle, where Michael King has an excellent reputation, is particularly strong in this area. The firm acts for animal and arts charities, providing advice regarding the restructuring of charities, hiving-off of schools to other charities, and charity commission schemes. They have also acted for Roman Catholic religious and educational charities for over 150 years. *Tozers* also enjoy an established reputation in the field, acting for a wide variety of religious, educational and other charities including two national charities and an AIDS trust. Richard King at the firm is particularly well regarded for his expertise.

Of the other firms that have been highly recommended *Osborne Clarke,* where Robert Johnson is well known, has considerable expertise in corporate charities and substantial land-owning charities. One of its partners has experience as a council member of the Sue Ryder Foundation. *Wansbroughs Willey Hargrave* is also well regarded, and Mark Woodward at the firm is known for undertaking the estab-

lishment of new charities, reorganizations and charity commission investigations.

HIGHLY REGARDED – SOUTH WEST & WALES	
OSBORNE CLARKE *Bristol*	STONE KING & WARDLE *Bath*
TOZERS *Exeter*	WANSBROUGHS WILLEY HARGRAVE *Bristol*
WILSONS *Salisbury*	
BURGES SALMON *Bristol*	CLARKE WILLMOTT & CLARKE *Taunton*
EVERSHEDS, CARDIFF *Cardiff*	HUGH JAMES JONES & JENKINS *Cardiff*
MORGAN BRUCE *Cardiff*	THRINGS & LONG *Bath*
BOYCE HATTON *Torquay*	DAVIES AND PARTNERS *Gloucester*
EDWARDS GELDARD *Cardiff*	FORD SIMEY DAW ROBERTS *Exeter*
LESTER ALDRIDGE *Bournemouth*	LOOSEMORES *Cardiff*
MEADE–KING *Bristol*	MICHELMORES *Exeter*
PARKER BULLEN *Salisbury*	RICKERBY JESSOP *Cheltenham*

Other notable practitioners in the South West include John Emmerson at *Wilsons* who has particular expertise in handling work for disabled, educational and sporting charities.

In Wales, *Hugh James Jones & Jenkins* is pre-eminent in charitable work ranging from the establishment of charities to advising trustees. The firm is particularly involved with the Presbyterian Church of Wales and also acts for one Trust corporation.

LEADING INDIVIDUALS – SOUTH WEST & WALES
John C. Emmerson *Wilsons*
Robert I. Johnson *Osborne Clarke*
A. Michael H. King *Stone King & Wardle*
A. Richard G. King *Tozers*
Mark Woodward *Wansbroughs Willey Hargrave*

MIDLANDS

The wide-ranging charities practice of *Anthony Collins* is highly-respected where Romaine Thompson, a full-time charities specialist, has an excellent reputation. She advises on formation, reorganizations, incorporation, amalgamation, dissolution, trading, trusteeship and constitutional matters. *Shakespeares*, where Gary De'Ath is well-regarded, has particular expertise in handling both welfare and educational charities.

HIGHLY REGARDED – MIDLANDS	
ANTHONY COLLINS *Birmingham*	GATELEY WAREING *Birmingham*
LEE CROWDER *Birmingham*	MARTINEAU JOHNSON *Birmingham*
SHAKESPEARES *Birmingham*	WRAGGE & CO *Birmingham*
HARVEY INGRAM *Leicester*	MANDER HADLEY & CO *Coventry*
TALLENTS GODFREY *Newark-on-Trent*	

Other notable practices include *Martineau Johnson, Gateley Wareing* and *Wragge & Co. Martineau Johnson,* where Hugh Carslake heads the department, has an extensive charities practice which includes work for the Church of England. Also recommended at the firm is Michael Fea. Stephen Gateley at *Gateley Wareing* has particularly strong ecclesiastical connections, and work undertaken includes acting for various religious orders and schools. *Wragge & Co* also strong in this area, handle both welfare and educational charities.

LEADING INDIVIDUALS – MIDLANDS

Hugh Carslake	*Martineau Johnson*
Gary R. De'Ath	*Shakespeares*
J.M.G. Fea	*Martineau Johnson*
Stephen Gateley	*Gateley Wareing*
Romaine Thompson	*Anthony Collins*

EAST ANGLIA

A number of firms with considerable expertise in this area are based in Norwich, which has several substantial charities. At *Cozens-Hardy & Jewson,* Matthew Martin has an excellent reputation for all aspects of charitable law, in particular ecclesiastical charities and welfare organisations.

HIGHLY REGARDED – EAST ANGLIA

COZENS–HARDY & JEWSON *Norwich*		**EVERSHEDS, NORWICH** *Norwich*	
LEATHES PRIOR *Norwich*		**MILLS & REEVE** *Norwich*	
GREENWOODS *Peterborough*		**LEEDS DAY** *Sandy*	
TAYLOR VINTERS *Cambridge*			

John Herring and Christopher Jackson at *Mills & Reeve* both enjoy strong reputations in the field, and act for a number of Cambridge colleges. *Eversheds* have an expanding practice in this area. The firm acts for NHS Trusts advising on hospital-based endowment funds and charities created by hospital consultants. Philip Norton and John Perowne have been particularly recommended at the firm for their depth of experience in the field. Anthony Hansell at *Leathes Prior* is also highly regarded for his substantial charity law experience.

LEADING INDIVIDUALS – EAST ANGLIA

J.W.F. Herring	*Mills & Reeve*
C.E.H. Jackson	*Mills & Reeve*
Matthew T. Martin	*Cozens–Hardy & Jewson*
A.P. Hansell	*Leathes Prior*
Philip Norton	*Eversheds*
John Perowne	*Eversheds*

NORTH WEST

Lawrence Holden at *Brabner Holden Banks Wilson* is the pre-eminent practitioner in the area. A member of the National Charity Law Association, he undertakes formations, trading subsidiaries, and general administration for a variety of charities.

HIGHLY REGARDED – NORTH WEST

BRABNER HOLDEN BANKS WILSON *Liverpool*		
ALSOP WILKINSON *Liverpool*		**BIRCH CULLIMORE** *Chester*
HILL DICKINSON DAVIS CAMPBELL *Liverpool*		**OSWALD GOODIER & CO** *Preston*
COBBETT LEAK ALMOND *Manchester*		**GEORGE DAVIES & CO** *Manchester*
HALLIWELL LANDAU *Manchester*		**PANNONE & PARTNERS** *Manchester*
WEIGHTMAN RUTHERFORDS *Liverpool*		

Alsop Wilkinson is well known for offering specialist advice to universities, further education colleges and others in the education sector. Other leading firms include *Oswald Goodier & Co* which acts for educational, private and public charities, charitable companies and trusts, *Birch Cullimore* and *Hill Dickinson Davis Campbell.* The latter acts for British Red Cross, health authority charities, Roman Catholic Charities and AIDS charities.

LEADING INDIVIDUALS – NORTH WEST

Lawrence Holden	*Brabner Holden Banks Wilson*

NORTH EAST

Of the firms highly regarded for charity work, *Ford & Warren* advise educational and religious charities, while, *Malcolm Lynch* has a particular expertise in the trading subsidiaries of charities. Malcolm Lynch himself is a well-known specialist in this field. Tony Lawton at *Grays* has particular expertise in dealings and management of charity land and property

HIGHLY REGARDED – NORTH EAST

GRAYS *York*	**MALCOLM LYNCH** *Leeds*
BOOTH & CO. *Leeds*	**FORD AND WARREN** *Leeds*
IRWIN MITCHELL *Sheffield*	**PINSENT CURTIS**
BROOKE NORTH AND GOODWIN *Leeds*	**ROLLIT FARRELL & BLADON** *Hull*
WILKINSON MAUGHAN *Newcastle-upon-Tyne*	

and formation of charities, as well as advising educational charities, schools and colleges. *Booth & Co* are also well-known for their work in charity law, as are *Pinsent Curtis.*

LEADING INDIVIDUALS – NORTH EAST

F. Tony Lawton	*Grays*
Malcolm Lynch	*Malcolm Lynch*

SCOTLAND

The leading firms have seen an increase in charitable work over the last year, particularly the incorporation of charities as companies in order to secure limited liability. Those with the strongest reputations include *Balfour & Manson - Nightingale & Bell, Bell & Scott WS, W & J Burness WS, Lindsays WS* and *T C Young & Son.* Also well-regarded are *Dundas & Wilson CS* and *Tods Murray WS,* the latter specialising in work relating to nature conservation bodies and landowners.

HIGHLY REGARDED – SCOTLAND

BALFOUR & MANSON *Edinburgh*	**BELL & SCOTT WS** *Edinburgh*
W & J BURNESS WS *Edinburgh*	**DUNDAS & WILSON CS** *Edinburgh*
LINDSAYS WS *Edinburgh*	**TODS MURRAY WS** *Edinburgh*
T.C. YOUNG & SON *Glasgow*	
GILLESPIE MACANDREW *Edinburgh*	**MACROBERTS** *Glasgow*
McGRIGOR DONALD *Glasgow*	**SHEPHERD & WEDDERBURN** *Edinburgh*

Lindsays WS has established specialist expertise in the incorporation of charitable companies. The firm also has experience across a wide range of charitable purposes, including education, heritage and religion, and has a niche specialisation in building preservation and conservation work. David Reith heads the department and is particularly well regarded amongst his peers for his expertise.

Balfour & Manson – Nightingale & Bell has particular expertise in charities involved in special needs and mental and physical disability. A partner at the firm has been appointed to the Scottish Hospital Endowments Research Trust. *Bell & Scott WS* also has close connections with specialist needs charities, and offers expertise in relation to the Arts where a number of organisations have charitable status.

LEADING INDIVIDUALS – SCOTLAND

Andrew M. Kerr	*Bell & Scott WS*
Simon A. MacKintosh	*W & J Burness WS*
David S. Reith	*Lindsays WS*

LEADERS IN CHARITIES

LONDON

Brown, Graham Stephen
See under Trusts & P.Tx.

Carpenter, Michael S.E.
See under Trusts & P.Tx.

Dollimore, J.D.
Trowers & Hamlins, London (0171) 831 6292.

Hill, Judith L.
Farrer & Co, London (0171) 242 2022. Partner in Private Client Department.

Specialisation: Main area of practice is charity law, including the establishment of charities, constitutional issues and trading companies. Also experienced in general private client work, covering trusts, wills, capital taxation and art and heritage law. Contributor to Trust Law International, The Charity Law and Practice Review and Charity World Bulletin. Regularly addresses conferences on charity law topics.

Prof. Membership: Law Society, Holborn Law Society, International Bar Association, Charity Law Association (Committee Member).

Career: Joined *Farrer & Co* in 1973, qualifying in 1975. Moved to *Shoosmiths & Harrison* in Northampton in 1979, until 1981. Re-joined *Farrer & Co* in 1985. Partner 1986.

Personal: Born 8th October 1949. Attended Brighton & Hove High School 1956-69, Newnham College, Cambridge 1969-72. Member of Board of Royal Hospital and Home, Putney. Leisure pursuits include running and reading. Lives in London.

Lloyd, Stephen T.
Bates, Wells & Braithwaite, London (0171) 251 1122. Partner in Charity and Company Commercial Department.

Specialisation: Main area of practice is charity work, acting for a large number of leading charitable organisations on a wide range of matters, including constitutional, contract,

property and charity law. Also provides all forms of legal advice to small and medium sized businesses. Co-author of 'Barclays Guide to the Law for the Small Business'. Author of 'Charities: The New Law' and 'Charities, Trading and the Law' and of numerous articles. Gave at least 20 lectures in 1994.

Prof. Membership: Charity Law Association, UK Environmental Law Association

Career: With *Freshfields* 1975-78. Qualified in 1977. With *Frizzell Group Ltd* 1978-80. Joined *Bates, Wells & Braithwaite* in 1980 and became a Partner in 1984.

Personal: Born 17th July 1951. Educated at Bristol University 1969-72 (History) and Cambridge University 1972 (Law). Trustee of three charities. Recreations include reading, cycling, theatre and music. Lives in Greenwich.

Macfadyen, Michael R.
See under Trusts & P.Tx.

Meakin, Robert
Lovell White Durrant, London (0171) 236 0066. Qualified 1987. Charities Department. Offers all aspects of charity advice.

Middleton, Fiona
Bates, Wells & Braithwaite, London (0171) 251 1122. Partner in Charity Department.

Specialisation: Deals with all aspects of law relating to charities and other voluntary organisations. Author (with Andrew Phillips) of 'Charity Investment, Law & Practice' and 'Charities, The New Law' (with Stephen Lloyd). Member of the NCVO/ Charity Commission working party on trustee training which produced the report 'On Trust: Increasing the Effectiveness of Charity Trustees and Management Committees'.

Prof. Membership: Charity Law Association.

Career: Lecturer in Law, Kings College, London University 1972-79. Legal Adviser to the Charity Commission 1979-87. Joined *Bates, Wells & Braithwaite* in 1988 and became a Partner in 1990.

Personal: Born 18th January 1948. Trustee of the Family Welfare Association and Barnardos. Recreations include gardening, bee keeping and opera. Lives in Crowborough, E. Sussex.

Mimpriss, Peter
Allen & Overy, London (0171) 330 3000. Qualified 1967. Partner 1972. Private Client Department. Main areas of practice are private client and charities. Born 22.8.1943.

Paisner, Martin D.
Paisner & Co, London (0171) 353 0299. Qualified 1970. Partner 1972. Head of Private Client. Specialises in all aspects of trusts (both UK and overseas), including charitable organisations both of a grant-making and functional nature.

Phillips, Andrew
Bates, Wells & Braithwaite, London (0171) 251 1122. Founding Partner.

Specialisation: Main areas of practice are charities, business law and defamation. Author of 'Charitable Status: A practical handbook', now in its fourth edition; 'Charity Investment: Law and Practice'; and 'The Living Law', a guide to the law for young people. Also an occasional freelance journalist, and a regular broadcaster, particularly as Legal Eagle on BBC 2's Jimmy Young Show.

Prof. Memberships: Law Society.

Career: Qualified 1964. Founded *Bates Well & Braithwaite, London* in 1970. Still Senior Partner. Co-founder in 1971 and first Chairman of the Legal Action Group. Founder and first Chairman of the Citizenship Foundation in 1989 (continuing). Initiated the Lawyers in the Community scheme.

Personal: Born 15th March 1939. Attended Culford and Uppingham schools, then Trinity Hall, Cambridge. Trustee of Guardian newspapers and various charities. Member of National Lottery Charities Board. Non-Executive Director of four companies. Leisure pursuits include politics, golf, cricket, history and the arts. Lives in Sudbury, Suffolk.

Piper, Anne-Marie
Paisner & Co, London (0171) 353 0299. Qualified 1988. Partner. Private Client and Charities Department. Work covers all aspects of charity law. Secretary of Charity Law Association. Born 27.1.1958.

Reburn, Vanessa
Lovell White Durrant, London (0171) 236 0066.

Sinclair Taylor, James
Sinclair Taylor & Martin, London (0181) 969 3667. Qualified 1975. Partner 1981. Also deals with housing associations, schools and local authorities.

Stewart, Michael
Hempsons, London (0171) 836 0011.

Syed, M. Catriona
Norton Rose, London (0171) 283 6000.

Weil, S.P.
Bircham & Co In Association with Dyson Bell Martin, London (0171) 222 8044.

REGIONS

Brooks, Kenneth
BrookStreet des Roches, Witney (01993) 771616. Partner handling charity, commercial property and company work.

Specialisation: Charity clients include Oxfam, the International Non Governmental Organisation Training and Research Centre, the Zambesi Society (UK), Merton College, Oxford, the Oxford Union Society, the Hamilton Trust, the Oxford Philosophy Trust. Commercial clients include Blockbuster Entertainment Corporation, Rhino Group plc, Barclays Bank, Discovery Zone (UK) Ltd and Bright Reasons Group Plc, Research Machines plc, Historical Collections Group plc, Oxford, Swindon & Gloucester Co-Operative Society Ltd, The Co-Operative Bank plc, Oxford Economic Research Associates Ltd, The Milk Group Ltd, Maison Blanc Ltd, the Maizegrowers Association, The American Pizza Company Ltd, Oxford Cable Ltd, Tothlord International (UK) Ltd.

Prof. Membership: Association of Charity Lawyers, Thames Valley Commercial Lawyers Association, European Law Group, Law Society.

Career: Qualified in 1982. With *Linnells* in Oxford from 1982 to 1994, as a Partner from 1985. Co-founder of *Brookstreet des Roches* in April 1994.

Personal: Born 23rd January 1956. Lives in Witney.

Burchfield, J.R.
Nabarro Nathanson, Reading (01734) 504700. Qualified 1978. Partner 1983. Head of Charity Group. Handles constitutions of

charities and the impact of charity law. Also private client work. Born 22.2.1954.

Carslake, Hugh
See under Ecclesiastical.

De'Ath, Gary R.
Shakespeares, Birmingham (0121) 632 4199. Partner in Private Client Department.

Specialisation: Main areas of practice are wills, trusts, administration of estates, enduring powers of attorney, receivership under the Court of Protection and charities (formation, operation and fund-raising). Has addressed the National Association of Hospice Fund-raisers and the Institute of Charity Fund-raising Managers.

Prof. Membership: West Midlands Charitable Trusts Group, The Institute of Charity Fund-raising Managers, The Charity Law Association, The Society of Trust and Estate Practitioners.

Career: Qualified in 1976. Joined *Shakespeares* in 1986 and became a Partner in 1989.

Personal: Born 21st December 1951. Educated at Gilberd School, Colchester 1963-70 and Kings College, University of London 1970-73. Fund-raising Sub-Committee Member for Turning Point (Birmingham); Director and Secretary of Birmingham Readers and Writers Festival Ltd and Sandwell Crossroads Care Attendant Scheme Ltd; Trustee of Freshwinds Charitable Trust. Trustee of Al Furquan school. Company Secretary to Newtown Cultural Project Ltd. Spiritual Healer.

Emmerson, John C.
See under Trusts & P.Tx.

Fea, J.M.G.
Martineau Johnson, Birmingham (0121) 200 3300.

Gateley, Stephen
Gateley Wareing, Birmingham (0121) 236 8585. Qualified 1966. Partner 1967. Charity Trust and Private Client Department. Main area of practice is charity trusts.

Hansell, A.P.
Leathes Prior, Norwich (01603) 610911. Qualified 1964. Partner 1985. Private Client Department. Work covers charity, probate, trusts, conveyancing, tax planning and notarial work.

Herring, J.W.F.
Mills & Reeve, Norwich +44 (0) 1603 660155.

Holden, Lawrence
Brabner Holden Banks Wilson, Liverpool (0151) 236 5821. Senior Partner.

Specialisation: Principal area of practice involved advising a number of major Housing Associations and charities. Also deals with general property and private client work.

Acted on large scale transfers in Runcorn and Warrington. Advised in relation to many charitable incorporations and group structures. Author of a number of articles on computers and the law and law practice management and legal education.

Prof. Membership: Law Society, Charity Law Society, National Federation of Housing Association Solicitors' Group, Society for Computers and Law.

Career: Qualified in 1965 while with *Brabner Holden*, became a Partner in 1966 and now Senior Partner. Past President Liverpool Law Society, President of Council Liverpool University. Deputy Lieutenant of Merseyside.

Personal: Born 19th September 1940. Attended Liverpool College 1951-59, then Liverpool University 1959-62. Leisure pursuits include fell walking, gardening and wood sculpture. Lives in Birkenhead.

Jackson, C.E.H.
Mills & Reeve, Norwich +44 (0) 1603 660155.

Johnson, Robert I.
See under Litigation (Commercial).

Kerr, Andrew M.
See under Media & Entertainment.

King, A. Michael H.
Stone King & Wardle, Bath (01225) 337599. Qualified 1974. Partner 1975. Heads Charity and Education Unit of Commercial Department.

King, A. Richard G.
Tozers, Exeter (01392) 424444. Qualified 1979. Partner 1983. Charities and Schools Department. Education work also covered.

Lawton, F. Tony
Grays, York (01904) 634771. Qualified 1966. Partner 1967. Main area of practice is charity law, including conveyancing of charity property, formation of charities and negotiating with Charity Commissioners. Work is also undertaken in connection with education, unincorporated associations and housing associations.

Lynch, Malcolm
Malcolm Lynch, Leeds (0113) 2429600. Qualified 1983. Partner 1989. Charity law. Work covers charities (especially those with trading subsidiaries), ESOPs and local government law. Born 29.4.1955.

MacKintosh, Simon A.
W & J Burness WS, Edinburgh (0131) 226 2561. Partner in Private Client Department.

Specialisation: Main areas of practice are tax, trusts and charities. Work includes tax planning, heritage property, charity law and practice and trust establishment, variation and practice. Also handles commercial trusts, pensions and ESOPs. Co-author of 'Revenue Law in Scotland', 1987. Member of Law Society of Scotland Revenue Law Committee.

Prof. Membership: Law Society of Scotland, Society of Trust and Estate Practitioners, International Academy of Estate and Trust Law.

Career: Qualified in 1982. Joined *W&J Burness WS* in 1980, becoming a Partner in 1985. Non-executive Director of Macphie of Glenbervie Ltd and Croftinloan (Holdings) Ltd.

Personal: Born 2nd February 1957. Attended Edinburgh Academy 1964-70, Glenalmond Academy 1970-74, Cambridge University 1975-78 and Edinburgh University 1978-80. Leisure interests include gardening, golf and rugby. Lives in Edinburgh.

Martin, Matthew T.

Cozens–Hardy & Jewson, Norwich (01603) 625231. Qualified 1967. Partner 1969. Property, Trusts and Estates Department. Main areas of practice are charity law and administration. Commercial and agricultural property work is also covered.

Norton, Philip

Eversheds, Norwich (01603) 272727. Qualified 1984. Partner 1990. Private Capital Group. Main area of work covers the affairs of the elderly and mental incapacity.

Perowne, John

Eversheds, Norwich (01603) 272727.

Poulter, A.G.

Morrell Peel & Gamlen, Oxford (01865) 242468. Qualified 1971. Partner 1975. Private Client and Charities Department.

Rees, John

See under Ecclesiastical.

Reith, David S.

Lindsays WS, Edinburgh (0131) 229 1212. Qualified 1974. Partner 1976. Managing Partner 1994. Main area of practice are commercial property and charities, especially building preservation and other conservation work. Born 15.4.1951.

Thompson, Romaine

Anthony Collins, Birmingham (0121) 200 3242. Partner and Head of Charities Department.

Specialisation: Main area of practice is charities. Work includes charity formation, registration, restructuring and reorganisation, compliance with charity commission requirements, charity commission schemes and the formation and tax efficient use of trading subsidiaries. Also handles fund-raising advice and agreements, as well as advising on corporate structure of charities; NHS trusts on charity law and compliance; on trustees rights and duties and providing trustee training for directors and trustees of charities. Pioneered a fixed fee legal health-check 'Legal Audit' service. Has particular experience in dealing with ecclesiastical and Christian charities. Contributor on occasional basis to NGO Finance; contributor to client newsletter produced by *Anthony Collins*. Lectures on charity law for clients and on (Law Society CPD approved) courses. Former tutor at Faculty of Law, University of Birmingham.

Prof. Membership: Association of Charity Lawyers, Society of Trusts and Estates Practitioners.

Career: Qualified in 1988. Worked at *Pinsent & Co.* 1986-89. Joined *Anthony Collins* in 1989, becoming a Partner in 1993.

Personal: Born in 1964. Attended Trinity Hall, Cambridge.

Woodward, Mark

Wansbroughs Willey Hargrave, Bristol (0117) 926 8981. Associate in Private Client Department; Head of Charity Unit.

Specialisation: Acts for a growing number of large national charities as well as smaller local ones. Although he handles all aspects of charity work, is particularly interested in establishing new charities and acting for charities in legacy disputes. Also handles charity commission investigations.

Prof. Membership: Bristol Law Society.

Career: Qualified in 1985, having joined *Freshfields* in 1983. Worked as a Legal Officer for the Charity Commission, London, 1987-88, before joining *Wansbroughs Willey Hargrave* in 1988. Became an Associate in 1990.

INTERNATIONAL SECTION

The international section lists foreign law firms based in London. It also lists the foreign connections of English law firms: their branch offices overseas and the foreign languages spoken at their UK offices. The section is located just before the main solicitors' A-Z.

CIVIL LIBERTIES

AT the forefront of this field are a small number of dedicated firms handling cases on prisoners' rights, actions against the police, public order and discrimination. A recent trend has been the increased number of such cases being referred to the European Court of Human Rights. Civil liberties work frequently overlaps with other areas of law such as crime, employment and immigration. As a result, a number of firms highlighted here also feature in other sections.

LONDON

Bindman & Partners and *B.M. Birnberg & Co* are widely respected for both the quality and range of their civil liberties work. Geoffrey Bindman of *Bindman & Partners* and Gareth

LEADING FIRMS – LONDON	
BINDMAN & PARTNERS	B.M. BIRNBERG & CO
CHRISTIAN FISHER	SIMONS MUIRHEAD & BURTON
STEPHENS INNOCENT	

Peirce of *B.M. Birnberg & Co* have first rate reputations. At *Simons Muirhead & Burton*, another firm well represented in this area, Larry Grant combines civil liberties work with

HIGHLY REGARDED – LONDON	
DEIGHTON GUEDALLA	FISHER MEREDITH
TAYLOR NICHOL	WINSTANLEY-BURGESS

his immigration practice. Louise Fisher of *Christian Fisher & Co* and Mark Stephens of *Stephens Innocent* are well known civil liberties lawyers with established reputations. Other recommended firms are *Fisher Meredith, Deighton Guedalla, Winstanley-Burgess* and *Taylor Nichol.*

LEADING INDIVIDUALS – LONDON	
Geoffrey Bindman	Bindman & Partners
Gareth Peirce	B.M. Birnberg & Co
Louise Christian	Christian Fisher
Larry Grant	Simons Muirhead & Burton
Mark H. Stephens	Stephens Innocent
Robert J. Winstanley	Winstanley-Burgess

SOUTH EAST

The Logan Partnership is highly regarded in this field and has been involved in a number of miscarriage of justice cases, including the 'Guildford Four' and 'Maguire Seven' campaigns.

HIGHLY REGARDED – SOUTH EAST
THE LOGAN PARTNERSHIP Guildford

MIDLANDS

In Birmingham, *Tyndallwoods* has a highly regarded civil liberties practice headed by Mark Phillips. In addition to its

LEADING FIRMS – MIDLANDS
TYNDALLWOODS Birmingham

mental health and asylum work, the firm pursues miscarriages of justice and actions against the police, and has taken a number of cases to the European Court of Human Rights. *George Jonas & Co's* civil liberties work stems

HIGHLY REGARDED – MIDLANDS	
BARRIE WARD & JULIAN GRIFFITHS Nottingham	GEORGE JONAS & CO Birmingham

mainly from its strong criminal practice. The firm's Stephen Jonas is highly experienced in bringing actions against the police. Julian Griffiths of *Barrie Ward & Julian Griffiths* in Nottingham has also been recommended to us.

LEADING INDIVIDUALS – MIDLANDS	
Julian Griffiths	Barrie Ward & Julian Griffiths
Steven Jonas	George Jonas & Co
Mark Phillips	Tyndallwoods

NORTH

In the North West, *Edwards Frais Abrahamson* handles all aspects of civil liberties work and is particularly well known for undertaking womens' and prisoners' rights cases.

LEADING FIRMS – NORTH
EDWARDS FRAIS ABRAHAMSON Liverpool

Elkan Abrahamson, who has a strong reputation in this field, has established a network of prisoners' rights solicitors. *Robert Lizar* was another firm recommended to us.

HIGHLY REGARDED – NORTH	
IRWIN MITCHELL Sheffield	ISON HARRISON & CO Leeds
JOHN HOWELL & CO Sheffield	ROBERT LIZAR Manchester

In the North East, *Ison Harrison & Co*, well known for its criminal practice, also undertakes actions against the police, inquests and prisoners' rights cases. Ruth Bundey is well regarded in this field. *Irwin Mitchell* is another firm experienced in bringing actions against the police. At *John Howell & Co*, Danny Simpson pursues miscarriages of justice and complaints on behalf of prisoners.

LEADING INDIVIDUALS – NORTH	
Elkan Abrahamson	Edwards Frais Abrahamson
Ruth Bundey	Ison Harrison & Co
Danny Simpson	John Howell & Co

LEADERS IN CIVIL LIBERTIES

LONDON

Bindman, Geoffrey

Bindman & Partners, London (0171) 833 4433. Senior Partner.

Specialisation: Specialises in civil liberties and human rights, media law, defamation, anti-discrimination and general litigation. Author of numerous articles in the professional and national press on these subjects, and has broadcast frequently. Has represented the International Commission of Jurists, International Bar Association, Amnesty International, and other bodies in human rights missions in several countries including the former Soviet Union, South Africa, Chile, Uganda, Namibia, Malaysia, Palestine and Northern Ireland. Edited the Report of the International Commission of Jurists on the rule of law in South Africa, Co-author with Lord Lester QC of 'Race and Law.' (Longman & Penguin, 1972).

Prof. Memberships: Law Society (Member of the Race Relations Committee and the Human Rights Working Party). Chairman, Discrimination Law Association.

Career: Established *Bindman & Partners* in 1974. From 1966 to 1976 was Legal Adviser to the Race Relations Board and thereafter until 1983 to the Commission for Racial Equality. Visiting professor, U.C.L.A (1982). Honorary Visiting Professor of Law at University College London and an Honorary Fellow in Civil Legal Process at the University of Kent.

Personal: Born 3rd January 1933. Attended Newcastle RGS and Oriel College, Oxford. Former Deputy Leader of the London Borough of Camden and Chairman of the Legal Action Group and Amnesty Lawyers' Group. Founder and first Chairman of Camden Community Law Centre. Vice-President of World University Service. Treasurer of Article 19. Trustee of the Wordsworth Trust, and a member of the Management Committee of One World Action, and of the Editorial Board of the British Journalism Review. Lives in London.

Christian, Louise

Christian Fisher & Co, London (0171) 831 1750. Partner in Civil Litigation Department.

Specialisation: Main area of practice is administrative law/judicial review, inquests, trades union and employment work, personal injury and disaster law, actions against the police and government departments and housing and immigration work. Acts for two

trades unions (the NUM and UCATT). Acted for the families in the Marchioness disaster inquest. Author of articles on policing and civil liberties; disaster law; safety; and the law on corporate manslaughter. Appears frequently on TV, most recently on 'Question Time'.

Prof. Membership: Civil Liberties Trust, Law Society Human Rights Working Party, Association of Personal Injury Lawyers, Immigration Law Practitioners Association, Inquest Lawyers Group, British Panel of the International Federation of Human Rights, Advisory Boards of Kurdistan Human Rights Project and the Redress Trust. Law Society Personal Injury Panel member.

Career: Qualified in 1978 while at *Lovell White & King*. Solicitor, Plumstead Community Law Centre 1979-81, then Advisor to the GLC Police Committee 1981-84. Co-founded *Christian Fisher* with Michael Fisher in November 1985.

Personal: Attended St. Anne's College, Oxford 1970-73. Involved in human rights visits to the former Yugoslavia and the Kurdish areas of Turkey and Iraq. Parliamentary candidate for the Labour Party 1987. Lives in London.

Grant, Larry

See under Immigration & Nationality.

Peirce, Gareth

See under Crime: General.

Stephens, Mark H.

See under Defamation.

Winstanley, Robert J.

Winstanley-Burgess, London (0171) 278 7911. Qualified 1973. Partner specialising in civil liberties work.

REGIONS

Abrahamson, Elkan

Edwards Frais Abrahamson, Liverpool (0151) 707 1212. Qualified 1983. Partner 1991. Litigation Department. Main areas of practice are prisoners' rights and child care.

Bundey, Ruth

See under Immigration & Nationality.

Griffiths, Julian

Barrie Ward & Julian Griffiths, Nottingham (0115) 9412622.

Jonas, Steven

George Jonas & Co, Birmingham (0121) 212 4111. Partner specialising in crime and personal injury work.

Specialisation: Deals with all areas of crime, from the most serious (e.g. murder) to minor traffic offences, with particular development recently in white collar and commercial crime. Acts for both legal aid and private clients. Also handles personal injury work, including road traffic accidents and factory accidents, with particular emphasis on medical negligence. Acts for both legal aid and private clients in this area also. Has been involved with several high profile criminal cases (e.g. 'Home Alone' Heidi Colwell) and personal injury cases (e.g. 'failed vasectomy', Mr & Mrs Stobie). Author of publications in the 'New Law Journal' on costs in criminal cases. Has a large amount of media experience involving newspapers, radio and television, both local and national.

Prof. Membership: Law Society, Birmingham Law Society, Personal Injury Panel, AVMA, APIL, Liberty.

Career: Qualified in 1981. Joined *George Jonas & Co.* as a Partner in 1982. Became Senior Partner in 1993. Chairman of Birmingham Young Solicitors Group 1989-90. Member of Birmingham Law Society's Council since 1990 (Library Committee since 1990, Civil Litigation Committee 1991-1995 and Criminal Litigation Committee since 1995). Member of Legal Aid Board No.6 Area Committee and of the Law Society Personal Injury Panel from 1994.

Personal: Born 30th December 1956. Educated at Moseley School, Birmingham until 1975, then Manchester University 1975-78. School Governor in 1974. Enjoys mountaineering, listening to music and good food and wine. Lives in Birmingham.

Phillips, Mark

Tyndallwoods, Birmingham (0121) 454 7996. Qualified 1981. Partner 1988. Civil Liberties Department. Specialises in immigration and public law, miscarriages of justice and Mental Health Review Tribunals. Born 10.5.1947.

Simpson, Danny

John Howell & Co, Sheffield (0114) 250 1000. Qualified 1984. Partner 1990. Head of Criminal Department. Principal area of practice covers crime, miscarriages of justice and civil liberties.

COLLECTIVE INVESTMENT SCHEMES

THIS heading covers a range of investment schemes and vehicles whereby investors pool their resources which are then managed on their behalf by professional investment managers. These schemes offer the investor the opportunity to spread risks.

A distinction can be drawn between an 'investment trust', a publicly listed company whose shares are traded on the Stock Exchange with fixed share capital, and an open ended 'unit trust' – a legal trust fund which issues units representing the value of the underlying holdings in the portfolio. Under unit trusts, units can be repurchased, hence the term, 'open ended'. In an investment trust, the shares are sold on the Stock Exchange. Investment trusts are permitted to borrow additional funds to purchase investments, in turn providing the potential benefits of 'gearing'; unit trusts are not permitted to gear. UK-based authorised unit trust schemes are subject to various regulatory controls. The schemes themselves and their format must be authorised by the Securities and Investments Board (SIB), the marketing will be regulated by the PIA and the managers by IMRO. Investment trusts must comply with the Stock Exchange Listing Rules, but are not regulated by SIB. Thus, lawyers will be involved in establishing and advising on the appropriate structure and regulation of schemes and also advise on matters such as drafting of scheme documentation, appointment and removal of trustees and managers and the restructuring and amalgamation of schemes.

There is also a trend towards 'globalisation' of the fund industry. New collective investment vehicles are being structured, with appropriate tax advice for investment in emerging markets.

LONDON

It is generally the larger City firms which have strong reputations for both overseas and UK investment scheme work. The leading firms handling overseas investment work are *Linklaters & Paines, Clifford Chance, Simmons & Simmons* and *Slaughter and May* with *Macfarlanes, Norton Rose* and *Lovell White Durrant* having excellent reputations.

Frere Cholmeley Bischoff and *Clifford Chance* are pre-eminent for their UK work.

LEADING FIRMS – LONDON – MAINLY UK	
CLIFFORD CHANCE	FRERE CHOLMELEY BISCHOFF
LINKLATERS & PAINES	LOVELL WHITE DURRANT
MACFARLANES	SIMMONS & SIMMONS
ROWE & MAW	SLAUGHTER AND MAY

These firms will also have an expertise in associated investment vehicles such as limited partnerships, and will bring to bear a capability in general corporate work. UK tax planning is essential here, given that one object of the collective investment scheme will be to ensure a more favourable tax situation than investing directly in the underlying investments.

LEADING FIRMS – LONDON – MAINLY OFFSHORE	
CLIFFORD CHANCE	LINKLATERS & PAINES
LOVELL WHITE DURRANT	MACFARLANES
NORTON ROSE	SIMMONS & SIMMONS
SLAUGHTER AND MAY	

Leading practitioners include Timothy Herrington of *Clifford Chance*, Richard Millar of *Frere Cholmeley Bischoff*, Paul Harris of *Linklaters & Paines*, Richard Slater of *Simmons*

HIGHLY REGARDED – LONDON – MAINLY OFFSHORE	
ALLEN & OVERY	ASHURST MORRIS CRISP
S J BERWIN & CO	FRESHFIELDS
HERBERT SMITH	TRAVERS SMITH BRAITHWAITE

& Simmons and Colin Hall of *Slaughter and May. Turner Kenneth Brown* formerly boasted a notable reputation in this area although their highly recommended Timothy Cornick has now moved to *Macfarlanes*, enhancing their capability.

LEADING INDIVIDUALS – LONDON		
Timothy C. Cornick *Macfarlanes*	Colin Hall *Slaughter and May*	Paul I. Harris *Linklaters & Paines*
Timothy Herrington *Clifford Chance*	J. Richard Millar *Frere Cholmeley Bischoff*	Richard E.H. Slater *Simmons & Simmons*
Bridget C. Barker *Macfarlanes*	James Barlow *Clifford Chance*	W. Nigel Campion-Smith *Travers Smith Braithwaite*
Dominic M.B. Clarke *Herbert Smith*	Simon F.T. Cox *Norton Rose*	R. James N. Cripps *Slaughter and May*
W. Iain Cullen *Simmons & Simmons*	Ben Hawkes *Clifford Chance*	D.H. Ive *Rowe & Maw*
Tim J. Marsden *Norton Rose*	A.S. McWhirter *Freshfields*	Paul M. Nelson *Linklaters & Paines*
Ian M.S. Swabey *Norton Rose*	Pamela M. Thompson *Frere Cholmeley Bischoff*	

SOUTH WEST

Firms specialising in collective investment schemes, namely advising on and drafting scheme documentation rather than

simply offering FSA advice, are rare outside London. However, *Burges Salmon* have a recognised practice, with Christopher Godfrey well known for his expertise in this area.

SCOTLAND

A number of firms in Scotland have developed specialist investment practices, unsurprisingly given Scotland's traditional strength in the financial and investment industry. *Dundas & Wilson CS* and *Shepherd & Wedderburn WS* are pre-eminent, with both firms fielding sizeable teams dealing with a range of investment trust, unit

trust, open ended investment company and other investment fund work. Also with recognised expertise are *Dickson Minto WS* and, especially in the area of unit trusts, *Tods Murray WS*.

Leading practitioners are Christopher Athanas and Philip Mackay at *Dundas & Wilson CS* and Martin Thurston Smith at *Tods Murray WS*.

LEADERS IN COLLECTIVE INVESTMENT SCHEMES

LONDON

Barker, Bridget C.
Macfarlanes, London (0171) 831 9222. Qualified 1983. Partner 1988. Company, Commercial and Banking Department. Specialises in financial services and on-shore and off-shore investment funds.

Barlow, James
Clifford Chance, London (0171) 600 1000. Partner. Principal area of practice encompasses collective investment schemes and financial services.

Campion-Smith, W. Nigel
See under Company/Commercial.

Clarke, Dominic M.B.
Herbert Smith, London (0171) 374 8000. Partner in Company Department.

Specialisation: Specialises in investment funds within the UK and overseas and in the regulation of the financial services and insurance industries. His work in connection with investment funds includes the formation and restructuring of investment trusts, limited partnerships, unit trusts, common investment funds for charities, off-shore funds and other investment vehicles. His regulatory practice covers the application of regulations governing the financial services and insurance industries. Other areas of expertise include acting for trustees of debenture and loan stock issues, the raising of private sector finance by housing associations and the Broadcasting Act.

Career: Qualified in 1975. Became a Partner at *Herbert Smith* in 1987.

Personal: Educated at Leeds University.

Cornick, Timothy C.
Macfarlanes, London (0171) 831 9222. Qualified 1982. Partner in the Company, Commercial and Banking Department. Specialises in collective investment schemes, particularly unit trusts.

Cox, Simon F.T.
Norton Rose, London (0171) 283 6000. Qualified 1980. Partner 1988. Corporate and Financial Department. Specialises in international and domestic corporate finance (including investment funds).

Cripps, R. James N.
Slaughter and May, London (0171) 600 1200. Qualified 1980. Specialises in collective investment schemes for international equities, debt securities, and non-corporate investments.

Cullen, W. Iain
See under Commodities.

Hall, Colin
Slaughter and May, London (0171) 600 1200. Qualified 1969. Partner 1978. Company/Commercial Department. Main areas of practice are corporate finance and investment funds. Born 23.4.1945.

Harris, Paul I.
Linklaters & Paines, London (0171) 606 7080. Qualified 1969. Joined *Linklaters & Paines* in 1967. Head of investment funds group. Main area of practice is collective investment schemes, advising on the establishment, marketing and listing of investment funds and related corporate finance transactions.

Hawkes, Ben
Clifford Chance, London (0171) 600 1000. Partner. Specialises in investment business/collective investment schemes, international investments and off-shore corporations.

Herrington, Timothy
Clifford Chance, London (0171) 600 1000. Partner. Principal area of practice is investment funds and financial services.

Ive, D.H.
Rowe & Maw, London (0171) 248 4282. Partner in Corporate Taxation Department.

Specialisation: Experienced in all aspects of taxation, especially in relation to financial services, collective investment schemes, unit trusts, offshore funds and life assurance taxation. Drafted the current trust deed of M&G Group plc Charifund Unit Trust. Author of articles in various tax journals, including 'British Tax Review' and 'Tax Journal'. Lecturer on tax topics, especially collective investment schemes and unit trusts.

Prof. Membership: Law Society.

Career: Qualified in 1972. Worked with *Allen & Overy* 1976-84. Spent 1 year at the Tax Bar (1984-85), then joined *Rowe & Maw* in

June 1985. Became a Partner in 1986.

Personal: Born 2nd January 1950. Attended Highgate School 1963-68, then Birmingham University 1968-71. Chairman of the Association of Liberal Democrat Lawyers. Leisure pursuits include opera and swimming. Lives in London.

Marsden, Tim J.

Norton Rose, London (0171) 283 6000. Qualified 1984. Partner 1993. Corporate and Financial Department. Specialises in financial services and investments. Born 9.9.1961.

McWhirter, A.S.

See under Financial Services.

Millar, J. Richard

Frere Cholmeley Bischoff, London (0171) 615 8000. Joint Chairman and Partner in Company Department.

Specialisation: Main area of practice is collective investment schemes: has acted for managers of authorised unit trusts since 1965 and for promoters of offshore funds and managers of unauthorised trusts subsequently. Also advises generally on financial services law as well as broader company law. Regular speaker at conferences.

Prof. Membership: Law Society, IBA. Member of Law Society's Company Law Committee and Chairman of its Sub-committee on Collective Investment Schemes.

Career: Qualified in 1963. Joined *Bischoff & Co.* in 1965, becoming a Partner in 1967 and Senior Partner and Managing Partner in 1990. Firm merged with *Frere Cholmeley* in 1993.

Nelson, Paul M.

See under Financial Services.

Slater, Richard E.H.

Simmons & Simmons, London (0171) 628 2020. Partner in Corporate Department.

Specialisation: Corporate work with a particular emphasis on the financial services industry. Transactional advice includes public and private company take-overs and

acquisitions, joint ventures, initial share offerings and flotations. Work in the financial services industry covers the formation and promotion of investment vehicles of all types, the acquisition and disposal of financial services businesses and the reconstruction and merger of investment trust companies, unit trusts and other investment entities.

Prof. Memberships: Law Society Company Law Committee, CBI Company Law Panel.

Career: Qualified in 1977, after joining *Simmons & Simmons* as an articled clerk in 1975. Became a Partner in the Corporate Department in 1981.

Personal: Born 9th November 1950. Attended City University 1979-82, then Cambridge University 1982-84. Lives in London.

Swabey, Ian M.S.

Norton Rose, London (0171) 283 6000. Qualified 1969. Partner 1973. Corporate and Financial Department. Specialises in corporate finance, collective investment, financial services and banking.

Thompson, Pamela M.

Frere Cholmeley Bischoff, London (0171) 615 8000. Partner in Company/ Commercial Department.

Specialisation: Main areas of practice are collective investment schemes and pooled investments. Handles onshore schemes such as authorised and unauthorised unit trusts and limited partnerships and offshore schemes such as trusts, open ended companies and closed ended funds. Also handles general financial services work, including regulatory advice, structuring, taxation and marketing investment schemes. Contributor to Taxation on Unitisations. Has attended various conferences including the 4th Annual Offshore Funds Conference on Marketing Funds Throughout Europe.

Prof. Membership: Association of Women Solicitors.

Career: Qualified in 1982, having joined *Bischoff & Co.* in 1980. Became a Partner in 1986.

Personal: Born in 1956. Attended St Hilda's College, Oxford 1974-78. Leisure interests include horse racing, swimming, cinema and food. Lives in London.

REGIONS

Athanas, Christopher N.

Dundas & Wilson CS, Edinburgh (0131) 228 8000. Qualified 1966. Partner 1969. Corporate Department. Specialises in Corporate Financial Services, handling all aspects of collective investment schemes. Born 26.8.1941.

Dunsire, David N.

Tods Murray WS, Edinburgh (0131) 226 4771. Qualified 1982. Partner 1986. Corporate and Commercial Department. Specialises in unit trusts, timesharing, acquisitions and disposals, MBOs and start-ups.

Godfrey, Christopher M.J.

See under Corporate Finance.

Mackay, Philip

Dundas & Wilson CS, Edinburgh (0131) 228 8000. Qualified 1982. Partner 1986. Corporate Department. Main areas of practice are financial services and company law. Born 1957.

Thurston Smith, Martin H.

Tods Murray WS, Edinburgh (0131) 226 4771. Qualified 1977. Partner 1978. Corporate and Commercial Department. Specialises in unit trusts, pensions, securities and banking work.

Watt, James P.

Dundas & Wilson CS, Edinburgh (0131) 228 8000. Qualified 1976. Partner 1977. Head of Corporate Financial Services Unit and of Pensions and Employee Benefit Group. Born 14.4.1943.

FIRMS OF ACCOUNTANTS

Accountants specialising in litigation support are listed in the accountants' A-Z, with details of the services they offer to solicitors, from forensic accounting to intellectual property or business valuations. This section is found immediately after the main solicitors' A-Z.

COMMODITIES

'COMMODITIES' describes either oil and metal products or 'soft' (eg: foodstuffs) goods that are traded between countries. As a specialist area of law, commodities is split between two main activities: advising on contracts and disputes relating to the actual trading of commodities, (known as 'physicals'); and the law relating to trading of contracts on the futures and derivatives markets, both on and off exchange.

LONDON

Given the position of London as an international financial centre, and the fact that the major trade associations and the UK terminal markets are based in London, commodities work is dominated by City firms.

Clients will typically include trading houses, UK and internationally based brokers, dealers and managers, trade associations, oil companies, speculators, such as hedge funds, and the exchanges themselves.

Traditionally, pre-eminence has been given to the 'physical' side of commodities work. It is also important to bring out the 'futures' side. We have therefore split the analysis of firms into these two categories (some firms will obviously overlap).

PHYSICALS

For strength and depth *Middleton Potts* retains its leading position in the field, with five partners and two assistants devoted to commodity or mixed commodity/shipping work. Christopher Potts and David Lucas both have strong reputations in the physicals commodity field.

LEADING FIRMS – LONDON – PHYSICALS	
MIDDLETON POTTS	RICHARDS BUTLER
CLIFFORD CHANCE	HILL TAYLOR DICKINSON
INCE & CO.	LOVELL WHITE DURRANT
SINCLAIR ROCHE & TEMPERLEY	TURNER & CO

Richards Butler is securely in second position with four partners and at least four assistants devoted to commodities

work. David Pullen is considered to be at the forefront in this area. The firm has been involved in a large number of arbitrations this year.

Hill Taylor Dickinson with one consultant and two partners does a substantial amount of commodities work. The recent appointment of Derek Kirby Johnson as consultant is a coup for the firm as he was a senior adviser to GAFTA.

HIGHLY REGARDED – LONDON – PHYSICALS	
CLYDE & CO	HERBERT SMITH
HOLMAN, FENWICK & WILLAN	THE SIMKINS PARTNERSHIP
SIMMONS & SIMMONS	THOMAS COOPER & STIBBARD
HOLMES HARDINGHAM	MORE FISHER BROWN
SHAW AND CROFT	

Among the other recommended firms in the physicals area, *Turner & Co* has a good niche practice, and Paul Turner is highly recommended. *Sinclair Roche & Temperley* has a practice led by Ben Leach. *Clyde & Co* under Clive Thorp is said to be expanding out of its traditional oil based practice. *Lovell White Durrant* has a practice with a key player in Ian Ward. *Ince & Co* has been assisted by the opening of a new office in Singapore, and Stuart Shepherd, and Jonathan Lux have been recommended to us. *Holman Fenwick & Willan* has also been recommended to us in the physicals context, as has *Thomas Cooper & Stibbard*.

FUTURES

The leading futures firm is *Clifford Chance* where James Barlow and Mark Harding have both been recommended.

LEADING FIRMS – LONDON – FUTURES	
CLIFFORD CHANCE	
M.W. CORNISH & CO	DENTON HALL
SIMMONS & SIMMONS	

A major niche player in the derivatives market is *M.W. Cornish & Co* where Martin W Cornish is highly regarded. *Simmons & Simmons* with Iain Cullen and Jonathan Melrose both highly recommended and *Denton Hall,* with Robert Finney recommended, complete the more specialist futures list.

LEADING INDIVIDUALS – LONDON – PHYSICALS		
John Bassindale *Clifford Chance*	C. David Lucas *Middleton Potts*	Christopher R. Potts *Middleton Potts*
David M. Pullen *Richards Butler*		
Richard D. Black *Middleton Potts*	John F. Emmott *Richards Butler*	Dominic Free *The Simkins Partnership*
D.J. Hickey *Ince & Co*	Anthony Holmes *Holmes Hardingham*	Jeffrey E. Isaacs *Hill Taylor Dickinson*
N. Andrew Iyer *Ince & Co*	Derek Kirby Johnson *Hill Taylor Dickinson*	Ben Leach *Sinclair Roche & Temperley*
Jonathan S. Lux *Ince & Co*	Adrian Moylan *More Fisher Brown*	Stuart W. Shepherd *Ince & Co*
Richard Swinburn *Richards Butler*	Clive Thorp *Clyde & Co*	Paul Turner *Turner & Co*
Nicholas Walser *Holmes Hardingham*	W. Ian R. Ward *Lovell White Durrant*	

HIGHLY REGARDED - LONDON - FUTURES

CLYDE & CO	LINKLATERS & PAINES
LOVELL WHITE DURRANT	MIDDLETON POTTS
NORTON ROSE	RICHARDS BUTLER
SINCLAIR ROCHE & TEMPERLEY	TURNER & CO

As would be expected both *Middleton Potts* and *Richards Butler* claim a capability in this area, as do *Clyde & Co, Linklaters & Paines, Lovell White Durrant, Norton Rose,* where Peter Martyr has been recommended, *Sinclair Roche & Temperley* and *Turner & Co.*

LEADING INDIVIDUALS - LONDON - FUTURES

James Barlow *Clifford Chance*	Martin W. Cornish *M.W. Cornish & Co*	W. Iain Cullen *Simmons & Simmons*
Robert Finney *Denton Hall*	Mark Harding *Clifford Chance*	
Pauline Ashall *Linklaters & Paines*	Anthony Hickinbotham *Linklaters & Paines*	Lynn Johansen *Clifford Chance*
Peter M. Martyr *Norton Rose*	Jonathan Melrose *Simmons & Simmons*	Tim Plews *Clifford Chance*

LEADERS IN COMMODITIES

LONDON

Ashall, Pauline
See under Financial Services.

Barlow, James
See under Collective Investment Schemes.

Bassindale, John
Clifford Chance, London (0171) 600 1000. Partner. Principal areas of practice are commodities, international trade, and shipping disputes. Also handles general maritime work, oil and gas, trade finance and letters of credit.

Black, Richard D.
Middleton Potts, London (0171) 600 2333. Partner in Shipping and Commodities Litigation Department.

Specialisation: Wide experience since 1978 of maritime and commodity arbitrations and Commercial Court hearings relating to shipping, trading, insurance and commercial litigation disputes with a particular emphasis on charterparty and cargo claims and commodity disputes including GAFTA, FOSFA, the crude oil and petroleum product trade and LME arbitrations. Clients include international trading houses, oil majors and traders, P&I and charterers' liability clubs, ship owners, charterers and marine insurers. Also handles commercial litigation. Cases have included Deutsche Schactbau und Tiefborgcsellschaft v. Raknoc & Shell International; Kloeckner v. Gatoil; Hong Kong & Shanghai Banking Corporation v. Kloeckner; the M.V. 'P', Phibro Energy v. Nissho Iwai and Bomar Oil; ICI v. Montedison (UK) Ltd; Ferrarini v. Magnol Shipping; Shell International Petroleum Company v. Transmor (Bermuda) Ltd; Shell Company of Australia v. Natship Bagging Services; Shell Eastern Petroleum v. Mobil Shipping; Plakoura Maritime v. Shell International; Tradax v. Pagnan; European Grain & Shipping v. Hall; European Grain & Shipping v. Dansk Land Brugs; Middle East Marketing v. M. Golodetz; Frahuil SA v. Tankrederi Ahrenkeil; and EF Hutton v. Mofarrij.

Prof. Membership: Law Society.

Career: Qualified in 1977. Joined *Middleton Potts* from *Coward Chance* in 1984, becoming a Partner in 1985.

Personal: Born 22nd March 1951. Holds an LLB from Manchester, 1969-72. Leisure interests include golf, tennis, chess and reading. Lives in Cobham.

Cornish, Martin W.
M.W. Cornish & Co, London (0171) 600 0910. Senior Partner 1991.

Specialisation: Main area of practice is full range of commodities and related derivatives and funds transactions including structuring exchange and OTC and on-shore and off-shore products. Other main area of work is financial services and securities documentation and regulation, particularly leveraged transactions and related security/netting issues. Author of numerous articles in the professional press. Regular speaker at conferences and seminars.

Prof. Memberships: Law Society

Career: Qualified in 1980. Partner with *Simmons & Simmons* 1986-88, then European Legal Director at *Shearson Lehman Hutton* 1988-91. Established *M.W. Cornish & Co.* in 1991 as Senior Partner.

Personal: Born 28th February 1955. Attended Millfield School 1970-74, then Downing College, Cambridge 1974-76. Leisure pursuits include tennis and golf. Lives in Ingatestone, Essex.

Cullen, W. Iain
Simmons & Simmons, London (0171) 628 2020. Partner in Corporate Department.

Specialisation: Handles all types of work relating to commodities, futures and options, unit trusts, offshore funds and investment management. Author of numerous articles in the professional press. Regular speaker at conferences and seminars.

Prof. Membership: Law Society, International Bar Association, American Bar Association, European Managed Futures Association, Board of Editors of Futures International Law Letter, Advisory Board of The Futures and Derivatives Law Review, Advisory Board of World Securities Law Report.

Career: Qualified in 1980, having joined *Simmons & Simmons* in 1977. Became a Partner in 1986.

Personal: Born 13th May 1953. Took a BA in Law in 1975. Lives in London.

Emmott, John F.
Richards Butler, London (0171) 247 6555. Qualified 1978. Qualified 1978. Partner 1986. Shipping Unit. Specialises in international trade and commodities. Educated at the University of Sydney (BA, LLB). Born 1953.

Finney, Robert
Denton Hall, London (0171) 242 1212. Partner in Banking and Financial Markets Group.

Specialisation: Main areas of practice are: Securities and derivatives dealing, investment management and related regulatory matters; capital markets, especially derivative products and structured finance, including securitisation; Funds; and Commodities (covering non-contentious work in respect of physicals and futures, including OTC derivatives). Author of various articles, especially in 'Futures and Options World' and Butterworths' 'Journal of International Banking and Finance Law'. Has addressed seminars and conferences on regulatory and derivatives issues.

Prof. Membership: Law Society, ICSA (FCIS), Futures & Options Association, US Managed Futures Association, UK Association of Compliance Officers.

Career: Qualified in Scotland 1979, (England and Wales 1991). In-house counsel with Pearson Group, then with Credit Suisse First Boston and Morgan Stanley International before joining *Denton Hall* in 1990. Became a Partner in 1992.

Personal: Born 9th April 1955. LLB Edinburgh University 1977. Leisure interests include theatre and cycling.

Free, Dominic

The Simkins Partnership, London (0171) 631 1050. Partner in Litigation Department.

Specialisation: Litigation and arbitration of commercial disputes particularly in relation to international business transactions and intellectual property matters.

Career: Qualified in 1985.

Personal: Born 16th November 1956. Educated in New Zealand (LLB, Auckland 1979) and the USA (LLM, Cornell University 1982).

Harding, Mark

See under Financial Services.

Hickey, D.J.

Ince & Co, London (0171) 623 2011.

Hickinbotham, Anthony

Linklaters & Paines, London (0171) 606 7080. Qualified 1968. Joined 1973. Main areas of practice are project finance, mergers and acquisitions and the regulation of commodities and futures exchanges and their clearing systems.

Holmes, Anthony

Holmes Hardingham, London (0171) 283 0222. Qualified 1964.

Isaacs, Jeffrey E.

Hill Taylor Dickinson, London (0171) 283 9033.

Iyer, N. Andrew

Ince & Co, London (0171) 623 2011. Solicitor specialising in Commodities Law and Shipping Law.

Specialisation: Principal areas of practice are shipping and commodities work, covering dry and wet shipping disputes involving both litigation and arbitration, and the full range of contentious and non-contentious physicals and futures work, including disputes on GAFTA, FOSFA, Coffee Trade Federation, Refined Sugar Association and London Metal Exchange contracts. Also deals with all area of oil trading. Handled multi-jurisdictional complex coffee trading dispute involving physical and futures swaps and transactions; and the first section 13A, Arbitration Act case which dramatically changed the law of arbitration in relation to delays "the BOUCRAA". Other main areas of work are letter of credit disputes, insurance, construction and engineering disputes in all forums. Articles written are: 'Legal Effects of War on International Trade Contracts', 'Letters of Credit and the Doctrine of Strict Compliance', and co-author 'Nomination of Vessels Under FOB and CiF Contracts'.

Prof. Membership: Law Society, GAFTA,

FOSFA, LMAA (via *Ince & Co.*).

Career: Trained with *Middleton Potts* then joined *Ince & Co* in 1991.

Personal: Born 10th December 1966. Attended Tettenhall College 1972-84 and Essex University 1984-88. Leisure pursuits include music, rugby, literature and motor sport. Lives in London.

Johansen, Lynn

Clifford Chance, London (0171) 600 1000.

Johnson, Derek Kirby

Hill Taylor Dickinson, London (0171) 283 9033.

Leach, Ben

Sinclair Roche & Temperley, London (0171) 638 9044. Partner in Litigation Department.

Specialisation: Main area of work is commodity trades, from litigation and arbitration to drafting and advising on commodity sales contracts and associated documentation. Other main area of work is shipping and oil trade litigation. Instructed in several of the milestone commodity trade cases in the last 15 years, e.g. Bunge v. Tradax (H.L. 1981), Italgrani v. Sosimage (C.A. 1986), State Trading Corporation v. Golodetz (C.A. 1989), Cargill v. Kadinopoulos (H.L. 1992). Conducted over 100 arbitrations before GAFTA, FOSFA, Refined Sugar Association, London Metal Exchange, London Rice Brokers' Association and various other hard and soft commodity trade associations in London and abroad. Contributed to the Law Commission Working Group on title to goods forming part of a bulk. Articles on topics related to the commodity trades for various periodicals and the national press (e.g. Lloyd's List and the Financial Times).

Prof. Memberships: Law Society

Career: Articled to *Richards Butler* in 1969, qualified as a solicitor in 1971, joined *Sinclair Roche & Temperley* in 1975 and became a Partner in 1978.

Personal: Born 24th October 1945. Attended Leeds University 1965-68 Leisure pursuits include family life, gardening and art. Lives in Hadley Wood, Herts.

Lucas, C. David

Middleton Potts, London (0171) 600 2333. Partner in Commercial Litigation Department.

Specialisation: Main area of practice is commodities and shipping. Extensive experience of arbitration and litigation, acting for commodity trading houses (including the majors), oil companies and traders, shipowners, insurers and P&I Clubs. Major cases handled include Bremer v Vanden-Avenne, 'The Montone', 'The Caspian Sea', 'The Pegase', 'The Afovos', 'The Golden Bear' and 'The Future Express'.

Prof. Memberships: Law Society

Career: Qualified in 1972. Associate, *Crawley & de Reya* 1974-76, then joined *Middleton Potts* as a Partner.

Personal: Born 15th December 1947. Attended St Paul's School 1960-65, then Bristol University 1966-69.

Lux, Jonathan S.

See under Shipping & Maritime Law.

Martyr, Peter M.

Norton Rose, London (0171) 283 6000. Qualified 1979. Partner 1985. Commercial Litigation Department. Also head of Insurance Group. Main areas of practice are insurance, commodities and marine work, in addition to ship management. Born 31.3.1954.

Melrose, Jonathan

Simmons & Simmons, London (0171) 628 2020. Partner in Corporate Department.

Specialisation: Handles all types of work relating to commodities, derivatives, collective investment vehicles and investment management. Regular speaker at conferences and seminars.

Prof. Membership: International Bar Association, Union Internationale des Avocats, Law Society, The Securities Institute, Member of Commodities Committee of the Futures and Options Association, Joint Editor of the Financial Services Newsletter of the Union Internationale des Avocats.

Career: Qualified 1985, having joined *Simmons & Simmons* in 1983. Became a Partner in 1991.

Personal: Born 21st April 1959. Holds an MA (Hons) Oxon, 1981. Lives in London.

Moylan, Adrian

More Fisher Brown, London (0171) 247 0438. Qualified 1980.

Plews, Tim

Clifford Chance, London (0171) 600 1000.

Potts, Christopher R.

Middleton Potts, London (0171) 600 2333. Senior Partner at *Middleton Potts*.

Specialisation: Work covers litigation and arbitration in commodities, shipping law and both marine and non-marine insurance. Major cases handled include 'The Cebu', 'The Adelfa', Bremer v. Soules & Scott, Berger v. Gill & Duffus. Lectures to trade audiences.

Prof. Memberships: Law Society

Career: Qualified in 1965. Partner at *Crawley & de Reya* 1967-76. Founding Partner of *Middleton Potts* in 1976, and is currently Senior Partner.

Personal: Born 1st July 1939. Attended University of London 1958-61. Lives in London.

Pullen, David M.

See under Shipping & Maritime Law.

Shepherd, Stuart W.

Ince & Co, London (0171) 623 2011. Partner specialising in shipping and commodities work.

Specialisation: Main area of practice is shipping. Handles all aspects of dry work, with particular emphasis on carriage of goods by sea and charterparty disputes. Other area of expertise is commodities: involved in advising those trading in various commodities, in particular oil, oil products and commodities traded on GAFTA terms, with particular emphasis on litigation. Cases have included 'Lefthero' (C.A. 1992), 'Boucraa' (H.L. 1993) and 'Mathraki' (Oil trading case, 1989). Author of articles on a number of shipping matters. Speaks at Lloyds of London shipping seminars and on the GAFTA Trade Education course.

Prof. Membership: IBA, LMAA, and through *Ince & Co.*, GAFTA, FOSFA and Refined Sugar Association.

Career: Qualified in 1984, having joined *Ince & Co.* in 1982. Became a Partner in 1990.

Personal: Born 17th October 1959. Attended Bexhill Grammar 1971-78, then University College, Cardiff 1978-81. Leisure interests include golf and skiing. Lives in London/Alfriston, East Sussex.

Swinburn, Richard

Richards Butler, London (0171) 247 6555. Qualified 1988. Solicitor. International Trade and Commodities Department. Born 25.2.1963.

Thorp, Clive

See under Shipping & Maritime Law.

Turner, Paul

Turner & Co, London (0171) 480 7991. Founder Partner handling Commodities.

Specialisation: Work includes trade arbitrations before the Sugar Associations, GAFTA, FOSFA, Cocoa Association, Coffee Trade Federation and Rice Association. Also handles oil disputes, bills of lading and charter party disputes, largely before commercial courts or the London Maritime Arbitrators Association. Acted for Gill & Duffus against Riunda Futures, for S A Sucre Export against Northern Rivershipping Co., and in the Galatia case for Golodetz.

Prof. Membership: Law Society, Associate Member of the Sugar Association of London.

Career: Qualified 1973. Partner with *Thomas Cooper & Stibbard* from 1977-85. Founder Partner of *Turner & Co.* in 1985.

Personal: Born 16th September 1948. Attended Skegness Grammar School 1960-67, then University College, London, 1967-70. Leisure interests include badminton, walking, travelling and eating. Lives in Esher, Surrey.

Walser, Nicholas

Holmes Hardingham, London (0171) 283 0222. Partner specialising in 'dry' shipping law.

Specialisation: 'Dry' shipping law, including commodity trade disputes. Work covers charterparty disputes, cargo loss/ damage claims, and international sale contracts including agricultural commodities (GAFTA and FOSFA contracts) and oil trading. Major cases include the 'TFL Prosperity' (1984) and Soules v.Intertradex (1991). Fluent French. Working knowledge of German.

Prof. Membership: Law Society, AIJA.

Career: Qualified in 1977. Partner in *Ingledew Brown Bennison & Garrett* 1979-89. A Founding Partner of *Holmes Hardingham* in 1989.

Personal: Born 31st December 1952. Attended Cambridge University (MA 1975). Lives in London.

Ward, W. Ian R.

See under Shipping & Maritime Law.

CD-ROM EDITION

This edition of the directory is available on a CD-ROM which includes both DOS and Windows versions. It can be loaded onto a network, and works with virtually any IBM compatible PC. The full contents of the printed directory are made available to the computer user who will have the advantage of rapid search, retrieval and cross-referencing.

COMPANY/COMMERCIAL

A S always, 'company/commercial' specialists are difficult to pin down. One firm's notion of what constitutes company commercial work will rarely coincide with another's. The largest firms have separate departments manned by specialists covering the whole range of company commercial matters as opposed to a department manned by company/commercial generalists. Many firms also seek to differentiate between corporate and commercial matters, with corporate finance constituting the bulk of their work-load. For others, commercial law may include areas like franchising or even EU law. To be consistent with previous years, we are adopting a broad definition to include a firm's capability right across the company commercial spectrum. Three types of information have been relied upon: a firm's own capability measured by its size; public knowledge including press reports; and its reputation among other lawyers, in private practice and in-house. Although pure corporate finance work is dealt with elsewhere in the directory, some cognisance needs to be taken of that capability in assessing the overall strength of a firm's company/commercial department.

LONDON

In order to compare like with like, we have divided the leading London commercial firms into four groups according to their number of fee-earners. All the largest firms are recognised as having outstanding company commercial departments, but this year the three that stand out are *Freshfields, Linklaters & Paines* and *Slaughter and May,* with many of their individual practitioners being especially recommended including Nigel Boardman and Tim Freshwater at *Slaughter and May,* David Cheyne at *Linklaters & Paines* and Gavin Darlington and Vanessa Knapp at *Freshfields.*

The true extent of the success of these firms can best be seen by looking at the various 'league tables' that exist. For UK private company take-overs in 1994, *Slaughter and May* tops the table by value of deals completed, with *Freshfields* in second place and *Linklaters & Paines* in third. Judged by the number of deals, *Freshfields* comes top, with *Slaughter and May* second.

In KPMG's summary of flotations from 1 January 1993 to 31 December 1994, *Linklaters & Paines* and *Slaughter and May* share second place with 20 deals apiece as solicitor to the company. *Linklaters & Paines* tops the table as 'solicitor to the issue', with 38 London listings compared with *Freshfield's* second place 28. *Slaughter and May* came fourth in that table.

Freshfields have had an excellent year acting amongst others for Courtaulds Textiles, Honda Motor Co, BP International, London Regional Transport and Rolls-Royce. Meanwhile *Linklaters & Paines* has advised on Russia's biggest-ever public share offering for cash, launched by Red Octo-

ber, a Moscow based confectionary company. It was also involved in the raising of cash to finance a gold mine in Kazakstan, advising the sponsors Williams de Broe. Closer to home *Linklaters & Paines* acted for Allied-Lyons in the bid for the Pedro Domecq Group. *Slaughter and May* advised EMAP in its purchase of Maclean Hunter European Publishing and Portals Group in the £682m offer from De La Rue. It also represented Wellcome in the bumper bid by Glaxo.

LEADING FIRMS – LONDON – 250+ FEE-EARNERS	
FRESHFIELDS	LINKLATERS & PAINES
SLAUGHTER AND MAY	
ASHURST MORRIS CRISP	CLIFFORD CHANCE

In the privatisation field *Freshfields* can claim the distinction of having done more privatisation business than any other law firm in the world, with *Clifford Chance* coming a creditable seventh. (The big surprise in this table is the fourth placing of *Watson, Farley & Williams.*) Finally, it is interesting to note that (notwithstanding the ambitious plans of the big regional firms to encroach on the corporate work that would previously have been the monopoly of the City firms) *Slaughter and May* and *Allen & Overy* have been chosen as the legal advisers in the recommended bid by Misys for ACT, one of the biggest companies in Birmingham, in preference to their usual Birmingham advisers.

HIGHLY REGARDED – LONDON – 250 PLUS FEE-EARNERS	
ALLEN & OVERY	HERBERT SMITH
LOVELL WHITE DURRANT	NORTON ROSE
SIMMONS & SIMMONS	
CAMERON MARKBY HEWITT	DENTON HALL
McKENNA & CO	NABARRO NATHANSON
WILDE SAPTE	

Ashurst Morris Crisp continues to impress with their essentially UK based company/commercial capability and lead the chasing group along with *Clifford Chance.*

Jeremy Brownlow (who led the team that advised CPC (UK) Ltd on the acquisition of Dalgety plc's Golden Wonder Pot Noodle business) and Peter Brooks at *Clifford Chance* and Jeremy Hill at *Ashurst Morris Crisp* are all recommended. These two firms led the KPMG table of leading solicitors in the period 1 January 1990 - 31 December 1994 for the number of MBO deals completed. *Ashurst Morris Crisp* also came third in the summary of flotations by 'solicitor to the issue' and topped the table of 'solicitor to the company'.

As part of its continuing internationalism *Clifford Chance* opened its latest offices in Vietnam and Prague in contrast to

Slaughter and May which has taken the decision to close its Frankfurt office. Closer to home *Clifford Chance* headed the table in 'Corporate Money' as the top firm of solicitors for deals in terms of value. Its company/commercial capability in London now comprises 51 specialist partners and 159 assistants.

Ashurst Morris Crisp can field 32 partners worldwide with commercial work accounting for 45 % of the firm's total workload. During the past year the firm has advised MAI plc on Rothschild's offer for Anglia Television Group and Allied Domecq on their recent disposals. *Clifford Chance* had a notable success this year when it was chosen to represent Glaxo in its bid for Wellcome (represented by *Slaughter and May*). City lawyers agree that the bid work will be good for *Clifford Chance's* corporate profile.

Our next grouping of firms with the most highly-regarded company/commercial departments consists of *Allen & Overy, Herbert Smith, Lovell White Durrant, Norton Rose* and *Simmons and Simmons*. *Allen & Overy's* corporate department consists of 35 specialist partners and undertakes the full range of commercial work, although the firm is primarily recognised for its banking and finance practice and related insolvency/corporate restructuring work. One of its developing specialisations is in the area of privatisation, having undertaken 16 privatisations world-wide (making it the fifth ranking UK firm carrying out this work). In more mainstream UK work, the firm was 7th by reference to the number of private company deals, by reference to deal value, and 10th for acting as 'solicitor to the issue' in the table of London Listings 1992-94. The firm's Charles Morgan has been particularly recommended.

Lovell White Durrant is another firm with a reputation for banking and reconstruction work, because of which it has managed to flourish during the recessionary years. Its corporate practice has to some extent developed from this success and the firm has acted for a number of high profile clients including Mirror Group and Granada. During 1994 the firm acted in more than 43 completed transactions, each in excess of £1 million including the takeover of LWT (Holdings) plc by Granada Group plc and advising British & Commonwealth on the offer of its shareholding in Exco PLC. The firm also benefited from the publicity surrounding its selection to act for ING in the takeover of the Barings Group.

Although it has been claimed that *Herbert Smith* has seen better days, it continues to be an international firm of distinction. The Corporate Services department has a complement of 45 specialist partners engaged in a number of high profile matters including acting for BSkyB (on its £4billion flotation and debt refinancing), Eurotunnel, Enterprise Oil (in its £1.5billion hostile bid for Lasmo) and the privatisation of British Coal. In the area of joint-ventures, the firm has acted for the AA on its joint-venture with Hambros and features particularly heavily in the former USSR. 'Corporate Money' shows that the firm has increased its share of deals done by reference to value, from 10th in 1992, to 5th in 1993 and 3rd in 1994.

Norton Rose received the accolade this year in the survey published by Global Research compiled from interviews with large international financial institutions by coming first as UK solicitors in terms of overall service it offered clients. The KPMG New Issues Statistics showed that *Norton Rose* had acted for the company in 18 London listings, placing it second. It ranked fifth in the table of 'solicitors to the issue'. In the 'Acquisitions Monthly' league table of lawyers acting on UK private takeovers, the firm managed to turn in a strong performance coming fourth, up from 12th position the previous year. The firm believes that leadership of the *Norton Rose* M5 Group has helped it to defend itself from price pressure and increasing attack from medium-sized firms. The firm acted for BMW AG in its purchase of Rover Group Holdings from British Aerospace.

Simmons & Simmons seems to be maintaining its position this year, continuing to attract clients with its reputation for finance and banking work and insolvency and reconstruction practice. It has continued its international expansion by opening a new office in Abu Dhabi. The firm has been advising Railtrack plc on the privatisation of the railway network and acted as English legal advisers to the controlling shareholders of the Pedro Domecq group in the £739 million takeover by Allied Lyons plc (*Linklaters & Paines* acted for Allied-Lyons).

Finally we would recommend *Cameron Markby Hewitt, Denton Hall, McKenna & Co., Nabarro Nathanson,* and *Wilde Sapte* in this last group of leading firms. *Cameron Markby Hewitt* has had a relatively quiet year although it advised the Wellcome Trust in Glaxo's takeover bid. Corporate/commercial work accounts for 20% of the firm's total work-load, which tends to be of a less international flavour than that of some of its competitors. Although the firm has offices in Brussels, no UK partners are stationed there. This contrasts with *Denton Hall* which maintains branches in seven foreign jurisdictions including five partners in Hong Kong. In other respects this has been a year of mixed fortunes for *Denton Hall* with a spate of heavily rumoured redundancies, one round of which was particularly savage, affecting the firm's morale. The company/commercial department has a strong list of media clients including UIP, the MCA-Paramount-MGM film distributor and CIC Video, its sister company. The firm acted for Thames Television in connection with its global joint venture with the BBC in satellite Television broadcasting and Talk Radio on its successful application for a national independent radio licence. In the retail sector the firm acted for J. Sainsbury in its takeover of Texas Homecare. Internationally the firm was part of a consortium acting on behalf of the Government of Pakistan in the sale of shares in the Pakistan Telephone Company.

Like *Denton Hall, McKenna & Co* is another firm which has suffered mixed fortunes in the past couple of years and which is striving to be an international presence, particularly in East and Central Europe. It has branches in Prague, Budapest, Warsaw and Moscow. Its major clients in this area include the World Bank, BAT plc, Aeroflot and the Russian Government. Back home, the firm acts for

BAe, Blockbuster, BAT and Samuel Montagu. On the corporate side the firm was placed joint eleventh with *Allen & Overy* in the KPMG Summary of flotations by 'solicitor to the issue', and eighteenth in the list of 'solicitor to the company'.

Nabarro Nathanson will have boosted its company/commercial capability with its merger with *Turner Kenneth Brown* (the firm now having a Reading office to add to its presence in Doncaster, Hull and Sheffield). Meanwhile *Wilde Sapte* continues with its international corporate strategy, opening offices in Hong Kong and Tokyo to add to its existing offices in France and the U.S.

Practitioners who are particularly highly regarded are listed in the accompanying table.

LEADING INDIVIDUALS – LONDON – 250+ FEE-EARNERS

Nigel P.G. Boardman *Slaughter and May*	**David W. Cheyne** *Linklaters & Paines*	**Gavin L.B. Darlington** *Freshfields*
Tim G. Freshwater *Slaughter and May*	**Vanessa Knapp** *Freshfields*	**David T.R. Lewis** *Norton Rose*
Charles ap Simon *Freshfields*	**John S. Armstrong** *Cameron Markby Hewitt*	**Chris Ashworth** *Ashurst Morris Crisp*
Stephen G. Barnard *Herbert Smith*	**Christopher Boddington** *Nabarro Nathanson*	**Andrew C. Brackfield** *Linklaters & Paines*
Jeremy Brownlow *Clifford Chance*	**Peter Brooks** *Clifford Chance*	**John Byrne** *Nabarro Nathanson*
J.W.Anthony Cann *Linklaters & Paines*	**William F. Charnley** *Simmons & Simmons*	**Adrian S. Clark** *Ashurst Morris Crisp*
Tim N. Clark *Slaughter and May*	**Stephen J. Cooke** *Slaughter and May*	**Andrew R. Curran** *Lovell White Durrant*
James P.L. Davis *Freshfields*	**Andrew Daws** *Denton Hall*	**Anthony C. Dove** *Simmons & Simmons*
Ian F. Elder *Allen & Overy*	**Stuart J. Evans** *Simmons & Simmons*	**Roger J. Finbow** *Ashurst Morris Crisp*
Mike Francies *Clifford Chance*	**Richard W. Godden** *Linklaters & Paines*	**Keith G. Godfrey** *Allen & Overy*
Edwin Godfrey *Simmons & Simmons*	**Philip Goodwin** *Denton Hall*	**Peter L. Graham** *Norton Rose*
Giles I. Henderson CBE *Slaughter and May*	**Jeremy G. Hill** *Ashurst Morris Crisp*	**Peter R.J. Holland** *Allen & Overy*
Glen W. James *Slaughter and May*	**Peter D.S. King** *Linklaters & Paines*	**Henry E.St.L. King** *Denton Hall*
William John Langford Knight *Simmons & Simmons*	**Daniel Kossoff** *Clifford Chance*	**J. Terence Kyle** *Linklaters & Paines*
Graeme Levy *Olswang*	**Anthony D. Macaulay** *Herbert Smith*	**Dan Mace** *Lovell White Durrant*
M.A.F. Macpherson *Ashurst Morris Crisp*	**Charles P. Morgan** *Allen & Overy*	**Margaret Mountford** *Herbert Smith*
B.J. O'Brien *Freshfields*	**John Osborne** *Clifford Chance*	**Colin Overbury** *Allen & Overy*
Alan D. Paul *Allen & Overy*	**Michael Pescod** *Slaughter and May*	**Richard Price** *McKenna & Co*
Mark S. Rawlinson *Freshfields*	**Andrew Philip Richards** *Freshfields*	**Anthony M.V. Salz** *Freshfields*
Jeremy Sivyer *Simmons & Simmons*	**Graham Smith** *Clifford Chance*	**Michael Sullivan** *Linklaters & Paines*
C.William Y. Underhill *Slaughter and May*	**Edward I.Walker-Arnott** *Herbert Smith*	**P.B.Wayte** *Alsop Wilkinson*

LEADING LONDON FIRMS 100-250 FEE EARNERS

The list of this group of firms is headed by three firms with an excellent reputation for corporate work, although, as with the larger firms, all the firms listed here have good overall capabilities with differing areas of specialities. *Travers Smith Braithwaite*, *Macfarlanes* and *S J Berwin & Co* have continued to demonstrate their ability to handle high quality work and by virtue of their reputations

edge ahead of the remaining firms in this group. It is difficult to assess the extent to which this reputation is really for corporate finance and venture capital capabilities (for which they are particularly well-known) or for the more general company/commercial area, the subject of this section.

LEADING FIRMS – LONDON – 100-250 FEE-EARNERS

S J BERWIN & CO	**MACFARLANES**
TRAVERS SMITH BRAITHWAITE	
BERWIN LEIGHTON	**GOULDENS**
STEPHENSON HARWOOD	**THEODORE GODDARD**
BAKER & McKENZIE	**EVERSHEDS**
FIELD FISHER WATERHOUSE	**FRERE CHOLMELEY BISCHOFF**
RICHARDS BUTLER	**ROWE & MAW**
TAYLOR JOYNSON GARRETT	

HIGHLY REGARDED – LONDON – 100-250 FEE-EARNERS

D J FREEMAN	**LAWRENCE GRAHAM**
TITMUSS SAINER DECHERT	**WATSON, FARLEY & WILLIAMS**
ALSOP WILKINSON	**BARLOW LYDE & GILBERT**
BEACHCROFT STANLEYS	**CLYDE & CO**
DAVIES ARNOLD COOPER	**MASONS**
RADCLIFFES CROSSMAN BLOCK	**REYNOLDS PORTER CHAMBERLAIN**
SINCLAIR ROCHE & TEMPERLEY	**TROWERS & HAMLINS**

Company/commercial accounts for 44% of the work-load of *Macfarlanes'* practice. On the corporate side the firm has had another excellent year placing fourth in KPMG's league table of firms acting in MBOs and seventh in the 'Acquisitions Monthly' August 1994 public takeover league. The KPMG flotation league table showing solicitors acting for the company on flotations during the period from January 1992-September 1994 also shows *Macfarlanes* at seventh place. The firm also has a strong commercial practice; during the last year it has acted for Grolsch in their joint venture with Bass in relation to brewing and distributing the Grolsch band in the UK, Ben & Jerry's Ice Cream in setting up their operations, and Reebok in relation to their distribution activities in Europe.

On the face of it *Travers Smith Braithwaite* is similar in profile to *Macfarlanes*, both medium-sized firms with predominantly corporate practice 'punching' well above their weight. In fact *Travers Smith Braithwaite* claims special advantages in being smaller, arguing greater partner involvement for their clients than would be the case at the big City firms. Combined corporate and commercial work accounts for just over 40% of the firm's total workload with the company/commercial department fielding 17 specialist partners. The firm acts for over 50 listed companies which puts them amongst the top dozen or so in the UK. The firm is in the top six for the number of flotations it advised on, according to 'Acquisitions Monthly'. It advised Hanson on the £460 million flotation of Beazer plc and continues to advise the Bank of England on CREST (the new paperless trading system). It also advised on the dissolution of the Scottish Marketing Board and the new arrangements for the marketing of milk in Scotland. The department boasts two well-known practitioners in Alan Keat and Nigel Campion-Smith.

S.J.Berwin's reputation does not seem to have suffered from the high-level departures to *Coudert Brothers*. The firm itself does not claim to have a traditional company/commercial department, but rather prefers to split its work-load as 39% corporate finance and 12% media. However the firm is able to field some 25 specialist partners in the non-contentious commercial field. This departmental split reveals the firm's strengths in corporate finance, and particularly, in venture capital and servicing its media clients. Clients include Bright Reasons Restaurants (formerly Pizzaland), Ladbroke Group plc (when it advised on the sale of Texas Homecare to Sainsburys) and The British Land Company acting in connection with the Swiss Centre in central London. The firm recently lost Graeme Levy to *Olswang*.

Alsop Wilkinson is particularly known for its work in connection with development capital and acts for a number of institutional providers of equity and debt finance. It has developed a sound MBO practice taking seventh place nationally in the KPMG league table for the period 1 January 1990 to 31 December 1994, although of course the firm is not purely based in London having substantial presences in Liverpool and Manchester and developing its international practice with staffed offices in Hong Kong and New York.

Baker & McKenzie continues to flourish as a result of its international practice and for its (London) size boasts an impressive client list including Asda plc, Canon (UK) Ltd, Wang UK Ltd, Kelloggs GB and Sony UK, although some of these are joint clients. The firm scored notable success coming a very close second to *Freshfields* in the

table of world-wide privatisation work done by law firms. Both firms were well ahead of the third placed US firm.

Like *S.J.Berwin*, *Berwin Leighton's* commercial strengths lie in its corporate finance expertise and in advising on financial aspects of Media and Entertainment. The firm placed ninth in the 'Acquisitions Monthly' table of top 20 legal advisers on UK private takeovers and seventh in the table of solicitors to the company for London listings for the period 1 January 1993-30 June 1994. The firm boosted this capability further by appointing two venture capital specialists from the old *Turner Kenneth Brown*. Half of the firm's commercial group's fee income derives from film finance work, and in the past year the firm has acted for the Royal Bank of Canada on an $80 million funding, acted for the Disney Group, acted for the Bolshoi Ballet on its Far East Tour and has entered the inter-active market acting for an EMI/PMI joint venture for children's inter-active programming with The Children's Company.

Gouldens has been steadily consolidating its position opening an office in Moscow in January 1994 to add to its recent Hong Kong addition. In the 'Acquisitions Monthly' league table of top 20 legal advisers in UK public takeovers it placed a creditable 10th, ahead of such firms as *Norton Rose*, *Denton Hall* and *Berwin Leighton*. The firm advised Hanson plc on its offer for Scholes Group plc and Imperial Tobacco Limited on its technology transfer arrangements in China.

This year waved good-bye to *Jaques & Lewis*, which took the bold decision to ditch its name and become part of the *Eversheds* 'group' of firms. Whether this will have a significant effect in the future is impossible to assess although clearly this gives *Eversheds* a foot-hold in the City and a small international presence, and presumably the old *Jaques & Lewis* may gain access to *Eversheds* impressive provincial client list. *Eversheds* apparently is the fastest recruiter of clients among the top ten firms.

After a couple of difficult years, with a series of well-publicised restructurings and a non-merger with the afore-mentioned *Eversheds*, *Theodore Goddard* seems to be recovering with slightly improved gross fees figures but generated by fewer fee earners. The firm placed 16th in a recent table of worldwide privatisation work done by law firms.

Stephenson Harwood's commercial base remains broad, covering joint ventures, EU/competition law, distribution and franchising work, as well as general commercial transactions. It also has a growing reputation for privatisation and redevelopment work. In addition to work on port privatisations, container line operation and airport ownership transactions, the firm is currently involved in two government privatisations.

Field Fisher Waterhouse seems to be developing something of a privatisation specialism undertaken by its corporate finance department which fields five specialist artners. Major clients include the Department of Employment, Department of Environment, and British Railways Board. The firm advised on the privatisation of Bournemouth International Airport and the sale of

Thomas Cook Business Travel Division to Amex. The firm also has specialist departments dealing with travel and tourism and the hotel industry with three partners. The main company/commercial department consists of 12 partners. The firm acts for BAT, Mitsubishi Corporation, Whitbread plc and Japan Airlines amongst others.

Frere Cholmeley Bischoff, where company/commercial accounts for 33% of the firm's workload, advise on a full range of commercial activity. In the technology and intellectual property fields the firm handles joint ventures, copyright and design protection, distribution agreements and computer contract negotiation. With its network of European offices, the firm is geared towards the needs of its international clients. In particular, the London-based Anglo-German group advises on commercial issues throughout the European Union.

Other firms recommended are *Rowe & Maw* and *Lawrence Graham*. *Rowe & Maw's* fifteen company/commercial partners generate 46% of the firm's workload, and recently acted in the acquisition of Dillons and in the sale of Rumbelows for Thorn EMI. *Lawrence Graham* has had an active year advising on a whole range of commercial matters, including acquisitions, joint ventures, flotations, management buy-outs, sale of assets and sponsorship agreements.

LEADING INDIVIDUALS – LONDON – 100-250 FEE-EARNERS

Christopher Tite *Stephenson Harwood*	**Timothy R.B. Anderson** *Reynolds Porter Chamberlain*	**Mark Beattie** *Davies Arnold Cooper*
Peter R.M. Bond *Taylor Joynson Garrett*	**Patrick Burgess** *Gouldens*	**Robert P. Burrow** *S J Berwin & Co*
W. Nigel Campion-Smith *Travers Smith Braithwaite*	**Nigel M. Carrington** *Baker & McKenzie*	**Kevin J. Dean** *Sinclair Roche & Temperley*
Martin L.G. Dillon *Taylor Joynson Garrett*	**Adam Greaves** *Gouldens*	**Robert J. Jones** *Berwin Leighton*
Alan M. Keat *Travers Smith Braithwaite*	**N. Anthony Leifer** *D J Freeman*	**John C. Longdon** *Travers Smith Braithwaite*
Antony S.R. Mair *Stephenson Harwood*	**Margaret A. Moore** *Travers Smith Braithwaite*	**Simon Morgan** *Frere Cholmeley Bischoff*
Charles N. Ouin *Lawrence Graham*	**Robin M. Preston** *Theodore Goddard*	**Richard J. Spiller** *D J Freeman*
Michael Steinfeld *Titmuss Sainer Dechert*	**Peter F. Stone** *Berwin Leighton*	**Michael J. Storar** *Lawrence Graham*
Robert H. Sutton *Macfarlanes*	**Richard L. Thomas** *Sinclair Roche & Temperley*	**Peter Turnbull** *Macfarlanes*
Charles Wander *Davies Arnold Cooper*		

LEADING LONDON FIRMS 50-100 FEE EARNERS

Despite their smaller size the leading firms in this group all have reputations that match their rivals'. *Bird & Bird* is the first firm to appear in this list and though primarily

LEADING FIRMS – LONDON – 50-100 FEE-EARNERS

BIRD & BIRD	**NICHOLSON GRAHAM &**
PAISNER & CO	**JONES**

known for its intellectual property and telecommunications expertise, company/commercial matters comprise 42% of its total workload with the firm able to field 11 specialist partners.

Nicholson Graham & Jones is a small City firm of 35 partners with a predominantly commercial practice with corporate/commercial work accounting for 40% of its total; the firm is structured according to cross-departmental units including specialist units advising on corporate rescue, mergers and acquisitions, MBOs (for which the firm featured in the KPMG leading solicitors table), media and entertainment and venture capital. Among corporate deals in which the firm has been involved during the past year are the £93 million cross border acquisition and placing of the Singer & Friedlander Group plc, the £50 million MBO of Levington Group ltd and the £50 million disposal of TJH Group Ltd.

Paisner & Co is a small firm which is known for doing 'higher quality' than would normally be expected for a firm of its size, and has long been associated with two major clients, Forte and GUS. Recent transactions by the firm include the demerger and flotation of ALPHA Airports Group plc, the restructuring of Ascot Holdings plc and Huntleigh Technology plc and the MBO of Gardner Merchant.

The remaining firms in our table all have good general company/commercial reputations commensurate with their size. *Pannone Pritchard Englefield* is included in this list by virtue of its reputation for international commercial work, particularly with regard to Germany. The next two names on the list, *Dibb Lupton Broomhead* and *Hammond Suddards* belong to the two regional firms making serious inroads on the London corporate

HIGHLY REGARDED – LONDON – 50-100 FEE-EARNERS

CHARLES RUSSELL	DIBB LUPTON BROOMHEAD
HAMMOND SUDDARDS	LEWIS SILKIN
MANCHES & CO	MISHCON DE REYA
SPEECHLY BIRCHAM	WEDLAKE BELL
BAILEYS SHAW & GILLETT	BIDDLE & CO
BOODLE HATFIELD	PANNONE PRITCHARD ENGLEFIELD

scene and it is clear from their achievements to date that they are making their presence felt. Their London offices have already established good reputations although it is fair to say that their major impact is still outside the capital and for this reason both firms are dealt with in more detail elsewhere.

LEADING INDIVIDUALS – LONDON – 50-100 FEE-EARNERS

Andrew P. Baker *Wedlake Bell*	**Clare Grayston** *Lewis Silkin*	**Michael S.M. Johns** *Nicholson Graham & Jones*
Stephen M. Rosefield *Paisner & Co*	**John C.B. South** *Charles Russell*	**Keith G. Stella** *Paisner & Co*
Martin Webster *Biddle & Co*	**Martin A.S. Winter** *Biddle & Co*	

LEADING LONDON FIRMS 1-50 FEE EARNERS

Three firms within the smallest category have received especial recommendations for their company commercial work. *Allison & Humphries* has developed a commercial reputation particularly in respect of the telecommunications and entertainment industries, acting for corporations rather than individuals. It acts for the BBC, various UK cable companies and a major Hollywood studio.

LEADING FIRMS – LONDON – 1-50 FEE-EARNERS	
ALLISON & HUMPHREYS	FOX WILLIAMS
MEMERY CRYSTAL	OLSWANG
WARNER CRANSTON	

Fox Williams is unusual for its size in that 60% of its workload has an international element to it, acting as it does for a large number of clients from the US, Europe and the Far East. Combined commercial and corporate work accounts for 43% of the firm's total. The firm recently advised on a worldwide travel industry joint venture and the acquisition by a Far Eastern motor manufacturer of a national distribution network.

According to *Memery Crystal* 45% of its workload is company/commercial. With only 13 partners, the firm nonetheless has a special flotations & capital raising department with three specialist partners and an acquisitions and disposals department also with three partners. The firm advised on 3i's investment in ICS Group and the relisting of Upton & Southern.

Warner Cranston, a small City firm with ambition has nine specialist company/commercial and corporate finance partners in its Pickford's Wharf office handling 35% of the firm's workload. In almost all its deals the other side is represented by one of the major law firms. It is known also for its American and French clientele.

Fox & Gibbons has a predominantly commercial practice with company/commercial accounting for some 40% of its workload, fielding a team of nine specialist partners. The firm also has strong links with the Middle East having associated offices in Yemen, Kuwait, Lebanon and Saudi Arabia.

Two firms with a reputation for entertainment and media work which have developed a name for company/commercial expertise are *Harbottle & Lewis* and *Olswang*. Company/commercial matters now account for 25% of *Harbottle & Lewis'* workload which is also more international than might be imagined. December of last year saw *Simon Olswang & Co.* announce a change of name and a change of location, with the firm now practising as *Olswang* from its new offices in Long Acre. In its typically aggressive fashion, the firm sees itself as a market leader in commercial law relating to film, television, radio and the new electronic media. Of its 18 partners, nine are company/commercial specialist partners with company/commercial work accounting for 33% of the total workload.

HIGHLY REGARDED – LONDON – 1-50 FEE-EARNERS	
FARRER & CO	FORSYTE SAUNDERS KERMAN
FOX & GIBBONS	HARBOTTLE & LEWIS
HOWARD KENNEDY	OSBORNE CLARKE
AMHURST BROWN COLOMBOTTI	BARNETT ALEXANDER CHART
CAMPBELL HOOPER	COUDERT BROTHERS
COURTS & CO	EDWIN COE
EVANS DODD	FINERS
GLOVERS	GREGORY, ROWCLIFFE & MILNERS
HOBSON AUDLEY	JOELSON WILSON & CO
LANE & PARTNERS	LAWRENCE JONES
LAYTONS	MARRIOTT HARRISON
MAXWELL BATLEY	MIDDLETON POTTS
RAKISONS	WALSH LAWSON

Amhurst Brown Colombotti features in our list because of its expertise in international commercial matters, especially involving Italy and Germany.

LEADING INDIVIDUALS – LONDON – 1-50 FEE-EARNERS		
Timothy D. Birt *Osborne Clarke*	Adrian J.A. Bott *Olswang*	Peter Carter *Forsyte Saunders Kerman*
Peter M. Crystal *Memery Crystal*	Paul Di Biase *Forsyte Saunders Kerman*	Ian B. Fagelson *Warner Cranston*
David N. Godfrey *Middleton Potts*	Colin M. Howes *Harbottle & Lewis*	Edward Marston *Barnett Alexander Chart*
Nigel Miller *Fox Williams*	Stephen L. Sidkin *Fox Williams*	Jon P.L Sweet *Marriott Harrison*

SOUTH EAST

The leading company/commercial firms in the South East are *Blake Lapthorne, Clarks, Cole & Cole* and *Donne Mileham & Haddock*. Of these firms, *Blake Lapthorne*, the largest in the region fielding 11 specialist partners, received the greatest number of recommendations. The firm undertakes a variety of work for major coporate clients and has recently acted for British Rail in the privatisation of two operating companies. Caroline Williams is held in high regard.

Clarks in Reading, is recognised as one of the most dynamic firms in the region and counts BMW among its clients. The company department benefits from a team of predominantly City trained lawyers including the highly

LEADING FIRMS – SOUTH EAST	
BLAKE LAPTHORN *Fareham*	CLARKS *Reading*
COLE and COLE *Oxford*	DONNE MILEHAM & HADDOCK *Brighton*
CRIPPS HARRIES HALL *Tunbridge Wells*	MANCHES & CO *Oxford*
SHOOSMITHS & HARRISON *Banbury*	THOMSON SNELL & PASSMORE *Tunbridge Wells*
DALLAS BRETT *Oxford*	PITMANS *Reading*

recommended Richard Lee who undertakes a range of work including venture capital, public issues, company acquisitions, management buy-outs and banking.

HIGHLY REGARDED – SOUTH EAST	
BRACHERS *Maidstone*	KIMBELL & CO *Milton Keynes*
LINNELLS *Oxford*	NABARRO NATHANSON
RAWLISON & BUTLER *Crawley*	THOMAS EGGAR VERRALL BOWLES *Chichester*
CHURCH ADAMS TATHAM *Reigate*	GARRETT & CO *Reading*
PICTONS *St. Albans*	SHERWIN OLIVER *Portsmouth*
BUSS MURTON *Tunbridge Wells*	B.P. COLLINS & CO *Gerrards Cross*
FENNEMORES *Milton Keynes*	MUNDAYS *Esher*
PARIS SMITH & RANDALL *Southampton*	STEVENS & BOLTON *Guildford*

Company/commercial work comprises 23% of the caseload at *Cole & Cole* which has six partners dedicated to the area. Joe Pillman (who has recently handled the management buy-outs of Early's of Witney plc and Cambridge Industries Ltd) is the firm's leading practitioner in this field.

Practitioners at *Donne Mileham & Haddock* handle technical business matters from the firm's Brighton and Crawley offices. Andrew Trotter, who heads the company/commercial department, undertakes a variety of work including company sales and purchases, management buy-outs, franchising, computer contracts and intellectual property agreements.

Other highly recommended firms include *Cripps Harries Hall, Manches & Co, Shoosmiths & Harrison* and *Thomson Snell & Passmore*.

Andrew Fermor heads the team of four specialists at *Cripps Harries Hall* which has recently advised on the purchase of a manufacturing company with a £12million turnover, the sales of a timber importer for £2.5million and a group of shopfitting companies for £1million and the demerger of a hotel group with a £7million turnover.

Company/commercial work accounts for 23% of the business at *Manches & Co* which has five specialist partners advising public and private companies.

Shoosmiths & Harrison (with ten specialist partners) and *Thomson Snell & Passmore* (which has seven partners operating from Tunbridge Wells, Maidstone and Tonbridge) both provide a comprehensive service to their corporate clients.

LEADING INDIVIDUALS – SOUTH EAST
Richard Lee *Clarks*
Jonathan Loake *Dallas Brett*
J.C. Pillman *Cole and Cole*
Andrew Trotter *Donne Mileham & Haddock*
Caroline A. Williams *Blake Lapthorn*
James H.T. Chatfield *Rawlison & Butler*
Andrew Fermor *Cripps Harries Hall*
Brian J. Haynes *Church Adams Tatham*
John C. Hutchinson *Pitmans*
Rosemary Martin-Jones *Nabarro Nathanson*
W.M. James Partridge *Thomson Snell & Passmore*
David R. Stanning *B.P. Collins & Co*
T.H. Walton *B.P. Collins & Co*

Shoosmiths & Harrison has recently handled the management buy-outs of a number of companies including Wilson Connolly plc, Ekco Packaging Ltd and Intermotor.

Other highly experienced firms include *Dallas Brett* (where Jonathan Loake is held in high regard) and *Pitmans*. *Brachers, Kimbell & Co, Linnells, Nabarro Nathanson, Rawlison & Butler* and *Thomas Eggar Verrall Bowles* are also noted for their expertise in the field.

SOUTH WEST

Burges Salmon and *Osborne Clarke* are the leading company/commercial firms in the South West. *Burges Salmon* has a strong team in Alan Barr, David Marsh (who also lectures on company law and financial services for Bristol Law Society) and Roger Hawes. The firm has been involved in some major transactions including the flotations of Gaymer Group Europe Ltd at £140 million and Badgerline Group at £47 million, and the £38 million takeover of Yorkshire Rider by Badgerline.

LEADING FIRMS – SOUTH WEST	
BURGES SALMON *Bristol*	OSBORNE CLARKE *Bristol*
BEVAN ASHFORD *Bristol*	BOND PEARCE *Plymouth*
WANSBROUGHS WILLEY HARGRAVE *Bristol*	

Osborne Clarke's company/commercial department includes the highly regarded Simon Beswick (who advised on the English aspects of a £400 million international joint venture between Knorr Bremse AG and Allied Signal Inc.), Chris Curling, Bruce Roxburgh, James Massey-Collier and Jeremy Simon. The firm has been involved in some major transactions in the last twelve months (35 of which exceeded £1m net worth) including the £120m MBO of Hollis Industries, a £35m hostile bid by Beverley Group plc for James Wilkes plc and the £50m flotations of Litho Supplies plc and Chesterton International plc.

Other highly recommended firms include *Bevan Ashford, Bond Pearce* and *Wansbroughs Willey Hargrave*.

HIGHLY REGARDED – SOUTH WEST	
EVERSHEDS *Bristol*	LESTER ALDRIDGE *Bournemouth*
VEALE WASBROUGH *Bristol*	
ANSTEY SARGENT & PROBERT *Exeter*	CHARLES RUSSELL *Cheltenham*
CLARKE WILLMOTT & CLARKE *Taunton*	COLES MILLER *Poole*
FOOT & BOWDEN *Plymouth*	LYONS DAVIDSON *Bristol*
STEELE RAYMOND *Bournemouth*	STEPHENS & SCOWN *Exeter*

Company/commercial work comprises 15% of the caseload at *Bevan Ashford* which has a team of ten specialists operating from the firm's Bristol, Exeter and Taunton offices. Paul Cooper, who heads the department, is particularly recommended.

Bond Pearce and *Wansbroughs Willey Hargrave* both provide a comprehensive service which includes business acquisitions, disposals and financing, MBOs, company restructuring and mergers and Stock Exchange/USM listings.

Other notable firms include *Lester Aldridge, Veale Wasbrough, Anstey Sargent & Probert, Clarke Wilmott & Clarke, Steele Raymond* and *Stephens & Scown.*.

LEADING INDIVIDUALS – SOUTH WEST

R. Alan Barr	*Burges Salmon*
Simon A. Beswick	*Osborne Clarke*
Paul Cooper	*Bevan Ashford*
Chris J. Curling	*Osborne Clarke*
David J. Marsh	*Burges Salmon*
B.O. Roxburgh	*Osborne Clarke*

Roger Acock	*Bond Pearce*
Derek J. Bellew	*Veale Wasbrough*
Nigel Campbell	*Veale Wasbrough*
Nicholas C.P. Cockcroft	*Wansbroughs Willey Hargrave*
Richard Coombs	*Anstey Sargent & Probert*
Roger Geoffrey Hawes	*Burges Salmon*
Mark R.L. Lewis	*Foot & Bowden*
Paul D. Longland	*Steele Raymond*
James P. Massy-Collier	*Osborne Clarke*
Christopher J. Mitchell	*Cartwrights*
Simon Rous	*Bevan Ashford*
Jeremy P. Simon	*Osborne Clarke*
Anthony R.H. Welford	*Veale Wasbrough*

WALES

Cardiff firms tend to take the lion's share of company/commercial work in Wales.

The highly regarded Roderick Thurman at *Edwards Geldard* handles principally corporate matters and has recently advised on the acquisition by Welsh Water plc of Acer Group Ltd, and the sale of B.I.G. Batteries to Exide. The firm is the only non-London practice to appear on the Citibank panel of lawyers.

LEADING FIRMS – WALES

EDWARDS GELDARD	*Cardiff*	**EVERSHEDS**	*Cardiff*
MORGAN BRUCE	*Cardiff*		

Roger Thomas is *Eversheds'* outstanding practitioner, handling the full range of commercial and corporate matters including acquisitions, joint ventures and MBOs.

The profile of *Morgan Bruce* continues to rise. It has acted for TBI plc in the acquisition of Cardiff-Wales airport, for Ryan Group Ltd in connection with its bids in the British Gas privatisation and for radio station Swansea Sound. The firm recently announced the opening of a London office in Fleet Street.

HIGHLY REGARDED – WALES

BEVAN ASHFORD	*Cardiff*	**FRANCIS & CO**	*Newport*
HUGH JAMES JONES & JENKINS	*Cardiff*		

Other highly experienced firms include *Bevan Ashford, Francis & Co* and *Hugh James Jones & Jenkins*.

LEADING INDIVIDUALS – WALES

Roger Thomas	*Eversheds*
Roderick J. Thurman	*Edwards Geldard*

MIDLANDS

Company/commercial work in the Midlands continues to be dominated by the 'big four' commercial firms in Birmingham. Of these firms, *Pinsent Curtis* and *Wragge & Co* are marginally ahead in terms of sheer expertise with *Edge & Ellison* and *Eversheds* ranking a close second.

LEADING FIRMS – MIDLANDS

PINSENT CURTIS	*Birmingham*	**WRAGGE & CO**	*Birmingham*
EDGE & ELLISON	*Birmingham*	**EVERSHEDS**	*Birmingham*

Company/commercial work accounts for 37% of the business at *Pinsent Curtis* which undertakes work for large corporate clients including advice on mergers and acquisitions, flotations, Stock Exchange and takeovers, venture capital and joint ventures. David Hughes, who heads the unit, is well-respected.

Wragge & Co has made its public company debut in the 'Acquisitions Monthly' tables by acting for Birkby and Suter. The firm is particularly known for its corporate finance expertise. Eminent practitioners in the company department include Michael Whitehouse, Charles Hughes and John Crabtree.

HIGHLY REGARDED – MIDLANDS

DIBB LUPTON BROOMHEAD *Birmingham*	**GATELEY WAREING** *Birmingham*
MARTINEAU JOHNSON *Birmingham*	
BROWNE JACOBSON *Nottingham*	**FREETH CARTWRIGHT HUNT DICKINS** *Nottingham*
HEWITSON BECKE + SHAW *Northampton*	**HOWES PERCIVAL** *Northampton*
KENT JONES and DONE *Stoke-on-Trent*	**LEE CROWDER** *Birmingham*
SHAKESPEARES *Birmingham*	**SHOOSMITHS & HARRISON** *Northampton*
FOSTER BAXTER COOKSEY *Wolverhampton*	**GEORGE GREEN & CO** *Warley*
GOODGER AUDEN *Burton-on-Trent*	**HERBERT WILKES** *Birmingham*
HIGGS & SONS *Brierley Hill*	**KEELY SMITH & JOBSON** *Lichfield*
KNIGHT & SONS *Newcastle-under-Lyme*	**RIGBEYS** *Birmingham*

Edge & Ellison's reputation mainly lies in management buy-out work where Digby Jones (who heads the commercial department) is particularly recommended. The firm has recently been reported in 'The Hambros Company Guide' as the fastest recruiter of plc clients among the

LEADING INDIVIDUALS – MIDLANDS

Digby M. Jones	*Edge & Ellison*
John Crabtree	*Wragge & Co*
Stephen L. Duffield	*Eversheds*
David J. Hughes	*Pinsent Curtis*
Christopher W. Hughes	*Wragge & Co*
Michael Whitehouse	*Wragge & Co*

top ten law firms in the country. *Eversheds,* which operates from Birmingham, Nottingham and Derby, boasts an enviable client list and has significant corporate finance expertise.

Outside Birmingham, *Browne Jacobson* in Nottingham, and the trio of Northampton firms, *Hewitson Becke & Shaw, Shoosmiths and Harrison* and *Howes Percival* are all well-regarded for their company and commercial work.

EAST ANGLIA

East Anglia's leading company/commercial firms are *Eversheds* (Ipswich and Norwich) and *Mills & Reeve.* At *Eversheds* Andrew Croome is a contributor to two Tolleys publications, 'Company Law' and 'The Directors' Handbook' and specialises in both company law and banking. Jerome Misso and Terry Gould (who handles all aspects of company law, and has extensive experience in the media industry, particularly newspapers and commercial radio) are also highly recommended. The firm has recently acted in the hostile bid for Suffolk Group Radio plc.

LEADING FIRMS – EAST ANGLIA	
EVERSHEDS *Norwich*	**MILLS & REEVE** *Norwich*
HEWITSON BECKE + SHAW *Cambridge*	**TAYLOR VINTERS** *Cambridge*

At *Mills & Reeve*, Ian Alexander-Sinclair handles the full range of corporate and commercial work, including mergers and acquisitions and corporate finance. Also highly regarded is Nicholas Fischl who advises on corporate finance, MBOs, joint ventures, commercial agreements and computer/IT agreements.

Other highly recommended firms include *Hewitson Becke & Shaw* and *Taylor Vinters.* At *Hewitson Becke & Shaw*, Bridget Kerle advises corporate clients on funding, acquisitions and disposals, flotations and MBOs and handles employee share schemes for growing and quoted companies. Also noted for her experience in the field is Fiona Crawley who specialises in all types of commercial agreements and intellectual property. Her practice also covers corporate work, acting for a number of pharmaceutical and biotechnology companies.

HIGHLY REGARDED – EAST ANGLIA	
BIRKETTS *Ipswich*	**GREENWOODS** *Peterborough*
LEATHES PRIOR *Norwich*	**PRETTYS** *Ipswich*
COZENS–HARDY & JEWSON *Norwich*	**HOWES PERCIVAL** *Ipswich*
LEEDS DAY *Sandy*	
BANKES ASHTON *Bury St. Edmunds*	**GOTELEE & GOLDSMITH** *Ipswich*
GREENE & GREENE *Bury St. Edmunds*	

Company/commercial work accounts for 26% of the caseload at *Taylor Vinters* which undertakes acquisition and sales work, reconstructions, venture capital, investment and MBOs/ins. John Short (who also lectures on the subject) is the firm's leading light. Gerard Fitzsimmons is also held in high regard.

Other firms noted for their experience in the field include *Birketts, Greenwoods* (and Michael Evans in particular), *Leathes Prior* and *Prettys.*

LEADING INDIVIDUALS – EAST ANGLIA	
Ian Alexander-Sinclair	*Mills & Reeve*
Andrew Croome	*Eversheds*
Nicolas J. Fischl	*Mills & Reeve*
Bridget A. Kerle	*Hewitson Becke + Shaw*
John Short	*Taylor Vinters*
Fiona Crawley	*Hewitson Becke + Shaw*
M.J. Evans	*Greenwoods*
Gerard Fitzsimons	*Taylor Vinters*
Terry Gould	*Eversheds*
Jerome Jude Misso	*Eversheds*

NORTH WEST

Addleshaw Sons & Latham emerges as the leading firm in the North West with outstanding practitioners in Keith Johnston, Paul Lee and Andrew Needham. The firm represents clients on a regional and a national scale and is recognised for its excellent regulatory and corporate finance work. Recent transactions have included North West Water plc's acquisition of the UK operations of Wallace and Tiernan and the sale of its engineering company to Bechtel Inc, the sale of NFC's waste management business for £115 million and the management and employee buy-outs of GM Buses North for £37 million.

LEADING FIRMS – NORTH WEST	
ADDLESHAW SONS & LATHAM *Manchester*	
ALSOP WILKINSON *Liverpool*	**EVERSHEDS** *Manchester*
CHAFFE STREET *Manchester*	**HALLIWELL LANDAU** *Manchester*
HAMMOND SUDDARDS *Manchester*	

Other highly regarded firms include *Eversheds* and *Alsop Wilkinson. Eversheds* boasts Edward Pysden, the most consistently recommended practitioner in the region, who for the last three years has been voted top North West corporate lawyer by readers of 'Insider' magazine. The firm is active in the public issues market, acting for Vymura on its flotation and for N.M. Rothschild & Sons on the admission of Aromascan plc to the USM. On the buy-in/buy-out front, the firm acts for venture capitalists, mezzanine lenders and buy-in/out teams (high profile transactions have included the buy-outs of GM Buses South for £25 million and the Ferranti Components Division from the Receivers of Ferranti) whilst acquisition work has included the sale by Co-operative Wholesale Society of its food manufacturing division for £100 million.

Alsop Wilkinson's company/commercial department comprises an eleven partner team (operating from Liverpool and Manchester) which includes Roger Lane-Smith, Michael Prince and Richard Paton. The firm is reported to have advised in more MBOs than any other North West firm in the last four years and is particularly known for development capital work.

Other firms noted for their expertise in the field include *Chaffe Street* which has Robert Street as its outstanding practitioner, *Halliwell Landau* (where Alexander Craig and Clive Garston have been recommended) and *Hammond Suddards*.

NORTH EAST

Dibb Lupton Broomhead and *Hammond Suddards* maintain their position as leading company/commercial firms in the North East, claiming third and fourth places respectively in the league tables for advising buy-out houses in MBOs (only *Ashurst Morris Crisp* and *Clifford Chance* out-performing them).

Dibb Lupton Broomhead has one of the largest company/ commercial departments in the region (nationally the firm has 31 partners specialising in the field). Andrew Darwin heads the team in Leeds that advises public and private companies, financial institutions, public bodies and insurance companies on flotations, mergers and acquisitions, and MBOs in addition to general commercial contract law.

The department at *Hammond Suddards* undertakes a substantial amount of work for major clients (the firm acts on a full service basis for 20% of the Yorkshire based, publicly held companies). Major transactions have included acting for Hoylake Investments Ltd (James Goldsmith consortium) in its bid for BAT Industries plc, Pembridge Investments Ltd in its hostile takeover of DRG plc for £700m and Amerpharm Group in the disposal of its pharmaceutical business to E Merck for US$400 million.

Other highly recommended firms include *Booth & Co, Eversheds* (Leeds), *Pinsent Curtis* and *Dickinson Dees*.

Booth and Co has completed over 200 deals in the past 12 months with an aggregate value of over £1 billion. Clients include 3I Group plc, Abbeycrest plc, Leeds University and Leeds Metropolitan University. Ian MacIntosh, Timothy Wheldon and Maurice Cowen are experienced in the field.

Eversheds (which reports a doubling of overall fee income in the past five years) has recently represented John Waddington plc in the sale of its games divisions, Next plc and Yorkshire Food Group plc. David Gray and Toby Tilly are held in high regard.

Pinsent Curtis (a recent merger between *Simpson Curtis* and *Pinsent & Co*) is now the 16th largest practice in the country with a pool of over 50 quoted companies including Mirror Group, Kwiksave and Yorkshire Water among its clients. The highly recommended Sean Lippell and Andrew Walker are among a strong team that advises on company formations, trading agreements, joint ventures and partnerships.

Dickinson Dees maintains its position as the pre-eminent firm in Newcastle, both in terms of size and reputation. The firm has recently advised on the flotations of The Go-Ahead Group and Parkdean Leisure at £40.5 and £13.5m respectively and the MBOs of the ceramic and syalon business of Cookson Group plc and EBR Polythene plc. Graham Wright, Nigel Bellis and John Flynn are highly recommended.

Other notable firms include *Eversheds* (Newcastle), *Wilkinson Maughan, Robert Muckle,* where Ian Gilthorpe and Hugh Welch have been recommended (the firm has increased its turnover by 22% in the last twelve months), *Walker Morris* where Ian Gilbert and Peter Smart have advised on the £57m MBO of Goldsborough Healthcare plc, the £75m flotation of the same company and the £6.7m management buy-in of Dunne & Co;

Ward Hadaway which has Peter Allen as its outstanding practitioner, and *Wilkinson Maughan* which has 16 fee-earners specialising in company/commercial law and has recently advised on the purchase of The Bakers Oven by Greggs plc, the MBO of Tyneside Waste Paper and a joint venture investment in Australia for The Pointing Group of Companies.

LEADING INDIVIDUALS – NORTH EAST		
Peter R. Allan *Ward Hadaway*	Nigel D. Bellis *Dickinson Dees*	David John Gray *Eversheds*
Graham Wright *Dickinson Dees*		
Maurice C. Cowen *Booth & Co.*	Andrew Darwin *Dibb Lupton Broomhead*	Andrew J. Davison *Wilkinson Maughan*
John Flynn *Dickinson Dees*	David C. Foster *Watson Burton*	Ian M. Gilbert *Walker Morris*
Ian M. Gilthorpe *Robert Muckle*	Richard Holt *Nabarro Nathanson*	C. Sean Lippell *Pinsent Curtis*
Ian W. McIntosh *Booth & Co.*	Peter C. Smart *Walker Morris*	Michael I. Spriggs *Wilkinson Maughan*
Toby H. Tilly *Eversheds*	Andrew W. Walker *Pinsent Curtis*	H.B. Welch *Robert Muckle*
Timothy J. Wheldon *Booth & Co.*		

SCOTLAND

McGrigor Donald, Maclay Murray & Spens and *Dundas & Wilson* vie for position as the leading commercial firm in Scotland. All three have a presence in two major Scottish commercial centres: Edinburgh and Glasgow, and also a London connection.

LEADING FIRMS – SCOTLAND	
DUNDAS & WILSON CS Edinburgh	MACLAY MURRAY & SPENS Glasgow
McGRIGOR DONALD Glasgow	
DICKSON MINTO WS Edinburgh	LEDINGHAM CHALMERS Aberdeen
MACROBERTS Glasgow	PAULL & WILLIAMSONS Aberdeen
SHEPHERD & WEDDERBURN Edinburgh	TODS MURRAY WS Edinburgh

McGrigor Donald's commercial department advises on a broad spectrum of work for clients ranging from small businesses to large scale operations involving public utilities and multinationals. Morag McNeill is highly recommended.

The commercial department at *Maclay Murray & Spens* (which boasts the highly regarded Bruce Patrick and Magnus Swanson) provides corporate advice on mergers & ac-quisitions and partnerships for public and private companies.

Dundas & Wilson's leading light is Christopher Campbell although the department also has a notable practitioner in Philip Mackay. The firm has handled some major cases in recent months including the capital reorganisation of Tullis Russell Ltd valued at £37 million, acting for Scottish Hydro-Electric plc in deals worth £40 million and the purchase by UK Consumer Electronics Ltd of the rental business of Clydesdale Group plc for £8.3 million.

Other highly recommended firms include *Dickson Minto* which has eight partners specialising in the subject including the well-respected Bruce Minto, *Ledingham Chalmers*, where company/commercial work accounts for 20% of the firm's business (David Laing is recommended) and *MacRoberts* (Ian Dickson is the most consistently recommended practitioner in Scotland).

HIGHLY REGARDED – SCOTLAND	
BIGGART BAILLIE & GIFFORD *Glasgow*	BIRD SEMPLE *Glasgow*
BRODIES WS *Edinburgh*	W & J BURNESS WS *Edinburgh*
DORMAN JEFFREY & CO *Glasgow*	
BOYDS *Glasgow*	IAIN SMITH & CO *Aberdeen*
JAMES & GEORGE COLLIE *Aberdeen*	McCLURE NAISMITH ANDERSON & GARDINER *Glasgow*
PETERKINS *Aberdeen*	STRONACHS *Aberdeen*
THORNTONS WS *Dundee*	

LEADING INDIVIDUALS – SCOTLAND		
Sidney Barrie *Paull & Williamsons*	Gordon A. Buchan *Paull & Williamsons*	Christopher R.J. Campbell *Dundas & Wilson*
Ian Dickson *MacRoberts*	John Gardiner *Bird Semple*	Paul W. Hally *Shepherd & Wedderburn*
David K. Laing *Ledingham Chalmers*	Philip Mackay *Dundas & Wilson CS*	Morag McNeill *McGrigor Donald*
Alan R. McNiven *Paull & Williamsons*	Iain M.C. Meiklejohn *Shepherd & Wedderburn*	Bruce W. Minto *Dickson Minto WS*
Bruce R. Patrick *Maclay Murray & Spens*	John C. Rafferty *W & J Burness WS*	Roy Roxburgh *Iain Smith & Co*
Andrew F. Sleigh *W & J Burness WS*	Magnus P. Swanson *Maclay Murray & Spens*	
David M. Allan *Stronachs*	Kenneth G. Chrystie *McClure Naismith Anderson & Gardiner*	Stephen Cook *McGrigor Donald*
Maureen S. Coutts *Dundas & Wilson CS*	Neil Cunningham *MacRoberts*	A. Brian Dorman *Dorman Jeffrey & Co*
Hugh Fraser *Stronachs*	Eric R. Galbraith *Dorman Jeffrey & Co*	Gordon Hopkirk *Iain Smith & Co*
Neil C. Hunter *Peterkins*	Kevan MacDonald *Dickson Minto WS*	Malcolm McIver *Bird Semple*
J. Stuart Russell *Boyds*	John A.T. Rutherford *Ledingham Chalmers*	Alfred C. Shedden *McGrigor Donald*
W.W. Campbell Smith *Biggart Baillie & Gifford*	Michael J. Walker *Maclay Murray & Spens*	

Paull & Williamsons boasts the highly regarded Sidney Barrie, Alan Macniven and Gordon Buchan, whilst *Shepherd & Wedderburn's* leading lights are Paul Hally and Iain Meikeljohn. Commercial work accounts for 24% of the caseload at *Tods Murray*.

Roy Roxburgh of *Iain Smith & Company* also featured prominently in our research.

Other firms noted for their expertise in the area include *Biggart Baillie & Gifford, Bird Semple* (where John Gardiner is particularly recommended), *Boyds* and *Brodies*.

NORTHERN IRELAND

While there has been some growth in inward investment in the province in the aftermath of last year's ceasefire, firms have yet to experience a significant upturn in work in this area.

Belfast firms dominate in the field: the leading practitioners include Stanley Hill at *Carson & McDowell*, Peter Rankin and Ian Dawson at *Cleaver Fulton & Rankin,* Brian Garrett at *Elliott Duffy Garrett*, John Irvine at *L'Estrange & Brett*, Stratton Mills and Ivan Selig at *Mills Selig*.

HIGHLY REGARDED – NORTHERN IRELAND

CARSON & McDOWELL	*Belfast*	CLEAVER FULTON & RANKIN	*Belfast*
ELLIOTT DUFFY GARRETT	*Belfast*	JOHNS ELLIOT	*Belfast*
L'ESTRANGE & BRETT	*Belfast*	MILLS SELIG	*Belfast*
TUGHAN & CO	*Belfast*		

HARRISON, LEITCH & LOGAN	*Belfast*	C & H JEFFERSON *Belfast*
JOHNSONS	*Belfast*	McKINTY & WRIGHT *Belfast*
NORMAN WILSON & CO		O'REILLY STEWART *Belfast*

Other firms with recognised expertise in the field include *Johns Elliott* and *Tughan & Co.*

Many firms carry out agency work for English solicitors.

LEADING INDIVIDUALS – NORTHERN IRELAND

Ian D. Dawson	*Cleaver Fulton & Rankin*
Brian Garrett	*Elliott Duffy Garrett*
W. Stanley Hill	*Carson & McDowell*
John W. Irvine	*L'Estrange & Brett*
W. Stratton Mills	*Mills Selig*
Peter J. Rankin	*Cleaver Fulton & Rankin*
Ivan Selig	*Mills Selig*

LEADERS IN COMPANY/COMMERCIAL

LONDON

Anderson, Timothy R.B.
Reynolds Porter Chamberlain, London (0171) 242 2877. Partner in Company/Commercial Department.

Specialisation: General company commercial. Work includes mergers and acquisition, share issues, joint ventures, franchising, distribution, software contracts, pharmaceutical law, competition law and partnership law.

Prof. Membership: Law Society, Holborn Law Society.

Career: Qualified in 1986. Joined *Reynolds Porter Chamberlain* in 1984, becoming a Partner in 1989.

ap Simon, Charles
Freshfields, London (0171) 936 4000. Partner in Corporate Department.

Specialisation: Main area of practice is corporate and corporate finance. Advises corporate and merchant banking clients on corporate, stock exchange and take- over related issues, including securities issues, joint ventures and private acquisitions and disposals.

Prof. Membership: Law Society and City Solicitors' Company.

Career: Qualified in 1977. Worked at Mullens & Co Stockbrokers 1969-71 and Cazenove & Co Stockbrokers 1971-75.

Joined *Freshfields* in 1977, becoming a Partner in 1982.

Personal: Born 28th June 1947. Attended Epsom College 1960-65 and Christ's College Cambridge 1966-69 (MA, LLB). Leisure interests include opera and wine. Lives in London and Warwickshire.

Armstrong, John S.
Cameron Markby Hewitt, London (0171) 702 2345.

Specialisation: Partner in the corporate/commercial department. Specialises in all non-contentious areas of information technology and intellectual property law including patents, trademarks, designs, copyright, confidential information, technology transfer, licensing, computer and technology contracts. Also handles commercial work including contracts for both goods and services covering distribution, agency, franchising, joint ventures, supply and purchase.

Career: Joined Cameron Markby Hewitt in 1986. Partner 1990.

Personal: Educated at Southampton University 1979-82. Born 1960. Lives in Haywards Heath, W. Sussex.

Ashworth, Chris
Ashurst Morris Crisp, London (0171) 638 1111. Partner 1986. Specialises in mergers and acquisitions, corporate restructuring and corporate finance work.

Baker, Andrew P.
Wedlake Bell, London (0171) 395 3000. Partner 1982 in Company/Commercial Department.

Specialisation: Commercial and Corporate. Acts for a wide range of listed companies, brokers and venture capitalists with regard to mergers and acquisitions, equity issues and flotations. Speaker at seminars and conferences with regard to corporate governance and buying and selling companies.

Career: Articled with *Slaughter and May* in 1970. Qualified 1972 joining the commercial department of *Slaughter and May*. Joined *Wedlake Bell* 1979 becoming a partner in 1982. Head of Corporate Department 1985 to 1992. Currently Business Development partner. Also President of the international association of independent commercial law firms, TELFA (Trans European Law Firms Association) and member of the CISCO corporate governance sub-committee.

Personal: Born 12th October 1946. LLB(Hons) Birmingham 1969. Lives in Surrey. Also a Director of The Global Group plc, The Egyptian-British Chamber of Commerce and Chairman of Telegraph Hill Estates plc.

Barnard, Stephen G.
Herbert Smith, London (0171) 374 8000. Partner in Corporate Department.

Specialisation: Heads one of the firm's general corporate groups dealing with a broad range of company and commercial work including corporate finance, mergers and acquisitions, venture capital transactions and privatisations. His work involves acting for a number of listed clients as well as financial intermediaries and institutions.

Career: Qualified in 1974. Partner at *Herbert Smith* since 1983.

Personal: Educated at Southampton University.

Beattie, Mark

Davies Arnold Cooper, London (0171) 936 2222. Qualified 1979. Partner 1986. Specialises in sale and purchase of companies, competition law and shareholder agreements and disputes.

Birt, Timothy D.

Osborne Clarke, London (0171) 600 0155. Qualified 1985. Partner 1988. Specialises in mergers and acquisitions, start-ups and venture and development capital. Born 23.7.1958.

Boardman, Nigel P.G.

Slaughter and May, London (0171) 600 1200. Qualified 1975. Joined 1973. Partner specialising in corporate finance, corporate and commercial work, including IPO's, MBO's, take-overs, private acquisitions and joint ventures. Also handles banking and capital markets matters.

Boddington, Christopher

Nabarro Nathanson, London (0171) 493 9933. Qualified 1966. Partner 1977. Company Department. Advises small and medium sized companies. Also has expertise of Eastern European work.

Bond, Peter R.M.

Taylor Joynson Garrett, London (0171) 353 1234.

Bott, Adrian J.A.

Olswang, London (0171) 208 8888. Partner and Head of Corporate Group.

Specialisation: Main areas of practice are corporate and finance. Since 1980, has been consistently involved in activities ranging from M&A, MBOs and MBIs, through flotations, rights issues, placings and other means of financing, to Venture Capital (acting for both providers and consumers), both in domestic and international transactions. Clients are predominantly quoted or subsidiaries of multinationals. Many have an electronics or media bias. Also active in banking work (covering a wide range of secured and unsecured lending transactions, involving all types of facilities and financial instruments), corporate joint ventures and a broad spectrum of commercial contracts and employee share schemes. Has handled numerous consortium arrangements, leading a variety of consortia in bids for various TV and radio broadcasting licences (ITV Channel 3 and Channel 5, and INRI (Classic FM)).

Prof. Membership: Law Society, British Venture Capital Association.

Career: Qualified in 1980. *Rooks Rider* 1978-87, from 1984 as a Partner. Partner at Olswang from 1988.

Personal: Born 9th June 1956. Charterhouse School 1969-73, Manchester University 1974-77 and Guildford Law School 1977.

Brackfield, Andrew C.

Linklaters & Paines, London (0171) 606 7080. Qualified 1980. Specialises in company law, including securities issues, privatisations, joint ventures, reorganisations, disposals and acquisitions.

Brownlow, Jeremy

See under Corporate Finance.

Brooks, Peter

Clifford Chance, London (0171) 600 1000. Partner. Company and commercial specialist with an emphasis on corporate finance, mergers and acquisitions.

Burgess, Patrick

Gouldens, London (0171) 583 7777. Partner and Head of Company Department.

Specialisation: Corporate finance and international specialist. Recent activities include advising on drafting of the new Stock Exchange Yellow Book, membership of the Stock Exchange Working Party on smaller companies and the Alternative Investment Market Panel of the London Stock Exchange, and tax and legislation advice to the Unquoted Companies Group. Speaker at numerous conferences and seminars.

Career: Qualified in 1972. Joined *Gouldens* in 1968 and became a Partner in 1974.

Personal: Born 31st October 1944. Recreations include sailing, shooting, rowing, reading and opera. Lives in London and Chichester.

Burrow, Robert P.

S J Berwin & Co, London (0171) 837 2222. Qualified 1975. Partner 1985. Corporate Finance Department. Specialises in international mergers and acquisitions and investment funds.

Byrne, John

Nabarro Nathanson, London (0171) 493 9933. Qualified 1985. Partner 1990. Company and Commercial Department. Specialises in contract negotiation, for both goods and services. Born 28.12.1958.

Campion-Smith, W. Nigel

Travers Smith Braithwaite, London (0171) 248 9133 or 696 0998. Partner in Corporate Department.

Specialisation: Main areas of practice are corporate finance (including public offerings, listings, mergers and acquisitions) and financial services, including formation of collective investment schemes and custodial and trustee arrangements.

Prof. Membership: Law Society.

Career: Qualified in 1978, having joined *Travers Smith Braithwaite* in 1976. Became a Partner in 1982.

Personal: Born 10th July 1954. Attended King George V School Southport 1965-69, Royal Grammar School, High Wycombe 1969-71 and St John's College, Cambridge 1972-75. Lives in Guildford.

Cann, J.W.Anthony

See under Corporate Finance.

Carrington, Nigel M.

Baker & McKenzie, London (0171) 919 1000. Managing Partner. Member of the Corporate Department.

Specialisation: Principal area of practice involves international corporate transactions including mergers, acquisitions, joint ventures and privatisations. Other main area of practice is commercial legal work including distribution, agency, direct selling and sports sponsorship agreements. Editor of 'Acquiring Companies and Businesses in Europe' (Wiley Chancery Law 1994).

Prof. Membership: Law Society, City of London Law Society.

Career: Joined *Baker & McKenzie* as an Articled Clerk in 1979, qualified in 1981. Assigned to Chicago Office (Foreign Trade Department) 1983-84 and became a Partner in 1987. Appointed Managing Partner of the firm's London office in 1994.

Personal: Born 1st May 1956. MA Jurisprudence, St John's College, Oxford.

Carter, Peter

Forsyte Saunders Kerman, London (0171) 637 8566. Qualified 1974. Partner 1978. Company and Commercial Department. Handles general commercial work and corporate finance. Born 11.5.1949.

Charnley, William F.

See under Corporate Finance.

Cheyne, David W.

See under Corporate Finance.

Clark, Adrian S.

Ashurst Morris Crisp, London (0171) 638 1111. Qualified 1983. Partner 1990. Company Department. Seconded to Takeover Panel 1988-1990.

Clark, Tim N.

Slaughter and May, London (0171) 600 1200. Qualified 1976. Partner 1983. Specialises in commercial, corporate and building society law, including finance, M&As and building society conversions.

Cooke, Stephen J.

Slaughter and May, London (0171) 600 1200. Qualified 1984. Partner 1991. Company/Commercial Department. Handles general company and commercial law and M&As. Born 7.3.1959.

Crystal, Peter M.
See under Sports Law.

Curran, Andrew R.
Lovell White Durrant, London (0171) 236 0066. Qualified 1971. Main areas of practice are corporate finance and tax. Born 1947.

Darlington, Gavin L.B.
Freshfields, London (0171) 936 4000. Qualified 1974. Partner 1980. Corporate Department. Main area of practice covers mergers and acquisitions, joint ventures and corporate finance matters. Born 27.6.49.

Davis, James P.L.
Freshfields, London (0171) 936 4000. Qualified 1970. Partner. Corporate Department. Specialises in mergers and acquisitions and other corporate and corporate finance transactions.

Daws, Andrew
Denton Hall, London (0171) 242 1212. Partner in Corporate Group, Company and Commercial Department.

Specialisation: Main areas of practice are corporate and M&A. Experience includes acquisition and sales of private and quoted companies, acquisition and sales of assets, joint ventures, privatisation and general corporate work, particularly in energy and media industries. Major clients include Associated Newspapers Holdings Ltd, Rentokil Plc, Bertlesmann, Bemrose Corporation Plc, Allied Leisure Plc, Total, CIPFA and The Southern Company Inc.

Career: Qualified in 1967. Assistant Solicitor at *Markbys* 1967-69; Solicitor (Tax and Trusts) Bank of London and South America Ltd 1969-71. Joined *Denton Hall* in 1971, becoming a Partner in 1975.

Personal: Born in 1943. Attended The King's School, Grantham, and Exeter University (1964 LLB Hons 2:1). Bracton Law Prize 1964. Leisure interests include golf, squash and family.

Dean, Kevin J.
Sinclair Roche & Temperley, London (0171) 638 9044. Qualified 1979. Partner 1985. Head of Company/Commercial Department. Specialises in international M&As and in transportation and leisure.

Di Biase, Paul
Forsyte Saunders Kerman, London (0171) 637 8566. Partner in Company and Commercial Department.

Specialisation: Principal areas of practice are mergers and acquisitions and corporate finance, including sales and acquisitions of companies and businesses, MBO's and MBI's, flotations and takeovers. Also deals with partnership matters (including establishing, monitoring, incorporating and dissolving professional partnerships), commercial agreements and banking. Important

matters handled include Hays MBO and flotation; Ryman MBI, flotation and agreed takeover; City Merchant Developers MBO, reverse into USM Shell and agreed takeover; Perrings Furnishing sale to MBO; Moyses Stevens MBI; British Car Auctions sale and Ripolin (Decor 8) MBO and trade sale. Individual charge-out rate is £270 per hour.

Prof. Membership: Law Society.

Career: Qualified in 1961. Partner with *Forsyte Saunders Kerman* since 1965. Chairman of the firm's Partnership Board.

Personal: Born 21st July 1934. Educated at Rutlish School, Merton 1947-53 and University College, Oxford 1954-57. Director of family service industry companies. Board Member and Lessee of the Richmond Golf Club. Leisure interests include golf, cinema, theatre, travel food and wine. Lives in Weston Green, Esher, Surrey.

Dillon, Martin L.G.
Taylor Joynson Garrett, London (0171) 353 1234.

Dove, Anthony C.
Simmons & Simmons, London (0171) 628 2020. Qualified 1969. Partner 1973. Corporate Department. Work includes advice on acquisitions and financing. Born 22.7.1945.

Elder, Ian F.
Allen & Overy, London (0171) 330 3000. Qualified 1984. Partner 1989. Corporate Department. Main area of practice is company/commercial. Also handles energy law.

Evans, Stuart J.
Simmons & Simmons, London (0171) 628 2020. Partner in Corporate Department.

Specialisation: Handles corporate and corporate finance transactions of all kinds, including IPO's, public and private takeovers and general company law. 1994/5 transactions include London Stock Exchange flotations of Graham Group plc, Partco Group plc and Templeton Latin America Investment Trust plc; the introduction to the LSE of Franklin Resources, Inc; Coutts Consulting Group plc's acquisition of Alternative International Ltd; and the recommended offer by Graham Group plc for Erith plc. Author of the chapter on Transactions in 'A Practitioner's Guide to the Stock Exchange Yellow Book': now in its Seventh Edition.

Prof. Membership: City of London Law Society Company Law Sub-Committee.

Career: Qualified in 1972. With *Slaughter and May* 1972-79. Joined *Simmons & Simmons in 1979, Partner since 1981.*

Personal: Born 31st December 1947. Educated at the Royal Grammar School, Newcastle-upon-Tyne 1956-66, Leeds University 1966-69. Leisure interests include pictures and squash.

Fagelson, Ian B.
Warner Cranston, London (0171) 403

2900. Partner in Company/Commercial Department.

Specialisation: Handles corporate and financial transactions, including corporate finance, mergers and acquisitions and banking. Wide experience of both public and private corporate and financial transactions, including complex international mergers and acquisitions, disposals, financings, restructurings, debt and equity issues (public and private) and joint ventures. Also deals with insurance and reinsurance, including the establishment of innovative structured reinsurance programmes. University lecturer 1977-79. Subsequently regular conference and seminar lecturer on corporate and banking topics.

Prof. Membership: Law Society, International Bar Association, American Bar Association.

Career: Qualified in 1980, having joined *Warner Cranston* in 1979. Became a Partner in 1981.

Personal: Born 22nd April 1952. Educated at the University of Southampton 1970-73 (LLB) and Oxford University 1973-75 (BCL). Enjoys theatre, reading and loafing. Lives in London.

Finbow, Roger J.
See under European Community & Competition.

Francies, Mike
Clifford Chance, London (0171) 600 1000. Partner. Principal area of practice is company/commercial. Also handles media and communications law.

Freshwater, Tim G.
See under Corporate Finance.

Godden, Richard W.
See under Corporate Finance.

Godfrey, David N.
Middleton Potts, London (0171) 600 2333. Head of Non-contentious Department.

Specialisations: Main areas of practice are corporate and commercial, banking and finance, insurance and reinsurance, and employment law. Has handled the acquisition by a major foreign insurance company of the controlling interest in a Lloyd's broker, a tender in the privatisation of the short term export credit business of ECGD, the merger of two Italian banks, the restructuring of debt in the liquidation of EFIM, and transactions in distressed debt and value impaired assets; has also supervised the handling of major Euro C.D. and Depository Receipt Programmes.

Prof. Membership: Law Society.

Career: Qualified in 1968. Assistant at *Herbert Oppenheimer, Nathan & Vandyk* 1958-1970. Assistant and then Partner of *Crawley and de Reya* 1970-1976. One of the Founding Partners of *Middleton Potts* in 1976.

Personal: Born 16th November 1943. Educated at Uppingham School 1957-62, then Bristol University 1962-65. Leisure interests include photography, antiques and travelling. Lives in London.

Godfrey, Keith G.
See under Corporate Finance.

Godfrey, Edwin
Simmons & Simmons, London (0171) 628 2020. International Managing Partner and head of Commercial Group.

Specialisation: Currently responsible for the firm's overseas business, including eight overseas offices. Main area of practice is commercial/corporate. Work includes acquisitions, disposals, joint ventures, supply contracts, I.P. licensing and commercial agreements in general. Has particular experience in industries including pharmaceuticals, waste management, motors and electrical equipment and in acting for foreign multi-nationals. Editor of 'Joint Ventures' in Butterworths Encyclopaedia of Forms and Precedents and of 'Law Without Frontiers' (Kluwer/IBA 1995). Has organised and chaired sessions on the international legal profession at numerous IBA conferences throughout the world; has presented several other lectures on commercial law topics. Broadcast on 'Retention of Title' on Legal Network Television.

Prof. Membership: International Bar Association, (member of Council, Section on Business Law, member of standing committee on professional ethics); Law Society; City of London Law Society (vice-chairman, commercial law sub-committee); British-Italian Law Association; British-Russian Law Association; South-Western Legal Foundation (Dallas, Texas) (member of advisory board, International and Comparative Law Center).

Career: Qualified in 1971. Articled Clerk and Assistant Solicitor at *Norton Rose Botterell & Roche* 1968-72. Joined *Simmons & Simmons* in 1972, becoming a Partner in 1977. Appointed International Managing Partner 1995.

Personal: Born 20th October 1947. Attended Repton School (Scholar) 1961-65 and Queens' College, Cambridge (Scholar, MA Cantab) 1965-68. Freeman of the City of London. Fellow of the Royal Society of Arts; Governor of Abel Smith JMI School, Hertford; Member of Hertford Deanery Synod. Fluent in German, French, Dutch and Italian. Lives in Hertford.

Goodwin, Philip
Denton Hall, London (0171) 242 1212. Partner in Corporate Group, Company and Commercial Department.

Specialisation: Main areas of practice are corporate finance and M&A take-overs. Experience includes mergers and acquisitions, corporate finance, joint ventures, banking, financial and securities markets (regulation and transactional), commercial agreements

and public company flotations. Has special interest and experience in transactions for Japanese clients.

Prof. Membership: Member Japan Association.

Career: Worked at *Fairbridge Ardene & Lawton,* Cape Town, 1975-77; admitted in 1977 as Attorney/Conveyancer, South Africa (Cape Provincial Division); worked at *Coward Chance* 1979-85: admitted as a solicitor in England and Wales in 1981. Joined *Denton Hall* in 1985, becoming a Partner in 1987.

Personal: Born in 1950. Attended Wynberg Boys' School, Cape Town, South Africa; University of Cape Town, South Africa (1974 BA LLB cum laude); and Trinity Hall, Cambridge, 1978. Leisure interests include sport, music and theatre.

Graham, Peter L.
Norton Rose, London (0171) 283 6000. Qualified 1971. Partner 1977. Company and Financial Department. Work includes M&As, reconstructions, joint ventures and financial services.

Grayston, Clare
Lewis Silkin, London (0171) 227 8004. Qualified 1985. Partner 1987. Corporate Department. Specialises in mergers and acquisitions and general corporate finance work. Born 18.12.1960.

Greaves, Adam
Gouldens, London (0171) 583 7777. Partner in Company/Commercial Department.

Specialisation: Very diversified practice covers venture capital, management buy-outs and buy-ins, joint ventures, mergers and acquisitions (private and public), flotations, corporate finance, corporate reconstructions, banking and project finance and commercial agreements and ventures. Major clients include the Domnick Hunter Group Plc, Persona Group Plc, Quiligotti Plc, Nash Sells & Partners Ltd, BancBoston Capital and Maritime Transport Services Ltd.

Career: Qualified in 1982. Joined *Nabarro Nathanson* in 1980, joining and becoming a Partner of *Gouldens* in 1986.

Personal: Born 9th July 1958. Attended Bradfield College 1972-76, Selwyn College, Cambridge 1976-79 and Guildford College of Law 1979-80. Leisure interests include fly fishing (member of the Red Sea Casters), bridge, hockey, walking and cooking. Lives in London.

Henderson CBE, Giles I.
Slaughter and May, London (0171) 600 1200. Qualified 1970. Partner 1975. Senior Partner 1993. Company/Commercial Department. Specialises in privatisations, acting both for HM Government and for companies being privatised.

Hill, Jeremy G.
Ashurst Morris Crisp, London (0171) 638 1111. Partner in Company/Commercial

Department.

Specialisation: Head of Insurance. Lloyd's of London and London Market: handles all non-contentious matters, particularly policy wordings; acquisition, disposal, flotation of agencies, brokers and insurance and reinsurance companies; regulatory issues; captive insurance vehicles; insurance reconstructions and insolvencies; and creation and registration of Lloyd's Corporate Members. Acted in the flotation of Delian Lloyd's Investment Trust PLC, HCG Lloyd's Investment Trust PLC and Archer Dedicated PLC and the establishment of London Processing Centre. Author of 'Willis Corroon Guide to Directors' and Officers' Liability', and of articles in many publications on Lloyd's and the London Insurance market. Author of commercial contracts book to be published by FT Law & Tax in 1995.

Prof. Membership: Chartered Insurance Institute, Law Society.

Career: Qualified in 1984. Joined *Ashurst Morris Crisp* in 1982, spending a year seconded to Lloyd's of London in 1985, and becoming a Partner in 1992.

Personal: Born 4th November 1958. Attended Bootham School, York 1972-77 and Pembroke College, Oxford 1977-80. Leisure interests include sailing, fishing and antiques. Lives in London.

Holland, Peter R.J.
See under Corporate Finance.

Howes, Colin M.
Harbottle & Lewis, London (0171) 629 7633. Qualified 1981. Partner 1984. Company/Commercial Department. Acts mainly for clients in the aviation, media/entertainment and leisure industries.

James, Glen W.
Slaughter and May, London (0171) 600 1200. Qualified 1976. Partner. Specialises in general company and commercial law, including corporate finance, flotations, M&As, reconstructions and MBO's.

Johns, Michael S.M.
Nicholson Graham & Jones, London (0171) 628 9151. Managing Partner and Joint Head of Company and Commercial Department.

Specialisation: Main area of practice is corporate finance. Work includes acquisitions, mergers, venture capital, buy-outs, equity issues, yellow book work and general corporate work for public listed companies. Head of sports group; acts for organisations and individuals in the sports field including sponsors and sports organisers. Has spoken at seminars both in the UK and USA on subjects such as buy-outs, international strategic activities, law firm management and sports sponsorship.

Prof. Membership: Institute of Directors, Law Society.

Career: Qualified in 1968. Joined *Nicholson*

Graham & Jones in 1972, becoming a Partner in 1973, Joint Head of Company/Commercial Department in 1982 and Managing Partner in 1987. Chairman of Merchant Retail Group Plc and a Director since 1979.

Personal: Born 18th October 1943. Attended Marlborough College 1957-62. Leisure interests include cricket, golf, gardening and theatre. Lives in London.

Jones, Robert J.
Berwin Leighton, London (0171) 623 3144. Partner in Corporate Department.

Specialisation: Corporate finance specialist with an emphasis on rescues. Since 1989 has been responsible for the corporate rescues of Eagle Trust, LEP, Brown & Jackson and Davies & Newman (Dan-Air). Also handles venture capital and MBOs.

Prof. Membership: Law Society.

Career: Qualified in 1974. Joined *Berwin Leighton* in 1975 and became a Partner in 1981.

Personal: Born 22nd April 1949. Educated at King's College School, Wimbledon 1963-67 and Emmanuel College, Cambridge 1968-71. Leisure interests include golf. Lives in Oxshott, Surrey.

Keat, Alan M.
Travers Smith Braithwaite, London (0171) 248 9133 or 696 0998. Qualified 1966. Partner 1970. Company Department. Company law specialist. Born 12.5.1942.

King, Peter D.S.
Linklaters & Paines, London (0171) 606 7080. Qualified 1981. Partner 1990. Specialises in corporate finance, advising companies and investment banks on all types of corporate transaction.

King, Henry E.St.L.
Denton Hall, London (0171) 242 1212. Corporate Group, Company and Commercial Department.

Specialisation: Main areas of practice are international trade, media and publishing, and international tax. Specialises in international business transactions including mergers and acquisitions, joint ventures and taxation with an international emphasis.

Prof. Membership: Non-executive Director and Chairman of Rentokil Group plc. Director of City Centre Restaurants plc and Brambles Investments plc.

Career: Articled and qualified with *Denton Hall Burgin* 1964 (Henry Strouts Prize). Became a Partner in 1967.

Personal: Born in 1936. Attended Whitgift Middle School and Fitzwilliam College, Cambridge (MA, LLB). Leisure interests include travel, theatre and music.

Knapp, Vanessa
Freshfields, London (0171) 936 4000. Qualified 1981. Partner 1988. Corporate Department. Main area of practice is

company/commercial. Also handles financial services work. Born 3.11.1956.

Knight, William John Langford
See under Corporate Finance.

Kossoff, Daniel
Clifford Chance, London (0171) 600 1000. Partner. Specialises in company and commercial work, including corporate finance, mergers and acquisitions and corporate restructuring.

Kyle, J. Terence
See under Capital Markets & Securitisation.

Leifer, N. Anthony
D J Freeman, London (0171) 583 4055. Partner in Company Commercial Department.

Specialisation: Handles a broad range of corporate law with particular reference to the property and media fields. Also media law, including non-contentious contract and commercial advice, particularly in television related industries. Acted in the Argent Group Plc flotation, Isosceles (Gateway) refinancing, Spitalfields Development Group joint venture, the Barlow Clowes insolvency, Chancery administration and numerous film and television financings for Channel 4. Coauthor of 'Profits of Crime and their Recovery' - the Report of the Committee chaired by Sir Derrick Hodgson.

Prof. Membership: Law Society. Copinger Society.

Career: Qualified in 1972, having joined *D J Freeman* in 1970. Became a Partner in 1975.

Personal: Born 17th September 1945. LLB (London) 1968 and LLM (University of California) 1969. Enjoys tennis and cookery. Lives in London.

Levy, Graeme
Olswang, London (0171) 208 8888. Qualified 1985.

Lewis, David T.R.
Norton Rose, London (0171) 283 6000. Qualified 1972. Partner 1977. Corporate and Financial Department. Main areas of practice include company/commercial, listings and take-overs.

Longdon, John C.
Travers Smith Braithwaite, London (0171) 248 9133 or 696 0998.

Macaulay, Anthony D.
See under Corporate Finance.

Mace, Dan
See under Corporate Finance.

Macpherson, M.A.F.
Ashurst Morris Crisp, London (0171) 638 1111.

Mair, Antony S.R.
Stephenson Harwood, London (0171) 329 4422. Partner in Corporate Department.

Specialisation: Main areas of practice are EC and competition law, particularly regulations affecting insurers and the art trade, as well as general commercial law, including joint ventures, mergers and acquisitions. Author of 'The Bus Industry & UK Competition Policy' in 'Transport Law and Policy', Nov. 1993. In 1994 addressed a UK conference on reinsurance litigation and gave talks at British Law Week in Milan entitled 'Le iniziative della Comunità Europea nel settore dell'arte', and at the IBA Conference in Melbourne on Agency, Distribution, Licensing and Franchising Agreements.

Prof. Membership: IBA, Law Society Solicitors European Group.

Career: Qualified in 1976. With *Holman Fenwick & Willan* 1976-88. Became a Partner there in 1979. Joined *Stephenson Harwood* as a Partner in December 1988.

Personal: Born 1946. Educated at Reading School 1957-64 and Magdalen College, Oxford 1964-67. Leisure interests include The Arts and writing novels.

Marston, Edward
Barnett Alexander Chart, London (0171) 434 4011. Qualified 1976. Partner in Company/Commercial Department.

Specialisation: Responsible for corporate finance and health service units. Regular speaker and writer on the PFI (with particular reference to NHS projects), out-sourcing and risk money transactions from early stage to flotation. Member of Law Society and Fellow of Institute of Directors.

Miller, Nigel
Fox Williams, London (0171) 628 2000. Partner in Commercial Department.

Specialisation: Main area of practice is commercial and intellectual property, including commercial and trade agreements, intellectual property licensing, joint ventures, product liability, consumer law and contracts, computer law and contracts and competition law. Has particular expertise in relation to information technology matters and interactive media and multimedia law. Also advises local authorities on compulsory and voluntary competitive tendering and the EC public procurement regime. Author of 'Compulsory Competitive Tendering and the Local Government Act 1988', and numerous articles on commercial law matters in business and trade journals. Regular speaker on legal issues on the Accelerated Growth Programme and at local government seminars on compulsory competitive tendering. Speaker at a CBI conference on product liability. Broadcast on "Product Safety" on Legal Network Television (November 1994).

Prof. Membership: Law Society, Society for Computers and the Law, The British Interactive Multimedia Association and Clarity.

Career: Qualified in 1983, having joined *Herbert Oppenheimer, Nathan Vandyk* in 1981. Became an Associate Partner at *Oppenheimers* in 1987. On dissolution of the firm joined *Denton Hall Burgin & Warren* and elected to the partnership there in February 1989. Founded *Fox Williams* in March 1989.

Personal: Born 28th May 1959. Educated at Rugby School 1972-76, the Hebrew University of Jerusalem 1976-77, and Manchester University 1977-80. Leisure interests include tennis (Chandos LTC), photography and computers. Lives in London.

Moore, Margaret A.

Travers Smith Braithwaite, London (0171) 248 9133 or 696 0998. Partner in Corporate Department.

Specialisation: Work includes strategic alliances and joint ventures, partnerships, commercial agreements, company and business disposals and acquisitions, intellectual property, EC law and competition.

Prof. Membership: Competition Law Association, Solicitors European Group, French Chamber of Commerce, City of London Solicitors Company.

Career: Studied at Durham University (BA Hons) 1980. Qualified in 1984. Joined *Travers Smith Braithwaite* in 1986, becoming a Partner in 1990.

Morgan, Simon

Frere Cholmeley Bischoff, London (0171) 615 8000. Partner in Company and Commercial Department.

Specialisation: General corporate advice to businesses and professional advisers including advising business start-ups, joint ventures, equity issues, acquisitions, disposals and take-overs. Also handles media and entertainment work, particularly in the cable, satellite TV and radio sectors. Recent transactions have included advising Pacific Telesis Group on the disposal of 8 UK cable franchises in three separate sales; advising Cox Cable Communications on its acquisitions of interests in UK Gold, UK Living and SBC CableComms; advising Interactive Network Limited, an interactive television operator, in connection with a number of equity issues and working on the financial restructuring of Allied Radio PLC. Author of various articles concerning cable and satellite television.

Prof. Membership: Law Society

Career: Qualified in 1987. Joined *Frere Cholmeley Bischoff* in 1985, becoming a Partner in 1994.

Personal: Born 25th June 1963. Attended Oakwood Comprehensive School 1974-79, Thomas Rotherham College 1979-81 and Pembroke College, Cambridge 1981-84. Leisure interests include tennis, reading, theatre, television, cinema and concerts. Lives in London.

Morgan, Charles P.

Allen & Overy, London (0171) 330 3000. Qualified 1978. Partner 1985. Corporate and commercial work includes building societies, consumer credit, collective investment schemes, leasing and securitisations.

Mountford, Margaret

See under Corporate Finance.

O'Brien, B.J.

See under Corporate Finance.

Osborne, John

Clifford Chance, London (0171) 600 1000. Partner. Main area of practice is company and commercial work.

Ouin, Charles N.

Lawrence Graham, London (0171) 379 0000.

Specialisation: Partner in the Company and Commercial department specialising in commercial contracts and general corporate work. Practice covers sales of businesses and companies, MBOs, venture capital, corporate restructuring, joint ventures and tenders. Also deals with public sector contracts and externalisations. Advised the Government on the establishment of the National Lottery.

Career: Qualified 1973. Assistant solicitor, Holloway Blount & Duke 1973-76. Partner, Blyth Dutton 1976-92. Partner, Lawrence Graham since 1992. Non-executive director of William Sinclair Holdings Plc.

Personal: Educated at Sherborne School and the College of Law. Leisure pursuits include sailing, fishing, architecture and theatre.

Overbury, Colin

See under European Community & Competition.

Paul, Alan D.

See under Corporate Finance.

Pescod, Michael

See under Corporate Finance.

Preston, Robin M.

Theodore Goddard, London (0171) 606 8855. Qualified 1969. Partner 1976. Specialises in intellectual property, information technology and general commercial work. Born 30.9.1943.

Price, Richard

McKenna & Co, London (0171) 606 9000.

Rawlinson, Mark S.

See under Corporate Finance.

Richards, Andrew Philip

See under Corporate Finance.

Rosefield, Stephen M.

Paisner & Co, London (0171) 353 0299. Qualified 1977. Partner 1980. Company Commercial Department. Main area of practice is corporate finance. Born 19.12.1952.

Salz, Anthony M.V.

See under Corporate Finance.

Sidkin, Stephen L.

Fox Williams, London (0171) 628 2000. Partner in Commercial Section, Company and Commercial Department.

Specialisation: Specialises in trading agreements, particularly agency, distributorship, R&D, manufacturing, marketing and joint venture agreements, especially for health-care companies. Other area of practice is competition law. Frequently deals with OFT and European Commission. Cases include extensive retail pharmacy franchise agreements for leading chain; series of cross-border loyalty marketing programmes; Competition Act investigation by Monopolies & Mergers Commission into Unichem Limited (1988-89); Fair Trading Act investigation by Monopolies and Mergers Commission into Fine Fragrances (1992-93). Also handled world-wide critical illness pharmaceutical licensing arrangements and international pharmaceutical and marketing licence. Author of 'Product Tampering in the United Kingdom' (1993) and of numerous articles, material and book reviews which have appeared in national and specialist press. Member of supervisory board of European law firm network; Member and Secretary of City of London Law Society Commercial Law Sub-Committee 1987-92; Deputy Chairman since 1992. Gave extensive lectures on the Commercial Agents Regulations 1993-94. Broadcast on "Product Safety" (November 1994) and "The Commercial Agents Regulations" (March 1995) on Legal Network Television.

Prof. Membership: Law Society, Solicitors European Group, Competition Law Association, International Business Law and EEC Law standing commissions of the Association Internationale des Jeunes Avocats.

Career: Qualified in 1981. Articled at *Fitzhugh Eggar & Port*, Brighton, 1979-81. Assistant Solicitor at *Norton Rose* 1981-84 and *Oppenheimers* 1984-88 (Associate Partner 1988). Partner Elect at *Denton Hall* 1988-89; founded *Fox Williams* 1989.

Personal: Born 1956. Attended King's College, University of London (Laws Hons) and, Guildhall University London (MA Business Law). Admitted freedom of the Worshipful Company of Solicitors of the City of London 1987. Leisure interests include travel, international affairs, chess and snooker. Lives London.

Sivyer, Jeremy

Simmons & Simmons, London (0171) 628 2020. Partner in Commercial and Trade Law Department.

Specialisation: Principal area of practice is company and commercial work, with particular emphasis on trading relations. Work includes commercial agreements, joint ventures, trade finance, Islamic banking, private company work, comparative law, dispute resolution, motor car law, international countertrade and offset.

Prof. Membership: Law Society, West Africa Committee, International Bar Association.

Career: Qualified 1979 while with *Simmons & Simmons* and became a Partner in 1984.

Personal: Born 13th May 1955. Attended Royal Liberty School 1966-73, then Sheffield University, 1973-76. Leisure pursuits include cricket and gardening.. Lives in Saffron Walden.

Smith, Graham
Clifford Chance, London (0171) 600 1000. Partner. Main area of practice is commercial work, with specialisation in competition and computer law.

South, John C.B.
Charles Russell, London (0171) 203 5123. Senior Partner.

Specialisation: Main areas of practice are corporate finance, joint ventures and mergers. Has particular experience in property related company and commercial transactions. Led borrower's legal team in attempted refinancing of 300m of Speyhawk PLC loans with 47 banks; acted for BIS Group (jointly) in US $100m sale to Nynex Corporation; and acted for Speyhawk PLC throughout its life.

Prof. Membership: Law Society.

Career: Qualified in 1961. Partner in predecessor firms since 1970; these merged to become *Charles Russell* in 1987.

Personal: Born in 1937. Attended Blundell's School 1951-55. Chairman of Peter Minet Charitable Trust. Treasurer of the French Hospital. Leisure interests include golf, walking, theatre and sport. Lives in London W2.

Spiller, Richard J.
See under Insurance & Reinsurance.

Steinfeld, Michael
Titmuss Sainer Dechert, London (0171) 583 5353. Partner in Corporate Department.

Specialisation: Corporate finance, mergers and acquisitions, and general company and commercial work.

Career: Qualified in 1970, having joined *Titmuss Sainer & Webb* (now *Titmuss Sainer Dechert*) in 1968. Became a Partner in 1972.

Personal: Born in 1943. Educated at Pembroke College, Oxford. Interests include skiing, football, good food and France. Lives in London.

Stella, Keith G.
Paisner & Co, London (0171) 353 0299. Qualified 1978. Partner 1980. Company Department. Specialises in corporate finance, including mergers and acquisitions. Born 3.12.1954.

Stone, Peter F.
Berwin Leighton, London (0171) 623 3144. Partner in Corporate Department.

Specialisation: Principal area of practice is general commercial work including IT, IP, media and distribution. Also handles UK and EC competition and merger control. Conference speaker on EC merger control and film distribution. Co-author of Practical Commercial Precedents -Entertainment Section (Longmans); and EC Merger Control (Japanese Institute of International Business Law).

Prof. Membership: London Solicitors' Company (Member Commercial Law Sub-Committee), American Film Marketing Association (Arbitration Panel Member).

Career: Qualified 1968 while with *Wright Webb Syrett*. Director of European Business Affairs Metro-Goldwyn-Mayer 1970-74, then returned to *Wright Webb Syrett* as a Partner. Joined *Berwin Leighton* as a Partner in 1983.

Personal: Born 3rd October 1943. Educated at Kingston Grammar School and Nottingham University (LLB 1965). Lives in London.

Storar, Michael J.
Lawrence Graham, London (0171) 379 0000. Partner in Company/ Commercial Department.

Specialisation: Main area of practice is corporate finance, covering mergers and acquisitions, flotations, listings and venture capital. Also handles advertising and marketing. Advised the Government and the Director General of the National Lottery on its structure and start up.

Career: Qualified in 1981. Worked at *Ashurst Morris Crisp* 1978-83. Joined *Blyth Dutton* in 1983, which merged to become *Lawrence Graham*.

Personal: Born 25th October 1955. Attended Cranleigh School 1963-73, Camberwell 1973-4 and Birmingham 1974-7. Lives in Suffolk.

Sullivan, Michael
Linklaters & Paines, London (0171) 606 7080.

Sutton, Robert H.
See under Advertising & Marketing.

Sweet, Jon P.L
Marriott Harrison, London (0171) 209 2000. Partner in Corporate Department.

Specialisation: Main area of practice is corporate and commercial, principally venture capital, mergers and acquisitions and general corporate finance. Handles a mix of private and public company work, but primarily private company. Has a broad range of experience in company/ business sales and purchases, complex company and group restructurings, financings (debt and equity) and joint ventures as well as more general commercial advice such as agency and distribution. Past experience has included the full range of stock exchange and take over code work. Also handles banking and insolvency.

Prof. Membership: Law Society, Associate Member of BVCA.

Career: Qualified in 1982. Worked at *Slaughter and May* 1980-90 (including 1986-88 in the Hong Kong office). Partner at *Iliffes* 1990-93, and at *Marriott Harrison* since 1993.

Personal: Born 7th March 1956. Attended Trinity College Glenalmond 1969-74, Brunel University 1975-79 and Guildford Law College 1979-80. Leisure interests include target rifle shooting, motor sport and classic cars. Lives in London.

Thomas, Richard L.
Sinclair Roche & Temperley, London (0171) 638 9044. Qualified 1981. Partner 1989. Company/Commercial Department. Main areas of practice are acquisitions and joint ventures, with 14 years experience in the UK and Netherlands. General Editor of 'Company Law in Europe (Butterworths)'. Born 16.6.1957.

Tite, Christopher
Stephenson Harwood, London (0171) 329 4422.

Specialisation: Partner in Corporate Department specialising in Transport law including port privatisation and development; ownership and operation of railway infrastructure and networks; road haulage; offshore supply industry; airport ownership and container line operation. Other specialisation is infrastructural projects, structuring commercial transactions (including privatisations) acting for both public and private sector clients in urban regeneration schemes, infrastructure investment and project finance. Author of 'Privatisation of Ports and Port Services: Managing Change Within the Legal Framework'. Member of Editorial Advisory Board, 'International Company and Commercial Law Review', Legal Contributor 'Port Development International' and speaker at World Port Privatisation Conference, September 1994.

Career: Qualified in 1985 and with Holman, Fenwick & Willan 1985-89. Joined Stephenson Harwood in 1989 and became a Partner in 1990.

Personal: Born 1959. Advisory Council Member, Camden Training Centre.

Turnbull, Peter
Macfarlanes, London (0171) 831 9222. Qualified 1968. Partner 1974. Head of Company, Commercial and Banking Department. Specialises in equity financing, development capital and MBOs.

Underhill, C. William Y.
See under Corporate Finance.

Walker-Arnott, Edward I.
Herbert Smith, London (0171) 374 8000. Senior Partner in Corporate Department.

Specialisation: Has extensive experience as a company lawyer and as a commercial lawyer involved in insolvency, banking, insurance, securities, employment, tax, venture capital, management buy-outs, intellectual property rights, media and broadcasting, accountancy, sport, monopolies, competition, EC law and takeovers and mergers. He led the firm's privatisation teams for Britoil, British Gas and British Coal and participated in the team on electricity. He sat on the Cork Enquiry into insolvency law between 1977 and 1982, the report of which resulted in the enactment of the Insolvency Act 1986. He was one of the first nominated members of the Council of Lloyds (sitting on the Council from 1983 to 1989) and chaired the Investigations Committee at Lloyds in the late 1970's and early 1980's.

Career: Qualified in 1963 and became a Partner at *Herbert Smith* in 1968. Currently Senior Partner.

Personal: Educated at London University (LL.M).

Wander, Charles
Davies Arnold Cooper, London (0171) 936 2222. Qualified 1979. Partner and Head of Corporate Department. Specialises in general commercial law, corporate finance and banking.

Wayte, P.B.
Alsop Wilkinson, London (0171) 248 4141.

Webster, Martin
Biddle & Co, London (0171) 606 9301. Partner in Company Commercial Department.

Specialisation: Main area of practice are corporate finance and share option schemes. Acted in the establishment of Parliamentary Broadcasting United Ltd, the vehicle for the dissemination of Parliamentary broadcasting.

Prof. Membership: Institute of Taxation, Law Society.

Career: Qualified in 1983. Joined *Biddle & Co* in 1981, becoming a Partner in 1987.

Personal: Born 1st July 1958. Attended Christ's College, Cambridge, 1976-79. Leisure interests include music, theatre and golf. Lives in London W9.

Winter, Martin A.S.
Biddle & Co, London (0171) 606 9301. Head of Company Commercial Department.

Specialisation: Main areas of practice are venture capital, joint ventures, acquisitions and disposals.

Prof. Membership: British Venture Capital Association (by firm).

Career: Qualified in 1978. Assistant Solicitor at *Norton Rose*, 1979-84. Joined *Biddle & Co* in 1984. Partner in 1985.

Personal: Born 13th April 1954. Graduated in English from St Edmund Hall, Oxford, 1975. Nationally ranked waterskier.

Acock, Roger
Bond Pearce, Plymouth (01752) 266633.

Alexander-Sinclair, Ian
Mills & Reeve, Norwich +44 (0) 1603 660155. Partner in Company Department.

Specialisation: Main area of practice is company law, covering mergers and acquisitions and corporate finance. Other area is commercial, including joint ventures and distribution and agency agreements.

Allan, Peter R.
Ward Hadaway, Newcastle upon Tyne (0191) 261 2651. Partner in Commercial Department.

Specialisation: Main areas of practice are mergers and acquisitions and corporate work, including sales and purchases of companies, acquisitions abroad and Yellow and Blue Book work. Has acted in reverse takeover transactions. Major clients include Crabtree Group PLC. Contributor to newspapers and periodicals circulating in the North East. Addresses seminars. Charge-out rate is £130 per hour.

Prof. Membership: Law Society.

Career: Qualified in 1960. Lecturer at Gibson & Wheldon 1960-61. Senior lecturer at Durham University 1961-62. Part-time lecturer at Durham University 1962-65. Examiner in law. Joined *Ward Hadaway* in 1962, becoming a Partner in 1964 and Senior Partner 1990.

Personal: Born 5th July 1936. Attended Queen Elizabeth Grammar School, Hexham 1947-54, then St Catharine's College, Cambridge 1954-57 (MA, 1st Class Honours in Law). Council Member of Northern Region CBI. Trustee of Beamish Museum. Board Member of Prince's Youth Business Trust.

Allan, David M.
Stronachs, Aberdeen (01224) 643573.

Barr, R. Alan
See under Corporate Finance.

Barrie, Sidney
Paull & Williamsons, Aberdeen (01224) 621621. Qualified 1973. Partner in the Corporate Department specialising in MBOs and aquisitions and disposals. Born 14.6.1950.

Bellew, Derek J.
Veale Wasbrough, Bristol (0117) 925 2020. Qualified 1967. Managing Partner. Company Commercial Department. Work includes sale and purchase, MBOs and progressive partnerships.

Bellis, Nigel D.
Dickinson Dees, Newcastle upon Tyne (0191) 261 1911. Qualified 1977. Partner 1982. Company and Commercial Depart-

ment. Handles flotations, mergers and acquisitions and IT contracts. Born 11.5.1953.

Beswick, Simon A.
See under Corporate Finance.

Buchan, Gordon A.
Paull & Williamsons, Aberdeen (01224) 621621.

Campbell, Christopher R.J.
Dundas & Wilson CS, Glasgow Glasgow (0141) 221 8586. Qualified 1982. Partner 1987. Corporate Department. Main areas of practice are mergers and acquisitions, corporate recovery and insolvency. Born 1.12.1958.

Campbell, Nigel
Veale Wasbrough, Bristol (0117) 925 2020.

Chatfield, James H.T.
Rawlison & Butler, Crawley (01293) 527744. Partner and Head of Corporate Department.

Specialisation: 16 years experience of UK and international corporate and commercial work. This has included cross-border work, investment in the UK and Europe, joint ventures, commercial agreements and financing. He has advised UK and non-UK companies on mergers and acquisitions and on setting up in Europe. Has acted for Plcs making strategic acquisitions in the UK, Europe and worldwide, and in reorganisations of companies. Has carried out speaking engagements for the CBI, DTI, Union Internationale des Avocats and at the firm's seminars. Has travelled extensively on business in North America, Europe, Africa and the Middle East.

Prof. Membership: Law Society (Member of Solicitors European Group), Union Internationale des Avocats (Member of Commission on the Future of the Lawyer).

Career: Worked for *Linklaters & Paines* 1974-1984, with a year at Swiss Bank Corporation International in London (1980-81). Qualified in 1977. Joined *Rawlison & Butler* as a Partner and Head of Corporate Department in 1984. Currently Chairman of the firm's Management Committee.

Personal: Born in 1952. Educated at Ardingly College, Sussex 1965-70 and Trinity College Oxford 1970-73 (M.A. in History). Leisure interests include cricket, theatre, literature, history and gardening. Member of the MCC.

Chrystie, Kenneth G.
McClure Naismith Anderson & Gardiner, Glasgow (0141) 204 2700. Senior Partner in Corporate Department.

Specialisation: Handles general corporate and commercial work, particularly commercial contracts, licensing agreements, commercial arbitrators and intellectual property. Handles clients in the whisky, engineering, banking, textiles and building industries as well as in the public sector. Author of the section on Commercial Credits in the 'Encyclopaedia of Scots Law', as well as the Scottish section in the 'International Handbook on Contracts of Employment'. Former part-time lecturer on commercial law and speaker at various law and accountancy conferences.

Prof. Membership: Law Society of Scotland, Insolvency Lawyers Association, International Bar Association, Intellectual Property Lawyers Association.

Career: Qualified in 1968. Joined *McClure Naismith Anderson & Gardiner* in 1969 and became a Partner in 1973. Awarded doctorate in Commercial Law in 1973. Member of the DTI Steyn Committee on Arbitration Law Reform.

Personal: Born 24th November 1946. Educated at Glasgow University 1964-68 and the University of Virginia (1971). Chairman of the Hugh Fraser Foundation. Leisure pursuits include golf, skiing and tennis. Lives in Glasgow.

Cockcroft, Nicholas C.P.

See under Corporate Finance.

Cook, Stephen

See under Corporate Finance.

Cooke, Darryl J.

See under Corporate Finance.

Coombs, Richard

Anstey Sargent & Probert, Exeter (01392) 411221. Qualified 1979. Partner 1994. Commercial Department. Specialises in all aspects of corporate and corporate finance law. Born 16.3.1954.

Cooper, Paul

Bevan Ashford, Bristol (0117) 923 0111. Partner and Head of Company and Commercial Department in Bristol.

Specialisation: Main area of practice covers corporate finance and company and business disposals and acquisitions. Responsible for numerous transactions involving clients receiving venture capital, as well as acting for venture capitalists, such as Charterhouse, Kleinwort Benson, Natwest Ventures and Singer & Friedlander, when they have made investments. Also deals with Stock Exchange and Company Offer documents, handling all Yellow Book work for listed clients. Experienced in requirements for prospectuses, circulars and listing particulars. Acted for the institutional investors in Radiodetection Limited (1993), acquisition of Smiles Brewery Company (1992) and subsequent BES prospectus for Smiles Traditional Inns PLC and Smiles Traditional Inns II PLC, as well as the flotation of MITIE Group PLC and numerous class 1 transactions for MITIE.

Prof. Membership: Law Society.

Career: Qualified in 1977, having joined *Boodle Hatfield* in 1975. Moved to *Norton*

Rose Botterel & Roche in 1978. Left to join *Bevan Ashford* in 1980, becoming a Partner in 1981.

Personal: Born 6th February 1953. Attended Oxford School 1964-70, then Selwyn College, Cambridge 1971-74. Director of Westward Commercial Vehicles Ltd and Witwood Food Products Ltd.

Coutts, Maureen S.

See under Corporate Finance.

Cowen, Maurice C.

Booth & Co., Leeds (0113) 283 2000. Partner in Corporate Department.

Specialisation: Main areas of practice are corporate and corporate finance.

Prof. Membership: Law Society.

Career: Qualified in 1970. Worked at *Slaughter and May* 1968-73. Joined *Booth & Co.* in 1973, becoming a Partner in 1975.

Personal: Born 29th January 1946. Attended Sheffield University 1964-67 (LLB). Board Member of Leeds Financial Services Initiative. Leisure interests include opera, music, literature and walking. Lives in Ilkley.

Crabtree, John

See under Corporate Finance.

Craig, I. Alexander

See under Corporate Finance.

Crawley, Fiona

Hewitson Becke + Shaw, Cambridge (01223) 461155. Qualified 1980. Partner 1985 Company and Commercial Department. Specialises in commercial agreements and intellectual property.

Croome, Andrew

See under Banking.

Cunningham, Neil

MacRoberts, Glasgow (0141) 332 9988.

Curling, Chris J.

Osborne Clarke, Bristol (0117) 923 0220. Qualified 1976. Partner 1980. Company/Commercial Department. Main area of practice is corporate, covering acquisitions, disposals, new issue work and shareholder/boardroom/partnership break-ups. Born 21.4.1950.

Darwin, Andrew

See under Corporate Finance.

Davison, Andrew J.

Wilkinson Maughan, Newcastle-upon-Tyne (0191) 261 1841. Partner in Company Commercial Department.

Specialisation: General Company Law and commercial law with particular reference to public company, corporate finance, and mergers and acquisitions work.

Prof. Membership: Law Society, Newcastle upon Tyne Incorporated Law Society, Food

Law Group.

Career: Qualified in 1985. Joined *Wilkinson Maughan* in 1983, becoming a Partner in 1986. Member of Law Society's Standing Committee on Company Law since 1991. Secretary of Northumbrian Fine Foods since 1987. Secretary of the Copenhagen Club of International Lawyers since 1991.

Dawson, Ian D.

Cleaver Fulton & Rankin, Belfast (01232) 243141.

Dickson, Ian

MacRoberts, Glasgow (0141) 332 9988. Partner in Corporate Department.

Specialisation: Main area of practice is corporate law, including acquisitions, corporate finance, banking, joint ventures, 'Yellow Book' and commercial contracts. Also handles nuclear energy and electricity. Recent cases include: Railtrack (Scotland), reorganisation of the British Railway Industry; Johnston Press plc's recommended offer for Halifax Courier (Holdings) Ltd and relative Placing; John Dickie Holdings MBO; Benedetti Holdings Financing; Royal Bank Development Capital/Paramount Clubs Financing. Has lectured at Strathclyde University; speaker at Law Society, CA Institute and other conferences.

Prof. Membership: Law Society of Scotland, International Bar Association, American Bar Association Institute of Directors.

Career: Qualified in 1971. Joined *MacRoberts* in 1973, becoming a Partner in 1977. Non-executive Director of Johnston Press plc.

Personal: Born 10th April 1950. Attended Hillhead High School, Glasgow 1962-68; then Strathclyde University 1968-71. Chairman of Friends of the Beatson Oncology Centre. Leisure interests include music, golf and football. Lives in Glasgow.

Dorman, A. Brian

Dorman Jeffrey & Co, Glasgow (0141) 221 9880. Partner in Corporate Department.

Specialisation: Main area of practice is corporate, including contract, corporate finance, information technology, employment, mergers and acquisitions and purchase and sale of private companies. Also handles the financing of sports stadia, including The Rangers Bond, The Arsenal Bond, The Hammers Bond and The Murrayfield Debenture (for Scottish Rugby Union). Scottish legal adviser to Argyll in its bid for Distillers; House of Fraser in its take-over of Army & Navy stores; Vaux in sale of Lorimer's Breweries; Bank of Scotland in its electronic fund transfer contract with DHSS and for Alexander & Alexander Services Inc in its acquisition of one of the UKs largest actuarial partnerships. Occasionally gives papers at seminars of the Law Society of Scotland.

Prof. Membership: Law Society of Scotland, Fellow of the Institute of Management.

Career: Qualified in 1969. Joined *Dorman*

Jeffrey & Co. as a Partner in 1979.

Personal: Born in 1945. Attended Hillhead High School, Glasgow 1950-63, then University of Glasgow 1963-67. Member of Master Court, Incorporation of Coopers of Glasgow (Deacon 1989-90). Leisure interests include current affairs, music and occasional golf. Lives in Hurlford, Ayrshire.

Duffield, Stephen L.
Eversheds, Birmingham (0121) 233 2001. Qualified 1977. Partner in the Commercial Department with particular expertise in the motor, manufacturing and brewing industries. Born 17.6.1951

Evans, M.J.
Greenwoods, Peterborough (01733) 555244.

Fermor, Andrew
Cripps Harries Hall, Tunbridge Wells (01892) 515121. Qualified 1974. Partner 1979. Commercial Division. Practice covers general company/commercial and commercial property work. Born 1949.

Fischl, Nicolas J.
See under Corporate Finance.

Fitzsimons, Gerard
Taylor Vinters, Cambridge (01223) 423444. Partner and Head of Company and Commercial Department.

Specialisation: Practice focuses on acquisitions and disposals, venture capital, corporate finance for private and public companies, MBO's, MBI's, joint ventures, banking and insolvency (including taking and enforcing security), advising receivers and company reconstructions. Also handles general company and commercial law. Occasional lecturer for Cambridge University Extramural Studies Board.

Prof. Membership: Law Society, Society of Practitioners of Insolvency (Associate Member).

Career: Qualified in 1984 after articles with *Coward Chance*. With *Shearman & Sterling$, New York 1985-86 and Coward Chance* 1986-87. Joined *Taylor Vinters* in 1987 and became a Partner in 1989.

Personal: Born 28th August 1959. Educated at Cranbrook School, Kent and University College, Oxford 1978-81. Lives in Cambridge.

Flynn, John
Dickinson Dees, Newcastle upon Tyne (0191) 261 1911. Qualified 1979. Partner 1986. Corporate Department. Work includes M&As, flotations, rights issues and joint ventures. Born 1.6.1959.

Foster, David C.
Watson Burton, Newcastle upon Tyne (0191) 232 3101.

Fraser, Hugh
Stronachs, Aberdeen (01224) 643573.

Galbraith, Eric R.
Dorman Jeffrey & Co, Glasgow (0141) 221 9880.

Gardiner, John
Bird Semple, Glasgow (0141) 221 7090.

Garrett, Brian
Elliott Duffy Garrett, Belfast (01232) 245034.

Garston, Clive R.
Halliwell Landau, Manchester (0161) 835 3003.

Gilbert, Ian M.
Walker Morris, Leeds (0113) 283 2500. Partner in Corporate Department.

Specialisation: Main area of practice is management buy-outs and venture capital. Has been involved in venture capital and development capital for 15 years, acting on both sides. Since 1985 has been involved in numerous MBO's of varying size and complexity. Also deals with public and private company acquisitions and disposals, flotations and share issues, with wide ranging experience from acting for a range of listed public companies. Transactions handled include a 57 million MBO of Goldsborough Healthcare Plc, a 27 million MBO of City Technology Ltd, a 6.7 million MBI of Dunn &Co Menswear, and a 75 million flotation of Goldsborough Healthcare Plc. Author of 'Earnouts' in 'Acquisitions Monthly' (June 1993).

Career: Qualified in 1981. With 3i Group Plc 1979-85, latterly as Senior Legal Advisor. Joined *Walker Morris* in 1985 and became a Partner in 1986.

Personal: Born 22nd July 1957. Educated at Sheffield University 1975-78. Recreations include tennis, walking, squash and icing children's birthday cakes. Lives in Wetherby.

Gilthorpe, Ian M.
Robert Muckle, Newcastle-upon-Tyne (0191) 232 4402. Partner in Commercial Department. Managing Partner.

Specialisation: Main area of practice is corporate finance, including MBO's, acquisitions, disposals, sources of finance, debt re-structuring and flotation. Also handles insolvency work. Licensed Insolvency Practitioner.

Prof. Membership: Law Society.

Career: Qualified in 1978, having joined *Robert Muckle* in 1976. Became a Partner in 1979.

Personal: Born 9th May 1953. Educated at Oundle School 1967-72 and Leeds University 1973-75. Director of a foundry company. Enjoys cricket and golf. Lives in Newcastle upon Tyne.

Gould, Terry
Eversheds, Norwich (01603) 272727. Qualified 1977. Partner 1981. Corporate Department. Work includes company sales and acquisitions, corporate finance and insolvency work.

Gray, David John
Eversheds, Leeds (0113) 243 0391. Partner and Head of Company Department.

Specialisation: Handles all aspects of corporate finance work including fund raising through flotation, venture and development capital and other share issues, advising PLCs on yellow book requirements, MBOs, M&A and blue book work. Also handles significant or complex commercial agreements of all types. In the last 12 months acted for John Waddington plc in its £42 million acquisition of IMCA Holdings together with associated rights issue and its £50 million sale (in 6 days) of Waddingtons Games to Hasbro; acts inter alia for Peter Black Holdings plc, Jerme & Sons plc and Heywood Williams plc in respect of their M&A work, and acted for Farnell Electronics plc in its 80 million disportent of its manufacturing business in March 1995.

Prof. Membership: Law Society.

Career: Qualified in 1979. Became a Partner in 1982 and Head of Company Department in 1992.

Personal: Born 9th January 1955. Member of Yorkshire and Humberside CBI Council. Attended Leeds Grammar School 1963-73, then Magdelene College, Cambridge 1973-76. Leisure interests include golf (playing), horse racing (ownership), cricket and other sports as a spectator. Lives near Knaresborough.

Hally, Paul W.
Shepherd & Wedderburn WS, Edinburgh (0131) 228 9900. Partner in Corporate Department.

Specialisation: Main area of practice is corporate finance. Work includes mergers and acquisitions, MBOs, development and venture capital, banking and insolvency.

Prof. Membership: Law Society of Scotland, Society of Writers to the Signet, Institute of Directors.

Career: Qualified in 1983. Worked at *Fyfe Ireland WS* 1982-4 and joined *Shepherd & Wedderburn WS* in 1984, becoming a Partner in 1987.

Personal: Born 23rd June 1959. Holds an LLB (Hons) Dip LP Edinburgh (1977-84).

Hawes, Roger Geoffrey
See under Corporate Finance.

Haynes, Brian J.
Church Adams Tatham & Co, Reigate (01737) 240111. Qualified 1966. Partner 1967. Handles company and commercial work. Born 8.6.1940.

Hill, W. Stanley
Carson & McDowell, Belfast (01232) 244951.

Holt, Richard
Nabarro Nathanson, Sheffield (0114) 278 6666. Qualified 1984. Partner 1985. Company and Commercial Department. Practice covers general corporate and commercial work and partnership law.

Hopkirk, Gordon
Iain Smith & Company, Aberdeen (01224) 645454.

Hughes, David J.
See under Corporate Finance.

Hughes, Christopher W.
Wragge & Co, Birmingham (0121) 233 1000. Qualified 1966.

Hunter, Neil C.
Peterkins, Aberdeen (01224) 626300.

Hutchinson, John C.
Pitmans, Reading (01734) 580224.

Irvine, John W.
L'Estrange & Brett, Belfast (01232) 230426.

Johnston, Keith
Addleshaw Sons & Latham, Manchester (0161) 832 5994. Partner in Corporate Finance and Commercial Department.

Specialisation: Principal area of practice is corporate finance and company commercial work including mergers and acquisitions and 'yellow book'. Other main area of work involves joint ventures between public and private sectors relating to economic development, regeneration and transport initiatives. Major deals (1990-95) include Tootal Group plc's recommended offer from Coats Viyella plc (subsequent contested bid); Simon Engineering plc's recommended offer for The Robertson Group plc; North West Water Group plc's acquisition of the UK operations of Wallace & Tiernan (as part of worldwide acquisition), North West Water Group plc's sale of its Engineering Company to Bechtel Inc, Gave Cadbury Report Lecture with Sir Adrian Cadbury in October 1993.

Prof. Membership: Law Society. Chairman: North West Company Secretaries Forum.

Career: Qualified in 1976, while at *Addleshaw Sons & Latham*. Became a Partner in 1981. Member of Management Board of *Addleshaw Sons & Latham*. 1991-94 Member of Board of *Norton Rose* M5 Group.

Personal: Born 3rd July 1952. Attended Bootle Grammar School 1963-70, then London University 1970-73 (External). Governor of The Grange School, Hartford, Cheshire. Leisure pursuits include badminton (Manchester League), chess and armchair spectator of sports. Lives in Sale, Cheshire.

Jones, Digby M.
Edge & Ellison, Birmingham (0121) 200 2001. Senior Partner of *Edge & Ellison*.

Specialisation: Heads teams of company law and corporate finance lawyers; has acted in numerous management buy-outs. Personally represents six major public companies and a substantial number of private companies, many emanating from management buyouts. Has acted in several high-profile bids and currently sits as non-executive director on the boards of Woodcote Industries Limited and Douglas Concrete Holdings Limited, where he is Chairman.

Prof. Membership: Member of the National Council and the West Midlands Regional Council of the Confederation of British Industry.

Career: Qualified in 1980, having joined *Edge & Ellison* in 1978 after a period in the Royal Navy. Became a Partner in 1984, Deputy Senior Partner in 1990, and in May 1995, the youngest Senior Partner of a major practice in the country.

Personal: LLB(Hons) from University College, London. Enjoys theatre, supports CBSO and races (badly) a Sierra Cosworth. Lives in Worcestershire.

Kerle, Bridget A.
Hewitson Becke + Shaw, Cambridge (01223) 461155. Qualified 1977. Partner 1980. Company Commercial Department. Advises corporate clients on funding, acquisitions and disposals, flotations and MBOs. Born 1953.

Laing, David K.
Ledingham Chalmers, Aberdeen (01224) 408408.

Lane-Smith, Roger
See under Corporate Finance.

Lee, Paul
See under Corporate Finance.

Lee, Richard
Clarks, Reading (01734) 585321. Qualified 1976. Partner 1986. Company Department. Work covers corporate finance, venture capital, public issues, acquisitions and MBOs, banking and employee share schemes. Born 16.6.1947.

Lee, Richard N.F.
Addleshaw Sons & Latham, Manchester (0161) 832 5994. Qualified 1984. Partner 1988. Company and Corporate Finance Department. Handles corporate finance and general corporate work.

Lewis, Mark R.L.
Foot & Bowden, Plymouth (01752) 675000. (London 0171 222 5165). Partner in Commercial/Commercial Department.

Specialisation: Practice covers the full range of domestic corporate finance activities including private and public mergers and acquisitions, flotations and secondary issues on the London Stock Exchange, and privatisations. Also handles company and commercial work, including joint ventures and other strategic commercial agreements, and cross border mergers and acquisitions.

Prof. Membership: Law Society

Career: Qualified in 1978. Joined *Foot & Bowden* as a Partner in 1995.

Personal: Born 1953. Attended Millfield School 1965-71 and Exeter College, Oxford 1972-75 (Exhibitioner). Lives in Exeter.

Lippell, C. Sean
See under Corporate Finance.

Loake, Jonathan
Dallas Brett, Oxford (01865) 791990. Qualified 1979.

Longland, Paul D.
Steele Raymond, Bournemouth (01202) 294566. Partner in Company Department.

Specialisation: Main area of practice is company law, covering mergers and acquisitions, corporate finance and business formations. Other area is insolvency, partnership and a wide range of commercial contracts.

Prof. Membership: Law Society.

Career: Qualified in 1981. Articled Clerk and Assistant Solicitor at *Allen & Overy*. Now partner and head of *Steele Raymond's* Company Department. First class honours Law Society Finals. Received Clements Inn Prize, Daniel Reardon Prize and City of London Solicitors' Company Prize.

Personal: Born 1954. Nottingham University (LLb Hons) and Keble College, Oxford (1978 BCL). Leisure interests; walking and music.

MacDonald, Kevan
Dickson Minto WS, Edinburgh (0131) 225 4455. Qualified 1982. Partner 1987. Corporate Department. Main areas of practice are corporate and commercial, pensions, and oil and gas law. Born 7.7.1958.

Mackay, Philip
See under Collective Investment Schemes.

Marsh, David J.
See under Corporate Finance.

Martin-Jones, Rosemary
Nabarro Nathanson, Reading (01734) 504700. Qualified 1967. Partner 1995. Company/Commercial Department. Covers a range of non-contentious work with particular focus on the information technology and communications sector and charities. Born 26.1.1943.

Massy-Collier, James P.
Osborne Clarke, Bristol (0117) 923 0220.

McIntosh, Ian W.
Booth & Co., Leeds (0113) 283 2000.

Qualified 1983.

McIver, Malcolm

Bird Semple, Glasgow (0141) 221 7090. Qualified 1958. Senior Partner. Specialises in corporate and partnership law. Former tutor in Jurisprudence at the University of Glasgow.

McNeill, Morag

McGrigor Donald, Glasgow (0141) 248 6677.

McNiven, Alan R.

Paull & Williamsons, Aberdeen (01224) 621621.

Meiklejohn, Iain M.C.

Shepherd & Wedderburn WS, Edinburgh (0131) 228 9900. Partner in Corporate Department.

Specialisation: Main areas of practice are corporate finance, mergers and acquisitions, banking, company law and insolvency law. Scottish Editor of 'International Bank Secrecy'.

Prof. Membership: Law Society of Scotland, International Bar Association, Society of Practitioners of Insolvency.

Career: Apprenticed to *Allan Dawson Simpson & Hampton* 1976-78. Qualified in 1976 and joined *Shepherd & Wedderburn WS*. Became a Partner in 1982.

Personal: Born 3rd November 1954. Educated at Edinburgh Academy 1961-72 and Edinburgh University 1972-76. Director of the Scottish Trust for Underwater Archaeology; Trustee of John Muir Association; Director of Stagecoach ESOP Trust Limited.

Mills, W. Stratton

Mills Selig, Belfast (01232) 243878.

Minto, Bruce W.

Dickson Minto WS, Edinburgh (0131) 225 4455. Qualified 1981. Founding Partner 1985. Corporate Department. Work includes stock exchange listings, Yellow Book work, mergers and acquisitions and institutional finance. Born 30.10.1957.

Misso, Jerome Jude

Eversheds, Ipswich (01473) 233433. Qualified 1989. Partner 1995. Corporate Department. Born 27.10.1963.

Mitchell, Christopher J.

Cartwrights, Bristol (0117) 929 3601. Partner and Head of Commercial Client Department.

Specialisation: Main area of practice is company commercial work, handling mergers and acquisitions, corporate finance, joint ventures, commercial contracts, the 'tie' and beer supply agreements. Was involved in the MBI of the Magic Pub Co (1994), the MBO of Bredon Group Ltd (1994), the Bristol City FC contested management take over (1993), the MBI of Discovery Inns Ltd (1992), the rule 9

bid for Stanley Gibbons Holdings Plc (1993), funding and shareholders arrangements for Bristol Harry Ramsdens Fish Restaurant (1993), and the Paramount case, regarding detention rights of a regional airport against a company in administration(1992).

Prof. Membership: Law Society, SBO

Career: Qualified in 1981. Joined *Cartwrights* in 1986 and became a Partner in 1987. Company Secretary, Bristol City Football Club.

Personal: Born 3rd October 1957. Educated at Portsmouth Grammar School 1969-73. Brockenhurst College, Hampshire 1973-75 and St. Catherine's College, Oxford 1975-78. Recreations include sport, hill walking and all things French. Lives in Bristol.

Needham, Andrew

See under Corporate Finance.

Partridge, W.M. James

Thomson Snell & Passmore, Tunbridge Wells (01892) 510000. Partner in Commercial Department.

Specialisation: Deals with company and commercial matters including advice on the structure and formation of companies and partnerships, acquisition and disposal of companies and un-incorporated business, all types of commercial agreements including joint ventures, agency and distribution, sub-contracting, all matters concerning intellectual property, particularly copyright, patent and trade mark licensing.

Career: Qualified in 1983. Trained and practised in London before joining *Thomson Snell & Passmore* in 1986. Became a Partner in 1987.

Personal: Born 14 March 1958. Educated at Lancing College and Trinity College, Cambridge BA(CANTAB) 1977-80. Other interests: member of the Territorial Army. Lives at High Hurstwood in East Sussex.

Paton, Richard

Alsop Wilkinson, Liverpool.

Patrick, Bruce R.

Maclay Murray & Spens, Edinburgh (0131) 226 5196. Qualified 1973. Partner (Company Department). Managing Partner 1991-94. Work includes venture capital, management buy-outs and insolvencies. Acted in receivership of Clydesdale Group plc. Born 26.11.1945.

Pillman, J.C.

Cole and Cole, Oxford (01865) 791122. Qualified 1977. Partner 1983. Company Commercial Department. Handles general company law. Born 7.7.1952.

Prince, Michael J.

See under Corporate Finance.

Pysden, Edward

See under Corporate Finance.

Rafferty, John C.

See under Corporate Finance.

Rankin, Peter J.

Cleaver Fulton & Rankin, Belfast (01232) 243141.

Rous, Simon

Bevan Ashford, Bristol (0117) 923 0111.

Roxburgh, Roy

Iain Smith & Company, Aberdeen (01224) 645454. Partner in Company & Commercial Department.

Specialisation: Main areas of practice are mergers and take-overs, MBO's, MBI's and corporate insolvency, acting for both purchasers and vendors of businesses, investors both private and institutional, and receiverships. Involvement in insolvency is generally on a specialist basis. Author of a chapter on diligence for the ICAS 'Insolvency Case Book'. Convener since 1993 of the Law Society/ICA's Insolvency Specialist Group which meets annually.

Prof. Membership: Law Society of Scotland (Member of Insolvency Solicitors Committee since 1992, and Insolvency Specialist Accreditation Panel since 1994), S.P.I.

Career: Qualified in 1974. Joined *Iain Smith & Co* as a Partner in 1977. External Examiner JIEB since 1993 and External Examiner at Robert Gordon University since 1992. Notary Public.

Personal: Born 29th September 1950. Educated at Dunfermline High School 1961-68 and Edinburgh University 1968-72. Recreations include ski-ing, golf and football. Lives in Aberdeen.

Roxburgh, B.O.

Osborne Clarke, Bristol (0117) 923 0220.

Russell, J.Stuart

Boyds, Glasgow (0141) 221 8251. Partner in Corporate Department.

Specialisation: Work includes corporate finance, banking work, mergers, acquisitions, disposals, MBOs/ MBIs, media and entertainment law, intellectual property, venture capital, contracts and agreements, business start-ups and partnership. Member of Company Law Committee of Law Society of Scotland; member of DTI Working Party on review of Sections 151-158 of Companies Act 1985; conference speaker on company law generally and corporate governance.

Prof. Membership: Law Society of Scotland, International Bar Association/American Bar Association.

Career: Qualified in 1984. Joined *Boyds* in 1989, becoming a Partner in 1991.

Personal: Born 1960. Lives in Rhu, near Helensburgh.

Rutherford, John A.T.

Ledingham Chalmers, Aberdeen (01224) 408408.

Selig, Ivan
See under Corporate Finance.

Shedden, Alfred C.
McGrigor Donald,   Glasgow (0141) 248 6677.

Short, John
Taylor Vinters,   Cambridge (01223) 423444. Partner in Company/ Commercial Department.

Specialisation: Work covers acquisitions and sales, reconstructions, venture capital, investment, and MBO/MBI's. Also handles insolvency and banking, advising receivers and liquidators. Advises on taking and enforcing security. Occasional lecturer in legal topics at Madingley Hall, Cambridge.

Prof. Membership: Law Society, Associate Member of Society of Practitioners of Insolvency.

Career: Qualified 1974. Trainee and solicitor at *Prettys*, Ipswich, 1972-75; Assistant Solicitor at *Coward Chance*, London, 1976-78. Joined *Taylor Vinters* in 1979. Became a Partner in 1982. Secretary of Cambridgeshire and District Law Society, 1983-87.

Personal: Born 28th December 1949. Attended Sheffield University 1968-71. Leisure interests include walking, music and photography. Lives in Lolworth, near Cambridge.

Simon, Jeremy P.
See under Corporate Finance.

Sleigh, Andrew F.
See under Insolvency.

Smart, Peter C.
Walker Morris,   Leeds (0113) 283 2500. Managing Partner and Head of Corporate Department.

Specialisation: Main areas of practice are corporate finance, M & A work, venture capital and shareholder disputes.

Prof. Membership: Law Society.

Career: Qualified in 1979, having joined *Walker Morris* in 1977. Became a Partner in 1981 and Managing Partner in 1993.

Personal: Born 5th September 1950. Attended Leeds Metropolitan University, taking a BA (Hons) in 1976. Leisure interests include watching rugby union Internationals. Lives in Leeds.

Smith, W.W. Campbell
Biggart Baillie & Gifford,   Glasgow (0141) 228 8000. Qualified 1972. Partner 1974. Head of Corporate Department. Work includes acquisitions, disposals, joint ventures and MBOs/MBIs. Born 17.5.1946.

Spriggs, Michael I.
Wilkinson Maughan,   Newcastle-upon-Tyne (0191) 261 1841. Partner in Company/ Commercial Department.

Specialisation: Main area of practice is corporate finance, covering MBOs, MBIs,

mergers and acquisitions, joint ventures, shareholder disputes and listed company work. Also experienced in public sector work, with particular experience of privatisation and development work. Legal Practice Course external examiner. Member of advisory board of Durham University Careers Advisory Service.

Prof. Memberships: Law Society, CBI, BURA.

Career: Banker with Standard Chartered Bank, Hong Kong 1979-81. Trained at *Frere Cholmeley*, London. Qualified as a solicitor in 1985. Joined *Wilkinson Maughan*, becoming Partner in 1987.

Stanning, David R.
B.P. Collins & Co,   Gerrards Cross (01753) 889995. Partner in Company Commercial Department.

Specialisation: Originally specialised in employment law, which led to greater involvement in company commercial work of all types, including MBO's, acquisitions, disposals, distribution and agency, joint ventures and shareholders agreements and disputes. Has experience of addressing seminars locally on employment matters, directors' responsibilities, acquisitions and 'business angels' investment.

Prof. Membership: Chamber of Commerce.

Career: Qualified in 1970. Joined *B.P. Collins & Co* in 1975 and became a Partner in 1978.

Personal: Born 16th May 1945. Educated at Canford School, Dorset 1958-63 and St. Andrews University 1963-66. Local Councillor 1982-86. Chairman of Parent Staff Association of Haileybury Junior School 1992-94. Enjoys golf, ski-ing, sailing and life generally. Lives in Taplow, Bucks.

Street, Robert H.
See under Corporate Finance.

Swanson, Magnus P.
See under Corporate Finance.

Thomas, Roger
Eversheds,   Cardiff (01222) 471147. Qualified 1969. Partner 1969. Head of Company and Commercial Department. Advises private and public sector clients on a range of commercial and corporate matters, including MBO's, joint ventures, mergers, inward investment and business development. Born 22.7.1945.

Thurman, Roderick J.
Edwards Geldard,   Cardiff (01222) 238239. Qualified 1973. Partner 1977. Senior Partner 1995. Head of Company and Commercial Department 1983-1995. Main areas of practice are corporate finance and M&A.

Tilly, Toby H.
Eversheds,   Middlesbrough (0642) 247456. Qualified 1971. Partner 1989. Company and Commercial Department. Practice

covers general corporate and commercial work and corporate finance.

Trotter, Andrew
Donne Mileham & Haddock,   Brighton (01273) 329833. Partner and head of Company Commercial Department.

Specialisation: Main area of practice is company sales and purchases, including management buy-outs and corporate finance. Also handles general company commercial work, including franchising, computer contracts and intellectual property agreements. Recently addressed the Institute of Bankers on acquisition finance.

Career: Qualified in 1981. At *Withers* 1979-83 and *Norton Rose* 1983-85. Joined *Donne Mileham & Haddock* in 1985 and became a Partner in 1986.

Personal: Born 5th August 1954. Educated at Lancing College and Oxford. Lives near Lewes, East Sussex.

Walker, Andrew W.
See under Corporate Finance.

Walker, Michael J.
Maclay Murray & Spens,   Glasgow (0141) 248 5011. Qualified 1976. Managing Partner. Company Department. Specialises in mergers and acquisitions, acting for listed company clients.

Walton, T.H.
B.P. Collins & Co,   Gerrards Cross (01753) 889995. Qualified 1985. Partner 1988. Barrister 1965. Company/Commercial Department. Specialises in company and business acquisitions and disposals.

Welch, H.B.
See under Banking.

Welford, Anthony R.H.
Veale Wasbrough,   Bristol (0117) 925 2020. Qualified 1981. Partner 1988. Company/Commercial Department. Work includes corporate finance, acquisitions and disposals. Born 19.1.1957.

Wheldon, Timothy J.
Booth & Co.,   Leeds (0113) 283 2000. Qualified 1983.

Whitehouse, Michael
Wragge & Co,   Birmingham (0121) 233 1000. Qualified 1977. Partner 1987. Specialises in corporate transactions including MBOs, M&As and joint ventures. Born 21.10.1952.

Williams, Caroline A.
Blake Lapthorn,   Fareham (01489) 579990.

Wright, Graham
Dickinson Dees,   Newcastle upon Tyne (0191) 261 1911.

COMPUTER LAW & I.T.

COMPUTER law and information technology are becoming ever more important areas of practice. Whilst most firms with commercial or intellectual property departments are able to provide advice on the legal issues involved, a number of firms have developed specialised IT departments, often employing practitioners with expertise gained in the industry.

LONDON

Clifford Chance emerges as the pre-eminent IT firm in London. The IT unit, headed by Christopher Millard (widely regarded as London's leading IT lawyer), comprises 24 specialists with substantial experience of the complex commercial, regulatory and technical issues characteristic of the information technology business. The firm advises manufacturers, distributors and users of hardware products; software developers, distributors and users; and providers and users of computer-based services. Vanessa Marsland, Graham Smith and David Griffiths are also held in high regard.

Other highly recommended firms include *Baker & McKenzie, Bird & Bird* and *Masons*.

LEADING FIRMS – LONDON	
CLIFFORD CHANCE	
BAKER & McKENZIE	BIRD & BIRD
MASONS	
DIBB LUPTON BROOMHEAD	FIELD FISHER WATERHOUSE
HAMMOND SUDDARDS	HOPKINS & WOOD
LOVELL WHITE DURRANT	

Baker & McKenzie has an excellent IT unit, boasting distinguished lawyers such as Donald Jerrard, who is a member of the editorial board for 'Computer Law and Practice' and 'Computer Law and Security Report', and Harry Small, who is a contributor to Sweet & Maxwell's 'IT Encyclopaedia'. The firm has a very strong client base, jointly advising computer giants such as Canon (UK) Ltd and CSC Computer Sciences Ltd, and also advising Sony UK Ltd, Sun Microsystems Europe and Wang (UK) Ltd.

Bird & Bird's IT department comprises seven specialist partners. The highly respected Hamish Sandison heads the formidable team that includes Trevor Cook, Christopher Rees, Roger Bickerstaff, Simon Chalton (formerly of *Masons*) and Hilary Pearson (ex- *Simmons & Simmons*) and undertakes facility management (FM), regulatory, contract, Electronic Data Interchange, protection, procurement and outsourcing work.

Masons has a strong and experienced computer department handling a wide range of contentious and non-contentious work for major users and suppliers on a domestic and international scale. The firm has developed particular expertise in facility management, document image processing and

safety critical systems. Rachel Burnett, Robert McCallough and Richard Susskind are well respected.

The IT unit at *Nabarro Nathanson* (which makes its first appearance in this list following the recent merger with *Turner Kenneth Brown*) numbers six specialists who offer a comprehensive service to suppliers and users. A substantial part of the firm's work is undertaken at the Reading office.

Firms noted for their expertise in computer law/information technology include *Dibb Lupton Broomhead, Hammond Suddards, Hopkins & Wood, Field Fisher Waterhouse* and *Lovell White Durrant*.

Dibb Lupton Broomhead enjoys a national reputation, in part due to the work undertaken by David Barrett (considered to be a leading authority on outsourcing). The firm advises on the protection and licensing of software, facilities contracts and Data Protection Act, produces a quarterly newsletter and holds regular IT seminars throughout the country.

Hammond Suddards' unit addresses the full range of IT legal requirements for no less than 75 major suppliers and public and private sector users.

Simon Rendell at *Hopkins & Wood* handles contentious and non-contentious work, IPR and Electronic Data Interchange (EDI) for suppliers and users.

Ranald Robertson at *Field Fisher Waterhouse* is highly experienced and advises major public and private institutions on a variety of matters including procurement contracts, licensing and protection.

HIGHLY REGARDED – LONDON	
BRISTOWS COOKE & CARPMAEL	DENTON HALL
LINKLATERS & PAINES	MILLER & CO
NABARRO NATHANSON	OLSWANG
SIMMONS & SIMMONS	TARLO LYONS
ALLISON & HUMPHREYS	ALSOP WILKINSON
ARNOLD SEGAL	ASHURST MORRIS CRISP
BROBECK HALE and DORR INTERNATIONAL	CAMERON MARKBY HEWITT
CHARLES RUSSELL	COUDERT BROTHERS
DAVIES ARNOLD COOPER	EVERSHEDS
FORSYTE SAUNDERS KERMAN	FRESHFIELDS
GARRETT & CO	GOULDENS
HARBOTTLE & LEWIS	HERBERT SMITH
HYLTON-POTTS	McKENNA & CO
MISHCON DE REYA	NEEDHAM & GRANT
RADCLIFFES CROSSMAN BLOCK	RICHARDS BUTLER
ROWE & MAW	THE SIMKINS PARTNERSHIP
SLAUGHTER AND MAY	STEPHENSON HARWOOD
TAYLOR JOYNSON GARRETT	THEODORE GODDARD
TITMUSS SAINER DECHERT	WITHERS

Lovell White Durrant's group comprises six practitioners dealing exclusively with computer-related matters. The firm represents major industry clients, software houses and user clients in the banking, insurance and media fields.

Other recommended firms include *Olswang* which provides corporate, commercial and intellectual property advice, *Bristows Cooke & Carpmael* which handles contentious and non-contentious work and *Linklaters & Paines* which advises on supply, maintenance and FM agreements and computer-related disputes.

Highly recommended practitioners include Clifford Miller of *Miller & Company,* a niche practice advising suppliers and users on a variety of contentious and non-contentious work, Michael Rhodes of *Coudert Brothers,* a regular contributor to and editor of 'Computer Law and Practice', Ian Walden at *Tarlo Lyons* who represents manufacturers, software houses and suppliers, Richard Kemp, who has recently moved from *Hammond Suddards* to *Garrett & Co* in order to develop its IT practice and Christopher Hoyle who has recently moved from *Hopkins & Wood* to American Law firm *Brobeck Hale & Dorr.*

LEADING INDIVIDUALS – LONDON		
Donald G. Jerrard *Baker & McKenzie*	**Christopher Millard** *Clifford Chance*	**Hamish R. Sandison** *Bird & Bird*
Harry Small *Baker & McKenzie*		
David Barrett *Dibb Lupton Broomhead*	**Rachel Burnett** *Masons*	**Simon Chalton** *Bird & Bird*
Trevor M. Cook *Bird & Bird*	**Christopher R. Hoyle** *Brobeck Hale & Dorr International*	**Richard H. Kemp** *Garrett & Co*
Vanessa Marsland *Clifford Chance*	**Clifford Miller** *Miller & Co*	**Hilary Pearson** *Bird & Bird*
Simon Rendell *Hopkins & Wood*	**Michael Rhodes** *Coudert Brothers*	**D. Ranald C. Robertson** *Field Fisher Waterhouse*
Graham Smith *Clifford Chance*	**Ian Walden** *Tarlo Lyons*	
Roger Bickerstaff *Bird & Bird*	**Gillian Bull** *Tarlo Lyons*	**Stephen Digby** *Withers*
David H. Griffiths *Clifford Chance*	**Laurence M. Kaye** *The Simkins Partnership*	**Robert McCallough** *Masons*
Christopher W. Rees *Bird & Bird*	**Arnold Segal** *Arnold Segal*	**Nigel Stamp** *The Simkins Partnership*
Richard Susskind *Masons*	**Michael J.B. Webster** *Rowe & Maw*	**Philip G. Westmacott** *Bristows Cooke & Carpmael*
N.D. Wildish *Nabarro Nathanson*		

SOUTH EAST

The leading computer firms in the South East are *Dallas Brett* and *Shoosmiths & Harrison.* Both firms undertake commercial work, advising major hardware and software suppliers and users on contract and licensing matters. Paul Klinger (consultant to *Shoosmiths & Harrison*) is considered a leading authority, whilst Anna Booy (*Dallas Brett*) is highly recommended.

Marcus O'Leary (formerly of *Garrett & Co*) is, at the time of going to print, in the process of launching a niche practice: *The Law Offices of Marcus O'Leary.* Considered to be an eminent practitioner at the forefront of computer law, Marcus O'Leary has acted for many leading international technology companies in complex matters and will no doubt carve a position in the market.

HIGHLY REGARDED – SOUTH EAST	
DALLAS BRETT *Oxford*	**NABARRO NATHANSON**
SHOOSMITHS & HARRISON *Banbury*	
GARRETT & CO *Reading*	**THE LAW OFFICES OF MARCUS J. O'LEARY**
MORRELL PEEL & GAMLEN *Oxford*	
DONNE MILEHAM & HADDOCK *Brighton*	**PENNINGTONS** *Basingstoke*

Tony Bailes (formerly of *Turner Kenneth Brown)* heads the IT team at *Nabarro Nathanson* that comprises five specialists and advises on a full range of contentious and non-contentious issues for some of the largest domestic and international computer suppliers and users.

LEADING INDIVIDUALS – SOUTH EAST
Tony G. Bailes *Nabarro Nathanson*
Paul Klinger *Shoosmiths & Harrison*
Anna C.H. Booy *Dallas Brett*
Marcus O'Leary *The Law Offices of Marcus J. O'Leary*
Christine Reid *Morrell Peel & Gamlen*

Morrell Peel & Gamlen advises on software and licensing matters for media companies. Christine Reid is held in high regard.

SOUTH WEST

Anstey Sargent & Probert, Burges Salmon, Charles Russell and *Osborne Clarke* whilst being experienced in computer-related litigation, have, in the main, established reputations for non-contentious work.

Anstey Sargent & Probert is particularly experienced in software licensing. Edward Probert has been recommended.

Jeremy Holt, Secretary of the Law Specialist Committee of the British Computer Society, heads *Charles Russell's* computer law group. In addition to advising clients such as W H Smith, British Computer Society and Kode International plc, they regularly produce a number of publications on computer law.

Osborne Clarke's computer unit, headed by Alan Wood, comprises four specialists handling a variety of work. The firm has developed particular expertise in IT procurement and facilities management and advises clients in the public and private sector.

HIGHLY REGARDED – SOUTH WEST	
ANSTEY SARGENT & PROBERT *Exeter*	BURGES SALMON *Bristol*
CHARLES RUSSELL *Cheltenham*	OSBORNE CLARKE *Bristol*
LESTER ALDRIDGE *Bournemouth*	TOWNSENDS *Swindon*
WANSBROUGHS WILLEY HARGRAVE *Bristol*	
LYONS DAVIDSON *Bristol*	

Lester Aldridge has a strong reputation for computer-related litigation.

LEADING INDIVIDUALS – SOUTH WEST
Jeremy Holt *Charles Russell*
E.A.W. Probert *Anstey Sargent & Probert*
Alan P. Wood *Osborne Clarke*

Wansbroughs Willey Hargrave acts for software houses and producers on a whole range of non-contentious issues.

WALES & MIDLANDS

In Wales, *Edwards Geldard* and *Eversheds* Cardiff office have well established reputations in all aspects of computer law, particularly on the intellectual property side. Phillip Rees at *Edwards Geldard* has developed particular expertise in FM and EDI arrangements and is highly recommended.

HIGHLY REGARDED – WALES & MIDLANDS	
DIBB LUPTON BROOMHEAD *Birmingham*	EDWARDS GELDARD *Cardiff*
EVERSHEDS *Cardiff*	EVERSHEDS *Nottingham*
HEWITSON BECKE + SHAW *Northampton*	SHOOSMITHS & HARRISON *Northampton*
WRAGGE & CO *Birmingham*	
GOODGER AUDEN *Burton-on-Trent*	PINSENT CURTIS *Birmingham*
MARTINEAU JOHNSON *Birmingham*	

Eversheds Nottingham, *Dibb Lupton Broomhead* and *Wragge & Co* take the lions share of computer-related work in the Midlands. *Eversheds* advises both suppliers and users in the public and private sector. The IT team, headed by the highly respected Nigel Sternberg specialises in outsourcing, FM, turnkey arrangements, distribution and licensing.

LEADING INDIVIDUALS – WALES & MIDLANDS
Bill Jones *Wragge & Co*
Neil Maybury *Dibb Lupton Broomhead*
Phillip Rees *Edwards Geldard*
Nigel P. Sternberg *Eversheds*

Dibb Lupton Broomhead and *Wragge & Co* both handle a wide range of contentious and non-contentious work for some major IT clients. Neil Maybury of *Dibb Lupton Broomead*, (formerly a partner at *Pinsent & Co*) is a member of the FAST Legal Advisory Group and the Law Society Technology Committee and is considered to be highly experienced. Bill Jones of *Wragge & Co* is well respected.

In Cambridge, *Hewitson Becke + Shaw* advises on systems supply agreements, development, distribution and joint ventures.

NORTH WEST

The leading computer law firms in the North West are *Alsop Wilkinson, Halliwell Landau, Masons and Slater Heelis*.

Alsop Wilkinson advises IT based clients and large institutions on a wide range of software issues and turnkey agreements. The computer unit comprises four specialist partners headed by George Godar.

HIGHLY REGARDED – NORTH WEST	
ALSOP WILKINSON *Liverpool*	HALLIWELL LANDAU *Manchester*
MASONS *Manchester*	SLATER HEELIS *Manchester*

Halliwell Landau provides commercially based advice to professional and institutional clients. Jonathan Moakes is highly recommended.

LEADING INDIVIDUALS – NORTH WEST
George W. Godar *Alsop Wilkinson*
Jonathan Moakes *Halliwell Landau*
Zoe Ollerenshaw *Masons*
Peter B.A. Renshaw *Slater Heelis*

Masons undertakes the full range of non-contentious work including technology transfer and computer bureau agreements. Zoe Ollerenshaw is well respected, as is Peter Renshaw of *Slater Heelis*.

NORTH EAST

Oxley & Coward emerges as the leading practice in the North East, with John Yates considered to be the doyen of computer law in the North. The firm has an enviable client base, advising on a wide range of contentious and non contentious work. John Yates and his team regularly provide in-house training schemes for clients and other interested parties.

Alistair Maughan and his team at *Dibb Lupton Broomhead* are also held in high regard. The IT unit advises on all aspects of computer law, specialises in Data Protection Act work and software protection and is one of the few practices in the UK to make available a video conferencing facility.

LEADING FIRMS – NORTH EAST
OXLEY & COWARD *Rotherham*
DIBB LUPTON BROOMHEAD *Bradford*

Other firms with experience in the field include *Booth & Co, Eversheds* Leeds, *Masons* and *Pinsent Curtis*.

Ian Sampson at *Booth & Co* advises financial institutions, public and private companies and governmental departments.

Eversheds' (Leeds) IT unit comprises eight specialists, some of who are dual qualified or have experience in industry. Dai Davis is well respected.

Masons has opened a new office in Leeds to service its clients in the North East of England. Shelagh Gaskill has quickly established a reputation as a leading authority in computer law.

HIGHLY REGARDED – NORTH EAST	
EVERSHEDS *Leeds*	HAMMOND SUDDARDS *Leeds*
MASONS	
BOOTH & CO. *Leeds*	PINSENT CURTIS

Michael Peeters at *Pinsent Curtis* advises public sector bodies and government departments on procurement work. The firm also represents a number of software houses and computer companies.

LEADING INDIVIDUALS – NORTH EAST	
John Yates *Oxley & Coward*	
Dai Davis *Eversheds*	
Shelagh Gaskill *Masons*	
Michael P.D. Peeters *Pinsent Curtis*	
Alistair Maughan *Dibb Lupton Broomhead*	
Ian C. Sampson *Booth & Co.*	

SCOTLAND

Dundas & Wilson CS (and particularly Lorne Byatt), *MacRoberts*, where David Flint is held in high regard and *McGrigor Donald* (Shonaig Macpherson is a rising star) were the most frequently recommended among the Scottish firms with IT expertise.

HIGHLY REGARDED – SCOTLAND	
DUNDAS & WILSON CS *Edinburgh*	McGRIGOR DONALD *Glasgow*
MACROBERTS *Glasgow*	

LEADING INDIVIDUALS – SCOTLAND	
Lorne Byatt *Dundas & Wilson CS*	
David Flint *MacRoberts*	
Shonaig Macpherson *McGrigor Donald*	
Fiona M.M. Nicolson *Maclay Murray & Spens*	

LEADERS IN COMPUTER LAW & I.T.

LONDON

Barrett, David

Dibb Lupton Broomhead, London (0171) 600 0202. Bar 1978. Partner and Head of Information Technology and Telecommunications Unit; Head of Regulatory and Commercial Group.

Specialisation: Main area of practice is IT and telecommunications regulatory law. Also handles public sector and public procurement, EC law, and non-contentious intellectual property work. Advised HM Government on outsourcing of Inland Revenue, DSS and DoT computer operations. Also a number of major private sector companies involved in outsourcing their information technology or in significant procurements. Has advised major computer companies on issues including technology transfer, major transactions, licensing, software protection, outsourcing and applications for telecommunications licenses. Legal correspondent for Business & Technology Magazine. Has spoken widely at conferences.

Prof. Membership: Law Society, Computer Law Association, Computer Law Group, Society for Computers and Law.

Career: Qualified as a Barrister in 1978 and as a solicitor in 1990. Senior Legal Adviser at IBM 1979-89, then Partner at *Theodore Goddard* from 1989-93. Joined *Dibb Lupton Broomhead* in 1993.

Personal: Born 30th April 1953. Attended King's School, Tynmouth, then Gonville & Caius College, Cambridge, taking First Class Honours. Then attended University of Michigan Law School. Leisure interests include motorsports, sailing, swimming, music and theatre. Lives in Harpenden.

Bickerstaff, Roger

Bird & Bird, London (0171) 415 6000. Partner in Company Department.

Specialisation: Principal area of practice is information technology and telecommunications. Work encompasses all aspects of IT law, including contract negotiation, dispute resolution, protection of rights, impact of EC legislation and impact of new technology (e.g. Internet). Also advises on all aspects of EC/GATT procurement law. Clients include the Government Centre for Information Systems (CCTA) and major private sector IT purchasers.

Prof. Membership: Society for Computers and Law.

Career: Qualified in 1990. At Linklaters & Paines 1990-92. Joined *Bird & Bird* in 1992 and became a Partner in 1995.

Personal: Born 1961. Attended King's College, Cambridge 1980-84. Lives in London.

Bull, Gillian

Tarlo Lyons, London (0171) 405 2000. Consultant, 1993. Information Technology unit.

Specialisation: Principal area is general non-contentious computer and IT law, particularly for businesses trading in a digital environment (eg stock, futures and commodity exchanges; banks; data supply); system, software, cabling and network and telecoms procurement; manufacture development and supply agreement; services, FM, disaster recovery and maintenance contracts; licences, distribution and standard agreements; due diligence and contract audits. Also deals with competition and EU law issues relating to IT. Contributor to *Croner's Model Business Contracts* and *Croner's Guide to IT*. Member of editorial panel of *Computer Law and Security Report*.

Career: Qualified 1991. Lecturer in information Management, London Business School 1983-88; articled with Turner Kenneth Brown 1988-91; joined Tarlo Lyons as a consultant in 1993.
Professional Membership: Real Time Club (Convenor, Caucus on ICT and Law, April 1995), City of London Solicitors Company.

Personal: Born 26th November 1944. MA (Jurisprudence) from Lady Margaret Hall, Oxford.

Burnett, Rachel

Masons, London (0171) 490 4000. Qualified 1980. Partner 1994. Computer Law Group. Principal area of practice is advising, drafting and negotiating IT industry transactions for suppliers and users including related commercial and regulatory matters.

Chalton, Simon

Bird & Bird, London (0171) 415 6000. Consultant to Information Technology Group.

Specialisation: Computer law including intellectual property rights in computer programs and databases; computer system procurement; computer-related contracts; computer-related liabilities, disputes and ADR (WIPO listed mediator); data protection; competition law and European and international law relating to computers and telecommunications. Co-editor: Sweet & Maxwell's 'Encyclopedia of Data Protection'; co-author 'Data Protection Law'; consultant contributor 'Encyclopedia of Information Technology Law'. Editorial Board member: Computer Law and Security Report; Computer Law and Practice; The Data Law Report (USA) and frequent contributor to many other legal and professional journals. Conference speaker at an international level.

Prof. Membership: Law Society, International Bar Association,(Chairman of Computer and Database Committee), British Computer Society (Chairman of Intellectual Property Committee and Deputy-Chairman of Professional Issues Board), National Computing Centre (Chairman of Legal Group), Chartered Institute of Arbitrators (Fellow), Society for Information Management (USA)(Member of Procurement working group). College of Law Practice Management (USA) (Fellow).

Career: Qualified 1958. Solicitor, subsequently Partner and Senior Partner with *Dibb Lupton & Co* in Leeds until 1989. Consultant to *Dibb Lupton Broomhead 1989-93*. Consultant to *Masons* 1993-94. Joined *Bird & Bird*, 1995.

Personal: Born 1932. Lives in High Kilburn near York.

Cook, Trevor M.
See under Intellectual Property.

Digby, Stephen
Withers,   London (0171) 936 1000. Solicitor Corporate Department. Head of Intellectual Property Group.

Specialisation: Main areas of practice are intellectual property, media and I.T. law. Has particular experience of European I.T. directives, formulation of UK Government policy and commercial agreements for the exploitation of I.P. rights in the I.T., entertainment and leisure industries. Legal Advisor to EURIM (European Infomatics Market) and the all-party parliamentary group on European and UK I.T.

Career: Qualified Australia 1984. Qualified Barrister 1992. Qualified Solicitor 1995. Joined *Withers* in January 1992.

Griffiths, David H.
Clifford Chance,   London (0171) 600 1000. Partner 1990. Media, Computer and Communications Group. Specialises in computer law, communications and multimedia. Born 13.2.1958.

Hoyle, Christopher R.
See under Telecommunications.

Jerrard, Donald G.
Baker & McKenzie,   London (0171) 919 1000. Partner and Head of Intellectual Property Department.

Specialisation: Main areas of practice are intellectual property, information technology and competition law, including patent, trade mark and copyright litigation, technology transfer, computer contracts, computer disputes, and competition law (domestic and EC). Acted in Mitsubishi Electric Corporation's acquisition of Apricot computers and defended a patent infringement claim concerning Sony Walkman personal stereos. Has written numerous articles on IP and IT law. Member of the editorial board of 'Computer Law and Practice' and 'Computer Law and Security Report'. Speaker and Chairman at many conferences, especially on IT law, in the UK and abroad.

Prof. Membership: Law Society, London Computer Law Group.

Career: Qualified in 1976 and joined *Baker & McKenzie* in 1977. Became Head of Department in 1983 and a Partner in 1985. Board Member, Federation against Software Theft (1988-91). Chairman, Fast Legal Advisory Group (1988-91).

Personal: Born 21st March 1950. Educated at Winchester College (1963-68) and Emmanuel College, Cambridge (1969-73). Leisure pursuits include swimming, tennis, watching most sports and landscape gardening. Lives in Greatham, near Liss, Hampshire.

Kaye, Laurence M.
The Simkins Partnership,   London (0171) 631 1050. Partner. Head of Publishing and Multimedia.

Specialisation: Work includes information and publishing law (print and electronic), IT law, multimedia contract work, I.P. advice for major newspapers, lobbying work and preparation of position papers, advice to publishing industry bodies, IT contracts, trade mark licensing, general company/ commercial work, M&A work, licensing and distribution contracts, and UK and EU competition law. Member of the Intellectual Property Rights Sub Committee, part of the DTI's Multimedia Industry Advisory Group and DTI Experts Group on the proposed Legal Protection of Databases. Regular writer, lecturer and seminar presenter on new media/multimedia issues.

Prof. Membership: Law Society, IBA's Society for Computers & the Law, British Interactive Multimedia Association.

Career: Qualified in 1975, having joined *Brecher & Co.* in 1973. Left in 1980 to co-found Company and Commercial Department at *Saunders Sobell*. Joined *The Simkins Partnership* in 1994.

Personal: Born 1st September 1949. Attended Haberdashers' Askes School, Elstree, then the Sorbonne, and then Sidney Sussex College, Cambridge. Leisure interests include tennis, jogging, yoga, playing the saxophone, cinema, theatre and family life.

Kemp, Richard H.
Garrett & Co,   London (0171) 628 4767. Partner in Corporate Department.

Specialisation: Main areas of practice are computers, I.T. and telecommunications. Offers a full service IT legal acquisition legal service for major users of IT, telecoms and computers. Handles all aspects of operators, commercial, EC competition, I.P. acquisition and licensing, and regulatory work for industry suppliers. Other main area of practice is commercial law, involving the drafting and negotiation of complex operational and commercial contracts. Recent projects have included acting for a UK facilities management supplier on contractual documentation for a 7.5m four year FM agreement with a major US publishing house, acting for a UK electronic information supplier on a 20m five year agreement with a UK securities institution, and acting for a major UK County Council on a 20m integrated network acquisition for a police authority. Author of numerous articles for professional computer law periodicals. On the editorial panel of Computer Law and Security Reports; IT International editor of the Computer Law Association Bulletin. Chaired UK Panel of World Computer Law Congress, San Diego, in 1993.

Prof. Memberships: FAST, IBA, CLA, SEG, Law Society, CIPA (associate member), SCL.

Career: Qualified in 1980, having joined *Clifford & Turner* in 1978. Joined *Hopkins & Wood* in 1984, becoming a Partner in 1985. Joined *Hammond Suddards* in 1992 as a Partner.

Personal: Born 8th July 1956. Attended Cambridge University 1974-77, then the Universite Libre de Bruxelles 1978-79. Lives in London.

Marsland, Vanessa
See under Intellectual Property.

McCallough, Robert
Masons,   London (0171) 490 4000. Partner and Head of I.T. Department.

Specialisation: Specialises in computer and technology disputes. Leads a team of contentious and non-contentious lawyers, personally supervising the contentious technology team. Is involved in project management disputes relating to software engineering, hardware and software procurement disputes, integration of mainframes and PC networks, etc. Important matters handled include a software dispute arising from the failure of the London Ambulance Service's computer assisted dispatch system to work; Georg Fischer v. Multi Construction (CA - computerised random access warehouse - petition pending to HoL); Frazer Williams v. Prudential (CA - software system - question of "subject to contract") and Wessex Regional Health Authority v. CFM/

WISL (well publicised dispute as to failure to implement computer health service - known as the "Wessex" litigation). Clients include Chubb (indemnity insurers), ICL, CFM, the Stock Exchange and Norwegian Telecom (now Telenor), specialist software houses, public utilities and management consultants. Has lectured to the British Computer Society, Birmingham Law Society (use of technology) and the Defence Research Agency, as well as for commercial organisations (e.g. Euroforum) and universities.

Prof. Membership: Hong Kong Law Society, English Law Society, the N.C.C.

Career: Qualified in 1975. At *Hill & Perks,* Norwich 1975-78. Member of Attorney General's Chambers in Hong Kong 1978-83. Joined *Masons* (Hong Kong) in 1983. Became a Partner in 1984.

Personal: Born 30th May 1950. Educated at Eltham Green Comprehensive School 1960-68 and Leicester University 1969-72 (LL.B Hons). Interests include walking, fishing and computer games. Lives in Orpington.

Millard, Christopher
Clifford Chance, London (0171) 600 1000. Partner. Principal area of practice is computer, communications and multimedia work.

Miller, Clifford
Miller & Company, London (0181) 503 0084. Qualified 1984. Founding Partner. Ten years" Top Ten' international City law firm experience in Intellectual Property, Computer and European Law.

Pearson, Hilary
Bird & Bird, London (0171) 415 6000. Partner in Information Technology Group.

Specialisation: Main area of practice is computer law. Worked in the Silicon Valley 1980-83, becoming involved in the start of the personal computer industry. Since then has represented a wide range of hardware, software and component suppliers. Other area of practice is intellectual property. Author of 'Computer Contracts' (1983) and 'Commercial Exploitation of Intellectual Property' (1990).

Prof. Membership: American Bar Association, Computer Law Association, Licensing Executives Society, American I.P. Law Association.

Career: Qualified 1976. New Court, Temple 1977-80; *Rosenblum, Parrish & Bacigalupi,* San Francisco 1980-83; *Arnold White & Durkee,* Houston 1983-90. *Simmons & Simmons,* London 1990-95. Joined *Bird & Bird* in 1995. Member of the Californian Bar 1981 and Texas Bar 1984; US Patent Attorney.

Personal: Born 1943. Holds BA/ MA (Oxon) Hons Physics 1965-69, and LLB (London) 1975.

Rees, Christopher W.
Bird & Bird, London (0171) 415 6000. Managing Partner.

Specialisation: Principal area of practice is computer law covering all aspects of non-contentious work and resolving complex licensing disputes. Also specialist advice to multimedia companies of an "external general counsel" nature including rights acquisition, licensing, distribution policies tax and corporate governance. Involved in multinational dispute resolution in multimedia with Japanese and US Vendors. Author of 'Patents for Software: The Holy Grail for the Computer Industry' (Copyright World) and 'The Quest for Quality' (Law Society Gazette). Presents two-day seminar: 'Negotiating Software Contracts'.

Career: Qualified in 1979. Managing Partner of *Bird & Bird* since 1993.

Personal: Born 1955. Attended Christ's College, Cambridge 1973-76. Lives in London.

Rendell, Simon
Hopkins & Wood, London (0171) 404 0475. Partner and Head of IT and Telecommunications. Head of Commercial Department.

Specialisation: In addition to IT and telecommunications, advises on EC Competition law, UK Restrictive Trade Practices, Intellectual Property and all aspects of commercial law. Advises manufacturers, importers, distributors and OEM's. Advises on multimedia software development, intellectual property protection, tendering for contracts, contractual negotiations, trade practices, unfair competition law and outsourcing and systems integration. For telecommunications, advises carriers, service providers and re-sellers, users of telecom services, radio-communication operators, satellite services operators, importers and manufacturers of such equipment and various businesses engaged in providing communication services. Advises on legal and regulatory issues and developments. Obtained the first UK international simple resale licence used by DTI. Consultant editor for IT Law Today and International Computer Law Adviser. Lectures on all aspects of IT law.

Prof. Membership: FAST Legal Advisory Group, Public Network Operators Interest Group, Competition Law Association.

Career: Qualified 1991. Appointed Partner and Head of Department in 1991. Previously qualified as a Barrister in 1986.

Personal: Born 5th November 1962. Attended Cambridge University 1981-84 (BA Hons). Leisure interests include rugby, golf, squash and chess. Lives in Richmond, London.

Rhodes, Michael
Coudert Brothers, London (0171) 248 3000. Associate in Corporate, Computer and Communications Department.

Specialisation: Work covers I.T. and telecommunications, I.P., competition and public procurement. Editor and regular contributor to 'Computer Law and Practice' (Tolley); contributor to 'Telecomms Users'

Guide to Regulations' 1995-96 (CommEd) and 'Telecommunications Law and Practice' (Sweet & Maxwell). Regular conference speaker.

Career: Qualified 1989. Joined *Coudert Brothers* as an associate in 1993.

Personal: Born 13th May 1964. Attended Manchester University 1982-85 (BSc-physics), then QMW, London 1988-90 (LLM - IP and competition law).

Robertson, D. Ronald C.
Field Fisher Waterhouse, London (0171) 481 4841. Head of Information Technology Law Group.

Specialisation: Main area of practice is IT work. Advises a mixture of UK and overseas user and supplier clients on computing, telecoms and multimedia mattters. Includes IT procurement, oursourcing and supply, distribution agreements, software acquisition and licensing, IP protection, software piracy, business ventures, EDI, IT/ IP aspects of corporate reconstructions and computer disputes. Author of 'Legal Protection of Computer Software' and Computer Contracts section of Butterworths Forms and Precedents. Contributor to Encyclopaedia of Information Law. Lectures both in UK and overseas on IT law matters. Editorial Panels of Computer Law and Security and IT Law Today.

Prof. Memberships: Law Society, British Computer Society, Worshipful Company of Information Technologists, FAST Legal Advisory Group (Chairman of FAST, 1985-86), London Computer Law Group, Director of Computer Law Association. Inc.

Career: Business Affairs, EMI Music 1974-80. Qualified 1980. Legal Services Manager, CAP/ SEMA 1980-87. Joined *Stephenson Harwood* 1987, Partner 1988. Left to join *Field Fisher Waterhouse* in 1993 as a Partner.

Personal: Born 23rd April 1948. Attended University of Auckland, New Zealand 1969-72. Lives in London.

Sandison, Hamish R.
Bird & Bird, London (0171) 415 6000. Partner in Company Department and member of Information Technology Group.

Specialisation: Main area of practice is IT law. Acts for both public bodies and private sector companies on IT procurement. Heads team representing CCTA (the Government's IT Procurement agency). Intellectual property and multimedia work is also covered, especially advising on copyright law. Clients include Motion Picture Export Association of America and numerous scientific and technical publishers. European Counsel to Software Publishers Association. Co-Author of 'Computer and Software Protection Law', 1989. Contributing Editor 'International Copyright and Neighbouring Rights', 1990. Lectures frequently in both UK and US. Appears on Legal Network T.V.

Prof. Memberships: Council of Institute of Intellectual Property, FAST Legal Advisory

Group, Intellectual Property Committee of the British Computer Society.

Career: Admitted to Washington DC Bar 1980. Qualified in UK 1989. Joined *Bird & Bird* 1992 as a Partner.

Personal: Born 1952. Attended University College School, London 1960-70, Jesus College, Cambridge 1971-74, then University of California, Berkeley 1974-75. Lives in Usk, Gwent.

Segal, Arnold

Arnold Segal, London (0171) 242 8122. Sole Practitioner.

Specialisation: Principally computer and IT law including software licensing, distribution, copyright, hardware, maintenance, turnkey, and facilities management. Has lectured frequently to professional audiences, user groups and law courses. Contributor on patents, designs and trade marks to the Lawyers' Remembrancer.

Prof. Membership: Law Society, FAST Legal Advisory Group, Society for Computers and Law, BCS.

Career: Assistant Legal Adviser/Company Secretary Alcan Aluminium. Legal Adviser to Morgan Crucible. Partner *Spark & Co.* Established *Arnold Segal* in 1986. Associated with *Rosenblatt* since 1994.

Personal: Born 17th July 1943. Attended King's College, London. Leisure pursuits include travel, theatre, cinema and reading. Lives in London.

Small, Harry

Baker & McKenzie, London (0171) 919 1000. Partner in Intellectual Property and Information Technology Department.

Specialisation: Principal area of practice is IT Law, including computer litigation, software protection and IT contracts (especially out sourcing). Other main area of work is IP law, covering enforcement of IP rights, copyright and designs law and multimedia contracts. Acted in many significant computer systems disputes and on the MDIS management buyout. Contributor to Sweet & Maxwell IT Encyclopaedia and author of numerous articles on IP and IT law for various legal periodicals. Regularly addresses conferences and is lecturer on designs on Bristol University Intellectual Property Diploma course.

Prof. Membership: Law Society, Computer Law Group, Patent Solicitors Association.

Career: Articled with *Linklaters & Paines* 1979-81 and then Assistant Solicitor 1981-86. Joined *Baker & McKenzie* in 1986 and became a Partner in 1989.

Personal: Born 20th April 1957. Attended St. Alban's Grammar School 1968-75, then Oriel College, Oxford 1975-78. Leisure pursuits include travel, railways, computers, books and sleeping. Lives in London.

Smith, Graham

See under Company/Commercial.

Stamp, Nigel

The Simkins Partnership, London (0171) 631 1050. Solicitor in the Company/Commercial Department responsible for IT and member of the cross departmental multi-media group.

Specialisation: Main area of practice is information technology and multi-media law (contentious and non-contentious). Has 10 years experience in senior management in the IT industry. Advises on, negotiates and drafts all major IT contracts for both suppliers and users including advice on UK and EU competition law and data protection registration and compliance. Advises on disputes between suppliers and users, involving both hardware and software including litigation in all major courts. Advises on multimedia projects, including all contractual, rights clearance and royalty issues and financing for both on-line and fixed media products and services. Other area of practice is intellectual property law including copyright and trade mark licensing and trade mark registration and infringement. Cases handled have included a negligence and breach of contract action against a plc software house; non-textual infringement of copyright in software dispute; computer insurance third party recovery litigation for a high street bank and financial data distribution and licensing agreements for a daily newspaper. Speaker at seminars and conferences on the EU Directives on software and data protection.

Prof. Membership: Law Society, Society for Computers & Law.

Career: Qualified in 1993. IT Systems Consultant, IMS International, London 1977-80; Head of Management Information Systems, NEC, London 1985-86; Head of Systems Development, Nomura International, London 1986-89; Solicitor with *Saunders Sobell Leigh & Dobin* from 1993-4, joined *The Simkins Partnership* in 1994.

Personal: Born 3rd July 1954. Holds an LLB from Essex University, 1983. Leisure interests include music, tennis, golf, skiing and reading. Lives in Wimbledon.

Susskind, Richard

Masons, London (0171) 490 4000. Special Adviser. Consulting Department.

Specialisation: Principal area of practice is information technology advising on the use of IT by lawyers and giving specialist advice on major computer transactions and disputes. Other main area of practice is legal risk management, advising large organisations on identifying and controlling the legal risks arising from their operations and activities. Involved in technology support for the Channel Tunnel disputes and outsourcing and development projects for the London Stock Exchange. Clients include the European Commission and numerous Government Departments. Author of three books and numerous articles. Visiting Professor, Centre for Law, Computers and Technology. Charge-out rate is £200-£250 per hour.

Prof. Membership: Honorary Member, Society for Computers and the Law; Court Liveryman, Worshipful Company of Information Technologists.

Career: Tutor, Oxford University 1984-86. With Ernst & Young 1986-89. Special Adviser at *Masons* from 1989. Management Board Member from 1994.

Personal: Born 28th March 1961. Educated at Glasgow University (LL.B 1st Class Hons, 1982 and Diploma in Legal Practice, 1983) and Balliol College, Oxford (Doctorate, D.Phil, Computers and Law). Leisure pursuits include running, reading and playing with children. Lives in Bushey.

Walden, Ian

Tarlo Lyons, London (0171) 405 2000. The Tarlo Lyons Information Technology Law Senior Research Fellow in the Centre for Commercial Law Studies, Queen Mary & Westfield College, seconded during 1995 to the EC. Advisor to *Tarlo Lyons* IT Law Unit.

Webster, Michael J.B.

Rowe & Maw, London (0171) 248 4282. Qualified 1967. Partner 1973. Company/commercial Department. Information Technology and Communications Group. Specialises in a wide range of non-contentious agreements involving software/hardware transfer and/or supply. Born in 1942.

Westmacott, Philip G.

Bristows Cooke & Carpmael, London (0171) 400 8000. Partner in Intellectual Property Department.

Specialisation: The full range of intellectual property work, contentious and non-contentious, with an emphasis on disputes involving, and advice to, the IT and computer industries. Has given evidence as an expert on UK IP law in US proceedings. Cases include, for the plaintiff, IBM v. Phoenix, Monsanto v. Maxwell M Hart and Monsanto v. Stauffer and, for the defendant, Smith Myers Communications Ltd v. Motorola and Norton Christensen v. Foseco. Lecturer and marker on the Bristol University Diploma in Intellectual Property Law and Practice.

Prof. Membership: Law Society, Associate of Chartered Institute of Patent Agents, London Computer Law Group, AIPPI.

Career: Undergraduate trainee at Tube Investments Ltd 1971-74. Joined *Bristows Cooke & Carpmael* on qualification in 1978 and became a partner in 1985.

Personal: Born 15th April 1954. Educated at Cambridge University 1972-75 (Engineering and Law). Enjoys sailing, walking, skiing and cycling. Lives in London.

Wildish, N.D.

Nabarro Nathanson, London (0171) 493 9933.

Bailes, Tony G.

Nabarro Nathanson, Reading (01734) 504700. Qualified 1975. Partner 1995. Head of Infotech Communications and Multimedia Group. Born 15.5.1951.

Booy, Anna C.H.

Dallas Brett, Oxford (01865) 791990. Qualified 1987. Partner 1995. Intellectual Property Department. Practice covers all aspects of intellectual property as well as entertainment law and retail law. Born 19.6.1962.

Byatt, Lorne

Dundas & Wilson CS, Edinburgh (0131) 228 8000. Qualified 1981. Associate 1990. Corporate Department. Main area of practice is intellectual property, especially hi-tech matters. Also handles information technology work. Born in 1955.

Davis, Dai

Eversheds, Leeds (0113) 243 0391. Partner.

Specialisation: Main areas of practice are computer and technology law. Advises on sale of computer systems, licensing of computer systems, intellectual property, joint ventures, development agreements and facility management agreements. Also advises on the safety of technological products, and on compliance with technology related European Union legislation such as Electromagnetic Compatibility Directive. Acts in DTI funded project Fresco: a Framework for the Evaluation of Safety Critical Objects. Author of chapters in Safety Aspects of Computer Control and in the Comparative Law Year Book of International Business 1993. Contributor to Computing and Control Engineering Journal. Speaker at more than 12 conferences per year; co-opted legal expert to BSI committee QMS/ 23/ 1 and to IC Committee TC 56 Legal Working Group.

Prof. Membership: Member of Institution of Electrical Engineers; Honorary Scientific Member of International Association of Cybernetics; Honorary Member of Center for International Legal Studies; Member of Licensing Executives Society.

Career: Joined *Eversheds Hepworth & Chadwick* in 1987; became a Partner in 1992.

Personal: Born 2nd March 1958. Took a Physics MA at Keble College, Oxford 1976-79; then Computing Science at Newcastle University 1981-83. Leisure interests include tennis, reading and cooking. Lives in Boston Spa.

Flint, David

See under Intellectual Property.

Gaskill, Shelagh

Masons, Leeds. Partner 1994. Technology Department. Information law specialist.

Godar, George W.

Alsop Wilkinson, Manchester (0161) 834 7760. Partner in Intellectual Property & Computer Law Department.

Specialisation: Principal area of practice is intellectual property, commercial, computers and competition. Handles both litigation and advisory work in relation to patents, trade marks, copyright, design rights, technology, franchising, software and hardware. Also deals with EC law, including public procurement. Has been involved in engineering, technology and pharmaceutical litigation, including claims arising out of the collapse of the Milford Haven box girder bridge, subsidence at Oldbury nuclear power station, the collapse of the Emley Moor television mast and the Ronan Point tower block. Has spoken at conferences on trade marks, intellectual property licensing, technology transfer and computer contracts.

Prof. Membership: Law Society, Solicitors European Group, Society for Computers and Law, London Solicitors Litigation Association, International Trademark Association, Federation Against Software Theft.

Career: Qualified in 1974. Partner with *Wilkinson Kimbers* from 1975 and Head of Intellectual Property and Computer Law Department from 1985. Partner with *Alsop Wilkinson* from 1988. Admitted as a solicitor in Hong Kong in 1988.

Personal: Born 11th November 1948. Educated at Nottingham High School 1959-67 and King's College, Cambridge 1968-71 (MA, Mechanical Sciences and Law). Interests include theatre, running, classic cars and travel. Lives in Berkhamsted, Herts.

Holt, Jeremy

Charles Russell, Swindon (01793) 617444. Partner specialising in computer law.

Specialisation: Advises on all aspects of non-contentious work including software rights, system purchase agreements and maintenance contracts.

Prof. Membership: Society for Computers and Law, British Computer Society.

Career: Qualified in 1980, became a partner in *Charles Russell* in 1986.

Personal: Born 1956. Leisure interests include military history and long distance running.

Jones, Bill

Wragge & Co, Birmingham (0121) 233 1000. Qualified 1984. Partner 1990. Main area of practice is computer law and information technology, handling both contentious and non-contentious matters. Born 12.7.1947.

Klinger, Paul

Shoosmiths & Harrison, Reading (01734) 498765. Qualified 1980. Sole Principal 1991. Main area of practice is computer law: computer consultant to *Shoosmiths & Harrison*. Also handles commercial and employment law. Born 4.8.1946.

Macpherson, Shonaig

See under Intellectual Property.

Maughan, Alistair

Dibb Lupton Broomhead, Sheffield (0114) 272 0202. Partner in Commercial and Regulatory Department.

Specialisation: Regional Head of the firm's IT and telecommunications practice. Acts for government departments (e.g. the DSS in Lytham St. Anne's, Inland Revenue), educational bodies and manufacturing entities all over the north. Specialises in IT, multimedia and technology acquisition/ supply contracts. Work is mainly non-contentious and divided equally between major government contracts and contracts for private sector clients. Handled the Inland Revenue Information Technology Office outsourcing and the DVOIT privatisation (first privatisation of a UK government executive agency). Author of several articles on computer law and export controls. Has lectured on outsourcing of IT, multimedia, export controls and acquiring computer systems.

Prof. Membership: Law Society, New York State Bar, NY State Bar Association, Society for Computers and the Law, Computer Law Association.

Career: Qualified in 1987. With *Boodle Hatfield* 1985-89, then *Crowell & Moring* in Washington D.C, 1989-92. Qualified in New York in 1990. At *Theodore Goddard* 1992-93, before joining *Dibb Lupton Broomhead* in 1993. Became a Partner in 1994.

Personal: Born 22nd August 1963. Educated at Bradford Grammar School (to 1981), Leicester University (to 1984). and the New York Bar (1990). Recreations include sport.

Maybury, Neil

See under Intellectual Property.

Moakes, Jonathan

See under Intellectual Property.

Nicolson, Fiona M.M.

Maclay Murray & Spens, Glasgow (0141) 248 5011.

O'Leary, Marcus

The Law Offices of Marcus J. O'Leary, Reading (01734) 880245. Principal.

Specialisation: Main area of practice is IT, including the drafting and negotiation of computer and software distribution, development, evaluation and licensing arrangements. All areas covered especially multi-media, disaster recovery, software piracy and hardware/software disputes. Other principal area of practice is intellectual property where experience encompasses copyright, design, patent, biotechnology, trade mark, passing off, confidential information, advertising, trade libel, music, media and entertainment, franchising and character merchandising issues as well as intellectual property health checks and hi-tech litigation.

Acts for many leading international technology companies including Dell Computer Corporation, CompuServe and Cognos. Author of a number of articles in the in the IP/IT press and consulted by them. Has been interviewed by the BBC on software piracy issues.

Prof. Membership: Law Society, Society for Computers and the Law, Legal Advisory Group to the Federation against Software Theft, Intellectual Property Advisory Committee Forum, BioIndustry, Association, Japan Association.

Career: Called to the Bar in 1984. Solicitor in 1990. Manager of Legal Affairs at Hewlett Packard, and an Intellectual Property Lawyer for the United Biscuits Group. Formerly Head of IP/IT at Garrett & Co and at Pitmans. Set up own law offices in 1995.

Personal: Born 31st October 1952. Educated at London University and the Inns of Court School of Law. Enjoys sailing, writing, learning Japanese and Judo. Occasional rock climber. Lives in Eversley, Hampshire.

Ollerenshaw, Zoe

Masons, Manchester (0161) 877 3777. Qualified 1987. Solicitor in Computers and Communications Group. All types of computer contracts. Also handles technology transfer and IP licensing.

Peeters, Michael P.D.

Pinsent Curtis, Leeds (0113) 244 5000. Partner in Commercial Department.

Specialisation: Principal area of practice is information technology law including major I.T. procurement contracts, data protection, telecommunications, electronic trading, software licensing and distribution, and dispute resolution. Other main area of work is intellectual property law, particularly international software copyright. Frequently addresses seminars and conferences. Registered Trade Mark Agent.

Career: *Clifford Chance* 1986 until 1992, then became Head of I.T. Law Unit at *Simpson Curtis* in Leeds.

Probert, E.A.W.

Anstey Sargent & Probert, Exeter (01392) 411221. Partner in commercial department specialising in Employment and Intellectual Property.

Specialisation: Main area of specialisation is employment law, with particular emphasis on negotiating and drafting employment contracts, staff handbooks and advising on disciplinary and redundancy procedures. Other area of expertise in intellectual property with a particular emphasis on computer software licensing. Lectured for several years on employment law to the Exeter University MBA course and on computer and management issues to Solicitors. Author of employment section of part work to be published by Longmans in 1995 and chaired Employment Lawyers Group of QLG in 1984.

Prof. Membership: Society for Computers & Law; Employment Lawyers Association.

Career: Qualified in 1978 with *Anstey Sargent & Probert* after articles with Gouldens. Became a partner in 1982.

Personal: Born 13 March 1953. Attended Clifton College and Christs College, Cambridge. Leisure interests include windsurfing, running, badminton, 'Tractions Avant' and computers. Lives in Exeter.

Rees, Phillip

Edwards Geldard, Cardiff (01222) 238239. Partner and Joint Head of Intellectual Property Department.

Specialisation: Deals with all aspects of IT and telecoms work, in particular, FM and EDI arrangements, multi media and banking technology. Other area of specialism is media and entertainment, in particular animation, international co-production work, character merchandising and defamation. Also deals with general intellectual property work and public sector and utilities IT procurement. Regular conference speaker.

Prof. Membership: Intellectual Property Commission of the European Lawyers Association, Society for Computers and the Law, CBI Public Procurement Contact Group, Producer's Alliance for Cinema and Television, Institute of Arbitrators, British Computer Society, National Computer Centre Legal Group.

Career: Qualified in 1986 after articles with *Peter Carter Ruck & Partners*. With *Alsop Wilkinson* 1986-88. Joined *Edwards Geldard* in 1988, Partner in 1991.

Personal: Born 18th March 1961. Educated at the University of Anglia 1979-82.

Reid, Christine

Morrell Peel & Gamlen, Oxford (01865) 242468. Partner.

Specialisation: Advises on, negotiates and drafts a wide range of computer and information technology contracts; software development, software licensing, hardware sales, support and maintenance, facilities management, disaster recovery, use of on-line systems, research and collaboration agreements, distribution and agency agreements.

Prof. Membership: Law Society, Society for Computers and Law.

Career: Qualified 1981. Partner in 1986.

Personal: Born 1954. Educated St Hilda's College Oxford.

Renshaw, Peter B.A.

See under Corporate Finance.

Sampson, Ian C.

Booth & Co., Leeds (0113) 283 2000. Partner in Intellectual Property Department.

Specialisation: Main areas of specialisation are information technology and non-contentious intellectual property. Work includes licensing, facilities management, turnkey

contracts, development and collaboration agreements, know-how and technology licensing, and sponsorship and endorsement agreements. Major clients include Oxford Molecular Group Plc and Scottish Provident Institution. Lecturing includes Leeds Business School/ Institute of Directors seminars, European Study Conferences (eg International Patent Symposium, Munich, March 1994; 'Keeping Control of Your Licensees', April 1995) and at Capitol University, Columbus, Ohio (EC Antitrust Law Guest Lecturer, October 1990 and 1992).

Prof. Membership: LES, IBA, Society for Computers and Law.

Career: Qualified at *Baker & McKenzie* in 1987. With *Baker & McKenzie* 1987-88. Joined *Booth & Co* in 1988. Became a Partner in 1992.

Personal: Born 13th October 1960. Educated at the University of Kent 1980-83. Enjoys cross country running. Lives in Sicklinghall, North Yorkshire.

Sternberg, Nigel P.

See under Education.

Wood, Alan P.

Osborne Clarke, Bristol (0117) 923 0220. Qualified 1975. Partner 1988. Intellectual Property Department. Emphasis on information technology, franchising, publishing and technology transfer. Born 29.8.1951.

Yates, John

Oxley & Coward, Rotherham (01709) 374091. Partner in Commercial Department.

Specialisation: Main area of practice is computer and I.T. law, including computer contracts and disputes. Clients include national and international computer companies, health authorities, NHS trusts and other public bodies. Author of numerous articles on all aspects of computer law. Regular speaker on outsourcing and computer disputes.

Prof. Membership: Society of Computers and Law.

Career: Qualified in 1984. IBM In-house lawyer 1984-87. Partner at *Theodore Goddard* in Computer Group, 1987-93. Joined *Oxley & Coward* as a Partner in 1993.

Personal: Born 8th May 1959. Attended Leeds University (LLB) and Oxford University (BCL). Leisure interests include mountaineering and rock climbing. Lives in Sheffield.

CONSTRUCTION & CIVIL ENGINEERING

FIRMS practising in construction law tend to be divided into those dealing with 'pure' construction law (such as pre-contract advice, contract documentation and disputes) and those which have a bias towards indemnity work (representing architects/surveyors/engineers or their insurers in professional negligence claims). Of the latter category, this list includes only those firms that are particularly well known within the construction industry. A complete list of professional indemnity specialists can be found elsewhere in the Directory.

LONDON

Our research shows that the two most highly recommended construction firms in London are *Masons,* the largest in the field and *Fenwick Elliott,* a relatively small practice but one which has risen considerably in reputation.

LEADING FIRMS – LONDON	
FENWICK ELLIOTT	MASONS
FREEDMAN CHURCH	
BAKER & McKENZIE	BRISTOWS COOKE & CARPMAEL
DAVIES ARNOLD COOPER	McKENNA & CO
ROWE & MAW	WINWARD FEARON

Of the two, *Masons* is marginally ahead in terms of expertise, having a very strong team in John Bishop, Anthony Bunch, Martin Harman and Mark Lane. Nationwide, the firm has in excess of 100 specialist fee-earners.

HIGHLY REGARDED – LONDON	
ALLEN & OVERY	CLIFFORD CHANCE
DIBB LUPTON BROOMHEAD	FRESHFIELDS
LINKLATERS & PAINES	LOVELL WHITE DURRANT
McGRIGOR DONALD	NABARRO NATHANSON
ALSOP WILKINSON	ASHURST MORRIS CRISP
S J BERWIN & CO	BERWIN LEIGHTON
BRECHER & CO	DENTON HALL
D J FREEMAN	EVERSHEDS
EVERSHEDS	FORSYTE SAUNDERS KERMAN
FOX & GIBBONS	GLOVERS
GOULDENS	HEXTALL, ERSKINE
LANE & PARTNERS	NORTON ROSE
PARK NELSON THOMPSON QUARRELL	ROSLING KING
SIMMONS & SIMMONS	SPEECHLY BIRCHAM
STEPHENSON HARWOOD	TROWERS & HAMLINS
WEDLAKE BELL	
FIELD FISHER WATERHOUSE	VIZARDS
WARNER CRANSTON	

The firm is equally well known for contentious and non-contentious work and handles a wide range of contract, project finance, arbitration, litigation and ADR work on both a national and an international scale.

By contrast, *Fenwick Elliott* has only 13 fee earners. The firm advises public and private sector clients on complex construction and engineering projects, both on- and off-shore, although the larger part of their practice is within the UK. The firm is particularly strong on the litigation side and has conducted some important cases in recent months. Robert Fenwick Elliott (regarded as a leading authority) has written a textbook on litigation within the construction industry and is the editor of the 'Construction Industry Law Letter'.

Freedman Church, (a recent merger between the niche construction practices *Freedmans* and *Church & Church*) is perceived to be more active in the market place than in previous years, with Victoria Russell, Peter Shaw and Christopher Bourgeois all being recommended. The firm has seven specialist partners and five assistant solicitors, two of whom are dual qualified, and deals with a wide variety of work for contractors, sub-contractors, property investors and public bodies.

LEADING FIRMS – LONDON – PROFESSIONAL INDEMNITY	
BEALE AND CO	BERRYMANS
KENNEDYS	

Larger firms with highly regarded construction practices include *Baker & McKenzie, Bristows Cooke & Carpmael, Davies Arnold Cooper, McKenna & Co, Rowe & Maw* and *Winward Fearon.*

Bristows Cooke & Carpmael's construction unit comprises six specialist partners, headed by the highly regarded James Hudson, who has recently been appointed as Chairman of the Official Referee's Association. The firm's work includes a large volume of litigation, (including reported cases such as ICI plc v. Bovis Construction Ltd) and arbitration for major clients within the construction and engineering industries.

HIGHLY REGARDED – LONDON – PROFESSIONAL INDEMNITY	
ALASTAIR THOMSON & PARTNERS	BARLOW LYDE & GILBERT
FISHBURN BOXER	REYNOLDS PORTER CHAMBERLAIN
BEACHCROFT STANLEYS	CAMERON MARKBY HEWITT
JARVIS & BANNISTER	ORCHARD
PARK NELSON THOMPSON QUARRELL	

Davies Arnold Cooper's construction practice is a significant force both in the UK and internationally. Work carried out includes arbitration, litigation, contract formation advice and procurement. Daniel Gowan and John Bolton have been recommended.

McKenna & Co is perceived to have a slightly lower profile than in previous years, although the construction department is still very active and has a strong team in Ann Minogue, Peter Long, Henry Sherman and Trevor Butcher. The firm has a sound reputation for construction work with an international flavour and has specialists in its foreign offices (particularly Hong Kong).

The construction departments at *Rowe & Maw* and *Winward Fearon* are best known for building litigation. John Rushton and Tony Blackler of *Rowe & Maw* and David Cornes at *Winward Fearon* are highly experienced.

Other firms with notable construction practices include *Allen & Overy, Clifford Chance, Freshfields, Linklaters & Paines, Lovell White Durrant* and *Nabarro Nathanson* which has been recommended for non-contentious building work.

Allen & Overy, in addition to providing construction-related advice to its corporate clients, also advises governments and major international contractors on build, operate and transfer schemes and other joint ventures, energy, leisure and airport projects.

Clifford Chance is renowned for contentious international arbitration, John Beechey having been recommended as an authority.

The highly regarded Sally Roe heads *Freshfields'* construction group which comprises seven specialist partners primarily advising employers and contractors.

Linklaters & Paines has a thriving construction practice acting for clients in the public and private sectors. Marshall Levine is held in high regard.

Lovell White Durrant is known for international work and in particular major projects which have recently included road projects in China, water projects in Eastern Europe and the Middle East and an airport project in the Far East. Nicholas Gould has been recommended.

Individual practitioners who have been highly recommended include David Miles of *Glovers* and Suzanne Reeves of *Wedlake Bell*.

The firms most frequently recommended for professional indemnity work include *Berrymans, Beale & Co* and *Kennedys*. Other firms with sound reputations include *Alastair Thompson & Partners, Barlow Lyde & Gilbert, Orchard* (Andrea Burns has been highly recommended) and *Reynolds Porter Chamberlain*.

SOUTH EAST

Shadbolt & Co has an outstanding reputation both nationally and internationally. Assisted by a team of five specialist partners, Richard Shadbolt handles contentious and non-contentious work for major contractors including Kier and Amey.

HIGHLY REGARDED – SOUTH EAST	
BALDOCKS *Guildford*	COLE and COLE *Oxford*
CRIPPS HARRIES HALL *Tunbridge Wells*	DONNE MILEHAM & HADDOCK *Brighton*
HAROLD BENJAMIN *Harrow*	MERRICKS *Chelmsford*
PENNINGTONS *Basingstoke*	SHADBOLT & CO *Reigate*

Other firms with expertise in construction law include *Cole and Cole, Cripps Harries Hall* which represents a number of residential developers, *Donne Mileham & Haddock* which provides advice on all aspects including project structuring and financing *Harold Benjamin & Collins, Merricks* and *Penningtons*, the latter three mainly handling litigation work.

LEADING INDIVIDUALS – SOUTH EAST
Peter Ashford *Cripps Harries Hall*
Susan Nadine Batstone *Donne Mileham & Haddock*
Richard A. Shadbolt *Shadbolt & Co*

SOUTH WEST

Laytons and *Masons* emerge as the pre-eminent construction practices in the South West. Both firms are renowned for their contentious work and in particular for representing contractors and sub-contractors.

John Redmond and Nicholas Guppy of *Laytons* and Mark Collingwood and Adam Harris of *Masons* are held in high regard.

Burges Salmon represents public bodies, contractors and sub-contractors, professionals, funders, insurers and suppliers and has an excellent reputation both for conten-

LEADING INDIVIDUALS – LONDON		
John Bishop *Masons*	**A.J.M. Blackler** *Rowe & Maw*	**John Bolton** *Davies Arnold Cooper*
Anthony Bunch *Masons*	**Andrea Burns** *Orchard*	**David L. Cornes** *Winward Fearon*
Robert J. Fenwick Elliott *Fenwick Elliott*	**Daniel Gowan** *Davies Arnold Cooper*	**Martin Harman** *Masons*
James J.S. Hudson *Bristows Cooke & Carpmael*	**Mark Lane** *Masons*	**Marshall F. Levine** *Linklaters & Paines*
Peter J. Long *McKenna & Co*	**David Miles** *Glovers*	**Ann Minogue** *McKenna & Co*
Suzanne Reeves *Wedlake Bell*	**Sally Jean Roe** *Freshfields*	**John Michael Rushton** *Rowe & Maw*
Victoria E. Russell *Freedman Church*	**Henry C. Sherman** *McKenna & Co*	
John Beechey *Clifford Chance*	**Christopher Bourgeois** *Freedman Church*	**Martin Bridgewater** *Nabarro Nathanson*
Robert Bryan *Simmons & Simmons*	**Simon Burch** *Linklaters & Paines*	**Trevor Butcher** *McKenna & Co*
Terry Fleet *Berwin Leighton*	**Michael R. Gibson** *Berwin Leighton*	**R. Nicholas H. Gould** *Lovell White Durrant*
Geoff Haley *S J Berwin & Co*	**Joseph Hannah** *Fenwick Elliott*	**Jonathan Hosie** *Baker & McKenzie*
Michael Mendelblat *Nabarro Nathanson*	**David W. Race** *Nicholson Graham & Jones*	**M.D. Regan** *Rowe & Maw*
James W. Shaw *Kennedys*	**Peter R. Shaw** *Freedman Church*	**Georgina Squire** *Rosling King*
Simon J.A. Tolson *Fenwick Elliott*	**John J. Ward** *Beale and Co*	**Christopher John Wright** *Warner Cranston*

tious and non-contentious work. Marcus Harling is regarded as a leading authority.

Bevan Ashford's construction unit comprises nine specialist practitioners, six of whom operate from the Bristol Office. The firm advises on a variety of contentious and non-contentious matters although the Cardiff office is primarily litigation based.

HIGHLY REGARDED – SOUTH WEST

LAYTONS *Bristol*	MASONS *Bristol*
BEVAN ASHFORD *Bristol*	BOND PEARCE *Plymouth*
BURGES SALMON *Bristol*	TOWNSENDS *Swindon*
VEALE WASBROUGH *Bristol*	WANSBROUGHS WILLEY HARGRAVE *Bristol*
LYONS DAVIDSON *Bristol*	OVER TAYLOR BIGGS *Exeter*
STONES *Exeter*	

Firms noted for their expertise on the professional indemnity side of construction law include *Veale Wasbroughs* (Roger Hoyle) and *Wansbrough Willey Hargrave* (John Vasey). Both firms also handle non-contentious work.

Outside Bristol, the leading construction practice is *Bond Pearce* which is well known for building litigation and professional indemnity work.

Townsends makes its first appearance in our recommended section this year. The firm handles a broad spectrum of work, including litigation and draws on expertise from a variety of established disciplines.

LEADING INDIVIDUALS – SOUTH WEST

Mark Collingwood *Masons*	
John V. Redmond *Laytons*	
W. Nicholas Guppy *Laytons*	
Marcus Harling *Burges Salmon*	
Adam Harris *Masons*	
Roger V. Hoyle *Veale Wasbrough*	
John R. Vasey *Wansbroughs Willey Hargrave*	

WALES

Cardiff firms tend to take the lion's share of construction work in Wales.

Hugh James Jones & Jenkins has long been at the forefront of building litigation work, although the firm also handles a substantial amount of professional indemnity work, representing major insurers. Michael Jefferies and Michael Jones are both experienced litigators.

HIGHLY REGARDED – WALES

EDWARDS GELDARD *Cardiff*	HUGH JAMES JONES & JENKINS *Cardiff*
KELLER PINNEY *Cardiff*	MORGAN BRUCE *Cardiff*

Other firms with notable practices include *Edwards Geldard, Keller Pinney* and *Morgan Bruce*.

All three firms advise on a broad range of contentious and non-contentious work, arbitration and ADR. *Keller Pinney* has, in addition, developed expertise in professional indemnity work.

LEADING INDIVIDUALS – WALES

Michael G. Jefferies *Hugh James Jones & Jenkins*	
Michael L.N. Jones *Hugh James Jones & Jenkins*	

MIDLANDS

The leading Midlands construction firms are *Edge & Ellison, Eversheds* (particularly Harry Forrester), *Pinsent Curtis,* and *Wragge & Co* (where Andrew Manning-Cox has been highly recommended), all of whom handle a broad range of contentious and non-contentious work.

HIGHLY REGARDED – MIDLANDS

EDGE & ELLISON *Birmingham*	EVERSHEDS *Birmingham*
FREETH CARTWRIGHT HUNT DICKINS *Nottingham*	GATELEY WAREING *Birmingham*
HACKING ASHTON *Newcastle-under-Lyme*	MARTINEAU JOHNSON *Birmingham*
NEIL F. JONES & CO *Birmingham*	PINSENT CURTIS *Birmingham*
WRAGGE & CO *Birmingham*	

Neil F. Jones & Co is a niche construction firm representing employers, contractors and sub-contractors and professionals and their insurers in all aspects of construction and indemnity work. The highly regarded founding partner, Neil Jones, has now retired but remains with the firm on a consultancy basis. Kevin Barrett has also been recommended.

LEADING INDIVIDUALS – MIDLANDS

Kevin John Barrett *Neil F. Jones & Co*	
Harry O. Forrester *Eversheds*	
Neil F. Jones *Neil F. Jones & Co*	
Frances M. Kirkham *Edge & Ellison*	
Andrew Manning-Cox *Wragge & Co*	

EAST ANGLIA

Mills & Reeve is the leading construction practice in the region, with Ronald Plascow regarded as an authority in the field. The firm has recently undergone a period of expansion and now boasts a number of construction specialists from City of London firms in addition to its existing team.

HIGHLY REGARDED – EAST ANGLIA

EVERSHEDS *Norwich*	GREENWOODS *Peterborough*
MERRICKS *Ipswich*	MILLS & REEVE *Norwich*

Greenwoods is also noted for its expertise in the field. Involved with major industrial, retail, public and commercial schemes, the construction unit draws on experience from a number of disciplines and is able to advise on any issue, whether contentious or non-contentious.

Other firms with experience include *Eversheds* and *Merricks*.

LEADING INDIVIDUALS – EAST ANGLIA

Ronald H. Plascow *Mills & Reeve*	

NORTH WEST

Masons maintains its position as the North West's premier construction firm, handling major construction and engineering work. Like its London counterpart, it has an international reputation. Edward Davies, Peter Wood and Ian Radford have been highly recommended.

LEADING FIRMS – NORTH WEST

DAVIES ARNOLD COOPER Manchester	**MASONS** *Manchester*

Davies Arnold Cooper undertakes the full range of construction and engineering work and represents a number of major clients in the industry. The firm is particularly well known for building litigation, partly due to the reputation of Andrew Willcock.

Other firms noted for their expertise include *Addleshaw Sons & Latham* (where Huw Baker is highly regarded), *Cobbett Leak Almond* (particularly Philip Hodson), *Dibb Lupton Broomhead* and *Kirk Jackson* where Kenneth Salmon has been recommended.

HIGHLY REGARDED – NORTH WEST

ADDLESHAW SONS & LATHAM Manchester	**COBBETT LEAK ALMOND** *Manchester*
DIBB LUPTON BROOMHEAD Manchester	**KIRK JACKSON** *Manchester*
ALSOP WILKINSON *Liverpool*	**DAVIES WALLIS FOYSTER** *Liverpool*
FREEDMAN CHURCH	**HAMMOND SUDDARDS** *Manchester*
INGHAM CLEGG & CROWTHER *Preston*	
AARON & PARTNERS *Chester,,*	**COLEMANS** *Manchester*
HILL DICKINSON DAVIS CAMPBELL Liverpool	**LACE MAWER** *Manchester*
WEIGHTMAN RUTHERFORDS *Liverpool*	

All of these firms undertake a broad range of contentious and non-contentious work. *Addleshaw Sons & Latham* is particularly known for representing developers and sub-contractors, while *Kirk Jackson* has a reputation for litigation and arbitration.

Davies Wallis Foyster are also noted for their expertise in the field.

LEADING INDIVIDUALS – NORTH WEST

Edward Davies *Masons*	
Andrew Willcock *Davies Arnold Cooper*	
Huw J. Baker *Addleshaw Sons & Latham*	
Philip Hodson *Cobbett Leak Almond*	
Ian Radford *Masons*	
Kenneth T. Salmon *Kirk Jackson*	
Peter Wood *Masons*	

NORTH EAST

In Leeds *Booth & Co, Dibb Lupton Broomhead, Hammond Suddards* and *Walker Morris* have excellent reputations for construction work. *Booth & Co* and *Dibb Lupton Broomhead* are considered to be marginally ahead in terms of sheer expertise, having outstanding practitioners such as Richard Cockram (*Booth & Co*) and Bruce Bentley (*Dibb Lupton Broomhead*). Both firms undertake the full range of contentious and non-contentious work. *Dibb Lupton Broomhead* is particularly known for building litigation.

The construction unit at *Hammond Suddards* undertakes contentious work for contractors, sub-contractors and employers. Mark Hilton and David Moss are held in high regard.

Walker Morris advises on non-contentious matters including contract and warranty negotiations and has had some notable victories in relation to professional negligence and defect claims.

HIGHLY REGARDED – NORTH EAST

BOOTH & CO. *Leeds*	**DIBB LUPTON BROOMHEAD** *Bradford*
DICKINSON DEES *Newcastle upon Tyne*	**EVERSHEDS** *Leeds*
EVERSHEDS *Newcastle upon Tyne*	**HAMMOND SUDDARDS** *Leeds*
MASONS	**NABARRO NATHANSON** *Doncaster*
ROBERT MUCKLE *Newcastle-upon-Tyne*	**WALKER MORRIS** *Leeds*
WATSON BURTON *Newcastle upon Tyne*	
DENISON TILL *York*	**HAY & KILNER** *Newcastle-upon-Tyne*

In Newcastle, *Dickinson Dees, Robert Muckle* where Roderick Gordon is held in high regard, and *Watson Burton* (Robert Langley) are acknowledged for their expertise in building litigation.

Eversheds construction practice comprises 17 fee-earners (three of whom are partners) operating from the Leeds office and three specialist partners (headed by Nigel Robson) in the Newcastle office. The firm has recently acquired new clients in the power generation and offshore engineering industries and the public sector. Alison Staniforth (Leeds) has been highly recommended.

LEADING INDIVIDUALS – NORTH EAST

Bruce Bentley *Dibb Lupton Broomhead*
Richard Cockram *Booth & Co.*
Roderick C.P.R. Gordon *Robert Muckle*
Mark W. Hilton *Hammond Suddards*
Robert Lennox Langley *Watson Burton*
David J. Moss *Hammond Suddards*
Nigel.R. Robson *Eversheds*
Alison J. Staniforth *Eversheds*

SCOTLAND

The most frequently recommended firms in Scotland include *MacRoberts* and *McGrigor Donald*.

MacRoberts construction department comprises three specialist partners dealing exclusively with non-contentious work and two handling litigation and arbitration cases. James Arnott and David Henderson are considered to be highly experienced in the field.

The construction department at *McGrigor Donald* operates from the Glasgow office. The team of three specialist partners headed by Brandon Nolan deals with a range of non-contentious issues, but is particularly known for building litigation. Vincent Connor is also highly regarded.

HIGHLY REGARDED – SCOTLAND

BIGGART BAILLIE & GIFFORD *Glasgow*	BIRD SEMPLE *Glasgow*
BISHOP AND ROBERTSON	W & J BURNESS WS *Edinburgh*
CHALMERS *Glasgow*	
DUNDAS & WILSON CS *Edinburgh*	LINDSAYS WS *Edinburgh*
MACROBERTS *Glasgow*	McGRIGOR DONALD *Glasgow*
SIMPSON & MARWICK WS *Edinburgh*	STEEDMAN RAMAGE WS *Edinburgh*

ALEX MORISON & CO WS *Edinburgh*	BALFOUR & MANSON *Edinburgh*
DORMAN JEFFREY & CO *Glasgow*	GILLESPIE MACANDREW *Edinburgh*
HENDERSON BOYD JACKSON *Edinburgh*	

Dundas & Wilson CS has a sound reputation, with construction work comprising 15% of the firm's workload. Alastair Morrison heads the team of four that represents a number of well known companies with construction interests.

Other firms with notable construction practices include *Bird Semple, Bishop & Robertson Chalmers* and *W & J Burness WS.*

LEADING INDIVIDUALS – SCOTLAND

James M. Arnott *MacRoberts*	
Vincent Connor *McGrigor Donald*	
David J. Henderson *MacRoberts*	
Alan D. MacKay *Lindsays WS*	
Alastair Morrison *Dundas & Wilson CS*	
Brandon E. Nolan *McGrigor Donald*	
Lindy A. Patterson *Bird Semple*	
Andrew L. Renton *Simpson & Marwick WS*	
Murray W.A. Shaw *Biggart Baillie & Gifford*	
John A. Welsh *Bishop and Robertson Chalmers*	

Bird Semple (particularly Lindy Patterson) and *Bishop & Robertson Chalmers* (John Welsh) have sound reputations for building litigation and arbitration, whilst *W & J Burness WS* has been recommended for non-contentious work.

Biggart Baillie & Gifford (Murray Shaw), *Lindsays WS* (Alan MacKay), *Simpson & Marwick WS* (Andrew Renton) and *Steedman Ramage WS* are also prominent.

NORTHERN IRELAND

Although the number of disputes arising in this area has probably fallen in the last year, several firms retain strong

HIGHLY REGARDED – NORTHERN IRELAND

JOHNS ELLIOT *Belfast*	L'ESTRANGE & BRETT *Belfast*
MILLS SELIG *Belfast*	TUGHAN & CO *Belfast*
CARSON & McDOWELL *Belfast*	CLEAVER FULTON & RANKIN *Belfast*
ELLIOTT DUFFY GARRETT *Belfast*	McKINTY & WRIGHT *Belfast*

practices within the field. Samuel Beckett at *L'Estrange & Brett* is a well-known specialist, as is Maurice Butler at *Johns Elliot* who sits on the Northern Ireland Housing Executive. Keith Cowan, who is also a member of the Executive, and Christine McClelland at *Tughan & Co* have excellent reputations for construction work. Brian Ham is highly regarded at *Mills Selig.*

LEADING INDIVIDUALS – NORTHERN IRELAND

Samuel R. Beckett *L'Estrange & Brett*	
Maurice R. Butler *Johns Elliot*	
Keith C.E. Cowan *Tughan & Co*	
Brian E. Ham *Mills Selig*	
Christine E.A. McClelland *Tughan & Co*	

LEADERS IN CONSTRUCTION & CIVIL ENGINEERING

LONDON

Beechey, John
See under Arbitration.

Bishop, John
Masons, London (0171) 490 4000. Senior Partner. Chairman of the Board, and Partner in Construction and Engineering Department.

Specialisation: Worked on projects in over 20 countries in Europe, Africa, Middle East and Far East and has substantial UK practice. Major projects include LRTS and Second Harbour Crossing in Hong Kong, Cairo Plaza, and the Channel Tunnel. Particular interests include international arbitration, ADR, cost effective litigation and use of technology. Non-contentious work includes joint ventures, all types of project documentation, BOT schemes, negotiating and drafting of contracts, insurances, guarantees, performance bonds, quality assurance, procurement, project management and project execution contracts. Contentious work involves litigation, arbitration, and ADR in the UK and internationally.

Prof. Memberships: Past Chairman (now Presdient) of Official Referees Solicitors Association; Member of Official Referees Users Committee, OR's Rules Committee, OR's IT Committee, ADR Committee, Past Member Law Society, Civil Litigation Committee, ICE Sub Committee on Expert Evidence, Founder Member of CEDR, previously served on (inter alia) Chartered Institute of Arbitrators' Committees on new forms of arbitration and ADR, British Academy of Experts Sub Committee, Blundel Memorial lecturer; Editorial Board of Construction Law Journal.

Career: Qualified 1971, becme a partner in 1972. Admitted in Hong Kong 1983. Managing Partner 1986-1990 and Senior Partner from 1990.

Personal: Attended Sherborne School. LLB Hons Queen Mary College, University of London. Leisure interests include golf, riding, tennis and bonfires.

Blackler, A.J.M.
Rowe & Maw, London (0171) 248 4282. Qualified 1967.

Bolton, John
Davies Arnold Cooper, London (0171) 936 2222. Qualified 1987. Partner 1991. Construction Department. Principal area of practice is construction litigation and arbitration. 25 years' construction industry experience. Born 29.9.1943.

Bourgeois, Christopher
Freedman Church, London (0171) 353 1330. Partner in Construction Department.

Specialisation: Principal area of practice is construction and engineering, and on and off-shore gas and oil contract law. Advises employers, main contractors, specialist sub-contractors, professionals and insurers on all forms of contract, standard form and "bespoke", and all points of practice and procedure. Also practises in environmental and planning law, as well as defamation actions. Clients include national and international construction and engineering companies (including process engineering), UK and foreign companies engaged in the manufacture of electrical and other technical components, UK and foreign government agencies, water companies, professional indemnity insurers, health trusts and developers. Lectures to local authorities, architects, engineers, quantity surveyors and management on building and engineering contracts, contentious and non-contentious matters, company reorganisations and environmental matters. Charge-out rate is £185 per hour.

Prof. Membership: Society of Construction Law, Worshipful Company of Arbitrators. Fellow of the Chartered Institute of Arbitrators.

Career: Qualified in 1975. Joined *Freedmans* in 1977 and became a Partner in 1979.

Personal: Born 17th May 1946. Leisure interests include shooting, coaching rugby, vintage car and property restoration. Lives in Abinger, Surrey.

Bridgewater, Martin

Nabarro Nathanson, London (0171) 493 9933. Qualified 1976. Hong Kong 1978. Partner 1984. Head of Construction Department. Main area of practice is non-contentious construction work. Mediation work is also covered.

Bryan, Robert

Simmons & Simmons, London (0171) 628 2020. Partner and Head of Construction Group.

Specialisation: Main field of activity concerns contentious and non- contentious construction law. Non-contentious work includes the preparation of and advice on construction contracts, consultant's appointments, collateral warranties, bonds, guarantees and other related documentation on a wide variety of projects for developers, funders, contractors and consultants both in the UK and overseas. Contentious work has been of an equally varied nature, with the resolution of disputes either by High Court litigation, domestic and international arbitration or ADR. Author of articles for the Pipeline Industries Guild and *British Property Review* and the publication of the firm's quarterly Development and Construction Law Newsletter.

Prof. Membership: Society of Construction Law, Official Referees' Solicitor's Association.

Career: Qualified in 1981. Joined *Simmons & Simmons* in 1985, becoming a Partner in 1987.

Personal: Born 6th March 1955. Holds a BA (Hons) in Law.

Bunch, Anthony

Masons, London (0171) 490 4000. Partner in Construction Department.

Specialisation: Has experience in all aspects of contentious and non-contentious matters relating to construction law. Has drafted a full range of contracts for major projects (including BOT schemes) in the UK and the Far East on behalf of employers, major contractors and international consultants. Has conducted

proceedings to all levels, including the House of Lords, and in other countries including Hong Kong, Singapore and China. Also handles arbitration and ADR work. Acted in the Channel Tunnel House of Lords case. Author of numerous articles on dispute resolution and in particular ADR. Speaks widely on construction issues.

Prof. Membership: Chartered Institute of Arbitrators.

Career: Qualified in 1978, having joined *Masons* in 1976. Became a Salaried Partner in 1980 and Equity Partner in 1982. Admitted as a Solicitor in Hong Kong in 1985; Senior resident Partner in Hong Kong office 1985-90. Became Managing Partner in 1991.

Personal: Born 8th February 1953. Holds a BA (Hons) from Nottingham. Leisure interests include music and theatre. Lives in Radlett, Herts.

Burch, Simon

Linklaters & Paines, London (0171) 606 7080. Qualified 1974. (NZ), 1991 (England and Wales). Partner 1994. Construction Department. Experienced in project structuring and construction contract documentation.

Burns, Andrea

Orchard, London (0171) 600 2448. Qualified 1983. Partner 1995. Head of Property and Construction. Handles both contentious and non-contentious aspects of construction and property.

Butcher, Trevor

McKenna & Co, London (0171) 606 9000. Partner in Construction Group.

Specialisation: Main areas of practice are construction and civil engineering, including procurement strategy, contract drafting, contract advice and disputes both in the UK and internationally. Experienced in construction and civil engineering matters in Germany and Central and Eastern Europe. Seconded for two years to the Canary Wharf project. During 1994 based in Hong Kong advising the Hong Kong Government on projects related to the new airport. Author of various articles, on such issues as architects' liability in Germany and France (*Architects Journal*) and reviews of NEC and NHS project management agreement (*Construction Law*). Speaker at a number of conferences on subjects including project management, construction in Russia and collateral warranties.

Prof. Membership: Society of Construction Law.

Career: Qualified in 1986, having joined *McKenna & Co.* in 1984. Became a Partner in 1992.

Personal: Born 10th February 1960. Graduated from Leicester University in 1983.

Cornes, David L.

Winward Fearon, London (0171) 836 9081. Founding Partner.

Specialisation: Gives advice to those in-

volved in building, civil engineering and the construction professions (architects, engineers and quantity surveyors) and their insurers. Has handled High Court and arbitration work, including abroad. Involved in major non-contentious projects including private finance. Author of 'Design Liability in the Construction Industry', contributor to 'Construction Contract Policy' and writes articles for *New Builder* magazine. Joint author of 'Collateral Warranties'. CEDR Mediator. Arbitrator. Regular speaker at conferences in the UK and occasionally abroad.

Prof. Membership: Fellow of the Institution of Civil Engineers, Fellow of the Chartered Institute of Arbitrators, Law Society, Society of Construction Law, Official Referees Solicitors Association, International Bar Association.

Career: Qualified in 1979. Worked with contractors and consulting engineers before joining *Masons* in 1976. Partner *Fenwick Elliott & Co.*, 1982-85, before founding *Winward Fearon* in 1986.

Personal: Born 31st August 1944. Attended King's College, University of London. Member of Electoral Reform Society and Charter 88. Leisure interests include walking, travelling, opera. Lives near Berkhamsted, Herts.

Fenwick Elliott, Robert J.

Fenwick Elliott, London (0171) 956 9354. Senior Partner in Construction Department.

Specialisation: Senior Partner of firm, which specialises in construction law. Emphasis on resolution of disputes in the area of building and civil engineering contracts. Also advises on the drafting of building contracts. Has handled many large cases, including Norwich Union v. Schol in a claim for £113 million. Author of 'Building Contract Litigation', now in its fourth edition. Qualified CEDR mediator. Has made TV and video programmes for TEN and others, and contributed to numerous conferences.

Prof. Membership: ORSA (Official Referees Solicitors Association) Committee Member.

Career: Qualified 1977. Worked at *Masons* from 1976 to 1980 before founding *Fenwick Elliott* in 1980.

Personal: Born 17th March 1952. Attended Eastbourne College 1965-69, then the University of Kent 1969-72. Leisure interests include music and motorbikes. Lives in London.

Fleet, Terry

Berwin Leighton, London (0171) 623 3144. Partner in Construction Department.

Specialisation: Principal area of practice is construction law advising on building and civil engineering projects in the UK and internationally, including procurement strategy, contract drafting and negotiation, bonds, warranties, insurance, contract advice and disputes. Has advised in connection with major projects in the UK, the Carribean, Europe (including Eastern Europe), Africa, the Middle East and the Far East. Currently involved in the New Parliamentary Building and a major retail development in the UK, a commercial development in Hungary and a textile mill in Asia. Clients include institutions, government departments, funders, developers, major construction and engineering companies and professional architectural and civil engineering consultants. Has written articles in *Construction Law, Building, Estates Gazette* and *Chartered Surveyor Weekly*. Speaks at conferences on construction law matters.

Prof. Membership: The Law Society, International Bar Association and Society of Construction Law.

Career: Qualified in 1980. Articled at *Heald & Nickinson* 1977-79 and moved to *Speechly Bircham* 1979-80. Legal Advisor to Costain Group 1980-82, Babcock International 1982-84 and International Construction Division, Trafalgar House 1984-87. Joined *Berwin Leighton* in 1987 before becoming a Partner in 1988.

Personal: Born 9th November 1954. Attended Southampton University (graduated 1976 LLB Hons.). Leisure interests include flying, golf, swimming and family. Lives in Twickenham.

Gibson, Michael R.

Berwin Leighton, London (0171) 623 3144. Partner in Construction Department.

Specialisation: Handles all aspects of law and practice relating to construction procurement, advising authorities, developers, funds, Government agencies, health trusts, contractors and professional designers on their contracts for the design and construction of major building or engineering projects and resolution of disputes arising from them.

Prof. Membership: Society of Construction Law.

Career: Qualified in 1977. Worked in the legal department of Costain Group 1975-78. Head of Legal Department, Construction Division, Trafalgar House, 1981-87. Joined *Berwin Leighton* as a Partner in 1987.

Personal: Born 19th February 1952. Educated at St. Edward's School, Oxford 1965-70 and Southampton University 1970-74. Enjoys golf, football and wine. Lives in London.

Gould, R. Nicholas H.

Lovell White Durrant, London (0171) 236 0066. Qualified 1967. Partner 1971. Energy and Construction Group. 25 years' experience of contentious and non-contentious aspects of construction and engineering contracts in the UK and worldwide.

Gowan, Daniel

Davies Arnold Cooper, London (0171) 936 2222. Qualified 1983. Partner 1987. Construction Department. Work includes contract drafting and reviewing, joint ventures, arbitration and litigation.

Haley, Geoff

S J Berwin & Co, London (0171) 837 2222. Qualified 1971. Partner 1993. Development and Construction Department.

Specialises in BOT type financing for infrastructure, and in creating legal structures for energy, transportation, water and urban renewal projects.

Hannah, Joseph

Fenwick Elliott, London (0171) 956 9354.

Specialisation: Partner specialising in construction litigation, contract drafting and advisory work. Litigation practice covers defects, loss and expense and all the usual construction claims across the full range of private and public projects. Project work includes privately financed infra-structure and electricity generation projects in Asia, construction management agreements and company acquisitions. Regularly lectures on various aspects of construction law.

Prof. Membership: ORSA; Society of Construction Law; BMELC.

Career: Qualified 1985. *Fenwick Elliott* since 1989, partner since 1991.

Personal: Treasurer of British Middle-East Law Council. Leisure pursuits include skiing, theatre, opera and travelling. Born 24th August 1962. Lives in London.

Harman, Martin

See under Arbitration.

Hosie, Jonathan

Baker & McKenzie, London (0171) 919 1000.

Specialisation: Senior associate in the Construction and Engineering Law Department handling drafting of documentation and resolution of construction and property disputes, with a particular emphasis on arbitration. Recent cases include representing a developer against a £10m management contractor's claim in a 4-party arbitration before the Official Referee; acting for a major Australian mining concern in a dispute under the International Chamber of Commerce arbitration rules; representing and advising a number of commercial property tenants in respect of a large dilapidations claim and rent review arbitrations. Has also represented and advised main contractors and sub-contractors in numerous claims for payment in respect of variations to their scope of works, claims for delay and disruption, acceleration costs, extensions of time, quantum meruit and claims for damages for breach of construction contracts generally. Has written a number of articles for various professional publications on construction related topics such as set-off, liquidated damages and global claims. Regularly addresses conferences and seminars on the legal aspects of construction and arbitration. Prepared *Baker & McKenzie's* submission to the DTI on the 1994 Arbitration Bill.

Prof. Membership: Society of Construction Law (Council member); Official Referees' Solicitors Association; Chatered Institute of Arbitrators; Arbitration Club, King's College Branch (Vice Chairman).

Career: Qualified 1984. Joined *Baker & McKenzie's* Construction and Engineering Law Department in 1989.

Personal: Educated at the University of Wales (LL.B Hons) and at King's College, London (MSc Construction Law and Arbitration) 1989-91. Winner of the Alfred Hudson Prize awarded by Society of Construction Law 1993. Interests include family and Manchester United FC. Born 5th December 1958. Lives in London.

Hudson, James J.S.

Bristows Cooke & Carpmael, London (0171) 400 8000. Partner in Commercial Litigation Department. Head of Construction Law Group.

Specialisation: Principal area of practice is construction and civil engineering law. Has extensive experience of litigation and arbitration in this field. Acts for employers, contractors, specialist subcontractors and professionals. Important cases have included Minter v. WHTSO and ICI v. Bovis and Others. Speaker at construction seminars.

Prof. Membership: Official Referees Solicitors Association (Chairman), Society of Construction Law, International Bar Association.

Career: Called to the Bar in 1972. Qualified as a solicitor in 1977. Joined *Bristows Cooke & Carpmael* in 1979 and became a Partner in 1984.

Personal: Born 13th May 1949. Educated at Winchester College 1962-66 and King's College, London (LL.B Hons, 1971). Leisure activities include golf, tennis and cricket. Lives in Wittersham, Kent.

Lane, Mark

Masons, London (0171) 490 4000. Partner in Construction and Engineering Department.

Specialisation: Main area of practice is contract drafting and dispute resolution. Work includes ICC arbitrations, domestic litigation and contract drafting for international and UK construction projects. Also deals with EU public procurement advising contracting authorities (including government departments, agencies and utilities) on tendering procedures and structuring the tendering procedures under PFI schemes. Acted for Eric Cumine Associates on Harbour City litigation in Hong Kong. Member of the firm's team on the Channel Tunnel and Canary Wharf projects and a number of PFI projects. Has extensive African experience including matters in Nigeria, Gambia, Ghana, Mozambique and Kenya.

Prof. Membership: Society of Construction Law; IBA (Committee T); European Construction Institute (Chairman of European Legislation Task Force).

Career: Qualified in 1975. Partner at *Masons* since 1988.

Personal: Born 18th March 1950. Educated at Cranleigh School 1962-67 and Trinity College, Cambridge 1968-72. Lives in London.

Levine, Marshall F.

Linklaters & Paines, London (0171) 606 7080. Qualified 1982. Partner and head of the Construction and Engineering Unit. Involved in construction and engineering, property development and joint ventures.

Long, Peter J.

McKenna & Co, London (0171) 606 9000. Partner in Construction Department.

Specialisation: Specialist in construction law with over 17 years experience advising contractors, consultants and employers in the construction industry. Includes drafting and negotiation of construction contracts, consultancy agreements, collateral warranties, concession agreements and operating and maintenance agreements. Also advising on contractual claims against and by contractors and consultants, dispute resolution procedures and conduct of litigation, arbitration and ADR procedures. Experienced in all kinds of construction projects including large-scale commercial buildings, civil engineering projects and process plant and heavy engineering. Contributor of articles to the construction press, the 'McKenna & Co. Law Letter' and 'McKenna & Co. Construction Law Bulletin'. Speaker at construction law seminars. Accredited mediator with CEDR (Centre for Dispute Resolution).

Prof. Membership: Law Society, Society of Construction Law, Official Referees Solicitors Association, Associate of the Chartered Institute of Arbitrators, CEDR Board Member.

Career: Qualified in 1977, having joined McKenna & Co. in 1975. Became a Partner in 1984. Worked in Hong Kong office 1981-1985, having qualified as a solicitor in Hong Kong in 1981.

Personal: Born 18th October 1950. Attended Balliol College, Oxford 1969-1973 (1st Class Honours in Classics). Leisure interests include music and family. Lives in Hampton Hill, Middlesex.

Mendelblat, Michael

Nabarro Nathanson, London (0171) 493 9933. Qualified 1979. Partner specialising in construction and engineering law, especially acting for public bodies.

Miles, David

Glovers, London (0171) 629 5121. Partner in Construction Department.

Specialisation: Has specialised in construction since 1978. Deals with the contract negotiations, joint venture agreements, claims involving both arbitration and litigation acting both for employers and contractors in the UK and overseas. Acted in the cases Rees Hough Viking Grain and St Martins. Involved in ADR being a founding steering committee member of CEDR. Contributing Author 'Construction Conflict Management and Resolution', and 'Coastal and Estuarial Harbour Engineers Reference Book.' Member of CEDR faculty and lecturer on ADR. Mediator (CEDR/BAE). Individual charge-out rates are £180-220 per hour.

Prof. Membership: C.I.Arb, Society of Construction Law.

Career: Commission Royal Artillery (1966-

1971). Joined Alan Wilson & Co. in 1978, becoming a Partner in 1979. Merged with Glover & Co. in 1986.

Personal: Born 22nd June 1946. Haileybury 1960-64. Chairman of Moreton Cricket Club. Leisure interests: tennis, cricket, opera. Lives in North Moreton, Oxon.

Minogue, Ann

McKenna & Co, London (0171) 606 9000. Partner in Construction Group.

Specialisation: Principal area of work is procurement advice and drafting building and construction-related contracts for major developments and projects. Other main area of work is construction disputes. Drafted standard forms for ACA and BPF. Handled construction work on Broadgate, Canary Wharf, and Minster Court. Contributes two monthly column to 'Building' magazine. Lectures on construction issues.

Prof. Membership: Society of Construction Law, Construction Management Forum, BPF Construction Committee, Anglo American Real Property Trust, 'Justice' Committee (legal remedies for home-owners).

Career: Joined McKenna & Co. in 1978 as an Articled clerk. Qualified in 1980 and became a Partner in 1985.

Personal: Born 17th October 1955. Attended Aylesbury Girls' High School 1966-73, then Clare College, Cambridge 1974-77. Speaks Russian. Leisure pursuits include films and tennis. Lives in Buckinghamshire.

Race, David W.

Nicholson Graham & Jones, London (0171) 628 9151. Partner in Company/Commercial Department.

Specialisation: Main areas of practice are construction and engineering law. Handles major infrastructure projects, particularly in transport and international project work in process engineering and related fields. Also undertakes general commercial work including project finance, joint ventures, procurement tendering and contracting particularly in the public sector. Major clients include Blue Circle Industries PLC, London Underground Limited and European Passenger Services Limited. Author of various articles for professional journals. Visiting lecturer to Crown Agents on international procurement and engineering law.

Prof. Membership: Institute of Arbitrators, Society of Construction Law.

Career: Qualified in 1974. Joined Nicholson Graham & Jones as a Partner in 1987. Before qualifying worked in overseas banking 1969-71 and subsequently was legal adviser to Mass Transit Railway Corp., Hong Kong 1978-82 and Chief Solicitor to Blue Circle Industries PLC 1985-87.

Personal: Born 19th May 1947. Attended Barnard Castle School 1957-65 and Birmingham University 1965-68. Executive Member and Director of Befrienders International: The Samaritans Worldwide. Leisure interests include fly fishing. Lives in Wye, near Ashford, Kent.

Reeves, Suzanne

Wedlake Bell, London (0171) 395 3000. Partner in Litigation Department.

Specialisation: Construction. Acts for all sectors of the industry, particularly specialist subcontractors, consulting engineers and insurers. Non-contentious work focuses on consultants, developers and financial institutions. Contributor to industry publications. Frequent speaker to industry seminars and conferences. Has close association with major subcontractor organisations.

Prof. Membership: Law Society, Official Referees Solicitors Association.

Career: Qualified in 1979. Joined Wedlake Bell the same year, becoming a Partner in 1986. Currently Head of Litigation Department and Construction Group.

Personal: Born 13th August 1955. LLB (Exon) 1976. Lives in London.

Regan, M.D.

Rowe & Maw, London (0171) 248 4282. Partner in Construction and Engineering Department.

Specialisation: Advises contractors, employers and professionals, and also insurers, particularly in relation to professional indemnity matters.

Prof. Membership: Law Society, Chartered Institute of Arbitrators, Society of Construction Law.

Career: Qualified in 1980, having joined Rowe & Maw in 1978. Became a Partner in 1985.

Personal: Born 4th October 1955. Attended Westcliff High School 1969-74, then Pembroke College, Oxford 1974-77. Leisure interests include watching cricket. Lives in London.

Roe, Sally Jean

Freshfields, London (0171) 936 4000. Partner in Litigation Department.

Specialisation: Head of Construction and Engineering Group. Extensive experience of litigation and arbitration in these fields, acting for employers and contractors. Also handles non-contentious projects including property developments, rail, road and power projects. Other areas of practice cover all aspects of commercial property litigation including rent review, and advising UK utilities companies on the application of the EC Procurement Regime. Author of the 'Freshfields Guide to Management Contracting Law and Practice' (1994); Contributor to 'Emden's Construction Law'.

Prof. Membership: City of London Solicitors Company.

Career: Qualified in 1981. Worked at Dawson & Co, Lincoln's Inn, as an Articled Clerk 1979-81, Assistant Solicitor 1981-5 and Partner 1985-88. Joined Freshfields in 1988, becoming a Partner in 1990.

Personal: Born 4th September 1956. Attended Wakefield Girls' High School

1965-74 and St Hilda's College, Oxford 1974-77. Leisure interests include walking, skiing, sailing and theatre. Lives in London.

Rushton, John Michael

Rowe & Maw, London (0171) 248 4282. Partner in Construction Department.

Specialisation: Acts or has acted for all sides of the construction industry: developers, building owners, main contractors, sub-contractors, insurers and trade association arbitrators regarding building and civil engineering projects. Also handles litigation and arbitration. Cases have involved dredging, ground conditions, mechanical and electrical disputes, decontamination contracts, fee claims and recovery of loss and expense and extensions of time. Acts for the Chartered Institute of Arbitrators. Lectures both for private and for public organisations. Accredited mediator with the Centre for Dispute Resolution. Has some advocacy experience in the High Court and before arbitrators.

Prof. Membership: Chartered Institute of Arbitrators (Fellow), Society of Construction Law. Firm has corporate or associate membership of British Academy of Experts and Confederation of Construction Specialists.

Career: Qualified 1975. Joined *Rowe & Maw* in 1980, becoming a Partner in 1981.

Personal: Born 22nd March 1950. Attended Uppingham 1963-68, then Sidney Sussex College, Cambridge, 1969-72. Freeman of the Worshipful Company of Arbitrators. Leisure interests include MCC and family life: he has two children. Lives in Loughton.

Russell, Victoria E.

Freedman Church, London (0171) 353 1330. Partner in Construction Department.

Specialisation: Handles construction and engineering matters with a special emphasis on litigation and arbitration. Advises employers, main contractors, specialist subcontractors and members of the professional team on a variety of points of law, practice and procedure. Has dealt with a number of complex construction matters, some arising from the various JCT and ICE standard forms of contract and others from "tailor made" contractual arrangements. Fluent German speaker. Practising arbitrator and occasional lecturer. Charge-out rate is £185 per hour.

Prof. Membership: ORSA, IBA (Business Section), LCIA, Society of Construction Law (Council Member), Chartered Institute of Arbitrators (Fellow (1991) and Member of Arbitration and ADR Committees). Member of the Court of Assistants of the Worshipful Company of Arbitrators and Chairman of its Charitable Trust.

Career: Qualified and joined *Freedmans* (now *Freedman Church*) in 1981. Became a Partner in 1985.

Personal: Born 12th October 1956. Educated at Benenden School, Kent 1968-73 and Exeter University 1974-77 (LL.B Hons). Member of Benenden School Trust and Alumni Board of Exeter University. Leisure

time spent responding to the challenges of two small sons. Lives in West London.

Shaw, James W.

Kennedys, London (0171) 638 3688. Partner in Commercial Department.

Specialisation: Apart from corporate and commercial work, main areas of practice are construction and insurance. Since 1982 has developed a department specialising in advising architects, engineers, contractors and sub-contractors on their terms of appointment and related contracts, building contracts, and on issues arising during the construction phase of projects. Drafts new commercial insurance policies for insurance companies developing and launching new products. Author of various articles on commercial law topics. Has given seminars and lectures to public and clients on construction law and on insurance related topics. Participates in the in-house training of staff.

Career: Qualified in 1979, having joined *Waterhouse & Co.* in 1977. Joined *Kennedy's* in 1980. Assistant Solicitor in Company\Commercial Department 1980-84. Became a Partner in 1984.

Personal: Born 9th May 1955. Took a BA from Oxford, 1976. Leisure interests include music and theatre.

Shaw, Peter R.

Freedman Church, London (0171) 353 1330. Senior Partner specialising in construction and engineering law.

Specialisation: Handles both contentious and non-contentious matters. Non-contentious work includes contract procurement, commercial drafting, collateral warranties, bonds, funding agreements, professional service agreements, project insurance, legal audits, contract adminstration procedures and BOT and PFI projects. Also provides representation in all forms of arbitration tribunal and ADR, pleading and affidavit drafting, opinions and advices. Examples of contentious work include advising clients in an arbitration dispute with a main contractor regarding design and construction work during the building of a railway in Jordan for the transport of phosphates (FIDIC contract); acting for clients as plaintiffs in litigation concerning the construction of a hospital in Suva, Fiji (JCT contract); representing plaintiffs in disputes with quarry owners concerning the construction of a £25 million mineral processing and crushing plant in the UK (I Chem E contract), and joint action in court by services engineering companies against oil rig jacket constructors in one of the English North Sea fields involving the joining of the Oil Companies Consortium as third parties (amended ICE contract). Clients include national and international construction companies, government agencies, health trusts and professional indemnity insurers in construction design disciplines. Contributor to legal section in trade/ professional publications that circulate in the construction industry. Also presents seminars and lectures

to various bodies and institutions involved in the construction industry. Member of the British Academy of Experts Committee on "The Language of ADR". Charge-out rate is £185 per hour.

Prof. Membership: Official Referees Solicitors Association (Committee Member), Reading Construction Forum, IBA Business Section.

Career: Qualified in 1980. With *Freedmans/ Freedman Church* since 1973. Became a Partner in 1980 and Senior Partner in 1991.

Personal: Born 10th January 1946. Educated at Huddersfield Grammar School and the University of Lancaster (BA Hons in History). Interests include golf, sailing, skiing, gardening, walking and good food and wine. Lives in London and Dartmouth.

Sherman, Henry C.

McKenna & Co, London (0171) 606 9000. Partner in Construction Group.

Specialisation: Main areas of practice are domestic and international litigation, arbitration and other construction disputes work including: acting for owners, funders, developers, consultants and contractors in relation to major construction disputes in Hong Kong, the Middle East, North Africa and the United Kingdom and advising them in relation to issues arising during the course of projects and the interim resolution of disputes by formal or other means. Has also undertaken work in Germany in conjunction with *McKenna & Co's* German associates for consultants, contractors and others, advising them as to terms of appointment, contractual disputes and other matters. Regularly addresses seminars and workshops and writes on legal subjects in the construction press.

Prof. Membership: Society of Construction Law, Official Referees Solicitors' Association.

Career: Qualified in 1977. Worked at *Frere Cholmeley* 1975-83. Joined *McKenna & Co* in 1983, becoming a Partner in 1986. Spent 1985-7 in Hong Kong.

Personal: Born 16th February 1952. Attended University of Oxford 1970-73 (BA) and University of Aix-Marseilles 1973-4. Leisure interests include idling whenever possible with his family on the Isle of Wight. Lives in Teddington, Middlesex.

Squire, Georgina

Rosling King, London (0171) 353 2353. Qualified 1983. Partner 1985. Litigation Department. Principal areas of practice are property and construction disputes acting for banks, insurers and investors.

Tolson, Simon J.A.

Fenwick Elliott, London (0171) 956 9354. Partner specialising in construction litigation and arbitration.

Specialisation: Has specialised in construction law since qualification. Major emphasis is on heavyweight Official Referee business and construction arbitration. Important cases handled include West Faulkner Associates v.

London Borough of Newham (CA); Team Services PLC v. Kier Management & Design Ltd (CA); John Lelliot (Contracts) Ltd v. Byrne Bros (Formwork) Ltd and Russell Bros (Paddington) Ltd v. John Lelliot Management Ltd. Clients include major contractors, consultants (all disciplines), local authorities, government departments, educational and professional bodies. Regular lecturer for IBC on construction-related matters. Author of contract module for construction law, litigation and regulation course at King's College Centre of Construction Law. Regular contributor to Television Education Network on commercial transactions law.

Prof. Membership: Law Society; Fellow of Chartered Institute of Arbitrators (1994); Official Referees Solicitors Association; Society of Construction Law; Fellow of the Faculty of Building (1988).

Career: Has been with *Fenwick Elliot* since qualification in 1987. Became a Partner in 1989.

Personal: Born 18th November 1959. Holds a BA (Hons) in Law (1982). Interests include off-roading (4x4), motor cycling, cycling, things mechanical (especially engines) and travel. Lives in London.

Ward, John J.
Beale and Company, London (0171) 240 3474. Qualified 1975. Partner 1977. Construction Department. Specialises in construction law as well as health and safety in the construction industry.

Wright, Christopher John
Warner Cranston, London (0171) 403 2900. Partner 1984. Litigation Department (Construction Group).

Specialisation: Principal area of practice is construction litigation. Handles a wide variety of matters acting for contractors, sub-contractors, professional indemnity insurers and employers. Has particular expertise in arbitration and ADR. Also deals with non-contentious construction work, including drafting building contracts and terms of appointment/collateral warranties for architects and employers. Has acted in numerous High Court actions and international and domestic arbitrations, including disputes in South America, the Middle East and Europe. Has lectured on a variety of construction issues and ADR to clients and outside organisations.

Prof. Membership: Fellow of the Chartered Institute of Arbitrators (Secretary of London Branch); Official Referees' Solicitors' Association (Committee Member); Law Society; International Bar Association.

Career: Qualified in 1976. With *Coward Chance* 1976-79 and *McKenna & Co* 1979-83. Joined *Warner Cranston* as a Partner in 1984.

Personal: Born 2nd May 1952. Educated Hereford Cathedral School 1963-69 and St. John's College, Cambridge 1970-73 (BA 1973, MA 1977). Leisure interests include golf, cricket, wine tasting and theatre. Lives in Richmond, Surrey.

Arnott, James M.
MacRoberts, Glasgow (0141) 332 9988. Senior Partner and member of Litigation Department.

Specialisation: Main area of practice is construction, both contentious and non-contentious, including High Court and arbitration proceedings negotiation, insurance claims arising in the construction sphere and drafting and negotiation of contracts. Also handles commercial litigation: contractual and delictual business issues. Has handled many leading construction cases in both Scotland and English arbitrations. Contributor to 'Building Contracts' in the Stair Memorial Society. Author of papers for IBA, ICLR, IBL, Law Society and other commercial bodies. Frequent speaker on construction matters.

Prof. Membership: Law Society of Scotland, Writer to the Signet, Solicitor to the Supreme Court, International Bar Association.

Career: Qualified in 1956. Joined *MacRoberts* in 1962, becoming Partner in 1963. Former Convenor of Law Reform Committee of Law Society of Scotland and Convenor of Law Society Working Party on Arbitration. Chairman of Committee of Law Society on Construction Specialism. Secretary and Legal Adviser to Scottish Building Contracts Committee. Director and Secretary of Scottish Council for International Arbitration.

Personal: Born 22nd March 1935. Attended Merchiston Castle School 1948-53, then University of Edinburgh 1953-56. Leisure interests include cricket. Lives in Edinburgh.

Ashford, Peter
Cripps Harries Hall, Tunbridge Wells (01892) 515121. Qualified 1986. Partner 1991. Commercial Litigation Department. Principal area of practice is construction litigation.

Baker, Huw J.
Addleshaw Sons & Latham, Manchester (0161) 832 5994. Partner in Commercial Litigation Department.

Specialisation: Work covers all aspects of contentious and non-contentious construction and engineering work.

Prof. Membership: Society of Construction Lawyers.

Career: Qualified in 1987 while with *Mckenna & Co*, then joined *Booth & Co* in Leeds in 1990. Joined *Addleshaw Sons & Latham* in 1993 as a Partner in the commercial litigation department.

Personal: Born 22nd September 1962. Graduated from Cambridge University in 1984 with First Class Honours in Law. Leisure pursuits include gardening, walking and reading. Lives in Hebden Bridge, West Yorkshire.

Barrett, Kevin John
Neil F. Jones & Co, Birmingham (0121)

643 1010. Qualified 1985. Partner 1989. Handles construction litigation and arbitration as well as non-contentious construction.

Batstone, Susan Nadine
Donne Mileham & Haddock, Brighton (01273) 329833. Qualified 1985. Partner 1990. Litigation Department. Handles a range of corporate, construction, professional negligence and other litigation.

Beckett, Samuel R.
L'Estrange & Brett, Belfast (01232) 230426.

Bentley, Bruce
Dibb Lupton Broomhead, Sheffield (0114) 276 0351. Partner in Litigation Group. Head of Construction Law Unit.

Specialisation: Engineering project work. Involves contracts for the implementation of building and engineering development projects and the negotiation and drafting of development agreements, construction and engineering contractors and related documents relating to office and industrial developments, disputes and arbitrations between public and private employers and contractors. Delivered a paper at first International Construction Management Conference, UMIST, 1992. Lectured on building contract terms, collateral warranties, JCT insurance clauses and JCT insolvency provisions. Contributor to Construction Management and Resolution.

Prof. Memberships: Society of Construction Law.

Career: Qualified with *Oxley & Coward*, Rotherham, 1971. Partner 1972. Left to join *Dibb Lupton Broomhead* as Partner in 1986.

Personal: Born 1st December 1946. Attended King Edward VII School, Sheffield, then Birmingham University 1965-68. Leisure pursuits include architecture, football and the Stock Exchange. Lives in Sheffield.

Butler, Maurice R.
Johns Elliot, Belfast (01232) 326881.

Cockram, Richard
Booth & Co., Leeds (0113) 283 2000. Partner in Construction Department.

Specialisation: Construction building and civil engineering, litigation, arbitration and drafting. Visiting lecturer at Leeds Metropolitan University for the Master's degree in Construction Law and Arbitration.

Prof. Membership: Fellow of the Chartered Institute of Arbitrators. Member, Society of Construction Lawyers.

Career: Qualified 1973. Partner at *McKenna & Co.* from 1986-89; joined *Booth & Co.* as a Partner in 1989.

Personal: Born 4th November 1947. Attended Cambridge University 1967-70: holds an MA. Leisure interests include books and walking. Lives in Leeds.

Collingwood, Mark
Masons, Bristol (0117) 9226622. Partner in Construction and Civil Engineering Department.

Specialisation: Heads the seven lawyer Construction Department in the Bristol office. Specialist construction lawyer since qualification. Particular specialisms include litigation, arbitration and dispute resolution generally, contract and project documentation negotiation and drafting. Has acted in many 'heavyweight' construction cases – civil engineering and building in the UK and abroad. Drafted project documentation for £350m dockyard redevelopment scheme. Recent reported cases have included Wessex v. HLM. Lectures frequently on the law relating to the construction industry.

Prof. Membership: Law Society, Faculty of Building.

Career: Qualified in 1980. Articled at *Crossman Block and Keith* 1978-80, before joining *Masons*. Became a Partner in 1985.

Personal: Born 19th December 1954. Attended Durham University, taking a BA in law and politics. Leisure interests include tennis. Has three young children.

Connor, Vincent
McGrigor Donald, Glasgow (0141) 248 6677. Qualified 1989. Partner 1995. Litigation Department. Handles mainly construction litigation, including representing clients in court and at arbitration.

Cowan, Keith C.E.
Tughan & Co, Belfast (01232) 553300.

Davies, Edward
Masons, Manchester (0161) 877 3777. Partner in Construction Department.

Specialisation: Main area of practice is construction and engineering work, together with technology expertise. Includes projects throughout UK and abroad involving building, civil engineering, transportation, water and energy matters. Advises on all forms of litigation, arbitration, drafting of contracts, warranties, insurance and bonds. Trained in the field of ADR as a mediator by American Arbitration Association in San Francisco. Lectures extensively on all aspects of construction and engineering law to individual companies and on continuing education courses. Joint co-ordinator of CIB task group working on conflict management and dispute resolution in the construction industry.

Prof. Memberships: Law Society, Society of Construction Law, American Arbitration Association, Chairman steering group of joint venture between UMIST and *Masons* researching into construction industry disputes.

Career: Qualified in 1982. Joined *Masons* in 1986 in London. Became Partner and moved to the Manchester office on its establishment in 1989.

Personal: Born 25th May 1958. Attended Leeds Grammar School until 1975; Manchester University 1976-79 (LLB); College

of Law, Guildford 1980-81 then Kings College, London 1988-90 (part-time MSc). Leisure pursuits include walking. Lives in Manchester.

Forrester, Harry O.
Eversheds, Birmingham (0121) 233 2001. Qualified 1970.

Gordon, Roderick C.P.R.
Robert Muckle, Newcastle-upon-Tyne (0191) 232 4402. Partner in Construction and Planning Department.

Specialisation: Main area of practice covers construction and engineering disputes, including High Court, arbitration and Alternative Dispute Resolution work as well as non-contentious work. Regularly addresses seminars for North-East region of Building Employers Confederation.

Prof. Memberships: Official Referees Solicitors Association.

Career: Qualified in 1988 with *Braby & Waller*. Moved to *Masons* in 1989, then to *Robert Muckle* as a partner in 1993.

Personal: Born 17th March 1959. Attended Charterhouse School 1972-77, then Bristol University 1978-81. Spent three years as an officer in the Army. Leisure Pursuits include riding, golf and sailing. Lives in Corbridge, Northumberland.

Guppy, W. Nicholas
Laytons, Bristol 0117 929 1626. Qualified 1976. Partner 1992. Construction Law Department. Main areas of practice are construction litigation and arbitration.

Ham, Brian E.
Mills Selig, Belfast (01232) 243878.

Harling, Marcus
Burges Salmon, Bristol (0117) 939 2000. Qualified 1985. Partner 1992. Construction Department. Head of Construction & Engineering Unit. Handles a wide range of contentious and non-contentious work.

Harris, Adam
Masons, Bristol.

Henderson, David J.
MacRoberts, Glasgow (0141) 332 9988. Partner in Construction Department.

Specialisation: Main area of practice is construction and engineering law. Covers litigation and arbitration on behalf of employers, contractors and sub-contractors. Also advises on and drafts contracts, warranties, and professional appointments. Joint Author of Scottish Building Contract Committee's Practice Guide on Insolvency in the Construction Industry. Has contributed to 'Building Trade and Industry'. Lectures at numerous seminars to building industry on construction related topics. Has addressed seminars for Law Society of Scotland, Institute of Arbitrators and Glasgow and Strathclyde Universities.

Prof. Membership: Associate of Chartered Institute of Arbitrators (ACIArb).

Career: Qualified in 1979, having joined *MacRoberts* in 1977. Became Partner in 1983. Accredited by Law Society of Scotland as Specialist in Construction Law (1994).

Personal: Born 18th July 1955. Attended Kilmarnock Academy until 1973, then Edinburgh University 1973-77. Lives in Giffnock, Glasgow.

Hilton, Mark W.
Hammond Suddards, Leeds (0113) 234 3500. Partner in Litigation Department.

Specialisation: Main area of practice is construction law. Acts on behalf of contractors, sub-contractors and employers in relation to contractual disputes in all areas of construction, in arbitration and litigation. Also handles commercial litigation work. Acted in Duquemin v. Slater and Preston v. Torfaen.

Prof. Membership: ORSA, Chartered Institute of Arbitrators.

Career: Qualified in 1982. Worked at *Last Suddards* in Bradford 1980-82, *Barlow Lyde & Gilbert* 1982-84 and rejoined *Last Suddards* (later Hammond Suddards) in 1984, becoming a Partner in 1985.

Personal: Born 15th July 1958. Attended Wrekin College 1972-76 and University of Leeds 1976-79. Leisure interests include swimming, scuba diving, skiing and tennis. Lives in Harrogate.

Hodson, Philip
Cobbett Leak Almond, Manchester (0161) 833 3333. Qualified 1969. Partner 1974. Litigation Department. Handles general commercial litigation including construction work and professional negligence. Born 2.10.1944.

Hoyle, Roger V.
Veale Wasbrough, Bristol (0117) 925 2020. Partner in Commercial Litigation Department.

Specialisation: Construction law. Has extensive experience of construction claims relating to design and construction defects in new buildings, disputes on contract conditions and the liability of professionals and their insurers.

Prof. Membership: Committee Member of the Official Referees Solicitors Association, Law Society (London and Bristol).

Career: Qualified in 1971. Joined *Stanley Wasbrough*, now *Veale Wasbrough*, in 1972. Became a Partner in 1973.

Personal: Born 6th March 1947. Educated at Sedbergh School. Leisure interests include trekking and walking, photography, family, food and wine. Lives in Bristol.

Jefferies, Michael G.
Hugh James Jones & Jenkins, Cardiff (01222) 224871. Qualified 1972. Partner 1972. Construction and Civil Engineering

Department. Has specialised in construction law for 20 years and also professional indemnity. Born 21.11.1947.

Jones, Michael L.N.

Hugh James Jones & Jenkins, Cardiff (01222) 224871. Qualified 1966. Senior Partner 1970. Head of Civil Litigation Department. Principal area of practice is general commercial litigation. Also handles construction litigation.

Jones, Neil F.

Neil F. Jones & Co, Birmingham (0121) 643 1010.

Kirkham, Frances M.

Edge & Ellison, Birmingham (0121) 200 2001.

Langley, Robert Lennox

Watson Burton, Newcastle upon Tyne (0191) 232 3101. Partner in Commercial Litigation Department. Also member of construction unit.

Specialisation: Specialises in construction law and professional indemnity. Head of Commercial Litigation. Handles contractual disputes in construction, engineering and fabrication. Also undertakes professional indemnity and professional negligence work, both tortious and contractual. Has acted in a wide range of disputes including those in the construction process, injunctive work particularly in the context of off-shore fabrication and engineering, minority oppression and a number of major arbitrations. Clients include fundholders, developers, further education institutions, design consultants, estate surveyors and valuers, foreign lawyers and underwriters. Regular speaker at conferences and seminars including the RICS National Briefing Conference for Building Surveyors.

Prof. Membership: Law Society, Official Referees Solicitors Association, Chartered Institute of Arbitrators, Centre for Dispute Resolution.

Career: Qualified in 1979. Articled at *Watson Burton*, Newcastle upon Tyne. Partner in 1981.

Personal: Educated at Oxford University (BA Jurisprudence 1974). Leisure interests include yachting, skiing, the hills, history, the novels of Patrick O'Brian. Local preacher in methodist church. Lives in Newcastle upon Tyne.

MacKay, Alan D.

Lindsays WS, Edinburgh (0131) 229 1212. Partner in Litigation Department.

Specialisation: Main areas of practice are building and construction arbitration and litigation. Acts for contractors, sub-contractors and employers in building and civil engineering work both contentious and non-contentious. Also handles insurance claims (both sides), contract issues and personal injury work. Has undertaken several major arbitrations. Lectures for the Law Society of Scotland and the Chartered Institute of Arbiters.

Prof. Membership: Law Society of Scotland, Society of Writers to the Signet, Chartered Institute of Arbiters (associate member).

Career: Qualified in 1968. Joined *Lindsays WS* as a Partner in 1987.

Personal: Born 19th January 1944. Attended George Watson's College 1952-62 and Edinburgh University 1962-65. Leisure interests include golf, reading, theatre and family. Lives in Edinburgh.

Manning-Cox, Andrew

Wragge & Co, Birmingham (0121) 233 1000. Qualified 1980. Partner 1985. Head of construction and employment teams, handling all areas of contentious and non-contentious construction and employment law. Born 23.4.1956.

McClelland, Christine E.A.

See under Environmental Law.

Morrison, Alastair

Dundas & Wilson CS, Glasgow (0141) 221 8586. Qualified 1989. Partner 1994. Heads Construction and Engineering Unit. Provides legal and strategic advice on all aspects of construction projects. Born 8.10.1962.

Moss, David J.

Hammond Suddards, Leeds (0113) 234 3500. Partner in Construction and Engineering Unit.

Specialisation: Principal area of practice is contentious construction and engineering industry claims. Wide experience of the standard form of building and engineering contract (including JCT, ICE, RMR '80, MF/I, IMechEE). Has advised main mechanical subcontractors on numerous power stations, waste incinerators and chemical process plants and both contractors and employers on various 'build' schemes. Part-time lecturer at the University of the City of Leeds. Addresses conferences and seminars both internal and external.

Prof. Membership: O.R.S.A., ACIAArb, Society of Construction Law.

Career: Qualified in 1986. Joined *Hammond Suddards* in 1990.

Personal: Born November 1961. Educated at Edge End High School, Nelson. University of Sheffield 1980-83. The College of Law Guilford. Leisure activities include cricket, football and golf. Lives in Addingham.

Nolan, Brandon E.

McGrigor Donald, Glasgow (0141) 248 6677. Qualified 1980. Partner 1987. Litigation Department. Head of Construction and Engineering Unit. Deals with a range of issues arising under standard form contracts, as well as construction drafting.

Patterson, Lindy A.

Bird Semple, Edinburgh (0131) 459 2345.

Qualified 1982. Partner 1988. Litigation Department. Main areas of practice are construction and civil engineering disputes. Born 12.9.1958.

Plascow, Ronald H.

Mills & Reeve, Cambridge Int+44 (01223) 64422. Partner in Construction and Civil Engineering Department.

Specialisation: Has practised both the contentious and non-contentious aspects of construction exclusively since 1982. Has experience of most forms of standard contracts used in the UK and the Fidic Contracy abroad. Also has experience of both large and smaller scale disputes in the courts, arbitration, ADR techniques and advising on interpretation of contracts. Prepares and drafts contracts and related documents, such as bonds and warranties. Editor of Arbitration Practice and Procedure, Interlocutory and Hearing Problems (Lloyds of London Press Ltd). Regularly addresses conferences and meetings arranged in East Anglia by RICS, RIBA, ICE and CIArb.

Radford, Ian

Masons, Manchester.

Specialisation: Principal area of practice is engineering and construction contract dispute resolution. Also involved in drafting building and civil engineering contract documentation. Significant cases handled include Waverley v. Carnaud Metalbox (the leading authority on s.5 Arbitration Act 1979) and Dew Goup v. North West Water (the only Court of Appeal authority on the valuation of variations pursuant to the ICE terms of contract). Clients include several multinational engineering/construction companies and cable television companies. Regular speaker at seminars and conferences. Charge out rate £140-160 per hour.

Career: Gonville and Caius College, Cambridge 1977 - 1980 BA (1980); MA (1983). Articled with Lawford & Co of Gray's Inn, London. Worked and admitted as a solicitor in Queensland, Australia 1986-1990. Partner at Masons from 1992.

Personal: Born 19th October 1959. Lives in Hazel Grove, Cheshire. Spends time outside of work in traffic jams on M63 and taming unruly children.

Redmond, John V.

Laytons, Bristol (0117) 929 1626. Qualified 1976. Partner 1983. Head of Construction Law 1992. Main area of practice is construction work, especially arbitration and litigation, with some contract and non-contentious work undertaken.

Renton, Andrew L.

Simpson & Marwick WS, Edinburgh (0131) 557 1545. Qualified 1984. Partner 1989. Commercial Litigation Department. Main area of specialisation is commercial litigation with a particular emphasis on building and engineering disputes.

Robson, Nigel.R.

Eversheds, Newcastle upon Tyne (0191) 261 1661. Qualified 1977. Partner 1980. Construction and Engineering Unit. Principal area of practice is contentious construction and engineering matters. Born 23.5.1951.

Salmon, Kenneth T.

Kirk Jackson, Manchester (0161) 794 0431. Partner in Construction Law Department.

Specialisation: Main area of work is building and civil engineering disputes, both in court and at arbitration, and advising on contract documentation. Conducts in-house seminars for clients and recently a seminar for Manchester Law Society.

Prof. Membership: Law Society, Official Referee's Solicitors Association, Northern Arbitration Association, Manchester Law Society.

Career: Qualified 1973 while at *Kirk Jackson* and became a Partner in 1975.

Personal: Born 16th April 1946. Leisure pursuits include tennis, five-a-side soccer, hill-walking, music and reading. Lives in Warrington.

Shadbolt, Richard A.

Shadbolt & Co, Reigate (01737) 226277. Senior Partner.

Specialisation: Main area of practice is construction law, including work on engineering and major projects, with experience in UK and internationally since 1967. Particular experience of structuring and drafting of contracts for major projects and construction. Litigation and arbitration work covered as well as environmental, trade and other commercial matters. Involved with the drafting of the widely praised Association of Consultant Architects standard contract form. Author of articles in professional and other periodicals and occasional lecturer on International Construction Contracts. Regular speaker at professional conventions and international conferences on construction contract and other legal topics.

Prof. Memberships: Law Society, Law Society of Hong Kong, American Bar Association (Associate Member), International Bar Association, Inter-Pacific Bar Association, British Association for Central and Eastern Europe, British Consultants Bureau.

Career: Joined *E T Ray & Co.* in Bletchley in 1965. Joined 1968. Joined *McKenna & Co.* in London in 1967. Partner, *McKenna & Co.* in London, Brussels, Bahrain, Hong Kong, Singapore, Tokyo and Jakarta, from 1971 until 1991. Established *Shadbolt & Co.* as Senior Partner in 1991.

Personal: Born 18th December 1942. Attended Okehampton Grammar School 1954-60; King's College, London 1961-64 then College of Law, Guildford 1967. Leisure pursuits include family life.

Shaw, Murray W.A.

Biggart Baillie & Gifford, Glasgow

(0141) 228 8000. Qualified 1982. Partner in the litigation department specialising in construction law and insolvency law. Work also includes planning law. Born 25.9.57.

Staniforth, Alison J.

Eversheds, Leeds (0113) 243 0391. Partner in Litigation Department (Head of Construction and Engineering).

Specialisation: Principal area of practice is construction and engineering disputes and general commercial litigation. Work includes litigation, arbitration and ADR on the JCT family of contracts, ICE contracts, bespoke contracts (including joint ventures, both domestic and international) and advice on FIDIC forms. Also deals with non-contentious construction and engineering work, including drafting and negotiating amendments to standard and bespoke forms of contracts, warranties, performance bonds, parent company guarantees and professional appontments. Important matters handled include developments at the University of York for a science park, student accomodation, teaching facilities and science laboratories; a facilites management agreement for the Benefits Agency; contract procurement, advice and drafting for North Hull HAT. Other clients include Heywood Williams, N G Bailey, Yorkshire Electricity, British Waterways Board, Weir Pumps Ltd, Cameron Taylor Bedford and Hays Specialist Distribution Ltd. Lecturer at Leeds Metropolitan University (MSc in Arbitration and Construction Law). Regular conference speaker for e.g. APM, RICS, CIOB and the Institute of Structural Engineers. Charge-out rate is £150-£220 per hour.

Prof. Membership: CIARB, ORSA, Common Purpose Graduate, OPP 2K, Network.

Career: Qualified in 1985. With *Herbert Smith* 1983-86. Joined *Hepworth & Chadwick* in 1986 and became a Partner at *Eversheds Hepworth & Chadwick* in 1991.

Personal: Born 13th December 1957. Educated at Leeds University 1976-79 (LL.B) and Trinity Hall, Cambridge 1980-83 (MLitt). Interests include golf, embroidery and gardening. Lives in Harrogate.

Vasey, John R.

Wansbroughs Willey Hargrave, Bristol (0117) 926 8981. Head of Construction Department.

Specialisation: Work includes defects claims, claims for additional payment and professional indemnity claims, in both arbitration and court forums. Acts for developers, contractors and insurers in often high value and high profile litigation. Also handles all aspects of non-contentious work.

Prof. Membership: Official Referee's Solicitors Association, Law Society.

Career: Qualified in 1980. Worked at *Oppenheimer Nathan & Vandhyke* 1981-83; *McKenna & Co.* 1984-87. Joined *Wansbroughs Willey Hargrave* in 1988, becoming a Partner in 1990.

Welsh, John A.

Bishop and Robertson Chalmers, Glasgow (0141) 248 4672. Partner in the Litigation Division.

Specialisation: Main area of practice is construction law, including professional negligence claims against engineers, architects and surveyors, arbitrations, drafting and advising on construction law contracts, appointments and warranties. Author of an article in *The Structural Engineer* (December 1993) entitled 'To Certify or Not?'. Submitted paper on 'Professional Responsibility for Surveys and Inspections' at Glasgow University in June 1991. Speaker at conferences on collateral warranties and methods of procurement under building contracts.

Prof. Membership: Law Society of Scotland, Royal Faculty of Procurators in Glasgow.

Career: Qualified in 1968. Assistant Solicitor and Partner at *Robertson Chalmers & Auld* 1969-86. Partner with *Bishop and Robertson Chalmers* from 1986. Accredited by the Law Society of Scotland as a Specialist in Construction Law in 1993 and as a Solicitor-Mediator in 1994.

Personal: Born 12th September 1945. Educated at Glasgow University 1963-66. Enjoys golf and fishing. Lives in Bearsden.

Willcock, Andrew

Davies Arnold Cooper, Manchester (0161) 839 8396. Qualified 1972. Partner 1993. Construction Department. Main areas of practice are construction and commercial property litigation. Born 13.9.1945.

Wood, Peter

Masons, Manchester (0161) 877 3777. Called to bar 1979 (Solicitor 1985) Partner in Construction and Engineering Department.

Specialisation: Handles all aspects of contentious and non-contentious construction and engineering law. Also deals with all aspects of energy law. Has handled numerous reported cases including Lorne Stewart v. William Sindall, Walter Lawrence v. Commercial Union Props, Emson v. Protea, AMEC v. Crown House and Davy v. Tate & Lyle. Former editor of *Construction Law Journal*; currently editorial board member. Lectures extensively on construction and engineering law.

Prof. Membership: Law Society, Northern Arbitration Association, Energy Industries Council.

Career: Qualified for the Bar in 1979 and as a solicitor in 1985. Joined *Masons* in 1982, becoming a Partner in 1985 and Senior Partner in Manchester office in 1989. Editor of *Construction Law Journal* in 1988 and editorial board member in 1991. Council Member Northern Arbitration Association in 1992.

Personal: Born 17th August 1956. Attended Altrincham Grammar School to 1975, and King's College London to 1978. Leisure interests include DIY and family. Lives in Prestbury, Cheshire.

CONSUMER LAW

CONSUMER law is divided into two main areas: the provision of goods and services (including product liability and recall, trading standards, terms and conditions, and food law) and financial services (including consumer credit, hire purchase, standard form and other finance documentation).

The Sale and Supply of Goods Act 1994 and the Sale of Goods (Ammendment) Act 1994 came into force on 3rd January 1995. This has had significant implications, especially with regard to company terms and conditions. Companies which supply consumer goods or services (including banks and insurance companies) have also been affected by the Unfair Terms in Consumer Contracts Regulations 1994, which came into force on 1st July 1995. This has also generated significant work regarding the revision of terms of business.

Further recent trends include the increase in 'due diligence' defences in trading standards cases, constant change in food law generated by technical processes including genetic developments, and increasing caution in product recall cases with companies tending towards recall if a problem arises.

LONDON

Firms with particularly strong reputations for their expertise in food law include *Murray & Company* and *Simmons &*

LEADING FIRMS - LONDON

MURRAY & CO	SIMMONS & SIMMONS
BARLOW LYDE & GILBERT	WEDLAKE BELL
ALLEN & OVERY	BERWIN LEIGHTON
BIDDLE & CO	DENTON HALL
FOX WILLIAMS	PAISNER & CO
TITMUSS SAINER DECHERT	

Simmons. *Murray & Company*, where Margaret Murray has been consistently recommended, represents numerous food companies and food manufacturers and is particularly well known for undertaking work for Uni-lever. Margaret Murray, who is nationally recognised for her expertise in all aspects of food law, particularly labelling, product safety, advertising and intellectual property, is also Chair of the Food Law Group which furthers the interests and education of food lawyers throughout the country.

Simmons & Simmons is well regarded for its strong team dealing with all aspects of consumer law and has particular expertise in food law (Gareth Davies has been recommended). The firm also has experience in handling work in connection with the supply of goods and services to the consumer.

Other firms highly recommended for expertise in food law include *Barlow Lyde & Gilbert*, *Wedlake Bell*, *Paisner & Co*, *Biddle & Co* and *Fox Williams*.

Stuart Hall at *Barlow Lyde & Gilbert* has an excellent reputation in this field, as has Peter Whatmuff at *Wedlake Bell*. Both firms are strong throughout the whole of the consumer spectrum, with *Barlow Lyde & Gilbert*, having particular expertise on the contentious side of consumer law.

Paisner & Co, whose clients include Forte, Burberrys and Courts Plc, are known for acting on behalf of retailers, manufacturers and wholesalers. Jonathan Kropman at the firm has an established reputation for consumer credit and hire purchase, guarantees and extensions, product safety, food safety and package tour regulations.

Julian Harris at *Biddle & Co*, who represents numerous food manufacturers and hotel groups, and Nigel Miller at *Fox Williams,* are both highly regarded for their expertise in the field. Nigel Miller is known particularly for his advice on the new unfair contract terms and sale of goods legislation, mentioned above.

HIGHLY REGARDED - LONDON

CHARLES RUSSELL	NABARRO NATHANSON
BAKER & McKENZIE	BLACK GRAF & CO
FORSYTE SAUNDERS KERMAN	LEWIS SILKIN
LOVELL WHITE DURRANT	MACFARLANES
PENNINGTONS	

Firms specialising in acting for retailers include *Allen & Overy*, *Berwin Leighton*, *Titmuss Sainer Dechert* and *Denton Hall*. *Titmuss Sainer Dechert* which advises the British Rail Consortium, has particular expertise in finance documentation, consumer credit and sale of goods and services. Simon Leonard at the firm has been recommended for his expertise in food law, trade descriptions, consumer protection and consumer credit.

LEADING INDIVIDUALS - LONDON

Gareth John Davies	*Simmons & Simmons*
Stuart Hall	*Barlow Lyde & Gilbert*
Julian A. Harris	*Biddle & Co*
Jonathan R. Kropman	*Paisner & Co*
Simon Leonard	*Titmuss Sainer Dechert*
Margaret Murray	*Murray & Co*
William L. King	*Macfarlanes*
Nigel Miller	*Fox Williams*
Dennis Rosenthal	*Forsyte Saunders Kerman*
Peter W. Whatmuff	*Wedlake Bell*

SOUTH EAST

The leading firms in the South East are *Brutton & Co, Clarks* and *Hepherd Winstanley & Pugh*. *Brutton & Co,* where Derek Snatt is highly recommended, has an excellent reputation for consumer work, especially with regard to product liability. *Clarks* also has an established reputation in relation to product liability which stems from its connections with the motor industry.

HIGHLY REGARDED – SOUTH EAST	
BRUTTON & CO *Portsmouth*	CLARKS *Reading*
HEPHERD WINSTANLEY & PUGH *Southampton*	

Anthony Askham leads the team at *Hepherd Winstanley & Pugh*, which acts mainly on behalf of retailers. Anthony Askham is particularly well regarded amongst his peers, and handles matters including Sunday trading, shopping hours, trading standards, and health and safety. He is also the author of numerous consumer law books.

LEADING INDIVIDUALS – SOUTH EAST
Anthony John Askham *Hepherd Winstanley & Pugh*
Derek P. Snatt *Brutton & Co*

SOUTH WEST & WALES

Among those firms who have developed a particular expertise in consumer credit and sale of goods issues are *Bond Pearce* and *Wolferstans*, where Paul Johnson has been recommended. *Bond Pearce* has a reputation for acting on behalf of banks and lending institutions on finance house documentation as well as handling trading standards prosecutions and the insurance aspect of product liability.

HIGHLY REGARDED – SOUTH WEST & WALES	
BOND PEARCE *Plymouth*	EVERSHEDS *Cardiff*
HUGH JAMES JONES & JENKINS *Cardiff*	LESTER ALDRIDGE *Bournemouth*
WOLFERSTANS *Plymouth*	

In Dorset, *Lester Aldridge* maintains its national reputation as consumer credit specialists, handling both contentious and non-contentious matters.

LEADING INDIVIDUALS – SOUTH WEST & WALES
Paul B. Johnson *Wolferstans*

The recommended consumer law specialists in Wales are *Eversheds* and *Hugh James Jones & Jenkins*. *Eversheds*, based in Cardiff, advises finance companies, clearing houses and building societies on all aspects of the Consumer Credit Act, and particularly on drafting documentation and the obligations of financiers under the Act. The firm's work in relation to consumer credit has been highly acclaimed.

Hugh James Jones & Jenkins has broad expertise in the field, and is particularly well known for drink and retail related work.

MIDLANDS & EAST ANGLIA

In Norwich, *Eversheds* has an excellent reputation in this area. Owen Warnock at the firm has a national reputation as a food law expert, with extensive experience including food and drink manufacturing, labelling and presentation, advertising and sales promotions, product liability and recall. The firm represents several PLCs including Bernard Matthews, and acted in the recent sale of Colmans.

The Birmingham branch of *Eversheds* also has a broad expertise in consumer law, and is particularly well known for its consumer credit work.

HIGHLY REGARDED – MIDLANDS & EAST ANGLIA	
BROWNE JACOBSON *Nottingham*	EDGE & ELLISON *Birmingham*
EVERSHEDS *Birmingham*	EVERSHEDS *Norwich*
PINSENT CURTIS *Birmingham*	SHOOSMITHS & HARRISON *Northampton*

Other notable practices in the area include *Browne Jacobson*, *Edge & Ellison*, *Pinsent Curtis* and *Shoosmiths & Harrison*. *Edge & Ellison* has a strong reputation in undertaking contentious work, whilst *Browne Jacobson* has considerable experience in relation to Sunday trading law, food law and trading standards. *Pinsent Curtis* is particularly well known for its capability in the law relating to financial services and the provision of goods and services. *Shoosmiths & Harrison* has been recommended for expertise in all aspects, and especially in defending proceedings under the Food Safety Act. The firm is particularly known for their work in product recall and labelling, and environmental health and consumer credit.

LEADING INDIVIDUALS – MIDLANDS & EAST ANGLIA
Owen Warnock *Eversheds*

NORTH

Of the leading firms in the region, *Elliott & Co* has particular expertise in food law, trading standards and health & safety issues. Barry Holland, at the firm, has an excellent reputation. *Andrew M Jackson* has a niche specialism in medicines and food, due largely to the expertise of Hugh Smith, who has an excellent reputation for his knowledge of the Medicines Act and food labelling regulations.

HIGHLY REGARDED – NORTH	
ANDREW M. JACKSON *Hull*	CUFF ROBERTS *Liverpool*
ELLIOTT & CO *Manchester*	EVERSHEDS *Leeds*
LAWSON COPPOCK & HART *Manchester*	PINSENT CURTIS *Leeds*

Other notable practices include *Cuff Roberts* (which has a number of major food clients and is experienced in food safety and hygiene matters), *Pinsent Curtis* (which has major clients in the brewing sector), and *Lawson Coppock & Hart* which acts for suppliers of consumer goods and is well known for its work in the mail order trade sector. N. Broady is known for his considerable expertise in this field.

LEADING INDIVIDUALS – NORTH

Neil H. Broady	*Lawson Coppock & Hart*
Barry K. Holland	*Elliott & Co*
Hugh E. Smith	*Andrew M. Jackson*

In Leeds, *Eversheds* continues to be well respected for its expertise in consumer law, with the team continuing to expand its activities and client base in the provision of consumer credit advice to finance houses, retailers, banks and building societies. The firm also has an excellent reputation for handling work in relation to food law.

SCOTLAND

The leading firm in Scotland in this area is *McClure Naismith Anderson & Gardiner*, which has an experienced department specialising in consumer credit. The firm has

HIGHLY REGARDED – SCOTLAND

McCLURE NAISMITH ANDERSON & GARDINER *Glasgow*

been recommended for its work acting for finance houses, banks, credit card companies and leasing companies. Frank Johnstone at the firm has an excellent reputation.

LEADING INDIVIDUALS – SCOTLAND

Frank R. Johnstone *McClure Naismith Anderson & Gardiner*

LEADERS IN CONSUMER LAW

LONDON

Davies, Gareth John
Simmons & Simmons, London (0171) 628 2020. Partner in Commercial Department.
Specialisation: Specialises in the food and drink industry. Scientific and technical adviser to EU Commission (DGVI) on Designations of Geographic Origin and Specific Character. Advises on all matters relating to composition labelling and regulation of food and drink. Has handled various acquisitions and disposals of food processing and distribution businesses, advice and compliance with compositional regulations, labelling regulations and free circulation of products in the EU and relations with the EU Commission, MAFF and local regulatory authorities, including prosecutions. Clients include Booker PLC, Procter & Gamble, E & J Gallo and Ferminich. Contributor (re sale of goods) to Butterworth's 'Encyclopedia of Forms & Precedents'. Lectures regularly on all aspects of food law.
Prof. Membership: Law Society, Food Law Group (Committee Member).
Career: Qualified in December 1979 (England & Wales) and May 1981 (Hong Kong). Partner at *Simmons & Simmmons* since 1989.
Personal: Born 5th July 1955. Educated at the University of Sheffield 1973-76 (LL.B Hons) and the City of London Polytechnic 1978-81 (MA, Business Law). Leisure interests include sailing, cookery, board games and history. Lives in Enfield.

Hall, Stuart
Barlow Lyde & Gilbert, London (0171) 247 2277. Qualified 1975.

Harris, Julian A.
See under Licensing & Leisure.

King, William L.
See under Advertising & Marketing.

Kropman, Jonathan R.
Paisner & Co, London (0171) 353 0299. Qualified 1981. Partner 1986. Company Department. Handles corporate and commercial, boitech, IP and health law work. Born 8.9.1957.

Leonard, Simon
Titmuss Sainer Dechert, London (0171) 583 5353. Partner and Head of Commercial Department.
Specialisation: General area of practice is Commercial Law including intellectual property advice on rights and contracts and competition. Special interest in consumer law includes pyramid selling, franchising charitable fundraising and unfair contract terms.
Prof. Membership: Law Society. Consumer Credit Trade Association.
Career: Qualified 1969. Assistant Solicitor with *Jaques Partners*, Lusaka, Zambia 1971-76, then joined *Titmuss Sainer Webb* (now *Titmuss Sainer Dechert*) and became a Partner in 1982.
Personal: Born 1944. Attended Durham University 1962-65. Leisure pursuits include sailing, swimming and walking. Lives in Sevenoaks.

Miller, Nigel
See under Company/Commercial.

Murray, Margaret
Murray & Company, London (0181) 944 1335. Partner and food law specialist.
Specialisation: Specialises in advising manufacturing companies, wholesalers and retailers on food law. Work includes advice on the advertising, marketing and manufacturing of food under UK and EC legislation and monitoring consumer legislation in relation to the sale of fast moving consumer products. Clients include CPC (UK) Ltd, Quaker Oats Ltd, Nurdin & Peacock plc and Perrier (UK) Ltd. Addresses food industry and packaging industry conferences. Publishes *The Food Lawyer*.
Prof. Membership: Food Law Group (Chairman), Association of Women Solicitors.
Career: Qualified in 1974. Legal Advisor to Unilever Plc and it's subsidiaries 1974-86. Group Legal Advisor to BOC Ltd 1986-87. Founded *Murray & Company* in 1987.
Personal: Attended Leeds University. Leisure interests include golf, historical buildings conservation, bridge and opera. Lives in Wimbledon.

Rosenthal, Dennis
See under Asset Finance & Leasing.

Whatmuff, Peter W.
Wedlake Bell, London (0171) 395 3000. Partner in Company Commercial Department.
Specialisation: Practice focuses on food law including advertising, labelling and marketing of food, sales promotions, trade marks, passing off, licensing and environmental work. Has dealt with food law issues for major dairy companies/ organisations and for other food companies. Publishes food law newsletter.

Prof. Membership: Law Society, Food Law Group, German-British Chamber of Industry and Commerce.

Career: Qualified in 1975. Became a Partner at *Ellis & Fairbairn* in 1984 and a partner at *Wedlake Bell* in 1988.

Personal: Attended Ashville College, Harrogate and the University of East Anglia. Leisure interests include German life and culture, theatre and swimming.

REGIONS

Askham, Anthony John
Hepherd Winstanley & Pugh, Southampton (01703) 632211. Senior Partner and head of Litigation Department.

Specialisation: Main area of practice is retail law, covering Sunday trading, shopping hours, European shopping hours, trading standards, health and safety, consumer protection and consumer safety. Also handles employment law, unfair dismissals, wrongful dismissal and discrimination cases. Acted in Torfaen Borough Council v. B&Q plc and Stoke on Trent and Norwich City Councils v. B&Q plc, both in the European Court; and Stoke on Trent CC v. B&Q plc (1984 HL). Major clients include B&Q Plc, Woolworth's Plc, Superdrug Plc and Comet Plc. Author of 'EC Sunday Trading Rules' (Butterworths 1990) and 'A Guide to the Sunday Trading

Act 1994' (Butterworths 1994). Individual charge-out rate is £125 per hour.

Prof. Membership: Solicitors European Group, Associate Member of the Institute of Chartered Arbitrators.

Career: Qualified in 1968. Joined *Hepherd Winstanley & Pugh* in 1963, becoming a Partner in 1970. Deputy District Judge and part-time Chairman Special Education Needs Tribunal.

Personal: Born 28th December 1945. Attended Hurstpierpoint College, Sussex (1954-62). Clerk to the Governors at Copythorne Primary School, Hampshire. Leisure interests include watching all sports, education issues and a general interest in politics. Lives in Southampton.

Broady, Neil H.
Lawson Coppock & Hart, Manchester (0161) 832 5944.

Holland, Barry K.
See under Licensing & Leisure.

Johnson, Paul B.
Wolferstans, Plymouth (01752) 663295. Qualified 1975. Partner handling commercial property work, business transfers, licensing and consumer law.

Johnstone, Frank R.
McClure Naismith Anderson &

Gardiner, Glasgow (0141) 204 2700. Partner specialising in Consumer Credit Law and asset recovery.

Specialisation: Consumer Credit Law. Represents a number of Finance Houses, Leasing Companies, Banks and Creditcard Companies, with particular emphasis on litigation/debt recovery. Convener of the Consumer Law Committee of the Law Society of Scotland and has lectured on Consumer Credit Law for the Law Society.

Career: Qualified 1982, joined present firm in 1985. Became a partner in 1988.

Personal: Born 12th October, 1957. Graduated M.A., LL.B., Glasgow University, British Universities Lightweight Boxing Champion 1979 - Runner up 1980.

Smith, Hugh E.
Andrew M. Jackson & Co, Hull (01482) 325242. Qualified 1983. Partner 1991. Commercial Litigation Department. Specialises in contractual disputes, professional negligence, defamation and passing off.

Snatt, Derek P.
Brutton & Co, Portsmouth (01705) 812711. Qualified 1974.

Warnock, Owen
See under Employment Law.

INDEXES TO PROFILES

Solicitors' Profiles The index to leading solicitors profiled in the specialist lists is located immediately after the section containing in-house lawyers' profiles. This index also includes heads of company legal departments.

Barristers' Profiles Leading barristers' profiles are indexed within the main Barristers' Index located at the end of the directory. Names of profiled barristers are set in bold type.

CORPORATE FINANCE

IF the recession is over, boom times still seem far away. The beginning of the year saw an upturn in merger and acquisitions with the Glaxo bid for Wellcome, Cadbury Schweppes going for Dr Pepper, and Texas being carried off by Sainsbury. Since then, however, activity has been intermittent and the market remains in the words of one commentator 'nervously optimistic'. Big deals are still happening but competition for them remains intense. There is a sense that businesses, still recession-shy, are reverting to their core activities. This provides promising territory for those companies which are on the hunt for new additions to their businesses.

LONDON

Many practitioners have mentioned the increasing internationalisation of their work. One manifestation of this is the recent hirings by *Linklaters & Paines, Clifford Chance* and *Allen & Overy* of U.S. lawyers expert in U.S. listing rules. These hirings are significant in that they are specifically designed to enhance these firms' corporate finance and capital markets edge by providing one-stop shopping for their clients when advice on U.S. securities law is required in a transaction. It remains to be seen whether the other leading firms will follow suit.

All of the top ten have excellent corporate finance teams. While it is generally accepted that *Slaughter and May, Linklaters & Paines* and *Freshfields* are especially strong in their mergers and acquisitions capability, and *Ashurst Morris Crisp, Clifford Chance, Macfarlanes* and *Allen & Overy* are more renowned on the Management Buy Out (MBO) side, it is important to remember that all the leading firms are more than capable across the entire corporate finance spectrum.

We should stress the ability of some of the smaller firms in this area. Outside the top 20 firms it is possible for smaller, so called 'boutique' firms to offer a perfectly good and probably cheaper service. We therefore wish to avoid this specialist list being biased in favour of the biggest firms.

Slaughter and May, with its reputation founded on an unparalleled depth of transactional experience in the mergers and acquisitions (M&A) field, continues to be perceived by the profession as the leading firm for the area as a whole, with Michael Pescod, Tim Freshwater, Nigel Boardman and William Underhill all highly recommended classical corporate finance lawyers, specialising in M&A and equity rating work and less frequently MBO work. *Slaughter and May* also continues to do well in external rankings of the top firms' performance and has more blue-chip clients than any other firm (see 'Crawford's Directory' for a 1995 listing and the 'Hambro Company Guide'). High profile transactions this year include advising Wellcome in the Glaxo bid (Michael Pescod) and advising Cadbury Schweppes in its acquisition of Dr Pepper.

LEADING FIRMS – LONDON	
LINKLATERS & PAINES	SLAUGHTER AND MAY
ASHURST MORRIS CRISP	CLIFFORD CHANCE
FRESHFIELDS	
ALLEN & OVERY	HERBERT SMITH
LOVELL WHITE DURRANT	MACFARLANES
NORTON ROSE	SIMMONS & SIMMONS
TRAVERS SMITH BRAITHWAITE	

While the remaining elite firms have received similar recommendations, looking at the field as a whole *Linklaters & Paines* follows as a close second to the leader. It comes second to *Slaughter and May* in the number of its blue-chip clients (see 'Crawford's Directory') and in M&A work, while topping the KPMG Flotations table by solicitor to the issue, placing second by solicitor to the company. Names that were repeatedly recommended to us are Leonard Berkowitz, Anthony Cann and David Cheyne. High profile transactions this year include Cadbury's bid for Dr Pepper, where the firm advised the underwriter Kleinwort Benson to the offerer Cadbury. The firm also acted (jointly) for SmithKline Beecham in its £1.5 billion bid for Diversified Pharmaceutical Services and advised Lloyds Bank plc on its bid for Cheltenham & Gloucester. The firm also acted for SmithKline Beecham on the UK aspects of the sale of its global animal health arm to US drugs giant Pfizer Inc for US $1.4 billion.

HIGHLY REGARDED – LONDON	
BAKER & McKENZIE	S J BERWIN & CO
BERWIN LEIGHTON	CAMERON MARKBY HEWITT
DENTON HALL	EVERSHEDS
FRERE CHOLMELEY BISCHOFF	GOULDENS
McKENNA & CO	NABARRO NATHANSON
RICHARDS BUTLER	ROWE & MAW
STEPHENSON HARWOOD	TAYLOR JOYNSON GARRETT
THEODORE GODDARD	WILDE SAPTE
D J FREEMAN	FIELD FISHER WATERHOUSE
FOX WILLIAMS	LAWRENCE GRAHAM
NICHOLSON GRAHAM & JONES	OLSWANG
PINSENT CURTIS	TITMUSS SAINER DECHERT
WARNER CRANSTON	WATSON, FARLEY & WILLIAMS
ALSOP WILKINSON	BARNETT ALEXANDER CHART
DAVIES ARNOLD COOPER	HOBSON AUDLEY
HOWARD KENNEDY	LEWIS SILKIN
MANCHES & CO	MEMERY CRYSTAL
PAISNER & CO	RAKISONS
SINCLAIR ROCHE & TEMPERLEY	SPEECHLY BIRCHAM
WEDLAKE BELL	

Freshfields does not have as many blue-chip clients as the two firms above. It has always had an excellent reputation and in recent years its own perception is that it has been

LEADING INDIVIDUALS – LONDON

Nigel P.G. Boardman *Slaughter and May*	**Tim G. Freshwater** *Slaughter and May*	
Leonard T. Berkowitz *Linklaters & Paines*	**J.W. Anthony Cann** *Linklaters & Paines*	**David W. Cheyne** *Linklaters & Paines*
Charles S.H. Geffen *Ashurst Morris Crisp*	**Geoffrey.S. Green** *Ashurst Morris Crisp*	**Alan M. Keat** *Travers Smith Braithwaite*
J.R.H. Kitching *Lovell White Durrant*	**Margaret Mountford** *Herbert Smith*	**Alan D. Paul** *Allen & Overy*
Michael Pescod *Slaughter and May*	**Mark S. Rawlinson** *Freshfields*	**Andrew Philip Richards** *Freshfields*
Anthony M.V. Salz *Freshfields*	**Kevin Tuffnell** *Macfarlanes*	**C. William Y. Underhill** *Slaughter and May*
Anthony Alexander *Denton Hall*	**Charles M. Allen-Jones** *Linklaters & Paines*	**C.P. Ashcroft** *Rowe & Maw*
Chris Ashworth *Ashurst Morris Crisp*	**James Baird** *Clifford Chance*	**Jonathan E. Blake** *S J Berwin & Co*
Richard D. Bond *Herbert Smith*	**Jeremy Brownlow** *Clifford Chance*	**Peter Brooks** *Clifford Chance*
William F. Charnley *Simmons & Simmons*	**David Childs** *Clifford Chance*	**Adrian S. Clark** *Ashurst Morris Crisp*
Julia Clarke *Clifford Chance*	**Marco Compagnoni** *Lovell White Durrant*	**Stephen J. Cooke** *Slaughter and May*
Peter M. Crystal *Memery Crystal*	**James P.L. Davis** *Freshfields*	**Anthony C. Dove** *Simmons & Simmons*
James. M. Featherby *Slaughter and May*	**Anthony Fine** *Barnett Alexander Chart*	**Mike Francies** *Clifford Chance*
Richard W. Godden *Linklaters & Paines*	**Keith G. Godfrey** *Allen & Overy*	**D. Graham** *Freshfields*
Patrick Graves *Ashurst Morris Crisp*	**Michael E. Hatchard** *Skadden, Arps*	**Peter R.J. Holland** *Allen & Overy*
William J. L. Knight *Simmons & Simmons*	**Adrian G. Knight** *Ashurst Morris Crisp*	**Matthew Layton** *Clifford Chance*
David T.R. Lewis *Norton Rose*	**Anthony Lewis** *Cameron Markby Hewitt*	**Anthony D. Macaulay** *Herbert Smith*
Dan Mace *Lovell White Durrant*	**Jonathan Macfarlane** *Macfarlanes*	**D.J. Macfarlane** *Ashurst Morris Crisp*
Stephen J. Machin *Ashurst Morris Crisp*	**Lynn McCaw** *Nabarro Nathanson*	**L.G. McFadden** *Freshfields*
A.J.R. Newhouse *Slaughter and May*	**B.J. O'Brien** *Freshfields*	**S.J. Phillips** *Slaughter and May*
Simon Laurence Sackman *Norton Rose*	**Jeremy Nigel Sheldon** *Ashurst Morris Crisp*	**Adam Signy** *Clifford Chance*
Robert C. Stern *Slaughter and May*	**Robert H. Sutton** *Macfarlanes*	**Peter Turnbull** *Macfarlanes*
Edward I. Walker-Arnott *Herbert Smith*	**Sean M. Watson** *McKenna & Co*	**T.O.G. Wethered** *Linklaters & Paines*
Christine J. Williams *Fox Williams*		

closing the gap between itself and *Linklaters & Paines*. As a firm, *Freshfields* has certainly been involved over the past year in most of the major deals, and the close connection with the Bank of England as a major client and an increase in its already strong representation with merchant banks has consolidated its position. In 1994's 'Acquisitions Monthly' yearly summary the firm comes second to *Slaughter and May* for public takeovers and is second to *Linklaters & Paines* in the KPMG summary of flotations by solicitor to the issue. Amongst its practitioners, Anthony Salz, Mark Rawlinson and Andrew Richards were especially recommended to us.

As a firm pre-eminently dedicated to corporate finance, *Ashurst Morris Crisp* perhaps does not receive the praise it deserves for its achievements in the field. Although smaller than the big three, in the field of MBO/ Venture Capital, *Ashurst Morris Crisp* certainly punches above its weight. Even disregarding its placing as top MBO adviser by 'Legal Business' in March '95, the firm has an equally high reputation amongst fellow practitioners. Most frequently mentioned were Charles Geffen and Geoffrey Green as well as Adrian Clark and Chris Ashworth. *Ashurst Morris Crisp* advised EXCO on its £215.5m flotation, acted for MAI and NM. Rothschild & Sons on Rothschild's £299m offer for Anglia Television Group plc and Alcatel Cable on the £600m acquisition of the STC Submarine Systems from Northern Telecom.

Clifford Chance has continued to follow the trend of internationalisation that it has committed itself to and with its strong banking and capital markets teams, makes full use of its extensive overseas network of offices. It has a continuing reputation for MBO work, but also has a strong classical corporate finance team. Among those repeatedly recommended to us were Peter Brooks, Jeremy Brownlow, Mike Francies, Matthew Layton and James Baird. Recent high profile transactions include advising Glaxo on the Wellcome bid and acting for Swiss Bank Corporation in its bid for SG Warburg. The firm also recently advised fund management company Govett & Co on its agreed bid for US fund managers Duff & Phelps. The firm has been active in the coal industry privatisation largely acting for the Government. After previously acting on the RJB Mining deal and the Celtic and Tower employee buy-outs, the firm again represented the Department of Trade and Industry on the disposal of all Scottish coal companies to Mining Scotland.

Allen & Overy is well-regarded and seen as a City firm with a good strength in depth. It is on the back of its banking reputation that it is often given the corporate side of an MBO, and it has a very strong reputation for its practice in this area with Alan Paul being most frequently mentioned. High profile transactions include advising the purchaser and investors in relation to the management buy-in of The Sweater Shop (£150m financing) and advising Swiss Bank in relation to the takeover bid by Trafalgar House for Northern Electric.

Herbert Smith has been involved in several high-profile deals, apart from well publicised privatisations, such as the 12 Regional Electricity Boards and British Coal, which reached its peak at the end of 1994. Other deals include advising the financial advisers to Glaxo in its bid for Wellcome (Lazard Brothers and Lazard Freres), and the BskyB flotation as well as the National Power/PowerGen offering where the firm acted for Kleinwort Benson and BZW. Of the *Herbert Smith* team names that were most frequently mentioned to us are Edward Walker-Arnott, Margaret Mountford and Anthony Macaulay.

Norton Rose received its greatest accolade recently in the survey published by 'Euromoney' subsidiary 'Global Research', entitled "Financial Lawyers on Lawyers 1995", where the firm was ranked first for mergers and acquisitions on a world wide basis. The firm has also been ranked fifth for international privatisations, (in the 1994 report by 'Privatisation International') with several successful privatisations in the emerging market of Eastern Europe. Among the corporate finance team the names most frequently mentioned are David Lewis and Simon Sackman.

Lovell White Durrant's most high profile transaction recently has been advising ING on its takeover of the Barings Group. Others include acting for Teneco Inc and Albright & Wilson on the flotation of Albright & Wilson at a value of £470 million, and for Robert Fleming on Glaxo's bid for Wellcome. Although known for its first-rate insolvency practice *Lovell White Durrant*, despite its size and international presence, still lags behind the big five both among clients and fellow practitioners in the perception they have of its corporate finance practice. Nevertheless it continues to have a steady profile which the firm may be trying to raise with the appointment of Lesley MacDonagh as one of the firm's two managing partners. Dan Mace and Marco Compagnoni were most frequently recommended to us in the context of corporate finance.

Although considerably smaller than the other leading firms *Macfarlanes* has an excellent reputation for its corporate finance capability. 'Hambro Company Guide' puts them tenth in the number of Stock Exchange clients (third in relation to fastest growing stock exchange clients and first in relation to Stock Exchange clients with fastest growing earnings), while 'Euromoney Research' ranks them tenth equal among UK law firms. Recent high profile transactions include advising on the flotation of Flemings Resources Investment Trust with a £50 million market capitalization and an agreed bid by Groupama for Lombard of £83 million. The firm is currently advising BAA on its bid for Holvis, the Swiss group, which is involving the firm in ground breaking territory in Switzerland.

Travers Smith Braithwaite has a reputation disproportionate to its small size. The firm features strongly in all the corporate finance league tables, and for M & A work the firm is regarded as being top ten. The firm can claim to act for over 50 listed companies. It recently advised Hanson on the £460 million flotation of Beazer Plc, and the acquisition of Heron. The firm is also active in the venture capital field, dealing with eight or nine venture houses. It acted for the management in the £60 million bid for Porton International plc and for NatWest Ventures and the bidding vehicle Chief Co Holdings plc in the £33 million bid for Vivat Holdings plc, where both targets were quoted companies.

Rather bigger than *Travers Smith Braithwaite* is *Simmons & Simmons,* fielding 28 specialist corporate finance partners. Recent work includes advising Railtrack plc on the privatisation of the railway network, Capital Radio on its £32 million acquisition of Southern Radio plc, and acting as English legal advisers to the controlling shareholders of the Pedro Domecq group in the takeover by Allied-Lyons.

Denton Hall recently acted for J. Sainsbury plc and Homebase Ltd on the acquisition of the Texas Homecare Group for £290 million. The *Denton Hall* team was led by Anthony Alexander who also advised United Newspapers plc on the purchase of ten magazine articles from Northern & Shell plc and advised the governments of the Czech Republic, Slovakia and Latvia on their mass privatisation programmes.

There are other firms within this 'highly recommended' group which may also have particular areas of expertise within the corporate finance field such as *S J Berwin & Co* which has a strong reputation for venture capital. *Nabarro Nathanson* has been particularly active in British Coal matters, recently acting for British Coal in the sale of its smokeless fuel subsidiary, Coal Products, to the management and employee team. The *Nabarro Nathanson* team was led by Lynn McCaw, formerly in-house at British Coal.

Gouldens have a strong corporate finance department, which has acted for several plcs, and major banks. The firm was instructed by Coal Investments plc on two rights issues and placings which raised £17.6m and has also carried out considerable high value mergers and acquisition work. It has been involved in transactions in the CIS and the Far East.

Finally there are a number of smaller practices, such as *Fox Williams* and *Memery Crystal,* which have especially strong corporate finance capabilities in relation to their size, or niche strengths such as *Barnett Alexander Chart* which is a market leader in local authority MBOs. *Memery Crystal* led by Peter Crystal, recently acted for Inkhold Ltd, in the sale of its ICS Group in a management and employee buy-out worth £78 million.

Nicholson Graham Jones recently advised merchant bank Singer & Friedlander in its acquisition of a 55% controlling stake in Carnegie, the international broking house, from Nordbanken of Sweden.

SOUTH EAST

The South East is not an area recognised for the strength of its corporate finance work and South East firms cannot match firms from other regions in the size and depth of their practice. They rarely, if ever, feature in the various league tables of deals, which help to give an indication of firms' performance in the corporate finance world. Whether cause

LEADING FIRMS – SOUTH EAST	
BLAKE LAPTHORN *Fareham*	**CLARKS** *Reading*
DONNE MILEHAM & HADDOCK *Brighton*	**SHOOSMITHS & HARRISON** *Banbury*

or effect, clients are always going to be tempted by the proximity of London, or depending on their location, Birmingham. These temptations notwithstanding, there are a number of respected firms throughout the South East which deal with corporate finance matters on a regular basis. The principal corporate finance firms are *Donne Mileham & Haddock* and *Blake Lapthorn* on the south coast; *Rawlison & Butler* and *Burstows* in Crawley, and in the Thames Valley, *Dallas Brett, Manches & Co* and *Cole and Cole* in Oxford, and *Clarks* and *Pitmans* in Reading. With offices in Northampton, Reading and Southampton *Shoosmiths & Harrison* are also well known for their corporate finance expertise.

HIGHLY REGARDED – SOUTH EAST	
BURSTOWS *Crawley*	**COLE and COLE** *Oxford*
DALLAS BRETT *Oxford*	**MANCHES & CO** *Oxford*
PITMANS *Reading*	**RAWLISON & BUTLER** *Crawley*

Recommended at *Donne Mileham & Haddock,* a practice headquartered in Brighton and with five branch offices and 200 staff, is Andrew Trotter. The firm has recently acted for the Avonex Group Limited on its acquisition of Reliant Motors Limited and for the Midland Enterprise Fund for the South East.

Blake Lapthorn has eleven specialist partners in the company/commercial department, with commercial work accounting for a third of the firm's total. The firm has a good corporate finance client in British Rail, and it recently acted in an MBO of BICC Vero Electronics Group.

In West Sussex, James Chatfield has been recommended at *Rawlison & Butler.* The firm fields two specialist partners in the corporate finance department, with company/ commercial work accounting for a fifth of its total workload. The firm handles traditional M&A work, MBOs and venture capital. In the same area *Burstows* also handles corporate matters.

LEADING INDIVIDUALS – SOUTH EAST
James H.T. Chatfield *Rawlison & Butler*
Andrew Trotter *Donne Mileham & Haddock*
Peter G. Angel *Manches & Co*
Andrew E. Heathcock *Paris Smith & Randall*
Richard Lee *Clarks*
Jonathan Loake *Dallas Brett*

In the Oxford area, three firms stand out for their corporate law capability. *Cole and Cole,* a large local firm, has recently acted for the Wychwood Brewery Company and for the management team in the MBO of Cambridge Industries, a leading supplier of consumer satellite equipment. *Manches & Co,* besides its London practice, has a substantial corporate presence in Oxford where it fields five specialist partners dealing with MBOs and MBIs, M & A work, venture capital and general corporate advice.

Dallas Brett, an up and coming commercial practice more commonly known for its intellectual property expertise, is developing a reputation for company/commercial work including corporate finance matters, handling M&A work, acting for a venture capital fund, and advising on MBOs. Jonathan Loake is particularly recommended.

Clarks in Reading undertakes the full range of corporate finance activity including MBO and MBI work, listed company matters (the firm is currently advising on the UK end of a New York listing), and venture capital, acting for BZW Private Equity in this region. Richard Lee has a good reputation.

Shoosmiths & Harrison is the pre-eminent firm in the Northampton area and is one of the leading commercial firms throughout the South East. Its team covers all aspects of corporate work including MBOs, venture capital and full listings including those for Eurovein plc and Radstone Technology plc.

SOUTH WEST

Osborne Clarke and *Burges Salmon* continue to dominate the corporate finance scene in the South West.

LEADING FIRMS – SOUTH WEST	
BURGES SALMON *Bristol*	**OSBORNE CLARKE** *Bristol*

At *Osborne Clarke* Simon Beswick, Chris Curling and Jeremy Simon make up the core of the corporate finance team. During the past year the firm has been involved in the flotation of Chesterton International for £50 million and has advised Colleagues Group plc in their flotation through an £8 million placing. The firm did well in KPMG's summaries of

HIGHLY REGARDED – SOUTH WEST	
BEVAN ASHFORD *Bristol*	**BOND PEARCE** *Plymouth*
VEALE WASBROUGH *Bristol*	**WANSBROUGHS WILLEY HARGRAVE** *Bristol*
CARTWRIGHTS *Bristol*	**CHARLES RUSSELL** *Cheltenham*
DAVIES AND PARTNERS *Gloucester*	**LAWRENCE TUCKETTS** *Bristol*
LESTER ALDRIDGE *Bournemouth*	**STEELE RAYMOND** *Bournemouth*

flotations by solicitor to the issue and to the company. In 1994 the firm acted in 35 corporate transactions worth more than £1 million. It advised the Bank of Scotland in the senior debt financing for the MBO of Dartington Crystal, South Western Electricity plc in the establishment of wind farm joint venture projects and Horlicks in the sale of operations to Dairygold. June 1995 saw the firm assisting Frost Group in its £83 million acquisition of Burmah Castrol's UK petrol retailing and wholesale operations to create the UK's fifth largest petrol retailer.

At *Burges Salmon* Alan Barr, Christopher Godfrey and David Marsh are all recommended for their corporate finance work. KPMG's summary of flotations by solicitor to the company in 1994 shows that the firm advised on four London listings (compared to *Osborne Clarke*'s three) and on two as solicitor to the issue (three for *Osborne Clarke*). The firm recently advised on the purchase by Cricket St. Thomas Dairies of Devon Dairy for £14 million.

Bevan Ashford is known as a 'boutique firm' active in the MBO field rather than as a general corporate finance specialist. Paul Cooper received more individual recommendations than anyone else, which is obviously a testament to the high quality of his and the firm's work. The firm has acted for Natwest Ventures and Foreign and Colonial Ventures in the £25 million fund raising for Cricket St. Thomas Dairies and represented the employees on their buy-out of Tower Colliery as part of the privatisation of British Coal.

Three other firms in this area which have received recommendations for their corporate finance work are *Bond Pearce*, *Veale Wasbrough* and *Wansbroughs Willey Hargrave*.

WALES

Government in past years has poured considerable sums of money into the Welsh economy through the Welsh Development Agency. This has helped to stimulate corporate finance activity, although the firms we list rely primarily on a range of corporate work, including much company/commercial work.

Eversheds in Wales is the firm most likely to be recommended for corporate finance, boasting the largest team of dedicated corporate finance lawyers in South Wales (including notable practitioners in Lawrence James and

Alan Whiteley). The firm has been involved in a number of high profile transactions last year, including acting for Celtic Energy Limited in its purchase of South Wales opencast coalfield from British Coal and setting up the joint venture between South West Electricity plc and CableTel for the South Wales cable television franchises. The firm is perceived as increasing its lead over its rivals in this area of practice.

Duncan Macintosh, heading up the corporate finance team at *Morgan Bruce,* has been recommended for his expertise

in this field. Other firms with a recognised capability are *Edwards Geldard*, along with *Hugh James Jones & Jenkins* and *Bevan Ashford.*

MIDLANDS

Four firms continue to dominate corporate finance in this area: *Wragge & Co, Eversheds, Edge & Ellison* and *Pinsent Curtis*. Of these four, *Wragge & Co* is acknowledged as the leading firm, probably followed by *Pinsent Curtis*, although the closer links being forged between the *Eversheds* firms may yet pose a challenge to this pre-eminence.

Dibb Lupton Broomhead, having entered Birmingham last year, is still trying to develop a market for itself. It is too early to say whether it will present a serious competitive threat. A disappointment for the Birmingham firms was the choice of traditional City firms to act in the recommended bid by Misys for ACT (one of the biggest companies in Birmingham) in preference to their usual Birmingham legal advisers. This seems to fly in the face of recent trends and could be indicative of the hard fight the regional firms may have in persuading clients to stay with them for larger transactions.

Wragge & Co's Ian Metcalfe is considered to be at the forefront of corporate finance in the Midlands. Stephen Braithwaite and John Crabtree are also highly recommended. The firm acts for over 90 listed public companies and can field a team of fifty lawyers based at its single Birmingham office. The firm ranked sixteenth in the 'FT's' top MBO table to 30/9/94 and in the 12 months to May 1994 the corporate finance team advised on over 100 transactions with an aggregate value of more than £540 million. It advised West Midlands Travel on its £244 million merger with National Express in what is claimed to be the biggest M&A transaction worked on by a regional firm. The firm also acted for PowerGen plc on its acquisition from Procarbon AB of a facility at Mersey Dock in Liverpool, and for Innovative Technologies Group plc on what was the last flotation on the USM.

HIGHLY REGARDED – MIDLANDS

GATELEY WAREING *Birmingham*	MARTINEAU JOHNSON *Birmingham*
BLYTHE LIGGINS *Leamington Spa*	DIBB LUPTON BROOMHEAD *Birmingham*
EDWARDS GELDARD *Derby*	FREETH CARTWRIGHT HUNT DICKINS *Nottingham*
GEORGE GREEN & CO *Warley*	HARVEY INGRAM *Leicester*
KENT JONES and DONE *Stoke-on-Trent*	SHAKESPEARES *Birmingham*
SHOOSMITHS & HARRISON *Northampton*	

Milton Psyllides and Peter McHugh of *Eversheds* continue to be highly recommended. The firm has been involved in several high profile deals including the flotation of Partco Group plc and Ryland Group plc where it acted for the company, and Silvermines Group plc's takeover of Molynx plc, and BSG International plc's takeover of Jessups plc.

LEADING INDIVIDUALS – MIDLANDS

Ian Metcalfe *Wragge & Co*	
Andrew Eastgate *Pinsent Curtis*	
David J. Hughes *Pinsent Curtis*	
Digby M. Jones *Edge & Ellison*	
Milton N. Psyllides *Eversheds*	
Amanda Allen *Pinsent Curtis*	
Stephen Braithwaite *Wragge & Co*	
Paul Cliff *Edge & Ellison*	
David J. Cooke *Pinsent Curtis*	
John Crabtree *Wragge & Co*	
Patrick John Green *Pinsent Curtis*	
Alan Edward Greenough *Pinsent Curtis*	
Simon D.V. Gronow *Pinsent Curtis*	
David S. Haggett *Eversheds*	
David W. Hamlett *Wragge & Co*	
Susan Lewis *Eversheds*	
Peter J. McHugh *Eversheds*	
Christopher D. Rawstron *Edge & Ellison*	
Michael R. Seabrook *Eversheds*	

Edge & Ellison has always been best known for its MBO expertise, in which it tends to have a higher profile than the other big three. Digby Jones is pre-eminent at the firm and is very well known on the Birmingham scene. There has been some criticism however that the firm lacks the depth of talent of the other big three firms and that it has a disproportionately small share of the top 20 largest Midlands companies by market capitalisation. However at the beginning of the year the firm appeared for the first time in three 'Acquisitions Monthly' tables. The firm recently helped Forward Group plc to complete the acquisition of Exacta Circuits Ltd and took the company from the USM to the Official List. It also advised on the flotation of Universal Ceramic Materials plc and the £193m recommended offers by Plantsbrook Group plc on behalf of Service Corporation International plc.

Pinsent Curtis has two notable practitioners in Andrew Eastgate and David Hughes. Alan Greenough has also been recommended. The firm is perceived as having strength in depth and following the merger, can claim that it is in the Top

Ten of firms acting for listed clients. The firm last year acted in seven flotations and 12 MBOs. It also acted for British Bus plc on the acquisition of Caldaire Holdings and then for the Caldaire Group in the acquisition of the holding company of Maidstone & District Transport Limited.

After the big four, *Gateley Wareing* and *Martineau Johnson* are firms that have a definite expertise in corporate finance, notwithstanding the fact that they have much smaller teams than the leading firms.

EAST ANGLIA

Firms in this region with a corporate finance capability all have established company/commercial practices. *Mills & Reeve* and *Eversheds* (Norwich) stand out, while *Hewitson Becke & Shaw* is also recognised in the area and *Taylor Vinters* is seen as having increasing expertise.

LEADING FIRMS – EAST ANGLIA

EVERSHEDS *Norwich*	MILLS & REEVE *Norwich*

At *Mills & Reeve* Nicolas Fischl is highly recommended. The firm claims that their work comprises 25% MBO; 25% raising finance and 50% acquisitions and disposals. The firm has acted for Sentry Farming Group plc on its full listing following its transfer from the USM, Blakes Holidays on the disposal of its holiday cottage letting business to Thomson Holidays and the flotation of the Ethical Group plc on Nasdaq. It also acted for Norfolk Health Commission on the privatisation of its accounting and payroll operations to the MBO team.

HIGHLY REGARDED – EAST ANGLIA

HEWITSON BECKE + SHAW *Cambridge*	TAYLOR VINTERS *Cambridge*
BIRKETTS *Ipswich*	GREENWOODS *Peterborough*

Andrew Croome of *Eversheds* (Norwich) is another highly recommended local practitioner. The firm has recently advised on a placing and public offering of up to £30m shares for Nursing Homes Properties plc, and the negotiation of up to £25m loan facility for the purchase and lease-back of care homes.

LEADING INDIVIDUALS – EAST ANGLIA

Nicolas J. Fischl *Mills & Reeve*
Fiona Crawley *Hewitson Becke + Shaw*
Andrew Croome *Eversheds*
John Short *Taylor Vinters*

Hewitson Becke & Shaw are able to field a team of six corporate finance specialists from their Cambridge office and cover all aspects of corporate finance activity. Fiona Crawley of their Peterborough office has also been recommended.

At *Taylor Vinters* John Short has also been recommended as a corporate finance practitioner and was currently engaged on a reverse takeover at the time of publication. In Peterborough *Greenwoods* has been recommended principally in connection with its work for EMAP.

NORTH WEST

Addleshaw Sons & Latham is acknowledged to be the leading corporate finance firm in the North West. Keith Johnston, Paul Lee, Andrew Needham and Paul Devitt are all highly recommended. The team has recently been strengthened by the addition of Darryl Cooke, formerly of *Halliwell Landau*, and a highly rated practitioner in the area who has written books on MBOs and venture capital. The firm covers the full range of corporate finance activity. High profile deals during 1994 include advising Charterhouse Tilney Securities Ltd, sponsor and stockbroker to the flotation of JJB Sports plc by way of a placing, with total market capitalization of £64.5m. The firm also advised on the highest value MBO for 1994, the £63.5m acquisition of the business of Holt Lloyd international from the Morgan Crucible Company.

LEADING FIRMS – NORTH WEST

ADDLESHAW SONS & LATHAM *Manchester*	
ALSOP WILKINSON *Liverpool*	**EVERSHEDS** *Manchester*

Edward Pysden at *Eversheds* in Manchester is considered to be one of the leading practitioners of corporate finance in the North West. Fielding a strong team *Eversheds,* has been involved in several high profile transactions including the sale by Co-operative Wholesale Society of its food manufacturing division for £100m, the merger of Sheppard Group with Coopers Holdings to form European Metal Recycling Ltd and acting for Vymura on its flotation.

HIGHLY REGARDED – NORTH WEST

DIBB LUPTON BROOMHEAD *Manchester*	**HALLIWELL LANDAU** *Manchester*
HAMMOND SUDDARDS *Manchester*	
CHAFFE STREET *Manchester*	**GARRETT & CO** *Manchester*
SLATER HEELIS *Manchester*	**WACKS CALLER** *Manchester*
BRABNER HOLDEN BANKS WILSON *Liverpool*	**DAVIES ARNOLD COOPER** *Manchester*
DAVIES WALLIS FOYSTER *Liverpool*	**INGHAM CLEGG & CROWTHER** *Preston*
KUIT, STEINART, LEVY *Manchester*	**PANNONE & PARTNERS** *Manchester*

Alsop Wilkinson has a strong presence in Liverpool, where the highly regarded Michael Prince is based, with other offices in Manchester and London. The firm ranks highly in national compilations for MBO transactions and handles the whole range of corporate finance activity. They recently acted for the joint administrative receivers of Shrigley Park Limited in the sale of Shrigley Hall Hotel Golf & Country Club for £8 million to Paramount Hotels Limited.

Dibb Lupton Broomhead, Halliwell Landau, and *Hammond Suddards* make up the next grouping, with Alexander Craig and John Whatnall of *Halliwell Landau* both being highly recommended.

Of the smaller firms, *Slater Heelis* is well-respected, especially for public company work. For a 'boutique' service, *Chaffe Street's* Robert Street is well known, although there is a perception that the firm does not have the resources for bigger transactions.

Wacks Caller has recently expanded by recruiting from the company commercial department of *Fox Brooks Marshall*.

LEADING INDIVIDUALS – NORTH WEST

Edward Pysden *Eversheds*	
Darryl J. Cooke	*Addleshaw Sons & Latham*
I. Alexander Craig	*Halliwell Landau*
Roger Gough	*Alsop Wilkinson*
William E. Holt	*Dibb Lupton Broomhead*
Keith Johnston	*Addleshaw Sons & Latham*
Roger Lane-Smith	*Alsop Wilkinson*
Paul Lee	*Addleshaw Sons & Latham*
Richard N.F. Lee	*Addleshaw Sons & Latham*
Andrew Needham	*Addleshaw Sons & Latham*
Kevin Philbin	*Wacks Caller*
Michael J. Prince	*Alsop Wilkinson*
Peter B.A. Renshaw	*Slater Heelis*
Robert H. Street	*Chaffe Street*
M.C. Warburton	*Slater Heelis*
Richard Burns	*Hammond Suddards*
P. Devitt	*Addleshaw Sons & Latham*
John Jackson	*Davies Arnold Cooper*
John Whatnall	*Halliwell Landau*

Garrett & Co despite its close connection with Arthur Anderson has not as yet managed to make an impact on the North West, (unlike its newer venture in the Midlands). However, having the resources of a major accountancy firm behind it, the firm can afford to be patient in building a reputation.

NORTH EAST

The out-standing corporate finance firm in the North East is *Eversheds* (Leeds), with David Gray, Ian Richardson, and Stephen Hopkins all being highly recommended. Major transactions for 1994 included acting for the management

LEADING FIRMS – NORTH EAST

BOOTH & CO. *Leeds*	**DIBB LUPTON BROOMHEAD** *Bradford*
EVERSHEDS *Leeds*	**HAMMOND SUDDARDS** *Leeds*
PINSENT CURTIS *Leeds*	

team in the MBO at the Birmingham Post for £130 million, and in the MBO at Leyland DAF trucks for £40m. It recently advised in the £24m buy-out of Crompton Lighting from BTR, one of the biggest MBOs in the region for some years. The team has also acted for many venture and development capitalists and has an unparalleled strength in this area.

HIGHLY REGARDED – NORTH EAST

DICKINSON DEES *Newcastle upon Tyne*	**ROBERT MUCKLE** *Newcastle-upon-Tyne*
WALKER MORRIS *Leeds*	
WARD HADAWAY *Newcastle upon Tyne*	**WATSON BURTON** *Newcastle upon Tyne*
WILKINSON MAUGHAN *Newcastle-upon-Tyne*	
BROOKE NORTH AND GOODWIN *Leeds*	**EVERSHEDS** *Newcastle upon Tyne*
IRWIN MITCHELL *Sheffield*	**NABARRO NATHANSON** *Doncaster*
ROLLIT FARRELL & BLADON *Hull*	**TEEMAN LEVINE** *Leeds*
WAKE SMITH *Sheffield*	

Hammond Suddards is another North East firm with an excellent reputation for its corporate finance expertise, with Noel Hutton being especially recommended. The firm now acts for twenty per cent of all Yorkshire based public companies, including ten of the top thirty.

Booth & Co's Maurice Cowen has been highly recommended to us. Major deals this year include advising Oxford Molecular Group plc on its £5.93m acquisition of Oregon software company Cache Scientific Inc from Tekronix, and advising Powell Duffryn plc on its acquisition of shares in Teesside and Humberside Holdings Limited for £90m. The firm continues to have a strong reputation for its corporate work notwithstanding the presence of the aggressively placed *Dibb Lupton Broomhead* and *Hammond Suddards*. Indeed it has completed over 200 deals in the twelve months to June 1995 and has an impressive client list.

LEADING INDIVIDUALS – NORTH EAST

David John Gray *Eversheds*	
Maurice C. Cowen *Booth & Co.*	
Andrew Darwin *Dibb Lupton Broomhead*	
Paul D. Emmett *Walker Morris*	
Ian M. Gilbert *Walker Morris*	
Stephen Martyn Hopkins *Eversheds*	
C. Noel Hutton *Hammond Suddards*	
C. Sean Lippell *Pinsent Curtis*	
Nick Painter *Garrett & Co*	
Andrew Pike *Hammond Suddards*	
Ian Ashley Richardson *Eversheds*	
Peter C. Smart *Walker Morris*	
Andrew W. Walker *Pinsent Curtis*	

Following its merger, *Pinsent Curtis* now has a combined strength of 97 partners and staff of 650, making it the 16th largest practice in the country, and is able to field an excellent corporate finance team notwithstanding the much-publicised departure of several of its corporate partners to *Garrett & Co* midway through 1994. Prior to the merger there had been a perception that *Simpson Curtis* (as it then was) was being left behind by *Dibb Lupton Broomhead*, *Hammond Suddards* and *Eversheds*. The firm has advised Independent Parts Group plc on its flotation and the £25.5m flotation of Hill Hire plc. The firm also advised The Bradford Property Trust plc on their successful bid for Harborne Tenants Limited and acted for FKI plc on the US$120m private placing by its subsidiary FKI Industries Inc. Sean Lippell has been

recommended as a leading practitioner.

Andrew Darwin is a leading corporate finance lawyer at *Dibb Lupton Broomhead*. The firm has always been at the forefront of corporate finance in the North East and its star is now firmly in the ascendant. In 1994 the firm was the third favourite in acting for buy-out houses in MBOs with only two City firms being preferred over it. As a whole, the firm scores highly for MBOs, for flotations and M&A work.

Finally, of the remaining firms that were especially recommended, *Walker Morris* should be noted, having the capable Peter Smart in its team. High profile transactions from last year include a £5.5m MBO of the Factory Shops Ltd from Peter Black plc and a £13m vendors' placing for Kalon Group plc.

In Newcastle *Dickinson Dees* continues to dominate the corporate finance scene both in terms of its size and reputation. *Robert Muckle* is a firm with an increasing reputation for corporate finance matters and was involved in the listing of Gus Carter plc, the rights issue at G.M. Firth Holdings plc and the sale of Eldiss Caravans Consett Ltd. Other firms in the area which are highly regarded are *Ward Hadaway* and *Watson Burton*. In Sheffield, *Irwin Mitchell's* recent merger with *Kershaw Tudor* has enhanced its corporate services strength.

SCOTLAND

The perception of the profession is that the gap between the major top five firms and the rest has widened in these hard post-recessionary times. It is said that margins are coming down and the bigger firms are encroaching on work that once was the preserve of smaller firms.

LEADING FIRMS – SCOTLAND

DUNDAS & WILSON CS *Edinburgh*	**McGRIGOR DONALD** *Glasgow*
DICKSON MINTO WS *Edinburgh*	**MACLAY MURRAY & SPENS** *Glasgow*
SHEPHERD & WEDDERBURN *Edinburgh*	

Dickson Minto WS, Dundas & Wilson CS, Maclay Murray & Spens, McGrigor Donald and *Shepherd & Wedderburn WS* have again dominated the corporate finance field and constitute the list of pre-eminent firms in Scotland. Of these, *Dundas & Wilson CS* and *McGrigor Donald* slightly edge in front of the competition for general corporate finance work.

HIGHLY REGARDED – SCOTLAND

BIGGART BAILLIE & GIFFORD *Glasgow*	**BIRD SEMPLE** *Glasgow*
BRODIES WS *Edinburgh*	**W & J BURNESS WS** *Edinburgh*
DORMAN JEFFREY & CO *Glasgow*	**MACROBERTS** *Glasgow*
McCLURE NAISMITH ANDERSON & GARDINER *Glasgow*	**PAULL & WILLIAMSONS** *Aberdeen*
TODS MURRAY WS *Edinburgh*	
BELL & SCOTT WS *Edinburgh*	**MILLER SAMUEL & CO** *Glasgow*
STEEDMAN RAMAGE WS *Edinburgh*	**WRIGHT, JOHNSTON & MACKENZIE** *Glasgow*

In all the tables the names in each group are listed alphabetically.

At *Dundas & Wilson* both Maureen Coutts and David Hardie are thought of as excellent practitioners in the field. Among transactions the firm handled recently were the £27.5m placing of shares in Stagecoach Holdings plc, advising Dawson International plc on its £45m rights issue and acting as solicitor to the company and to the issue in the issue of £50m debenture stock in Scottish Eastern Investment Trust plc.Brian Dorman of *Dorman Jeffery & Co* is also highly regarded. In the past year the firm has advised on the sale of the business by Healthcare International (Scotland) Ltd to HCI Holdings Ltd and subsequent hive-down to, and sale of, HCI (Scotland) Ltd. It also advised on the MBO of Currie Line Ltd from Anchor Line plc and the acquisition by Helikopter Services A/S of Bond Holdings Ltd to create the largest helicopter service group worldwide.

McGrigor Donald acted for venture capitalists Murray Johnstone in the sale of British Coal's assets north of the border. The team was led by Stephen Cook. Also highly regarded at the firm is Morag McNeill.

LEADING INDIVIDUALS – SCOTLAND
Maureen S. Coutts *Dundas & Wilson CS*
David Hardie *Dundas & Wilson CS*
Christopher R.J. Campbell *Dundas & Wilson CS*
Stephen Cook *McGrigor Donald*
Alastair R. Dickson *Dickson Minto WS*
A. Brian Dorman *Dorman Jeffrey & Co*
Ian B. Inglis *Shepherd & Wedderburn*
Ian G. Lumsden *Maclay Murray & Spens*
Morag McNeill *McGrigor Donald*
Iain M.C. Meiklejohn *Shepherd & Wedderburn*
Bruce W. Minto *Dickson Minto WS*
Bruce R. Patrick *Maclay Murray & Spens*
John C. Rafferty *W & J Burness WS*
William G. Simmons *Tods Murray WS*
Magnus P. Swanson *Maclay Murray & Spens*
James R. Will *Shepherd & Wedderburn*

Dickson Minto is seen as a specialist corporate finance player, and has a London office of equal size and possibly greater repute than its Scottish base in Edinburgh. With a focus on MBOs, the firm came second only to *Clifford Chance* in MBO deals in the UK in 1991. The firm also featured in the KPMG flotations table as acting in seven London listings as solicitor to the company.

Maclay Murray & Spens' Bruce Patrick and Magnus Swanson, and James Will and Iain Meiklejohn from *Shepherd & Wedderburn WS* have also been recommended as excellent corporate finance practitioners. During the past year *Maclay Murray & Spens* has advised on the £63m flotation of Robert Wiseman Dairies plc, the flotation of Wainhomes plc (the Chester-based housebuilder) and the £27m sale of Donprint International to Jarvis Porter Group plc. The firm has also advised on numerous MBOs.

Shepherd & Wedderburn showed particularly well in the KPMG league table of solicitors acting in flotations in the two year period to 31 December 1994, advising on seven issues as solicitor to the issue and eight as solicitor to the company. The firm recently acted in the sale of Exacta Circuits Ltd to Forward Group plc.

Other firms with a definite corporate finance capability include *Biggart Baillie & Gifford, Brodies WS, W & J Burness WS, McClure Naismith Anderson & Gardiner, Tods Murray WS, MacRoberts, Bird Semple* (it will be interesting to see how its demerger will affect it) and *Paull & Williamsons*.

Biggart Baillie & Gifford acted for Bank of Scotland and Clydesdale Bank in the acquisition by Mining (Scotland) Ltd of all of British Coal's assets in Scotland.

NORTHERN IRELAND

The leading firms in this field include *Johns Elliott* where David Leitch is a well-known specialist. At *L'Estrange & Brett* Brian Henderson has considerable expertise in corporate finance, dealing with the financing of mergers and acqui-

HIGHLY REGARDED – NORTHERN IRELAND	
JOHNS ELLIOT *Belfast*	**L'ESTRANGE & BRETT** *Belfast*
MILLS SELIG *Belfast*	**TUGHAN & CO** *Belfast*
CARSON & McDOWELL *Belfast*	**CLEAVER FULTON & RANKIN** *Belfast*
ELLIOTT DUFFY GARRETT *Belfast*	

sitions, MBOs, finance, leasing and securitisation, receivables and asset-based financing, debt reorganization, flotations and share issues. *Mills Selig* are also well regarded for mergers and acquisitions, specialists including Bill McCann, Richard Fulton and Ivan Selig. At *Tughan & Co* Phyllis Agnew and John Mills are highly thought of in this area. Other leading firms in the field include *Carson & McDowell, Cleaver Fulton & Rankin* and *Elliott Duffy Garrett*.

LEADING INDIVIDUALS – NORTHERN IRELAND
B.E. Phyllis M. Agnew *Tughan & Co*
Richard Fulton *Mills Selig*
Brian L. Henderson *L'Estrange & Brett*
David A. Leitch *Johns Elliot*
R. William C. McCann *Mills Selig*
John W. Mills *Tughan & Co*
Ivan Selig *Mills Selig*

In all the tables the names in each group are listed alphabetically.

LONDON

Alexander, Anthony
Denton Hall, London (0171) 242 1212.

Allen-Jones, Charles M.
Linklaters & Paines, London (0171) 606 7080. Partner 1968. Corporate Department. Specialisms include equity issues, public and private acquisitions, reorganisations and projects.

Ashcroft, C.P.
Rowe & Maw, London (0171) 248 4282. Qualified 1977.

Ashworth, Chris
See under Company/Commercial.

Baird, James
Clifford Chance, London (0171) 600 1000. Partner. Specialises in management buyouts\buyins, leveraged acquisitions and new issues.

Berkowitz, Leonard T.
Linklaters & Paines, London (0171) 606 7080. Qualified 1970. Partner 1972. Main area of practice is corporate law.

Blake, Jonathan E.
S J Berwin & Co, London (0171) 837 2222. Qualified 1979. Partner. Corporate Finance Department. Specialises in the establishment of funds, company structuring, and venture capital investment.

Boardman, Nigel P.G.
Slaughter and May, London (0171) 600 1200. Qualified 1975. Joined 1973. Partner specialising in corporate finance, corporate and commercial work, including IPO's, MBO's, take-overs, private acquisitions and joint ventures. Also handles banking and capital markets matters.

Bond, Richard D.
Herbert Smith, London (0171) 374 8000. Partner and Head of Company Department.

Specialisation: Wide ranging experience of corporate transactions, particularly in the fields of energy and privatisations. He is a Council Member of the Energy and National Resources Section of the International Bar Association and Chairman of its Oil Committee.

Career: Qualified in 1969. Partner with *Herbert Smith* since 1977.

Brownlow, Jeremy
Clifford Chance, London (0171) 600 1000. Main area of work is company and commercial including corporate finance and mergers and acquisitions.

Brooks, Peter
See under Company/Commercial.

Cann, J.W.Anthony
Linklaters & Paines, London (0171) 606 7080. Qualified 1972. Joined 1970, became Partner 1978. Partner specialising in general corporate work, mergers and acquisitions and issues.

Charnley, William F.
Simmons & Simmons, London (0171) 628 2020. Qualified 1987. Partner 1990. Corporate Department. Practice includes flotations, mergers and acquisitions and capital raising.

Cheyne, David W.
Linklaters & Paines, London (0171) 606 7080. Qualified 1974. Partner 1980. Main area of practice is company and corporate finance, including mergers and acquisitions, issues and general corporate work.

Childs, David
Clifford Chance, London (0171) 600 1000.

Clark, Adrian S.
See under Company/Commercial.

Clarke, Julia
Clifford Chance, London (0171) 600 1000.

Compagnoni, Marco
Lovell White Durrant, London (0171) 236 0066. Qualified 1987. Partner 1993. Corporate Department. Practice includes joint ventures, MBO's, MBI's and mergers and acquisitions. Born 3.5.1962.

Cooke, Stephen J.
See under Company/Commercial.

Crystal, Peter M.
See under Sports Law.

Davis, James P.L.
See under Company/Commercial.

Dove, Anthony C.
See under Company/Commercial.

Featherby, James. M.
Slaughter and May, London (0171) 600 1200. Qualified 1983. Partner since 1990. Specialises in commercial work including mergers, acquisitions and joint ventures.

Fine, Anthony
Barnett Alexander Chart, London (0171) 434 4011. Partner in Company & Commercial Department.

Specialisation: Principal areas of work are MBOs, MBIs, and development capital. Has-

completed in excess of 35 MBO/MBI development capital deals over the last 5 years. Firm is a market leader in local authority MBOs. Also heavily engaged in advising on externalisation of public sector services. Has completed 25 facilities management arrangements in the fields of IT, leisure, and airport management. Has advised on buying and selling DSO's and advised councils (or their consultants) on management of change issues and outsourcing. Author of numerous articles in various publications. Has lectured extensively on subjects such as The Transfer of Undertakings Regulations and externalisation issues.

Francies, Mike
See under Company/Commercial.

Freshwater, Tim G.
Slaughter and May, London (0171) 600 1200. Qualified 1969. Joined 1967. Handles mergers and acquisitions, corporate finance, and general corporate work. Also covers international investment and capital markets.

Geffen, Charles S.H.
Ashurst Morris Crisp, London (0171) 638 1111. Qualified 1984. Partner 1991. Company Department. Born in 1959.

Godden, Richard W.
Linklaters & Paines, London (0171) 606 7080. Qualified 1982. Joined 1980. Has experience of a wide range of corporate and corporate finance transactions.

Godfrey, Keith G.
Allen & Overy, London (0171) 330 3000. Qualified 1976. Partner 1981. Corporate Department. Main area of practice is corporate finance. Born 21.1.1951.

Graham, D.
Freshfields, London (0171) 936 4000.

Graves, Patrick
Ashurst Morris Crisp, London (0171) 638 1111.

Green, Geoffrey.S.
Ashurst Morris Crisp, London (0171) 638 1111. Qualified 1975. Partner 1979. Head of Company Department. Principal area of work is corporate finance, particularly buy-outs, acting primarily for equity institutions.
Born 3.9.1949.

Hatchard, Michael E.
Skadden, Arps, Slate, Meagher & Flom, London (0171) 248 9929. Partner specialising in corporate finance and M&A.

Specialisation: Main areas of practice are corporate finance, in particular international securities offerings, and cross-border M&A.

Career: Qualified 1980 with *Theodore God-*

dard, partner 1985. Joined *Skadden, Arps* as a partner in 1994 with responsibility for the English law aspects of global equity offerings and cross-border transactions.

Personal: Born 21st November 1955.

Holland, Peter R.J.
Allen & Overy, London (0171) 330 3000. Qualified 1968. Partner 1972. Corporate Department. Work includes acquisitions, mergers, new issues and privatisations in the UK.

Keat, Alan M.
See under Company/Commercial.

Kitching, J.R.H.
Lovell White Durrant, London (0171) 236 0066.

Knight, William John Langford
Simmons & Simmons, London (0171) 628 2020. Head of Corporate Department.

Specialisation: Main area of practice involves corporate finance and company work. Author of Acquisition of Private Companies (6th ed.) and member of Editorial Board of PLC magazine.

Prof. Memberships: Chairman Law Society Company Law Committee 1990-93, Institute of Advanced Legal Studies Research Committee, CCBE (Conseil Barreaux de La Communnaute Europeenne) Company Law Committee.

Career: Qualified in 1969. Partner at *Simmons & Simmons* 1973. Admitted as Hong Kong Solicitor 1979, and Head of Hong Kong office 1979-82. Leader of one of the corporate finance groups 1984-94. Appointed head of corporate department 1994.

Knight, Adrian G.
Ashurst Morris Crisp, London (0171) 638 1111. Qualified 1984. Partner 1992. Company Department. Specialises in mergers and acquisitions and corporate transactions.

Layton, Matthew
Clifford Chance, London (0171) 600 1000. Partner. Particular emphasis on domestic and international management/leveraged buy-outs and venture capital.

Lewis, David T.R.
See under Company/Commercial.

Lewis, Anthony
Cameron Markby Hewitt, London (0171) 702 2345. Qualified 1972.

Macaulay, Anthony D.
Herbert Smith, London (0171) 374 8000. Partner in Corporate Finance Department.

Specialisation: Experienced in company and commercial matters, especially corporate finance work, including takeovers and flotations. Has particular expertise in relation to the Takeover Code (having spent two years at the Takeover Panel) and insider dealing.

Career: Qualified in 1974. Became a Partner at *Herbert Smith* in 1983.

Personal: Educated Keble College, Oxford.

Mace, Dan
Lovell White Durrant, London (0171) 236 0066. Qualified 1970. Partner 1976. Corporate Finance and Company Law Group. Practice covers company and securities law, M&A and collective investment schemes.

Macfarlane, Jonathan
Macfarlanes, London (0171) 831 9222. Qualified 1980. Partner 1985. Corporate, Commercial & Banking Department. Specialises in corporate finance and mergers and acquisitions.

Macfarlane, D.J.
Ashurst Morris Crisp, London (0171) 638 1111.

Machin, Stephen J.
Ashurst Morris Crisp, London (0171) 638 1111. Qualified 1980. Partner 1987. Head of Tax Department. Specialises in corporate tax, M&A and international matters with emphasis on South Africa. Born 9.11.1954

McCaw, Lynn
Nabarro Nathanson, London (0171) 493 9933.

McFadden, L.G.
Freshfields, London (0171) 936 4000. Partner 1991. Main practice areas are; mergers and acquisitions (public and private), securities, offerings and joint ventures.

Mountford, Margaret
Herbert Smith, London (0171) 374 8000. Partner in Company Department.

Specialisation: Principal area of practice is corporate, corporate finance and commercial matters. Advises corporate clients and intermediaries (investment banks, brokers, etc) on a wide range of transactions including mergers, flotations, takeovers, private company and assets acquisitions/disposals, joint ventures and venture capital.

Prof. Membership: Law Society, British German Jurists Association.

Career: Qualified in 1976. Became a partner at *Herbert Smith* in 1983.

Personal: Born 24th November 1951. Educated at Strathearn School, Belfast 1963-70 and Girton College, Cambridge 1970-73 (MA). Leisure interests include opera and travel. Lives in London.

Newhouse, A.J.R.
Slaughter and May, London (0171) 600 1200. Qualified 1979.

O'Brien, B.J.
Freshfields, London (0171) 936 4000. Partner in Corporate Department.

Specialisation: Corporate finance including mergers and acquisitions, new issues: advis-

ing Lloyd's on its reconstruction.

Prof. Membership: Law Society.

Career: Qualified in 1978. Joined *Freshfields* in 1983 and became a Partner in 1986.

Personal: Born 27th October 1952. Educated at University College, London. Enjoys sport. Lives in London.

Paul, Alan D.
Allen & Overy, London (0171) 330 3000. Qualified 1980. Partner 1985. Corporate Department. Work covers corporate finance, particularly takeovers and MBOs, and equity linked financings, including flotations. Born 19.7.1954.

Pescod, Michael
Slaughter and May, London (0171) 600 1200. Qualified 1970. Partner 1977. Corporate Department. Main areas of practice are commercial and corporate law.

Phillips, S.J.
Slaughter and May, London (0171) 600 1200. Qualified 1985.

Rawlinson, Mark S.
Freshfields, London (0171) 936 4000.

Specialisation: Partner in the Corporate Department specialising in public and private mergers, acquisitions, disposals and joint ventures. Work also covers corporate finance and IPOs including flotations, rights issues and other issues. Publications include 'A Practitioners Guide to Corporate Finance and the Financial Services Act 1986' (contributor).

Career: Qualified 1984. Assistant solicitor, *Freshfields* 1984-90. Partner since 1990.

Personal: Educated at Haberdashers' Aske's School, Elstree and Sidney Sussex College, Cambridge 1976-80. Interests include family and sport. Born 3rd May 1957. Lives in London.

Richards, Andrew Philip
Freshfields, London (0171) 936 4000. Qualified 1980. Partner 1987. Corporate Department. Work includes mergers and acquisitions, joint ventures, securities offerings and insurance law. Born in 1956.

Sackman, Simon Laurence
Norton Rose, London (0171) 283 6000. Qualified 1977. Partner 1983. Corporate and Financial Department. Head of Corporate Finance Group. Main area of practice is M&A and other equity issues.

Salz, Anthony M.V.
Freshfields, London (0171) 936 4000. Qualified 1974. Partner 1980. Corporate Department. Main area of practice covers mergers and acquisitions and corporate finance matters. Member City of London Solicitors Company. Born 30.6.1950.

Sheldon, Jeremy Nigel
Ashurst Morris Crisp, London (0171)

638 1111. Partner in Company Department.

Specialisation: Principal area of practice is U.K. and international buyouts acting primarily for equity providers, including CINVen Limited, Candover Investments plc and BZW Private Equity Limited. Other areas of practice include establishing and marketing quoted and unquoted investment funds, mergers and acquisitions, flotations and other Stock Exchange transactions. Is a member of the media and communications group advising on the formation of cable, terrestrial and satellite joint ventures in the UK and overseas.

Career: Qualified in 1980. Became a Partner in 1987.

Personal: Born in 1952.

Signy, Adam
Clifford Chance, London (0171) 600 1000.

Stern, Robert C.
Slaughter and May, London (0171) 600 1200. Qualified 1986.

Sutton, Robert H.
See under Advertising & Marketing.

Tuffnell, Kevin
Macfarlanes, London (0171) 831 9222. Qualified 1984. Partner 1989. Company, Commercial & Banking Department. Specialises in corporate finance, venture capital, mergers and acquisitions and flotations.

Turnbull, Peter
See under Company/Commercial.

Underhill, C.William Y.
Slaughter and May, London (0171) 600 1200. Qualified 1983. Specialises in corporate finance, including acting for underwriters and issuers of securities, mergers and acquisitions, London Stock Exchange rules and regulations and FSA compliance. Also experienced in mortgage and other asset securitisation, and other mortgage-backed financing.

Walker-Arnott, Edward I.
See under Company/Commercial.

Watson, Sean M.
McKenna & Co, London (0171) 606 9000. Partner in Corporate Department.

Specialisation: Handles all areas of corporate finance including reconstructions, take-overs and mergers and venture capital, with primary specialisation in stock exchange transactions.

Prof. Membership: Law Society, City of London Solicitors Company.

Career: Qualified in 1972. Joined *McKenna & Co* in 1979, becoming a Partner in the same year.

Personal: Born 5th April 1948. Attended The Leys School, Cambridge, 1961-66 and Man-

chester University 1966-69. Leisure interests include tennis, golf, skiing, gardening and family. Lives in Weybridge, Surrey.

Wethered, T.O.G.
Linklaters & Paines, London (0171) 606 7080.

Williams, Christine J.
Fox Williams, London (0171) 628 2000. Partner in Corporate Department.

Specialisation: Principal area of practice is corporate finance. Work includes mergers and acquisitions, capital raising, financings, joint ventures and restructurings. Has acted on many sales of companies, both quoted and unquoted, including management buy-outs and buy-ins. Capital raising work has included venture capital, flotations and rights issues. Has represented banks and borrowers in connection with financings. Member of Company Law Sub-Committee of City of London Law Society. Other main area of practice is partnership law including drafting partnership deeds and advising on partnership disputes and partners leaving.

Prof. Membership: Law Society, City of London Law Society, International Bar Asssociation.

Career: Qualified in 1977. Partner at *Oppenheimers* 1981-88 and *Denton Hall* 1988-89. Formed and joined *Fox Williams* as a Partner in 1989.

Personal: Born 15th February 1953. Educated at St Annes's College, Oxford 1971-74. Leisure interests include theatre and cinema. Lives in London.

REGIONS

Agnew, B.E. Phyllis M.
Tughan & Co, Belfast (01232) 553300.

Allen, Amanda
Pinsent Curtis, Birmingham (0121) 200 1050. Partner in Corporate Department.

Specialisation: Handles all types of company and commercial work including mergers and acquisitions, MBO's/ MBI's, joint ventures, flotations, etc.

Career: Qualified in 1986. Partner at *Pinsent Curtis* since 1992.

Personal: Born 1st December 1960. Leisure intersts include golf, skiing and water skiing. Lives in Kidderminster.

Angel, Peter G.
See under Insurance & Reinsurance.

Barr, R. Alan
Burges Salmon, Bristol (0117) 939 2000. Qualified 1982. Partner 1988. Company Department. Also handles international business transactions and cross border transactions. Born 23.2.1958.

Beswick, Simon A.
Osborne Clarke, Bristol (0117) 923 0220. Qualified 1986. Partner 1989. Corporate Department. Work includes M&A, corporate finance and venture captial. Born 2.3.1961.

Braithwaite, Stephen
Wragge & Co, Birmingham (0121) 233 1000. Qualified 1973. Partner 1980. Corporate Finance specialist including M&A, buyouts and venture capital matters. Born 3.5.1947.

Burns, Richard
Hammond Suddards, Manchester (0161) 834 2222.

Campbell, Christopher R.J.
See under Company/Commercial.

Chatfield, James H.T.
See under Company/Commercial.

Cliff, Paul
Edge & Ellison, Birmingham (0121) 200 2001.

Cockcroft, Nicholas C.P.
Wansbroughs Willey Hargrave, Bristol (0117) 926 8981. Partner in Corporate Department.

Specialisation: Specialises in mergers and acquisitions, and corporate finance work, particularly share issues and institutional funding. He handles commercial work and is company secretary to a listed company, handling a wide range of joint ventures and acquisitions overseas. He is also an independent trustee of several pension funds and advises directors and other executives on their corporate duties and responsibilities.

Prof. Memberships: Securities Institute, Institute of Directors, Secretary to Bristol Law Society's Business and International Committee.

Career: Qualified 1980. 1978-80 with *Howard Kennedy and Rossi* in London. 1980-84, company solicitor to Trident Television plc, handling entertainment law, acquisitions and disposals. Joined *WWH* in 1984 to head up the corporate department. Partner in 1985.

Cook, Stephen
McGrigor Donald, Glasgow (0141) 248 6677.

Cooke, Darryl J.
Addleshaw Sons & Latham, Manchester (0161) 832 5994. Partner in Company and Commercial Department.

Specialisation: Principal areas of practice are venture capital, management buy-outs and corporate finance. Author of 'Management Buy-outs' (Longman).

Career: Became a Partner at *Addleshaw Sons & Latham* in 1995. Formerly at *Halliwell Landau*.

Personal: Born 1st January 1959. Educated

at Hulme Grammar School, Oldham, and Leeds University (LLB, LLM). Plays golf and squash in his spare time. Lives in Kerridge, Cheshire.

Cooke, David J.
See under Banking.

Cooper, Paul
See under Company/Commercial.

Coutts, Maureen S.
Dundas & Wilson CS, Edinburgh (0131) 228 8000. Qualified 1977. Partner 1984. Corporate Department specialising in Mergers & Acquisitions, Investments, Outsourcing and General Corporate and Commerical work. English qualified.

Cowen, Maurice C.
See under Company/Commercial.

Crabtree, John
Wragge & Co, Birmingham (0121) 233 1000. Qualified 1973. Partner 1976. Senior Partner, specialises in corporate and corporate finance work. Born 5.8.1949.

Craig, I. Alexander
Halliwell Landau, Manchester (0161) 835 3003. Qualified 1985. Partner 1989. Corporate Finance Department. Work includes MBOs, MBIs, flotations, mergers and acquisitions. Born 28.9.1957.

Crawley, Fiona
See under Company/Commercial.

Croome, Andrew
See under Banking.

Curling, Chris J.
See under Company/Commercial.

Darwin, Andrew
Dibb Lupton Broomhead, Leeds (0113) 243 9301.

Devitt, P.
Addleshaw Sons & Latham, Manchester (0161) 832 5994. Qualified 1988.

Dickson, Alastair R.
Dickson Minto WS, Edinburgh (0131) 225 4455.

Dorman, A. Brian
See under Company/Commercial.

Eastgate, Andrew
Pinsent Curtis, Birmingham (0121) 200 1050. Qualified 1980. Partner 1985. Company Department. Work includes mergers and acquisitions, flotations, MBOs and joint ventures. Born 14.5.1956.

Emmett, Paul D.
Walker Morris, Leeds (0113) 283 2500. Partner in Corporate Department.

Specialisation: Principal area of practice is corporate finance, mergers and acquisitions. Work includes flotations, rights issues, other forms of equity financing, acquisitions and disposals. Other main area of practice is general corporate advice. Important transactions have included the £550 million merger of Kalon Group PLC and Euridep, a £110 million hostile bid by Kalon Group PLC for Manders PLC, a £28 million rights issue by Cattle's PLC, the £26 million acquisition by Cattle's PLC of the Welcome Group of companies and the £75 million flotation of Goldsborough Healthcare PLC. Author of several articles in the *Yorkshire Post* and legal journals. Has spoken at seminars on new Stock Exchange listing rules and director's duties.

Prof. Membership: Law Society.

Career: Qualified in 1987. With *Slaughter & May* 1985-93. Joined *Walker Morris* as a Partner in 1993.

Personal: Born 7th November 1961. Educated at Cheadle Hulme School, Cheshire 1974-80 and King's Collge, London University 1981-84. Leisure activities include golf, reading amd politics. Lives in Leeds.

Fischl, Nicolas J.
Mills & Reeve, Norwich +44 (0) 1603 660155. Qualified 1979. Partner 1986. Company/Commercial Department. Work includes corporate finance, venture capital, joint ventures, commercial agreements and computer/IT. Born 1.4.1954.

Fulton, Richard
Mills Selig, Belfast (01232) 243878.

Gilbert, Ian M.
See under Company/Commercial.

Godfrey, Christopher M.J.
Burges Salmon, Bristol (0117) 939 2000. Qualified 1986. Partner 1990. Company/Commercial Department. Practice includes financial services with emphasis on collective investment schemes.

Gough, Roger
Alsop Wilkinson, Manchester (0161) 834 7760. Qualified 1985. Partner 1995. Corporate finance specialist handling acquisition and disposal of companies and businesses, MBO's, venture capital and reorganisations. Born 5.10.1960.

Gray, David John
See under Company/Commercial.

Green, Patrick John
Pinsent Curtis, Birmingham (0121) 200 1050. Qualified 1966. Partner 1975. Corporate Department. Handles company and commercial work in the public and private sector.

Greenough, Alan Edward
Pinsent Curtis, Birmingham (0121) 200 1050. Partner in Corporate Finance Department.

Specialisation: Yellow Book flotation work includes full listing, USM, Super Class 1, Class 1 circulars, vendor placings, placings, underwritings, international offerings, international placings and underwritings. Handles M&A for both private and public companies, including cross-frontier deals as well as MBO's/ MBI's and venture capital. 1994 deals include the MBO/ MBI of Kennings (£130 million).

Gronow, Simon D.V.
Pinsent Curtis, Birmingham (0121) 200 1050. Partner in Company Department.

Specialisation: Principally engaged in corporate matters undertaking "Yellow Book" work for public companies and merchant banks/brokers,including flotations, rights issues, takeover offers, acquisitions and disposals.

Prof. Membership: Law Society.

Career: Qualified in 1986.Joined *Pinsent Curtis* in 1984 and became a Partner in 1991.

Personal: Born 29th January 1961. Educated at Kings College Cambridge 1979-83. Lives in Edgbaston Birmingham.

Haggett, David S.
Eversheds, Birmingham (0121) 233 2001. Qualified 1965.

Hamlett, David W.
Wragge & Co, Birmingham (0121) 233 1000. Qualified 1980.

Hardie, David
Dundas & Wilson CS, Edinburgh (0131) 228 8000. Qualified 1976. Partner 1983. Corporate Department. Work includes flotations, rights issues, placings, takeovers, joint ventures and general corporate and contractual matters. Born 17.9.1954.

Hawes, Roger Geoffrey
Burges Salmon, Bristol (0117) 939 2000. Qualified 1984. Partner 1990. Company Department. Practice includes M&A, venture capital, corporate structuring, and public company work.

Heathcock, Andrew E.
Paris Smith & Randall, Southampton (01703) 635191. Partner in Company and Commercial Department.

Specialisation: Main area of practice includes over 15 years experience in all areas of corporate finance in the private sector, in particular dealing with 3i, LDC, Candover and NatWest.

Prof. Memberships: Law Society, Institute of Directors.

Career: Qualified with *Bird & Bird* 1977; *Lovell White & King* in 1979-81. Partner in charge of Commercial Department of *Boodle Hatfield* in Southampton 1981-90. Joined *Paris Smith & Randall* as a Partner in October 1990.

Henderson, Brian L.
L'Estrange & Brett, Belfast (01232) 230426.

Holt, William E.
Dibb Lupton Broomhead, Manchester (0161) 839 2266. Qualified 1971. Partner 1992. Main area of specialism is corporate finance and mergers and acquisitions. Born 28.12.1946.

Hopkins, Stephen Martyn
Eversheds, Leeds (0113) 243 0391.

Specialisation: Undertakes significant buy-out work with the management buy-out team, having lead the *Eversheds* team in the £40m buy-out of Leyland Trucks Manufacturing from the receivers of Leyland DAF Limited. Also handles other corporate finance and banking work. Acted for the management team in the £130m MBO of the Birmingham Post, acted for the Bank of Scotland in the £6m MBO of Saint Martin's Foods, acted in the £26m MBO of Crompton Lighting, acted in the £11m MBO of Fotoprocessing, acted for National Westminster Bank plc in the provision of £20m long term facilities to the University of Leeds.

Prof. Membership: Law Society, Licensed Insolvency Practitioner.

Career: Qualifed in 1984. Joined *Eversheds* in 1988. Became a Partner in 1991.

Personal: Born 17th March 1960. Attended Sheffield University 1978-1981. Leisure interests include golf, cricket and rugby. Lives near Wetherby.

Hughes, David J.
Pinsent Curtis, Birmingham (0121) 200 1050. Head of Corporate, Birghmingham.

Specialisation: Corporate finance, including mergers and aquisitions, takeovers and primary and secondary equity issues.

Career: Qualified in 1980. Became a Partner in 1987 and Head of Corporate in Birmingham in 1990. Worked at *Nabarro Nathanson* 1978-82, then *Slaughter and May* 1982-85, before joining *Pinsent & Co.* in 1985.

Personal: Born 19th March 1955. Attended Wolverhampton Grammar School 1966-73, then Jesus College, Oxford 1973-77.

Hutton, C. Noel
Hammond Suddards, Leeds (0113) 234 3500. Partner and Head of Corporate Department.

Specialisation: Specialises in mergers and acquisitions (principally by and on behalf of listed companies) and new issue work.

Career: Qualified in 1973. Partner at *Hammond Suddards* since 1977. Member of the firm's Executive.

Personal: Born 4th November 1949. Interests include sailing, motor sports and sport generally. Lives in Ilkley.

Inglis, Ian B.
Shepherd & Wedderburn WS, Edinburgh (0131) 228 9900.

Jackson, John
Davies Arnold Cooper, Manchester (0161) 839 8396. Qualified 1980. Partner 1985. Corporate Department. Work includes all aspects of corporate transactions. Born 10.11.1953.

James, Lawrence
Eversheds, Cardiff (01222) 471147. Qualified 1975. Partner 1980. Company Commercial Department. Main area of practice is corporate finance. Also handles partnerships and education law. Born 1951.

Johnston, Keith
See under Company/Commercial.

Jones, Digby M.
See under Company/Commercial.

Lane-Smith, Roger
Alsop Wilkinson, Manchester (0161) 834 7760.

Lee, Paul
Addleshaw Sons & Latham, Manchester (0161) 832 5994. Partner specialising in corporate finance.

Specialisation: Work covers acquisitions and sales, public issues, MBOs and venture capital. Also offers strategic advice to large private companies. Acted in the sale of NFCs waste management business for 115m in 1993; the sale of WMS Limited for 52m in 1993; the flotation of Canadian Pizza plc in 1993; and the MBO/EBO of GM Buses North for 37m in 1994. Addresses conferences and seminars on corporate finance matters.

Career: Qualified in 1970. Joined *Addleshaw Sons & Latham* in 1970, becoming a Partner in 1973 and Managing Partner in 1991. Member of Management Board of *Addleshaw Sons & Latham*.

Personal: Born 26th January 1946. Attended Manchester Central Grammar School, then Clare College, Cambridge. Director of several companies both public and private, including clothing, engineering and theatre companies. Chairman for the Governors of Chethams School of Music and a Feoffee of Chethams. Leisure interests include travel, wine and sport. Lives in Manchester.

Lee, Richard N.F.
Addleshaw Sons & Latham, Manchester (0161) 832 5994. Qualified 1984. Partner 1988. Company and Corporate Finance Department. Handles corporate finance and general corporate work.

Lee, Richard
See under Company/Commercial.

Leitch, David A.
Johns Elliot, Belfast (01232) 326881.

Lewis, Susan
Eversheds, Birmingham (0121) 233 2001. Qualified 1983.

Lippell, C. Sean
Pinsent Curtis, Leeds (0113) 244 5000. Partner and National Practice Head Corporate Department.

Specialisation: Corporate finance and company law deals with public issues, MBO/MBIs, mergers and acquisitions including UK, EC and international deals.

Prof. Membership: Law Society.

Career: Qualified in 1979 at *Simmons & Simmons*. Joined *Freshfields* in 1979, then moved to *Pinsent & Co* in 1984 becoming a Partner in the same year. Joined *Simpson Curtis* in 1987 as a Partner, became Head of Corporate Department in 1993, and Joint Chief Executive in 1994.

Personal: Born 21st September 1950. Attended Kelly College, Tavistock and Durham University. Leisure pursuits include running, reading and walking. Lives in Harrogate.

Loake, Jonathan
See under Company/Commercial.

Lumsden, Ian G.
Maclay Murray & Spens, Edinburgh (0131) 226 5196. Partner 1980. Corporate Department. Handles corporate finance, mergers and acquisitions. Born 19.3.1951.

Macintosh, Duncan J.G.
Morgan Bruce, Cardiff (01222) 385385. Qualified 1992. Partner 1992. Company Department. Main area of practice is corporate finance. Born 11.10.1957.

Marsh, David J.
Burges Salmon, Bristol (0117) 939 2000. Qualified 1968. Partner 1972. Joint Senior Partner. Company Commercial Department. Work includes flotations, acquisitions and disposals.

McCann, R. William C.
Mills Selig, Belfast (01232) 243878.

McHugh, Peter J.
Eversheds, Birmingham (0121) 233 2001. Chairman of National Corporate Practice Group.

Specialisation: Handles mainly public company work, acquisitions and disposals, management buy-outs and general corporate advice. Advised on the management buy-out of Hozelock Ltd and its subsequent flotation as Hozelock Group plc. Also acted in the management buy-out of Standard Fireworks Ltd.

Prof. Membership: Birmingham Law Society.

Career: Qualified in 1982. Became a Partner in *Eversheds Wells & Hind* in 1989.

Personal: Born 23rd July 1958. Lives in Bewdley, Worcestershire.

McNeill, Morag
See under Company/Commercial.

Meiklejohn, Iain M.C.
See under Company/Commercial.

Metcalfe, Ian
Wragge & Co, Birmingham (0121) 233 1000. Qualified 1983. Partner 1992. Corporate Finance Department. Main areas of practice are all aspects of yellow book and blue book work, mergers and acquisitions for listed companies, MBO's and MBI's. Born 10.2.1958.

Mills, John W.
Tughan & Co, Belfast (01232) 553300.

Minto, Bruce W.
See under Company/Commercial.

Needham, Andrew
Addleshaw Sons & Latham, Manchester (0161) 832 5994. Partner in Company and Commercial Department.

Specialisation: Handles corporate finance matters including, mergers and acquisitions, flotations and stock market issues, venture capital, and management buy-outs and buy-ins.

Prof. Membership: Law Society.

Career: Qualified in 1975. Joined *Addleshaw Sons & Latham* as a Partner in 1977.

Personal: Born 3rd September 1950. Educated at Trinity College, Cambridge 1968-72. Holds company directorships and is charity trustee. Leisure pursuits include squash, tennis, golf and skiing. Lives in Uppermill, Saddleworth.

Painter, Nick
Garrett & Co, Leeds (0113) 244 1954. Qualified 1983. Partner 1994. Corporate/Commercial Department. Main area of practice is corporate finance. Also deals with competition law, employee share schemes and local authority law. Born 3.2.1959.

Patrick, Bruce R.
See under Company/Commercial.

Philbin, Kevin
Wacks Caller, Manchester (0161) 957 8888. Qualified 1984. Partner, 1987. Company and Commercial Department. Main area is corporate finance and company/commercial matters. Born 12.06.59.

Pike, Andrew
Hammond Suddards, Leeds (0113) 234 3500. Senior Solicitor in Corporate Finance Department.

Specialisation: Experienced in all aspects of corporate finance work, including mergers, acquisitions and disposals, hostile and recommended takeovers, flotations and other public issues, MBO's and other venture capital transactions. Clients include UK listed

PLC's, merchant banks and other corporate finance advisers, major overseas corporations and private companies.

Prof. Membership: Law Society.

Career: Qualified in 1987. With *Linklaters & Paines* 1987-90. Joined *Hammond Suddards* in 1990.

Personal: Born 2nd November 1962. Educated at Ermysted's Grammar School, Skipton and Thirsk School 1974-81, then Jesus College, Cambridge 1981-84. Leisure activities include walking, mountaineering and rock-climbing. Lives in Calverley, Leeds.

Prince, Michael J.
Alsop Wilkinson, Liverpool (0151) 227 3060 and (0161) 834 7760. Qualified 1979. Partner 1986. Head of Northwest Corporate Department. Work includes MBOs, venture and development capital, mergers and acquisitions and flotations. Born 20.12.1954.

Psyllides, Milton N.
Eversheds, Birmingham (0121) 233 2001. Qualified 1978.

Pysden, Edward
Eversheds, Manchester (0161) 832 6666. Senior Partner specialising in Corporate and Commercial work.

Specialisation: Principal area of practice is corporate finance covering flotations, acquisitions, management buy-outs and all other stock exchange and non-contentious corporate work. Recently acted in flotations of Vymura and Canadian Pizza and the employee buy-out of Greater Manchester Buses South. Other main area of work is overseas contracting in Africa, Middle East and South America. For the last three years voted top North-West corporate lawyer by readers of Insider magazine.

Prof. Membership: Solicitors European Group, Securities Institute, Law Society, Institute for Fiscal Studies, North West Export Club.

Career: Articled at *Alexander Tatham* 1970-72 and became a Partner in 1974. Appointed Senior Partner of the firm (now *Eversheds, Manchester*) in 1993.

Personal: Born 6th May 1948. Attended Dulwich College 1959-60, King's School, Macclesfield 1960-66, and Manchester University 1966-69. Director of UMIST Ventures Board. Leisure pursuits include golf and squash. Lives in Macclesfield.

Rafferty, John C.
W & J Burness WS, Edinburgh (0131) 226 2561. Partner in Company Department.

Specialisation: Main areas of practice are company law and corporate finance. Work includes acquisition, sale and restructuring of listed and unlisted companies, and general corporate advice to a wide range of business and statutory bodies. Also handles share option schemes (both Revenue approved and non-approved) including the use of ESOPs.

Taught taxation at Edinburgh University for five years.

Prof. Membership: Law Society of Scotland, Securities Institute, Society of Writers to HM Signet.

Career: Qualified in 1975. Joined *W & J Burness* in 1973, becoming a Partner in 1979. Director of St Andrew Trust plc, an investment trust, since 1986.

Personal: Born 30th June 1951. Attended The Edinburgh Academy 1961-69 and Edinburgh University 1969-73. Leisure interests include gardening, hillwalking and skiing. Lives in Edinburgh.

Rawstron, Christopher D.
Edge & Ellison, Birmingham (0121) 200 2001. Head of Corporate Department.

Specialisation: Main area of practice is corporate finance. Work includes mergers and acquisitions, flotations, rights issues, MBOs, MBIs, disposals and general corporate advice. Sector experience covers automotive, retail and engineering. Has handled numerous acquisitions for quoted and unquoted companies; disposals; bids; flotations and reverse takeovers. Frequent author of articles for local press and specialist publications. Occasional lecturer to MBA students at Aston University. Frequent speaker at seminars.

Prof. Membership: Law Society.

Career: Qualified in 1986. Joined *Edge & Ellison* in 1984, becoming a Partner in 1990.

Personal: Born 29th July 1962. Attended Clitheroe Royal Grammar School 1978-80, Birmingham University 1980-83 and College of Law 1983-84. Member of the *Edge & Ellison* main board. Holds various trusteeships and directorships. Leisure interests include golf, Burnley FC and cricket. Lives in Hagley, near Stourbridge.

Renshaw, Peter B.A.
Slater Heelis, Manchester (0161) 228 3781. Qualified 1979. Partner in the Company and Commercial Department specialising in information technology and computer related work. Born 23.7.1954.

Richardson, Ian Ashley
Eversheds, Leeds (0113) 243 0391.

Specialisation: Handles all aspects of corporte finance work, venture capital, MBO's and MBI's, principal transactions including acting for the management team on the MBO of the Birmingham Post for £130m, Leyland DAF Vans £40m, Crompton Lighting £26m, Foto Processing £11m and the equity provider on Barrett Steel and Vivat Holdings. Acquisitions and Disposals.
Acting for CrestaCare Plc and Barr & Wallace Arnold Trust Plc in respect of their M&A work.
He is joint author of "Runnning a Partnership", published by Jordons.

Prof. Membership: Law Society.

Career: Qualified in 1983 and became a Partner in 1989.

Personal: Born on 23rd April 1959. Lives near Boroughbridge, North Yorkshire. Leisure interests: running, rugby and cricket.

Seabrook, Michael R.

Eversheds, Birmingham (0121) 233 2001. Qualified 1976. Partner 1986. Deputy Senior Partner (Birmingham). Corporate Services Department. Born 24.3.1952.

Selig, Ivan

Mills Selig, Belfast (01232) 243878.

Short, John

See under Company/Commercial.

Simmons, William G.

Tods Murray WS, Edinburgh (0131) 226 4771. Qualified 1981. Partner 1986. Corporate Department. Practice includes listed company work, M&A, banking and insolvency. Born in 1958.

Simon, Jeremy P.

Osborne Clarke, Bristol (0117) 923 0220. Qualified 1980. Partner 1985. Head of Corporate Department. Acts for a number of quoted companies, venture capitalists and professional partnerships.

Smart, Peter C.

See under Company/Commercial.

Street, Robert H.

Chaffe Street, Manchester (0161) 236 5800. Qualified 1975. Partner 1978. Company/Commercial Department. Work includes corporate finance, acquisitions and disposals, intellectual property and commercial contracts. Born 25.5.1951.

Swanson, Magnus P.

Maclay Murray & Spens, Glasgow (0141) 248 5011. Qualified 1982. Partner 1987. Corporate Department. Practice includes MBO's/ MBI's, M&A and joint ventures. Born 25.4.1958.

Thurman, Roderick J.

See under Company/Commercial.

Trotter, Andrew

See under Company/Commercial.

Walker, Andrew W.

Pinsent Curtis, Leeds (0113) 244 5000. Managing Partner in Corporate Department.

Specialisation: Corporate finance, including stock exchange issues, management buy-outs, take-overs, M and A and international law.

Prof. Membership: Law Society, Leeds Law Society, American Bar Association, International Bar Association.

Career: Qualified in 1969. Articled with *Linklaters & Paines.* Joined *Simpson Curtis* as a Partner in 1974. Head of Corporate Department 1990-93, Deputy Managing Partner 1993-94. Joint Chief Executive 1994-1995.

Personal: Born 9th January 1944. Attended Leeds Grammar School and Magdalene College, Cambridge 1963-66. Leisure interests include golf, riding, sailing, tennis, skiing and theatre. Lives in Leeds.

Warburton, M.C.

See under Banking.

Whatnall, John

Halliwell Landau, Manchester (0161) 835 3003. Qualified 1981. Partner 1987. Corporate Department. Practice includes banking

finance. Acted for mezzanine lender on Greater Manchester Buses.

Whiteley, Alan

Eversheds, Cardiff (01222) 471147. Qualified 1987. Partner 1989. Company Commercial Department. Main area of practice is corporate finance: mergers and acquisitions, corporate reorganisations, flotations, joint ventures, MBOs and venture capital. Born 10.4.1963.

Will, James R.

Shepherd & Wedderburn WS, Edinburgh (0131) 228 9900. Partner in Corporate Department.

Specialisation: Main areas of practice are Stock Exchange work, company law, mergers and acquisitions, take-overs and corporate finance, major start-ups and development capital, with emphasis on the technology sector. Recent work includes the flotations of Stagecoach Holdings, Magnum Power, Calluna and Vision Group.

Prof. Membership: Law Society of Scotland, Society of Writers to Her Majesty's Signet.

Career: Qualified in 1978. With *Tods Murray WS* 1978-79 and *Clifford Chance* 1980-81. Joined *Shepherd & Wedderburn* in 1981 and became a Partner in 1982.

Personal: Born 30th April 1955. Educated at Merchiston Castle and Aberdeen University.

Wynn-Jones, Richard T.

Burges Salmon, Bristol (0117) 939 2000. Qualified 1973. Partner 1983. Company/ Commercial Department. Main area of practice is transport related work. Born 27.8.1948.

EDITORIAL POLICY

Our policy is to identify leading practitioners entirely on merit. It is not possible to buy a place in our biographical lists: inclusion is based on a practitioner's expertise and professional reputation. The same applies to the lists of recommended law-firms and sets of chambers.

Enormous effort has been invested by our ten-strong research team (mainly solicitors and barristers) in canvassing recommendations and identifying leaders. We are confident in the overall accuracy of the results. However, mistakes and omissions are inevitable, and if readers have any suggestions regarding listings or rankings we should be very pleased to hear from them.

The lists will be revised on the basis of fresh research every year.

CRIME: GENERAL

GENERAL criminal work, ranging from motoring offences to violent crime, has traditionally been the province of the high street practice. The fixed fee system and the legal aid franchise have both taken their toll, forcing a number of these firms to concentrate on other, more lucrative areas of law.

Whilst a great many firms still undertake criminal work, this list concentrates on those which either have dedicated departments or boast individual practitioners who, through many years of experience in the field, are regarded as leading authorities.

LONDON

The most highly recommended criminal practices include *B.M.Birnberg & Co, Claude Hornby & Cox* and *T.V. Edwards.*

LEADING FIRMS – LONDON

B.M. BIRNBERG & CO	**CLAUDE HORNBY & COX**
T.V. EDWARDS	
EDWARD FAIL BRADSHAW & WATERSON	**FISHER MEREDITH**
HODGE JONES & ALLEN	**TAYLOR NICHOL**

B.M.Birnberg & Co is particularly known for representing ethnic communities and victims of oppression. Gareth Peirce, a highly experienced practitioner, specialises in major miscarriages of justice and has gained national acclaim representing The Guildford Four.

HIGHLY REGARDED – LONDON

DARLINGTON & PARKINSON	**DUTHIE HART & DUTHIE**
GILCHRISTS	**HENRY MILNER & CO**
MAGRATH & CO	**OFFENBACH & CO**
POWELL SPENCER & PARTNERS	**SAUNDERS & CO**
TUCKERS	**VICTOR LISSACK & ROSCOE**
SIMONS MUIRHEAD & BURTON	**WINSTANLEY-BURGESS**

Criminal work comprises 70% of the caseload of West End firm, *Claude Hornby & Cox,* where Christopher Green, a member of the Executive Council of the British Academy of Forensic Sciences, and Richard Hallam represent clients in private prosecutions and Courts Martial, in addition to conducting legally aided defence work.

T.V. Edwards, based in Mile End, has a number of specialists handling a variety of privately paid and legal aid cases. Anthony Edwards, author of a number of texts in the subject, with over twenty years experience in the field, was the most consistently recommended London practitioner.

Other firms with highly regarded criminal departments include *Edward Fail Bradshaw & Waterson, Fisher Meredith, Hodge Jones & Allen* and *Taylor Nichol.*

Edward Fail Bradshaw & Waterson, Fisher Meredith and *Hodge Jones & Allan* all have thriving criminal departments undertaking Magistrates and Crown Court work. *Fisher Meredith* is particularly known for representing clients in actions against the police. *Hodge Jones & Allen* has recently expanded following a recent merger with niche criminal practice, *Wyman & Walters* and now comprises eleven specialists.

Taylor Nichol, based in Finsbury Park, is a small practice with an excellent reputation. The firm has recently been involved in a number of high profile cases, most notably the M50 murder appeal and *R v. Hickey* (Carl Bridgewater case) now at the Divisional Court. James Nichol is held in high regard.

Other notable criminal practices with eminent practitioners include *Darlington & Parkinson,* where Kenneth Grant is highly recommended, *Duthie, Hart & Duthie* (and in particular Shaun Murphy) and *Offenbach & Co* (Bernard Carnell).

Individual practitioners recommended for their expertise include Stephen Gilchrist of *Gilchrists* and Henry Milner of *Henry Milner & Co.*

SOUTH EAST

Firms which are highly experienced in general criminal work include *Alistair Meldrum & Co* in Enfield and *Marsh Ferriman & Cheale* in Worthing.

LEADING FIRMS – SOUTH EAST

ALISTAIR MELDRUM & CO *Enfield*	**MARSH, FERRIMAN & CHEALE** *Worthing*
TWITCHEN MUSTERS & KELLY *Southend-on-Sea*	

Twitchen Musters & Kelly in Southend-on-Sea, boasts two practitioners awarded Higher Court Advocate status. The firm has been instructed in a number of high profile cases

LEADING INDIVIDUALS – LONDON

Bernard Carnell *Offenbach & Co*	**Anthony T.A. Edwards** *T.V. Edwards*	**Stephen Gilchrist** *Gilchrists*
Kenneth I Grant *Darlington & Parkinson*	**Christopher Green** *Claude Hornby & Cox*	**Mark Haslam** *Magrath & Co*
Stephen Hewitt *Fisher Meredith*	**Henry F. Milner** *Henry Milner & Co*	**Shaun P. Murphy** *Duthie Hart & Duthie*
James Nichol *Taylor Nichol*	**Gareth Peirce** *B.M. Birnberg & Co*	**Greg Powell** *Powell Spencer & Partners*
Howard Riddle *Edward Fail Bradshaw & Waterson*	**James Saunders** *Saunders & Co*	
Robert T.J. Brown *Darlington & Parkinson*	**Richard S. Hallam** *Claude Hornby & Cox*	**Bernard Huber** *Duthie Hart & Duthie*
Edward Preston *Edward Fail Bradshaw & Waterson*	**Robert Roscoe** *Victor Lissack & Roscoe*	**Robert J. Winstanley** *Winstanley-Burgess*

In all the tables the names in each group are listed alphabetically.

including *R v.Colin Ireland* (serial killings of homosexual men) and *R v. Sylvia Wignall* ('foxes in the wood' murder).

BLAKE LAPTHORN *Fareham*	BRADLEYS *Dover*
ERIC ROBINSON & CO *Southampton*	GARETH WOODFINE & PARTNERS *Bedford*
MAX BARFORD & CO *Tunbridge Wells*	PICTONS *St. Albans*
BERNARD CHILL & AXTELL *Southampton*	BERRY & BERRY *Tunbridge Wells*
STEPHEN RIMMER & CO *Eastbourne*	

Other notable criminal practices include *Blake Lapthorn, Eric Robinson & Co, Gareth Woodfine & Partners, Max Barford & Co* and *Pictons.*

In Dover, *Bradleys* specialises in customs cases.

SOUTH WEST

Bobbetts Mackan is the leading criminal practice in Bristol, with Anthony Miles the most consistently recommended so-licitor in the South West. The firm, in addition to representing

LEADING FIRMS – SOUTH WEST

BOBBETTS MACKAN *Bristol*

individual defendants, (Anthony Miles was instructed in the 'Fredrick West' case), also handles Courts Martial cases.

HIGHLY REGARDED – SOUTH WEST

CROSSE & CROSSE *Exeter*	JOHN BOYLE *Redruth*
STEPHENS & SCOWN *Exeter*	WOLFERSTANS *Plymouth*
WOOLLCOMBE BEER WATTS *Newton Abbot*	

Cornwall firms recommended for legal aid work include *John Boyle,* a niche practice which specialises in Crown Court advocacy and conducts all DTI prosecutions in West Cornwall, (John Boyle holds a Higher Courts Advocate qualification), *Crosse & Crosse,* which is particularly known for Youth Court work, and *Stephens & Scown.*

LEADING INDIVIDUALS – SOUTH WEST

Anthony Miles *Bobbetts Mackan*
John Boyle *John Boyle*
David J.L. Gabbitass *Wolferstans*
Derek S. Reed *Woollcombe Beer Watts*

Wolferstans and *Woollcombe Beer Watts* are Devon's pre-mier criminal firms, both handling a variety of legally aided and privately funded work. David Gabbitass of *Wolferstans,* and Derek Reed of *Woollcombe Beer Watts* are highly rec-ommended.

WALES

The leading criminal firms in Wales tend to be based in Car-diff; *Hallinans, Huttons* and *Leo Abse & Cohen* all have highly experienced criminal practitioners handling Magis-trates and Crown Court work. Martyn Prowell (*Hallinans*),

HIGHLY REGARDED – WALES

HALLINANS *Cardiff*	HUTTONS *Cardiff*
LEO ABSE & COHEN *Cardiff*	
GRANVILLE-WEST *Newport*	SPICKETTS *Pontypridd*
SPIRO GRECH & CO *Cardiff*	

Stuart Hutton of *Huttons* (instructed in the 'Rhonnda vigi-lante killing'), and Gwyn Jones of *Leo Abse & Cohen* are all held in high regard.

LEADING INDIVIDUALS – WALES

Stuart Hutton *Huttons*
Gwyn Jones *Leo Abse & Cohen*
Martyn Prowel *Hallinans*

MIDLANDS

In the West Midlands, firms with excellent reputations in the field include *George Jonas & Co* (primarily a legal aid prac-tice) and *Glaisyers,* where Charles Royle is held in particu-larly high regard.

HIGHLY REGARDED – MIDLANDS

BERRYMAN & CO *Nottingham*	FREETH CARTWRIGHT HUNT DICKINS *Nottingham*
GEORGE JONAS & CO *Birmingham*	GLAISYERS *Birmingham*
THE JOHNSON PARTNERSHIP *Nottingham*	
BARRIE WARD & JULIAN GRIFFITHS *Nottingham*	BRETHERTONS *Rugby*
ELLIOT MATHER SMITH *Chesterfield*	HAWLEY & RODGERS *Loughborough*
MARRON DODDS *Leicester*	NELSONS *Nottingham*
REES PAGE *Wolverhampton*	SILKS *Warley*
THE SMITH PARTNERSHIP *Derby*	WOODFORD-ROBINSON *Northampton*

Experienced East Midlands firms include *Freeth Cart-wright Hunt Dickins, Berryman & Co* and *The Johnson Part-nership* (legal aid and privately funded cases).

LEADING INDIVIDUALS – MIDLANDS

Charles Royle *Glaisyers*

EAST ANGLIA

The most widely regarded criminal practices in East Anglia tend to be centred in Norwich.

HIGHLY REGARDED – EAST ANGLIA

EVERSHEDS *Norwich*	FOSTERS *Norwich*
HUNT & COOMBS *Peterborough*	LEATHES PRIOR *Norwich*
OVERBURY STEWARD & EATON *Norwich*	THOMSON & CO *Cambridge*
LUCAS & WYLLYS *Great Yarmouth*	

Eversheds undertakes a substantial amount of court and road traffic work, while *Fosters, Leathes Prior* and *Overbury Steward & Eaton* all handle legal aid work (*Leathes Prior* is best known for civil liberties work, in particular representing hunt saboteurs and poll tax protesters).

In Cambridge, *Thomson & Co* has been awarded a legal aid franchise, and in Peterborough, *Hunt & Coombs* is reported to have a thriving criminal practice.

NORTH WEST

The North West of England remains a major centre in the field with a substantial number of firms having large specialist departments.

LEADING FIRMS – NORTH WEST	
BURTON COPELAND *Manchester*	
JONES MAIDMENT WILSON *Manchester*	TUCKERS *Manchester*

Burton Copeland maintains its position as the pre-eminent criminal practice in the region with 18 specialists dealing exclusively with adult crime, and two fee-earners handling youth court work, in Manchester and beyond. The highly regarded Ian Burton, renowned for commercial fraud work, heads the formidable team that includes Michael Mackey, Gillian Crossley and Nicholas Freeman.

HIGHLY REGARDED – NORTH WEST	
BETESH FOX & CO *Manchester*	BRIAN KOFFMAN & CO *Manchester*
R.M. BROUDIE & CO *Liverpool*	JACKSON & CANTER *Liverpool*
LINSKILLS *Liverpool*	MARTIN CUNNINGHAM *Manchester*
PAUL ROONEY & CO *Liverpool*	ROBERT LIZAR *Manchester*
RUSSELL JONES & WALKER *Manchester*	YAFFE JACKSON OSTRIN *Liverpool*
GARSTANGS *Bolton*	RUSSELL & RUSSELL *Bolton*
M.B. CUTTLE & CO *Manchester*	FARLEYS *Blackburn*
FORBES & PARTNERS *Blackburn*	

Hard on *Burton Copeland's* heels comes *Jones Maidment Wilson* and *Tuckers*.

Despite the loss of Alan Maidment, *Jones Maidment Wilson* remain at the forefront of criminal law with an excel-

LEADING INDIVIDUALS – NORTH WEST
G. Crossley *Burton Copeland*
N.F. Freeman *Burton Copeland*
M.P. Mackey *Burton Copeland*
Franklin Sinclair *Tuckers*
Barry M. Tucker *Tuckers*
Robert Broudie *R.M. Broudie & Co*
Julian Linskill *Linskills*
Anthony R. Ostrin *Yaffe Jackson Ostrin*
Paul Rooney *Paul Rooney & Co*

lent reputation. *Tuckers,* a niche practice, acts on behalf of both private and legally aided clients in all aspects of criminal law from drink driving to business crime, drugs and murder. Barry Tucker and Franklin Sinclair are both authorities in the field.

Manchester firms primarily known for legal aid work include *Martin Cunningham, Betesh Fox & Co, Brian Koffman & Co, Robert Lizar* and *Russell Jones & Walker.*

In Bolton, *Garstangs* and *Russell & Russell* are experienced in the field.

In Liverpool, firms with strong all-round reputations include *R.M Broudie & Co, Jackson & Canter, Linskills, Paul Rooney & Co* and *Yaffe Jackson Ostrin.*

Robert Broudie, Julian Linskill, Paul Rooney and Anthony Ostrin all have many years experience in the field.

NORTH EAST

Leeds firms with reputations in the field include *McCormicks* and *Russell Jones & Walker*

HIGHLY REGARDED – NORTH EAST	
LUMB & MACGILL *Bradford*	McCORMICKS *Leeds*
RUSSELL JONES & WALKER *Leeds*	SUGARÉ & CO *Leeds*
GRAHAME STOWE, BATESON *Leeds*	HENRY HYAMS & CO *Leeds*
LEVI & CO *Leeds*	MYER WOLFF & MANLEY *Hull*

In Bradford, *Lumb & Macgill* has six specialists, some of whom have rights of audience at the Crown Court. Kerry Macgill, in addition to representing clients such as Peter Sutcliffe, has developed a particular specialism defending solicitors facing fraud allegations.

LEADING INDIVIDUALS – NORTH EAST
Kerry M.P. Macgill *Lumb & Macgill*
Anthony Sugaré *Sugaré & Co*

Anthony Sugare of *Sugaré & Co* is particularly noted for road traffic work.

SCOTLAND

The leading criminal firms in Scotland include *Beltrami & Co, Gilfedder & McInnes, Gordon & Smyth* and *McCourts.*

LEADING FIRMS – SCOTLAND
BELTRAMI & CO *Glasgow*

Each of the above firms have solicitor advocates handling trials, appeals, bail applications and remits to the High Court.

Joseph Beltrami, senior partner at Glasgow firm *Beltrami & Co* was the first solicitor to appear before the Criminal Appeal Court and also the first to lead in a successful murder acquittal. John Macara of the same firm is well respected.

HIGHLY REGARDED – SCOTLAND	
GILFEDDER & McINNES *Edinburgh*	GORDON & SMYTH *Glasgow*
McCOURTS *Edinburgh*	
BLAIR & BRYDEN *Greenock*	CONDIES *Perth*

Also in Glasgow, *Gordon & Smyth* has three partners dealing exclusively with criminal work. Maurice Smyth is noted for his expertise.

Edinburgh firms *Gilfedder & McInnes* and *McCourts* both have highly respected practitioners in Brian Gilfedder and John McInnes at *Gilfedder & McInnes* and Alistair Duff, Douglas Main and Alexander Prentice at *McCourts.*

LEADING INDIVIDUALS – SCOTLAND

Joseph Beltrami	*Beltrami & Co*
Alistair J.M. Duff	*McCourts*
Brian G. Gilfedder	*Gilfedder & McInnes*
John D.M. Macara	*Beltrami & Co*
Douglas G. Main	*McCourts*
John S.F. McInnes	*Gilfedder & McInnes*
Alexander Prentice	*McCourts*
Maurice T. Smyth	*Gordon & Smyth*

NORTHERN IRELAND

Although paramilitary-based criminal work has virtually disappeared, the number of 'ordinary' criminal cases coming before the courts has markedly increased – drug-related offences particularly so. Consequently, those firms which previously specialised in 'political' criminal work are redirecting their attention towards general criminal cases.

Of the firms mentioned below, *Madden & Finucane*, where Peter J. Madden is a well regarded specialist, having acted in R v Miller and R v McMullan, was frequently recommended. The firm appears in the Magistrates and

HIGHLY REGARDED – NORTHERN IRELAND

DONELLY & WALL *Belfast*	**MADDEN & FINUCANE** *Belfast*
BABINGTON & CROASDAILE *Londonderry*	**BRENDAN KEARNEY KELLY** *Derry*
FLYNN & McGETTRICK *Belfast*	**MILLAR SHEARER & BLACK** *Cookstown*

Crown Courts, and undertakes civil liberties cases. At *Donelly & Wall* Patrick Donnelly and Dennis Moloney are highly regarded for their criminal work; they have acted in several recent highly publicised sexual offence cases concerning the clergy.

LEADING INDIVIDUALS – NORTHERN IRELAND

Patrick H. Donnelly	*Donelly & Wall*
Peter J. Madden	*Madden & Finucane*
Denis G.G. Moloney	*Donelly & Wall*

LEADERS IN CRIME: GENERAL

LONDON

Brown, Robert T.J.
Darlington & Parkinson, London (0181) 998 4343.

Carnell, Bernard
Offenbach & Co, London (0171) 434 9891. Senior Partner in Criminal Department.

Specialisation: Work includes commercial fraud, insider dealing, drug related crime, obscene publications and all areas of general crime. Particular experience of legal aid regulations and international and financial investigations. Acted in R v. Kellard and Others (Britannia Park Fraud trial, the longest in English history); BCCI Investigation; R v. Fisher (the first insider dealing trial); R v. Adelaja and Others (the first trial using computers); R v. Howard Marks and others (one of the largest and well-publicised drug cases); the inquest of Cynthia Jarrett (Tottenham riots); and R v Gay News Ltd and Lemon (Blasphemy trial) and numerous Divisional Court, Court of Appeal and House of Lords proceedings. Individual charge-out rate is usually £150-£170 per hour, depending on nature and seriousness of case.

Prof. Membership: Law Society.

Career: Qualified in 1972. Joined *Offenbach & Co* in 1976, becoming a Partner in 1982.

Personal: Born 13th December 1947. Attended LSE (1966-69) and Law College. Lives in London. Director of The Bubble Theatre Company. Former Director of Release.

Edwards, Anthony T.A.
T.V. Edwards, London (0171) 790 7000. Senior Partner. Criminal and Licensing Department.

Specialisation: Criminal law. Author of 'Standard Fees in the Magistrates Court: A Survival Guide'. Contributor to Criminal Law Society Practice Guides: 'Advising the Suspect in the Police Station', 'The Magistrates Court: a Guide to Good Practice' and 'The Crown Court - A Guide to Good Practice'. Regular contributor to Law Society Gazette and other periodicals. Lecturer on all aspects of criminal practice.

Prof. Membership: Law Society, London Criminal Courts Solicitors Association.

Career: Qualified in 1974, having joined *T.V. Edwards* in 1972. Became Senior Partner in 1993. Member of the Law Society Criminal Law Committee.

Personal: Born 6th December 1949. Attended Bristol University, taking a first class LLB in 1972. Leisure interests include walking and reading.

Gilchrist, Stephen
See under Crime: Fraud.

Grant, Kenneth I
Darlington & Parkinson, London (0181) 998 4343. Senior Partner in Criminal Department.

Specialisation: Handles white collar crime and general crime. Has been involved in a range of cases, from defending Cynthia Payne, to acting on behalf of two defendants in the Harrovian fraud, the largest alleged mortgage fraud to date, and the source of the largest single claim against the Solicitors Indemnity Fund (trial anticipated in 1995/96).

Prof. Membership: Law Society, Central and South Middlesex Law Society, London Criminal Courts Solicitors Association.

Career: Qualified in 1977. Joined *Darlington & Parkinson* in 1977 and became a

Partner in 1990. Chairman Ealing Duty Solicitor Committee, Member London Legal Aid Area Committee, Deputy Metropolitan Stipendiary Magistrate, Solicitor-Advocate (Higher Courts Criminal).

Personal: Born 14th November 1951. Educated at the University of Sussex. Leisure interests include opera and ballet. Lives in London.

Green, Christopher
Claude Hornby & Cox, London (0171) 437 8873. Partner in Criminal Department.

Specialisation: Wide experience of criminal litigation both in the civil and military courts. Engaged primarily for the Defence but conducts private prosecutions regularly. Legal Assessor to the disciplinary committees of a number of professions. Defends in professional disciplinary proceedings. Training Consultant with Central Law Training; presents Professional ethics and conduct courses and is a member of their Professional Skills Course Advocacy Team.

Prof. Membership: British Academy of Forensic Sciences, City of Westminster Law Society (Criminal Law Committee), London Criminal Courts Solicitors Association, Regional Duty Solicitor Committee.

Career: Qualified 1970 while with *Claude Hornby & Cox* and became a Partner in 1972.

Personal: Born 9th August 1944. Lives in London.

Hallam, Richard S.
Claude Hornby & Cox, London (0171) 437 8873. Partner in Criminal Litigation Department since 1989.

Specialisation: Crime. Has substantial experience of conducting cases in the Magistrates Courts, Higher Criminal Courts and before

Courts Martial in UK and Germany. Normally instructed as a defence advocate, but has experience of prosecuting for the CPS and will prosecute privately for individuals or organisations. Nationwide experience of prosecuting video piracy cases. Defends in professional disciplinary proceedings. Has successfully represented defendants facing allegations of murder, terrorism, large-scale drugs importation and fraud, but equally interested in defending clients charged with speeding or drink-driving.

Prof. Membership: City of Westminster Law Society, London Criminal Courts Solicitors Association, Legal Aid Practitioners Group.

Personal: Born 24th April 1948. Educated at the King's School, Canterbury and Oxford University. Lives in London.

Haslam, Mark

Magrath & Co, London (0171) 495 3003. Partner in Criminal Litigation Department.

Specialisation: Practice covers all areas of criminal defence work including white collar, large scale drugs allegations and murder and manslaughter cases. Has experience of Court Martial proceedings and defended Christine Dryland the wife of Major Dryland in a highly publicised murder trial in Germany. Also has a particualr specialisation in motoring cases including excess alcohol, careless driving and speeding. Regular broadcaster and lecturer on criminal legal affairs on radio, television and at seminars and conferences.

Prof. Membership: The Law Society, Secretary of the London Criminal Courts Solicitors Association, Westminster Law Society.

Career: Qualified in 1981, worked at *Claude Hornby & Cox* from 1979 to 1993. Became a partner at *Magrath & Co* in 1993.

Personal: Born 16 June 1957. Attended Wellington College, Berkshire 1971-1976 and Pembroke College, Cambridge, 1976 to 1979 (MA). Leisure interests include cricket, horse racing and the theatre. Lives in Cobham in Surrey.

Hewitt, Stephen

Fisher Meredith, London (0171) 622 4468. Senior Partner in Criminal Department.

Specialisation: All areas of criminal defence work, including advocacy, with lengthy experience of murder and major drug tafficking cases. Lecturer on aspects of criminal practice and co-author of "Legal Aid Practice Manual".

Prof. Membership: Law Society, London Criminal Courts Solicitors Association.

Career: Qualified 1980. Joined *Fisher Meredith* as partner in 1986.

Personal: Born 14th November 1953. Lives in London.

Huber, Bernard

Duthie Hart & Duthie, London (0181) 472 0138. Partner in Criminal Law Department.

Specialisation: Has fifteen years experience of handling a large and varied criminal law caseload with daily advocacy. Important cases include the "Baby Kim" murder (controversial case on the right to silence) and "Operation Own Goal" (collapsed trial in relation to organised football violence).

Prof. Membership: L.C.C.S.A., West Essex Law Society, Child Care Panel, Duty Solicitor Scheme (Committee Member).

Career: Qualified in 1980. Partner at *Duthie Hart & Duthie* since 1982.

Personal: Born 30th October 1955. Educated at Leeds University (LL.B Hons, 1977). Leisure interests include football, squash, golf and guinness. Lives in Wanstead.

Milner, Henry F.

Henry Milner & Co, London (0171) 831 9944. Principal of firm.

Specialisation: Main area of practice is criminal defence work. Has twenty years specialist experience defending in serious criminal cases of all types. Defence solicitor in all Brinks Mat robbery trials and many other important trials of the 1980s and 1990s. Author of 'Time Wasting at Magistrates Courts' in the Law Society Gazette.

Prof. Membership: Law Society.

Career: Qualified in 1975. Established *Henry Milner & Co.* in 1978.

Personal: Born 23rd April 1947. Holds a law degree from London School of Economics. Leisure interests include bridge, football and traditional American music. Lives in London.

Murphy, Shaun P.

Duthie Hart & Duthie, London (0181) 472 0138. Partner in Criminal Litigation Department.

Specialisation: Criminal law specialist. Advocate in criminal proceedings on a regular basis in courts throughout the London area. Recently qualified as a Higher Courts Advocate. Also a Privy Council Agent. Other areas of practice are care proceedings and civil litigation, primarily civil actions against the police. Also involved in some prosecution work on behalf of North East London Probation Service and the Port of London Authority. Member of Duty Solicitor Schemes (Newham and Thames) and a member of the Child Care Panel. Charge-out rate is £75 per hour, otherwise Legal Aid rates.

Prof. Membership: London Criminal Courts Solicitors Association, Criminal Law Solicitors Association, West Essex Law Society.

Career: Qualified in 1979 after articles at *Duthie Hart & Duthie*. Became a Partner in 1986.

Personal: Born 10th June 1956. Educated at Warwick University 1974-77 (LL.B Hons). School Governor. Enjoys most sports. Lives in Wanstead, London.

Nichol, James

Taylor Nichol, London (0171) 272 8336. Qualified 1984. Partner specialising in public

order and miscarriages of justice.

Peirce, Gareth

B.M. Birnberg & Co, London (0171) 403 3166.

Powell, Greg

Powell Spencer & Partners, London (0171) 624 8888. Qualified 1973. Senior Partner. Specialises in criminal defence work, including advocacy and conduct of serious criminal matters. Born 21.1.1948.

Preston, Edward

Edward Fail Bradshaw & Waterson, London (0171) 790 4032. Qualified 1981. Partner 1984. Handles all types, including white collar fraud. Member of the British Academy of Forensic Science.

Riddle, Howard

Edward Fail Bradshaw & Waterson, London (0171) 790 4032. Senior Partner in Criminal Department.

Specialisation: Main area of practice covers all areas of criminal law. Also handles licensing work. Author of 'Guide to Scholarly Publishings in Canada'. Lecturer in Law 1969; Editor Penguin Books; McGill University Press 1969-72. Social Science Research Council (Canada) 1972-76.

Prof. Membership: Law Society, NE London Law Society, London Criminal Courts Solicitors Association.

Career: Qualified in 1978. Joined *Edward Fail Bradshaw & Waterson* in 1976, becoming Senior Partner in 1985. Assistant Metropolitan Stipendiary Magistrate; Deputy Chairman of London Legal Aid Board Area Committee; Past Chairman of Thames Duty Solicitor Committee.

Personal: Born 13th August 1947. Attended Judd School 1958-65 and London School of Economics 1965-68. Leisure interests include rugby, tennis, cycling and visiting France. Lives in Bethersden, Kent.

Roscoe, Robert

Victor Lissack & Roscoe, London (0171) 240 2010. Qualified 1976. Partner 1978. Specialises in white collar fraud, serious criminal offences, and general crime. Born 14.4.1949.

Saunders, James

Saunders & Co, London (0181) 960 5611. Senior Partner.

Specialisation: Criminal Law; Legal Aid Franchise and Private Client. Covers all aspects of Criminal Law, particularly complex and heavy trials including fraud, serial murder, drugs, sexual offences, robbery, official secrets and civil liberties. Also deals with scientific, medical and other expert issues; DNA, computers, firearms, confiscation of assets, motoring and London Agent matters.

Career: Articled at the North Kensington Neighbourhood Law Centre. Qualified 1972. Established *Saunders & Co* in 1974.

Personal: Born 1948. Attended King Edward VII School, Sheffield and University of Leicester (LLB).

Winstanley, Robert J.

See under Civil Liberties.

See under Civil Liberties.

REGIONS

Beltrami, Joseph

Beltrami & Co, Glasgow (0141) 221 0981. Senior Partner specialising in criminal law.

Specialisation: Solicitor advocate specialising in criminal law. Instructed in more than 300 murder and manslaughter cases. Acted in the only two Scottish Royal Pardons this century on matters of substantive crime – Maurice Swanson in 1975 and Pat Meehan in 1976. In each case compensation was awarded to the client. Also acted in the cases of W.S.Ellis, A.Thompson, D. Boyle, Howard Wilson and Thos Docherty. First solicitor advocate to appear before the Criminal Appeal Court (1993) and the first to lead in a successful murder acquittal (June 1994). Author of 'The Defender' (1980), 'Beltrami's Tales of the Suspected' (1988), and 'A Deadly Innocence' (1989). Has written numerous articles for 'New Law Journal', 'Scottish Law Journal', the Police Federation, etc.

Prof. Membership: Solicitor Advocate, Solicitor to the Supreme Court.

Career: Qualified in 1953. Sergeant in the Intelligence Corps 1954-56. Senior and Founding Partner of *Beltrami & Co*, established in 1958.

Personal: Born 15th May 1932. Educated at St. Aloysius's College, Glasgow and Glasgow University. Recreations include bowls, soccer, snooker, writing and boxing. Lives in Bothwell.

Boyle, John

John Boyle, Redruth (01209) 213507. Qualified 1980. Founder Partner 1986. Crime specialist. Has practised as solicitor advocate before Crown Courts in Bodmin and Truro for 14 years prosecuting, defending and conducting jury trials. Born 22.6.1954.

Broudie, Robert

R.M. Broudie & Co, Liverpool (0151) 227 1429. Qualified 1972.

Crossley, G.

Burton Copeland, Manchester (0161) 834 7374. Qualified 1979.

Donnelly, Patrick H.

Donelly & Wall, Belfast (01232) 233157.

Duff, Alistair J.M.

McCourts, Edinburgh (0131) 225 6555. Partner in firm specialising in criminal defence work.

Specialisation: Solicitor-advocate with rights of audience before the High Court. Firm deals exclusively with criminal defence work, in all courts throughout Scotland. Represents the two Libyan suspects in the 'Lockerbie' prosecution. Represents some political groups. Regularly addresses seminars on criminal law.

Prof. Membership: Law Society of Scotland, Society of Solicitors in the Supreme Court in Scotland.

Career: Qualified in 1977. Procurator Fiscal 1977-81. Assistant and then Partner with *More & Co.*, Edinburgh 1981-91. Founding Partner of *McCourts* in 1991.

Personal: Born 21st May 1954. Educated at Glenrothes High School, Fife and Edinburgh University 1971-75 (LLB 1st Class Hons.). Enjoys football, reading and music. Lives in Edinburgh.

Freeman, N.F.

Burton Copeland, Manchester (0161) 834 7374. Qualified 1981.

Gabbitass, David J.L.

Wolferstans, Plymouth (01752) 663295. Partner specialising in criminal advocacy.

Specialisation: Regular advocate for prosecution and defence in the Crown Court and Magistrates' Courts and for the defence at Courts Martial for all branches of the services. Represents police officers at disciplinary hearings, solicitors at Solicitors' Disciplinary Tribunals and also appears at inquests. Former agent for the DPP, Treasury Solicitor and Bank of England. Currently agent solicitor for the DTI. Member of Justice Committee on Fraud Trials. Appears on television and radio, as well as regularly having articles published in the local press. Chairman S.S.A.T.

Prof Membership: Law Society, Fellow of the Chartered Institute of Arbitrators.

Career: Plymouth City Police 1956-59. Joined *Wolferstan Snell & Turner* in 1959 and became Partner in 1965. Became Senior Partner in 1980 and Managing Partner in 1986. President of Plymouth Law Society, 1987. Became director of Law Group UK in 1991, obtaining Higher Court advocacy rights in 1994.

Personal: Born 19th July 1935. Attended Huish's Grammar School, Taunton 1945-51. President of Plymouth Albion RFC, 1985-90. Past President of Rotary Club of Drake, Plymouth. Member of Management Committee of Somerset County Cricket Club and TCCB Discipline Committee. Lords Taverner. Leisure interests include cricket and rugby.

Gilfedder, Brian G.

Gilfedder & McInnes, Edinburgh (0131) 553 4333. Partner in Criminal Department.

Specialisation: Specialises in criminal law. One of the first solicitors to obtain rights of audience in the High Court.

Prof. Membership: Edinburgh Bar Association.

Career: Qualified in 1976. Procurator Fiscal Depute (Prosecutor) 1976-82. Legal assistant specialising in criminal law 1982-83. Sole Practitioner specialising in criminal law 1983-85. Since then Joint Senior Partner in *Gilfedder & McInnes*.

Personal: Born 19th October 1954. Educated at Holyrood Secondary School, Glasgow and Strathclyde University. Lives in Edinburgh.

Hutton, Stuart

Huttons, Cardiff (01222) 378621. Senior Partner. Criminal Department.

Specialisation: Has been primarily involved in criminal work for over 20 years. Also deals with child care, adoption and fostering. Has been on the Child Care Panel for over 10 years. Has handled some notable murder cases, one the subject of the 'Bloody Valentine' book, another a 'vigilante' killing in Penrhys, Rhondda, Mid Glamorgan. Former part time Chairman of Social Security Appeals tribunals. Has special interest in entertainment and media law.

Career: Qualified in 1975. With *Edwards Geldard* 1973-86 (as a Partner from 1976). Established own practice, *Hutton's*, in August 1986.

Personal: Born 21st October 1946. Lives in Cardiff.

Jones, Gwyn

Leo Abse & Cohen, Cardiff (01222) 383252. Partner in Advocacy Unit.

Specialisation: Handles all aspects of criminal litigation and advocacy, defending individuals and companies in respect of charges pursued by Crown Prosecution Service, DTI, local authorities, etc., as well as liquor licensing. All advocacy conducted through the medium of both English and Welsh. Makes regular appearances on BBC radio and TV in relation to legal matters arising from Wales.

Prof. Membership: Law Society, Cardiff Solicitor Advocacy Society.

Career: Qualified in 1984. Joined *Leo Abse & Cohen* in 1982, becoming a Partner in 1986.

Personal: Born 22nd July 1960. Attended Liverpool Polytechnic 1978-81 and College of Law Chester 1981-82. Chairman of Llamau Housing Society Ltd 1988-91. Leisure interests include eating out and travelling. Lives in Cardiff.

Linskill, Julian

Linskills, Liverpool (0151) 236 2224. Qualified 1975. Senior Partner. Handles heavy weight criminal cases, including murder, rape and major drugs allegations.

Macara, John D.M.

Beltrami & Co, Glasgow (0141) 221 0981.

Macgill, Kerry M.P.

Lumb & Macgill, Bradford (01274) 730666. Partner in Criminal Department.

Specialisation: Extensive experience of criminal matters. Handled over 40 homicide cases and recently worked on one of the largest drug importation cases in the UK. Represented 'Yorkshire Ripper', Peter Sutcliffe; Ian Wood, a Sheffield solicitor; and Arthur Hutchinson (a triple murderer in Sheffield). Prosecutes for the Department of Social Security in fraud cases. Also handles Child Care work and is a member of the Child Care Panel. Member of the Criminal Team setting up courses to assess prospective higher court Advocates.

Prof. Membership: Criminal Law Solicitors Association, Solicitors' Association of Higher Court Advocates.

Career: Qualified 1975. Joined *Lumb & Macgill* in 1978. Senior Partner. Deputy Stipendiary Magistrate 1989-95. Appointed recorder 1995.

Personal: Born 30th April 1950. Governor of Bradford Grammar School. Leisure pursuits include sailing, fell running and golf. Lives in Huddersfield.

Mackey, M.P.

Burton Copeland, Manchester (0161) 834 7374. Qualified 1974.

Madden, Peter J.

Madden & Finucane, Belfast (01232) 238007.

Main, Douglas G.

McCourts, Edinburgh (0131) 225 6555.

McInnes, John S.F.

Gilfedder & McInnes, Edinburgh (0131) 553 4333. Qualified 1982. Partner 1986. Specialises in all aspects of crime in the Sheriff and High Courts. Born 5.11.1955.

Miles, Anthony

Bobbetts Mackan, Bristol (0117) 929 9001. Qualified 1972. Partner 1974. Criminal Defence Department, specialising entirely in the preparation and advocacy in relation to defence of criminal allegations, including white collar crime and substantial courts-martial practice, born 12.2.1947.

Moloney, Denis G.G.

Donelly & Wall, Belfast (01232) 233157.

Ostrin, Anthony R.

Yaffe Jackson Ostrin, Liverpool (0151) 236 5555. Qualified 1965. Senior Partner. Experienced advocate before courts, tribunals and the traffic commissioner/licensing authority.

Prentice, Alexander

McCourts, Edinburgh (0131) 225 6555.

Prowel, Martyn

Hallinans, Cardiff (01222) 482316.

Reed, Derek S.

See under Crime: Fraud.

Rooney, Paul

Paul Rooney & Co, Liverpool (0151) 227 2851. Qualified 1970. Partner 1977. Deals with personal injury cases and crime. Born 15.3.45.

Royle, Charles

Glaisyers, Birmingham (0121) 233 2971. Qualified 1971. Managing Partner. Specialises in criminal law, licensing, liquor and gaming.

Sinclair, Franklin

Tuckers, Manchester (0161) 835 1414. Senior Partner.

Specialisation: In overall control of large criminal practice dealing in all aspects of criminal defence work. Particular specialisation as an advocate defending the rights of clients in a robust manner and dealing with many serious cases, including extensive involvement in preparation from the outset of a case to its conclusion. Has dealt with numerous murder cases and specialises, particularly, in large scale drugs' importation and armed robbery cases. Has recently dealt with the first case involving challenge to D.N.A evidence which initially was successful at the Court of Appeal.

Prof. Membership: Manchester Law Society. Solicitor Member of Criminal Justice Liaison Committee for the North-West. Committee Member of Criminal Law Solicitors' Association (C.L.S.A).

Career: Qualified 1982. Partner with Barry Tucker in *Tuckers Solicitors* since 1984.

Personal: Manchester Grammer School; Manchester University; College of Law, Chester. Married with three children. Interests include Golf, Environmental Issues, Gardening. Born 28th June 1958. Lives in Cheshire.

Smyth, Maurice T.

Gordon & Smyth, Glasgow (0141) 332 5705.

Sugaré, Anthony

Sugaré & Co, Leeds (0113) 244 6978. Senior Partner and founder of firm 1974.

Specialisation: Experienced advocate specialising in criminal and road traffic matters. Provides representation for defendants in all areas of criminal law, both legal aid and private. Wide expertise in representing sportsmen and sporting associations.

Prof. Membership: Leeds Law Society.

Career: Qualified in 1970. Founded and became Senior Partner of *Anthony Sugaré & Co.* in 1974. Member of the Leeds Duty Solicitor Committee. Criminal Law Officer of Leeds Law Society and Chairman of Solicitors Representatives on the Leeds Court Users Group.

Personal: Born 16th July 1943. Attended Leeds Grammar School and Manchester University. Leisure pursuits include rugby league, golf and horse racing. Lives in Leeds.

Tucker, Barry M.

Tuckers, Manchester (0161) 835 1414. Managing Partner specialising in serious and business crime matters.

Specialisation: Handling all aspects of criminal cases on behalf of privately-paying and legally-aided clients who are looking for a discreet and confidential legal representative whose aim is to prevent proceedings moving forward from investigation to prosecution. He is able to give advice and assistance prior to interview and if a prosecution develops will maintain full control over all proceedings through to conclusion. Casework July 1994 through to July 1995 including acquittals for clients charged with murder at the Old Bailey, fraud against the Local Authority at the Southwark Crown Court, industrialist's son charged with rape - Knightsbridge Crown Court. Cases currently being dealt with include the defence of the first defendant to be charged with male rape, prominent corporate fraudulent trading allegations and a Japanese industrialist's son facing trial on serious allegations. With a 24-hour team of solicitors and legal assistants this partner is able to deal sympathetically with clients caught in the criminal system who require immediate advice and assistance at any time of the day or night. Professional Membership: West London Law Society. London Criminal Courts Solicitors Association. Manchester Law Society.

Career: Qualified in 1981. Formed Tuckers Solicitors 1982.

Personal: Cheadle Hulme Grammar School. University of London LLB. Chester College of Law. Born 13th February 1955. Married, three children. Lives Central London. Interests include family and business.

CRIME: FRAUD

COMMERCIAL, or white collar defence work, including fraud, tax evasion, money laundering and insider dealing tends to be handled by specialist firms, commercial firms generally dealing with related civil matters, such as securing stolen assets by injunction and tracing.

A number of white collar frauds are now dealt with by the regulatory authorities rather than the criminal courts following a recommendation by the Royal Commission on Criminal Justice in 1993. As a result, an increasing number of commercial firms have developed the expertise to conduct investigations and disciplinary proceedings on behalf of the regulatory bodies in addition to advising their corporate clients on compliance.

LONDON

Peters & Peters and *Kingsley Napley* emerge as the leading commercial fraud practices in London, with *Burton Copeland* and *Simons Muirhead & Burton* ranking a close second.

LEADING FIRMS – LONDON	
KINGSLEY NAPLEY	PETERS & PETERS
BURTON COPELAND	SIMONS MUIRHEAD & BURTON
MAGRATH & CO	RUSSELL JONES & WALKER

Peters & Peters handles all forms of corporate fraud, cross border issues, extradition and mutual assistance, forensic tax and revenue work. It also deals with VAT and Customs infractions, insolvency crime and the regulatory activities of government and financial services institutions and has litigated cases in foreign jurisdictions. Monty Raphael (who was universally recommended during our research) with 25

HIGHLY REGARDED – LONDON	
OFFENBACH & CO	TITMUSS SAINER DECHERT
CLAUDE HORNBY & COX	GARSTANGS
NORTON ROSE	STEPHEN FIDDLER & CO
STEPHENSON HARWOOD	

years experience in the field, has advised the Roskill Committee and the Royal Commission on Criminal Justice in addition to founding and chairing the Business Crime Committee of the International Bar Association. Keith Oliver (in-

structed by Kevin Maxwell at the time of going to print) and Julia Balfour- Lynn are also held in high regard.

Kingsley Napley prides itself on the breadth of expertise that it is able to offer its clients at partner level. The firm undertakes Inland Revenue work (including back duty), VAT and Customs work and money laundering, and regulatory work for the Securities and Futures Authority. The firm has been involved in a number of high profile cases, including defending in 'Barlow Clowes', 'Guinness', 'BCCI' and 'Maxwell'. Most recently, it has acted for Nick Leeson in the Barings Bank collapse. The highly regarded John Clitheroe (involved in the 'Blue Arrow' litigation) has written a number of texts on the subject including 'Conducting a Criminal Defence' and 'Criminal Risks in International Trade'. Other well respected practitioners include Christopher Murray (a member of the British Academy of Forensic Sciences), Stephen Pollard (who acted for Lou Macari in the revenue prosecution of Swindon Town FC and in the 'PR futures' case), Michael Caplan (who sits as an assistant recorder) and Deborah Gehm.

The highly regarded Ian Burton of *Burton Copeland* heads a strong team that includes two former members of the Commercial Fraud Squad and undertakes a broad spectrum of work including Serious Fraud Office, Customs and Excise, Department of Trade and Industry and Inland Revenue prosecutions. The firm has acted in the 'Barlow Clowes', 'Maxwell Eagle Trust' and 'Blackspur plc' cases and is currently representing Robert Bunn in the Maxwell brothers trial. Also recommended is Jeffrey Bayes who has 20 years experience in the field.

Simons Muirhead & Burton's commercial fraud department has acted in the 'Blue Arrow', 'Maxwell', 'Nissan (UK) Ltd', 'Levitt Group' and 'Grupo Torras' cases. The firm boasts a number of excellent practitioners including Anthony Burton, David Kirk (author of 'Serious Fraud – Investigation and Trial') and Brian Spiro.

Other eminent firms include *Russell Jones & Walker* (Rod Fletcher heads the team that is currently representing Larry Trachtenberg in the 'Maxwell brothers' trial) and *Magrath & Co,* which is seen as an emerging force due to the presence of Aileen Colhoun and Christopher Magrath.

Other highly recommended firms include *Titmuss Sainer Dechert* and *Offenbach & Co*, where Bernard Carnell is well respected having acted in the 'Brittania Park Fraud' trial and *R v Fisher.*

LEADING INDIVIDUALS – LONDON		
Anthony Burton *Simons Muirhead & Burton*	Ian R. Burton *Burton Copeland*	John Clitheroe *Kingsley Napley*
David Kirk *Simons Muirhead & Burton*	Christopher Murray *Kingsley Napley*	Keith E. Oliver *Peters & Peters*
Stephen Pollard *Kingsley Napley*	Monty Raphael *Peters & Peters*	Brian Spiro *Simons Muirhead & Burton*
Julia M. Balfour-Lynn *Peters & Peters*	Jeffrey J. Bayes *Burton Copeland*	Michael Caplan *Kingsley Napley*
Bernard Carnell *Offenbach & Co*	Aileen Colhoun *Magrath & Co*	Louise Delahunty *Peters & Peters*
Rod Fletcher *Russell Jones & Walker*	Deborah Gehm *Kingsley Napley*	Christopher Magrath *Magrath & Co*
Joanne Rickards *Peters & Peters*		

In all the tables the names in each group are listed alphabetically.

FRAUD INVESTIGATION

Norton Rose and *Stephenson Harwood* emerge as the leading practices in the field, largely due to the reputations of James Bagge (*Norton Rose*) and Anthony Woodcock

(*Stephenson Harwood*) both of whom conduct financial services, accounting and insolvency investigations for regulatory bodies, advise companies on compliance and handle civil disputes arising out of fraudulent transactions.

HIGHLY REGARDED – LONDON – INVESTIGATIONS	
CLIFFORD CHANCE	LINKLATERS & PAINES
MACFARLANES	RICHARDS BUTLER
TITMUSS SAINER DECHERT	WILDE SAPTE
ALLEN & OVERY	BOODLE HATFIELD
CAMERON MARKBY HEWITT	DAVIES ARNOLD COOPER
DENTON HALL	D J FREEMAN
EVERSHEDS	HARRIS ROSENBLATT & KRAMER
HERBERT SMITH	KINGSLEY NAPLEY
LOVELL WHITE DURRANT	McKENNA & CO
MEMERY CRYSTAL	MISHCON DE REYA
PETERS & PETERS	PICKERING KENYON
RUSSELL JONES & WALKER	SIMMONS & SIMMONS
SLAUGHTER AND MAY	THEODORE GODDARD

Other highly recommended firms include *Clifford Chance* (David Mayhew), *Linklaters & Paines* (and in particular Graeme Brister), *Macfarlanes*, where Paul Phippen is held in high regard, *Richards Butler* (Roger Parker) and *Wilde Sapte,* where Richard Caird has been recommended.

LEADING INDIVIDUALS – LONDON – INVESTIGATIONS	
A. James S. Bagge *Norton Rose*	
Anthony J.J. Woodcock *Stephenson Harwood*	
Graeme R. Brister *Linklaters & Paines*	
Richard F. Caird *Wilde Sapte*	
David Mayhew *Clifford Chance*	
R.J. Parker *Richards Butler*	
C. Paul Phippen *Macfarlanes*	
John Potts *Clifford Chance*	

UP AND COMING – INVESTIGATIONS	
Bernard O'Sullivan *Titmuss Sainer Dechert*	

SOUTH, EAST ANGLIA & WALES

In the South East of England, John Mitchell at *Blake Lapthorn* heads the firm's Business Defence Unit which advises companies on compliance in areas such as consumer protection and health and safety (where breach may incur a criminal sanction). The unit also defends companies against regulatory charges and investigations by the tax authorities.

Other firms with experience in the field include *Allan Janes* (High Wycombe), *Donne Mileham & Haddock* in Lewes and Newhaven and *Warner Goodman & Streat* in Portsmouth.

HIGHLY REGARDED – SOUTH, EAST ANGLIA & WALES	
BLAKE LAPTHORN *Fareham*	BOBBETTS MACKAN *Bristol*
ALLAN JANES *High Wycombe*	DONNE MILEHAM & HADDOCK *Lewes, Newhaven*
EVERSHEDS *Norwich*	HALLINANS *Cardiff*
HUTTONS *Cardiff*	LEO ABSE & COHEN *Cardiff*
WARNER GOODMAN & STREAT *Portsmouth*	WOLFERSTANS *Plymouth*
WOOLLCOMBE BEER WATTS *Newton Abbot*	

In the South West, Bristol-based firm *Bobbetts Mackan* handles commercial fraud and white collar crime as part of its general criminal practice. Other firms in the region with experience in the field include *Wolferstans* and *Woollcombe Beer Watts.*

LEADING INDIVIDUALS – SOUTH, EAST ANGLIA & WALES	
John Mitchell *Blake Lapthorn*	

Wales' premier commercial fraud specialists include *Hallinans, Huttons* and *Leo Abse & Cohen,* while in East Anglia, *Eversheds'* Norwich office has advised corporate entities on regulatory compliance.

MIDLANDS

In the West Midlands, *Cartwright & Lewis*, *Edge & Ellison* and *Williamson & Soden* undertake a range of corporate and VAT fraud work.

HIGHLY REGARDED – MIDLANDS	
CARTWRIGHT & LEWIS *Birmingham*	EDGE & ELLISON *Birmingham*
WILLIAMSON & SODEN *Solihull*	

NORTH

Burton Copeland maintains its position as the premier firm in the region, with Ian Burton the North's most consistently recommended practitioner. The firm, which also has offices in London, enjoys a national reputation and has handled a number of high profile cases including acting for Naveed in the 'Arrows' litigation and Peter Clowes in the 'Barlow Clowes' case. Richard Smyth is also held in high regard.

LEADING FIRMS – NORTH	
BURTON COPELAND *Manchester*	

Other Manchester firms with experience in the field include *Pannone & Partners* and *Betesh Fox & Co,* (Andrew Kenyon has been recommended), while in Bolton, *Garstangs* undertakes white collar work as part of its general criminal practice.

In the North East of England, *Walker Morris* is renowned for handling serious fraud cases, tax prosecutions and customs and excise cases. Other firms which have been recommended include *McCormicks, Pinsent Curtis* and *Russell Jones & Walker* in Leeds, while in Sheffield *Irwin Mitchell* has established a business crime unit to cater for its commercial clients.

SCOTLAND

While there are a number of Scottish firms with general criminal practices, *Harper Macleod,* the commercial arm of *Ross Harper & Murphy* is the only firm with a department dedicated to commercial fraud work.

LEADERS IN CRIME: FRAUD

LONDON

Bagge, A. James S.
Norton Rose, London (0171) 283 6000. Qualified 1979. Partner 1993. Commercial Litigation Department. Principal area of work covers fraud and regulation. Born 7.12.1952.

Balfour-Lynn, Julia M.
Peters & Peters, London (0171) 629 7991. Partner in Litigation Department.

Specialisation: Principal area of practice is business crime, encompassing major cases instituted by the SFO, Inland Revenue, Customs and Excise and other regulatory authorities involving fraud, tax and securities offences, Customs infractions and general financial regulatory problems. French Speaker.

Prof. Membership: Law Society, The City of Westminster Law Society, Association Internationale des jeunes advocats (AIJA), International Bar Association

Career: Qualified 1984. Joined *Peters & Peters* in 1986 and became a Partner in 1988.

Personal: Attended University College, London. Lives in London.

Bayes, Jeffrey J.
Burton Copeland, London (0171) 430 2277. Partner in Commercial Fraud Department.

Specialisation: Has over thirty years experience of general crime including prosecuting. For the last 20 years has specialised in the defence of fraud cases including SFO, DTI, Inland Revenue and VAT cases. Also acts in extradition cases. Has handled cases with foreign elements, including advising with local lawyers concerning criminal law and extradition in USA, Scotland, France, Cyprus, Israel, Egypt, Sweden and Malta. Author of various articles and book reviews in Law Society Gazette, New Law Journal and Solicitors Journal. Has made numerous radio and television appearances and lectured on criminal law- especially fraud.

Prof. Membership: Law Society, London Criminal Courts Solicitors' Association (President 1989-90), Criminal Law Solicitors' Association (Chairman 1990-91). British Academy of Forensic Sciences (Executive Council Member 1995).

Career: Qualified 1963. Joined *Burton Copeland* as a Partner in 1991. Member of Law Society Criminal Law Committee since 1989; Former Member of Number 13 (London East) Legal Aid Area Committee.

Personal: Born 21st April 1939. Attended St Paul's School 1952-56 and London University (LLB, 1961). Freeman of the City of London. Former Chairman of Holloway Prison Board of Visitors. Leisure interests include family, cricket and rugby, travel, book-shop browsing and book collecting. Lives in London.

Brister, Graeme R.
Linklaters & Paines, London (0171) 606 7080. Partner in the Litigation Department. Qualified in 1979.

Burton, Anthony
Simons Muirhead & Burton, London (0171) 734 4499. Senior Partner.

Specialisation: Main area of practice is white collar crime. Represents entities and individuals, either those before the courts or those who are the subject of inquiry by investigatory or regulatory bodies. Also handles other criminal defence work and libel. Has acted in the Maxwell, BCCI, Bestwood and Brent Walker cases. Has written for law journals and national newspapers, and has lectured on criminal law.

Prof. Membership: Law Society, London Criminal Courts Solicitors Association and International Bar Association.

Career: Qualified 1972, joining *Simons Muirhead & Burton* as Partner in 1976.

Personal: Born 12th July 1947. Vice Chairman of the board of the Royal Court Theatre. Leisure interests include the Groucho club, theatre and cinema. Lives in London.

Burton, Ian R.
Burton Copeland, London (0171) 430 2277 & (0161) 834 7374. Partner in Commercial Fraud Department.

Specialisation: Specialises in crime, particularly fraud. Acted in the Barlow Clowes, Maxwell, Eagle Trust and Blackspur PLC cases.

Prof. Membership: L.C.C.S.A.

Career: Qualified in 1971. Joined *Burton Copeland* as a Partner in 1982.

Personal: Born 25th March 1947. Educated at Whittingehame College 1953-63. Enjoys family, food, wines, shooting and opera. Lives in London and Cheshire.

Caird, Richard F.
See under Crime: Fraud.

Caplan, Michael
Kingsley Napley, London (0171) 814 1200. Partner in Criminal Litigation Department.

Specialisation: Work includes criminal law, advocacy, extradition, gaming and licensing, and prosecuting for and advising professional bodies. Sits as an Assistant Recorder. Rights of audience in the Crown Court. Advises TEN on Criminal Law.

Career: Qualified in 1977. Joined *Kingsley Napley* in 1978 and became a Partner in 1982.

Personal: Born 3rd May 1953. Attended Kings College, London: LLB (Hons), AKC. Leisure interests include family, sport and reading. Lives in London.

Carnell, Bernard

See under Crime: General.

Clitheroe, John

Kingsley Napley, London (0171) 814 1200. Senior Partner.

Specialisation: Work covers white collar crime, international crime, tax and customs investigations and professional litigation. Also handles licensing and gaming. Author of 'Conducting a Criminal Defence', 'Criminal Risks in International Trade' and 'Data Protection in UK'. Recent major cases include Blue Arrow, Barlow Clowes, BCCI and Maxwell.

Prof. Membership: Law Society, London Criminal Courts Solicitors Association (President 1992-1993), British Academy of Forensic Sciences, International Bar Association.

Career: Qualified in 1958. Joined *Kingsley Napley* in 1962, becoming a Partner in 1965 and Senior Partner in 1994. Solicitor to Council for Professions Supplementary to Medicine; past member of Law Society Standing Committee on Criminal Law; member of the International Bar Association Committee on Business Crime and Vice-Chairman of the Committee on Criminal Law; member of the Law Society Advocacy Training Team; member of Solicitors Disciplinary Tribunal.

Personal: Born 3rd June 1935. Attended Royal Grammar School, Guildford. Leisure interests include reading, opera, theatre, sport and travel; member of Athenaeum Club, RAC, St James' Club. Lives in Kingston-upon-Thames.

Colhoun, Aileen

Magrath & Co, London (0171) 495 3003. Partner in Criminal Litigation Department.

Specialisation: Practice covers all areas of criminal work, particularly large scale white collar criminal defence work. Currently acting for one of the defendants in the Maxwell case. Defended in other SFO prosecutions. Defended Anthony Brindle in a widely publicised murder trial.

Prof. Membership: Law Society, London Criminal Courts Solicitors Association, International Bar Association, British Academy of Forensic Scientists, Westminster Law Society.

Career: Qualified in 1983. Worked at *Kingsley Napley* 1981-87, then *Powell Magrath & Spencer* 1987-90. Became a Partner at *Magrath & Co.* in 1990.

Personal: Born 14th September 1957. Attended University of Bristol 1976-79 (LLB), then University of Cambridge (MPhil in Criminology 1979-80). Leisure interests include reading, cinema and live music. Lives in London.

Delahunty, Louise

Peters & Peters, London (0171) 629 7991. Partner in Litigation Department.

Specialisation: Has extensive experience in business crime including defence of major prosecutions instituted by the SFO and the Crown Prosecution Service Fraud Investigation Group. International work includes conduct of the defence in criminal proceedings in another member state of the European Union, and advice on proceedings in the European Union, the USA and the Far East. Has wide experience in civil and commercial litigation including jurisdictional disputes, contempt, employment and civil and commercial fraud. Extensive advocacy experience in both domestic and overseas courts, including both conduct of the prosecution and the defence. Recent experience includes securing the acquittal of a defendant in a major prosecution instituted by the SFO after undertaking extensive preparation both in England and overseas, securing the acquittal of a solicitor in a major mortgage fraud prosecution, advising clients from the European Union and the Middle East on the issue of proceedings in England and the USA, and proceedings in the Chancery Division to recover substantial funds misappropriated as a result of fraud. She is one of three partners having knowledge of the French language.

Prof. Membership: Law Society, The City of Westminister Law Society, Hong Kong Law Society. London Criminal Courts Solicitors Association, International Bar Association and AIJA.

Career: Joined *Peters & Peters* in 1982 and qualified in 1984. Spent 4 years in Hong Kong between 1986 and 1990, practising in both criminal and commercial litigation for individuals and multinational companies based in the Pacific Basin. Returned to *Peters & Peters* in 1990 and became a Partner in 1991.

Fletcher, Rod

Russell Jones & Walker, London (0171) 837 2808. Partner and Head of Criminal and Business Investigations Department.

Specialisation: Main area of practice is criminal defence. Has particular involvement with white collar crime, business crime and major miscarriage of justice cases. Also regularly instructed in disciplinary cases. Represents individuals attending a number of government and other public inquiries. Acting in the Maxwell case, and miscarriage of justice cases, including the representation of the police officers prosecuted following the Birmingham Six, Guildford Four and Broadwater Farm investigations. Member of Justice/ British Institute of International and Comparative Law Committee, chaired by Mr Justice Phillips, investigating the advantages and disadvantages of the accusatorial and inquisitorial systems of criminal justice 1991-92.

Prof. Membership: Law Society, LCCSA, IBA

Career: Qualified in 1981. Worked with

Kingsley Napley, 1979-83. Left to join *Russell Jones & Walker* in 1983, becoming a Partner in 1985.

Personal: Born 21st April 1957. Attended Berkhamstead School, then Birmingham University 1975-8. Leisure interests include sailing, golf, cricket and music. Lives in London.

Gehm, Deborah

Kingsley Napley, London (0171) 814 1200. Partner in Criminal Department.

Specialisation: Main area of practice is crime and regulatory work. Experienced in general criminal work, especially fraud and investigations which potentially give rise to criminal liability (e.g. DTI investigations), regulatory investigations and proceedings before disciplinary tribunals. Acted in the Blue Arrow case. Also experienced in and deals with commercial litigation matters. Has spoken at various seminars and the 1992 UKACO Conference.

Prof. Membership: Law Society, City of London Solicitors.

Career: Qualified in 1986 with *Druces & Attlee*. Worked with *Linklaters & Paines* 1986-93. Joined *Kingsley Napley* as a Partner in January 1994.

Personal: Born 2nd February 1961. Attended Sir William Turner's VIth Form College 1977-79, then Bristol University 1979-82. Leisure interests include squash, badminton, tennis, opera. Lives in London.

Kirk, David

Simons Muirhead & Burton, London (0171) 734 4499. Partner in Criminal Department.

Specialisation: Commercial fraud, regulation, investigations. Acted in Blue Arrow, Nissan (UK) Ltd, Levitt Group, and Grupo Torras cases. Author of 'Serious Fraud-Investigation and Trial' and numerous articles. Has wide lecturing experience at conferences and seminars.

Prof. Membership: IBA.

Career: Qualified in 1989. Called to the Bar 1974. Worked at the office of the DPP 1976-85, and the Law Officers Department 1985-88. Partner at *Stephenson Harwood* 1989-94; joined *Simons Muirhead & Burton* as a Partner in 1994.

Personal: Born 2nd March 1949. Holds an English Language & Literature MA (Hons) degree from St Peter's College, Oxford, 1971. Lives in London.

Magrath, Christopher

See under Immigration & Nationality.

Mayhew, David

See under Litigation (Commercial).

Murray, Christopher

Kingsley Napley, London (0171) 814 1200. Qualified 1972. Partner and head of the Criminal Litigation Department. Specialises in all aspects of crime with a particular emphasis on white collar crime and fraud. Born 6.11.47.

O'Sullivan, Bernard

Titmuss Sainer Dechert, London (0171) 583 5353. Assistant Solicitor in Investigations Department.

Specialisation: Fraud and tax investigations. Acts principally as a defence lawyer in investigations undertaken by DTI, Customs & Excise and the Inland Revenue as well as financial regulatory work, banking prosecutions and extradition.

Prof. Membership: Law Society.

Career: Articled with *Titmuss Sainer & Webb* (now *Titmuss Sainer Dechert*) and qualified in 1992.

Personal: Born 1968. Birmingham University 1986-89 LLB. Leisure interests include sports and literature. Lives in London.

Oliver, Keith E.

Peters & Peters, London (0171) 629 7991. Qualified 1980. Partner 1983. Litigation Department. Specialises in business crime and commercial fraud litigation. Born 5.9.1956.

Parker, R.J.

Richards Butler, London (0171) 247 6555.

Phippen, C. Paul

Macfarlanes, London (0171) 831 9222. Qualified 1982. Partner 1989. Practice covers City fraud, regulatory and DTI work.

Pollard, Stephen

Kingsley Napley, London (0171) 814 1200. Partner in Criminal and Regulatory Department.

Specialisation: Practice covers all criminal work, including white collar fraud and 'city crime'. Also handles regulatory work and commercial litigation, including disciplinary proceedings before the self regulating organisations SFA, FIMBRA and LAUTRO. Acted for Rosemary Aberdour, for Lou Macari in the revenue prosecution of Swindon Town FC, and in the DPR Futures cases. Currently represents Nick Leeson, the Ex-Barings Trader. Lectures on criminal law to the Association of Women Solicitors' Returners course, and has appeared on TV and radio on criminal law matters.

Prof. Membership: AIJA, London Criminal Courts Solicitors' Association, City of London Solicitors.

Career: Qualified 1985. Worked at *Payne Hicks Beach* 1982-87, including 1984-5 as a Member of Secretariat of the European Commission of Human Rights, Strasbourg. Then worked at the Crown Prosecution Service 1987-88. Joined *Kingsley Napley* in 1989, becoming a Partner in 1990.

Personal: Born 5th September 1958. Attended Manchester Grammar School 1972-77, then Pembroke College, Oxford

1977-80. Leisure interests include reading, sport, theatre and family. Lives in Putney, London.

Potts, John

Clifford Chance, London (0171) 600 1000. Partner. Principal area of practice covers regulatory and financial services investigations and disciplinary proceedings, white collar crime, fraud, corporate/commercial disputes.

Raphael, Monty

Peters & Peters, London (0171) 629 7991. Senior Partner.

Specialisation: Main area of practice is business crime. Handles major cases involving fraud, tax and securities offences, customs infractions and general financial regulatory problems. Has specialised in commercial fraud for 25 years. Author of numerous articles and publications on the subject. Has spoken widely at conferences held by, among many others, the American Bar Association, American Bankers Association, American Society of Criminology, The Crown Agents, Commonwealth Secretariat, Jesus College, Cambridge, the Anglo-German Law Society and the Anglo-French Law Society.

Prof. Membership: Law Society, The City of Westminster Law Society, London Criminal Courts Solicitors' Association, British Academy of Forensic Science, International Bar Association, International Fiscal Association, British-German Jurists Association, International Association of Penal Law.

Career: Qualified 1962; has been a Senior Partner of *Peters & Peters* since 1983. In 1979 became the first Advocacy Training Officer appointed by the London Criminal Courts Solicitors' Association, (President 1982-84). Provided detailed written and oral evidence on the prosecution and trial of commercial fraud to the Roskill Committee and to the Royal Commission on Criminal Justice. Appointed Chairman of the Business Crime Committee of the Section on Business Law of the International Bar Association. Served as a member of the Home Office Working Party advising on the proposed alterations to 'right to silence' in 1988-89. Chairman of the White Collar Crime Unit at the Business School Liverpool. Assists the Council of Europe in its programme to help the emergent economies of Eastern Europe in their transition to a market economy.

Personal: Lives in London.

Rickards, Joanne

Peters & Peters, London (0171) 629 7991. Partner in Business Crime Department.

Specialisation: Principal area of practice is white collar crime encompassing SFO, FIG, DTI, Customs and Excise and Inland Revenue cases. Has extensive experience in all types of investment fraud, also disciplinary regulatory work involving SROs, the Solicitors' Complaints Bureau and the Joint Disciplinary Scheme of the Institute of Chartered Accountants. Prepared the first case to

make a successful application for dismissal under the Criminal Justice Act 1987 and has represented both suspects and witnesses in numerous s.2 inquiries. Also has experience of the banking tribunal of the Bank of England and directors' disqualification proceedings in the Companies Court.

Prof. Membership: Law Society, International Bar Association, Westminster Law Society.

Career: Qualified in 1989 while at *Peters & Peters* and became a Partner in 1992.

Personal: Born 7th October 1963. Attended University College, London 1982-85 (LL.B Hons). Lives in London.

Spiro, Brian

Simons Muirhead & Burton, London (0171) 734 4499. Partner in Criminal Litigation Department.

Specialisation: General criminal defence work including business crime, drugs law and serious offences against the person. Also fraud investigative work. Cases include the British Rail corruption trial, the NCP industrial espionage trial and the European Leisure trial. Regular contributor to legal journals and broadcaster.

Prof. Membership: Law Society, LCCSA, I.B.A.

Career: Qualified in 1984, having joined *Simons Muirhead & Burton* in 1982. Became Partner in 1986. Author of "Police Station Adviser's Index" (FT Law & Tax, September 1995).

Personal: Born 31st January 1959. Educated at Manchester Grammar School 1969-76 and Nottingham University 1976-79. Hon. Treasurer of the Association for the Prevention of Addiction 1986-88 and Chair of 'Alone in London Service' 1988-94.

REGIONS

Kenyon, A.D.

Betesh Fox & Co, Manchester (0161) 832 6131.

Mitchell, John

Blake Lapthorn, Fareham (01489) 579990. Partner in charge of Criminal Courts Department.

Specialisation: Main areas of practice are white collar and corporate fraud. Has specialised in criminal law since qualification and now concentrates on defending all types of commercial fraud prosecutions, including tax fraud. Also defends businesses against regulatory investigation, sanction and prosecution by local and national Government Departments and by Tax authorities.

Prof. Membership: Law Society.

Career: Qualified in 1979. Joined *Blake Lapthorn* in 1977, becoming a Partner in 1984.

Personal: Born 2nd March 1954. Attended Portsmouth Grammar School 1962-72, Pembroke College, Cambridge, 1973-76, and Guildford College of Law 1977. Lives in Bishops Waltham, Hampshire.

Robinson, Kevin J.

Irwin Mitchell, incorporating Kershaw Tucker, Sheffield (0114) 276 7777. Partner heading Businesss Crime Unit.

Acted in the major Iraqi arms export cases and also Astra/BMARC disqualification proceedings. Involved in arms export prosecutions in the US. Represents Company directors, managers and professionals charged with fraud, fraudulent trading and ancillary offenses. Also represents Corporations including multi-nationals and Plc's in criminal proceedings arising out of their commercial activities.

Career: Qualified in 1973. Joined *Irwin Mitchell* in 1974 became a partner in 1975. Former Treasurer of Criminal Law Solicitors Association. Higher Courts Rights of Audience 1995.

Smyth, R.

Burton Copeland, Manchester (0161) 834 7374. Qüalified 1977.

Woodcock, Anthony J.J.

Stephenson Harwood, London (0171) 329 4422. Partner and Head of Fraud and Regulation Unit.

Specialisation: Main area of practice is white collar crime and business and professional regulation, including fraud, insider dealing, and prosecuting and defending before professional disciplinary tribunals. Also deals with financial and professional investigations, conducting investigations for regulatory bodies in financial services, accounting and insolvency. Co-author of 'Serious Fraud: Investigation and Trial' (Butterworths). Speaker at conferences. Regular television appearances in relation to fraud and insider dealing enquiries.

Career: Called to the Bar 1976. At the Office of the DPP 1979-85 and the Office of the Treasury Solicitor 1985-87. With *Slaughter and May* 1987-90. Requalified 1989. Joined *Stephenson Harwood* 1990.

Personal: Born 1954. Educated at University College, London 1972-75. School Governor; Chairman of Education Act Appeal Committee. Interests include reading, cycling, running, swimming and music.

FIRMS OF ACCOUNTANTS

Accountants specialising in litigation support are listed in the accountants' A-Z, with details of the services they offer to solicitors, from forensic accounting to intellectual property or business valuations. This section is found immediately after the main solicitors' A-Z.

DEBT COLLECTION & FACTORING

MANY firms offer a computerised debt recovery service, while an increasing number (especially regional firms) have established distinct debt recovery departments attracting clients in their own right.

LONDON

Braby & Waller has one of the largest debt collection departments in the City and clients include major national and international manufacturers, distributors, communication providers and lenders.

LEADING FIRMS – LONDON

BRABY & WALLER

WILDE & PARTNERS

Also highly regarded is *Wilde & Partners* with a team of three partners advising on all aspects of trade and consumer debts including court investigations, seizure of assets, charging orders, credit control, summary judgements and High Court and County Court actions.

HIGHLY REGARDED – LONDON

DAVIES ARNOLD COOPER	STONEHAM LANGTON & PASSMORE
TARLO LYONS	UNDERWOOD & CO
WILDE SAPTE	
ALSOP WILKINSON	BARNETT ALEXANDER CHART
BEVERIDGE ROSS & PREVEZERS	EDGE & ELLISON
FRANKS, CHARLESLY	HEXTALL, ERSKINE
HOWARD KENNEDY	JEFFREY GREEN RUSSELL
KEENE MARSLAND	McKENNA & CO
NABARRO NATHANSON	SPRECHER GRIER
TUCKER TURNER KINGSLEY WOOD	

Other firms with strong debt collecting units include *Davies Arnold Cooper, Stoneham Langton & Passmore, Tarlo Lyons, Underwood & Co* and *Wilde Sapte. Davies Arnold Cooper*'s unit, part of the firm's insolvency department, is retained by high street and commercial banks. *Tarlo Lyons* offers a computerised service covering all aspects of routine debt recovery. Debt recovery forms around 15% of *Underwood & Co's* total workload and its clients include trade associations and recovery agencies.

SOUTH EAST

South East firms with substantial units include *Brachers, Cole and Cole, Cripps Harries Hall, Donne Mileham & Haddock, Matthew Arnold & Baldwin* and *Shoosmiths & Harrison.* Debt collection constitutes around 18% of *Brachers'* total workload and clients include charge card, building trade and shipping companies. The debt recovery department of *Donne Mileham & Haddock,* led by a member of the Institute of Credit Management, handles over 3,500

cases a year for commercial clients including overseas companies trading in U.K.

Also well- regarded are *Burt Brill & Cardens, Buss Murton (with two specialist partners), Ellison & Co* and *Mundays. Mundays'* department deals with recovery of debt for all types of trading activities and private clients. It also handles mortgage and rent arrears and small financial claims.

HIGHLY REGARDED – SOUTH EAST

BRACHERS Maidstone	BURT BRILL & CARDENS Brighton
BUSS MURTON Tunbridge Wells	COLE and COLE Oxford
CRIPPS HARRIES HALL Tunbridge Wells	DONNE MILEHAM & HADDOCK Brighton
ELLISON & CO Colchester	MUNDAYS Esher
SHOOSMITHS & HARRISON Banbury	
BLAKE LAPTHORN Fareham	BOYES TURNER & BURROWS Reading
CLARKS Reading	CLARKSON WRIGHT & JAKES Orpington
CLYDE & CO Guildford	FENNEMORES Milton Keynes
GLENISTERS Ruislip	LIGHTFOOTS Thame
LINNELLS Oxford	MATTHEW ARNOLD & BALDWIN Watford
MAX BARFORD & CO Tunbridge Wells	McGOLDRICK CAIRNS Dartford
MOORE & BLATCH Southampton	ORMEROD WILKINSON MARSHALL Croydon
RAWLISON & BUTLER Crawley	STEVENS & BOLTON Guildford
THOMSON SNELL & PASSMORE Tunbridge Wells	TURBERVILLE WOODBRIDGE Uxbridge
WHITE & BOWKER Winchester	WOODFORD & ACKROYD Southampton
WYNNE BAXTER GODFREE Lewes	

SOUTH WEST & WALES

Debt collection service is offered throughout the South West and the commercial centres of Wales. Those active in this field include *Clarke Willmott & Clarke, Francis & Co, Lester Aldridge, Osborne Clarke, Pardoes, Stephens & Scown, Veale Wasbrough* and *Wansbroughs Willey Hargrave.*

HIGHLY REGARDED – SOUTH WEST & WALES

CLARKE WILLMOTT & CLARKE Taunton	FRANCIS & CO Newport
LESTER ALDRIDGE Bournemouth	OSBORNE CLARKE Bristol
PARDOES Bridgwater	STEPHENS & SCOWN Exeter
VEALE WASBROUGH Bristol	WANSBROUGHS WILLEY HARGRAVE Bristol
ANSTEY SARGENT & PROBERT Exeter	BEVAN ASHFORD Bristol
BOND PEARCE Plymouth	BURGES SALMON Bristol
CARTWRIGHTS Bristol	DAVIES AND PARTNERS Gloucester
DICKINSON MANSER Poole	DOUGLAS-JONES & MERCER Swansea
EDWARDS GELDARD Cardiff	EVERSHEDS Cardiff
FAULKNERS Frome	FORD SIMEY DAW ROBERTS Exeter
GOWMANS Paignton	HUGH JAMES JONES & JENKINS Cardiff
LAWRENCE TUCKETTS Bristol	MICHELMORES Exeter
PORTER BARTLETT & MAYO Yeovil	RICKERBY JESSOP Cheltenham
SPICKETTS Pontypridd	STEELE RAYMOND Bournemouth
TOWNSENDS Swindon	TOZERS Exeter
TRUMP AND PARTNERS Bristol	WITHY KING & LEE Bath
WOOLLCOMBE BEER WATTS Newton Abbot	

In all the tables the names in each group are listed alphabetically.

All offer a computerised debt recovery service. *Francis & Co* also advises on credit control. *Wansbroughs Willey Hargrave* acts principally for insurance and consumer goods companies.

MIDLANDS

Firms with prominent debt collection units include *Warner Cranston*, *Edge & Ellison*, *Hewitson Becke & Shaw* and *Shoosmiths & Harrison*. The Coventry office of *Warner Cranston* deals almost exclusively with national and international computerised debt recovery for both trade and consumer debts.

HIGHLY REGARDED – MIDLANDS	
EDGE & ELLISON *Birmingham*	HATCHER ROGERSON *Shrewsbury*
HEWITSON BECKE + SHAW *Northampton*	SHOOSMITHS & HARRISON *Northampton*
WARNER CRANSTON *Coventry*	
BLAKEMORES *Coventry*	BLUNTS *Walsall*
BROWNE JACOBSON *Nottingham*	DIBB LUPTON BROOMHEAD *Birmingham*
EVERSHEDS *Birmingham*	EVERSHEDS, NOTTINGHAM
FOSTER BAXTER COOKSEY *Wolverhampton*	FREETH CARTWRIGHT HUNT DICKINS *Nottingham*
GATELEY WAREING *Birmingham*	GOODGER AUDEN *Burton-on-Trent*
HERBERT WILKES *Birmingham*	HOWES PERCIVAL *Northampton*
LANYON BOWDLER *Shrewsbury*	NEEDHAM & JAMES *Stratford upon Avon*
OWSTONS *Leicester*	PINSENT CURTIS *Birmingham*
ROYTHORNE & CO *Spalding*	SHACKLOCKS *Nottingham*
SHAKESPEARES *Birmingham*	TOLLER HALES *Northampton*
TRUMANS *Nottingham*	WILLCOX LANE CLUTTERBUCK *Birmingham*
WRAGGE & CO *Birmingham*	

As well as providing a computerised service to aid their clients' credit control requirements, *Edge & Ellison*'s unit reviews the enforceability of terms and conditions of payment. *Hewitson Becke + Shaw* has further increased its debt recovery service to include full credit management for clients who are primarily lending institutions and plcs.

Also active in this area is *Hatcher Rogerson* with two specialist partners. Commercial debt recovery forms around 9% of its total workload.

EAST ANGLIA

The leading firms include *Cozens-Hardy & Jewson*, *Eversheds* (Norwich and Ipswich) and *Greenwoods*. *Eversheds*, who acts for a major client throughout East Anglia, is currently handling a case load of more than 350 live matters for them.

LEADING FIRMS – EAST ANGLIA	
COZENS–HARDY & JEWSON *Norwich*	EVERSHEDS *Norwich*
GREENWOODS *Peterborough*	

Greenwoods has been selected by Railtrack following a beauty parade, to handle all of its debt recovery work (around 1,000 cases a year). Other firms with strong expertise in this field include *Birketts*, *Hewitson Becke + Shaw* and *Leeds Day*.

HIGHLY REGARDED – EAST ANGLIA	
BIRKETTS *Ipswich*	HEWITSON BECKE + SHAW *Cambridge*
LEEDS DAY *Sandy*	
BANKES ASHTON *Bury St. Edmunds*	CUNNINGHAM, JOHN *Thetford*
GOTELEE & GOLDSMITH *Ipswich*	GREENLAND HOUCHEN *Norwich*
HOWES PERCIVAL *Ipswich*	LEATHES PRIOR *Norwich*
MILLER & CO *Cambridge*	PRETTYS *Ipswich*

NORTH WEST

Bermans with five specialist partners, has developed a reputation as one of the pre-eminent debt recovery practices. Its commercial recovery department, whose services are also used internationally, handles bulk collection of commercial debts for companies, public bodies, receivers and liquidators.

LEADING FIRMS – NORTH WEST
BERMANS *Liverpool*

Also highly regarded are *Addleshaw Sons & Latham*, *Cobbett Leak Almond*, *Cuff Roberts*, *Davies Wallis Foyster*, *Eversheds* (Manchester) and *Lees Lloyd Whitley*.

Eversheds' department, headed by an associate partner, handles a range of recovery work including secured and unsecured lending and trade claims from major plc's and clearing banks to sole traders. *Lees Lloyd Whitley*'s department acts for commercial clients and government agencies including H.M. Customs & Excise.

HIGHLY REGARDED – NORTH WEST	
ADDLESHAW SONS & LATHAM *Manchester*	COBBETT LEAK ALMOND *Manchester*
CUFF ROBERTS *Liverpool*	DAVIES WALLIS FOYSTER *Liverpool*
EVERSHEDS *Manchester*	LEES LLOYD WHITLEY *Liverpool*
AARON & PARTNERS *Chester,,*	ALSOP WILKINSON *Liverpool*
DAVIES ARNOLD COOPER *Manchester*	HALLIWELL LANDAU *Manchester*
HILL DICKINSON DAVIS CAMPBELL *Liverpool*	WEIGHTMAN RUTHERFORDS *Liverpool*

NORTH EAST

Booth & Co, *Dibb Lupton Broomhead*, *Eversheds* (Leeds), *Hammond Suddards* and *Robert Muckle* continue to maintain their excellent reputations in debt recovery.

LEADING FIRMS – NORTH EAST	
BOOTH & CO. *Leeds*	DIBB LUPTON BROOMHEAD *Bradford*
EVERSHEDS *Leeds*	HAMMOND SUDDARDS *Leeds*
ROBERT MUCKLE *Newcastle*	

Booth & Co has a separate credit management department dealing with all aspects of debt recovery. *Eversheds'* department, consisting of four solicitors, is headed by Jeremy Sutcliffe: (National Chairman of the Eversheds Recoveries Group and a fellow of the Institute of Credit Management). The firm currently carries approximately 18,000 live files and retail clients include Club 24, IKANO and GE Capital. The firm recently accepted an invitation from European law firm, *Stanbrook & Partners*, to join their Pan-European debt recovery service. *Hammond Suddards'* computerised debt recovery department deals with commercial and consumer debts involving both High Court and County Court matters.

HIGHLY REGARDED – NORTH EAST		
CARRICK CARR & WRIGHT *Hull*	FORD AND WARREN *Leeds*	
LUPTON FAWCETT *Leeds*	READ HIND STEWART *Leeds*	
WILKINSON MAUGHAN *Newcastle*		
ANDREW M. JACKSON *Hull*	DICKINSON DEES *Newcastle*	
EVERSHEDS *Newcastle & Middlesbrough*	HAY & KILNER *Newcastle*	
IRWIN MITCHELL *Sheffield*	R.C. MOORHOUSE & CO *Leeds*	
NABARRO NATHANSON *Doncaster*	NELSON & CO *Leeds*	
PINSENT CURTIS	ROLLIT FARRELL & BLADON *Hull*	
WAKE SMITH *Sheffield*	WALKER MORRIS *Leeds*	
WANSBROUGHS WILLEY HARGRAVE *Leeds*	WARD HADAWAY *Newcastle*	
WILKIN CHAPMAN *Grimsby*		

Other firms with sound debt recovery practices include *Carrick Carr & Wright, Ford and Warren, Lupton Fawcett, Read Hind Stewart* and *Wilkinson Maughan.*

Ford and Warren handles all aspects of credit control and High Court and County Court debt recovery. *Lupton Fawcett's* department consisting of the former head of *Dibb Lupton Broomhead's* debt recovery service, is particularly experienced in handling contested cases. Major clients include Hewden Stewart plc, Dun and Bradstreet, the Royal Bank of Scotland and several national debt collection agencies. *Read Hind Stewart's* computerised department has expertise in High and County Court systems and credit control.

SCOTLAND

Firms with strong debt recovery practices include *Bonar Mackenzie WS, McClure Naismith Anderson & Gardiner* and *Morton Fraser Milligan WS.*

HIGHLY REGARDED – SCOTLAND	
BONAR MACKENZIE WS *Edinburgh*	McCLURE NAISMITH ANDERSON & GARDINER *Glasgow*
MORTON FRASER MILLIGAN *Edinburgh*	
BRODIES WS *Edinburgh*	DORMAN JEFFREY & CO *Glasgow*
KIDSTONS & CO *Glasgow*	
AITKEN NAIRN WS *Edinburgh*	ANDERSON FYFE *Glasgow*
BALFOUR & MANSON *Edinburgh*	BELL & SCOTT WS *Edinburgh*
BENNETT & ROBERTSON *Edinburgh*	BIRD SEMPLE *Glasgow*
BISHOP AND ROBERTSON	BLACKADDER REID JOHNSTON
CHALMERS *Glasgow*	*Dundee*
BOYDS *Glasgow*	BRUNTON MILLER *Glasgow*
FYFE IRELAND *Edinburgh*	HAMILTON BURNS & MOORE *Glasgow*
HENDERSON BOYD JACKSON *Edinburgh*	JAMES & GEORGE COLLIE *Aberdeen*
MACDONALDS *Glasgow*	MACROBERTS *Glasgow*
McGRIGOR DONALD *Glasgow*	MILLER SAMUEL & CO *Glasgow*
MITCHELLS ROBERTON *Glasgow*	ROBSON McLEAN WS *Edinburgh*
SHEPHERD & WEDDERBURN *Edinburgh*	SIMPSON & MARWICK WS *Edinburgh*
STORIE, CRUDEN & SIMPSON *Aberdeen*	STRONACHS *Aberdeen*
TINDAL OATTS *Glasgow*	TODS MURRAY WS *Edinburgh*
WRIGHT, JOHNSTON & MACKENZIE *Glasgow*	

Bonar Mackenzie's team consisting of three partners advises banks and building societies on the recovery of both

consumer and trade debts. *McClure Naismith Anderson & Gardiner* advises on high volume debt recovery, asset recovery and the drafting of credit documentation. Their clients include the Finance House Association, the Consumer Trade Association, finance houses, leasing companies, banks, building societies and credit card companies. Also active in this field are *Brodies WS, Dorman Jeffrey & Co.* (with one specialist partner) and *Kidstons & Co.*

NORTHERN IRELAND

Firms noted for their computerised debt recovery services include *Babington & Croasdaile* and *S.J.Diamond & Son.* The latter handles High Court and County Court collection of secured and unsecured debts for two major banks. It also deals with the collection of credit card debts, mortgage arrears and mortgage repossessions.

HIGHLY REGARDED – NORTHERN IRELAND	
BABINGTON & CROASDAILE *Londonderry*	S.J. DIAMOND & SON *Belfast*
CLEAVER FULTON & RANKIN *Belfast*	DONNELLY NEARY & DONNELLY *Newry*
HEWITT & GILPIN *Belfast*	JOHN McKEE & SON *Belfast*
O'REILLY STEWART *Belfast*	J.W. RUSSELL & CO *Newtonards*
WILSON NESBITT *Belfast*	

FACTORING AND INVOICE DISCOUNTING

Factoring and invoice discounting are being increasingly used as alternatives to bank finance. In factoring, the factor will take over the control of the sales ledger and credit management and provide the company with advanced payment against the outstanding debts/invoices (ranging from 33%-80% of their value). The balance of the debt will be paid to the company once the invoice is fully settled, after deduction of a service fee. Invoice discounting merely consists of a cash advance with credit management control remaining in the hands of the client.

LEADING FIRMS – LONDON – INVOICING & FACTORING	
WILDE & PARTNERS	
BOOTH & BLACKWELL	BRABY & WALLER
DAVIES ARNOLD COOPER	

Only a handful of solicitors have an expertise in representing large factoring companies which are often bank-owned. In London, *Wilde & Partners,* with over 90% of the UK market, is pre-eminent. Their team of five partners acts for most members of the Association of British Factors and Discounters.

The leading regional firm is undoubtedly *Bermans* in Liverpool. The firm has four partners specialising in factoring/invoice discounting, which accounts for 21% of the firm's workload.

LEADING FIRMS – NORTH WEST – INVOICING & FACTORING
BERMANS *Liverpool*

Other firms active in this field include London firms *Booth & Blackwell, Braby & Waller* and *Davies Arnold Cooper. Booth & Blackwell's,* unit consisting of two licensed insolvency practitioners, has been acting for factoring companies for nearly 20 years.

DEFAMATION

HIGH profile defamation work is largely concentrated in London and is commonly handled by niche practices or larger firms with specialist departments. By contrast, libel work for regional newspapers and broadcasters is usually conducted by local firms outside London.

Many practices have experienced litigation departments capable of conducting libel cases and offering pre-publication advice. This list contains only those firms which have established reputations in the field and have consistently been recommended for their work.

LONDON

No less than ten firms were consistently recommended as having outstanding defamation practices, their reputations largely based on an individual practitioner.

LEADING FIRMS – LONDON	
BIDDLE & CO	DAVENPORT LYONS
FARRER & CO	MISHCON DE REYA
OLSWANG	OSWALD HICKSON COLLIER
PETER CARTER-RUCK & PARTNERS	RICHARD C.M. SYKES
RUSSELL JONES & WALKER	SWEPSTONE WALSH

David Hooper at *Biddle & Co* has represented a number of MP's in libel actions against national newspapers and conducted cases on behalf of other well-known personalities including John Major. The firm also provides pre-publication advice for major publishers.

Davenport Lyons makes its first appearance in the list following the recent merger with leading niche defamation practice, *Wright Webb Syrett*. The firm now boasts eminent practitioners such as Kevin Bays and Philip Conway who are retained by nine of the national newspapers in addition to being the principal solicitors for 'Private Eye'. The firm also represents plaintiffs and has conducted cases on behalf of a number of personalities from the world of politics, sport and entertainment.

Robert Clinton of *Farrer & Co*, who received more recommendations than any other libel practitioner, is well known for both plaintiff work (having represented the Queen and other members of the Royal Family) and defence work, representing News International ('Sun' and 'News of the World') amongst other national newspapers.

Lovell White Durrant, previously ranked among the top ten defamation practices, will notice the loss of Geraldine Proudler (one of London's leading practitioners, who has moved to *Olswang*). This recent appointment has heightened *Olswang's* profile considerably. The firm now has a formidable team in Geraldine Proudler, Julia Palca and Caroline Kean who represent both plaintiffs and defendants including a number of national newspapers and magazines.

Brian Hepworth and Julie Scott-Bayfield at *Mishcon de Reya* both enjoy good reputations in the field, representing media giants such as Associated Newspapers, United Newspapers,

Mirror Group, Channel 4, Carlton, Central and Yorkshire TV.

Peter Carter Ruck & Partners has strength in depth in Nigel Tait, Alasdair Pepper, Andrew Stephenson and Peter Carter-Ruck himself who have gained a reputation for high profile plaintiff work. They also undertake defence work, representing a number of book and magazine publishers and two television companies. Guy Martin has also been recommended to us.

Oswald Hickson Collier and *Swepstone Walsh* primarily represent defendants. Both firms are retained by national and regional newspapers. Richard Shillito and Paul Davies at *Oswald Hickson Collier* represent The Financial Times and The Economist, whilst Roderick Dadak and Patrick Stewart of *Swepstone Walsh* undertake work for Associated and Express Newspapers. Rhory Robertson has been described as a rising star.

Any list would be incomplete without *Russell Jones & Walker* and in particular Barton Taylor who has gained a reputation acting for The Police Federation.

Other notable practitioners include Rupert Grey of *Crockers* (who in addition to handling a substantial amount of litigation and pre-publication advice for leading book and magazine publishers, also lectures on the subject), Keith Schilling of *Schilling & Lom*, (famous for his aggressive stance and for representing high profile glitterati) and Patrick Swaffer of *Goodman Derrick* (who provides both pre- and post-publication advice to the publishing and broadcasting industries).

HIGHLY REGARDED – LONDON	
CROCKERS	D J FREEMAN
GOODMAN DERRICK	SCHILLING & LOM
THEODORE GODDARD	
BINDMAN & PARTNERS	CLIFFORD CHANCE
DAVID PRICE & CO	DENTON HALL
HARBOTTLE & LEWIS	HEMPSONS
LEWIS SILKIN	MANCHES & CO
REID MINTY	RICHARDS BUTLER
SIMONS MUIRHEAD & BURTON	STEPHENS INNOCENT
TAYLOR JOYNSON GARRETT	

Also highly recommended are Richard Sykes of *Richard Sykes & Co* and David Price of *David Price & Co*, a niche defamation practice with a fast growing reputation and a number of high profile cases under its belt including Patricia Guppy v. Times Newspapers Ltd (acting for plaintiff) and British Data Management plc v. Boxer Commercial Removals plc – a landmark action (acting for plaintiffs). David Price also represents Scallywag, which frequently appears before the courts.

Other recommended firms include *Bindman & Partners* and in particular Geoffrey Bindman, who, whilst better known in the field of civil liberties, has an ever increasing defamation practice; *Clifford Chance*, where Michael Smyth has established a reputation in the field; *D.J. Freeman*, where Susan Aslan advises terrestrial and satellite broadcasting companies on libel issues; and *Stephens Innocent*, where Mark Stephens is well known for representing clients within the media.

LEADING INDIVIDUALS – LONDON

Kevin Bays *Davenport Lyons*	**Peter Carter-Ruck** *Peter Carter-Ruck & Partners*	**Robert G. Clinton** *Farrer & Co*
Philip Conway *Davenport Lyons*	**R. Dadak** *Swepstone Walsh*	**Paul Davies** *Oswald Hickson Collier*
Rupert C. Grey *Crockers*	**Brian J. Hepworth** *Mishcon De Reya*	**David Hooper** *Biddle & Co*
Caroline Kean *Olswang*	**M.C. Kramer** *Theodore Goddard*	**Julia Palca** *Olswang*
Alasdair G.T. Pepper *Peter Carter-Ruck & Partners*	**David Price** *David Price & Co*	**Geraldine Proudler** *Olswang*
Keith Schilling *Schilling & Lom*	**Richard A. Shillito** *Oswald Hickson Collier*	**P. Stewart** *Swepstone Walsh*
Patrick Swaffer *Goodman Derrick*	**Richard C.M. Sykes** *Richard C.M. Sykes*	**Nigel G.T.M. Tait** *Peter Carter-Ruck & Partners*
Barton Taylor *Russell Jones & Walker*		
Susan Aslan *D J Freeman*	**Geoffrey Bindman** *Bindman & Partners*	**Tim J. House** *Allen & Overy*
G. Martin *Peter Carter-Ruck & Partners*	**Robin Perrot** *Goodman Derrick*	**R. Robertson** *Swepstone Walsh*
Julie Scott-Bayfield *Mishcon De Reya*	**Michael Skrein** *Richards Butler*	**Michael Smyth** *Clifford Chance*
Mark H. Stephens *Stephens Innocent*	**Andrew James Stephenson** *Peter Carter-Ruck & Partners*	

SOUTH OF ENGLAND

Highly experienced practices in the South of England include *Knights, Bevan Ashford, Foot & Bowden* and *Osborne Clarke.*

Knights, a niche litigation firm in Tunbridge Wells, has two partners specialising in defamation. Matthew Knight has represented a number of companies in libel actions and is held in high regard.

HIGHLY REGARDED – SOUTH OF ENGLAND

BEVAN ASHFORD *Bristol*	**FOOT & BOWDEN** *Plymouth*
KNIGHTS *Tunbridge Wells*	**OSBORNE CLARKE** *Bristol*

In Bristol, *Bevan Ashford's* team of three specialists undertakes a broad range of work for media clients.

LEADING INDIVIDUALS – SOUTH OF ENGLAND

Anthony R. Jaffa *Foot & Bowden*
Matthew Knight *Knights*
David K. Ticehurst *Osborne Clarke*

David Ticehurst at *Osborne Clarke* represents HTV, GWR and Bristol United Press. The firm also acted in the Walker Wingsail litigation, in which record damages were awarded against an insured defendant.

Tony Jaffa at *Foot & Bowden* in Plymouth acts for a number of newspapers, television and radio stations.

MIDLANDS

In the Midlands, *Keely Smith & Jobson* and *Wragge & Co* have established reputations in the field.

HIGHLY REGARDED – MIDLANDS

KEELY SMITH & JOBSON *Lichfield*	**WRAGGE & CO** *Birmingham*

Peter Lax of *Keely Smith & Jobson* gives pre-publication advice to newspapers, whilst Gordon Harris at *Wragge & Co*

LEADING INDIVIDUALS – MIDLANDS

Gordon D. Harris *Wragge & Co*
Peter Lax *Keely Smith & Jobson*

is experienced in trade libel work. Both firms also represent plaintiffs.

NORTH

The only firms in the North of England with genuine expertise in defamation are *Brabner Holden Banks Wilson, Hempsons* and *Pannone & Partners.*

HIGHLY REGARDED – NORTH

BRABNER HOLDEN BANKS WILSON *Liverpool*	**HEMPSONS** *Manchester*
PANNONE & PARTNERS *Manchester*	

At *Brabner Holden Banks Wilson*, Mark Manley represents Radio City and Newsco Publishing (Business Insider) and is held in high regard.

LEADING INDIVIDUALS – NORTH

Mark J. Manley *Brabner Holden Banks Wilson*

Hempsons, the medical and healthcare specialists, gains its reputation from work carried out for the Medical Defence Union. The firm also represents local authorities and substantial commercial undertakings.

Pannone & Partners' work is largely plaintiff orientated, advising politicians and company directors.

SCOTLAND

The majority of defence work in Scotland is non-contentious pre-publication advice. Of the firms which have been involved in litigation, those with the strongest reputations are *Dundas & Wilson CS* which provides pre- and post-publication advice to newspapers and television companies and *James & George Collie* which acts for newspapers and publishers.

HIGHLY REGARDED – SCOTLAND

DUNDAS & WILSON CS *Edinburgh*	**JAMES & GEORGE COLLIE** *Aberdeen*

In all the tables the names in each group are listed alphabetically.

NORTHERN IRELAND

Defamation law in Northern Ireland is largely the preserve of Belfast firms. In addition to their contentious expertise, *C & J Black,* who act for the BBC, and *Cleaver Fulton & Rankin* are well known for their pre-publication work on

defendants but also undertakes some plaintiff work. At *Johns Elliott* James Hendron has an excellent reputation and long experience in defendant work. *Johnsons,* whose leading specialist is Paul Tweed, are known primarily for their plaintiff litigation, and have recently been involved in several widely publicised libel trials including *Eastwood v McGuigan.*

HIGHLY REGARDED – NORTHERN IRELAND	
C & J BLACK *Belfast*	CLEAVER FULTON & RANKIN *Belfast*
JOHNS ELLIOT *Belfast*	JOHNSONS *Belfast*

LEADING INDIVIDUALS – NORTHERN IRELAND	
James Hendron *Johns Elliot*	
M. Paul Spring *Cleaver Fulton & Rankin*	
Paul Tweed *Johnsons*	

behalf of major broadcasting and publishing concerns. Paul Spring at the latter firm is well known for acting for

LEADERS IN DEFAMATION

LONDON

Aslan, Susan

D J Freeman, London (0171) 583 4055. Qualified 1985. Partner 1991. Multimedia Group. Specialises in libel, advising terrestrial and satellite broadcasting companies and newspapers.

Bays, Kevin

Davenport Lyons, London (0171) 287 5353. Partner in 1982.

Specialisation: Defamation, publishing and media law. Principal solicitor for 'Private Eye' for the past eight years. Other publisher clients include Mirror Group Newspapers and Associated Newspapers. Also acts for plaintiffs in defamation cases. Handles general litigation with an entertainment bias and employment law. Currently acting for the Mirror Group in Michael Jackson's libel action concerning his plastic surgery.

Prof. Membership: Law Society.

Career: Qualified 1979, having joined *Wright Webb Syrett* in 1977. Became a Partner in 1982.

Personal: Born 24th April 1955. Leisure interests include skiing, golf, cricket, football and travelling. Chairman of Norman Cowans Benefit Committee 1993, Member of The Media Society and The Groucho Club.

Bindman, Geoffrey

See under Civil Liberties.

Carter-Ruck, Peter

Peter Carter-Ruck & Partners, London (0171) 353 5005. Senior Partner. Partner in Media, Intellectual Property and Trusts Department.

Specialisation: Principal areas of practice are libel and copyright litigation for plaintiffs and defendants and checking written matter for libel, contempt of court and copyright for newspapers, magazines and T.V. companies. Also advises on literary and financial trusts, probate and matrimonial matters. Has acted in many leading cases including the copyright action and subsequent negotiations leading to the production and vesting of the copyright in Kevin McClory, the producer of the James Bond Film 'Thunderball', the Hamilton and Howarth libel actions against the BBC and others, the case of Sir Ranulph Fiennes against Macleans Magazine and the King of Malaysia against the "Daily Mirror ". Clients have included the late Randolph Churchill, Winston Churchill, Edwina Currie, Teresa Gorman, Express Newspapers, Associated Newspapers, Time Warner, the late Lord Olivier and the late Sir Terence Rattigan. Has written 'Libel and Slander' (Butterworths), 'Copyright:Modern Law and Practice' and 'The Cyclist and The Law' and has contributed numerous articles on media and newspaper law for the *Newspaper Society*. Has spoken extensively on media law and has more recently taken part in debates at Cambridge, Oxford and Durham Universities. Charge out rate is £250 per hour, less for clearing material.

Prof. Membership: Member, The International Bar Association, Justice, International Commission of Jurists (English Section), the Solicitors Benevolent Association and the Institute of Journalists. Formerly specialist member of the Council of the Law Society and President of the City of Westminster Law Society.

Career: Qualified in 1937. Joined *Oswald Hickson, Collier & Co.* where he became Senior Partner 1945-81. Founded *Peter Car-*

ter-Ruck and Partners in 1982 as Senior Partner.

Personal: Born 26th February 1914. Educated at Thorpe House Preparatory School, St. Edward's School, Oxford, 1928-31. Past Governor of St. Edward's School, Oxford, 1950-78, former Chairman and Governor of Shiplake College, Henley, past President of the Media Society, Member of Council of Justice since 1968, past Commodore of the Law Society Yacht Club and past Commodore of the Ocean Cruising Club. Leisure interests include sailing, walking, field work, carpentry, wood-turning and photography. Lives in Great Hallingbury, Herts.

Clinton, Robert G.

Farrer & Co, London (0171) 242 2022. Partner. Head of Litigation, Managing Partner.

Specialisation: Main areas of practice are defamation and publishing related litigation. Involves extensive range of plaintiff and defendant work for prominent individuals and institutions, including newspaper and publishing companies. Pre- and post-publication advice including breach of confidence, contempt etc. Intellectual property work, covering general trademark and passing off work for commercial clients.

Prof. Memberships: Media Society. International Bar Association.

Career: Joined *Farrer & Co* in 1972. Became Partner in 1979.

Personal: Born 19th August 1948. Attended Brasenose College, Oxford 1967-71. Leisure pursuits include sailing. Lives in London.

Conway, Philip

Davenport Lyons, London (0171) 287 5353. Partner in Litigation Department.

Specialisation: Main area of practice is defamation, especially with regard to the newspaper and entertainment industries. Acted for Gorden Kaye (against the Sunday Sport), The Daily Star (against Gillian Taylforth) and Carmen Proetta (against The Sunday Times).

Prof. Memberships: Law Society (Member of Privacy and Defamation Working Committees).

Career: Qualified in 1984. Joined *Wright Webb Syrett* in February 1986. Became Partner in August 1988.

Personal: Born 15th April 1959. Attended Aldenham School 1972-77. Former Director Southend United Football Club. Member of The Media Society, Groucho Club and a Barker of The Variety Club of Great Britain.

Dadak, R.
Swepstone Walsh, London (0171) 404 1499. Qualified 1972. Senior Litigation Partner 1988. Main areas of practice are defamation and litigation. Intellectual property, commercial litigation and contempt work also undertaken. Born 20.1.1947.

Davies, Paul
Oswald Hickson Collier, London (0171) 583 5333. Partner in Media Department.

Specialisation: Principal area of practice is libel (defamation). Important cases handled include Morgan v. Odhams Press, Cassell and Broome and Spycatcher as well as cases relating to protection of journalist's sources, notably in re an Inquiry under the Company Securities (insider dealing) Act 1985, X v. Morgan-Grampian and others and in re Saunders. Also regarding the extent of common law privilege in Tsikata v. Newspaper Publishing [1994]. In addition to libel, practice covers all other aspects of media law - contempt of court, reporting restrictions, copyright, injunctions, advertising, computer misuse, competition law, betting, gaming and lotteries and newspaper competitions. Major clients include three national broadsheet newspapers, major regional newspaper groups, major trade business and specialist interest magazine publishers, Lloyd's syndicates and other insurers in the UK and abroad.

Prof. Membership: Law Society.

Career: Qualified in 1964. Partner at *Oswald Hickson Collier* since 1965. Born 13th May 1939. Educated at Beaumont College 1952-57. Leisure interests include reading, music and gardening. Lives in Cobham, Surrey.

Grey, Rupert C.
Crockers, London (0171) 353 0311. Partner in Litigation Department.

Specialisation: Main area of practice is libel: Head of Department of five fee-earners. Retained by leading book and magazine publishers and their insurers to advise on libel and allied matters prior to publication and to deal with post-publication claims. Also handles copyright: retained by syndication agencies, picture libraries and publishers to handle all matters connected with literary and photographic copyright. Cases have included Armand Hammer v. Random House, and Lloyds v. Independent Newspaper Publishers plc. Retained as expert witness on UK copyright by Reuters in a major trial in the USA. Author of guide books on copyright and libel, in addition to numerous articles on these subjects. Regularly lectures on libel to publishing houses, and gives seminars at Crockers. Also lectures on the implications of the electronic revolution for current licensing practice at major national conferences, and appeared on the Kilroy Silk programme to talk about the possible law of privacy.

Prof. Membership: Fellow of Royal Geographical Society.

Career: Qualified in 1975, having served Articles with *Farrer & Co*. Worked at *Wilde Sapte & Co*. 1975-77, then *Southall & Knight* 1978-79, before joining *Crockers* in 1981, becoming a Partner in 1983. Prior to this, held diverse jobs including Exploration Director with Barringer Research in the Fiji Islands, a roughneck on an oil rig in the Yukon, nickel prospector in West Australia, as a lumberjack in Western Canada and freelanced as a photographer and journalist.

Personal: Born 8th September 1946. Attended Wellington College in Berkshire, then University College, London. Honorary Solicitor and Trustee to Scientific Exploration Society (co-ordinating relief projects in Fiji and Panama), International Scientific Support Trust and Schools for Performing Arts Trust. Leisure interests include expeditions to wild and remote places (usually these days with children); supervised the construction of an important timberframe building in Sussex; professional photographer, designated best black and white photographer of the year in 1981 by Wild Life Publications. Lives in South Downs.

Hepworth, Brian J.
Mishcon De Reya, London (0171) 405 3711. Partner in Litigation Department.

Specialisation: Main areas of practice are defamation and media, including contempt and contentious copyright. Acts mainly for television, newspapers and publishers. Handles pre-publication clearance, injunctive work and post-publication litigation. Acted for broadcasters in successfully defending the injunctions concerning the broadcast of recorded interviews with mass murderers Dennis Nilsen and Beverly Allitt. Major clients include Central Television, Carlton Television, Yorkshire Television, Channel 4, Express Newspapers, Mirror Newspapers and Associated Newspapers. Occasional contributor to professional periodicals. Departmental charge-out rates vary from £125-£250 per hour for qualified staff.

Prof. Membership: Law Society, Media Society.

Career: Qualified in 1981. Partner at *Peter*

Carter-Ruck & Partners 1981-88. Joined *Mishcon de Reya* as a Partner in 1988.

Personal: Born 14th November 1950. Attended Salford Grammar School 1962-9 and King's College London 1969-72. Leisure interests include rugby and contemporary literature. Lives in St Albans.

Hooper, David
See under Media & Entertainment.

House, Tim J.
Allen & Overy, London (0171) 330 3000. Qualified 1986. Partner 1992. Litigation Department. Emphasis on banking and finance litigation and professional negligence. Born 15.12.1959.

Kean, Caroline
Olswang, London (0171) 208 8888. Partner in Litigation Department.

Specialisation: Main area of practice is defamation. Includes contentious and non-contentious work and media litigation for plaintiffs, defendants and insurers, advising on copy pre-publication and broadcast, copyright and passing off. Commercial/Property litigation work also covered. Speaks frequently on BBC Radio, has appeared on BBC TV News, and specialises in private seminars to companies and organisations on issues which include media handling/damage limitation and systems. Author of 'Considerations for the Libel Defendant', International Media Law; 'Ideas in Need of Protection', Television; 'Obscenity: Have the New Kids Come of Age?', International Media Law; 'Protection Rackets', Director magazine.

Prof. Memberships: Law Society, The Media Society (Council Member).

Career: Articled *Rubinstein Callingham*. Qualified 1985. Partner 1987. Left to join *Simon Olswang & Co*. as partner designate in 1988. Partner 1989.

Personal: Born 1960. Burford School 1971-78, Newnham College, Cambridge 1978-81. College of Law, Lancaster Gate 1981-82.

Kramer, M.C.
Theodore Goddard, London (0171) 606 8855. Qualified 1969. Partner 1978. Intellectual Property Group. Main area of practice is media related litigation. Born 11.10.1940.

Martin, G.
Peter Carter-Ruck & Partners, London (0171) 353 5005.

Palca, Julia
Olswang, London (0171) 208 8888. Partner and Head of Litigation Department 1987.

Specialisation: Main area of practice is media litigation. Represents both print and broadcast defendants, and some plaintiffs, in defamation, breaches of copyright and other media and entertainment-related disputes. Also advises mainly employers on all aspects of employment law, including unfair and wrongful dismissal, industrial relations and the application of restrictive covenants. Author of 'Employment Law Checklists' and numerous articles on media and employment issues. Acted as an in-house libel litigator to a major newspaper group 1985-86. Speaks on both media and employment law issues.

Career: Qualified in 1980. Joined *Olswang* in 1986, becoming Partner and Head of Litigation Group in 1987.

Pepper, Alasdair G.T.
Peter Carter-Ruck & Partners, London (0171) 353 5005. Partner in Media Litigation Department.

Specialisation: Main area of practice is media law, with emphasis on defamation and related areas, contempt, and copyright. Also covers general litigation, and has acted for public and private companies, newspapers, journalists, charities, politicians, celebrities and public figures.

Prof. Memberships: Law Society, IBA.

Career: Qualified in 1984. Has remained with *Peter Carter-Ruck & Partners* since qualification. Became a Partner in 1986.

Personal: Born 13th May 1960. Attended Radley College, then Guildford College of Law. Leisure interests include tennis, squash, riding and walking. Lives in Farnham, Surrey.

Perrot, Robin
Goodman Derrick, London (0171) 404 0606. Qualified 1970. Partner 1973. Litigation and Media Department. Specialises in defamation, broadcasting and publishing.

Price, David
David Price & Co, London (0171) 916 9911. Qualified 1990. Sole Practitioner 1993. Principal area of practice is defamation and media law. Also handles contract and tort matters for publishing clients. Born 16.10.63.

Proudler, Geraldine
Olswang, London (0171) 208 8888. Partner specialising in media and publishing work.

Specialisation: Main area of practice is media law. including defamation, contempt of court, breach of confidence, broadcasting complaints and associated matters. Acts for both plaintiffs and defendants including national and regional newspapers and magazines.

Prof. Memberships: Law Society, Media Society.

Career: Qualified 1980. Became a partner with *Lovell White & King* (Now *Lovell White Durrant* in 1987. Joined *Olswang* as a partner 1995.

Personal: Born 2 July 1956. BA Law at Nottingham University 1974-1977. Lives in London.

Robertson, R.
Swepstone Walsh, London (0171) 404 1499.

Schilling, Keith
Schilling & Lom, London (0171) 453 2500. Senior Partner handling defamation.

Specialisation: Main area of practice is media litigation especially libel. Represents insurers, broadcasters, newspapers, other publishers and many celebrities. Other areas of practice in media litigation include copyright, breach of confidence and passing off. Frequent contributor on libel, breach of confidence and copyright in the Entertainment Law Review.

Prof. Membership: Law Society, City of Westminster Law Society.

Career: Qualified in 1981. Articled at *Wright Webb Syrett* before forming *Schilling & Lom* in 1984.

Personal: Born 25th July 1956. Attended Bromley Technical High School for Boys 1967-72, City of London Polytechnic 1980-82. Leisure interests include reading, music, chess, squash, mountain walking and windsurfing. Lives in Hampstead.

Scott-Bayfield, Julie
Mishcon De Reya, London (0171) 405 3711.

Specialisation: Main areas of practice are defamation, media and copyright law. Main Clients: publishers, newspapers, authors and scriptwriters. Involved in all aspects of defamation work for both Defendant and Plaintiff. Advises on pre-publication work as well as handling litigation including injunctions. Writes, broadcasts and lectures on defamation. Recent cases: successful defence on behalf of Penguin Books Ltd of first major infringemnt of copyright case involving a world map; successful defence of blasphemy and public order actions against Penguin Books and Salman Rushdie regarding the Satanic Verses; successful defence of journalist Neil Hyde and INS News Group Limited against action for disclosure of source by Broadmoor Hospital.

Prof. Membership: Law Society, City of London Solicitors Company, Media Society, Holborn Law Society, Committee Member on Litigation Section.

Career: Qualified 1965 Samuel Herbert Easterbrook Prize. 1966-1981 Partner, *Oswald Hickson Collier & Co.* 1982-1988 Partner, *Peter Carter-Ruck and Partners*. Joined *Mishcon de Reya* as Partner in 1988.

Personal: Member of Reform, Groucho, Royal Ocean Racing Club. Interests include sailing and walking.

Shillito, Richard A.
Oswald Hickson Collier, London (0171) 583 5333. Partner in Media Department.

Specialisation: Main area of practice is defamation. Has acted for a large number of national, regional and trade press clients and their insurers. Other areas of expertise are contempt, reporting restrictions and copyright. Contributor to the Law Society's Gazette (annual review of libel). Has spoken

at various conferences and seminars, including seminars convened by the Newspaper Society.

Career: Qualified in 1976, having joined *Oswald Hickson, Collier & Co.* in 1973. Became a Partner in 1984. Previously a trainee journalist at Yorkshire Weekly Newspaper Group Limited, 1970-72.

Personal: Born 13th March 1948. Attended Westminster School, then Magdalen College, Oxford (1970, PPE (Hons)). Leisure interests include music and sailing. Lives in London.

Skrein, Michael
See under Litigation (Commercial).

Smyth, Michael
Clifford Chance, London (0171) 600 1000. Partner. Principal area of practice is commercial litigation and public law with emphasis on media and defamation.

Stephens, Mark H.
Stephens Innocent, London (0171) 353 2000. Senior Partner.

Specialisation: Has acted in numerous cases widely reported in the national media, such as the Taylor sisters and other contempt of court by media cases; miners case concerning having the decision to close 31 pits rendered illegal; Friendly Fire Inquest; BCCI collapse; Wingrove blasphemy case; Antoni and Alison; Sonia Sutcliffe libel trial; Linda Joyce (the Princess Royal's maid accused of stealing letters); Arthur Scargill; Boggs (the US money artist); seizure of fake works concerning the Matisse, Picasso and Utrillo estates; Dali and Magritte infringement of copyright actions. Has also handled the David Wilson employment/ trade union case; Repetitive Strain Injury cases; the Sinn Fein broadcasting ban; William Pye and Hugh Tessier (sculptors for Gatwick and Stansted airports); the Hoffman case under the new Copyright Act; Borzello case (Judicial Review of the Press Complaints Commission); the League Against Cruel Sports; and many malicious falsehood, Privy Counsel, Press Complaints Commission, libel and privacy matters. Experienced in European Court of Human Rights cases. Founded one of the first English law firms in Moscow and one of the first European Economic Interest Groupings of law firms for 1992. Lectures regularly on art and law, copyright, censorship and repetitive strain syndrome. Regularly presents and contributes on the full range of current legal issues for BSB. Also regularly contributes to television, radio and print media and has appeared on many TV networks, radio services and in print in almost every UK national newspaper.

Prof. Membership: Former President of North East London Law Society, Founder of Joint Ethics Committee for the Visual Arts, British Copyright Council, Editorial Board of 'Copyright World', Honorary Solicitor to the Contemporary Arts Society and the Public Art Development Trust, Law Society (public relations officer and parliamentary liaison officer).

Career: Qualified in 1982. Founded *Stephens Innocent* in 1982.

Personal: Born 7th April 1957. Attended London University. Freeman of the City of London. Legal Director of Artlaw 1982-84. Leisure interests include scuba diving, gardening and playing with his children. Lives in London.

Stephenson, Andrew James

Peter Carter-Ruck & Partners, London (0171) 353 5005. Partner in Litigation Department.

Specialisation: Main area of practice is defamation. Includes 12 years' experience acting both for plaintiffs, including government ministers, members of Parliament and sports and music personalities, and for defendants including book, magazine and newspaper publishers and television companies. Also experienced in media law generally, including the law of contempt, copyright and passing off work. Advised and assisted on chapter on defamation law in McNae's Essential Law for Journalists (12th ed.).

Prof. Memberships: Law Society, Media Society.

Career: Joined *Peter Carter-Ruck & Partners* in 1982. Qualified 1983. Became Partner in 1986.

Personal: Born 11th September 1956. Attended University College, London 1975-78. Council of Stock Exchange 1979-81. Leisure pursuits include literature and theatre. Lives in Wokingham, Berkshire.

Stewart, P.

Swepstone Walsh, London (0171) 404 1499.

Swaffer, Patrick

Goodman Derrick, London (0171) 404 0606. Partner in Media Department.

Specialisation: Main areas of practice are broadcasting and publishing. Includes pre- and post-publication advice on defamation, confidence and copyright, rights exploitation, contractual issues and regulatory advice for the broadcasting industry.

Career: Joined *Goodman Derrick* in 1974. Qualified 1976. Became Partner in 1979 in Media Department.

Personal: Born 12th February 1951. Lives in London.

Sykes, Richard C.M.

Richard C.M. Sykes, London (0171) 235 2508.

Tait, Nigel G.T.M.

Peter Carter-Ruck & Partners, London (0171) 353 5005. Partner in Media Department.

Specialisation: Main area of practice is media law, acting for plaintiffs and defendants and giving pre-publication advice. Cases of interest include Beta Construction v. Channel

4 (award of £568,000: highest ever libel award paid to a company); Vladimir Telnikoff v. Vladimir Matusevitch (first libel case to go to House of Lords for over a decade. Award of £240,000); Jack Slipper v BBC (£50,000 damages). A leading case on liability for republication); Jonathan Hunt (aged 6) v. The Sun (settlement of £35,000 plus costs to mother and son. Youngest ever libel plaintiff); Victor Kiam v. Sunday Times (£45,000 damages). Also undertakes personal injury work, acting for plaintiffs (highest award £755,000). Contributor to 'Carter-Ruck on Libel and Slander', 4th edition. Regular lecturer on media law and defamation. Member of Law Society Privacy and Defamation working committees.

Prof. Membership: Law Society. International Bar Association.

Career: Qualified in 1988, having joined *Peter Carter-Ruck and Partners* in 1986. Became a Partner in 1990.

Personal: Born 5th April 1963. Attended Nottingham University 1981-84. Leisure interests include family and squash. Lives in Clapham, London.

Taylor, Barton

Russell Jones & Walker, London (0171) 837 2808. Partner and Head of Commercial Litigation Department.

Specialisation: Defamation, acting only for Plaintiffs. Has acted successfully against all national daily and most Sunday newspapers and against most magazine and book publishers, and TV companies. Other area of practice is commercial litigation including in particular, professional negligence.

Prof. Membership: Law Society.

Career: Qualified 1971, joining *Russell Jones & Walker* as a Partner in 1977.

Personal: Born 3rd August 1944. Attended Hereford Cathedral School. Leisure interests include golf, tennis, family and friends.

REGIONS

Harris, Gordon D.
See under Franchising.

Hendron, James
Johns Elliot, Belfast (01232) 326881.

Jaffa, Anthony R.
Foot & Bowden, Plymouth (01752) 675000. Qualified 1980. Partner 1987. Handles libel, contempt of court and related law for media clients.

Knight, Matthew
Knights, Tunbridge Wells (01892) 537311. Qualified 1982. Senior Partner 1994. Litigation Department. Main area of practice is defamation. Also handles Judicial Review, crime and trespass. Born 2.4.1957.

Lax, Peter

Keely Smith & Jobson, Lichfield (01543) 414222. Partner in Commercial Litigation Department.

Specialisation: Main areas of practice are commercial litigation and defamation. Gives defamation advice particularly for newspaper publishers at a pre-publication stage. Handles construction and engineering litigation. Also insolvency litigation, giving advice to receivers, liquidators and company directors. Acted in the identification of Roy Cornes (accused of infecting women with HIV) and the reporting of threats by Birmingham City Football Club. Has addressed Society of Practitioners in Insolvency, Midlands Association of Insolvency Lawyers, Midlands Guild of Newspaper Editors.

Career: Qualified in 1982. Worked with *Duggan Lea & Co.* 1980-85, then *Pinsent & Co.* 1985-93, from 1988 as a Partner. Joined *Keely Smith & Jobson* in 1993 as Joint Head of Commercial Litigation Department.

Personal: Born 27th March 1958. Attended Barnard Castle School 1969-75, then Durham University 1976-79. Leisure interests include bridge and Birmingham Canal Society Work Parties. Lives in Lichfield.

Manley, Mark J.

Brabner Holden Banks Wilson, Liverpool (0151) 236 5821. Qualified 1987. Partner 1992. Specialises in defamation, acting for newspapers, radio stations, broadcasters and publishers.

Spring, M. Paul
Cleaver Fulton & Rankin, Belfast (01232) 243141.

Ticehurst, David K.
See under Employment Law.

Tweed, Paul
Johnsons, Belfast (01232) 240183.

ECCLESIASTICAL

THIS section includes details of firms and individuals with expertise in religious law of various denominations, although, strictly speaking, the term 'ecclesiastical law' refers exclusively to the law of the Church of England – the only church whose internal rules possess the status of law. Many of the lawyers listed below advise on Church of England matters but firms who regularly advise other religous denominations including Roman Catholic, Baptist and Methodist, are also covered in this section.

LONDON

Lee Bolton & Lee has a strong reputation in the field, having acted for the Church of England for many years. Peter Beesley and Nick Richens carry out employment and property as well as purely ecclesiastical and disciplinary work for the Dioceses of Canterbury, Hereford, Guildford and Ely. The former is a contributor to volume 13 of the 'Encyclopaedia of Forms and Precedents: Ecclesiastical Law.'

HIGHLY REGARDED – LONDON

LEE BOLTON & LEE	WINCKWORTH & PEMBERTON
ELLIS WOOD	WITHAM WELD
CAMERONS	POTHECARY & BARRATT
WANSBROUGHS WILLEY HARGRAVE	

Winckworth & Pemberton enjoy an equally strong reputation in the area, and also act for the Church of England, advising the Archbishop of Canterbury, and the bishops of London, Leicester, Rochester, Southwark, Oxford and Chelmsford, as well as the Dean and Chapter of St Pauls. David Faull, Paul Morris, Roger Filton and Michael Thatcher are all specialists, the latter offering a particular expertise in Church education and school law. The firm also advises on Roman Catholic law.

LEADING INDIVIDUALS – LONDON

Peter Frederick Barton Beesley	*Lee Bolton & Lee*
David Faull	*Winckworth & Pemberton*
Roger Filton	*Winckworth & Pemberton*
Paul C.E. Morris	*Winckworth & Pemberton*
N.J. Richens	*Lee Bolton & Lee*
Michael C. Thatcher	*Winckworth & Pemberton*
Nicolas J. Bellord	*Witham Weld*
Simon P.J. Howell	*Ellis Wood*

Nicolas Bellord at *Witham Weld* practises in relation to a range of denominations including Roman Catholic, Anglican, Orthodox and Eastern European, whilst Simon Howell at *Ellis Wood* is known for his work for the Roman Catholic Church.

SOUTH EAST

Winckworth & Pemberton are highly respected in this area. Dr Frank Robson, John Rees and Brian Hood cover all aspects of the field, the latter acting as the Registrar of the Diocese of Chelmsford. The firm provides the provincial registry for the Archbishop of Canterbury and registry for the Diocese of Oxford as well as dealing with property work for the Diocese of Rochester. The firm also acts as legal

HIGHLY REGARDED – SOUTH EAST

BRUTTON & CO *Portsmouth*	CLAYTONS *Luton*
THOMAS EGGAR VERRALL BOWLES *Chichester*	WHITE & BOWKER *Winchester*
WINCKWORTH & PEMBERTON *Chelmsford*	
CAMERONS *Harrow*	DONNE MILEHAM & HADDOCK *Brighton*
FURLEY PAGE FIELDING & BARTON *Canterbury*	GODWIN BREMRIDGE & CLIFTON *Winchester*
MARTIN TOLHURST PARTNERSHIP *Gravesend*	RODGERS HORSLEY WHITEMANS *Guildford*

secretary to the Bishop of Oxford. David Cheetham of *Claytons* provides the registry for the Diocese of St Albans, whilst Peter White at *White & Bowker* performs the same function in Winchester as well as acting for the Church of England as a legal secretary. Peter White also has expertise in the field of Methodist property. Clifford Hodgetts at

LEADING INDIVIDUALS – SOUTH EAST

David N. Cheetham	*Claytons*
Clifford L. Hodgetts	*Thomas Eggar Verrall Bowles*
Brian J. Hood	*Winckworth & Pemberton*
John Rees	*Winckworth & Pemberton*
Frank E. Robson	*Winckworth & Pemberton*
Peter M. White	*White & Bowker*
Owen Woodfield	*Martin Tolhurst Partnership*

Thomas Eggar Verall Bowles is highly regarded and acts for the Dean and Chapter of Westminster and for the Diocese of Chichester. Other notable firms include *Brutton & Co,* which acts as legal secretary for the Church of England and *Martin Tolhurst Partnership.* Owen Woodfield at the latter firm has a particularly strong reputation in the field. *Rodgers Horsley Whitemans* act for the Russian Orthodox Church.

SOUTH WEST & WALES

Firms which act for the Church of England in this region include *Harris & Harris, Osborne Clarke,* and *Michelmores* where Richard Wheeler is highly regarded for his expertise. *Parker Bullen* in Salisbury are well-known.

Among firms acting for the Roman Catholic Church, the most prominent are *Stone King & Wardle,* where Michael

HIGHLY REGARDED – SOUTH WEST & WALES

ANSTEY SARGENT & PROBERT	*Exeter*	HARRIS & HARRIS	*Wells*
HUGH JAMES JONES & JENKINS	*Cardiff*	MICHELMORES	*Exeter*
OSBORNE CLARKE	*Bristol*	PARKER BULLEN	*Salisbury*
STONE KING & WARDLE	*Bath*	TOZERS	*Exeter*

King has an established reputation, and *Tozers* where Richard King has been highly recommended for his expertise. Both firms are members of the executive committee of the Conference of Solicitors acting for Catholic dioceses and religious orders.

LEADING INDIVIDUALS – SOUTH WEST & WALES

A. Michael H. King	*Stone King & Wardle*
A. Richard G. King	*Tozers*
Richard K. Wheeler	*Michelmores*

In Wales, *Hugh James Jones & Jenkins* acts for several churches including the Baptist, Methodist and the Presbyterian Church of Wales.

MIDLANDS

All the firms listed either work for their local diocese or advise church clients, particularly on property and finance matters.

HIGHLY REGARDED – MIDLANDS

ANTHONY COLLINS	*Birmingham*	EDWARDS GELDARD	*Derby*
GATELEY WAREING	*Birmingham*	MANBY & STEWARD	*Wolverhampton*
MARTINEAU JOHNSON	*Birmingham*		
OWSTONS	*Leicester*	ROTHERAS	*Nottingham*

Martineau Johnson, Gateley Wareing, Manby & Steward and *Anthony Collins* all enjoy excellent reputations for their ecclesiastical work. Hugh Carslake at *Martineau Johnson* has an excellent reputation amongst his peers and is the Registrar of the Diocese of Birmingham. Stephen Gateley at *Gateley Wareing* is also well regarded and his workload includes acting for Roman Catholic Diocese.

LEADING INDIVIDUALS – MIDLANDS

James S. Battie	*Edwards Geldard*
Hugh Carslake	*Martineau Johnson*
Stephen Gateley	*Gateley Wareing*

Also recommended is James Battie at *Edwards Geldard* who deals with all aspects of ecclesiastical work including faculties and conveyancing.

EAST ANGLIA

Both firms listed below act for their local Diocesan registry. *Leeds Day* deals with faculties, including memorials in churchyards and handles general ecclesiastical matters

HIGHLY REGARDED – EAST ANGLIA

LEEDS DAY	*Sandy*	MILLS & REEVE	*Norwich*

including common and special marriage licences. One partner is registrar of the Diocese of Ely. *Mills & Reeve* handle all aspects of ecclesiastical law with particular emphasis on property work and one partner at the firm is registrar of the Diocese of Norwich.

NORTH WEST

In the North West, the firms listed are known to have strong connections with their local diocese. Alan MacAllester at *Birch Cullimore* is regarded as the pre-eminent practitioner in the region. He advises Bishops, Archdeacons, Diocesan

HIGHLY REGARDED – NORTH WEST

BIRCH CULLIMORE	*Chester*		
COBBETT LEAK ALMOND	*Manchester*	DAVIES WALLIS FOYSTER	*Liverpool*
HILL DICKINSON DAVIS CAMPBELL		OSWALD GOODIER & CO	*Preston*
Liverpool			

Board of Finance and Committees in matters of ecclesiastical law and canon law of the Church of England, as well as general points of law. He also acts as Registrar of the Diocese of Chester. Also recommended are *Cobbett Leak Almond* and *Davies Wallis Foyster* which advises the Church of England and *Hill Dickinson Davis Campbell* and *Oswald Goodier & Co* which acts on behalf of the Roman Catholic Church.

LEADING INDIVIDUALS – NORTH WEST

Alan K. McAllester	*Birch Cullimore*

NORTH EAST

Lionel Lennox of *Denison Till* emerges as the pre-eminent practitioner in the North East. He is the Diocesan Registrar of York and acting Legal Secretary to the Archbishop of York.

LEADING FIRMS – NORTH EAST

DENISON TILL	*York*

Other notable practitioners in the area who have been recommended for their expertise include Jeremy Mackrell at *Gordons Wright & Wright,* and Linda Box at *Dixon Coles & Gill,* of which both firms act for the Church of England and

HIGHLY REGARDED – NORTH EAST

GRAYS	*York*	RODGERS & HOWE	*Sheffield*
DIXON, COLES & GILL	*Wakefield*	GORDONS WRIGHT & WRIGHT	*Bradford*

the Methodist Church. *Rodgers & Howe,* which act for the Church of England, undertake property work for the Diocesan Registrar in Sheffield.

LEADING INDIVIDUALS – NORTH EAST

L. Lennox	*Denison Till*
L.M. Box	*Dixon, Coles & Gill*
Jeremy G.H. Mackrell	*Gordons Wright & Wright*

In all the tables the names in each group are listed alphabetically.

LEADERS IN ECCLESIASTICAL

LONDON

Beesley, Peter Frederick Barton
Lee Bolton & Lee, London (0171) 222 5381. Partner in Ecclesiastical Education and Charity Department.

Specialisation: Particular expertise in Church of England work. Chapter Clerk of St Alban's Cathedral; Joint Registrar of the Diocese of Ely; Registrar of the Diocese of Guildford; Joint Registrar of the Diocese of Hereford; Registrar of the Faculty Office of the Archbishop of Canterbury; Solicitor to the National Society; and to the Board of Education of the General Synod. Also handles education and charity work. Registrar of the Woodard Corporation. Joint Contributor to Volume 13 'Encyclopaedia of Forms and Precedents- Ecclesiastical Law'. Speaker at and promoter of several conferences and seminars on ecclesiastical charity and education matters.

Prof. Membership: Law Society, City of Westminster Law Society (ex-President), Ecclesiastical Law Association, Ecclesiastical Law Society.

Career: Qualified 1967. Joined *Lee Bolton & Lee* in 1968, becoming a Partner in 1969.

Personal: Born 30th April 1943. Attended Kings School Worcester, then Exeter University 1961-64 and College of Law 1964-65. Lives in London.

Bellord, Nicolas J.
Witham Weld, London (0171) 821 8211. Partner in Tax and Trusts Department.

Specialisation: Main area of practice is charities, advising on all aspects of the law with particular emphasis on religious charities including Roman Catholic, Anglican, Orthodox and Eastern European. Other area of practice is computer law: founder member and secretary of Society for Computers and the Law, 1975-84. Author of 'Computer Science and Law' (CUP 1980) and 'Computers for Lawyers' (Sinclair Browne 1983).

Prof. Memberships: Law Society, Society for Computers and the Law. British Cybernetics Society.

Career: Qualified 1963. Became a Partner in 1967. UK representative of the Committee of Experts on Legal Data Processing, Council of Europe, 1980-84.

Personal: Born 24th April 1938. Attended Downside School 1952-54, Fribourg University in Switzerland 1954-57, then Oxford 1957-60. Leisure interests include running a vineyard in Portugal. Lives near Haywards Heath.

Faull, David
Winckworth & Pemberton (incorporating Sherwood & Co), London (0171) 593 5000. Qualified 1954. Consultant 1994. Ecclesiastical Department.

Handles a mixture of ecclesiastical and housing work. Born 25.2.1929.

Filton, Roger
Winckworth & Pemberton (incorporating Sherwood & Co), London (0171) 593 5000.

Howell, Simon P.J.
Ellis Wood, London (0171) 242 1194.

Specialisation: Partner specialising in charity law. Practice covers both charitable trusts and property related work. Acts for major national Catholic charities, religious orders and dioceses. Also advises schools and colleges, mainly in the voluntary (Roman Catholic) sector. Has three times addressed conferences of Catholic Religious Orders on charity related matters.

Prof. Membership: The Charity Law Association; Conference of Solicitors Acting for Catholic Dioceses and Religious Orders (previously Secretary for 10 years).

Career: Qualified 1971. Assistant solicitor, Arnold Fooks Chadwick, 1972-76. Partner, Ellis Wood since 1976. Since 1989 a director of a medium size property investment company.

Personal: Educated at Cranleigh School, Surrey and the College of Law, Guildford. Previously Ward Clerk to a Ward in the City of London, and currently Clerk to a small City charity. Born 22nd February 1948. Lives near Bromley.

Morris, Paul C.E.
Winckworth & Pemberton (incorporating Sherwood & Co), London (0171) 593 5000. Partner and Head of Ecclesiastical and Education Law Department.

Specialisation: Head of Department since 1987; previously Joint Head of Institutional Property Department 1984-87, with expertise in commercial property law. Has acted in controversial cases involving clergy discipline, re-ordering of church buildings and re-development of redundant churches and church land.

Prof. Membership: Law Society, City of Westminster Law Society, Ecclesiastical Law Society, Ecclesiastical Law Association.

Career: Qualified in 1978. Joined *Winckworth & Pemberton* in 1978, becoming a Partner in 1981. Registrar and Bishop's Legal Secretary, Diocese of Southwark. Joint Registrar, Diocese of Leicester. Solicitor to Southwark Diocesan Board of Finance.

Personal: Born 21st September 1950. Attended Westminster Abbey Choir School 1960-64, Westminster School 1964-68 and UCNW Bangor 1968-72. Leisure interests include music and the family. Lives in West London and Charlbury, Oxfordshire.

Richens, N.J.
Lee Bolton & Lee, London (0171) 222 5381. Qualified 1985.

Thatcher, Michael C.
See under Education.

REGIONS

Battie, James S.
Edwards Geldard, Derby (01332) 31631.

Box, L.M.
Dixon, Coles & Gill, Wakefield (01924) 373467.

Carslake, Hugh
Martineau Johnson, Birmingham (0121) 200 3300. Qualified 1966. Partner 1974. Head of Private Client Department. Specialist in estate planning and ecclesiastical law. Born 15.11.1946.

Cheetham, David N.
Claytons, St. Albans (01727) 865765. Qualified 1971. Partner 1972. Senior Partner 1985. Ecclesiastical, Charity and General Property Department.

Gateley, Stephen
See under Charities.

Hodgetts, Clifford L.
Thomas Eggar Verrall Bowles, Chichester (01243) 786111. Also at Worthing and Horsham. Senior Partner.

Specialisation: Principal area of practice covers ecclesiastical and charities work. Registrar of the Diocese of Chichester and Legal Secretary to the Bishop of Chichester. Clerk to the Dean and Chapter of Chichester and its associated charities. Also acts as legal adviser to the Doam and Charter of Westminster. Other main area of work is private client and commercial conveyancing. Recent article in Law Society Gazette relating to Practise Rule 5- Hived Off Businesses.

Prof. Membership: Ecclesiastical Law Association, Law Society, Ecclesiastical Law Society.

Career: Qualified 1958. Joined *Thomas Eggar Verrall Bowles* in 1960, became a Partner in 1961, and Senior Partner in 1986. Director of Thesis- investment management company and financial advisors (1989).

Personal: Born 12 May 1934. Attended Bristol University 1953-56. Deputy Lieutenant of West Sussex. Trustee of Chichester Festival Theatre Ltd (1989). Governor of Westbourne House School Educational Trust. Leisure pursuits include fishing, tennis, golf, shooting, travel. Member of MCC. Lives in Graffham.

Hood, Brian J.

Winckworth & Pemberton (incorporating Sherwood & Co), Chelmsford. Qualified 1976. Partner 1977. Ecclesiastical Department (Chelmsford). Specialises in all aspects of ecclesiastical law. Born 8.2.1943.

King, A. Michael H.

See under Charities.

King, A. Richard G.

See under Charities.

Lennox, L.

Denison Till, York (01904) 611411. Qualified 1973. Partner 1987. Main area of practice is ecclesiastical law. Also handles town and country planning and charity law; notary public. Registrar of the Province and Diocese of York.

Mackrell, Jeremy G.H.

Gordons Wright & Wright, Bradford (01274) 733771.

McAllester, Alan K.

Birch Cullimore, Chester (01244) 321066. Partner and Diocesan Registrar of the Diocese of Chester.

Specialisation: Ecclesiastical law. Advises Bishop, Archdeacons, Diocesan Board of Finance and Committees in matters of ecclesiastical law and canon law of the Church of England and general points of law. Also deals with commercial property and charity law matters. Appointed Diocesan Registrar of the Diocese of Chester in 1983.

Prof. Membership: Law Society, Justice, Ecclesiastical Law Society, Ecclesiastical Law Association.

Career: Joined *Birch Cullimore* in 1964. Qualified in 1968 and became a Partner in 1972.

Personal: Born 21st August 1942. Attended Alsop High School, Liverpool to 1961, then St. Peter's College, Oxford 1961-64. Previously Chairman of Greater Merseyside Area Committee of NACAB, Chairman of Chester CAB Management Committee, Founder Vice Chairman of Chester Aid to the Homeless and Founder Chairman of Chester Womens Aid. Leisure pursuits include fly fishing, gardening and Scottish country dancing. Lives in Chester.

Rees, John

Winckworth & Pemberton (incorporating Sherwood & Co), Oxford (01865) 241974. Partner in Ecclesiastical, Education and Charities Department.

Specialisation: Main area of practice is ecclesiastical law. Deputy Registrar, Diocese of Oxford. Advises Province of Canterbury on Archbishop's overseas jurisdictions. Also handles education work: Oxford Diocesan Board of Education and Oxford Diocesan Education Services Limited. Has expertise with grant-maintained schools. Handled 1994 appeal to Court of Arches re St Luke Maidstone, the first appeal under the Care of Churches and Ecclesiastical Jurisdiction Measure 1991; mausolea disputes; and the constitution of the new province of Korea. Author of 'Alternative Episcopal Oversight' in Watts, 'Through a Glass' (Gracewing 1993) and 'Church and Housing' (1994).

Prof. Membership: Ecclesiastical Law Association, Ecclesiastical Law Society, Education Law Advisory Service.

Career: Qualified in 1976. Joined *Winckworth & Pemberton* in 1986, becoming a Partner in 1988.

Personal: Born 21st April 1951. Holds an LLB (So'ton 1972), MA (Oxon 1984) and MPhil (Leeds 1984). Clergyman (Church of England, Non-Stipendiary); part-time lecturer of Oxford Ministry Course. Leisure interests include photography and cycling. Lives in Oxford.

Robson, Frank E.

Winckworth & Pemberton (incorporating Sherwood & Co), Oxford (01865) 241974. Partner in Ecclesiastical Department.

Specialisation: Main area of practice is ecclesiastical law. Registrar to Diocese of Oxford since 1970; Registrar to Province of Canterbury and legal adviser to the Archbishop since 1982; Vice-Chairman of Legal Advisory Commission of the General Synod. Also handles education law: legal adviser to Oxford Diocesan Board of Education.

Prof. Membership: Ecclesiastical Law Association (Chairman 1984-86), Ecclesiastical Law Society.

Career: Qualified 1954. Joined *Winckworth & Pemberton* in 1958, becoming a Partner in 1960 and Senior Partner in 1990.

Personal: Born 14th December 1931. Attended Selwyn College, Cambridge 1954-57. Leisure interests include supporting Oxford United, fell walking and travel. Lives in Stanton St. John, Oxford.

Wheeler, Richard K.

Michelmores, Exeter (01392) 436244.

White, Peter M.

White & Bowker, Winchester (01962) 844440. Qualified 1970. Partner 1974. Ecclesiastical Law and Residential Property Department. Appointed Notary Public. Born 28.8.1945.

Woodfield, Owen

Martin Tolhurst Partnership, Rochester (01634) 843231.

EDITORIAL POLICY

Our policy is to identify leading practitioners entirely on merit. It is not possible to buy a place in our biographical lists: inclusion is based on a practitioner's expertise and professional reputation. The same applies to the lists of recommended law-firms and sets of chambers.

Enormous effort has been invested by our ten-strong research team (mainly solicitors and barristers) in canvassing recommendations and identifying leaders. We are confident in the overall accuracy of the results. However, mistakes and omissions are inevitable, and if readers have any suggestions regarding listings or rankings we should be very pleased to hear from them.

The lists will be revised on the basis of fresh research every year.

EDUCATION

LONDON

Of the firms that advise educational institutions, *Eversheds* and *Winckworth & Pemberton* emerge as the leading practices. The recent merger of *Eversheds* with *Jaques & Lewis* has combined the expertise of John Hall, who has a national

LEADING FIRMS – LONDON	
EVERSHEDS	EVERSHEDS
WINCKWORTH & PEMBERTON	
TEACHER STERN SELBY	
BEACHCROFT STANLEYS	BENNETT TAYLOR TYRRELL
LEE BOLTON & LEE	REYNOLDS PORTER CHAMBERLAIN
WITHAM WELD	

reputation, with that of John Glasson, who has considerable experience in this field. The firm offers a broad range of expertise, particularly in advising universities and colleges and their representative bodies. The team regularly offers advice on governance and constitutional issues, management and development of property assets, employment matters, purchaser and provider issues, judical review and various specialist education issues for over 100 universities and colleges. The team headed by John Hall, a contributor to "Education and the Law", has a wealth of experience, includes John Glasson who is company secretary for the Association of Colleges and acted in the winding up of the Inner London Education Authority, and, David Hetherington who advises the educational sector in relation to employment matters.

The established education practice at *Winckworth & Pemberton,* where Michael Thatcher heads the department, has grown significantly over the last three years, acting for Roman Catholic authorities, universities, higher & further education institutions and grant-maintained schools as well as commercial and charitable organisations which are involved in the education sector. Michael Thatcher has acted in various judicial reviews of Appeal Committee decisions and on behalf of the Commission for Racial Equality proceedings against Governors. He also speaks at conferences on various aspects of education law. Christopher Tipping, who heads the litigation department at the firm, is also well known for his work in the field.

Also highly regarded nationally is *Teacher Stern Selby,* with particular expertise in acting on behalf of students and parents and undertaking judicial review work. The firm handles cases against both state and public schools on a variety of matters including admissions, exclusions and school closures. The team also acts for voluntary associations, charities

and schools, and Jack Rabinowicz at the firm has an excellent reputation for such work. He is currently Chair of the Education Law Association and a member of the Council of Registration of Schools teaching Dyslexia.

Other firms with strong reputations in the area include *Reynolds Porter Chamberlain, Lee Bolton & Lee, Beachcroft Stanleys, Bennett Taylor Tyrrell* and *Witham Weld. Reynolds Porter Chamberlain* advise both independent and grant maintained schools on a whole range of legal issues including statutory controls and employment matters, and clients include teachers, unions and heads' associations.

Lee Bolton & Lee has a well regarded department comprising four partners which advises on all matters from establishing a new school to day-to-day operational and employment matters. The department is active in the grant-maintained sector advising school governors and trustees. *Beachcroft Stanleys* is particularly well regarded for handling funding matters on behalf of higher and further education institutions, and acts for both the Higher Education Funding Council for England and the Further Education Funding Council for England.

HIGHLY REGARDED – LONDON	
ALLEN & OVERY	NORTON ROSE
CHARLES RUSSELL	LAWFORD & CO
NABARRO NATHANSON	WOODROFFES

At *Bennett Taylor Tyrrell,* Richard Gold has been recommended for his expertise in the field, and the firm acts for schools and parents in all aspects of education law. Also recommended is *Witham Weld* which advises schools and colleges, their governors and trustees in matters of concern to staff, students and parents. Peter Hawthorne at the firm has acted in judicial reviews of pupil exclusions, governor removal, admission policies of Roman Catholic state maintained schools and religious special educational needs.

LEADING INDIVIDUALS – LONDON
John T. Hall *Eversheds*
Jack Rabinowicz *Teacher Stern Selby*
Richard Gold *Bennett Taylor Tyrrell*
Michael C. Thatcher *Winckworth & Pemberton*
John Glasson *Eversheds*
Peter J.M. Hawthorne *Witham Weld*
David Hetherington *Eversheds*
Christopher J. Tipping *Winckworth & Pemberton*

SOUTH EAST

Peter Liell, a sole practitioner, emerges as the leading specialist in the region, concentrating exclusively in the field of education law. He is widely acknowledged as the national expert in the field, with experience in school admissions, exclusion, transport, special needs and school closure. As a member of the executive committee of the Education Law Association, he edits the newsletter, and is often involved in giving seminars. As well as handling a number of high profile cases in the area, he also acts as a consultant to the firm *Winkworth & Pemberton*.

LEADING FIRMS – SOUTH EAST	
PETER LIELL *Oxford*	
THOMAS EGGAR VERRALL BOWLES *Chichester*	WOLLASTONS *Chelmsford*

Other well regarded firms include *Thomas Eggar Verrall Bowles* and *ollastons*. *Thomas Eggar Verrall Bowles* handles all aspects of education law, which includes acting for schools and colleges and undertaking cases concerning governors' liability. *Wollastons,* where Nicholas Cook is highly regarded, has particular expertise in the Education Reform Act and the Further and Higher Education Act. The firm acts primarily for grant maintained schools, and is a member of Educational Law Focus- a national group of independent solicitors advising higher and further education institutions.

HIGHLY REGARDED – SOUTH EAST	
GEPP & SONS *Chelmsford*	MORRELL PEEL & GAMLEN *Oxford*
WINCKWORTH & PEMBERTON *Chelmsford*	

Morrell Peel & Gamlen, based in Oxford, also has an established reputation in the field, and has for many years advised a major University and various schools, colleges and other educational establishments. The firm has also taken commissions from other universities, scientific research associations and further education colleges.

LEADING INDIVIDUALS – SOUTH EAST
Peter M. Liell *Peter Liell*
Nicholas D. Cook *Wollastons*

SOUTH WEST & WALES

Veale Wasbrough has an excellent reputation for its legal services to independent schools, serving over 400, and acts for the Governing Bodies Association, the Independent Schools Bursars Association and the Independent Association of Preparatory Schools. The team consists of seven partners who represent the University of Bristol. Robert Boyd, who is in charge of the Schools Unit and Christopher Southam, who advises on employment matters, both have substantial experience in the field.

LEADING FIRMS – SOUTH WEST & WALES	
HUGH JAMES JONES & JENKINS *Cardiff*	MICHELMORES *Exeter*
TOZERS *Exeter*	VEALE WASBROUGH *Bristol*

In Exeter, Michelmores act for a number of universities, schools and colleges, particularly in the context of property and finance-related work. They are founders of Education Law Focus. Malcolm Dickinson, who has an established reputation in the field, has been involved in raising significant sums of money from banks and other lenders for educational institutions.

HIGHLY REGARDED – SOUTH WEST & WALES	
A.E. SMITH & SON *Stroud*	STONE KING & WARDLE *Bath*
BOND PEARCE *Plymouth*	
MACFARLANE GUY *Bath*	STEELE RAYMOND *Bournemouth*

Tozers in Plymouth also have an active education practice, acting on behalf of voluntary aided, grant maintained and independent schools. The firm recently defended a High Court action brought by parents seeking to prevent the closure of a school.

LEADING INDIVIDUALS – SOUTH WEST & WALES
Robert P. Boyd *Veale Wasbrough*
Malcolm K. Dickinson *Michelmores*
Michael L.N. Jones *Hugh James Jones & Jenkins*
R.J. Love *A.E. Smith & Son*
Christopher A. Southam *Veale Wasbrough*

In Wales, *Hugh James Jones & Jenkins* has been recommended for its expertise in the field, acting mainly for pupils, parents and school governors. The department has particular strength in handling constitutional issues, claims against Local Education Authorities, and work relating to schools for the mentally disabled. Michael Jones at the firm has extensive knowledge in the field, particularly on Welsh language education.

MIDLANDS

Shakespeares are recommended for their experience in contractual, property and employment related matters for higher and further education institutions and grant maintained schools. The firm is a member of 'Education Law Focus' and Paul Pharoah who heads the team, recently acted in a high profile dispute over assets between a grant maintained school and local education authority.

The education team at *Martineau Johnson,* headed by Simon Arrowsmith, acts for eight universities and 17 further education corporations, independent and grant maintained schools, an Examination Board and a Diocesan Education

Council. Simon Arrowsmith deals with a variety of legal issues confronting educational organisations, from legisative reform and commercial funding to personnel questions involving students and staff.

LEADING FIRMS – MIDLANDS	
EVERSHEDS *Nottingham*	MARTINEAU JOHNSON *Birmingham*
SHAKESPEARES *Birmingham*	
DIBB LUPTON BROOMHEAD *Birmingham*	WRAGGE & CO *Birmingham*

In Nottingham, *Eversheds'* education unit headed by Nigel Sternberg handles such matters as employment issues, grants, governors' liability and joint ventures. The firm acts for over

HIGHLY REGARDED – MIDLANDS
BAND HATTON AND CO *Coventry*

30 further education colleges and Nottingham Trent University, and has developed an expertise in private finance initiatives for schools. Nigel Sternberg is Chair of the National Education Group within *Eversheds*.

LEADING INDIVIDUALS – MIDLANDS
Simon Arrowsmith *Martineau Johnson*
Paul Pharaoh *Shakespeares*
Nigel P. Sternberg *Eversheds*

EAST ANGLIA

Mills & Reeve has a substantial education practice and acts for the majority of the Cambridge colleges. Duncan Ogilvy, at the firm's Cambridge office, has a national reputation for his expertise in this area of law.

LEADING FIRMS – EAST ANGLIA	
EVERSHEDS *Norwich*	MILLS & REEVE *Norwich*

In Ipswich, *Eversheds'* multidisciplinary team acts for higher and further education institutions in North London, Herfordshire, Bedfordshire and the East Anglian counties of

HIGHLY REGARDED – EAST ANGLIA	
BIRKETTS *Ipswich*	HUNT & COOMBS *Peterborough*

Norfolk, Suffolk, Cambridgeshire and Essex. In addition, the firm acts for a number of grant maintained schools throughout the region and as part of *Eversheds* nationwide, provide a legal helpline to the Grant Maintained School Centre.

LEADING INDIVIDUALS – EAST ANGLIA
Philip W. George *Birketts*
Duncan M. Ogilvy *Mills & Reeve*

In all the tables the names in each group are listed alphabetically.

NORTH WEST

Eversheds advises about 20 colleges of further education, and undertakes work for higher education institutions and

LEADING FIRMS – NORTH WEST	
ADDLESHAW SONS & LATHAM *Manchester*	ALSOP WILKINSON *Liverpool*
EVERSHEDS *Manchester*	

universities. It also acts for grant-maintained schools, and participates in the *Eversheds* legal helpline. Advising opt-out schools, it handles such matters as ultravires issues, funding, employment, disciplinary and contractual matters. John Boordman is highly recommended.

HIGHLY REGARDED – NORTH WEST
BURNETTS *Carlisle*

Other firms in the region renowned for their expertise include *Alsop Wilkinson* and *Addleshaw Sons & Latham*. Alsop Wilkinson offers specialist advice to a number of education institutitions including the University of Liverpool and the Liverpool Institute of Performing Arts. In addition, the firm handles a large amount of property development for further education colleges and former polytechnics seeking to expand.

LEADING INDIVIDUALS – NORTH WEST
John Boardman *Eversheds*

Addleshaw Sons & Latham has considerable experience in education work and undertakes corporate and constitutional advice to further and higher education bodies.

NORTH EAST

In Leeds, *Eversheds* attracts work from numerous colleges of further and higher education, including Bradford & Ilkley

LEADING FIRMS – NORTH EAST	
EVERSHEDS *Leeds*	EVERSHEDS *Newcastle*
FORD AND WARREN *Leeds*	

Community College, North Hertfordshire College and Grimsby College of Technology and Arts. A particular speciality of the firm is the provision of advice on funding including loans to educational bodies in excess of £35 million. *Eversheds* in Newcastle act for 13 sixth form and further education colleges in the North East, advising particularly on education law and governance matters.

HIGHLY REGARDED – NORTH EAST
GRAYS *York*

Ford & Warren has also been recommended for its expertise, and Edward Brown at the firm is particularly highly regarded. The firm works closely with independent, grant maintained, and special needs schools.

LEADING INDIVIDUALS – NORTH EAST

David Ansbro	*Eversheds*
Edward V. Brown	*Ford and Warren*

SCOTLAND

Campbell Smith WS has specific expertise in relation to children with special educational needs, and is able to provide assistance to parents who are having difficulty in acquiring Records of Needs for their children and the placing of them

LEADING FIRMS – SCOTLAND

CAMPBELL SMITH WS *Edinburgh*

at special schools. The firm has handled a number of high profile cases against regional councils on behalf of pupils, including Aitken v Tayside Regional Council and Kinsman v Tayside Regional Council.

LEADERS IN EDUCATION

LONDON

Glasson, John
See under Administrative & Public Law.

Gold, Richard
Bennett Taylor Tyrrell, London (0171) 323 1100. Partner specialising in education work.

Specialisation: Education Law. Acts for schools and parents in all aspects of education law. Also covers property and private client work, including commercial and residential property matters , wills and trusts. Addressed conferences and seminars organised by IBC and Education Law Association and others.

Prof. Memberships: Education Law Association (ELAS) (Member of Executive Committee and Treasurer).

Career: Qualified 1968. Joined *Bennett Taylor Tyrrell* in 1990 as a Partner.

Personal: Born 21st October 1941. Attended William Ellis School 1953-61, then Trinity College, Cambridge 1961-65. Chair of Governors, William Ellis School 1978-87. Chair of Trustees, William Ellis School 1978-present. Chair of Governors, Ravenscroft School 1994-present. Govenor, Jewish Free School 1994-present. Leisure pursuits include music, theatre, reading and sport.

Hall, John T.
Eversheds, London (0171) 919 4500. Partner in Education Law Department.

Specialisation: Work includes governance, the Education Acts, employment law, industrial relations, judicial review, admissions, commercial law, funding and asset management. Clients include in excess of one hundred education institutions, mainly universities and colleges of higher and further education. Also handles company/commercial and employment. Contributor to 'Education and the Law', the 'Times Education Supplement' and education press. Lectures extensively to College Managers and Governors.

Prof. Membership: Law Society, Education Law Association, FRSA.

Career: Qualified in 1975. Partner at *Wedlake Saint* 1978-93. Chair, London Young Solicitors's Group, 1985; Company Secretary, Polytechnics and Colleges Employers' Forum, 1988; Governor, Barnet College of Further Education, 1992; Company Secretary, Colleges' Employers' Forum, 1992. Joined *Eversheds* in 1994 as a Partner.

Personal: Born 23rd December 1948. College Governor. Leisure interests include walking, history, art and Spain. Lives in Hadley Wood, Barnet, Herts.

Hawthorne, Peter J.M.
Witham Weld, London (0171) 821 8211. Partner in Litigation Department.

Specialisation: Main areas of practice are education and employment law. Advises schools and colleges, their governors and trustees in matters of concern to staff, students, parents, DFE LEAs and Charity Commission in providing education. Also advises religious orders and institutions on procedures for safeguarding their clients' welfare and furthering their work in a secular world. Has acted in judicial reviews of pupil exclusions, governor removal, admission policies of RC state-maintained schools and religious special educational needs. Lectured on child protection problems to conferences of religious orders.

Prof. Membership: Law Society, Education Law Association, Catholic Union.

Career: Qualified 1976, having joined *Witham Weld* in 1974. Became a Partner in 1978. Governor of Donhead (Wimbledon College Preparatory School) since 1990, St Christina's Independent Catholic Girls' School, London since 1993 and a Director of Myrrh Education from 1995.

Personal: Born 14th May 1949. Attended Beaumont College 1962-67, then LLB (Hons), London. Leisure interests include HCPT and family.

Hetherington, David
Eversheds, London (0171) 919 4500. Assistant Solicitor. Employment and Education Groups.

Specialisation: Main area of practice is advising the education sector, particularly higher and further education institutions, in relation to employment law matters. Also deals with other aspects of education law and, in relation to employment law matters, acts for clients outside the education sector.

Career: Qualified in 1975. With *Slaughter & May* 1979-90 as Assistant Solicitor in its Litigation Department. Associate with *Wedlake Saint*, where specialised in employment law, 1990-93. Joined *Eversheds* on 1st January 1994.

Personal: Educated at Wellington School and Magdalene College, Cambridge. Recreations include music, squash and walking. Lives in West Wickham, Kent.

Rabinowicz, Jack
Teacher Stern Selby, London (0171) 242 3191. Partner in Litigation Department.

Specialisation: Main areas of practice include education and personal injury work.

Prof. Memberships: Director of Disability Law Service, Chair of Education Law Association (ELAS), Steering Committee of Whooping Cough Claims, Action for Victims of Medical Accidents (AVMA), American Trial Lawyers Association (ATLA), Medico-Legal Society, Association of Personal Injury Lawyers (APIL), Law Society's Group for the Welfare of People with a Mental Handicap, Council of Registration of Schools teaching Dyslexia (CresTeD).

Career: Qualified in 1977. Currently a partner with *Teacher Stern Selby*.

Thatcher, Michael C.

Winckworth & Pemberton (incorporating Sherwood & Co), London (0171) 593 5000. Partner in Education, Ecclesiastical and Charities Department.

Specialisation: Acts for voluntary aided schools, grant maintained schools, voluntary controlled schools, Church of England and Roman Catholic boards of education and finance, further education colleges and local education authorities. Also acts for charities, airlines, and in general commercial and property law. Has acted in Judicial Review of Appeal Committee decisions, all types of disciplinary and appeal hearings, and Commission for Racial Equality proceedings against Governors. Author of various editorials in the specialist press. Has spoken at a wide range of conferences and seminars on various aspects of education law.

Prof. Memberships: Law Society; Ecclesiastical Law Association; Education Law Association.

Career: Qualified in 1968. From 1969 to 1989 was clerk to the Governors of St Clement Danes School, to St Clement Danes Parochial Charities and to Isaac Ducketts Trustees.

Personal: Born 19th May 1943. Attended Ardingly College 1956-60, then King's College, London 1961-64, and College of Law 1964-65. Clerk to the Worshipful Company of Cooks, Secretary to the Reunion des Gastronomes, Parish Councillor. Leisure interests include running, shooting, fishing and gardening. Lives in Guildford.

Tipping, Christopher J.

Winckworth & Pemberton (incorporating Sherwood & Co), London (0171) 593 5000. Partner in Litigation Department.

Specialisation: Handles ecclesiastical and education litigation, employment law, landlord and tenant matters (licensed properties and others) and leisure and entertainment law. Also deals with liquor licensing, acting for breweries, restaurant chains and other licensed property owners.

Prof. Membership: Law Society, City of Westminster Law Society.

Career: Parliamentary Research Assistant 1974-79. Lecturer in Economics at City & East London College 1972-79. Qualified in 1981, having joined *Winckworth & Pemberton* in 1979. Became a Partner in 1983. President of City of Westminster Law Society 1993-94.

Personal: Born in 1946. Educated at King Edward's, Birmingham 1957-65 and Selwyn College, Cambridge 1965-68. Lay Vicar at Westminster Abbey since 1971. Professional singer. Lives in Westminster.

Ansbro, David

Eversheds, Leeds (0113) 243 0391. Managing Partner and Head of Public Sector Unit.

Specialisation: Main areas of practice are public sector, local government and education. Acts for a wide variety of clients including local authorities, higher and further education institutions, TECs and Quangos including Coventry Technical College, Blackburn College, Bradford and Ilkley Community College, North Hertfordshire College, Grimsby College and North Hull Housing Action Trust. Cases have included major asset transfers and disputes for Further Education Colleges.

Prof. Membership: Law Society, Society of Local Authority Chief Executives.

Career: Qualified in 1969. Appointments have included Chief Executive of Leeds City Council, Chief Executive of Kirklees MBC, and Town Clerk and Chief Executive of York City Council. Now Member of the Local Government Commission and Director of Leeds TEC. Joined *Eversheds Hepworth & Chadwick* in 1991 as a Partner, becoming Managing Partner in 1994.

Personal: Born 3rd April 1945. Attended University of Leeds 1963-66. Member of two FE College Governing Bodies. Leisure interests include Manchester City FC, golf, theatre and cricket. Lives in Leeds.

Arrowsmith, Simon

Martineau Johnson, Birmingham (0121) 200 3300. Partner, Head of Education Department.

Specialisation: The department provides and/or co-ordinates a full in-house service to all institutional educational clients, principally universities, colleges and schools. Particular interests of expertise include: constitutional, public and administrative law, specialist contracts (including joint ventures with private sector partners), statutory interpretation and compliance, disciplinary and other management advice.

Career: qualified in 1984, having joined *Martineau Johnson* in 1982. Became a partner in 1987. Head of Education since 1992.

Boardman, John

Eversheds, Manchester (0161) 832 6666. Partner in Corporate Department.

Specialisation: Principal area of work is education law advising higher education, further education and grant-maintained schools. Other main area of work is franchising, acting for franchisors and franchisees. Contributes articles to various specialist education law and franchise publications and gives numerous lectures and seminars on these two areas.

Prof. Membership: ELAS, British Franchise Association, IFS, International Bar Association.

Career: Qualified 1979 while at *Alexander Tatham*, now *Eversheds Alexander Tatham* and became a Partner in 1986.

Personal: Born 26th July 1955. Attended Manchester Grammar School 1966-73 and Downing College, Cambridge 1973-76. Governor of City College, Manchester. Leisure pursuits include pottery, computers, films, books and music. Lives in Hayfield, Derbyshire.

Boyd, Robert P.

Veale Wasbrough, Bristol (0117) 925 2020. Partner in Commercial Department. (Education and Insurance).

Specialisation: Main area of practice is education work for independent schools. Partner in charge of Schools Unit serving over 400 independent schools and ISJC, GBA, ISBA, IAPS and ISAI. Also handles professional indemnity and personal injury litigation for insurers and plaintiffs. Has acted in numerous disputes under the parent contract relating to expulsions and unpaid fees (including Atholl School v. Denfield 1992), school closures and advice to governors on personal liabilities. Publications have included ISBA Members notes, numerous education templates, an article on Governors' liabilities (IAPS Bulletin) and pending items for the ISJC Bulletin. Has delivered many seminars and lectures and addressed district meetings of IAPS in 1993-94 and annual conferences of ISBA and IAPS in 1995.

Prof. Membership: Law Society, Academy of Experts (Council Member), Bristol Law Society, Bristol Medico Legal Society, ELAS.

Career: Qualified in 1972. Joined *Veale Wasbrough* as a Partner in 1988. Council of Bristol Law Society 1986-88; practising expert and Council Member of Academy of Experts 1989; Co-opted to Judicial Committee 1992.

Personal: Born 21st December 1946. Attended Stonyhurst College 1960-65 and Birmingham University 1966-69. Leisure interests include sailing and woodwork; charity pianist. Lives in Bristol.

Brown, Edward V.

Ford and Warren, Leeds (0113) 243 6601. Partner in Property and Trusts Department.

Specialisation: Main areas of practice are commercial property (for developers and investors), licensed property (for brewers and multiple retailers), charities (formation, administration and ecclesiastical) and education (independent and grant maintained schools).

Prof. Membership: Law Society, Leeds Law Society.

Career: Qualified in 1969, having joined *Ford & Warren* in 1967. Became a Partner in 1970.

Personal: Born 3rd February 1945. Attended Bootham School, York 1958-63, then Leeds

University, 1963-66. School governor of Ayton School, Great Ayton, North Yorkshire; and of Froebelian School, Leeds. Leisure interests include hockey and tennis. Lives in Leeds.

Cook, Nicholas D.

Wollastons, Chelmsford (01245) 211211. Qualified 1983. Partner 1986. Commercial and Commercial Property Department. Specialisms are commercial and commercial leasehold work and education advice to corporations. Born 19.4.1950.

Dickinson, Malcolm K.

Michelmores, Exeter (01392) 436244. Qualified 1980. Partner 1990. Company Commercial Department. Acts for a wide range of Education Institutions in the South West.

George, Philip W.

Birketts, Ipswich (01473) 232300. Qualified 1975. Partner 1976. Company Commercial Department. Handles education work, acting for a university and sixth form colleges and schools, particularly in contractual and constitutional matters. Born 15.8.1951.

Jones, Michael L.N.

See under Construction & Civil Eng..

Liell, Peter M.

Peter Liell, Oxford (01865) 242176. Qualified 1963. Principal 1979. Specialist practice in education law. Work includes school admission, exclusion, transport, special needs and school closure. Joint Editor of 'The Law of Education' since 1984. Born 15.11.1939.

Love, R.J.

A.E. Smith & Son, Stroud (01453) 757444.

Ogilvy, Duncan M.

Mills & Reeve, Cambridge (01223) 364422. Partner in Property Department.

Specialisation: Main area of practice is education. Acts for three of the four universities in East Anglia, the majority of the Cambridge colleges and seven universities elsewhere in England. Advises on finance, property and funding issues such as QIS, sales and leasebacks, etc. Other area of expertise is health. Acts for 15 Health Authorities and 32 NHS Trusts. Gives general property advice, including shared arrangements, usually with the voluntary sector for Care in the Community. A number of the more complex schemes involve Private Finance.

Pharaoh, Paul

Shakespeares, Birmingham (0121) 632 4199. Partner in Commercial Department.

Specialisation: Handles all kinds of commer-

cial agreements. Other area of practice is education: contractual, property and employment related matters for higher and further education institutions and GM Schools. Acted in a high profile dispute re: assets between a GM School and LEA. Author of articles in The Law Society Gazette and The Lawyer. Speaker at conference on Contracts for Schools.

Prof. Membership: Law Society, ELAS.

Career: Qualified in 1971. Joined *Shakespeares* (then *Bettinsons*) in 1969, becoming a Partner in 1973. Joint Honorary Secretary of Birmingham Law Society 1983-88. Honorary Secretary of West Midland Association of Law Societies 1988-91. Law Society Council Member since 1990.

Personal: Born 1947. Attended Manchester University 1965-68 and Liverpool College of Commerce 1968-69. Leisure interests include slow moving tennis and fell walking. Lives in Sutton Coldfield.

Southam, Christopher A.

See under Employment Law.

Sternberg, Nigel P.

Eversheds, Nottingham (0115) 950 6201. Qualified 1980. Partner 1987. Commercial Department. Head of *Eversheds'* Midland Education Team; specialist in constitution and management of educational establishments. Born 25.11.1954.

CD-ROM EDITION

This edition of the directory is available on a CD-ROM which includes both DOS and Windows versions. It can be loaded onto a network, and works with virtually any IBM compatible PC. The full contents of the printed directory are made available to the computer user who will have the advantage of rapid search, retrieval and cross-referencing.

EMPLOYEE BENEFITS/SHARE SCHEMES

As employee share schemes become an integral part of corporate strategy, it is the law firms with well established corporate finance departments which have developed the greatest expertise in this field. Such firms are concentrated in London, although some firms in the larger cities outside London do undertake good quality work.

LONDON

In London, the leading firms in this field are *Clifford Chance, Freshfields, Herbert Smith, Linklaters & Paines, Lovell White Durrant, Nabarro Nathanson, Nicholson Graham & Jones, Paisner & Co* and *Slaughter and May.*

LEADING FIRMS – LONDON	
CLIFFORD CHANCE	FRESHFIELDS
HERBERT SMITH	LINKLATERS & PAINES
LOVELL WHITE DURRANT	NABARRO NATHANSON
NICHOLSON GRAHAM & JONES	PAISNER & CO
SLAUGHTER AND MAY	

Clifford Chance enjoy a good reputation for their employee benefits work and advise on all tax and related aspects of employment, including taxation of remuneration packages, corporate PEPs, ESOPs and equity participation programmes. Robin Tremaine handles all aspects of employee share schemes. David Reid specialises in tax efficient remuneration techniques.

HIGHLY REGARDED – LONDON	
ALLEN & OVERY	ASHURST MORRIS CRISP
FIELD FISHER WATERHOUSE	SPEECHLY BIRCHAM
McKENNA & CO	SIMMONS & SIMMONS
TRAVERS SMITH BRAITHWAITE	

Freshfields is also a leading firm in the field of employee benefits. Simon Evans, a partner in the Employment Pensions and Benefits Department, has a particular expertise in share options, restricted share plans and ESOP arrangements, relating both to the establishment of schemes and the impact of corporate transactions on schemes.

Another City firm with a well established reputation is *Herbert Smith* which has specialist expertise in profit related

pay together with other common aspects of employee share schemes. The firm's major clients include BAT Industries, various water and electricity companies, British Gas and BSkyB. Colin Chamberlain is well regarded and is the author of 'Tolley's Practical Guide to Employees Share Schemes' published in 1994.

Linklaters & Paines another leading firm in this field, deal with documentation for a wide variety of UK and international employee share schemes and executive incentives. Janet Cooper is a pre-eminent practitioner having experience in relation to mergers, demergers, take overs, privatisations and flotations.

Lovell White Durrant have a substantial reputation for their employee benefits practice advising on all aspects of the structure and establishment of approved and unapproved employee share incentives, including ESOPS. Louise Whitewright is well regarded and has specialised in this field since 1987.

Nabarro Nathanson also have a high profile in this field, handling a variety of share schemes as well as more general aspects of employee taxation such as tax treatment of remuneration packages and severance arrangements. This includes share based schemes and profit related pay. Patrick Moon who is a partner in the Tax Department specialises in such work and has experience of restricted share plans and corporate PEPs, profit related pay and other cash-based incentives.

Another firm widely involved in this area is *Nicholson Graham & Jones* which advises on all types of employee incentive schemes, including share option schemes, ESOPs and international schemes. Michael Jacobs heads the Tax department and was the founder member of the Share Scheme Lawyers Group, an association of solicitors specialising in this field.

Paisner & Co are well regarded and David Cohen, a member of the corporate tax department, has emerged as a leading practitioner, acting mainly for small to medium sized quoted companies. An ESOP designed by his firm for a Scottish manufacturing firm, Tullis Russell, was recently recognised with an award by Proshare. He is the author of 'Employee Participation in Flotations 1987-1994'.

Slaughter and May provide advice on employee incentives such as profit-sharing schemes and share option schemes, whether Inland Revenue approved or not. They also assist clients, devise and establish schemes for profit related pay, deferred compensation, phantom options and share incentives. Edward Codrington specialises in employee incentive plans of all kinds.

LEADING INDIVIDUALS – LONDON		
Colin Ellis Chamberlain *Herbert Smith*	Edward A. Codrington *Slaughter and May*	David H.J. Cohen *Paisner & Co*
Janet Cooper *Linklaters & Paines*	Simon J.M. Evans *Freshfields*	Michael E.H. Jacobs *Nicholson Graham & Jones*
Patrick Moon *Nabarro Nathanson*	Robin Tremaine *Clifford Chance*	Louise Whitewright *Lovell White Durrant*
Graeme John Nuttall *Field Fisher Waterhouse*	Paul N. Randall *Ashurst Morris Crisp*	David Reid *Clifford Chance*

In all the tables the names in each group are listed alphabetically.

REGIONS

To the extent that this type of work exists outside London, it is handled by the larger firms with strong corporate bases, notably *Pinsent Curtis* in Birmingham and Leeds. David

LEADING FIRMS – REGIONS

ADDLESHAW SONS & LATHAM *Manchester*	**BOOTH & CO.** *Leeds*
WRAGGE & CO *Birmingham*	**PINSENT CURTIS** *Birmingham, Leeds*

Pett, based at their Birmingham office, is a nationally recognised leader in the field, having written a number of publications including 'A Practical Guide to Employee Share Schemes' (1989) and 'Employee Share Schemes Handbook' (1994). He advises on a range of share schemes including restrictive share schemes, employee buy-outs on privatisation and cash-based performance incentive schemes. His counterpart in the Leeds office is Judith Greaves, also recommended, who undertakes approved and unapproved schemes, ESOPs, employee buyouts and international schemes.

In Birmingham, *Wragge & Co* handle approved executive share option schemes and profit sharing schemes as well as employee benefit trusts and ESOPs. Peter Smith is the partner specialising in this work and has acted for companies such as United Industries plc and Symonds Engineering plc.

In Manchester, *Addleshaw Sons & Latham* undertake work in this field. Richard Hayes heads the Corporate Tax unit dealing with employee share schemes including ESOPs.

HIGHLY REGARDED – REGIONS

MALCOLM LYNCH *Leeds*	
BURGES SALMON *Bristol*	**EVERSHEDS** *Birmingham*
GARRETT & CO *Leeds*	**LYONS DAVIDSON** *Bristol*
OSBORNE CLARKE *Bristol*	

In Leeds the firm *Malcolm Lynch* has been involved in several bus company privatisations including those in Greater Manchester, Hartlepool and Chesterfield and has an employee based approach.

Also in Leeds, *Booth & Co* has an employee share scheme practice which was recommended for its expertise. The firm deals with all aspects of share options, profit sharing schemes and ESOPs.

In Bristol, *Burges Salmon* specialises in this field acting primarily for quoted companies.

LEADING INDIVIDUALS – REGIONS

David Pett *Pinsent Curtis*	
Richard John Burston *Eversheds*	
Judith A. Greaves *Pinsent Curtis*	
Richard Hayes *Addleshaw Sons & Latham*	
Peter W. Smith *Wragge & Co*	
Claire Wesley *Booth & Co.*	

LEADERS IN EMPLOYEE BENEFITS/SHARE SCHEME

LONDON

Chamberlain, Colin Ellis
Herbert Smith, London (0171) 374 8000. Partner in Employment Department.

Specialisation: Specialises in employee share schemes and benefit arrangements in the UK and overseas including employee cash incentives, ESOP's, corporate personal equity plans and profit-related pay. He is author of 'Tolley's Practical Guide to Employees' Share Schemes'.

Career: Qualified in 1977. Between 1985 and 1989 he worked as a director of the former CC&P, now part of Bacon & Woodrow. Became a Partner at *Herbert Smith* in 1989.

Personal: Educated at Sussex University.

Codrington, Edward A.
Slaughter and May, London (0171) 600 1200. Qualified 1976. Joined 1974. Deals with the establishment of all types of employee incentive plans, both cash and share based, including ESOP's, profit sharing schemes, savings related share option schemes and executive share option schemes. Also handles pensions work, including establishment of pensions schemes and advice in connection with flotations, privatisations, etc.

Cohen, David H.J.
Paisner & Co, London (0171) 353 0299.

Qualified 1980. Partner 1986. Corporate Tax Department. Handles mainly employee share schemes and employee benefits work. Chairman Share Scheme Lawyers Group. Born 15.12.55.

Cooper, Janet
Linklaters & Paines, London (0171) 606 7080. Qualified 1984. Partner 1991. Heads unit designing and drafting documentation for all types of UK and international employee share schemes and executive incentives. Involved in all aspects of these schemes on mergers, take-overs, demergers, flotations, privatisations, etc.

Evans, Simon J.M.
Freshfields, London (0171) 936 4000. Partner in Employment Pensions and Benefits Dept.

Specialisation: Main areas of practice are employee benefits and share schemes. Specialises in share option, restricted share plan and ESOP arrangements, relating both to establishment of schemes and advice on the impact of corporate transactions on schemes. Also handles employment law, notably executive appointments and dismissals and related advice. Acted in the London Weekend Television Management Incentive Scheme. Demergers have included Pearson/ Royal Doulton and English China Clays/ Camas. Also acted in litigation with the Inland Revenue relating to Reed Elsevier merger. Has addressed various lectures on share schemes,

including Euroforum 1994 Share Scheme Symposium.

Prof. Membership: Share Scheme Lawyers Group, Law Society.

Career: Qualified in 1983. Joined *Freshfields* in 1981, becoming a Partner in 1991.

Personal: Born 16th June 1957. Attended Rugby School 1970-75; MA from Sidney Sussex College, Cambridge, 1976-79. Lives in Staplehurst, Kent.

Jacobs, Michael E.H.
Nicholson Graham & Jones, London (0171) 628 9151. Partner . Head of the Tax Department.

Specialisation: Work includes corporate acquisitions and disposals, employee share schemes, VAT and international tax. Also handles trust law, charities, local government, privatisation and public sector bodies. Author of 'Tolley's Tax on Take-overs' and 'Tax on Take-overs' (6 editions); contributor to 'Tolley's Tax Planning' 1994-1995, and 'Tolley's VAT Planning' 1994-1995. Editor of Tolley's Trust Law International since 1989. Has published many articles in the professional press and lectures on taxation and trusts.

Prof. Membership: Trust Law Committee (Founder Member and Secretary) Share Scheme Lawyers Group (Founder Member and Vice-Chairman), FI Mgt; FRSA; Governor of the Tax Research Unit at Kings

College London and a member of the Taxation Sub-Committee - CISCO; International Bar Association, VAT Practitioners Group - Trafalgar Chapter; Charity Law Association; Society of Trust and Estate Practitioners; Director, Independent Trustee Limited; Globalex Inc.

Career: Articled at *Nicholson Graham & Jones* 1970, qualified 1972. Becoming a Partner 1976.

Personal: Born 21st May 1948. Attended St Paul's School (Scholar) 1961-66 and Birmingham University (LLB Hons) 1969; Admitted 1972. Leisure interests include sailing, skiing and reading. Lives in London.

Moon, Patrick

Nabarro Nathanson, London (0171) 493 9933. Qualified 1980. Partner 1986. Tax Department. Main areas of practice are employee benefits and share schemes and employee taxation generally. Born 8.5.1953.

Nuttall, Graeme John

Field Fisher Waterhouse, London (0171) 481 4841.

Specialisation: Partner in the Business Tax Department specialising in all aspects of business taxation. Particular interest in employee share schemes and intellectual property taxation. Has advised on the employee ownership aspects of privatisations both in the UK and overseas in Bulgaria, Romania and Slovenia. Publications include 'Employee Ownership - Legal and Tax Aspects' (co-author) 1987; 'Share Incentives for Employees' (co-author) 1990; 'Butterworths Tax Planning' (looseleaf service) (contributor); 'Butterworths UK Corporate Finance' (2nd edition 1992) (contributor); 'Nelson-Jones and Nuttall's Tax Tables' (5 editions) (co-author); 'Nuttall's Tax Tables 1994-95'; 'Sponsorship Endorsement and Merchandising' (co-author) 1990. Regularly addresses conferences both in the UK and internationally on tax and employee share schemes. Frequently called on to assist in lobbying Government for tax and other changes to encourage employee ownership.

Prof. Membership: Associate of the Institute of Taxation since 1985; member of the Share Schemes Lawyers Group since 1989; member of the Taxation Committee of the Intellectual Property Institiute.

Career: Qualified 1984. Assistant solicitor, Field Fisher Martineau 1984-88. Partner since 1988. Spent six months on secondment to Touche Ross & Co. in 1987.

Personal: Educated at Price's Grammar School, Fareham, Hants. and Peterhouse, Cambridge (MA law) 1978-81. Lives in Blackheath, London.

Randall, Paul N.

Ashurst Morris Crisp, London (0171) 638 1111. Qualified 1984. Partner and head of the Employment Department. Born 26.1.1960.

Reid, David

Clifford Chance, London (0171) 600 1000. Partner. Handles succession planning for private companies.

Tremaine, Robin

Clifford Chance, London (0171) 600 1000. Partner. Principal area of practice is employee share schemes. Also handles corporate tax and VAT.

Whitewright, Louise

Lovell White Durrant, London (0171) 236 0066. Qualified 1986. Joined and qualified with *Lovell White Durrant* in 1986. Specialist in employee benefits and employee share schemes since 1987. Advises on all aspects of design, structure, establishment and operation of approved and unapproved employee share incentive schemes (including ESOPS).

REGIONS

Burston, Richard John

Eversheds, Birmingham (0121) 233 2001. Senior Associate in Tax Department.

Specialisation: Main area of specialism is share incentive schemes. Experience of all kinds of schemes, including approved and unapproved schemes, executive, SAYE and profit sharing schemes, ESOPs, restricted share plans and long-term incentive schemes. Has advised quoted and unquoted companies on share scheme issues in the context of management and employeee buyouts, flotations, takeovers, renewal of existing schemes and introduction of new schemes. Also provides general advice on employee taxation. Gave share scheme advice on the flotations of Hozelock Group plc, Partco Group plc and Automotive Precision Holdings plc and assisted the *Eversheds* Manchester office in establishing an ESOP in the employee buyout of Greater Manchester Buses South. Is currently advising a number of quoted companies on the renewal of their executive schemes and on the introduction of long term share incentive schemes. Frequently talks at seminars for clients and prospective clients of the firm on share incentive schemes.

Prof. Membership: Law Society.

Career: Qualified in February 1988. Whole career has been spent at *Eversheds*. Became a Associate in May 1991 and a Senior Associate in May 1994.

Personal: Born 13th August 1962. Educated at New College, Telford 1978-80 and U.C.W. Aberystwyth 1980-83 (LL.B). Leisure pursuits include mountaineering and long distance walking, travelling, dining out and going to the theatre. Lives in Birmingham.

Greaves, Judith A.

See under Tax (Corporate).

Hayes, Richard

Addleshaw Sons & Latham, Manchester (0161) 832 5994. Partner in Corporate Tax Department.

Specialisation: Head of Corporate Tax Unit providing specialist tax services to the firm.

Specialises in employee share schemes including ESOPs. Involved in the establishment and subsequent operation of the employer ownership arrangements of BAXI Partnership Ltd, the major North West based employee owned company. Speaks regularly on the subject of ESOPs to seminars.

Prof. Membership: Law Society, Manchester Law Society.

Career: Qualified in 1972. Joined *Addleshaw Sons & Latham* in 1973, becoming a Partner in 1975. Secretary of the Manchester Incorporated Law Library Society.

Personal: Born 31st October 1947. Attended Trinity Hall, Cambridge (MA 1969, LLB 1970). Committee Member of the Manchester Midday Concerts Society. Leisure interests include railways, opera, classical music and sheep. Lives in Chapel-en-le-Frith.

Pett, David

Pinsent Curtis, Birmingham (0121) 200 1050. David Pett, 39, is National Practice Head of Tax and Pensions and an acknowledged specialist in the fields of corporate tax and employee share schemes. The author of "Employee Share Schemes Handbook" (Longmans), he has fifteen years' experience in advising a range of UK and overseas companies and individuals in relation to all aspects of UK and international tax planning.

Smith, Peter W.

Wragge & Co, Birmingham (0121) 233 1000. Qualified 1978. Partner 1982. Specialises in corporate tax, employees' share schemes and public authority law and finance. Born 11th October 1952.

Wesley, Claire

Booth & Co., Leeds (0113) 283 2000.

Specialisation: Head of corporate tax department specialising in corporate taxation and employee share schemes. Corporate tax practice covers all aspects of corporation tax, capital gains tax, VAT, employment related taxation, mergers and acquisitions, management buy-outs and corporate finance related work, tax and VAT disputes, tax planning. Employee share schemes practice includes all aspects of share option schemes, profit sharing schemes, other share and cash incentive arrangements and ESOPs. Has published various articles on share schemes and employee incentives. Regular speaker at seminars on share schemes, ESOPs, employee benefits, corporate tax and VAT.

Prof. Membership: The Law Society.

Career: Qualified 1989. Assistant solicitor, *Frere Cholmeley* 1989-1992. Assistant solicitor, *Walker Morris*, Leeds 1992-1994. Joined *Booth & Co.* February 1994.

Personal: Educated at Malvern Girls' College 1975-1981, New College, Oxford 1982-1985 and the College of Law 1985-1986. Leisure pursuits include opera, music, theatre, wine, cooking, tennis, skiing and keeping fit. Born 4th December 1963. Lives in Harrogate.

EMPLOYMENT LAW

LONDON

Firms practising employment law can be divided into those which act mainly for employers (and also provide employment advice for directors and senior executives) and the 'trade union firms' which act mainly for employees. This is an area of practice where the reputation of individual lawyers is stronger than that of law firms. It was stressed by practitioners that clients choose to go to a particular lawyer rather than a firm for employment law advice.

MAINLY FOR EMPLOYERS

The leading individuals in this area are very well known. The two outstanding names are Fraser Younson of *Baker & McKenzie* and Janet Gaymer of *Simmons & Simmons* who is also currently head of the Employment Lawyers Association. These two practitioners were almost universally recommended and are generally considered to be at the forefront of their field.

A number of other individuals were singled out for their expertise. Georgina Keane of *Titmuss Sainer Dechert* was very highly regarded. Barry Mordsley of *Harris Rosenblatt & Kramer*, Stephen Levinson of *Paisner & Co*, Simon Jeffreys of *McKenna & Co* and Julian Roskill of *Rowe & Maw*, are regarded as well established specialists having extensive experience in acting for employers.

Jane Mann is also seen as an expert by her peers and the impact of her move to *Fox Williams* from *Denton Hall* continues to be felt despite this transfer having taken place well over a year ago. With the merging of *Jaques & Lewis* with *Eversheds*, Elaine Aarons will no doubt play a part in developing the profile of *Eversheds* as far as employment law is concerned. Her work in this field has included advising public and private companies, public sector employers and sen-

ior management on matters such as service agreements, board room disputes and restrictive covenants.

LEADING FIRMS – LONDON – MAINLY EMPLOYERS	
BAKER & McKENZIE	SIMMONS & SIMMONS
EVERSHEDS	FOX WILLIAMS
HARRIS ROSENBLATT & KRAMER	PAISNER & CO
ROWE & MAW	TITMUSS SAINER DECHERT
LOVELL WHITE DURRANT	NORTON ROSE
SLAUGHTER AND MAY	

Melanie Tether is also a very highly regarded employment lawyer who was formerly of *Norton Rose* but has now transferred to the Bar and is based at *Old Square Chambers*. Her move to the Bar is a loss to the employment expertise of *Norton Rose*. Similarly, the recent exit of Jill Andrew is likely to have an adverse effect on the capabilities of *Dibb Lupton Broomhead*. Jill Andrew is now with a specialised employment firm, *Langley & Co*.

HIGHLY REGARDED – LONDON – MAINLY EMPLOYERS	
CLIFFORD CHANCE	LANGLEY & CO
McKENNA & CO	STEPHENSON HARWOOD
WARNER CRANSTON	
CHARLES RUSSELL	DENTON HALL
DIBB LUPTON BROOMHEAD	D J FREEMAN
FRESHFIELDS	HERBERT SMITH
HILL TAYLOR DICKINSON	LEWIS SILKIN
LINKLATERS & PAINES	MACFARLANES
MISHCON DE REYA	MONIER–WILLIAMS & BOXALLS
OSBORNE CLARKE	

LEADING INDIVIDUALS – LONDON

David Cockburn * *Pattinson and Brewer*	Janet Gaymer *Simmons & Simmons*	Fraser R. Younson *Baker & McKenzie*
Elaine Aarons *Eversheds*	Jill Andrew *Langley & Co*	Catherine F.N. Brearley *Stephenson Harwood*
Simon Jeffreys *McKenna & Co*	Georgina Keane *Titmuss Sainer Dechert*	Stephen E. Levinson *Paisner & Co*
Jane Mann *Fox Williams*	Barry Mordsley *Harris Rosenblatt & Kramer*	Julian W. Roskill *Rowe & Maw*
Michael Short * *Rowley Ashworth*		
Elizabeth J. Adams *Beachcroft Stanleys*	Michael Burd *Lewis Silkin*	Stephen Cavalier * *Brian Thompson & Partners*
Edward J.O. Cooper * *Russell Jones & Walker*	Stephanie Dale *Denton Hall*	David Dalgarno *Warner Cranston*
Pamela A. Benady Davies *Monier–Williams & Boxalls*	James Davies *Lewis Silkin*	John R. Farr *Herbert Smith*
Ronald D. Fox *Fox Williams*	David Green *Charles Russell*	D.A. Harper *Lovell White Durrant*
Gillian Howard *Mishcon De Reya*	Howard R. Jacobs *Slaughter and May*	Raymond J. Jeffers *Linklaters & Paines*
Jane Moorman *D J Freeman*	Christopher C. Osman *Clifford Chance*	David C. Warner *Warner Cranston*
Andrew P.F. Williamson *Lovell White Durrant*		

UP AND COMING

Simon Auerbach * *Pattinson and Brewer*	Ian Hunter *Fox Williams*

* ACTS MAINLY FOR EMPLOYEES

In all the tables the names in each group are listed alphabetically.

Another recent development was the bolt-on at the London office of *Osborne Clarke* of the senior members of the employment team from *Hill Taylor Dickinson.*

A name that the Directory has come across for the first time this year has been Howard Jacobs of *Slaughter and May* who has been recommended for his expertise in this area (and also for his capacity to undertake pensions work). Catherine Brearley of *Stephenson Harwood* was also commended. She is the joint author of 'Employment Covenants and Confidential Information: Law Practice and Technique', written along with Selwyn Bloch of *2 Crown Office Row.*

A number of other firms are well-known for their employment practices. At *Lovell White Durrant,* David Harper is the leading figure – his area of practice includes unfair dismissal, trade union disputes and discrimination. A small firm with a good reputation is *Warner Cranston.* Their senior partner, David Warner, specialises in employment law relating to senior executives: service agreements, share options and director's responsibilities. At the same firm David Dalgarno advises clients on management changes, redundancies and transfers of undertakings. He is a former barrister and handles a substantial amount of advocacy and litigation work. Christopher Osman, head of the employment unit at *Clifford Chance* is well regarded, and also edits 'Harvey on Industrial Relations' and 'Employment Law'. *Freshfields'* employment department has handled several high profile terminations and members have contributed to 'Tolley's Employment Law'.

MacFarlanes is particularly known for its employment work in relation to the advertising and marketing industry. It acted for the old Saatchi & Saatchi agency when it was attempting to enforce garden leave and restrictive covenants against three leaving executives.

Denton Hall deals with employment contracts and termination, senior management arrangements and industrial relations. Stephanie Dale is highly regarded. At *Linklaters & Paines,* the leading employment lawyer is Raymond Jeffers whose work includes transfers of business, restraint of trade and occupational health and safety. Pamela Benady Davies of *Monier-Williams & Boxalls* also has a good reputation. At West End firm *Lewis Silkin,* James Davies counts several major advertising agencies amongst his clients. His particular areas of interest include EC law, discrimination law and the transfer of undertakings.

Other firms with good employment law departments are *Mishcon De Reya, D J Freeman, Herbert Smith* and *Charles Russell.*

MAINLY FOR EMPLOYEES

David Cockburn of *Pattinson & Brewer* is extremely well regarded and considered to be the leading employment specialist acting for employees. He is adept at dealing with collective trade union disputes and has acted in a number of notable cases including the National Docks Strike (1989) and the Tilbury Dockers Unfair Dismissal Case. He also acted for RMT in last years dispute with Railtrack. Other recommended names include Michael Short of *Rowley Ashworth* and Edward Cooper of *Russell Jones & Walker.*

Prominent firms include *Robin Thompson & Partners* and *Brian Thompson & Partners* which are due to amalgamate their expertise in the form of a merger in the near future. Stephen Cavalier of *Brian Thompson & Partners* was singled out as an up and coming practitioner. *Russell Jones & Walker* are another firm involved in this field of employment

LEADING FIRMS – LONDON – MAINLY EMPLOYEES	
PATTINSON AND BREWER	
BRIAN THOMPSON & PARTNERS	**ROBIN THOMPSON & PARTNERS**
RUSSELL JONES & WALKER	

law, deriving a great deal of their work from their historical trade union connections and adding to the foundations of their well established personal injury practice. *Bindman & Partners* was recommended particularly for its expertise in discrimination matters as were *Hodge Jones & Allen. Lawford & Co* were also recommended for their work for employees.

HIGHLY REGARDED – LONDON – MAINLY EMPLOYEES	
BINDMAN & PARTNERS	**HODGE JONES & ALLEN**
LAWFORD & CO	

An interesting phenomenon in this field has been the recent geographical redistribution of work away from London in favour of the larger provincial cities. While this was primarily generated by cost factors and the impact of the recession, it will be interesting to see in the coming years whether such firms continue to retain such work. Certainly the larger regional firms are very keen to emphasise their client base as deriving from a wide geographical spread and their ability to seduce work away from firms in the capital. However one prominent London employment lawyer justified higher costs in London by stating that 'a Rolls Royce fee results in a Rolls Royce service'.

SOUTH EAST

The leading individual by far in this region was Sue Ashtiany of *Cole & Cole* located in Oxford. Her pre-eminence extends

LEADING FIRMS – SOUTH EAST
COLE and COLE *Oxford*

well beyond her own geographical vicinity and she justifiably enjoys a national reputation for her employment expertise. She heads a specialist department in employment and

HIGHLY REGARDED – SOUTH EAST	
DONNE MILEHAM & HADDOCK *Brighton*	**HEDLEYS** *East Horsley*
BLANDY & BLANDY *Reading*	**BOYES TURNER & BURROWS** *Reading*
BRACHERS *Maidstone*	**CLARKS** *Reading*
CLARKSON WRIGHT & JAKES *Orpington*	**CRIPPS HARRIES HALL** *Tunbridge Wells*
GIRLINGS *Canterbury*	**HORWOOD & JAMES** *Aylesbury*
PATTINSON AND BREWER *Chatham*	**PICKWORTHS** *Watford*
ROBIN THOMPSON & PARTNERS *Ilford*	**STEVENS & BOLTON** *Guildford*
UNDERWOODS *St. Albans*	

discrimination law and acts for several major clients in the public and private sector. She also has taken a number of cases for the Equal Opportunities Commission and has been instructed by the Commission for Racial Equality.

From a regional viewpoint the firms of note are *Hedleys*, with Judith Gleeson, based in East Horsley and *Donne Mileham & Haddock*, with Quintin Barry, which handles a substantial number of sex and race discrimination claims. The firm is also a member of the Armed Forces Pregnancy Dismissal Group which co-ordinates the claims of service women dismissed from the services due to pregnancy.

LEADING INDIVIDUALS – SOUTH EAST	
Sue Ashtiany	Cole and Cole
Quintin Barry	Donne Mileham & Haddock
Judith A.J.C. Gleeson	Hedleys
Colin C. Henney	Henmans

Colin Henney, at *Henmans* in Oxford, handles the full range of employer and employee work, including appearing before EATs, and is also involved in ACAS training.

SOUTH WEST

David Ticehurst of *Osborne Clarke* is a highly regarded employment practitioner who also sits as a part time recorder. He is head of both the Employment unit and Media unit at

LEADING FIRMS – SOUTH WEST			
BOND PEARCE	Plymouth	BURGES SALMON	Bristol
OSBORNE CLARKE	Bristol	VEALE WASBROUGH	Bristol

his firm, and has a broad range of experience including industrial disputes, wrongful and unfair dismissals, restrictive covenants and major restructuring of industry. He has experience both in Industrial and Employment Appeal Tribunals and in conducting cases before the High Court.

HIGHLY REGARDED – SOUTH WEST			
BEVAN ASHFORD	Bristol	CARTWRIGHTS	Bristol
LESTER ALDRIDGE	Bournemouth	MACFARLANE GUY	Bath
PATTINSON AND BREWER	Bristol	ROBIN THOMPSON & PARTNERS	Bristol
THRINGS & LONG	Bath	WANSBROUGHS WILLEY HARGRAVE	Bristol

Christopher Southam, of *Veale Wasbrough* also has a high profile in this field. The firm has acted for a number of PLCs, public utilities and local authorities and NHS trusts. It has

LEADING INDIVIDUALS – SOUTH WEST	
Nikki Duncan	Bond Pearce
George M. Dyson	Burges Salmon
Christopher A. Southam	Veale Wasbrough
David K. Ticehurst	Osborne Clarke
Anthony Brown	Wansbroughs Willey Hargrave
Nicholas Moore	Osborne Clarke
David J. Owens	Bevan Ashford

also been involved in a number of high profile cases including *Dawes v Avon Ambulance Service*. In Plymouth, Nikki Duncan of *Bond Pearce* is very well regarded. Her experience of employment law has embraced litigation, discrimination and the employment aspects of corporate transactions.

George Dyson, of *Burges Salmon* is also recommended. He has experience of both individual and collective labour law including collective agreements and service agreements. He has also dealt with TUPE, dismissals, discrimination, restraint of trade, industrial tribunals and internal disciplinary hearings as well as negotiations with trade unions.

Two well respected Bristol firms are *Bevan Ashford*, where David Owens in particular handles dismissal issues, transfers of undertakings and discrimination work, and *Cartwrights*. Finally there is Anthony Brown, whose work at *Wansbroughs Willey Hargrave* includes the drafting of employment contracts and the development of innovative ways of rewarding employees.

WALES

Vivian Du-Feu of *Eversheds* in Cardiff is the most prominent name in this region and also has an excellent reputation nationally. The employment department is the largest in the

LEADING FIRMS – WALES	
EVERSHEDS	Cardiff

area comprising a total of 13 fee earners working exclusively in this field. The firm has a widespread client base having represented at industrial tribunals employers from Plymouth in the South to Fort William in the North. His firm handles

HIGHLY REGARDED – WALES			
EDWARDS GELDARD	Cardiff	HOWARD PALSER GROSSMAN HERMER & PARTNERS	Cardiff
MORGAN BRUCE	Cardiff		
LEO ABSE & COHEN	Cardiff	ROBIN THOMPSON & PARTNERS	Cardiff

all aspects of both contentious and non-contentious work including industrial relations advice, sex and race discrimination, restructuring, redundancy matters and variation of contracts. Clients include British Steel, South Wales Electricity, University of Wales College of Cardiff and NHS Trusts in Wales. The firm also runs employment law training programmes for its clients.

LEADING INDIVIDUALS – WALES	
Vivian J. Du-Feu	Eversheds

Other firms in this area which handle employment law work are *Morgan Bruce, Edwards Geldard* and *Howard Palser Grossman Hermer & Partners. Robin Thompson & Partners* and *Leo Abse & Cohen* are both firms based in Cardiff acting for employees and trade unions.

MIDLANDS

Colin Goodier of *Pinsent Curtis* is highly regarded for his employment law expertise. He is currently head of the litigation department at the Birmingham branch of this firm and has experience of both individual and collective labour law. Formed from the recent amalgamation of the Leeds firm *Simpson Curtis* and the Birmingham firm, *Pinsent & Co*, *Pinsent Curtis* combines two very strong employment departments resulting in a formidable national presence.

LEADING FIRMS – MIDLANDS

EDGE & ELLISON *Birmingham*	EVERSHEDS *Birmingham*
PINSENT CURTIS *Birmingham*	WRAGGE & CO *Birmingham*

Martin Hopkins of *Eversheds*, Birmingham heads a team of eight full time employment lawyers. He has experience in discrimination and maternity work and is co-author of 'The Maternity Manual'. He also has experience advising on health and safety matters, and on a number of collective employment law issues including union deregulation and strike ballots.

HIGHLY REGARDED – MIDLANDS

DIBB LUPTON BROOMHEAD *Birmingham*	HIGGS & SONS *Brierley Hill*
HOWES PERCIVAL *Northampton*	SHOOSMITHS & HARRISON *Northampton*
FOSTER BAXTER COOKSEY *Wolverhampton*	MOSS LATHAM & TOONE *Loughborough*
OWSTONS *Leicester*	ROWLEY ASHWORTH *Birmingham*
ROWLEY DICKINSON *Birmingham*	SHAKESPEARES *Birmingham*

James Retallack of *Edge & Ellison* was recommended and heads the Employment Unit acting mainly for employers. Andrew Manning Cox of *Wragge & Co* enjoys a reputation in this field despite also having a substantial general commercial litigation practice. In Dudley, Roger Field of *Higgs & Sons* has a good reputation. His work arises primarily from a strong retail client base and he acts mainly for employers. Another leading figure is Alan Jones at *Dibb Lupton's* Birmingham office. His work includes executive severance and drafting and enforcing restrictive covenants. Other recommended firms are *Shoosmiths & Harrison* in Nottingham, and *Howes Percival* in Northampton, where Peter Thompson is well regarded.

LEADING INDIVIDUALS – MIDLANDS

Colin J. Goodier *Pinsent Curtis*
Martin W. Hopkins *Eversheds*
James K. Retallack *Edge & Ellison*
Roger Field *Higgs & Sons*
Alan G. Jones *Dibb Lupton Broomhead*
Andrew Manning-Cox *Wragge & Co*
Peter Thompson *Howes Percival*

UP AND COMING

Martin Chitty *Pinsent Curtis*

EAST ANGLIA

Norman Lamb of *Steele & Co* in Norwich has developed a strong reputation based on his involvement in the actions

LEADING FIRMS – EAST ANGLIA

EVERSHEDS *Norwich*	HEWITSON BECKE + SHAW *Cambridge*
MILLS & REEVE *Norwich*	STEELE & CO *Norwich*

against the Ministry of Defence which concerned the unfair dismissal of servicewomen on the grounds of pregnancy. He is chairman of the Armed Forces Pregnancy Dismissal Group, a joint venture involving over 300 law firms nationwide in similar actions against the Ministry of Defence.

Nicholas Sayer of *Hewitson Becke & Shaw* is based in Cambridge. The firm deals with matters of unfair dismissal, sex and race discrimination, injunctive relief, trade secrets and confidentiality. It also handles collective issues including trade disputes.

HIGHLY REGARDED – EAST ANGLIA

COZENS–HARDY & JEWSON *Norwich*	PRETTYS *Ipswich*
TAYLOR VINTERS *Cambridge*	
GOTELEE & GOLDSMITH *Ipswich*	GREENE & GREENE *Bury St. Edmunds*
GROSS & CO. *Bury St. Edmunds*	LEATHES PRIOR *Norwich*

Individuals were recommended from the *Eversheds* offices in this region, most particularly Owen Warnock based in Ipswich and Tracy Yates in Norwich. His branch of *Eversheds* along with the Norwich branch act for both employers and employees including 13 of the 25 health trusts in East Anglia and also for eight FE colleges. Employment matters dealt with cover all aspects including discrimination, equal pay and negotiated service agreements for senior executives and directors.

LEADING INDIVIDUALS – EAST ANGLIA

Norman P. Lamb *Steele & Co*
Nicholas T. Sayer *Hewitson Becke + Shaw*
Colin J. Tweedie *Mills & Reeve*
Owen Warnock *Eversheds*
Nicola Brown *Mills & Reeve*
Robert Dillarstone *Greenwoods*
Tracy Yates *Eversheds*

Colin Tweedie of *Mills & Reeve* is located in Norwich. Acting mainly for employers he has experience of handling service contracts, dismissal claims and redundancy matters. Nicola Brown of this firm is based in Cambridge and has a good reputation in advising health authorities on employment issues.

Other firms worthy of mention in this area are Cambridge based *Taylor Vinters*, *Cozens-Hardy & Jewson* in Norwich and *Prettys* in Ipswich. Robert Dillarstone, who heads the Employment and Employee Benefits department at *Greenwoods* in Peterborough, is highly regarded.

NORTH WEST

Malcolm Pike of *Addleshaw Sons & Latham*, Manchester, has a solid national reputation. He advises on conditions of employment, personnel policies and collective agreements, industrial tribunals, trade union matters and employment aspects of the sale and reorganisation of companies and businesses.

LEADING FIRMS – NORTH WEST

ADDLESHAW SONS & LATHAM *Manchester*	DIBB LUPTON BROOMHEAD *Manchester*
MACE & JONES *Liverpool*	

Thomas Nicholls of *Dibb Lupton Broomhead*, Manchester, who heads the department of Human Resources, also enjoys a national reputation. Much of the success of his firm in the field of employment law has been attributed to him. His particular expertise lies in boardroom disputes, contract variation and discrimination law.

HIGHLY REGARDED – NORTH WEST

COBBETT LEAK ALMOND *Manchester*	EVERSHEDS *Manchester*
HAMMOND SUDDARDS *Manchester*	WHITTLES *Manchester*
ALSOP WILKINSON *Liverpool*	DAVID PHILLIPS & PARTNERS *Bootle*
DAVIES ARNOLD COOPER *Manchester*	DAVIES WALLIS FOYSTER *Liverpool*
NIGHTINGALES *Manchester*	
BRIAN THOMPSON & PARTNERS *Liverpool*	DAVIS BLANK FURNISS *Manchester*
ELLIOTT & CO *Manchester*	HOWARTH GOODMAN *Manchester*
LEES LLOYD WHITLEY *Liverpool*	TAYLORS *Blackburn*
WEIGHTMAN RUTHERFORDS *Liverpool*	

Mace & Jones in Liverpool acts for NHS trusts, local authorities, Training and Enterprise councils and companies nationwide. It has acted in *Lavery v Plessey Telecommunications*, a case concerning maternity leave.

Another recommended name in this region, Sue Nickson of *Hammond Suddards*, is based in Manchester and handles employment matters for both public and private sector clients, including retail, manufacturing and construction companies.

Charles Hantom of Whittles in Manchester acts for several trade unions. Michael Grierson of *Cobbett Leak Almond* was also recommended to us, as was the Manchester office of *Eversheds*.

LEADING INDIVIDUALS – NORTH WEST

K. Martin Edwards *Mace & Jones*
M.I. Grierson *Cobbett Leak Almond*
Charles C. Hantom *Whittles*
Thomas Nicholls *Dibb Lupton Broomhead*
Sue Nickson *Hammond Suddards*
Malcolm J. Pike *Addleshaw Sons & Latham*
Mary Clarke *Alsop Wilkinson*
Nicolas J. Harney *Nightingales*
Paul Lockett *Davies Arnold Cooper*
H. Andrea McWatt *Davies Wallis Foyster*
Peter Norbury *Eversheds*
P. Quinn *David Phillips & Partners*

NORTH EAST

Leeds has a strong concentration of employment law expertise, with a number of recommendations being made for practitioners there.

LEADING FIRMS – NORTH EAST

PINSENT CURTIS	
BOOTH & CO. *Leeds*	BRIAN THOMPSON & PARTNERS *Leeds*
DIBB LUPTON BROOMHEAD *Bradford*	EVERSHEDS *Leeds*
HAMMOND SUDDARDS *Leeds*	ROLLIT FARRELL & BLADON *Hull*
SHORT RICHARDSON & FORTH *Newcastle upon Tyne*	

John McMullen of *Pinsent Curtis* is highly respected. He is considered to be the leading authority on transfer of undertakings and is the author of 'Business Transfers and Employee Rights'. The Leeds employment department acts for a number of Universities, NHS Trusts and multi-national corporations, attracting work from a nationwide client base and acting for both employers and employees.

HIGHLY REGARDED – NORTH EAST

DICKINSON DEES *Newcastle upon Tyne*	FORD AND WARREN *Leeds*
JACKSONS *Middlesbrough*	WALKER MORRIS *Leeds*
BRIDGE MCFARLAND SOLICITORS *Grimsby*	IRWIN MITCHELL *Sheffield*
NABARRO NATHANSON *Doncaster*	ROBERT MUCKLE *Newcastle-upon-Tyne*
WARD HADAWAY *Newcastle upon Tyne*	
GARRETT & CO *Leeds*	GORDONS WRIGHT & WRIGHT *Bradford*
PATTINSON AND BREWER *York*	READ HIND STEWART *Leeds*
ROBIN THOMPSON & PARTNERS *Hull*	SAMUEL PHILLIPS & CO *Newcastle*

Thomas Flanagan, head of the Employment Law Department at Booth & Co, has experience of all aspects of this field. In particular, he has advised on disciplinary issues and tax and corporate aspects of termination packages and the impact of EC law.

LEADING INDIVIDUALS – NORTH EAST

John McMullen *Pinsent Curtis*
J. Howard Bryan *Eversheds*
Thomas D. Flanagan *Booth & Co.*
Pauline A. Molyneux *Rollit Farrell & Bladon*
Timothy D. Russell *Hammond Suddards*
Michael C. Short *Short Richardson & Forth*
John Bridge *Bridge McFarland Solicitors*
Christopher J. Chapman *Brian Thompson & Partners*
Kevin J. Fletcher *Jacksons*
Keith Hearn *Ford and Warren*

Timothy Russell of *Hammond Suddards* was also recommended. His firm acts for BACS, Baring Asset Management, Credit Lyonnais (UK), IMRO and LIFFE.

Howard Bryan of *Eversheds*, who heads the employment team was also recommended. The firm acts principally for employers and has clients drawn from both the public and private sector including the National Freight Consortium PLC and Asda. The firm also has experience of dealing with collective employment law issues.

In Newcastle, Michael Short of *Short Richardson & Forth* is considered to be the leading employment specialist and has over twenty years' experience in this field. In Hull, Pauline Molyneux of *Rollit Farrell & Bladon* has an equivalent standing. She has a great deal of experience in both contentious and non-contentious matters. Other firms worthy of note in the area are *Dibb Lupton Broomhead* in Sheffield and Leeds, and *Brian Thompson & Partners* in Sheffield.

Other firms worthy of mention are *Jacksons* in Middlesbrough, where Keith Fletcher is highly regarded, and *Ford & Warren* in Leeds, where Keith Hearne was recommended to us. Of the larger firms not already mentioned, *Walker Morris* in Leeds does some employment work as does Newcastle-based *Dickinson Dees*.

SCOTLAND

The leading employment law firm north of the border is *Mackay Simon*, based in Edinburgh. This is a deserved position as it is the only Scottish law firm to devote itself exclusively to employment law. Malcolm MacKay is the founding

LEADING FIRMS – SCOTLAND

MACKAY SIMON *Edinburgh*	**MACROBERTS** *Glasgow*
BURNSIDE KEMP FRASER *Aberdeen*	**HARPER MACLEOD** *Glasgow*
KIDSTONS & CO *Glasgow*	**MORTON FRASER MILLIGAN** *Edinburgh*

partner of this firm and was highly recommended. He handles all aspects of employment law and has a particular interest in industrial relations, transfer of undertakings and the law relating to discrimination.

HIGHLY REGARDED – SCOTLAND

DUNDAS & WILSON CS *Edinburgh*	**THE FRANK LEFEVRE PRACTICE** *Aberdeen*
PAULL & WILLIAMSONS *Aberdeen*	**RAEBURN CHRISTIE** *Aberdeen*
SIMPSON & MARWICK WS *Edinburgh*	**TINDAL OATTS** *Glasgow*
BRODIES WS *Edinburgh*	**DIGBY BROWN & CO** *Glasgow*
DRUMMOND MILLER WS *Edinburgh*	**ROBIN THOMPSON & PARTNERS** *Edinburgh*
TILSTON MACLAURIN *Glasgow*	
BALFOUR & MANSON *Edinburgh*	**BISHOP AND ROBERTSON CHALMERS** *Glasgow*
BLACKADDER REID JOHNSTON *Dundee*	**DORMAN JEFFREY & CO** *Glasgow*
GILLESPIE MACANDREW *Edinburgh*	**JAMES & GEORGE COLLIE** *Aberdeen*
LEDINGHAM CHALMERS *Aberdeen*	**McGRIGOR DONALD** *Glasgow*
MUNRO & NOBLE *Inverness*	**SHEPHERD & WEDDERBURN** *Edinburgh*
THORNTONS WS *Dundee*	**WRIGHT, JOHNSTON & MACKENZIE** *Glasgow*

In all the tables the names in each group are listed alphabetically.

The expertise of Malcolm Mackay is very closely followed by that of Raymond Williamson of *MacRoberts* in Glasgow, both of whom practise wholly in employment law. Raymond

LEADING INDIVIDUALS – SCOTLAND

Malcolm R. Mackay *Mackay Simon*	
Raymond M. Williamson *MacRoberts*	
Iain F. Atack *Kidstons & Co*	
David M. Burnside *Burnside Kemp Fraser*	
Reginald G. Christie *Raeburn Christie*	
John R. Griffiths *Simpson & Marwick WS*	
Frank H. Lefevre *The Frank Lefevre Practice*	
Euan R. MacLeod *Dundas & Wilson CS*	
Rod McKenzie *Harper Macleod*	
William S.C. Speirs *Tindal Oatts*	
David L. Stewart *Morton Fraser Milligan*	
James K. Tierney *Paull & Williamsons*	
Isabel J. Anderson *Drummond Miller WS*	
Alistair M. Cockburn *Tilston MacLaurin*	
R. Craig Connal *McGrigor Donald*	
Nicol M. Hosie *Ledingham Chalmers*	
D. Ian K. MacLeod *Shepherd & Wedderburn*	
William A. Meiklejohn *Blackadder Reid Johnston*	
David D. Whyte *Bishop and Robertson Chalmers*	
David S. Williamson *Brodies WS*	
James D. Young *McGrigor Donald*	

Williamson has extensive experience in this field acting primarily for employers, including advising on employer management of staff and on redundancies and disciplinary matters. He is the holder of the Specialist Authorisation from the Law Society of Scotland in Employment Law.

David Burnside of *Burnside Kemp & Fraser* is also experienced having handled industrial tribunal cases since 1967 primarily in the areas of redundancy, unfair dismissal, sex and race discrimination and transfer of undertakings. The firm has acted for a number of private companies in this field.

Rod McKenzie of *Harper McLeod* in Glasgow is a partner in the litigation department specialising in employment law. The firm acts for a number of major public companies, trade unions and the Equal Opportunities Commission and acts for both applicants and respondents. David Stewart of *Morton Fraser Milligan* was also well recommended and has extensive experience in handling trade union and employee based work.

In Aberdeen, Reginald Christie of *Raeburn Christie* has experience of acting for the oil industry. The firm has a particular emphasis on handling contract formation and termination.

Also in Aberdeen, Frank Lefevre of the *Frank Lefevre Practice* has a good reputation in acting for employees.

Iain Atack, senior partner at *Kidstons & Co* in Glasgow was mentioned to us. The firm has particular expertise in contentious work. Another Glasgow firm mentioned to us was *Tindal Oats* where William Speirs is a specialist. Two Edinburgh firms recommended to us are *Simpson & Marwick WS*, where

John Griffiths practices employment law in addition to his main area of practice in medical negligence, and *Dundas & Wilson CS* where Euan MacLeod is head of the Employment Group. An Aberdeen firm worth mentioning is *Paull & Williamsons*, whose leading individual is James Tierney.

Although, the Scottish Bar is outside the province of this directory, Ian Truscott should be mentioned as the leading employment Advocate. His expertise was universally endorsed.

NORTHERN IRELAND

Adam Brett at *L'Estrange & Brett* is a highly regarded specialist in the field, offering advice to the public and private sector. His clients include Queen's University in Belfast.

HIGHLY REGARDED – NORTHERN IRELAND	
CARSON & McDOWELL *Belfast*	CLEAVER FULTON & RANKIN *Belfast*
ELLIOTT DUFFY GARRETT *Belfast*	JONES AND CASSIDY *Belfast*
L'ESTRANGE & BRETT *Belfast*	TUGHAN & CO *Belfast*
C & H JEFFERSON *Belfast*	JOHNS ELLIOT *Belfast*
MILLS SELIG *Belfast*	

Henry Coll at *Elliott Duffy Garrett* enjoys an excellent reputation for employment work. He also acts for educational clients, including a university together with a number of quangos and commercial and institutional undertakings, dealing with dismissal and discrimination claims. At *Carson*

& McDowell William Turtle is highly respected for his work which is carried out almost entirely on behalf of employers. The niche employment firm of *Jones & Cassidy* acts for three large banking institutions, a major university and a number of trade unions. The firm's specialists Beverley Jones and Fiona Cassidy have been involved in two important cases which raised issues of European law. At *Tughan & Co* Grahame Loughlin is a well known figure who acts for a broad range of manufacturing and service clients. Patrick

LEADING INDIVIDUALS – NORTHERN IRELAND	
Henry A. Coll	*Elliott Duffy Garrett*
Grahame Loughlin	*Tughan & Co*
Adam T.G. Brett	*L'Estrange & Brett*
William B.W. Turtle	*Carson & McDowell*
Fiona A. Cassidy	*Jones and Cassidy*
S.M. Patrick Cross	*Cleaver Fulton & Rankin*
Beverley Jones	*Jones and Cassidy*
R. William C. McCann	*Mills Selig*

Cross heads a busy team at *Cleaver Fulton & Rankin*, taking instructions from public limited companies, local businesses, universities and schools, governmental bodies and charities. The firm also carries out agency work for English solicitors. William McCann at *Mills Selig* acts for a range of employers including Northern Bank Ltd and Group Four.

LEADERS IN EMPLOYMENT LAW

LONDON

Aarons, Elaine

Eversheds, London (0171) 919 4500. Partner in Employment and Pensions Group.

Specialisation: Main area of practice is employment law, advising public and private companies, public sector employers and senior management on all aspects of the employment relationship, including contracts, service agreements, board room disputes, restrictive covenants, stress, discrimination and employment related litigation. Has lectured for Industrial Relations Services, Euroforum, the French Chamber of Commerce and at the 1994 Annual Conference of the Employment Lawyers Association. Regularly invited to speak to private business audiences. Editor of Tolley's 'Journal of Employment Law and Practice'.

Prof. Membership: Employment Lawyers Association (elected as the Association's Training Co-ordinator and as a member of its Management Committee), International Bar Association (Labour Law Committee), Industrial Law Society, Employment Law Sub-Committee of City of London Solicitors Society, London South Industrial Tribunal Users Committee.

Career: Qualified in 1982 and has specialised in employment law since that date.

Practised for 9 years with *Norton Rose*. Joined *Jaques & Lewis* (now Eversheds, London) as Employment Partner in 1989.

Personal: Born 7th February 1958. Attended Manchester High School for Girls 1969-1976, then Kings College, London 1976-79. Leisure time is devoted to her three children, charitable fund raising and entertaining. Lives in London.

Adams, Elizabeth J.

Beachcroft Stanleys, London (0171) 242 1011. Qualified 1980. Partner 1986. Employment Department. Advises clients in the public and private sectors in relation to employment and labour relations law.

Andrew, Jill

Langley & Co, London (0171) 814 6637. Principal.

Specialisation: Handles all aspects of contentious and non-contentious employment law. Acted in Payne & others v Port of London Authority (longest ever Industrial Tribunal). Frequent contributor to legal and personnel publications. Regular lecturer. Media contributions have included Newsnight, Panorama, Business Breakfast and Kilroy.

Prof. Membership: Employment Lawyers Association, City of London Solicitors Company.

Career: Qualified in 1981. Joined Langley & Co in 1995. Formerly partner and Head of

Employment Law at Masons and the London Employment Department of Dibb Lupton Broomhead. Director of London Chamber of Commerce since 1992. Chairman of Social Legislation Committee of London Chamber of Commerce 1989-94. Vice Chairman of Employment Affairs Committee of London Chamber of Commerce since 1994. Chairman Employment Lawyers Group 1987-89 and 1991-94.

Personal: Born 8th March 1956. Attended Exeter University (LLB(Hons)) and London School of Economics (MSc in Industrial Relations and Personnel Management). Local Councillor for London Borough of Bromley. School Governor. Lives in Bromley.

Auerbach, Simon

Pattinson and Brewer, London (0171) 405 3033. Qualified 1985. Partner. Employment Department. Practices in all areas of employment law, particularly industrial conflict, transfers of undertakings and trade union law. Born in 1961.

Brearley, Catherine F.N.

Stephenson Harwood, London (0171) 329 4422. Qualified 1989. Partner in the Corporate Department and head of the Employment and Pensions Group. Handles all aspects of employment law with particular emphasis on restrictive covenants and confidential information. Born 12.1.1957.

Burd, Michael

Lewis Silkin, London (0171) 227 8000.

Cavalier, Stephen

Brian Thompson & Partners, London (0171) 637 9761. Qualified 1986. Partner 1989. Main area of practice is employment and trade union law. Also handles personal injury work. Born 26.2.1962.

Cockburn, David

Pattinson and Brewer, London (0171) 405 3033. Qualified 1975. Partner 1978. Employment & Trade Union Law Department. Work includes all aspects of individual and collective labour law. Born 30.11.1948.

Cooper, Edward J.O.

Russell Jones & Walker, London (0171) 837 2808. Partner and Head of Employment Law Department.

Specialisation: Principal area of practice is trade union and employment law. Advises on a wide range of industrial employment and constitutional issues. Also covers administrative law, including a number of judicial review or proposed judicial review cases. Has advised on new police terms and conditions of service, union mergers, Inland Revenue information technology privatisation, and acted in judicial review of Home Secretary on making of police regulations. Clients include the Police Federation and trade unions in the public and private sectors. Author of the trade union section of Butterworths 'Encyclopedia of Forms and Precedents'. Charge-out rate is £130-£175 per hour.

Prof. Membership: Industrial Law Society.

Career: Qualified in 1984. With *Simmons & Simmons* 1982-85. Joined *Russell Jones & Walker* in 1985 and became a Partner in 1988.

Personal: Born 12th June 1959. Educated at Bristol University 1977-80. Leisure interests include jazz, cricket, theatre and tennis. Lives in Putney, London.

Dale, Stephanie

Denton Hall, London (0171) 242 1212. Partner in Employment Group, Litigation Department.

Specialisation: Covers the whole range of contentious and non-contentious employment law. Work includes employment contracts and termination, director + senior management arrangements, industrial relations, discrimination issues, redundancies, review and rationalisation of employment practices for employers, and transactional work including Transfer of Undertakings Regulations. Seconded to British Airways 1990-91 to advise on a wide range of employment issues. Speaker at professional conferences and writer of articles.

Prof. Membership: International Bar Association, Industrial Law Society, Institute of Personnel and Development, Devonshire House Management Club, ILPA.

Career: Qualified 1985. Legal Adviser,

A.T.L. (Teacher's Trade Union) 1986-87. Joined *Denton Hall* in 1987 and became a Partner in 1993.

Personal: Educated at the University of Newcastle 1979-82 (LL.B).

Dalgarno, David

Warner Cranston, London (0171) 403 2900. Partner and Head of Employment Department.

Specialisation: Employment. Advises mainly corporate clients on managing change, redundancy and reorganisation, acquisitions and disposals, discrimination, trade unions, collective and industrial action as well as individual employment issues. Handles a substantial amount of advocacy and litigation work. Has presented many seminars and training programmes to clients.

Prof. Membership: Employment Lawyers Association, City of London Law Society, Employment Law Sub Committee, Industrial Law Society.

Career: Called to the Bar in 1978. Joined Courtaulds Ltd's Industrial Relations Unit in 1979 and moved to the legal department 1982-87. Joined *Warner Cranston* in 1987 and became Partner and Head of Employment Department in 1989.

Personal: Born in 1955. Educated at Hatfield School 1969-74 and Warwick University 1974-77. Leisure pursuits include gardening, travelling and wine tasting. Lives in Surrey.

Davies, Pamela A. Benady

Monier–Williams & Boxalls, London (0171) 405 6195. Partner.

Specialisation: Has specialised in all aspects of employment law since 1971. Acted for Mr Shove in the leading case on compensation for dismissal, Shove v. Downs Surgical plc. Clients include major public companies and banks, advising personnel directors and in-house lawyers.

Career: Called to the Bar in 1955. Practised in partnership *Benady & Benady*, Gibraltar, as a barrister and solicitor. First woman barrister to appear in a Court Martial. Co-editor of 'Phipson on Evidence'. Qualified as a Solicitor in 1971 and joined *Rowe & Maw*, becoming a Partner in 1974. Left in 1985. Now a Partner in *Monier-Williams & Boxalls*.

Davies, James

Lewis Silkin, London (0171) 227 8000. Qualified 1988. Solicitor in Litigation Department (Employment Group). Acts for a wide range of employers and employees in all types of employment-related matters. Also deals with immigration, especially business migration. Born 26.2.1962.

Farr, John R.

Herbert Smith, London (0171) 374 8000. Partner and Head of Employment Section.

Specialisation: His experience relates to both contentious and non-contentious matters and includes injunction applications in

connection with restrictive covenants, competing businesses and group defections; boardroom terms of employment, disputes and dismissals; business transfers and redundancies; pension disputes and Ombudsman referrals; discrimination claims, equal pay investigations and trade union disputes. He also deals with partnership disputes, director's disqualification and has defamation experience.

Career: Qualified in 1974. Became a Partner at *Herbert Smith* in 1982.

Personal: Educated at London University.

Fox, Ronald D.

Fox Williams, London (0171) 628 2000.

Specialisation: Main areas of practice are employment law and partnership law. Specialises in negotiating payments on termination of employment and in advising partners in professional firms. Advises on the sale and purchase of companies and businesses. Recent cases include departures from the boards of listed companies and partnership disputes. Author of ten commercial publications, including 'Payments on Termination of Employment' (in its third edition). Also author of numerous articles in the professional and national press.

Prof Membership: IBA, Law Society, City of London Law Society, Employment Lawyers' Association.

Career: Qualified 1972. Senior Partner at *Fox Williams* from 1989.

Personal: Born 27th September 1946. Member of the Institute of Directors and Fellow of the Royal Society of Arts.

Gaymer, Janet

Simmons & Simmons, London (0171) 628 2020. Head of Employment Law Department.

Specialisation: Employment Law. Work covers collective and individual, contentious and non-contentious matters and occupational health and safety. Acted for the Ministry of Defence on the contractorisation of the Royal Dockyards and for Railtrack on the British Rail privatisation. Written numerous articles on employment law and is a frequent lecturer on employment law topics.

Prof. Memberships: UIA, IBA, Institute of Advanced Legal Studies (Friend).

Career: Articled with *Simmons & Simmons* in 1971, qualified in 1973 and became a Partner in 1977. Currently Head of Employment Law Department.

Personal: Born 11th July 1947. Attended Nuneaton High School for Girls 1958-65, then St Hilda's College, Oxford 1966-70. Read LLM at London School of Economics 1976-78. Leisure pursuits include theatre, music and learning to play the flute. Lives in Effingham.

Green, David

Charles Russell, London (0171) 203 5052. Partner in Employment and Employee

Benefits Unit, Company/ Commercial Department.

Specialisation: Handles all aspects of employment law, including individual employment rights, employee benefits, contractual and policy documentation, discrimination, health and safety, equal opportunities, wrongful dismissal, redundancy, protection of confidentiality and goodwill, collective labour law, immigration and employment issues resulting from mergers and acquisitions. Member of editorial board of Croners Employee and Industrial Relations Briefing. Author of various articles in a range of publications, including Management Consultancy and Tolleys Employment Law. Author of 'Business Basics Staff'. Has spoken at and chaired a number of seminars.

Prof. Membership: Association of Employment Lawyers.

Career: Qualified in 1978. Worked at *Taylors Newmarket* 1976-83 (from 1981 as a Partner); then *McKenna & Co.* 1983-85 and *Clifford Chance* 1985-91. Joined *Charles Russell* in 1991 as a Partner.

Personal: Born 1953. Attended John Lyon School, Forest School and University of London. Committee Member of Downham Town FC. Follows all forms of sports. Leisure interests include gardening. Lives in Downham Market, Norfolk.

Harper, D.A.

Lovell White Durrant, London (0171) 236 0066. Qualified 1978. Partner 1986. Deals with labour and employment issues under national and European law, both contentious and non-contentious.

Howard, Gillian

Mishcon De Reya, London (0171) 405 3711.

Hunter, Ian

Fox Williams, London (0171) 628 2000. Assistant Solicitor in the Employment and Immigration section of the Company Commercial Department.

Specialisation: Main area of practice is employment law. Specialises in negotiation of payments on termination of employment, the Transfer of Undertakings Regulations, immigration and sex and race discrimination. Has handled departures from the boards of listed companies. Co-author of 'Britain's Invisible Earnings'. Regular contributor to The Observer and The Times, as well as to the Hong Kong Standard. Author of numerous articles in the national and professional press.

Prof. Membership: Law Society, Employment Lawyers' Association.

Career: Qualified in 1989 with *Druces & Attlee.* Left to join *Fox Williams* as an Assistant Solicitor in 1990.

Personal: Born 20th July 1961. Attended Campbell College, Belfast, then Bristol University. Interests include writing and current affairs. Lives in London.

Jacobs, Howard R.

Slaughter and May, London (0171) 600 1200. Qualified 1977. Partner specialising in employment and pensions work and employee incentives.

Jeffers, Raymond J.

.**Linklaters & Paines,** London (0171) 606 7080. Qualified 1980. Joined 1978. Employment and Employee Benefits Group. Work includes transfer of businesses, restraint of trade, and European works councils.

Jeffreys, Simon

McKenna & Co, London (0171) 606 9000. Partner and Head of Employment Group.

Specialisation: Has specialised in employment and labour relations law since qualifying, advising predominantly employer clients in the public and private sectors on all aspects of their legal relationship with employees and trade unions. Work includes contractual documentation, corporate policies towards employees, workforce reductions, negotiations with trade unions, anti-discrimination law, employee and trade union aspects of mergers, acquisitions and disposals, together with general advice on all aspects of the day to day employment relationship and the resolution of disputes with employees and trade unions. Has advised on and established approved and unapproved employee share ownership schemes in public and private companies. Has appeared as an advocate in the Industrial Tribunal and has conducted litigation for clients in the Employment Appeal Tribunal, County Court, High Court and Court of Appeal. Frequently advises clients on interpretation of legislation and the impact of proposed legislation. Has spoken at numerous conferences and seminars. Contributor of employment precedents to Longmans 'Practical Commercial Precedents' and author of various articles.

Prof. Membership: Employment Lawyers Association, Industrial Law Society, City of London Law Society (Member of Employment Law Sub-Committee).

Career: Joined *McKenna & Co* in 1980 and qualified in 1982. Became a Partner in 1988.

Keane, Georgina

Titmuss Sainer Dechert, London (0171) 583 5353. Partner and Head of Employment Unit.

Specialisation: Handles all aspects of employment law, discrimination and trade unions, as well as employee benefits including share option schemes and ESOPS. Has conducted numerous speaking engagements at conferences, training for the Institute of Personnel and Development, and in-house training for clients.

Prof. Membership: Employment Lawyers Association, Industrial Law Society.

Career: Qualified in 1988. Called to the Bar in 1975, practised at the common law Bar until 1984. Then became Employment Law

Adviser to the Confederation of British Industry. Joined *Titmuss Sainer & Webb* (now *Titmuss Sainer Dechert*) in 1986 as Head of Employment Unit; became a Partner in 1988.

Personal: Born 3rd February 1954. Leisure interests include theatre and horse riding. Lives in London.

Levinson, Stephen E.

Paisner & Co, London (0171) 353 0299. Qualified 1976. Partner 1979. Head of Employment Department. Has dealt with cases at all levels from the Industrial Tribunal to the House of Lords, including advocacy. Born 12.2.1949.

Mann, Jane

Fox Williams, London (0171) 628 2000. Partner in Employment and Immigration Section, Company/ Commercial Department.

Specialisation: Covers all aspects of employment law for companies and individuals, and also executive immigration including work permits. Has a particular interest in sex discrimination law. Author of a chapter in Tolleys book on employment law. Frequent lecturer at conferences.

Prof. Memberships: Founder Member of Employment Lawyers Association and currently its Secretary. Former Treasurer of the Immigration Law Practitioners Association. Member of the Industrial Law Society; the Employment Law Sub-Committee of the City of London Law Society; The International Bar Association and The American Immigration Lawyers Association. Associate Member of the Institute of Personnel and Development.

Career: Qualified 1981. Worked at *McKenna & Co.* 1979-86, then at *Denton Hall* until 1994, where became a Partner. Joined *Fox Williams* in 1994 as a Partner.

Personal: Born 1957. Attended Cambridge University 1975-78.

Moorman, Jane

D J Freeman, London (0171) 583 4055. Qualified 1984. Partner 1992. Litigation Department (Head of Employment Group). Matters covered include transaction work, contracts of employment, discrimination law, director and other dismissals and industrial relations policy. Born 12.5.1958.

Mordsley, Barry

Harris Rosenblatt & Kramer, London (0171) 242 3254. Partner in Employment Department.

Specialisation: Work includes drafting and advising on contracts of employment and handbooks, terms and conditions, including restrictive covenants, and competition clauses. Also handles partnership law and company law. Has prepared cases for the Industrial Tribunal and Employment Appeals Tribunal as well as High Court and County Court in all areas of employment law and appeared as an advocate in them, including unfair dismissal, redundancy, trade union matters, sex discrimination, race discrimination, equal pay and transfer of undertakings. Co-author of Butterworths Employment Law Guide and author of various articles appearing in journals such as Modern Law Review, the New Law Journal, Employment Law Briefing and Digest and Croners. Has spoken at numerous conferences both in Britain and abroad.

Prof. Memberships: Law Society (on Employment Law Committee), Employment Lawyers Association (on General Committee) and the sub-committees of Publishing, Training and Legislation. Industrial Law Society. Fellow of the Institute of Personnel and Development.

Career: From 1972 to 1989 ran own solicitor's practice specialising in labour law. Joined *Harris, Rosenblatt & Kramer* as a Partner in 1989. A Chairman of Industrial Tribunals (England and Wales) 1984.

Personal: Born 19th January 1947. LLB (1969) and LLM (1972). Leisure interests include theatre, music, current affairs and sports, particularly squash, tennis and cricket. Lives in London.

Osman, Christopher C.

Clifford Chance, London (0171) 600 1000. Partner 1981. Head of Employment Unit. Specialises in all aspects of individual and collective employment law. Born 7.4.1951.

Roskill, Julian W.

Rowe & Maw, London (0171) 248 4282. Partner and Head of Employment and Industrial Relations Group.

Specialisation: Has been dealing with all aspects of employment and industrial relations work since 1974, including employment contracts, personnel policies, work permits, sex and race discrimination, redundancies, dismissals, restrictive covenants, unfair and wrongful dismissals, industrial disputes and employment aspects of acquisitions and sales. Acted in Dupont Steels v. Sirs (1980); the 1984 Fleet Street Dispute; John Michael Design v. Cooke (1987); Rolls Royce Motor Cars v. Price (1993); Rolls Royce Motor Cars v. Mair (1993) and New Victoria Hospital v. Ryan (1993). Writes articles and booklets for Croner Publications and Personnel Today; regular speaker on a variety of employment topics.

Prof. Membership: Law Society, City of London Solicitors Company, Employment Lawyers Association, Industrial Law Society.

Career: Qualified in 1974. Joined *Rowe & Maw* in 1986, becoming a Partner in 1988. Member of Editorial Advisory Board of Croner's Industrial Relations Briefing since 1991. Member of Management and Training Committees of Employment Lawyers Association since 1993. Vice Chairman of Employment Sub-Committee of City of London Solicitors Company since 1993 (previously Secretary for three years).

Personal: Born 22nd July 1950. Attended Horris Hill 1958-1963, then Winchester College 1963-69. Leisure interests include tennis and photography. Lives in London.

Short, Michael

Rowley Ashworth, London (0181) 543 2277. Partner and Head of Trade Union & Employment Law Department.

Specialisation: Handles trade union and employment law for employees and unions. Work includes trade union constitution, rules, amalgamations etc., collective employment law (including industrial action) and individual employment law (including discrimination). Also deals with defamation and pensions litigation. Is currently representing dismissed employees in litigation arising from administrative receiverships of Leyland Daf, Swan Hunter and Ferranti. Lectures occasionally.

Prof. Membership: Law Society, Industrial Law Society.

Career: With *Lovell White & King* 1977-80. Qualified in 1979. With *Lawford & Co* 1980-87 (Partner from 1983). Joined *Rowley Ashworth* as a Partner in 1988.

Personal: Born 2nd May 1951. Educated at St. Philips Grammar School, Birmingham 1962-69 and Sussex University 1970-73 (BA in Philosophy).

Warner, David C.

Warner Cranston, London (0171) 403 2900. Senior Partner in Employment Law.

Specialisation: Principal area of practice is employment law with particular reference to senior executives, including service agreements, share options, directors' responsibilities, financial structuring, pensions and termination. Other main area of work is company/ commercial.

Prof. Membership: Law Society, United Oxford and Cambridge Universities Club.

Career: Qualified in 1973 while with *Polden Bishop & Gale*, then with *Lovell White & King* 1973-78. Based in Brussels office for two years. Founder of *Warner Cranston* in 1979.

Personal: Born 28.8.1947. Attended Whitgift School, Croydon 1957-65, then St Edmund Hall, Oxford 1965-68. Past Master of Worshipful Company of Makers of Playing Cards. Leisure pursuits include rare breeds and barges. Lives in London.

Williamson, Andrew P.F.

Lovell White Durrant, London (0171) 236 0066. Qualified 1980. Partner 1980. Employment Group. Deals with all aspects of employment and labour law. Born 1942.

Younson, Fraser R.

Baker & McKenzie, London (0171) 919 1000. (Bar 1975)Partner in Employment Department.

Specialisation: Main area of practice is employment law, covering executive

termination, employment aspects of mergers and acquisitions, sex and race discrimination, restrictive covenants, unfair dismissal and redundancy, wrongful dismissal, collective labour law, industrial disputes, EC labour law, Industrial Tribunal advocacy and compensation claims. Author of Employment Law Handbook, Employment Law and Business Transfers - A Practical Guide, Croner's Industrial Relations Law, and contributor to PLC and the Law Society Gazette on employment law issues. Lectures extensively on labour law.

Prof. Memberships: Law Society, Industrial Law Society, Vice-Chairman of Employment Lawyers Association.

Career: Qualified for the Bar in 1975, and for the Law Society in 1987. Previously Employment Law Adviser to British Aerospace Group HQ, and previously Editor of IDS Brief. Joined *Baker & MacKenzie* in 1983, becoming a Partner in 1990.

Personal: Born 11th November 1952. Attended Oxford University. Lives in Woodhurst, Cambs.

Coll, Henry A.

Elliott Duffy Garrett, Belfast (01232) 245034.

Loughlin, Grahame

Tughan & Co, Belfast (01232) 553300.

Brett, Adam T.G.

L'Estrange & Brett, Belfast (01232) 230426.

Turtle, William B.W.

Carson & McDowell, Belfast (01232) 244951.

Cassidy, Fiona A.

Jones and Cassidy, Belfast (01232) 642290.

Cross, S.M. Patrick

Cleaver Fulton & Rankin, Belfast (01232) 243141.

Anderson, Isabel J.

Drummond Miller WS, Edinburgh (0131) 663 9568. Partner specialising in employment law.

Specialisation: Main area of practice is employment law. Certified by Law Society of Scotland as a specialist in this field. Has 14 years experience in general chamber practice and court work. Researched and wrote the first drafts of 'Mental Health: A Guide to the Law in Scotland' (Butterworths Scottish Legal Education Trust).

Prof. Membership: Law Society of Scotland, Industrial Law Group.

Career: Qualified in 1982, having joined *Drummond Miller WS* in 1980. Became Partner in 1985. Currently Senior Partner with responsibility for offices in Midlothian.

Personal: Born 29th May 1957. Attended Dunoon Grammar 1969-74, then Edinburgh University 1975-79 (LLB Hons). Notary Public and Writer to the Signet. Chairman of Midlothian Enterprise Trust Ltd. Lay Leader in Independent Christian Church. Leisure pursuits include walking, boating, skiing, tennis, bird watching and spoken French. Lives in Edinburgh.

Ashtiany, Sue

Cole and Cole, Oxford (01865) 791122. Qualified 1986. Partner 1989. Employment and Intellectual Property Department. Main area of practice is employment and discrimination law. Has acted for the Equal Opportunities Commission.

Atack, Iain F.

Kidstons & Co, Glasgow (0141) 221 6551. Senior Partner.

Specialisation: Main area of practice is employment law: accredited as a specialist by the Law Society of Scotland. Advises mainly employers on all aspects of Employment law. Represents at Tribunals in Scotland and England. Also handles general civil litigation and factoring law. Advises on contractual disputes, covering claims for damages for personal injuries. Advises invoice factors on all commercial matters. Major clients include several large Plc's operating both in England and Scotland, together with many medium sized companies. Lectures for Law Society at PQLE conferences and the Scottish Young Lawyers' Association. Tutor in Advocacy & Pleading at Glasgow University.

Prof. Membership: Law Society of Scotland, Royal Faculty of Procurators in Glasgow, Industrial Law Group. Member Law Society of Scotland Employment Law Committee.

Career: Qualified in 1971. Joined *Kidstons & Company* in 1972, becoming a Partner in 1975 and Senior Partner in 1993. Council Member of Royal Faculty of Procurators 1989-92. Committee Member of Industrial Law Group since 1984. Chairman of NHBC Appeal Tribunal since 1990.

Personal: Born 22nd November 1947. Attended Kelvinside Academy, Glasgow 1954-66, then St Andrew's University 1966-69. Leisure interests include walking and skiing. Lives in Killearn.

Barry, Quintin

Donne Mileham & Haddock, Brighton (01273) 329833. Chairman. Partner 1961. Company and Commercial department.

Specialisation: Main area of practice is employment law. Advises on all aspects and conducts employment related litigation, including advocacy before industrial tribunals and EAT. Also advises on general commercial law. Major clients include Forbuoys plc, Vosper Thornycroft (UK) Ltd, East Sussex Health Authority, various NHS trusts, University of Sussex. Regularly addresses

conferences and seminars. Charge out rate - up to £120 per hour.

Prof. Membership: ELA, Law Society, Sussex Law Society, Legal Aid Practitioners Group.

Career: Qualified 1958. Assistant solicitor, *Cronin & Son* 1959-60. Assistant solicitor, *Mileham Scatliff & Allen* 1960-62. Partner, *Mileham Scatliff & Allen* 1962-70. Managing Partner, *Donne Mileham Haddock* 1970-91, Chairman 1991 to date. Part-time Chairman Industrial Tribunal 1994 to date.

Personal: Born on 7th March 1936. Educated at Eastbourne College and Open University. Principal hobby is the study and writing of history. Chairman Southern FM, Deputy Chairman South Downs Health NHS Trust. Lives in Shoreham-by-Sea, West Sussex.

Bridge, John

Bridge McFarland Solicitors, Grimsby (01472) 348566.

Brown, Anthony

Wansbroughs Willey Hargrave, Bristol (0117) 926 8981. Partner in Commercial Litigation Department.

Specialisation: All contentious and non-contentious aspects of employment law, including drafting employment contracts and disciplinary procedures, employee renumeration and representation at tribunals and courts. Also handles all types of business disputes, including disputes with suppliers and infringement of intellectual property rights.

Prof. Membership: Industrial Law Society, Industrial Tribunal Users Consultative Committee, Institute of Credit Management.

Career: Qualified in 1983. Worked at *Laytons* 1981-83, *Osborne Clarke* 1983-84 and *Wansbroughs Willey Hargrave* from 1984. Became a Partner in 1988.

Brown, Nicola

Mills & Reeve, Cambridge + 44(0)1223 364422.

Bryan, J. Howard

Eversheds, Leeds (0113) 243 0391. Partner and Head of Litigation Department.

Specialisation: Has been an employment specialist for more than 20 years with considerable experience of Tribunals and advocacy. Since 1980 has been responsible for the establishment and running of the firm's Employment Group, consisting of 2 Partners and 8 assistants within the Litigation department. In addition to contentious work, the Employment Group advises on the Acquired Rights Directive and the Transfer of Undertakings Regulations, advice on collective agreements and Trade Union law (discrimination and equal pay), advice on suitability and enforcement of restrictive covenants and issues relating to confidentiality, and the conduct of litigation relating to those matters. Has recently advised major institutions on re-

location and redundancy issues, a major plc on all aspects of plant closure and other employers on introduction of contract flexibilty (i.e. annual hours contracts). Successfully argued before an Industrial Tribunal the application of Transfer Regulations to the Catering Licence at the Science Museum (one of the first such cases), and took a case to the Court of Appeal in June 1994 involving dismissal of dockworkers for industrial action as the main or principal reason for dismissal. North East Regional adviser to the British Printing Industries Federation.

Prof. Membership: Employment Lawyers Association, Industrial Law Society, British German Jurists Association.

Career: Qualified and joined *Eversheds Hepworth & Chadwick* in 1968. Became a Partner in 1971.

Personal: Born 24th April 1944. Educated at Silcoates School and Leeds University. Governor of Silcoates School since 1977. Member of Leeds Law Society 1980-1994. Interests include sailing in Scotland, squash, tennis and ski-ing. Lives in York.

Burnside, David M.

Burnside Kemp Fraser, Aberdeen (01224) 624602. Senior Partner in Court Department.

Specialisation: Main area of practice is employment. Has handled industrial tribunal cases since 1967 in the fields of redundancy, unfair dismissal, sexual and racial discrimination and Transfer of Undertakings. Acts for a number of major clients in these matters. Accredited by the Law Society of Scotland as an Employment Law Specialist. Also handles personal injury work. Since 1970 has worked predominantly for claimants. Has substantial experience of offshore cases, although also deals with many cases involving injury at work or in road traffic accidents. Joint lead negotiator in Piper Alpha for claimants. Group spokesman for steering committees on other matters such as helicopter crashes: Chinook, Brent and Cormorant. Author of articles in local newspapers on employment law matters. Gives occasional lectures for Aberdeen University, the Law Society IPM and other outside babies. Has considerable media experience arising from matters of local interest.

Prof. Membership: Law Society of Scotland, Society of Advocates in Aberdeen, Association of Personal Injury Lawyers, Aberdeen Bar Association.

Career: Qualified in 1966. Established *Messrs Burnside Advocates* as Senior Partner in 1989; firm became *Burnside Kemp Fraser* in 1994. President of Junior Chamber of Commerce, Aberdeen, 1978-79; President of Aberdeen Bar Association 1987-89; Board Member of Legal Defence Union since 1990; Scottish convenor and member of National Executive Committee of APIL since 1990.

Personal: Born 5th March 1943.

Chapman, Christopher J.

Brian Thompson & Partners, Sheffield (0114) 270 1556.

Specialisation: Consultant to Brian Thompson & Partners. Also has 25 years of personal injury litigation and employment law. Involved in the Mineworkers' Pension Scheme litigation; acted for the Yorkshire Area of the NUM during the 1984/85 Miners Strike; represented Arthur Scargill in his action against the South Yorkshire Police. Frequent lecturer and television and radio broadcaster. Chairman of Industrial Tribunals (part-time).

Prof. Membership: Law Society; Industrial Law Society; Haldane Society.

Career: Qualified in 1972. Assistant solicitor, W H Thompson 1972-73. Partner, Casson & Co. 1973-79. Since 1979, partner at Brian Thompson & Partners. Consultant to Brian Thompson & Partners - August 1995 onwards. Appointed part-time Chairman of Industrial Tribunals-July 1995.

Personal: Educated at Lewis County Grammar School for Boys 1959-66, London School of Economics 1966-69, and at Birmingham College of Commerce 1969-70. Governor of Northern College. Keen amateur artist. Born 8th December 1947. Lives in Sheffield.

Chitty, Martin

Pinsent Curtis, Birmingham (0121) 200 1050.

Christie, Reginald G.

Raeburn Christie & Co, Aberdeen (01224) 640101. Qualified 1971. Partner 1975. 15 years experience advising in relation to and conduct of Industrial Tribunals, methods of employment termination and financial provision and drafting of employment documentation. Born 1.7.1948.

Clarke, Mary

Alsop Wilkinson, Manchester (0161) 834 7760.

Cockburn, Alistair M.

Tilston MacLaurin, Glasgow (0141) 332 5666. Qualified 1972. Partner 1974. Litigation Department. Employment Law Department. Represents employers before industrial tribunals. Born 8.3.1950.

Connal, R. Craig

McGrigor Donald, Glasgow (0141) 248 6677. Qualified 1977. Partner 1980. Litigation Department. Main area of practice is employment law. Also covers contentious areas of planning, especially inquiries. Born 7.7.54.

Dillarstone, Robert

Greenwoods, Peterborough (01733) 555244. Partner and Head of Employment and Employee Benefits Department.

Specialisation: Handles all aspects of employment law, almost exclusively for employers.

Prof. Membership: Employment Lawyers Association, Industrial Law Society, Discrimination Practitioners Association.

Career: Joined *Greenwoods* in 1984 and qualified in 1986. Became a Partner in 1989.

Personal: Born 15th October 1961. Educated at University College, London 1980-83 (LLB Hons). Leisure activities include playing football and juggling (balls, not files). Lives in Peterborough.

Du-Feu, Vivian J.

Eversheds, Cardiff (01222) 471147. Qualified 1979. Partner 1984. Head of Litigation and Employment Department. Handles contentious and non-contentious matters for the private and public sector. Work includes advocacy at industrial tribunals and EATs. Author of three Cronor Employment books. Born 17.3.1954.

Duncan, Nikki

Bond Pearce, Plymouth (01752) 266633. Qualified 1979. Partner 1985. Commercial Division. Main area of practice is employment law including litigation, employment aspects of corporate transactions and discrimination.

Dyson, George M.

Burges Salmon, Bristol (0117) 939 2000. Qualified 1972. Partner 1977. Commercial Litigation Employment Unit. Main area of practice is employment work, acting for both employers and employees. Also experienced in contentious commercial work.

Edwards, K. Martin

Mace & Jones, Liverpool (0151) 236 8989. Partner in the Commercial Department, Employment Law Unit.

Specialisation: Employment law specialist with extensive advocacy experience in Industrial Tribunals and before the Employment Appeal Tribunal. Advises on all aspects of industrial relations law and acts for major clients in the public and private sectors throughout the UK. Also expert in relation to computer contracts. Major cases include Lavery v. Plessey Telecommunications (maternity leave). Advised on film 'Letter to Brezhnev'. Author of 'Dismissal Law', 'Managing Redundancies', 'Careers in the Law', 'How to get the Best Deal from your Employer', 'Understanding Computer Contracts' and numerous articles. Lectures frequently and has appeared on 'Legal Network' (TV Programme on Tribunals).

Prof. Membership: Law Society, Liverpool Law Society, Employment Lawyers Association, Society for Computers and Law, Society of Authors, Crime Writers Association.

Career: Qualified in 1980 while at *Mace & Jones*. Became a Partner in 1984.

Personal: Born 7th July 1955. Attended Balliol College, Oxford 1974-77. Leisure pursuits include writing crime novels about Liverpool Solicitor Harry Devlin, the first of which was nominated for the best first crime novel of 1991. Lives in Lymm, Cheshire.

Field, Roger

Higgs & Sons, Brierley Hill (01384) 76411. Qualified 1970. Partner 1974. Employment Department. Handles all aspects: 75 per cent employer, 25 per cent employee. Emphasis on national retailer clients. Born 13.1.1946.

Flanagan, Thomas D.

Booth & Co., Leeds (0113) 283 2000. Partner. Head of Employment Law Department.

Specialisation: Main area of practice is employment law, providing a full range of advice to individuals, partnerships, companies and institutions, including a number of banks, building societies, local authorities, health authorities and NHS Trusts, universities and colleges and clients in the industrial, manufacturing, retail and health care sectors plus Central Government Agencies. Experienced in drafting service agreements and other employment documents and policies. Handles work covering industrial relations, sex and race discrimination, variation and management of terms of employment, disciplinary issues, redundancy, unfair and wrongful dismissal, advice on tax and corporate aspects of termination packages and the impact of EC law, as well as the Transfer of Undertakings Regulations and their impact on corporate transactions, including contracting out, in the public and private sectors. Acted in Royal Bank of Scotland v. Guthrie (concerning return to work part-time after maternity) and London and Solent v. Brookes (enforcement of a non-dealing restriction against a former employee). Has provided advice on TUPE and contracting out to a number of local authorities, high street banks and major retailers and on equalisation of pension and retirement ages post Barber to a major corporate group, bank and building society. Is advising a number of clients in different sectors on part-timers claiming access to pension benefits. Author of the chapters on Transfer of Undertakings Regulations, Variation of Contract, Employment and Self-Employment in 'Tolley's Employment Law'. Has had articles and letters published in various journals including 'IPM Newsletter', 'Local Government Chronicle', the UK Regional Handbook of the LSCA, 'Acquisitions Monthly', 'The Financial Times', 'The Telegraph' and the 'Yorkshire Post'. Has given public seminars on various topics, including to non-executive directors on executive packages, to the Local Government Lawyers Association on TUPE and CCT. Gives frequent sector-based or client-based seminars on topics of current interest to them.

Prof. Membership: Employment Lawyers Association, Industrial Law Society, Institute of Personnel and Development.

Career: Qualified in 1979. With *Brian Thompson & Partners* in Manchester 1980-84, then *Barlow Lyde & Gilbert* in London until June 1985. Joined *Speechly Bircham* in 1985 and became a Partner in 1988. Joined *Booth & Co.* as a Partner in 1992.

Personal: Born 16th January 1954. Educated at London University 1972-76. Interests include playing folk and blues guitar, photography, art, theatre, reading and listening to blues and jazz. Lives in Harrogate.

Fletcher, Kevin J.

Jacksons, Middlesbrough (01642) 244154. Senior Partner and head of Company/Commercial Department.

Specialisation: Principal area of practice is employment law advising and representing mainly employers in all aspects, both contentious and non-contentious. Advocates in tribunals throughout the country. Also handles company/commercial work and commercial litigation. Important cases handled recently include: Dhanjal v. British Steel, a test case on Sikhs and hard hats in the steel industry; Hoggans v. British Bakeries Ltd, a multi-applicant case on changes to terms and conditions of employment. Also dealt with the privatisation and sale of the Tees and Hartlepool Port Authority in 1992. Major clients include British Steel plc, British Bakeries Ltd, Black and Decker, National Rivers Authority and the National Farmers Union. Part-time chairman of Industrial Tribunals in 1991. Regularly gives seminars to clients, local professional bodies and employers' associations.

Prof. Membership: Law Society and Employment Lawyers' Association.

Career: Qualified in 1971. Appointed a Partner at *Jacksons* in 1972. Became Senior Partner in 1995.

Personal: Born 6th March 1947. Educated at Hull Grammar School 1958-65; St Catharine's College, Cambridge 1965-68 and The College of Law, Guildford 1968-69. Also a non-executive director of Cleveland Ambulance NHS Trust. Leisure interests include music, sport, art, reading and travel. Lives in Middlesbrough.

Gleeson, Judith A.J.C.

Hedleys, East Horsley (01483) 284567. Partner in Litigation Department.

Specialisation: Main area of practice is employment law, offering employer/employee and litigation advice, on such matters as contract drafting and dispute resolution. Member of Union Law Panel. Also handles commercial litigation. Acted in Gately v. United Airlines on transfer of undertakings. Has made regular radio broadcasts and occasional TV appearances since 1983.

Prof. Membership: Industrial Law Society, Employment Lawyers Association.

Career: Qualified in 1981. Joined *Hedleys* in 1981, becoming a Partner in 1988. Legal Adviser to Leatherhead CAB since 1984. Appointed Part time Chairman of Industrial Tribunals in 1994 and visiting Industrial Fellow, Kingston University.

Personal: Born 24th August 1955. Attended Lady Margaret Hall, Oxford 1973-77. Leisure interests include reading and modern art. Lives in Leatherhead, Surrey.

Goodier, Colin J.

Pinsent Curtis, Birmingham (0121) 200 1050. Qualified 1972. Partner 1987. Head of Litigation Department. Main area of practice is employment law. Also experienced in defamation and general commercial litigation.

Grierson, M.I.

Cobbett Leak Almond, Manchester (0161) 833 3333. Partner in Commercial Department.

Specialisation: Main area of practice is employment and labour law, acting for the brewing, leisure, engineering and newspaper industries and industry in general. Adviser to NW Brewers & Licensed Retailers Association, a BPIF regional solicitor, and adviser to several large companies and organisations. Also handles any employment related issues in any work place such as pensions and remuneration packages. Acted in the 'Messenger' dispute with NGA.

Prof. Membership: Law Society, Employment Lawyers Association, Licensing Executives Society.

Career: Joined *Cobbett Leak Almond* in 1967 and qualified in 1970. Became a Partner in ????.

Personal: Born 6th August 1944. Educated at Lincoln College, Oxford 1963-66. Leisure interests include sport, music, literature and languages. Lives in Pendle, Lancashire.

Griffiths, John R.

See under Medical Negligence.

Hantom, Charles C.

Whittles, Manchester (0161) 228 2061. Senior Partner.

Specialisation: Main areas of practice are employment, trade union and industrial. Handles Industrial Tribunal and EAT work. Undertakes advocacy for industrial tribunals. Also handles High Court Injunctive proceedings. Predominantly Trade Union practice. Gives occasional seminars for Trade Union clients.

Prof. Membership: Employment Lawyers Association.

Career: Qualified 1967. Joined *Whittles* in 1969, becoming a Partner in 1972.

Personal: Born 24th January 1942. Attended Windermere Grammar School 1954-60, Nottingham University 1960-63, and College of Law 1966. Leisure interests include fishing, walking, house renovations, classic cars and outdoor pursuits. Lives in Bowden.

Harney, Nicolas J.

Nightingales, Manchester (0161) 832 6722. Partner in Litigation Department.

Specialisation: Specialises in employment law, advising mainly employers, but employee work also undertaken. Experienced advocate in the Industrial Tribunals and Employment Appeal Tribunal. Main areas: unfair dismissal, redundancy, equal pay, transfer of undertakings, trade union law,

race and sex discrimination, drafting service agreements, Wages Act cases. Also undertakes commercial litigation, including engineering and construction contract claims in the High Court and Arbitrations. Clients include members of the GEC Group. British Aerospace, Ricardo Aerospace, Kemira Fertilisers, Osram. Charge out rate: £110 - £125.

Prof. Membership: Law Society, Manchester Law Society.

Career: Qualified 1973. Director of Goldberg Ensemble Ltd. Member of the Board of Manchester YMCA. Partner 1978. Notary Public.

Personal: Born 17th November 1948. Educated De La Salle College (Salford) and Hull University (LLB 1970). Leisure pursuits include music, badminton and sailing. Lives in Worsley, Manchester.

Hearn, Keith

Ford and Warren, Leeds (0113) 243 6601.

Henney, Colin C.

Henmans, Oxford (01865) 722181. Partner in Commercial Department.

Specialisation: Sole area of practice is employment. Handles the full range of employee and employer work, both contentious and non-contentious. Has appeared before EAT as well as undertaking almost all advocacy in cases before ITs. Major clients include DAS Legal Expenses Insurance, TWR Group, Baxter Healthcare and British Bio-tech. Involved in ACAS training, giving seminars at individual conciliation officer workshops since 1990.

Prof. Membership: Employment Lawyers' Association, Industrial Law Society.

Career: Qualified in 1982. Articled with *Rickerby Jessop Flint* 1980-82; joined *Henmans* in 1983, becoming a Partner in 1987; Managing Partner 1991-3.

Personal: Born 25.11.1957. Attended Daniel Stewart's and Melville College, Edinburgh 1962-75, and Oxford University 1976-79 (Law, BA). Leisure interests include music, golf and languages. Lives in Eynsham, Oxfordshire.

Hopkins, Martin W.

Eversheds, Birmingham (0121) 233 2001. Partner and Head of Employment and Pensions.

Specialisation: Main area of practice is employment and industrial relations law. Has wide experience of handling all types of contentious and non-contentious employment work in both the public and private sector. Particular strength in discrimination and maternity law. Heads team of 8 full time specialist employment lawyers. Co-author of 'Health and Safety: Are You at Risk?' (1993) and of 'The Maternity Manual' (1994). Speaks regularly on employment issues in all types of forum, particularly at the IPD events.

Career: Qualified in 1982. Joined *Eversheds*

Wells & Hind in 1980, becoming a Partner in 1989, Head of Litigation in 1991 and Head of Employment and Pensions Department in 1994.

Personal: Born 28th October 1957. Attended Warwick School 1971-76 and Coventry University 1976-79. Leisure interests include travel, theatre and family. Lives in Lighthorne, near Warwick.

Hosie, Nicol M.

Ledingham Chalmers, Aberdeen (01224) 408408. Qualified 1975. Partner 1977. Litigation Department. Main areas of practice are employment and personal injuries claims. Part-time Chairman of Industrial Tribunals since 1978. Born 18.1.1951.

Jones, Alan G.

Dibb Lupton Broomhead, Birmingham (0121) 200 1188. Qualified 1978. Partner 1983. Human Resources Department. Specialises in employment law. Born 17.5.1953.

Jones, Beverley

Jones and Cassidy, Belfast (01232) 642290.

Lamb, Norman P.

Steele & Co, Norwich (01603) 627107. Qualified 1984. Partner 1987. Commercial Department. Specialises in employment work, particularly tribunal advocacy, unfair dismissal, redundancy, sex and race discrimination and the Equal Treatment Directive. Also does non-contentious employment work. Born 16.9.1957.

Lefevre, Frank H.

The Frank Lefevre Practice, Aberdeen (01224) 208208. Founding Partner in Litigation Department.

Specialisation: Main areas of practice are employment law and personal injury claims. Also handles all aspects of court practice. Acted in the Piper Alpha disaster in 1988 and handled 33 of the 35 claims in the Ocean Odyssey explosion in 1988.

Prof. Membership: Law Society of Scotland, Aberdeen Society of Advocates (President).

Career: Qualified in 1958. Founded *The Frank Lefevre Practice* in 1970. Chairman of Quantum Claims Compensation Specialists Ltd, Britain's first specialist 'no win no fee' company.

Personal: Born 4th December 1934. Attended Aberdeen University 1953-58 (MA, LLB). Leisure interests include golf, squash and music. Lives in Aberdeen.

Lockett, Paul

Davies Arnold Cooper, Manchester (0161) 839 8396. Partner in Corporate Department.

Specialisation: Covers all areas of corporate work, particularly transaction based work. Particular experience in management buyouts. Also does employment work, principally acting on behalf of employers.

Major clients include Hoopsafe plc; James Halstead Group plc; North West Water Group plc; Yates Brothers Wine Lodges plc; Air Kilroe Limited; Avonmore Dairies (UK) Limited; Four Seasons Hotel (Investments) Ltd; Hertel (UK) Limited; KDL Limited; River Wall Properties Ltd; Systemhouse (UK) Ltd; Tameside Care Group Ltd; Whiteley Electronics Ltd. Contributes to DAC reports and regional publications on corporate and employment matters. Frequent provider of lecture workshop presentations to clients and intermediaries. Has made regular radio appearances on corporate and employment matters. Charge-out rate £150/hour

Prof. Membership: The Law Society.

Career: Qualified 1986. Was at *Chaffe Street* 1985-87 and then *Marsons* 1987-91. Joined *Davies Arnold Cooper* in 1991, becoming a partner in 1994.

pr. Born 1st February 1962. Attended De La Salle College 1973-80, Manchester University 1980-83 and the College of Law, Chester 1983-84. Leisure pursuits include ski-ing, golf and theatre. Lives in Sale.

Mackay, Malcolm R.

Mackay Simon, Edinburgh (0131) 220 2900. Partner.

Specialisation: Practices only in the field of employment law. Co-author of 'Employment Law Update' in the Journal of the Law Society of Scotland; Co-editor of Greens Employment Law Bulletin. Lectures in employment law at various Universities. Particular interests - Industrial Relations, Transfer of Undertakings and Discrimination.

Prof. Membership: Society to Writers of HM Signet; Member of Institute of Personnel and Development. Law Society of Scotland Employment Law Committee.

Career: Qualified in 1975. Founded *Mackay WS* now *Mackay Simon* in 1988.

Personal: Born 24th January 1953. Attended Edinburgh University. Lives in Edinburgh.

MacLeod, D. Ian K.

Shepherd & Wedderburn WS, Edinburgh (0131) 228 9900. Partner in Litigation Department.

Specialisation: Main areas of practice are general commercial litigation and employment law. Accredited as Employment Law Specialist by Law Society of Scotland. Solicitor in Scotland to Department of Employment. Also solicitor in Scotland to HM Customs & Excise and to Health and Safety Executive. Occasional lecturer in post qualification legal education; Member of Court of Session Rules Council.

Prof. Membership: Law Society of Scotland, WS Society, Scottish Law Agents Society, Edinburgh Bar Association.

Career: Qualified in 1960. Joined *Shepherd & Wedderburn WS* in 1957, becoming a Partner in 1964.

Personal: Born 19th April 1937. Attended

Edinburgh University 1955-59 (MA, LLB). Governor of Rannoch School and Church Elder.

MacLeod, Euan R.

Dundas & Wilson CS, Edinburgh (0131) 228 8000. Partner in Litigation Department.

Specialisation: Main areas of practice are employment law (Head of Employment Law Group and accredited by the Law Society of Scotland as an Employment Law Specialist); and commercial litigation.

Prof. Membership: Law Society of Scotland, Society of Writers to HM Signet, Scottish Law Agents Society.

Career: Qualified in 1967. Joined *Dundas & Wilson CS* as a Partner in 1972.

Personal: Born 17th January 1944. Attended Edinburgh University 1962-65 (LL.B). Leisure interests include theatre, walking and reading. Lives in Edinburgh.

Manning-Cox, Andrew

See under Construction & Civil Eng..

McCann, R. William C.

See under Corporate Finance.

McKenzie, Rod

Harper Macleod, Glasgow (0141) 221 8888. Qualified 1982. Partner in the Litigation Department specialising in employment law. Practice also includes building and construction litigation. Born 1.7.1958.

McMullen, John

Pinsent Curtis, Leeds (0113) 244 5000. Partner and Head of Employment Unit.

Specialisation: Employment law (all aspects). Leading authority on transfer of undertakings. Part-time Professor of Labour Law at University of Leeds. Author "Business Transfers and Employee Rights", "Butterworths Employment Law Guide", "Tolley's Employment Law" (Joint) and numerous articles in business and legal journals.

Prof. Membership: MIPD. FRSA. Law Society's Employment Law Committee. Industrial Law Society Executive Committee.

Career: Qualified in 1978. With *Rotheras* 1978-80. Fellow in Law at Girton College, Cambridge 1980-86. Bye Fellow since 1986. Partner, *Rotheras* 1986-91. Partner and Head of the Employment Unit, *Simpson Curtis* 1991.

Personal: Born 29th March 1954. Educated Emmanuel College, Cambridge (BA 1975, 1st (Class Hons), MA 1979, PhD 1993).

McWatt, H. Andrea

Davies Wallis Foyster, Liverpool (0151) 236 6226. Partner specialising in all aspects of employment law both contentious and non-contentious.

Meiklejohn, William A.

Blackadder Reid Johnston, Dundee

(01382) 229222. Qualified 1973. Partner 1978. Commercial Department. Accredited as a specialist in employment law by the Law Society of Scotland.

Molyneux, Pauline A.
Rollit Farrell & Bladon, Hull (01482) 323239. Partner in Litigation Department.

Specialisation: Head of Employment Law Unit. Covers all aspects, contentious and non-contentious, including review and drafting of documentation, advocacy before Tribunals, the conduct of High Court cases and advising on employment consequences of commercial sales. Has undertaken a variety of Tribunal cases including sex and race discrimination claims; applications by Trade Unions for an interim order and for a protective award; cases involving the application of the Transfer of Undertakings Regulations and cases involving injunctions to enforce post-termination employment restrictions. Author of articles in various law journals.

Prof. Membership: Employment Lawyers Association, Industrial Law Society, Law Society.

Career: Qualified in 1977. Worked at *Clifford Turner* 1977-79, *Field Fisher and Martineau* 1979-84. Senior lecturer at the College of Law, Lancaster Gate, 1984-86; *Clifford Chance* 1986-89. Joined *Rollit Farrell & Bladon* as a Partner in 1989. Part-time Chairman of Industrial Tribunals (appointed 1995).

Moore, Nicholas
Osborne Clarke, Bristol (0117) 923 0220. Partner and Head of Employment Unit.

Specialisation: Has specialised in Employment Law and Industrial Relations since 1971. Represents major employers in a wide range of commercial sectors. Also responsible for the *Hill Taylor Dickinson* commodities team, with personal involvement principally on disputes under GAFTA, FOSFA and LRBA. Regularly speaks at external and internal conferences and seminars.

Prof. Membership: Law Society, Member of CBI Employment Law Panel.

Career: Qualified 1971, having joined *Hill Dickinson & Co.* in 1969. Became a Partner in 1976.

Personal: Born December 1947. Attended Oundle School 1960-64, then Trinity College, Cambridge, 1965-68. Leisure interests include family, riding, gardening and country sports. Lives near Tunbridge Wells.

Nicholls, Thomas
Dibb Lupton Broomhead, Manchester (0161) 839 0202. Regional Managing Partner and Head of Human Resources Law.

Specialisation: Main areas of practice are employment and discrimination. Has practised in this field continuously since 1982. *Dibb Lupton Broomhead* has the largest national team of employment law specialists (25). Also holds the position of regional managing partner for the Manchester office of the

firm. Experienced advocate, reported cases include Commission for Racial Equality v. Lambeth and Sharma v. British Gas. Author of Tolley's Discrimination Law Handbook. Lectures widely on employment issues.

Prof. Membership: Employment Lawyers Association.

Career: Qualified in 1980 for the Bar and 1990 as a Solicitor. Legal Officer, Commission for Racial Equality 1982-88. Worked with *Paisner & Co.* 1988-92. Joined *Dibb Lupton Broomhead* in 1992 as a Partner and Head of Human Resources Law.

Personal: Born 2nd July 1953. Member of Armstrong Siddeley owners club. Leisure interests include classic cars and politics. Lives in Manchester.

Nickson, Sue
Hammond Suddards, Manchester (0161) 834 2222. Partner in charge of Manchester Employment Unit of three specialist solicitors.

Specialisation: Handles a full ambit of contentious and non-contentious employment law issues ranging from public to the private sector, including retail, manufacturing and construction companies. Also handles NHS Trust work. Has contributed to various journals, and lectures frequently.

Prof. Membership: Law Society, Employment Lawyers Association, Member of Salford University Council.

Career: Qualified in 1988. Worked at *Pannone & Partners* 1986-94, as a Partner from 1991 and as Head of Employment Department from 1992. Joined *Hammond Suddards* as a Partner in 1994.

Personal: Born 1st January 1964. Holds a First Class Honours Degree from Caius College, Cambridge 1982-85, with a TAPP postgraduate scholarship. Associate Member of Institute of Linguists. Leisure interests include motor bike riding, ballroom dancing and theatre.

Norbury, Peter
Eversheds, Manchester (0161) 832 6666.

Owens, David J.
Bevan Ashford, Bristol (0117) 923 0111. Partner in Commercial Litigation Department.

Specialisation: Main area of practice is employment law, including both contentious and non-contentious work. Particular experience in dismissal cases, transfer of undertakings (especially in relation to public sector) and discrimination issues. General commercial litigation also undertaken, including intellectual property, insolvency and company work.

Prof. Memberships: Bristol Law Society, Employment Lawyers' Association, Society of Computers and Law.

Career: Joined *Bevan Ashford* in 1982. Qualified 1984. Partner 1990.

Personal: Born 23rd July 1958. Attended Oxford University 1977-80.

Pike, Malcolm J.
Addleshaw Sons & Latham, Manchester (0161) 832 5994. Partner. Head of Employment Unit.

Specialisation: Main areas of practice are employment and industrial relations. Includes drafting and advising on terms and conditions of employment, personnel policies and collective agreements, industrial tribunals and other trade union matters, defending and prosecuting High Court and industrial tribunal proceedings and advising on employment aspects of the sale and reorganisation of companies and businesses. Various publications include 'The Lawyers Factbook', 'Essential Facts Employment' and Butterworths Encyclopaedia of Forms and Precedents. Regular speaker at seminars and conferences. Acted in Doughty v. Rolls Royce Plc (1992) and Micklefield v. SAC Technology Ltd (1990).

Prof. Membership: Law Society, Employment Lawyers Association, Industrial Law Society, Manchester Industrial Relations Society, IBA.

Career: Qualified in 1984 with *Hepworth & Chadwick* in Leeds. Moved to *Freshfields*, London in 1984. Left to join *Addleshaw Sons & Latham*, Manchester, as a Partner in 1992.

Personal: Born 22nd August 1959. Attended Leicester University 1978-81. Leisure pursuits include golf. Lives in Wilmslow, Cheshire.

Quinn, P.
David Phillips & Partners, Bootle (0151) 922 5525.

Retallack, James K.
Edge & Ellison, Birmingham (0121) 200 2001. Partner and Head of the Employment Unit.

Specialisation: All aspects of employment, human resource and Industrial Relations law.

Prof. Membership: Law Society, Employment Lawyers Association, Birmingham Industrial Tribunal Users Committee.

Career: Qualified in 1981. Joined *Edge & Ellison* in 1981, becoming a Partner in 1988.

Personal: Born 8th July 1957. Attended Malvern College 1970-74 and Manchester University 1975-78. Leisure interests include reading, skiing, gardening and American Football. Lives in Worcester.

Russell, Timothy D.
Hammond Suddards, Leeds (0113) 234 3500. Partner in Corporate Department.

Specialisation: Specialises in employment law. Head of Employment Law Unit. Has handled many major transfer of undertakings and sex discrimination cases. An advocate for over 100 industrial tribunal cases. Contributor to many publications and journals, including 'Personnel Today', 'Modern Management', 'Lloyd's List', 'The Estates Gazette' and the Law Society's 'Gazette'. Principal speaker for the Industrial Society and lecturer for Commerce and Industry Group. Regularly speaks at seminars and has made radio and television appearances. Practical approach based on in-house commercial experience.

Prof. Membership: Law Society, Employment Lawyers Association, Industrial Law Society, Local Chamber of Commerce.

Career: Worked with *Wilde Sapte* 1982-86. Qualified in 1985 and was Ciba Geigy's legal adviser 1986-87. Senior legal adviser at Lloyds Bank 1987-91. Joined *Hammond Suddards* in 1991 and became a Partner in 1992.

Personal: Born 17th June 1960. Educated at Pocklington School and Cambridge University. Enjoys all sports. Lives in Leeds.

Sayer, Nicholas T.
Hewitson Becke + Shaw, Cambridge (01223) 461155. Qualified 1987. Partner 1993. Head of Employment Law Department. Principal area of practice is contentious employment matters, particularly injunctive relief. Also deals with non-contentious employment matters. Born 26.9.1961.

Short, Michael C.
Short Richardson & Forth, Newcastle upon Tyne (0191) 232 0283. Founder Partner in Employment Law Department.

Specialisation: Has twenty years' experience in employment law, acting on both sides of industry and dealing with the full range of employment law matters including appearing before Industrial Tribunals regularly throughout the country and lecturing regularly on employment law matters to Companies.

Prof. Membership: Member of the Employment Lawyers Association.

Career: Qualified in 1967. Senior Partner and founding Partner of *Short Richardson & Forth* since 1978.

Personal: Born 20th April 1943. Attended Durham University LLB (Hons) 1964. Leisure interests include theatre. Lives in Newcastle-upon-Tyne.

Southam, Christopher A.
Veale Wasbrough, Bristol (0117) 925 2020. Partner in Company/Commercial Department.

Specialisation: Main area of practice is employment. Handles all aspects of employment law, both individual and collective, for both employers and employees. Author of several articles; joint author of 'Croner Industrial Relations Law', 'AIDS and Employment Law' and 'Jordans Secretarial Administration' (in preparation). Has conducted several seminars and lectures on all aspects of employment law. Runs in-house training for employers on employment law. Part-time lecturer for Bristol University's Legal Practice Course.

Prof. Membership: Law Society, Employment Lawyers Association.

Career: Qualified in 1974. Joined *Veale Was-*

brough as a Partner in 1988. Member of Industrial Tribunal Users Committee.

Personal: Leisure interests include guitar, music and sport. Lives in Upper Weare, near Axbridge, Somerset.

Speirs, William S.C.
Tindal Oatts, Glasgow (0141) 221 8012.

Stewart, David L.
Morton Fraser Milligan WS, Edinburgh (0131) 556 8444. Partner in Litigation Department; Head of Commercial Litigation.

Specialisation: Main area of practice is commercial and maritime litigation and employment law. Certified as an Employment Law specialist by the Law Society of Scotland. Gives frequent lectures to courses organised by the Law Society and other bodies.

Prof. Membership: Law Society of Scotland, WS Society.

Personal: Born 18th March 1942. Attended Trinity Hall, Cambridge University 1961-64 and Edinburgh University 1964-67. Leisure interests include skiing and sailing. Lives in Edinburgh.

Thompson, Peter
Howes Percival, Northampton (01604) 230400.

Ticehurst, David K.
Osborne Clarke, Bristol (0117) 923 0220. Qualified 1975. Partner 1980. Head of Employment Unit, Head of Media Unit. Employment work specialises in contentious and non contentious matters, industrial tribunal, wrongful dismissal and restrictive covenants. Holder of Higher Courts (All Proceedings) Qualification. Born 1.5.1950.

Tierney, James K.
Paull & Williamsons, Aberdeen (01224) 621621.

Tweedie, Colin J.
Mills & Reeve, Norwich +44 (0) 1603 660155. Qualified 1978. Partner 1985. Employment Law Department. Has specialised exclusively in employment law since qualification. Deals with all aspects, mainly for employers. Born 29.6.1953.

Warnock, Owen
Eversheds, Norwich (01603) 272727. Qualified 1982. Partner 1985. Employment Department. Main area of practice is employment law. Food and drink law also covered, with particular interest in labelling and advertising. Born in 1957.

Whyte, David D.
Bishop and Robertson Chalmers, Glasgow (0141) 248 4672. Partner in Litigation Department.

Specialisation: Main area of practice is employment law. Has 10 years practical experience. Holds a Law Society of Scotland

certificate as an employment law expert. Also handles debt recovery, divorce and general civil litigation. Lectures on employment law and debt recovery.

Prof. Membership: Industrial Law Group (Scotland) Industrial Law Society.

Career: Qualified in 1976. Joined *Bishop & Robertson Chalmers* in 1976. Became a Partner in 1981.

Personal: Born 1st July 1954. Attended Kelvinside Academy 1959-72 and Glasgow University 1972-76. Enjoys sailing and hill-walking. Lives in Glasgow.

Williamson, David S.
See under Litigation (Commercial).

Williamson, Raymond M.
MacRoberts, Glasgow (0141) 332 9988. Partner in Court Department.

Specialisation: Specialist in employment law since the early 1970's. Advises on the drafting of contracts of employment, on management of staff, on redundancies and disciplinary matters. Also experienced in representing clients' interests before industrial and other tribunals. Holder of Specialist Authorisation from the Law Society of Scotland in Employment Law. Convener of the Law Society's Employment Law Committee and Chairman of the Employment Law Specialisation Committee. Lectures extensively on employment matters for the University of Glasgow, Strathclyde University and the Law Society of Scotland and has been an external examiner on employment law at Glasgow University. Author of the chapter on employment law in Greene & Fletcher's 'The Law and Practice of Receivership in Scotland'.

Prof. Membership: Law Society of Scotland, Royal Faculty of Procurators in Glasgow.

Career: Joined *MacRoberts, Solicitors* in 1968 and qualified in the same year. Became a Partner in 1972.

Personal: Born 24th December 1942. Educated at the High School of Glasgow 1949-60 and the University of Glasgow 1960-66. Governor of the Royal Scottish Academy of Music and Drama, Chairman of the John Currie Singers Ltd and Governor of the High School of Glasgow. Chairman Scottish Childrens Music Foundation in Scotland, Trustee Scottish International Piano Competition. Leisure interests include music and gardening. Lives in Glasgow.

Yates, Tracy
Eversheds, Norwich (01603) 272727. Qualified 1986. Partner 1992. Employment Department. Advocates in Industrial Tribunals and also handles immigration work. Born 16.6.1962.

Young, James D.
McGrigor Donald, Edinburgh (0131) 226 7777. Qualified 1975. Partner 1979. Litigation Department. Has broad experience of all commercial litigation and specialises in employment law. Born 26.2.1950.

ENERGY & UTILITIES

ENERGY lawyers advise the oil, gas, coal, nuclear and electricity industries on a range of matters including regulatory issues, competition law, corporate matters and project finance. Utilities work involves a similar range of advice to the formerly state-owned service sector, now largely privatised.

UK firms have developed a high level of expertise in the energy field over the last few years with the privatisation and deregulation of the home market. This has placed them in a strong position to expand their operations overseas and many are now involved in large-scale projects in Asia, Eastern Europe and the Middle East.

LONDON

The two leading firms in London are *Denton Hall* and *Herbert Smith*. *Denton Hall,* with one of the largest energy practices in the City, has a strong team in David Moroney, James Dallas and Malcolm Groom (who is particularly well regarded for gas-related work). The firm handles a broad spectrum of work for clients in the oil, gas, mining and electricity industries and has recently advised on privatisation and legislative issues and the planning and negotiation of major international energy and mineral projects. The firm has a substantial presence in both the domestic and international fields (Blanche Sas at the Moscow office has been particularly recommended).

LEADING FIRMS – LONDON

DENTON HALL	HERBERT SMITH
FRESHFIELDS	LINKLATERS & PAINES
McKENNA & CO	
ALLEN & OVERY	ASHURST MORRIS CRISP
CLIFFORD CHANCE	NABARRO NATHANSON
NORTON ROSE	SLAUGHTER AND MAY

Herbert Smith's energy department handles international concession negotiations, unitisation agreements, privatisations and trading, exploration, engineering and service contracts. Richard Bond, who has been involved in the high profile Britoil, British Gas, water, electricity and coal privatisations is the firm's outstanding practitioner, although Stephen Barton and Alan Jowett are also highly recommended.

Also highly regarded are the energy and utilities departments of *Linklaters & Paines, Freshfields* and *McKenna & Co.*

Linklaters & Paines boasts eminent practitioners in Stuart Salt and Richard Jones (formerly in-house at British Petroleum and now practice manager of the firm's Moscow office) who handle a variety of contentious and non-contentious work. The firm is active across all sectors but is particularly known for financing of major projects.

The energy team at *Freshfields* undertakes a broad spec-

trum of work, although its expertise lies mainly in corporate acquisitions and mergers, joint ventures, project finance, pollution and environmental work. Members of the firm have recently acted for the State Electricity Board of Maharashtra on a power station project at Dabhol in India, and oil field development in Siberia and the Komi Republic.

McKenna & Co has a strong practice particularly in the electricity sector. It also has expertise in corporate and project financing, regulatory and infrastructure work for utility industries, and waste management work. Fiona Woolf (an authority in the electricity sector) and Robert Lane are well-respected.

Other firms with highly regarded energy practices include *Allen & Overy, Ashurst Morris Crisp, Clifford Chance, Nabarro Nathanson, Norton Rose* and *Slaughter and May.*

Allen & Overy, has an excellent reputation in the electricity, water, oil and gas sectors. Roger Davies handles, in the main, oil and gas acquisition and operational issues and has been involved in North Sea development and Interconnecta gas pipeline work. Doran Doeh, who heads the Moscow team, focuses on gas supply and upstream oil work as well as some downstream marketing to petrol stations. Ian Elder (electricity) is also highly regarded.

Clifford Chance advise petroleum, mining and electricity companies, oil traders and transporters and construction and offshore service companies. Jeremy Carver has an excellent reputation, particularly for upstream work, and represents national and government owned oil companies, often in relation to petroleum development contracts. He has also been involved in drafting oil-related legislation for foreign governments, and has handled Kuwait's claims for damage caused to their infrastructure by Iraq. Paul Simpson is also held in high regard.

Nabarro Nathanson is particularly known for its expertise in the coal sector, although partner Mark Saunders has been recommended for oil and gas work having acted for almost all the oil majors. Gareth Jones and Robert Tudway are also well regarded by their peers.

Norton Rose has a particular reputation for its work in the oil, gas and electricity sectors and is renowned for project finance work within the energy field. The highly regarded Michael Taylor has expertise in all aspects of major energy projects.

HIGHLY REGARDED – LONDON

S J BERWIN & CO	CLYDE & CO
FRERE CHOLMELEY BISCHOFF	INCE & CO.
LOVELL WHITE DURRANT	PENNINGTONS
BAKER & McKENZIE	BROWN COOPER
CAMERON MARKBY HEWITT	EVERSHEDS
FIELD FISHER WATERHOUSE	HOBSON AUDLEY
LAWRENCE GRAHAM	LE BOEUF LAMB GREENE & MACRAE
RICHARDS BUTLER	SIMMONS & SIMMONS
TEACHER STERN SELBY	TRAVERS SMITH BRAITHWAITE
WALTONS & MORSE	WATSON, FARLEY & WILLIAMS

In all the tables the names in each group are listed alphabetically.

Another large city firm strong in the oil, gas and electricity sectors is *Slaughter and May* which has been involved in utilities privatisation work as well as oil and gas acquisitions and gas infrastructure work. Martin Roberts is considered an authority.

The last firm to be mentioned in the group, *Ashurst Morris Crisp,* has the fastest growing practice in the field. Ian Johnson (uniformly recommended by all practitioners canvassed), who heads the energy and major projects team, has expertise across the whole range of oil, gas and electricity work. Paul Griffin, formerly at *Denton Hall,* (who has spoken at numerous lectures on the privatisation and de-regulation of the gas industries) is a recent appointment and will no doubt enhance the firm's gas buying expertise. Geoffrey Picton-Turbervill, who specialises in oil and gas transactions and power generation and distribution projects, is also highly regarded.

Although not in the same league as the firms mentioned above, a number of other firms deserve a mention for their expertise in the field. *Clyde & Co* represent oil producing and exploration companies, oil traders, refineries and petrochemical producers. Their work includes joint ventures, exploration and production agreements. Peter Felter who heads the Energy, Trade and Asset Finance Group is experienced in pipeline agreements, joint ventures and tariffing. *Ince & Co*, though better known as a shipping firm, have an energy group dealing with the oil and gas industries from exploration, production and refining to transportation and trading.

Penningtons handles a broad spectrum of energy work ranging from oil and gas to coal mines and power production. Martin Byatt advises on all aspects of the exploration, production, processing, storage, distribution and sale of oil, gas, coal and minerals. His colleague Michelle Dunne also handles oil and gas work including joint operating agreements, transportation, licensing, gas and asset sales.

Lovell White Durrant represents oil, gas and mineral exploration businesses and electricity generation companies. The firm also advises on downstream activities. *Frere Cholmeley Bischoff* is best known for oil and gas work in Moscow. Work carried out includes advising oil companies in the process of establishing new joint ventures or joining existing joint ventures, and the refinancing of oil refineries. Another firm well regarded in the area is *S J Berwin & Co.*

Individual practitioners to feature prominently in our research include Alan Jones and Garry Pegg, both of whom have recently left *Clifford Chance* to join US firm *Le Boeuf Lamb Greene & Macrae.*

LEADING INDIVIDUALS – LONDON

Richard D. Bond *Herbert Smith*	**Jeremy Carver** *Clifford Chance*	**James Dallas** *Denton Hall*
Roger G. Davies *Allen & Overy*	**Doran Doeh** *Allen & Overy*	**Ian Johnson** *Ashurst Morris Crisp*
Alan Jones *Le Boeuf Lamb Greene & Macrae*	**David Moroney** *Denton Hall*	**M.J.D. Roberts** *Slaughter and May*
S.R. Salt *Linklaters & Paines*	**Mark Saunders** *Nabarro Nathanson*	**Michael P.G. Taylor** *Norton Rose*
Fiona Woolf *McKenna & Co*		
Stephen J. Barton *Herbert Smith*	**Michael Brothwood** *Denton Hall*	**Martin Byatt** *Penningtons*
F.H. Coffell *Field Fisher Waterhouse*	**Michelle A. Dunne** *Penningtons*	**Ian F. Elder** *Allen & Overy*
Peter Felter *Clyde & Co*	**Paul Griffin** *Ashurst Morris Crisp*	**Malcolm Groom** *Denton Hall*
Geoff Haley *S J Berwin & Co*	**Gareth Jones** *Nabarro Nathanson*	**Richard Jones** *Linklaters & Paines*
R.A. Jowett *Herbert Smith*	**Robert C. Lane** *McKenna & Co*	**Garry Pegg** *Le Boeuf Lamb Greene & Macrae*
Geoffrey Picton-Turbervill *Ashurst Morris Crisp*	**Blanche Sas** *Denton Hall*	**Stephen T. Sayer** *Richards Butler*
Paul Simpson *Clifford Chance*	**Paul H. Stacey** *Slaughter and May*	**Robert Tudway** *Nabarro Nathanson*
John Verrill *Lawrence Graham*		

SOUTH EAST

Clyde & Co is the only firm in the region with a team dedicated to energy and utility work. The firm was heavily involved in the Piper Alpha disaster and the Emerald Field litigation and represents a number of multi-national oil companies and their insurers.

HIGHLY REGARDED – SOUTH EAST

CLYDE & CO *Guildford*

SOUTH WEST & WALES

Veale Wasbrough has established a name in the field, largely due to the reputation of Tim Smithers who advises on energy inquiries, easement acquisitions and pipeline advice. The firm is particularly known for bulk easement acquisitions, pipelines and public inquiries and has experience in the law relating to the conversion of waste into energy and combined heat power.

Three firms in the region with reputations for wind farm work are Plymouth-based *Bond Pearce,* Bristol-based *Osborne Clarke* and *Hugh James Jones & Jenkins* in Cardiff.

Osborne Clarke in addition acts on behalf of several providers of utilities while *Hugh James Jones & Jenkins* is also regarded for its work in electricity and mining law.

HIGHLY REGARDED – SOUTH WEST & WALES

BOND PEARCE *Plymouth*	COLES MILLER *Poole*
EDWARDS GELDARD *Cardiff*	FOOT & BOWDEN *Plymouth*
HUGH JAMES JONES & JENKINS *Cardiff*	OSBORNE CLARKE *Bristol*
VEALE WASBROUGH *Bristol*	

Other firms in the region with experience in the energy and utilities sectors include *Coles Miller* in Dorset which undertakes mineral extraction and exploration work and advises on off-shore drilling and pipelines, and *Edwards Geldard* which advises several electricity and water utilities on infrastructure, supply and purchase and regulatory compliance and also has experience of renewable energy project work. *Foot & Bowden* has expertise in all aspects of mining and mineral law and is particularly well regarded for mineral site development work.

LEADING INDIVIDUALS – SOUTH WEST & WALES

Tim M.D. Smithers *Veale Wasbrough*

MIDLANDS

Much of the work in the Midlands is concerned with mining and mineral extraction. It is therefore not surprising that the two leading individuals are Simon Hambly at *Kent Jones and Done* and Tony Bell at *Knight & Sons*, both specialists in mining law. *Kent Jones & Done* has traditionally had close connections with the mining industry, although more recently it has acquired a number of clients within the waste disposal industry. *Knight & Sons* has an excellent reputation for its work in sand and gravel extraction.

HIGHLY REGARDED – MIDLANDS

EDGE & ELLISON *Birmingham*	EDWARDS GELDARD *Derby*
KENT JONES and DONE *Stoke-on-Trent*	KNIGHT & SONS *Newcastle-under-Lyme*
MARTINEAU JOHNSON *Birmingham*	PINSENT CURTIS *Birmingham*
WRAGGE & CO *Birmingham*	

Edge & Ellison is also known within in the mining law sector and acts for several major quarrying companies. Over the years the firm has developed a particular specialism in waste disposal and management law including advising on the issues arising from the generation of heat and power from waste. The firm has also been recommended for oil and gas work.

Firms in the region with expertise in the electricity sector include *Edwards Geldard* whose work includes infrastructure, supply and purchase agreements, and also renewable energy work, *Martineau Johnson* which, in addition to electricity work, also has experience in the water sector, acting for several utilities and, *Pinsent Curtis*.

LEADING INDIVIDUALS – MIDLANDS

Tony Bell *Knight & Sons*
Simon Hambly *Kent Jones and Done*

Wragge & Co, traditionally known for its involvement in waste to energy plants and general waste management work, has extended its client base, now advising a number of different public utilities. The firm, in addition has developed a specialism in non-fossil fuel related work.

NORTH

The two leading practitioners in the North of England are Neil Brown at *Eversheds* and Brian Wake at *Aaron & Partners*.

HIGHLY REGARDED – NORTH

AARON & PARTNERS *Chester*	EVERSHEDS *Leeds*
DICKINSON DEES *Newcastle upon Tyne*	EVERSHEDS *Newcastle upon Tyne*
HAMMOND SUDDARDS *Leeds*	NABARRO NATHANSON *Doncaster*
PINSENT CURTIS	WATSON BURTON *Newcastle upon Tyne*
WILKINSON MAUGHAN *Newcastle-upon-Tyne*	

Neil Brown, who heads the Utilities Group at *Eversheds*(Leeds) advises on all aspects of energy law. Recent transactions have included advising in a major gas fired power station project. The firm not only has an excellent reputation in the electricity sector, where it is involved in both core and non-core regulated areas, but also in the gas sector, where it has undertaken second tier licensing work.

Brian Wake at *Aaron & Partners* in addition to advising public and private companies on environmental and waste management issues, is also well known for mineral extraction and quarrying.

Other firms with a reputation in the field include *Eversheds*(Newcastle) which has experience across the electricity, oil and gas sectors and *Dickinson Dees* which handles acquisition and joint venture work, advises on environmental, development and construction issues and advises clients in the supply and transportation industries.

Other firms worthy of note include *Hammond Suddards* which has developed a specialism in the renewable energy sector (in particular wind farms) in addition to handling electricity, gas and water work and *Nabarro Nathanson* which has a number of clients in the coal, gas and electricity sectors and also advises on waste to energy work.

Pinsent Curtis, Watson Burton (electricity) and *Wilkinson Maughan* (water) also advise private and public organisations on a variety of issues.

LEADING INDIVIDUALS – NORTH

A.Neil Brown *Eversheds*
Brian Wake *Aaron & Partners*

SCOTLAND

Dundas & Wilson CS is strong in all aspects of the energy and utilities field and has been recommended for its mineral development work. Donald Cumming (a partner in the energy department) acted in the privatisation of the Scottish electricity industry and has also been involved in power station projects for Scottish Hydro-Electric plc.

Shepherd & Wedderburn has a broad client base, but is particularly known for electricity work, advising several Scottish electricity companies. Patrick Andrews (an authority on renewable energy projects) and James Saunders are held in high regard.

HIGHLY REGARDED – SCOTLAND	
BIGGART BAILLIE & GIFFORD *Glasgow*	DUNDAS & WILSON CS *Edinburgh*
MACROBERTS *Glasgow*	McGRIGOR DONALD *Glasgow*
SHEPHERD & WEDDERBURN *Edinburgh*	
CAMERON MARKBY HEWITT *Aberdeen*	DORMAN JEFFREY & CO *Glasgow*
LEDINGHAM CHALMERS *Aberdeen*	SIMPSON & MARWICK WS *Edinburgh*
TODS MURRAY WS *Edinburgh*	

Many of the other energy specialists in Scotland advise the oil and gas industries. *Cameron Markby Hewitt* is principally involved in the financing and refinancing of oil projects with an upstream emphasis, although the firm is also known for environmental work within the energy field. *Dorman Jeffrey & Co* advises on bidding, applications, concessions, acquisitions, and disposals of licences. *Ledingham Chalmers* handle oil exploration and production work in former Soviet Union territory. *Simpson & Marwick WS* in addition to acting for oil clients, has strong ties with the domestic electricity industry.

LEADING INDIVIDUALS – SCOTLAND
Patrick Andrews *Shepherd & Wedderburn*
Donald I. Cumming *Dundas & Wilson CS*
Ian Dickson *MacRoberts*
David C.H. Ross *Biggart Baillie & Gifford*
James Saunders *Shepherd & Wedderburn*

Individual practitioners to feature prominently in our research include David Ross of *Biggart Baillie & Gifford*, who advises the electricity and gas industries and Ian Dickson of *MacRoberts* who has been recommended for his work within the nuclear power industry.

LEADERS IN ENERGY & UTILITIES

LONDON

Barton, Stephen J.
Herbert Smith, London (0171) 374 8000. Partner in International Finance and Banking Group, Company Department.

Specialisation: Wide ranging corporate and commercial practice, with particular experience in project financing, advising oil and gas companies and in electricity related matters. He is also involved in insolvency work and in that connection is the contributing editor of the Insolvency division of 'Butterworth's Company Law Service' and is responsible for the firm's corporate insolvency group.

Career: Qualified in 1971. Partner at *Herbert Smith* since 1978.

Personal: Educated at Cambridge University (First Class Honours).

Bond, Richard D.
See under Corporate Finance.

Brothwood, Michael
Denton Hall, London (0171) 242 1212. Partner in Energy and Natural Resources Group.

Specialisation: Main area of practice is energy law. As senior legal adviser to British Gas Corporation, was responsible for drafting and negotiating numerous major contracts for the purchase of natural gas from both UK and Norwegian Shelf. Also covered EEC and UK Competition law, asset disposal programs and legal aspects of relations with the government. As senior legal adviser to the British Steel Corporation, was responsible for international joint ventures and construction projects and for legal aspects of integration of British Steel into the European Community. Cases have included drafting and negotiating LNG purchase contract for Algeria; giving advice as a Consultant to Danish National Oil and Gas Company in connection with EC law issues; advising on numerous regulatory and competition matters and EC law relating particularly to third party access; and advising and drafting UK gas transportation agreements. Legal Expert to the European Parliament, in connection with its proposals for third party access to gas and electricity networks; project leader for Phare Legislation/ Regulation project on the European Energy Charter. Member of the editorial boards of the European Law Review and the Oil and Gas Law and Taxation Review. Has written and lectured widely on European and Energy Law.

Prof. Membership: Law Society, Solicitors' European Group, International Bar Association.

Career: Qualified in 1959. Worked at *Slaughter and May* 1956-65; Counsel to Casey Lane & Mittendorf, New York, 1965-67; Senior Legal Adviser to British Steel Corporation 1967-74. Resident Partner at *Freshfields*, Paris, 1974-81; Senior Legal Adviser for British Gas Corporation 1981-85; Partner with *Denton Hall* since 1985.

Personal: Born 22nd September 1932. Holds an MA in law from Cambridge, 1953-56. Leisure interests include cycling, walking, gardening and French culture. Lives in London.

Byatt, Martin
Penningtons, London (0171) 457 3000. Partner in Company Commercial Department (Natural Resources and Corporate Finance Units).

Specialisation: Main area of practice is energy law. Handles all aspects of the commercial, regulatory, environmental and financing aspects of the exploration for and extraction, production, processing, storage, distribution and sale of oil, gas, coal, base and precious metals and minerals generally. Also handles corporate finance work, covering all aspects of Yellow Book work including flotations, rights issues and prospectuses. Has handled international natural resource joint ventures and financing of cross border natural resource projects.

Prof. Membership: Law Society, International Bar Association.

Career: Qualified in 1968. Partner in own practice 1970-93. Joined *Penningtons* as a Partner in 1993.

Personal: Born 7th March 1946. Attended College of Law. Leisure interests include horse riding, gardening and wine appreciation. Lives in Cambridgeshire.

Carver, Jeremy
Clifford Chance, London (0171) 600 1000. Partner. Practice includes arbitration and public international law.

Coffell, F.H.
Field Fisher Waterhouse, London (0171) 481 4841. Partner Commercial Property Department. Head of Pipeline Services Unit.

Specialisation: Practice covers acquisition, disposal and development of commercial property including industrial sites, oil and gas terminals and facilities and the construction of cross-country pipelines. Acts for a number of major UK oil and gas companies and pipeline operators. Present involvement includes gas and gas oil connections to proposed new power stations.

Prof. Membership: Law Society.

Career: Qualified 1974, having joined *Field Fisher Waterhouse* in 1972. Became a Partner in 1978.

Personal: Born 23rd November 1948. Attended King Henry VIII School, Coventry and Magdalen College, Oxford.

Dallas, James
Denton Hall, London (0171) 242 1212. Partner in Energy and Natural Resources Group, Company/Commercial Department.

Specialisation: Experienced in oil and gas work; gas, electricity and rail privatisation and regulation in the UK and internationally; utility regulation; private finance initiative projects in the UK. Regular speaker at conferences on privatisation and regulation issues. Editor (Rail) of the *Utilities Law Review*.

Prof. Membership: Law Society; UK Oil Lawyers Group; CRI (committee member).

Career: Qualified 1979 while articled with a City firm. Joined *Denton Hall* in 1985 and became a Partner in 1986.

Personal: Born 21st April, 1955. Attended Eton and St Edmund Hall College, Oxford 1973-76 (MA Jurisprudence).

Davies, Roger G.

Allen & Overy, London (0171) 330 3000. Qualified 1972. Partner 1976. Corporate Department. Work covers oil/gas.

Doeh, Doran

Allen & Overy, London (0171) 330 3000. Moscow (007501) 9404500. Qualified 1973. Barrister. Solicitor 1987. Joined firm 1986. Has over twenty years' experience of UK and international energy transactions, principally related to oil and gas and electricity. Partner, Head of Moscow office. Born 14.5.1948.

Dunne, Michelle A.

Penningtons, London (0171) 457 3000. Partner in Corporate Department (Natural Resources and Corporate Finance Units).

Specialisation: Main area of practice is energy. Handles all aspects of upstream oil and gas work, including joint operating agreements, unit operating agreements, transportation, licensing, gas sales and asset sales and purchases and swaps. Also handles corporate finance, covering all aspects of Yellow Book work including flotations, rights issues and prospectuses.

Prof. Membership: Law Society, International Bar Association.

Career: Qualified in 1979 (Scotland) and 1985 (England). Worked at *Biggart Baillie & Gifford WS* 1979-81. Britoil PLC 1981-84, Exploration Consultants Limited 1984-5 and *M.P. Byatt & Co* 1985-93. Joined *Penningtons* as a Partner in 1993.

Personal: Attended Glasgow University 1974-77. Leisure interests include skiing, gardening and wine appreciation.

Elder, Ian F.

See under Company/Commercial.

Felter, Peter

Clyde & Co, London (0171) 623 1244. Qualified 1992.

Griffin, Paul

Ashurst Morris Crisp, London (0171) 638 1111. Qualified 1981. Partner 1995. Energy and Major Projects Department. Work covers privatisation, regulation and competition.

Groom, Malcolm

Denton Hall, London (0171) 242 1212. Partner in Company and Commercial Department (Energy and Natural Resources Group).

Specialisation: Areas of expertise include oil and gas licences and production sharing agreements, joint ventures and project financing, long-term gas purchase contracts, gas marketing, pipeline finance, construction and carriage arrangements. Has substantial international experience, including former Soviet Union countries, Europe, Australia and Africa.

Prof. Membership: International Bar Association.

Career: Qualified in 1974 after articles at *Linklaters & Paines*. Legal Adviser, Union Oil Co., California 1974-83. Joined *Warrens* as a Partner in 1983.

Personal: Born 16th June 1950. Educated at Kingston Grammar School. Manchester Grammar School and Trinity Hall, Cambridge (1st Class Hons in Law). Leisure pursuits include marathon running and chess.

Haley, Geoff

See under Construction & Civil Eng..

Johnson, Ian

Ashurst Morris Crisp, London (0171) 638 1111. Partner in Company Department.

Specialisation: Energy and natural resources, all aspects of oil and gas law. Has particular expertise with international power projects. Author of articles on energy law matters. Speaker at international energy conferences.

Prof. Memberships: Institute of Petroleum, Association of International Petroleum Negotiators, UK Energy Lawyers Group.

Career: *Linklaters & Paines* 1975-79, Counsel for Europe, Middle East and Africa at Unocal Corporation. Joined *Ashurst Morris Crisp* as Partner in 1991.

Personal: MA, LL.M Downing College, Cambridge 1970-74.

Jones, Alan

Le Boeuf Lamb Greene & Macrae, London (0171) 626 3000. Partner. Work covers privatisations in UK oil, gas and power sectors.

Jones, Gareth

Nabarro Nathanson, London (0171) 493 9933. Qualified 1980. Partner 1986. Company and Commercial Department, Energy Group.

Jones, Richard

Linklaters & Paines, London 7 095 929 9797. Qualified 1971. Practice Manager, Moscow Office. Oil, gas and energy specialist.

Jowett, R.A.

Herbert Smith, London (0171) 374 8000. Partner 1986. Company Department. Main area of practice is corporate finance.

Lane, Robert C.

McKenna & Co, London (0171) 606 9000. Partner specialising in utilities law and regulation.

Specialisation: Extensive experience of electricity projects and restructurings in the UK and overseas. Adviser to The National Grid Company plc. From 1988 to 1990 advised on the restructuring of the England and Wales

electricity industry, including drafting the Grid Code for the England and Wales system, extensive involvement in the design of the regulatory regime and pooling arrangements and drafting/advice on many of the other documents (e.g. those dealing with connection to and use of the system). Also adviser to Northern Ireland Electricity plc on its restructuring and privatisation and the ESI Reform Unit of the State Government of Victoria (which involved consideration of and scoping of the regulatory, contractual and code structures and critiquing the licences, codes and contracts). He has also worked on power purchase agreements relating to Electricidade de Portugal and the Public Power Corporation of Greece and advised on all aspects of the restructuring of the electricity supply industry in Orissa, India. Regular speaker at conferences throughout the world.

Prof. Membership: International Bar Association (Member of Section on Energy and Natural Resources Law and vice-chairman of Utilities Law Committee).

Career: Qualified in 1982. Joined *McKenna & Co* seven years ago.

Personal: Educated at University College, London.

Moroney, David

Denton Hall, London (0171) 242 1212. Partner in Company and Commercial Department (Energy and Natural Resources Group).

Specialisation: Specialises in energy and natural resources law. Work includes international projects and transactions, privatisation, and drafting of legislation for developing markets. Particular expertise in oil and gas, electricity and mining sectors. In addition to UK, international experience includes former Soviet counties, S.E Asia, Australia and Africa. Considerable experience in-house. Experienced conference lecturer.

Prof. Membership: International Bar Association (Section on Energy & Natural Resources Law - Vice-Chairman and Treasurer).

Career: Qualified as a Solicitor in New South Wales 1969. Legal and Lands Manager, Burmah Oil, London & Australia 1969-77. UK Legal Adviser, Deminex Oil and Gas, London 1977-80. Uranium Contracts Manager and Corporate Solicitor, Western Mining Corporation Ltd, Melbourne 1980-81. General Counsel, International Energy Development Corporation, Switzerland and UK 1981-86. Solicitor *Allen Allen & Hemsley*, Sydney 1987-88. Qualified in England & Wales and joined *Denton Hall* in 1988. Became a Partner in 1989.

Personal: Born 20th October 1945. Educated at the University of Sydney (LL.B).

Pegg, Garry

Le Boeuf Lamb Greene & Macrae, London (0171) 626 3000. Partner. Emphasis on oil and gas, privatisation and project work.

Picton-Turbervill, Geoffrey

Ashurst Morris Crisp, London (0171)

638 1111. Qualified 1985. Partner 1994. Company Department (Energy and Major Projects Group).

Roberts, M.J.D.
Slaughter and May, London (0171) 600 1200. Qualified 1969. Joined *Slaughter and May* 1967. Partner 1975. Practice includes energy, projects and project finance.

Salt, Stuart R.
Linklaters & Paines, London (0171) 606 7080.

Sas, Blanche
Denton Hall, London \$IMoscow 00 7 502 213 9210\$N. *Fax 00 7 502 213 9214.* Head of Moscow Office.

Specialisation: Specialist in energy legislation in Eastern Europe and former Soviet Union; international and comparative law in relation to petroleum regimes; downstream energy law in particular, oil trading; energy sales contracts (gas, oil, coal, uranium and electricity); pipeline law; privatisation and regulation of electricity and gas industries. Editor of *Oil and Gas Law and Taxation Review* and author of numerous publications on energy law.
Professional Membership: International Bar Association.

Career: Community Development Officer at Tayside Regional Council 1976-1979. Lecturer in petroleum law at Dundee University 1985-91. Joined *Denton Hall* in 1991.

Personal: Born 28th March, 1948. Attended Dalhousie University, Canada (BSc, Maths) 1968 and University of Dundee (LLB) 1982. Currently completing a PhD in law at the European University Institute in Florence. Fluent French and Italian.

Saunders, Mark
Nabarro Nathanson, London (0171) 493 9933. Qualified 1985. Partner 1990. Energy and Corporate Department. Seconded to Occidental Petroleum as in-house counsel in 1985.

Sayer, Stephen T.
See under European Union/Competition.

Simpson, Paul
See under Major Projects/Infrastructure.

Stacey, Paul H.
See under Major Projects/Infrastructure.

Taylor, Michael P.G.
Norton Rose, London (0171) 283 6000. Partner, Head of the Energy Group at *Norton Rose* and leads the firm's project finance team.

Specialisation: Project finance, energy and natural resources and construction. Led the team on the Emerald oil field project, acting for the then operator of the field, and on the Peterborough and Keadby power station projects, acting for the project company. Advised on the Brigg and Medway power stations; power projects in the Gulf, Italy, Malaysia, Northern Ireland, Pakistan and Portugal; renewable energy projects; mining joint ventures and a wide variety of oil, gas and LNG projects in the UK

and overseas. A member of the editorial board of Oil and Gas Law and Taxation Review and contributing editor to Butterworth's Financial Services Law and Practice. Co-author of a book on oil and gas joint ventures.

Prof. Membership: Law Society, International Bar Association and UK Energy Lawyers' Group.

Career: Qualified 1972. Joined *Norton Rose* in 1974, becoming a Partner in 1979.

Tudway, Robert
Nabarro Nathanson, London (0171) 493 9933. Qualified 1973. Partner 1995. Company Department. Practice focuses on electricity supply law and power generation projects. Born 28.4.1947.

Verrill, John
See under Insolvency.

Woolf, Fiona
McKenna & Co, London (0171) 606 9000. Partner in Utilities Group.

Specialisation: Main areas of practice are electricity, gas and transport projects, financings, restructurings and regulation. Worked exclusively on banking and project finance transactions in Bahrain, 1982-85. Acted in the Channel Tunnel project, as one of the lead negotiators on the Concession Agreement and the Treaty with British and French Governments. Led a team of 40 people acting for The National Grid Company plc on the privatisation of the Electricity Supply Industry in England and Wales (for which she continues to act) and advised on the Northern Ireland Electricity restructuring and privatisation. Advised Electricidade de Portugal on the Tapada do Outeiro and Pego power projects and the project to bring natural gas to Portugal. Worked on the Lavrion power project in Greece for the Public Power Corporation and the privatisation of the transmission system of Argentina. Has worked on restructurings, utility regulation and privatisations in Malaysia, Thailand, Australia, Canada, India and California. Also advised the Department of Transport on the Channel Tunnel Rail Link, and the Department of Economic Development in Northern Ireland on the introduction of natural gas to the province. Contributor to 'Utilities Law Review'; regular speaker at conferences.

Prof. Membership: Council Member of the Law Society, Chairman of the International Committee.

Career: Qualified in 1973. Worked at *Coward Chance* 1973-78 before joining *McKenna & Co.* in 1978. Became a Partner in 1981.

Personal: Born 11th May 1948. Attended Keele University 1966-70. Leisure interests include wine and opera. Lives in Esher, Surrey.

REGIONS

Andrews, Patrick
Shepherd & Wedderburn WS, Edinburgh (0131) 228 9900. Partner in Commercial Property Department.

Specialisation: Main areas of practice are commercial property and contracts. Work has included the privatisation of Scottish Electricity Companies; the proposed interconnection between Scotland and Northern Ireland and various renewable energy projects and the property aspects of telecommunications infrastructure. Has particular knowledge of infrastructure and wayleaving.

Prof. Membership: Law Society, WS Society.

Career: Qualified in 1984. Articled *Dundas & Wilson CS* 1984-86. Joined *Shepherd & Wedderburn WS* in 1987, becoming a Partner in 1989.

Personal: Born 10th April 1962. Holds an LLB/DipLP from Aberdeen University. Leisure interests include sailing, hill walking, cycling and gardening. Lives in Edinburgh.

Bell, Tony
Knight & Sons, Newcastle-under-Lyme (01782) 619225.

Brown, A.Neil
See under Telecommunications.

Cumming, Donald I.
Dundas & Wilson CS, Edinburgh (0131) 228 8000. Qualified 1974. Partner 1981. Corporate Department. Main areas of practice are electricity and privatisations. Born 3.10.1952.

Dickson, Ian
See under Company/Commercial.

Hambly, Simon
Kent Jones and Done, Stoke-on-Trent (01782) 202020.

Ross, David C.H.
Biggart Baillie & Gifford, Glasgow (0141) 228 8000. Qualified 1972. Partner 1977. Corporate Department. Specialises in electricity and gas law, covering drafting and negotiation of a wide variety of energy related contracts.

Saunders, James
Shepherd & Wedderburn WS, Edinburgh (0131) 228 9900. Partner in Corporate Department.

Specialisation: Main areas of practice are energy law and I.P. (including computer law). Advises on electricity agreements and on I.P. agreements including licensing and turnkey. Also advises on telecommunications law, giving advice on supplier and infrastructure agreements.

Prof. Membership: Intellectual Property Committee of Law Society of Scotland.

Career: Qualified in 1984. Trainee with *McClure Naismith,* Glasgow 1983-85. Worked for ICI plc 1986-87 and *Freshfields* 1987-93. Joined *Shepherd & Wedderburn WS* in 1993.

Smithers, Tim M.D.
See under Property (Commercial).

Wake, Brian
See under Environmental Law.

ENVIRONMENTAL LAW

ALTHOUGH environmental law has been recognised as a distinct discipline for some years, it never quite achieved the lucrative status that the early 90's promised and many lawyers who took it up have now dropped it. Environmental law nevertheless remains an important and growing area, with an experienced sector of the profession dedicated to it.

This list highlights those firms which have set up specialist environmental units, drawing on a wealth of expertise from various established disciplines. Solicitors servicing specific industries such as shipping have been included under the appropriate section.

LONDON

Simmons & Simmons emerges as the pre-eminent firm with an eight-strong specialist unit headed by Stephen Tromans who is generally regarded as the doyen of environmental law. Kathy Mylrea is also held in high regard. The firm advises a wide range of industrial and commercial companies and has recently advised the Ministry of Defence and Railtrack. Assisted by the litigation department, the unit handles both criminal and civil proceedings, for both defendant and plaintiff. Advice has been given on a pro bono basis to the Environmental Law Foundation, British Trust for Ornithology, Campaign for the Protection of Rural England and the Tidy Britain Group.

LEADING FIRMS – LONDON	
McKENNA & CO	SIMMONS & SIMMONS
ALLEN & OVERY	FRESHFIELDS
LEIGH DAY & CO	
ASHURST MORRIS CRISP	BRISTOWS COOKE & CARPMAEL
CLIFFORD CHANCE	NABARRO NATHANSON

McKenna & Co retains a high profile, winning a coveted contract with the European Commission to advise the EU on environmental liability. It is particularly strong on regulatory issues, Pamela Castle having been consistently recommended. The firm also runs an environmental telephone 'hotline' for clients paying a retainer.

Other firms with highly experienced environmental units include *Freshfields, Allen & Overy, Clifford Chance, Nabarro Nathanson, Ashurst Morris Crisp* and *Bristows Cooke & Carpmael.*

Freshfields is noted for its broad-ranging expertise. On the litigation side the firm has a strong team in Paul Bowden, Malcolm Forster and Robert Lewis, whilst Paul Watchman is highly regarded for his transactional work.

Allen & Overy is strong within the financial sector with Owen Lomas advising corporate and banking clients on a variety of environmental issues.

Clifford Chance is best known for environmental litigation, representing defendant companies and their insurers in both criminal and civil proceedings. Christopher Napier has

recently acted for Coalite Products Ltd in a landmark action against Royal Insurance (UK) Ltd and CPC (UK) Ltd in the Court of Appeal defending prosecutions brought in respect of river pollution. On the non-contentious side, the environmental team advised the government in the British Coal privatisation and British Rail in the railway privatisation.

Nabarro Nathanson's environmental unit comprises eight specialists, five of whom operate from its Northern office. In addition to representing major institutions in the public and private sectors, the team advises mineral and waste operators, power generation clients, regulators and owners and developers of Brown Field Sites. Thomas Symes has been recommended.

Trevor Adams at *Ashurst Morris Crisp* is best known for acquisition-related work although the firm also offers 'freestanding' environmental advice to its corporate clients.

Bristows Cooke & Carpmael has heightened its profile with the appointment of Richard Burnett-Hall (formerly a partner at *McKenna & Co*). The environmental group provides a comprehensive service to industry clients and to other professionals and is considered by most practitioners to be a major competitor.

Leigh Day & Co has a national reputation and is generally regarded as the market leader in plaintiff litigation. Martyn Day, who has been recommended by many practitioners in the field, heads a team of twelve lawyers who specialise in personal injury and nuisance claims. The firm has represented clients such as the Sellafield and Dounreay leukaemia victims and the Docklands residents in their claims against the LDDC and Olympia and York.

HIGHLY REGARDED – LONDON	
S J BERWIN & CO	BERWIN LEIGHTON
DENTON HALL	HERBERT SMITH
SHINDLER & CO	
ALSOP WILKINSON	BAKER & McKENZIE
BARLOW LYDE & GILBERT	BATES, WELLS & BRAITHWAITE
BERRYMANS	BRECHER & CO
DAVIES ARNOLD COOPER	EVERSHEDS
GOULDENS	LAWRENCE GRAHAM
LINKLATERS & PAINES	LOVELL WHITE DURRANT
NICHOLSON GRAHAM & JONES	NORTON ROSE
ROWE & MAW	STEPHENSON HARWOOD
CAMERON MARKBY HEWITT	CHARLES RUSSELL
FRERE CHOLMELEY BISCHOFF	LAYTONS
PENNINGTONS	ROSS & CRAIG

Individual practitioners noted for their expertise include Andrew Waite of *Berwin Leighton* who handles land, waste and corporate based environmental work, Patricia Thomas of *S.J. Berwin* (editor of 'Environmental Liability' and 'Water Pollution: Law & Liability'), John Salter, a consultant at *Denton Hall* and Clare Deanesly at *Gouldens* who specialises in waste management, landfill and contaminated land.

David Brock of *Herbert Smith*, John Garbutt of *Nicholson Graham & Jones*, David Cuckson of *Stephenson Harwood* and Andrew Wiseman of *Shindler & Co* are also held in high regard.

SOUTH EAST

Andrew Bryce & Co emerges as the leading environmental firm in the South East. Andrew Bryce (former head of *Cameron Markby Hewitt's* environmental department) is considered a leading authority and regularly contributes to articles and seminars on the subject. The firm was launched as a niche practice earlier this year and already enjoys a national reputation.

Other highly experienced firms include *Donne Mileham & Haddock, Hepherd Winstanley & Pugh, Thomas Eggar Verrall Bowles* and *White & Bowker.*

Donne Mileham & Haddock's environmental group, headed by Tony Allen (a member of the Law Society's Planning and Environmental Committee) advises a range of industrial and agricultural clients on a variety of matters including the licensing of waste disposal and waste transfer stations, contaminated land problems and actions in respect of statutory breaches. Members of the unit also lecture on environmental law topics.

Hepherd Winstanley & Pugh and *Thomas Eggar Verrall Bowles* primarily operate as support for their larger commercial property departments. They have nevertheless established reputations in the field. Robert Davies (*Hepherd Winstanley & Pugh*) is particularly recommended.

White & Bowker's environmental department comprises three partners dealing with a range of non-contentious matters. John Steel is considered to be an authority on mineral extraction, tipping and waste licences.

Other firms which are prominent in the field include *Brachers, Blake Lapthorn* (particularly Colin Barlow), *Griffith Smith* and *Penningtons.*

SOUTH WEST

The most highly recommended firms in the South West include *Lawrence Tucketts, Bond Pearce* and *Clarke Willmott & Clarke.*

Within this trio, *Lawrence Tucketts* is considered to be marginally ahead in terms of expertise, with a strong environmental team in Craig Begg, Sue Otty and Stephen Pasterfield. The firm provides a comprehensive service and has particular expertise in the law as it relates to waste disposal, contaminated land and water pollution.

At *Bond Pearce*, Marcus Trinick and his team of six specialists have developed considerable experience in waste and mineral work and especially renewable energy projects.

Clarke Willmott & Clarke is one of the few firms in the region equally strong in both contentious and non-contentious matters. Tim Hayden at the Taunton office has been recommended on the litigation side (prosecution and defence work for statutory bodies and private clients).

Other firms with notable practices include *Bevan Ashford*, which has five specialists operating from Bristol, Exeter and Plymouth, *Eversheds* Bristol (waste, water, contaminated land and litigation), *Osborne Clarke,* whose environmental team has particular experience in due diligence investigations and renewable energy projects and *Veale Wasbrough,* where Tim Smithers has been recommended for waste, waste to energy joint venture agreements and contaminated land.

WALES

Both *Eversheds* Cardiff and *Morgan Bruce* have sound reputations in environmental law.

Eversheds' environmental unit comprises three specialists, headed by the highly regarded Martin Warren. The firm specialises in waste and water law, contaminated land and environmental litigation for public and private institutions. Martin Warren has given expert evidence for the Royal Commission on Environmental Pollution.

Morgan Bruce advises the coal mining and other heavy industries on compliance matters, and public and private companies on due-diligence. Clients such as Associated British Ports and Cardiff Bay Development Corporation are advised on contaminated land redevelopment projects. The firm also has a substantial environmental litigation practice.

MIDLANDS

Firms which have developed specialist expertise in environmental law include *Eversheds* (Nottingham), *Pinsent Curtis* and *Wragge & Co.*

The bulk of the environmental work at *Eversheds* tends to be litigation based, defending companies in regulatory and private prosecutions and statutory nuisance proceedings. On the non-contentious side, the firm advises on a whole range of compliance and due-diligence matters.

Pinsent Curtis' environmental practice is largely transactional, the unit handling the environmental issues arising in the course of property development or corporate acquisitions.

Wragge & Co's environmental team has developed particular expertise in waste management, water law, pollution control and contaminated land.

EAST ANGLIA

Hewitson Becke & Shaw and *Mills & Reeve* have the most highly respected environmental departments in the region.

Hewitson Becke & Shaw is particularly active in contaminated land issues, providing advice on civil and criminal activity to clients, property lawyers and financial institutions. The firm also has experience of the waste industry. Peter Brady is well-known in this field.

Mills & Reeve's environmental team is headed by the highly regarded Beverley Firth, who has a national reputation in both environmental and planning law. The firm advises on all aspects of environmental law and specialises in waste disposal, land contamination and pollution.

Richard Buxton of *Richard Buxton*, a niche environmental practice, tends to represent the objector. Regarded as a leading authority on water, nature conservation and noise (particularly aircraft noise), he advises statutory bodies, environmental charities, local authorities, professionals on a referral basis, and individuals. Recent high profile cases

include successfully representing six local authorities against the Department of Transport in the 'night-flight' litigation and representing the RSPB in the 'Lappel Bank' litigation (awaiting a decision by the ECJ at the time of going to print).

NORTH WEST

Firms in the North West with substantial experience in environmental law include *Aaron & Partners, Addleshaw Sons & Latham, Alsop Wilkinson, Eversheds* and *Halliwell Landau.*

HIGHLY REGARDED – NORTH WEST	
AARON & PARTNERS *Chester,,*	ADDLESHAW SONS & LATHAM *Manchester*
ALSOP WILKINSON *Liverpool*	EVERSHEDS *Manchester*
HALLIWELL LANDAU *Manchester*	
ELLIOTT & CO *Manchester*	HILL DICKINSON DAVIS CAMPBELL *Liverpool*
MASONS *Manchester*	PANNONE & PARTNERS *Manchester*

The environmental unit at *Aaron & Partners* comprises three specialist partners, headed by Brian Wake (founder and Chairman of North West section of Environmental Law Association). The firm specialises in mineral extraction, waste disposal, contaminated land and work under the Environmental Protection Act.

Addleshaw Sons & Latham's environmental unit primarily operates to provide corporate support, the firm has also developed expertise in landfill and sewage.

Eversheds is particularly known for environmental litigation, representing clients faced with prosecution by the NRA, HMIP, water companies and local authorities.

LEADING INDIVIDUALS – NORTH WEST
Roger Lancaster *Halliwell Landau*
Brian Wake *Aaron & Partners*

Halliwell Landau undertakes a broad range of environmental work, including advice on EPA compliance. Roger Lancaster has been highly recommended.

NORTH EAST

The most highly recommended firms in Leeds are *Booth & Co* and *Eversheds*.

Booth & Co's environmental unit advises on waste, contaminated land, integrated pollution control and air and water pollution. The firm has also prosecuted on behalf of the National Rivers Authority and the Health & Safety Executive. Victoria Joy and John Pike are both held in high regard.

HIGHLY REGARDED – NORTH EAST	
BOOTH & CO. *Leeds*	DIBB LUPTON BROOMHEAD *Bradford*
DICKINSON DEES *Newcastle upon Tyne*	EVERSHEDS *Leeds*
EVERSHEDS *Newcastle upon Tyne*	HAMMOND SUDDARDS *Leeds*
IRWIN MITCHELL *Sheffield*	NABARRO NATHANSON *Doncaster*
PETER WILBRAHAM & CO *Leeds*	PINSENT CURTIS
ROLLIT FARRELL & BLADON *Hull*	
GODLOVE PEARLMAN *Leeds*	

Paul Smith, based in the Leeds office, is head of *Eversheds* environmental law team, which comprises 33 lawyers nationally. The firm conducts a substantial amount of environmental work including defence of prosecutions (for which they are best known), compliance and due-diligence. Paul Smith, who co-writes the CCH Environmental Manual and appeared as guest speaker at the IBA international conference, is regarded as a leading authority. Stuart Bell (formerly at *Hammond Suddards*) has recently joined the team.

Other Leeds firms with notable practices include *Dibb*

Lupton Broomhead, Hammond Suddards, where Michael Shepherd is recommended, *Peter Wilbraham & Co*, where environmental law compliments the planning practice and *Pinsent Curtis*.

In Newcastle, *Dickinson Dees* is highly experienced in the conduct of environmental impact assessments. The firm regularly advises two major utilities.

LEADING INDIVIDUALS – NORTH EAST
Stuart Bell *Eversheds*
Timothy J. Driver *Eversheds*
Victoria Joy *Booth & Co.*
John D. Pike *Booth & Co.*
Michael Renger *Nabarro Nathanson*
Michael L. Shepherd *Hammond Suddards*
Paul A. Smith *Eversheds*
Peter Wilbraham *Peter Wilbraham & Co*

Timothy Driver at *Eversheds* has been recommended for his work in relation to water pollution.

Nabarro Nathanson's environmental unit comprises five specialists who act for the water, energy and mineral industries. The Doncaster office (due to relocate to Sheffield at the time of going to print) conducts all of the contentious environmental work, representing defendants and prosecuting authorities in major high profile cases. Michael Renger, who heads the unit, has been highly recommended.

SCOTLAND

The two firms most regularly recommended for environmental law are *Brodies* and *Morton Fraser Milligan*.

The environmental law group at *Brodies* draws on expertise from a number of disciplines advising on transactional, remediation and due-diligence work. The firm also conducts a substantial amount of litigation for companies falling foul of the statutory authorities. Charles Smith (Treasurer of the Scottish Branch of UKELA) is held in high regard.

Environmental law at *Morton Fraser Milligan* is also a cross-departmental discipline (Donald Reid is held in high regard) which advises on pollution, waste management and contaminated land, and undertakes environmental audit and impact assessments.

HIGHLY REGARDED – SCOTLAND	
BRODIES WS *Edinburgh*	W & J BURNESS WS *Edinburgh*
DUNDAS & WILSON CS *Edinburgh*	McGRIGOR DONALD *Glasgow*
MORTON FRASER MILLIGAN *Edinburgh*	THORNTONS WS *Dundee*
TODS MURRAY WS *Edinburgh*	
BISHOP AND ROBERTSON CHALMERS *Glasgow*	
DORMAN JEFFREY & CO *Glasgow*	STEEDMAN RAMAGE WS *Edinburgh*

Other firms with notable practices include *W & J Burness* where Kenneth Ross and Martin Sales advise on landfill, waste control and contaminated land, *Dundas & Wilson CS* (particularly Kenneth Cumming), *McGrigor Donald*, *Thorntons* (Michael Blair) and *Tods Murray*.

LEADING INDIVIDUALS – SCOTLAND

Norman Robert Oliver *Biggart Baillie & Gifford*	
J. Michael G. Blair *Thorntons WS*	
Kenneth M. Cumming *Steedman Ramage WS*	
Ian A.H. McPake *Tods Murray WS*	
Donald A. Reid *Morton Fraser Milligan*	
Kenneth A. Ross *W & J Burness WS*	
Kenneth C. Ross *Bishop and Robertson Chalmers*	
Martin Sales *W & J Burness WS*	
Charles Smith *Brodies WS*	

All these firms provide advice on a variety of contentious and non-contentious matters. *Thorntons* has, in addition, particular experience in the waste disposal industry, while *Tods Murray* has developed expertise in river pollution and renewable energy projects (Ian McPake is highly regarded).

NORTHERN IRELAND

Environmental law in Northern Ireland is still in its infancy, although it is expected to become an increasingly fertile area of work for the profession. A number of the environmental

HIGHLY REGARDED – NORTHERN IRELAND

CARSON & McDOWELL *Belfast*	**CLEAVER FULTON & RANKIN** *Belfast*
TUGHAN & CO *Belfast*	

provisions enacted in England and Wales by the Environmental Protection Act 1990 have yet to come into force in Northern Ireland. Consequently, firms are involved largely in preparatory or consultancy work in this area.

LEADING INDIVIDUALS – NORTHERN IRELAND

Neil C. Faris *Cleaver Fulton & Rankin*	
Christine E.A. McClelland *Tughan & Co*	

Regarded as leaders in this emerging field, *Cleaver Fulton & Rankin* offer a consultancy service on national and EC environmental issues. The firm's Neil Faris is highly regarded as an expert in the area, and has contributed, in conjunction with the Department of the Environment, to 'Green Triangle', a textbook on the subject. At *Tughan & Co* Christine McClelland advises on contentious and non-contentious aspects of existing and incoming legislation, giving particular attention to anticipating potential problems. *Carson & McDowell* are also well regarded for their consultancy services, environmental reviews and agency work.

LEADERS IN ENVIRONMENTAL LAW

LONDON

Adams, Trevor
Ashurst Morris Crisp, London (0171) 638 1111. Senior Associate.

Specialisation: Main area of practice is environmental law. Includes mergers and acquisitions, property transactions, lending, environmental litigation, legal auditing, environmental management systems and compliance advice. Experienced in the acquisition of a secondary lead smelting business, waste import/export advice, auditing in healthcare industry. Joint editor of UKELA Journal.

Prof. Membership: UKELA, Society of Chemical Industry, Royal Society of Chemistry.

Career: Environmental Researcher and Lecturer, Queen's University, Belfast 1976-82. Sewage Sludge Research, Rothamstead Experimental Station 1982-84. Joined *McKenna & Co* in 1984. Joined *Ashurst Morris Crisp* in 1990. Senior Associate 1992.

Personal: Born 6th June 1951. Obtained B.Sc. 1973, Ph.D. (Chemistry) 1980. Hon. Legal Advisor to Herts. & Middx. Bat Protection Society. Lives in Harpenden, Herts.

Ashley, Alan
Stringer Saul, London (0171) 631 4048.

Bowden, Paul
See under Litigation (Commercial).

Brock, David M.J.
Herbert Smith, London (0171) 374 8000. Partner in Planning and Environmental Group.

Specialisation: Has a wide ranging planning, environmental and minerals law practice, advising on new settlements, urban regeneration, minerals and waste planning, judicial review and parliamentary environmental aspects of corporate transactions. Experienced advocate. Contributor to 'Commercial Environmental Law and Liability' (Longman).

Career: Qualified in 1980. Partner at *Herbert Smith* since 1989.

Personal: Born in 1954. Educated at Dame Allan's Boys School, Newcastle, Marylebone Grammar School and University College, London (LL.B). Practising Christian. Enjoys opera, skiing and modern art. Resides in Saffron Walden.

Burnett-Hall, Richard H.
Bristows Cooke & Carpmael, London (0171) 400 8000. Head of Environmental Law Group.

Specialisation: Environmental law. Handles all aspects of UK and EC environmental law and regulation, and their impacts on business transactions and activities; also technology protection and exploitation. Author of "Environmental Law", a legal practitioners' text-book, published by Sweet & Maxwell 1995. Has written and given numerous articles and papers on environmental issues.

Prof. Memberships: Law Society, UK Environmental Law Association (Council Member), Chartered Institute of Patent Agents (Fellow), European Patent Attorney.

Career: Qualified as Chartered Patent Agent 1966. Qualified as solicitor and partner *McKenna & Co*. in 1974. Joined *Bristows*

Cooke & Carpmael 1995.

Personal: Born 5th August 1935: Trinity Hall, Cambridge 1956-59 (BA Natural Sciences 1959; MA 1963).

Castle, Pamela
McKenna & Co, London (0171) 606 9000. Partner in Environmental Law Group.

Specialisation: Handles a range of environmental law matters. Provides compliance advice on all areas of UK and EC environmental law, in particular the regulatory control of emissions to air and water, the transport, labelling and disposal of waste, the handling and storage of hazardous substances and health and safety at work. Advised the water and electricity industries on environmental issues before and during privatisation and acted for the Department of the Environment in Northern Ireland on the restructuring of the water industry there. Has advised local authorities on the transfer of their waste disposal functions into arms-length companies in relation to contaminated land issues. Conducts environmental audits and advises on the results, especially in the context of mergers and acquisitions and property transactions, with particular focus on contaminated land issues. Also advises on the terms of waste disposal contracts and on the liabilities of owners and occupiers of waste disposal sites and the generators of waste, as well as defending criminal prosecutions in the magistrates court by regulatory authorities. Council Member of the Environmental Auditors Registration Association. Member of the CBI Environmental Protection Water and Effluent Panel and the NRA Flood Defence Committee. On the Environmental Committee of the Association of British Healthcare Industries. Frequently speaks at public conferences and has had a number of articles published in journals such as *Oil and Gas Law and Taxation Review* and *European Construction Lawyer*.

Prof. Membership: Law Society, UK Environmental Law Association, City of London Solicitors Company, Institute of Wastes Management, Institute of Environmental Assessment (accredited environmental auditor), Royal Society of Chemistry, Fellow of the Royal Society of Arts.

Career: With Shell Chemical Company, New York 1965-67. Head of European Operations of Paul de Haen, Inc., New York (research company associated with the pharmaceutical industry) 1967-84. Joined *McKenna & Co* in 1986 and became a Partner in 1994.

Personal: Born 7th September 1941. Educated at the University of London (Queen Mary College) 1960-63 (BSc, 1st Class Hons in Chemistry) and the College of Law 1984-86. Interests include music, reading, theatre and walking. Lives in London.

Cuckson, David M.

Stephenson Harwood, London (0171) 329 4422. Partner in Property Department.

Specialisation: Head of Environmental Law Group. Specific work includes issues relating to contaminated land, environmental warranties, renewable energy projects and waste management. Also handles public sector conveyancing, including property law work relating to education, local government and other public bodies. Author of various articles on environmental law topics. Convenor of UKELA waste working party, addressing conferences and seminars.

Prof. Membership: UK Environmental Law Association.

Career: Qualified in 1978. Held various posts in local government, most recently as Borough Secretary and Solicitor to Test Valley Borough Council. Joined *Stephenson Harwood* in 1989, becoming a Partner in 1992.

Personal: Born 1942. Fitzwilliam College, Cambridge 1961-65. United Reformed Church Minister 1966-74.

Dawson, Andrew

Alsop Wilkinson, London (0161) 834 7760. Qualified 1988. Associate. Head of Planning & Environment Unit (North West). Also handles CPO, local authority law and public law.

Day, Martyn

Leigh Day & Co, London (0171) 242 1775. Qualified 1981. Partner 1987. Environment Department. Main area of practice is environmental law, heading team of 12 lawyers acting against polluters. Complex personal injury work also covered. Born in 1957.

Deanesly, Clare

Gouldens, London (0171) 583 7777. Part-

ner and Head of Environmental Law Group.

Specialisation: Principal area of practice is environmental law, dealing with waste management, landfill and contaminated land cases. Also handles general commercial property work including landlord and tenant matters and retail and development work. Acted for the Landfill Division of ARC (Greenways) in their acquisition of Econowaste from Tarmac plc 1993 and for London Brick Ltd concerning sale of substantial airspace to Shanks & McEwan. Other major clients have included Hanson Plc and Drinkwater Sabey Ltd (part of BFI). Author of 'Badlands: Essential Environmental Law for Property Professionals' (1993) and author of various articles on waste management property issues for professional publications. Environmental contributor to T.E.N. Video Network (the lawyers' educational channel). Speaker on waste management issues at conferences and seminars. Individual charge-out rate varies depending on type of job, degree of complexity and other relevant factors.

Prof. Membership: Law Society, UKELA.

Career: Qualified in 1977 while at *Field Fisher Martineau*. Joined *Gouldens* in 1978 and became a Partner in 1980.

Personal: Born 30th May 1953. Attended Church of England College for Girls, Birmingham 1957-71, then Southampton University 1971-74 (LLB Hons). Leisure pursuits include family, skiing, walking, tennis, travel and theatre. Lives in London.

Forster, Malcolm

Freshfields, London (0171) 936 4000. Litigation Department (Environment Group).

Specialisation: Advises and represents on regulatory challenges and liability disputes in the environmental field. Manages preparation of environmental statements for major projects and ensures statutory compliance. Gives environmental support for international investment, including project financing. Handles environmental issues in Eastern Europe and has special interest in matters with transitional and transnational elements; advises international organisations. Editor of Environmental Law & Management, Editor, author or contributor to numerous books and articles in legal journals. Professor of International Environmental Law at the Durrell Institute for Conservation and Ecology, at the University of Kent. Council Member, United Kingdom Environmental Law Association.

Prof. Membership: International Bar Association, Selden Society.

Career: Qualified in 1992, having joined *Freshfields* in 1991. Director of the Centre for Environmental Law at the University of Southampton 1973-84 and 1987-91. General Counsel for the Commission on Environmental Law at the International Union for Conservation of Nature and Natural Resources, Bonn, Germany, 1984-87.

Personal: Born 22nd October 1948. Attended University of Southampton 1967-70. Interests include ecclesiastical law, naval his-

tory, legal history and equestrianism. Lives in East Wellow, Hants.

Garbutt, John

Nicholson Graham & Jones, London (0171) 628 9151. Partner and Head of Planning and Environment Unit.

Specialisation: Deals with all areas of planning and environmental law, including appeals, development plans, environment disputes, audits and policy. Specialises in minerals, waste management, and land contamination in the UK and Europe. Also handles compulsory purchase and rating work, including Lands Tribunal hearings. Has acted in major planning inquiries concerning minerals, waste management, leisure developments, and in judicial reviews. Formerly chief executive of waste management and industrial minerals divisions at Blue Circle Industries and head of their environmental affairs office. Major clients include United Biscuits PLC, Blue Circle PLC, Surrey County Council, Essex County Council, Norfolk County Council, Universal Flavors Ltd, Levington plc, Southern Water PLC and Unilever plc. Author of 'Environmental Law - A Practical Handbook' and 'Waste Management Law: A Manager's Handbook'. Contributing author 'Commercial Environmental Law and Liability' (Longman). Has lectured extensively in universities and at conferences. The firm is a member of the Land Pollution Consortium.

Prof. Membership: Law Society (Member of Planning Panel), UK Environmental Law Association, CBI Minerals Committee and Environmental Protection Panel, Mining & Mineral Law Group.

Career: Qualified in 1963. Local government solicitor 1965-69. General Manager of Environmental Affairs Office, Blue Circle Industries (1978-85) and Chief Executive, Blue Circle Industrial Minerals 1986-88. Chief Executive, Blue Circle Waste Management 1989. Joined *Nicholson Graham & Jones* in 1990 and became a Partner in 1991.

Personal: Born 23rd February 1939. Local councillor. Leisure interests include golf, theatre, cinema, travel and music. Lives in Hampshire.

Greenwood, Brian J.
See under Planning.

Griffith, Robin
Clifford Chance, London (0171) 600 1000.

Handler, Thomas J.

Baker & McKenzie, London (0171) 919 1000. Partner in Commercial Litigation Department and Environmental Law Group.

Specialisation: Principal areas of practice are environmental law, covering a broad range of corporate, regulatory and liability issues, and commercial litigation, including arbitration, international aspects, contract and tort, in particular product liability, and alternative dispute resolution. Major clients include contractors, state-owned instrumentalities, foreign corporations and English companies in the fields of manufacture and supply of products, including pharmaceuticals and medical devices and the provision of services. Contributor to and editor of the *Baker & McKenzie* publication 'Regulating the European Environment'. Editorial consultant of *Environmental Law Brief* and legal consultant to the Environmental Law Foundation publication *ELFline*. Trained mediator. Maximum charge-out rate of 260 per hour.

Prof. Membership: Law Society, UK Environmental Law Association, ICC Environmental Committee, International Association of Defense Counsel, British Hungarian Society.

Career: Qualified in England & Wales in 1966. Admitted as a solicitor in New South Wales, Australia in 1962. Became a Partner at *Baker & McKenzie* in 1973. Advisor to the Foundation for International Environmental Law and Development. Member of the Executive Committee of the Environmental Law Foundation. Chairman of Environmental Resolve.

Personal: Born 25th May 1938 in Budapest, Hungary. Educated at Fort Street Boys' High School, Sydney 1951-55 and the University of Sydney, New South Wales 1956-62 (BA 1958, LL.B 1962). Fluent in Hungarian and has some German and French. Leisure activities include the arts, cross country skiing and photography. Charity Trustee. Lives in London.

Lewis, Robert
Freshfields, London (0171) 936 4000. Partner in Litigation Department.

Specialisation: Main area of practice is environmental law including environmental due diligence for corporate and property transactions, authorisation appeals and advice and environmental impact assessment. Other main area of work is planning law including planning appeals and inquiries and general planning law advice. An Author and Editor of Tolley's Environmental Handbook (1994) and co-author of Environmental Liability (1990). Member of the editorial board 'Environmental Law and Management'.

Prof. Membership: UK Environmental Law Association, Law Society, British Property Federation.

Career: Qualified in 1977. Joined *Freshfields* 1988 and became a Partner in 1991.

Personal: Born 31st December 1951. Attended St John's College, Oxford and gained 1st Class Honours Degree in Law. Lives in Hitchin.

Lomas, Owen
Allen & Overy, London (0171) 330 3000. Qualified 1980. Head of Environmental Law Group 1992. Partner 1995. Handles all aspects of UK and EC environmental law, including regulatory compliance, environmental liabilities, waste management: responsibilities of waste producers and packaging waste. Born 16.3.1955.

Mylrea, Kathy
Simmons & Simmons, London (0171)

628 2020. Qualified 1992. Partner 1994. Environmental Law Department. Advises on all aspects of UK and EU environmental law including regulatory matters, transaction work, criminal and civil litigation, environmental assessment and environmental audits. Born 6.11.1958.

Napier, Christopher
Clifford Chance, London (0171) 600 1000. Partner. Area of practice is commercial litigation with special expertise in environmental and health and safety litigation (civil and criminal), environmental insurance and environmental law generally.

O'Keeffe, Jacqui
S J Berwin & Co, London (0171) 837 2222. Qualified 1982. Senior Solicitor 1989. Construction, Development and Environmental Group.

Polden, Daniel
Ross & Craig, London (0171) 262 3077.

Redman, Michael
See under Planning.

Rose, Michael
S J Berwin & Co, London (0171) 837 2222. Qualified 1954.

Salter, John
Denton Hall, London (0171) 242 1212. Chairman of Environmental Law Group. Consultant.

Specialisation: Principal area of work covers all aspects of health, safety and environment law. Other main area of work is planning, covering all aspects of major projects. Acted on Hamilton Oil Company Ltd's Irish Sea Development. Lecturer at Imperial College and King's College, London, and expert in TV Series 'The Law is Yours'. Publications include Corporate Environmental Responsibility - Law and Practice (1992); Directors' Guide to Environmental Issues (1992); European Environmental Law (1994). Contributor to UK Oil and Gas Law - Land Use, Planning and Environment (1994), Halsbury's Laws of England (vol. 58) Environment (1986) and Vaughan's Law of the European Communities (1990). Numerous articles and publications for Oil and Gas Law and Taxation Review, Journal of Planning and Environment Law, European Environmental Law Review, Journal of Energy and Natural Resources Law.

Prof. Membership: Law Society (member of Planning Panel), RTPI, RSA, RGS, EARA, CIArb, Member of the Council International Bar Association, and Section on Business Law; Chair, International Law Committee ABA, Fellow, Institute of Management. Hon. Mem. Bar of Madrid.

Career: Qualified in 1959 while at *Denton Hall & Burgin* and became a Partner in 1961. Currently Chairman of the Environmental Law Group. On Management Committee of Lindsey Oil Refinery 1965-68; Burmah Total Refineries Trust 1971-81 and EMI Ltd 1975-79. Chaired On-Shore Gas Gathering Group 1980-81.

Personal: Born 2nd May 1932. Attended Queen Elizabeth's School then, Ashridge College. University education: Lincoln College Oxford and King's College, London. Hon. Fellow University of Dundee; Visiting Fellow and Member of the Court, Cranfield University. Member of Senior Common Room, Lincoln College, Oxford. Freeman of the City of London and of City of Glasgow. Governor of Lady Bowell's School and Copthorne School. Leisure pursuits include the arts, archaeology, sailing and tennis. Lives in Sevenoaks.

Symes, Thomas
Nabarro Nathanson, London (0171) 493 9933. Qualified 1981. Partner in Environmental Department. Advises on all aspects of health and safety regulations including the Management of Health and Safety at Work Regulations. Particular emphasis on mining and minerals. Work also includes IPC authorisations and waste regulation.

Thomas, Patricia E.
S J Berwin & Co, London (0171) 837 2222. Qualified 1974. Partner 1981. Planning and Construction Department. Principal area of work is planning and local government law, including highways, land drainage, water matters and conservation issues. Editor of 'The Planning Factbook'.

Tromans, Stephen R.
Simmons & Simmons, London (0171) 628 2020. Partner and Head of Environmental Law Department.

Specialisation: Work covers waste management, due diligence, environmental litigation, contaminated land, pollution control, water resources and environmental audit and compliance. Has acted recently in the environmental aspects of the contractorisation and sale of major defence establishments, for Railtrack plc on rail privatisation and for a wide range of major industrial companies, banks and public authorities. Author of 'Planning Law, Practice and Precedents'(1990), 'Environmental Protection Act 1990' (1991, 2nd edition 1993), and 'Contaminated Land' (1994). Associate Lecturer at University of Cambridge and at Kings College, London. Very frequent speaker in the UK and abroad.

Prof. Membership: UKELA (Chairman), specialist advisor to House of Lords Environment Committee; former Chairman of Environmental Law Sub-Committee of the Law Society.

Career: Qualified 1981. Lecturer at Cambridge University 1981-87, then a Partner at *Hewitson Becke + Shaw* from 1987-90. Joined *Simmons & Simmons* as a Partner in 1990.

Personal: Born 2nd February 1957. Attended Selwyn College, Cambridge 1975-78. Lives in Cambridge.

Waite, Andrew
Berwin Leighton, London (0171) 623 3144. Environmental specialist and Senior Solicitor.

Specialisation: Main area of practice: land contamination, waste and corporate based environmental work. Specialist in environmental liability and pollution controls, dealing principally with contaminated land, waste management and water resources issues. Also handles noise, integrated pollution controls and air pollution, advises on environmental liabilities in corporate and property transactions and legal issues involved in establishing and operating environmental management systems. Clients advised include English Partnerships, Blue Circle, British Gas, Tesco, Tarmac, Smith & Nephew, Prudential Property Management, Geest, TransAmerica Corporation, Rolls Royce and Lex Service plc. Advises Waste Facilities Audit Association (whose members include Royal Ordnance, British Telecom, Duracell, SmithKline Beecham, Glaxco, Boots, ICI, Zeneca, IBM, Rolls Royce and British Airways), on waste management issues and the Brown Lands Group (whose members include Blue Circle, British Gas, National Power, Prudential Portfolio Managers, British Coal, Ministry of Defence and Railtrack) on law and policy developments relating to contaminated land; has been consulted by the Bulgarian government with regard to their proposed legislation on noise; and numerous other clients on all areas of environmental law. Member of the International Court of Environmental Arbitration and Conciliation. Member of CBI ad hoc working party on environmental liability and Chairman of the UKELA working party on contaminated land. Editor of Butterworths' Environmental Handbook and writer on all aspects of environmental law (UK section), and author of numerous articles on all aspects of environmental law. Frequent speaker at national and international conferences on environmental law, with TV and radio experience.

Prof. Memberships: Vice-President of the European Environmental Law Association, Co-founder and member of the Council of Management of the UK Environmental Law Association.

Career: Qualified 1975, Lecturer in law at Southampton University from 1980-88; acting director of the Centre for Environmental Law at Southampton University 1984-87; visiting Professor in at the University of Georgia. Head of Environmental Law Group at *Masons* 1988-90 and Co-ordinator of the Environment Group at *Linklaters & Paines* 1990-93. Joined *Berwin Leighton* in 1993.

Personal: Born 25th February 1950. Attended Lincoln College, Oxford, 1969-72. Leisure interests include history, wildlife, theatre, cinema and walking in the countryside. Lives in Chandlers Ford, Hampshire.

Watchman, Paul

Freshfields, London (0171) 936 4000. Property Department: Environment Group.

Specialisation: Principal area of work is environmental law, including contaminated land, water and oil pollution, waste management, ballast water, energy industry and transport

matters. Other main area of work is planning law, covering mineral developments (including coal mining and coastal superquarries), planning inquiries and retail office and business developments. Author or co-author of 'Liability for Contaminated Land', 'Green's Guide to Environmental Law', 'Housing Act 1987', 'Crime and Regulation', 'The Local Ombudsman' and 'Homelessness and the Law in Great Britain'. Author of over 50 articles for a variety of professional publications. Lectures regularly on planning and environmental law.

Prof. Membership: Law Society, Law Society of Scotland.

Career: Qualified as a Scottish Solicitor in 1977. Socio/Legal Fellowship University of Glasgow 1977-79, then Lecturer/Senior Lecturer in Law 1979-89. Associate Partner *Brodies WS* 1990-91 and Partner 1991-92. Joined *Freshfields* in 1992 and qualified as an English Solicitor in 1994, Partner Freshfields, 1995.

Personal: Born 17th November 1952. Attended Strathclyde University 1971-75. Visiting Professor, Department of Land Economy/Centre for Environmental Law and Policy, Aberdeen University. Leisure pursuits include golf and fishing. Lives in London and St. Andrews.

Wiseman, Andrew

Shindler & Co, London (0171) 283 6376. Partner in Environmental Law Unit.

Specialisation: Practice covers the full range of environmental matters including noise, waste, contaminated land and pollution. Member of London Waste Regulation Authority. Visiting lecturer at Brunel University. Has addressed numerous conferences and seminars and been interviewed on TV and radio.

Prof. Membership: UK Environmental Law Association (Secretary of Planning and Environmental Impact Assessment Working Party), US Environmental Law Institute, City of London Law Society (Planning and Environmental Law Sub-Committee), Environmental Law Foundation.

Career: Qualified in 1989. Became a Partner at *Shindler & Co* in 1993.

Personal: Fellow of the Royal Society of Arts. Local Councillor.

REGIONS

Faris, Neil C.

Cleaver Fulton & Rankin, Belfast (01232) 243141.

Allen, Anthony J.R.

Donne Mileham & Haddock, Lewes (01273) 480205. Partner.

Specialisation: Main area of practice is town planning. Head of Planning and Environmental Law Unit 1976-93, and Partner in charge of DM & H Planning Services since 1993. Also in charge of environmental law

unit. Has acted in housing and retail development, health authority and university cases, in cases regarding waste deposit licensing, waste transfer stations, planning and licensing, statutory nuisance prosecutions, objections to a waste power plant and mineral extraction. Author of various articles on planning topics. Recent seminar topics have included Environmental Law- The European Background, The Environmental Protection Act Part 1- Integrated Pollution Control, and Trading in Europe- Environmental Aspects.

Prof. Membership: LMRTPI, International Bar Association, European Environmental Law Sub Committee, Environmental Law Foundation, European Environmental Law Association, British Nordic Lawyers Association, UK Environmental Law Association.

Career: MA (Cantab). Qualified in 1970, having joined *Donne Mileham & Haddock* in 1969. Became a Partner in 1976. Member of the Law Society Planning and Environmental Law Committee.

Barlow, Colin P.

Blake Lapthorn, Fareham (01489) 579990. Partner 1968. Head of Environmental and Planning Unit.

Specialisation: Main area of practice is planning and environmental law. Also a senior member of the employment department. Involved in planning appeals re mineral extraction, landfill and "wind farm" development. Lectures frequently to architects, surveyors and planning consultants on environmental law matters.

Prof. Memberships: Royal Town Planning Institute (Legal Associate), Law Society (Member of Planning Panel), Law South Group of Solicitors.

Career: Qualified in 1959. Joined *Blake Lapthorn* in 1967 and became a Partner in 1968.

Personal: Born 18th August 1935. Attended Nottingham University 1953-56. Member of Independent Board of Visitors to RN Detention Quarters. Member of MCC. Leisure pursuits include cricket and walking. Lives in Havant.

Begg, Craig

See under Planning.

Bell, Stuart

Eversheds, Leeds (0113) 243 0391. Environmental Consultant.

Specialisation: Main area of work covers environmental law including environmental audits and the preparation of environmental statements. Also advises on planning and administrative law matters including rating and highways. Advised national and regional utilities on a range of issues from the construction of overhead power lines to the development of water treatment works. Currently advising a private developer on the development of a Waste Technology Park involving a variety of waste disposal, management and recycling uses. Also advising the National Rivers Authority on the pollution of groundwater from the closure of mines in the Durham coalfield and nationally. Author of 'Environmental Law: The Law and Policy Relating to the Protection of the Environment' (Blackstone Press) and 'Commercial Environmental Law and Liability' (Longmans). Case Editor of the Environmental Law Reports. Honorary Lecturer in Environmental Law at Leeds University.

Prof. Membership: UKELA

Career: Called to the Bar in 1987. Head of Environmental Law Unit at *Dibb Lupton Broomhead* 1989-92, then joined *Hammond Suddards* as a member of the Environmental Law Group.

Blair, J. Michael G.

Thorntons WS, Forfar (01241) 872683. Qualified 1982. Partner 1986. Private Client Department. Handles agricultural and environmental matters, including the purchase and sale of estates and large farm properties and succession planning. Also acts in capital tax matters.

Brady, Peter J.

Hewitson Becke + Shaw, Cambridge (01223) 461155. Partner and head of the Development Division specialising in planning and environmental work. Born 1954.

Bryce, Andrew John

Andrew Bryce & Co, Colchester (01376) 563123. Head of Planning and Environment Group.

Specialisation: Main area of practice is environmental law, including waste management, contaminated land, water law, corporate banking and property due diligence and environmental management. Other area of practice is planning and environmental issues on major projects. Author of numerous magazine articles and papers. Has spoken at many conferences in the UK and abroad.

Prof. Membership: Law Society, UK Environmental Law Association (Chairman 1988-91), City of London Law Society (Vice Chairman, Planning and Environment Sub-Committee).

Career: Qualified in 1971, having joined *Cameron Markby Hewitt* in 1969. Became a Partner in 1973. Vice-Chair of UKELA 1987-8, and Chairman of UKELA 1988-91. Vice Chair of City of London Law Society, Planning and Environmental Sub-Committee, since 1990.

Personal: Born 31st August 1947. Attended Thorpe Grammar School, Norwich to 1965, then Newcastle University 1965-68. Leisure interests include birdwatching, tennis, walking, decorative arts and music. Lives in Coggeshall, Essex.

Buxton, Richard

Richard Buxton, Cambridge (01223) 328933. Sole Practitioner, environmental lawyer.

Specialisation: Mainly water, nature conservation, environmental assessment and noise

work. Also contaminated land and nuisance. Advises statutory bodies, charities, local authorities, private clients and other solicitors on policy and disputes. Issues include EC conservation law, abstraction licensing and other water problems, environmental assessment (ranging from afforestation of Scottish moorland to expansion of Heathrow airport), and judicial review cases including actions, two successful, for local authorities over night flights into London airports and for RSPB on nature conservation issues. Lectures on these topics.

Prof. Membership: UK Environmental Law Association (Council Member). Institute of Environmental Assessment.

Career: Qualified 1978 with *Farrer & Co*. Joined *Sinclair Roche & Temperley* 1978, handling shipping disputes work. Legal adviser to Japan Line, Tokyo 1981-84. Environmental consultancy work, Nova Scotia 1986-89, mainly advising Canadian government agencies on marine and fisheries issues. Returned to England 1989. Joined *Mills & Reeve*. Independent since 1990.

Personal: Born in 1953. Lives and works in Cambridge.

Cumming, Kenneth M.

Steedman Ramage WS, Edinburgh (0131) 226 3781.

Davies, Robert

Hepherd Winstanley & Pugh, Southampton (01703) 632211. Partner in the Commercial Department.

Specialisation: Principal area of practice covers environmental aspects of major commercial property transactions. Other main area of work is general corporate, including commercial property and business sales and purchases and commercial agreements. Defended Marwell Zoological Park against charge of polluting controlled waters. Gives seminars on environmental law matters to clients and professional bodies.

Prof. Membership: UKELA.

Career: Qualified in 1973 while with *Hepherd Winstanley & Pugh* and became a Partner in 1975.

Personal: Born 24th March 1949. Attended Southampton University 1967-70. Leisure pursuits include gardening and spending time on the Isle of Skye. Lives in Upham, near Bishops Waltham.

Driver, Timothy J.

Eversheds, Newcastle upon Tyne (0191) 261 1661. Qualified 1981. Partner 1992. Planning and Environmental Law Partner attached to Property Department. Has 25 years experience in planning work including 19 years in local government. Born 7.7.1949.

Firth, Beverley J.

Mills & Reeve, Cambridge +44(0)1223 364422. Partner: Planning and Environment specialising in all aspects of environmenmtal law and town and Country planning.

Hayden, Tim

Clarke Willmott & Clarke, Taunton (01823) 337474. Qualified 1981. Partner 1985. Advocacy Department. Main area of practice is environmental law. Also handles commercial criminal work. Born 10.12.1956.

Joy, Victoria

Booth & Co., Leeds (0113) 283 2000. Environmental Consultant in Environmental Unit.

Specialisation: Principal area of work is advising on technical aspects of environmental issues arising from corporate transactions, lender/ investor liability and enforcement actions. Experienced in environmental auditing, energy efficiency and advising on regulatory compliance, pollution control and land remediation. Contributor of numerous articles on environmental subjects in various trade, environmental and technical journals. Presented papers on environmental topics at various conferences and seminars, including EU, Energy Efficiency Office and DTI events.

Prof. Membership: Graduate Member of Institution of Mechanical Engineers, UKELA, Leeds Environmental Business Forum.

Career: Design Engineer, Department of Environment, 1982-85. Technical Consultant, Fabric Care Research Association, Harrogate 1985-88, then became Environmental Services Manager for British Textile Technology Group in Leeds. Joined *Booth & Co.* in 1993 as Environmental Consultant.

Personal: Born 26th February 1960. Attended St. Hilda's College, Oxford (BA 1982) and Glasgow University (MSc 1986). Leisure pursuits include cinema, wine and travel. Lives in Otley.

Lancaster, Roger

See under Planning.

McClelland, Christine E.A.

Tughan & Co, Belfast (01232) 553300.

McPake, Ian A.H.

Tods Murray WS, Edinburgh (0131) 226 4771. Qualified 1971. Partner *Ranken & Reid* 1973 Partner *Tods Murray* 1990. Commercial Property Department. Also handles environmental work (Convenor UK Environmental Law Association).

Oliver, Norman Robert

Biggart Baillie & Gifford, Edinburgh 0131 226 5541. Qualified 1988. Partner in the corporate department specialising in environmental law and commercial contracts. Work also covers corporate law and intellectual property. Born 21.12.1952.

Otty, Sue

See under Planning.

Pasterfield, Stephen

See under Planning.

Pike, John D.
See under Property (Commercial).

Reid, Donald A.
Morton Fraser Milligan WS, Edinburgh (0131) 556 8444. Partner and Head of Environmental Law Group.

Specialisation: Advises on all aspects of environmental law and liability including legislative compliance, property transactions, civil litigation and corporate environmental strategy, with a particular emphasis on European and international environmental law. Also handles agricultural law, advising on purchase and sale of agricultural property and tenancy disputes. Frequent contributor to environmental law journals. Lecturer to universities and industrial groups throughout the UK and abroad.

Prof. Membership: UK Environmental Law Association (Treasurer), CBI Environment Committee, Law Society of Scotland Environment Committee.

Career: Qualified in 1968. Joined *Morton Fraser Milligan WS* as a Partner in 1975.

Personal: Born 14th February 1945. Educated at George Watson's College 1949-62 and Edinburgh University 1962-66. Leisure interests include sailing, hill walking and blues piano. Lives in Aberdour, Fife.

Renger, Michael
See under Planning.

Ross, Kenneth A.
W & J Burness WS, Edinburgh (0131) 226 2561. Partner in Commercial Property Department.

Specialisation: Deals primarily with developers and retailers and major overseas investors. Acts for developers and funders in major public sector disposals. Contributes to Conferences on planning law, environmental law, VAT and commercial leases.

Prof. Membership: Environmental Law Committee of the Law Society of Scotland.

Career: Qualified in 1978. Joined *W&J Burness* in 1983, becoming Partner in 1986.

Personal: Born 18th January 1957. Studied law at Edinburgh University. Leisure interests include rugby, tennis, golf.

Ross, Kenneth C.
Bishop and Robertson Chalmers, Glasgow (0141) 248 4672. Partner in Business Law Division. Head of Environmental Law Group.

Specialisation: All aspects of environmental law, with particular reference to contaminated land and waste. Frequent lecturer to conferences, and author of articles regarding a variety of environmental law topics, particularly contaminated land and its connection with commercial property transactions, waste management licences and other waste issues.

Prof. Membership: UK Environmental Law Association, Union des Avocats Europeenes.

Career: Qualified in 1982. Joined *Robertson*

Chalmers & Auld in 1984 and became a Partner the same year. Became a Partner in *Bishop and Robertson Chalmers* in 1986.

Personal: Born 30th September 1958. Graduate of Glasgow University (LLB 1st Class Hons 1980). Spare time interests include archaeology. Lives in Glasgow.

Sales, Martin
See under Planning.

Shepherd, Michael L.
Hammond Suddards, Leeds (0113) 234 3500. Partner in Litigation Department. Head of Environmental Law Group.

Specialisation: Main areas of practice are commercial litigation, Environmental, Food Safety and Health and Safety litigation.

Prof. Membership: Law Society.

Career: Qualified in 1969. Worked in Town Clerk's office, Manchester 1966-72. Joined *Hammond Suddards* in 1972, becoming a Partner in 1974.

Personal: Born 26th September 1944. Attended Bradford Grammar School 1954-1963, then The Queen's College, Oxford 1963-66. Leisure interests include cricket, football, golf and foreign languages (Portuguese, French and Spanish). Lives in Ilkley.

Smith, Paul A.
Eversheds, Leeds (0113) 243 0391. Partner in Commercial Litigation Department.

Specialisation: Main area of practice is environmental law. Heads *Eversheds'* National Environmental Law Group, having established the unit in 1988. Acts principally for major industrial companies in the UK, US and Europe. Also covers employment law. Member of *Eversheds'* Employment Group, dealing with a broad range of employment work, particularly regarding Transfer of Undertakings issues. Successfully took the River Derwent test case to the House of Lords. In the crisis management field he acted in the Hickson & Welch Castleford incident, the Hickson International Cork incident and the Silentnight Industrial dispute and the Associated Octel fire at Ellesmere Port. Acted in Hayward v Provident Financial Corporation (for Hayward), the leading case on executive garden leave. Co-Author of College of Law Environment Law and Environmental Manual to be published by CCH Publications. Has lectured for IBC, Industrial Society, ACAS, College of Law, CBI, European Business Seminars, US Mining Congress in Florida on the Environment and Employment. Regular contributor to BBC radio programmes.

Prof. Membership: UKELA, Law Society, Industrial Law Society, ABA, IBA.

Career: Qualified in 1982, having joined *Freshfields* in 1980. Joined *Eversheds Hepworth & Chadwick* in 1984 and became a Partner in 1987.

Personal: Born 14th November 1956. Attended Warwick University 1975-79.

Lecturer at the College of Law; Governor of Richmond House School. Member of Hickson International Plc Supervisory Board. Member of Steering Group of Urban Mines UK. Professional Puppeteer. Lives in Menston, West Yorks.

Smith, Charles
Brodies WS, Edinburgh (0131) 228 3777. Partner in Corporate Department.

Specialisation: Advises on environmental law and liability generally and in respect of land, water and air pollution, sales and purchases of land, assets and shares, leases and security/banking transactions. Also handles banking and insolvency law, including loan transactions (secured and unsecured) and receiverships. Assisted in preparation of a report on contaminated land in Scotland for Scottish Enterprise. Advised on Ravenscraig Steelworks Site and the privatisation of Rosyth Royal Dockyard. Edited for Publication 'Scots Law and the Environment: Liability for Contaminated Land' by the environmental law group at *Brodies WS*.

Prof. Membership: Law Society of Scotland, United Kingdom Environmental Law Association, Royal Society of Arts, Commerce and Manufactures.

Career: Qualified in 1987, having joined *Brodies WS* in 1985. Became a Partner in 1990.

Personal: Born 21st October 1960. Attended Perth Academy 1972-78, Exeter College, Oxford 1978-82, then University of Edinburgh 1982-85. Lives in Edinburgh.

Smith, Peter
Stephens & Scown, Exeter (01392) 210700. Qualified 1980. Associate. Specialisation is the EPA 1990 as it relates to waste disposal privatisation by county councils.

Smithers, Tim M.D.
See under Property (Commercial).

Steel, John R.
See under Agriculture & Bloodstock.

Trinick, Marcus
Bond Pearce, Plymouth (01752) 266633. Qualified 1983. Partner 1991. Commercial Property Division. Has specialised in planning and environmental law for more than twelve years with particular expertise in energy developments.

Wake, Brian
Aaron & Partners, Chester (01244) 315366. Qualified 1978.

Warren, Martin H.
Eversheds, Cardiff (01222) 471147. Qualified 1985. Partner 1989. Environmental Law Department. Main area of practice is acting for defendants in complex environmental litigation. Also health and safety. Born 12.2.1961.

Wilbraham, Peter
See under Planning.

EUROPEAN UNION/COMPETITION

LONDON

Linklaters & Paines and *Slaughter and May* are considered to be marginally the best in this field.

LEADING FIRMS – LONDON

LINKLATERS & PAINES	**SLAUGHTER AND MAY**
ALLEN & OVERY	**CLIFFORD CHANCE**
FRESHFIELDS	**LOVELL WHITE DURRANT**
SIMMONS & SIMMONS	
S J BERWIN & CO	**HERBERT SMITH**
NORTON ROSE	

Linklaters' London office boasts a very strong team that includes David Hall and William Allan, while Chris Bright heads our up-and-coming list.

Slaughter and May's outstanding reputation is due in part to Malcolm Nicholson, who was the most highly recommended individual by some distance. New partners William Sibree and Laura Carstensen are also highly regarded. The team is most noted for its mergers-related work in its London office.

Naturally both of these firms have strong Brussels offices.

Lovell White Durrant is widely regarded as the best Brussels office belonging to a UK law firm, with a reputation for all-round EC law expertise. John Pheasant is its leading partner in Brussels, whilst in London, Philip Collins, Simon Polito, Michael Hutchings and Lesley Ainsworth are all highly regarded.

Freshfields' renowned M&A practice guarantees a strong presence in this area of work; John Davies is managing partner of the Brussels office, whilst in London Nicholas Spearing heads a strong team that includes Rachel Brandenburger, a new addition to our list of leading individuals.

Clifford Chance's Brussels team, headed by the experienced Ulick Bourk, is well thought of. The London team is less well-known but includes rising stars James Wheaton and John Osborne.

Simmons & Simmons' reputation rests largely on the excellence of Peter Freeman and Martin Smith in London.

HIGHLY REGARDED – LONDON

ASHURST MORRIS CRISP	**BAKER & McKENZIE**
BRISTOWS COOKE & CARPMAEL	**CAMERON MARKBY HEWITT**
CHARLES RUSSELL	**CLEARY, GOTTLIEB, STEEN & HAMILTON**
DENTON HALL	**EVERSHEDS**
EVERSHEDS	**McKENNA & CO**
SINGLETONS	**WATSON, FARLEY & WILLIAMS**
ALSOP WILKINSON	**CLYDE & CO**
HOLMAN, FENWICK & WILLAN	**RICHARDS BUTLER**
STEPHENSON HARWOOD	**TAYLOR JOYNSON GARRETT**
THEODORE GODDARD	

Allen & Overy's outstanding figure is Michael Reynolds, head of the firm's London and Brussels European and Competition Law Group, whilst in Brussels Colin Overbury, former director of the EC mergers task force, works as a consultant.

LEADING INDIVIDUALS – LONDON

Malcolm G.C. Nicholson *Slaughter and May*		
David Aitman *Denton Hall*	**W. Allan** *Linklaters & Paines*	**Ulick Bourke** *Clifford Chance*
Rachel Brandenburger *Freshfields*	**Philip G.H. Collins** *Lovell White Durrant*	**C. John Cook** *Norton Rose*
John G. Davies *Freshfields*	**Peter J. Freeman** *Simmons & Simmons*	**David F. Hall** *Linklaters & Paines*
M.B. Hutchings *Lovell White Durrant*	**Stephen D. Kon** *S J Berwin & Co*	**Dorothy Livingston** *Herbert Smith*
Julian Maitland-Walker *Charles Russell*	**Lynda Martin Alegi** *Baker & McKenzie*	**J.E. Pheasant** *Lovell White Durrant*
S.W. Polito *Lovell White Durrant*	**Michael J. Reynolds** *Allen & Overy*	**Mario Seragusa** *Cleary, Gottlieb, Steen & Hamilton*
Martin Smith *Simmons & Simmons*	**D.N. Spearing** *Freshfields*	**James Wheaton** *Clifford Chance*
Richard P. Whish *Watson Farley & Williams*		
Lesley M. Ainsworth *Lovell White Durrant*	**C.R. Bright** *Linklaters & Paines*	**Laura Carstensen** *Slaughter and May*
P.P. Chappatte *Slaughter and May*	**David Church** *Eversheds*	**Martin A. Coleman** *Norton Rose*
Julian Ellison *Ashurst Morris Crisp*	**Roger J. Finbow** *Ashurst Morris Crisp*	**Frank L. Fine** *Eversheds*
Richard J.H. Fleck *Herbert Smith*	**James Flynn** *Linklaters & Paines*	**D. Guy** *Theodore Goddard*
Katherine Holmes *Richards Butler*	**Rosalind Kellaway** *Eversheds*	**Guy I.F. Leigh** *Theodore Goddard*
Avril C.B. Martindale *Bristows Cooke & Carpmael*	**Anthony L. Morris** *Linklaters & Paines*	**Edward J. Nodder** *Bristows Cooke & Carpmael*
John Osborne *Clifford Chance*	**Colin Overbury** *Allen & Overy*	**Stephen T. Sayer** *Richards Butler*
Jonathan W. Scott *Herbert Smith*	**E. Susan Singleton** *Singletons*	**John P. Wotton** *Allen & Overy*

UP AND COMING

Alec Burnside *Linklaters & Paines*	**William Sibree** *Slaughter and May*	**Trevor I. Soames** *Norton Rose*

In all the tables the names in each group are listed alphabetically.

Other firms excelling in this field include *Herbert Smith* (Dorothy Livingston, Richard Fleck and Jonathan Scott), *Norton Rose* (John Cook and Trevor Soames) and *SJ Berwin* (Stephen Kon), which is the leading medium-sized firm.

Individuals with excellent reputations include Lynda Martin Alegi of *Baker & McKenzie*, David Aitman of *Denton Hall*, Professor Richard Whish of *Watson Farley & Williams* and Julian Maitland-Walker of *Charles Russell*. Diana Guy and Guy Leigh of *Theodore Goddard* have been heavily involved in the *Magill* case before the ECJ on behalf of an American trade group.

Having practised at both *Slaughter and May* and *Bristows Cooke & Carpmael*, Susan Singleton founded *Singletons*, a niche practice in 1994. A dedicated EC/competition lawyer and author of several texts in the area, she provides a high quality service at rates which are considerably lower than the average commercial practice.

The best-regarded firm in Brussels is *Cleary, Gottlieb Steen & Hamilton*, an American firm which also has an office in London.

SOUTH OF ENGLAND & WALES

Firms in the South East with expertise in the area include *Clyde & Co* and *Mundays*.

Clyde & Co's European department comprises seven specialists who operate from the London and Guildford offices. The firm advises on regulation and competition law, stated aids, free movement of goods and agricultural subsidies.

HIGHLY REGARDED – SOUTH OF ENGLAND & WALES	
EDWARDS GELDARD *Cardiff*	ELLIS JONES *Bournemouth*
CLYDE & CO *Cardiff*	EVERSHEDS *Cardiff*
MORGAN BRUCE *Cardiff*	MUNDAYS *Esher*
OSBORNE CLARKE *Bristol*	VEALE WASBROUGH *Bristol*

At *Mundays*, Bryan Harris, formerly a senior official of the European Commission, provides advice on a consultancy basis. The firm is a member of Eurolink (a facility providing direct communication with lawyers throughout Europe).

In the South West of England *Osborne Clarke* and *Veale Wasbrough* are experienced in the field.

Osborne Clarke is particularly active with associate offices in Copenhagen, Paris, Lyons and Brussels. The Bristol office has two specialist partners dealing primarily with competition law, intellectual property and public procurement.

Veale Wasbrough also has two specialists advising on the effect of Article 85 and block exemptions on marketing and licensing arrangements. The firm recently hosted the AGM for the Association of European Lawyers.

LEADING INDIVIDUALS – SOUTH OF ENGLAND & WALES
Stephen Chappell *Ellis Jones*
Rose D'Sa *Edwards Geldard*
Bryan Harris *Mundays*

Edwards Geldard is the leading firm in Cardiff advising on EU/competition issues. The firm has particular expertise in

competition law, public procurement, employment and environmental law. Rose D'Sa is highly recommended.

Ellis Jones makes its first appearance in the list this year, largely due to the reputation of its consultant, Steven Chappel, a former local government solicitor with many years' experience in advising local authorities on EC matters.

MIDLANDS & EAST ANGLIA

A number of large commercial firms in the Midlands have developed expertise in the area. Of these, *Eversheds*, *Martineau Johnson* and *Pinsent Curtis* have been most frequently recommended.

HIGHLY REGARDED – MIDLANDS & EAST ANGLIA	
EVERSHEDS *Birmingham*	EVERSHEDS *Norwich*
MARTINEAU JOHNSON *Birmingham*	PINSENT CURTIS *Birmingham*
WRAGGE & CO *Birmingham*	

Eversheds Birmingham office advises on distribution and agency agreements, contractual disputes and time share. Stephen Duffield is held in high regard.

Martineau Johnson boasts Geraldine Tickle (formerly a partner at *Wragge & Co*), who enjoys a national reputation in the field.

LEADING INDIVIDUALS – MIDLANDS & EAST ANGLIA
Stephen L. Duffield *Eversheds*
Geraldine Tickle *Martineau Johnson*

In East Anglia, *Eversheds* Norwich office has three specialist partners dealing with a variety of EC and competition issues, with a particular emphasis on food matters.

NORTH

In the North West *Addleshaw Sons & Latham, Eversheds* and *Lace Mawer* are held in high regard.

Addleshaw Sons & Latham's expertise covers EC/EEA competition rules, restrictive and anti-competition practices, merger control, public procurement and state aids. Garth Lindrup and Jonathan Davey have been recommended.

HIGHLY REGARDED – NORTH	
ADDLESHAW SONS & LATHAM *Manchester*	BOOTH & CO. *Leeds*
EVERSHEDS *Leeds*	EVERSHEDS *Newcastle upon Tyne*
HAMMOND SUDDARDS *Leeds*	
ALSOP WILKINSON *Liverpool*	IRWIN MITCHELL *Sheffield*
LACE MAWER *Manchester*	PINSENT CURTIS
READ HIND STEWART *Leeds*	

Lace Mawer's European department comprises three specialist partners advising on clearance, exports, distribution and agency agreements, IP, franchises and M&A's

Highly experienced firms in the North East include *Booth & Co, Eversheds, Hammond Suddards, Irwin Mitchell* and *Read Hind Stewart*.

Gillian Holding at *Booth & Co* advises on OFT and EC notifications and investigations in addition to other aspects of competition law.

Eversheds has three specialist partners operating from Leeds and Newcastle, who handle a substantial amount of European work from general advice to competition compliance.

LEADING INDIVIDUALS – NORTH

Jonathan W. Davey	*Addleshaw Sons & Latham*
Gillian E. Holding	*Booth & Co.*
Garth Lindrup	*Addleshaw Sons & Latham*

Hammond Suddards EC group has recently expanded with the appointment of four further lawyers, and is now among the six largest UK law firms operating in Brussels.

Irwin Mitchell and *Read Hind Stewart* both offer general commercial advice, *Read Hind Stewart* has strong links with Germany.

SCOTLAND

Firms in Scotland which handle European law work on a regular basis include *W & J Burness, Dundas & Wilson, Maclay Murray Spens, MacRoberts, McGrigor Donald* and *Morton Fraser Milligan*. All have access to legal services throughout Europe and, with the exception of *MacRoberts*, all have associated offices within the EC.

HIGHLY REGARDED – SCOTLAND

W & J BURNESS WS *Edinburgh*	MACLAY MURRAY & SPENS *Glasgow*
DUNDAS & WILSON CS *Edinburgh*	MACROBERTS *Glasgow*
McGRIGOR DONALD *Glasgow*	MORTON FRASER MILLIGAN *Edinburgh*
STEEDMAN RAMAGE WS *Edinburgh*	

James McLean (*W & J Burness*), William Brown of *Maclay Murray Spens* (considered an authority), David Flint of *MacRoberts* and Michael Dean (*McGrigor Donald*) have all been recommended.

LEADING INDIVIDUALS – SCOTLAND

William Brown	*Maclay Murray & Spens*
Michael Dean	*McGrigor Donald*
David Flint	*MacRoberts*
James A. McLean	*W & J Burness WS*

NORTHERN IRELAND

Cleaver Fulton & Rankin have a consultancy unit which provides information and advice to clients on all areas of EU law.

HIGHLY REGARDED – NORTHERN IRELAND

CLEAVER FULTON & RANKIN *Belfast*

Specialists in the EU aspects of particular fields such as company, environment, employment and human rights law are mentioned in the appropriate sections.

LEADERS IN EUROPEAN UNION/COMPETITION

LONDON

Ainsworth, Lesley M.
Lovell White Durrant, London (0171) 236 0066. Qualified 1981. Partner 1988. Principal area of work is UK and EU competition law and EU law generally. Born 17.4.1957.

Aitman, David
Denton Hall, London (0171) 242 1212. Partner in Competition and EC Group, Company and Commercial Department.

Specialisation: Practice covers all areas of EC and domestic competition law, particularly in the energy, transport, manufacturing, retail, communications and media sectors. Advises on EC law in relation to internal market law, public procurement and state aids, and handles regulatory work in connection with privatised utilities and privatisations, including notifications and complaints to the European Commission, the Office of Fair Trading, the Monopolies and Mergers Commission, Oftel, the Restrictive Practices Court and the DTI. Editor of section on intellectual property licensing in Butterworth's 'Encyclopedia of Competition Law'. Lectures on EC and UK competition law and is a regular contributor of articles to the legal and trade press.

Prof. Membership: Competition Law Asso-

ciation, International Bar Association.

Career: Qualified in 1982 after articles at *Denton Hall*. Became a Partner of the firm in 1988.

Personal: Born 11th April 1956. Educated at Clifton College, Bristol, then Sheffield University 1975-78 (English Literature) and the Royal Academy of Music (1978). Leisure interests include music, theatre, reading, wind-surfing and skiing.

Allan, W.
Linklaters & Paines, London (0171) 606 7080.

Bourke, Ulick
Clifford Chance, London Brussels (00 322) 533 5911. Partner. Principal area of practice is EU/competition law, including its application to publicly owned enterprises and state aids. Practice also covers EU regulatory law.

Brandenburger, Rachel
Freshfields, London (0171) 936 4000. Partner. Competition and Regulatory Law, London and Brussels.

Specialisation: Principal areas of practice are EC and UK anti-trust competition and regulatory law. Has led many cases in front of the EC and UK regulators, including the Of-

fice of Fair Trading, the Monopolies and Mergers Commission, industry specific regulators (OFTEL and others) and the European Commission. Acts for major corporate clients across a broad range of industry sectors (including telecommunications and media) and from many different countries (the Americas and continental Europe, as well as the UK). Co-editor of the mergers section in Butterworths 'Competition Law Encyclopedia' and author of articles on competition/anti-trust and telecommunications matters. Has also spoken at conferences and seminars.

Prof. Membership: Solicitors European Group, City of London Law Society (Competition Law Sub-Committee).

Career: Articled with Freshfields; qualified in 1979; became a partner in 1988.

Personal: Born 2nd April 1954. Educated at North London Collegiate School 1961-72 and Hilda's College, Oxford 1973-76 (MA Jurisprudence).

Bright, C.R.
Linklaters & Paines, London (0171) 606 7080.

Burnside, Alec
Linklaters & Paines, London (0171) 606 7080.

Carstensen, Laura

Slaughter and May, London (0171) 600 1200. Qualified 1987. Partner 1994. Specialises in UK and EU competition law.

Chappatte, P.P.

Slaughter and May, London (0171) 600 1200. Qualified 1982. Partner 1989. Main area of practice is European and UK competition law. Also commercial and trade law.

Church, David

Eversheds, London (0171) 919 4500. Partner in Brussels Office.

Specialisation: Specialises in European and commercial law. Responsible for EU advice and affairs service from Brussels office. Coordinates advice to inward investors to continental Europe. Acted in Kent Kirk (ECJ fisheries case). Editor and contributor to *Brussels Focus* (monthly EU news and data).

Prof. Membership: Law Society (member of International Awareness Working Group) ABA, IBA.

Career: Qualified in 1975. Partner at *Eversheds* since 1992.

Personal: Born 1950. Educated at Felsted School 1959-67 and University College, London 1968-71. Interests include cinema. Lives in Brussels and Kelvedon.

Coleman, Martin A.

Norton Rose, London (0171) 283 6000. Qualified 1977. Partner specialising in EC law and UK and European competition law. Born 19.11.52.

Collins, Philip G.H.

Lovell White Durrant, London (0171) 236 0066. Qualified 1973. Partner specialising in UK and EC competition law. Member of EC Competition Law Sub-Committee of City of London Solicitors Company. French speaker. Born in 1948.

Cook, C. John

Norton Rose, London (0171) 283 6000. Qualified 1990. Partner 1990. Competition and EC Unit. Principal areas of practice are competition law, EC law, utilities regulation and public law. Born 2.2.1952.

Davies, John G.

Freshfields, London (0171) 936 4000.

Ellison, Julian

Ashurst Morris Crisp, London (32-1) 537 6895. Qualified 1982. Resident partner in the Brussels office. Specialises in competition law, international joint ventures and intellectual property.

Finbow, Roger J.

Ashurst Morris Crisp, London (0171) 638 1111. Qualified 1977. Partner 1984. Company Department. Main areas of practice are corporate/commercial and competition law. Born 13.5.1952.

Fine, Frank L.

Eversheds, London Brussels (00) 32 2 230 8058. European Counsel in EC and Competition Law Group.

Specialisation: Advises companies on the EU competition aspects of commercial agreements, including mergers and joint ventures. Has established antitrust compliance programmes for companies operating in oligopolistic industries and has conducted antitrust audits and investigations. Other areas of practice include food and beverage law and insurance law. Author of 'Mergers and Joint Ventures in Europe: The Law and Policy of the EEC'. Editor of *EC Merger Control Annual Review* and EU correspondent for *ABA European Law Bulletin*. Regular speaker at conferences and seminars and author of numerous articles in legal journals.

Prof. Membership: Member of California and Washington DC Bars.

Career: Admitted to the California Bar in 1983 and the Washington DC Bar in 1991. Conseiller Juridique, Belgium since 1986. Practised in California 1982-85 before moving to Belgium. With *Dobson, Sinisi & Associates*, Brussels 1987-90, then *Frere Cholmeley Bischoff*, Brussels 1990-93. European Counsel with *Jaques & Lewis* (now *Eversheds*), Brussels from October 1993.

Personal: Born 31st July 1952. Educated at Loyola University of Los Angeles (BA., Philosophy, 1974); Loyola Law School, Los Angeles (J.D., 1982); Cambridge University (LL.M., 1986) and the Hague Academy of International Law (Certificate, 1986). Awarded a Doctorate from Cambridge University in EU Competition Law in 1995. Leisure activities include travel, snorkelling, climbing and guitar. Lives in Brussels, Belgium.

Fleck, Richard J.H.

Herbert Smith, London (0171) 374 8000. Partner in EC and Competition Law Section.

Specialisation: Handles EC and competition law, commercial disputes and accounting law. Has extensive experience of references of proposed merger and monopoly situations to the Monopolies and Mergers Commission and on other competitive and regulatory matters such as investigations under the Competition Act. Also of European competition authorities, the Department of Trade and the Bank of England. Other areas of expertise include major commercial disputes and advising major accounting firms and the Institute of Chartered Accountants on technical and accounting matters. He is the only lawyer on the Auditing Practices Board.

Career: Qualified in 1973. Partner at *Herbert Smith* since 1979.

Personal: Educated at Southampton University.

Flynn, James

Linklaters & Paines, London (Brussels) 32 2 513 78 00. Qualified 1984. Partner 1993. Brussels Office. Specialises in EC and competition/state aid law including ECJ and Court of First Instance litigation.

Freeman, Peter J.

Simmons & Simmons, London (0171) 628 2020. Head of EC and Competition Law and Managing Partner of Commercial and Trade Law Department.

Specialisation: Main area of practice is the law of the European Community including its competition law, the EEA, and UK competition law including mergers, RTPA and monopolies. Cases have included MMC investigations into the supply of beer and the supply of carbonated drinks. Joint General Editor (with Richard Whish) of 'Butterworths Competition Law'. Vice Chairman of the Regulatory Policy Institute, Oxford.

Prof. Membership: IBA, UIA, Law Society, Competition Law Association.

Career: Qualified 1977, and as a Barrister (Middle Temple) 1972. Joined *Simmons & Simmons* in 1973 and became a Partner in 1978.

Personal: Born 2nd October 1948. Attended Kingswood School, Bath, 1961-66, then Trinity College, Cambridge 1967-71, and Universite Libre de Bruxelles 1972-73. Vice President of British Maritime Charitable Foundation. Leisure interests include naval history and music. Lives in Cambridge.

Guy, D.

Theodore Goddard, London (0171) 606 8855.

Hall, David F.

Linklaters & Paines, London (0171) 606 7080. Qualified 1969. Partner 1976. Specialises in EC and competition law, also mergers and acquisitions, and state aid. Formerly in legal service at the EC Commission in Brussels. Also chairman, competition working party of UK Bars and Law Societies. Co-author of EEC Anti-trust Law: Principles and Practice (Butterworths 1975).

Holmes, Katherine

Richards Butler, London (0171) 247 6555. Qualified 1990. Partner in the Corporate & Commercial Department specialising in EC law and European and UK competition law.

Hutchings, M.B.

Lovell White Durrant, London (0171) 236 0066. Qualified 1973. Partner 1981. Principal area of work is UK and EU competition law (monopolies, mergers and restrictive practices). Also deals with EC and EU law generally with a particular emphasis on internal market, trade, social affairs and transport. Born 8.11.1948

Kellaway, Rosalind

Eversheds, London (0171) 919 4500. Partner in Company Commercial Department. Head of *Eversheds* national EC and Competition Law Group.

Specialisation: Main areas of practice are EC and UK competition law. Work includes Fair Trading Act enquiries, Restrictive Trade Practices Act matters, public procurement and competitive tendering by local government, competition law advice in connection with utilities, and complaints. Also handles related commercial work, including distribution, agency agreements, supply agreements, licensing agreements, and complex contract work generally. Writes and speaks regularly.

Prof. Membership: Solicitors European Group, Competition Law Association, CBI Competition Law Committee.

Career: Qualified in 1984. Joined *Jaques & Lewis* (now Eversheds) in 1981, becoming a Partner in 1989.

Personal: Born 10th June 1957. Attended Lewes Priory School and the University of Sussex 1979 (BA Law with French). Leisure interests include riding. Lives in Lewes.

Kon, Stephen D.

S J Berwin & Co, London (0171) 837 2222. Qualified 1980. Partner in the EU/Competition Law Department. Advises widely on EU law, particularly EU and UK competition law. Born 26.9.1949.

Leigh, Guy I.F.

Theodore Goddard, London (0171) 606 8855. Qualified 1974. Partner 1978. EU and Competition Group. Has experience before EU and national courts and administrative bodies. Born 22.11.1944.

Livingston, Dorothy

Herbert Smith, London (0171) 374 8000. Partner and Joint Head of EC and Competition Law Group.

Specialisation: Her areas of expertise cover the full range of EU and UK competition law, including restrictive agreements, monopolies, anti-competitive practices, abuse of dominant position, mergers, public procurement, state aids and utility regulation. Also handles international finance and banking matters in which her areas of expertise include financing arrangements for international joint ventures, disputes relating to cross-border payments, including those arising from insolvencies, governmental embargoes and misappropriation of funds. She is the joint author of 'Longmans Competition Law Sources' and of 'Competition Law and Practice' and has contributed a chapter on cross border payment systems to 'European Cash Management'. Sits on the advisory board of the Centre for European Law at King's College, London.

Prof. Membership: City of London Law Society (Member of Banking Law and EC and Competition Law Sub-Committees), Finance Leasing Association (Member of European Committee).

Career: Qualified in 1972. With *Herbert Smith* since articles. Became a Partner in 1980.

Personal: Educated at St Hugh's College, Oxford.

Maitland-Walker, Julian

Charles Russell, London (0171) 203 5000. Partner in EC & Competition Law Group.

Specialisation: Main area of Practice is European trade and competition law including UK restrictive trade practices, monopolies and merger control, state aids, public procurements and anti-dumping issues. Has acted in several references to the MMC, including Beer Supply, Motor Vehicle Distribution and the Pharmaceutical Industry. Other areas of practice include intellectual property, registration and licensing, agency distribution, franchising, joint ventures and R&D agreements. Editor of the *European Competition Law Review* and author of several texts including 'A Guide to European Company Laws' (Sweet & Maxwell), 'EC Insurance Directives' and 'EC Banking Directives' (Lloyds of London Press).

Martin Alegi, Lynda

Baker & McKenzie, London (0171) 919 1000. Partner in EC, Competition and Trade Department.

Specialisation: Main area of practice is competition law. Also distribution, franchising, computers and I.T. Author of competition chapter in Sweet & Maxwell's 'Encyclopaedia of Information Technology Law'.

Prof. Membership: Law Society, Competition Law Society. International Bar Association.

Career: Qualified in 1977, having joined *Baker & McKenzie* in 1975. Became a Partner in 1981. Member of the CBI Competition Panel. Member of the Institute of Directors Law Committee.

Personal: Born 7th March 1952. Educated at Cambridge University (MA in Law, 1973) and the Institute of European Studies, Brussels (1975). Lives in London.

Martindale, Avril C.B.

See under Intellectual Property.

Morris, Anthony L.

Linklaters & Paines, London (0171) 606 7080. Since 1976, specialised in competition law (EC and UK) and regulatory work, including four years as Head of Brussels office.

Nicholson, Malcolm G.C.

Slaughter and May, London (0171) 600 1200. Qualified 1972. Head of firm's EC/Competition Group. Advises a wide range of clients (including governments) on a full range of EC, Competition and Regulatory matters.

Nodder, Edward J.

See under Intellectual Property.

Osborne, John

See under Company/Commercial.

Overbury, Colin

Allen & Overy, London (0171) 330 3000. Qualified 1955. Since 1993, a consultant in the Corporate (Competition) Department, having worked for the EC Commission 1974-93 and Director, Directorate-General for Competition 1986-93. Born 13.1.1931.

Pheasant, J.E.

Lovell White Durrant, London Brussels (322) 647 0660. Qualified 1979. Partner 1985. Competition and EU Department. Principal area of practice is EC and UK Competition. Also deals with general EU trade law matters. Advocate in European Commission and Courts proceedings and before the Monopolies and Mergers Commission in UK. Born 19.12.1953.

Polito, S.W.

Lovell White Durrant, London (0171) 236 0066. Qualified 1976. Partner 1982. EC and UK Competition and Trade Department. Work includes merger clearance work involving EC merger task force, OFT, MMC, and monopoly and competition investigations. Born 11.3.1949.

Reynolds, Michael J.

Allen & Overy, London Brussels (00) 32 2 230 2791. Qualified 1977. Partner 1981. Head of EC Department. Main areas of practice are EC law and UK anti-trust law; also active in the Central and Eastern Europe Practice Group. Born 8.10.1950.

Sayer, Stephen T.

Richards Butler, London (0171) 247 6555. Partner in Commercial and EC Group.

Specialisation: Main areas of practice are competition and energy. Advises on takeover bids on competition issues. Acted for the bidder in a hostile bid when a reference to the MMC was avoided by negotiating undertakings with the OFT to dispose of certain of the target's business. This was the first occasion on which such undertakings were given. Has also negotiated a number of undertakings and variations to undertakings with the OFT, including extensions of the deadline for disposals due to changes in economic circumstances, and has acted in a number of monopolies references. Represents the European Commission in relation to certain energy matters and also represents Middle Eastern Government on energy. Also deals with commercial and intellectual property. He is a contributor to Longman's 'Practical Commercial Precedents' on distribution agreements and author of the chapter on joint ventures in Longman 'Law Tax and Finance'. Has lectured extensively on international law and joint ventures, agency distribution and competition issues.

Prof. Membership: Law Society, Society of English and American Lawyers, International Bar Association, City of London Solicitors Company.

Career: Qualified in 1968, having joined *Richards Butler* in 1969. Became a Partner in 1974.

Personal: Born 8th July 1945. Interests include racquets, real tennis, golf and theatre. Lives in London.

Scott, Jonathan W.
Herbert Smith, London (0171) 374 8000. Qualified 1981. Partner 1988. EC/Competition Department. Work includes mergers, joint ventures, anti-trust investigations and cases before the ECJ.

Seragusa, Mario
Cleary, Gottlieb, Steen & Hamilton, London (00 322) 287 2000.

Sibree, William
Slaughter and May, London (0171) 600 1200. Qualified 1988. Partner 1993. EC/Competition Department. Deals with all areas of UK and EC competition law. Born 19.3.1961.

Singleton, E. Susan
Singletons, Harrow (0181) 864 0835. Senior Partner of firm since 1994.

Specialisation: Main area of practice is EC Competition law, particularly relating to commercial agreements and intellectual property. Handles compliance, competition law and mergers and joint ventures, notifications, abuse of market power, licensing and EU law generally, including directives and public procurement. Also handles intellectual property, commercial and computer\I.T. law. Advises on ownership of rights, licences, EU intellectual property directives, general commercial law, agency (particularly Commercial Agents (Council Directive) Regulations), distribution and contract law. Acted in ready mixed concrete investigations and in various EC notifications. Author of Financial Times Management Report 'EC Competition Law - a Practical Guide for Companies', Introduction to Competition Law', 'Getting Value from Professional Advisers' and 'Daily Express: You and the Law', and contributor to ten other books including Croner's:- 'I.T. Guide', 'Europe' and 'Model Business Contracts'. Editor of Comparative Law of Monopolies book and journals - I.T. Law Today and Trading Law and joint editor of Tolley's Computer Law and Practice. Speaking at 36 conferences in 1995. Publishes an average of 17 articles on the law per month.

Prof. Membership: Competition Law Association, Licensing Executives Society, Law Society, Society of Computers and Law, Computer Law Association and Institute of Export.

Career: Qualified 1985, having joined *Nabarro Nathanson* in 1983. Joined *Slaughter and May* in 1985, then *Bristows Cooke & Carpmael* in 1988. Established *Singletons* in 1994.

Personal: Born 14th December 1961. Attended Westfield School, Newcastle-upon-Tyne 1972-79, then Manchester University 1979-82 and Chester Law College 1982-3. Leisure interests include sightsinging, piano, computers, skiing, reading, writing and children. Lives in Harrow.

Smith, Martin
Simmons & Simmons, London (0171)

628 2020. Partner.

Specialisation: Main area of practice is European Community Law with particular emphasis on competition work (both EC and UK). Has experience of dealing with all the main EC and UK competition law authorities. His experience extends to a number of regulated industries, notably water and radio. Also undertakes more general commercial work, usually with a significant competition law or regulatory element. Author of three major divisions of the three-volume 'Butterworths Competition Law'. Has also written a number of articles. Frequently speaks at conferences and seminars.

Prof. Membership: Law Society, City of London Solicitors' Company Competition Law Sub-Committee. Solicitors European Group, International Bar Association, American Bar Association.

Career: Qualified in 1981. Joined *Simmons & Simmons* in 1977, becoming a Partner in 1986, having worked at *Dechert Price & Rhoads* (Philadelphia) 1978 and *Linklaters & Paines* 1983-5.

Personal: Born 27th August 1955. Attended St Catharine's College, Cambridge 1974-77 (MA) and University of Pennsylvania (LLM) 1978-9. Leisure interests include sport, music and walking. Lives in London.

Soames, Trevor I.
Norton Rose, London (0171) 283 6000. Qualified 1989. Partner 1994. Based in Brussels office: (010) 322 237 6111. EC and Competition Law Unit. Specialises in competition and regulatory law.

Spearing, D.N.
Freshfields, London (0171) 936 4000. Head of Competition Group.

Specialisation: Main area of practice is EC/Competition law. Extensive experience in monopolies, mergers and restrictive practices cases at both UK and EC levels. Acted for leading companies in recent MMC inquiries into coffee, car prices, perfumes and ice-cream. Merger clearances for range of clients including GEC, Nestlé, Reed Elsevier, Forte and Powergen. Co-Author of 'Mergers' section of Butterworth's Competition law. Numerous contributions to legal journals.

Prof. Memberships: Law Society, City of London Solicitors Company, Former Chairman Solicitors' European Group.

Career: Joined *Gordon, Dadds & Co.* in 1976, qualifying in 1978. Left to join *Freshfields* in 1978. Partner 1984. Head of Competition Group.

Personal: Born 4th May 1954. Attended Caterham School 1965-72, then Hertford College, Oxford 1972-75. Leisure pursuits include family, travel and golf. Lives in Haslemere, Surrey.

Wheaton, James
Clifford Chance, London (0171) 600 1000. Partner 1978. EC and Competition Department. Principal area of practice is EC and

competition law. Also public procurement and government contracts. Born 13.11.1948.

Whish, Richard P.
Watson Farley & Williams, London (0171) 814 8000. Partner and Head of EC and Competition Law Department. Professor of Law, King's College London, University of London.

Specialisation: Main areas of practice are UK and EC competition law including mergers, joint ventures, distribution agreements, licenses of intellectual property rights, and particularly the energy and transport sectors. Author of several books including 'Competition Law' 3rd edition (Butterworths, 1993); Co-editor of Butterworths Competition Law, 1991; Editor of Volume 47 of Halsbury's Laws of England (Trade and Industry); contributor to Chitty on Contracts on Competition Law.

Prof. Memberships: Member of the Executive Council of the Centre of European Law at King's College, London; Member of the Advisory Board of the Centre for the Study of Regulated Industries; Member of the Editorial Board of the European Business Law Review.

Career: Qualified 1977. Lecturer in Law at Bristol University 1978-88, then Reader in Commercial Law at Bristol University 1988-90. Joined *Watson Farley & Williams* in 1989.

Personal: Born 23rd March 1953. Holds a BA, BCL Oxon. Leisure interests include opera, travelling, gardening and India. Lives in London and Marshfield.

Wotton, John P.
Allen & Overy, London (0171) 330 3000. Qualified 1978. Partner in the Competition Department specialising in European Community, competition and broadcasting law. Born 7.5.1954.

Brown, William
Maclay Murray & Spens, Edinburgh (0131) 226 5196. Qualified 1983. Partner 1992. Company Department. Main area of practice is European Community and Competition. Born 25.4.1959.

Chappell, Stephen
Ellis Jones, Bournemouth (01202) 525333. Qualified 1965. Consultant 1993. Advises on local government law, public procurement and European employment law. Born 9.12.1938.

D'Sa, Rose
Edwards Geldard, Cardiff (01222) 238239. International Relations Consultant.

Specialisation: Main area of practice is European Community Law, covering general commercial, competition law, agency and distribution, EC public procurement and EC employment law. Also handles public international law, including law of the Commonwealth and international human rights law. Cases have covered matters including competition law procedures (regulation 17), State aids, public procurement (including the Services Directive) and EC Employment law (such as the acquired rights directive and TUPE). Author of 'European Community Law and Civil Remedies in England and Wales' and of various articles in the European Business Law Review, Arbitration, Law Society's Gazette and the national and Welsh media. Legal Consultant to the 1990 Commonwealth Law Ministers Meeting in New Zealand. Visiting Fellow at the Institute of Advanced Legal Studies (London) for 1991-92 in European Community Law. Consultant and Speaker at the 1993 Commonwealth Law Conference (Cyprus). Co-ordinator of European Commission FORCE pilot project on 'Europe Without Frontiers: Legal Barriers to Cross Border Trade' (1991-94).

Prof. Membership: Institute of Directors, Wales Chamber of Commerce, Welsh Centre for International Affairs, Commonwealth Lawyers Association, International Law Association, AIJA, Solicitors European Group.

Career: Qualified as a Barrister in 1981. Lecturer in Law at University College, Cardiff 1982-83 and the University of Bristol 1984-85. Worked at the Human Rights Unit, Commonwealth Secretariat (London) 1985-88. International Relations Consultant for *Edwards Geldard* since 1989.

Personal: Born 7th October 1957. Holds an LLB (First Class Honours 1979, PhD 1982). Barrister (Middle Temple) 1981. Leisure interests include playing tennis for Dinas Powys Club and for Wales. Lives in Newport.

Davey, Jonathan W.

Addleshaw Sons & Latham, Manchester (0161) 832 5994. Partner in EC Competition & Commercial Department.

Specialisation: Main areas of work are agency, distribution, franchising, joint ventures, state aids, public procurement, UK and EC competition law (including the law relating to restrictive practices, mergers and anti-competitive behaviour). Also deals with other commercial agreements (particularly with international dimensions) including drafting and advising generally on commercial agreements, sale of goods and unfair contract terms legislation. Co-author of 'A Guide to the Commercial Agents Regulations' (CCH). Co-author of UK chapter in 'Commercial Agency and Distribution Agreements' (Graham & Trotman). Has lectured widely on the Commercial Agents Regulations and on other commercial law topics to audiences of lawyers and businessmen.

Prof. Membership: Association Internationale des Jeunes Avocats, CBI National Consumer Law Advisory Panel, North West Solicitors European Group.

Career: Joined *Addleshaw Sons & Latham* in 1986 and qualified in 1988. Became an Associate in 1992 and a Partner in 1994.

Personal: Educated at Manchester University 1982-85 (LL.B Hons) and the College of Law, Chester 1985-86 (1st Class Hons in Law Society Final Examination). Treasurer, Manchester University Law Graduates Association (MULGA). Enjoys hill walking, travel and good food. Lives near Knutsford.

Dean, Michael

McGrigor Donald, Glasgow (0141) 248 6677. Qualified 1986. Partner in the Corporate Department specialising in EC and Competition law. 15.1.1960.

Duffield, Stephen L.

See under Company/Commercial.

Flint, David

See under Intellectual Property.

Harris, Bryan

Mundays, Esher (01372) 467272. A special consultant to Mundays advising on European Community policy and law.

Specialisation: Advises generally on the administrative, legislative and policy making procedures of the EC institutions; and particularly on questions involving the competition rules and intellectual property rights (patents, trade marks, copyright etc). He was a senior official of the Commission of the European Community from 1973 to 1983 and served as Head of the Intellectual Property Division.

During the last 20 years he has written and lectured extensively on legal and economic matters. He has written several full-length books ["The Law of the European Communities", [Butterworths, 1973]; "Franchising in the European Community", [Longmans, 1991], and "Lobbying in the European Community", [MacMillan, 1992]; has contributed numerous articles to learned or specialised journals, including The European Law Review, [London, England], The Journal of Law and Technology, [Concord, NH, USA], The Common Market Law Review [Leyden, The Netherlands], The International Law Contract Law Review [Lausanne, Switzerland], and the European Intellectual Property Review [Oxford, England]; he also wrote the section on the Common Agricultural Policy [Title "Agriculture"] for the Fourth Edition of Halsbury's Laws and is author of "The Law of the European Communities", [Supplement to Halbury's Laws, Third Edition]. He is Editor of the monthly publication, "Competition Law in the European Communities", published by the Monitor Press in England, with an international readership.

He helped to found, and is a Council Member of, the Common Law Institute of Intellectual Property.

Holding, Gillian E.

Booth & Co., Leeds (0113) 283 2000. Partner in Corporate Department.

Specialisation: Principal area of practice is European, competition and public procurement law. Work includes UK and EU merger control advice; OFT, MMC and European Commission enquiries and investigations; restrictive trade practices advice and advice to public and private sector clients on public purchasing regulations. Also handles commercial work including agency and distribution agreements and international joint ventures. Acted in Newitt/Dunlop Slazenger International (leading EC case on distribution networks). Has spoken at various conferences, including CBI (Northern Region), Leeds in October 1994.

Prof. Membership: Law Society, Solicitors European Group (current Chairman of Yorkshire and Humberside branch), UAE, IAJA.

Career: Qualified in 1984 with *Linklaters & Paines* until August 1990 (1986 - 1988 in Paris office). Joined *Booth &Co.* in September 1990 and became a partner in 1992.

Personal: Born 4th March 1959. Educated at the University of Birmingham 1977-81 (LL.B Hons, Law with French), Université de Limoges, France 1979-80 (Diplome d'études juridiques Français) and City University 1983-85 (MA in Business Law). Leisure interests include walking, painting, food, travel, French cinema and literature. Lives in Leeds.

Lindrup, Garth

Addleshaw Sons & Latham, Manchester (0161) 832 5994. Partner and Head of EC and Competition Department.

Specialisation: Work includes mergers and joint ventures, distribution, agency and franchising, public procurement, state aid, restrictive and anti-competitive practices, dominant positions and complex monopolies. Particular sectors include motor vehicles, books, beer, milk, air transport, buses, steel and pharmaceuticals. Editor, 'Butterworths Competition Law Handbook'; author of articles for the Law Society Gazette, New Law Journal and SEG Journal. Honorary lecturer in EC law, Manchester University. Chairman, Law Society's Solicitors European Group 1994/95.

Prof. Membership: IBA, LIDC, Competition Law Association, Law Society.

Career: Qualified in 1975. Joined *Addleshaw Sons & Latham* in 1979 and became a Partner in 1984. Member of Law Society's 1992 (subsequently International) Awareness Working Party, 1989-93.

Personal: Born 1948. Holds BA, LLM (Cantab).

McLean, James A.

See under Intellectual Property.

Tickle, Geraldine

Martineau Johnson, Birmingham (0121) 200 3300. Qualified 1983. Associate 1995. Main area of practice is competition and EC law. Also handles general commercial work. Born 11.2.1951.

FAMILY/MATRIMONIAL

LONDON

The firms most frequently recommended include *Manches & Co, Gordon Dadds, Farrer & Co, Charles Russell, Collyer-Bristow* and *Withers.*

Manches & Co, where Jane Simpson and Helen Ward have been consistently recommended, gained Richard Sax fol-

LEADING FIRMS – LONDON	
CHARLES RUSSELL	COLLYER–BRISTOW
FARRER & CO	GORDON DADDS
MANCHES & CO	
DAWSON CORNWELL & CO	MILES PRESTON & CO
WITHERS	
KINGSLEY NAPLEY	MISHCON DE REYA
SEARS TOOTH	

lowing their recent merger with *Rubinstein Callingham Polden & Gale.* Richard Sax enjoys a strong reputation in the field which should strengthen the department at the firm even further. They have all at one time been officers of and remain members of the Solicitors Family Law Association (SFLA) and are members of the International Academy of Matrimonial Lawyers. Both Richard Sax and Helen Ward sit as Deputy District Judges at the Principal Registry. They, and their team, totalling four partners and eight assistants, have considerable experience in all areas of family law work, financial and children, domestic and international, married and unmarried.

Gordon Dadds is also seen as a leading firm with partners belonging to the Solicitors Family Law Association, Inter-

national Academy of Matrimonial Lawyers and the Family Mediators Association. The department headed by Douglas Alexiou covers all areas of matrimonial and family law and has six partners specialising in family work including Gill Doran and James Harcus who are also highly regarded.

Farrer & Co has a strong family department whose clients have included the Prince Of Wales and the Duke Of York. *Charles Russell,* also highly recommended, is acting for Camilla Parker-Bowles in her divorce. The firm has a strong department incorporating specialist partners Peter George, David Davidson and William Longrigg, all of whom have considerable experience. In addition to acting for clients whose affairs are governed exclusively by English law, members of the department have frequently acted in cases with an international aspect.

Collyer-Bristow is also among the foremost family law practices within London, and Jeremy Levison who heads the department is particularly well regarded. He is treasurer and secretary of the European branch of the International Academy of Matrimonial Lawyers. Clients of the department include many senior professionals, senior executives from commerce and industry and well established names in the field of entertainment and the arts. The firm is nominated solicitors on the Lord Chancellor's Child Abduction Panel, and is also involved in many cases with an international element.

The well regarded team at *Withers* consists of partners Diana Parker, Andrew Gerry and Charles Doughty. The team has particular expertise in handling cases embracing complex international dimensions, all of which entail careful consideration of financial issues and taxation consequences.

Other highly recommended firms include *Dawson Corn-*

LEADING INDIVIDUALS – LONDON		
Douglas Alexiou *Gordon Dadds*	Pamela Collis *Kingsley Napley*	John Cornwell *Dawson Cornwell & Co*
David Davidson *Charles Russell*	Sandra S. Davis *Mishcon De Reya*	Gill Doran *Gordon Dadds*
Charles Doughty *Withers*	Peter George *Charles Russell*	Andrew Gerry *Withers*
James Harcus *Gordon Dadds*	Jeremy Levison *Collyer–Bristow*	William Longrigg *Charles Russell*
Diana C. Parker *Withers*	Miles Preston *Miles Preston & Co*	Maggie Rae *Mishcon De Reya*
Richard Sax *Manches & Co*	Fiona Shackleton *Farrer & Co*	Jane Simpson *Manches & Co*
Ray Tooth *Sears Tooth*	Helen Ward *Manches & Co*	
Peter J. Alexander *Dawson & Co*	Sian E. Blore *Farrer & Co*	Paul Butner *Wright Son & Pepper*
Elspeth Chapman *Barnett Sampson*	Felicity Crowther *Bindman & Partners*	Michael J. Drake *Collyer–Bristow*
J. Fisher *Gordon Dadds*	Judith Goodman *Goodman Ray*	Naomi Goodman *Gordon Dadds*
David M. Hodson *Frere Cholmeley Bischoff*	Grant Howell *Charles Russell*	Frances Hughes *Bates, Wells & Braithwaite*
Maryly La Follette *Charles Russell*	David. J. Leverton *Payne Hicks Beach*	Alan Marco *Baileys Shaw & Gillett*
Claire Meltzer *Collyer–Bristow*	Richard Parry *Farrer & Co*	Eileen Pembridge *Fisher Meredith*
Susan Philipps *Penningtons*	Simon Pigott *Collyer–Bristow*	Peggy Ray *Goodman Ray*
Sara Robinson *The Simkins Partnership*	Geoffrey M. Rutter *S. Rutter & Co*	Jonathan Walsh *Stephenson Harwood*

UP AND COMING
Jane Keir *Kingsley Napley*

In all the tables the names in each group are listed alphabetically.

well & Co, Miles Preston & Co, Sears Tooth, Kingsley Napley and *Mishcon de Reya. Dawson Cornwell & Co,* where John Cornwell is highly regarded, is a leading family practice with six full-time matrimonial specialists, all of whom are members of the SFLA. *Miles Preston & Co* is a niche matrimonial and family law practice formed in May 1994 by three experienced partners in the field. Miles Preston is highly

HIGHLY REGARDED – LONDON

ANTHONY GOLD, LERMAN & MUIRHEAD	BAILEYS SHAW & GILLETT
BATES, WELLS & BRAITHWAITE	BINDMAN & PARTNERS
DAVID DU PRÉ	DAVID TRUEX AND CO
DAWSON & CO	FISHER MEREDITH
FRERE CHOLMELEY BISCHOFF	GOODMAN RAY
PAYNE HICKS BEACH	REYNOLDS PORTER CHAMBERLAIN
THE SIMKINS PARTNERSHIP	STEPHENSON HARWOOD
WILFORD MCBAIN	

BARNETT SAMPSON	BECKMAN & BECKMAN
BOODLE HATFIELD	DUNDONS
FORSYTE SAUNDERS KERMAN	HODGE JONES & ALLEN
MARGARET BENNETT	OSMOND GAUNT & ROSE
PENNINGTONS	RADCLIFFES CROSSMAN BLOCK
RUSSELL-COOKE, POTTER & CHAPMAN	S. RUTTER & CO
TAYLOR JOYNSON GARRETT	WEDLAKE BELL
WRIGHT SON & PEPPER	

BRECHER & CO	CURRY CH. HAUSMANN POPECK
EDWARD FAIL BRADSHAW & WATERSON	E. EDWARDS SON & NOICE
GULBENKIAN HARRIS ANDONIAN	HUNTERS
RUSSELL JONES & WALKER	SIMMONDS CHURCH SMILES

recommended by his peers and is president of the International Academy Of Matrimonial Lawyers. Ray Tooth at *Sears Tooth* is well known for his matrimonial work. He has a reputation for an aggressive approach, but nevertheless has an excellent reputation amongst other lawyers in the field. *Kingsley Napley* is well known for its family and matrimonial work, handling cases concerning childcare through to cohabitation and complex financial matters on divorce. Pamela Collis at the firm is particularly highly regarded. Maggie Rae and Sandra Davis at *Mishcon de Reya* are both very well regarded by competitors. Apart from having a good name in divorce work, they have also cornered a sizable niche in matters involving children, most notably child abuction cases. Both *Kingsley Napley* and *Mishcon de Reya* also handle a certain amount of legal aid work.

Of other firms with a strong reputation for their work relating to children, *Goodman Ray, Wilford McBain* and *Reynolds Porter Chamberlain* have been particularly recommended.

SOUTH EAST

Numerous firms in the South East specialise in the area of family and matrimonial work, and many firms in the region balance legal aid and private client casework, such as *Cole and Cole* which has a large matrimonial practice.

Eric Robinson & Co is particularly known for its substantial legal aid practice. *Griffith Smith* and *Blandy & Blandy*

are known for their efforts in the field of conciliation and mediation, and the latter firm has two partners who are members of the Family Mediators Association.

HIGHLY REGARDED – SOUTH EAST

BALDOCKS *Guildford*	BLANDY & BLANDY *Reading*
BOWER & BAILEY *Oxford*	COLE and COLE *Oxford*
DONNE MILEHAM & HADDOCK *Brighton*	ERIC ROBINSON & CO *Southampton*
GIRLINGS *Canterbury*	GRIFFITH SMITH *Brighton*
GRIFFITHS ROBERTSON *Reading*	LEONARD GRAY *Chelmsford*
THOMSON SNELL & PASSMORE *Tunbridge Wells*	

BERRY & BERRY *Tunbridge Wells*	BUSS MURTON *Tunbridge Wells*
COFFIN MEW & CLOVER *Portsmouth*	CRIPPS HARRIES HALL *Tunbridge Wells*
HENMANS *Oxford*	ILIFFES BOOTH BENNETT *Uxbridge*
LINNELLS *Oxford*	MACDONALD OATES *Petersfield*
MATTHEW ARNOLD & BALDWIN *Watford*	MAX BARFORD & CO *Tunbridge Wells*
PARIS SMITH & RANDALL *Southampton*	PENNINGTONS *Basingstoke*
PICTONS *St. Albans*	STEVENS & BOLTON *Guildford*
TWITCHEN MUSTERS & KELLY *Southend-on-Sea*	WOODFORD & ACKROYD *Southampton*
WYNNE BAXTER GODFREE *Lewes*	

Most of the firms handling divorce work also advise on child care matters, with many solicitors members of The Law Society's Children Panel. Firms particularly well known for their work in child care matters include *Bower & Bailey, Donne Mileham & Haddock* and *Griffiths Robertson. Leonard Gray* continues to handle a large caseload of child care matters, primarily representing abused children, and *Girlings* and *Thomson Snell & Passmore* are known for handling child abuction cases with an international element. *Baldocks* has an established reputation for its expertise in adoption cases.

SOUTH WEST

Many firms in the South West have strong family practices. Among the most prominent, *Bond Pearce* handle all aspects of marriage or relationship breakdown. The team, where

HIGHLY REGARDED – SOUTH WEST

BOND PEARCE *Plymouth*	BURGES SALMON *Bristol*
FOOT & BOWDEN *Plymouth*	GILL AKASTER *Plymouth*
HARTNELL & CO *Exeter*	LESTER ALDRIDGE *Bournemouth*
STEPHENS & SCOWN *Exeter*	TOZERS *Exeter*
TRUMP AND PARTNERS *Bristol*	VEALE WASBROUGH *Bristol*
WOLFERSTANS *Plymouth*	

CLARKE WILLMOTT & CLARKE *Taunton*	

BARCAN WOODWARD *Bristol*	BATTENS *Yeovil*
BEVAN ASHFORD *Bristol*	BOBBETTS MACKAN *Bristol*
CARTWRIGHTS *Bristol*	COLES MILLER *Poole*
COODES *St. Austell*	FAULKNERS *Frome*
KIRBY SIMCOX *Bristol*	LAWRENCE TUCKETTS *Bristol*
NALDER & SON *Truro*	STONE KING & WARDLE *Bath*
STONES *Exeter*	WANSBROUGHS WILLEY HARGRAVE *Bristol*
WITHY KING & LEE *Bath*	WOOLLCOMBE BEER WATTS *Newton Abbot*

Wendy Boyce enjoys an established reputation, has particular expertise in issues concerning the Child Support Act and matters involving substantial assets and business interests.

Burges Salmon, where Catherine Hallam is well regarded, has a strong reputation for handling complex financial disputes involving large sums of money. A firm particularly well known for child law work, both public and private, is *Foot & Bowden* where Margaret Bonner has been recommended for her involvement in cases concerning adoption, abduction, divorce and ancillary relief.

The department at *Gill Akaster* headed by Jacqueline Ashley has a family specialist team with particular strength in child care work. *Wolferstans* also has strength in handling child law, where Jeremy Bennett is on the Plymouth Child Care Support group and heads the childrens' department at the firm. Phillip Thorneycroft, the partner at *Wolferstans* who heads the matrimonial department, has particular expertise in advising on claims to pensions assets upon divorce as well as covering all aspects of matrimonial work.

Phillip Kidd at *Tozers* has recently opened a specialist child care office in Torquay. The team consists of three members of the Law Society Children Panel and the entire office is devoted to child care and related work. *Hartnell & Co,* a niche practice, has been highly recommended. The team of three is headed by Norman Hartnell, who has contributed to 'Family Law' and is Co-ordinator of the Family Mediators Association (Devon) and is an accredited FMA mediator.

LEADING INDIVIDUALS – SOUTH WEST	
Jacqueline S. Ashley	*Gill Akaster*
John D. Bedford	*Veale Wasbrough*
Jeremy Bennett	*Wolferstans*
Margaret Bonner	*Foot & Bowden*
Wendy Boyce	*Bond Pearce*
Catherine Hallam	*Burges Salmon*
Norman A. Hartnell	*Hartnell & Co*
Philip E. Kidd	*Tozers*
Michael P. Lowry	*Stephens & Scown*
Philip M. Thorneycroft	*Wolferstans*
David W. Woodward	*Trump and Partners*

The team at *Veale Wasbrough* has a high reputation for all areas of work but especially substantial financial matters in which John Bedford has particular expertise. The firm is also a Matrimonial Legal Aid franchise holder. *Stephens & Scown* in Cornwall, where Michael Lowry is well known, has one of the largest family departments in that area and has particular experience in large ancillary relief work.

David Woodward at *Trump & Partners* is also highly regarded and the firm has been involved in a number of reported cases over the last 12 months.

Lester Aldridge in Dorset is widely recognised for its wide ranging work handled by its sizeable family department. In Somerset, *Clarke Willmott & Clarke* has established a strong reputation for child care work.

WALES

Two firms that emerge as clear leaders for family law are *Hallinans* and *Leo Abse & Cohen. Hallinans*, where Robert Edwards has an established reputation, handles all aspects

HIGHLY REGARDED – WALES	
HALLINANS *Cardiff*	**HUGH JAMES JONES & JENKINS** *Cardiff*
LEO ABSE & COHEN *Cardiff*	**LOOSEMORES** *Cardiff*
SPICKETTS *Pontypridd*	
EVERSHEDS *Cardiff*	**GRANVILLE-WEST** *Newport*

including advocacy in the Magistrates Court and in the High Court. The firm is also known for its expertise in matters relating to child care law. *Leo Abse & Cohen* has a strong team dealing exclusively with family matters, particularly co-habitation disputes, child care proceedings and disputes relating to the Children Act. Other well regarded family practices include *Hugh James Jones & Jenkins* and *Loosemores* The latter firm has significant experience in dealing with financial settlements and children work.

LEADING INDIVIDUALS – WALES	
Robert Nigel Edwards	*Hallinans*

Spicketts has built a strong reputation in Pontypridd and the surrounding valley for its expertise in family matters.

MIDLANDS

Many firms in the Midlands have excellent reputations in family law. Firms particularly well known for child care expertise include *Blair Allison & Co, Wace Morgan, Morton Fisher, R.Gwynne & Sons* and *Nelsons,* all of which have solicitors who are members of the Law Society's Children

HIGHLY REGARDED – MIDLANDS	
BLAIR ALLISON & CO *Birmingham*	**R. GWYNNE & SONS** *Wellington*
MORTON FISHER *Worcester*	**NELSONS** *Nottingham*
RUPERT BEAR & CO *Nottingham*	**TYNDALLWOODS** *Birmingham*
WACE MORGAN *Shrewsbury*	
ADIE EVANS & WARNER *Birmingham*	**BLAKESLEY RICE MACDONALD** *Chesterfield*
BLYTHE LIGGINS *Leamington Spa*	**ELLIOT MATHER SMITH** *Chesterfield*
GLAISYERS *Birmingham*	**GOODGER AUDEN** *Burton-on-Trent*
HADEN STRETTON SLATER MILLER *Walsall*	**HUNT & COOMBS** *Oundle*
LYON CLARK *West Bromwich*	**PARKINSON WRIGHT** *Worcester*
SHARP & PARTNERS *Nottingham*	**TRUMANS** *Nottingham*
VARLEY HIBBS & CO *Coventry*	**WARREN & ALLEN** *Nottingham*
WOODFORD-ROBINSON *Northampton*	

Panel. *Morton Fisher* has a substantial practice which includes acting in care proceedings and in proceedings for Hereford and Worcester County Council. The firm has expertise in divorce financial matters, particularly for business and farming clients and has been involved in many substantial cases in the High Court with regard to children and finance. *Tyndallwoods,* a firm which covers all aspects, also runs a 24 hour help line for female victims of domestic violence run by female lawyers. *Rupert Bear & Co,* a sole practice dealing exclusively with family law matters, is also well regarded.

EAST ANGLIA

A number of firms in East Anglia provide excellent advice on a broad range of family matters from the financial consequences of divorce to Children Act provisions. *Miller & Co*

HIGHLY REGARDED – EAST ANGLIA	
EVERSHEDS *Norwich*	FOSTERS *Norwich*
GREENWOODS *Peterborough*	HUNT & COOMBS *Peterborough*
MILLER & CO *Cambridge*	MILLS & REEVE *Norwich*
THOMSON & CO *Cambridge*	WARD GETHIN *King's Lynn*
COZENS–HARDY & JEWSON *Norwich*	OVERBURY STEWARD & EATON *Norwich*
PALMER WHEELDON *Cambridge*	RUDLINGS & WAKELAM *Thetford*

in Cambridge is well known. Both Rosemary Carter and Rosemary Sands enjoy first rate reputations. They are trained mediators, and were involved in setting up the Family and Divorce centre in Cambridge, an umbrella referral organisation that mediates between separating and divorcing couples.

Mills & Reeve also have one of the leading family specialist teams in the region. Bruce Wilson at the firm is well known for his expertise in handling cases of weightier financial matters, and Roger Bamber, who is an accredited member of the Family Mediators Association, has been highly recommended. He regularly lectures and is joint author of 'Pensions and Insurance on Family Breakdown.'

Greenwoods in Peterborough has been highly recommended for its excellent family law team comprising of Nigel Long, Jane Proctor and Maureen Pring, which covers all aspects of care and family work.

LEADING INDIVIDUALS – EAST ANGLIA
Roger Bamber *Mills & Reeve*
Rosemary E. Carter *Miller & Co*
Nigel H. Long *Greenwoods*
Maureen Pring *Greenwoods*
E. Jane Proctor *Greenwoods*
Rosemary Sands *Miller & Co*
A. Saul *Fosters*
Rachel Silver *Thomson & Co*
David Sisson *Eversheds*
Bruce Wilson *Mills & Reeve*

Other recommended firms include *Thomson & Co*, where Rachel Silver has been recommended for her child care expertise, and *Eversheds* where David Sisson has been highlighted as an excellent practitioner in the field. Firms in the

list with particular expertise in child care work and who have representatives on The Law Society Children Panel include *Fosters & Co, Hunt & Coombs* and *Ward Gethin.* Andrew Saul at *Foster & Partners* has been recommended for his expertise.

NORTH WEST

A number of firms in the region have large departments, enjoying established reputations in the field. *Morecroft Urquhart* has a strong reputation for divorce work and advises

HIGHLY REGARDED – NORTH WEST	
FARLEYS *Blackburn*	GREEN & CO *Manchester*
JONES MAIDMENT WILSON *Manchester*	LACE MAWER *Manchester*
MORECROFT URQUHART *Liverpool*	NIGHTINGALES *Manchester*
PANNONE & PARTNERS *Manchester*	
BIRCHALL BLACKBURN *Preston*	BURNETTS *Carlisle*
CUFF ROBERTS *Liverpool*	FORBES & PARTNERS *Blackburn*
JACKSON & CANTER *Liverpool*	ROWLANDS *Manchester*
STEPHENSONS *Leigh*	

on adoption with four of the firm's solicitors members of the Children Panel. *Farleys,* where Kathryn Hughes is well regarded, also has a large department with broad ranging experience. Kathryn Hughes is also a contributing editor for 'Butterworths Family Law' service and sits as an Assistant Recorder. Beth Wilkins has moved from *Davies Arnold Cooper* to join the team at *Pannone & Partners* headed by

LEADING INDIVIDUALS – NORTH WEST
Lorraine Baldwin *Green & Co*
Michael Green *Green & Co*
Iain M. Hamilton *Jones Maidment Wilson*
Peter Hardman *Nightingales*
Kathryn Lesley Hughes *Farleys*
Catherine Jones *Pannone & Partners*
John McGoldrick *Jones Maidment Wilson*
Paula Milburn *Jones Maidment Wilson*
Nigel G. Shepherd *Lace Mawer*
Beth Wilkins *Pannone & Partners*

Catherine Jones, which now consists of three specialist partners handling all aspects of private family law including divorce, finance, children and adoption. *Green & Co* is a niche practice with expertise in all aspects of law relating to children. Michael Green himself has been recommended and also Loraine Baldwin, a partner at the firm. Also highly recommended is *Jones Maidment Wilson* which handles all types of children cases and has five Children Panel members. Iain Hamilton, John McGoldrick and Paula Milburn have all been recommended at the firm for their expertise. Peter Hardman at *Nightingales* and Nigel Shepherd at *Lace Mawer* also have established reputations in the field.

NORTH EAST

Two leading commercial firms, *Booth & Co* and *Dickinson Dees*, are highly regarded for their expertise in family work. *Booth & Co* undertakes the whole range of work within its

HIGHLY REGARDED – NORTH EAST

ANDREW M. JACKSON *Hull*	BOOTH & CO. *Leeds*
CRANSWICK WATSON *Leeds*	DICKINSON DEES *Newcastle upon Tyne*
GORDONS WRIGHT & WRIGHT *Bradford*	GOSSCHALKS *Hull*
GRAHAME STOWE, BATESON *Leeds*	HENRY HYAMS & CO *Leeds*
IRWIN MITCHELL *Sheffield*	JONES MYERS *Leeds*
SAMUEL PHILLIPS & CO *Newcastle-upon-Tyne*	ZERMANSKY & PARTNERS *Leeds*

ARCHERS *Stockton-on-Tees*	ASKEWS *Redcar*
GODLOVE PEARLMAN *Leeds*	GRAHAM & ROSEN *Hull*
JACKSONS *Middlesbrough*	PHILIP HAMER & CO *Hull*
PINSENT CURTIS	PUNCH ROBSON *Middlesbrough*
SINTON & CO *Newcastle upon Tyne*	

family unit, and handles divorce, separation and children cases often with an international element. David Salter at the firm is highly regarded by his peers and was elected as a fellow of the International Academy of Matrimonial Lawyers. He has also been involved in editing numerous publications including 'Pensions and Insurance on Family Breakdown' produced by the Norton Rose M5 Family Law Business Group. *Dickinson Dees* is particularly well known for its expertise in major divorce cases and substantial financial

LEADING INDIVIDUALS – NORTH EAST

David A. Salter *Booth & Co.*
Barry N. Speker *Samuel Phillips & Co*

provision. Barry Speker at *Samuel Phillips & Co* has been recommended particularly for his child care work as have *Jones Myers, Henry Hyams & Co* and *Gordons Wright & Wright*. A number of firms have well regarded all round family law practices including *Andrew M. Jackson & Co, Gosschalks, Grahame Stowe, Bateson & Co, Irwin Mitchell, Zermansky & Partners* and *Cranswick Watson*.

SCOTLAND

Firms which were particularly highly recommended include *Anne Hall Dick & Co, Balfour & Manson – Nightingale &*

HIGHLY REGARDED – SCOTLAND

ANNE HALL DICK & CO *Kilmarnock*	BALFOUR & MANSON *Edinburgh*
BURNETT & REID *Aberdeen*	DRUMMOND MILLER WS *Edinburgh*
ERSKINE MacASKILL *Edinburgh*	GILMORE LEWIS *Edinburgh*
IAIN SMITH & CO *Aberdeen*	LOUDONS WS *Edinburgh*
MORTON FRASER MILLIGAN *Edinburgh*	ROSS & CONNEL *Dunfermline*
ROSS HARPER & MURPHY *Glasgow*	RUSSEL & AITKEN WS *Denny*
RUSSELLS *Glasgow*	
DUNDAS & WILSON CS *Edinburgh*	GILLESPIE MACANDREW *Edinburgh*
WALKER LAIRD *Paisley*	

Belland *Loudons WS*, all of which have strong family departments. *Anne Hall Dick & Co* has a particularly impressive background in mediation work whilst *Balfour & Manson – Nightingale & Bell* is known for its expertise in international custody disputes. *Loudons WS,* along with *Gilmore Lewis,* maintain strong links with women's welfare organisations. *Ross & Connel* in Dunfermline offers child law expertise and *Russells* offers particular expertise in child abuction cases. *Drummond Miller WS,* which has a strong department covering a broad range of areas, also handles cases including emergency legal aid and child abduction. Other highly recommended firms include *Burnett & Reid, Erskine MacAskill & Co, Iain Smith & Company, Ross Harper & Murphy WS* and *Morton Fraser Milligan WS*.

LEADING INDIVIDUALS – SCOTLAND

Ian L.S. Balfour *Balfour & Manson*
Joan Catto *Burnett & Reid*
Clare Craig *Anne Hall Dick & Co*
Anne Dick *Anne Hall Dick & Co*
Sarah R. Erskine *Erskine MacAskill*
John M. Fotheringham *Ross & Connel*
Andrew T.F. Gibb *Balfour & Manson*
Sheila Gilmore *Gilmore Lewis*
C. Margaret A.F. Gimblett *Russel & Aitken WS*
Alasdair Loudon *Loudons WS*
G. Leonard R. Mair *Morton Fraser Milligan*
Andrew Grant McCulloch *Drummond Miller WS*
Maureen McGowan *Morton Fraser Milligan*
Fiona Paterson *Drummond Miller WS*
Iain Patience *Iain Smith & Co*
Margaret Scanlan *Russells*
Caroline Smith *Loudons WS*

NORTHERN IRELAND

Many firms in the province offer family services, including the large commercial practices. In general, the latter do so only to privately-paying clients. Legal aid-funded work is handled by the smaller and less commercially-oriented firms.

HIGHLY REGARDED – NORTHERN IRELAND

BABINGTON & CROASDAILE *Londonderry*	CLEAVER FULTON & RANKIN *Belfast*
S.J. DIAMOND & SON *Belfast*	HEWITT & GILPIN *Belfast*
JOHNS ELLIOT *Belfast*	WILSON NESBITT *Belfast*
C & J BLACK *Belfast*	CARSON & McDOWELL *Belfast*
ELLIOTT DUFFY GARRETT *Belfast*	MILLAR SHEARER & BLACK *Cookstown*
J.W. RUSSELL & CO *Newtonards*	

Among the commercial firms William Cross at *Cleaver Fulton & Rankin* is well known for all aspects of family work including adoption and wardship matters. At *Johns Elliott* Vera Woods is a highly regarded specialist. Stephen Gillespie at *Hewitt & Gilpin* is widely known for his expertise in the field. *Carson & McDowell, C & J Black* and *Elliott Duffy Garrett* all provide a full service to private clients.

Among the smaller firms Janet Beveridge at *S J Diamond & Sons* has an excellent reputation. At *Babington & Croasdaile* Hilary Carmichael carries out wardships, divorce, separation agreements and financial arrangements. Lorraine Stevenson of *Wilson Nesbitt* is highly thought of in the field. Other recognised firms include *J W Russell & Co* and Millar *Shearer & Black*.

LEADING INDIVIDUALS – NORTHERN IRELAND	
Vera W. Woods	*Johns Elliot*
Janet Beveridge	*S.J. Diamond & Son*
Hilary Carmichael	*Babington & Croasdaile*
William Cross	*Cleaver Fulton & Rankin*
Stephen Gillespie	*Hewitt & Gilpin*
Lorraine Stevenson	*Wilson Nesbitt*

LEADERS IN FAMILY/MATRIMONIAL

LONDON

Alexander, Peter J.
Dawson & Co, London (0171) 404 5941. Qualified 1970. Partner 1993. Matrimonial Department. 25 years' experience as a matrimonial specialist. Born 16.11.1943.

Alexiou, Douglas
Gordon Dadds, London (0171) 493 6151. Senior Partner and Head of Family Law Department.

Specialisation: Covers all areas including divorce, judicial separation, financial disputes, co-habitation, children (including Children Act applications, Child Support Act) and international aspects (including recognition and enforcement). Chairs London Regional Group (SFLA); lectures, gives TV, radio, magazine and newspaper interviews; workshop leader at the 'Big Money' conference.

Prof. Membership: Law Society, Solicitors Family Law Association (Chairman of London Regional Group), International Academy of Matrimonial Lawyers (Vice President, European Chapter), City of Westminster Law Society, Member of the Family Mediators Association.

Career: Qualified in 1970. Joined *Gordon Dadds* in February 1971, and was made a Partner later that year. Became Senior Partner in 1986. Director of Tottenham Hotspur Football Club since 1980. Chairman 1982-84. Director of Tottenham Hotspur Plc 1983-91 and 1993 to date.

Personal: Born 24th May 1942. Attended St Paul's School 1955-59, Kings College London (LLB Hons) 1965 and College of Law. Leisure interests include golf, tennis and association football. Lives in Kingston-upon-Thames.

Blore, Sian E.
Farrer & Co, London (0171) 242 2022. Qualified 1979.

Butner, Paul
Wright Son & Pepper, London (0171) 242 5473. Partner in Matrimonial Department.

Specialisation: Family law. Principally divorce, children and ancillary relief. Has represented a number of leading public figures. Former member of SFLA Main Committee and founder member. Ex-Parish Councillor (and Chairman) during the 1970s.

Prof. Membership: Law Society, Solicitors Family Law Association.

Career: Admitted in 1960. Joined *Watkins Pulleyn* in 1961, becoming a Partner in 1962. Amalgamated with *Wright Son & Pepper* in 1990.

Personal: Born 13th August 1937. Attended Uppingham School 1950-54. Leisure interests include travelling and sitting in the sun. Lives in London.

Chapman, Elspeth
Barnett Sampson, London (0171) 935 9161.

Specialisation: Partner in the Family Department. Specialises in substantial ancillary relief applications, often with an international, trust or offshore aspect. Also undertakes private children's applications. Has written a number of articles and book reviews.

Prof. Membership: Founder member and current Treasurer of the Solicitors Family Law Association; accredited member of the Family Mediators Association.

Career: Qualified in 1972. Partner at Finers 1973-84. Partner at Barnett Sampson (formerly Barnett Chapman Murray) since 1984.

Personal: Educated at Howells School, Denbigh 1957-63 and University College, London (LL.B 1968). Leisure pursuits include travel, horse riding, cooking, reading and gardening. Born 8th August 1945. Lives in London.

Collis, Pamela
Kingsley Napley, London (0171) 814 1200. Head of Family Department.

Specialisation: Financial and other disputes arising on divorce; the breakdown of non-marital relations; children disputes with many cases involving a foreign element. Contributor to legal journals on matters relating to family law.

Prof. Membership: SFLA (Committee Member London Regional Group), Justice.

Career: Qualified 1981. Joined *Kingsley Napley* in 1982 and became a Partner in 1984. Committee member London Solicitors Litigation Association 1987-89. Member Principal Registry Family Division Users Group since 1993.

Personal: Born 9th March 1957. Attended Rosemead School for Girls, then Bristol University (LLB 1978). Leisure pursuits include windsurfing, books and family life. Lives in London.

Cornwell, John
Dawson Cornwell & Co, London (0171) 242 2556. Partner handling family and matrimonial and private client matters.

Specialisation: Main areas of practice are family and matrimonial work (private law only). Practises on own account as a mediator. Deputy District Judge in Principal Registry since 1987. Also handles private client matters, including administration of estates, trusts and wills. Writes articles in SFLA newsletters and for 'Family Law'. Has frequently addressed conferences.

Prof. Membership: SFLA, FMA.

Career: Qualified in 1969. Founding Partner of *Dawson Cornwell* in 1972. Founder of the SFLA, Chairman 1982-87 and returned to the Committee in 1994. Co-founder of FMA, Vice Chairman 1992-93 and Board Member from inception until 1994. Deputy District Judge since 1987.

Personal: Born 21st September 1943. Educated at St. Paul's School 1957-62 and Bristol University 1962-65. Leisure interests include theatre, cricket and cider-making. Lives in London.

Crowther, Felicity
Bindman & Partners, London (0171) 833 4433. Partner in Family Department.

Specialisation: Work includes ancillary relief, residence and contract, cohabitation disputes and international child abduction.

Prof. Membership: Solicitors Family Law Association, Family Mediators Association.

Career: Qualified in 1974. Joined *Bindman & Partners* in 1974, becoming a Partner in 1976.

Personal: Born 14th January 1947. Lives in London.

Davidson, David
Charles Russell, London (0171) 203

5114. Partner in Family Law Department.

Specialisation: Handles all areas of family law. Has written and broadcast on the subject.

Prof. Membership: Solicitors Family Law Association, International Academy of Matrimonial Lawyers.

Personal: Born 30th January 1947. Edinburgh University to 1968 (LLB).

Davis, Sandra S.

Mishcon De Reya, London (0171) 405 3711. Head of Family Department.

Specialisation: Work includes international and domestic 'big money' cases, international child abduction, divorce and separation, cohabitation disputes and contact and residency disputes. Author of 'International Child Abduction' (1993) and numerous articles. Lectured to the 1st World Family Congress in Sydney, 1993 and the IBA Conferences, 1993 and 1994. Chaired, and lectured at the *Mishcon de Reya* and IBC conferences on 'Big Money', 'International Child Abduction' and 'Middle Money'. Lord Chancellor's Department panel solicitor; Radio 4 'You & Yours' panel member.

Prof. Membership: Solicitors Family Law Association, Holborn Law Society, Law Society. Fellow of the International Academy of Matrimonial Lawyers; Fellow of the RSA.

Career: Qualified in 1981. Joined *Mishcon de Reya* in 1979, becoming a Partner in 1984. Staff Partner on firm's Management Board.

Personal: Born 3rd July 1956. Attended University of Sussex 1974-78 and Universite Aix-en-Provence, France, and studied European Studies/ Law. Leisure interests include travel, painting and photography. Lives in London. Married with two children.

Doran, Gill

Gordon Dadds, London (0171) 493 6151. Partner in Family & Matrimonial Department.

Specialisation: Has specialised in family and matrimonial work for 20 years. Has written articles about family matters, addressed conferences and done committee work for the SFLA. Individual charge-out rate is £200 per hour.

Prof. Membership: International Academy of Matrimonial Lawyers, Family Mediators Association.

Career: Qualified in 1974. Joined *Gordon Dadds* in 1979 and became a Partner in 1982.

Personal: Born 28th September 1949. Educated at The Abbey School 1960-68 and Manchester University 1968-71. Leisure interests include music, opera and horses. Lives in London.

Doughty, Charles

Withers, London (0171) 936 1000. Partner in Family Department.

Specialisation: Family law specialist.

Prof. Membership: IAML, SFLA.

Career: Qualified in 1961, having joined

Withers in 1958. Became a Partner in 1963.

Personal: Born 21st December 1935. Educated at Eton 1948-53 and Magdalen College, Oxford 1955-58. Leisure interests include fishing and hunting. Lives in London.

Drake, Michael J.

Collyer–Bristow, London (0171) 242 7363. Partner in Matrimonial Department.

Specialisation: Handles all areas of matrimonial and family law. Also deals with litigation and business law, including contract and commercial advice, employment advice and commercial litigation. Author of various textbooks, SFLA publications and articles. On the Editorial Board of 'The Family Practitioner'. Has lectured and broadcast on radio and television.

Prof. Membership: SFLA (National Committee 1987 to 1994).

Career: Qualified in 1971. Joined *Collyer-Bristow* as a Partner in 1984.

Personal: Born 14th August 1947. Educated at Haberdasher's Askes's, Elstree (to 1965) and Selwyn College, Cambridge (to 1968). Recreations include travel, arts, reading and tennis. Lives in London.

Fisher, J.

Gordon Dadds, London (0171) 493 6151. Qualified 1988.

George, Peter

Charles Russell, London (0171) 203 5098. Partner in Family Department.

Specialisation: Handles all areas of family law.

Prof. Membership: Solicitors Family Law Association. Family Mediators Association, International Academy of Matrimonial Lawyers, International Society of Family Law, Council for Family Proceedings.

Personal: Born 12th January 1935. Attended Ampleforth. Leisure interests include people, music, bridge and chess.

Gerry, Andrew

Withers, London (0171) 936 1000. Qualified 1977. Partner 1979. Family Law Department. Practices exclusively family law.

Goodman, Judith

Goodman Ray, London (0171) 254 8855. Qualified 1980. Partner 1985. Principal area of practice is divorce, ancillary relief and Children Act work, including care work. Born 23.3.1955.

Goodman, Naomi

Gordon Dadds, London (0171) 493 6151.

Harcus, James

Gordon Dadds, London (0171) 493 6151. Partner in Family Department.

Specialisation: Specialises in matrimonial finance and taxation, children, cohabitation and pre-marital contracts. Acted in Robinson

v. Robinson 1982 (case involving setting aside for material non-disclosure) and Cornick v Cornick 1994 (Barder priciples). Co-author of an article in Family Law Vol. 17 (1987) 'Child Maintenance-A Fresh Look'. Has lectured for the Solicitors Family Law Association and the Institute of Financial Planning.

Prof. Membership: Fellow of the International Academy of Matrimonial Lawyers.

Career: Qualified in 1974. Joined *Gordon Dadds* in 1980 and became a Partner in 1981. Treasurer of the Solicitors Family Law Association 1982-87.

Personal: Born 15th April 1949. Educated at Exeter University 1968-71. Leisure interests include riding, skiing and gardening. Lives in London.

Hodson, David M.

Frere Cholmeley Bischoff, London (0171) 615 8000. Partner in Family Law Group.

Specialisation: Principal area of practice is financial aspects of family breakdown, with emphasis on cases involving complex or substantial assets or an international element. Regular lecturer and writer on family law. Author of "Business of Family Law" (Jordans), editor of "SFLA Guide to Family Law in Europe" and of "Family Law in Europe" (Butterworths).

Prof. Membership: Solicitors Family Law Association National Committee, Good Practice Committee (Chairman), International Committee and Training Committee; Fellow, International Academy of Matrimonial Lawyers; IBA Family Law Committee; Lawyers Christian Fellowship; Society of Computers and the Law; Course Director, Diploma in Law; Trustee, Marriage Resource counselling organisation. Also Deputy District Judge of Principal Registry of the Family Division.

Career: Qualified 1978. After working in legal aid and mixed practices in Southampton and Birmingham, joined *Theodore Goddard* in 1985 and moved with Family Law Group to *Frere Cholmeley Bischoff* in 1991.

Personal: Born October 1953. Educated at Southampton and Leicester University. Married. Lives in Guildford. Leisure interests include holidays, photography, scuba diving and hill walking.

Howell, Grant

Charles Russell, London (0171) 203 5000.

Hughes, Frances

Bates, Wells & Braithwaite, London (0171) 251 1122. Partner and Head of Family Law Department.

Specialisation: Practice covers the full range of family law, especially international cases, child abduction and cases involving trust law or complex offshore corporate entities. Clients include City professionals, entertainment clients and other lawyers.

Writes, lectures and broadcasts on family law.

Prof. Membership: International Academy of Matrimonial Lawyers; SFLA (on London Regional Committee); Accredited FMA Mediator.

Career: Qualified in 1981. Assistant at *Theodore Goddard*. Joined *Bates Wells & Braithwaite* to establish the Family Department in 1983 and became a Partner in 1984.

Personal: Born 15th June 1954. Educated at Ursuline Convent School 1965- 72 and St Anne's College, Oxford 1973-76. School Governor. Enjoys opera and gardening. Lives in London and Wiltshire.

Keir, Jane
Kingsley Napley, London (0171) 814 1200.

La Follette, Maryly
Charles Russell, London (0171) 203 5000.

Leverton, David. J.
Payne Hicks Beach, London (0171) 465 4300. Partner in Family Law Department.

Specialisation: Head of Family Law Department: member of International Academy of Matrimonial Lawyers. Very experienced specialist in all aspects of matrimonial law with particular expertise in complex financial matters and in negotiating financial settlements.

Career: Qualified 1958 at Ridsdale & Son of Westminster: joined *Payne Hicks Beach* in 1959. Became Partner in 1963. Managing Partner of firm. Member of Solicitors Disciplinary Tribunal.

Personal: Born 8th September 1935. Educated at The Haberdashers' Askes' School, Hampstead. Enjoys fine art, music and rugby. Lives in London.

Levison, Jeremy
Collyer–Bristow, London (0171) 242 7363. Partner in Family/ Matrimonial Department.

Specialisation: Head of Matrimonial Department, leading a team of 10 specialist lawyers. Founder member of the SFLA and the International Academy of Matrimonial Lawyers (Secretary and Treasurer of its European Chapter). Responsible for opening the firm's New York office, established primarily to deal with American/ European matrimonial issues. Author of various articles on matrimonial matters. Has lectured, broadcast and appeared at conferences and seminars.

Prof. Membership: Solicitors Family Law Association, International Academy of Matrimonial Lawyers.

Career: Qualified in 1974 and worked for *Theodore Goddard* until 1980. Joined *Collyer-Bristow* as a Partner in 1980.

Personal: Born 3rd February 1952. Educated at Charterhouse School 1965-69 and the University of Kent 1970-73. Enjoys fine art, music, cricket, classic cars and France. Lives in London.

Longrigg, William
Charles Russell, London (0171) 203 5000. Partner in Family Department.

Specialisation: Main areas of practice are divorce, ancillary relief and child-related work (private law).

Prof. Membership: Solicitors Family Law Association (Member SFLA Mediation Committee; Secretary SFLA London Regional Group).

Career: Qualified in 1987. Joined *Charles Russell* in 1985, becoming a Partner in 1992.

Personal: Born 6th July 1960. Attended Dragon School, Oxford 1968-73, Shrewsbury School 1973-78 and Warwick University 1979-82. Leisure interests include drawing, writing and junk shops. Lives in London.

Marco, Alan
Baileys Shaw & Gillett, London (0171) 837 5455. Qualified 1965. Partner 1972. Head of Family Group. Work covers all areas with emphasis on financial provision applications. Deputy District Judge at Principal Registry of the Family Division.

Meltzer, Claire
Collyer–Bristow, London (0171) 242 7363. Partner in Matrimonial Department.

Specialisation: Main areas of practice are matrimonial and family law. Author of various articles.

Prof. Membership: FMA, SFLA.

Career: Qualified in 1979. Partner in *Theodore Goddard* 1983-85. Joined *Collyer-Bristow* as a Partner in 1985.

Personal: Holds a BA Hons. Lives in London.

Parker, Diana C.
Withers, London (0171) 936 1000. Partner in Family Law Department.

Specialisation: Exclusively family law. Co-author of Longman's Practical Matrimonial Precedents' and 'Know How for Family Lawyers'. Author of articles in professional journals and elsewhere. Occasional lecturer, speaker at conferences and contributor to the media.

Prof. Membership: Solicitors Family Law Association (SFLA); Family Mediators Association (FMA); International Academy of Matrimonial Lawyers (IAML).

Personal: MA (Cantab) MPhil (Cantab).

Parry, Richard
Farrer & Co, London (0171) 242 2022. Qualified 1976. Partner 1983. Litigation Department. Main areas of practice are family law and civil litigation. Born 6.12.1951.

Pembridge, Eileen
Fisher Meredith, London (0171) 622 4468. Senior Partner and Head of Family Department.

Specialisation: Deals with all aspects of fam-

ily law, but especially complex ancillary relief on divorce and other financial matters. Has always taken on legal aid work. Will also handle defamation, generally where there are important public issues to address. Handled the Sutcliffe defamation actions. Has written various opinion pieces in 'New Law Journal', 'Family Law' and the Law Society's 'Gazette'. Has lectured on the Children Act and addressed sessions on Family Law at the Law Society's National Conference.

Prof. Membership: Law Society (Council Member for London South since 1990, Chair of Family Law Committee since 1992, on Courts and Legal Services Committee since 1987, Human Rights Committee since 1993 and Equal Opportunities Committee since 1994), SFLA, LAPG (Committee Member since 1982 and Chair 1987-88). International Family Law Association.

Career: Worked as a freelance interpreter for the UN 1967-73 and casually thereafter until 1983. Qualified in 1975. Co-founder of *Fisher Meredith* in 1975, now 65 strong. Challenged Law Society cnvention by standing for election of President, July 1995.

Personal: Born 15th March 1944. Educated at Worcester Girls' Grammar School; Newnham College, Cambridge (Natural Sciences degree and postgraduate Russian), and Bath University (postgraduate language studies).FRSA interests include Human Rights/Amnesty, animal welfare, sailing, horse-riding, hill-walking, vegetable-growing and reading novels in French, Russian and Spanish. Lives in Dulwich Village, London.

Philipps, Susan
Penningtons, London (0171) 457 3000. Partner and Head of Family Law Department.

Specialisation: Covers all areas of family and matrimonial law.

Prof. Membership: Solicitors Family Law Association. Serves on Education Committee of the SFLA.

Career: Qualified in 1984. Joined *Ward Bowie* in 1982 and became a partner in 1986 on merger with *Penningtons*. Head of Family Law Department since 1994.

Personal: Born 9th April 1957. Lives in London.

Pigott, Simon
Collyer–Bristow, London (0171) 242 7363. Partner in Family Law Department.

Specialisation: Handles all aspects of matrimonial and family work.

Prof. Membership: SFLA, Chairman of Family Mediators Association.

Career: Qualified in 1982. Worked at *Wright Webb Syrett* 1978-81 and *Theodore Goddard* 1983-85. Joined *Collyer-Bristow* in 1985, becoming a Partner in 1987.

Personal: Born 29th October 1956. Attended Mill Hill School 1970-74, Southampton University 1974-77 and College of Law 1977-78 and 1981-82. Lives in Wolverton, Hants.

Preston, Miles

Miles Preston & Co, London (0171) 583 0583. Founding Partner 1994.

Specialisation: Practises exclusively in matrimonial and family law. Individual charge-out rate is £200 + VAT per hour.

Prof. Membership: Solicitors Family Law Association, International Academy of Matrimonial Lawyers.

Career: Qualified in 1974. Partner with *Radcliffes & Co.* 1979-94. Served on Sir Gervaise Sheldon's Family Law Liaison Committee 1982; Founder Member SFLA 1982; served on main Committee of SFLA 1982-88; Chaired working party on procedure 1982-88; Founder Member of IAML 1986; Governor IAML 1986-89; Parliamentarian to Main Committee 1989; President of English Chapter 1989; President of European Chapter 1989-92; President Elect of Main Academy 1992-94. President of Main Academy since 1994. Member of the President's International Family Committee (chaired by Mr Justice Thorpe) since 1994.

Personal: Born in 1950. Attended Shrewsbury School 1963-68. Leisure interests include food and travel. Lives in Blackheath, London.

Rae, Maggie

Mishcon De Reya, London (0171) 405 3711. Partner. Family Department. Work includes divorce, children, adoption, employment and education. Also all aspects of family and children work.

Specialisation: Work includes divorce, children, adoption, employment and education. Also all aspects of family and children work. Author of 'Women and the Law', 'Children and the Law', 'First Rights' and 'Child Care Law'. Lectured at Warwick University. Undertakes frequent teaching, lecturing and writing assignments. Individual charge-out rate is £185 per hour.

Prof. Membership: Solicitors Family Law Association, Education Law Association, British Association for Adoption and Fostering, Inter Country Adoption Lawyers Association, International Academy of Matrimonial Lawyers, Fellow of the RSA.

Career: Qualified in 1973. Barrister 1973-77. Partner at *Hodge Jones & Allen* 1978-92. Joined *Mishcon de Reya* in 1992, becoming a Partner in 1993.

Personal: Born 20th September 1949. Attended Great Yarmouth High School 1961-68 and University of Warwick 1968-71. School Governor (Chair). Leisure interests include walking, cooking and gardening. Lives in London.

Ray, Peggy

Goodman Ray, London (0171) 254 8855.

Robinson, Sara

The Simkins Partnership, London (0171) 631 1050. Partner and Head of Family Department.

Specialisation: Particular expertise in negotiation of financial settlements following the separation of married and unmarried couples, investigation and location of matrimonial assets and enforcement of matrimonial orders. Also negotiation of residence and contact issues relating to children. Solicitor mediator with the Family Mediators Association, mediating comprehensively in relation to all of the above issues. Acts for a number of high profile pop star and media clients. Author of the Scandinavian chapters in the 'Solicitors Family Law Association Guide to Family law in Europe'. National Press Officer for the Solicitors Family Law Association.

Prof. Membership: Solicitors Family Law Association, Family Mediators Association, Law Society.

Career: Qualified in 1981. With *Jacobs & Kane* 1982-88, and *Jacobs Pearson Robinson* 1988-90. Joined *The Simkins Partnership* as Partner and Head of Family Department in 1990. Committee Member of The European Committee of the SFLA, the London Regional Group of the SFLA, and the Central & South London Group of the Family Mediators Association.

Personal: Born 23rd January 1955. Educated at Leeds University 1974-77. Secretary of Spare Tyre Theatre Company. Enjoys eating, drinking good wines, listening to music, photography, gardening, interior decorating, the company of friends and coastal walking. Lives in Chiswick, London.

Rutter, Geoffrey M.

S. Rutter & Co, London (0171) 628 8641/4. Head of Family Department.

Specialisation: Many years experience in family law, principally involving substantial financial issues resulting from marriage breakdown. Considerable knowledge of and experience in the investigative elements of domestic and international work including offshore trusts and structures. Regularly advises on the commercial and tax considerations involved in financial negotiations and settlements.

Sax, Richard

Manches & Co, London (0171) 404 4433. Partner in Family Department.

Specialisation: Advises on all areas of family law, particularly complex financial and children issues arising from matrimonial and relationship breakdown including International, Trust and Tax aspects.

Prof. Membership: Solicitors Family Law Association. International Academy of Matrimonial Lawyers, Law Society.

Career: Qualified in 1967. 1968 Partner and subsequently Managing Partner at *Rubinstein Callingham* (which merged with Manches in 1994). Sits as a Deputy District Judge at the Principal Registry. Past Chairman of the Solicitors Family Law Association. Member of Law Society Family Law Committee. Board Member Family Mediators Association. Member Advisory

Board Institute of Family Therapy, Family Mediation Service. Co-Author "Know how for Family Lawyers", published by Longmans.

Personal: Born 26th December 1938. Attended Tonbridge School, Scholar St John's College Oxford. National service. Member MCC. Liveryman Skinners Company. Married with three daughters. Leisure: Family. Gardening. Archaeology. Visiting Churches and Art Galleries. Watching cricket. Current affairs. Theatre.

Shackleton, Fiona

Farrer & Co, London (0171) 242 2022. Partner in Litigation Department.

Specialisation: Principal area of practice is family law. Author of 'The Divorce Handbook'.

Prof. Membership: SFLA, IAML.

Career: Qualified in 1980. Became a Partner with *Brecher & Co* in 1982. Joined *Farrer & Co* in 1984 and became a Partner in 1987.

Personal: Born 26th May 1956. Attended Benenden School and Exeter University. Governor of Benenden School since 1985. Leisure pursuits include opera, bridge, entertaining and shopping. Lives in London.

Simpson, Jane

Manches & Co, London (0171) 404 4433. Partner and Head of Family Law Department.

Specialisation: Deals in particular with divorce and the financial issues arising, children, tax, and the commercial implications of divorce and separation. Also the international aspects of divorce and separation, forum shopping and child abduction. Has addressed and chaired many family law conferences and seminars, and appeared on radio and television. Member of working party to recommend rule changes towards more cost effective and resolution-centred litigation.

Prof. Membership: Solicitors Family Law Association, International Academy of Matrimonial Lawyers, Law Society.

Career: Qualified in 1967. Marriage Guidance Counsellor 1972-77. Joined *Manches & Co* as a Partner and Head of Family Law Department in 1977. Member of Management Board from 1990. Founder member of Solicitors Family Law Association (1982), Chairman of its Education Committee 1982-90, Chairman 1993-95.

Personal: Born 15th July 1942. Educated at Channing School, Highgate, and London University 1961-64. Non-executive director of Tavistock and Portman NHS Trust from 1994. Leisure interests include reading, walking, music and food. Lives in London. Married with two daughters and a son.

Tooth, Ray

Sears Tooth, London (0171) 499 5599.

Walsh, Jonathan

Stephenson Harwood, London (0171) 329 4422. Head of Matrimonial and Family Department.

Specialisation: Many years experience of family, matrimonial and private client work. Has addressed conferences on various aspects of family law.

Prof. Membership: SFLA.

Career: Qualified in 1968. Previously Head of Litigation Department and Matrimonial and Family Department at *Joynson-Hicks* and later at *Taylor Joynson Garrett*, where he was also Head of the Private Client Department. Joined *Stephenson Harwood* as a Partner in 1991.

Personal: Born 1944. Educated at Eton College 1957-62 and Sorbonne University 1962-64. Enjoys tennis, real tennis and shooting.

Ward, Helen

Manches & Co, London (0171) 404 4433. Partner in Family Law Department.

Specialisation: Handles all areas of family law, particularly financial aspects of matrimonial and relationship breakdown.

Prof. Membership: Solicitors Family Law Association, International Academy of Matrimonial Lawyers, Law Society.

Career: Qualified in 1978. Partner at *Ward Bowie* from 1978, which subsequently became *Penningtons*. Joined *Manches & Co* as a partner in July 1994. Sits as a Deputy District Judge in the Principal Registry.

Personal: Born 28th May 1951. Attended King Alfred School, London 1955-69 and Birmingham University 1970-73. Chief leisure interest is her family, music and her garden.

REGIONS

Ashley, Jacqueline S.

Gill Akaster, Plymouth (01752) 500111. Qualified 1984. Partner 1985. Head of Family Department. Main areas of practice are public law, child-care and ancillary relief. Born 28.4.1950.

Baldwin, Lorraine

Green & Co, Manchester (0161) 834 8980.

Balfour, Ian L.S.

Balfour & Manson, Edinburgh (0131) 225 8291. Qualified 1955. Partner 1959. Senior Partner. Family practice covers divorce, separation, custody, access, aliment, capital payments and particularly abduction.

Bamber, Roger

Mills & Reeve, Cambridge (01223) 64422. Qualified 1981. Partner 1988. Family Department. Work includes financial provision, children law, divorce, and Inheritance Act claims. Born 5.2.1955.

Bedford, John D.

Veale Wasbrough, Bristol (0117) 925 2020. Qualified 1961. Partner 1964. Family Law Department. Handles all aspects including the breakdown of unmarried relationships, children and finance. Born 14.4.1936.

Bennett, Jeremy

Wolferstans, Plymouth (01752) 663295.

Beveridge, Janet

S.J. Diamond & Son, Belfast (01232) 243726.

Bonner, Margaret

Foot & Bowden, Plymouth (01752) 675000. Qualified 1985. Partner 1986. Family Law Department. Acts in cases concerning children in both public and private law. Born 31.8.1946.

Boyce, Wendy

Bond Pearce, Plymouth (01752) 266633. Qualified 1980. Partner 1987. Private Client Division. Main area of practice is family law, and involves substantial assets, business interests and pensions.

Carmichael, Hilary

Babington & Croasdaile, Londonderry (01504) 49531.

Carter, Rosemary E.

Miller & Co, Cambridge (01223) 66741. Qualified 1978. Joined *Miller & Co.* as Partner in 1987. 18 years experience of family law and five years experience of family mediation.

Catto, Joan

Burnett & Reid, Aberdeen (01224) 644333. Qualified 1968. Partner 1991. Family law practice includes divorce and ancillary issues such as custody, access and adoptions.

Craig, Clare

Anne Hall Dick & Co, Kilmarnock (01563) 42797. Qualified 1969. Partner 1991. Family Law Department. Specialises in family law and family law mediation. Born 6.6.1948.

Cross, William

Cleaver Fulton & Rankin, Belfast (01232) 243141.

Dick, Anne

Anne Hall Dick & Co, Kilmarnock (01563) 42797. Qualified 1973. Partner. Main area of practice is family, mediation and matrimonial work as well as arbitration. Born 31.12.1949.

Edwards, Robert Nigel

Hallinans, Cardiff (01222) 482316. Partner in Family Department.

Specialisation: Principal area of practice is matrimonial and care work, dealing with personal representation from the Magistrates Court through to the High Court. Specialises in complicated financial and property issues and representing both guardians and parents in care proceedings (including advocacy at all stages up to High Court). Also handles domestic conveyancing, mainly as an offshoot of matrimonial work. Deputy Chairman of South Glamorgan Family Practitioners Committtee. Former Vice Chairman of the South Wales Family Law Association.

Prof. Membership: Law Society, Family Law Association, Child Care Panel.

Career: Qualified in 1975. Became a Partner at *Hallinans* in 1980.

Personal: Born 26th February 1948. Educated at Penarth Grammar School 1960-67 and the University of Wales, Aberystwyth 1967-70 (LLB). Captain of Glamorganshire Golf Club and Member of Welsh Solicitors Golf Team. Also enjoys gardening, reading and travel. Lives in Penarth, South Glamorgan.

Erskine, Sarah R.

Erskine MacAskill & Co, Edinburgh (0131) 557 1520. Partner.

Specialisation: Main area of practice is family law, covering matrimonial, separations, agreements, violence, financial arrangements, child law, custody, children in care and children's hearings. Also handles other civil court work, damages and criminal work. Acts for Shakti Women's Aid and has become involved in cases concerning marital disputes amongst ethnic minorities, child sexual abuse, non-accidental injury cases and abduction cases. Gave a family mediation child abduction seminar; on advisory group of Child Law Centre; on Management Group managing housing for sexually abused young women.

Prof. Membership: SSC (Solicitor to the Supreme Court).

Career: Qualified in 1980. Joined *Erskine Macaskill & Co* in 1984 as a Partner.

Personal: Born 21st January 1953. Educated at St. Brides' School, Helensburgh, then Edinburgh University 1971-73 and 1978-79. Leisure interests include politics, hill walking, bird watching and reading. Lives in Edinburgh.

Fotheringham, John M.

Ross & Connel, Dunfermline (01383) 721156.

Gibb, Andrew T.F.

Balfour & Manson, Edinburgh (0131) 225 8291. Qualified 1971. Partner 1975. Litigation Department. Main areas of practice are family, education and employment law. Born 17.8.1947.

Gillespie, Stephen

Hewitt & Gilpin, Belfast (01232) 323254.

Gilmore, Sheila

Gilmore Lewis, Edinburgh (0131) 662 1933.

Gimblett, C.Margaret A.F.

Russel & Aitken WS, Denny (01324) 822194. Qualified 1972. Partner 1974. Family and Child Care Department. Has handled separation agreements, divorces and all associated work for ten years.

Green, Michael

Green & Co, Manchester (0161) 834 8980. Qualified 1970. Partner 1993. Main areas of practice are child care and family law, principally in the public sector of child care law.

Hallam, Catherine

Burges Salmon, Bristol (0117) 939 2000. Qualified 1984. Partner 1988. Private Client Department. Specialises in separation, family breakdown and complex financial settlements. Born 6.4.1958.

Hamilton, Iain M.

Jones Maidment Wilson, Manchester (0161) 832 8087. Partner in Family Department.

Specialisation: Childcare and adoption. Children Panel Member since 1985. Also considerable experience of matrimonial finance and private law childrens cases. Contributor of articles on child care for various professional publications. Frequent speaker at seminars concerned with children's law. Work mainly legally aided, private client charge-out rate is £100-£100 per hour.

Prof. Membership: Law Society Family Law Committee; SFLA; Association of Lawyers for Children; Child Concern (Past Chairman); BAAF; IRCHIN; NAGALRO.

Career: Qualified in 1974 while with *Walls, Johnston & Co*. Past President Stockport Law Society. Assistant Recorder on Northern Circuit. Joined *Jones Maidment Wilson* in 1994. Member of Manchester Family Courts Business Committee and Courts Forum. Interviewer for Law Society Children Panel. Family Law Committee member since 1994. Holder of Higher Courts (All Proceedings) qualification.

Personal: Born 11th November 1948. Leisure pursuits include cooking, music and reading. Lives in Stockport.

Hardman, Peter

Nightingales, Manchester (0161) 832 6722.

Hartnell, Norman A.

Hartnell & Co, Exeter (01392) 421777. Principal. Family Law specialist.

Specialisation: Main areas of practice are family law, child care law and family mediation. Member of Law Society Children Panel; accredited mediator with FMA; joint organiser of Devon Family Forum (interdisci-

plinary group); former member of Plymouth Family Courts Business and Services Committees. Has acted for children in a number of private law cases, and handled substantial ancillary relief and children cases. Author of articles and book reviews in 'Family Law'. Has lectured to social workers, Education welfare officers, conciliation services, the Exeter Diocesan FLAME Group and an International Mediation Conference (Barbican) 1992.

Prof. Membership: Family Mediators Association (Co-ordinator for Devon area); Devon and Cornwall SFLA (past Secretary); Devon & Exeter Law Society.

Career: Qualified in 1979. Established own specialist family law firm in 1991. Previously Partner with *Dunn & Baker* from 1988. Assistant Solicitor with *Stones* in Exeter 1985-87. Previous positions with *Rimmers*, Aylesbury; *Reynolds Parry-Jones*, High Wycombe; *Landons*, Brentwood and *Whiskers*, Harlow and Epping.

Personal: Born 1st October 1953. Attended Aylesbury Grammar School, then Selwyn College, Cambridge (1974-76, MA) and Chester College of Law 1978. Leisure interests include walking, enjoying Devon, local church activities and his young family. Lives in Exeter.

Hughes, Kathryn Lesley

Farleys, Blackburn (01254) 668844. Qualified 1985. Partner 1985. Family Law Department. Specialises in child care, ancillary relief in divorce, and law relating to cohabitation.

Jones, Catherine

Pannone & Partners, Manchester (0161) 832 3000. Qualified 1977. Partner 1990. Family Department. Handles divorce and judicial separation, children disputes and financial provision. Born 6.8.1950.

Kidd, Philip E.

Tozers, Torquay (01803) 291898. Qualified 1985. Partner based at Torquay office (which has specialist child facilities) dealing almost exclusively with childcare work.

Long, Nigel H.

Greenwoods, Peterborough (01733) 555244.

Loudon, Alasdair

Loudons WS, Edinburgh (0131) 662 4193. Founding Partner.

Specialisation: Main area of practice is family law, including divorce, custody, adoption and children's panel work. Also handles reparation work. Acts in Court of Session and Sheriff Court. Former tutor in criminal advocacy at Edinburgh University. Accreditted by the Law Society of Scotland as a specialist in Family Law and Child Law.

Prof. Membership: WS Society, Edinburgh Bar Association (Vice President).

Career: Qualified in 1978. Apprentice at

Tods, Murray & Jamieson WS 1978-80. Qualified Assistant at *Warner & Co*. 1980-82 and Partner 1982-92. Founded *Loudons WS* in 1992.

Personal: Born 7th April 1956. Attended Dundee University 1974-78. Leisure interests include golf (member of Bruntsfield Links and Luffness New) and football (Hearts Season Ticket holder). Lives in Edinburgh.

Lowry, Michael P.

Stephens & Scown, Exeter (01392) 210700. Qualified 1983. Partner 1990. Family Law Department. Particular specialisation is ancillary relief claims. Born 8.12.1957.

Mair, G. Leonard R.

Morton Fraser Milligan WS, Edinburgh (0131) 556 8444. Partner in Civil Litigation Department.

Specialisation: Main areas of practice are family law, ADR and mediation. Has covered a wide range of work over a 21 year period and has developed ADR and mediation skills since 1993. Has also handled reparation and contract work in general practice over 21 years. Mediator with Family Mediation Service; Accredited Mediator with CEDR; Accredited 'solicitor-mediator' with Law Society of Scotland.

Prof. Membership: Law Society of Scotland, Writers to the Signet.

Career: Qualified in 1975. Joined *Morton Fraser Milligan WS* in 1972, becoming a Partner in 1977.

Personal: Born 5th September 1949. Attended Stirling University 1967-71 and Edinburgh University 1971-73. Council Member of Lothian Marriage Counselling Service. Leisure interests include fly fishing, sailing and the arts. Lives in Pencaitland.

McCulloch, Andrew Grant

See under Personal Injury.

McGoldrick, John

Jones Maidment Wilson, Manchester (0161) 832 8087. Partner and Head of Family Department.

Specialisation: Specialist child care lawyer for 5 years, mainly representing children. Acted in Manchester Satanic Ritual Abuse case. Trainer for Manchester University on the Children Act.

Prof. Membership: Child Concern.

Career: Joined *Jones Maidment Wilson* in 1979. Qualified in 1981. Children Panel Member. Member of Committee of Child Concern and Editor of Newsletter.

Personal: Born 17th July 1956. Enjoys football and computers. Lives in Stockport.

McGowan, Maureen

Morton Fraser Milligan WS, Edinburgh (0131) 556 8444.

Milburn, Paula
Jones Maidment Wilson, Manchester (0161) 832 8087.

Paterson, Fiona
Drummond Miller WS, Edinburgh (0131) 226 5151. Associate in Sheriff Court Department.

Specialisation: Main area of practice is family law. Work includes divorce, child law and children's hearings. Tutor at the University of Edinburgh LLB Course in commercial law.

Prof. Membership: Law Society of Scotland, Edinburgh Bar Association Council Member.

Career: Qualified in 1991. Joined *Drummond Miller WS* in 1989, becoming an Associate in 1993.

Personal: Born 9th January 1966. Attended University of Edinburgh: LLB (Hons) 1988, DipLP 1989. Lives in Edinburgh.

Patience, Iain
Iain Smith & Company, Aberdeen (01224) 645454. Qualified 1979.

Pring, Maureen
Greenwoods, Peterborough (01733) 555244.

Proctor, E. Jane
Greenwoods, Peterborough (01733) 555244.

Salter, David A.
Booth & Co., Leeds (0113) 283 2000. Partner and Head of Family Department.

Specialisation: Handles all aspects of family law, but principally ancillary relief. Also deals with inheritance claims. Author or Joint Author of 'Humphreys Family Proceedings', 'Matrimonial Consent Orders and Agreements' and 'Family Courts: Emergency Remedies and Procedures'. Editor of 'Pensions and Insurance on Family Breakdown' and 'Longman Litigation Practice'. Contributor to 'Insolvency on Family Breakdown' and 'Butterworths Family Law Service'. Frequent lecturer on family law topics.

Prof. Membership: SFLA (Vice-Chairman) Law Society, (Member of Family Law Committee), International Academy of Matrimonial Lawyers (Fellow).

Career: Qualified in 1972. Joined *Booth & Co.* in 1975, becoming a Partner in 1978. Recorder (North Eastern Circuit); Member of Family Proceedings Rules Committee; Member of Supreme Court Procedure Committee Family Division Sub-Committee.

Personal: Born 27th August 1948. Attended Pembroke College, Cambridge. Governor of Harrogate International Festival. Leisure interests include classical music, especially church music. Lives in Harrogate.

Sands, Rosemary
Miller & Co, Cambridge (01223) 66741. Partner heading Family Law Department.

Specialisation: Work includes divorce, ancillary relief, wardship, adoption and children (public law). Member of the SFLA Education Committee. Helps organise seminars for it and for other organisations. Trained FMA mediator. Chair of Cambridge Family & Divorce Centre. Hon Adviser for local CAB. Vice Chair Legal Aid Board Area Committee.

Prof. Membership: Law Society, SFLA, FMA, ALC, BAAF, Chair of Cambridge Guardian ad litem advisory panel. Member Children Panel.

Personal: Born 19th December 1932. LLB 1954; Practised as Barrister (Middle Temple) 1956-1964. Married: two daughters.

Saul, A.
Fosters, Norwich (01603) 620508.

Scanlan, Margaret
Russells, Glasgow (041) 332 4176.

Shepherd, Nigel G.
Lace Mawer, Manchester (0161) 236 2002.

Silver, Rachel
Thomson & Co, Cambridge (01223) 562002.

Sisson, David
Eversheds, Norwich (01603) 272727.

Smith, Caroline
Loudons WS, Edinburgh (0131) 662 4193. Partner dealing with family law and adoption.

Specialisation: Ten years experience dealing exclusively with family law and adoption, mainly in the Sheriff Court. Member of local panel of Reporting Officers/ Curators ad litem for adoption proceedings. Experienced in the preparation of custody reports for Sheriff Court. Notary Public. Writer to the Signet.

Prof. Membership: Family Law Association, Edinburgh Bar Association.

Career: Qualified MB.Ch.B in 1979 and worked as a hospital doctor 1979-82. Trainee and assistant *Warner & Co.* 1985-88. Qualified in 1986. Assistant in Litigation Department at *Morton Fraser Milligan WS* 1988-93. Joined *Loudons WS* as an Associate in October 1993. Partner July 1994.

Personal: Born 23rd June 1955. Educated at St. Denis School, Edinburgh 1960-73 and Edinburgh University 1973-79 and 1982-85. Leisure interests include reading, swimming, gardening and spending time with her 2 children. Lives in Edinburgh.

Speker, Barry N.
See under Medical Negligence.

Stevenson, Lorraine
Wilson Nesbitt, Bangor (01247) 271035.

Thorneycroft, Philip M.
Wolferstans, Plymouth (01752) 663295. Partner 1990. Head of Matrimonial Depart-

ment.

Specialisation: Main areas of practice are child-care and family law. Acts on behalf of parents and children in Care proceedings in related matters. Deals with private matters, divorce, ancillary relief, injunctions, and domestic violence matters. Lectured on child-care update to a conference run jointly by Plymouth University and Plymouth Law Society. Has made a number of appearances on local radio dealing with such issues as sexual abuse, cohabitation contracts and the effect of pensions on divorce.

Prof. Membership: Solicitors Family Law Association, Member of Children Panel, founder member of the Plymouth Child-care Support Group. Associate Member of the National Association of Guardians ad Litem and Reporting Officers.

Career: Qualified in 1982. Joined *Wolferstans* in 1982, becoming a Partner in 1990. Member of Plymouth University Law Degree Validation Committee. Vice Captain of the Plymouth Eleven Hockey Team.

Personal: Born 2nd December 1957. Attended Chesterfield Grammar School 1970-76, Hull University 1976-79 and Chester Law College 1979-80. Leisure interests include hockey, skiing, music and Sheffield Wednesday. Lives in Plymouth.

Wilkins, Beth
Pannone & Partners, Manchester (0161) 832 3000. Qualified 1981. Partner 1985. Family Department. Specialises in child-related work, divorce, matrimonial finance and cohabitation matters.

Wilson, Bruce
Mills & Reeve, Norwich +44 (0) 1603 660155.

Woods, Vera W.
Johns Elliot, Belfast (01232) 326881.

Woodward, David W.
Trump and Partners, Bristol (0117) 929 9901. Partner in Family Law Department.

Specialisation: Main areas of practice are divorce, ancillary relief and children. Acted in Richardson 1994 1FLR 188 and B v. B 1995 IFLR 9.Contributor to Western Daily Press. Experience includes cable television work.

Prof. Membership: SFLA, Law Society.

Career: Qualified in 1975. Joined *Trump & Partners* in 1979, becoming a Partner in 1981.

Personal: Born 10th January 1950. Holds an LLB from Bristol. Leisure interests include cycling, badminton and cricket. Lives in Bristol.

FINANCIAL SERVICES

THE concept of financial services traditionally relates to The Financial Services Act 1986 and the regulatory framework which it created. The need for financial services advice arises in three broad areas:

1. Transactional compliance advice: this is required in relation to transactional activity, such as advising on a merger, takeover or acquisition.
2. Pure compliance work: advice as to procedures required to comply with new or existing regulations.
3. Advice relating to enforcement and disciplinary actions taken by the regulators.

However, the concept, 'financial services', also refers to the regulation of other financial areas such as the insurance market and the specialist rules relating to Lloyd's; the rules of The Stock Exchange; advice relating to building society activity; new EU developments, and so forth.

The self regulatory bodies are becoming tougher in their attitudes to regulatory enforcement. This can be seen, for example, in the recent criticism levelled at the pension industry for encouraging individuals to opt out of their occupational pension schemes where it was inappropiate to do so. The PIA has now taken up the ensuing litigation.

This section does not include the everyday provision of investment advice to clients as being within the definition of Financial Services.

LONDON

The larger City firms have specialist departments advising on all aspects of regulation and compliance in the financial

LEADING FIRMS – LONDON	
CLIFFORD CHANCE	LINKLATERS & PAINES
FRESHFIELDS	
SLAUGHTER AND MAY	TRAVERS SMITH BRAITHWAITE

services industry. At the top of our list are *Linklaters & Paines* and *Clifford Chance*, whose departments are headed by Paul Nelson and Tim Herrington respectively. Both firms provide a complete service to institutions, companies and regulatory bodies. *Freshfields* and *Slaughter and May* handle advisory and regulatory work for financial institutions and Self Regulatory Organisations (SROs), and are also highly recommended.

HIGHLY REGARDED – LONDON	
ALLEN & OVERY	S J BERWIN & CO
CAMERON MARKBY HEWITT	LOVELL WHITE DURRANT
NORTON ROSE	SIMMONS & SIMMONS
WILDE SAPTE	

In all the tables the names in each group are listed alphabetically.

Margaret Chamberlain at *Travers Smith Braithwaite* heads a well regarded financial services department. In addition to its work for various institutions, financial intermediaries and companies, the firm advised the Bank of England on Crest, the new system for paperless trading in listed companies.

LEADING INDIVIDUALS – LONDON	
Mark Harding	Clifford Chance
Timothy Herrington	Clifford Chance
G.W. Morton	Freshfields
Paul M. Nelson	Linklaters & Paines
Pauline Ashall	Linklaters & Paines
James Barlow	Clifford Chance
Margaret Chamberlain	Travers Smith Braithwaite
A.S. McWhirter	Freshfields
S.J. Morris	Cameron Markby Hewitt
Paul Phillips	Allen & Overy
Richard J.L. Stones	Lovell White Durrant

Other recommended firms include *Allen & Overy*, *Cameron Markby Hewitt*, *Simmons & Simmons*, *Lovell White Durrant*, *Norton Rose* and *S J Berwin*, all of which advise both the regulators and the regulated.

SOUTH EAST

Two firms feature in our list for providing FSA advice, *Griffith Smith* in Brighton and *Hodkinsons* in Locks Heath, both of which cover all aspects of compliance work.

HIGHLY REGARDED – SOUTH EAST	
GRIFFITH SMITH Brighton	HODKINSONS Locks Heath

SOUTH WEST & WALES

In the South West region, the leading firms are *Burges Salmon*, *Osborne Clarke* and *Wansbroughs Willey Hargrave*. *Osborne Clarke* is a founder member of the Association of Solicitors Investment Managers and acts for FIMBRA and other regulatory bodies. *Lester Aldridge* is considered to be the main Dorset practice offering compliance advice.

LEADING FIRMS – SOUTH WEST & WALES	
BURGES SALMON Bristol	OSBORNE CLARKE Bristol
WANSBROUGHS WILLEY HARGRAVE Bristol	
EVERSHEDS Cardiff	HUGH JAMES JONES & JENKINS Cardiff
LESTER ALDRIDGE Bournemouth	

In Wales *Eversheds* and *Hugh James Jones & Jenkins* are well regarded for their expertise in FSA matters.

HIGHLY REGARDED – SOUTH WEST & WALES	
BISHOP LONGBOTHAM & BAGNALL *Trowbridge*	DAVIES AND PARTNERS *Gloucester*
EDWARDS GELDARD *Cardiff*	RICKERBY JESSOP *Cheltenham*
STEELE RAYMOND *Bournemouth*	THRINGS & LONG *Bath*

MIDLANDS

Wragge & Co, Pinsent Curtis, Edge & Ellison and *Eversheds* all have expertise in providing specialist compliance advice. *Blythe Liggins* is also well regarded.

LEADING FIRMS – MIDLANDS	
EDGE & ELLISON *Birmingham*	EVERSHEDS *Birmingham*
PINSENT CURTIS *Birmingham*	WRAGGE & CO *Birmingham*

HIGHLY REGARDED – MIDLANDS	
BLYTHE LIGGINS *Leamington Spa*	

EAST ANGLIA

Eversheds provides advice on all aspects of financial services. *Hansell Stevenson* is one of the few firms in East Anglia to provide a separate financial services department giving specialised FSA and compliance advice.

HIGHLY REGARDED – EAST ANGLIA	
EVERSHEDS *Norwich*	HANSELL STEVENSON *Norwich*

NORTH WEST

All the firms listed here regularly advise on FSA matters. *Addleshaw Sons & Latham* is well known in this field especially for compliance advice and unit trusts. *Eversheds* (Anthony Gold) is also well regarded, acting mainly, though not exclusively, for investors.

LEADING FIRMS – NORTH WEST	
ADDLESHAW SONS & LATHAM *Manchester*	ALSOP WILKINSON *Liverpool*
EVERSHEDS *Manchester*	

HIGHLY REGARDED – NORTH WEST	
BERMANS *Liverpool*	CHAFFE STREET *Manchester*
DAVIES WALLIS FOYSTER *Liverpool*	HALLIWELL LANDAU *Manchester*
PANNONE & PARTNERS *Manchester*	

LEADING INDIVIDUALS – NORTH WEST	
Antony Gold *Eversheds*	

NORTH EAST

All the leading firms in this region are well regarded for their FSA abilities. *Booth & Co* is a good example of a firm which

LEADING FIRMS – NORTH EAST	
BOOTH & CO. *Leeds*	DIBB LUPTON BROOMHEAD *Bradford*
DICKINSON DEES *Newcastle*	EVERSHEDS *Leeds*
HAMMOND SUDDARDS *Leeds*	PINSENT CURTIS *Leeds*

has developed financial services expertise through an institutional client base. The firm has a strong reputation in the field of FSA compliance, advising UK and overseas clients

HIGHLY REGARDED – NORTH EAST	
MALCOLM LYNCH *Leeds*	WANSBROUGHS WILLEY HARGRAVE *Leeds*

on all aspects of authorisation, structure and conduct. Other firms well known for compliance advice and investor protection include *Dibb Lupton Broomhead, Dickinson Dees, Eversheds, Hammond Suddards* and *Pinsent Curtis*.

SCOTLAND

Dundas & Wilson CS, Shepherd & Wedderburn WS, and *Tods Murray WS* all have strong connections in the investment and unit trust industries. *McGrigor Donald, Dickson Minto WS* and *Bird Semple* were also recommended.

LEADING FIRMS – SCOTLAND	
DUNDAS & WILSON CS *Edinburgh*	SHEPHERD & WEDDERBURN *Edinburgh*
TODS MURRAY WS *Edinburgh*	
BIRD SEMPLE *Glasgow*	DICKSON MINTO WS *Edinburgh*
McGRIGOR DONALD *Glasgow*	

HIGHLY REGARDED – SCOTLAND	
BRODIES WS *Edinburgh*	FYFE IRELAND *Edinburgh*
MACLAY MURRAY & SPENS *Glasgow*	

LONDON

Ashall, Pauline
Linklaters & Paines, London (0171) 606 7080. Qualified 1987. Partner 1992. Specialises in financial services and banking regulation in the UK and EC.

Barlow, James
See under Collective Investment Schemes.

Chamberlain, Margaret
Travers Smith Braithwaite, London (0171) 248 9133 or 696 0998.

Harding, Mark
Clifford Chance, London (0171) 600 1000. Partner. Principal area of practice is commodities, derivatives and international financial services regulation.

Herrington, Timothy
See under Collective Investment Schemes.

McWhirter, A.S.
Freshfields, London (0171) 936 4000. Qualified 1979. Partner in 1985. Tax Department. Main area of practice is collective investment schemes; also handles corporate taxation.

Morris, S.J.
Cameron Markby Hewitt, London

(0171) 702 2345. Partner in Financial Services Group.

Specialisation: Advises banks, life offices and fund managers on compliance matters; advises fund managers and insurers on establishment in the UK; and advises and represents clients in their dealings with SIB and the SROs, including advising on investigations and before disciplinary and appellate tribunals. Author of 'Financial Services: Regulating Investment Business'. Contributor to Journal of Financial Regulation and Compliance (Member of editorial board). Chairman of five annual conferences for IMRO and LAUTRO members on compliance organised by IBC.

Prof. Membership: United Kingdom Association of Compliance Officers.

Career: Qualified in 1982, having joined *Cameron Markby Hewitt* in 1980. Became a Partner in 1988.

Personal: Born 24th January 1958. Attended Cambridge University. Member of Council, London Topographical Society. Leisure interests include travel and cartography. Lives in Islington.

Morton, G.W.
Freshfields, London (0171) 936 4000.

Nelson, Paul M.
Linklaters & Paines, London (0171) 606 7080. Qualified 1981. Partner 1987. Regula-

tory Practice Department. Specialises in the regulation of securities, banking and insurance firms.

Phillips, Paul
Allen & Overy, London (0171) 330 3000. Qualified 1988. Partner 1994. Specialises in financial services, including regulation, FSA, Banking Act, and SRO rules (SFA/IMRO/PIA).

Stones, Richard J.L.
Lovell White Durrant, London (0171) 236 0066. Qualified 1980. Partner 1987. Corporate Finance and Company Law Group. Specialises in financial services and market law and regulation. Born 1948.

REGIONS

Gold, Antony
See under Litigation (Commercial).

EDITORIAL POLICY

Our policy is to identify leading practitioners entirely on merit. It is not possible to buy a place in our biographical lists: inclusion is based on a practitioner's expertise and professional reputation. The same applies to the lists of recommended law-firms and sets of chambers.

Enormous effort has been invested by our ten-strong research team (mainly solicitors and barristers) in canvassing recommendations and identifying leaders. We are confident in the overall accuracy of the results. However, mistakes and omissions are inevitable, and if readers have any suggestions regarding listings or rankings we should be very pleased to hear from them.

The lists will be revised on the basis of fresh research every year.

FRANCHISING

LONDON

Both *Eversheds* and *Field Fisher & Waterhouse* are nationally recognised as premier firms in this area of law.

Eversheds' national and international practice is franchisor dominated. One of their franchise partners was formerly head of *Dibb Lupton Broomhead*'s unit and the legal director of Prontaprint. Their expertise includes structuring domestic and international franchise arrangements, drafting legal documentation and advising on competition law and compliance procedures. Martin Mendelsohn of the firm has advised Eastern European Governments and the Indonesian Government on the establishment of national franchise associations. He also advised the Polish Anti-Monopoly Office on franchising and competition law.

LEADING FIRMS – LONDON	
EVERSHEDS	FIELD FISHER WATERHOUSE
DAVID BIGMORE & CO	

Field Fisher Waterhouse's team, acting predominantly for franchisors, has had a buoyant year. Last year it acted for International Franchise Systems Inc. in acquiring the master franchise of Domino's Pizza. It recently represented the franchisee action group in the buy-out of the Athena franchise. Other major transactions include advising Threshers (the largest off-licence chain in the UK) on franchising out its retail outlets and Modern Security Systems who are currently franchising their domestic installation operations throughout the UK. The firm also advised Bass on the possible conversion of its pub leases into franchises and Greenalls on the restructuring of their pub franchise. In addition, Mark Abell with over 30 years' experience of franchising, has been appointed to advise the United Nations WIPO on international franchising.

HIGHLY REGARDED – LONDON	
PETERS & PETERS	ROSS & CRAIG
CHURCH ADAMS TATHAM	PAISNER & CO
PINSENT CURTIS	STONES PORTER
ALLEN & OVERY	BRISTOWS COOKE & CARPMAEL
CLIFFORD CHANCE	HOWARD KENNEDY
NABARRO NATHANSON	PENNINGTONS
SIMMONS & SIMMONS	TAYLOR JOYNSON GARRETT

Also highly respected is *David Bigmore & Co*, which represents international and domestic franchisors as well as franchise associations. Other firms with strong franchising practices include and *Peters & Peters* and *Ross & Craig*. The former's international franchising transactions are principally connected with Canada, USA and Eastern Europe. *Ross & Craig* acts for both franchisors and franchisees particularly in the food and retail industries. It is currently representing a South African fast-food chain. The firm's expertise includes advising on franchise and

development area agreements, funding and the setting up of master licences.

All the above-mentioned firms are among the few London firms affiliated to the British Franchise Association. In addition, Mark Abell (*Field Fisher Waterhouse*), David Bigmore (*David Bigmore & Co*), Raymond Cannon (*Peters & Peters*) and Martin Mendelsohn (*Eversheds*) are all members of the BFA Legal Committee.

LEADING INDIVIDUALS – LONDON	
P. Mark Abell *Field Fisher Waterhouse*	
Martin Mendelsohn *Eversheds*	
David Bigmore *David Bigmore & Co*	
Raymond Cannon *Peters & Peters*	
Paul Heatherington *Eversheds*	
Jonathan Horne *Sylvester, Amiel, Lewin and Horne*	

SOUTH EAST

Mundays continues to maintain its excellent reputation in the domestic and international arena. It represents franchisors, franchisees and franchise associations. The department handles joint ventures, franchise disputes, international franchising and franchise agreements including funding agreements. Their wide client base includes John Menzies UK Ltd, Pret à Manger, Service Group plc, Securicor Pony Express, Paint Magic, Ribbon Revival and Microplay Franchising Inc. Domestically, it represents the Texas and Kall Kwik Franchise Associations.

LEADING FIRMS – SOUTH EAST		
MUNDAYS *Esher*		
BURSTOWS *Crawley*	**OWEN WHITE** *Slough*	

Also highly respected are *Owen White* and *Burstows*. The former continues to advise international licensors, particularly from the USA and Canada, seeking to establish or reinforce their networks in the UK. Advice is also given to multinational companies in France and Germany wishing to expand in the UK and in the Far East. *Burstows'* clients, mainly franchisees, are primarily in the retail and service industries. It has recently acted for Veedy Services (trading name Tekclean) and the United Business Group.

HIGHLY REGARDED – SOUTH EAST	
CHURCH ADAMS TATHAM *Reigate*	CRIPPS HARRIES HALL *Tunbridge Wells*
DONNE MILEHAM & HADDOCK *Brighton*	

Other recommended firms include *Church Adams Tatham & Co* which acts primarily for franchisors in the food sector, *Cripps Harries Hall* (franchisors and franchisees) and *Donne Mileham & Haddock* (franchisors and franchisees in the retail and service industries).

Burstows, Mundays and *Owen White* are affiliated members of the BFA. Leading franchising specialists include Caroline Armitage (*Burstows*), Anton Bates (*Owen White*) and Manzoor Ishani (*Mundays*). In addition, Anton Bates (*Owen White*) who is legal advisor to the BFA, and Manzoor Ishani (*Mundays*) are members of the BFA Legal Committee. The former also represented the BFA on the European Franchise Federation's Legal Committee.

SOUTH WEST & WALES

The Bristol firms of *Lawrence Tucketts* and *Osborne Clarke* are among the most highly respected in this area of law. Both practices advise franchisors and franchisees on a range of matters including the setting up of international networks, funding and the drafting of franchise agreements. *Lawrence Tucketts* is also an affiliated member of the BFA.

Other recommended firms include *Bond Pearce* and *Wansbroughs Willey Hargrave*. The former's clientele is primarily from the service, retail and distribution sectors. *Wansbroughs Willey Hargrave* specialises in master licences, area development licences and expansion, distributor agreements, funding and start ups (including the creation of franchise agreements). The firm is currently acting for a national network of building maintenance franchisees consisting of 32 franchises and for a hi-fi retail chain on the structure and arrangement of its branches as franchises.

Sue Cook (*Lawrence Tucketts*), Robin Staunton (*Lawrence Tucketts*) and Alan Wood (*Osborne Clarke*) are among the leading franchising practitioners in the South West.

In all the tables the names in each group are listed alphabetically.

MIDLANDS

Pinsent Curtis continues to maintain its dominance in the field of franchising, acting for over 70 UK franchisors including Dolland & Aichison. Its clients range from fast food chains to retailers and carpet cleaners. The firm is also increasingly involved in master franchising, particularly in connection with the USA. where it recently obtained a master licence for Microplay in the video game industry. John Pratt of the firm has an excellent reputation and is a member of the BFA Legal Committee.

Also highly regarded is *Wragge & Co* which acts for both franchisors and franchisees in the domestic and international domain. As well as advising on franchising agreements and management buy-outs for franchise companies, it offers a comprehensive start-up service which includes financial arrangements. Their clients include Chemical Express, Autella Components Ltd, Rosemary Conley Fitness Club, Links Careers Service and Linkmaster Ltd. Gordon Harris of *Wragge & Co* has been highly recommended.

Both *Pinsent & Co* and *Wragge & Co* are affiliated members of the BFA.

Other recommended firms include *Dibb Lupton Broomhead* (an affliated member of the BFA), *Eversheds* (Birmingham) and *Goodger Auden*. All three firms act for franchisors and franchisees with *Eversheds* having particular expertise in leisure industry franchising. *Dibb Lupton Broomhead*'s expertise covers franchise disputes including franchise-related litigation and arbitration proceedings. Last year it acted on behalf of two major lending banks in connection with the establishment of a large number of franchised Burger King outlets. *Goodger Auden* handles a fair amount of international franchising, particularly in Eastern and Western Europe.

EAST ANGLIA

Leathes Prior, which acts for both franchisors and franchisees, continues to maintain its excellent reputation. It has particular expertise in multiple party actions and international master licence agreements where it acts for US, Canadian and UK franchisors. Its US and Canadian clients include Metal Supermarkets, Advance Nursing Agencies and M & B Marquees. In the past 12 months, the firm has been handling an increasing amount of franchising work in the motor dealership field where it represents Toyota, SAAB, Audi, BMW and Nissan motor dealers, amongst others.

LEADING FIRMS – EAST ANGLIA

LEATHES PRIOR *Norwich*	
EVERSHEDS *Norwich*	

Eversheds' team in Norwich which includes a former *Leathes Prior* franchising specialist, has also been consistently recommended. It acts exclusively for franchisors. In addition to handling domestic franchising, the firm has expertise in international master licences arrangements especially in relation to Singapore, the USA, Ireland and France.

HIGHLY REGARDED – EAST ANGLIA

STEELE & CO *Norwich*	**TAYLOR VINTERS** *Cambridge*

Both *Leathes Prior* and *Eversheds* (Norwich) are among the few firms affliated to the British Franchise Association. *Steele & Co* (acting for franchisors and franchisees) and *Taylor Vinters* also have sound licensing practices.

LEADING INDIVIDUALS – EAST ANGLIA

R. Jonathan Chadd *Leathes Prior*	
John Chambers *Eversheds*	
G.C. Wilcock *Leathes Prior*	

Leading practitioners include Jonathan Chadd (*Leathes Prior*), John Chambers (*Eversheds – Norwich*) and Gavin Wilcox (*Leathes Prior*).

NORTH WEST

The niche practice of *Howard Jones & Co*, acting for both franchisors and franchisees, is widely acknowledged as one of the prominent firms in this field. As well as advising on general franchising matters, it handles EC aspects of franchising and franchise litigation. Its clients are predominantly in the retail, food and hairdressing industries. The Manchester firm of *Addleshaw Sons & Latham* is also well regarded for its franchisor dominated expertise.

LEADING FIRMS – NORTH WEST

HOWARD JONES & CO *Liverpool*	
ADDLESHAW SONS & LATHAM *Manchester*	

Other recommended firms include *Colemans* (acting for both franchisors and franchisees), *Dibb Lupton Broomhead, Eversheds* (Manchester) which has particular expertise in advising franchisors and franchisees in the financial services sector, and *Goldsmith Williams*.

Colemans recently co-sponsored the British Franchise exhibition. *Dibb Lupton Broomhead* 's clients include franchisors, franchise consultants, funders and franchisees. It was recently involved in the £10 million launch of Genesis Restaurants who plan to open a franchise chain of 25 Burger King restaurants in the North West and Midlands. *Goldsmith*

HIGHLY REGARDED – NORTH WEST

COLEMANS *Manchester*	**DIBB LUPTON BROOMHEAD** *Manchester*
EVERSHEDS *Manchester*	**GOLDSMITH WILLIAMS** *Liverpool*
COBBETT LEAK ALMOND *Manchester*	**DAVIES WALLIS FOYSTER** *Liverpool*
HALLIWELL LANDAU *Manchester*	**HILL DICKINSON DAVIS CAMPBELL** *Liverpool*
WEIGHTMAN RUTHERFORDS *Liverpool*	

Williams' franchisee clients are mainly in the freight packaging, retail, hairdressing and food industries. It also has substantial experience in handling franchisee group actions.

BFA affiliated members in the North West include *Addleshaw Sons & Latham, Dibb Lupton Broomhead, Eversheds* (Manchester) and *Howard Jones & Co.*

LEADING INDIVIDUALS – NORTH WEST

George E. Howard Jones *Howard Jones & Co*	
Garth Lindrup *Addleshaw Sons & Latham*	
John Boardman *Eversheds*	
Edward R. Goldsmith *Goldsmith Williams*	

Leading licensing specialists include George Howard Jones (*Howard Jones & Co*) and Garth Lindrup (*Addleshaw Sons & Latham*).

NORTH EAST

Eversheds (Leeds) has an excellent reputation (acting for both franchisors and franchisees), being one of the few local firms recognised by the British Franchise Association as an affiliate. It recently advised Alphagraphics Printshops in the

LEADING FIRMS – NORTH EAST

EVERSHEDS *Leeds*	

negotiation of its UK master licence with Alphagraphics Inc., and Next Plc on its international retail franchise agreement. Other recent clients include Decorating Den Inc. and the UK kitchen and bathroom franchisor, Welman Intoto. James Hodgson of the firm has been consistently recommended.

HIGHLY REGARDED – NORTH EAST

ROLLIT FARRELL & BLADON *Hull*	**WAKE SMITH** *Sheffield*
BOOTH & CO. *Leeds*	
ANDREW M. JACKSON *Hull*	**IRWIN MITCHELL** *Sheffield*
PINSENT CURTIS *Leeds*	

Rollit Farrell Bladon, which acts for a number of car importers, is one of a few firms in the North East with a specialisation in motor franchising agreements. It also has expertise in the caravan industry. *Wake Smith & Co's* franchising practice is predominantly franchisee-based in sectors such as takeaway food, stationary printing, carpet cleaning and lock masters. Another recommended firm in Leeds is *Booth & Co.*

LEADING INDIVIDUALS – NORTH EAST

James Hodgson *Eversheds*	

SCOTLAND

The franchising of ScotRail as part of the Government's rail privatisation programme has lead to a growth of work in this

area. *Brodies* and *Levy & Macrae*, both affiliated members of the BFA, are widely recognised as the leading firms. The former represents both franchisors and franchisees.

Also recommended is *Steedman Ramage WS* which acts primarily for franchisors in, inter alia, the purchase and disposal of franchised outlets and the drafting of franchise agreements.

Leading practitioners include Julian Voge (*Brodies*) and Anthony Caplan (*Levy Macrae*).

LEADERS IN FRANCHISING

LONDON

Abell, P. Mark

Field Fisher Waterhouse, London (0171) 481 4841. Partner in Intellectual Property Department.

Specialisation: Main areas of practice are franchising and licensing. Work covers negotiating, drafting and advising generally on international and domestic area and unit franchises, fractional franchises, concessions, technology transfers, merchandising and sponsorship. Also advises the United Nations WIPO on the appropriate legal regime in developing countries. Other area is distribution: negotiating, drafting and advising generally on the distribution of branded products and beer internationally and domestically. Acted in the Moosehead decision of the EC Commission, an important trademarks and anti-trust case. Author of 'The Franchise Option', 'The International Franchise Option', 'European Franchising- Law and Practice in the European Community Vol. I & II', 'International Technology Transfer for Profit' and over 300 articles on franchising, licensing and I.P. Expert adviser to WIPO. Visiting lecturer at QMW University of London. Lectures regularly in the USA, Japan, PRC and Europe. Editorial Board Member of Trade Mark World.

Prof. Membership: IFA, IBA, UIA, LES, Society of Franchising, British Franchise Association.

Career: Qualified 1978. Joined *Field Fisher Waterhouse* in 1984 and became a Partner in 1987.

Personal: Born 19th February 1957. Attended Southampton University 1975-78. Vice President of UIA's Franchise Commission. BFA Legal Committee Member. Leisure interests include Japanese and Chinese cultural activities (Japanese speaker), keeping fit, opera, swimming and tennis.

Bigmore, David

David Bigmore & Co, London (0171) 583 2277. Franchising and Company/ Commercial Department.

Specialisation: Has specialised in franchising since 1986. Has acted for numerous international franchisors, domestic franchisors and large franchise associations. Also handles mergers and acquisitions and corporate law, with twenty years experience of take-overs and general corporate work. Author of numerous articles. Other experience includes lecturing and conducting seminars.

Prof. Memberships: Law Society, BFA, Member of BFA's Legal Committee.

Career: Qualified in 1972. Set up *David Bigmore & Co.* in 1992.

Personal: Born 27th March 1948. Attended Merchant Taylor's School, Crosby, 1957-64, Bedford Modern School 1964-66, and Worcester College, Oxford, 1966-69. Leisure interests include squash and tennis. Lives in Holmwood, Dorking.

Cannon, Raymond

Peters & Peters, London (0171) 629 7991. Senior Partner in Commercial and Corporate Department.

Specialisation: Domestic and international commercial and corporate dealings. Emphasis on distribution, franchising, joint ventures, trade marks and intellectual property. Principally involved in Canada, USA, European Union and Eastern Europe. Regular speaker at various international conferences, seminars and symposiums on the international dimension of business, including IFA Conventions in Mexico and London and AIJA Congresses in Copenhagen, Munich and Spain. Addressed major franchise exhibitions in London and Toronto and the Anglo US Trade Association in Los Angeles. Contributing author to 'The Com-

plete Guide to Franchising in Canada' (Macmillan) and 'Franchises: Dollars & Sense' (Kendall/ Hunt). Frequent contributor to commercial and legal publications. Currently writing a book on European Union Business Law.

Prof. Membership: Law Society, British Franchise Association, (member of Senior Legal Committee), member of the European Franchise Federation Legal Committee, American Bar Association and International Bar Association. Established the franchise group of the Association of International des Jeunes Advocates (AIJA). International representative on Advisory Board of Council of Franchise Suppliers (USA) and a member of the International Affairs Committee (IFA).

Career: Qualified 1955. Joined *Peters & Peters* in 1958 and became Senior Partner in 1960.

Personal: Born 13th November 1933. Chairman of Governors of Jews Free School; Chairman of Board of Education - United Synagogue. Leisure pursuits include bridge, skiing, swimming and travel. Lives in Kenton.

Heatherington, Paul

Eversheds, London (0171) 919 4500. Partner in Company/Commercial Department.

Specialisation: Franchising. Has handled numerous UK and international franchising transactions. Author of articles in the legal and franchising press. Has lectured widely on franchising in the UK and abroad.

Career: Qualified in 1980 (also admitted in Ireland and Northern Ireland). Partner at *Bennett Wainright & Richardson* in Newcastle upon Tyne 1981-89. Legal Director of Prontaprint Ltd 1989-93. Partner in charge of franchising at *Dibb Lupton Broomhead* 1993-94. Joined *Jaques & Lewis* (now Eversheds) Franchising Group as a Partner in 1994.

Personal: Born 11th May 1948. Educated at Newcastle upon Tyne Polytechnic 1978-80. Married with two teenage children. Leisure pursuits include Rugby and Genealogy. Lives Shotley Bridge, County Durham.

Horne, Jonathan

Sylvester, Amiel, Lewin and Horne, London (0171) 723 0931. Qualified 1980. Partner in Franchising and Commercial Property Department. Specialises in franchise agreements.

Mendelsohn, Martin

Eversheds, London (0171) 919 4500. Partner in Company and Commercial Department. Head of *Eversheds* national Franchising Group.

Specialisation: Has 36 years' experience of handling a wide range of commercial, corporate and international transactions. Has particular expertise in franchising, distribution, agency and licensing transactions, both domestic and international, as well as UK and EC competition law. Has been active in many parts of the world in providing support and assistance to Franchise Associations. Has twice visited Indonesia to advise its Government at the request of the ILO and UNDP as well as visiting Eastern Europe at the request of the OECD to explain franchising to Government Departments. Visiting Professor of Franchising and Director of the Centre for Franchise Research at City University Business School. Member of the International Institution for the Unification of Private Law (UNIDROIT) study group on franchising. Member of the American Bar Association's Forum Committee on Franchising. Current publications include 'The Guide to Franchising' (5th edition), and 'How to evaluate a Franchise' (5th edition) and 'The Ethics of Franchising' (2nd edition). He is also co-author of several publications, including 'How to Franchise your Business' (3rd edition) 'Franchising and the Block Exemption Regulation' and 'Franchising'. Editor of the 'Journal of International Franchising and Distribution Law' and editor of and contibutor to 'Franchising in Europe'. Legal consultant to the British Franchise Association. Assisted in the introduction of a franchising law course by Queen Mary & Westfield College, London University as a subject for the University's Master of Law Degree and lectures regularly there. Frequent lecturer at conferences and seminars worldwide. Regular contributor to journals and publications. Was first chairman of the International Franchising Committee of the International Bar Association.

Prof. Membership: Fellow of the Chartered Institute of Arbitrators, Law Society, International Bar Association, American Bar Association.

Career: Qualified in 1959. Joined *Jaques & Lewis* (now Eversheds) as a partner in 1992.

Personal: Born 6th November 1935. Lives in Stanmore, Middlesex.

REGIONS

Armitage, Caroline D.

Burstows, Crawley (01293) 534734. Qualified 1986. Partner 1990. Commercial Unit. Main areas of practice include mergers, acquisitions, disposals and franchises. Has acted in £500,000 to £15 million transactions, share structurings and management buyouts. Born 11.7.1960.

Bates, Anton B.

Owen White, Slough (01753) 536846. Partner leading the Commercial Department.

Specialisation: Main area of practice is franchising. Legal Advisor to British Franchise Association since advising founder members and drafting constitution in 1977. Has advised scores of franchisors and franchisees including international companies in the UK, coming to the UK and exporting from the UK. Other area of practice is licensing and intellectual property. Acts for household names in the franchising industry and in injunction proceedings where necessary. Author of many articles in various specialist magazines and newspapers. Organiser and speaker at countless seminars in the UK (for the BFA) and abroad.

Prof. Membership: Law Society, Chartered Institute of Arbitrators, British Franchise Association.

Career: Qualified in 1967. After 5 years as a Partner in a large city firm, joined *Owen White* as a Partner in 1973. A Chairman of the Legal Aid Board Area Committee. Past Chairman of the Central and South Middlesex Law Society. Legal Advisor to the British Marine Industries Federation.

Personal: Born 22nd November 1941. Attended Warwick School 1953-60, then the University of Birmingham 1960-63. Leisure interests include yachting. Lives in Camberley, Surrey.

Boardman, John

Eversheds, Manchester (0161) 832 6666. Partner in Corporate Department.

Specialisation: Principal area of work is education law advising higher education, further education and grant-maintained schools. Other main area of work is franchising, acting for franchisors and franchisees. Contributes articles to various specialist education law and franchise publications and gives numerous lectures and seminars on these two areas.

Prof. Membership: ELAS, British Franchise Association, IFS, International Bar Association.

Career: Qualified 1979 while at *Alexander Tatham*, now *Eversheds Alexander Tatham* and became a Partner in 1986.

Personal: Born 26th July 1955. Attended Manchester Grammar School 1966-73 and Downing College, Cambridge 1973-76. Governor of City College, Manchester. Leisure pursuits include pottery, computers, films, books and music. Lives in Hayfield, Derbyshire.

Caplan, Anthony M.

Levy & McRae, Glasgow (0141) 307 2311.

Chadd, R. Jonathan

Leathes Prior, Norwich (01603) 610911. Qualified 1980. Partner 1986. Commercial Department. Principal area of practice is franchising and intellectual property. Born 14.8.1953.

Chambers, John

Eversheds, Norwich (01603) 272727.

Cook, Sue

Lawrence Tucketts, Bristol (0117) 929 5252.

Goldsmith, Edward R.

Goldsmith Williams, Liverpool (0151) 231 1292. Qualified 1977. Partner 1984. Responsible for quality and the BS5750. Also Legal Aid franchising. Born 21.9.1952.

Harris, Gordon D.

Wragge & Co, Birmingham (0121) 233 1000. Qualified 1984. Partner 1990. Main areas of practice are franchising, intellectual property and defamation, with media and merchandising work also covered. Born 13.10.1959.

Hodgson, James

See under Intellectual Property.

Ishani, Manzoor G.K.

Mundays, Esher (01372) 467272. Partner and Head of Franchising Unit.

Specialisation: Principal area of practice (for over 16 years) is UK and international franchising, including franchise dispute resolution and joint ventures with overseas companies. Over past three years has helped UK companies franchise into more than 22 countries. Other main area of work is EC Competition Law.

Has advised Holland & Barratt, HSS-Hire Shops, Beefeater Restaurants, Clifford Dairies, Conaco, Cullens, Dolland & Aichison, Securicor Pony Express, Early Learning Centres, (John Menzies [UK] Ltd), The Meteorological Office, Prontaprint, One Stop Community Stores [Portsmouth and Sunderland Newpapers Plc]. E. Moss Chemists (UniChem Plc), Sketchley, Pizza Express and 3M among others.

Regular columnist on legal and commercial aspects of franchising to Business Franchise Magazine, Franchise World, Business Money Magazine and Enterprise Magazine. Author of "The European Community" (Fourmat Publishing [Tolley] 1992) and co-author of "Franchising in the UK"; (Second Edition, Fanchise World Publications 1989); "Franchising in Europe" (Second Edition, Cassey Publications 1993); "Franchising in Canada" (MacMillan Canada 1992); and "The Business Franchise Guide-Franchise Handbook" (Fourth Edition, CGB Publishing 1994). European Contributing Editor:

World Franchise & Business Report (USA). European Franchise Correspondent: Exposure Magazine (USA). International Franchise Correspondent: Aspiring Millionaire Magazine. Advisory Editor: Journal of International Franchising and Distribution Law (1986-1991).

Lectures frequently on legal and commercial aspects of franchising topics to businessmen, academics and lawyers worldwide and has done so for International Franchise Association, International Bar Association, British Franchise Association, National Westminster Bank, The Royal Bank of Scotland, City of Westminster Law Society and University of Maryland, USA. Legal Advisor to the Franchise Consultants Association.

Prof. Membership: British Franchise Association (Legal Committee), International Bar Association (Franchise Committee - Section of Business Law), American Bar Association (Forum Committee on Franchising), International Association of Lawyers (Franchising Committee), International Association of Young Jurists (Working Commission on Franchising), Association of Swiss Arbitrators.

Career: Qualified 1976. Previously a Partner with City practice. Joined *Mundays* as a partner in 1992.

Personal: Born 6th October 1949. Attended St. Edmund's School Canterbury 1963-68, then University of St. Andrews 1969-72. Leisure pursuits include classic cars and reading. Lives in Oxshott, Surrey.

Jones, George E. Howard

Howard Jones & Company, Liverpool (0151) 231 1577. Qualified 1972. Senior Partner 1976. Commercial Department. Handles corporate/commercial work including commercial property, commercial agreements, franchising. Born 30.8.1946.

Lindrup, Garth

See under European Union/Competition.

Masih, Jane

Owen White, Slough (01753) 536846. Partner in Company & Commercial Department.

Specialisation: Main area of practice is commercial work related to the computer industry, advising several major companies regarding a broad range of commercial issues, including negotiating and drafting documentation. Also handles franchising and intellectual property, advising both franchisors and franchisees, with a wide range of experience over the last 6 years. has negotiated and advised on the appointment of several US franchise systems to UK franchisors. Has lecturing experience, addressing local interest groups, including the Chamber of Commerce.

Prof. Membership: Law Society, Thames Valley Commercial Lawyers Association, Women in Commerce.

Career: Qualified in 1987, having joined *Owen White* in 1986. Became a Partner in 1989.

Personal: Born 27th May 1962. Educated at Yeovil Girl's School 1973-78 and Yeovil College 1978-80, then Keele University 1980-84. Committee Member of Thames Valley Chamber of Commerce (Slough area). Leisure pursuits include gardening, swimming and keeping fit. Lives in Sunbury on Thames.

Pratt, John

Pinsent Curtis, Birmingham (0121) 200 1050. Qualified 1976. Partner 1993. Company Department. Main area of practice is franchising, for one hundred UK franchisors; also handles competition law. Born 26.4.1951.

Pyper, T.E.

Lawrence Tucketts, Bristol (0117) 929 5252. Qualified 1970.

Staunton, R.M.

Lawrence Tucketts, Bristol (0117) 929 5252. Qualified 1984.

Voge, Julian C.A.

Brodies WS, Edinburgh (0131) 228 3777. Partner 1987. Corporate Department. Main areas of practice are corporate and contract law, including franchising and licensing. Author of chapters on Scots law for 'Franchising Law and Practice' and 'International Franchising Law'.

Prof. Membership: Law Society of Scotland, Writer to the Signet. Also admitted as a solicitor in England and Wales.

Career: Qualified 1982. Articled at *Tods Murray*. Then worked at *Brodies* and *Berwin Leighton*, before re-joining *Brodies* as a Partner in 1987.

Personal: Born 3rd February 1958. Attended Daniel Stewarts & Melville College 1964-76, then University of Edinburgh 1976-80. Lives in Edinburgh.

Walley, Ray D.

Mundays, Esher (01372) 467272. Partner in Intellectual Property Department and Managing Partner.

Specialisation: Principal area of practice is intellectual property, especially trade marks, copyright, and software issues, including the licensing and disposal of rights. Also specialises in franchising, licensing and distribution. Has recently advised on the franchising aspects of a Texas/Homecare matter. Clients include E.Moss Pharmacists (Unichem plc), Presto Print, Golf Land, ICS Identcode Systems and Yonex. Is a contributor to *Franchise World* and *Business Franchise*. Has conducted two lecture tours of the U.S. under the title of "Building a Bridge To The United States Of Europe" and has spoken extensively at conferences in the U.K. and in Europe.

Prof. Membership: Chair of Surrey European Business Association, member of Institute of Directors, Chartered Institute of Bankers and Director of Surrey Training & Enterprise Council.

Career: Qualified in 1976. Became a Partner in *Mundays* in 1976 and Managing Partner in 1992.

Personal: Born 29th July 1944. Educated at King Edward VII G.S., Sheffield 1956-62, and at Durham University. Law Society Qualification 1972-76. At Lloyds Bank 1963-72. Leisure interests include acting as Governor, Horse Rangers Association, tennis, computing and walking. Lives in Oxshott, Surrey.

Wilcock, G.C.

Leathes Prior, Norwich (01603) 610911. Qualified 1974. Partner 1975. Commercial Department. Principal areas of practice are landlord and tenant business, property law and franchising. Born 9.12.1948.

Wood, Alan P.

See under Computer Law & I.T.

HEALTH & SAFETY

LONDON

The regulatory aspects of health and safety law have traditionally been dealt with by either in-house lawyers or specialist health and safety managers. However, as the legislation affecting this field becomes more extensive and complex, companies are increasingly consulting lawyers in private

LEADING FIRMS – LONDON	
MASONS	McKENNA & CO
NABARRO NATHANSON	

practice. It is those firms with a high level of industrial expertise which have been best placed to take advantage of this trend, and the leading firms include *McKenna & Co, Masons* and *Nabarro Nathanson.* All these firms are defendant firms and tend to be instructed by insurance companies or have expertise in the regulatory aspects of the field. The best known plaintiff firms tend to be those which regularly act on behalf of trade unions and they are listed in the Employment section of the directory.

HIGHLY REGARDED – LONDON	
BARLOW LYDE & GILBERT	VIZARDS

Mark Tyler at *McKenna & Co* has a strong reputation and is on the Confederation of British Industry Health and Safety Consultative Committee. His work includes monitoring new legislation for clients, and risk and crisis management. He also undertakes various health and safety litigation including enforcement actions, criminal prosecutions and employers' liability claims. Alison Brown at the firm has also been recommended for her expertise. *Masons,* where Christopher Dering is well known, has a reputation for health and safety compliance advice in the construction industry.

LEADING INDIVIDUALS – LONDON	
Christopher Dering *Masons*	
Thomas Symes *Nabarro Nathanson*	
Mark Tyler *McKenna & Co*	

UP AND COMING
Alison F. Brown *McKenna & Co*

Thomas Symes at *Nabarro Nathanson* advises on all aspects of health and safety regulations. Work in the last twelve months has included rewriting British Coal health and safety policy and acting in the Lyon Bay canoeing tragedy, as well as general policy and risk assessment advice. Other notable firms in the area are *Vizards* and *Barlow Lyde & Gilbert.*

Environmental and employment aspects of health and safety are covered by the specialists lists dealing with these two subjects.

SOUTH WEST & WALES

Osborne Clarke emerges as the leading firm in the South West. Richard Bretton, head of the unit, has a national reputation for his pioneering health and safety work. The firm advises on procedures and risk assessments for the prevention of costly accidents, and undertakes a wide range of accident claims for both insurers and claimants. Richard Bretton launched the unique Health and Safety Club last October which aims to prevent disasters. The club's facilities include a 24 hour advice line, workshops for the exchange of inform-

LEADING FIRMS – SOUTH WEST & WALES
OSBORNE CLARKE *Bristol*

ation, regular notes and advice about new regulations and other developments, and access to a comprehensive health and safety library. Richard Bretton has also been involved in high profile health and safety cases over the past year including gaining record 'nervous shock' damages of £1.3m for businessman Peter Vernon following the death of his two daughters, and the landmark case involving an accident on a bouncy castle resulting in potential £1m damages.

HIGHLY REGARDED – SOUTH WEST & WALES	
BEVAN ASHFORD *Bristol*	EVERSHEDS *Cardiff*
HUGH JAMES JONES & JENKINS *Cardiff*	LESTER ALDRIDGE *Bournemouth*
ROBIN THOMPSON & PARTNERS *Bristol*	ROWLEY ASHWORTH *Exeter*
LYONS DAVIDSON *Bristol*	VEALE WASBROUGH *Bristol*

Richard Byrne at *Lester Aldridge,* who is highly regarded, advises on health and safety matters and also undertakes prosecutions for the Health and Safety Executive. Other notable firms include *Bevan Ashford,* where Richard Annandale has been recommended, *Rowley Ashworth* and *Robin Thompson & Partners*

LEADING INDIVIDUALS – SOUTH WEST & WALES
Richard Bretton *Osborne Clarke*
Richard Annandale *Bevan Ashford*
Richard Byrne *Lester Aldridge*
Michael L.N. Jones *Hugh James Jones & Jenkins*
Martin H. Warren *Eversheds*

In Wales, *Eversheds* has expertise in this highly specialised area of law and Martin Warren, a partner at the firm and co-author of a book on health and safety law, has been recommended. Michael Jones at *Hugh James Jones & Jenkins* has also been recommended.

MIDLANDS

Following departmental reorganisation in 1994, health and safety at *Eversheds* is dealt with by the Retail & Regulatory team within the litigation department. The team acts principally for clients in the retail and leisure sector and consists of advocates whose specialisation is in the magistrates courts, as well as other tribunals such as local authority licensing committees. After liquor licensing, health and safety has been the largest part of the team's work, ranging from advice on health and safety assessments to the conduct of a three-day trial.

HIGHLY REGARDED – MIDLANDS

EDGE & ELLISON *Birmingham*	EVERSHEDS *Birmingham*

Edge & Ellison is also known for its defence and prosecution work under health and safety regulations.

NORTH

Nabarro Nathanson has an established reputation in this area of work, with a strong team of five headed by Gareth Watkins who has been highly recommended. The team gives advice to clients on health and safety policies, organisation and structure and EU Directives, as well as providing advice and representation in connection with inquests, public

LEADING FIRMS – NORTH

NABARRO NATHANSON *Doncaster*

inquiries and prosecutions. *Eversheds* also has a large specialist health and safety unit, due to its substantial industrial, construction and insurance client base. The team acts exclusively for defendants and has acted in numerous high profile

HIGHLY REGARDED – NORTH

DAVIES ARNOLD COOPER *Manchester*	DAVIES WALLIS FOYSTER *Liverpool*
EVERSHEDS *Leeds*	FORD AND WARREN *Leeds*
HALLIWELL LANDAU *Manchester*	

cases including the fire at Hickson & Welch Limited in 1992 which was subject to a Government inquiry under the auspices of the Health and Safety Executive. Paul Burnley at the firm is particularly well known for his work in the field.

LEADING INDIVIDUALS – NORTH

Gareth Watkins *Nabarro Nathanson*
Paul Burnley *Eversheds*
Christopher Phillips *Halliwell Landau*

Christopher Phillips, a personal injury specialist who moved from *Hammond Suddards* to *Halliwell Landau* last year, also undertakes health and safety work, covering all aspects.

LEADERS IN HEALTH & SAFETY

LONDON

Brown, Alison F.
McKenna & Co, London (0171) 606 9000. Assistant Solicitor in Healthcare Department.

Specialisation: Advises on civil and criminal aspects of a wide range of health and safety matters and acts for companies faced with criminal prosecutions, inquests and claims for damages. Handles related litigation, including product liability litigation medical negligence claims and warranty claims. Has written several articles for legal journals and spoken at conferences and seminars.

Career: Joined *McKenna* in 1988 and qualified in 1990.

Personal: Born 12th June 1966. Educated at Latymer Grammar School, Edmonton 1977-84 and Bristol University 1984-87.

Dering, Christopher
Masons, London (0171) 490 4000.

Symes, Thomas
See under Environmental Law.

Tyler, Mark
McKenna & Co, London (0171) 606 9000. Partner in Healthcare Group.

Specialisation: Main areas of practice are health and safety and product liability. Contributor to 'Buildings and Health: The Rosehaugh Guide to the Design Construction and Management of Buildings', 'A New Balance: A Guide for Property Owners and Developers', and 'Environmental Issues in Construction' - CIRIA Special Report, and Facilities Management Handbook.

Prof. Membership: Law Society, CBI Health and Safety Consultative Committee, CBI Consumer Affairs Panel.

Career: Joined *McKenna & Co* in 1984 and qualified in 1986. Became a Partner in 1992.

Personal: Born 10th October 1960. Educated at Sir William Borlase's Grammar School, Marlow, Worcester College, Oxford and Kings College, London.

REGIONS

Annandale, Richard
Bevan Ashford, Bristol (0117) 923 0111.

Specialisation: Partner in the NHS litigation department with ten years experience acting for health authorities and trust hospitals in a wide variety of medical negligence claims. Practice also covers risk management and

health and safety work. For the past ten years has acted for health authorities and trust hospitals on employer and public liability claims involving health and safety issues, and in particular manual handling, ASBESTOSIS, COSHH and RSI.

Career: Qualified 1977. Partner since 1993. Director of QRM Healthcare Limited (*Bevan Ashford's* healthcare risk management company) since 1993.

Personal: Educated at Manchester University (LL.B) 1968-71. Born 25th April 1950. Lives in Bristol.

Bretton, Richard
Osborne Clarke, Bristol (0117) 923 0220. Qualified 1978. Partner 1993. Litigation Department. Main area of practice is health and safety; also handles personal injury and medical negligence. Born in 1954.

Burnley, Paul
Eversheds, Leeds (0113) 243 0391.

Byrne, Richard
Lester Aldridge, Bournemouth (01202) 786161.

Specialisation: Advises on health and safety legislation, company health and safety policies and organisation. Provides representation in connection with Health and Safety at Work Act prosecutions. Advises and represents the Health and Safety Executive in prosecutions. Part time industrial tribunal chairman.

Prof. Membership: Law Society, Employment Lawyers Association.

Career: Qualified in 1978. Joined *Lester Aldridge* 1983 becoming a partner in 1984.

Personal: Born 19 January 1955. Enjoys walking, skiing, reading and travel. Fellow of

The Royal Geographical Society. Lives near Romsey, Hampshire.

Jones, Michael L.N.
See under Construction & Civil Eng..

Phillips, Christopher
Halliwell Landau, Manchester (0161) 835 3003. Qualified 1982. Partner and head of the Personal Injury and Health and Safety Department. Specialised in disease related matters. Born 17.7.1953.

Warren, Martin H.
See under Environmental Law.

Watkins, Gareth
Nabarro Nathanson, Doncaster (0130) 234 4455. Qualified 1980. Partner 1990. Litigation Department. Main area of practice is health and safety. Also handles occupational health and industrial diseases. Born 7.3.1956.

HEALTH CARE

THE NHS Trust is a huge corporate client with a vast array of needs to be serviced. Firms acting on behalf of NHS trusts will handle not only medical negligence defence work but also a range of commercial matters. NHS Trust work relating to employment, IT, environmental (including waste management and contaminated land) and medical negligence, are dealt with elsewhere in the directory under the appropriate headings.

Perhaps one of the most significant developments is in the commercial sphere, particularly in connection with the Private Finance Initiative (PFI) which has created a demand for specialist skills in this area from traditional healthcare practices.

The proliferation of NHS Trusts has increased the potential work for solicitors within the health sector, and the number of firms with relevant expertise is increasing to meet this demand.

LONDON

Of the firms well known for their healthcare practices, *Beachcroft Stanleys* has a strong health law group offering a comprehensive service. The group embraces some 45 lawyers and other professionals managed by nine partners, and most of their time is spent on health care related matters for NHS clients. The experienced team provides legal services

LEADING FIRMS – LONDON

BEACHCROFT STANLEYS	**CAPSTICKS**
LE BRASSEUR J TICKLE	

to some 90 health service bodies including Trusts, Regional Health Authorities, District Health Authorities and Family Health Service Authorities. The firm recently won one of the two contracts to act for Guy's and St. Thomas's NHS Trust. Gay Wilder, a partner at the firm, has been highly recommended for this area of work, particularly with regard to issues concerning patient care.

HIGHLY REGARDED – LONDON

BERRYMANS	**HEMPSONS**
NABARRO NATHANSON	
BIRD & BIRD	**CLYDE & CO**
DAVIES ARNOLD COOPER	**MACFARLANES**
McKENNA & CO	**PINSENT CURTIS**
CHURCH ADAMS TATHAM	

Capsticks, where Brian Capstick has been highly recommended, also has an excellent reputation for healthcare work, acting for the NHS, and has four doctors within the team. The firm offers a high quality of work across the spectrum and has been acting for regional and district health

authorities since the 1970's. Brian Capstick is particularly well known for his work in relation to judicial reviews of health service powers and allocation of health service resources.

Le Brasseur J Tickle also has an established reputation for its expertise in health care law. With ten partners, the firm handles clinical and dental negligence, criminal and regulatory law, class actions, risk management, mental health and community care law, administrative law and NHS estates. Stephen Janisch at the firm has been particularly recommended for his expertise.

LEADING INDIVIDUALS – LONDON

Brian Capstick	*Capsticks*
Gay E. Wilder	*Beachcroft Stanleys*
Cheryl Blundell	*Berrymans*
Stephen Janisch	*Le Brasseur J Tickle*
N. Paul Ridout	*Nabarro Nathanson*

Nabarro Nathanson's Health and Community Care department, which is headed by Paul Ridout, has rapidly demonstrated an ability to provide a full range of services to healthcare clients. In addition to expertise in traditional fields of medical negligence, employment and personal injury, the firm has a growing reputation in regulation, operation, acquisition and funding of private health care facilities, hospitals and nursing homes. Among its clients are health authorities in East Sussex, East and West Kent and Stockport, and among providers, Takare PLC, Care UK PLC and Court Cavendish Group PLC. The team also advises on private finance schemes for the development of public hospitals.

Hempsons has long been renowned for its expertise in the field of medical and healthcare law, advising a range of healthcare organisations on all aspects of law and ethics, mental health and community care law, administrative and NHS regulatory law.

Berrymans medical law service is co-ordinated by Cheryl Blundell and consists of a strong team specialising in the field. Major clients for the team include a number of London and provincial NHS trusts and private hospitals. The group has recently been involved in producing a risk management guide for NHS trusts.

Other notable practices which offer a complete range of advice to NHS trusts include *Clyde & Co, Bird & Bird, McKenna & Co, Davies Arnold Cooper, Pinsent Curtis, Macfarlanes* and *Church Adams Tatham & Co. Macfarlanes'* workload has included in particular, advising a number of clients on PFI. Particular transactions which the team has been involved include the development of a patient hotel at Aintree, the reprovision of medical facilities with private sector funding and the development of hospitals for private patients.

SOUTH EAST

Wansbroughs Willey Hargrave has opened a new office in Winchester where Tim Wright heads the health sector team. The group acts for over 30 NHS Trusts, regional health authorities and related organisations in the South East.

LEADING FIRMS – SOUTH EAST

WANSBROUGHS WILLEY HARGRAVE

The firm's caseload ranges from medical negligence and general health service law to employment, commercial, IT and property law advice. The team recently acted in a prominent case involving a persistent vegetative state patient and obtained an order to withdraw feeding.

HIGHLY REGARDED – SOUTH EAST

CHURCH ADAMS TATHAM *Reigate*		CLARKS *Reading*
CLYDE & CO *Guildford*		

Clyde & Co's office at Guildford offers the complete range of advice to NHS trusts and has a strong specialist team comprising of four full time healthcare lawyers. *Clarks* are also well known in the area and have acted for health bodies for over 30 years. The firm's clients include health authorities and trusts spread over a wide geographical area. The services the firm offers include establishing NHS trusts, and handling employment issues, property transactions and various medico legal problems. The firm also takes an active role in litigation and training for the NHS. At *Church Adams Tatham & Co*, the Reigate office works alongside the London office in providing health care legal advice.

LEADING INDIVIDUALS – SOUTH EAST

Tim L. Wright *Wansbroughs Willey Hargrave*

SOUTH WEST & WALES

Bevan Ashford is regarded as one of the leading firms in this area, and has a considerable depth of experience in acting for health authorities in a broad range of issues. Advice to health authorities has been a major specialism of the firm and it has developed one of the largest teams of health lawyers in the country. They recently won one of the two contracts to act

LEADING FIRMS – SOUTH WEST & WALES

BEVAN ASHFORD *Bristol*

for Guy's and St. Thomas's NHS Trust. Work handled includes contracts for hospital services, income generation, health authority transfer assets, surplus land disposals, medical negligence, hospital building disputes and risk management services. The firm is increasingly involved in advice to health authorities on donated assets, trustees' responsibilities and charitable funds generally. Jill Broadhead and Paul Barber at the firm are particularly well regarded in the field.

HIGHLY REGARDED – SOUTH WEST & WALES

MORGAN BRUCE *Cardiff*	OSBORNE CLARKE *Bristol*

In all the tables the names in each group are listed alphabetically.

Osborne Clarke, also has a strong reputation in this field, and has acted for many years for health authorities in relation to medical claims, inquests, property, employment and commercial work, as well as in relation to medical ethical problems.

In Wales, *Morgan Bruce* has built up a strong reputation in this field. It has advised health authorities, inter alia, on their powers to fund and participate in multi-million pound 'community-care' projects, and on the procedures to be followed in connection with the closure of hospitals.

LEADING INDIVIDUALS – SOUTH WEST & WALES

P.H. Barber *Bevan Ashford*
Jill Broadhead *Bevan Ashford*

EAST ANGLIA

Mills & Reeve is nationally known for its specialist expertise in this field and acts for 43 NHS Trusts and Health Authorities across the UK. It handles the majority of NHS work in East Anglia. The firm advises purchasers and providers of health care including NHS Trusts, family health service authorities and GP practices. The team has tremendous

LEADING FIRMS – EAST ANGLIA

MILLS & REEVE *Norwich*

strength in all aspects of healthcare, in particular, medical negligence, mental health, employment, property management and environmental issues, capital projects and management issues. Stephen King and Howard Weston at the firm are renowned for their expertise in healthcare law.

LEADING INDIVIDUALS – EAST ANGLIA

Stephen King *Mills & Reeve*
Howard W. Weston *Mills & Reeve*

NORTH

Hempsons, in the North West is particularly strong in this field, whilst in the North East *Wansbroughs Willey Hargrave* which recently merged with *Oxley & Coward's* Sheffield office has considerable expertise. The large team, incorporating five partners, acts for around 55 health service organisations including NHS Trusts, Health Authorities and FHSA's. The team acted in the 'Beverley Allitt affair',

HIGHLY REGARDED – NORTH

HEMPSONS *Manchester*	PINSENT CURTIS *Leeds*	
SMITH & GRAHAM *Hartlepool*	WANSBROUGHS WILLEY HARGRAVE *Leeds*	
WILKINSON MAUGHAN *Newcastle-upon-Tyne*		
BLACKHURST PARKER & YATES *Preston*	DAVIES ARNOLD COOPER *Manchester*	
DICKINSON DEES *Newcastle upon Tyne*		

advising the hospital, district and regional Health Authorities and is currently handling post traumatic stress claims from families of the victims. Diane Hallatt, a partner at the firm, has been particularly highly recommended for her expertise in the field. *Wilkinson Maughan,* where Ronald Bradbeer is well regarded, is another North Eastern firm with an established reputation for healthcare work. It acts for a significant number of NHS trusts both in its own region and in London.

Smith & Graham also has a strong healthcare practice, acting for a number of NHS trusts, predominantly North East based and also an NHS Trust in Kent. Most of the firm's partners are involved on a regular basis with health service clients advising on a whole host of matters, including vesting of assets, joint venture projects, IP, risk management as well as employment law, general litigation and medical negligence. The firm also holds seminars on health related topics throughout the country.

LEADING INDIVIDUALS – NORTH

Ronald B. Bradbeer	*Wilkinson Maughan*
Diane Hallatt	*Wansbroughs Willey Hargrave*

The large department at *Pinsent Curtis* handles all aspects of healthcare, acting for over 20 NHS Trusts and health authorities. The team has particular expertise in PFI, and is at present dealing with PFI projects to the value of £250 million. The team was also involved in the first major 'externalisation' for a regional health authority.

Other recommended firms include *Blackhurst Parker & Yates, Davies Arnold Cooper* and *Dickinson Dees.*

MENTAL HEALTH

Many of the firms highlighted for healthcare also undertake mental health work, most notably *Mills & Reeve* in East Anglia and *Hempsons* in their London and North West offices. Also strong in London for mental health work are *Capsticks and Le Brasseur J Tickle.*Other firms with notable practioners in the area of mental health law are listed seperately below.

LEADING INDIVIDUALS – LONDON – MENTAL HEALTH

Lucy Scott-Moncrieff	*Scott-Moncrieff, Harbour & Sinclair*

LEADING INDIVIDUALS – SOUTH WEST & WALES – MENTAL HEALTH

Alun B. Cole	*Morgan Bruce*
Neil P. Confrey	*Confreys*
Graham J. Miles	*Morgan Bruce*

LEADING INDIVIDUALS – NORTH – MENTAL HEALTH

Timothy F. Durkin	*Myer Wolff & Manley*
Peter Charles Edwards	*Peter Edwards & Co*

LEADERS IN HEALTH CARE

LONDON

Blundell, Cheryl
Berrymans, London (0171) 638 2811.

Specialisation: Partner in charge of Medical Law Services at Berrymans, where she practices in health related matters acting for NHS Trusts, Royal Colleges and Insurers of Private Hospitals. Her work encompasses: Medical Negligence, Employers' Public and Product Liability together with Risk and Claims Management advice.

Career: Graduated from Exeter University in 1982 and was admitted as a solicitor in 1985.

Prof. Membership: Is a member of the Institute of Risk Management and its Health Sector Special Interest Group.

Capstick, Brian
Capsticks, London (0181) 780 2211. Partner 1980. Senior Partner. Specialises in hospital and health service law, representing health authorities and trusts and is the author of numerous publications in this field.

Janisch, Stephen
Le Brasseur J Tickle, London (0171) 836 0099.

Ridout, N. Paul
Nabarro Nathanson, London (0171) 493 9933. Partner. Head of Health and Community Care Department. Specialises in corporate advice to NHS Trusts and health authorities and to businesses active in the health sector. Particular emphasis on commercial and regulatory matters. Born 1948.

Scott-Moncrieff, Lucy
Scott-Moncrieff, Harbour & Sinclair, London (0171) 242 4114. Qualified 1978. Partner 1992. Mental health law specialist, representing patients who apply for Mental Health Review Tribunals and on judicial reviews against MHRTS, local authorities and the Home Secretary.

Wilder, Gay E.
Beachcroft Stanleys, London (0171) 242 1011. Qualified 1982. Partner 1989. Health Law Department. Principal area of practice is medical negligence, handling claims for health service bodies.

REGIONS

Bacon, Paul
Bryan & Armstrong, Mansfield (01623) 24505. Qualified 1974. Senior Partner 1980. Criminal Department. Specialises in mental health law. Also deals with criminal work, representing defendants, especially those with a mental disorder. Born 13.6.1948.

Barber, P.H.
Bevan Ashford, Bristol (0117) 923 0111.

Bradbeer, Ronald B.
Wilkinson Maughan, Newcastle-upon-Tyne (0191) 261 1841. Managing Partner and Senior Litigation Partner.

Specialisation: Principal area of practice is medical negligence. Has been principal legal advisor to area health authorities and trusts for many years and has specialised in medical negligence for over 25 years. Also handles commercial disputes specialising in commercial contracts, industrial tribunal cases and construction matters.

Prof. Membership: Accredited Mediator with Centre for Dispute Resolution, Law Society.

Career: Joined *Wilkinson Maughan* in 1960. Qualified in 1963. Became a Partner in 1967 and Managing Partner in 1993.

Broadhead, Jill
See under Medical Negligence.

Burdett, David M.
Browne Jacobson, Nottingham (0115) 950 0055. Qualified 1972. Partner 1976. Main area of practice is Mental Health Law. Law Society Panel Member since its inception and Tribunal representative since 1978 at special and local hospitals. Born 3.9.1946.

Cole, Alun B.
See under Administrative & Public Law.

Confrey, Neil P.
Confreys, Cardiff (01222) 458080. Sole Practitioner. Fax (01222) 497080.

Specialisation: Main area of practice is mental health law. Law Society Panel Member since 1985 for tribunal representation. Specialist sole practitioner since 1993. Law Society interviewer for panel membership. Also handles social security law: has advised and represented claimants since commencing articles in 1983. Presents training on all aspects of the Mental Health Act for solicitors, volunteer advisers, health authority medical, nursing and administrative staff and social workers.

Prof. Membership: Law Society MHRT Panel, Mind Legal Network, Volunteer Legal Adviser for Saneline and NSF.

Career: Qualified in 1985. Lay Member of local Social Security Appeal Tribunal 1985-88. Appointed part time Chair of Special Educational Needs Tribunal in 1994.

Personal: Born 6th January 1958. Holds Degree in Law from LSE, 1981. Diplomas in Discrimination Law and Civil Liberties Law from Bristol University, 1990 and 1991. Works from home.

Durkin, Timothy F.
Myer Wolff & Manley, Hull (01482) 223693.

Edwards, Peter Charles
Peter Edwards & Co, Hoylake (0151)632 6699. Qualified 1975. Specialist Mental Health Review Tribunal Practice. For 23 years has represented patients detained under the Mental Health Act 1983 wishing to appeal against their sections.

Hallatt, Diane
See under Medical Negligence.

Keen, Andrew
Anthony Collins, Birmingham (0121) 200 3242. Qualified 1988. Specialist in Mental Health law. Advises on all aspects of Mental Health Act and Care in the Community legislation. Born 26.5.1964.

King, Stephen
Mills & Reeve, Norwich +44 (0) 1603 660155. Partner in Health Care Team.

Specialisation: Specialises in professional negligence, including medical negligence. Acts for NHS Trusts, Health Commissions and Authorities, advising on claims made against them for damages and on insurance arrangements for non-clinical negligence cover. Also covers mental health law, coroners inquests, drug trials, and acts as client partner for all health care clients. Acted in the first self-funded structured settlement in East Anglia financing the payment of substantial damages in a brain damage case. Regular lecturer to hospitals on health care law, negligence, risk management and awareness and claims management.

Lloyd, Jon
Young & Lee, Birmingham (0121) 772 5012. Qualified 1976. Partner 1984. Main areas of practice are mental health and disability law, Mental Health Review Tribunals, Court of Protection, Wills & EPA's. Born 25.10.1951.

Miles, Graham J.
See under Medical Negligence.

Miller, Stephen
Harper Macleod, Glasgow (0141) 221 8888. Qualified 1990. Partner 1994. Litigation Department. Main area of practice is employment, both applicant and respondent. Also handles mental health work. Born 5.1.1965.

Ward, Adrian
Turnbull & Ward, Glasgow (0141) 881 2357.

Weston, Howard W.
See under Medical Negligence.

Wright, Tim L.
See under Medical Negligence.

EDITORIAL POLICY

Our policy is to identify leading practitioners entirely on merit. It is not possible to buy a place in our biographical lists: inclusion is based on a practitioner's expertise and professional reputation. The same applies to the lists of recommended law-firms and sets of chambers.

Enormous effort has been invested by our ten-strong research team (mainly solicitors and barristers) in canvassing recommendations and identifying leaders. We are confident in the overall accuracy of the results. However, mistakes and omissions are inevitable, and if readers have any suggestions regarding listings or rankings we should be very pleased to hear from them.

The lists will be revised on the basis of fresh research every year.

HOUSING ASSOCIATIONS

LONDON

The pre-eminent firms that emerge in this area include *Trowers & Hamlins, Devonshires, Winckworth & Pemberton, Prince Evans, Manches & Co* and *Lewis Silkin.*

Trowers & Hamlins, has a national reputation, acting for some 220 associations throughout the country, including the Housing Corporation and Chartered Institute of Housing. The team, comprising 13 specialist partners has particular expertise in advising clients involved in Large Scale Voluntary Transfer (LSVT). It has advised 23 out of the 31 LSVT successfully completed at the end of May 1994. The firm is also active in housing finance, and has advised on all types of private finance, from stock issues to securitisation of housing association rents. The team has also been involved in Private Finance Initative (PFI). Leading practitioners at the firm who have been particularly recommended to us are Ian Graham, Ian Doolittle, Jonathan Adlington, Jennifer Gubbins and Rosemary Hart.

LEADING FIRMS – LONDON

DEVONSHIRES	LEWIS SILKIN
MANCHES & CO	PRINCE EVANS
TROWERS & HAMLINS	WINCKWORTH & PEMBERTON

The niche practice *Devonshires* act for over 80 registered housing associations nationwide, including the London & Quadrant Housing Trust Circle and New Islington and Hackney, East London and Thames Valley housing associations. The strong team, including ten partners, advises on consortium developments, stock transfers, shared ownership and other property matters.The firm also has strength in relation to housing association finance and acts for a number of funders including TSB Bank plc and Hambros Bank Ltd. The team also act for a group of hous- ing associations in relation to finance matters.

*Winckworth & Pemberton,*where Andrew Murray and Keith Jenkins have excellent reputations, acts for a large number of housing associations. Andrew Murray is particularly well known for project finance and project development work.

Also highly regarded are Louis Robert and Trevor Morley at *Prince Evans.*Work undertaken in the department includes construction, development and planning advice, financing new initatives and buying, selling and management of property.

HIGHLY REGARDED – LONDON

ALLEN & OVERY	ASHURST MORRIS CRISP
DAWSON & CO	EDWIN COE
EVANS BUTLER WADE	FLADGATE FIELDER
HODGE JONES & ALLEN	LAWRENCE GRAHAM
STONES PORTER	
BINDMAN & PARTNERS	CAMPBELL HOOPER
G.L. HOCKFIELD & CO	PENNINGTONS
RODGERS & BURTON	

Lewis Silkin acts for some 60 housing associations. The team, headed by Gillian Bastow, has five specialist partners and has been involved in private funding schemes. *Manches & Co,* where Richard Frost has an established reputation, is active in housing association law and practice and is a member of the Housing Corporation panel of solicitors.

SOUTH EAST

Coffin Mew & Clover has particular strength in housing associations and currently acts for more than 20 active housing association clients. The firm is by far the largest specialist in the region and has three specialist partners in the department. The team has advised one of the members of a consortium in the first securitisation issue for UK housing associations with Nomura Bank. The team also has considerable experience in housing association development and funding.

LEADING FIRMS – SOUTH EAST

COFFIN MEW & CLOVER Portsmouth	CRIPPS HARRIES HALL Tunbridge Wells

Cripps Harries Hall undertakes substantial housing association work in the South East, including development projects, financing, tenancy and contracts. The team, incorporating two specialist partners, acts for a housing association which took over a District Council's housing stock. It has also been involved in the refinancing of a housing association in which £72 million was raised.

Other notable practices in the region are *Penningtons, Sherrards, Owen White, Whiskers* and *Marsons Solicitors.*

LEADING INDIVIDUALS – LONDON

Jonathan P.N. Adlington *Trowers & Hamlins*	Ian Doolittle *Trowers & Hamlins*	Ian D. Graham *Trowers & Hamlins*
Jennifer M. Gubbins *Trowers & Hamlins*	Louis Robert *Prince Evans*	
Gillian Bastow *Lewis Silkin*	Richard Frost *Manches & Co*	Rosemary D. Hart *Trowers & Hamlins*
Allan James Hudson *Devonshires*	Keith Jenkins *Winckworth & Pemberton*	Charles J.E. Leach *Ashurst Morris Crisp*
Trevor E. Morley *Prince Evans*	Andrew J. Murray *Winckworth & Pemberton*	Charles Pigott *Hodge Jones & Allen*
Simon Randall C.B.E. *Lawrence Graham*	Julian Roberts *Devonshires*	Duncan A. Salmon *Campbell Hooper*
Chris Smith *Stones Porter*	Andrew Thomas *Lewis Silkin*	

In all the tables the names in each group are listed alphabetically.

SOUTH WEST & WALES

Among the practices which handle this specialist type of work, *Hugh James Jones & Jenkins* emerge as one of the most active housing association firms in the region. The strong team with five specialist partners acts for over 20 housing associations, and has considerable expertise in collateral warranties, building contracts, land acquisition, development agreements, performance and other bonding arrangements as well as arbitration and building litigation.

In Exeter, *Cann & Hallett* has a recognised capabilty in the field, acting for housing associations covering the whole of the South West area ranging from Hampshire to Cornwall. *Bevan Ashford* and *Burges Salmon* also have established reputations for their housing association practices.

MIDLANDS

Anthony Collins offers a comprehensive service for housing associations, with particular expertise in joint ventures with local authorities, management funding arrangements

and conveyancing. Clients of the firm include Bromford Carinthia Housing Association Ltd, Focus Housing Association Ltd and Trident Housing Ltd. Martin Knox has been recommended for his expertise.

Rigbeys also handle all aspects of housing association work, including Large Scale Voluntary Transfers. They act for numerous housing associations including Sanctuary Housing Association Ltd.

, Of the other firms recommended in the region, *Gateley Wareing* has had a particularly long involvement in the field.

NORTH

The London-based *Trowers & Hamlins* is recognised as a leading firm nationally and their housing association expertise is available in the Manchester Office. Graham Turner who heads the Manchester team, has particular expertise in the transfer of New Town stock.

Brabner Holden Banks Wilson also has an excellent reputation. With five specialist partners, they act for numerous housing associations in the North including Merseyside Improved Houses, Liverpool Housing Trust Ltd and Merseyside Housing Association. Over the last twelve months, the team has had substanial involvment in the Private Finance Initative.

Croftons act for several major housing associations including Northern Counties Housing Association and Manchester and District Housing Association. The team, headed by Richard Clarke, consists of three partners and one assistant solicitor. It has handled empty property initiatives, various new building schemes, mortgage financing and general property acquisitions and disposals.

Michael Gaskell who has 12 years' experience working for housing associations, has recently joined Manchester firm *Slater Heelis*. The firm has established expertise in a number of key areas, which enables the firm to offer the full range of skills to clients involved in social housing.

Michael Rhatigan, who has built a strong reputation in the region for housing association work, has joined *Eversheds* in Manchester, developing this side of the firm's practice.

Of the other firms in the North which have been recommended for this area of work, *Walker Charlesworth & Foster* has a well regarded team, acting for many local housing associations and some national ones.

NORTHERN IRELAND

Wilson Nesbitt act for the largest housing association in the province, and offer particular expertise in housing stock transfers.

HIGHLY REGARDED – NORTHERN IRELAND
WILSON NESBITT *Belfast*

SCOTLAND

There are several firms in Scotland which have long-standing connections with housing associations, offering advice on property transactions, constitutions, investment

HIGHLY REGARDED – SCOTLAND	
ALAN J. BAILLIE *Dundee*	**ANDERSON FYFE** *Glasgow*
BAIRD & CO *Kirkcaldy*	**BRECHIN ROBB** *Glasgow*
W & J BURNESS WS *Edinburgh*	**SHEPHERD & WEDDERBURN** *Edinburgh*
MACLEOD & MACCALLUM *Inverness*	**T.C. YOUNG & SON** *Glasgow*

powers, financing and contractual arrangements with Scottish Homes. Of the firms recommended, *Brechin Robb* acts for 28 housing associations, and has particular expertise in Large Scale Voluntary Transfers, whilst *W & J Burness WS,* where Paul Pia is well regarded, advise the Scottish Federation of Housing Associations. *Anderson Fyfe* also has a recognised capability in the field, and acts for 13 Scottish Housing Associations.

Shepherd & Wedderburn WS advise on all aspects, including large scale voluntary transfers, and Kareen Moffat has been recommended. Also well known in this field are Kenneth Swinton at *Alan J. Baillie* and Charles Milne at *Baird & Co* who has particular expertise in property acquisition and shared ownership.

LEADING INDIVIDUALS – SCOTLAND
Charles M. Milne *Baird & Co*
Kareen E. Moffat *Shepherd & Wedderburn*
Paul D. Pia *W & J Burness WS*
Kenneth W. Swinton *Alan J. Baillie*

LEADERS IN HOUSING ASSOCIATIONS

LONDON

Adlington, Jonathan P.N.
Trowers & Hamlins, London (0171) 831 6292. Partner in Property Department.

Specialisation: Principal area of practice is housing law, acting for Housing Associations on all aspects of their affairs including acquisition, development and letting of property, structures and the raising of finance. Other main area of work covers all aspects of commercial property including planning, acquisition, development and funding. Lectures frequently for Institute of Bankers, Council of Mortgage Lenders, Institute of Housing, National Federation of Housing Associations and commercial bodies.

Bastow, Gillian
Lewis Silkin, London (0171) 227 8000. Qualified 1981. Partner 1984. Property Department. Experience includes funding and development.

Doolittle, Ian
See under Local Government.

Frost, Richard
Manches & Co, London (0171) 404 4433. Qualified 1970. Partner 1971. Head of Housing Association Group.

Graham, Ian D.
Trowers & Hamlins, London (0171) 831 6292. Partner in Housing Association Department.

Specialisation: Main area of practice is housing association work, including group structures, powers, consortium development, assured and secure tenancies, management contracts with local authorities, large scale voluntary transfers, joint ventures to provide student/ nurses accomodation, shared ownership, care in the community schemes and partnership schemes with local authorities. Also deals with NHS work, including joint ventures with housing associations, care in the community, grant agreements and purchase contracts. Author of articles on many of the above issues and an experienced speaker.

Gubbins, Jennifer M.
Trowers & Hamlins, London (0171) 831 6292. Partner in Company and Commercial Department.

Specialisation: One of the firm's leading practitioners in corporate finance law, including stock/bond issues, loans and the acquisitions/transfer of companies and undertakings with particular reference to public sector areas including housing associations and universities. Has acted in significant and innovative capital market transactions including the first securitisation of housing association rent. On the editorial board of *Charity Law & Practice Review* and has written for a wide range of publications including *The Journal of Property Finance*, *Local Government News* and *The Daily Telegraph*. Has spoken for IBC seminars, the Chartered Institute of Housing and the National Federation of Housing Associations, and is a member of the CBI Company Law Panel, CBI Commercial Law Panel, Institute of Investment Management and Research Panel on Earnings Per Share.

Hart, Rosemary D.
Trowers & Hamlins, London (0171) 831 6292. Partner in Housing Section.

Specialisation: Works almost exclusively for housing associations covering all aspects including land acquisition, security aspects of development involving public and private finance, consortium developments, volume build, package deals, deferred purchase arrangements and nomination agreements. On the disposals side involved in drafting documentation for all types of letting, including shared ownership, leasehold schemes for the elderly, assured tenancies and shared equity schemes with leases or mortgages. Acts for associations in leaseback schemes, private sector leasing schemes and housing associations as managing agents with a number of London Boroughs involving management agreements, guarantees and other types of schemes dealing with homelessness; also care in the community schemes. Regular author and speaker.

Hudson, Allan James
Devonshires, London (0171) 628 7576. Partner in Housing Association Development and Finance Department.

Specialisation: Principal area of practice is housing association development and private finance. Deals with complex consortium developments of sites and provision of private finance to housing associations. Also patient hotels. Practice also covers commercial property work, including acquisition, disposal and management of investment property. Has done pioneering work on patient hotels in Glasgow, Liverpool and Nottingham. Handled the development of a site at Isledon

Road in the London Borough of Islington and the German Hospital site in the London Borough of Hackney. Clients include Circle Thirty Three Housing Trust Ltd, New Islington & Hackney Housing Association, Scandinavian Patient Hotels Ltd, London Borough of Camden, East London Housing Association Ltd, Windsor Life Assurance Company Ltd and Langbourn Property Services Ltd (part of Kleinwort Benson). Charge-out rate is £150 per hour.

Career: Qualified in 1978. At *Penningtons* 1978-81, *Nabarro Nathanson* 1981-82 and *Knapp Fishers* 1982-84. Joined *Devonshires* in 1984 and became a Partner in 1985.

Personal: Born 7th July 1954. Educated at Poole Grammar School and Durham University (BA 1st Class Hons). Leisure interests include theatre, cinema and gardening. Lives in Godalming.

Jenkins, Keith
Winckworth & Pemberton (incorporating Sherwood & Co), London (0171) 593 5000. Partner in Housing and Local Government Department.

Specialisation: Closely involved with the Housing Association movement for about twenty years, he specialises in Housing, Co-ops and local authorities. He has made a significant contribution to the growth and development of social housing. He is regarded as one of the most imaginative achievers in this sector.

Prof. Membership: NFHA Lawyers Sub-Group.

Career: Qualified in 1974. Joined Winckworth & Pemberton in 1972, becoming a partner in 1977. He is the firm's Managing and Finance Partner.

Personal: Born 10th May 1949. Read law at Lincoln College, Oxford. Leisure interests include reading, rock music and motorcycles. Lives in London.

Leach, Charles J.E.
Ashurst Morris Crisp, London (0171) 638 1111. Qualified 1978. Partner 1989. Handles housing transfers, development and public sector.

Morley, Trevor E.
Prince Evans, London (0181) 567 3477. Partner in Housing and Public Sector Department.

Specialisation: Experienced in all aspects of housing association finance, including banking facilities and capital markets issues, with particular emphasis on shared ownership finance. Also undertakes LCHO work, including acquisitions, development, consortium arrangements, long and short term funding, disposals and vires issues. He is a committee member of Network Housing Association, and has lectured extensively on housing related topics.

Personal: Born 28th December, 1953. Lives in Cobham.

Murray, Andrew J.
Winckworth & Pemberton (incorporating Sherwood & Co), London (0171) 593 5000. Partner in Housing and Local Government Department.

Specialisation: Main area of practice is housing association law, with particular expertise in project finance and project development. Addresses various seminars organised by professional bodies and clients.

Prof. Membership: Law Society.

Career: Qualified in 1987. Joined *Winckworth & Pemberton* in 1988, becoming a Partner in 1989.

Personal: Attended Manchester University 1978-81 (English Language and Literature). Lives in Richmond, Surrey.

Pigott, Charles
Hodge Jones & Allen, London (0171) 482 1974. Qualified 1984. Partner 1991. Acts for individuals in possession, disrepair and homelessness matters.

Randall C.B.E., Simon
Lawrence Graham, London (0171) 379 0000. Partner, Head of Local and Public Authority Unit.

Specialisation: Principal area of practice is public sector work advising local authorities on externalisation, charitable trusts, local government re-organisation, housing action trusts, Housing Association and Health Service work and compulsory competitive tendering. Involved in large scale voluntary transfers of housing stock to Housing Associations. Advised William Waldegrave, Housing Minister, on implementation of Housing Act 1988, and subsequently, Michael Howard. Non-executive Director (and currently Vice-Chairman) Bethlem Royal and Maudsley Special Health Authority since 1971. Member London Drug Policy Forum. Member of Editorial Board of Roof magazine. Author of many articles and pamphlets on local government and social issues ranging from the private rented sector, privatisation and large scale voluntary sector to drug abuse among young people. Organised many seminars on health service, housing and local government related matters on behalf of the Association of District Councils, the London Boroughs Association and CIPFA.

Prof. Membership: Law Society, Chairman London Boroughs' Association Housing and Social Services Committee, Chairman London Area Mobility Scheme and Homes Across London, Single Homeless in London Working Party, Housing Consultative Council, London Committee for Accessible Transport, Social Housing Association Ltd.

Career: Articled with *Lawrence Graham* and became a Partner in 1970. Chairman London Borough of Bromley Housing Committee 1971-76 and Leader of the Council 1976-81. Member Greater London Council 1981-86.

Personal: Born 1944. Attended Bickley Hall

Preparatory School, Westminster School and the College of Law, Lancaster Gate. Appointed CBE in June 1991 for Housing Work in London. Chairman Kelsey Housing Association Ltd and Director Kelsey Care Ltd: recently formed to provide sheltered and supported housing for those with learning disabilities and the mentally ill. Member of Management Committee of Broomleigh Housing Association Ltd. Leisure pursuits include the Cotswolds, collecting English postal history, antiquarian books and Masons Ironstone pottery. Lives in Sevenoaks.

Robert, Louis
Prince Evans, London (0181) 567 3477. Senior Partner in Housing and Public Sector Department.

Specialisation: Principal area of practice is new initiatives and joint ventures in housing. Also handles housing association corporate matters and funding. Acted in the redevelopment of the Blackbird Leys Estate, Oxford, Hackney initiative, DOE recycling of HAG element of non local authority plans and PPG 3 Section 106 Agreements (producing non set-aside receipts for local authorities to facilitate redevelopment). Has written articles on a variety of housing issues and lectured extensively on a range of housing related topics. Member of the NFHA Legal Working Party.

Career: Qualified in 1969. Became a Partner at *Prince Evans* in 1972. Now Senior Partner.

Personal: Born 23rd July 1943. Lives in Ealing, London.

Roberts, Julian
Devonshires, London (0171) 628 7576. Partner in Conveyancing and Constitutional Department.

Specialisation: Principal area of practice is Housing Association work. Extensive experience of all aspects of Housing Association transactions. Lectures to Secretaries of Housing Associations.

Prof. Membership: Law Society.

Career: Qualified 1965 while with *Devonshires* and became a Partner in 1968.

Personal: Born 25th March 1941. Attended Trinity Hall, Cambridge 1960-63. Leisure pursuits include fishing. Lives in London.

Salmon, Duncan A.
Campbell Hooper, London (0171) 222 9070. Partner in Construction and Litigation Department.

Specialisation: Has extensive experience in residential and commercial construction contracts, housing association developments, professional appointments, joint venture documentation, warranties, lending agreements, and contentious construction matters. Advises major developers, housing associations, contractors, banks, national charities and professional firms.

Prof. Membership: Law Society.

Career: Qualified in 1981, having joined *Campbell Hooper* in 1979. Became a Partner in 1984.

Personal: Born 12th October 1956. Attended Exeter University. Commodore Law Society Yacht Club. Leisure interests include sailing and skiing. Lives in Belsize Park, London.

Smith, Chris

Stones Porter, London (0171) 248 9991. Partner in Housing Association Department.

Specialisation: Principal area of practice covers all aspects of Housing Association work with particular expertise in employment law, constitutional work and Care in the Community. Other main area of practice is development work including consortium arrangements. Acted on consortium arrangements for Blackbird Leys development in Oxford.

Career: Qualified in 1978. Became a Partner with *Asshetons* in 1980 and in the merged firm of *Manches & Co.*, then joined *Stones Porter* as a Partner in 1993.

Personal: Born 22 October 1953. Attended University College, Cardiff 1972-75. Leisure pursuits include golf and squash. Lives in Godalming.

Thomas, Andrew

Lewis Silkin, London (0171) 227 8000. Qualified 1974. Partner 1976. Property Department. All aspects of Housing Association matters.

REGIONS

Clarke, R.J.A.

Croftons, Manchester (0161) 834 4391. Qualified 1976. Partner 1979. Property/Housing Association Department. Wide experience in housing association work including acquisition, development and funding.

Gaskell, Michael

Slater Heelis, Manchester 017172 882244. Partner specialising in housing and property law with a particular emphasis on housing association related work. Born 31.5.1956.

Holden, Lawrence

See under Charities.

Knox, Martin

Anthony Collins, Birmingham (0121) 200 3242. Qualified 1980. Partner 1989. Head of Housing and Local Government Department. Main areas of practice are housing association work, and local government law. Born in 1956.

Milne, Charles M.

Baird & Co, Cupar (01334) 656644. Partner in Cupar office.

Specialisation: Principal area of practice is housing law, housing association work, conveyancing and commercial leasing. Acted in cases relating to damages for injury caused by dampness in dwellings. Also handles employment law and some criminal and matrimonial work. Recently co-ordinated major housing association refinancing project.
Born 23.7.1954.

Moffat, Kareen E.

Shepherd & Wedderburn WS, Edinburgh (0131) 228 9900. Qualified 1984. Partner 1989. Commercial Property Department. Also involved in health care and Care in the Community projects.

Pia, Paul D.

W & J Burness WS, Edinburgh (0131) 226 2561. Qualified 1971. Partner 1974. Corporate Department. Main area of practice is business formations.

Rhatigan, Michael

Eversheds, Manchester (0161) 832 6666. Qualified 1977. Partner in Commercial Property Department, specialising in Housing Association work and general commercial property.

Swinton, Kenneth W.

Alan J. Baillie, Dundee (01382) 202444.

Turner, Graham F.

Trowers & Hamlins, Manchester (0161) 833 9293. Partner 1976. Head of Manchester office. Housing law specialist. Born 28.1.1947.

IMMIGRATION & NATIONALITY

I MMIGRATION law can be divided into two categories according to the type of work that firms specialise in. We have defined the first category as Nationality, Family and Human Rights.

The second category has been termed 'Business Immigration'. This involves services to commercial bodies wishing to transfer employees and personnel internationally.

LONDON

NATIONALITY, FAMILY & HUMAN RIGHTS

The two leading firms in this field are *Jane Coker & Partners* and *Winstanley Burgess*.

LEADING FIRMS – LONDON	
	– PERSONAL IMMIGRATION
JANE COKER & PARTNERS	WINSTANLEY-BURGESS
BINDMAN & PARTNERS	B.M. BIRNBERG & CO
DEIGHTON GUEDALLA	

Jane Coker & Partners is a two partner law firm located in north London, handling all aspects of work including deportation, family reunion cases, asylum appeals, representation and judicial review. Jane Coker, the founding partner, enjoys an outstanding reputation for this type of work and has been involved in a number of cases including the Marchan case involving the deportation of EC nationals. Jawaid Luqmani of this firm is also well regarded. *Winstanley Burgess,* based in Islington with a strong legal aid base, has a particular expertise in refugee work and has acted in the important case of Re Sivakumaran, which was a European Court of Human Rights decision. Both David Burgess, who is the joint UK representative to the European Legal Network on Asylum, and Christopher Randall were highly recommended.

HIGHLY REGARDED – LONDON	
	– PERSONAL IMMIGRATION
TAYLOR NICHOL	WESLEY GRYK
WILSON & CO	
CHRISTIAN FISHER	
GOLDKORN DAVIES MATHIAS	MAURICE COHEN & CO

Other leading firms are *B.M.Birnberg & Co, Deighton Guedella* and *Bindman & Partners*. *B.M.Birnberg & Co,* based near London Bridge, undertake all aspects in this field of immigration law including political asylum cases, deportation and illegal entries. Nigel Leskin is well regarded for his immigration expertise, ably assisted by Fiona Lindsley. *Deighton Guedella* is a two partner firm concentrating on civil liberties litigation with an excellent reputation for asylum law. Vicky Guedella is well regarded and has a special emphasis on refugee issues including unaccompanied children. *Bindman & Partners'* expertise includes work permits, EC immigration law, comparative and international migra-

tion. Alison Stanley of this firm was highly recommended.

Other highly regarded firms in this field include *Taylor Nichol,* where Mark Ashford and Carolyn Taylor were recommended, *Wilson & Co, Christian Fisher* and *Wesley Gryk.*

LEADING INDIVIDUALS – LONDON	
	– PERSONAL IMMIGRATION
Jane Coker	*Jane Coker & Partners*
David C.W. Burgess	*Winstanley-Burgess*
Vicky Guedalla	*Deighton Guedella*
Christopher W. Randall	*Winstanley-Burgess*
Mark Ashford	*Taylor Nichol*
Louise Christian	*Christian Fisher*
Maurice Cohen	*Maurice Cohen & Co*
Wesley Gryk	*Wesley Gryk*
Nigel Leskin	*B.M. Birnberg & Co*
Fiona Lindsley	*B.M. Birnberg & Co*
Jawaid Luqmani	*Jane Coker & Partners*
Alison Stanley	*Bindman & Partners*
Carolyn S. Taylor	*Taylor Nichol*
UP AND COMING	
Trevor Wornham	*Wilson & Co*

BUSINESS IMMIGRATION

At the outset it should be stressed that a small number of firms, despite being listed under 'Business Immigration', also have a very good reputation for their immigration work in the non-business field. These firms are *Baileys Shaw & Gillett, Bates Wells & Braithwaite, Gherson & Co* and *Simons Muirhead Burton.*

LEADING FIRMS – LONDON	
	– BUSINESS IMMIGRATION
BAILEYS SHAW & GILLETT	CAMERON MARKBY HEWITT
NICHOLSON GRAHAM & JONES	SIMONS MUIRHEAD & BURTON
STURTIVANT & CO	
BATES, WELLS & BRAITHWAITE	GHERSON & CO

The leading firms for business immigration are *Cameron Markby Hewitt, Baileys Shaw & Gillett* and *Simons Muirhead & Burton. Cameron Markby Hewitt* advise principally on work permits, business applications, domestic employees, sole representatives, independent means and investor applications. The firm also has experience in handling investor applications for persons bringing £1 million plus to the UK. Julia Onslow-Cole heads the immigration and nationality group and has an excellent reputation in this field. She acts for a number of financial institutions and PLC companies in the UK.

Baileys Shaw & Gillett, has particular expertise in matters pertaining to the work permit scheme. It has strong international connections including an office in Abu Dhabi and has acted for both UK based clients operating overseas and foreign companies. Elspeth Guild is attached to the company/commercial department but specialises in immigration law. She is very highly regarded especially for her expertise in relation to the European Community.

Simons Muirhead & Burton handles all areas of immigration enjoying a strong reputation for its business immigration work. It has also undertaken preparation and representation before the immigration appellate authorities and applications for judicial review where necessary. Larry Grant is very well known in this field.

HIGHLY REGARDED – LONDON – BUSINESS IMMIGRATION	
BAKER & McKENZIE	MAGRATH & CO
NORTON ROSE	SIMMONS & SIMMONS
GULBENKIAN HARRIS ANDONIAN	LEWIS SILKIN
McKENNA & CO	STEPHENSON HARWOOD
WARNER CRANSTON	
ALSOP WILKINSON	CAMPBELL HOOPER
EVERSHEDS	EVERSHEDS
FLADGATE FIELDER	FOX WILLIAMS
HARBOTTLE & LEWIS	OSMOND GAUNT & ROSE
RADCLIFFES CROSSMAN BLOCK	

Other leading firms include *Sturtivant & Co* and *Nicholson Graham & Jones. Sturtivant & Co* is a small but highly specialised law firm undertaking immigration work primarily in the business context. The firm, founded in 1985, has dealt with matters relating to work permits, business residence and other residence categories. The principal of this firm is Karen Sturtivant who enjoys a very good reputation for her expertise in this field.

Nicholson Graham & Jones have experience in dealing with work permits, business and sole representative permits, applications for persons of independent means, and nationality. It also has experience of advising on matters relating to tax status in this context. Jackie Thompson heads the immigration department and has conducted seminars for such bodies as the Foreign Banks Association and the Commonwealth Banks Association.

Other firms with an excellent reputation in this field of work are *Baker & McKenzie, Bates Wells & Braithwaite, Gherson & Co, Magrath & Co, Norton Rose* and *Simmons & Simmons. Baker & McKenzie* handle employment related immigration law, including work permits and entry clearance for sole representatives, self-employed businessmen and investors. Samia Garrush was recommended for her experience in this field. *Bates Wells & Braithwaite* has experience of advising corporations and individuals on business immigrations including Home Office and Department of Employment practice concessions. Philip Trott is a partner in the immigration and employment department and a former chairman of the Immigration Law Practitioners Association. Peter Moss has experience of dealing with work

permits and applications for entry clearance for businessmen and overseas representatives.

Gherson & Co are a specialist immigration law firm established in 1988, handling all aspects of immigration law but dealing primarily with business immigration. The firm has dealt with executive relocation and the admission of entrepeneurs and investors. It has a number of foreign connections including connections with the Indian sub-continent. The firm also has a number of US and Japanese corporate clients. David Webb has extensive experience in this field and has acted for business people, investors, writers and artists. Roger Gherson is well known for his work in this field.

Magrath & Co have six practitioners acting in this field and enjoy a very good reputation. Christopher Magrath is a founding member and senior partner in the immigration and employment department. He is the author of 'Working in the United Kingdom – A Guide for Foreign Nationals'.

Norton Rose and *Simmons & Simmons,* have substantial expertise in business immigration. *Norton Rose* deals with its immigration work within its corporate services group and acts for a number of large financial institutions, hotels and catering and leisure industry clients. Helen Jorgensen has handled cases in this field for over fourteen years. *Simmons & Simmons* cover work permit applications, training and work experience permit applications and other applications allowing overseas nationals to work in Britain for British employers. The firm acts for a number of financial institutions and other corporate clients. Hilary Belchak who has over ten years' experience in this area, was recommended.

LEADING INDIVIDUALS – LONDON – BUSINESS IMMIGRATION	
Larry Grant	*Simons Muirhead & Burton*
Elspeth Guild	*Baileys Shaw & Gillett*
Julia Onslow-Cole	*Cameron Markby Hewitt*
Karen L. Sturtivant	*Sturtivant & Co*
Jackie Thompson	*Nicholson Graham & Jones*
Peter Alfandary	*Warner Cranston*
Bernard Andonian	*Gulbenkian Harris Andonian*
Hilary Belchak	*Simmons & Simmons*
Vanessa Cranswick	*Cameron Markby Hewitt*
Samia Garrush	*Baker & McKenzie*
Roger M. Gherson	*Gherson & Co*
Paul Gulbenkian	*Gulbenkian Harris Andonian*
Helen Michelle Jorgensen	*Norton Rose*
Lesley Kemp	*Magrath & Co*
Christopher Magrath	*Magrath & Co*
Peter Moss	*Bates, Wells & Braithwaite*
Caron Pope	*Cameron Markby Hewitt*
Tim Reed	*Sturtivant & Co*
Philip Trott	*Bates, Wells & Braithwaite*
David Webb	*Gherson & Co*
Peter Wyatt	*Gulbenkian Harris Andonian*

In all the tables the names in each group are listed alphabetically.

SOUTH EAST

Gordon Denson of *Woodford & Ackroyd* in Southampton, undertakes immigration work as an important part of his overall caseload. He has conducted a number of immigration appeals and has experience of handling asylum work. He has a particular expertise for immigration issues relating to the Indian sub-continent and to South African citizens of British ancestry.

HIGHLY REGARDED – SOUTH EAST	
LINNELLS *Oxford*	WOODFORD & ACKROYD *Southampton*
ERIC ROBINSON & CO *Southampton*	MARSONS SOLICITORS *Bromley*
WOLLASTONS *Chelmsford*	

Other firms in this area include *Wollastons* in Chelmsford advising corporate entities on work permits and immigration arrangements for dependants, acting as it does for a number of companies employing foreign nationals. *Eric Robinson & Co*, again in Southampton and *Marsons* in Bromley have also undertaken immigration law work.

HIGHLY REGARDED – SOUTH EAST – PERSONAL IMMIGRATION
E. EDWARDS SON & NOICE *Ilford*

In Oxford, *Linnels* have very recently set up an immigration practice with the assistance of the very highly regarded Philip Turpin, formerly of *McGrath & Co,* in Birmingham.

LEADING INDIVIDUALS – SOUTH EAST
Gordon F. Denson   *Woodford & Ackroyd*
Philip B.C. Turpin   *Linnells*

SOUTH WEST & WALES

Eversheds in Cardiff has experience of handling immigration matters for staff from overseas, acting particularly for Japanese firms based in Wales.

HIGHLY REGARDED – SOUTH WEST & WALES
EVERSHEDS *Cardiff*
BOBBETTS MACKAN *Bristol*

MIDLANDS

Birmingham is a very important area for family/human rights immigration. The two leading immigration firms in this region are *McGrath & Co* and *Tyndallwoods*. The immi-

LEADING FIRMS – MIDLANDS	
McGRATH & CO *Birmingham*	**TYNDALLWOODS** *Birmingham*

gration department at *McGrath & Co* enjoys an excellent reputation, undertaking work relating to visitors, students,

work permits, family settlement, asylum, deportation and illegal entry. *Tyndallwoods* have experience of dealing with marriage and family reunion cases, political asylum and business related immigration. Mark Phillips enjoys a good reputation for his work in this field.

LEADING INDIVIDUALS – MIDLANDS
Mark Phillips   *Tyndallwoods*

EAST ANGLIA

This particular geographical region undertakes very little by way of immigration work. However firms known to undertake such work are *Gross & Co*, and *Leathes Prior*. *Gross & Co* based in Bury St. Edmunds primarily deal with business

HIGHLY REGARDED – EAST ANGLIA	
GROSS & CO. *Bury St. Edmunds*	LEATHES PRIOR *Norwich*

immigration where Graeme Kirk practises in this field. *Leathes Prior* are located in Norwich and have dealt with both business and personal immigration work.

LEADING INDIVIDUALS – EAST ANGLIA
Tim J. Cary   *Leathes Prior*
Graeme D. Kirk   *Gross & Co.*

NORTH WEST

LEADING FIRMS – NORTH WEST
RAMSBOTTOM & CO *Blackburn*

Ramsbottom & Co deal with business immigration and family/ human rights immigration work. Edward Slinger of this firm is highly regarded and has experience of appearing

HIGHLY REGARDED – NORTH WEST	
EDWARDS FRAIS ABRAHAMSON *Liverpool*	JACKSON & CANTER *Liverpool*
DAVIS BLANK FURNISS *Manchester*	J. KEITH PARK & CO *St. Helens*

before Immigration Appeal Tribunals. In Liverpool, *Edward Frais Abrahamson* deal with all aspects including refugee and family reunion cases. Also in Liverpool *Jackson & Canter* handle a wide range of work including student and asylum cases where Andrew Holroyd has experience of business immigration, particularly for businesses owned by ethnic minorities.

LEADING INDIVIDUALS – NORTH WEST
Edward Slinger   *Ramsbottom & Co*
Andrew Holroyd   *Jackson & Canter*
Peter Simm   *Edwards Frais Abrahamson*

NORTH EAST

The two leading firms in this field are *Ison Harrison & Co* and *David Gray & Co.*

DAVID GRAY & CO *Newcastle upon Tyne*	**ISON HARRISON & CO** *Leeds*

Ison Harrison & Co based in Leeds, is well known for its work for refugees in this field. Ruth Bundey is very well regarded. In Newcastle, *David Gray & Co* has a good reputation for its immigration work particularly family settlement, student immigration, political asylum and refugee work.

SAMUEL PHILLIPS & CO *Newcastle-upon-Tyne*

Also in Newcastle, *Samuel Philips & Co* undertake work in this field.

Ruth Bundey *Ison Harrison & Co*
David Gray *David Gray & Co*

LEADERS IN IMMIGRATION & NATIONALITY

LONDON

Alfandary, Peter
Warner Cranston, London (0171) 403 2900.

Andonian, Bernard
Gulbenkian Harris Andonian, London (0171) 937 1542. Partner in Immigration and Nationality Law Department.

Specialisation: Principal area of practice is UK immigration and nationality law and US immigration. Deals with UK business immigration including work permit applications and business and sole representative applications; preparation and submission of business and investor plans; independent means and refugee asylum applications. Also handles appeals against Home Office or Entry Clearance Officer decisions and cases before the Adjudicator, Immigration Appeal Tribunals and judicial review. Acted in the case of Livingstone, a significant immigration decision. Experienced in all aspects of US business immigration. Contributor of numerous articles for The Law Society Gazette, Solicitors Journal, International Legal Practitioner, Immigration and Nationality Law and Practice, West London Law Society Newsletter. Lectures on immigration at the LSE and other universities and also to other solicitors specialising in immigration law at ILPA training sessions; reviewed for The Law Society Gazette book entitled:- "Immigration: The Law and Practice" by Michael Supperstone QC and Declan O'Dempsey. Also deals with general commercial litigation, matrimonial finance and property disputes and has a speciality in intellectual property.

Prof. Membership: Executive Committee Member of Immigration Law Practitioners Association, a member of the International Bar Association, Law Society, West London Law Society, Holborn Law Society.

Career: Qualified 1985 while at *Gulbenkian Harris Andonian*, and became a Partner in 1986.

Personal: Born 11th September 1949. Attended City of London and Thames Valley Universities. Obtained Distinction in Intellectual Property for the MA Degree. Leisure pursuits include reading, rambling, table tennis, snooker, swimming. Lives in Osterley, Middlesex.

Ashford, Mark
Taylor Nichol, London (0171) 272 8336.

Belchak, Hilary
Simmons & Simmons, London (0171) 628 2020. Partner in Litigation Department.

Specialisation: Main areas of practice are UK immigration and nationality law. Has eleven years experience in this field. Presently covering corporate immigration such as work permits, immigration advice to high net worth individuals wishing to settle in the UK and nationality issues. Contributor to 'Central and Eastern European Business Law Review' IBA journal 'International Legal Practitioner' and 'Corporate Counsel's International Adviser'. Has spoken at ILPA and the immigration committees of IBA and IPBA annual conferences as well as to groups representing personnel managers in banking and legal field.

Prof. Membership: ILPA, IBA, IPBA, AILA. Vice Chair IPBA's Immigration Committee.

Career: Qualified in 1984. Senior lecturer at North London Polytechnic 1971-81; worked at *Winstanley Burgess* 1982-84 and *Clinton Davis & Co.* 1984-88. Joined *Simmons & Simmons* in 1988, becoming a Partner in 1994.

Personal: Born 17th March 1949. Holds an LLB (1970) and LLM (1971). Leisure interests include opera and cinema. Lives in London.

Burgess, David C.W.
Winstanley-Burgess, London (0171) 278 7911. Partner in Immigration Department.

Specialisation: Main area of practice is immigration, including refugee work. Acted in Re M (H.L.), asylum case involving Ministers' liability to contempt; and Re Sivakumaran (H.L. and European Court of Human Rights), 'refugee' definition case. Also acted in NSH, Gulf War detainees, and Chahal cases which concerned national security (C.A.). Author of various articles concerning immigration matters. Has appeared on television and radio, as well as lecturing at seminars in Europe.

Prof. Membership: Law Society, Immigration Law Practitioners Association, Refugee Legal Group, European Legal Network on Asylum (Joint UK Representative).

Career: Qualified in 1972. Partner at *Winstanley-Burgess* from 1975.

Personal: Born 25th September 1947. Attended Cambridge University (MA, 1969). Lives in London.

Christian, Louise
See under Civil Liberties.

Cohen, Maurice
Maurice Cohen & Co, London (0171) 267 2967. Principal.

Specialisation: Main area of practice is immigration, handling all aspects. Particular expertise in the field of political asylum applications. Also handles business applications, marriage settlement, family reunion and nationality applications. Among many notable appeals, acted in a case concerning Sweden as a third country case being ruled unfit for asylum seekers.

Prof. Membership: Immigration Law Practitioners Association.

Career: Qualified in 1988. Assistant Solicitor at *Teacher Stern & Selby* 1988-92. Principal of *Maurice Cohen & Co* since 1992.

Personal: Born 7th November 1963. Attended Leeds University 1982-85 and College of Law 1986. Lives in London.

Coker, Jane
Jane Coker & Partners, London (0181) 885 1415. Qualified 1980. Partner 1982. Specialises in immigration, covering deportation, asylum, appeals representation and judicial review, and contempt of court. Born 11.7.1954.

Cranswick, Vanessa

Cameron Markby Hewitt, London (0171) 702 2345. Qualified 1993. Assistant Solicitor. Immigration Group. Covers all areas of UK immigration and nationality (except asylum and refugee work).

Garrush, Samia

Baker & McKenzie, London (0171) 919 1000. Paralegal in Immigration Department.

Specialisation: Handles employment-related immigration law, including work permits, entry clearance for sole representatives, entry clearance for self-employed businessmen and investors. Also deals with UK nationality law, including work permit holders who acquire settled status, holders of entry clearance under other categories, and their dependents. Has addressed seminars and workshops and contributed to articles regarding the changes in the immigration rules.

Prof. Membership: Immigration Law Practitioners Association, Law Society's Immigration Law Sub-Committee.

Career: Joined *Baker & McKenzie* in 1982.

Personal: Born 26th September 1954. Holder of Joint BA degree in French and Italian (1977) and Postgraduate Certificate of Education (1979). Founder member of property management company. Youth leader for St. Dunstan's Youth Club. Leisure interests include ballroom dancing, visiting National Trust Properties and country walking.

Gherson, Roger M.

Gherson & Co, London (0171) 355 2282. Principal of firm.

Specialisation: Practices exclusively in immigration and nationality. Work includes work permits, business investors, sole representations, writers and artists visas, appeals before the adjudicators and the Tribunal, as well as judicial review matters in the High Court.

Prof. Membership: Law Society, Immigration Law Practitioners' Association.

Career: Qualified in 1981. Established *Gherson & Co.* in 1988.

Personal: Born 24th August 1954. Attended University College, London 1975-78.

Grant, Larry

Simons Muirhead & Burton, London (0171) 734 4499. Partner in Immigration and Nationality Department.

Specialisation: Handles all areas of law and practice including applications to the Home Office, Department of Employment and overseas posts; preparation and representation before immigration appellate authorities; and applications for judicial review. Co-editor of 'Civil Liberty: the NCCL Guide'; co-author of 'Immigration Law and Practice', and 'Immigration and Asylum Emergency Procedures' and Consultant Editor of 'Tolley's Immigration and Nationality Law and Practice'. Gives regular seminars on immigration law.

Prof. Membership: Law Society, Immigration Law Practitioners Association.

Career: Qualified in 1967. Legal Officer, National Council for Civil Liberties 1970-74, solicitor, Law Clinic at the University of Kent 1974-77. Partner at *Seifert Sedley Williams* 1977-91. Partner at *Simons Muirhead & Burton* since 1991. Founder member and former Chair of the ILPA. Member of Immigration Law sub-committee of Law Society.

Personal: Born 1943. Leisure interests include travel, theatre, crosswords and soccer. Lives in Ickham, near Canterbury.

Gryk, Wesley

Wesley Gryk, London (0171) 240 8485.

Guedalla, Vicky

Deighton Guedalla, London (0171) 490 5518. Qualified 1987. Co-founding Partner 1990. Main areas of practice are immigration and asylum law and civil liberties. Special emphasis on refugee issues, including unaccompanied children.

Guild, Elspeth

Baileys Shaw & Gillett, London (0171) 837 5455. Qualified 1989. Head of Immigration Group, specialising in UK immigration and nationality law including matters relating to the work permit scheme. Member of the Council of Justice.

Gulbenkian, Paul

Gulbenkian Harris Andonian, London (0171) 937 1542. Immigration Department.

Specialisation: Principal area of practice covers business and private immigration and nationality law including nationality applications, UK immigration and advice and obtaining work permits. Other main area of work covers family, defamation and general litigation. Appointed Part-time Immigration Adjudicator 1989 and Assistant Recorder in the Crown Court 1992. Joint editor of European Immigration Law & Business and author of numerous articles in legal and other journals.

Prof. Membership: Law Society, Institute of Directors, Immigration Law Practitioners Association, European Immigration Lawyers Group, Solicitors Family Law Association and the British Armenian Lawyers Association. Fellow of the Royal Society of Arts (FRSA).

Career: Qualified in 1964 while with *Penningtons, Lewis & Lewis.* Joined *Isadore Goldman & Son* in 1966 and became Administration Partner in charge of Litigation Department 1970. Became Senior Partner of *Gulbenkian Harris Andonian & Isadore Goldman* in 1989.

Personal: Born 23rd March 1940. Attended King's College School, Wimbledon 1953-58, then London School of Economics 1958-61. Trustee of a number of charitable trusts including an Associate Trust of the Calouste Gulbenkian Foundation (the St. Sarkis Charity Trust), the Foundation for International Health, the Serio Ensemble and a number of trusts for the benefit of the Armenian community. Leisure pursuits include walking, music, tennis and squash. Lives in Weybridge, Surrey.

Jorgensen, Helen Michelle

Norton Rose, London (0171) 283 6000. Qualified 1982. Corporate Services Department. 13 years' experience of business related immigration work and inward investment related immigration.

Kemp, Lesley

Magrath & Co, London (0171) 495 3003.

Leskin, Nigel

B.M. Birnberg & Co, London (0171) 403 3166. Solicitor. Immigration and Criminal Department. Specialises in immigration work.

Lindsley, Fiona

B.M. Birnberg & Co, London (0171) 403 3166.

Luqmani, Jawaid

Jane Coker & Partners, London (0181) 885 1415.

Magrath, Christopher

Magrath & Co, London (0171) 495 3003. Senior Partner in Immigration and Employment Department.

Specialisation: Practice has substantially specialised in immigration and nationality law since 1985, primarily in the corporate field of executive expatriate transfer on a global basis, as well as for numerous individual clients over the last nine years. Also practises employment law in both contentious and non-contentious circumstances. Co-author of 'Practitioners Guide to the Police and Criminal Evidence Act 1984' (Longmans) and 'Working in the United Kingdom- A Guide for Foreign Nationals' (Handbook). Has published numerous articles in both professional and commercial magazines. Has made many conference addresses worldwide over the last twenty years, on immigration and employment related issues arising from expatriate transfer and relocation. Regular broadcaster on legal affairs, in particular with LBC and London Radio since 1983.

Prof. Membership: Law Society, ILPA, American Immigration Lawyers Association, International Bar Association, London Criminal Courts Solicitors' Association.

Career: Qualified in 1975. Admitted to New York Bar in 1986. Set up *Magrath & Co* as Senior Partner in 1990.

Personal: Born 12th May 1948. Attended Campbell College, Belfast, 1961-66 and Trinity College Dublin (BA degree) 1972. Leisure interests include tennis, restaurants, dogs and skiing. Lives in London.

Moss, Peter

Bates, Wells & Braithwaite, London (0171) 251 1122. Immigration and Nationality Advisor.

Specialisation: Advises on immigration and nationality matters and conducts advocacy in appeals. Main area of practice covers commercial immigration: work permits and applications for entry clearance as businessmen or overseas representatives. Other main area of work is for private clients including persons of independent means, self-employed artists, nationality, family visit and asylum cases. Author of articles for Immigration Law and Practice and the Hong Kong Law Society Gazette. Sometime lecturer at the University of West of England and the College of Law. Organised and participated in various Immigration Law Practitioners' Association Seminars and Panel discussions.

Prof. Membership: Treasurer of Immigration Law Practitioners' Association.

Career: HM Immigration Officer, Dover 1973-75. Immigration Counsellor with the United Kingdom Immigrants Advisory Service 1975-76, then Senior Counsellor 1976-89. Immigration and Nationality Advisor with *Thomson Snell & Passmore* 1989-92, then joined *Bates Wells & Braithwaite.*

Personal: Born 11th July 1949. Attended Bridgewater School, Worsley 1954-68, then Manchester University 1969-71. Leisure pursuits include walking and horseracing. Lives in London.

Onslow-Cole, Julia

Cameron Markby Hewitt, London (0171) 702 2345. Partner and Head of UK Immigration and Nationality Group.

Specialisation: Heads team of solicitors who also practise exclusively in this area. Acts for many financial institutions and PLC companies in the UK, advising principally on corporate immigration matters. In addition advises private clients on all types of application, save asylum and refugee. Particular expertise in investor and business related immigration. Voted Expert's Expert by Legal Business in 1993. Contributing co-editor of Butterworths Immigration Law Service. Author of numerous articles. Has lectured and spoken at conferences in South Africa, Japan, Hong Kong, the USA and in Europe.

Prof. Membership: Member of Immigration Law Sub-Committee of Law Society, Vice Chairman of International Bar Association, Migration & Nationality Committee and Member of Immigration Law Practitioners Association.

Career: Qualified 1984. Worked for British Coal 1982-86, then *Simmons & Simmons* as Head of UK Immigration and Nationality Department 1986-90. Joined *Cameron Markby Hewitt* in 1990 as Head of UK Immigration and Nationality Group, Partner from 1991.

Personal: Born 30th September 1959. Took an LLB(Hons) in 1981, Law Society exams in 1982.

Pope, Caron

Cameron Markby Hewitt, London (0171) 702 2345. Qualified 1990. Assistant Solicitor. Immigration Group. Covers all areas of UK immigration law (apart from asylum and refugee cases).

Randall, Christopher W.

Winstanley-Burgess, London (0171) 278 7911. Qualified 1985. Partner 1990. Immigration Department. Handles refugee law, judicial review and general immigration law. Born in 1959.

Reed, Tim

Sturtivant & Co, London (0171) 486 9524. Assistant Solicitor in Immigration Department.

Specialisation: Main area of practice is UK immigration, work permit and nationality law, with over ten years experience. Also handles immigration law of other European countries.

Prof. Membership: Immigration Law Practitioners Association, Middle East Legal Practitioners Forum, British Legal Association.

Career: Qualified in 1993, having joined *Sturtivant & Co* in 1985. Fellow of the Institute of Legal Executives 1989.

Personal: Born 14th September 1963. Attended Kings School Canterbury and College of Law 1993. Lives in London.

Stanley, Alison

Bindman & Partners, London (0171) 833 4433.

Sturtivant, Karen L.

Sturtivant & Co, London (0171) 486 9524. Qualified 1980. Principal 1985. Immigration and Nationality specialist. Emphasis on business clients, as well as handling a full range of private client immigration work.

Taylor, Carolyn S.

Taylor Nichol, London (0171) 272 8336. Qualified 1983.

Thompson, Jackie

Nicholson Graham & Jones, London (0171) 628 9151. Solicitor and Head of Immigration Unit.

Specialisation: Executive immigration including work permits, business and sole representative permits, applications for investors and persons of independent means and nationality. Also advises on the impact of immigration and nationality on tax status. Particularly strong in private client, medical and academic immigration. Has contributed to articles in The Sunday Times, The Guardian, Taxation, The Lancet, Law Society Gazette, Solicitors Journal, British Arab Yearbook, Chamber of Commerce Magazines, Immigration and Nationality Law and Practice and The Lawyer. Speaks regularly at seminars including IBA, Foreign Banks Association, the Commonwealth Banks

Association and the British Medical Association; has arranged the Immigration Law Practitioners conferences attended by representatives of the Home Office and Employment Department; gives talks to those in academic and medical fields, accountants and bankers.

Prof. Membership: Immigration Law Practitioners Association including Business Sub-Committee, IBA.

Career: Qualified in 1986. Articled at *Speechly Bircham* 1984-86, joined *Nicholson Graham & Jones* in 1986.

Personal: Born 6th April 1962. Attended Southampton University 1980-83. Leisure interests include food, wine and snorkelling. Lives in Ealing, London.

Trott, Philip

Bates, Wells & Braithwaite, London (0171) 251 1122. Partner in Immigration and Employment Department.

Specialisation: Principal area of practice is commercial immigration law, advising individuals and corporations on how they can be economically active in the UK and advising on Home Office and Department of Employment practices and concessions. Regular lecturer on professional courses on immigration and employment law issues. Lecturer at the University of West England. Assisted in production of educational video on Immigration Law for Legal Network T.V. Author of articles for Immigration and Law Practice, Hong Kong Law Society Gazette and co-author of forthcoming text book on immigration law and tax.

Prof. Membership: Law Society, Immigration Law Practitioners' Association (Executive Committee), Employment Lawyers Association, American Immigration Lawyers' Association.

Career: Articled with *Dale Parkinson & Co.* 1977-78 and *Lawford & Co.* 1978-79. Qualified in 1979 and made a Partner in 1982. Joined *Thomson Snell & Passmore* as Head of Immigration and Employment Law Department in 1989, and moved to *Bates, Wells & Braithwaite* in 1992.

Personal: Born 5th June 1952. Attended Portsmouth Grammar School 1964-71, then Oxford Polytechnic 1971-73. Gained LLB at University College, London 1973-76. Fluent in French. Hon. Legal Adviser to Holborn Citizens Advice Bureau. Leisure pursuits include sailing, swimming, cycling, hill walking, flying and travelling. Lives in Teddington.

Webb, David

Gherson & Co, London (0171) 355 2282. Partner.

Specialisation: Handles exclusively immigration and nationality law. Work includes employment and business related immigration law (business persons, work permit holders, investors, representatives of overseas firms, writers and artists); family reunion (entry clearance and variation applications in respect of immediate and extended family members); political asylum applications; students, visitors and other temporary categories; advocacy before the immigration appellate authority; applications for Judicial Review to the High Court; and nationality analysis and acquisition of citizenship. As a result of his involvement in Bangladesh 'family' cases in the mid 1980s and Hindu 'marriage' cases in recent years, he has developed strong links with the Indian sub-continent. In addition he has represented numerous US and Japanese corporate clients and regularly assists senior staff in relocating to the UK. Co-author of 'Immigration Emergency Procedures' he has published many articles on immigration law in legal journals. An experienced ILPA lecturer, he has frequently appeared on BBC television and radio and speaks at numerous conferences organised by private bodies.

Prof. Membership: Immigration Law Practitioners' Association (elected Executive Committee Member on a number of occasions), American Immigration Lawyers Association, Law Society.

Career: Qualified in 1991; previously a Member of the Institute of Legal Executives. Employed as an Immigration Consultant at Tower Hamlets Law Centre 1983-87, and legal advisor at *Ault McGrath & Co.* 1987-88. Worked at *Baker & McKenzie* 1988-93, then *Simons Muirhead & Burton* 1993-94, before joining *Gherson & Co.* in 1994.

Personal: Born 18th December 1959. Attended University of Birmingham, Faculty of Law (LLB Hons 1982). Interests include local and national politics, legal and journalistic writing and international travel. Lives in London.

Wornham, Trevor
Wilson & Co, London (0181) 808 7535.

Wyatt, Peter
Gulbenkian Harris Andonian, London (0171) 937 1542. Fax (0171) 938 2059. Partner in Immigration Department.

Specialisation: Main areas of practice are immigration and nationality law. Handles all aspects including work permits, businessmen, sole representatives, independent means, investor, writers and artists applications, nationality and citizenship applications, and refugee and asylum cases. Also handles conveyancing and company work. Addresses conferences.
Prof. Immigration Law Practitioners Association. Membership: Law Society, International Bar Association, West London Law Society.

Career: Qualified in 1980. Previously worked for a Central London Practice in London, Saudi Arabia and USA. Joined *Gulbenkian Harris Andonian* in 1992, becoming a Partner in 1994.

Personal: Born 27th October 1953. Attended Fettes College Edinburgh 1967-72, Dundee University 1972-75 and College of Law

1976. Leisure interests include skiing and golf. Lives in London.

REGIONS

Bundey, Ruth
Ison Harrison & Co, Leeds (0113) 286 1455. Qualified 1980. Partner 1986. Has specialised in crime and immigration work since 1980.

Cary, Tim J.
Leathes Prior, Norwich (01603) 610911. Qualified 1978. Partner 1984. Handles plaintiff personal injury cases and immigration and nationality law. Born 15.2.1954.

Denson, Gordon F.
Woodford & Ackroyd, Southampton (01703) 321000. Partner in Immigration Department.

Specialisation: Work covers all areas of immigration, nationality and asylum law. Conducts own appeals before adjudicators. Other areas of practice are commercial and conveyancing. Has undertaken personal visits to India to organise visas for children on compassionate grounds.

Prof. Membership: JCWI.

Career: Qualified 1975. Joined *Woodford & Ackroyd* 1976. Partner 1980. Deputy Coroner for Southampton and New Forest District 1993.

Personal: Born 22nd May 1950. Rotary member. Leisure interests include road running, walking, ornithology and foreign travel.

Gray, David
David Gray & Co, Newcastle upon Tyne (0191) 232 9547. Qualified 1970. Founding Principal 1979. Main area of practice is immigration. Work includes family settlement, nationality illegals, students, political asylum and refugees. Born 16.11.1944.

Holroyd, Andrew
Jackson & Canter, Liverpool (0151) 708 6593. Partner in Immigration and Small Business Department.

Specialisation: Principal area of practice covers all aspects of immigration law including business immigration matters, with an emphasis on dealing with small businesses operated by ethnic minorities. Chairman of Legal Aid and Advice Sub-Committee, Liverpool Law Society, for seven years, overseeing CAB rota schemes of free legal advice and involved in Positive Action Scheme to encourage black entrants to the legal profession.

Prof. Membership: Law Society, Immediate past President of Liverpool Law Society. ILPA.

Career: Qualified 1974 while with *Alsop Stevens Batesons* in Liverpool, then joined *Jackson & Canter*. Became a Partner in 1977.

Personal: Born 13th April 1948. Attended Bradford Grammar School and Nottingham University. Governor of Archbishop Blanch School. Local Methodist Preacher and Circuit Steward of the Liverpool South Circuit. Leisure pursuits include music and walking. Lives in Liverpool.

Kirk, Graeme D.
Gross & Co., Bury St. Edmunds (01284) 763333. & (0171) 935 5541. Qualified 1981. Partner in Immigration and Commercial Department.

Specialisation: Principal area of practice is immigration and nationality law. Other main area of work is company/commercial for private companies and businesses, including foreign businesses seeking to establish a UK presence. Handles work permit, self-employment, business sole representative and independent means cases. Addressed IBA conferences in Montreal, Cannes, London, New Orleans and Australia and has given seminars in South Africa and the UK.

Prof. Membership: Law Society, IBA, ILPA, Solicitors European Group.

Career: Qualified in 1981. Assistant solicitor with *Radcliffes & Co.* 1981-84, then joined *Gross & Co.* in 1984 and became a Partner in 1986. Appointed Chairman of NIS Group November 1992. Currently Secretary of the Migration & Nationality Committee of the International Bar Association. Senior Partner of Gross & Co from January 1995.

Personal: Attended University of East Anglia. Past Chairman of Bury St. Edmunds Round Table. Leisure pursuits include cricket, badminton, opera and the violin. Lives in Bury St. Edmunds.

Phillips, Mark
See under Civil Liberties.

Simm, Peter
Edwards Frais Abrahamson, Liverpool (0151) 707 1212. Qualified 1982. Partner 1991. Immigration Department. All aspects, particularly family reunion, refugee cases and European Court/Commission.

Slinger, Edward
Ramsbottom & Co, Blackburn (01254) 672222. Qualified 1961. Senior Partner. Handles immigration and nationality and general litigation. Makes regular appearances before adjudicators and Immigration Appeal Tribunals. Born 2.2.1938.

Turpin, Philip B.C.
Linnells, Oxford (01865) 248607. Qualified 1992. Partner 1992. Immigration Department. Deals with matters involving visitors, students, work permits, family settlement, asylum, deportation and illegal entry. Born 4.9.1957.

INSOLVENCY

WITH the recession tailing off, insolvency work takes on an increasing corporate rescue/recovery and restructuring flavour, enabling practices with strong banking and corporate units to apply their expertise accordingly.

LONDON

The established players continue to dominate most major insolvency work. Both *Allen & Overy* and *Lovell White Durrant* have formidable reputations for corporate insolvency and are still regarded as the leaders despite stiff competition from others.

LEADING FIRMS – LONDON	
ALLEN & OVERY	LOVELL WHITE DURRANT
CAMERON MARKBY HEWITT	WILDE SAPTE
CLIFFORD CHANCE	DENTON HALL

Allen & Overy's well-established strength is reflected in its recent involvement in the receiverships of Ferranti International, Health Care International and Athena Posters, in addition to continuing work on Queen's Moat, Canary Wharf and Heron Group reschedulings. It has also been dealing with a number of voluntary arrangements in the Maxwell private companies.

Lovell White Durrant likewise has been involved in several large insolvencies including BCCI (acting for liquidators, Touche Ross), Olympia & York, Arrows and the Maxwell collapse. It also advised the creditor banks in the Heron International restructuring. Major receiverships handled include Rosehaugh, the Melville Group and certain Peter de Savary companies. In the recent Barings administration, the firm advised Robert Fleming & Co on the acquisition of Barings Group businesses. Its team also acted in bankruptcy proceedings against Robert Montague (former chief executive of Tiphook) and Martyn Deaner (managing director of Midland & Scottish Resources).

Cameron Markby Hewitt (particularly strong in administrative receiverships and property based insolvency), and *Wilde Sapte* have excellent reputations. *Cameron Markby Hewitt* has been acting recently for the receivers on the sale of Reliant Robin and advising on the exit strategies of three major reconstructions. It continues to act for the administrators of Atlantic Computers in connection with the litigation brought by British & Commonwealth's administrators. The administrators of Polly Peck were also represented by the firm in its scheme of arrangement. The team is furthermore developing a strong expertise in advising insolvent airlines.

Wilde Sapte's extensive expertise encompasses both corporate and personal insolvency. Their team comprises 20 full time insolvency fee-earners. Clients include banks, directors and insolvency office holders from all the major accountancy firms. It recently acted for the administrative receivers

of Leyland Daf Ltd and the Lancer Boss group, and the administrators of Paramount Airways Ltd.

Also highly regarded are *Clifford Chance* and *Denton Hall*. In addition to its formidable insurance insolvency expertise, *Clifford Chance* handles a large amount of mainstream insolvency matters including property receiverships. Examples include the Speyhawk, Butler's Wharf and Mountleigh receiverships. The firm also has wide experience in cases involving asset tracing, fraud claims and recovery.

Denton Hall currently representing the Trustees in Bankruptcy of Roger Levitt is pre-eminent in personal insolvency. It does, however, have an excellent corporate insolvency practice (particularly for contentious work), acting frequently for the Official Receiver as provisional liquidator. The firm is retained by Price Waterhouse in the Roxburghe Guarantee Corporation's administration. It also advises Barclays Bank on the insolvency aspects of environmental warranties and liabilities. Michael Steiner and Howard Morris of *Denton Hall* are members of the International Advisory Board to the Federal Agency of Insolvency (Bankruptcy) of the Russian Federation.

HIGHLY REGARDED – LONDON	
DIBB LUPTON BROOMHEAD	HAMMOND SUDDARDS
LAWRENCE GRAHAM	NABARRO NATHANSON
NORTON ROSE	SIMMONS & SIMMONS
STEPHENSON HARWOOD	
ALSOP WILKINSON	DAVIES ARNOLD COOPER
FRESHFIELDS	HERBERT SMITH
ISADORE GOLDMAN	RICHARDS BUTLER
SLAUGHTER AND MAY	SPRECHER GRIER
ASHURST MORRIS CRISP	BAKER & McKENZIE
BARLOW LYDE & GILBERT	BERWIN LEIGHTON
BOOTH & BLACKWELL	CARRICK READ INSOLVENCY
EDWIN COE	EVERSHEDS
GOULDENS	HILL TAYLOR DICKINSON
HOWARD KENNEDY	JEFFREY GREEN RUSSELL
LINKLATERS & PAINES	MACFARLANES
MACKENZIE MILLS	McKENNA & CO
NICHOLSON GRAHAM & JONES	OSBORNE CLARKE
PAISNER & CO	PICKERING KENYON
RAKISONS	REID MINTY
STONES PORTER	TAYLOR JOYNSON GARRETT
THEODORE GODDARD	TITMUSS SAINER DECHERT
TRAVERS SMITH BRAITHWAITE	UNDERWOOD & CO

Other firms consistently recommended for their sound insolvency base are *Dibb Lupton Broomhead, Hammond Suddards, Lawrence Graham, Nabarro Nathanson, Norton Rose, Simmons & Simmons* and *Stephenson Harwood*.

Dibb Lupton Broomhead has extensive experience in both corporate and personal insolvency. It represented leisure industry chief, John Broome in negotiations with his trade creditors over the possible acceptance of an individual voluntary arrangement. *Hammond Suddards'* expertise extends to corporate rescues and company reorganisations. The firm also acted in the Maxwell case on Israeli realisations and for building societies in the Kentish and Declan Kelly collapses.

Some of *Lawrence Graham's* major activities include acting for Credit Suisse in the Brent Walker receivership, pioneering the CVA scheme for listed companies and advising the directors of Polly Peck and British & Commonwealth. It was also involved in Keith Prowse's receivership.

Recent high profile transactions in which *Norton Rose* was involved include Maxwell Communication Corporation plc, Rafidain Bank (provisional liquidation), Windsor Safari Park Ltd (administrative receivership), Riverbus Ltd (liquidation) and London United Investments plc (administration). It is also experienced in advising on reconstruction schemes and voluntary arrangements.

Simmons & Simmons continues to handle major reconstructions such as Heron, Brent Walker and Hawthorn Leslie. The team is also involved in the receiverships of Peter de Savary's companies and the administrations of Team Lotus (advising Robson Rhodes) and the Travers Morgan Group (advising Arthur Andersen). It additionally has expertise in large multi-national insolvencies and settlements such as the Carrian Holdings liquidation and property insolvencies, acting for Security Pacific, Mitsibushi Trust & Banking Corporation and Paribas.

Stephenson Harwood has dealt with several litigation-driven insolvencies such as Bishopsgate (handling the Maxwell pension funds recovery and the liquidation of the trustee company), BCCI and British & Commonwealth (acting for Ernst & Young). Other receiverships handled include that of Embassy Greenly (Arthur Andersen), Colin Farley (Kidsons Impey), Miles Kent (Touche Ross) and The Leasing Group (Levy Gee).

The insolvency practices of *Alsop Wilkinson, Davies Arnold Cooper, Freshfields, Herbert Smith, Richards Butler* and *Slaughter and May* are also well-regarded.

In addition to mainstream insolvency work, *Alsop Wilkinson* is active in insurance insolvency, bankruptcy, corporate rescues and reconstructions. It acted for the joint administrators of Polly Peck and the liquidators of Maxwell Communications International Ltd. Other clients include Royal Bank of Scotland and overseas banks.

In the past year, *Herbert Smith* has advised on a number of high profile cases including British & Commonwealth (advising Kleinwort Benson and Coopers & Lybrand), Maxwell Communications (acting for the administrators), BCCI, Polly Peck, Blade Investments and Midland & Scottish Energy.

Richards Butler's team consisting of two licensed insolvency practitioners recently represented a clearing bank in a major property receivership involving a value in excess of £40 million. *Slaughter and May* has been appointed to act for the administrators, Ernst & Young in the Barings collapse.

Among the smaller firms, *Isadore Goldman* and *Sprecher Grier* are regarded as the leading players. The former's expertise includes the disposal and acquisition of insolvency assets. Its team includes a former member of the Cork Committee and a part time Deputy Registrar in Bankruptcy. *Sprecher Grier's* expertise encompasses corporate rescues and restructuring. Their clients include Arthur Andersen, Ernst & Young, Grant Thornton and Leonard Curtis & Co. Major cases handled include Brightlife Ltd and Cranley Mansions Ltd.

Those consistently recommended as leading specialists include Mark Andrews (*Wilde Sapte*), Mark Gill (*Wilde Sapte*), Christopher Grierson (*Lovell White Durrant*), Christopher Hanson (*Lovell White Durrant*), Peter Horrocks (*Lovell White Durrant*), Nicholas Segal (*Allen & Overy*), Michael Steiner for personal insolvency (*Denton Hall*), Gordon Stewart (*Allen & Overy*), Peter Totty (*Allen & Overy*) and John White (*Cameron Markby Hewitt*).

INSURANCE INSOLVENCY

London tends to generate the bulk of insurance insolvency work due to the concentration of the insurance market in the City. This remains an area in which very few City law firms specialise despite the fact that it is currently one of the most active fields of insolvency.

LEADING INDIVIDUALS – LONDON

Mark B. Andrews *Wilde Sapte*	Mark S. Gill *Wilde Sapte*	Christopher K. Grierson *Lovell White Durrant*
Christopher Hanson *Lovell White Durrant*	Peter G. Horrocks *Lovell White Durrant*	Nicholas Segal *Allen & Overy*
Michael Steiner *Denton Hall*	Gordon C. Stewart *Allen & Overy*	Peter G. Totty *Allen & Overy*
John J. White *Cameron Markby Hewitt*		
Nigel Barnett *Wilde Sapte*	Richard J.S. Bethell-Jones *Wilde Sapte*	Ashley R.B. Booker *Clifford Chance*
Margaret Cole *Stephenson Harwood*	Ian Fletcher *Richards Butler*	Stephen J. Foster *Cameron Markby Hewitt*
Stephen Gale *Hammond Suddards*	D.A. Gregory *Lovell White Durrant*	Ian Stephen Grier *Sprecher Grier*
John Houghton *Simmons & Simmons*	David John Kidd *Cameron Markby Hewitt*	Sandy Pratt *Norton Rose*
Michael Prior *Nabarro Nathanson*	Paul A. Rhodes *Dibb Lupton Broomhead*	Josanne Rickard *Freshfields*
James H.D. Roome *Simmons & Simmons*	Jonathan E.F. Rushworth *Slaughter and May*	Danny Schaffer *Isadore Goldman*
David Jeremy Steinberg *Clifford Chance*	John Verrill *Lawrence Graham*	Geoffrey Woolf *Stephenson Harwood*
Richard W. Wright *Dibb Lupton Broomhead*		

UP AND COMING

Dan Hamilton *Cameron Markby Hewitt*	Judith P. Naylor *Allen & Overy*	

In all the tables the names in each group are listed alphabetically.

LEADING FIRMS – LONDON – INSURANCE

LEADING FIRMS – LONDON – INSURANCE	
CLIFFORD CHANCE	
DAVIES ARNOLD COOPER	**LOVELL WHITE DURRANT**
STEPHENSON HARWOOD	

Clifford Chance has carved out a substantial practice in insurance insolvency and it is undoubtedly the premier firm. Major transactions include drafting the KWELM administration scheme which was the largest general insurance insolvency and advising on the English & American insolvency. Other clients include Bermuda Fire & Marine, Orion Insurance, Trinity, ACC, Fremont, Monument and Confederation. Andrew Wilkinson of the firm has a formidable reputation in this field.

HIGHLY REGARDED – LONDON – INSURANCE	
ALSOP WILKINSON	**D J FREEMAN**
HERBERT SMITH	
ALLEN & OVERY	**CAMERON MARKBY HEWITT**
FRESHFIELDS	**HOLMAN, FENWICK & WILLAN**
SLAUGHTER AND MAY	

Also highly respected are *Davies Arnold Cooper, Lovell White Durrant* and *Stephenson Harwood.* The former's reputation is in insurance insolvency involving schemes of arrangement. It acts for insurance insolvency accountancy firms, reinsurance companies and for market groupings comprising creditors of insolvent insurance companies. Companies' schemes of arrangement in which it was involved include the Charter Reinsurance Co Ltd, RMCA Re, Municipal General Insurance Ltd and ICS UK Ltd.

LEADING INDIVIDUALS – LONDON – INSURANCE
Peter J.M. Fidler *Stephenson Harwood*
Nigel Montgomery *Davies Arnold Cooper*
Sandy Shandro *Clifford Chance*
R. Spencer *Lovell White Durrant*
Andrew Wilkinson *Clifford Chance*

Lovell White Durrant advises the provisional liquidators of Orion Insurance (Price Waterhouse), London and Overseas Insurance (Price Waterhouse) and Stockholm Re (Bermuda). It also acts for a group of US creditors (which includes Dow Corning, Dow Chemical and Owens-Illinois) claiming against the KWELM companies.

Stephenson Harwood has been involved in several major insurance insolvencies including Andrew Weir, Bryanston, Trinity and Chancellor (where their clients are principally Price Waterhouse and Touche Ross).

Other recommended firms include *Allen & Overy, Alsop Wilkinson, Cameron Markby Hewitt, D J Freeman, Freshfields, Herbert Smith* (advising the Policyholders Protection Board), *Holman Fenwick Willan* and *Slaughter and May.*

Alsop Wilkinson represented the joint administrators of English & American Insurance Co and the liquidators of Devonshire Insurance Underwriting Ltd. *D J Freeman*'s strength lies in handling insolvencies involving pools such as those in relation to English & American, Weavers and Orion. *Herbert Smith* recently had a substantial involvement

in devising and settling the terms of major schemes of arrangement. In the past 12 months, the firm was involved in major insurance insolvencies and reorganisations including English & American, KWELM, Bryanston, Trinity, MMI, Oaklife, MGI and Scan Re.

SOUTH EAST

The Reading firm of *Boyes Turner & Burrows,* whose insolvency work extends to London and Gloucester, is one of the leading firms. The firm's traditional forte has been in the personal insolvency field and it is currently involved in a £45m bankruptcy. The firm also represented seven partners in the Help and Woolfe IVA. It also has expertise in corporate insolvency.

LEADING FIRMS – SOUTH EAST	
BOYES TURNER & BURROWS *Reading*	
BURSTOWS *Brighton, Crawley*	**COLE and COLE** *Oxford*
SHERWIN OLIVER *Portsmouth*	

Other firms with excellent reputations include *Burstows* (Brighton and Crawley), *Cole and Cole* and *Sherwin Oliver. Burstows*' insolvency unit continues to expand with the recent recruitment of another specialist. It has cornered the lion's share of major insolvency work in the immediate area, including an increasing amount of restructuring work. It is the appointee for the Treasury Solicitor on directors' disqualification matters and recently advised the nominee in the first partnership voluntary arrangements for a firm of solicitors.

HIGHLY REGARDED – SOUTH EAST	
LAMPORT BASSITT *Southampton*	**PARIS SMITH & RANDALL** *Southampton*
PARROTT & COALES *Aylesbury*	
BOODLE HATFIELD *Southampton*	**B.P. COLLINS & CO** *Gerrards Cross*
PITMANS *Reading*	**STEVENS & BOLTON** *Guildford*
BRACHERS *Maidstone*	**BRAIN & BRAIN** *Reading*
CLARKS *Reading*	**CRIPPS HARRIES HALL** *Tunbridge Wells*
DONNE MILEHAM & HADDOCK *Brighton*	**HEPHERD WINSTANLEY & PUGH** *Southampton*
PENNINGTONS *Basingstoke*	

Sherwin Oliver handles both corporate and personal insolvency. Regular instructions are received from Price Waterhouse, Coopers & Lybrand, Cork Gully in Gloucester, Grant Thornton, KPMG, Ernst & Young and Touche Ross. The firm has been involved in nearly 10 % of the total number of administration orders granted in the country in recent years.

Lamport Bassitt and *Paris Smith & Randall* are among the prominent Southampton insolvency practices, handling both corporate and personal insolvency. The former's strength lies primarily in receivership matters where in the past four years it has been involved in a major receivership of a quoted PLC. *Paris Smith & Randall* handles both contentious and non-contentious matters, with an increasing pension flavour. It acts for major insolvency practitioners, the local Official Receiver and has an expanding workload for Trustees in Bankruptcy.

Also well-regarded is *Parrott & Coales*, specialising in both corporate insolvency (particularly company realisations) and personal insolvency. It acts for accountants, individuals and companies.

Other recommended firms include *Boodle Hatfield* (strong in individual voluntary arrangements), *B.P.Collins & Co*, *Pitmans* and *Stevens & Bolton*. About 70 % of *Stevens & Bolton's* insolvency work is in the corporate domain with an emphasis on receivership and liquidation. It receives instructions from major accountancy firms, in addition to advising directors on their liabilities.

LEADING INDIVIDUALS – SOUTH EAST	
Christopher Branson *Boyes Turner & Burrows*	
Nigel Stuart Craig *Sherwin Oliver*	
David C. Oliver *Sherwin Oliver*	
Bruce J. Potter *Cole and Cole*	
Andrew C. Taylor *Burstows*	
Malcolm H. Le Bas *Paris Smith & Randall*	
Sean Kelly *Lamport Bassitt*	
Ian R. Taylor *Parrott & Coales*	
Clive H. Thomson *Paris Smith & Randall*	

Leading individuals include Christopher Branson (*Boyes Turner & Burrows*), Nigel Craig (*Sherwin Oliver*), David Oliver (*Sherwin Oliver*), Bruce Potter (*Cole & Cole*) and Andrew Taylor (*Burstows*).

SOUTH WEST

Both *Bond Pearce* and *Osborne Clarke* continue to maintain their dominant positions in corporate insolvency. The former's team comprises five licensed insolvency practitioners. They recently handled the Redruth Brewery receivership resulting in the sale of the business for £1.25m and the creditors' voluntary liquidation of Berkeley Applegate (Investment Consultants). *Bond Pearce's* clients are almost exclusively banks (it acts for two of the four clearing banks and two major foreign banks), finance houses, specialised lending institutions and regional insolvency practitioners.

LEADING FIRMS – SOUTH WEST	
BOND PEARCE *Plymouth*	OSBORNE CLARKE *Bristol*
ANSTEY SARGENT & PROBERT *Exeter*	BURGES SALMON *Bristol*

Osborne Clarke, traditionally strong in receivership matters, continues to handle a substantial amount of company directors' disqualification work for the Treasury Solicitor. The firm has two licensed insolvency practitioners and their clients include NatWest (South West and Wales), building societies and life companies.

Another firm with an excellent regional presence in corporate insolvency is *Burges Salmon* whose team includes a licensed insolvency practitioner. Its clients are primarily banks and receivers. The firm, additionally has the largest

agricultural insolvency practice in the country, stemming from its formidable agricultural expertise.

HIGHLY REGARDED – SOUTH WEST	
LAYTONS *Bristol*	LESTER ALDRIDGE *Bournemouth*
RICKERBY JESSOP *Cheltenham*	TRUMP AND PARTNERS *Bristol*
WANSBROUGHS WILLEY HARGRAVE *Bristol*	
CLARKE WILLMOTT & CLARKE *Taunton*	STONES *Exeter*
VEALE WASBROUGH *Bristol*	
BEVAN ASHFORD *Bristol*	BOYCE HATTON *Torquay*
BRETHERTON PRICE ELGOODS *Cheltenham*	CAMERON MARKBY HEWITT *Bristol*
DAVIES AND PARTNERS *Gloucester*	HARRIS & HARRIS *Wells*
LAWRENCE TUCKETTS *Bristol*	MEADE–KING *Bristol*
PENNINGTONS	STEELE RAYMOND *Bournemouth*
STEPHENS & SCOWN *Exeter*	TRETHOWANS *Salisbury*
WILSONS *Salisbury*	

Anstey Sargent & Probert in Exeter has consistently been recommended as the market leader for personal insolvency, covering all matters including individual voluntary arrangements. It also handles corporate insolvencies but its widespread reputation is primarily in the personal insolvency domain.

Other Bristol firms with sound insolvency practices include *Laytons, Trump & Partners, Veale Wasbrough* and *Wansbroughs Willey Hargrave*. The team at *Trump & Partner* specialises in both corporate and personal insolvency. It acts nationally for the Insolvency Service (37 offices in England and Wales) on the prosecution of directors and bankrupts.

Veale Wasbrough acts for banks, lending institutions and insolvency practitioners in both personal and corporate insolvency. Its clients include Bristol & West Building Society, Lloyds bank, Coopers & Lybrand, Ernst & Young, BDO, Stoy Hayward, Touche Ross and Neville Russell. *Clarke Willmott & Clarke's* Taunton office with one licensed insolvency practitioner and *Rickerby Jessop* (corporate and personal insolvency) are also well regarded in this field.

LEADING INDIVIDUALS – SOUTH WEST	
Hamish Anderson *Bond Pearce*	
Patrick D. Cook *Osborne Clarke*	
Stephen A. Lawson *Anstey Sargent & Probert*	
Guy W. Stobart *Burges Salmon*	
Victor Tettmar *Bond Pearce*	
Robert R.G. Bourns *Trump and Partners*	
Anthony Harris *Laytons*	
Derek S. Jones *Rickerby Jessop*	
Peter Rees *Wansbroughs Willey Hargrave*	

Lester Aldridge has a well-established regional insolvency practice. Its sizeable insolvency unit specialises in administration, receiverships and all other aspects of corporate insolvency. Clients include regional offices of two clearing banks, major accountancy firms and second group banks.

Leading practitioners include Hamish Anderson (*Bond Pearce*), Patrick Cook (*Osborne Clarke*), Stephen Lawson (*Anstey Sargent & Probert*), Guy Stobart (*Burges Salmon*) and Victor Tettmar (*Bond Pearce*).

WALES

Edwards Geldard and *Morgan Bruce* are the leading practices in non-contentious corporate insolvency. *Edwards Geldard* has recently recruited an insolvency lawyer from *Wilde Sapte* to head its banking and insolvency team. The firm handles a large amount of work for Barclays bank in South Wales, as well as having close links with Citibank.

LEADING FIRMS – WALES	
EDWARDS GELDARD *Cardiff*	MORGAN BRUCE *Cardiff*
EVERSHEDS *Cardiff*	HUGH JAMES JONES & JENKINS *Cardiff*

Morgan Bruce's expertise covers the core areas of insolvency as well as advice on refinancing, rescheduling and security issues. Clients include Coopers & Lybrand, Ernst & Young, KPMG, banks, financial institutions and breweries.

HIGHLY REGARDED – WALES	
BEVAN ASHFORD *Cardiff*	DOLMANS *Cardiff*

Eversheds (Cardiff) with its sound banking connections, is also highly regarded for corporate insolvency. It acts predominantly for administrative receivers, the main firms of insolvency practitioners and two major clearing banks. Recent insolvencies handled include the John Williams Foundries' administration (one of the largest administrations in South Wales) and the receivership of Pyrok Group involving several jurisdictions. Also recommended for corporate insolvency is *Bevan Ashford* in Cardiff particularly for receiverships.

Hugh James Jones & Jenkins is regarded as the main firm for contentious insolvency work (especially personal insolvency). Its team includes a licensed insolvency practitioner, and acts for banks, accountants, minority shareholders, directors and professional individuals (mainly accountants and architects). It also handles misfeasance proceedings and the defence of directors of insolvent companies. Also recommended for its contentious insolvency work is *Dolmans* in Cardiff.

LEADING INDIVIDUALS – WALES
Karl Baranski *Edwards Geldard*
R. Bleddyn V. Rees *Morgan Bruce*
Catrin Wyn Thomas *Hugh James Jones & Jenkins*
Philip D. Vaughan *Eversheds*

Notable specialists in this field include Karl Baranski (*Edwards Geldard*), Catrin Thomas (*Hugh James Jones & Jenkins*), Bleddyn Rees (*Morgan Bruce*) and Philip Vaughan (*Eversheds*).

MIDLANDS

Both *Eversheds* in Birmingham and *Wragge & Co* are recognised as the leaders in this field. The former advises insolvency practitioners on all aspects of corporate and individual insolvency with a slight emphasis on non-contentious corporate insolvencies. It continues to act for Coopers & Lybrand in the timeshare receivership of Walton Hall. The firm was also involved in the receiverships of European Network Engineering Group Plc (acting for KPMG) and Peter Storm Ltd (acting for Price Waterhouse), and the Alexander Theatre liquidation (acting for Ernst & Young).

LEADING FIRMS – MIDLANDS	
EVERSHEDS *Birmingham*	WRAGGE & CO *Birmingham*
EDGE & ELLISON *Birmingham*	PINSENT CURTIS *Birmingham*

There has been a big shift in *Wragge & Co's* insolvency practice towards solvent reconstructions and turnaround work as the number of receiverships decreases. It handles a considerable amount of intensive care and support operations for banks and companies. The firm also deals with mainstream corporate insolvency for all major West Midlands based insolvency practitioners. It is also experienced in disqualification of delinquent directors proceedings. Recent transactions include advising Arthur Andersen and Price Waterhouse on the receiverships and sales of Bacons Shoes Group and the Hawk Cycles business (manufacturing and retail) respectively.

HIGHLY REGARDED – MIDLANDS	
GATELEY WAREING *Birmingham*	MARTINEAU JOHNSON *Birmingham*
SHOOSMITHS & HARRISON *Northampton*	
BROWNE JACOBSON *Nottingham*	FREETH CARTWRIGHT HUNT DICKINS *Nottingham*
HARVEY INGRAM *Leicester*	HEWITSON BECKE + SHAW *Northampton*
HOWES PERCIVAL *Northampton*	KEELY SMITH & JOBSON *Lichfield*
KNIGHT & SONS *Newcastle-under-Lyme*	OWSTONS *Leicester*
RIGBEYS *Birmingham*	ROYTHORNE & CO *Spalding*
THE SMITH PARTNERSHIP *Derby*	WHATLEY, WESTON & FOX *Worcester*

The insolvency teams of *Edge & Ellison* and *Pinsent Curtis* are also highly regarded, both with strong banking connections. *Edge & Ellison* has undertaken a significant proportion of cross-border insolvency, including asset disposals and worldwide litigation. It is one of the few Birmingham firms with in-depth expertise in asset tracing operations on a worldwide basis. One such case handled is the National Plant and Transport plc administration. *Pinsent Curtis* has links with all major accountancy firms in addition to its close links with Barclays.

LEADING INDIVIDUALS – MIDLANDS
David J. Cooke *Pinsent Curtis*
Jeff Drew *Eversheds*
Richard Haywood *Wragge & Co*
John C.P. Sullivan *Edge & Ellison*
Brendan G. McGeever *Gateley Wareing*

In all the tables the names in each group are listed alphabetically.

Other firms with sound reputations include *Gateley Waring* (corporate and personal insolvency), *Martineau Johnson* and *Shoosmiths & Harrison* (acting primarily for financial institutions).

David Cooke *(Pinsent Curtis)*, Jeff Drew (*Eversheds, Birmingham)*, Richard Haywood *(Wragge & Co)* and John Sullivan *(Edge & Ellison)* are among the leading insolvency specialists.

EAST ANGLIA

The insolvency departments of *Eversheds* (Norwich) and *Mills & Reeve* (Norwich and Cambridge) continue to dominate the scene for corporate insolvencies. *Eversheds* handles primarily receiverships and liquidations (contentious and non-contentious). It acts regularly for Coopers & Lybrand, KPMG, Ernst & Young, Grant Thornton and BDO Stoy Hayward. The firm has developed a niche practice in advising insolvency practitioners on potential personal liabilities, especially with regards to environmental risks. One such case was the House of Lords' Cambridge Water case. Currently they are representing receivers in two instances, one involving a suit by guarantors.

LEADING FIRMS – EAST ANGLIA	
EVERSHEDS *Norwich*	**MILLS & REEVE** *Norwich*
LEATHES PRIOR *Norwich*	

Mills & Reeve's practice is very much administrative receivership oriented, although it does handle all aspects of corporate insolvency. Its clients are almost exclusively banks, specialised lending institutions and insolvency practitioners. They include Coopers & Lybrand, KPMG, Ernst & Young, Arthur Andersen, Touche Ross, BDO Stoy Hayward, Pannell Kerr Forster and Kidsons Impey.

Leathes Prior with two licensed insolvency practitioners, continues to maintain its stronghold in personal bankruptcy work which includes acquisition and disposal of businesses, security appraisal and bad debts. It also handles corporate insolvency.

HIGHLY REGARDED – EAST ANGLIA	
HEWITSON BECKE + SHAW *Cambridge*	**PALMER WHEELDON** *Cambridge*
TAYLOR VINTERS *Cambridge*	
BIRKETTS *Ipswich*	
COZENS–HARDY & JEWSON *Norwich*	**LEEDS DAY** *Sandy*
PRETTYS *Ipswich*	

Other notable firms include *Hewitson Becke + Shaw, Taylor Vinters* (specialising in receiverships, liquidations and corporate rescue) and *Birketts* (mainly corporate insolvency). *Hewitson Becke + Shaw* handles both corporate and personal insolvency including LPA receiverships. *Taylor Vinters* advises a major clearing bank on corporate and individual voluntary arrangements affecting customers. Its clients include most of Cambridgeshire's leading insolvency practitioners and Grant Thornton in Bedford and Ipswich.

Also recommended is *Palmer Wheeldon*, especially for personal insolvency. It is active in insolvency-related litigation and recently advised a liquidator in a compulsory winding-up on wrongful trading and misfeasance claims in excess of £200,000

LEADING INDIVIDUALS – EAST ANGLIA
Bryony J. Falkus *Mills & Reeve*
Paul Matthews *Eversheds*
Anthony J.G. McGurk *Eversheds*
Peter S.A. Nicholls *Leathes Prior*
Mark Robert Oakley *Leathes Prior*
Simon G. Biggin *Hewitson Becke + Shaw*
Ian Philip Mather *Palmer Wheeldon*
Graeme G. Menzies *Mills & Reeve*

Bryony Falkus *(Mills & Reeve)*, Paul Matthews – contentious *(Eversheds)*, Anthony McGurk – non-contentious *(Eversheds)*, Peter Nicholls *(Leathes Prior)* and Mark Oakley *(Leathes Prior)* are among the leaders for insolvency.

NORTH WEST

Addleshaw Sons & Latham, Alsop Wilkinson and *Slater Heelis* are widely recognised as the market leaders. *Addleshaw Sons & Latham* handles both corporate and personal insolvency with its strong expertise in banking generating a large amount of insolvency work in the past years (23% of the firm's total workload). It has been involved in several major cases including the Keith Prowse, Doctus Group, ELS, Kumar Brothers and Habit Group receiverships.

LEADING FIRMS – NORTH WEST	
ADDLESHAW SONS & LATHAM *Manchester*	**ALSOP WILKINSON** *Liverpool*
SLATER HEELIS *Manchester*	

Alsop Wilkinson specialises in corporate administrations, voluntary arrangements, administrative receiverships and the receivership of nursing homes. Principal clients include the Royal Bank of Scotland, UCB Bank and NM Rothschild & Sons Ltd as well as all major accountancy firms. It advised Price Waterhouse and Hill Samuel Bank upon the receivership of English Ironstone Ltd, and Levy Gee as receivers of John Wood Steel Drum Ltd. Other major receiverships include that of 4 Play Plc (advised Leonard Curtis & Partners) and Warwick & Bailey Ltd (advised Royal Bank of Scotland and Ernst & Young). *Slater Heelis'* insolvency team, consisting of two licensed insolvency practitioners, acts predominantly for liquidators and receivers.

Also strongly recommended are *Davies Wallis Foyster, Dibb Lupton Broomhead, Eversheds* (Manchester), *Halliwell Landau* and *Hammond Suddards.* The first has a particular strength in brewing and licensing insolvency. The majority of its work (liquidations, receiverships, administration, bankruptcies and voluntary arrangements) is handled in the Manchester office. Currently, the firm is representing creditors, NWS Trust, in the bankruptcy of some of Deacon Goldrein's partners. It also acted for Liverpool Marina's administrators.

Dibb Lupton Broomhead handles mainstream corporate and personal insolvency as well as bank reconstructions and rescheduling work. *Eversheds* (Manchester) handles a substantial amount of high value receiverships. Recent examples include Clydesdale Group plc (Grant Thornton), Polycost Ltd, (Ernst & Young), George Drew plc (Grant Thornton), Reliance Mercury Ltd (Ernst & Young) and Holemasters Ltd (Price Waterhouse). It also recently advised a German bank concerning a £10m set-off claim arising out of Barings Brothers' administration.

HIGHLY REGARDED – NORTH WEST	
DAVIES WALLIS FOYSTER *Liverpool*	DIBB LUPTON BROOMHEAD *Manchester*
EVERSHEDS *Manchester*	HALLIWELL LANDAU *Manchester*
HAMMOND SUDDARDS *Manchester*	
BERMANS *Liverpool*	CUFF ROBERTS *Liverpool*
DAVIES ARNOLD COOPER *Manchester*	
AARON & PARTNERS *Chester*	CHAFFE STREET *Manchester*
COBBETT LEAK ALMOND *Manchester*	HILL DICKINSON DAVIS CAMPBELL *Liverpool*
MACE & JONES *Liverpool*	WACKS CALLER *Manchester*

Halliwell Landau handles substantial receivership and administration cases. Its team of three partners acted on behalf of the receivers of a Midlands based house developer which resulted in a £10 million disposal of the business. *Hammond Suddards* specialises in receiverships, administrations and the sale and purchase of insolvent companies.

LEADING INDIVIDUALS – NORTH WEST
Egan R. Brooks *Slater Heelis*
Peter R. Manning *Alsop Wilkinson*
Shân Spencer *Addleshaw Sons & Latham*
Richard Glithero *Eversheds*
Duncan R. Haymes *Hammond Suddards*
Andrew L. Livesey *Halliwell Landau*

UP AND COMING
John Joyce *Slater Heelis*

Other notable firms include *Bermans* (whose corporate insolvency practice is predominantly in the brewing, leisure and factoring sectors), *Cuff Roberts* and *Davies Arnold Cooper.*

Among the numerous specialists, Egan Brooks (*Slater Heelis*), Peter Manning (*Alsop Wilkinson*) and Shân Spencer (*Addleshaw Sons & Latham*) are recognised as leaders in this field.

NORTH EAST

Dibb Lupton Broomhead, which has one of the largest regional insolvency practices, *Hammond Suddards* and *Walker Morris* have been consistently recommended as the leading firms.

Dibb Lupton Broomhead handles all aspects of insolvency including IVAs, bankruptcy, bank reconstructions and rescheduling of loans. It does however have a particular strength in liquidations due to its well-established debt recovery practice. The firm recently advised the Administrative Receivers (from Arthur Andersen) of Regent Leisureship Ltd who sold the Carvynick Golf and Country Club in Cornwall to Earlmoor Properties Ltd.

LEADING FIRMS – NORTH EAST	
DIBB LUPTON BROOMHEAD *Bradford*	WALKER MORRIS *Leeds*
EVERSHEDS *Leeds*	HAMMOND SUDDARDS *Leeds*
PINSENT CURTIS *Leeds*	

Hammond Suddards was involved in the reorganisations of Ward Group plc, Hughes Group plc and Devalit (UK). The firm also specialises in property insolvencies. *Walker Morris'* team consisting of five partners, has a particular strength in advising office-holders and lenders on turnaround, corporate rescues and intensive care. The firm also advised on a number of successful debt for equity swaps and other restructurings. Major insolvencies handled include the £25m Cam Shipping Group administration and the £12m Pilcher Group receivership.

Both *Eversheds* in Leeds and *Pinsent Curtis* have solid reputations for corporate insolvency work. The former's team comprises five full time specialists including three licensed insolvency practitioners. As well as dealing with receiverships, administrations, bankruptcy and IVA, *Eversheds* acts for creditors and companies in re-structuring matters. Also handled are LPA receiverships (with an emphasis on public houses, night clubs and hotels) and agricultural receiverships.

Pinsent Curtis' emphasis is on receiverships where it acts for the 'big six' accountancy firms and three of the clearing banks. Of the seven receiverships in Leeds in 1994, it was involved in at least two – the Corton Beach Plc receivership, and the Brown International Group Plc (which included Capital Airlines).

HIGHLY REGARDED – NORTH EAST	
DICKINSON DEES *Newcastle*	ROBERT MUCKLE *Newcastle*
BOOTH & CO. *Leeds*	CARRICK READ INSOLVENCY *Leeds*
WILKINSON MAUGHAN *Newcastle*	
BROOKE NORTH AND GOODWIN *Leeds*	IRWIN MITCHELL *Sheffield*
LUPTON FAWCETT *Leeds*	R.C. MOORHOUSE & CO *Leeds*
ROLLIT FARRELL & BLADON *Hull*	WARD HADAWAY *Newcastle*
WATSON BURTON *Newcastle*	

The leading Newcastle firms are *Dickinson Dees* and *Robert Muckle,* both handling corporate and personal insolvency. The former's team has had a good year, particularly in receivership matters. The firm has recently handled receivership sales with a gross value of assets sold exceeding £10 million. Its expertise also extends to agricultural receiverships, the appointment of receivers to Industrial & Provident Societies and the conversion of bankruptcies into IVA. The firm acts for the Treasury Solicitor and the Official Receivers in Stockton-on-Tees and Newcastle-upon-Tyne.

Robert Muckle's team consisting of two licensed insolvency practitioners, advises major clearing and secondary banks, building societies, and the 'Big Six' accountancy firms on all aspects of administration, receivership and restructuring. Also handled are misfeasance, wrongful trading and directors' disqualification matters. Notable cases include advice to the administrative receivers of Swan Hunter and the administrative receivers on the handover of Slaley Hall receivership.

Booth & Co, the niche practice of *Carrick Read Insolvency* and *Wilkinson Maughan* have well established insolvency practices. All of *Carrick Read Insolvency*'s partners are licensed insolvency practitioners and they cover both personal and corporate insolvency matters.

LEADING INDIVIDUALS – NORTH EAST

Peter Cranston *Dibb Lupton Broomhead*	
Christopher W. Jones *Hammond Suddards*	
Philip J. Mudd *Walker Morris*	
William Ballmann *Booth & Co.*	
Christopher Garwood *Carrick Read Insolvency*	
Ian M. Gilthorpe *Robert Muckle*	
Julian Horrocks *Eversheds*	
Mark S. Jackson *Dibb Lupton Broomhead*	
Jonathan D. Jeffries *Pinsent Curtis*	
Andrew Laycock *Carrick Read Insolvency*	
John A. Pennie *Dickinson Dees*	
Catherine Mary Wood *Robert Muckle*	

Among the numerous insolvency specialists, Peter Cranston (*Dibb Lupton Broomhead*), Christopher Jones (*Hammond Suddards*) and Philip Mudd (*Walker Morris*) have consistently been recommended as leaders in this field.

SCOTLAND

Insolvency work tends to revolve around Glasgow, Aberdeen and Edinburgh, with Glasgow cornering the lion's share. *Dorman Jeffrey & Co* has a formidable position in corporate insolvency work and is undoubtedly the premier firm. It is one of the few Scottish firms with a separate corporate recovery and insolvency department, and this work forms around 37% of the firm's total workload. Currently the bulk of it relates to receiverships and major reconstructions. Clients include banks and leading accountancy firms. It was involved in the Maxwell, Leyland DAF, Ferranti, HCI and Scottish Heritable Trust cases.

Also highly respected are *Dundas & Wilson* and *MacRoberts*. The former handling primarily corporate insolvency, is currently acting for the joint liquidators of Clydesdale Group plc and six of its subsidiaries, one of the largest liquidations in Scotland. Other cases include acting for the receivers of Encap UK Ltd and of Arthur Armstrong & Co. Ltd (appointed by the Royal Bank of Scotland and NatWest respectively). *MacRoberts'* team consisting of four partners handles both personal and corporate insolvency.

Other firms with strong reputations include *W & J Burness* and *Shepherd & Wedderburn*. The former's team consisting of an accredited insolvency specialist was recently involved

in the second largest receivership in Scotland, having acted for the receivers (Coopers & Lybrand) of Galloway Cheese Co Ltd. Major insolvencies in which *Shepherd & Wedderburn* was involved include BCCI, British & Commonwealth as well as the Air Ecosse administration.

LEADING FIRMS – SCOTLAND

DORMAN JEFFREY & CO *Glasgow*	
DUNDAS & WILSON CS *Edinburgh*	**MACROBERTS** *Glasgow*
W & J BURNESS WS *Edinburgh*	**SHEPHERD & WEDDERBURN** *Edinburgh*

Also consistently recommended are *Biggart Baillie & Gifford, Bird Semple, Iain Smith & Co* (with three Law Society accredited insolvency specialists), *Maclay Murray & Spens* (two accredited insolvency practitioners) and *McGrigor Donald.*

Biggart Baillie & Gifford with an accredited insolvency specialist has a particular strength in litigious insolvency work, having defended the first wrongful trading action. Other major cases include Balfour Beatty concerning the position of trust funds in a receivership and EFT v Gresham House (the rights of a guarantor to challenge a liquidation damage clause).

Bird Semple specialises in receiverships, liquidations and company voluntary arrangements. *Maclay Murray & Spens* acted for the joint receivers of Clydesdale Group in negotiating the sale of the business as a going concern.

HIGHLY REGARDED – SCOTLAND

BIGGART BAILLIE & GIFFORD *Glasgow*	**BIRD SEMPLE** *Glasgow*
IAIN SMITH & CO *Aberdeen*	**MACLAY MURRAY & SPENS** *Glasgow*
McGRIGOR DONALD *Glasgow*	
ANDERSON FYFE *Glasgow*	**BENNETT & ROBERTSON** *Edinburgh*
BISHOP AND ROBERTSON CHALMERS *Glasgow*	**McCLURE NAISMITH ANDERSON & GARDINER** *Glasgow*
PAGAN MACBETH *Cupar*	**STRONACHS** *Aberdeen*
WRIGHT, JOHNSTON & MACKENZIE *Glasgow*	
BOYDS *Glasgow*	**BRODIES WS** *Edinburgh*
DICKSON MINTO WS *Edinburgh*	**FYFE IRELAND** *Edinburgh*
KIDSTONS & CO *Glasgow*	**MACDONALDS** *Glasgow*
MORTON FRASER MILLIGAN *Edinburgh*	**PAULL & WILLIAMSONS** *Aberdeen*
STEEDMAN RAMAGE WS *Edinburgh*	**TINDAL OATTS** *Glasgow*
TODS MURRAY WS *Edinburgh*	

Other Glasgow firms with a sound insolvency practices include *Anderson Fyfe, Bishop and Robertson Chalmers, McClure Naismith Anderson & Gardiner* and *Wright Johnston & Mackenzie. Anderson Fyfe's* clients include major credit and national finance companies. It is known for insolvency related litigation having acted for the successful liquidators in two of the leading cases in Scotland on directors misfeasance (Blin v Johnston) and unfair preferences (Nicoll v Steelpress). The firm is the external litigation consultant for Scottish Enterprise.

Bishop and Robertson Chalmers advises on corporate and personal insolvency, and corporate rescues, whilst *McClure*

Naismith Anderson & Gardiner is known for receiverships. Also well-regarded are *Bennett & Robertson, Pagan Macbeth* and *Stronachs,* all of which have Law Society accredited insolvency practitioners.

Leading insolvency specialists include Yvonne Brady (*Dorman Jeffrey & Co*), Christopher Campbell (*Dundas & Wilson*), Ian Cuthbertson (*Dorman Jeffrey & Co*), David Flint (*MacRoberts*), Paul Hally (*Shepherd & Wedderburn*) and Andrew Sleigh (*W & J Burness*).

NORTHERN IRELAND

Firms with prominent insolvency practices include *Carson & McDowell, Cleaver Fulton & Rankin, L'Estrange & Brett, Napier & Sons* and *Tughan & Co.* The insolvency team of *Tughan & Co* which consists of a licensed insolvency practitioner, acts for the Official Receiver. *L'Estrange & Brett* handles the usual spectrum of corporate insolvency matters including wrongful trading and personal liability issues.

LEADERS IN INSOLVENCY

LONDON

Andrews, Mark B.
Wilde Sapte, London (0171) 246 7000. Partner and Head of Insolvency Group.

Specialisation: Main area of work is insolvency, advising on administrations, receiverships, liquidations, bankruptcies, voluntary arrangements, work-outs and re-structurings and directors' liabilities. Other main area of work is banking, advising on insolvency, security and restructuring issues. Acted in receiverships of Leyland DAF Ltd, Harrap Publishing Ltd, Coloroll Group, and Lockwoods Foods. Member of Editorial Board for Insolvency Bulletin and Receivers, Administrators & Liquidations Quarterly. Member CLSC Insolvency Law Sub-Committee. Regularly chairs and addresses conferences on insolvency issues.

Prof. Memberships: Law Society, City of London Solicitors Company, Society of Practitioners of Insolvency, Insolvency Lawyers Association, AEPPC, INSOL and IBA.

Career: Articled with *Clark & Son* Reading 1974-76. Joined *Wilde Sapte* in 1976 and became a Partner in 1979. Became Head of Insolvency in 1991.

Personal: Born 12th July 1952. Attended Reading Grammar School 1963-69, then Hertford College, Oxford 1970-73. Trustee of Pimlico Opera. Leisure pursuits include music, playing the French horn, singing, history, ornithology and farming. Lives in London.

Barnett, Nigel
Wilde Sapte, London (0171) 246 7000. Partner in Insolvency Group.

Specialisation: Handles all aspects of insolvency, but with particular emphasis on insolvency litigation. Cases include: The Reject Shop PLC, Lancer Boss Group Plc, Leyland Daf Ltd, Resort Hotels Plc, Aldermanbury Trust Plc and Nyckeln Finance Co Ltd.

Prof. Membership: International Bar Association, Insolvency Lawyers Association, SPI, AEPPC.

Career: Qualified in 1985. Partner at *Wilde Sapte* since 1991.

Personal: Educated at Southampton University 1979-82 and Guildford College of Law 1983-84.

Bethell-Jones, Richard J.S.
Wilde Sapte, London (0171) 246 7000. Partner in Banking and Finance Department.

Specialisation: Specialist in banking. Areas of practice include banking, secured and unsecured lending, including management and leveraged buy-outs and project finance, drafting and take up of security, rescheduling and work-outs and sale of loan assets, administra-

tions and administrative receiverships. Also handles insurance insolvency. Acted for the administrators of Fairbriar Plc and the German trustee and paying agent for ECU and DM bonds issued by Maxwell Communications Corporations. Acts for banks, administrative receivers and administrators. Contributor to numerous publications and journals. Has spoken at a number of seminars.

Prof. Membership: City of London Law Society, International Bar Association, Society of Practioners of Insolvency, Insolvency Lawyers Association.

Career: Qualified in 1970. Partner in *Wilde Sapte* from 1974.

Personal: Born 16th September 1945. Educated at St Johns School Leatherhead 1957-63 and Churchill College, Cambridge 1964-67. Leisure pursuits include tennis, sailing and cinema. Lives in London.

Booker, Ashley R.B.
Clifford Chance, London (0171) 600 1000. Partner. Principal area of work is insolvency. Acts for insolvency practitioners, banks and corporate clients.

Cole, Margaret
Stephenson Harwood, London (0171) 329 4422. Qualified 1985. Partner 1990. Litigation Department. Specialises in complex banking recovery matters and asset tracing (civil fraud).

Fidler, Peter J.M.

Stephenson Harwood, London (0171) 329 4422. Qualified 1967. Partner 1984. Banking Department. Insolvency & Asset Recovery Group. Principal area of practice is insolvency. Other main area is banking. Born 16.3.1942.

Fletcher, Ian

Richards Butler, London (0171) 247 6555. Qualified 1971. (Scotland) and 1978 (England). Partner 1987. Main area of practice is corporate insolvency law against general corporate law background. Born 16.2.1948.

Foster, Stephen J.

Cameron Markby Hewitt, London (0171) 702 2345. Partner in Banking & Insolvency Department.

Specialisation: Principal area of practice is insolvency. Work includes advising banks on domestic banking questions and pre-insolvency issues, including options to maximise recovery and advising Insolvency Practitioners in receiverships, administrations and liquidations. Other main area of practice is UK and US distressed debt funds, advising on documentation and insolvency issues. Has lectured to the Institute of Bankers, SPI and for various commercial lecture providers on banking and insolvency topics.

Prof. Membership: Law Society, Insolvency Lawyers Association, AEPPC.

Career: Qualified in 1989. Became a Partner at *Cameron Markby Hewitt* in 1991.

Personal: Born 4th January 1958. Educated at Pembroke College, Cambridge. Interests inlcude walking, music and film. Lives in London.

Gale, Stephen

Hammond Suddards, London (0171) 628 4767. Partner in Insolvency and Corporate Recovery Department. London Office.

Specialisation: Principal area of practice is corporate rescue and company reorganisation. Has wide experience of acting for banks and other financial institutions in work-outs and reorganisations. Also has considerable insolvency related experience, particularly in corporate insolvencies. Has acted in Maxwell case on Israeli realisations and for building societies in the Kentish and Declan Kelly collapses. Has written numerous articles on insolvency-related topics and lectured widely on specialist areas.

Prof. Membership: Law Society, Institute of Credit Management, SPI, IPA, AEPPC.

Career: Qualified in 1982. Associate Partner with *Simpson Curtis* 1984, then Partner with *Masons & Marriott* in Hong Kong, 1985. Joined *Hammond Suddards* in 1985 as a Partner.

Personal: Born 15th October 1957. Attended Blackpool Grammar School and Sixth Form College, then Sheffield University. Leisure pursuits include fell walking, windsurfing,

horseriding, skiing and classical music. Lives in London and Holmfirth.

Gill, Mark S.

Wilde Sapte, London (0171) 246 7000. Partner in Banking Litigation Department.

Specialisation: Specialises in contentious litigation for banks, often involving insolvency related issues. Acts mainly for banks. Lectures widely on banking and insolvency topics.

Prof. Membership: Licensed insolvency practioner, Member of the Society of Practioners for Insolvency, Associate Member of AEPPC.

Career: Qualified in 1977. Articles with *Alsop Stevens & Batesons* 1975-77. Lecturer for The College of Law 1977-79. Joined *Wilde Sapte* in 1979. Became a partner in 1985.

Personal: Born 15th March 1953. Educated at St. Anselm's Colllege, Birkenhead and University College London (LL.B). Lives in London.

Gregory, D.A.

Lovell White Durrant, London (0171) 236 0066.

Grier, Ian Stephen

Sprecher Grier, London (0171) 831 9027. Partner in Litigation and Insolvency Department.

Specialisation: Deals with all aspects of corporate and individual insolvency, principally working for administrative receivers, liquidators and trustees in bankruptcy as well as for banks and creditors. Substantial involvement in rescue schemes for limited companies, partnerships and individuals by way of corporate and individual voluntary arrangements. Also has considerable experience in relation to court appointed receiverships and LPA receiverships. Other main area of practice is corporate litigation including contractual disputes, construction work, intellectual property, banking litigation and debt recovery. Important cases have included Re Brightlife Limited (leading case on fixed and floating charges); Re Cranley Mansions Limited (leading case in relation to individual voluntary arrangement); Scottish Enterprise v. Bank of East Asia Limited (in relation to law of set off - appeal pending in House of Lords). Clients include one of the clearing banks, merchant banks, a substantial number of firms of insolvency practitioners and major firms of chartered and certified accountants, international airlines and international employment agencies. Lectures widely to the SPI, firms of chartered accountants and other professional bodies in relation to the law and practice of insolvency. Co-author of three published works on corporate and individual insolvency and of numerous articles. Charge-out rate is £245 per hour.

Prof. Membership: Law Society, Society of Practitioners of Insolvency (Member of the Small Practices Issues Committee).

Career: Qualified in 1972. Joined with David Sprecher to form *Sprecher Grier* in 1984.

Personal: Born 23rd February 1945. Educated at London University (LL.B 1967, LL.M 1968). Governor of a number of schools. Former local councillor. Leisure interests include theatre, playing poker and bridge. Lives in London.

Grierson, Christopher K.

Lovell White Durrant, London (0171) 236 0066.

Hamilton, Dan

Cameron Markby Hewitt, London (0171) 702 2345. Qualified 1988. Partner 1994. Banking Department. Principal area of practice is insolvency and reconstruction.

Hanson, Christopher

Lovell White Durrant, London (0171) 236 0066. Qualified 1965. Partner 1968. Insolvency and Corporate Recovery Department. Main area of practice covers corporate insolvency and banking law, with a particular emphasis on the employment aspects of insolvency. Born 20.4.1940.

Horrocks, Peter G.

Lovell White Durrant, London (0171) 236 0066. Qualified 1968. Partner 1975. Head of Insolvency. Work includes liquidations, receiverships, administrations and other contentious commercial matters (frequently internationally). Born 25.6.1944.

Houghton, John

Simmons & Simmons, London (0171) 628 2020. Partner in Corporate Department.

Specialisation: Principal area of practice is insolvency and reconstructions. Work includes rescues and reconstructions, administrations, receiverships and liquidations and cross-border insolvencies. Recently handled the Team Lotus administration, the Travers Morgan administrations, and the de Savary companies receiverships. Also recently advised on the Heron reconstruction, the reconstruction of a large hotels group and the rescue of a high profile manufacturing company.

Prof. Membership: Society of Practitioners of Insolvency, Law Society, Insolvency Lawyers Association, and the European Insolvency Practitioners Association.

Career: Qualified in 1989, became a Partner in 1994.

Personal: Born 20th February 1962. Educated at Brunel University and University College, London 1980-84 (LL.B Hons, First Class) 1984-85 (LL.M). Interests include wine, Manchester United, music and an E-Type. Lives in London.

Kidd, David John

Cameron Markby Hewitt, London (0171) 702 2345. Partner in Insolvency Department.

Specialisation: Principal area of practice is administrations, receiverships and liquidators acting for administrators, receivers and liquidations all areas, including in particular dispute resolution and cross-border issues. Also handles fraud and commercial litigation. Experience in general commercial litigation, particularly fraud, obtaining Mareva and Anton Piller relief and asset tracing. Acted in Sugar Properties (Derisley Wood) Ltd (bloodstock receivership), Aveling Barford Group of Companies (manufacturing receivership), Atlantic Computer Group of Companies (company leasing administration) and Polly Peck International Plc (electronics, leisure and fresh produce administration). Acted for Court appointed receiver in Derby v. Weldon litigation. Clients include Arthur Andersen, Coopers & Lybrand, Price Waterhouse, Touche Ross, KPMG, banks and creditors. Has lectured at conferences organised by Euroforum, IBC and the Society of Practitioners of Insolvency. Charge-out rate is £270 per hour.

Prof. Membership: Law Society, Society of Practitioners of Insolvency (Assoc.), Society of Insurance Receivers.

Career: Qualified in New Zealand in 1982. Barrister and Solicitor with *Simpson Grierson Butler White* 1982-83. Joined *Cameron Markby Hewitt* in 1984 and became a Partner in 1990. Qualified as a solicitor in England and Wales in 1989.

Personal: Born 8th April 1959. Educated at St Paul's Collegiate School, Hamilton, New Zealand 1972-76 and Auckland University (LL.B/ BCom) 1977-81. Chairman, Crescent Amenity Group. Leisure interests include cricket, theatre, golf and sailing. Lives in London.

Montgomery, Nigel

Davies Arnold Cooper, London (0171) 936 2222. Partner in charge of insurance Insolvency and Corporate Rescue/Insolvency Departments.

Specialisation: Principal area is advising provisional liquidators, scheme administrators, liquidators and creditors of insolvent insurers/reinsurers on schemes of arrangement and on accelerated run-off in solvent cases. Advising on schemes of arrangement for RMCA Re; ICS Re; Charter Re; MGI; ICS UK. Also advises receivers, administrators, supervisors of CVAs and banks on corporate insolvency and companies, banks and shareholders on rescue and turnaround strategies. Acted in the receiverships of Clarke Foods/Lyons Maid and for a major bidder for Ferranti receivership assets. Frequently lectures and writes on insurance insolvency in UK and USA. Is a licensed Insolvency Practitioner.

Prof. Membership: Law Society; Society of Practitioners of Insolvency; Society of Insurance Receivers; AEPPC; Insolvency Lawyers Association.

Career: Qualified 1981.

Personal: Born 1956. Attended Cambridge

University. Leisure pursuits include wild-life conservation, old cars and target rifle shooting. Lives in Kent.

Naylor, Judith P.

Allen & Overy, London (0171) 330 3000. Qualified 1986. Partner. Banking Department. Specialises in all aspects of insolvency law. Born 15.9.1961.

Pratt, Sandy

Norton Rose, London (0171) 283 6000. Qualified 1978. Partner 1988. Corporate & Financial Department. Main areas of practice are corporate rescue and insolvency.

Prior, Michael

Nabarro Nathanson, London (0171) 493 9933.

Rhodes, Paul A.

Dibb Lupton Broomhead, London (0171) 600 0202.

Rickard, Josanne

Freshfields, London (0171) 936 4000.

Roome, James H.D.

Simmons & Simmons, London (0171) 628 2020. Partner in Corporate Department.

Specialisation: Principal area of practice is insolvency and reconstructions. Work includes restructurings, corporate insolvency, cross-border and multinational insolvency, receivership, enforcement, administration, liquidations and contentious insolvency. Also handles general corporate work. Has addressed conferences on enforcement of security, employees and insolvency and secondary insolvency litigation. Author of miscellaneous articles on insolvency issues.

Prof. Membership: Society of Practitioners of Insolvency, Law Society, Insolvency Lawyers Association, European Insolvency Practitioners Association.

Career: Qualified in 1984 and in Hong Kong in 1985. Became Partner at *Simmons & Simmons* Hong Kong office in 1987 and at London office in 1988. Licensed Insolvency Practitioner from March 1990.

Personal: Born 7th October 1958. Educated at Wellington College 1971-76 and Southampton University 1978-81 (LL.B Hons). Leisure pursuits include yachting. Lives in London.

Rushworth, Jonathan E.F.

Slaughter and May, London (0171) 600 1200. Qualified 1974. Joined 1974. Company and Corporate Finance. Particular expertise in capital markets (especially trustees).

Schaffer, Danny

Isadore Goldman, London (0171) 242 3000. Partner.

Specialisation: Specialises in all aspects of insolvency including related litigation and bank recovery. Licensed Insolvency Practi-

tioner.

Prof. Membership: Society for Practitioners of Insolvency, Insolvency Lawyers Association.

Career: Qualified in 1975. Partner at *Isadore Goldman* since 1978. Appointed Deputy Registrar in Bankruptcy at High Court in February 1992.

Personal: Born 2nd September 1950. University of Birmingham 1969-71. Spare time activities include being a football referee. Lives in London.

Segal, Nicholas

Allen & Overy, London (0171) 330 3000. Qualified 1982. Partner 1989. Main areas of practice are banking, commercial law and insolvency. Work includes corporate reorganisations, rescues, administrations, receiverships, liquidations, schemes of arrangement, other insolvency proceedings and commercial disputes.

Shandro, Sandy

Clifford Chance, London (0171) 600 1000. Qualified 1978 (British Columbia); 1992 (England & Wales). Partner in Insolvency Department. Specialises in insolvency work. Born 14.7.1951.

Spencer, R.

Lovell White Durrant, London (0171) 236 0066.

Steinberg, David Jeremy

Clifford Chance, London (0171) 600 1000. Partner 1994. Insolvency Department. Specialises in insolvency and corporate restructuring.

Steiner, Michael

Denton Hall, London (0171) 242 1212. Partner in Litigation Department.

Specialisation: Main area of practice is insolvency and corporate reconstruction. Specialises in all areas of insolvency law, including official and unofficial corporate reconstruction, administrative receiverships and liquidations, personal insolvency (including voluntary arrangements) and asset recovery, particularly in relation to trans-national insolvencies. Acts for provisional liquidators on public interest petitions and has advised regulatory bodies.

Prof. Membership: International Bar Association Creditors Rights Section (Joint Chairman of Sub-Committee on Model International Bankruptcy Legislation); Bar and Law Society's Joint Working Party on Insolvency Law; City of London Solicitors' Insolvency Society Sub-Committee.

Career: Qualified in 1964. Partner with *Booth & Blackwell* 1964-90. Joined *Denton Hall* as a Partner in 1990. Solicitor member of the Lord Chancellor's Insolvency Rules Advisory Committee 1986-92. Consultant to the Czech Government on privatisation with responsibility for insolvency legislation. Adviser to the Russian Federation Ministry on Insolvency.

Personal: Born in 1938. Educated at St. Paul's School, London and Lincoln College, Oxford (MA 1961). Leisure pursuits include theatre, cinema and walking the dog.

Stewart, Gordon C.

Allen & Overy, London (0171) 330 3000. Qualified 1980. Partner 1989. Banking Department. Main areas of practice are business reconstruction and insolvency. Handled administrations of Maxwell Private Companies and receiverships of Ferranti and Athena. Born 16.5.1956.

Totty, Peter G.

Allen & Overy, London (0171) 330 3000. Qualified 1964. Partner in Banking Department. Work covers banking, debt rescheduling, work-outs and insolvency. Born 10.6.1938.

Verrill, John

Lawrence Graham, London (0171) 379 0000. Partner in Company Commercial Department.

Specialisation: Main area of practice is insolvency, including corporate insolvency, banking, restructuring, voluntary arrangements, receiverships and liquidations. Also handles oil and gas law. Work covers all aspects of upstream asset management, including sales and purchases, transportation and joint ventures. Acted in the company voluntary arrangement of London Securities PLC and gives advice to boards of British and Commonwealth and Polly Peck after administration orders made. Author of Butterworths Insolvency Meetings Manual, (to be published 1995). Frequent speaker on insolvency topics.

Prof. Membership: Insolvency Practitioners Association, Society of Practitioners in Insolvency, Insolvency Lawyers Association, UK Energy Lawyers Group, International Bar Associations Section on Energy Law.

Career: Qualified in 1981. Joined *Lawrence Graham* in 1983, becoming a Partner in 1986. Trainee and Assistant Solicitor at *Ward Bowie*, Basingstoke 1978-82.

Personal: Born 25th March 1954. Attended University College School Hampstead, then University College, London. Leisure interests include rowing, sailing and sea fishing. Lives in Barnes, London.

White, John J.

Cameron Markby Hewitt, London (0171) 702 2345. Partner and Head of Banking and Insolvency Department.

Specialisation: Insolvency work includes multi-bank support operations, administrations and administrative receiverships. Banking work includes clearing bank lending, property and project finance, trade finance and syndicated facilities. Acted for the administrators of Polly Peck, the examiner of the Maxwell Communication Corporation and the administrators of Air

Europe. Addresses around twenty conferences per year including several for the Chartered Institute of Bankers.

Prof. Memberships: Law Society, Chartered Institute of Bankers, Society of Practitioners in Insolvency, Insolvency Lawyers Association, International Bar Association, City of London Solicitors Company, Association Europeénne des Practiciens des Procédures Collectives.

Career: Qualified in 1963. Having joined *Cameron Markby Hewitt* in 1957, became a Partner in 1964. Fellow of the Chartered Institute of Bankers.

Personal: Born 6th July 1938. Leisure interests include hockey, cricket and port. Lives in London. Clubs. Athenaeum and West Herts.

Wilkinson, Andrew

Clifford Chance, London (0171) 600 1000. Partner. Principal area of practice is corporate insolvency and reconstruction work encompassing cross-border insolvencies, all aspects of insurance company and intermediary reconstruction and transactions against an insolvency background including work-outs and rescues.

Woolf, Geoffrey

Stephenson Harwood, London (0171) 329 4422. Qualified 1970. Partner 1975. Banking Department (Insolvency and Asset Recovery Group). Specialises in corporate insolvency and reconstruction.

Wright, Richard W.

Dibb Lupton Broomhead, London (0171) 600 0202.

REGIONS

Anderson, Hamish

Bond Pearce, Plymouth (01752) 266633. Qualified 1973. Partner and licensed insolvency practitioner 1977. Banking and Insolvency Division. Specialises in banking and building society law, asset finance and insolvency (all aspects under Insolvency Act 1986).

Ballmann, William

Booth & Co., Leeds (0113) 283 2000. Partner and Head of Insolvency Department.

Specialisation: Handles all aspects of contentious and non-contentious corporate and personal insolvency work. Also covers related banking work. Contributor of articles and updates to 'Insolvency Practitioner'. Speaker at SPI conferences and seminars.

Prof. Membership: Law Society, SPI, Insolvency Lawyers Association, AEPPC.

Career: Qualified in 1983. Joined *Booth & Co.* as Partner and Head of Insolvency Department in 1992.

Personal: Born 1955. Attended Esher Grammar School and the University of Leeds (LLB 1978). Leisure interests include skiing,

scuba diving, classic car restoration, food and wine, and golf.

Baranski, Karl

Edwards Geldard, Cardiff (01222) 238239.

Le Bas, Malcolm H.

Paris Smith & Randall, Southampton (01703) 635191. Partner in Commercial Department.

Specialisation: Principal area of practice since 1972 has been insolvency and sales and purchases of businesses, including MBO's. Has an extensive practice acting for both vendors and purchasers. Clients include national firms of insolvency practitioners, the Insolvency Service and a significant number of local companies, including work for PLC's. Individual charge-out rate of 130 per hour.

Prof. Membership: Law Society.

Career: Qualified in 1964. Became a Partner at *Paris Smith & Randall* in 1969. Managing Partner since 1993.

Personal: Born 28th October 1941. Educated at Worksop College 1955-59. Governor, Southampton Institute; Hon. Solicitor to Hampshire County Cricket Club; Secretary, Mayflower Theatre Trust; Chairman Southern Newspapers PLC Pension Fund. Past President Trojans Sports Club. Trustee of Wessex Cancer Trust. Interests include cricket, rugby union, cinema, theatre and jazz. Lives in Southampton.

Bell, D. Graham

Wright, Johnston & Mackenzie, Glasgow (0141) 248 3434. Qualified 1987. Partner 1993. Litigation Department. Main area of practice is insolvency. Also handles commercial repossession.

Bennett, David A.

Bennett & Robertson, Edinburgh (0131) 225 4001. Qualified 1962. Partner 1964. Main area of practice is company, commercial and insolvency law. Certified Specialist in Insolvency Law.

Biggin, Simon G.

Hewitson Becke + Shaw, Cambridge (01223) 461155. Qualified 1983. Partner 1990. Litigation Department. Work covers all aspects of corporate and personal insolvency.

Bourns, Robert R.G.

Trump and Partners, Bristol (0117) 929 9901. Qualified 1980. Partner 1987. Business Client/ Company Commercial Department. Principal area of practice is insolvency work.

Brady, Yvonne T.

Dorman Jeffrey & Co, Glasgow (0141) 221 9880. Partner in Insolvency Department.

Specialisation: Main area of practice is corporate reconstruction and insolvency. Also deals with licensing, mainly in insolvency situations. Currently contributing two chapters to 'A Scottish Insolvency Casebook', due for publication in autumn 1994. Regularly convenes and lectures at Institute of Chartered Accountants seminars. Presents seminars for Law Society courses and lectures at Joint Insolvency Examination Board seminars.

Prof. Membership: Law Society.

Career: Qualified in 1984, having joined *Dorman Jeffrey & Co.* in 1982. Became a Partner in 1990.

Personal: Born 3rd July 1961. Educated at Strathclyde University 1978-82. Leisure pursuits include cooking, entertaining and reading (mainly thrillers and biographies). Lives in Glasgow.

Branson, Christopher

Boyes Turner & Burrows, Reading (01734) 597711. Partner in Insolvency Group.

Specialisation: Principal area of practice is corporate and individual insolvency. Acts for receivers, liquidators and administrators in corporate insolvency situations and for trustees in bankruptcy as well as nominees and supervisors in CVA'S and IVA'S. Advises banks and financial institutions on security and lending issues. Also advises upon debt collection (Head of the firm's Debt Collection Unit). Clients include Cork Gully, Coopers & Lybrand, Ernst & Young, KPMG, Price Waterhouse, Touche Ross and Barclays Bank. Has lectured at SPI South conferences as well as giving internal lectures and talks to accountancy firms. Charge-out rate of £150 per hour.

Prof. Membership: Law Society, IPA, SPI.

Career: Qualified in 1981. At *Hewett Pim & Dixon* 1981-1987 (Partner from 1983). Partner at *Boyes Turner & Burrows* from 1988.

Personal: Born in 1955. Educated at Kingston University 1975-78 (BA Hons in Law). Leisure activities include windsurfing, mountain biking and squash. Lives in Caversham, Reading.

Brooks, Egan R.

Slater Heelis, Manchester (0161) 228 3781.

Campbell, Christopher R.J.

See under Company/Commercial.

Chaplin, David H.

Anderson Fyfe, Glasgow (0141) 248 4381. Partner in Commercial Department.

Specialisation: Main area of practice is corporate insolvency. Work includes receiverships, liquidations and administrations. Licensed Insolvency Practitioner; accredited specialist in insolvency law. Also handles debt recovery. Solicitor for major credit card company and national finance companies. External litigation consultant for Scottish Enterprise. Wrote Scottish section of 'Voluntary Liquidations and Receiverships'

by Grier & Floyd; and 'Personal Insolvency' (Scottish Sections) for Grier & Floyd. Gives training lectures to Accountant Insolvency Practitioners.

Prof. Membership: Law Society of Scotland, Institute of Credit Management.

Career: Qualified in 1972. Joined *Anderson Fyfe* in 1970, becoming a Partner in 1975.

Personal: Born 23rd January 1950. Attended Glasgow University 1967-70. Leisure interests include sailing, motoring and walking. Lives in Bearsden.

Clarke, John B.

Pagan Macbeth, Cupar (01334) 657000. Qualified 1977. Partner 1994. Commercial and Insolvency Department. Licensed Insolvency Practitioner.

Cook, Patrick D.

Osborne Clarke, Bristol (0117) 923 0220. Qualified 1983. Partner 1986. Insolvency Department. Has acted for office holder in some 450 administrative receiverships, 300 Law of Property Act receiverships and eight administration orders. Born 11.7.1956.

Cooke, David J.

See under Banking.

Craig, Nigel Stuart

Sherwin Oliver, Portsmouth (01705) 832200. Qualified 1981. Partner 1989. Corporate/Commercial and Corporate Rescue Department. Main areas of practice are corporate restructuring, mergers, acquisitions and disposals, with and without insolvency related issues. Born 16.12.1956.

Cranston, Peter

Dibb Lupton Broomhead, Leeds (0113) 243 9301. Qualified 1981. Partner 1989. Banking and Corporate Recovery Department. Main areas of practice are insolvency, banking and security. Born 27.7.1956.

Cuthbertson, Ian J.

Dorman Jeffrey & Co, Glasgow (0141) 221 9880. Partner in Corporate Reconstruction and Insolvency Department.

Specialisation: Main area of practice is corporate reconstruction, acting mainly for banks, and corporate insolvencies, acting mainly for receivers, administrators and liquidators. Also corporate, mainly banking and investment related. Consultant to 'Law of Corporate Insolvency in Scotland' (St. Clair & Drummond Young, 2nd ed., Butterworths). Has lectured to the Law Society of Scotland and Institute of Chartered Accountants in Scotland at educational courses and at seminars with accountants and banks. On the panel of examiners for JIEB.

Prof. Membership: Law Society of Scotland, Insolvency Practitioners Association, Society of Practitioners in Insolvency, Insolvency Lawyers Association, Royal Faculty of Procurators in Glasgow.

Career: Qualified in 1972. Became a Notary

Public in 1975 and Licensed Insolvency Practitioner in 1986. Joint founding Partner of *Dorman Jeffrey & Co.* in 1979.

Personal: Born 8th May 1951. Educated at the University of Glasgow. Leisure interests include sport, reading and music. Lives in Milngavie.

Drew, Jeff

Eversheds, Birmingham (0121) 233 2001. Partner in Insolvency and Banking Group.

Specialisation: Advises insolvency practitioners in connection with all aspects of insolvency law and banks in connection with the taking and realising of charges. Speaks widely at conferences and seminars.

Prof. Membership: Society of Practitioners of Insolvency.

Career: Qualified in 1980. Worked at *Wragge & Co.* 1978-82, then *Edge & Ellison* 1982-92 (from 1984 as a Partner). Joined *Eversheds Wells & Hind* as a Partner in 1992.

Personal: Born 12th October 1954. Attended Solihull School and St Edmund Hall, Oxford 1974-77. Leisure interests include tennis, squash and badminton. Lives in Birmingham.

Falkus, Bryony J.

Mills & Reeve, Norwich +44 (0) 1603 660155. Partner in Corporate Department.

Specialisation: Main area of practice is corporate insolvency specialising in receiverships and administrations, acting for banks, specialised lending institutions and insolvency practitioners. Also handles banking and insolvency work. Major clients include Coopers and Lybrand, KPMG and other accountants.

Career: Qualified 1976. Partner at *Pickering Kenyon* 1978-90. Consultant *Mills and Reeve* 1990-92 and made a Partner in 1992.

Personal: Born 10th July 1952. Attended St Felix School, Southwold 1961-70 and Coventry University BA Hons (Business Law) 1970-73. Member of the Regional Board, Princes Youth Business Trust. Leisure interests include travel, gardening and theatre. Lives in Alpington, Norwich.

Flint, David

See under Intellectual Property.

Garwood, Christopher

Carrick Read Insolvency, Hull (01482) 211160. Senior Partner

Specialisation: Has specialised in all aspects of personal and corporate insolvency since 1975 and is an authorised insolvency practitioner. Through Senior Partnership with associated firm *Carrick Garwood Devine* also deals with general commercial work.

Prof. Memberships: Law Society, Insolvency Lawyers Association (Founder member and 1993/4 President), SPI, IPA, AEPPC.

Career: Qualified 1973 before establishing *Carr & Garwood*, which merged in 1979 to become *Carrick Carr & Garwood*. Was licensed to act as an insolvency practitioner in 1986 after working on the Law Society Committee dealing with the 1985 Insolvency Act. Established *Carrick Read Insolvency* in 1990, and in 1992 established the primarily commercial practice of *Carrick Garwood Devine*: currently Senior Partner of both.

Personal: Born 15th June 1949. Attended Pocklington School 1959-67, then Worcester College, Oxford 1967-70. Leisure interests include golf. Lives in Wansford, near Driffield, East Yorkshire.

Gilthorpe, Ian M.
See under Company/Commercial.

Glithero, Richard
Eversheds, Manchester (0161) 832 6666. Qualified 1986. Partner 1991. Banking and Insolvency Department. Advises office holders on all legal matters arising from corporate recovery and insolvency. Born 14.1.1953.

Hally, Paul W.
See under Company/Commercial.

Haymes, Duncan R.
Hammond Suddards, Manchester (0161) 834 2222. Partner in Insolvency and Corporate Recovery Department.

Specialisation: Banking and insolvency law. Has addressed conferences and seminars.

Prof. Membership: Law Society; Society of Practitioners of Insolvency; Insolvency Lawyers Association.

Career: Joined *JW Hollows & Co* in 1975, moving to *Pilkington Brothers* in 1980. From 1983-90, was at *William Prior & Co* and from 1990-92, was at *Addleshaw Sons & Latham*. Joined *Hammond Suddards* as a Partner in 1992.

Personal: Born in 1953. Graduated from Trent Polytechnic in 1974. Lives in Manchester.

Haywood, Richard
See under Banking.

Hollerin, Gordon C.
Bird Semple, Glasgow (0141) 221 7090. Qualified 1980. Partner 1985. Litigation Department. Practice includes receiverships, liquidations and company voluntary arrangements. Born 23.1.1957.

Horrocks, Julian
Eversheds, Leeds (0113) 243 0391.

Specialisation: Partner in the Insolvency Department specialising in all aspects of insolvency and insolvency related problems.

Prof. Membership: SPI: AEPPC.

Career: Qualified 1981. Partner since 1988.

Personal: Stowe School, Buckingham 1970-75, Birmingham University 1975-78. Leisure pusuits include destroying internal memos, family, golf and snooker. Born 27th December 1956.

Harris, Anthony
Laytons, Bristol (0117) 929 1626. Qualified 1971. Bristol managing partner and part of the Company, Commercial & Insolvency Department. Specialises in all aspects of insolvency law. Born 14.5.1946.

Jackson, Mark S.
Dibb Lupton Broomhead, Leeds (0113) 243 9301.

Jeffries, Jonathan D.
Pinsent Curtis, Leeds (0113) 244 5000. Partner and Head of Corporate Recovery.

Specialisation: Advises insolvency practitioners on all aspects of insolvency and banks and other financial institutions on re-financing and security. Acted for the administrators of Charnley Davies Limited, James Ferguson Holdings Plc (of which Barlow Clowes was a subsidiary). Advised members of Brown Group, Corton Beach PLC and Just Leather Plc. Lectures frequently to banks and accountants on many aspects of corporate recovery, debt recovery and banking law.

Jones, Christopher W.
Hammond Suddards, Leeds (0113) 234 3500. Executive Partner. Partner in Insolvency and Corporate Recovery Department.

Specialisation: Principal area of practice covers insolvency and bank recovery, acting for leading accountancy firms and major clearing banks. Also handles general commercial litigation. Acted in re-organisations of Ward Group plc, Hughes Foods plc and Devalit (UK). Lectured to Society of Practitioners in Insolvency.

Prof. Membership: Law Society, Insolvency Practitioners' Association, Society of Practitioners in Insolvency, Institute of Credit Management.

Career: Qualified in 1977 while with *Sampson Wade & Co.* Joined *Hammond Suddards* as a Partner in 1984.

Personal: Born 1953. Attended Fulneck Boys School, Pudsey to 1972 and Nottingham University 1972-75. Member of Leeds United FC 100 Club, Moortown Golf Club, Ilkley Rugby Club and Ilkley Tennis Club. Leisure pursuits include sport, rock music, Spain and cars. Lives in Burley-in-Wharfedale, West Yorkshire.

Jones, Derek S.
Rickerby Jessop, Cheltenham (01242) 222022. Qualified 1983. Partner and Head of Insolvency and Recoveries Department. Principal areas of practice are rescue procedures and insolvency avoidance.

Joyce, John
Slater Heelis, Manchester (0161) 228 3781.

Kelly, Sean
Lamport Bassitt, Southampton (01703) 634931. Partner in Company and Commercial Department.

Specialisation: Specialises in company and commercial work and insolvency, acting for accountants, banks and the leisure industry.

Prof. Membership: Law Society.

Career: Qualified in 1976. Partner at *Lamport Bassitt* since 1978.

Personal: Born 8th January 1951. Lives in Winchester.

Lang, J. Russell
Bishop and Robertson Chalmers, Glasgow (0141) 248 4672. Qualified 1976. Partner 1982. Business Law Division, Corporate Unit. Has specialised in personal and corporate insolvency and corporate rescue work since 1976. Licensed Insolvency Practitioner as a specialist, accredited by Law Society of Scotland in Insolvency Law.

Lawson, Stephen A.
Anstey Sargent & Probert, Exeter (01392) 411221. Qualified 1969. Partner 1973. Insolvency Department. Handles all areas of corporate and personal insolvency, including LPA receiverships. Also handles bank litigation and professional negligence, including acting as expert witness in these fields. Born 27.8.1945.

Laycock, Andrew
Carrick Read Insolvency, Leeds (0113) 243 2911. Partner.

Specialisation: Main area of practice is insolvency. Handles small to medium receiverships (maximum asset value 2 million), CVAs, administrations, liquidations, bankruptcy and IVAs. Transactions have included numerous heavy engineering cases, the insolvency of Hull Grammar (the first charity administration order), and the administration of Doncaster RLFC. Contributor to Insolvency Intelligence, Solicitors Journal, and Legal Executive Journal. Regularly addresses conferences to bankers, accountants and the SPI. Honorary Solicitor to the Bankruptcy Association.

Prof. Membership: Insolvency Lawyers Association, SPI, AEPPC.

Career: Qualified in 1983. *Established Carrick Read Insolvency* in 1980 with Chris Garwood.

Personal: Born 5th December 1957. Attended St Michael's College, Leeds 1970-1976: Emmanuel College Cambridge 1977-1980. Leisure interests include rugby and cricket. Lives in Thorner, near Wetherby.

Livesey, Andrew L.
Halliwell Landau, Manchester (0161) 835 3003. Qualified 1985. Partner 1991. Insolvency Department. Handles all types of corporate insolvency and bank recovery work. Born 23.8.1960.

Macfarlane, John
McGrigor Donald, Glasgow (0141) 248 6677. Qualified 1971. Partner 1990. Company Department. Corporate insolvency specialist.

Manning, Peter R.

Alsop Wilkinson, Manchester (0161) 834 7760. Qualified 1986. Partner 1989. Insolvency Department. Acted in Polly Peck and Maxwell litigations and other high profile receiverships. Also handles commercial litigation, banking and security work. Regularly lectures on behalf of the SPI. Born 1959.

Mather, Ian Philip

Palmer Wheeldon, Cambridge (01223) 355933. Partner in Litigation Department.

Specialisation: Principal area of practice is insolvency. Advises insolvency practitioners on all aspects of insolvency law. Other main area of practice is employment law. Adviser to a number of companies, some employing over 1,000 people. Routinely undertakes advocacy in the Industrial Tribunal. Largest employer client is the Royal British Legion Attendants Co Ltd. Charge-out rate subject to negotiation on insolvency matters.

Prof. Membership: Law Society; Associate Member of the Society of Practitioners of Insolvency; Member of Lawnet's Insolvency Unit Management Committee.

Career: Partner since 1986. Managing Partner since 1992.

Personal: Born 13th June 1958. Educated at York University (BA in Economics, 1979) and Newcastle Polytechnic 1981-82 (CPE and Law Society Finals). Council Member of Cambridge & District Chamber of Commerce since March 1994.

Matthews, Paul

See under Litigation (Commercial).

McGeever, Brendan G.

Gateley Wareing, Birmingham (0121) 236 8585. Qualified 1983. Partner 1986. Senior Partner. Partner in Banking and Insolvency Department. Acts on all aspects of insolvency law. Born 11.2.1958.

McGurk, Anthony J.G.

Eversheds, Norwich (01603) 272727. Qualified 1989. Partner 1995. Company/Commercial Department. Handles company matters and non-contentious insolvency work. Born 28.6.1961.

McIlvride, Rhoderick R.

Anderson Fyfe, Glasgow (0141) 248 4381. Partner in Litigation/Insolvency Department.

Specialisation: Corporate and personal insolvency and insolvency related litigation. Has acted for liquidators, receivers and trustees in a wide range of insolvencies and insolvency related litigation since 1981. Acted for the successful liquidators in two of the leading cases in Scotland on directors misfeasance (Blin v. Johnstone) and unfair preferences (Nicoll v. Steelpress). Has lectured for the Institute of Chartered Accountants in Scotland and to the Staff of the Accountant in Bankruptcy for Scotland.

Prof. Membership: Licensed Insolvency Practitioner and accredited by Law Society

of Scotland as an Insolvency Specialist.

Career: Qualified in 1981. Joined *Anderson Fyfe* in 1982, becoming a Partner in 1984.

Personal: Born 19th January 1957. Attended Glasgow University 1975-79 (LLB Hons). Lives in Glasgow.

Menzies, Graeme G.

Mills & Reeve, Cambridge + 44(0)1223 364422. Partner in Commercial Litigation Department.

Specialisation: Main areas of work are commercial advice and business dispute resolution, including arbitration and ADR, banking litigation, credit management, intellectual property and product liability, Office of Fair Trading investigation.

Merson, James T.

Stronachs, Aberdeen (01224) 643573. Qualified 1974. Partner 1978. Litigation Department. Certified by Law Society of Scotland as a specialist in Insolvency Law.

Mudd, Philip J.

Walker Morris, Leeds (0113) 283 2500. Partner and Head of Banking and Insolvency Department.

Specialisation: Deals with insolvency and banking issues for lenders, insolvency practitioners and corporate clients with an emphasis on debt restructuring and corporate rescue in addition to mainstream insolvency, lending and realisation work. Acted for lender in reconstruction of UK Land plc. Recent work includes Administration of CAM Shipping Group, Receivership of Pilcher Group and liquidation of MedChoice Holidays. Contributor to 'Insolvency Law and Practice'. Speaker at local and regional SPI conferences.

Prof. Membership: Society of Practitioners of Insolvency, Insolvency Lawyers Association.

Career: Qualified 1983, and joined *Walker Morris* the same year. Became a Partner in 1985. Licensed insolvency practitioner.

Personal: Born 19th January 1959. Attended Bristol University 1977-80. Leisure interests include music, skiing and sailing. Lives in Huddersfield.

Nicholls, Peter S.A.

Leathes Prior, Norwich (01603) 610911. Qualified 1978. Partner 1979. Licensed Insolvency Practitioner. Head of Banking and Insolvency Department. Principal area of practice is banking and insolvency and associated civil litigation. Also handles commercial property and planning. Born 12.11.1952.

Oakley, Mark Robert

Leathes Prior, Norwich (01603) 610911. Qualified 1983. Partner 1986. Banking and Insolvency Department. Principal area of practice is insolvency. Also handles employment law and industrial relations. Born 5.4.1958.

Oliver, David C.

Sherwin Oliver, Portsmouth (01705) 832200. Senior Partner in Insolvency and Litigation Department.

Specialisation: Practice covers all areas of corporate and individual insolvency, acting for all of the major insolvency practitioners in the Southern region and some outside. Acts for three major banks and various firms of chartered surveyors in relation to LPA receiverships. Also handles general civil litigation and major fraud prosecution. Work includes contract disputes involving claims in excess of £5 million each, obtained an Administration Order in relation to a Lloyds managing agent company with claims against it of approximately £90 million and a major fraudulent trading case, representing one director of a company with a deficiency in excess of £12 million. Has lectured to Portsmouth University, LawNet, Chambers of Commerce and the Insolvency Practitioners Association. Charge-out rate is £135 per hour.

Prof. Membership: Law Society, Insolvency Lawyers Association, AEPPC, Chartered Institute of Arbitrators, Institute of Directors, Society of Practitioners of Insolvency.

Career: Senior Litigation Partner at *Sherwin Oliver* since 1985. Fellow of Chartered Institute of Arbitrators since 1993. Appointed Deputy District Judge in January 1994.

Personal: Born 13th March 1944. Leisure interests include golf, tennis, walking, swimming, films and theatre. Trustee of two national charities. Lives in Portsmouth.

Patrick, Bruce R.

See under Company/Commercial.

Pennie, John A.

Dickinson Dees, Newcastle upon Tyne (0191) 261 1911. Qualified 1981. Partner 1985. Company and Commercial Department. Specialises in all aspects of corporate and personal insolvency.

Potter, Bruce J.

Cole and Cole, Oxford (01865) 791122.

Rees, Peter

Wansbroughs Willey Hargrave, Bristol (0117) 926 8981. Partner and Head of Insolvency Department.

Specialisation: Licensed insolvency practitioner. One of first solicitors in England to qualify by passing joint insolvency examination (1991). Also handles banking and secured lending. Contributor to Company Law Handbook. Occasional conference speaker.

Prof. Membership: Society of Practitioners of Insolvency.

Career: Qualified in 1989; having previously practised as a Barrister. Joined *Wansbroughs Willey Hargrave* in 1990, becoming a Partner in 1992.

Personal: Born 21st September 1957.

Birmingham University 1976-79. School Governor.

Rees, R. Bleddyn V.
Morgan Bruce, Cardiff (01222) 385385. Qualified 1986. Partner 1989. Company/ Commercial Department. Handles mainly corporate insolvency and banking matters.

Roxburgh, Roy
See under Company/Commercial.

Shaw, Murray W.A.
See under Construction & Civil Eng..

Sleigh, Andrew F.
W & J Burness WS, Glasgow (0141) 248 4933. Partner in Company Department.

Specialisation: Main areas of practice are private company and commercial contract work. Provides advice on all areas of private company activity including mergers and acquisitions, venture capital investment, restructuring, banking transactions, shareholder or directors disputes, asset acquisition and commercial contracts. Also handles insolvency work with emphasis on the receivership field. Acted in the receiverships of Lafferty Construction Ltd, Aerotech (formerly Allivane International Ltd), Forth Valley Homes and Galloway Cheese. Author of numerous articles. Law Society of Scotland Accredited Specialist in Insolvency Law. Has spoken at many conferences.

Prof. Membership: Law Society of Scotland, International Bar Association.
Careeer: Qualified in 1981. Foreign Associate at *Steptoe & Johnson*, Washington DC 1983-84. Partner at *McClure Naismith Anderson & Gardiner* 1987-94. Joined *W & J Burness WS* as a Partner in 1994.

Personal: Born 11th September 1957. Educated at Glasgow Academy 1965-74, and the Universities of Glasgow 1974-79, Amsterdam 1981-82 and Virginia 1982-83. Director of Dairsie House School. Leisure interests include golf, football, movies and family life. Lives in Glasgow.

Spencer, Shân
Addleshaw Sons & Latham, Manchester (0161) 832 5994. Partner in Insolvency and Banking Department.

Specialisation: Deals with the full range of insolvency matters with the emphasis on corporate insolvency including administrative receiverships, administrations, liquidations (both compulsory and voluntary) and corporate voluntary arrangements. Also acts for banks in recovery matters and risk positions. Has acted in cases including Keith Prowse, ELS, Kumar Brothers, Doctus plc, Habit Group and Paddy Hopkirk Limited. Addresses SPI conferences.

Prof. Membership: Society of Practitioners of Insolvency, Law Society of England and Wales, Insolvency Lawyers Association, Insolvency Practitioners Association, Association Europeene des Practiciens des Procedures Collective.

Career: Qualified in 1977. Partner at *William Prior & Co.* 1980-90. Joined *Addleshaw Sons & Latham* as a Partner in 1990. Member of the North West Regional Committee of the SPI since 1992.

Personal: Attended Altrincham Grammar School 1964-71 and Sheffield University 1971-74. Leisure interests include theatre, sport and music. Lives in Altrincham.

Stobart, Guy W.
Burges Salmon, Bristol (0117) 939 2000.

Sullivan, John C.P.
Edge & Ellison, Birmingham (0121) 200 2001. Partner in Banking and Insolvency Department.

Specialisation: Handles banking and insolvency work of all types.

Prof. Membership: Member of Society of Practitioners in Insolvency.

Career: Qualified in 1980. Joined *Edge & Ellison* in 1978, becoming a Partner in 1987.

Personal: Born 10th August 1956. Attended Oxford University 1974-77.

Swanson, Magnus P.
See under Corporate Finance.

Taylor, Ian R.
Parrott & Coales, Aylesbury (01296) 82244.

Taylor, Andrew C.
Burstows, Crawley (01293) 534734. Qualified 1983. Specialises in all aspects of corporate and personal insolvency. Conducts directors disqualification cases on behalf of the DTI.

Tettmar, Victor
Bond Pearce, Plymouth (01752) 266633. Qualified 1985. Partner 1991. Banking and Insolvency Department. Work includes all aspects of non-contentious insolvency including realisation as well as security auditing and enforcement.

Thomas, Catrin Wyn
Hugh James Jones & Jenkins, Cardiff (01222) 224871. Qualified 1983. Partner 1986. Commercial Litigation Department. Head of Insolvency and Debt Recovery Unit. Practice covers all aspects of personal, partnership and corporate insolvency. Also banking litigation and litigation between directors. Born 26.9.1956.

Thomson, Clive H.
Paris Smith & Randall, Southampton (01703) 635191. Qualified 1978. Partner and Head of Litigation. Deals with insolvency and litigation.

Vaughan, Philip D.
See under Banking.

Wood, Catherine Mary
Robert Muckle, Newcastle-upon-Tyne (0191) 232 4402. Partner in Commercial Litigation Department.

Specialisation: In insolvency work advises receivers, administrators, liquidators, nominees, supervisors and trustees on appointments and on the conduct of insolvencies. Advises on claims for preference, transactions at an undervalue, misfeasance, wrongful trading and directors' disqualification. In banking practice undertakes monitoring of intensive care and potential insolvency situations, recovery of loans and enforcement of guarantees, debt security review, realisation of security and the priority of payments.

Prof. Membership: Law Society, Society of Practitioners of Insolvency, Insolvency Practitioners Association, Licensed Insolvency Practitioner.

Career: Qualified in 1984, having joined *Robert Muckle* in 1981. Became a Partner in 1985.

Personal: Born 13th May 1959. Attended Newcastle University 1977-80 and College of Law, Chester 1980-81. Governor of Gateshead College. Leisure interests include reading and music.

FIRMS OF ACCOUNTANTS

Accountants specialising in litigation support are listed in the accountants' A-Z, with details of the services they offer to solicitors, from forensic accounting to intellectual property or business valuations. This section is found immediately after the main solicitors' A-Z.

INSURANCE & REINSURANCE

WHERE readers require information on marine and aviation insurance they should refer to the 'Shipping' and 'Aviation' sections. Professional indemnity firms and practitioners have been included in a separate category within the 'Professional Negligence' section.

LONDON

Insurance work in London divides naturally into four categories: reinsurance, non-contentious insurance, the Lloyds litigation and general claims insurance.

REINSURANCE

The bulk of reinsurance work is concentrated in London. It has become a leading centre for reinsurance arbitrations and the reputation of the Commercial Court has attracted foreign companies to litigate here.

LEADING FIRMS – LONDON – RE-INSURANCE	
BARLOW LYDE & GILBERT	
CAMERON MARKBY HEWITT	CLIFFORD CHANCE
CLYDE & CO	DAVIES ARNOLD COOPER
HERBERT SMITH	HOLMAN, FENWICK & WILLAN
INCE & CO.	
ELBORNE MITCHELL	LOVELL WHITE DURRANT
NORTON ROSE	

The pre-eminent firm in this field is *Barlow Lyde & Gilbert* which dominates the reinsurance market in the UK. It acts for specialist reinsurance companies, Lloyd's syndicates and direct insurers faced with reinsurance problems. Clients also include brokers, underwriting agents and run-off specialists. Colin Croly is the head of the Reinsurance Division and held in very high regard – he advises on all areas of reinsurance including contract wording and dispute resolution.

Another dominant firm in the reinsurance market is *Ince & Co.* which deals with all aspects of reinsurance litigation. The firm's practice covers all aspects of UK and international reinsurance. It recently acted in *Charter Re. v Feltrim*, which considered the 'pay as paid' principle. The firm's clients include underwriters, assureds and brokers. Peter Rogan is the most highly regarded reinsurance specialist at *Ince & Co.* He concentrates on the London market and treaty reinsurance disputes and he also has a good reputation for litigation work.

Clyde & Co. has an established reinsurance team specialising in the drafting and interpretation of reinsurance contracts. Michael Payton is a very well established reinsurance practitioner – his experience has included energy and marine insurance, E&O insurance and bloodstock insurance . He has been involved in litigation involving Piper Alpha, and the Palau power station.

The reinsurance practice at *Davies Arnold Cooper* has a formidable reputation. They acted for Coopers & Lybrand in the *Charter Re.* case referred to above. Michael Dobias heads their litigation department and was recommended for his work in this field. *Cameron Markby Hewitt* acts for reinsurance companies and brokers. The firm is particularly strong in litigation, having acted in a number of major reinsurance disputes. Mark Elborne has a high profile acting principally for insurers of banks and financial institutions, Lloyd's agents and brokers. He advises on the handling of reinsurance arbitration and litigation.

Another firm recommended for its substantial expertise in this field was *Herbert Smith*. Advising on questions of policy liability and reinsurance coverage, it recently acted for a leading reinsurance company over reinsurance arrangements for terrorist damage. Several members of their reinsurance team are highly regarded. David Higgins has been with the firm since 1971. Many of the cases he has handled have had an international element. Michael Munden has advised on most aspects of reinsurance dispute. Martin Bakes has acted for major UK brokers and errors and omissions insurers. All three have been recommended to us for their considerable expertise in this field.

Holman, Fenwick & Willan advises its clients, including brokers and reinsurers, on all aspects of reinsurance and retrocessional business. Reinsurance partner John Duff is highly respected. *Clifford Chance* also enjoys a high profile in the reinsurance arena. It has acted for reinsurance brokers both inside and outside Lloyd's underwriting agencies. Terry O'Neill was recommended to us and has experience in drafting reinsurance documentation.

HIGHLY REGARDED – LONDON – RE-INSURANCE	
FRESHFIELDS	LINKLATERS & PAINES
WALTONS & MORSE	
ALSOP WILKINSON	D J FREEMAN
FISHBURN BOXER	JARVIS & BANNISTER
KENNEDYS	REYNOLDS PORTER CHAMBERLAIN
SIMMONS & SIMMONS	STEPHENSON HARWOOD
BERWIN LEIGHTON	EVERSHEDS
PAISNER & CO	

Other leading firms are *Elborne Mitchell, Lovell White Durrant* and *Norton Rose*. *Elborne Mitchell* has acted for several Lloyd's syndicates, Centre Re, NRG Victory Re and Prudential Assurance. Recent cases in which the firm has been involved are 'Simner v New India' and 'Trade Indemnity v Njord Ab'. Both Tim Akeroyd and Ed Stanley of this firm were recommended to us. *Lovell White Durrant* is involved in all aspects of reinsurance including the conduct of substantial multi-party litigation and arbitration, reinsurance cover and regulation. John Powell, who deals with all aspects of reinsurance litigation and Peter Taylor, who concentrates on the companies market, were recommended to us.

Norton Rose undertakes work in this field under the

auspices of their Insurance Group and has acted in a number of notable reinsurance disputes including 'Sail v Farex' and 'Syndicate 947 v The Black Sea and Baltic'.

Prominent amongst other firms which were recommended to us are *Freshfields*, *Linklaters & Paines* and *Waltons & Morse*. *Freshfields* has been involved in the KWELM litigation, a substantial reinsurance dispute with Deutsche Ruck raising issues of non-disclosure, illegality and letters of credit. Raj Parker undertakes reinsurance work and handles claims for brokers and intermediaries. He has acted in the Johnson Mathey Bankers insurance claims. *Linklaters & Paines* acts for policy holders, brokers, Lloyd's syndicates and agencies and reinsurance companies. Cases undertaken have included 'Yasuda Fire and Marine Insurance Company

of Europe Ltd v Orion Marine Insurance Underwriting Agency Ltd and anor'. *Waltons & Morse* has experience in acting for Lloyd's of London, overseas insurance companies and a major UK clearing bank.

Other well known firms whose expertise in this field was commended to us include *Simmons & Simmons* and *Fishburn Boxer*. The former has an insurance litigation team within its Commercial Litigation group. The firm's experience has included advising merchant banks on the securitisation of reinsurance receivables. *Fishburn Boxer* undertake reinsurance litigation and arbitration work and act for Lloyd's syndicates and reinsurance companies. Stephen Leonard was recommended for his expertise in this field; his practice includes the drafting of reinsurance documentation.

LEADING INDIVIDUALS – LONDON – RE-INSURANCE

Colin V. Croly *Barlow Lyde & Gilbert*	**P.J.H. Rogan** *Ince & Co*	
Tim Akeroyd *Elborne Mitchell*	**Martin J. Bakes** *Herbert Smith*	**Michael Dobias** *Davies Arnold Cooper*
John P.J. Duff *Holman, Fenwick & Willan*	**Mark E.M. Elborne** *Cameron Markby Hewitt*	**Peter Farthing** *Clyde & Co*
David E.A. Higgins *Herbert Smith*	**Francis Mackie** *Norton Rose*	**David A. McIntosh** *Davies Arnold Cooper*
Michael R. Munden *Herbert Smith*	**Terry O'Neill** *Clifford Chance*	**Michael Payton** *Clyde & Co*
John F. Powell *Lovell White Durrant*	**Ed Stanley** *Elborne Mitchell*	
Andrew Alan Bandurka *Holman, Fenwick & Willan*	**Steven Anthony Blair** *Alsop Wilkinson*	**Leon Boshoff** *Clifford Chance*
Steven C. Fox *Ince & Co*	**Simon K.P.T. Greenley** *Reynolds Porter Chamberlain*	**Alexander N. Hamer** *Reynolds Porter Chamberlain*
John Hanson *Barlow Lyde & Gilbert*	**Alan Hepworth** *Ince & Co*	**David R. Kendall** *D J Freeman*
Stephen M. Leonard *Fishburn Boxer*	**Stephen Lewis** *Clifford Chance*	**Kenneth McKenzie** *Davies Arnold Cooper*
Michael Mendelowitz *Barlow Lyde & Gilbert*	**Gerald O'Mahoney** *Davies Arnold Cooper*	**Raj D. Parker** *Freshfields*
Jonathan Sacher *Paisner & Co*	**Nicholas Sinfield** *Davies Arnold Cooper*	**Peter L. Taylor** *Lovell White Durrant*
Christian Wells *Lovell White Durrant*	**Vere A. Wheatley** *Cameron Markby Hewitt*	

In all the tables the names in each group are listed alphabetically.

NON-CONTENTIOUS INSURANCE

Non-contentious insurance work involves corporate and regulatory work undertaken specifically for insurance companies, including flotations.

LEADING FIRMS – LONDON – NON-CONTENTIOUS

CLIFFORD CHANCE	**CLYDE & CO**
FRESHFIELDS	**HERBERT SMITH**
LOVELL WHITE DURRANT	

The leading firms in this area of insurance law are *Clyde & Co* and *Clifford Chance*. At *Clyde & Co*. Verner Southey, head of the corporate department, specialises principally in insurance work. At *Clifford Chance* Katherine Coates, deals with mergers, acquisitions, joint ventures, and UK and EU regulatory matters, acting for both life and general insurers.

Freshfields enjoys a good reputation for this type of work. Philip Richards deals with mergers, acquisitions and restructuring matters. The firm acts for a number of mutual life companies, insurance brokers and Lloyd's market partici-

pants. *Herbert Smith* can also claim considerable expertise in this field with Marian Pell whose practice lies predominantly within life insurance work. *Lovell White Durrant* is another City firm with a substantial reputation in this field, with John Young specialising in advising insurance companies and related businesses on corporate and regulatory matters.

HIGHLY REGARDED – LONDON – NON-CONTENTIOUS

CROCKERS	**D J FREEMAN**
HOLMAN, FENWICK & WILLAN	**LINKLATERS & PAINES**
MANCHES & CO	**SLAUGHTER AND MAY**
TITMUSS SAINER DECHERT	**WALTONS & MORSE**
ASHURST MORRIS CRISP	

Other firms recommended to us for non-contentious insurance were *Waltons & Morse, Manches & Co., DJ Freeman, Slaughter and May, Crockers, Linklaters & Paines, Titmuss Sainer Dechert* and *Holman, Fenwick & Willan*.

LEADING INDIVIDUALS – LONDON – NON-CONTENTIOUS

Hugh Hovey Bohling	Waltons & Morse
Katherine Coates	Clifford Chance
Marian Pell	Herbert Smith
Andrew Philip Richards	Freshfields
Verner Southey	Clyde & Co
John Young	Lovell White Durrant
R. James N. Cripps	Slaughter and May
Jeremy G. Hill	Ashurst Morris Crisp
Richard D. Hudson	Crockers
G.M. Ridley	Slaughter and May
Michael Smith	Titmuss Sainer Dechert
Richard J. Spiller	D J Freeman

LLOYD'S LITIGATION

The Lloyd's litigation between the Names and the Lloyd's syndicates has continued to dominate the headlines. Although there are a large number of firms involved, a few firms and individuals in particular have established an impressive reputation.

LEADING FIRMS – LONDON – LLOYD'S LITIGATION

CAMERON MARKBY HEWITT	ELBORNE MITCHELL
REYNOLDS PORTER CHAMBERLAIN	RICHARDS BUTLER
WILDE SAPTE	D.J. FREEMAN

Acting for the Names, *Richards Butler* are prominent, with Mark Connoley and Stuart Beare the two leading individuals there. *Wilde Sapte* with Philip Rocher have established a high profile acting for Gooda Walker, as have *DJ Freeman*, where David Tiplady has established a good reputation.

Acting for the defendants in this action, *Reynolds Porter Chamberlain* with Simon Greenley have played a prominent part as have *Cameron Markby Hewitt* with Michael Wadsworth and Belinda Schofield and *Elborne Mitchell* with Tim Akeroyd and Andrew Pincott.

HIGHLY REGARDED – LONDON – LLOYD'S LITIGATION

CLYDE & CO	DAVIES ARNOLD COOPER
HOLMAN, FENWICK & WILLAN	
BARLOW LYDE & GILBERT	CLIFFORD CHANCE
LOVELL WHITE DURRANT	MANCHES & CO
McKENNA & CO	MORE FISHER BROWN
NORTON ROSE	OSWALD HICKSON COLLIER
DENTON HALL	HERBERT SMITH
HEXTALL, ERSKINE	PAISNER & CO

Other firms involved in this litigation are *Holman, Fenwick & Willan, Clyde & Co.* and *Davies Arnold Cooper* acting for the E&O underwriters, *Clifford Chance*, acting for the managing agents, *Lovell White Durrant, Barlow Lyde & Gilbert, McKenna & Co.*, acting for accountants, *Manches & Co., Oswald Hickson Collier* and *More Fisher Brown*.

LEADING INDIVIDUALS – LONDON – LLOYD'S LITIGATION

Mark F. Connoley	Richards Butler
Philip Rocher	Wilde Sapte
Tim Akeroyd	Elborne Mitchell
Andrew Alan Bandurka	Holman, Fenwick & Willan
Stuart N. Beare	Richards Butler
Simon K.P.T. Greenley	Reynolds Porter Chamberlain
Andrew Pincott	Elborne Mitchell
B.A. Schofield	Cameron Markby Hewitt
David Tiplady	D J Freeman
Michael Henry Wadsworth	Cameron Markby Hewitt
Paul Wordley	Holman, Fenwick & Willan
Timothy Brentnall	Elborne Mitchell
Clive Brown	Cameron Markby Hewitt
Tim Burton	McKenna & Co
John P.J. Duff	Holman, Fenwick & Willan
Mark E.M. Elborne	Cameron Markby Hewitt
Alexander N. Hamer	Reynolds Porter Chamberlain
Kenneth McKenzie	Davies Arnold Cooper
Michael Payton	Clyde & Co
Richard Slowe	S J Berwin & Co

GENERAL CLAIMS INSURANCE

General claims insurance, also known as 'direct' or 'primary' insurance, relates to disputes about the liability of an insurance company after a claim has been made, most often in areas of fire, motor and accident insurance. Professional indemnity insurance is dealt with in the Professional Negligence section.

LEADING FIRMS – LONDON

BARLOW LYDE & GILBERT	BEACHCROFT STANLEYS
BERRYMANS	CAMERON MARKBY HEWITT
CLYDE & CO	DAVIES ARNOLD COOPER
HEXTALL ERSKINE	HOLMAN, FENWICK & WILLAN
INCE & CO.	KENNEDYS
REYNOLDS PORTER CHAMBERLAIN	

General claims insurance is a wide field of practice undertaken all over the country, and it is difficult to highlight particular firms. However the firms listed in this section have established reputations for such work.

Most of the leading insurance firms are also expert in handling general claims insurance. *Barlow Lyde & Gilbert, Ince & Co.* and *Clyde & Co.* all come into this category.

However there are a number of firms whose insurance practice is defined by the strength of their general claims work. Such firms would include *Kennedys* whose work in this area has included directors' and officers' liability, political and credit risks and product liability. *Reynolds Porter Chamberlain* have substantial experience in policy drafting and interpretation and also handle directors' and officers' liability. *Hextall Erskine* have a niche specialisation in motor insurance.

HIGHLY REGARDED – LONDON

CLIFFORD CHANCE	ELBORNE MITCHELL
HERBERT SMITH	
McKENNA & CO	
ALASTAIR THOMSON & PARTNERS	DENTON HALL
EDWARD LEWIS	EDWIN COE
ELLIOTT & CO	EVERSHEDS
FORSYTE SAUNDERS KERMAN	JARVIS & BANNISTER
LAWRENCE GRAHAM	LLOYD COOPER
MACKRELL TURNER GARRETT	PAISNER & CO
PICKERING KENYON	ROWE & MAW
SEDGWICK, DETERT, MORAN & ARNOLD	TITMUSS SAINER DECHERT
VIZARDS	WOODROFFES

Beachcroft Stanleys handle areas such as employers' liability, public liability, including pollution, and construction cases.

LEADING INDIVIDUALS – LONDON

Graham Harris *Richards Butler*	
B.A. Schofield *Cameron Markby Hewitt*	

SOUTH EAST

Clyde & Co handle a large volume of high quality insurance and reinsurance work. Ray Bell is involved in Lloyd's litigation work.

HIGHLY REGARDED – SOUTH EAST

BERRYMANS *Southampton*	CLYDE & CO *Guildford*
MANCHES & CO *Oxford*	
ARGLES & COURT *Maidstone*	
HODKINSONS *Locks Heath*	

Berrymans were also recommended for their general claims insurance work. *Hodkinsons* is known for its insurance fraud expertise. Peter Angel, known for his involvement in Lloyd's litigation work, is based at the Oxford office of *Manches & Co.*

LEADING INDIVIDUALS – SOUTH EAST

Peter G. Angel *Manches & Co*	
Raymond Bell *Clyde & Co*	

SOUTH WEST & WALES

Humphreys & Co are one of the very few provincial law firms to be recommended for their expertise in reinsurance. *Wansboroughs Willey Hargrave* in Bristol is known for general claims insurance work. Its specialist team, whose service is enhanced by its London office, is particularly experienced in policy drafting, risk management for self-insureds and handling subrogated recovery claims.

Lyons Davidson, also in Bristol, undertake motor claims, policy disputes, insurers' outlay recoveries and employers' liability.

HIGHLY REGARDED – SOUTH WEST & WALES

EVERSHEDS *Cardiff*	HUMPHREYS & CO *Bristol*
WANSBROUGHS WILLEY HARGRAVE *Bristol*	
CAMERON MARKBY HEWITT *Bristol*	CARTWRIGHTS *Bristol*
CLYDE & CO *Cardiff*	LEO ABSE & COHEN *Cardiff*
LYONS DAVIDSON *Bristol*	

In Wales, *Eversheds* in Cardiff have considerable experience in handling policy disputes, general insurance litigation and policy drafting.

MIDLANDS

A number of Midland firms advise insurance companies on policy drafting. *Wragge & Co.* advise composites insurers and the Lloyd's market on a wide range of policy issues. The firm has experience of advising underwriters and insurance brokers too. Also in Birmingham, both *Pinsent Curtis* and *Eversheds* have experience of policy drafting and disputes.

HIGHLY REGARDED – MIDLANDS

SHOOSMITHS & HARRISON *Northampton*	WRAGGE & CO *Birmingham*
EVERSHEDS *Birmingham*	PINSENT CURTIS *Birmingham*
BERRYMAN & CO *Nottingham*	BULLER JEFFRIES *Birmingham*
IRWIN MITCHELL *Birmingham*	ROWLEY DICKINSON *Birmingham*

EAST ANGLIA

In both Cambridge and Norwich, *Mills & Reeve* have a substantial presence in insurance law with six specialist partners. The firm has a particular expertise in litigation.

HIGHLY REGARDED – EAST ANGLIA

MILLS & REEVE *Norwich*

NORTH WEST

The Manchester office of *Davies Arnold Cooper* was recommended for its general claims insurance work. It also has experience of regulatory and corporate matters in an insurance context. *Elliott & Company*, also in Manchester, deals with market regulation and insurance disputes. *James Chapman & Co.* are well regarded; the firm cites policy interpretations and disputes as particular specialisms.

HIGHLY REGARDED – NORTH WEST

DAVIES ARNOLD COOPER *Manchester*	ELLIOTT & COMPANY *Manchester*
JAMES CHAPMAN & CO *Manchester*	KEOGH RITSON *Bolton*
WEIGHTMAN RUTHERFORDS *Liverpool*	
ALSOP WILKINSON *Liverpool*	EVERSHEDS *Manchester*
HILL DICKINSON DAVIS CAMPBELL *Liverpool*	LACE MAWER *Manchester*
PETER RICKSON AND PARTNERS *Preston*	VAUDREYS *Manchester*

In all the tables the names in each group are listed alphabetically.

Outside Manchester, the two North West firms of note for insurance work are *Keogh Ritson* in Bolton and in Liverpool, *Weightman Rutherfords,* who act for the Motor Insurers' Bureau.

LEADING INDIVIDUALS – NORTH WEST

Kevin P. Finnigan *James Chapman & Co*	
David J. Teasdale *James Chapman & Co*	

NORTH EAST

The Leeds office of *Pinsent Curtis* was recommended, handling most aspects of general claims insurance with an aptitude for litigation. *Hammond Suddards,* another Leeds firm,

HIGHLY REGARDED – NORTH EAST

DIBB LUPTON BROOMHEAD *Bradford*	**EVERSHEDS** *Leeds*	
HAMMOND SUDDARDS *Leeds*	**PINSENT CURTIS** *Leeds*	
WANSBROUGHS WILLEY HARGRAVE *Leeds*		
EVERSHEDS *Newcastle upon Tyne*	**IRWIN MITCHELL** *Sheffield*	

are well known for their experience and undertake a broad range of work. Both the Leeds offices of *Dibb Lupton Broomhead* and *Eversheds* were highlighted for their expe-

rience in the field. *Wansboroughs Willey Hargrave* undertake insurance regulatory advice and policy drafting.

LEADING INDIVIDUALS – NORTH EAST

Julia M.C. Monteith *Wansbroughs Willey Hargrave*	

SCOTLAND

Only a small number of firms offer insurance law expertise. However a number of insurance companies have their headquarters based in Scotland and so a number of Scottish firms have experience of handling non-contentious insurance work. *McGrigor Donald* were recommended for their dealings with life insurance companies where they have a good

HIGHLY REGARDED – SCOTLAND

DUNDAS & WILSON CS *Edinburgh*	**McGRIGOR DONALD** *Glasgow*
SHEPHERD & WEDDERBURN *Edinburgh*	
BIGGART BAILLIE & GIFFORD *Glasgow*	

reputation for undertaking regulatory work. *Shepherd & Wedderburn* has been involved in the flotation of an independent insurance company and acts for some life insurance companies based north of the border. *Dundas & Wilson* in Edinburgh have also been recommended for their work in the field of non contentious insurance.

LEADERS IN INSURANCE & REINSURANCE

LONDON

Akeroyd, Tim
Elborne Mitchell, London (0171) 320 9000. Managing Partner. Qualified 1971. Partner 1974. Specialist areas of practice are insurance and reinsurance litigation, including Lloyd's litigation and professional indemnity defence. Born 1947.

Bakes, Martin J.
See under Professional Negligence.

Bandurka, Andrew A.
Holman, Fenwick & Willan, London (0171) 488 2300. Qualified 1989. Called to Bar 1985. Partner 1993. Insurance/reinsurance Department. Principal area of practice is reinsurance/insurance related litigation. Born 31.12.1956.

Beare, Stuart N.
See under Shipping & Maritime Law.

Blair, Steven Anthony
Alsop Wilkinson, London (0171) 248 4141. Qualified 1972. Partner specialising in insurance and reinsurance dispute resolution in London and the US. Born 26.11.1947.

Bohling, Hugh Hovey
Waltons & Morse, London (0171) 623 4255. Qualified 1983. Partner 1987. Head of Corporate and Banking Group. Practice covers London insurance market work including Lloyd's of London, mergers and acquisitions and corporate finance. Born 1.8.1957.

Boshoff, Leon
Clifford Chance, London (0171) 600 1000. Lloyd's office. Partner. Principal area of practice is insurance and reinsurance.

Brentnall, Timothy
Elborne Mitchell, London (0171) 320 9000.

Brown, Clive
Cameron Markby Hewitt, London (0171) 702 2345. Partner in Insurance and Aviation Groups.

Specialisation: Main area of practice is professional indemnity, particularly Lloyds Brokers E&O work. Has acted in many claims in all classes of insurance. Other area of practice is aviation: has acted regularly for the London insurance market in relation to substantial aviation claims. Author of several articles on the liability of brokers and frequently conducts loss control seminars for brokers.

Prof. Membership: Law Society, City of London Law Society, IBA, Lawyers Flying Association.

Career: Qualified in 1976, having been admitted as a South African attorney in 1971. Became a Partner in *Hewitt Woollacott & Chown* in 1977, which merged to become *Cameron Markby Hewitt.* Appointed Joint Managing Partner May 1994.

Personal: Born 6th March 1944. Attended St John's College, Johannesburg, University of Stellenbosch, and Jesus College, Cambridge. Yacht Club Commodore. Leisure interests include flying and sailing. Lives in Cambridge.

Burton, Tim
McKenna & Co, London (Lloyd's) (0171) 929 1250. Partner in Insurance and Reinsurance Group, based in Lloyd's.

Specialisation: Main area of practice is market dispute resolution, including major litigation and arbitrations. Particular areas of expertise are reinsurance disputes, claims against brokers and other insurance professionals and the Lloyd's Market. Acts for a number of the larger Lloyd's brokers and is currently heavily involved in defending a number of the Lloyd's Names actions. Non-contentious expertise includes drafting wordings, advising on regulatory matters and acting for insurance entities in corporate transactions. Acted in the Howden, PCW and Spicer & White disputes at Lloyd's; in the E I Du Pont de Nemours & Co. v. I C Agnew & Others (law governing Lloyd's policies; insurability of punitive damages) and NV Rotterdamse Assurantickas (reinsurance; broker's duties; illegality) actions. Recently successfully defended Lloyd's leader of marine facility (leading underwriter clauses; duty to following market). Currently defending Syndicate Auditors in leading "long-tail" Names' action, Merrett 418 and international broker in relation to a French Market placement. Legal columnist of 'Insurance Law and Claims'; author of 'Insuring the Product Liability Risk' (1993). Has also written numerous articles in the Insurance Press. Has spoken at a wide range of conferences and seminars both at home and abroad.

Prof. Membership: British Insurance Law Association, City of London Solicitors Association, Law Society of England and Wales.

Career: Qualified in 1982. Articled at *Simanowitz & Brown* 1978-80. Solicitor at *Kenwright & Cox* 1981-83 and *Kingsley Napley* 1983-85. Joined *McKenna & Co.* in 1985, becoming a Partner in 1989.

Personal: Born in 1956. Attended Southampton University 1975-78. Being a father to three young children, his leisure interests are necessarily limited to eating good food and occasionally cooking it. Lives in Surrey.

Coates, Katherine
Clifford Chance, London (0171) 600 1000. Partner. Principal area of practice is non-contentious insurance (corporate and regulatory). Also deals with corporate finance, investment funds and other financial services.

Connoley, Mark F.
Richards Butler, London (0171) 247 6555. Partner in Shipping Unit.

Specialisation: Work includes mainstream shipping, charterparty and bills of lading, war risk insurance, marine insurance, non-marine insurance and reinsurance and Lloyd's matters.

Career: Qualified 1980. Partner at *Richards Butler* since 1987.

Personal: Born 1955. Attended St Edmund Hall, Oxford (Jurisprudence).

Cripps, R. James N.
Slaughter and May, London (0171) 600 1200. Qualified 1980. Specialises in collective investment schemes for international equities, debt securities, and non-corporate investments.

Croly, Colin V.
Barlow Lyde & Gilbert, London (0171) 247 2277. Qualified 1974. Partner 1980. Head of Reinsurance Division. Advises on all areas of reinsurance including contract wording and dispute resolution. Born 9.10.1949.

Dobias, Michael
Davies Arnold Cooper, London (0171) 936 2222. Qualified 1975. Partner 1980. Head of Litigation Department. Main areas of practice are commercial and insurance litigation, both domestic and international. Born 28.9.1950.

Duff, John P.J.
Holman, Fenwick & Willan, London (0171) 488 2300. Partner in Reinsurance Department.

Specialisation: Main areas of practice are reinsurance and professional indemnity. Author of various articles and a frequent speaker worldwide.

Career: Qualified in 1982. Joined *Holman Fenwick & Willan* in 1983, becoming a Partner in 1987.

Elborne, Mark E.M.
Cameron Markby Hewitt, London (0171) 702 2345. Partner in Insurance and Reinsurance Department.

Specialisation: Principal areas of practice involve acting in claims and disputes for Insurers and Reinsurers of Banks and Financial Institutions, Accountants, Financial Advisers and Stockbrokers, Lloyd's Agents and Lloyd's Brokers; advising Insurers and Reinsurers on policy wordings and construction in insurance and reinsurance contracts; acting in major reinsurance arbitration and litigation disputes and advising Reinsurers generally with clients in the London market, Europe, Middle and Far East, USA and Bermuda. Lectured in Bermuda at International Reinsurance Congress and in Hong Kong and London at various conferences on financial institutions insurance, Directors' and Officers' liability cover and on reinsurance.

Prof. Membership: Law Society, Chartered Institute of Insurers, Society of Insurance Receivers.

Career: Qualified 1983 while at *Cameron Markby Hewitt* and became a Partner in 1988.

Personal: Born 22nd January 1958. School Trustee. Leisure pursuits include golf, swimming, tennis, shooting and opera. Lives near Uppingham, Rutland. Married with 5 children.

Farthing, Peter
Clyde & Co, London (0171) 623 1244. Qualified 1974. Partner 1977. Main areas of practice are insurance/reinsurance and commercial litigation. Born 12.1.1949.

Fox, Steven C.
Ince & Co, London (0171) 623 2011. Qualified 1983. Partner 1989. Specialises in insurance and reinsurance.

Greenley, Simon K.P.T.
Reynolds Porter Chamberlain, London (0171) 242 2877. Partner in Insurance and Professional Indemnity Department.

Specialisation: Main area of practice is insur-

ance, reinsurance and professional liability litigation. Work covers litigation for errors and omissions underwriters, including banks and other financial institutions and intermediaries, Lloyd's underwriting agents, brokers, accountants, surveyors, directors and officers. Acts in non-marine insurance and reinsurance disputes, principally Lloyd's syndicates, including commercial risks, property and building society block policies, fine arts and jewellers' block policies. Also handles policy disputes and liability litigation (US, European and domestic). Currently involved in a number of high profile Lloyd's Syndicate disputes.

Prof. Memberships: Law Society

Career: Qualified in 1980. Became a Partner in 1983.

Personal: Born 29 January 1957. Attended Stowe School 1970-75, then College of Law 1976-79. Leisure interests include golf, tennis, rackets, squash, arts, antique furniture and Japanese porcelain. Hurlingham Club and Walton Heath Golf Club. Lives in London.

Hamer, Alexander N.
Reynolds Porter Chamberlain, London (0171) 242 2877. Partner in Insurance and Professional Indemnity Department.

Specialisation: Main area of practice is insurance and professional liability litigation. Handles litigation for errors and omissions underwriters including Lloyd's underwriting agents, accountants, financial advisers and institutions. Gives general insurance and policy advice. Has acted in a number of Lloyd's syndicate disputes, and acts for Lloyd's syndicates.

Prof. Membership: Law Society and Institute of Taxation.

Career: Qualified in 1984. Became a partner in *Reynolds Porter Chamberlain* in 1989.

Personal: Born 20th September 1959. Attended Exeter University (LLB Hons 1981). Leisure interests include sailing, windsurfing and music. Lives in Farnham, Surrey.

Hanson, John
Barlow Lyde & Gilbert, London (0171) 247 2277. Partner.

Specialisation: Main areas of practice are insurance brokers, property insurance and reinsurance. Author of various articles; co-editor and joint author of Lloyd's of London Press 'Reinsurance Practice and the Law'. Author of All Risks Property Insurance textbook published by Lloyd's of London Press 1995. Has made regular conference appearances, particularly with DYP and EuroForum.

Career: Admitted in England 1977. Admitted as a Barrister and Solicitor in Western and Northern Australia in 1978. Partner Commercial Litigation in Australia 1981-5. Joined *Barlow Lyde & Gilbert* in 1986, becoming a Partner in 1987.

Personal: Born 19th January 1952. Attended

Oxford University. Jurisprudence 1973; Law Society Part II 1974. Lives in Whitstable, Kent.

Harris, Graham

See under Litigation (Commercial).

Hepworth, Alan

Ince & Co, London (0171) 623 2011. Qualified 1988. Partner 1995. Specialises in insurance and reinsurance. Born 28.8.1962.

Higgins, David E.A.

Herbert Smith, London (0171) 374 8000. Partner and Head of Insurance Litigation Section.

Specialisation: Specialises in insurance and reinsurance law. Many of his cases have an international element requiring advice on jurisdiction and choice of law.

Career: Qualified in 1970 and joined *Herbert Smith* in 1971. Became a Partner of the firm in 1977.

Personal: Educated at St. Peter's School, York and Newcastle University.

Hill, Jeremy G.

See under Company/Commercial.

Hudson, Richard D.

Crockers, London (0171) 353 0311. Qualified 1957. Senior Partner specialising in insurance work.

Kendall, David R.

D J Freeman, London (0171) 583 4055. Partner and Head of Insurance Department.

Specialisation: Main area of practice is reinsurance. Acts for Lloyd's syndicates, for major UK and overseas insurers and reinsurers, for liquidators and for Lloyd's brokers in litigation and arbitration. Has particular experience of advising on pool and syndicate group reinsurance programmes and on insurance coverage. Advises on regulatory, structural and management issues affecting Lloyd's, particularly in relation to run-off and corporate capital. Lloyd's panel arbitrator. Cases have included Suncorp v Milano (pools/reinsurance), Finnish Marine v Protective National (jurisdiction), Munich Re v Weavers (reinsurance), Milano v Walbrook (reinsurance) and Re A Company 1991 (insurance insolvency). Regularly contributes articles to Re Actions, Lloyd's List and other insurance publications. Speaks regularly at conferences and *DJ Freeman* seminars.

Prof. Membership: Law Society, Federation of Insurance and Corporate Counsel, BILA, ARIAS, LMAA, British-German Jurists and SEG.

Career: Qualified in 1981. Worked at *Hedleys* 1979-87, from 1985 as a Partner. Joined *DJ Freeman* in 1988 as a Partner, becoming Head of Department in 1993.

Personal: Born 17th September 1955. Holds an LLB (Hons) 1976, and MA (Business Law) 1982.

Leonard, Stephen M.

Fishburn Boxer, London (0171) 925 2884. Partner since 1992 in Insurance and Reinsurance Litigation Department.

Specialisation: Principal area of practice is insurance and reinsurance litigation and arbitration. Advises insurers and reinsurers in a wide array of actual and potential disputes. Also advises in relation to Lloyd's litigation. Other main area of practice is product development including drafting insurance and reinsurance documentation. Acts for Lloyd's syndicates and insurance and reinsurance companies.

Personal: Born 16th June 1959. Educated at St Edmund Hall, Oxford 1978-82 (BA in Law). Holds an LL.M in Commercial Law from the University of London (1988).

Lewis, Stephen

Clifford Chance, London (0171) 600 1000. Partner. Principal area of practice is insurance and reinsurance law.

Mackie, Francis

Norton Rose, London (0171) 283 6000. Qualified 1976.

McIntosh, David A.

Davies Arnold Cooper, London (0171) 936 2222. Partner in Litigation Department.

Specialisation: Main areas of practice are commercial, insurance and pharmaceutical litigation. Foremost UK and international litigator and arbitrator. Author of over one hundred published papers and articles; has addressed numerous conferences and seminars, including the IADC Conference on insurance law at the Waldorf-Astoria in new Work in 1994; Chairing in the Product Liability Day at the IBA conference in New Orleans; and chairing the IBC conference on claims management in 1993. Since becoming Senior Partner, *Davies Arnold Cooper* has quadrupled in size.

Prof. Membership: Law Society, American Bar Association, Society of English and American Lawyers, Chartered Institute of Arbitrators, United States International Association of Defence Counsel, Defence Research and Trial Lawyers Association of America, Arson Prevention Bureau.

Career: Qualified in 1969. Joined *Davies Arnold Cooper* in 1962, becoming Senior Partner in 1976. Member of the Joint Committee of the Senate of the Bar and Law Society which made recommendations to the Lord Chancellor on the proposed US/ UK Reciprocal Enforcements Convention and on allied jurisdictional matters; Member of the Law Society's Working Party which made recommendations in the context of the Lord Chancellor's Review of Civil Justice with regard to personal injury litigation; Member of the International Bar Association and a Vice Chairman of its Committee on Consumer Affairs, Advertising, Unfair Competition and Products Liability. Chairman of the Disaster Litigation Worldwide Programme in Stras-

bourg in 1989. Member of the Board of Editors of the Journal of Products and Toxic Liability. Member of the Executive Committee of Centre of Advanced Litigation at Nottingham Law School. Member of the Supreme Court Procedures Committee. member of the Editorial Advisory Board of 'The Litigator'.

Personal: Born 10th March 1944. Leisure interests include travelling, playing golf, keeping fit, and principally his family. Lives in London and Loughton.

McKenzie, Kenneth

Davies Arnold Cooper, London (0171) 936 2222. Qualified 1978. Partner 1986. Litigation. Insurance/reinsurance litigator specialising in risks and institutions, professional indemnity and Lloyd's related matters.

Mendelowitz, Michael

Barlow Lyde & Gilbert, London (0171) 247 2277. Qualified 1989. Partner. Reinsurance Division. Specialises in all aspects of insurance and reinsurance, including environmental liability and insolvency.

Munden, Michael R.

Herbert Smith, London (0171) 374 8000. Partner in Insurance Department.

Specialisation: Acts both for major insurance companies and for syndicates at Lloyd's on most aspects of insurance and reinsurance disputes, frequently involving foreign jurisdictions, including for many of the major insurance organisations in the City of London and around the world.

Career: Qualified in 1972. Became a Partner at *Herbert Smith* in 1980.

Personal: Educated at Southampton University.

O'Mahoney, Gerald

Davies Arnold Cooper, London (0171) 936 2222. Partner in Commercial Litigation Department.

Specialisation: Handles commercial litigation and arbitration, insurance, reinsurance, professional indemnity and liability. Has written several articles on law reform and Lloyds disciplinary procedures. Charge-out rate is £175-£225 per hour.

Prof. Membership: Law Society.

Career: Started as a Legal Executive. Previously with *Robert Gore & Co* 1977-82 and *Colombotti & Partners* 1983-85. Qualified in 1984. Joined *Davies Arnold Cooper* in 1985 and became a Partner in 1987.

Personal: Born 1st November 1953. Educated at Gunnersbury Grammar School 1965-70 and the College of Law 1982-83. Interests include golf, rugby, good food and wine, reading and current affairs. Lives in London.

O'Neill, Terry

Clifford Chance, London (0171) 600 1000. Partner. Principal area of work is insurance and reinsurance law.

Parker, Raj D.
Freshfields, London (0171) 936 4000. Partner in Litigation Department.

Specialisation: Main area of practice is insurance and reinsurance work, including the Johnson Matthey Bankers insurance claims (1984-1990), Eras environmental impairment liability litigation (1990-1994); claims for brokers; intermediaries and banks on mortgage liability claims; claims against Insurance Ombudsman Bureau; acts for Lloyd's in Central fund and related litigation and enquiries. Contributor to forthcoming Lloyd's of London Press 'Insurance Coverage Disputes' and author of articles. Regular speaker at insurance industry seminars. Also deals with sports law, acting for the Football Association in all advisory and contentious work. Acted in the Hillsborough proceedings, the battle to establish the Premier League, recent disciplinary hearings, sits on working parties.

Prof. Membership: Law Society; Society of Solicitor Advocates.

Career: Attended Bar School (1983). and practised as a barrister until 1985. At the Corporation of Lloyd's for a year 1985-86 on an Inquiry. Joined *Freshfields* in 1986 and became a Partner in 1993.

Personal: Born 19th September 1960. Educated at Christ's College 1972-79 and Southampton University 1979-82. Recreations include sport, music, theatre and ornithology. Lives in London.

Payton, Michael
Clyde & Co, London (0171) 623 1244.

Pell, Marian
Herbert Smith, London (0171) 374 8000. Partner and Head of Insurance Section of Company Department.

Specialisation: Has expertise in mergers and acquisitions, demutualisation, restructuring of insurance businesses, establishment, authorisation and regulation of insurance businesses and insurance intermediaries and of the drafting of insurance policies. Has particular experience of the concerns of mutual life companies.

Career: Qualified in 1976 and became a Partner at *Herbert Smith* in 1984.

Personal: Educated at Southampton University.

Pincott, Andrew
Elborne Mitchell, London (0171) 320 9000. Senior Partner. Qualified 1974. Partner 1982. Chairman of British Insurance Law Association 1986-1988. Specialist areas of practice are reinsurance, including financial reinsurance and insurance market problems; advisory work, including insurance contract and product wordings, insurance and reinsurance disputes, litigation and arbitration. Born 1949. Leisure: Opera, theatre design and gardens. Resides: London.

Powell, John F.
Lovell White Durrant, London (0171) 236 0066. Qualified 1970. Partner. Extensive experience of insurance dispute resolution (particularly marine) and reinsurance dispute resolution.

Richards, Andrew Philip
See under Corporate Finance.

Ridley, G.M.
Slaughter and May, London (0171) 600 1200. Qualified 1971.

Rocher, Philip
Wilde Sapte, London (0171) 246 7000. Partner in Litigation Department.

Specialisation: Insurance and reinsurance litigation specialist. Handles political and credit risk coverage disputes and recovery actions, directors and officers liability insurance, insurance company insolvency and Lloyd's Names litigation. Acted for plaintiff policyholders in House of Lords test case on the Policyholders Protection Board, for the plaintiff Names (3092) in the Gooda Walker litigation claiming £620 million, and a member of the creditors committee of the 'Kwelm' companies. Regular speaker at conferences in the UK and abroad.

Prof. Membership: Law Society, London Litigation Solicitors Association, American Bar Association.

Career: Qualified and joined *Wilde Sapte* in 1981. Became a Partner in 1985. Partner in charge of the firm's New York office 1988-92.

Personal: Born 5th February 1956. Attended Ashville College, Harrogate (to 1974) and Birmingham University 1975-78. Recreations include golf and football. Lives in London.

Rogan, P.J.H.
Ince & Co, London (0171) 623 2011. Partner in Insurance and Reinsurance Department.

Specialisation: Main area of practice is reinsurance, with emphasis on the London market, marine and non-marine, treaty reinsurance disputes. Also handles marine and aviation insurance disputes. Recently handled Pan Atlantic v Pine Top. Author of various publications; regularly addresses Insurance Seminars.

Prof. Membership: Law Society, ARIAS.

Career: Qualified in 1977. Worked at *Willis Faber & Dumas* from 1975-7, before joining *Ince & Co.* in 1977. Became a Partner in 1982.

Personal: Born 17th December 1950. Attended Stellenbosch University in South Africa, then Kings College London. Leisure interests include family, theatre, tennis, golf and skiing. Lives in London.

Sacher, Jonathan
Paisner & Co, London (0171) 353 0299. Qualified 1981. Partner 1984. Reinsurance

and insurance litigation and arbitration. Member of British Insurance Law Association.

Schofield, B.A.
Cameron Markby Hewitt, London (0171) 702 2345. Partner in Insurance and Reinsurance Department.

Specialisation: Principal area of practice is handling of professional indemnity claims against accountants, actuaries, Lloyd's Agents and insurance brokers, acting for insurers and insured. In addition advising on general insurance and reinsurance matters including advising on policy wording construction.

Prof. Membership: Law Society.

Career: Qualified in 1980 became a partner in *Cameron Markby Hewitt* in 1986.

Personal: Date of Birth: 11th June 1956.

Sinfield, Nicholas
Davies Arnold Cooper, London (0171) 936 2222.

Specialisation: Partner specialising in professional indemnity, coverage and reinsurance litigation. Practice also covers fire and property insurance coverage disputes, with an emphasis on fraud, and asset recovery and tracing. Interesting cases include the JD Wood consequential insurance litigation; Asbestos London Market Coverage disputes; defence of RMH Outhwaite (Underwriting) Agency in Names litigation; Judicial Review process of PIA Pensions. Regularly addresses conferences and recently lectured as a guest of Stamford Law School on catastrophe excess of loss insurance. Has written various articles on insurance and fraud, and insurance/reinsurance coverage issues.

Prof. Membership: Law Society; British Insurance Law Association, Arson Prevention Bureau.

Career: Qualified 1984. Reynolds Porter Chamberlain 1984-1987. Davies Arnold Cooper since 1987, partner since 1989.

Personal: Educated at Bedford School 1965-1977, University College, London 1977-1980 and at the College of Law 1981. Leisure pursuits include ergometer training and gym training. Born 22nd March 1959. Lives in Chiswick.

Slowe, Richard
S J Berwin & Co, London (0171) 837 2222. Qualified 1970. Partner in Litigation Department specialising in advocacy. Fifteen years commercial and common law experience at the Bar.

Smith, Michael
Titmuss Sainer Dechert, London (0171) 583 5353. Senior Partner and Partner in Financial Services Department.

Specialisation: Deals exclusively with non-contentious work relating to Lloyd's of London, acting on the acquisition, disposal and merger of underwriting agents and brokers, transfer of their businesses and raising corporate capital at Lloyd's. Advises on all related aspects of their businesses, including regulatory, disciplinary and insolvency issues affecting underwriting agents, brokers and their directors. Author of several articles on Lloyd's of London.

Prof. Membership: Lloyd's Hardship Scheme Advisory Panel.

Career: Qualified in 1970, having joined *Titmuss Sainer & Webb* (now *Titmuss Sainer Dechert*) in 1968. Became a Partner in 1972 and Senior Partner in 1990.

Personal: Born in 1945. Educated at Cheltenham College. Enjoys opera, skiing and good food and wine. Non-executive director of Cater Allen Syndicate Management Ltd. Lives near Guildford.

Southey, Verner

Clyde & Co,   London (0171) 623 1244. Qualified 1977. Qualified 1977 in England. Partner 1986. Head of Corporate Department. Handles corporate and non-contentious work principally in the insurance sector, Lloyd's, London market and international. Born 1.10.1942.

Spiller, Richard J.

D J Freeman,   London (0171) 583 4055. Qualified 1980. Partner 1985. Company/commercial lawyer specialising in insurance. Also handles insolvency work. Fluent German speaker.

Stanley, Ed

Elborne Mitchell,   London (0171) 320 9000. Qualified 1984. Partner 1989. Specialist areas of practice are reinsurance, insurance and professional indemnity disputes. Born 1959. Leisure: football and playing keyboards. Resides: London.

Taylor, Peter L.

Lovell White Durrant,   London (0171) 236 0066. Qualified 1988. Partner 1993. Insurance and Reinsurance Department. Specialises in reinsurance dispute resolution.

Tiplady, David

D J Freeman,   London (0171) 583 4055. Qualified 1991. Partner 1992. Insurance Litigation Department. Main area of work is

representing Lloyd's Names. Born 26.12.1946.

Wadsworth, Michael Henry

See under Professional Negligence.

Wells, Christian

Lovell White Durrant,   London (0171) 236 0066.

Specialisation: Partner in the Insurance and Reinsurance Group. Practice involves advising Lloyd's underwriting agents, London market institutions and mutual insurance associations on the conduct of insurance business and markets, including current issues such as pollution claims, accounts settlement systems, security and insolvency.

Career: Qualified 1980. Partner since 1986.

Wheatley, Vere A.

Cameron Markby Hewitt,   London (0171) 702 2345. Partner in Insurance and Reinsurance Department.

Specialisation: Main area of practice is reinsurance and the defence of brokers in direct and reinsurance disputes; also defends Lloyd's agents.

Career: Qualified in 1982. Practised in New York 1985-89. Admitted as a lawyer in New York state 1987. Joined *Cameron Markby Hewitt* in 1989, becoming a Partner in 1992.

Personal: Born 1st May 1957. Attended Bristol University 1976-79 and Guildford Law School 1979-80.

Wordley, Paul

Holman, Fenwick & Willan,   London (0171) 488 2300. Qualified 1994. Partner 1994. Insurance and Reinsurance Department. Principal area of practice is insurance/reinsurance industry disputes. Born 12.7.1959.

Young, John

Lovell White Durrant,   London (0171) 236 0066. Qualified 1981. Partner 1987. Specialises exclusively in advising insurance companies and related businesses in the UK and Europe on corporate and regulatory matters.

Angel, Peter G.

Manches & Co,   Oxford (01865) 722106. Partner in the Company & Commercial Department.

Specialisation: General corporate finance and venture capital work, with particular interest in corporate and regulatory aspect of the Lloyds insurance market. Regular speaker at seminars on corporate finance topics.

Career: Qualified 1970.

Personal: Born 27th July, 1946. Attended Maidstone Grammar School 1959-64 and then University College, London. Board member of The College of Estate Management. Lives in Oxford.

Bell, Raymond

Clyde & Co,   Guildford (01483) 31161. Qualified 1984.

Finnigan, Kevin P.

James Chapman & Co,   Manchester (0161) 236 7772.

Monteith, Julia M.C.

Wansbroughs Willey Hargrave,   Leeds (0113) 244 1151. Partner in General Insurance Department.

Specialisation: Head of Environmental Law Unit. Acts for insurers and self-insureds to assess civil liabilities for pollution damage, define policy coverage and defend against personal injury claims. Also experienced in all aspects of personal injury including employers' and public liability, MIB and road traffic accident work. Speaks regularly at seminars.

Prof. Membership: UK Environmental Law Association, CORE (Centre for Organisations relating to the Environment).

Career: Qualified 1985 after articles with *Willey Hargrave*. Became a Partner at *WWH* in 1989.

Teasdale, David J.

James Chapman & Co,   Manchester (0161) 236 7772.

INTELLECTUAL PROPERTY

THIS section divides intellectual property rights into two parts; patent work, which requires an element of scientific expertise, and non-patent work.

A firm's strength in information technology and other commercial sectors requiring IP work, such as the publishing and entertainment industries, will be reflected in the relevant sections of this directory.

LONDON

PATENT

Bird & Bird is regarded as the best patents firm in the United Kingdom. Its IP group comprises eight partners (most notably Trevor Cook, David Harriss and Hamish Sandison) and 19 assistants handling a variety of litigious, transactional and advisory work particularly in the information technology, and pharmaceutical/biotechnology sectors.

LEADING FIRMS – LONDON – MAINLY PATENT	
BIRD & BIRD	BRISTOWS COOKE & CARPMAEL
CLIFFORD CHANCE	HERBERT SMITH
NEEDHAM & GRANT	SIMMONS & SIMMONS
TAYLOR JOYNSON GARRETT	
BAKER & McKENZIE	LINKLATERS & PAINES
LOVELL WHITE DURRANT	

Bristows Cooke & Carpmael also boasts an outstanding patents team headed by Ian Judge, whose track record includes 'Beecham v Bristol-Myers' and 'DuPont v Akzo' in the House of Lords. Sally Field has also been highly recommended. *Simmons & Simmons* is regarded as having the best IP department in a large firm. Kevin Mooney is its outstanding practitioner in patents. Gerald Kamstra and Mark Hodgson are also highly recommended.

HIGHLY REGARDED – LONDON – MAINLY PATENT	
ALLEN & OVERY	ASHURST MORRIS CRISP
DENTON HALL	EVERSHEDS
FRESHFIELDS	HAMMOND SUDDARDS
HOPKINS & WOOD	MASONS
McKENNA & CO	NABARRO NATHANSON
NORTON ROSE	SLAUGHTER AND MAY

Although *Clifford Chance* has lost some of its best IP specialists of late, it still has an impressive team including David Perkins and Alan Bryson.

Herbert Smith will sorely miss Christopher Tootal, the leading UK patents lawyer, soon to retire.

Needham & Grant is the leading niche firm in this area, largely owing to Gregor Grant's outstanding reputation in patent litigation. The firm has recently conducted patent-related litigation for Unilever, Access, Christie-Tyler, Murex Diagnostics, British Gas and Johnson Electric.

Baker & Mckenzie and *Linklaters & Paines* also possess highly rated patents teams.

Linklaters & Paines, in addition to a substantial amount of 'core' patent litigation, were at the time of going to print, involved in three out of the four major biotechnology patent actions.

Taylor Joynson Garrett, while still very strong in this area, has suffered a major loss in the form of Isabel Davies' departure to *Eversheds*. The IP department now comprises four specialist partners headed by the very capable Richard Price.

Ashurst Morris Crisp has made major progress in patents thanks to the arrival of Ian Starr (formerly the number two IP partner at *Clifford Chance*).

Hammond Suddards owes its standing to the highly-rated Laurence Cohen, whilst *Dibb Lupton Broomhead* can draw on its strength in the North. *Denton Hall* is also starting to make an impact thanks to Clive Thorne and James Irvine.

NON-PATENT

To list every firm capable of simple transactional non-patent IP work would not be helpful to the reader. The firms listed here are those which are either particularly recommended for their work on 'soft' IP (i.e. trade marks, passing off, copyright, confidential information and anti-counterfeiting) or which can justifiably boast a significant, stand-alone IP practice.

LEADING FIRMS – LONDON – MAINLY NON-PATENT	
BIRD & BIRD	BRISTOWS COOKE & CARPMAEL
SIMMONS & SIMMONS	
BAKER & McKENZIE	CLIFFORD CHANCE
EVERSHEDS	HAMMOND SUDDARDS
LOVELL WHITE DURRANT	ROUSE & CO
TAYLOR JOYNSON GARRETT	
HERBERT SMITH	MASONS
NEEDHAM & GRANT	SLAUGHTER AND MAY

The strongest patents firms are also invariably strong in other areas of intellectual property. However, there are firms more notable for their work in soft IP rather than patents.

HIGHLY REGARDED – LONDON – MAINLY NON-PATENT	
ALLEN & OVERY	DENTON HALL
HOPKINS & WOOD	LINKLATERS & PAINES
MONIER–WILLIAMS & BOXALLS	
ALSOP WILKINSON	BRIFFA & CO
CAMERON MARKBY HEWITT	CROCKERS
FARRER & CO	FORSYTE SAUNDERS KERMAN
FRESHFIELDS	GOULDENS
HOBSON AUDLEY	LEWIS SILKIN
MANCHES & CO	MAYCOCK'S
McKENNA & CO	NORTON ROSE
PETTMAN SMITH	REYNOLDS PORTER CHAMBERLAIN
ROITER ZUCKER	TITMUSS SAINER DECHERT

In all the tables the names in each group are listed alphabetically.

Besides its heavyweight presence in patents, *Bristows Cooke & Carpmael* can boast the talents of the rapidly-emerging Sally Field and Paul Walsh; the latter acts for the British Producers and Brand Owners Group. The firm also acts for IBM, Kodak and Glaxo.

Simmons & Simmons has Helen Newman, who is particularly noted for her trade marks expertise.

Sheer weight of departmental expertise keeps patent-oriented *Bird & Bird* near the top in this area, whilst *Lovell White Durrant* is also regarded as one of the best 'soft' IP firms, with both David Latham and Nicholas Macfarlane highly recommended.

Despite the presence of Christopher Tootal, *Herbert Smith* has slipped somewhat owing to the departure of anti-counterfeiting expert Anthony Willoughby to *Rouse & Co*, which is surely the best niche firm for non-patent IP.

Eversheds is sure to make progress with 'passing off' expert Isabel Davies of 'Jif Lemon' fame.

Taylor Joynson Garrett, Baker & McKenzie and *Clifford Chance* each have very strong all-round IP departments.

Making headway in non-patent IP is *Slaughter and May* (Nigel Swycher has become its first IP partner) and *Masons*, whose first appearance on our IP listings is largely due to Stephen Aldred's arrival from *Clifford Chance*.

LEADING INDIVIDUALS – LONDON

Laurence J. Cohen *Hammond Suddards*	Trevor M. Cook *Bird & Bird*	Isabel Davies *Eversheds*
Sally A. Field *Bristows Cooke & Carpmael*	Gregor Grant *Needham & Grant*	David Harriss *Bird & Bird*
Donald G. Jerrard *Baker & McKenzie*	Ian M. Judge *Bristows Cooke & Carpmael*	Vanessa Marsland *Clifford Chance*
Kevin M. Mooney *Simmons & Simmons*	David Perkins *Clifford Chance*	Richard Price *Taylor Joynson Garrett*
Hamish R. Sandison *Bird & Bird*	Harry Small *Baker & McKenzie*	Robert Z. Swift *Linklaters & Paines*
Christopher P. Tootal *Herbert Smith*	Anthony J.T. Willoughby *Rouse & Co*	
P. Mark Abell *Field Fisher Waterhouse*	Stephen Aldred *Masons*	Robert J. Anderson *Lovell White Durrant*
David Barrett *Dibb Lupton Broomhead*	Robert T. J. Bond *Hobson Audley*	Jeremy R.C. Brown *Linklaters & Paines*
Alan Bryson *Clifford Chance*	Miles Gaythwaite *Bird & Bird*	David J.S. Gibbins *Needham & Grant*
Rupert C. Grey *Crockers*	Michael L. Hart *Baker & McKenzie*	Mark T. Hodgson *Simmons & Simmons*
John Hull *Wilde Sapte*	James Irvine *Denton Hall*	Gerald Simon Kamstra *Simmons & Simmons*
David A. Latham *Lovell White Durrant*	David Llewelyn *Llewelyn Zietman*	Morag Macdonald *Bird & Bird*
Nicholas R. Macfarlane *Lovell White Durrant*	Avril C.B. Martindale *Bristows Cooke & Carpmael*	Christopher Millard *Clifford Chance*
William J. Moodie *Herbert Smith*	Gary Moss *Taylor Joynson Garrett*	Helen Newman *Simmons & Simmons*
Edward J. Nodder *Bristows Cooke & Carpmael*	David Charles Petterson *Taylor Joynson Garrett*	David Sills *Monier–Williams & Boxalls*
Catriona Smith *Allen & Overy*	Ian C. Starr *Ashurst Morris Crisp*	Hugh W.J. Stubbs *Freshfields*
Peter D. Taylor *Clifford Chance*	Clive Thorne *Denton Hall*	Paul A. Walsh *Bristows Cooke & Carpmael*
Robin G. Whaite *Linklaters & Paines*		

UP AND COMING

Nick Gardner *Herbert Smith*	James Marshall *Lovell White Durrant*	Glyn Morgan *Taylor Joynson Garrett*
Nigel Swycher *Slaughter and May*		

SOUTH EAST

Firms in the South East recommended for their expertise in the field include *Dallas Brett, The Law Offices of Marcus J. O'Leary, Donne Mileham & Haddock* and *Nabarro Nathanson*.

The nationally acclaimed Hugh Brett, of *Dallas Brett*, in addition to having written numerous articles on anti-trust law, copyright, patent licensing and technology transfer, is a member of the Intellectual Property Committee of The Law Society and the founder and editor of the 'European Intellectual Property Review'.

Garrett & Co will mourn the loss of Marcus O'Leary, a well respected practitioner who is equally known for his work in IT as IP. Marcus J.O'Leary has recently launched *The Law Offices of Marcus O'Leary*, a niche practice, which aims to provide a low cost, high quality service.

The intellectual property department at *Donne Mileham &*

Haddock advises on both contentious and non-contentious work. Timothy Aspinall has been recommended.

HIGHLY REGARDED – SOUTH EAST

DALLAS BRETT *Oxford*	DONNE MILEHAM & HADDOCK *Brighton*
THE LAW OFFICES OF MARCUS J. O'LEARY	NABARRO NATHANSON
BRAIN & BRAIN *Reading*	MORRELL PEEL & GAMLEN *Oxford*
PENNINGTONS *Basingstoke*	PITMANS *Reading*
SHOOSMITHS & HARRISON *Banbury*	

Nabarro Nathanson makes its first appearance in this list following the recent merger with *Turner Kenneth Brown*. The firm now boasts the excellent Tony Bailes, who, in addition to handling a broad spectrum of intellectual property work, specialises in IP issues as they affect the computer industry.

SOUTH WEST

There are relatively few firms in the South West with sizeable intellectual property departments, the reputation of the firm tending to rest with that of the individual practitioner.

Osborne Clarke's strength lies with Alan Wood, a trademark specialist who formerly practised at *Linklaters & Paines*. The IP department, comprising three specialist partners, also conducts a substantial amount of IP-related litigation.

Wansbroughs Willey Hargrave is also well respected, Andrew Braithwaite having been recommended.

Laytons has developed particular expertise in licensing and technology transfer and is at the forefront of intellectual property law in the region. Richard Brown is held in high regard.

Robert Humphreys of *Humphreys & Co*, is a new addition to the list, having been highly recommended for patents work.

Other notable firms include *Every & Phillips and Dunnings, Lester Aldridge* and *Wiggin and Co.*

WALES

Cardiff firms take the lion's share of intellectual property work in Wales. *Edwards Geldard, Eversheds* and *Morgan Bruce* all handle a variety of patent and 'soft' IP work, including litigation.

MIDLANDS

A frenzy of retirements and departures from Midlands IP departments has severely undermined the premier status of *Pinsent Curtis* and *Wragge & Co*. News of Rupert Hughes's retirement from *Wragge & Co* was swiftly followed by the announcement that Neil Maybury, head of *Pinsent Curtis'* IP department, was moving to *Dibb Lupton Broomhead* to develop its Birmingham IP practice. As a result, *Pinsent Curtis'* IP unit is in the throes of a major reorganisation.

Eversheds' reputation for IP comes from its Nottingham office, where Lionel Howard heads the department. The firm has particular expertise in intellectual property matters within the textile industry.

Martineau Johnson, in addition to boasting the highly recommended William Barker, has gained in strength through the arrival of Marie McMorrow from *Wragge & Co*.

Firms seen as developing their practices in IP include *Freeth Cartwright Hunt Dickens* and *Browne Jacobson*.

Neil Martin-Kaye of *Martin-Kaye & Partners* is considered to be very experienced in the field.

EAST ANGLIA

Hewitson Becke + Shaw's IP practice remains the strongest in the region, with partner Ian Craig and assistant Neil Ackermann (newly recruited from *Pettman Smith*) both recommended. The firm has recently expanded its practice to cover the

In all the tables the names in each group are listed alphabetically.

bio-technology field, advising start-up and established companies in Europe and the United States.

HIGHLY REGARDED – EAST ANGLIA

EVERSHEDS Norwich	GREENWOODS Peterborough
MILLS & REEVE Norwich	TAYLOR VINTERS Cambridge
LEATHES PRIOR Norwich	

Other recommended firms include *Eversheds* (Norwich) which specialises in the food and drink advertising industry, *Greenwoods* (particularly Philip Sloan), *Mills & Reeve* where Glynne Stanfield is held in high regard and *Taylor Vinters* where Isabel Napper is considered an authority.

LEADING INDIVIDUALS – EAST ANGLIA

Niel Ackermann	Hewitson Becke + Shaw
Ian Craig	Hewitson Becke + Shaw
Isabel Napper	Taylor Vinters
Philip Sloan	Greenwoods
G. Stanfield	Mills & Reeve

NORTH WEST

As in the Midlands, it has been a turbulent year in IP in the North West. Philip Woods, the North West's outstanding IP practitioner, left *Eversheds* at the end of 1994 to set up as a sole practitioner. *Addleshaw Sons & Latham* lost two IP lawyers (including the renowned Glyn Gowans) and *Wacks Caller* lost recent recruit Riaz Bowmer to *Alsop Wilkinson*.

LEADING FIRMS – NORTH WEST

PHILIP WOODS & CO Stockport

Meanwhile, national heavyweights *Masons, Dibb Lupton Broomhead* and *Eversheds* were still looking for IP practitioners in Manchester at the time of writing.

HIGHLY REGARDED – NORTH WEST

ADDLESHAW SONS & LATHAM Manchester	ALSOP WILKINSON Liverpool
DAVIES WALLIS FOYSTER Liverpool	HALLIWELL LANDAU Manchester
KUIT, STEINART, LEVY Manchester	PHILIP CONN & CO Manchester
TAYLORS Blackburn	WACKS CALLER Manchester
HILL DICKINSON DAVIS CAMPBELL Liverpool	LAWSON COPPOCK & HART Manchester

Notable practitioners include Robert Stoker at *Addleshaw Sons & Latham,* Jonathan Moakes at *Halliwell Landau* and Ian Morris at *Philip Conn & Co.*

LEADING INDIVIDUALS – NORTH WEST

Philip D. Woods	Philip Woods & Co
Riaz Bowmer	Alsop Wilkinson
George W. Godar	Alsop Wilkinson
Jonathan Moakes	Halliwell Landau
A. Ian Morris	Philip Conn & Co
Robert R. Stoker	Addleshaw Sons & Latham

UP AND COMING

Gill Duddy	Alsop Wilkinson

NORTH EAST

Dibb Lupton Broomhead is generally regarded as having the leading IP practice in the North East, handling a substantial

LEADING FIRMS – NORTH EAST

DIBB LUPTON BROOMHEAD Bradford	
EVERSHEDS Leeds	LUPTON FAWCETT Leeds
PINSENT CURTIS Leeds	
HAMMOND SUDDARDS Leeds	

amount of contentious and non-contentious work. Richard Sutton is considered a leading authority. The firm's in-house patent agents have particular expertise in computer technology, EC and foreign patents.

HIGHLY REGARDED – NORTH EAST

BOOTH & CO. Leeds	GARRETT & CO Leeds
IRWIN MITCHELL Sheffield	WALKER MORRIS Leeds

Other highly recommended firms include *Eversheds* (Leeds), *Pinsent Curtis* (where Stephen Chandler is held in high regard) and *Lupton Fawcett* (John Sykes).

LEADING INDIVIDUALS – NORTH EAST

Stephen B.J. Chandler	Pinsent Curtis
Richard Sutton	Dibb Lupton Broomhead
John R.H. Sykes	Lupton Fawcett
Richard Boardman	Garrett & Co
James Hodgson	Eversheds
Richard A. Kempner	Booth & Co.

SCOTLAND

McGrigor Donald emerges as the leading intellectual property practice, with Shonaig Macpherson highly recommended. The firm handles the full range of contentious and non-contentious work for a broad client base.

LEADING FIRMS – SCOTLAND

McGRIGOR DONALD Glasgow	
DUNDAS & WILSON CS Edinburgh	MACLAY MURRAY & SPENS Glasgow
MACROBERTS Glasgow	

Other highly recommended firms include *Dundas & Wilson CS, Maclay Murray & Spens* and *MacRoberts.*

HIGHLY REGARDED – SCOTLAND

W & J BURNESS WS Edinburgh	DICKSON MINTO WS Edinburgh
SEMPLE FRASER WS Glasgow	
DORMAN JEFFREY & CO Glasgow	HOLMES MACKILLOP Glasgow
SHEPHERD & WEDDERBURN Edinburgh	STEEDMAN RAMAGE WS Edinburgh
WRIGHT, JOHNSTON & MACKENZIE Glasgow	

Lorne Byatt at *Dundas & Wilson CS* has developed a specialism in intellectual property rights within the information technology sector, whilst Fiona Nicolson at *Maclay Murray & Spens* has cornered the market within the education sector.

Ian Inglis is noted for his expertise on the contentious side.

MacRoberts boasts David Flint, who is considered to be experienced in the full range of intellectual property work.

LEADING INDIVIDUALS – SCOTLAND

Lorne Byatt	*Dundas & Wilson CS*
David Flint	*MacRoberts* '
Shonaig Macpherson	*McGrigor Donald*
Kenneth D.B. McLew	*Holmes Mackillop*
Fiona M.M. Nicolson	*Maclay Murray & Spens*
Ian G. Inglis	*Maclay Murray & Spens*
John A.D. Innes	*Dundas & Wilson CS*
Scott Kerr	*Dickson Minto WS*
Kenneth McCracken	*Wright, Johnston & Mackenzie*
James A. McLean	*W & J Burness WS*
L. Annette Pairman	*W & J Burness WS*
James Saunders	*Shepherd & Wedderburn*
David Semple	*Semple Fraser WS*

NORTHERN IRELAND

Cleaver Fulton & Rankin and *Carson & McDowell* offer expertise in copyright and trade marks work, while the former firm are also experienced in passing off and patents matters. *C & H Jefferson* and *Harrison, Leitch & Logan* also carry out work in this field.

HIGHLY REGARDED – NORTHERN IRELAND

CARSON & McDOWELL	*Belfast*	**CLEAVER FULTON & RANKIN**	*Belfast*
HARRISON, LEITCH & LOGAN	*Belfast*	**C & H JEFFERSON**	*Belfast*

In all the tables the names in each group are listed alphabetically.

LEADERS IN INTELLECTUAL PROPERTY

LONDON

Abell, P. Mark
See under Franchising.

Aldred, Stephen
Masons, London (0171) 490 4000. Partner and Head of Intellectual Property Group.

Specialisation: Practice covers the full range of intellectual property work and includes disputes and transactions in relation to patents, copyright and design, trade secrets and trade marks. Acts for computer hardware and software suppliers, manufacturing, telecommunications and publishing companies.

Prof. Membership: CIPA, ITMA, INTA, AIPPI.

Career: Qualified 1977. At *Herbert Smith* 1975-79 and *Clifford Chance* 1980-93 (Partner from 1985). Joined *Mason* as a Partner in 1994.

Personal: Born 20th July 1952. Educated at Bolton School and Worcester College, Oxford (MA). Interests include theatre, sports and wine. Lives in Putney.

Anderson, Robert J.
Lovell White Durrant, London (0171) 236 0066. Qualified 1972. Partner 1978. Intellectual Property Department. All aspects of intellectual property work and technology related work.

Barrett, David
See under Computer Law & I.T.

Bond, Robert T. J.
Hobson Audley, London (0171) 248 2299. Qualified 1979. Partner 1995. IP/IT Department. Specialises in intellectual property and information technology.

Brown, Jeremy R.C.
Linklaters & Paines, London (0171) 606 7080. Joined 1978. Partner since 1982. Head of Intellectual Property, Technology and Communications Department.

Bryson, Alan
Clifford Chance, London (0171) 600 1000. Partner. Principal area of work is intellectual property.

Cohen, Laurence J.
Hammond Suddards, London (0171) 628 4767. Partner and Head of Intellectual Property Unit.

Specialisation: Contentious and non-contentious intellectual property matters including patents, trademarks, copyright, design right and trade secrets. Also deals with regulatory law, particularly in the area of agrochemicals and medicines. Acted in Linpac v. Eagleton; ICI v. ROHM and RAM; Games Workshop v Transworld Publishers; McDonald v. Graham; Dalgety v. Food Brokers. Author of 'World Litigation Law and Practice: Unit B1 England and Wales' (1986) and CIPA/ITMA Trade Marks Handbook section on Civil Litigation (1992). Contributor of numerous articles to a variety of specialist publications on intellectual property topics and regular conference speaker.

Prof. Membership: CIPA, ITMA, INTA, IBA, Law Society.

Career: Qualified 1976. Assistant Solicitor with *Bristows Cooke & Carpmael* from 1976, and became a Partner in 1981. Joined *Hammond Suddards* in 1992 and is currently Head of Intellectual Property Unit.

Personal: Born 12th September 1951. Attended Emmanuel College, Cambridge 1970-73. Leisure pursuits include tennis, squash and skiing. Lives in Radlett, Hertfordshire.

Cook, Trevor M.
Bird & Bird, London (0171) 415 6000. Partner in Intellectual Property Department.

Specialisation: Main areas of practice are litigation, transactional and advisory work in relation to patents, copyright and other intellectual property rights and associated regulatory law issues, particularly in the information technology and pharmaceutical/ biotechnology sectors. Contributor to 'Information Technology and the Law' and 'CIPA Guide to Patents Act'; co-author of 'Pharmaceuticals Biotechnology and the Law' and 'Copyright and the European Community'. Has addressed seminars in London, Berlin, Paris and New York on various intellectual property and computer law topics.

Prof Membership: Committee member of Intellectual Property Lawyers Association, member of Licensing Executives Society, associate member of Chartered Institute of Patent Agents, Secretary of the British Computer Society Intellectual Property Committee.

Career: Qualified in 1977. Joined *Bird & Bird* in 1974, became a Partner in 1981.

Personal: Born 1951. Attended Southampton University (BSc Chemistry, 1973). Lives in Woking, Surrey.

Davies, Isabel
Eversheds, London (0171) 919 4500. Partner and Head of Intellectual Property at Eversheds, London. Head of Eversheds national Intellectual Property Group.

Specialisation: Work includes patents, trademarks, copyright, designs, competition and EC law. Cases have included Jif, Coloplast v. Mentor 1994 and 175+ High Court Proceedings, Howley v. Dronsfield & Boode (UK) Ltd. Author of numerous articles in the professional press. Editor of TJG Intellectual Property Review 1991-94 and Eversheds IPEye intellectual property review 1994-5. Legal Editor of Journal of Brand Management and Country Correspondent for EIPR. Has spoken widely at conferences on I.P. issues, often taking the Chair.

Prof. Membership: ITMA, CIPA, ICC, INTA, ACG, ICC Anti-counterfeiting Committee, Task Force Leader on INTA International Committee, Member of INTA Forums Committee.

Career: Qualified in 1976. Worked at *Alsop Stevens*, then *Wragge & Co.*, 1979-85. Joined *Woodham Smith* as a Partner in 1985, *Taylor Joynson Garrett* in 1990, then *Jaques & Lewis* (now Eversheds) in 1994.

Personal: Born 30th May 1952. Attended St Albans Girls' Grammar School, Leicester University and Guildford College of Law. Leisure interests include travel, theatre, squash, skiing, food and wine. Lives in Twickenham.

Field, Sally A.
Bristows Cooke & Carpmael, London (0171) 400 8000. Partner in Intellectual Property Department.

Specialisation: Intellectual Property. Work covers advising on full range of intellectual property including patents, trade marks, copyright, designs and confidential information. Cases include Allen & Hanbury's (Glaxo) v. Generics, IBM v. Phoenix, and Kodak/ Kodiak. Writes articles for specialist periodicals such as Corporate Briefing and Trade Mark and Patents World. Regular speaker at intellectual property conferences and seminars.

Prof. Memberships: Law Society, Associate Member Chartered Institute of Patent Agents, Associate Member Institute of Trade Mark Agents.

Career: Articled with *Clifford Turner* 1979-81, then moved to *Bristows Cooke & Carpmael* in 1983. Became a Partner in 1987.

Personal: Born 16th May 1957. Attended Durham University 1975-78. Leisure pursuits include golf, tennis and skiing. Lives in London.

Gardner, Nick
Herbert Smith, London (0171) 374 8000. Partner in Intellectual Property and Technology Department.

Specialisation: Deals with intellectual property and technology, specialising in matters involving technical issues in the computing and electronics field.

Career: Qualified in 1988 and became a Partner at *Herbert Smith* in 1994.

Personal: Educated at the University of Nottingham.

Gaythwaite, Miles
Bird & Bird, London (0171) 415 6000. Partner in Intellectual Property Department.

Specialisation: Principal area of practice is patents, patent and know-how licensing, trade marks and copyright. Also pharmaceuticals and software. Important cases handled include L.B. Plastics v. Swish; Holtite v. Jost; Unilever v. Gillette; Societe Francaise Hoechst v. Allied Colloids Ltd; Kakkar v. Ferring; BICC plc v. Burndy Corporation and Amersham v. Corning.

Prof. Membership: Chartered Institute of Patent Agents, Licensing Executives Society, APRAM.

Career: With *Elkington & Fife*, Chartered Patent Agents 1967-74. Qualified as a Chartered Patent Agent in 1972. Joined *Bird & Bird* in 1974 and became a Partner in 1978.

Personal: Born 1943. Educated at Glasgow University 1960-64 (BSc, Chemistry) and Cambridge University 1964-67 (PhD, Organic Chemistry). Lives in London.

Gibbins, David J.S.
Needham & Grant, London (0171) 242 5866. Qualified 1984.

Grant, Gregor
Needham & Grant, London (0171) 242 5866. Qualified 1967. Partner 1971. Main area of practice is patent litigation and advice with particular emphasis on engineering, pharmaceuticals, biotechnology and chemical matters.

Grey, Rupert C.
See under Defamation.

Harriss, David
Bird & Bird, London (0171) 415 6000. Partner in Intellectual Property Department. Senior Partner.

Specialisation: Main area of practice is intellectual property litigation. Includes UK and international patent infringement litigation, trademark infringement, passing off, copyright infringement, design infringement and breach of confidence. Acted in Akzo/ Du Pont, Montedison/ ICI, Polaroid/ Kodak and Exxon/ Lubrizol. Member of Editorial Boards of World Intellectual Property Review and Patent World.

Prof. Memberships: Law Society, Chartered Institute of Patent Agents (Fellow).

Career: Qualified as Patent Agent 1969. Worked for AA Thornton & Co. 1965-70, then Langner Parry from 1970-73 (Chartered Patent Agents). Joined *Bird & Bird* in 1973. Qualified as a solicitor 1977. Partner 1977. Senior Partner 1993.

Personal: Born 1943. Attended Epsom College 1956-61, then Christ's College, Cambridge 1961-64. Lives in Chobham, Surrey.

Hart, Michael L.
Baker & McKenzie, London (0171) 919 1000. Partner in Intellectual Property and Information Technology Law Department.

Specialisation: Principal area of practice is contentious and non-contentious IP and IT Law. Work includes copyright, trade marks and passing off, patents and trade secrets, computer and IT disputes, broadcasting and media law. Also deals with government regulations and trade libel. Has represented various trade bodies in lobbying activities relating to UK and EU legislative proposals. Important cases include Mattel v. Hasbro (defended Hasbro in the Barbie/ Sindy copyright dispute); Gianni Versace v. Independent on Sunday (represented Gianni Versace in defamation claim) and Toppy v. S.R.Gent (represented Toppy (owners of Episode Stores) in major joint venture dispute). Contributor to Sweet & Maxwell's 'Encyclopedia of Information Technology'. Has written numerous articles on IP and IT issues. Radio 4 "Today" programme adviser on copyright law issues. Frequently speaks at seminars.

Prof. Membership: Anti-counterfeiting Group, AIPPI, Intellectual Property Lawyers Association.

Career: Qualified in 1983. With *Linklaters & Paines* 1983-87. Joined *Baker & McKenzie* in 1987 and became a Partner in 1990.

Personal: Born 12th August 1959. Educated at City of London School 1970-77 and Exeter College, Oxford 1977-80. Leisure activities include theatre, cinema, horse racing, tennis and hockey. Lives in London.

Hodgson, Mark T.
Simmons & Simmons, London (0171) 628 2020. Partner in Intellectual Property Department. Head of Pharmaceutical and Medical Group.

Specialisation: Specialises in patent litigation in the U.K. courts and qualified as a European Patent Attorney in the European Patent Office. Also handles pharmaceutical matters, including litigation and regulatory issues, product liability, advertising, parallel importation, clinical trial contracts and biotechnology matters. Acted in respect of Smith Kline and French Laboratories Ltd.(Cimetidine) Patents, Bonzel v. Intervention, R v. Licensing Authority ex parte Smith Kline and French Laboratories Ltd. and Biogen v. Medeva. Clients include Eli Lilly and Smith Kline Beecham. Has written numerous articles for legal and pharmaceutical journals and lectures extensively on matters such as E.C. medical device regulations, patent term restoration and clinical fraud.

Prof. Membership: Member Law Society, Committee member of Intellectual Property Lawyers Association.

Career: Qualified in 1983 whilst at *Woodham Smith* 1981-85. Joined *Simmons and Simmons* in 1985 where he became a Partner in 1989.

Personal: Educated at Barnard Castle School 1969-77 and at Emmanuel College Cambridge 1977-80. Chester Law School 1981. Leisure interests include Newcastle United F.C.. Lives near Gamglingay, Cambs.

Hull, John

Wilde Sapte, London (0171) 246 7000. Qualified 1979. Partner 1990. Commercial Litigation Department. Principal area of practice is intellectual property. Born 22.6.1951.

Irvine, James

Denton Hall, London (0171) 242 1212. Partner in Industrial IP Group, Litigation Department.

Specialisation: Specialises in IP litigation, particularly patent and trademark litigation and anti-counterfeiting work for international companies. Clients in industries ranging from computer software to fashion accessories. Co-author of chapter on Hong Kong in book about IP rights in Hong Kong and other countries. Lectures on IP issues. Regular contributor of articles to IP magazines.

Prof. Membership: Institute of Trade Mark Agents (Associate Member), Chartered Institute of Patent Agents, Marques, Law Society of Scotland, AIPPI, INTA.

Career: Admitted in Scotland in 1983 and in Hong Kong in 1984. With *Johnson Stokes & Master* in Hong Kong 1984-88. Joined *Denton Hall* in 1988 and became a Partner in 1990. In the firm's Hong Kong office 1988-92.

Personal: Born 24th August 1959. Educated at Aberdeen University 1977-82 (LL.B Hons, DLP). Interests outside the law include golf and bridge.

Jerrard, Donald G.

See under Computer Law & I.T.

Judge, Ian M.

Bristows Cooke & Carpmael, London (0171) 400 8000. Partner in Intellectual Property Department.

Specialisation: Intellectual property. Work covers litigation and licensing of the full range of intellectual property, including patents, trade marks, copyright, designs and confidential information. Involved in major patent cases such as Beecham v. Bristol Myers and Du Pont v. Akzo (both H.L.) and Chiron v Organon Teknika. Speaker at seminars on specialist intellectual property topics.

Prof. Memberships: Law Society, Chartered

Institute of Patent Agents (Associate Member), Committee Member - Intellectual Property Lawyers Association (formerly Patent Solicitors Association, AIPPI.

Career: Joined *Bristows Cooke & Carpmael* 1964, became a Partner in 1969. Representative of the Patent Solicitors Association on the Oulton Committee on Patent Litigation 1986-87. Non-executive director of the Pilot Pen Company (UK) Ltd since 1979.

Personal: Born 4th December 1941. Attended Cambridge University (BA 1963, MA 1967).

Kamstra, Gerald Simon

Simmons & Simmons, London (0171) 628 2020. Partner in Intellectual Property Department.

Specialisation: Principal area of practice is intellectual property law, including litigation within the pharmaceutical and biotechnology industries. Acted in SmithKline & French v. Evans Medical, Bonzel & Schneider (Europe) v. Intervention & Advanced Cardiovascular Systems and Chiron Corporation & Ortho Diagnostics v. Organon/Akzo & United Biomedical. Clients include Eli Lilly and Company. Has written numerous articles for legal journals including *Computer Law and Practice* , *Patent World* and *Journal of Biotechnology in Healthcare*. Is a regular speaker at conferences.

Prof. Membership: Member Intellectual Property Advisory Committee of BioIndustry Association and Associate Member of Chartered Institute of Patent Agents. European Patent Attorney.

Career: Qualified in 1986. Joined *Simmons & Simmons* 1986 where he became a Partner in 1992.

Personal: Born 13th May 1954. Educated at Hymers College, Hull 1963-71, Keble College, Oxford 1972-75 (Psychology & Physiology), Leicester University 1975-80 (Ph.D in Neuroendocrinology) and Trent Polytechnic 1982-84. Leisure interests include running, swimming and travel. Lives in London and Essex.

Latham, David A.

Lovell White Durrant, London (0171) 236 0066. Qualified 1980. Partner 1988. Intellectual Property Department. Principal area of practice is trademarks, patents, and IT.

Llewelyn, David

Llewelyn Zietman, London (0171) 739 1010. Founding Partner specialising in intellectual property law.

Specialisation: Main area of practice is intellectual property. Deals with all aspects, both contentious and non-contentious. Also covers information technology and pharmaceutical law. Important cases handled include CIBA-GEIGY v. Parke Davis [1993] (for defendant) and Neutrogena v. L'Oreal [1994-5] (also for defendant). Has been involved in a number of major IP related transactions and cases, many cross-border.

Clients come principally from the cosmetics, food and drink, pharmaceuticals and retail sectors. Also computer companies (especially software) and multimedia. Author of numerous articles published in legal journals including *Corporate Briefing*, *Intellectual Property in Business* and *Practical Law for Companies*.

Has also delivered many conference papers in the UK and abroad. Senior Visiting Fellow in Intellectual Property, Centre for Commercial Law Studies, Queen Mary and Westfield College, London. Charge-out rate is £160 per hour (daily and weekly rates available on request).

Prof. Membership: Law Society, Pharmaceutical Trade Marks Group, International Trademark Association.

Career: Research Fellow at Max Planck Institute for Patent, Copyright and Competition Law, Munich 1980-81. Qualified in 1985. With *Linklaters & Paines* 1982-87, then Partner at *McKenna & Co* 1987-94. Founded *Llewelyn Zietman* in July 1994.

Personal: Born 15th July 1956. Educated at Wallingford Grammar School 1967-74, Southampton University 1974-77 (LL.B) and Worcester College, Oxford 1978-79 (BCL, 1st Class Hons). German speaker. Lives in London NW6.

Macdonald, Morag

Bird & Bird, London (0171) 415 6000. Partner in Intellectual Property Department.

Specialisation: Work includes litigation, transactional and advisory work in relation to patents, trade marks, copyright and other intellectual property rights. Also handles electronics and computer law. Acted in Mentor/ Hollister and Compaq/ Dell. Has addressed seminars in London, Beijing and Budapest on various intellectual property topics.

Prof. Membership: CIPA, ITMA, INTA, ECTA.

Career: Called to the Bar in 1984. Qualified as a Solicitor in 1988, having joined *Bird & Bird* in 1985. Became a Partner in 1989.

Personal: MA in Mathematics, Physics and Law from Cambridge.

Macfarlane, Nicholas R.

Lovell White Durrant, London (0171) 236 0066. Qualified 1977. Partner 1980. Intellectual Property Department. Work covers contentious and non-contentious intellectual property and competition matters. Born February 1952.

Marshall, James

Lovell White Durrant, London (0171) 236 0066. Called to the Bar 1986. Solicitor. Intellectual Property and Technology Department. Deals with all areas of IP. Born 9.4.1963.

Marsland, Vanessa

Clifford Chance, London (0171) 600 1000. Partner. Principal area of work is intellectual property, with particular interest in computer, media and telecommunications.

Martindale, Avril C.B.

Bristows Cooke & Carpmael, London (0171) 400 8000. Partner specialising in intellectual property.

Specialisation: Main area of practice covers intellectual property. Deals with commercial, advisory and transactional aspects of intellectual property, including in particular EC and competition law relevant thereto. Author of various articles on intellectual property and EC law, as well as being a regular speaker at intellectual property conferences.

Prof. Membership: Law Society of England & Wales, Law Society of Scotland, Licensing Executives Society, Competition Law Society, INTA.

Career: Qualified in Scotland in 1985. With Scottish firm *Dickson Minto WS* 1985-88, then *McKenna & Co.* 1988-93. Qualified in England & Wales in 1992. Joined *Bristows Cooke & Carpmael* as a Partner in 1993.

Personal: Born 1st June 1961. Educated at Glasgow University 1978-83. Enjoys travel, skiing, tennis and hill-walking. Lives in London.

Millard, Christopher

See under Computer Law & I.T.

Moodie, William J.

Herbert Smith, London (0171) 374 8000. Partner in Intellectual Property and Technology Department.

Specialisation: Specialises in intellectual property law, particularly involving the electronics, communications and patent fields and all aspects of computer related intellectual property work.

Career: Qualified in South Africa 1975 and in England and Wales 1979. Became a Partner at *Herbert Smith* in 1984.

Personal: Educated at the University of Cape Town (B.Sc (Eng) Elec.) and the University of South Africa.(LL.B)

Mooney, Kevin M.

Simmons & Simmons, London (0171) 628 2020. Senior Partner in Intellectual Property Department.

Specialisation: Principal area of practice is patent litigation, especially in the pharmaceutical industry. Important cases handled included Beecham Group Ltd v. Bristol-Myers Co [1978] (infringement and revocation action concerning Hetacillin, in High Court, Court of Appeal and House of Lords - a leading case on non-literal infringement); Anheuser-Busch Inc. v. Budejovicky Budvar Narodny Podnik [1984] (passing-off case concerning the "Budweiser" trade mark); Generics (UK) Ltd v. Smith Kline & French Laboratories Ltd [1992] (European Court decision relating to the application of the Treaty of Rome to a licence of right under pharmaceutical patents in the UK), and Biogen v. Medeva Plc (patent infringement/ validity ac-

tion in Patents Court and EPO. Patent relates to Hepatitis B virus antigen). Also handles product liability work. Acts for Gallaher in the smoking and health litigation. Clients include Smith Kline Beecham, Eli Lilly, Courtaulds, Union Carbide, Procter & Gamble, Intel Inc, Gallaher and Norsk Hydro. Member of Nuffield Bioethics Council Working Party on Human Tissue (report published April 1995). Experienced speaker at seminars and conferences. Charge-out rate is around £250 per hour.

Prof. Membership: ABA, AIPLA, AIPPI, City of London Solicitors Company (Member of Intellectual Property Sub-Committee).

Career: Qualified in 1971. Partner at *Simmons & Simmons* since 1973.

Personal: Born 14th November 1945. Educated at Bristol University (LL.B 1968). Leisure activities include gardening and supporting Q.P.R. Lives in Ealing, West London.

Morgan, Glyn

Taylor Joynson Garrett, London (0171) 353 1234.

Moss, Gary

Taylor Joynson Garrett, London (0171) 353 1234. Partner in Intellectual Property Department.

Specialisation: Practice covers all areas of intellectual property, but with particular emphasis on patents, biotechnology, information technology and technology transfers. Handles both contentious and non-contentious matters within the field of information technology including licence disputes, fitness for purpose disputes and copying/ plagiarism disputes. Examples of important cases handled are Pall Corporation v. Commercial Hydraulics, SKM v. Wagner Spraytech and, currently, Amgen v. Boehringer Mannheim & Genetics Institute (major litigation relating to biotechnology patents). Clients include Amgen Inc, AT&T Global Information Solutions, Visa and Pall Corporation. Member of the Editorial Board of *The Biotechnolgy Law Report*. Has spoken at seminars on information technology and acquisitions/ protection of computer hardware and software.

Prof. Membership: Law Society (Member of Intellectual Property Sub-Committee), International Intellectual Property Group, Information Technology Practice Group (Chairman).

Career: Qualified in 1977. With *Clifford Turner* 1977-79, then *Woodham Smith* 1979-90 (Partner from 1981). Joined *Taylor Joynson Garrett* as a Partner in 1990.

Personal: Born 7th April 1953. Educated at the University of Leicester 1971-74 (1st Class Hons) and the College of Law (1st Class Hons). Recreations include theatre, opera and golf. Lives in London.

Newman, Helen

Simmons & Simmons, London (0171) 628 2020. Partner and Head of Intellectual

Property Department.

Specialisation: Principal area of practice is advising on a wide range of contentious and non-contentious intellectual property matters. Conducts litigation involving patents, know-how, copyright, designs and trade marks in the UK, and co-ordinates or instructs corresponding litigation overseas. Other main area of work is advising on the acquisition, disposal, re-structuring and exploitation of intellectual property rights portfolios. Has spoken at a number of conferences on intellectual property matters.

Prof. Membership: International Trademark Association, Institute of Trade Mark Agents, MARQUES, Anti-Counterfeiting Group, European Communities Trade Mark Association, American Bar Association.

Career: Articled with *Simmons & Simmons*. Qualified 1980 and became a Partner in 1985.

Nodder, Edward J.

Bristows Cooke & Carpmael, London (0171) 400 8000. Partner in Intellectual Property Department.

Specialisation: Advises on the full range of contentious and non-contentious intellectual property, including patents, trade marks, copyright, designs and confidential information, computers and IT and biotechnology. This includes advice on all aspects of European competition and harmonisation laws as they impact on intellectual property, including the European Patent Office and the Community Trade Mark Office. Amongst numerous cases, acted for the plaintiff in 3M v. Rennicks and Gillette v. Edenwest and for the defendant in Murray v. NEC and Howard v. United Biscuits. Has been involved in opposition proceedings at European Patent Office for British Gas and developed the trade marks aspects of the X/ Open Branding Programme for Open IT Systems. Author of articles for specialist periodicals such as 'Corporate Briefing' and 'Patent World'. Regular speaker at intellectual property and European law conferences and seminars.

Prof. Membership: Law Society, Associate Member of Chartered Institute of Patent Agents, AIPPI.

Career: Joined *Bristows Cooke & Carpmael* in 1978. Became a Partner in 1986.

Personal: Born 29th June 1956. Educated at Cambridge University 1974-77 (MA in Natural Sciences and Law). Vice-Chairman of Friends of Lewes. Enjoys opera, chamber music, tennis, gardening and the Languedoc. Lives in Lewes, Sussex.

Perkins, David

Clifford Chance, London (0171) 600 1000. Partner. Principal area of practice is intellectual property encompassing patents, designs, trademarks copyright and trade secrets, competition and antitrust law, pharmaceuticals and biotechnology.

Petterson, David Charles

Taylor Joynson Garrett, London (0171)

353 1234. Consultant in Intellectual Property Department.

Specialisation: Principal area of practice is litigation and commercial agreements relating to patents, trade marks, passing off and designs and EC anti-competition law relating to intellectual property. Important cases handled include Smith Kline French Laboratories Ltd v. Sterling Winthrop (1975) (appeal to House of Lords), York Tailer Holdings Ltd v. Registrar of Trade Marks [1982] (appeal to the House of Lords) and C Van der Lely NV v. Ruston's Engineering Co Ltd [1993]. Major clients include Autoliv AB, The Jacob's Bakery Ltd, Kellogg Company of Great Britain Ltd, Lledo plc. Regularly gives talks to ITMA students.

Prof. Membership: Chartered Institute of Patent Agents (Associate), European Communities Trade Mark Practitioners Association, Institute of Trade Mark Agents (Associate), Law Society, London Solicitors Litigation Association, Licensing Executives Society, Solicitors' Benevolent Association.

Career: Qualified in 1961. Partner at *Woodham Smith* 1963-90. Consultant with *Taylor Joynson Garrett* since 1990. Deputy District Judge, Patents County Court, from 1991.

Personal: Born 28th January 1939. Educated at Chigwell School 1950-55. Lay Reader. Other interests include running, railway preservation and motorcycles. Married with two children. Lives in Brentwood.

Price, Richard

Taylor Joynson Garrett, London (0171) 353 1234. Partner in Intellectual Property Department.

Specialisation: Intellectual property specialist dealing with patents, trade marks, copyright, confidential information and trade libel litigation, IP intensive acquisitions and disposals and licensing. Important cases handled include successful appeal to House of Lords concerning Asahi Chemical's Patent Application in 1991 (priority of competing patent applications and the need for an enabling disclosure; brought UK back into line with Europe; first IP case ever taken to House of Lords by a Japanese company), Reckitt & Colman Plc v Borden Inc [1990] (successful prevention of JIF lemon lookalike. House of Lords), Unilever v Johnson Wax [1989] (successful defence of a trade mark infringement action re LIFEBOUY/LIFEGUARD and rectification of Unilever's marks) and Lancer Boss v Henley Forklift [1975] (one of the few patent cases to go as far as an enquiry into damages).

Prof. Membership: The Intellectual Property Lawyer's Association (formerly Patent Solicitors Association (Chairman), City of London Solicitors' Company, Law Society, Solicitors European Group, AIPPI (UK).

Career: Qualified in 1970. With *Joynson-Hicks & Co* 1968-75 (partner 1973-75), then Partner at *Courts & Co* 1975-77 and at *Woodham Smith* 1977-90. Joined *Taylor Joynson Garrett* as a Partner in 1990.

Personal: Born 7th January 1946. Educated at Kingston Grammar School 1957-64 and Bristol University (LLB) 1964-67. Leisure interests include wildlife, tennis and sailing. Trustee, British Ornithologist's Club. Lives in London.

Sandison, Hamish R.

See under Computer Law & I.T.

Sills, David

Monier–Williams & Boxalls, London (0171) 405 6195. Qualified 1970. Partner 1970. Acts for governmental organisations dealing with wines and private spirit trade interests on specific commercial assignments.

Small, Harry

See under Computer Law & I.T.

Smith, Catriona

Allen & Overy, London (0171) 330 3000. Qualified 1982. Partner 1992. Litigation & Intellectual Property Department. Main areas of practice are intellectual property and IT litigation.

Starr, Ian C.

Ashurst Morris Crisp, London (0171) 638 1111. Partner in Intellectual Property Group.

Specialisation: Handles all aspects of patents, trade marks, designs, copyright and trade secrets. Has specialised in this area since 1978.

Prof. Membership: CIPA, ITMA, INTA, AIPLA, AIPPI, ECTA and Union.

Career: Qualified in 1979. Worked at *Crossman Block* 1977-80, then *Clifford Chance* 1980-93 (Partner from 1984). Joined *Ashurst Morris Crisp* as a Partner in 1993.

Personal: Born 9th May 1954. Attended St Paul's School 1967-72 and Caius, Cambridge 1973-76. Leisure interests include golf. Lives in Moor Park.

Stubbs, Hugh W.J.

Freshfields, London (0171) 936 4000. Partner 1977. Hong Kong Office 1986-1990.

Specialisation: Head of Intellectual Property Department, handling a wide range of matters relating to copyright, patents, trade marks and designs. Author and co-author of various articles in International Legal Practitioner.

Prof. Membership: International Bar Association (Vice Chairman of Section on General Practice; Chairman of Civil Litigation Committee 1988-92).

Personal: Born 6th August 1946. Attended Exeter University. Lives at Hampton Court, London.

Swift, Robert Z.

Linklaters & Paines, London (0171) 606 7080. Qualified 1967. Partner 1976. Intellectual Property, Technology and Communications Department. 25 years experience in all aspects of the intellectual property field. Born 13.8.1941.

Swycher, Nigel

Slaughter and May, London (0171) 600 1200. Qualified 1987.

Taylor, Peter D.

Clifford Chance, London (0171) 600 1000. Partner. Principal area of practice is intellectual property matters generally and advertising and marketing work.

Thorne, Clive

Denton Hall, London (0171) 242 1212. Partner in Intellectual Property Group, Litigation Department.

Specialisation: Specialises in contentious intellectual property work, including copyright law, patents, trade marks, passing off, marketing law, computer law and trade secrets. Also commercial litigation, arbitration and employment law. Fellow of the Chartered Institute of Arbitrators. Co-author of 'Intellectual Property - the New Law' and author of 'Sony Guide to Home Taping Intellectual Property: The New Law'. Lectures on and has written numerous articles about intellectual property.

Prof. Membership: Patent Solicitors Association, International Trade Mark Association, Institute of Trade Mark Agents (Associate Member), Anti-counterfeiting Group, Computer Law Group, Chartered Institute of Patent Agents (Associate Member).

Career: Qualified in 1977. At *Beachcroft & Co* 1977-80 and *Baker & McKenzie* 1980-84. Admitted in Hong Kong in 1984 and Victoria, Australia in 1985. Joined *Denton Hall* as a Partner in 1987.

Personal: Born 21st January 1952. Educated at Trinity Hall, Cambridge 1971-74 (BA Hons in Law). Interests outside the law include politics, playing the flute, opera and English music.

Tootal, Christopher P.

Herbert Smith, London (0171) 374 8000. Qualified 1967. Partner 1968. Intellectual Property Department. Main area of work is patent law, particularly in the pharmaceutical and biotechnology industries. Qualified Chartered Patent Agent. Former Chairman of the Patent Solicitors Association. Current President of the British Group of the International Association for the Protection of Industrial Property.

Walsh, Paul A.

Bristows Cooke & Carpmael, London (0171) 400 8000. Partner in Intellectual Property Department.

Specialisation: Practice spans both contentious and non-contentious intellectual property matters including computer contracts and related disputes. Legal adviser to the British Producers and Brand Owners Group, an alliance of leading manufacturers in the FMCG industry concerned with lookalike products. Also interested in emergency interlocutory applications, Anton Piller Orders and Mareva injunctions, and has been appointed by the High Court to supervise in the conduct of such orders. Cases include Pilkington v. PPG (confidential information arbitration), PPG v. Pilkington (anti-trust arbitration), Assidoman Multipack v. Mead Corporation and Altertext Inc. v. Advanced Data Communications Ltd. Lecturer on technology transfer litigation, trade mark law, biotechnology law and Anton Piller Orders. Author of various articles for *Trade Mark World* and *Corporate Briefing*.

Prof. Membership: Licensing Executives Society, Associate Member of the Institute of Trade Mark Agents, European Community Trade Mark Association, Law Society.

Career: Qualified and joined *Bristows Cooke and Carpmael* in 1983. Became a Partner in 1988.

Personal: Born 21st December 1956. Educated at Salvatorian College 1968-75 and Oxford University 1976-79. Leisure interests include tennis, squash, literature and wine. Lives in London.

Whaite, Robin G.

Linklaters & Paines, London (0171) 606 7080. Qualified 1980. Partner 1989. Intellectual Property, Technology and Communications Department. Focuses on the chemical and computer industries.

Willoughby, Anthony J.T.

Rouse & Co, London (0171) 345 8888. Qualified 1970. Partner 1994. Recently joined from *Herbert Smith*. Partner in Intellectual Property section of their Litigation Department. Particular experience in Anton Piller orders and Mareva injunctions. Born 29.9.1944.

REGIONS

Bowmer, Riaz

Alsop Wilkinson, Manchester (0161) 834 7760.

Ackermann, Niel

Hewitson Becke + Shaw, Cambridge (01223) 461155.

Aspinall, Timothy John Mellor

Donne Mileham & Haddock, Brighton (01273) 329833. Partner and Head of Litigation Department.

Specialisation: Practice focuses on intellectual property and computer related litigation and other heavy weight commercial litigation cases concerning high technology products and services. Work covers the full range of intellectual property litigation including copyright, design rights, trademarks, patents, passing off and breaches of confidential information. Also handles information technology disputes. Acted for the successful defendant in the reported patent dispute Hughes Rediffusion v. Link-Miles (a multi-

million pound patent infringement claim concerning visual displays on flight simulators). Clients include several major flight simulator companies, a major US conglomerate quoted on New York Stock Exchange with subsidiaries throughout Europe, NHS Trusts and academic institutions. Lectures to other lawyers around the country. Charge out rate is £120-£150 per hour.

Prof. Membership: Society for Computers and the Law, Law Society.

Career: Qualified in 1982. Spent a year at West Sussex County Council before joining *Donne Mileham & Haddock* in 1983. Appointed Partner in 1987 and Head of Litigation Department in 1994.

Personal: Born 30th June 1956. Educated at Huddersfield New College 1967-74, York University 1975-78 (BA Hons, History) and Leeds Law School 1979-80 (CPE and LSF). Plays golf and enjoys cricket and theatre. Trustee of local charity. Lives in Brighton.

Bailes, Tony G.

See under Computer Law & I.T.

Barker, William T.

Martineau Johnson, Birmingham (0121) 200 3300. Partner, Head of Intellectual Property Department.

Specialisation: Areas of practice include contentious and non-contentious intellectual property and computer law. Experienced in anti-counterfeiting and has particular experience of trade marks, copyright and patents. Has written various articles on the protection and enforcement of intellectual property rights and has addressed seminars in Birmingham and Singapore. Experienced in the application and execution of Anton Piller Orders and is on the Birmingham Law Society list of supervising solicitors.

Prof. Membership: Anti-counterfeiting Group and Licensing Executives Society.

Career: Articled: *Laces & Co*, Liverpool; Qualified 1986; Assistant Solicitor, *Pinsent & Co* 1986-1990; Associate, 1990-1991; Partner, *Martineau Johnson* 1992.

Personal: Born 4th January 1962. Educated at Merchant Taylors School, Crosby, Liverpool. BSc in Law and Mathematics. Leisure interests include tennis, member Edgbaston Priory LTC and golf, member Moor Hall Golf Club.

Boardman, Richard

Garrett & Co, Leeds (0113) 244 1954. Partner in Intellectual Property and Anti-Trust Group.

Specialisation: Handles all aspects of commercial and dispute related intellectual property work together with associated anti-trust matters. This work covers patents, trade marks (including registrations), copyright, design right, confidential information and passing off. Also deals with character and personality merchandising, media and entertainment law and information technology (including multimedia). Represents a

wide range of clients from international corporations to smaller private companies in the United Kingdom and abroad (particularly in the United States). Recent work has been in areas as diverse as chemicals, biotechnology, engineering, retailing, manufacturing, publishing, media and entertainment, advertising and information technology. Regular author of articles and speaker on IP matters.

Prof. Membership: Law Society, Licensing Executives Society, Chartered Institute of Patent Agents (Associate).

Career: Qualified in 1989. Employed as trainee solicitor, assistant and associate at *Simpson Curtis* 1987-1994. Joined *Garrett & Co* in 1994. Appointed partner in 1995.

Braithwaite, Andrew L.

Wansbroughs Willey Hargrave, Bristol (0117) 926 8981. Partner in Company/Commercial Department.

Specialisation: Main areas of practice are commercial and intellectual property transactional work. Advises retail chains on branding, software houses and health sector organisations on computer program licensing and distribution, independent TV producers on productions and sports bodies on sponsorship and merchandising. Addresses regional seminars on software contracts and I.P. licensing.

Prof. Membership: Society for Computers and the Law, British Association for Sport and the Law, Secretary of Bristol Channel (media network).

Career: Qualified in 1985. Worked with *Ingledew Brown Bennison & Garrett* 1983-85, then *Finers* 1985-88. Joined *Wansbroughs Willey Hargrave* in 1989, becoming a Partner in 1990.

Brett, Hugh

Dallas Brett, Oxford (01865) 791990. Founder Partner and Head of Intellectual Property Department:

Specialisation: Intellectual property specialist dealing with patents, trade marks, designs and copyrights, confidentiality arrrangements, publishing and multi-media agreements, software protection and exploitation of intellectual property rights. Experience of handling major problems in connection with intellectual property transactions including licensing and sale of intellectual property rights in the fields of entertainment, publishing and brand management. Is a member of the intellectual property section of the British Computer Society which reviews legal developments affecting the protection and licensing of software. Also sits on the intellectual property committee of the Law Society and on The Copyright Tribunal, the body established to determine disputes involving copyright licensing schemes. Has lectured in the UK and abroad on intellectual property matters and has acted as an expert for the European Commission on technology transfer and copyright issues raised by multi-media.

Author of articles on anti-trust law, copyright matters, patent licensing and technology transfer and has written books on *The Patents Act 1977* and the protection of computer software. Founder and co-editor of *European Intellectual Property Review* and founder and member of *The Institute of Intellectual Property*, a charitable body having as one of its objects the underwriting of common law principles within the European Union.

Prof. Membership: Law Society, British Literary and Copyright Association.

Career: Qualified with *Linklaters & Paines*. Co-founder of *Dallas Brett* in 1981.

Personal: Born 14th June 1941. Educated at Keble College, Oxford. Leisure pursuits include fishing. Lives in Oxford.

Brown, Richard G.
Laytons, Bristol (0117) 929 1626. Qualified 1976. Partner 1986. Company and Commercial Department. Handles all aspects, including employment and pensions. Born 11.4.1952.

Byatt, Lorne
See under Computer Law & I.T.

Chandler, Stephen B.J.
Pinsent Curtis, Leeds (0113) 244 5000. Leeds. Partner in Commercial Department.

Specialisation: Intellectual property, including protection, exploitation and enforcement of patents, trade marks, copyrights, design rights and trade secrets, as well as consultancy in the management of IP. Acted in Provident Financial Plc v. Halifax Building Society, Acts for Holliday Chemical Holdings Plc in chemical and pharmaceutical patent matters, worked for the National Health Service in developing a framework for the management of its intellectual property.

Career: Qualified in 1980. Partner in 1985.

Personal: Born 5th November 1955. Educated St. John's College, Cambridge 1974-77.

Craig, Ian
Hewitson Becke + Shaw, Cambridge (01223) 461155. Qualified 1982. Partner 1985. Intellectual Property Group, undertaking nothing but intellectual property work, including advising on copyright (including computer copyright), patents, unregistered design right, registered design right, trademarks, passing off and breach of confidentiality. Born in 1949.

Duddy, Gill
Alsop Wilkinson, Manchester (0161) 834 7760.

Flint, David
MacRoberts, Glasgow (0141) 332 9988. Partner in Corporate and Commercial Department.

Specialisation: Corporate and commercial matters including business start-ups, reorgan-

isations, partnerships, commercial contracts, patents, trade marks, copyright and other intellectual property licensing, computer and technology contracts, agency and distribution agreements, restrictive practices and competition law in terms of both EU and UK law, as well as EU matters generally. Has given evidence to House of Lords Select Committee on European Affairs in relation to competition procedures, the European Court of First Instance and European Community Competition Practice. Author of numerous articles in, amongst other publications, 'The Accountant's Magazine', JLSS and the 'Journal of the Glasgow Chamber of Commerce'. Author of 'Liquidation in Scotland' (Jordan & Sons Ltd, 2nd edition 1990) and Scottish Insolvency Editor of 'Gore-Browne on Company Law'. UK Rapporteur 'Company Mergers and Take-overs'. FIDE Congress, Madrid 1990. Extensive lecturing experience on a variety of subjects. Member of Joint Working Party of Scottish, English and Northern Irish Law Societies and Bars on Competition Law (since 1981). Member of Law Society of Scotland Intellectual Property Law and International Relations Committees. Licensed Insolvency Practitioner.

Prof. Membership: Licensing Executives Society, Insolvency Practitioners Association, Society of Practitioners of Insolvency, Institute of Credit Management, The Computer Law Association Inc., Union Internationale des Avocats, UK Association for European Law. American Bar Association (Associate).

Career: Qualified in 1979. Assistant in *Mac-Roberts* Company and Commercial Department 1979-84 and Partner from May 1984. Admitted Notary Public 1980. Chairman of Scottish Lawyers European Group since 1985.

Personal: Educated at the High School of Glasgow 1964-73, the University of Glasgow (LLB 1976 and LLM 1982), and the Europa Instituut, Universiteit van Amsterdam (Diploma in European Integration 1978). Director of Giltech Ltd, The Shareholding & Investment Trust Ltd, and Advoc Ltd.

Godar, George W.
See under Computer Law & I.T.

Hodgson, James
Eversheds, Leeds (0113) 243 0391. Partner in Intellectual Property Group.

Specialisations: Intellectual Property, both contentious and non-contentious including trade marks, passing off, copyright, designs, patents, know-how, trade secrets and confidential information. Particular expertise in enforcement and anti-piracy work including obtaining, service and execution of Anton Piller orders on behalf of Plaintiff and as "Supervising Solicitor". Franchising, including advice on trademark protection, franchisor/franchisee agreements and enforcement of post-termination obligations and restrictive covenants. Has lectured extensively in the UK and USA on the protection and enforce-

ment of intellectual property rights.

Prof. Memberships: Executive Communications Committee International Trademark Association; New York Licensing Executives Society; Anti-Counterfeiting Group; British Franchise Association; Australian Business in Europe.

Career: Qualified in 1984. Previous positions: *Baker & McKenzie* (Hong Kong and London), *Eversheds, Jaques & Lewis* (Head of Intellectual Property).

Personal: Graduated in Laws (LLB Hons) from King's College, University of London. JELF Medal in Laws. Leisure interests include entertaining visitors to North Yorkshire, local history, travel and general outdoor pursuits. Lives in York.

Howard, Lionel M.
Eversheds, (0115) 950 6201. Qualified 1961. Partner 1965. Commercial Department, Intellectual Property Unit. Has 25 years experience in all areas of IP including commercial licensing and prosecuting and defending proceedings for infringement. Born 6.1.1937.

Howard, Lionel M.
Eversheds, Nottingham (0115) 950 6201. Partner in Commercial Department: Head of Intellectual Property Group.

Specialisation: Has 25 years' experience in all aspects of IP, both contentious and non-contentious, including commercial licensing and prosecuting and defending proceedings for infringement. Has particular experience in Mechanical Engineering Patent Infringement actions. Acted on the purchase of IP valued at over £40 million in the management buy-out by Kenwood from Thorn EMI, and Boots plc v. Superdrug. Author of IP articles in the Law Society Gazette, Nottingham business journals and various other publications. Lectures regularly on all aspects of intellectual property.

Prof. Membership: Law Society, Institute of Patent Agents, Institute of Trade Mark Agents, AIPPI, LES, National Computer User's Forum.

Career: Qualified in 1961. Magistrates Clerk 1961-65; Chairman of National Insurance Appeal Tribunal since 1973 and of Disability Appeal Tribunal since 1993; Regional Chairman of LES 1986-91. Chairman of Legal Working Group of National Computer User's Forum. Joined *Evershed Wells & Hind* 1986 as a partner, having been a partner in previous firm since 1965.

Personal: Born 6th January 1937. Attended Liverpool College in 1955. President (twice) and District Secretary of Rotary.

Humphreys, Robert A.
Humphreys & Co, Bristol (0117) 929 2662. Senior Partner in commercial department.

Specialisation: Principally intellectual property and reinsurance.

Prof. Membership: Law Society.

Career: Qualifed 1981. With *Simmons & Simmons* 1979-85. Partner *Cartwrights* 1985-86. Co-founded *Humphreys & Co* 1986.

Personal: Born 1953. Educated Dr Morgan's School, Bridgwater and New College, Oxford. Leisure interests include cricket. Lives near Bristol.

Inglis, Ian G.

Maclay Murray & Spens, Edinburgh (0131) 226 5196. Qualified 1959. Partner 1961. Litigation Department. Main areas of practice are intellectual property, shipping and maritime.

Innes, John A.D.

See under Litigation (Commercial).

Jones, Bill

See under Computer Law & I.T.

Kempner, Richard A.

Booth & Co., Leeds (0113) 283 2000. Partner in Intellectual Property Department.

Specialisation: Handles both commercial and litigious work involving patents, copyright, trade marks, designs, confidential information and passing off. Also deals with information technology, media and entertainment law (contentious and non-contentious). Recent matters include IP joint ventures for Digital Equipment, William Hill, and Yorkshire Water and licensing deals covering areas ranging from technology transfer to the works of Philip Larkin. Major clients include Asda, William Hill, Digital Equipment Co, Yorkshire Chemicals and Games Workshop. Speaks widely on a number of intellectual property topics nationally and internationally. Author of various articles and contributor to 'Joint Ventures', published by Longmans.

Prof. Membership: LES, Law Society, Honorary Representative Canada (UK) Chamber of Commerce, INTA (International Committee Member)

Career: Qualified in 1987. With *Linklaters & Paines* 1985-90. Joined *Booth & Co* in 1990 and became a Partner in 1992.

Personal: Born 30th July 1962. Educated at Durham University 1981-84. Recreations include jogging, bridge, cinema and family. Lives in Leeds.

Kerr, Scott

Dickson Minto WS, Edinburgh (0131) 225 4455. Qualified 1985. Solicitor. Main area of practice is intellectual property: registering, transferring and licensing trade marks and patents.

Lewis, John

Freeth Cartwright Hunt Dickins, Nottingham (0115) 9369369. Qualified 1974.

Macpherson, Shonaig

McGrigor Donald, Edinburgh (0131) 226 7777. Qualified 1984. Partner 1992. Corporate Department. Handles all aspects of intellectual property. Born 29.9.1958.

Martin-Kaye, Neil

Martin-Kaye & Partners, Telford (01952) 291757. Qualified 1960. Founder and Senior Partner 1983. Business Law Department. Main areas of practice are technology transfer, licensing and intellectual property law, as well as international business law. Born 20.6.1934.

Maybury, Neil

Dibb Lupton Broomhead, Birmingham (0121) 200 1188. Partner in and Head of Intellectual Property Department.

Specialisation: Intellectual property work includes patents, copyright, trade mark matters, unfair business competition (contentious and non-contentious), EC law and media law. Also handles information technology law, covering all types of computer contracts and computer dispute work. Acted for Business Software Alliance in the first UK civil action to restrain corporate overuse of software. Has extensive lecturing experience and is trained as a mediator.

Prof. Membership: FAST Legal Advisory Group, Birmingham Law Society Technology Committee.

Career: Qualified in 1969. Joined *Pinsent & Co.* in 1974, becoming a Partner in 1975. Society of Computers and Law General Council 1977-88, Chairman of Law Committee of Society of Computers and Law 1986-88. Chairman of ACUA 1991-93.

Personal: Born 25th August 1943. Attended King Edward's School, Birmingham and Birmingham University. Leisure interests include tennis, squash, opera, gardening and flying. Lives in Much Wenlock, Shropshire.

McCracken, Kenneth

Wright, Johnston & Mackenzie, Glasgow (0141) 248 3434. Qualified 1987. Partner specialising in patents and IP licensing.

McLean, James A.

W & J Burness WS, Edinburgh (0131) 226 2561. Partner in Company Department.

Specialisation: Main area of practice is intellectual property, covering certification and collective marks, trade dress and get-up, designs, copyright (particularly in an industrial context) and other intellectual property rights. Also handles banking, lending, security and public affairs, including conflict and interaction of security and insolvency laws (especially of Scotland and England). Cases and transactions have included Harris Tweed Act 1993 and Ross v. Lord Advocate 1986 (TSB). Author of 'Oil Financing and Securities' in Stair Memorial Encyclopaedia; 'Security over Intellectual Property- a Scottish Perspective' and 'Reservation of Property- All Sums'. Addresses seminars on intellectual property issues.

Prof. Membership: Law Society of Scotland,

Society of Writers to Her Majesty's Signet, Scottish Lawyers European Group, and Competition Law Association.

Career: Qualified in 1972. Joined *W&J Burness WS* in 1972, becoming a Partner in 1974. Member of various Law Society of Scotland committees.

Personal: Born 25th April 1947. Attended Dunoon Grammar School to 1952, Fettes College to 1960, Cambridge University to 1965 and Edinburgh University to 1968. Leisure interests include theatre, swimming and cycling. Lives in Edinburgh.

McLew, Kenneth D.B.

Holmes Mackillop, Glasgow (0141) 221 5232.

McMorrow, Marie F.

Martineau Johnson, Birmingham (0121) 200 3300. Associate in the Intellectual Property Department.

Specialisation: Main area of practice is intellectual property litigation. Includes UK and international patent and trade mark infringement, passing off, copyright and design infringement and breach of confidence. Work includes competition and EC law litigation. A particular area of expertise is the field of anti-counterfeiting, acting on behalf of clients in a wide range of manufacturing and licensing sectors.

Prof. Membership: Licensing Executives Society and Anti-Counterfeiting Group.

Career: Articled: *Wragge & Co*, Birmingham in 1987; qualified 1989. Associateship: *Wragge & Co*, May 1993. Joined *Martineau Johnson*, February 1995.

Moakes, Jonathan

Halliwell Landau, Manchester (0161) 835 3003. Qualified 1984. Partner 1989. Intellectual Property Department. Work covers patents, designs, and technology.

Morris, A.Ian

Philip Conn & Co, Manchester (0161) 833 9494. Partner specialising in intellectual property work.

Specialisation: Principal area of practice is intellectual property. Work encompasses all areas of patents, trademarks, copyright, registered design, breach of confidence, passing off and competition, both contentious and non-contentious. Also handles general commercial litigation including contract, company, professional negligence and banking. Was involved in the House of Spring litigation, reported extensively between 1982 and 1987 (Republic of Ireland and UK). Has also handled a patent revocation action on behalf of a major plc, an international cross licensing agreement, international trademark litigation (cosmetics) and numerous Anton Piller Orders, Mareva injunctions and trials in all areas of practice. Clients include public utilities, international textile, cosmetics, engineering and bio-technology companies. Co-author of 'Morris & Quest:

Design - The Modern Law and Practice'(Butterworths). Has given lectures and spoken at various conferences in the UK and USA.

Prof. Membership: Law Society, Licensing Executives Society.

Career: Qualified in 1974. Founding Partner of *Philip Conn & Co* in 1975.

Personal: Born 16th April 1951. Educated at Manchester University 1968-71 (LL.B Hons). Synagogue President. Member of Legal Friends of the Hebrew University. Fellow of the Royal Society of Arts. Leisure activities include tennis, walking, bridge, reading, music and watching cricket. Lives in Manchester.

Napper, Isabel
Taylor Vinters, Cambridge (01223) 423444.

Nicolson, Fiona M.M.
See under Computer Law & I.T.

O'Leary, Marcus
See under Computer Law & I.T.

Pairman, L. Annette
W & J Burness WS, Edinburgh (0131) 226 2561. Qualified 1980.

Roper, Jeremy James
Dibb Lupton Broomhead, Birmingham (0121) 200 1188.

Saunders, James
See under Energy & Utilities.

Semple, David
Semple Fraser WS, Glasgow (0141) 221 3771.

Sloan, Philip
Greenwoods, Peterborough (01733) 555244.

Stanfield, G.
Mills & Reeve, Cambridge (01223) 64422. Qualified 1985. Partner 1990. Company Department. Main area of practice is arranging innovative funding specifically for educational institutions and health authorities. Born 1961.

Stoker, Robert R.
Addleshaw Sons & Latham, Manchester

(0161) 832 5994. Partner in Intellectual Property Department.

Specialisation: Work includes the acquisition, exploitation and enforcement of patents, trade marks, copyright and designs, confidential information and related areas of competition law. Other areas of practice are media and entertainment and information technology including all types of computer contracts involving the acquisition, disposal or licensing of software, hardware purchase and maintenance, facilities management and computer bureau agreements. Has dealt with the IP aspects of pharmaceutical and healthcare joint ventures and the acquisition of portfolios of international agrochemical products, the merchandising of various internationally known brands and various total solution computer hardware and software installation transactions. Former lecturer at University College of Wales, Aberystwyth. Has spoken on various intellectual property and information technology related topics in the UK and USA.

Prof. Membership: Licensing Executives Society, INTA, LIDC, Solicitors European Group, Law Society.

Career: Qualified in 1981. Assistant Secretary at ICI Paints 1987-89. Joined *Addleshaw Sons & Latham* in 1989 and became a Partner in 1991.

Personal: Born 5th June 1953. Educated at Sir William Borlase's School, Marlow 1964-71 and St Catharine's College, Cambridge 1972-75 and 1976-77. Leisure interests include angling, music, journalism, photography and Sunderland A.F.C. Lives in Whitegate.

Sutton, Richard
Dibb Lupton Broomhead, Leeds (0113) 243 9301. Partner in Intellectual Property Department.

Specialisation: Principal area of practice is contentious intellectual property matters with an emphasis on litigation of patents, trade marks, copyright and designs. Other main area of work is advice on and licensing of IP rights generally. Handled a variety of reported IP decisions from Solar Thompson v. Barton (1977) to Provident Financial plc v. Halifax Building Society (1994).

Prof. Membership: Law Society, Patent Solicitors' Association, Patent Litigators' Association, Chartered Institute of Patent

Agents (Associate).

Personal: Qualified 1973. With *Cleary Gottlieb Steen Hamilton* in New York 1973-74 and *Goldsmith Chartier Delvolve* in Paris 1974. Started specialist IP Department at *Dibb Lupton Broomhead* in 1976 and in 1990 introduced patent and trade mark agents to provide filing and prosecution services.

Personal: Born 5th May 1947. Attended Charterhouse School 1960-65 and the Royal Agricultural College, Cirencester. Governor of Bramcote School, Scarborough. Lives near York.

Sykes, John R.H.
Lupton Fawcett, Leeds (0113) 246 9696. Qualified 1984. Partner and head of the Intellectual Property and Information Technology Department. Handles all types of Intellectual Property work.

Wood, Alan P.
Osborne Clarke, Bristol (0117) 923 0220. Qualified 1975. Partner 1988. Intellectual Property Department. Emphasis on information technology, franchising, publishing and technology transfer. Born 29.8.1951.

Woods, Philip D.
Philip Woods & Co, Stockport (0161) 429 6767.

Specialisation: Sole practitioner specialising in all aspects of intellectual property and computer law, both contentious and non-contentious.

Prof. Membership: Chartered Institute of Patent Agents; Institute of Trade Mark Agents; UNION; FICPI; AIPPI; Society for Computers and Law; Committee Member of LES (North West Group); TIPLA (founder member).

Career: Qualified 1974. Admitted Hong Kong 1975. Deacons (Hong Kong) 1975-81. Partner, Wilkinson & Grist (Hong Kong) 1981-89. Partner, Eversheds Alexander Tatham (head of IP Department) 1989-94. Chairman of Eversheds National IP Group until 1994.

Personal: Leisure pursuits include classic cars, wines, walking, reading and gardening. Lives in Prestbury, Cheshire. Born 23rd December 1950.

LICENSING

LONDON

Allen & Fraser, specialising in liquor and entertainment licensing, has a formidable national reputation in this field, but is facing increasing competition from *Field Fisher Waterhouse, Kingsford Stacey, Richards Butler* and *Vallance Lickfolds*, all of whom are highly regarded.

LEADING FIRMS – LONDON

ALLEN & FRASER	
FIELD FISHER WATERHOUSE	KINGSFORD STACEY
RICHARDS BUTLER	VALLANCE LICKFOLDS

Field Fisher Waterhouse specialise in liquor and entertainment licensing too. Its clients include public houses, hotels, clubs, wine bars, off-licences and supermarkets. *Kingsford Stacey's* clients are in the brewery and leisure industries.

HIGHLY REGARDED – LONDON

JEFFREY GREEN RUSSELL	LOXLEYS
PAISNER & CO	PULLIG & CO
BIDDLE & CO	GREGORY, ROWCLIFFE & MILNERS
BAKER & McKENZIE	DAVIES ARNOLD COOPER
EVERSHEDS	HOWARD KENNEDY
JOELSON WILSON & CO	KINGSLEY NAPLEY
LAWRENCE GRAHAM	LEWIS SILKIN
NABARRO NATHANSON	NICHOLSON GRAHAM & JONES
OSBORNE CLARKE	RAKISONS

Richards Butler, specialising in betting, gaming and liquor licensing, acts for multinational companies, sole independent operators and multi-leisure complexes, amongst others. The firm's nationwide licensing practice is headed by Elizabeth Southorn, a former *Penningtons* licensing partner. It is experienced in contested late night licences and in obtaining licences for new leisure developments. *Vallance Lickfolds* specialises in all aspects of liquor, betting and gaming licensing, in addition to advising on the sale and leasing of licensed premises.

Also consistently recommended are *Jeffrey Green Russell, Loxleys, Paisner & Co* and *Pullig & Co. Jeffrey Green Russell* cover liquor, betting, gaming, public entertainment and lottery licensing on a nationwide basis. It handled the licensing work for UK's first multi-activity centre and was also involved in obtaining the first permanent 24-hour public entertainment licence for the 'Ministry of Sound' in Southwark. Licensing partner, Julian Skeens is a member of the British

Entertainment and Discotheque Association and the International Association of Gaming Attorneys.

Loxleys is strong on liquor and gaming matters, and it also handles some entertainment licensing. *Paisner & Co's* relatively new licensing team acts primarily for the retail, leisure and brewery industries on liquor licensing and regulatory matters including licensing appeals. It has also handled over 200 Children's Certificate applications nationally for a major chain. *Pullig & Co*, specialising in liquor and entertainment licensing, represents a national brewer.

Recommended for gaming licensing with a particular emphasis on casino licensing is *Biddle & Co*. The firm acts for one of London's top casinos and a major leisure company on all aspects of gaming law. Currently involved in proposals to legalise casino gaming in Eire and the establishment of the first casino in Dublin, its experience in casino matters also extends internationally, particularly to France, Switzerland and Greece.

Among the numerous licensing practitioners, Robert Edney (*Kingsford Stacey*), Peter Glazebrook (*Field Fisher Waterhouse*), David Lavender (*Allen & Fraser*), Elizabeth Southorn (*Richards Butler*) and Lawrence Stevens (*Vallance Lickfords*) have been consistently recommended as leaders in this field.

SOUTH EAST

Woodford & Ackroyd, one of the premier firms for betting licensing, is rapidly expanding its licensing presence.

LEADING FIRMS – SOUTH EAST

WOODFORD & ACKROYD *Southampton*	
ALLAN JANES *High Wycombe*	BLAKE LAPTHORN *Fareham*

Having acted for Ladbrokes for over 30 years, it has extensive experience in a range of matters including compliance with the Lottery and Betting Acts and licensing advocacy for both applicants and opponents. From April 1995 onwards, it will be handling all Ladbrokes' licensing work in the North. It advises the Pizza Hut chain and casino companies. It is also expert in track licensing.

Also highly regarded are *Allan Janes* and *Blake Lapthorn*. The former is particularly recommended for contentious betting licensing including the handling of licensing appeals. It acts for Arthur Prince bookmakers and has handled a large number of betting office applications and objections in recent years. It also represents a major operator of public

LEADING INDIVIDUALS – LONDON

Robert Edney *Kingsford Stacey*	Peter G. Glazebrook *Field Fisher Waterhouse*	F.D. Lavender *Allen & Fraser*
Elizabeth Southorn *Richards Butler*	Lawrence E. Stevens *Vallance Lickfolds*	
Craig Baylis *Paisner & Co*	Graeme Harris *Loxleys*	Julian A. Harris *Biddle & Co*
Christopher Hepher *Pullig & Co*	Julian M. Skeens *Jeffrey Green Russell*	Robin Walter *Allen & Fraser*

In all the tables the names in each group are listed alphabetically.

houses in London and the home counties (including three of the largest units in the City). *Blake Lapthorn* whose clients include regional and national brewers, is especially known for its liquor licensing.

COLE and COLE *Oxford*	DONNE MILEHAM & HADDOCK *Brighton*
BLANDY & BLANDY *Reading*	BRACHERS *Maidstone*
BRAIN & BRAIN *Reading*	BRUTTON & CO *Portsmouth*
FITZHUGH GATES *Brighton*	GIRLINGS *Canterbury*
HEPHERD WINSTANLEY & PUGH *Southampton*	PENNINGTONS *Basingstoke*
ARGLES & COURT *Maidstone*	BUSS MURTON *Tunbridge Wells*
GLANVILLES *Portsmouth*	LAMPORT BASSITT *Southampton*
MULLIS & PEAKE *Romford*	RAWLISON & BUTLER *Crawley*
THOMSON SNELL & PASSMORE *Tunbridge Wells*	TURBERVILLE WOODBRIDGE *Uxbridge*

Other well-established licensing practices include *Cole & Cole* and *Donne Mileham & Haddock*. The former acts for two major regional brewers. The other has for many years acted for leading operators in the licensed, retail and leisure sectors (including marinas and leisure complexes). Its expertise includes betting, gaming, club law, bingo, lotteries, public entertainment, liquor licensing and licensing appeals.

Other recommended firms include *Blandy & Blandy* (liquor licensing), *Brachers, Brain & Brain, Brutton & Co* (liquor licensing), *Fitzhugh Gates* (liquor licensing), *Girlings, Hepherd Winstanley & Pugh* (liquor licensing) and *Penningtons*.

Walter J.B. Cha *Blake Lapthorn*
David Leslie Hay *Allan Janes*
Michael J. Messent *Woodford & Ackroyd*

Leading specialists in this field include Walter Cha (*Blake Lapthorn*), David Hay (*Allan Janes*) and Michael Messent (*Woodford & Ackroyd*).

SOUTH WEST

Cartwrights and *Eversheds* (Bristol) maintain their positions at the front of the licensing field. *Cartwrights* is particularly strong in off- and on- licences as well as gaming and cinema licences (including multiplex operations). Its licensing team has had an excellent year, handling around 2000 successful nightclub applications and the application for the largest bingo club. Their clients include BHS and Marks & Spencer for off-licence work, Bass Plc for on-licence matters, First Leisure Corporation Plc for on-licence and entertainment work and Rank Organisation Plc for gaming matters. Hotel chains and pubs which it acts for include Novotel, Stakis, Wolverhampton Dudley breweries and Magic Pub Co Ltd. The firm also represents Tesco, Safeway, UCI and MGM.

CARTWRIGHTS *Bristol*	EVERSHEDS, BRISTOL *Bristol*
FYNN & PARTNERS *Bournemouth*	

Eversheds (Bristol) acts principally for breweries, licensed property companies, independent operators, multiple specialist off-licences and convenience stores. Clients include Grand Metropolitan, Oddbins and 7-Eleven. In 1994, it supervised about 6,500 pub licences renewals (10 % of all pubs in England and Wales) and was advisor to a group of multiple retailers on Home Office review of night cafe licences.

The newly established *Fynn & Partners*, which comprises the old licensing department of *Penningtons* (Bournemouth), is also a leading firm in the region. Its partners have extensive experience in applications for gaming permits, club registration certificates, betting office licences, bookmaker permits, off-licences, public entertainment and cinema licences.

LESTER ALDRIDGE *Bournemouth*	
BEVAN ASHFORD *Bristol*	BOND PEARCE *Plymouth*
CLARKE WILLMOTT & CLARKE *Taunton*	RICKERBY JESSOP *Cheltenham*
BEVISS & BECKINGSALE *Axminster*	BOYCE HATTON *Torquay*
FOOT & BOWDEN *Plymouth*	FORD SIMEY DAW ROBERTS *Exeter*
FRANK & CAFFIN *Truro*	OSBORNE CLARKE *Bristol*
STEPHENS & SCOWN *Exeter*	STONES *Exeter*
WOLFERSTANS *Plymouth*	WOOLLCOMBE BEER WATTS *N'ton Abbot*

Also well-regarded, *Lester Aldridge* is particularly strong in liquor licensing. Clients include one of the leading country health hotels and a major South West brewery. The firm are the nominated solicitors for the Bournemouth Hotels and Restaurants Association. It also handles casino licensing.

Other recommended firms include *Bevan Ashford*, (strong on liquor and entertainment licensing), *Bond Pearce, Clarke Wilmott & Clarke* and *Rickerby Jessop* (which acts for breweries and leisure complexes).

Practitioners recognised as leaders in licensing include Tim Davies (*Cartwrights*), Kathryn Eardley (*Cartwrights*), Lionel Fynn *(Fynn & Partners*), David Hamilton (*Cartwrights*), Julia Palmer (*Fynn & Partners),* Michael Parrott *(Cartwrights)* and Jeremy Philips (*Eversheds* (Bristol)).

Timothy L. Davies *Cartwrights*
Lionel C. Fynn *Fynn & Partners*
Jeremy Phillips *Eversheds*
Kathryn Eardley *Cartwrights*
David J. Hamilton *Cartwrights*
Julia C. Palmer *Fynn & Partners*
Michael Kindersley Parrott *Cartwrights*
Graham Gover *Fynn & Partners*
Sandra D. Graham *Fynn & Partners*
Colin Patrick *Lester Aldridge*

WALES

The two leading firms are *Gaskell Rhys & Otto Jones* and *Morgan Bruce*, both known for their liquor licensing expertise. The former concentrates on personal licensing but also acts for a major brewer. *Morgan Bruce,* with licensing teams in Cardiff and Swansea, advises one of the big six breweries on all of its licensing matters in Wales and the South. It also acts for one of the largest convenience store chains, advising on off-licence applications.

LEADING FIRMS – WALES	
GASKELL RHYS & OTTO-JONES *Cardiff*	**MORGAN BRUCE** *Cardiff*

Other recommended firms include *Cartwrights Adams & Black* (predominantly liquor licensing) and *Hugh James Jones & Jenkins*. The former also handles public entertainment, betting and gaming licensing. The firm acts for individual applicants, a local brewery and national hotel groups. *Hugh James Jones & Jenkins* has expertise in licensed clubs matters and entertainment and gaming licensing (particularly the licensing of amusement arcades).

Since the merger of *Eversheds* (Cardiff) with *Holt Phillips* in Bristol (a leading South West licensing practice), *Eversheds* has been developing a notable licensing presence in Wales.

HIGHLY REGARDED – WALES	
CARTWRIGHTS ADAMS & BLACK *Cardiff*	**EVERSHEDS,** *Cardiff*
HUGH JAMES JONES & JENKINS *Cardiff*	
BEVAN ASHFORD *Cardiff*	**DAVID & SNAPE** *Bridgend*
DOLMANS *Cardiff*	**GROSSMAN HERMER SELIGMAN** *Cardiff*

Notable practitioners in this field include Robin Havard *(Morgan Bruce)*, John Otto-Jones *(Gaskell Rhys & Otto Jones)* and Rosemary Morgan *(Morgan Bruce*, Swansea).

LEADING INDIVIDUALS – WALES
Michael Robin Havard *Morgan Bruce*
Rosemary Morgan *Morgan Bruce*
John Alcwyn Otto-Jones *Gaskell Rhys & Otto-Jones*

MIDLANDS

WEST MIDLANDS

One of the pre-eminent firms in the West Midlands for licensing is *Edge & Ellison*, specialising in liquor, betting and gaming licences. It handles all aspects including new applications, protection orders and transfers.

LEADING FIRMS – MIDLANDS	
EDGE & ELLISON *Birmingham*	**POPPLESTON ALLEN** *Nottingham*
ANTHONY COLLINS *Birmingham*	**KENNETH CURTIS & CO** *Birmingham*
SHACKLOCKS *Nottingham*	**YOUNG & PEARCE** *Nottingham*

In all the tables the names in each group are listed alphabetically.

Both *Anthony Collins* and *Kenneth Curtis & Co* also have excellent reputations in this field. The former's expertise lies principally in liquor licensing including applications for on/off-licences. It also covers public entertainment licences, special hours certificate, restaurant licences, protection orders/transfers and secured lending on licensed premises for brewers. It was additionally involved in obtaining a Justices' conditional licence for the National Indoor Sports Arena in Birmingham. Major clients include Wolverhampton & Dudley Breweries plc, Camerons and West Midlands Taverns Ltd. *Kenneth Curtis & Co* is experienced in liquor, betting and gaming licensing.

Also highly regarded is the Birmingham office of *Eversheds* with three full-time specialists. Liquor licensing forms the largest part of its licensing practice. It acts for Bass Taverns in relation to acquisition work in Midlands and the North, as well as handling the management of Bass' Midlands estate and protection orders and licence renewals on a national basis. Its expertise also extends to pub conversions, new applications and supermarket licensing. Other clients include Greenalls (locally) and one of Hilton Hotels' guest houses.

Recommended leaders for licensing include Anthony Collins *(Anthony Collins)*, Anthony Curtis *(Kenneth Curtis & Co)* and Andrew Potts *(Edge & Ellison)*.

EAST MIDLANDS

Poppleston Allen, one of the few niche licensing firms, has a formidable reputation particularly for discotheque and late night licensing. A large proportion of its clients are

HIGHLY REGARDED – MIDLANDS	
EVERSHEDS *Birmingham, Nottingham*	**IRONSIDES RAY & VIALS** *Northampton*
CHALLINOR ROBERTS COOKSEY *Cradley Heath*	**ELLIS MOXON** *Stoke-on-Trent*
FREETH CARTWRIGHT HUNT DICKINS *Nottingham*	**GOODGER AUDEN** *Burton-on-Trent*
HOWES PERCIVAL *Northampton*	**KNIGHT & SONS** *Newcastle-under-Lyme*
LANYON BOWDLER *Shrewsbury*	**LYON CLARK** *West Bromwich*

in the leisure industry and include European Leisure and Kingfisher Leisure plcs, both of whom it acts for nationally, First Leisure, Rank Leisure, Meadowhall, Simpsons and, restaurant chain Muswell. The firm is also becoming increasingly involved with university union leisure facilities. Susanna Poppleston is the legal correspondent for the Licensee and Morning Advertiser, whilst Jeremy Allen is the official solicitor for BEDA. (British Entertainment & Discotheque Association).

Shacklocks and *Young & Pearce* have excellent local reputations. The former acts for Mansfield Brewery plc on new applications, objections, transfers, trade outlets and licensing appeals including Crown Court matters. It also represents a number of sports clubs, restaurants and off-licences.

Young & Pearce undertakes liquor, betting and gaming licensing work. It continues to advise several breweries, plcs, off-licences and individuals on new applications, expansion and acquisition plans, and Children's Certificate applications. The firm also does a substantial amount of work for the leisure industry, particularly holiday villages, and golf and tennis complexes.

Also strongly recommended is *Ironsides Ray & Vials*, especially for off-licence work. Most of the firm's work is either dealing with objections on behalf of the Leicestershire police or for the German discount supermarket group, Aldi Stores, for whom it acts on a nationwide basis.

LEADING INDIVIDUALS – MIDLANDS

Jeremy Allen *Poppleston Allen*	
Susanna Poppleston *Poppleston Allen*	
Andrew J. Potts *Edge & Ellison*	
Anthony Ralph Collins *Anthony Collins*	
Anthony G. Curtis *Kenneth Curtis & Co*	
John Pearce *Young & Pearce*	
Robin K. Wilson *Shacklocks*	
Malcolm Radcliffe *Ironsides Ray & Vials*	
David A. Young *Eversheds*	

UP AND COMING

Susanna Davies *Edge & Ellison*
Stephanie Perraton *Edge & Ellison*
Deborah Shaw *Edge & Ellison*

Jeremy Allen (*Poppleston Allen*), John Pearce (*Young & Pearce*), Susanna Poppleston (*Poppleston Allen*) and Robin Wilson (*Shacklocks*) are among the widely recognised leaders for licensing.

EAST ANGLIA

Among the few firms with a well-established licensing and leisure practice, *Howes Percival* has an excellent reputation. The recruitment of leading specialist, Simon Nicholls (formerly a partner of *Overbury Steward & Eaton*) has further strengthened that reputation. The firm's work is primarily in the liquor field, although it does handle some gaming, entertainment and betting licensing. Clients include Scottish & Newcastle, Tollemache & Cobbold Brewery Ltd, Dunstan Hall Hotel and Glynian (Leisure Parks) Ltd.

LEADING FIRMS – EAST ANGLIA

HOWES PERCIVAL *Ipswich*	**MILLS & REEVE** *Norwich*

Also highly regarded is *Mills & Reeve*. It undertakes gaming and holiday camp licensing, as well as mainstream licensing work.

HIGHLY REGARDED – EAST ANGLIA

EVERSHEDS, *Norwich*	**KENNETH BUSH & CO** *King's Lynn*
GREENWOODS *Peterborough*	

Other recommended firms include *Eversheds* (Norwich) and *Kenneth Bush & Co*. The former's expertise covers applications for justices, licences, renewal of gaming certificates, and transfers and protection orders for various licences. The latter's sound local reputation is primarily in the leisure industry. The firm acts for around 20-30 holiday

parks across the coast in relation to applications for licensing certificates for bingo, facilities, drinks and food.

LEADING INDIVIDUALS – EAST ANGLIA

Anthony F.R. Jordan *Mills & Reeve*
Alan Kefford *Howes Percival*
Simon J. Nicholls *Howes Percival*

Notable practitioners include Alan Kefford (*Howes Percival*), Anthony Jordan (*Mills & Reeve*) and Simon Nicholls (*Howes Percival*) who currently devotes 75-80% of his time in licensing work.

NORTH WEST

Weightman Rutherfords is one of the leading firms for off-licensing. It also handles general liquor licensing, public entertainment, betting and gaming. Clients include two off-licences nationally Allied Breweries, the police authority (handling objections/revocations of betting office licences) and independent bookmakers.

LEADING FIRMS – NORTH WEST

WEIGHTMAN RUTHERFORDS *Liverpool*	
COBBETT LEAK ALMOND *Manchester*	
DAVIES WALLIS FOYSTER *Liverpool*	**ELLIOTT & COMPANY** *Manchester*

Cobbett Leak Almond (which has close links with the North West Brewers' & Licensed Retailers' Association), *Davies Wallis Foyster* and *Elliott & Company* all have excellent reputations.

Cobbett Leak Almond's team consisting of five specialist partners acts for Bass plc, the Boddington Group plc, Whitbread, Marston Thompson & Evershed and Joseph Holt plc, amongst others.

HIGHLY REGARDED – NORTH WEST

BERMANS *Liverpool*	
BULLIVANT JONES & COMPANY *Liverpool*	**DAVIES ARNOLD COOPER** *Manchester*
EVERSHEDS *Manchester*	**A. HALSALL & CO** *Birkenhead*
ADDLESHAW SONS & LATHAM *Manchester*	**BARKER, BOOTH & EASTWOOD** *Blackpool*

Davies Wallis Foyster advised a major supermarket operator on the licensing aspects of their acquisition of around 100 outlets in Scotland. Other clients include major brewers, independent pub operators, two of the largest supermarket operators in GB and a leading specialist off-licence operator.

In liquor licensing, *Elliott & Company* acts for the country's largest firm of wine warehouse retailers, major off-licence chains and an independent brewery in the North West. In betting and gaming, the firm acts for one of the 'big three' licensed betting office operators, a major football pools company and numerous smaller operators.

Bermans (liquor licensing), *Bullivant Jones & Company* (liquor licensing), *Davies Arnold Cooper, Eversheds* (Manchester), and *A.Halsall & Co* all have well-established licensing practices.

The recruitment of Nigel Copeland from the niche licensing practice of *Copeland Lyons,* has further strengthened *Bermans'* licensing presence in the North. Clients include clubs, individuals and those in the brewing and leisure industries.

Bullivant Jones & Company acts primarily for retailers and wholesalers requiring justices licence. *Davies Arnold Cooper* advises on all aspects of liquor, gaming and entertainment licensing. It recently handled the licensing work for Valedrome involving indoor sports and track matters; also advises a large leisure company dealing with bingo.

Eversheds, (Manchester) is one of the few North West firms specialising primarily in gaming licensing. It continues to act for the Stanley Leisure Group with nineteen casinos from Edinburgh to the South coast of England. The firm is also instructed by Stanley Racing, the fourth largest bookmaker in the UK with around 400 betting shops.

LEADING INDIVIDUALS – NORTH WEST

Hamish K. Lawson *Cobbett Leak Almond*
David Morgan *Weightman Rutherfords*
James C.M. Davies *Davies Wallis Foyster*
Nicholas H. Dickinson *Davies Wallis Foyster*
Barry K. Holland *Elliott & Company*
Mark D. Owen *Weightman Rutherfords*
Nigel Copeland *Copeland Lyons*
Anthony Horne *Davies Arnold Cooper*
Christopher R. Johnson *A. Halsall & Co*
Simon David Allen Jones *Cobbett Leak Almond*

Individuals consistently recommended as leading licensing specialists include James Davies (*Davies Wallis Foyster,* Manchester), Nicholas Dickinson (*Davies Wallis Foyster,* Liverpool), Barry Holland (*Elliott & Company*), Hamish Lawson (*Cobett Leak Almond*), David Morgan *(Weightman Rutherfords)* and Mark Owen (*Weightman Rutherfords*).

NORTH EAST

Gosschalks is consistently recommended as one of the premier firms in the country for betting, bingo, nightclub and public houses licensing. It handles all aspects of licensing but is especially known for handling difficult contested licensing applications. It advises numerous national clients including William Hill, First Leisure and Yates' Wine Lodges.

Other highly regarded licensing practices include *Dibb Lupton Broomhead, Goodswens, McKenzie Bell* and *Mincoff Science & Co.* The bulk of *Dibb Lupton Broomhead's* licensing practice is in liquor licensing although it does handle public entertainment, bingo, gaming and lottery licensing. Its clients include regional and national brewers, public

house operators, major hotel chains, leisure groups, supermarket and cinema operators, and individual enterpreneurs.

LEADING FIRMS – NORTH EAST

GOSSCHALKS *Hull*	
DIBB LUPTON BROOMHEAD *Bradford*	**GOODSWENS** *Middlesbrough*
McKENZIE BELL *Sunderland*	**MINCOFF SCIENCE & GOLD** *Newcastle-upon-Tyne*

Goodswens' expertise includes liquor, entertainment and gaming licensing. Hotels, bars, public houses, off licences, social and night clubs, restaurants, casinos and sports centres are part of the firm's wide-ranging clientele. In recent years, the firm has been instructed by Police Forces and by Licensing Benches in licensing appeals.

McKenzie Bell's has a solid reputation in liquor and public entertainment licensing. In addition to advising on all forms of licensing applications including late licences, it is experienced in dealing with revocations and opposed renewals. Clients represented include four nationally- known breweries or brewery owned chains, night clubs and public houses. It has also undertaken liquor licence work on behalf of Northumbria Police since 1985.

The licensing expertise of *Mincoff Science & Co* lies in liquor, gaming, amusements and lottery. Major clients include Rank, Mecca and Scottish & Newcastle as well as statutory authorities. *Goodswens, McKenzie Bell* and *Mincoff Science & Gold* are co-founders of the 'Lawyers for Licensing North' consortium.

Also consistently recommended is the newly established niche practice of *John Gaunt & Partners*, co-founded by John Gaunt, a former licensing partner from *Wake Smith & Co.* Its forte is liquor licensing, contentious and non-contentious, which forms 40% of its total workload. John Gaunt has been retained as regional licensing solicitor by a major brewer for 13 years and the firm's client base extends to East Midlands. It also handles litigation work for the brewing and leisure industries.

HIGHLY REGARDED – NORTH EAST

JOHN GAUNT & PARTNERS *Sheffield*	
GODLOVE PEARLMAN *Leeds*	**SMITH & GRAHAM** *Hartlepool*
DOBERMAN HORSMAN *Middlesbrough*	**EATON SMITH & DOWNEY** *Huddersfield*
FORD AND WARREN *Leeds*	**GORDONS WRIGHT & WRIGHT** *Bradford*
IRWIN MITCHELL *Sheffield*	**LISTER CROFT PARTNERSHIP** *Wakefield*
LUPTON FAWCETT *Leeds*	**PINSENT CURTIS** *Leeds*
READ HIND STEWART *Leeds*	**WALKER MORRIS** *Leeds*

Other firms with sound licensing practices include *Godlove Pearlman* whose strength is in off-licence work, and *Smith & Graham* innovator of the Club Care scheme for Workingham's clubs. Clients of *Smith & Graham's* Leisure Industry Group established in 1994, include breweries, public house operators and licensed premises estates. It acts for Pubmaster – the largest non-brewery pub operator.

Martin Cowell (*Dibb Lupton Broomhead*), Les Green (*Gosschalks*) who has a national reputation, Richard Hall (*Goodswens*), Austen Science (*Mincoff Science & Co*) and

William Temperley (*McKenzie Bell*) are among the recommended leaders for licensing.

LEADING INDIVIDUALS – NORTH EAST	
Richard Leslie Green *Gosschalks*	
M. Cowell *Dibb Lupton Broomhead*	
Richard Hall *Goodswens*	
Austen Science *Mincoff Science & Gold*	
William B. Temperley *McKenzie Bell*	
John R.T. Gaunt *John Gaunt & Partners*	

SCOTLAND

John Batters & Co, Brunton Miller, J & A Hastie SSC and *R & J.M. Hill Brown* are the four premier firms for liquor licensing. The highly specialised practice of *John Batters & Co* also handles gaming matters, licensing appeals and the purchase of licensed premises.

LEADING FIRMS – SCOTLAND	
BRUNTON MILLER *Glasgow*	**J. & A. HASTIE SSC** *Edinburgh*
R. & J.M. HILL BROWN *Glasgow*	**JOHN BATTERS & CO** *Glasgow*

Brunton Miller's clients include major brewers, supermarket chains, medium-sized companies with a number of licensed premises and individual shopkeepers with off-sales licences. It is particularly experienced in handling Licensing Board appearances, all of which are exclusively dealt with by partners.

J & A Hastie's expertise includes gaming, betting and entertainment licensing involving public houses, clubs and hotels. It also handles acquisitions and disposals of licensed businesses, and applications for late hours catering licences. The firm has a substantial connection with the hotel and restaurant industry and has been Scottish Secretaries and legal advisers for the British Hospitality Association for 45 years. Other clients include Top Rank Ltd and Scottish Highlands Hotels.

HIGHLY REGARDED – SCOTLAND	
ROBIN MORTON SOLICITORS	
GRIGOR & YOUNG *Elgin*	**JOHNSTON & HERRON** *Lochgelly*
McARTHUR STANTON *Dumbarton*	**McGRIGOR DONALD** *Glasgow*
PAULL & WILLIAMSONS *Aberdeen*	
BLACKADDER REID JOHNSTON *Dundee*	**BRODIES WS** *Edinburgh*
DORMAN JEFFREY & CO *Glasgow*	**HARPER MACLEOD** *Glasgow*
JAMES & GEORGE COLLIE *Aberdeen*	**LEDINGHAM CHALMERS** *Aberdeen*
LINDSAYS WS *Edinburgh*	**MACKINTOSH & WYLIE** *Kilmarnock*
MACROBERTS *Glasgow*	**MORTON FRASER MILLIGAN** *Edinburgh*
PAGAN OSBORNE *Cupar*	**SHEPHERD & WEDDERBURN** *Edinburgh*
STEEDMAN RAMAGE WS *Edinburgh*	**THORNTONS WS** *Dundee*
TINDAL OATTS *Glasgow*	

R & J.M. Hill Brown represents a wide spectrum of licensed trade clients, with particular emphasis on the enter-

tainment industry. It covers new licence applications, court representations and renewal/review of existing licences. Clients include two major leisure chains, a national supermarket group, a Scottish pubs/restaurants subsidiary of an international drinks company and a national hotel chain.

Robin Morton Solicitors, established in May 1995, has been consistently recommended for liquor licensing. Robin Morton – a former licensing partner of *McClure Naismith Anderson & Gardiner* – has acted for several major organisations and individuals in licence applications and board appearances. His expertise extends to the sale and purchase of licensed premises. He has been involved in a number of important cases including Mount Charlotte Investments v. City of Glasgow Licensing Board.

LEADING INDIVIDUALS – SCOTLAND	
John A. Batters *John Batters*	
John C. Cummins *R. & J.M. Hill Brown*	
Douglas S. Dalgleish *Brunton Miller*	
John A. Loudon *J. & A. Hastie SSC*	
John A.G. Gilmour *McArthur Stanton*	
Tom Johnston *Johnston & Herron*	
Peter J. Lawson *R. & J.M. Hill Brown*	
Archibald D. Maciver *Brunton Miller*	
David F. McLeod *Paull & Williamsons*	
Robin J.M. Morton *Robin Morton Solicitors*	

Other firms with established licensing practices include *Johnston & Herron, McArthur Stanton* and *Paull & Williamsons. Johnston & Heron* handles liquor licensing, including Licensing Board appearances and the sale, purchase and finance of licensed properties. *McArthur Stanton* is strong on liquor licensing, although it does handle bookmakers applications, hot food licensing, gaming permits and other associated work. Clients range from local hotels to major brewers.

Paull & Williamsons' emphasis is in liquor licensing and, the purchase, sale and leasing of licensed premises (includes the North East area). It has strong links with the hotel industry, having advised the developers of Aberdeen Quality Hotel and, the Jurys Hotel Group on the purchase of Pond Hotel in Glasgow.

Other recommended firms with accredited liquor licensing specialists include *Grigor & Young* and *McGrigor Donald*.

Leaders in this field include John Batters (*John Batters & Co*), John Cummins (*R & J. M. Hill Brown & Co*), Douglas Dalgleish (*Brunton Miller*), and John Loudon (*J & A Hastie*) (Convener of the Licensing Law Specialist Accreditation Panel).

NORTHERN IRELAND

E & L Kennedy is regarded as one of the leading practices in this field with licensing constituting around 20% of its total workload. It is especially known for liquor licensing and major clients include Stewarts Supermarkets Ltd. The firm is also one of the few firms with a specialism in pharmaceutical licensing and it advises Boots Chemist Ltd, amongst others.

It was recently involved in a judicial review of Pharmacy Practices Committee's refusal to grant a pharmacy contract for Bloomfield Centre.

ents primarily in the hotel and catering industries. The latter handles liquor licensing, club registrations, and entertainment and cinema licensing.

LEADING FIRMS – NORTHERN IRELAND

E. & L. KENNEDY *Belfast*

HIGHLY REGARDED – NORTHERN IRELAND

O'REILLY STEWART *Belfast*   **SHEAN DICKSON MERRICK** *Belfast*

Other firms with strong licensing expertise include *O'Reilly Stewart* and *Sheen Dickson & Merrick*. The former has cli-

LEADERS IN LICENSING

LONDON

Baylis, Craig

Paisner & Co, London (0171) 353 0299. Qualified 1981. Partner 1993. Litigation Department. Main areas of practice are environmental law, food health and safety, and licensing and leisure.

Edney, Robert

Kingsford Stacey, London (0171) 242 6784. Partner in Licensing Department.

Specialisation: Acts for major brewery clients and others in the leisure industry at all levels in relation to liquor and entertainment licensing and related work. Also handles planning and rating work and related litigation.

Career: Qualified in 1970, having joined *Kingsford Stacey* in 1968. Became a Partner in 1972.

Personal: Born 8th September 1946. Educated at Cambridge University (MA 1968). Chairman of local tennis club. Enjoys tennis, food and wine. Lives in Aston, near Stevenage.

Glazebrook, Peter G.

Field Fisher Waterhouse, London (0171) 481 4841. Partner in Licensing Department.

Specialisation: Main area of practice is liquor and entertainment licensing law. Work includes applications to the licensing justices for liquor licenses for public houses, hotels, clubs, wine bars and off-licenses including supermarkets. Also advises clients on food safety legislation, the Health & Safety at Work Act and related statutory provisions.

Harris, Graeme

Loxleys, London (0171) 377 1066. Partner in Licensing Department.

Specialisation: Acts for major companies and individuals on liquor licensing and Gaming Act matters. Also advises on entertainment licensing. Other area of practice is commercial property, acting for companies and individuals with particular reference to licensing and attendant matters. Has acted in a wide range of licensing cases related to liquor and entertainment licensing.

Prof. Memberships: Law Society, London

Brewery and Licensing Solicitors Association (Chairman).

Career: Qualified in 1960. Joined *Loxleys* in 1960, becoming a Partner in 1965.

Personal: Born 27th September 1936. Attended Westminster School 1950-54, then College of Law. Leisure interests include theatre, bowls and watching other sports. Lives in Eltham, London.

Harris, Julian A.

Biddle & Co, London (0171) 606 9301. Partner in Litigation Department.

Specialisation: Main area of practice is gaming licenses. Spent six years with solicitors for Gaming Board. Now acts for two major casinos and leisure companies. Also handles food law: acts for national and international food manufacturing and catering companies.

Prof. Membership: International Association of Gaming Attorneys, Food Law Group.

Career: Qualified in 1980. Worked at *Beechcroft Hyman Isaacs* 1978-80, *Gregory Rowcliffe & Co.* 1980-86, becoming a Partner in 1983; *Nicholson Graham & Jones* 1986-88 and *Shoosmiths & Harrison* 1988-93, as Partner and Head of Litigation in the London office. Joined *Biddle & Co.* as a Partner in 1993.

Personal: Born 15th May 1955. Attended Wellingborough School 1963-73 and Magdalene College, Cambridge 1974-77. Lives in Chiswick, London.

Hepher, Christopher

Pullig & Co, London (0171) 353 0505. Qualified 1979. Partner 1994. Licensing Department. Also handles licensing-related crime.

Lavender, F.D.

Allen & Fraser, London (0171) 437 4001. Qualified 1966. Senior Partner 1968. Licensing Department. Work covers liquor and entertainment law. Has appeared in 185 licensing tribunals from Aberdeen to Penzance. Born 23.8.1942.

Skeens, Julian M.

Jeffrey Green Russell, London (0171) 499 7020. Partner in charge of Licensing and Gaming Law Department.

Specialisation: Specialist in liquor licensing, betting, gaming, public entertainment and lotteries: undertakes cases nationwide. Cases successfully handled include the UK's first multi-activity centre, the UK's first permanent 24-hour public entertainment licence and the UK's largest licensed premises.

Prof. Membership: Law Society, Business in Sport and Leisure (Director), British Entertainment and Discotheque Association, Society for the Study of Gambling, International Association of Gaming Attorneys, European Society for the Study of Gambling.

Career: Qualified 1980. Joined *Jeffrey Green Russell* in 1987 as a Partner to establish the specialist Licensing and Gaming Department.

Personal: Born 26th December 1951. Holds an LLB (1974). Lives in Bristol.

Southorn, Elizabeth

Richards Butler, London (0171) 247 6555. Qualified 1974. Partner and head of the Licensing Department, specialising in all aspects of betting, gaming and liquor licensing law. Born 7.4.1950.

Stevens, Lawrence E.

Vallance Lickfolds, London (0171) 404 0707. Qualified 1954. Senior Partner 1989. Licensing Department.

Specialisation: all aspects of liquor licensing, betting and gaming and the purchase, sale and leasing of licensed premises. Born 8.12.1930.

Walter, Robin

Allen & Fraser, London (0171) 437 4001. Qualified 1975. Partner 1983. Licensing Department. Acts for several national companies.

REGIONS

Allen, Jeremy

Poppleston Allen, Nottingham (0115) 953 8500. Partner and Co-Founder.

Specialisation: Specialises in licensing and leisure work, including liquor, public entertainment, betting and gaming, and pay parties. Also handles associated crime work, including trades descriptions and breach of conditions. Solicitors to B.E.D.A. (British Entertainment and Discotheque Association). Major clients include European Leisure Plc, First Leisure Plc, Kingfisher Leisure Plc, Luminar Leisure, Rank Leisure Plc and Simpsons of Cornhill Plc. Charge out rate is 120/hour.

Prof. Membership: Law Society. Secretary Nottinghamshire Law Society 1977-84; President East Midlands Association of Local Law Societies (Secretary 1981-86). Founder Chairman Law Society's Child Care Working Party; member Law Society Council 1986-92; member Magistrates' Courts Rule Committee since 1982; Chairman Law Society's Criminal Law Committee 1987-1991; member Lord Chancellor's Efficiency Commission 1987-89; member of Home Office Review of Procedure Committee. Higher Courts (crime) Advocacy course leader.

Career: Qualified in 1970. Articled at *Johnstone Sharp & Walker* 1962-68 *Raleigh Industries* 1968-72. Joined *Hunt Dickins* in 1972, becoming a Partner in 1973 and Managing Partner in 1987. Co-founded *Poppleston Allen Licensing Solicitors* in 1994.

Personal: Born 5th July 1944. Attended Bedales and College of Law. Honorary solicitor Nottingham CAB and Nottinghamshire branch British Red Cross Society. Member of Beeston Hockey club and Park Tennis Club. Leisure interests include theatre, hockey, running and tennis. Lives in Nottingham.

Batters, John A.

John Batters and Company, Glasgow (0141) 427 6884. Qualified 1971. Founding Partner 1991. Main areas of practice are licensing, principally liquor and gaming; and commercial conveyancing. Born 19.6.1946.

Cha, Walter J.B.

Blake Lapthorn, Fareham (01489) 579990. Partner in Commercial Department.

Specialisation: Main area of practice is licensing: has specialised since 1985, acting for national and regional brewers. Also handles commercial conveyancing for licensed premises. Acts on behalf of brewers in landlord and tenant matters and acquisitions and disposals of premises. Assisted national brewers in complying with MMC report. Individual charge-out rate of £115 per hour.

Career: Qualified in 1983, having joined *Blake Lapthorn* in 1981. Became a Partner in 1987.

Personal: Born 9th August 1959. Married with two children. Leisure interests include rugby, golf, tennis, theatre and family. Lives in Southsea.

Collins, Anthony Ralph

Anthony Collins, Birmingham (0121) 200 3242. Qualified 1970. Founding Partner 1973. Licensing Department. Specialises in licensing work, primarily for brewers in the West Midlands. Born 23.6.1942.

Copeland, Nigel

Copeland Lyons, Manchester (0161) 834 5001. Partner specialising in liquor licensing and entertainment law.

Specialisation: Main area of practice since 1960 is liquor licensing and entertainment law. Successfully defended application for licence revocation in relation to the Hacienda Club. Has also acted for the Voyager Arndale Centre, Manchester and the Manchester Arena Complex.

Prof. Membership: British Legal Association, Law Society (London and Manchester).

Career: Qualified 1956. Commenced practice on own account in Manchester, 1960. In partnership with *Nigel Copeland Glickman & Co.*, 1963-74. In practice on own account, 1974-85. In partnership with *Burton Copeland*, 1985-93. Established new practice *Copeland Lyons* in 1993 with Anthony Lyons.

Personal: Born 20th August 1933. Attended Manchester Grammar School 1945-50, then Manchester University. Governor of Handicapped School. Leisure pursuits include stamp and coin collecting and model railways.

Cowell, M.

Dibb Lupton Broomhead, Sheffield (0114) 2760351. Partner in Litigation Department.

Specialisation: Main area of practice is licensing: has specialised since 1979. Established and became head of firm's licensing unit in 1989. Deals with all types of liquor licensing, as well as public entertainment, gaming and bingo licensing and lotteries. Acts for National and Regional brewers, various companies operating public houses, major hotel chains, leisure groups, supermarket operators and cinema operators together with individual entrepreneurs and licensees. Also handles white collar and corporate crime, covering fraud, health and safety, food safety and trading standards prosecutions. Has given various seminars on Licensing and Food Safety, including IBC conferences on Revocations.

Career: Qualified in 1975, having joined *Dibb Lupton Broomhead* in 1973. Became a Partner in 1979. Acting Provincial Stipendiary Magistrate.

Personal: Born 7th July 1950. Attended Repton School 1964-68 and Nottingham University 1969-72. Leisure interests include amateur dramatics, tennis, walking, music and cycling. Lives in Sheffield.

Cummins, John C.

R. & J.M. Hill Brown & Co, Glasgow (0141) 332 3265. Partner in Licensing Department.

Specialisation: Handles licensing, gaming, leisure and retail matters, representing a wide range of brewing, restaurant, retail and entertainment interests in the licensed trade. Author of 'Licensing Law in Scotland' (But-

terworths, 1993); contributor to 'Scots Law Times', 'Journal of the Law Society of Scotland' and 'Scottish Licensed Trade News'. Reporter for 'Scottish Civil Law Reports' and consultant editor of 'Licensing Review'. Accredited as a specialist in liquor licensing law by The Law Society of Scotland. Keynote speaker, first National Conference for Licensing Boards, Aberdeen, 1994. Contributor to various radio programmes. Law Society of Scotland 'Update' speaker. Member of Licensing Law Committee of the Law Society of Scotland.

Prof. Membership: Law Society of Scotland.

Career: Joined *R & JM Hill & Brown & Co.* in 1976. Qualified in 1978 and became a Partner in 1980.

Personal: Born in 1952. Educated at the University of Glasgow (M.A., 1974, LL.B. 1976). Leisure pursuits include motoring. Lives in Glasgow.

Curtis, Anthony G.

Kenneth Curtis & Co, Birmingham (0121) 356 1161. Qualified 1969. Senior Partner. Specialises in Off License Applications. Born 5.12.1944.

Dalgleish, Douglas S.

Brunton Miller, Glasgow (0141) 337 1199. Senior Partner.

Specialisation: Has been involved in licensing work for around thirty years. Widely experienced, acting for several major breweries and supermarket chains. Also handles general commercial work. Regular contributor to various licensed trade publications. Has addressed numerous conferences and seminar groups. Appeared on radio and is frequently mentioned in the press.

Prof. Membership: Law Society of Scotland.

Career: Qualified in 1956. Became Senior Partner of *Brunton Miller* in 1974. Member of Law Society Working Party on licensing law.

Personal: Born 26th December 1927. Attended Glasgow University 1949-55. Chairman of Dumbarton FC; Past President of Scottish Golf Union; Chairman of Caledonian Golf Travel Limited. Leisure interests include golf and football. Lives in Helensburgh.

Davies, James C.M.

Davies Wallis Foyster, Liverpool (0151) 236 6226. Senior Partner

Specialisation: Principal area of practice is liquor and gaming licensing. Acts for several major supermarket and off licence chains in the UK and also for casino and betting operators nationally. Also deals with corporate finance matters. Believed first English Solicitor to apply for supermarket off licence in Scotland. Made some of earliest Section 77 applications for public houses in North West England. Lectures nationally on licensing matters.

Prof. Membership: Law Society, Liverpool

Law Society, Manchester Law Society.

Career: Articled with *Layton & Co.* Qualified 1971. Partner in *Bullivant & Co* in Liverpool 1973-77. Founded *Davies Wallis* in 1977 and became Senior Partner of the merged firm *Davies Wallis Foyster* in 1989

Personal: Born 23rd October 1946. Attended Liverpool College, then Liverpool Polytechnic. Director of Royal Liverpool Children's NHS Trust. Leisure pursuits include fishing, shooting and the arts. Lives in Caldy, Wirral.

Davies, Timothy L.

Cartwrights, Bristol (0117) 929 3601. Partner in Licensing Department.

Specialisation: Handles all aspects of liquor, entertainment and gaming licensing both as adviser and advocate. Also liaises with commercial department partners in relation to licensing related acquisitions and disposals. Examples of major clients in each sector are Marks & Spencer (off-licence work), First Leisure Corporation Plc (on-licence and entertainment licensing work), Wadworth & Co (on-licence work), Stakis Plc (casino work) and Top Rank/Mecca (bingo work). Has run a series of licensing workshops for the trade and witness training exercises for clients.

Prof. Memberships: Bristol Law Society.

Career: Qualified 1978. Joined *Cartwrights* as an articled clerk in 1975 and has remained there since, except for two years as an employed legal adviser in commerce from 1982-84. Appointed Partner on his return in 1984.

Personal: Born 2nd April 1953. Attended Clifton College to 1971, then University College London 1971-74. Leisure interests include power boating and watching rugby. Lives in Bristol.

Davies, Susanna

Edge & Ellison, Birmingham (0121) 200 2001.

Dickinson, Nicholas H.

Davies Wallis Foyster, Liverpool (0151) 236 6226. Qualified 1975. Partner 1989. Head of Licensing Department. Main areas of practice are liquor licensing and food safety. Born 3.6.1943.

Eardley, Kathryn

Cartwrights, Bristol (0117) 929 3601. Partner in Licensing Department.

Specialisation: Specialises in the administration of licensed estates.

Career: Qualified in 1978, while articled with *George Brown & Co* and then moved to *Blatch & Co.* Spent six years with Hampshire Magistrates' Court Committee. Joined *Cartwrights* in 1988 and became a partner in 1990.

Personal: Educated at University of Sheffield, 1971. Lives in Bristol.

Fynn, Lionel C.

Fynn & Partners, Bournemouth (01202) 551991. Partner, and Head of Environmental Licensing and Planning Department.

Specialisation: Regular advocate in a wide range of planning environmental and licensing matters. One of the first solicitors in the country to conduct a Crown Court Licensing Appeal and has since acted in numerous such cases involving liquor licensing, betting and gaming subjects. Well known for his conduct of many Town Planning Appeals and has developed a speciality for cases involving High Court Challenges and Judicial Review. In the environmental field has handled numerous noise related Magistrates' Court proceedings and civil actions. His knowledge of noise related matters is greatly assisted by his outside involvement in sound recording. Major clients include Trust House Forte, Allied Leisure, Rank, Eldredge Pope and Hall & Woodhouse.

Prof. Membership: Law Society, International Visual Communications Association.

Career: Founder of the Bournemouth office of *Penningtons* (now *Fynn & Partners*) in 1969. Consulting Editor of Licensing Review. Lecturer at major seminars on Licensing and Planning subjects. Produced 'cassette law' audio series in collaboration with Oyez IBC and the Law Society and subsequently produced two Licensing videos. A third on the new Children's Certificates legislation was released late 1994 and has been widely acclaimed.

Personal: Born 14th April 1940. Attended Oratory School, Woodcote 1953-58. Leisure interests include writing, filming, photography, video, recording and editing music, squash and cricket. Trustee of the Myelin Project. Lives in Bournemouth.

Gaunt, John R.T.

John Gaunt & Partners, Sheffield (0114) 266 8664.

Specialisation: Main area of practising is licensing and leisure. Retained as regional licensing solicitor by a major brewer for 13 years. Has developed a wide client base, handling a number of important applications through the North and East Midlands. Also covers general commercial litigation, particularly in relation to the brewing and leisure industries and landlord and tenant matters. Has handled a number of high profile licensing applications, attracting significant media attention and coverage.

Prof. Membership: Law Society.

Career: Qualified in 1976. Became a Partner in Wake Smith & Co in 1977 and latterly a member of the firm's Management Committee.
Co-founded *John Gaunt & Partners*, a specialist commercial litigation and property practice in 1995.

Gilmour, John A.G.

McArthur Stanton, Dumbarton (01389) 762266. Partner in Licensing and Commercial Conveyancing Department. Offices in Clydebank, Dumbarton, Alexandria & Helensburgh.

Specialisation: Main area of practice is liquor licensing. Accredited by the Law Society of Scotland as a Specialist in Licensing. Main spheres of operation in tourist area of Dumbarton, Clydebank, Bearsden & Milngavie and Stirling & Argyll. Handles bookmakers applications, hot food licensing, gaming permits and other associated work.

Career: Qualified in 1961. Joined *McArthur Stanton* in 1962, becoming a Partner in 1966. President of Strathclyde Junior Chamber of Commerce 1972; Junior Chamber International Senator 1974; Director of Dumbarton District Enterprise Trust since 1985.

Personal: Born 17th November 1937. Attended Morrisons Academy, Crieff 1950-56, then Edinburgh University 1956-61. Honorary Sheriff at Dumbarton. Dean of Faculty of Dunbartonshire Solicitors 1988-90. Leisure interests include golf. Lives in Helensburgh.

Gover, Graham

Fynn & Partners, Bournemouth (01202) 551991. Associate in Environmental Licensing Department and Planning Department.

Specialisation: Main areas of practice are licensing and the leisure industry, including liquor, betting and gaming and public entertainment applications. With a background as a prosecutor and Local Authority solicitor, also conducts appeals and defends criminal proceedings in these subject areas and advises on planning, noise, environmental, health and safety and food safety issues. He is the regular writer on licensing topics for the Law Society Gazette and a regular speaker at training events and seminars.
Professional Membership: Law Society.

Career: LLB Brunel University. Qualified 1983. Magistrates Clerk 1980-1995. Prosecutor 1985-1988. Local Government Solicitor 1988-1993. Joined the Bournemouth office of *Penningtons* (now *Fynn & Parnters*) 1993, becoming Associate in 1994.

Personal: Born February 1957. Enjoys cinema, jazz music and being married. Lives in Poole.

Graham, Sandra D.

Fynn & Partners, Bournemouth (01202) 551991. Consultant in Environmental Licensing and Planning Department.

Specialisation: Main areas of practice are liquor and entertainment licensing for complete range of premises, betting and gaming licensing, public entertainment and other local authority licensing including cinemas and late night food premises and amusement centres. Advises on food health and safety. Particular experience of licensing issues relating to development of retail and leisure parks; licensing of new concept premises, sports and leisure related premises including league football club, golf clubs, ten-pin bowling centres, leisure centres, snooker clubs and holiday centres. Has represented major leisure plc from small limited company, with no licensing business, to national leisure status. Clients include major brewers and leisure operators. Experienced advocate before licensing committees of both Magistrates Courts and Local Authorities. Travels widely undertaking cases nationwide. Author of articles in numerous publications, correspondent to a catering magazine.

Professional Memberships: Food Law Group; Law Society.

Career: Qualified in 1984. Started career in pharmaceutical industry before obtaining law degree. Joined the Bournemouth office of *Penningtons*, then Ward Bowie, (now *Fynn & Partners*) in 1984 becoming a partner in 1987 and a consultant in 1993.

Personal: Leisure interests include squash, watersports, classical music, gardening and cake decorating. Member of British Sugar-craft Guild.

Green, Richard Leslie

Gosschalks, Hull (01482) 324252. Qualified 1969. Senior Partner 1993. Licensing & Leisure Department. Main area of practice is licensing and leisure work. Particular expertise in all matters relating to betting, gaming and liquor licensing. Joint Editor Patersons Licensing 1995. Born 18.8.1944.

Hall, Richard

Goodswens, Middlesbrough (01642) 218444. Partner in Commercial and Civil Litigation Department.

Specialisation: Principal area of practice is licensing and leisure. Deals with all aspects of liquor and entertainment licensing, gaming, sales and purchases of licensed premises and financing of operations. Clients include hotels, bars, public houses, off licences, social clubs, night-clubs, restaurants, casinos, sports and entertainment centres. Also handles civil litigation matters. Author of articles in various legal journals.

Prof. Membership: Lawyers for Licensing North.

Career: Qualified in 1970. Joined *Goodswens* in 1972, and became a Partner in 1973. Appointed Deputy District Judge in 1984.

Personal: Born 13th November 1945. Educated at Bradford Grammar School 1954-64 and Exeter University 1964-67. Leisure pursuits include chess. Lives in Castleton, North Yorkshire.

Hamilton, David J.

Cartwrights, Bristol (0117) 929 3601. Partner in Licensing Department.

Specialisation: Main area of practice is licensing, including applications for gaming, liquor, public entertainment, betting and similar licences, together with advice, assistance and representation in connection with existing licensed premises. Also provides advice and representation in connection with prosecutions of clients arising under consumer protection and in particular Food Safety Legislation. Joint author with Kerry Barker of 'Betting, Gaming and Lotteries'. (Fourmat Publishing 1993).

Career: Served in the Royal Navy for 3 years after leaving university, then pursued a career in industry. Studied for the Solicitors qualifying exam part-time 1973-76. Qualified and joined *Cartwrights* in 1976. Became a Partner in 1980.

Personal: Born 13th March 1934. Educated at Fitzwilliam House, Cambridge 1953-56 (MA Natural Sciences).

Havard, Michael Robin

Morgan Bruce, Cardiff (01222) 385385. Qualified 1981. Partner 1987. General Insurance Department. Born 7.5.1957.

Hay, David Leslie

Allan Janes, High Wycombe (01494) 521301. Qualified 1973. Partner 1978. Commercial and business services department. Main area of practice is liquor and betting licensing. Also handles planning and freehold and leasehold commercial property work. Born 2.6.1950.

Holland, Barry K.

Elliott & Company, Manchester (0161) 834 9933. Notary Public 1980. Partner in Licensing Department.

Specialisation: Acts for major off licence chains in England and Wales and for a national bookmaker. Also handles entertainment and liquor licensing for an international hotel chain. Other areas of practice are food safety and health and safety at work acting on a nationwide basis for national supermarket chains. Member of the national committee of the Food Law Group and co-ordinator of the enforcement sub-committee. Cases have included successful challenges of the liquor licensing policies of Sheffield and Birmingham, and the successful defence of a national supermarket chain in a substantial MAFF prosecution. Has lectured for the Law Society and given both in-house and client seminars on liquor, gaming licensing, food safety and health & safety.

Horne, Anthony

Davies Arnold Cooper, Manchester (0161) 839 8396.

Johnson, Christopher R.

A. Halsall & Co, Birkenhead (0151) 647 6323.

Johnston, Tom

Johnston & Herron, Lochgelly (01592) 780421. Qualified 1978. Partner 1979. Specialist in Liquor Licensing. Deals with purchase, sale and finance of licensed properties.

Jones, Simon David Allen

Cobbett Leak Almond, Manchester (0161) 833 3333. Qualified 1978. Partner 1982. Commercial Property Department. Also food, consumer protection, working standards and health and safety law.

Jordan, Anthony F.R.

Mills & Reeve, Norwich +44 (0) 1603 660155. Qualified 1960. Partner 1965. Litigation Department. Main areas of practice are professional indemnity and licensing and leisure. Born 21.7.1938.

Kefford, Alan

Howes Percival, Norwich (01603) 762103. Managing Partner for East Anglian offices and Head of firm's Liquor and Leisure Division.

Specialisation: Main area of practice covers all aspects of liquor and entertainment licensing. Also includes gaming matters. Addressed a number of seminars for representatives of the leisure industry.

Prof. Membership: Director of Anglian Archives plc and The Leisure Stop Ltd.

Personal: Born 1st May 1944. Attended Malvern College 1958-62, then University College, London 1963-66. Leisure pursuits include walking, running, cricket and Norwich City F.C. Lives in Norwich.

Lawson, Hamish K.

Cobbett Leak Almond, Manchester (0161) 833 3333. Partner in Commercial Property Department.

Specialiastion: Main area of practice is licensing. Acts for most of the breweries and major licensed retail operators represented in the north west, especially with regard to new site applications. Also handles food law, acting for two major national food manufacturers. Acted in Drury & Samuel Smith Old Brewery (Tadcaster) v. Scunthorpe Licensing Justices on surrender of licences. Firm advises North West Brewers and Licensed Retailers Association. Has addressed numerous conferences and seminars including 'The 24 Hour City' in Manchester in 1993.

Prof. Membership: Law Society of England and Wales, Manchester Law Society.

Career: Qualified in 1978. Joined *Cobbett Leak Almond* in 1976, becoming a Partner in 1981.

Personal: Born 23rd June 1951. Attended Oxford University 1969-72. Leisure interests include theatre (acting and directing) and sport. Lives in Bramhall, Cheshire.

Lawson, Peter J.

R. & J.M. Hill Brown & Co, Glasgow (0141) 332 3265. Partner in Licensing Department.

Specialisation: Principal area of practice is licensing. Deals with new license applications, provides an advice service to multiple operators and individuals, court representation (including trading standards, consumer protection, etc) and renewal/review service for existing clients. Also handles commercial/employment matters, providing a full commercial service, advice and representation in relation to employment law. Clients include most national brewers, supermarket chains and national entertainment companies. Has written various articles for trade magazines and lectured on Glasgow University Licensing Course. Co-presenter of licensing seminars throughout Scotland.

Prof. Membership: Law Society of Scotland.

Career: Qualified in 1981. Partner at *McSherry Halliday, Irvine* 1984-90. Joined *Hill Brown* as a Partner in 1990.

Personal: Born 25th March 1958. Educated at Peterhouse, Zimbabwe, Marr College, Troon and Glasgow University. Holds various directorships. Director of Tron Theatre, Glasgow. Leisure interests include theatre and skiing. Lives in Glasgow.

Loudon, John A.

J. & A. Hastie SSC, Edinburgh (0131) 556 7951. Senior Partner.

Specialisation: Main areas of practice are liquor licensing and gaming. Accredited as a specialist in liquor licensing by the Law Society of Scotland in July 1993. Also handles commercial work and intellectual property. Author of a number of articles on licensing matters in various journals. Lectures for Law Society, the University of Strathclyde, Law Society Update Courses and to other bodies.

Prof. Membership: SSC Society.

Career: Qualified in 1973. Joined *J.A. Hastie* in 1973, becoming a Partner in 1975 and Senior Partner in 1989.

Personal: Born 5th December 1949. Attended Edinburgh Academy 1955-68 and University of Dundee 1968-71. High Constable of Edinburgh. Member of Council of Law Society of Scotland. Leisure interests include skiing and shooting. Lives in Edinburgh.

Maciver, Archibald D.

Brunton Miller, Glasgow (0141) 337 1199. Partner.

Specialisation: Main area of practice is licensing. Extensive experience in all aspects of liquor licensing work. Also involved heavily in licensing under Civic Government (Scotland) Act such as public entertainment licences, street traders and late hours catering licences. Regular columnist in 'Scottish Licensed Trade News'. Has addressed many seminar groups on licensing matters.

Prof. Membership: Law Society of Scotland, Scottish Law Agents Society, Glasgow Bar Association.

Career: Qualified in 1982. Worked at *Levy & McRae* 1981-88, from 1984 as a Partner. Joined *Brunton Miller* in 1988 as a Partner. Accredited by the Law Society of Scotland as a Specialist in Liquor Licensing Law in 1993.

Personal: Born 13th December 1959. Attended Hutchesons' Grammar School 1972-77 and University of Strathclyde 1977-81. Leisure interests include sport (especially football), keeping fit, cinema and reading. Lives in Glasgow.

McLeod, David F.

Paull & Williamsons, Aberdeen (01224)

621621. Qualified 1978. Partner 1984. Commercial Property. Handles the purchase, sales and leasing of all types of commercial property.

Messent, Michael J.

Woodford & Ackroyd, Southampton (01703) 321000. Qualified 1971. Partner 1976. Licensing Department. Responsible for all aspects of licensing within the firm, with particular emphasis on betting licensing.

Morgan, David

Weightman Rutherfords, Liverpool (0151) 227 2601. Partner in Commercial Property Department.

Specialisation: Main area of practice is commercial property, acting for the leisure and drinks industry and for office and retail development. Also handles liquor licensing applications for on and off licences throughout the country. Gives regular seminars to main clients.

Prof. Membership: Law Society.

Career: Qualified in 1977, having joined *Weightman Rutherfords* in 1975. Became a Partner in 1979.

Personal: Born 2nd November 1952. Attended Newcastle-upon-Tyne University 1971-74. Leisure interests include golf and sailing. Lives in Birkenhead.

Morgan, Rosemary

Morgan Bruce, Cardiff (01222) 385385. Qualified 1964. Partner in Property Department. Born 15.3.1945.

Morton, Robin J.M.

Robin Morton Solicitors, Glasgow (0141) 248 7676. Partner in Licensing Department.

Specialisation: Handles liquor licensing, leisure and entertainment law. Acts for major organisations as well as individuals in obtaining and operating liquor licences, appearing at many boards throughout Scotland. Also acts for banks, purchasers and sellers in the property and commercial aspects relating to licensed premises. Has been involved in a number of reported cases, including one which resulted in a change of law (Mount Charlotte Investments v. City of Glasgow District Licensing Board). Accredited by the Law Society of Scotland as a specialist in liquor licensing. Regular contributor to 'Scottish Licensed Trade News' Legal Clinic. Frequently lectures on liquor licensing law and is a member of the Glasgow University Liquor Licensing Certificate teaching team.

Prof. Membership: Law Society of Scotland.

Career: Qualified in 1975. With *Brunton Miller,* Solicitors 1975-1978. Assistant Director of Legal Aid for the Hong Kong Government 1978-81. Partner with *Brunton Miller* 1981-88. Joined *McClure Naismith Anderson & Gardiner* as a partner in 1988, established *Robin Morton Solicitors* in 1995.

Personal: Born 1st October 1951. Educated

at Glasgow Academy 1961-69, then Glasgow University 1969-72. Leisure pursuits include music and football. Lives in Glasgow.

Nicholls, Simon J.

Howes Percival, Norwich (01603) 762103. Partner in Liquor and Licensing/Commercial Advocacy Division.

Specialisation: Principal area of practice is liquor and licensing acting for both private clients and companies in applications for and advice concerning liquor licenses, entertainment licenses, gaming applications and related matters. Other main area of practice is private client and company defence work including frauds, environmental health prosecutions, road traffic matters and defence work in relation to other criminal prosecutions, including defence advocacy. Has provided comment on specialist topics for press, radio and television.

Prof. Membership: Law Society.

Career: Qualified in 1979. Joined *Overbury Steward & Eaton*, Norwich in 1980 and became a Partner in 1985. Head of Criminal Litigation and Liquor and Licensing Department for 6 years. Joined *Howes Percival* as a Partner in April 1995.

Personal: Born 25th November 1955. Married with two small children. Leisure interests include skiing, mountain biking and running. Lives in Norwich.

Otto-Jones, John Alcwyn

Gaskell Rhys & Otto-Jones, Cardiff (01222) 225591.

Owen, Mark D.

Weightman Rutherfords, Liverpool (0151) 227 2601. Qualified 1987. Partner 1992. Licensing Department. Specialises in applications for off licences throughout the country. Also handles general liquor licensing, betting and gaming. Born 7.11.1961.

Palmer, Julia C.

Fynn & Partners, Bournemouth (01202) 551991. Partner in Environmental Licensing and Planning Department.

Specialisation: Main area of practice covers licensing work, from initial preparation through to advocacy before courts and committees. Experienced in applications for Gaming Permits and Part III Gaming Act Registration; Club Registration certificates; Betting Office licences and Bookmakers permits; Public Entertainment licences and Cinema Act licences. Also advises on late night food premises licensing, open air concerts and Goods Vehicle Operators licensing. Other area of practice is environmental law including applications for authorisation under the Environmental Protection Act, noise and other nuisance matters and Abatement Notice appeals and prosecutions. Advises on compliance with food law, especially the Food Safety Act 1990 and Regulations including Food Premises Registration; Health and Safety at Work Act 1974 etc. Also handles criminal law advocacy, including CPS agency and road traffic law. Has represented major leisure PLCs, breweries, companies managing public houses, one of the three major bookmakers and the largest Vineyard in the country, specialising in 'tailor made' licensing. Has obtained Full Justices on Licence for previously unlicensed premises within 22 days of instruction, as well as obtaining licences for major sports centres, leisure centres, holiday centres, cafe bars, public houses and off licences. Author of articles in numerous publications and has trained Justices in licensing law. Organises and addresses seminars and lectures in the fields of liquor licensing, health and safety requirements and Town and Country Planning matters.

Prof. Membership: UKELA. Lawyers Flying Association.

Career: Qualified in 1980. Court Clerk, Bournemouth Magistrates Court 1982-88. Joined the Bournemouth office of *Penningtons* in 1988 (now *Fynn & Partners*), becoming a Partner in 1991.

Personal: Born 11th April 1952. Leisure interests include gliding (Black Mountains Gliding Club), archery, clay pigeon shooting, walking, photography, classical music and crosswords. Lives in Bournemouth.

Parrott, Michael Kindersley

Cartwrights, Bristol (0117) 929 3601.

Specialisation: Partner specialising in all aspects of licensing law including liquor, entertainment and gaming licenses. Work also covers cinema licensing for major UK operators of multiplex cinemas. Practice involves applications for judicial review of interpretation and implementation of licensing justices' policy.

Career: Articles in Magistrates Courts Service, Cartwrights in 1985, appointed partner in 1987.

Personal: Educated at Exeter School 1965-71 and Leicester University 1972-1975. Leisure pursuits include squash, tennis, skiing and photography. Born 15th March 1953. Lives in Bristol.

Patrick, Colin

Lester Aldridge, Bournemouth (01202) 786161.

Specialisation: Chairman of the firm, partner and specialist in licensing law. Practice covers liquor, public entertainment, betting, gaming and licences for the celebration of marriages. Has written a number of articles on licensing matters for Hotel and Restaurant Association publications.

Prof. Membership: The Law Society.

Career: Qualified 1957. Partner, *Lester Aldridge* 1962. Chairman, *Lester Aldridge* since 1990.

Personal: Educated at Canford School, Wimborne 1948-1952. Law Society Finals 1957 (2nd Class honours). Hampshire Law Society Prize 1957. Bournemouth Law Society

Prize 1957. Trustee of the Bournemouth Orchestras Foundation. Governor of Canford School, Wimborne. President, Summer Music Society of Dorset. Leisure pursuits include music, theatre, food and wine, antiques, art, gardening, architecture, travel and the countryside. Born 28th August 1934. Lives in Poole, Dorset.

Pearce, John

Young & Pearce, Nottingham (0115) 959 8888. Partner in Licensing and Leisure and Commercial Department.

Specialisation: Experienced in licensing and leisure work involving public houses, clubs of all types, casinos, bingo halls, betting offices, leisure centres, off-licences and restaurants. Acts for major breweries and other PLCs in the East Midlands and elsewhere in the UK, as well as for many individuals and groups. Deals with acquisitions and sales of businesses as well as licensing. Has been involved in the licensing work for new public houses for major breweries, bingo halls, casinos and betting offices for other companies and individuals as well as other leisure complexes for golf, tennis and indoor cricket including the UK holiday villages for Center Parcs. Reviewed 'Betting, Gaming and Lotteries' by K. Barker and D.J. Hamilton. Has delivered various lectures and is available to address conferences and seminars.

Prof. Membership: Law Society, Nottinghamshire Law Society.

Career: Has been senior partner of *Young & Pearce* since qualifying in 1965. Member of the Young Solicitors Group London Committee 1970-77. Current President of the Nottinghamshire Law Society (1994-95).

Personal: Born 8th April 1940. Educated at Nottingham High School 1953-57. Chairman of Rufford Parish Council. Trustee of the Nottingham Union Rowing Club. Owner of 27 foot steam launch and 3 vintage tractors. Enjoys rowing, DIY, boating, painting and playing the drums. Lives in Rufford, near Newark.

Perraton, Stephanie

Edge & Ellison, Birmingham (0121) 200 2001.

Phillips, Jeremy

Eversheds, Bristol (0117) 9299555. Partner in Retail and Licensing Unit.

Specialisation: Main area of practice is licensing and leisure, acting on behalf of breweries, licensed property companies, independent operators, multiple specialist off licences and convenience stores throughout England and Wales. Also retail work, defending and advising companies concerning food safety, trades descriptions, weights and measures and environmental legislation. Regular contributor to legal journals concerning licensing matters. Conducts seminars on licensing law for national multiple operators, financial institutions and professional practices.

Prof. Membership: A.B.I.I.

Career: Partner in 1982, Co-founder of *Holt Phillips* in 1984.

Personal: Born 20th January 1954. Attended Harrow School 1967-71, then Southampton University 1972-75. Leisure time is devoted to family life. Lives in Orange End, outside Bristol.

Poppleston, Susanna

Poppleston Allen, Nottingham (0115) 953 8500. Partner and Co-founder.

Specialisation: Main area of practice is licensing and leisure. Work includes liquor, betting and gaming, public entertainment and pay parties. Legal correspondent and columnist for Licensee and Morning Advertiser, a trade paper for the licensed trade. Former Notts advocacy training officer; now advocacy trainer with the National Law Society. Major clients include European Leisure plc, First Leisure plc, Kingfisher Leisure plc, Luminar Leisure, Rank Leisure plc and Simpsons of Cornhill plc. Charge out rate is 120/hour.

Prof. Membership: Nottinghamshire Law Society (Former President), Law Society.

Career: LLB. Bristol 1969. Qualified in 1972. Articled at *Shacklocks* (subsequently merged with *Ashton Hill & Co.*) 1969-72, setting up own criminal department in 1972 and becoming a Partner in 1974. Set up and ran the first branch office in Nottingham. Co-founded *Temple Wallis* in 1979, which merged to create *Hunt Dickins* in 1987. First woman Vice-President of the Nottingham Law Students' Society. Co-founded *Poppleston Allen* in 1994.

Personal: Born 24th June 1948. Leisure interests include reading, cooking, fell walking and eating. Lives in Nottingham.

Potts, Andrew J.

Edge & Ellison, Birmingham (0121) 200 2001. Partner in Litigation Department.

Specialisation: Main area of practice is licensing: Head of a department of two associate partners and at least two other fee earners. Also handles employment law. Author of numerous articles in the professional press and has wide experience of addressing conferences and seminars.

Prof. Membership: Law Society, Birmingham Law Society.

Career: Qualified in 1971. Joined *Edge & Ellison* in 1970, becoming a Partner in 1976. Part time Industrial Tribunal Chairman since 1983.

Personal: Born 7th September 1944. Attended Aldewham School 1958-63 and Bristol University 1963-66. Leisure interests include tennis, hockey and cricket. Lives in Leamington Spa.

Radcliffe, Malcolm

Ironsides Ray & Vials, Leicester (0116) 251 5253. Partner in Licensing and Commercial Department.

Specialisation: Principal area of practice is licensing. Also handles commercial conveyancing. Acted for Leicestershire Police four years ago in revoking the licence for the largest night club in the city at that time ('Ritzy', owned by Rank Leisure) and about 18 months ago obtained the first full self-service supermarket off licence in the Chester Licensing Division. Major clients include Leicestershire Police; Aldi Stores; Leicester University and De Montfort University Student's Union. Has written a guide to the 1988 Licensing Act which was distributed to all major brewers and organisations in the leisure industry. Individual charge-out rate is normally £130 per hour.

Prof. Membership: Law Society, Solicitors Benevolent Association.

Career: Qualified in 1972. With *Ironsides Ray & Vials* (formerly *Ironsides*) since qualification. Became a Partner in 1974.

Personal: Born 22nd November 1948. Educated at Oakham School 1959-66. Parish Councillor and Vice Chairman of local primary school governors.

Science, Austen

Mincoff Science & Gold, Newcastle-upon-Tyne (0191) 281 6151. Managing Partner. Leisure Department Head.

Specialisation: Main area of practice is licensing, covering liquor licensing, gaming, amusements, and town and country planning. Also handles commercial property work. Acted in R v. Herrod, ex parte Leeds City District Council, a House of Lords decision on amusement premises; and R v. Newcastle upon Tyne Gaming Licensing Committee, ex parte Whiteheart Enterprises Ltd on the exhibition of statutory notices. Major clients include Rank, Mecca and Scottish & New-

castle. Editor of section on Clubs in Halsbury's Laws of England and Clubs and Betting and Gaming in Encyclopaedia of Forms and Precedents. Individual charge-out rate of £110 per hour.

Prof. Membership: Law Society Planning Panel, National Vice President of the British Amusement Caterers Trade Association.

Career: Qualified in 1961.

Personal: Born 11th August 1938. Attended Clifton College. Leisure interests include golf. Lives in Newcastle upon Tyne.

Shaw, Deborah

Edge & Ellison, Birmingham (0121) 200 2001.

Temperley, William B.

McKenzie Bell, Sunderland (0191) 567 4857. Partner in Licensing and Leisure Department.

Specialisation: Principal area of work covers liquor and public entertainment licensing including betting and theatre licences and all types of applications and offences under the Licensing Act 1964. Handles applications to Justices and local authorities and Appeals to Crown Court throughout five North Eastern counties. Other main area of work involves property matters relating to licensed premises. Handles objections and applications for late licences, revocations and opposed renewals on behalf of police and licensees.

Prof. Membership: Lawyers for Licensing North.

Career: Articled with *McKenzie Bell* and became a Partner in 1966.

Personal: Born 1940. Attended Bristol University 1958-61. Leisure pursuits include theatres and railways. Lives in Sunderland.

Wilson, Robin K.

Shacklocks, Nottingham (0115) 941 0789. Qualified 1970.

Young, David A.

Eversheds, Birmingham (0121) 233 2001. Partner in Litigation Department.

Specialisation: Main area of practice is liquor licensing, acting for retail and leisure clients. Work covers new licences, both on and off, revocations, structural alteration programmes and public entertainment licensing. Also handles general regulatory work including health and safety investigations, trading standards, food law, environmental health and environmental prosecutions. Examples of matters dealt with are the re-licensing of an international airport, a restaurant licence in a supermarket, major structural alterations programmes (several multi-site roll-out programmes) and petrol station forecourt shop off-licences. Is assisting Jeremy Phillips of *Eversheds* Bristol office as editor of a revised licensing guide (title to be confirmed). Speaker at in-house and external seminars and has appreared on local radio. Tends to work on a fee per project basis for licensing work (rather than an hourly rate).

Prof. Membership: Law Society, Food Law Group.

Career: Qualified in 1984. Became a Partner at *Eversheds* in 1993.

Personal: Born 11th October 1959. Educated at Solihull School 1971-78, University College, London 1978-81 and The College of Law, Chancery Lane 1981-82. Leisure time devoted to squash, family life and travel. Lives in Solihull.

EDITORIAL POLICY

Our policy is to identify leading practitioners entirely on merit. It is not possible to buy a place in our biographical lists: inclusion is based on a practitioner's expertise and professional reputation. The same applies to the lists of recommended law-firms and sets of chambers.

Enormous effort has been invested by our ten-strong research team (mainly solicitors and barristers) in canvassing recommendations and identifying leaders. We are confident in the overall accuracy of the results. However, mistakes and omissions are inevitable, and if readers have any suggestions regarding listings or rankings we should be very pleased to hear from them.

The lists will be revised on the basis of fresh research every year.

LITIGATION (COMMERCIAL)

ALMOST every law firm is capable of running a small contractual dispute for a client. This list is confined to firms and individuals that have a reputation for general heavyweight commercial litigation.

LONDON

Herbert Smith maintains its position as the pre-eminent commercial litigation firm in London, with a powerful team which, unusually, attracts clients purely for its litigation expertise. Charles Plant, David Gold (instructed in Tottenham Hotspur FC's Litigation against Terry Venables and the Football Association) and Lawrence Collins stand out as the firms leading lights. Other talented litigators include Julian Wilson, Campbell McLachlan and Ted Greeno, who recently conducted the 'Phillips v. BSkyB case'. The firm has recently handled some large and complex cases, most notably acting for Price Waterhouse in the BCCI litigation, Willis Corroon in the Kuwait Airways action and Quadrex in their appeal against a £180m damages award in favour of British & Commonwealth plc.

Linklaters & Paines and *Lovell White Durrant* emerge as *Herbert Smith's* closest rivals with large departments which operate as stand-alone profit centres.

Linklaters & Paines has three eminent practitioners in Christopher Style, Mark Humphries and Brinsley Nicholson. Diana Good, Kathryn Ludlow and John Turnbull are also highly regarded.

John Trotter is *Lovell White Durrant's* outstanding practitioner, Neil Fagan, Andrew Foyle (Hong Kong) and Russell Sleigh are also highly recommended.

Clifford Chance shows no signs of retreating from the forefront of the litigation scene. David Mayhew is one of the highest-ranked litigators and won a landmark victory for the Securities and Investments Board in an FSA case against Melton Medes Ltd, which was especially significant for the fact that Mayhew did the advocacy himself. Terry O'Neill (insurance litigation) and Tony Willis (financial and banking litigation) are also held in high regard.

The loss of Martin Hunter and Alan Redfern to the Bar has been a major loss to *Freshfields'* litigation department. Nevertheless, the firm remains prominent in the field with Paul Bowden and Paul Leonard both highly recommended.

Allen & Overy boasts London's top-ranked commercial litigator, David Mackie, and completes the 'big six' firms that stand head and shoulders above all others for commercial litigation in terms of the number of recommendations received.

Other well-regarded firms include *Norton Rose* where Michael Lee and Valerie Davies have been recommended, *Simmons & Simmons* (Paul Mitchard is well-respected in both litigation and ADR), *Stephenson Harwood* and *Slaughter and May*.

Other highly experienced individual practitioners include Robert Goldspink of *Denton Hall* and Alan Jenkins of *Frere Cholmeley Bischoff*.

LEADING FIRMS - LONDON

HERBERT SMITH	LINKLATERS & PAINES
LOVELL WHITE DURRANT	
ALLEN & OVERY	CLIFFORD CHANCE
FRESHFIELDS	

Smaller firms with dedicated litigation departments which featured prominently in our research include *Allison & Humphries,* which was involved in the high profile NRG case, *Barlow Lyde & Gilbert, Cameron Markby Hewitt, Ince & Co, Kennedys, Reynolds Porter Chamberlain* and *Mishcon de Reya* where Anthony Julius has been recommended.

HIGHLY REGARDED - LONDON

ASHURST MORRIS CRISP	DENTON HALL
D J FREEMAN	EVERSHEDS
FLADGATE FIELDER	FRERE CHOLMELEY BISCHOFF
LEWIS SILKIN	MANCHES & CO
McKENNA & CO	NORTON ROSE
PENNINGTONS	SIMMONS & SIMMONS
SLAUGHTER AND MAY	STEPHENSON HARWOOD
TRAVERS SMITH BRAITHWAITE	WILDE SAPTE
ALLISON & HUMPHREYS	BARLOW LYDE & GILBERT
BERRYMANS	CAMERON MARKBY HEWITT
CLYDE & CO	DAVIES ARNOLD COOPER
GOODMAN DERRICK	HAMLIN SLOWE
HOLMAN, FENWICK & WILLAN	INCE & CO.
KENNEDYS	MACFARLANES
MISHCON DE REYA	REYNOLDS PORTER CHAMBERLAIN
ALSOP WILKINSON	BAKER & McKENZIE
BEACHCROFT STANLEYS	BIDDLE & CO
BOWER COTTON & BOWER	BRECHER & CO
CHURCH ADAMS TATHAM	CLINTONS
CROSSMAN BLOCK	EDWIN COE
FORSYTE SAUNDERS KERMAN	FOX WILLIAMS
FRANKS, CHARLESLY	GOULDENS
GREGORY, ROWCLIFFE & MILNERS	HAMMOND SUDDARDS
HARBOTTLE & LEWIS	HARRIS ROSENBLATT & KRAMER
HOWARD KENNEDY	JEFFREY GREEN RUSSELL
KINGSFORD STACEY	LANE & PARTNERS
MACKRELL TURNER GARRETT	PICKERING KENYON
RAYNER, DE WOLFE	ROSLING KING
SEDDONS	SHERIDANS
STALLARDS	STRINGER SAUL
TARLO LYONS	WARNER CRANSTON
WEDLAKE BELL	ZAIWALLA & CO

In all the tables the names in each group are listed alphabetically.

SOUTH EAST

Blake Lapthorn, Cole and Cole, Cripps Harries Hall, Donne Mileham & Haddock and *Pitmans* have the largest litigation practices (in terms of size and workload) in the region.

Civil litigation comprises 36% of the workload of Hampshire firm *Blake Lapthorn,* which has a team of six specialist partners handling a variety of commercial disputes.

The litigation department at *Cole and Cole* in Oxford comprises four specialist partners who offer a range of services including construction, insurance, property, company and shareholder disputes.

Cripps Harries Hall's litigators, particularly known for construction and insurance matters, have recently conducted cases for a 'blue chip' construction company, a first-division assurance company and a major clearing bank.

Timothy Aspinall at *Donne Mileham & Haddock* heads a department which numbers 44 fee-earners operating from offices in Brighton, Crawley, Lewes and Worthing. In addition to handling general commercial disputes, the firm has developed specialist expertise in computer law, intellectual property, construction and insolvency and handles high profile cases for major clients in both the UK and abroad.

Pitmans, whose litigation department is largely known for representing clients in the hi-technology, construction and finance industries is also experienced in international trade.

Thomas Eggar Verrall Bowles (where commercial litigation makes up 18% of the firms practice) is also held in high regard.

Smaller firms with sound reputations in the field include *Buss Murton* in Tunbridge Wells, which has three full time specialists, and *Paris Smith & Randall* which was recently involved in the Obangi v. Stanborough Developments Ltd litigation.

SOUTH WEST

The leading litigation firms in Bristol are *Burges Salmon, Osborne Clarke* and *Wansbroughs Willey Hargrave.* Of this trio, *Osborne Clarke* is marginally ahead in terms of sheer expertise with a team of 13 specialist partners, five of whom operate from the London office. Robert Johnson, an aggressive negotiator, is the firm's leading light.

LEADING FIRMS – SOUTH WEST	
BURGES SALMON *Bristol*	**OSBORNE CLARKE** *Bristol*
LAYTONS *Bristol*	**WANSBROUGHS WILLEY HARGRAVE** *Bristol*

Burges Salmon is noted for its strength in depth and handles a variety of work, including partnership disputes, construction litigation and international contractual disputes. Adrian Llewelyn Evans is well respected.

Wansbroughs Willey Hargrave has 11 specialists within its litigation department and has developed a specialised loss unit to handle arson fraud investigations. *Laytons* was also consistently recommended and nudges at the shoulders of the 'big three' Bristol firms.

HIGHLY REGARDED – SOUTH WEST	
BOND PEARCE *Plymouth*	**LESTER ALDRIDGE** *Bournemouth*
TRETHOWANS *Salisbury*	**WILSONS** *Salisbury*
BEVAN ASHFORD *Bristol*	**CARTWRIGHTS** *Bristol*
CLARKE WILLMOTT & CLARKE *Taunton*	**DAVIES AND PARTNERS** *Gloucester*
EVERSHEDS *Bristol*	**FOOT & BOWDEN** *Plymouth*
LAWRENCE TUCKETTS *Bristol*	**LYONS DAVIDSON** *Bristol*
STEELE RAYMOND *Bournemouth*	**STEPHENS & SCOWN** *Exeter*
TRUMP AND PARTNERS *Bristol*	**VEALE WASBROUGH** *Bristol*
ANSTEY SARGENT & PROBERT *Exeter*	**BEVIRS** *Swindon*
CHARLES RUSSELL *Cheltenham*	**DICKINSON MANSER** *Poole*
HOOPER & WOLLEN *Torquay*	**LACEYS** *Bournemouth*
TOWNSENDS *Swindon*	**WOLFERSTANS** *Plymouth*

Other Bristol firms with experienced litigators include *Lawrence Tucketts, Lyons Davison* and *Veale Wasbrough.*

Further West, *Bond Pearce* handles a substantial number of cases and is regarded as the leading litigation firm outside Bristol. Simon Richardson is in the team that is especially well regarded for insurance, construction, property litigation and debt recovery.

LEADING INDIVIDUALS – SOUTH WEST
Robert I. Johnson *Osborne Clarke*
Adrian Llewelyn Evans *Burges Salmon*
Simon Richardson *Bond Pearce*

Commercial litgation comprises 22% of the workload at *Lester Aldridge,* one of the leading practices on the south coast. The firm has six partners handling a high volume of banking, financial and employment cases and is reported to have substantial overseas experience.

Other firms with experience in the field include *Trethowans* and *Wilsons* (both in Salisbury).

WALES

The four large Cardiff firms take the lion's share of work in this field. *Hugh James Jones and Jenkins* (universally recommended during our research) is particularly known for domestic and international insurance related litigation although the firm also has considerable expertise in construction, insolvency and partnership litigation. Michael Jefferies ranks high among the individual practitioners.

Morgan Bruce has a sizeable team which handles a substantial amount of general contract and commercial litigation although the department's reputation lies primarily in the field of insolvency. Phillip Howell-Richardson who heads the department is well respected by his competitors.

HIGHLY REGARDED – WALES	
EDWARDS GELDARD *Cardiff*	**EVERSHEDS** *Cardiff*
HUGH JAMES JONES & JENKINS *Cardiff*	**MORGAN BRUCE** *Cardiff*
BEVAN ASHFORD *Cardiff*	**CARTWRIGHTS ADAMS & BLACK** *Cardiff*
DOLMANS *Cardiff*	**DOUGLAS-JONES & MERCER** *Swansea*
GROSSMAN HERMER SELIGMAN *Cardiff*	**LEO ABSE & COHEN** *Cardiff*
LOOSEMORES *Cardiff*	
BEOR WILSON & LLOYD *Swansea*	

Edwards Geldard and *Eversheds* complete the quartet, both having experienced practitioners, Peter Jones at *Eversheds* is particularly highly recommended, and has a broad base of clients from within the region.

Of the smaller firms handling commercial litigation work, *Dolmans* and *Leo Abse & Cohen* are among the most highly experienced.

LEADING INDIVIDUALS – WALES
Philip Howell-Richardson *Morgan Bruce*
Michael G. Jefferies *Hugh James Jones & Jenkins*
Peter Jones *Eversheds*

MIDLANDS

Wragge & Co emerges as the most consistently recommended commercial litigation firm in the West Midlands, with twelve specialists who, in addition to servicing the firms corporate and property clients, also have a number of litigation-only clients. The litigation department, which already boasts highly recommended practitioners such as Quentin Poole, Richard Ellison and Nicola Mumford, has been further strengthened by the recent appointment of Paul Howard (formerly head of litigation at *Dibb Lupton Broomhead).*

LEADING FIRMS – MIDLANDS	
WRAGGE & CO *Birmingham*	
EDGE & ELLISON *Birmingham*	**EVERSHEDS** *Birmingham*
PINSENT CURTIS *Birmingham*	
BROWNE JACOBSON *Nottingham*	**GATELEY WAREING** *Birmingham*

Other highly recommended West Midlands firms include

Eversheds (Birmingham), *Edge & Ellison* and *Pinsent Curtis*.

Eversheds litigation department has created a number of product sub-groups such as property and construction, banking and insolvency, insurance and intellectual property, so tailoring the work to the needs of the client. In 1994, the firm conducted cases for a number of well known companies including Jaguar Cars, Mary Quant and Act Financial Systems Ltd. Sarah McKenna is well regarded. *Eversheds* Nottingham office is equally well known and conducts litigation on a national and international scale.

Edge & Ellison's litigation department numbers five specialists who represent clients such as the National Exhibition Centre, the Solicitors Indemnity Fund and Nottingham County Council. The firm recently acted in White v. Jones, a landmark case concerning the liability of solicitors in negligence to potential beneficiaries under a will. Digby Rose has been recommended.

HIGHLY REGARDED – MIDLANDS

MARTINEAU JOHNSON *Birmingham*	
ANTHONY COLLINS *Birmingham*	BLYTHE LIGGINS *Leamington Spa*
CARTWRIGHT & LEWIS *Birmingham*	CHALLINOR ROBERTS COOKSEY *Cradley Heath*
DIBB LUPTON BROOMHEAD *Birmingham*	FREETH CARTWRIGHT HUNT DICKINS *Nottingham*
HEWITSON BECKE+SHAW *Northampton*	HOWES PERCIVAL *Northampton*
IRWIN MITCHELL *Birmingham*	KEELY SMITH & JOBSON *Lichfield*
KENT JONES and DONE *Stoke-on-Trent*	REES EDWARDS MADDOX *Birmingham*
SHAKESPEARES *Birmingham*	SHOOSMITHS & HARRISON *Northampton*
FLINT, BISHOP & BARNETT *Derby*	OWSTONS *Leicester*

Pinsent Curtis handles litigation on both a domestic and international scale. Brian Hopkinson is particularly known for insurance and professional indemnity litigation.

Other West Midlands firms with excellent reputations include *Gateley Wareing, Martineau Johnson* and *Shakespeares*.

Both Northampton and Nottingham have a number of firms with substantial litigation departments. In Northampton, *Shoosmiths & Harrison, Hewitson Becke + Shaw* and *Howes Percival* all have experienced practitioners dealing with a variety of heavyweight contractual and commercial disputes.

In Nottingham, *Browne Jacobson* and *Freeth Cartwright Hunt Dickins* have respectable practices. *Challinor Roberts Cooksey* and *Kent Jones and Done* were also among the firms which were highly recommended.

LEADING INDIVIDUALS – MIDLANDS

Richard J. Ellison *Wragge & Co*
John Brian Hopkinson *Pinsent Curtis*
Paul Howard *Wragge & Co*
Brendan G. McGeever *Gateley Wareing*
Sarah L. McKenna (formerly Argyle) *Eversheds*
Quentin Poole *Wragge & Co*
Digby H. Rose *Edge & Ellison*
Andrew Nicolas Spooner *Martineau Johnson*

UP AND COMING

Nicola Mumford *Wragge & Co*

In all the tables the names in each group are listed alphabetically.

EAST ANGLIA

The two market leaders in East Anglia are *Eversheds* (Norwich) and *Mills & Reeve.*

Eversheds' litigation team provides a comprehensive service (from negotiating a settlement, to conducting High Court litigation) for its company clients. Paul Matthews, who specialises in insolvency litigation and Max Roessler, make their first appearances in our list.

LEADING FIRMS – EAST ANGLIA

EVERSHEDS *Norwich*	MILLS & REEVE *Norwich*
BIRKETTS *Ipswich*	GREENWOODS *Peterborough*
LEATHES PRIOR *Norwich*	MERRICKS *Ipswich*
PRETTYS *Ipswich*	

HIGHLY REGARDED – EAST ANGLIA

HEWITSON BECKE + SHAW *Cambridge*	HOWES PERCIVAL *Ipswich*

Mills & Reeve boasts Edward Callaghan, East Anglia's pre-eminent litigator, who is equally well known for banking, insolvency and construction litigation.

Other highly recommended firms include *Birketts*, where Robert Wright has been recommended, *Greenwoods, Leathes Prior, Merricks* and *Prettys,* where Peter Blake is highly regarded.

LEADING INDIVIDUALS – EAST ANGLIA

Peter Blake *Prettys*
Edward J. Callaghan *Mills & Reeve*
Paul Matthews *Eversheds*
Max Roessler *Eversheds*
Robert J. Wright *Birketts*

NORTH WEST

In Manchester, the leading commercial litigation firms include *Addleshaw Sons & Latham, Alsop Wilkinson, Halliwell Landau* and *Eversheds.*

Addleshaw Sons & Latham covers the whole range of commercial litigation including general contract, construction and property. John Gatenby (particularly known for disputes with an international flavour) and John Gosling are experienced practitioners.

Nigel Kissack and the litigation team at *Alsop Wilkinson* advise on disputes arising out of corporate and commodities transactions, in addition to litigating on a variety of breach of contract, sale of goods and shareholder claims for corporate and personal clients. Tony Winterburn has been described as a rising star.

The team of four specialist partners at *Halliwell Landau* handle building disputes, bond and surety claims, guarantees, shareholder and partnership disputes, agency distribution and general contract disputes. The firm has recently been involved in a number of major cases, most notably 'Perar v. General Surety & Guarantee Co Ltd' (Court of Appeal) and 'Trafalgar House v. General Surety & Guarantee Co Ltd', at the House of Lords at the time of going to print. Paul Thomas is held in high regard.

LEADING FIRMS – NORTH WEST	
ADDLESHAW SONS & LATHAM *Manchester*	ALSOP WILKINSON *Liverpool*
EVERSHEDS *Manchester*	HALLIWELL LANDAU *Manchester*
COBBETT LEAK ALMOND *Manchester*	DAVIES WALLIS FOYSTER *Liverpool*
HILL DICKINSON DAVIS CAMPBELL *Liverpool*	LACE MAWER *Manchester*

Eversheds' litigation department covers the whole spectrum of litigation services for banking and corporate clients. The firm also represents a number of educational establishments and local authorities. Antony Gold, (Chairman of the *Eversheds* national litigation group) and Mark Mattison, who heads the department in Manchester, are both highly recommended.

HIGHLY REGARDED – NORTH WEST	
AARON & PARTNERS *Chester,,*	BERG & CO *Manchester*
BERMANS *Liverpool*	BRABNER HOLDEN BANKS WILSON *Liverpool*
CHAFFE STREET *Manchester*	CUFF ROBERTS *Liverpool*
DIBB LUPTON BROOMHEAD *Manchester*	HAMMOND SUDDARDS *Manchester*
KUIT, STEINART, LEVY *Manchester*	SLATER HEELIS *Manchester*
TAYLORS *Blackburn*	
DAVIES ARNOLD COOPER *Manchester*	VAUDREYS *Manchester*

Other firms in Manchester with strong litigation practices include *Cobbett Leak Almond, Davies Arnold Cooper* and *Slater Heelis.*

In Liverpool, *Davies Wallis Foyster, Hill Dickinson Davis Campbell* and *Lace Mawer* (where litigation is 60% of the total workload) all have excellent litigation departments which are able to provide a broad range of services for clients in the public and private sectors. Edward Bootland and Christopher Sorrell at *Davis Wallis Foyster* was highly recommended.

Individual litigators who featured heavily in our research include Ian Tranter at *Chaffe Street* and Robert Moss at *Vaudreys.*

LEADING INDIVIDUALS – NORTH WEST
Edward Tjorn Bootland *Davies Wallis Foyster*
John Gatenby *Addleshaw Sons & Latham*
Antony Gold *Eversheds*
John A. Gosling *Addleshaw Sons & Latham*
Nigel J. Kissack *Alsop Wilkinson*
Mark Mattison *Eversheds*
Robert J. Moss *Vaudreys*
Rodger J. Pannone *Pannone & Partners*
R.A. Roper *Cobbett Leak Almond*
Paul M.A. Rose *Halliwell Landau*
Christopher R.J. Sorrell *Davies Wallis Foyster*
Paul A. Thomas *Halliwell Landau*
Ian Victor Keith Tranter *Chaffe Street*

UP AND COMING
Tony Winterburn *Alsop Wilkinson*

NORTH EAST

Booth & Co, Dibb Lupton Broomhead, Eversheds and *Hammond Suddards* take the lion's share of contentious work in Leeds.

Booth & Co's litigation department, whilst relatively small (the highly regarded John Priestley and one other partner undertake the majority of the work), has been involved in some high value cases in the past 12 months. The firm has also developed a credit managment services department which offers a debt recovery service as an alternative to litigation.

LEADING FIRMS – NORTH EAST	
BOOTH & CO. *Leeds*	DIBB LUPTON BROOMHEAD *Bradford*
EVERSHEDS *Leeds*	HAMMOND SUDDARDS *Leeds*

Dibb Lupton Broomhead is particularly known for engineering litigation and building society work (Andrew Chappell has been recommended).

Eversheds has the largest litigation department in the region with 12 partners who handle a large number of heavyweight cases for manufacturing, industrial and financial sector clients. The firm's reputation is such that it attracts work from outside the region and has recently been instructed on an international level.

HIGHLY REGARDED – NORTH EAST	
ANDREW M. JACKSON *Hull*	DICKINSON DEES *Newcastle*
EVERSHEDS *Newcastle*	FORD AND WARREN *Leeds*
HAY & KILNER *Newcastle*	IRWIN MITCHELL *Sheffield*
LUPTON FAWCETT *Leeds*	PINSENT CURTIS
READ HIND STEWART *Leeds*	WALKER MORRIS *Leeds*
WANSBROUGHS WILLEY HARGRAVE *Leeds*	
BROOKE NORTH AND GOODWIN *Leeds*	DENISON TILL *York*
GORDONS WRIGHT & WRIGHT *Bradford*	GOSSCHALKS *Hull*
LINSLEY & MORTIMER *Newcastle*	McCORMICKS *Leeds*
STAMP JACKSON & PROCTER *Hull*	TEEMAN LEVINE *Leeds*

Hammond Suddards also has a substantial department dealing with major commercial litigation in the UK and overseas. Other highly recommended firms include *Pinsent Curtis* and *Walker Morris.*

Smaller Leeds firms with sound reputations in the field include *Ford & Warren, Lupton Fawcett* and *Read Hind Stewart.*

In Newcastle, the litigation departments at *Dickinson Dees* and *Eversheds* are held in high regard. Both firms handle a broad spectrum of work, offering advice mainly to corporate clients on heavyweight contractual litigation, including construction.

Other notable firms in the region include *Irwin Mitchell* in Sheffield and *Andrew M. Jackson* in Hull.

LEADING INDIVIDUALS – NORTH EAST
Andrew Geoffrey Chappell *Dibb Lupton Broomhead*
John H.G. Heller *Hammond Suddards*
John C. Priestley *Booth & Co.*

In all the tables the names in each group are listed alphabetically.

SCOTLAND

The premier commercial litigation firms in Scotland include *Dundas & Wilson WS, Maclay Murray & Spens, McGrigor Donald* and *Simpson & Marwick WS*.

LEADING FIRMS – SCOTLAND

DUNDAS & WILSON CS Edinburgh	**MACLAY MURRAY & SPENS** Glasgow
McGRIGOR DONALD Glasgow	**SIMPSON & MARWICK WS** Edinburgh
W & J BURNESS WS Edinburgh	**SHEPHERD & WEDDERBURN** Edinburgh

All conduct a high volume of contentious work for their corporate and commercial clients; *McGrigor Donald* is particularly strong in the construction field, whilst *Simpson & Marwick WS* is renowned for insolvency work. Peter Anderson and Michael Wood, both of *Simpson & Marwick WS* were universally recommended.

HIGHLY REGARDED – SCOTLAND

BALFOUR & MANSON Edinburgh	**BIGGART BAILLIE & GIFFORD** Glasgow
BIRD SEMPLE Glasgow	**BISHOP AND ROBERTSON CHALMERS** Glasgow
BRECHIN ROBB Glasgow	**BRODIES WS** Edinburgh
DORMAN JEFFREY & CO Glasgow	**FYFE IRELAND** Edinburgh
MACROBERTS Glasgow	**MORTON FRASER MILLIGAN** Edinburgh
PAULL & WILLIAMSONS Aberdeen	**TODS MURRAY WS** Edinburgh
AITKEN NAIRN WS Edinburgh	**ANDERSON FYFE** Glasgow
BOYDS Glasgow	**HENDERSON BOYD JACKSON** Edinburgh
KIDSTONS & CO Glasgow	**RAEBURN CHRISTIE** Aberdeen
STRONACHS Aberdeen	**TINDAL OATTS** Glasgow
WRIGHT, JOHNSTON & MACKENZIE Glasgow	

Other highly recommended firms include *Brodies WS* (and in particular David Williamson), *W & J Burness WS* and *Shepherd & Wedderburn* where David Murby is held in high regard.

LEADING INDIVIDUALS – SCOTLAND

M.Peter Anderson Simpson & Marwick WS
James M. Arnott MacRoberts
J. Neil Cochran Dundas & Wilson CS
Kenneth M. Cumming Steedman Ramage WS
Ian J. Cuthbertson Dorman Jeffrey & Co

Neil Douglas Brechin Robb
Ian G. Inglis Maclay Murray & Spens
John A.D. Innes Dundas & Wilson CS
David F. Murby Shepherd & Wedderburn
Alayne Swanson Dundas & Wilson CS
David S. Williamson Brodies WS
Michael M. Wood Simpson & Marwick WS

NORTHERN IRELAND

Litigation is a key area for the major commercial firms in the province. *McKinty & Wright, C & H Jefferson, Elliott Duffy Garrett* and *Mills Selig* enjoy particularly strong reputations for their expertise in this field. At *McKinty & Wright* Owen Catchpole is a well-known specialist. At *C & H Jefferson* Ian Jefferson and Kenneth Rutherford act for large commercial and industrial clients involved in aircraft manufacture, ship-building, engineering, manufacturing and bio-chemical and textile industries. Michael Lynch at *Elliott Duffy Garrett* is known for his commercial litigation work. Brian Ham and Jeremy Mills at *Mills Selig* are also highly regarded.

Other firms which are highly esteemed for their litigation work include *Tughan & Co, Carson & McDowell, L'Estrange & Brett, Johns Elliot, Cleaver Fulton & Rankin* and *Francis Hanna & Co*.

HIGHLY REGARDED – NORTHERN IRELAND

ELLIOTT DUFFY GARRETT Belfast	**C & H JEFFERSON** Belfast
JOHNSONS Belfast	**McKINTY & WRIGHT** Belfast
MILLS SELIG Belfast	
C & J BLACK Belfast	**CARSON & McDOWELL** Belfast
CLEAVER FULTON & RANKIN Belfast	**FRANCIS HANNA & CO** Belfast
JOHNS ELLIOT Belfast	**L'ESTRANGE & BRETT** Belfast
TUGHAN & CO Belfast	

LEADING INDIVIDUALS – NORTHERN IRELAND

Michael P. Lynch Elliott Duffy Garrett
Owen Catchpole McKinty & Wright
Jeremy V.S. Mills Mills Selig
H.L. Ian Jefferson C & H Jefferson
Brian E. Ham Mills Selig
Kenneth Rutherford McKinty & Wright

LEADERS IN LITIGATION (COMMERCIAL)

LONDON

Anderson, Harry R.A.
Herbert Smith, London (0171) 374 8000. Partner in Commercial Litigation Department.

Specialisation: Heads one of the firm's general commercial litigation sections with substantial experience in litigation arising out of corporate transactions, such as claims for misrepresentation and breach of warranty.

Career: Joined *Herbert Smith* as an articled clerk in 1968. Qualified 1970. Partner since 1976.

Personal: Educated at Jesus College, Cambridge.

Archer, Nick J.
Slaughter and May, London (0171) 600 1200. Qualified 1981. Partner 1988. Litigation Department. Wide experience of handling major and complex domestic and international disputes. Born 1956.

Bowden, Paul
Freshfields, London (0171) 936 4000. Partner in Litigation Department.

Specialisation: Main area of practice is environmental litigation, acting for corporate defendants and their insurers. Acted for the defence in Merlin v. BNFL, Gillingham BC v. Medway (Chatham) Dock Co. Ltd, Sellafield and Dounreay Leukaemia Cases and THORP Judicial Reviews. An author and editor of 'Tolley's Environmental Law

Handbook' and contributor to 'Transnational Rules in International Commercial Arbitration'.

Prof. Membership: Advisory Board, Centre of Advanced Litigation;, Joint Bar/ Law Society Working Party on Civil Justice (1992-93); United Kingdom Environmental Law Association Practice and Procedure Working Group; International Nuclear Lawyers Association; Associate of Chartered Institute of Arbitrators.

Career: Qualified in 1981, having joined *Freshfields* in 1978. Became a Partner in 1987, having spent 1984-87 in the Singapore office. Also qualified as a Solicitor in Hong Kong in 1986.

Personal: Born 30th July 1955. Attended Bristol University, 1973-78.

Collins, Lawrence A.
Herbert Smith, London (0171) 374 8000. Partner in Commercial Litigation Department.

Specialisation: Leading practitioner in the field of international commercial litigation with particular emphasis on banking questions, competition and securities law, commercial fraud and arbitration. He has advised and represented several foreign governments and has rights of audience in the higher courts. He is general editor of 'Dicey and Morris on the Conflict of Laws' (12th edition, 1993).

Career: Qualified 1968. Partner at *Herbert Smith* since 1971.

Personal: Educated at Cambridge University and Columbia University, New York.

Davies, Valerie E.M.
Norton Rose, London (0171) 283 6000. Qualified 1979. Partner 1986. Commercial Litigation Department. Specialises in banking, insolvency and international litigation. Born 20.10.1952.

Fagan, N.J.
Lovell White Durrant, London (0171) 236 0066. Qualified 1971. Partner 1975. Litigation Department. Specialises in large corporate financial/ commercial litigation. Born 5.6.1947.

Foyle, Andrew W.
Lovell White Durrant, London (0171) 236 0066. Qualified 1974. Partner 1982. Principal area of practice is commercial litigation and arbitration.

Gold, David L.
Herbert Smith, London (0171) 374 8000. Qualified 1975. Partner 1983. Litigation Department. Handles general commercial litigation, company/partnership disputes, local authority law, computer law and injunctions. Born 1.3.1951.

Goldspink, Robert
Denton Hall, London (0171) 242 1212. Partner in Litigation Department.

Specialisation: Main areas of practice are international commercial litigation and arbitration. Has particular experience in advising companies who have been the victims of fraud on how to handle the issues arising and recover their losses. Has acted in cases including Alexander Howden, PCW, Lloyds litigation, Lonrho v. Fayed, and 'Operation Cheetah' (Liverpool and Derek Hatton). Member of joint working party of the general counsel of the Bar and the Law Society which in 1993 reviewed Britain's civil courts and made wide ranging recommendations for the reform of the English Civil Litigation process. Member of the 'Mariott' committee which produced draft legislation for the reform of British arbitration law, eventually taken up by the DTI. Member of the Advisory Board of the Centre of Advanced Litigation of Nottingham Law School. Advisory Committee Member of the International Litigation Practitioners' forum. Visiting lecturer at the University of Richmond, Virginia. Teaches law regularly at conferences and seminars .

Prof. Membership: City of London Law Society, London Litigation Solicitors' Association.

Career: Qualified in 1975. Joined *Denton Hall* in 1980, becoming a Partner in 1981.

Personal: Born 8th August 1949. Attended Eltham College 1959-67, then Cambridge University 1968-72 (receiving an MA & LLM). Leisure interests include gardening, fishing and watersports. Lives in Brampton, Cambs.

Good, Diana
Linklaters & Paines, London (0171) 606 7080. Qualified 1981. Partner 1988. Litigation Department. Deals with a range of commercial disputes including banking, insurance and tax litigation.

Grandison, Richard
Slaughter and May, London (0171) 600 1200. Qualified 1978. Partner specialising in commercial litigation and commercial judicial review.

Greeno, Ted
Herbert Smith, London (0171) 374 8000. Partner in Commercial Litigation Department.

Specialisation: Wide range of experience in both litigation and arbitration work spanning a number of commercial, industrial and professional sectors including the energy industry, engineering and construction, media, product liability and accountancy.

Career: Qualified 1983. Partner at *Herbert Smith* since 1989.

Personal: Educated at King's College, London.

Handler, Thomas J.
See under Environmental Law.

Harris, Graham
Richards Butler, London (0171) 247 6555.

Humphries, Mark
Linklaters & Paines, London (0171) 606 7080.

James, Simon
Clifford Chance, London (0171) 600 1000. Partner 1992. Litigation Department. Handles a range of commercial litigation, particularly banking, financial and regulatory litigation.

Jenkins, Alan D.
Frere Cholmeley Bischoff, London (0171) 615 8000. Former Head of Litigation.

Specialisation: Main area of practice is commercial litigation. Includes professional negligence, fraud, banking, breach of warranty, insurance/ reinsurance, Lloyd's work and unfair prejudice. Environmental law work also undertaken. Acted in BCCI-related litigation; Harrods (Buenos Aires) Ltd; Elton John v. Dick James Music and Alexander Howden-related litigation.

Prof. Memberships: Law Society, IBA (Committee on Environment, Committee on International Litigation), UIA, London Solicitors Litigation Association, RIIA, FRSA.

Career: Articled at *Frere Chomeley*, qualified 1977. Partner 1983. Previously Head of Litigation Department. Head of Environmental Group 1991.

Personal: Born 27th May 1952. Attended New College, Oxford.

Julius, Anthony
Mishcon De Reya, London (0171) 405 3711.

Kelly, Jonathan P.
Simmons & Simmons, London (0171) 628 2020. Partner in Commercial Litigation Department.

Specialisation: Main areas of practice are banking and financial services litigation, specialising in securities, commodities and derivatives disputes, and regulatory issues arising in these areas. Has also had broad experience of large scale commercial fraud actions. Further area of specialism is defamation with experience of advising both publisher defendants and a wide range of plaintiffs. Has handled securities and commodities disputes and regulatory investigations arising under The Financial Services Act, interest rates swaps litigation and claims of multi-jurisdictional international commercial fraud. Clients include UK, US and European commercial and investment banks, investment institutions, brokers and commodity houses and, in relation to defamation, UK public companies and Lloyd's insurers, foreign multi-nationals and international sports bodies and personalities.

Prof. Membership: Law Society, Society of

English and American Lawyers.

Career: Qualified in 1989 after articles at *Simmons & Simmons*. Became a Partner in 1995.

Personal: Born 11th August 1964. Educated at Stonyhurst College 1972-82, Balliol College, Oxford 1983-86 and The College of Law, Lancaster Gate, 1986-87. Leisure pursuits include salmon fishing, squash and tennis. Lives in Notting Hill, London.

Langton, Tim

Goodman Derrick, London (0171) 404 0606. Qualified 1978. Partner. Specialises in Commercial Litigation. Born 25.7.1953.

Lee, Michael J.A.

Norton Rose, London (0171) 283 6000. Qualified 1966. Partner 1973. Commercial Litigation Department. Main area of practice is international commercial arbitration and commercial and banking litigation. Born 22.6.1942.

Leonard, P.M.

Freshfields, London (0171) 936 4000. Qualified 1966. Partner 1972. Litigation Department. Handles general commercial, construction and engineering, insurance, commodities, insolvency and banking disputes. Also deals with private and public international law. Born 14.1.1942.

Ludlow, Kathryn

Linklaters & Paines, London (0171) 606 7080. Qualified 1988. Assistant Solicitor. Litigation Department. Work includes professional negligence, banking, DTI and disciplinary investigations.

Mackie, David L.

Allen & Overy, London (0171) 330 3000. Qualified 1971. Partner 1975. Head of Litigation Department. Covers all commercial disputes, with emphasis on banking, defence, energy, insurance and manufacturing. Advocate authorised to appear in High Courts. Recorder. Born 1946.

Mayhew, David

Clifford Chance, London (0171) 600 1000. Partner in the Litigation Department. Qualified in 1983.

McLachlan, Campbell A.

Herbert Smith, London (0171) 374 8000. Partner in Commercial Litigation Department.

Specialisation: Specialises in international commercial litigation including multi-national fraud, cross-border banking, international commercial arbitration and public and private international law. He is joint editor of *International Litigation News*, newsletter of the IBA Committee on International Litigation, and Rapporteur of the ILA Committee on the same subject.

Career: Qualified New Zealand 1984 and England and Wales 1991. Partner at *Herbert Smith* since 1992.

Personal: Educated at Victoria University of Wellington, New Zealand, the University of London and Hague Academy of International Law (Diploma cum laude).

Mitchard, Paul

Simmons & Simmons, London (0171) 628 2020. Head of Litigation.

Specialisation: Main areas of practice are international arbitration and litigation, covering the conduct of ICC, LCIA, RSA, Lloyd's arbitrations and commercial and financial disputes in the High Court in London. Also handles dispute resolution and mediation. Accredited CEDR mediator, member of CPR's panel of distinguished neutrals and a Fellow of the Chartered Institute of Arbitrators. Has represented domestic and international companies and State organisations in a number of major disputes. Has given seminars in Houston, Atlanta, Charlotte, Washington, Philadelphia and New York on international arbitration.

Prof. Membership: Law Society, American Bar Association, International Bar Association, City of London Solicitors' Company.

Career: Qualified in 1977. Worked at *Slaughter and May* 1977-84 in London and Hong Kong. Joined *Simmons & Simmons* in 1984, becoming a Partner in 1985 and Head of Litigation in 1994.

Personal: Born 2nd January 1952. Attended Taunton School 1960-70 and Lincoln College Oxford 1971-4. Leisure interests include squash, reading and walking. Lives in Amersham, Bucks.

Neate, Francis W.

Slaughter and May, London (0171) 600 1200. Qualified 1966. Partner since 1972. Head of litigation department. Wide experience of handling major and complex domestic and international disputes.

Nicholson, Brinsley

Linklaters & Paines, London (0171) 606 7080. Qualified 1971. Partner and head of the Litigation Department. Practice covers commercial litigation and arbitration including insolvency, financial services, investigations, banking and white collar crime. Born 11.4.1945.

O'Neill, Terry

See under Insurance & Reinsurance.

Plant, Charles W.

Herbert Smith, London (0171) 374 8000. Qualified 1969. Partner 1976. Head of Litigation Department. Work covers commercial litigation with an emphasis on media, oil and gas and construction industries. Born 1944.

Rink, John S.

Allen & Overy, London (0171) 330 3000. Qualified 1970. Managing Partner 1994. Litigation Department. Practice covers general commercial litigation including banking.

Born 25.10.1946.

Rochez, Nicholas

Davies Arnold Cooper, London (0171) 936 2222. Qualified 1979. Partner 1984. Managing Partner 1987-1992. Senior Litigation Partner. Specialist in insurance, reinsurance and employment law. Born 13.11.1954.

Rogan, P.J.H.

See under Insurance & Reinsurance.

Ryan, Kevin

Denton Hall, London (0171) 242 1212. Partner in Litigation Department.

Specialisation: Handles a range of commercial litigation, particularly in insurance and reinsurance. Also experienced in crisis management, professional negligence, fraud, environmental law and satellite communications.

Career: Qualified as a solicitor in New South Wales, Australia in 1980, and as a solicitor and barrister in Northern Territory Australia in 1982. Associate Partner *Hunt & Hunt*, Sydney, Australia 1984. Qualified in England and Wales in 1986. Joined *Denton Hall* in 1985 and became a Partner in 1988.

Personal: Born 6th December 1954. Educated at St Joseph's and Holy Cross, Sydney and the University of New South Wales 1972-77 (BA, Commerce, BA Law). Director and past President Australian Business in Europe.

Sandelson, Jeremy

See under Crime: Fraud.

Sigler, Peter

Nabarro Nathanson, London (0171) 493 9933. Qualified 1975. Partner 1982. Head of Litigation Department. Main area of practice is commercial litigation, including insolvency. Born 3.10.1948.

Skrein, Michael

Richards Butler, London (0171) 247 6555. Partner and Head of Commercial Litigation Group.

Specialisation: Work is mainly litigation, but also advisory, particularly in relation to insurance and also clearance work for broadcasting. Specialist areas of work include aviation, contempt of court, defamation, insurance, intellectual property (copyright, the law of confidence, patents, registered and unregistered trade marks) and judicial review. Has years of experience in the aviation, food and drink, insurance and media industries as well as many other areas of life after about 20 years as a litigation partner in a firm with very broad and notably international scope of practice.

Prof. Membership: Law Society; City of London Solicitors' Company; The City of London Solicitors' Company; 'Copinger Society', the Baltic Exchange.

Career: Articled *Richards Butler* 1971; qualified 1973; partner since 1976; head of litigation department 1990; lectured on copyright, trade libel and trademarks, chair of the 'Protecting the Media' series of conferences.

Personal: Born 1947. Educated at Oxford University (MA, Modern History) and the University of Southern California (MA, International Relations). Honor Society of Phi Kappa Phi.

Sleigh, Russell H.P.
Lovell White Durrant, London (0171) 236 0066. Qualified 1973. Partner, 1980. Litigation Department. Handles wide range of international commercial litigation; also handles media law issues.

Smart, Robert Tyndall
Dibb Lupton Broomhead, London (0171) 600 0202.

Stebbings, Simon Brent
Freshfields, London (0171) 936 4000. Partner. Member of Construction & Engineering and International Arbitration Groups.

Specialisation: Principal area of practice is construction disputes, acting for owners, contractors, designers and other professionals in all forms of disputes arising out of construction projects, particularly in the civil and process engineering industries. Other main area of practice is international commercial arbitration, advising and representing clients involved in commercial arbitrations, particularly those arising out of the construction industry.

Prof. Membership: Singapore Institute of Arbitrators.

Career: Qualified in 1983. Qualified Hong Kong in 1986. Partner at *Freshfields* since 1990.

Personal: Born 31st March 1958. Educated at St Albans School 1970-76 and Worcester College, Oxford 1977-80 (BA Hons in Jurisprudence). Recreations include clay pigeon shooting, running and scuba diving. Lives in St Albans.

Style, Christopher J.D.
Linklaters & Paines, London (0171) 606 7080. Qualified 1979. Joined 1977. Commercial litigation specialist, covering banking disputes and capital market problems, including defaults, reschedulings, state immunity and expropriation, investigations, disciplinary proceedings and jurisdictional issues. Also handles international arbitration.

Taylor, Ian
Freshfields, London]. Partner in Litigation Department.

Specialisation: Main area of practice is commercial litigation, particularly in relation to fraud and asset recovery. Represented the defendant in Armagas Ltd v. Mundogas SA ('The Ocean Frost'), and the plaintiff in Arab Monetary Fund v. Hashim. Represented clients in various DTI/ SFO cases, including the inquiries into Guinness, County Nat West (Blue Arrow) and House of Fraser. Author of

'Inquiries under S.432 (2) Companies Act 1985' in 'Banks and Remedies'.

Prof. Membership: Law Society; Member of Commercial Court Committee.

Career: Qualified in 1976, having joined *Freshfields* in 1974. Became a Partner in 1982 and Head of Litigation Department in 1991.

Personal: Born 20th June 1951. Attended Gonville & Caius College, Cambridge 1969-73. Lives in London.

Terry, Ian K.
Freshfields, London (0171) 936 4000. Partner in Litigation Department.

Specialisation: Specialises in commercial litigation and arbitration, particularly in relation to corporate finance, banking and insurance matters. Cases include representing Society of Lloyd's in Central Fund recovery litigation, co-ordinating U.S. proceedings on behalf of provisional liquidators of BCCI, representing Bank of England in case to recover stolen banknotes and representing defendant in Kleinwort Benson v. Malaysia Mining Corporation.

Career: Articled at *Freshfields* and qualified in 1980. Partner in 1986.

Personal: Born 26th July 1955. Educated at Leeds Grammar School 1963-73 and Keble College, Oxford 1973-77. Leisure interests include tennis, golf, skiing and opera. Lives in London.

Trotter, John G.
Lovell White Durrant, London (0171) 236 0066. Qualified 1977. Specialises in insurance and reinsurance dispute resolution, including professional negligence and media law.

Turnbull, John W.
Linklaters & Paines, London (0171) 606 7080. Qualified 1982. Partner 1989. Litigation Department. Specialises in corporate finance, financial services and professional negligence litigation.

Vaughan, Phillip
Simmons & Simmons, London (0171) 628 2020. Partner in Litigation Department.

Specialisation: Main areas of practice are contract and tort litigation, both domestic and international, including insolvency, fraud and asset recovery, professional negligence and breach of trust. Also handles product liability, covering manufacturers liability for defective products and personal injury. Acted in the liquidation of BCCI and in the defence of tobacco related product liability claims. Author of 'The Enforcement of Foreign Judgements in England and Wales' and 'Jurisdiction of National Courts of the European Union'. Recent lectures have included 'Mitigating the Loss: Civil remedies to recover Assets' in 1993 (First Annual Conference, International Regulation and Movement of Funds).

Prof. Membership: Law Society, American Bar Association.

Career: Qualified in 1979. Worked at *Radcliffes & Co* 1977-81. Admitted as a Solicitor in Hong Kong in 1986, having joined *Simmons & Simmons* in 1981. Became a Partner in 1985.

Personal: Born 1st May 1955. Attended Jesus College Cambridge 1973-76. Leisure interests include choral music, skiing and windsurfing, and photography. Lives in London.

Watson, Peter S.
Allen & Overy, London (0171) 330 3000. Qualified 1985. Partner in Litigation Department. Born 13.2.1956.

Willis, Tony
Clifford Chance, London (0171) 600 1000. Partner. Main area of work is commercial litigation, particularly banking and financial litigation and ADR.

Wilson, Julian
Herbert Smith, London (0171) 374 8000. Partner in Commercial Litigation Department.

Specialisation: Experienced in international litigation, particularly resulting from corporate, banking, securities related fraud and transnational insolvency. He has rights of audience in the higher courts and is co-editor of *International Litigation News*.

Career: Qualified 1984. Partner at *Herbert Smith* since 1990.

Personal: Educated at King George V School, Southport and Pembroke College, Oxford.

Wood, Jonathan
Clyde & Co, London (0171) 623 1244. Qualified 1977. Partner 1984. Commercial Litigation (International). Main area of practice is insurance and banking work. Born 11.6.1953.

Wyld, David
Macfarlanes, London (0171) 831 9222. Qualified 1974. Joined 1980. Partner 1981, Litigation Department. Specialises in commercial litigation, including insolvency and insurance, and Privy Council work.

REGIONS

Lynch, Michael P.
Elliott Duffy Garrett, Belfast (01232) 245034.

Catchpole, Owen
McKinty & Wright, Belfast (01232) 246751.

Mills, Jeremy V.S.
Mills Selig, Belfast (01232) 243878.

Anderson, M.Peter
Simpson & Marwick WS, Edinburgh (0131) 557 1545. Qualified 1975. Partner 1977. Commercial Litigation Department. Solicitor/Advocate. Work includes professional indemnity, aviation litigation and professional negligence.

Arnott, James M.
See under Construction & Civil Eng..

Aspinall, Timothy John Mellor
See under Intellectual Property.

Blake, Peter
Prettys, Ipswich (01473) 232121. Partner in Commercial Litigation Department.

Specialisation: Handles a range of commercial litigation including sale of goods, warranty claims, carriage of goods by road (domestic and CMR), freight forwarding and construction. Clients include insurance companies, road hauliers, freight forwarders and construction companies. Has had various articles published in the local press and business magazines. Charge-out rate is from £110 per hour.

Prof. Membership: Law Society, Eastern Builders Federation, Felixtowe Port User's Association.

Career: Qualified in 1987. Became a partner at *Prettys* in 1991.

Personal: Born 5th June 1963. Educated at King Edward VI School, Norwich 1973-81, Exeter University 1981-84 and Guilford College of Law 1984-85. Leisure interests include hockey (Chairman of Ipswich and East Suffolk Hockey Club), sport generally, walking, music and English literature. Lives near Ipswich.

Bootland, Edward Tjorn
Davies Wallis Foyster, Manchester (0161) 228 3702. Partner in Commercial Litigation Department.

Specialisation: Principal area of practice is general commercial contract disputes, asset leasing, hire purchase and sale of goods disputes involving large pieces of plant and machinery, trucks and cars. These include disputes as to title and quality as well as non-payment and recovery of assets. Clients include various finance houses and other trading and manufacturing companies. Experienced conference speaker. Course Di-

rector for Manchester Law Society Advocacy Training Courses.

Prof. Membership: Manchester Law Society (Member of council), Institute of Credit Management.

Career: Qualified in 1972. Partner at *Pricketts* 1974-79. Partner at *Foysters* from 1980 (*Davies Wallis Foyster* from 1989). Member of Legal Aid Appeals Committee since 1985. Deputy District Judge since 1992.

Personal: Born 5th October 1947. Educated at King's School, Macclesfield 1956-66 and Manchester University 1966-69. Colonel, Territorial Army (Royal Engineers). Member of Council of the Order of St. John, Greater Manchester. Leisure interests include skiing, walking, shooting, music, good food and wine. Lives in Mobberley, Cheshire.

Callaghan, Edward J.
Mills & Reeve, Norwich +44 (0) 1603 660155. Qualified 1974. Partner 1979. Commercial Litigation Department. Specialises in banking, insolvency and building/construction litigation.

Chappell, Andrew Geoffrey
See under Building Societies.

Cochran, J. Neil
See under Professional Negligence.

Cumming, Kenneth M.
Steedman Ramage WS, Edinburgh (0131) 226 3781.

Cuthbertson, Ian J.
See under Insolvency.

Douglas, Neil
See under Professional Negligence.

Ellison, Richard J.
Wragge & Co, Birmingham (0121) 233 1000. Qualified 1982. Partner 1991. Commercial Litigation Department. Main areas of practice are banking and finance litigation and resources work.

Gatenby, John
Addleshaw Sons & Latham, Manchester (0161) 832 5994. Head of Department. Corporate and Commercial Litigation.

Specialisation: Advises English and overseas private and public companies on international litigation and arbitration matters, including the enforcement of foreign judgements. Also advises on commercial contract disputes and professional negligence. Cases handled include BP Exploration Co (Libya) Ltd v. Hunt and Noirhomme v. Walklate. General editor of 'Recovery of Money', and has also written on discovery and inspection of documents. Has also contributed articles to 'Modern Law Review', 'Arbitration', and 'Litigation Letter'. Lectures regularly on civil procedure matters including discovery, Mareva injunctions, and arbitration.

Prof. Membership: Law Society, Chartered Institute of Arbitrators (Fellow), Institute of Credit Management, IBA, SEG, LSLA, Commonwealth Lawyers Association, Commercial Law League of America.

Career: Qualified in 1975. With *Linklaters & Paines* 1973-82. Head of Litigation at *Withers* 1983-84. Joined *Addleshaw Sons & Latham* in 1984, becoming a Partner in 1985.

Personal: Born 26th April 1950. Educated at West Hartlepool Grammar School 1962-68 and Trinity Hall, Cambridge 1968-72. Elder, Poynton Baptist Church.

Gold, Antony
Eversheds, Manchester (0161) 832 6666. Head of Commercial Litigation Department in Manchester. Chairman at Eversheds National Litigation Group.

Specialisation: Main area of practice is contract litigation arising from breaches of trading and other agreements in manufacturing, engineering and service industries. Also handles professional negligence, intellectual property and landlord and tenant. Other area of practice is financial services litigation arising out of or relating to the provision of financial services, the collapse of financial advisers, proceedings involving the allocation of trust funds, claims for and against banks, and disciplinary proceedings. Was involved in the Barlow Clowes, BCCI, Dunsdale Securities Ltd, and Lancashire and Yorkshire Assurance Society. Has extensive media experience and speaks at conferences and seminars. Recently involved in major disputes concerning takeovers and importation of contaminated waste.

Prof. Memberships: Law Society.

Career: Qualified 1983, joined *Eversheds Alexander Tatham* in 1984 and became a Partner in 1988. Chairman of *Eversheds'* National Commercial Litigation Group.

Personal: Born 26th August 1958. Attended Birkenhead School 1969-76, then Manchester University 1976-9 and Chester College of Law 1979-80. Leisure interests include mountain walking, literature, photography and walking the dog. Lives in Wilmslow, Cheshire.

Gosling, John A.
Addleshaw Sons & Latham, Manchester (0161) 832 5994. Partner in Corporate and Commercial Litigation Department.

Specialisation: Specialises in commercial litigation. Work handled includes commercial contract and tort cases, including professional negligence, property based disputes, and landlord and tenant. Has spoken at various conferences and seminars.

Prof. Membership: Law Society, Manchester Law Society.

Career: Qualified in 1984. Employed at *Addleshaw Sons & Latham* since 1982. Became partner in 1990.

Personal: Born 22nd July 1959. Educated at Shrewsbury School 1973-77 and Durham

University 1978-81. Leisure pursuits include sport and family. Lives in Wilmslow, Cheshire.

Ham, Brian E.
See under Construction & Civil Eng..

Heller, John H.G.
Hammond Suddards, Leeds (0113) 234 3500. Partner and Head of Litigation Department. Member of the Executive.

Specialisation: Main area of practice is commercial litigation, including warranty claims and contractual disputes. Also handles insurance litigation, acting for composite insurers and Lloyd's. Has experience of addressing seminars on commercial litigation issues.

Prof. Membership: Law Society.

Career: Articled with *Berwin Leighton* 1974-76. Qualified in 1976 and joined *Hammond Suddards* in the same year.

Personal: Born 7th September 1950. Educated at Bootham School 1964-68 and Sheffield University 1970-73. Enjoys reading, opera, running and skiing. Lives in Harrogate.

Hopkinson, John Brian
Pinsent Curtis, Birmingham (0121) 200 1050. Qualified 1972. Partner 1976. Managing Partner 1995. Litigation Department. Specialises in product liability and commercial contract litigation.

Howard, Paul
Wragge & Co, Birmingham (0121) 233 1000. Qualified 1975. Partner 1995. Commercial Litigation Department. Main areas of practice are corporate litigation and construction. Born 10.9.1948.

Howell-Richardson, Philip
Morgan Bruce, Cardiff (01222) 385385. Qualified 1975. Partner 1982. Head of Commercial Litigation. Handles heavyweight High Court litigation and arbitration. Born 21.6.1950.

Inglis, Ian G.
See under Intellectual Property.

Innes, John A.D.
Dundas & Wilson CS, Edinburgh (0131) 228 8000. Qualified 1965. Partner 1966. Litigation Department. Main area of practice is commercial litigation. Born 28.4.1940.

Jefferies, Michael G.
See under Construction & Civil Eng..

Jefferson, H.L. Ian
C & H Jefferson, Belfast (01232) 329545.

Johnson, Robert I.
Osborne Clarke, Bristol (0117) 923 0220. Qualified 1963. Partner 1967. Litigation Department. Main areas of practice include banking, charities, medical and educational work.

Jones, Peter
Eversheds, Cardiff (01222) 471147.

Kissack, Nigel J.
Alsop Wilkinson, Manchester (0161) 834 7760. Qualified 1969. Partner 1980. Litigation Department. Specialises in commercial contract, tort and intellectual property litigation. Born 8.4.1955.

Llewelyn Evans, Adrian
Burges Salmon, Bristol (0117) 939 2000. Qualified 1979. Partner 1984. Head of Commercial Litigation. Handles broadly based heavyweight litigation and arbitration. Born 5.8.1953.

Matthews, Paul
Eversheds, Norwich (01603) 272727. Qualified 1982. Partner 1985. Commercial Litigation Department. Deals with mainly contract-based litigation. Born 28.9.1953.

Mattison, Mark
Eversheds, Manchester (0161) 832 6666.

McGeever, Brendan G.
See under Insolvency.

McKenna (formerly Argyle), Sarah L.
Eversheds, Birmingham (0121) 233 2001. Partner in Litigation Department.

Specialisation: Work covers contract, negligence, insurance (including personal injury and medical negligence) and computer related litigation. Also handles intellectual property and defamation work. Marker for Law Society Final Examinations. Author of 'Strict Liability for Defective Products: a Changing Basis?' in NILQ. Tutor at Birmingham University 1982-83.

Prof. Membership: Law Society, Birmingham Law Society, Birmingham Medico Legal Society.

Career: Qualified in 1984. Articled at *Wragge & Co.* 1982-84. Joined *Eversheds Wells & Hind* in 1984, becoming a Partner in 1992.

Personal: Born 26th January 1959. Attended Queenswood School, Hartfield 1969-75; Loughborough Technical College, 1976-78 and Birmingham University 1978-81. Leisure interests include photography, music and swimming. Lives in Blockley, near Moreton-in-Marsh.

Moss, Robert J.
Vaudreys, Manchester (0161) 834 6877. Partner in Commercial Litigation Department.

Specialisation: Main area of practice is property-based litigation including all types of landlord and tenant disputes, banking recoveries work and insolvency and receivership litigation. Also handles general commercial matters of a contractual nature. Acted in Nationwide Ahmad v. Balakrishnan (Court of Appeal) [1995]. Clients include MEPC, Nationwide Building Society and Lloyds Bank.

Prof. Membership: Law Society.

Career: Qualified in 1985.

Personal: Born 1st November 1959. Educated at St Bede's College 1971-78 and Hull University 1978-82. School Governor. Leisure interests include shooting, cricket, football (watching) and golf (very badly). Lives in Marple.

Mumford, Nicola
Wragge & Co, Birmingham (0121) 233 1000. Qualified 1986. Partner 1993. Commercial Litigation Department. Specialises in corporate and insolvency litigation. Born 18.12.1960.

Murby, David F.
Shepherd & Wedderburn WS, Edinburgh (0131) 228 9900.

Pannone, Rodger J.
Pannone & Partners, Manchester (0161) 832 3000. Senior Partner.

Specialisation: Principal area of practice is multiple claim litigation. Acted in the British Midland air crash, Lockerbie air crash, Piper Alpha oil rig disaster, Zeebrugge ferry disaster, and for John Stalker and Ernest Saunders. Also deals with labour law and dispute resolution, acting for many multi-national companies. Regularly lectures, appears in the media and chairs conferences and seminars.

Prof. Membership: Vice President of the British Academy of Experts, President of the Law Society 1993-94, Fellow of the Royal Society of Arts.

Career: Qualified in 1969. Joined *Pannone & Partners* in 1973 and became Senior Partner in 1986. Member of the Lord Chancellor's Advisory Committee on Civil Justice 1986-89.

Personal: Born 20th April 1943. Director of the Manchester Concert Hall Ltd. Governor of the College of Law since 1990. Recreations include food, wine and walking slowly. Lives in Didsbury.

Poole, Quentin
Wragge & Co, Birmingham (0121) 233 1000. Qualified 1981. Partner 1985. Specialises in banking and insolvency litigation. Licensed Insolvency Practitioner. Born 7.1.1955.

Priestley, John C.
Booth & Co., Leeds (0113) 283 2000.

Richardson, Simon
Bond Pearce, Plymouth (01752) 266633. Qualified 1983. Partner 1991. Commercial Division. Specialises in business dispute, employment and pensions litigation.

Roessler, Max
Eversheds, Norwich (01603) 272727. Qualified 1981. Partner 1986. Commercial Litigation Department. Specialises in construction disputes and professional

negligence. Born 2.12.1956.

Roper, R.A.
Cobbett Leak Almond, Manchester
(0161) 833 3333. Partner in Litigation Department.

Specialisation: Principal area of practice is intellectual property. Work includes litigation on all types of trade mark, passing off, copyright and design right matters as well as mechanical and electrical patent proceedings. Also handles commercial litigation including large commercial contract disputes with overseas elements and/or competition law issues (e.g. Restrictive Trade Practices Act Article 85/86). Has considerable experience in injunction work including Anton Piller Orders both in intellectual property matters and commercial litigation. Important cases handled include McMillan Graham & Others v. R R UK Ltd (contempt of court for breach of interlocutory undertakings in passing off/ copyright case) and DTI v. D C Wilson and others (acted for the major intermediaries sued by the DTI in the Barlow Clowes collapse).

Prof. Membership: Law Society, Manchester Law Society, Licensing Executive Society.

Career: Qualified in 1979 while at *Cobbett Leak Almond*. Became a Partner in 1983.

Personal: Born 11th August 1953. Educated at Altrincham Grammar School 1964-71 and the University of Wales Institute of Science and Technology 1973-76 (LL.B Hons).

Rose, Digby H.
Edge & Ellison, Birmingham (0121) 200 2001. Head of Commercial Litigation.

Specialisation: Main areas of practice are commercial litigation and dispute resolution. Has wide experience covering contractual disputes, contentious intellectual property and computer work and professional negligence. Particular areas of interest include partnership disputes and claims relating to acquisition agreements. Recently acted in a major dispute arising out of the sale of a business to a Saudi Arabian corporation after litigation involving issues of jurisdiction. Has advised on the dissolution of medical and other professional partnerships and pension fund litigation. Regular contributor to Current Law Week: Focus on Civil Litigation.

Prof. Membership: Law Society, Birmingham Law Society.

Career: Qualified in 1975. Joined *Edge & Ellison* in 1979. Became Head of Commercial Litigation in 1990.

Personal: Born 16th September 1950. Attended Hurstpierpoint College 1964-68 and Gonville & Caius College, Cambridge 1969-72. Honorary Secretary of Birmingham Botanical and Horticultural Society. Leisure interests include music. Lives in Birmingham.

Rose, Paul M.A.
Halliwell Landau, Manchester (0161) 835 3003. Qualified 1973. Partner 1984. Insolvency Department. Principal area of practice is receivership and liquidations. Born 30.7.1948.

Rutherford, Kenneth
McKinty & Wright, Belfast (01232) 246751.

Sorrell, Christopher R.J.
Davies Wallis Foyster, Manchester (0161) 228 3702. Qualified 1979. Partner and Head of Litigation. Specialises in corporate recoveries and professional negligence. Born 25.10.1940.

Spooner, Andrew Nicolas
Martineau Johnson, Birmingham (0121) 200 3300. Partner and Head of Litigation Department.

Specialisation: Main area of practice is commercial litigation. Has acted in a wide range of commercial claims (both in the High Court and arbitration) involving breach of contract and tort. In particular, handles claims arising from product liability and defective goods and machinery in the engineering industry. Also handles banking work: including recovering money under guarantees, possession proceedings and other specialist banking litigation work. Has acted in a variety of large claims involving the engineering industry, including robots, cranes, mining equipment, diesel trains, plastic extrusions, computers, photocopiers, boilers and radiators. Author of articles for 'Court Brief'. Addressed an external conference on 'Summary Judgements and Interim Payments'. Chaired a firm's conference on 'Copyright' for a local Chamber of Commerce and gave a presentation on High Court litigation at a conference in Hong Kong. Has supervised the acquisition and installation of a fully computerised Document Management System for Martineau Johnson.

Prof. Membership: Chartered Institute of Arbitrators, Centre for Dispute Resolution.

Career: Qualified in 1978. Joined *Martineau Johnson* in 1976 (then *Johnson & Co.*), becoming a Partner in 1980 and Head of

Litigation in 1989. Became an Associate of the Chartered Institute of Arbitrators in 1989.

Personal: Born 5th May 1953. Holds an LLB (1975). Treasurer and Librarian of the Birmingham Book Club. Leisure interests include golf, cricket, squash and the arts.

Swanson, Alayne
See under Media & Entertainment.

Thomas, Paul A.
Halliwell Landau, Manchester (0161) 835 3003. Qualified 1979. Partner, 1981. Head of Litigation Department. Particular emphasis on property, negligence and professional indemnity.

Tranter, Ian Victor Keith
Chaffe Street, Manchester (0161) 236 5800. Qualified 1982. Partner 1989. Litigation practice includes employment law, shareholder disputes and injunctions. Born 20.10.1955

Williamson, David S.
Brodies WS, Edinburgh (0131) 228 3777. Partner in Litigation Department.

Specialisation: Solicitor advocate handling general commercial litigation and specialising in intellectual property and employment law. Experienced speaker at conferences and seminars. Lectured for over 5 years to University of Edinburgh Diploma students.

Career: Qualified in 1971. With *Simpson & Marwick* 1969-75, latterly as Partner. Joined *Brodies WS* as a Partner in 1976. Part time Industrial Tribunals Chairman.

Personal: Born in 1949. Educated at Royal High School, Edinburgh and University of Edinburgh. Leisure interests include cricket and hill walking. Lives in Edinburgh.

Winterburn, Tony
Alsop Wilkinson, Manchester (0161) 834 7760.

Wood, Michael M.
Simpson & Marwick WS, Edinburgh (0131) 557 1545. Qualified 1979.

Wright, Robert J.
Birketts, Ipswich (01473) 232300. Qualified 1975. Partner 1984. Litigation (Commercial) Department. Handles substantial commercial litigation and professional negligence.

LITIGATION (PROPERTY)

LONDON

The three most highly recommended property litigation firms in London are *Herbert Smith*, *Lovell White Durrant* and *Nabarro Nathanson*.

Herbert Smiths' litigation specialists not only handle disputes for their existing clients, but also attract work in their own right. Recent cases have included acting for Broadgate Square Ltd in its Court of Appeal victory over Lehman Brothers Ltd (a landmark rent review case). Lucy Hutchinson makes her first appearance in the list of leading practitioners.

LEADING FIRMS – LONDON

HERBERT SMITH	LOVELL WHITE DURRANT
NABARRO NATHANSON	
DIBB LUPTON BROOMHEAD	D J FREEMAN
LAWRENCE GRAHAM	MACFARLANES
MASONS	
ROWE & MAW	SIMMONS & SIMMONS

The litigation group at *Lovell White Durrant* is one of the largest in the UK with 15 lawyers dealing exclusively with property-related problems. The firm has handled some substantial cases in the last year, many of which were reported in the legal press. David Cox (who heads the department) and Anne Waltham were both highly recommended.

Nabarro Nathanson has eminent litigators in Iain Travers, Jennifer Rickard and Nicholas Cheffings, all of whom were universally recommended. The firm (pre-eminent in the non-contentious field) has 18 specialists handling all aspects of property work including landlord and tenant, vendor and purchaser and adjoining owners cases. Iain Travers (managing partner of the litigation department) was instructed in the two leading 'pre-emption rights' cases.

Other highly recommended firms include *Dibb Lupton Broomhead*, *DJ Freeman*, *Lawrence Graham* and *Macfarlanes*.

Lesley Webber (a fellow of the Chartered Institute of Arbitrators) heads *Dibb Lupton Broomheads'* property department which advises on rent reviews, lease renewals, dilapidations and service charge disputes, possession, forfeiture and ratings.

The litigation department at *DJ Freeman* boasts Christopher Hancock (one of the highest ranking practitioners in our research) who provides a comprehensive service including purchase and land development, landlord and tenant, nuisance and negligence claims. The firm acts for major domestic and international clients.

Lawrence Graham, and in particular Penny Francis, has established a strong following, undertaking work for UK and overseas institutions, property companies and occupiers. Anne Molyneux at *Masons*, who has recently addressed the Law Society National Conference on litigation, enjoys a reputation in the field. The firm has been involved in a substantial number of cases at the High Court, most recently, Inntrepreneur Estates v Boyes, Inntrepeneur v Mason and Little v Courage.

HIGHLY REGARDED – LONDON

BERWIN LEIGHTON	CHURCH ADAMS TATHAM
CLIFFORD CHANCE	DEWAR HOGAN
DRUCES & ATTLEE	LINKLATERS & PAINES
MAPLES TEESDALE	OLSWANG
PAYNE HICKS BEACH	RADCLIFFES CROSSMAN BLOCK
STEPHENSON HARWOOD	TITMUSS SAINER DECHERT
BOODLE HATFIELD	BRECHER & CO
CAMERON MARKBY HEWITT	FIELD FISHER WATERHOUSE
FORSYTE SAUNDERS KERMAN	MANCHES & CO
McKENNA & CO	PENNINGTONS

Rowe and Maw and *Simmons & Simmons* are also well-known in the field. Both firms handle a broad range of contentious work for their property clients in the public and private sectors. Michele Freyne (*Rowe and Maw*) and Carol Hewson (*Simmons & Simmons*) are held in high regard.

Individual practitioners who featured prominently in our research include Katie Bradford of *Linklaters & Paines*, Wendy Miller of *Clifford Chance*, Roger Cohen of *Berwin Leighton*, who has recently been instructed by the Property Holdings Directorate of the Department of the Environment on a £9 million claim in rent and service charges, Ken Duncan of *Stephenson Harwood* and Ronald Hogan (founder of the recently formed Property Litigation Association) who has launched *Dewar Hogan*, a niche property litigation prac-

LEADING INDIVIDUALS – LONDON

Katie Bradford *Linklaters & Paines*	**Nicholas Cheffings** *Nabarro Nathanson*	**Roger D. Cohen** *Berwin Leighton*
David Cox *Lovell White Durrant*	**Penelope J.L. Francis** *Lawrence Graham*	**Michele Freyne** *Rowe & Maw*
Christopher Hancock *D J Freeman*	**Carol Hewson** *Simmons & Simmons*	**Wendy Miller** *Clifford Chance*
Anne Molyneux *Masons*	**Jennifer Rickard** *Nabarro Nathanson*	**Iain Travers** *Nabarro Nathanson*
Anne Waltham *Lovell White Durrant*	**Lesley Webber** *Dibb Lupton Broomhead*	
Ken W. Duncan *Stephenson Harwood*	**Robert P. Highmore** *Radcliffes Crossman Block*	**Ronald D. Hogan** *Dewar Hogan*
Lucy Hutchinson *Herbert Smith*	**Evelyn Smith** *Titmuss Sainer Dechert*	

UP AND COMING

Marcus Robert Barclay *Olswang*		

In all the tables the names in each group are listed alphabetically.

tice. Making their first appearances in our leading practitioner list are Robert Highmore of *Radcliffes Crossman Block* (a member of the British Property Federation) and Marcus Barclay of *Olswang*, described as a rising star.

Of the smaller firms, *Church Adams Tatham & Co*, *Druces & Attlee*, *Maples Teesdale* and *Payne Hicks Beach* are especially noted for their expertise. *Claremont Smith* specialise in pension fund investments.

SOUTH EAST

Carole Peet of *Denton Hall* emerges as the leading practitioner in the region, undertaking a substantial amount of work for major property clients. Recent instructions have included

LEADING FIRMS – SOUTH EAST

DENTON HALL *Milton Keynes*

'National Westminster Bank plc v Co-operative Wholesale Ltd' (treatment of inducement clauses at review) and 'Commissioners for the New Towns v Cooper' (a landmark action which extended the categories of reliance on a mistake).

HIGHLY REGARDED – SOUTH EAST

BURSTOWS *Crawley*	**COFFIN MEW & CLOVER** *Portsmouth*
DONNE MILEHAM & HADDOCK *Brighton*	**HAROLD BENJAMIN & COLLINS** *Harrow*
SPARLING BENHAM & BROUGH *Colchester*	**THOMSON SNELL & PASSMORE** *Tunbridge Wells*
T.G. BAYNES & SONS *Bexleyheath*	**BRACHERS** *Maidstone*
CRIPPS HARRIES HALL *Tunbridge Wells*	**DEAN WILSON** *Brighton*
E. EDWARDS SON & NOICE	**RAWLISON & BUTLER** *Crawley*

Other well-regarded firms advising on a broad range of contentious property matters include *Burstows, Coffin Mew & Clover, Donne Mileham & Haddock, Harold Benjamin & Collins, Sparling Benham & Brough* and *Thomson Snell & Passmore,* which has two partners dealing exclusively with property litigation.

LEADING INDIVIDUALS – SOUTH EAST

Carole Peet *Denton Hall*

SOUTH WEST & WALES

Burges Salmon, with one of the largest property litigation teams, emerges as the leading practice in the region. Andrew Densham and Peter Rhys Williams are both highly experienced litigators.

LEADING FIRMS – SOUTH WEST & WALES

BURGES SALMON *Bristol*	**OSBORNE CLARKE** *Bristol*
VEALE WASBROUGH *Bristol*	

Other firms with dedicated property litigation practices include *Osborne Clarke* and *Veale Wasbrough* where Julie Exton is held in high regard.

Eversheds Bristol and *Wansbroughs Willey Hargrave* handle possession, dilapidations, lease renewal, insolvency and

rent review work. *Eversheds* is particularly known for work in the context of business tenancies.

HIGHLY REGARDED – SOUTH WEST & WALES

EVERSHEDS *Bristol*	**HUGH JAMES JONES & JENKINS** *Cardiff*
MORGAN BRUCE *Cardiff*	**WANSBROUGHS WILLEY HARGRAVE** *Bristol*
BEVAN ASHFORD *Bristol*	**FOOT & BOWDEN** *Plymouth*
LOOSEMORES *Cardiff*	**LYONS DAVIDSON** *Bristol*
PYE-SMITHS *Salisbury*	

In Wales, the leading property litigation firms include *Hugh James Jones & Jenkins* and *Morgan Bruce* which handle, in the main, landlord and tenant disputes.

LEADING INDIVIDUALS – SOUTH WEST & WALES

Julie A. Exton *Veale Wasbrough*

H. Andrew C. Densham *Burges Salmon*
Peter Rhys Williams *Burges Salmon*

MIDLANDS

Commercial firms with large commercial property practices take the lion's share of contentious property work in the Midlands. Of these firms, *Eversheds* (Nottingham and Derby),

LEADING FIRMS – MIDLANDS

EDGE & ELLISON *Birmingham*	**EVERSHEDS** *Nottingham, Derby*
PINSENT CURTIS *Birmingham*	**WRAGGE & CO** *Birmingham*

Edge & Ellison, Pinsent Curtis and *Wragge & Co* are particularly recommended. Suzanne Lloyd-Holt of *Wragge & Co* is

HIGHLY REGARDED – MIDLANDS

ANTHONY COLLINS *Birmingham*	**FREETH CARTWRIGHT HUNT DICKINS** *Nottingham*
LANYON BOWDLER *Shrewsbury*	**MARTINEAU JOHNSON** *Birmingham*
McGRATH & CO *Birmingham*	**SHOOSMITHS & HARRISON** *Northampton*
SYDNEY MITCHELL *Birmingham*	

noted for her expertise which includes litigation in dilapidation's, rent reviews, restrictive covenants and rights of light.

LEADING INDIVIDUALS – MIDLANDS

Suzanne Lloyd-Holt *Wragge & Co*

Jason Pinkney *Eversheds*
Gordon Scott *Edge & Ellison*

EAST ANGLIA

Eversheds and *Mills & Reeve* have the largest property litigation practices in the region with dedicated teams handling

LEADING FIRMS – EAST ANGLIA

EVERSHEDS *Ipswich, Norwich*	**MILLS & REEVE** *Norwich*

primarily landlord and tenant work. James Falkener heads *Mills & Reeve's* property litigation department, while at

STEELE & CO *Norwich*

Eversheds, Claire Watson co-ordinates the property litigation unit from the Ipswich office.

J.M.G. Falkner *Mills & Reeve*
Claire Watson *Eversheds*

NORTH WEST

In Manchester, *Cobbett Leak Almond* (P. Stone), *Halliwell Landau* and *Pannone & Partners* have well established property litigation departments, providing a comprehensive

COBBETT LEAK ALMOND	**HALLIWELL LANDAU**
Manchester	*Manchester*
PANNONE & PARTNERS *Manchester*	

service to their property clients. *Cobbett Leak Almond* handles a substantial volume of work for licensed premises.

J. KEITH PARK & CO *St. Helens*	**WEIGHTMAN RUTHERFORDS** *Liverpool*
ABSON HALL *Stockport*	**JACKSON & CANTER** *Liverpool*

In Liverpool, *Weightman Rutherfords* has developed a specialism in related professional indemnity work whilst in St. Helens *J Keith Park & Co* has formed a Mortgage Repossession Complaints Bureau as part of their service.

Ian D. Austin *Halliwell Landau*
Vincent B. O'Farrell *Pannone & Partners*
P.J.W. Stone *Cobbett Leak Almond*

NORTH EAST

Leeds firms with well-established property litigation departments include *Booth & Co*, *Dibb Lupton Broomhead*, *Eversheds* and *Pinsent Curtis*, all of which undertake the whole range of landlord and tenant work, including dilapidations,

BOOTH & CO. *Leeds*	**DIBB LUPTON BROOMHEAD**
	Bradford
EVERSHEDS *Leeds, Newcastle*	**PINSENT CURTIS** *Leeds*

In all the tables the names in each group are listed alphabetically.

s146 notices, chancery litigation, covenants and boundary disputes. In Newcastle, *Dickinson Dees* and *Eversheds*

DICKINSON DEES *Newcastle upon Tyne*	**NABARRO NATHANSON** *Doncaster*

(which has three partners dealing exclusively with contentious property work including Christopher Hugill) have sound reputations in the field while in Doncaster, *Nabarro Nathanson* acts for a wide range of clients including banks and building societies.

C.J. Hugill *Eversheds*
Philip O'Loughlin *Booth & Co.*

SCOTLAND

Highly recommended property litigation practices in Scotland include *Bird Semple* in Glasgow and *Brodies WS*, *Dundas & Wilson CS*, *Muclay Murray & Spens* (which has been involved in a series of ground-breaking decisions in connection with 'stay open' clauses), and *Shepherd & Wedderburn WS* in Edinburgh.

BIRD SEMPLE *Glasgow*	**BRODIES WS** *Edinburgh*
CONDIES *Perth*	**DUNDAS & WILSON CS** *Edinburgh*
GILLESPIE MACANDREW *Edinburgh*	**MACLAY MURRAY & SPENS** *Glasgow*
SHEPHERD & WEDDERBURN *Edinburgh*	**STEEDMAN RAMAGE WS** *Edinburgh*

NORTHERN IRELAND

Highly regarded firms in this field include *Carson & McDowell*, *Elliott Duffy Garrett*, *L'Estrange & Brett* and *Tughan & Co.*.

CARSON & McDOWELL *Belfast*	**CLEAVER FULTON & RANKIN** *Belfast*
ELLIOTT DUFFY GARRETT *Belfast*	**L'ESTRANGE & BRETT** *Belfast*
TUGHAN & CO *Belfast*	
HEWITT & GILPIN *Belfast*	**JOHN McKEE & SON** *Belfast*
O'REILLY STEWART *Belfast*	

Cleaver Fulton & Rankin advise on landlord and tenant issues, mortgage repossessions and compulsory purchase orders, while *Hewitt & Gilpin* have experience of mortgage debt recovery and possession actions as well as landlord and tenant disputes.

LEADERS IN LITIGATION (PROPERTY)

LONDON

Barclay, Marcus Robert

Olswang, London (0171) 208 8888. Partner in Litigation Department.

Specialisation: Principal area of practice is property litigation. Handles all aspects of commercial property litigation, including contentious lease renewals, forfeiture actions, rent review arbitrations, service charge disputes and privity actions. Also deals with insolvency including security enforcement for banks, and acting for liquidators and administrative receivers on all matters arising out of liquidations or receiverships. Important cases include Ropemaker Properties v. Noonhaven Ltd [1989] (considerations which will influence the Court to grant relief from forfeiture) and Commercial Union Life Assurance Co Ltd and another v. Woolworths PLC [1994] (binding variations to rights and obligations of landlord and tenant to be taken into account on rent review). Clients include major high street retailers, leading commercial property companies, banks and Insolvency practitioners.

Prof. Membership: Law Society.

Career: Qualified in September 1988. At *Rubinstein Callingham Polden & Gale* 1986-90. Joined *Simon Olswang* in August 1990. Became a Partner at *Olswang* in May 1994.

Personal: Born 12th December 1961. Educated at Holland Park School 1971-76, Abingdon School 1976-78 and Warwick University 1981-84. Leisure pursuits include music, sports, cooking, theatre and cinema. Lives in London.

Bradford, Katie

Linklaters & Paines, London (0171) 606 7080. Qualified 1982. Joined *Linklaters & Paines* in January 1992. Head of Property Litigation Unit. Work includes rent review, landlord and tenant, mortgages, professional negligence, land law and trusts. Also judicial review and administrative law.

Cheffings, Nicholas

Nabarro Nathanson, London (0171) 493 9933. Qualified 1983. Partner 1990. Property Litigation Department. Work includes judicial review, landlord and tenant, rent review arbitrations, contractual and development disputes and professional negligence. Born 24.1.1960.

Cohen, Roger D.

Berwin Leighton, London (0171) 623 3144. Partner in Litigation Department.

Specialisation: Main area of practice is property litigation including landlord and tenant, planning-related litigation, rating, ADR, and professional indemnity. Other areas are general commercial litigation and arbitration. Acted for Tesco Stores Ltd in planning gain

litigation, Prudential and Property Holdings. Major clients also include Legal and General. Conducts client seminars and regularly contributes articles to the property press.

Prof. Memberships: Associate Chartered Institute Of Arbitrators, Administrative Law Bar Association, City of London Solicitors Company, Law Society.

Career: Articled with *Donnelly & Elliott* in Gosport, then joined *Matthew Arnold & Baldwin* in Watford. Joined *Berwin Leighton* in 1984 and became a Partner in 1989. Head of Property Litigation Group.

Personal: Born 2nd June 1959. Attended Portsmouth Grammar School 1970-77. Leisure pursuits include soccer, music and reading. Lives in London.

Cox, David

Lovell White Durrant, London (0171) 236 0066. Qualified 1979. Partner 1985. Property Litigation Group. Main area of practice covers all types of litigation and advice on contentious aspects of property. Born 16.3.1956.

Duncan, Ken W.

Stephenson Harwood, London (0171) 329 4422. Qualified 1971. Partner 1977. Litigation Department. Principal area of work is property litigation.

Francis, Penelope J.L.

Lawrence Graham, London (0171) 379 0000. Partner in Litigation Department.

Specialisation: Main area of practice is property litigation, covering rent reviews, insolvency, shopping centre and portfolio management, lease renewals and dilapidations. Lectures for RICS, ARBRIX and other conferences.

Prof. Membership: Law Society, Women in Property, Property Litigation Club.

Career: Qualified in 1984. Worked at *Beachcroft Stanleys* 1982-88. Joined *Lawrence Graham* in 1989, becoming a Partner in 1991.

Personal: Born 9th November 1959. Attended University of Bristol 1978-81, then College of Law 1981-2. Leisure interests include ballet, eating and travel. Lives in London.

Freyne, Michele

Rowe & Maw, London (0171) 248 4282. Partner in Commercial Litigation Department.

Specialisation: Main area of practice is property litigation. Started first specialist team in 1980. This has grown into a team of 2 partners, 2 assistants, 1 legal executive and 2 trainees. Also specialises in matrimonial law (about 15% of total workload).

Prof. Membership: Solicitors Family Law Association

Career: Qualified in 1978. Joined *Rowe &*

Maw in 1979 and became a Partner in 1985. Group Managing Partner, Commercial Litigation 1993-94.

Hancock, Christopher

D J Freeman, London (0171) 583 4055. Partner specialising in property litigation.

Specialisation: Work includes disputes arising out of the purchase and redevelopment of land, development agreements, surveyors' negligence and commission claims, commercial landlord and tenant and management disputes, nuisance, rights of light, rent review, building defects and loss and expense claims.

Prof. Membership: Law Society.

Career: Qualified in 1982. Joined *DJ Freeman* in 1980 and became a Partner in 1987.

Personal: Born 19th September 1957. Attended Birmingham University (LLB 1979). Leisure interests include playing the piano, singing, concert-going, wine and family. Lives in Ealing.

Hewson, Carol

Simmons & Simmons, London (0171) 628 2020. Partner in Litigation Department.

Specialisation: Main area of practice is commercial litigation, with particular experience in all aspects of commercial property and landlord and tenant litigation. Acts for institutional landlords, property developers and banks, as well as for commercial and retail tenants. Also has extensive experience in rent review disputes, including arbitration, service charge disputes, forfeiture claims and litigation under the Landlord and Tenant Act 1954. Experienced in insolvency litigation, acting primarily for banks and insolvency practitioners. Acted for Brent Walker in connection with dispute over re-development of Elstree Film Studio site. Addressed seminars for Westminster Management Consultants on "Business Lease Renewals", for IBC on "Insolvency of Individuals" and "Introduction to Property Litigation" and for Euroforum on "Watertight Commercial Leases".

Prof. Memberships: Law Society; City of London Solicitors Company.

Career: Qualified in April 1980, after joining *Stephenson Harwood* as an articled clerk in 1978. Left for *Simmons & Simmons* in 1983, Partner in 1986.

Personal: Born 8th October 1955. Attended Kings College, London 1974-1977. Member of Committee of Management of Broomleigh Housing Association. Leisure pursuits include fell walking, skiing and cooking. Lives in London.

Highmore, Robert P.

Radcliffes Crossman Block, London (0171) 222 7040. Qualified 1982. Partner 1987. Head of Property Litigation Unit.

Extensive experience of property and landlord and tenant litigation.

Hogan, Ronald D.

Dewar Hogan, London (0171) 329 8846.

Specialisation: Work covers all aspects of contentious property matters and related litigation including rent and service charge disputes; professional negligence claims; making and resisting claims for possession, including redevelopment cases; rent reviews and dilapidation claims; enforcing and resisting the enforcement of legal charges and dealing with insolvency related property matters. Acted in Nikko Hotels (UK) Ltd v. MEPC (1991) and Re National Jazz Centre (1988). Has experience in dealing with problems caused by the Financial Services Act in the enforcement of securities. Author of a number of articles published in the property press; speaker at conferences and seminars on obtaining possession of redevelopment sites, tenant default and the property aspects of insolvency.

Prof. Membership: Law Society.

Career: Qualified in 1979. Member of *Nabarro Nathanson's* property litigation department prior to founding *Dewar Hogan* in 1991.

Personal: Leisure interests include sailing and other outdoor pursuits. Lives in London.

Hutchinson, Lucy

Herbert Smith, London (0171) 374 8000. Partner in Commercial and Property Litigation Department.

Specialisation: Deals with commercial and specialised property litigation, the former involving commercial disputes, professional negligence actions and Department of Trade and Industry investigations, the latter involving major property and landlord and tenant disputes.

Career: Qualified in 1982. Became a Partner at *Herbert Smith* in 1989.

Personal: Educated at Southampton University.

Miller, Wendy

Clifford Chance, London (0171) 600 1000. Partner in charge of Property Litigation Unit. Principal area of practice is property litigation.

Molyneux, Anne

Masons, London (0171) 490 4000. Partner and head of Property Litigation Department.

Specialisation: Handles all areas of High Court litigation. Cases have included Inntrepreneur Estates v. Boyes (covering European law, application of Article 85 and severance), Inntrepreneur v. Mason (covering the status of comfort letters) and Little v. Courage (covering status of option). Addressed Law Society National Conference on litigation; has addressed conferences on dilapidations, insolvency, litigation and rent review. Worked on a TEN video.

Prof. Membership: Law Society.

Career: Born 12th January 1959. Qualified in 1983. Associate at *Lawrence Messer & Co.*, before joining *Masons* in 1987. Became a Partner in 1989. Member of Ealing and Fulham Book Club. Lives in Ealing. Has two children and is a member of Working Mothers Group.

Rickard, Jennifer

Nabarro Nathanson, London (0171) 493 9933. Qualified 1983. Partner 1989. Property Litigation Department. Main area of practice is property litigation. Includes rent reviews, opposed redevelopments, construction of leases and property related insolvency work. Born 6.11.1958.

Smith, Evelyn

Titmuss Sainer Dechert, London (0171) 583 5353. Partner in Property Litigation Unit.

Specialisation: Work includes landlord and tenant, secured lending, real property disputes and property aspects of insolvency. Also handles general commercial litigation. Acted in London & Leeds United v. Paribas Ltd (rent review). Author of Landlord and Tenant Factbook.

Prof. Membership: Law Society, Justice.

Career: Barrister 1981-86, practising in general common law. Joined *Lovell White & King* in 1986, cross-qualifying in 1987. Joined *Titmuss Sainer & Webb* in 1989, becoming a Partner in 1992.

Personal: Born 6th October 1958. Attended University College of Wales, Aberystwyth (LLB) 1980. Inveterate traveller, moderately serious walker. Lives in London.

Travers, Iain

Nabarro Nathanson, London (0171) 493 9933. Qualified 1977. Partner 1980. Fellow of the Chartered Institute of Arbitrators. Head of Property Litigation Department. Main area of practice is property litigation. Acted in St. Bartholomew's Hospital Trustees v. British Railways Board and Techno Ltd v. Allied Dunbar Assurance Ltd. Born 6.9.1952.

Waltham, Anne

Lovell White Durrant, London (0171) 236 0066. Qualified 1982. Solicitor in Property Litigation Group. Handles all aspects of property litigation relating to landlord and tenant and real property matters. Born 4.3.1957.

Webber, Lesley

Dibb Lupton Broomhead, London (0171) 600 0202. Partner, Head of Property Litigation and Planning Department.

Specialisation: Principal area of practice is property litigation including rent reviews, lease renewals, dilapidations and service charge disputes, possession and forfeiture, rating and professional negligence actions. Other main area of work is town and country planning covering planning applications, agreements and appeals, local planning advice and representation, compulsory purchase orders and environmental assessments. Acted in PHIT v. Holding & Management, Shield Properties v. Anglo Overseas Transport Ltd, Zubaida v. Hargreaves and in the original arbitration of National Westminster Bank v. Arthur Young. Member of RICS Working Party on Landlord and Tenant Act 1954. Recent Articles include 'Independent Expert Determinations' for Property Review and 'Judge-Proof Awards' for Chartered Institute of Arbitrators.

Prof. Membership: Fellow of the Chartered Institute of Arbitrators, Honorary Member of ARBRIX.

Career: Qualified 1980 while with *Freshfields*. Joined *Masons* in 1984 and became a Partner and Head of the Property Litigation and Planning Department in 1984. Moved to London office of *Dibb Lupton Broomhead* in November 1993 to head Property Litigation and Planning Department.

Personal: Born 10th April 1956. Attended Birmingham University 1974-77. Leisure pursuits include family life, reading and theatre.

REGIONS

Austin, Ian D.

Halliwell Landau, Manchester (0161) 835 3003.

Densham, H. Andrew C.

See under Agriculture & Bloodstock.

Exton, Julie A.

Veale Wasbrough, Bristol (0117) 925 2020. Qualified 1983. Partner 1988. Property Services Department. Main area of practice is property litigation. Handles all aspects, especially commercial landlord and tenant. Born 17.10.1957.

Falkner, J.M.G.

Mills & Reeve, Norwich +44 (0) 1603 660155.

Hugill, C.J.

Eversheds, Newcastle upon Tyne (0191) 261 1661.

Lloyd-Holt, Suzanne

Wragge & Co, Birmingham (0121) 233 1000. Qualified 1974. Partner 1988. Specialises in property litigation work, including all aspects of contentious property, heavyweight dilapidations disputes, rent reviews, restrictive covenants and rights of light.

O'Farrell, Vincent B.

Pannone & Partners, Manchester (0161) 832 3000.

O'Loughlin, Philip

Booth & Co., Leeds (0113) 283 2000. Head of Property Litigation Department.

Specialisation: Rent review, dilapidations, property related professional negligence. Work also includes Landlord and Tenant 1954 applications, forfeiture, tenant default.

Career: Articled with *Simmons and Simmons*, qualified 1986; *Withers*, 1987-88; *Crossman Block* 1988-1991; joined *Booth & Co* 1991; becoming a Partner in May 1995.

Personal: Born 5 May 1960; attended Ipswich School 1971-1978; Cambridge University 1979-1982. Leisure interests include fellwalking, landscape photography, archaeology. Lives near Ilkley.

Peet, Carole
Denton Hall, Milton Keynes (0908) 690260. Partner: Head of Litigation Department.

Specialisation: Practice covers all aspects of contentious property law. Emphasis on landlord and tenant disputes, including rent reviews, business lease renewals, possession actions, dilapidation claims and litigation involving the refusal or withholding of licences. Contributes articles to Estates Gazette, Property Review, Lawyer, Lease Renewal and Rent Review. Lectures frequently to invited audiences.

Career: Qualified 1985. Assistant Solicitor with *Boodle Hatfield* 1985-88. Joined *Denton Hall* 1988 and became a Partner in 1993.

Personal: Born 1958. Lives in Milton Keynes and London.

Pinkney, Jason
Eversheds, Nottingham (0115) 950 6201. Qualified 1988.

Scott, Gordon
Edge & Ellison, Birmingham (0121) 200 2001.

Stone, P.J.W.
Cobbett Leak Almond, Manchester (0161) 833 3333. Qualified 1976.

Watson, Claire
Eversheds, Norwich (01603) 272727.

Williams, Peter Rhys
See under Agriculture & Bloodstock.

INDEXES TO PROFILES

Solicitors' Profiles The index to leading solicitors profiled in the specialist lists is located immediately after the section containing in-house lawyers' profiles. This index also includes heads of company legal departments.

Barristers' Profiles Leading barristers' profiles are indexed within the main Barristers' Index located at the end of the directory. Names of profiled barristers are set in bold type.

LOCAL GOVERNMENT

LOCAL authorities require advice on a broad range of legal matters, from litigation to contract work and conveyancing. Traditionally, a great proportion of this work has been handled by in-house legal departments with firms in private practice acting in support.

Firms dealing principally with health authorities, education and housing associations will be found listed under their respective areas.

LONDON

The leading local government firm is *Nabarro Nathanson* which advises over 90 local authorities, several development corporations and other public and private sector organisations. The highly respected David Hawkins (author

LEADING FIRMS – LONDON	
NABARRO NATHANSON	
ASHURST MORRIS CRISP	SHARPE PRITCHARD
BERWIN LEIGHTON	CLIFFORD CHANCE
DENTON HALL	D J FREEMAN

of the Compulsory Purchase volume of the 'Encyclopaedia of Forms and Precedents') advises on planning, compulsory purchase, rating and local authority financing deals. Also highly regarded are Carl Hopkins (particularly known for urban regeneration work) and Ray Ambrose who advises on the constitution and financing of local authorities and has been involved in the privatisation of the in-house service organisation for a London borough.

Other highly recommended firms include *Sharpe Pritchard* and *Ashurst Morris Crisp. Sharpe Pritchard's* traditional role in parliamentary agency work has facilitated their transition into local government. Trevor Griffiths is well regarded for compulsory competitive tendering (CCT) and local government reorganisation challenges. *Ashurst Morris Crisp* has a solid base of public sector clients and has gained prominence for urban renewal work acting for the London Docklands Development Corporation on high profile projects such as the Docklands Light Railway and Canary

Wharf. The firm has also acted for the London Borough of Hounslow on the redevelopment of Hounslow Town Centre.

Other notable firms include *DJ Freeman, Denton Hall, Clifford Chance,* which deals with all aspects of local government work including contracting out and public procurement, and *Berwin Leighton* where David Taylor advises over 40 local authorities and other public sector clients on redevelopment and CCT.

Firms with experience in the field include *Trowers & Hamlins,* where Ian Doolittle handles voluntary transfers, CCT, environmental work and housing stock transfers, *Eversheds* which provides a comprehensive service for its public sector and city council clients and *Titmuss Sainer Dechert* which represents local and other public authorities involved in major property or infrastructure projects (the firm is particularly known for town centre management and refurbishment work).

Individual practitioners to feature prominently during our research include Léonie Cowen (formerly the chief solicitor for the London Borough of Barnet) at *Léonie Cowen & Associates* who advises on the implementation of new methods of service provision and local government reorganisation.

HIGHLY REGARDED – LONDON	
EVERSHEDS	LAWRENCE GRAHAM
LÉONIE COWEN & ASSOCIATES	LOVELL WHITE DURRANT
TITMUSS SAINER DECHERT	TROWERS & HAMLINS
BARNETT ALEXANDER CHART	S J BERWIN & CO
FOX WILLIAMS	MASONS
NORTON ROSE	ROWE & MAW
SHINDLER & CO	SPEECHLY BIRCHAM
STONEHAM LANGTON & PASSMORE	WINCKWORTH & PEMBERTON
HERBERT SMITH	McKENNA & CO

She acted for Dartmouth Borough Council in the recent management buy-out of a number of its technical services. Others include David Hunter at *Lovell White Durrant* (finance, planning, rating, and compulsory purchase and compensation) and Simon Randall C.B.E. at *Lawrence Graham* who heads the firm's Local and Public Authority Unit, advising local authorities on externalisation, local government reorganisation and housing action trusts.

LEADING INDIVIDUALS – LONDON		
Tony Briam *Clifford Chance*	Léonie Cowen *Léonie Cowen & Associates*	David Hawkins *Nabarro Nathanson*
Carl W.V. Hopkins *Nabarro Nathanson*		
David Abram *Nabarro Nathanson*	Ray Ambrose *Nabarro Nathanson*	A.A. Child *Rowe & Maw*
Michael D. Cunliffe *Ashurst Morris Crisp*	Ian Doolittle *Trowers & Hamlins*	Anthony Fine *Barnett Alexander Chart*
Trevor Griffiths *Sharpe Pritchard*	Brian Hall *Clifford Chance*	Catherine Hand *Winckworth & Pemberton*
David Hunter *Lovell White Durrant*	Carol A. McCormack *Berwin Leighton*	Nigel Miller *Fox Williams*
Simon Randall C.B.E. *Lawrence Graham*	David Taylor *Berwin Leighton*	Edward B. Totman *D J Freeman*
Christine J. Williams *Fox Williams*		

In all the tables the names in each group are listed alphabetically.

SOUTH EAST

Blake Lapthorn in Fareham handles a broad spectrum of public sector and local government work. Recent instructions have included externalisation work for one of the London boroughs' service departments and advising a local authority social services department. *Underwoods* in St. Albans acts for local authorities handling funding, CCT and joint venture work.

HIGHLY REGARDED – SOUTH EAST	
BLAKE LAPTHORN *Fareham*	**CLARKS** *Reading*
GRIFFITH SMITH *Brighton*	**UNDERWOODS** *St. Albans*

Reading-based *Clarks* boasts Simon Dimmick, who is equally known for local government and planning work and has recently advised on the privatisation of local government services. In Brighton, *Griffith Smith's* Robert Hinton, a former chief executive and solicitor to a borough council, is held in high regard.

LEADING INDIVIDUALS – SOUTH EAST
Simon Dimmick *Clarks*
Robert Hinton *Griffith Smith*

SOUTH WEST & WALES

Bevan Ashford, while primarily known for planning, also undertakes municipal enterprise work. Malcolm Iley (based at the Plymouth office) has handled local authority transfers, CCTs and city centre redevelopments and recently acted in the London Borough of Croydon's transfer of Fairfield Halls.

HIGHLY REGARDED – SOUTH WEST & WALES	
BEVAN ASHFORD *Bristol*	**EDWARDS GELDARD** *Cardiff*
EVERSHEDS *Cardiff*	**MORGAN BRUCE** *Cardiff*
VEALE WASBROUGH *Bristol*	

In Cardiff, *Eversheds* has considerable experience in planning and development work as well as compulsory purchase and compensation matters. Eric Evans (a former chief officer in local government) has 30 years' public sector experience dealing with all areas of local government and has handled compulsory purchase orders for various bodies, including the Garden Festival of Wales. *Morgan Bruce*, while acting in a number of public sector contexts, is particularly known for externalisations. Peter Burgess, who heads the planning department, handles compulsory purchases and urban regeneration for public authorities. In Bristol, *Veale Wasbrough* are also known for their expertise in the field.

LEADING INDIVIDUALS – SOUTH WEST & WALES
Simon Baker *Veale Wasbrough*
Peter Burgess *Morgan Bruce*
Eric C. Evans *Eversheds*
Malcolm Iley *Bevan Ashford*
Huw R.C. Williams *Edwards Geldard*

MIDLANDS

Midlands firms with substantial local government practices tend to be centred in Birmingham: *Dibb Lupton Broomhead*, *Anthony Collins*, *Pinsent Curtis* and *Wragge & Co* all have dedicated departments.

HIGHLY REGARDED – MIDLANDS	
ANTHONY COLLINS *Birmingham*	**DIBB LUPTON BROOMHEAD** *Birmingham*
PINSENT CURTIS *Birmingham*	**WRAGGE & CO** *Birmingham*
BROWNE JACOBSON *Nottingham*	

Michael Orlik at *Dibb Lupton Broomhead* acts for four local authorities and has recently handled a compensation case following a large compulsory acquisition by a development corporation. *Anthony Collins* handles regeneration work for housing estates, CCTs and conveyancing for local authorities.

LEADING INDIVIDUALS – MIDLANDS
Michael Orlik *Dibb Lupton Broomhead*
A.J. Stacey *Pinsent Curtis*
Martin White *Pinsent Curtis*

Martin White heads the planning and local government department at *Pinsent Curtis* that advises on externalisation, CCT, contracts and tenders, planning and compulsory purchase, local authority finance, companies and property. The firm acts for a number of local authorities including the Black Country Development Corporation and also the Trafford Park Development Corporation.

EAST ANGLIA

The leading public sector and local government firms in the region are *Gotelee & Goldsmith* and *Steele & Co*.

HIGHLY REGARDED – EAST ANGLIA	
GOTELEE & GOLDSMITH *Ipswich*	**STEELE & CO** *Norwich*

Brian Morron at *Gotelee & Goldsmith* (former Deputy Borough Solicitor at Wandsworth LBC) has 22 years' experience in the field and advises on all matters concerning local authorities. The firm has decided not to compete in compulsory competitive tendering with local authority legal teams in their geographical vicinity.

LEADING INDIVIDUALS – EAST ANGLIA
Brian Morron *Gotelee & Goldsmith*

Steele & Co has heightened its profile following the firm's take over of Broadland District Council's entire legal department.

NORTH

Eversheds Leeds (which is generally regarded as having the best public sector department outside London) undertakes a broad range of work for central and local government and for quangos. The firm is also renowned for its expertise in EC public procurement, municipal training and CCT. *Eversheds* is another practice which has refused to engage in bidding

against local authority legal departments under the compulsory competitive tendering regime but is concentrating on assisting local authorities to prepare for compulsory competitive tendering. Stephen Cirell and John Bennett are widely regarded as leading authorities on CCT and have written a number of leading texts on the subject, the most recent of which, 'Competitive Tendering for Professional Services', was published in 1994.

HIGHLY REGARDED – NORTH

ALSOP WILKINSON *Liverpool*	**DICKINSON DEES** *Newcastle*
HALLIWELL LANDAU *Manchester*	**PANNONE & PARTNERS** *Manchester*
PINSENT CURTIS *Leeds*	
AARON & PARTNERS *Chester*	

In Manchester, *Pannone & Partners* advise local authorities on major projects, companies and partnerships between the public and private sectors, while Leeds-based *Pinsent Curtis* is one of the leading firms in externalisation work for local councils, acting for more than 20 local authorities

in this respect.

Dickinson Dees is particularly renowned for compulsory purchase and urban regeneration work and is currently acting in a proposed grant-aided project involving a 500 acre site in Londons' Docklands. The firm represents a number of major clients including the Tyne & Wear Development Corporation. Other firms representing urban development corporations include *Alsop Wilkinson* and *Halliwell Landau*.

LEADING INDIVIDUALS – NORTH

A. John Bennett *Eversheds*	
Stephen D. Cirell *Eversheds*	
David Ansbro *Eversheds*	
Roger Lancaster *Halliwell Landau*	

SCOTLAND

Harper Macleod is the only Scottish practice to have entered into a formal contractual relationship with a local authority. The firm provides legal services to Stirling District Council.

HIGHLY REGARDED – SCOTLAND

BRODIES WS *Edinburgh*	**W & J BURNESS WS** *Edinburgh*
HARPER MACLEOD *Glasgow*	

Brodies WS has established a Local Government Support Group which offers litigation services and a range of advice on planning/ environmental issues and compulsory purchase. *W & J Burness WS* also has a public sector group and advises a transport agency.

LEADERS IN LOCAL GOVERNMENT

LONDON

Abram, David
Nabarro Nathanson, London (0171) 493 9933. Partner. Planning Department.

Ambrose, Ray
Nabarro Nathanson, London (0171) 493 9933. Qualified 1975. Consultant. Public Sector Department. Specialises in local government and administrative law. Born 20.9.1937.

Briam, Tony
See under Property (Commercial).

Child, A.A.
Rowe & Maw, London (0171) 248 4282.

Cowen, Leonie
Leonie Cowen & Associates, London (0181) 964 4177.
Specialisation: Local Authority professional work and consultancy, especially externalisation, CCT, local authority powers, companies, public procurement, social serv-

ices, education, employment and finance. She is an accredited mediator. Acted for Quantum Care Ltd. in transfer of 31 homes for the elderly from Hertfordshire CC and in obtaining £30m development funding. Acted for Dartford BC in the MBO of its Direct Services Organisation and for numerous authorities in interest rate swaps litigation. Contributor to 'The Handbook of Local Authority Legal Practice' and author of many articles in legal and local government press. Regular speaker at conferences and seminars on local authority topics.
Prof. Membership: Law Society, Assoc. of District Secretaries.
Career: Spent 15 years in local government, latterly as Chief Solicitor to London Borough of Barnet and Director of Law & Admin./Deputy Chief Executive at London Borough of Camden. Founded her own practice in 1989.
Personal: Born 1950. Leisure interests include music and her family.

Cunliffe, Michael D.
See under Planning.

Doolittle, Ian
Trowers & Hamlins, London (0171) 831 6292. Partner in Public Sector Department.
Specialisation: Deals with all aspects of central and local government work, especially housing stock transfers. Also handles environmental matters, including all aspects of transactional and regulatory work, and in particular contaminated land and waste management. Practice and bulletin editor of 'Garner's Environmental Law' (Butterworth's). Author of the UK chapter in 'Environmental Law and Regulation' (Butterworth's) and various articles on housing and environmental issues. Regular speaker on public sector and environmental issues.

Fine, Anthony
See under Corporate Finance.

Griffiths, Trevor
See under Administrative & Public Law.

Hall, Brian
See under Planning.

Hand, Catherine

Winckworth & Pemberton (incorporating Sherwood & Co), London (0171) 593 5000. Partner in Housing and Local Government Department.

Specialisation: Has extensive experience of all aspects of legal work required by housing associations, including major urban regeneration schemes, private finance, employment law, constitutional issues, stock transfers and care in the community schemes. Also experienced in local government law, advising on powers and creation of companies, stock transfers, CCT and VCT. Has acted on eight completed large scale voluntary transfers, with three more currently in progress. Advised bidders in three of last year's VCT housing management contracts and a group of large housing associations on their report on corporate governance. Advised the DOE on the management agreement for the tenant's right to manage.

Prof. Membership: Law Society.

Career: Qualified 1978. Lecturer in Law at Queen Mary College, London 1978-79 and 1980-84. Lecturer in Law at the University of Kent 1979-80. In the Government Legal Service, Lord Chancellors Department 1984-89. Joined *Winckworth & Pemberton* in 1989.

Personal: Born 8th September 1954. Educated at Southampton University 1972-75 (LL.B 1st Class Hons). Chairman of Westminster Medical Research Trust. Trustee of START (a charity researching into skin disease). Lives in London.

Hawkins, David

See under Planning.

Hopkins, Carl W.V.

Nabarro Nathanson, London (0171) 491 6770. Qualified 1971. Partner 1987. Public Law and Urban Regeneration Department. Work covers advising on strategy, compulsory purchase, planning and litigation. Born 18.8.1945.

Hunter, David

Lovell White Durrant, London (0171) 236 0066.

Specialisation: Partner in the Local Government and Planning Group. Advises on all aspects of local government law, including finance, planning, rating, compulsory purchase and compensation, parliamentary work and highways.

Prof. Membership: Land Tribunal Consultative Committee; The Law Society Planning Panel.

Career: Qualified 1980. Solicitor in local government 1976-1987. Assistant solicitor, *Lovell White Durrant* 1987-1990. Partner since 1990.

McCormack, Carol A.

Berwin Leighton, London (0171) 623 3144. Partner in Property Department.

Specialisation: Principal area of work is ad-vising local authorities and other public sector clients on major commercial property transactions such as town centre redevelopment and refurbishment agreements. Also handles public sector and institutional property work, including grant-related work and the acquisition and disposal of commercial property generally. Presented workshops at Cipfa annual conferences 1991-94, to various local authority valuer associations and chaired workshop at British Council of Shopping Centres, Annual Conference 1993.

Prof. Membership: British Council of Shopping Centres, Committee Member of Women in Property.

Career: Articled with *Berwin Leighton* 1983-85 and became a Partner in 1989.

Personal: Born 22nd February 1961. Attended the Gillbrook School, Southpark Sixth Form College and Selwyn College, Cambridge. Leisure pursuits include reading, sewing and fly fishing. Lives in Chiswick.

Miller, Nigel

See under Company/Commercial.

Randall C.B.E., Simon

See under Housing Associations.

Taylor, David

Berwin Leighton, London (0171) 623 3144. Senior Associate in Property Department.

Specialisation: Main areas of practice are commercial property and local government. Broad commercial practice including acquisition development and joint ventures with specialist involvement for local authority and public sector clients. Recent transactions include the purchase of 50% interest in Little Britain for the Prudential and major lettings on behalf of the UK government. In addition to the Prudential major clients include British Land and AMEC.

Career: With *Lovell White & King* from 1974 to 1979. Joined *Berwin Leighton* in 1980 and became a Senior Associate in 1987.

Personal: Born 5th August 1956. Educated at Shooters Hill Grammar School. Leisure interests include classic cars. Lives in Smarden.

Totman, Edward B.

D J Freeman, London (0171) 583 4055. Partner in Property Department.

Specialisation: Principal area of work involves local government and public authorities, including controls on local authority finance and capital expenditure and on company participation, extent of powers, town centre development agreements, joint ventures between public and private sectors and property work for NHS Trusts. Other main area of work is general commercial property advice and agreements for funding, development, purchase, sale and lettings of all types of commercial property. General legal adviser to the Commission for the New Towns and deals with all major property sales in the Commission's 12 southern towns. Development projects include the Glades Centre, Bromley; the Swan Centre, Eastleigh; and Basildon and Cwmbran Town Centres. Author of various articles on public and private sector initiatives, local authority capital expenditure controls and 'clawback'. Has chaired and spoken at various conferences and seminars, especially for the Law Society's Local Government Group.

Prof. Membership: Law Society.

Career: Qualified 1970. With Greater London Council 1966-72, Abbey National Building Society 1972-74, Mercantile Credit Company Ltd 1974-79. Joined *D.J. Freeman* in 1979 and became a Partner in 1981.

Personal: Born 28th June 1942. Attended Wimbledon College, then King's College, London. Leisure pursuits include theatre, reading, swimming, tennis and 'Dingbats'. Lives in Ewell.

Williams, Christine J.

See under Corporate Finance.

REGIONS

Ansbro, David

See under Education.

Baker, Simon

See under Property (Commercial).

Bennett, A. John

Eversheds, Leeds (0113) 243 0391. Consultant in Public Sector Unit.

Specialisation: Work covers all aspects of contracting and tendering, including CCT, EC public procurement and municipal trading. Competition Editor for the Local Government Chronicle; Specialist Editor on Competition for the Encyclopaedia of Local Government Law, co-author of 'Compulsory Competitive Tendering: Law and Practice'; co-author of 'Municipal Trading'; co-author of 'EC Public Procurement; Law and Practice'; co-author of 'Compulsory Tendering for Professional Services'; co-author of over one hundred articles on public sector contracting. Has appeared on TV and addressed numerous conferences and seminars.

Prof. Membership: Law Society.

Career: Qualified in 1975. Became a Consultant in 1984. Previous appointments include *Malcolm Lynch* Solicitors in Leeds; Head of Public Law Group at Leeds Business School; Solicitor at the Department of Education and Science, Education Assets Board; Senior Contracts Solicitor at Brown & Root (UK) Ltd (Consultant to Esso, Shell, ELF and Mobil); *Peysner & Foley* Solicitors in Sheffield; *John Howell & Co.* Solicitors in Sheffield; and Solicitor for Nottinghamshire County Council.

Personal: Born 11th October 1950. Attended Universities of Nottingham and Sheffield. Leisure interests include wife and family, and outdoor pursuits. Lives in Leeds.

Burgess, Peter
See under Planning.

Cirell, Stephen D.
Eversheds, Leeds (0113) 243 0391. Partner in Public Sector Unit.

Specialisation: Principal area of practice covers compulsory competitive tendering, externalisation, market testing, municipal trading, European Community Public Procurement and public sector contracting generally. Other main area of work is local government law including housing, finance, planning, environmental health, education, social services and highways. Author 'CCT-Law & Practice', 'Municipal Trading' and 'Competitive Tendering for Professional Services'. Specialist editor to Encyclopaedia of Local Government Law. Specialist correspondent to the Local Government Chronicle and author of numerous articles for professional publications. Lectures frequently on CCT and related matters for commercial course organisers, professional organisations, local authorities and in-house.

Prof. Membership: Law Society.

Career: Qualified 1984 while with Stockport MBC. Assistant Solicitor, then Principal Solicitor with Dudley MBC 1984-88, then Head of Common Law/ Assistant Director at Leeds City Council 1988-93. Joined *Eversheds Hepworth & Chadwick* as a Partner in the Public Sector Unit in October 1993.

Personal: Born 3rd July 1960. Attended University College of Wales Aberystwyth 1978-81. Leisure pursuits include martial arts. Lives in Leeds.

Dimmick, Simon
Clarks, Reading (01734) 585321. Specialises in local government and planning law.

Evans, Eric C.
See under Planning.

Hinton, Robert
Griffith Smith, Brighton (01273) 324041. Partner in Public Law Department.

Specialisation: Main area of practice is town and country planning, handling all aspects of law, procedure and policy, including local inquiry advocacy. Also a specialist in the law and practice regarding taxi and private hire licensing, having advised many Taxi Associations and local authorities and conducted three seminars on this for the Law Society Local Government Group.

Prof. Membership: Legal Associate of Royal Town Planning Institute. Member of Law Society's panel of solicitors to act in planning cases.

Career: 27 years employment by local

authorities, the last 12 of these as Chief Executive and Solicitor to a Borough Council. Joined *Griffith Smith* in 1985.

Personal: Born 21st December 1936.

Iley, Malcolm
Bevan Ashford, Plymouth (01752) 256888. Partner specialising in public sector law and local government.

Specialisation: Main area of practice is public sector law with regard to local government, including local government law, planning and environmental and some European experience with particular reference to local authority transfers, compulsory purchase, CCT, education, competition, grants, town and city centre redevelopments. Acted in London Borough of Croydon transfer of Fairfield Halls, LAWDAC, in education transfers and parliamentary bills and has done work for UDC and urban regeneration. Author of several articles for local government press and local newspapers. Regular advisor and speaker on television, in newspapers and at seminars both national and regional.

Career: Qualified in 1976. Began career in the private sector in a commercial appointment. Transferred to local government and became City Solicitor and Deputy Chief Executive for Plymouth City Council, having held senior posts with Leeds City Council, Sussex and Norfolk. Joined *Bevan Ashford* in 1989 as a Partner.

Personal: Born 12th April 1950. Plymouth College Governor. F.E. Governor. Company Director, Trustee, Director of Environmental Trust and Business in the Community.

Lancaster, Roger
See under Planning.

Morron, Brian
Gotelee & Goldsmith, Ipswich (01473) 211121. Partner in Commercial Department.

Specialisation: Main areas of practice are local government, planning and employment law. 22 years' experience of local authority legal work: ex-Deputy Borough Solicitor at Wandsworth LBC. Chaired Associate Section of the Association of District Secretaries, 1988. Acted as Borough solicitor to the Royal Borough of Kingston Upon Thames while based in Suffolk. Managed six month contract in 1991 to transfer total housing stock of Suffolk Coastal District Council to a housing association. Currently managing three year and five year contracts with two other London Borough Councils. Member of Law Society's Planning Panel.

Prof. Membership: Law Society; Committee Member, Ipswich Solicitors Group.

Career: Qualified in 1976. Principal Planning Solicitor, London Borough of Haringey 1978-80, Deputy Borough Solicitor, London Borough of Wandsworth 1983-89. Joined *Gotelee & Goldsmith* in 1989, from 1990 as a partner.

Personal: Born 8th March 1949. Attended University of London (LSE), taking an LLB and LLM 1971-2. Executive Committee Member of Suffolk Book League. Lives in Framlingham, Suffolk.

Orlik, Michael
Dibb Lupton Broomhead, Birmingham (0121) 200 1188. Partner in Property Litigation Group.

Specialisation: Main area of practice is town and country planning, environmental law, highway law and compulsory purchase. Worked for four local authorities from 1967 to 1989. Currently has a number of local authority and developer clients. Also advises on local authority legislation, powers of local authorities and judicial review. Has represented numerous clients at local inquiries. Acted in the Skypark planning inquiry, the successful prosecution of a County Council for obstructing a highway and a lengthy Lands Tribunal case for compensation for compulsory acquisition by a development corporation. Author of 'An Introduction to Highway Law' (1993); contributes regular monthly column for the Surveyor. Has lectured on these topics at a number of seminars.

Prof. Membership: Law Society, Society of Local Authority Chief Executives. Evironmental Law Foundation, Education Law Association.

Career: Qualified in 1970. VSO teacher in West Africa 1965-66. Articled clerk and then solicitor with West Sussex C.C. 1967-77. Assistant County Solicitor at Buckinghamshire C.C. 1977-81. Assistant Chief Executive at Dorset C.C. 1981-84. Chief Executive of Surrey Heath B.C. 1984-89. Joined *Needham & James* as a Partner in 1990; firm merged with *Dibb Lupton Broomhead* in 1993.

Personal: Born 21st September 1943. Attended Oxford University 1962-65. School Governor of a secondary school and a primary school. Leisure interests include walking, cycling, bridge, theatre, reading and history. Lives in Birmingham.

Stacey, A.J.
Pinsent Curtis, Birmingham (0121) 200 1050.

White, Martin
See under Planning.

Williams, Huw R.C.
See under Planning.

MAJOR PROJECTS/INFRASTRUCTURE

LARGE scale infrastructure and major projects together constitute an area of increasing importance for the firms capable of handling this sort of work. Such work includes the financing of roads, railways, airports and hotels, particularly in areas of rapid economic development such as South-East Asia and Eastern Europe. For the first time, a separate section for firms and individuals with major projects and infrastructure financing expertise has been compiled. Specialists in asset finance and leasing appear elsewhere in the directory.

This is an area with a strong international aspect, characterised by fierce competition between English and US firms for the available work. Recently the struggle was intensified as leading US firm *Milbank Tweed Hadley & McCloy* hired project finance lawyers from *Clifford Chance*.

LONDON

Major projects and infrastructure is an area of expertise dominated by the large City firms who are able to benefit from their international presence and contacts. This is illustrated by the fact that the pre-eminent firms in London are *Allen & Overy, Clifford Chance* and *Linklaters & Paines*.

The leading firm is *Allen & Overy*. The firm advises sponsors, governments, construction companies and lenders on construction projects and project financings throughout the world. They are particularly highly regarded for their work in connection with airport construction, tolled motorways and transit systems, electricity generation, water treatment, oil and gas field development, refineries and telecommunications. Partner Graham Vinter is the author of 'Project Finance: A Legal Guide', and has been particularly recommended for his work in relation to finance for bridges, motorways, power stations, oil and gas, and Private Finance Initiative projects. Jonathan Horsfall Turner, Tony Humphrey, and Brian Harrison also have excellent reputations for their work in this field.

The next leading firm is *Clifford Chance*, offering expertise across the full range of major project work, and particularly known for project financing in oil and gas, natural resources and power, and infrastrucure projects. Anthony Bankes-Jones is known for representing international institutions such as the International Finance Corporation and the World Bank. John East, managing partner in the Hong Kong Office, has special expertise in transport infrastructure, power and petrochemical projects. Michael Bray, Tim Soutar, Peter Blake, Margaret Gossling, Rodney Short, Paul Simpson and Chris Wyman were also highly recommended.

Linklaters & Paines also have an excellent reputation in this area, dealing in particular with privatisations and telecommunications issues. Alan Black is well regarded for his involvement in a range of recent major projects including an airport development project for the Greek government, the Bangkok Expressway development for the Thai government,

and oil and gas projects in Nigeria and the Far East, as well as domestic Private Finance Initiative projects. Clive Ransome has been recommended for his work in the Far East and Stuart Salt and David Weber are both highly regarded in the field.

The second tier of firms in this area is also dominated by the large City firms. A firm strong in all aspects of project work, particularly with regard to roads, rail and bridges, petro-chemical plants, private power and private prisons projects is *Norton Rose*. Michael Taylor has considerable experience in North Sea oil and gas financing, as well as independent power projects in the U.K. Jon Ellis is well respected for his work in all aspects of the field and Peter Haslam has been recommended for his work in Hong Kong.

LEADING FIRMS – LONDON	
ALLEN & OVERY	CLIFFORD CHANCE
LINKLATERS & PAINES	
FRESHFIELDS	HERBERT SMITH
NORTON ROSE	SLAUGHTER AND MAY
ASHURST MORRIS CRISP	DENTON HALL
McKENNA & CO	

Freshfields act in all types of major projects and infrastructure work worldwide. Roger McCormick, head of the firm's International Project Finance Group, has been involved in oil and gas transactions in the North Sea, South East Asia, North Africa, Sudan and the Ivory Coast. Other notable project finance work includes an Italian high speed rail project, the Point Fortin Methanol Plant in Trinidad, and the IFC/Apicorp White Nile pipeline in Sudan. Edward Evans has also been highly recommended.

Another firm known for their work in this area is *Herbert Smith*. Andrew Preece has experience in oil, gas, minerals, electricity, water, infrastructure and telecommunications projects. Stephen Barton has acted in the Eurotunnel project.

HIGHLY REGARDED – LONDON	
BAKER & McKENZIE	S J BERWIN & CO
BERWIN LEIGHTON	CAMERON MARKBY HEWITT
FOX & GIBBONS	LOVELL WHITE DURRANT
MACFARLANES	RICHARDS BUTLER
SIMMONS & SIMMONS	STEPHENSON HARWOOD
WATSON, FARLEY & WILLIAMS	WILDE SAPTE

Slaughter and May also have acknowledged expertise in this area. St John Flaherty has been highly recommended for his work in the Far East, including limited recourse financing and documentation for the Hong Kong Eastern Harbour Tunnel. Martin Roberts, Tom Kinnersley, and Paul Stacey have very good reputations.

The third tier of firms in this area comprises *Denton Hall, Ashurst Morris Crisp,* and *McKenna & Co. Denton Hall* have a particularly strong practice in projects related to the energy and utilities sectors. They are also well respected for their work in construction and property projects. David Moroney has been recommended for his work in energy-related projects. A firm with a growing reputation for projects work is *Ashurst Morris Crisp* where both Mark Elsey and Ian Johnson have been highly recommended. Ian Johnson has particular expertise with international power projects. Lastly, *McKenna & Co* have an excellent reputation for their work in the electricity sector. They are involved in electricity related projects in India, Pakistan and the U.S. Fiona Woolf is highly regarded for this work. The firm is also involved in the Channel Tunnel rail link, gas work in Portugal, and work across the other domestic utilities. Robert Phillips has a reputation for developing competitive tenders and setting up the bidding contracts process, as well as for advising on responses to competitive bidding arrangements.

The firms listed above all have a first class reputation for major project work. But there are a number of other firms in London who have expertise in handling this type of work.

A firm which has recently expanded into Eastern Europe is *Baker & McKenzie*; they have been instructed on the development of the M1/M15 motorways in Hungary. *S J Berwin & Co* enjoy a specialist expertise in large and complex projects in the fields of transport, energy, water treatment, private power generation, waste to energy schemes and urban renewal. *Berwin Leighton* act for a number of leading retail and property sector clients in this field.

Cameron Markby Hewitt have advised on many major projects including the construction of a light railway in Ankara, the reorganization of road and rail systems in Crawley, the construction of highways and toll roads in Italy, and the construction of an extension to the Croydon tram links scheme.

Another firm with wide-ranging experience in the field is *Lovell White Durrant*. Their clients have included lenders and borrowers involved with construction projects in Hong Kong; bank syndicates providing pre-export finance to Africa, South Africa and Eastern Europe; and American buyers under long-term gas supply contracts from Africa. In addition, *Richards Butler* is well known for its energy-related work in this sector and *Simmons & Simmons* are well regarded for their structured finance work. *Watson Farley & Williams'* advice on project finance in a number of areas has included oil and gas transactions in the former Soviet Union. Also known for their work in this field are *Wilde Sapte, Fox & Gibbons, Stephenson Harwood* and *Macfarlanes*.

LEADING INDIVIDUALS – LONDON

Anthony Bankes-Jones *Clifford Chance*	**Alan W. Black** *Linklaters & Paines*	**Michael Bray** *Clifford Chance*
George Crozer *White & Case*	**John H.M. East** *Clifford Chance*	**St. J.A. Flaherty** *Slaughter and May*
Jonathan Horsfall Turner *Allen & Overy*	**Anthony R. Humphrey** *Allen & Overy*	**Kenneth MacRitchie** *Milbank, Tweed, Hadley & McCloy*
Roger S. McCormick *Freshfields*	**Robert J. Phillips** *McKenna & Co*	**Andrew D. Preece** *Herbert Smith*
Clive B. Ransome *Linklaters & Paines*	**M.J.D. Roberts** *Slaughter and May*	**Tim Soutar** *Clifford Chance*
Michael P.G. Taylor *Norton Rose*	**Ray Vickers** *Skadden, Arps, Slate, Meagher & Flom*	**Graham D. Vinter** *Allen & Overy*
Fiona Woolf *McKenna & Co*	**Chris Wyman** *Clifford Chance*	
Stephen J. Barton *Herbert Smith*	**Peter Blake** *Clifford Chance*	**Nicholas Buckworth** *Milbank, Tweed, Hadley & McCloy*
Jon Ellis *Norton Rose*	**Mark Elsey** *Ashurst Morris Crisp*	**Edward T.H. Evans** *Freshfields*
Phillip Douglas Fletcher *Milbank, Tweed, Hadley & McCloy*	**Margaret Gossling** *Clifford Chance*	**Brian W. Harrison** *Allen & Overy*
Peter Haslam *Norton Rose*	**Ian Johnson** *Ashurst Morris Crisp*	**Thomas A. Kinnersley** *Slaughter and May*
David Moroney *Denton Hall*	**Stuart R. Salt** *Linklaters & Paines*	**Rodney Short** *Clifford Chance*
Paul Simpson *Clifford Chance*	**John M. Skelton** *Macfarlanes*	**Paul H. Stacey** *Slaughter and May*
Bill Voge *Latham & Watkins*	**David H. Weber** *Linklaters & Paines*	

SCOTLAND

Perhaps unsurprisingly, two of three leading firms in Scotland, *W & J Burness WS* and *Dundas & Wilson CS* both have a strong involvement in oil and gas projects in the North Sea.

HIGHLY REGARDED – SCOTLAND

W & J BURNESS WS *Edinburgh*	**DUNDAS & WILSON CS** *Edinburgh*
SHEPHERD & WEDDERBURN *Edinburgh*	

W. & J. Burness WS have also done work in power station financing. James McLean is noted for his major project work, and has written about oil financing issues.

Dundas & Wilson CS have been involved in work for banks and other providers of finance in connection with oil, gas and electricity projects. Michael Stoneham has been recommended for his finance expertise in connection with these projects.

Shepherd & Wedderburn WS have been involved in project finance work in relation to construction and infrastructure developments; recently they were involved in the construction of the Skye Bridge.

LEADING INDIVIDUALS – SCOTLAND

James A. McLean *W & J Burness WS*
Michael P. Stoneham *Dundas & Wilson CS*

In all the tables the names in each group are listed alphabetically.

LEADERS IN MAJOR PROJECTS/INFRASTRUCTURE

LONDON

Bankes-Jones, Anthony
Clifford Chance, London (0171) 600 1000. Partner. Principal area of practice is securitisation, project financing, banking and international finance.

Barton, Stephen J.
See under Energy & Utilities.

Black, Alan W.
Linklaters & Paines, London (0171) 606 7080. Qualified 1976. Partner 1983. Head of Project Finance Group. Extensive experience acting for governments, sponsors and lenders on major projects for transport, airports and aviation, oil, gas and derivative products.

Blake, Peter
Clifford Chance, London (0171) 600 1000. Partner. Projects Department. Main area of practice is energy and infrastructure projects financed on a limited recourse basis.

Bray, Michael
See under Banking.

Buckworth, Nicholas
Milbank, Tweed, Hadley & McCloy, London (0171) 448 3000. Partner in Project Finance Department.

Specialisation: Advising project developers and financial institutions on all aspects of the structuring, negotiation, development and financing of major infrastructure projects in the UK, Europe and Asia. Currently involved in advising on projects in the Oman, India and Pakistan as well as in Spain and Italy. Regular participant in industry conferences and in client focused presentations and working groups.

Career: Qualified in 1986. With *Clifford Chance* 1984-94. Joined *Milbank, Tweed, Hadley & McCloy* as a Partner in 1994.

Personal: Born 2nd February 1961. Educated at Dundee University (LL.B Hons, 1983). Leisure activities include skiing, squash, golf, music and cinema.

Crozer, George
White & Case, London (0171) 726 6361.

East, John H.M.
Clifford Chance, London (0171) 600 1000. Partner 1976. Managing/ Senior Partner in Hong Kong Office since 1991. Specialises in asset/ project finance (especially transport infrastructure, power and petrochemical projects) and ship financing. Born in 1947.

Ellis, Jon
Norton Rose, London (0171) 283 6000. Qualified 1985. Partner 1992. Banking Department. Main area of practice is project finance.

Elsey, Mark
Ashurst Morris Crisp, London (0171) 638 1111. Qualified 1985. Partner 1994. Main area of practice is the commercial and financial aspects of infrastructure and energy projects.

Evans, Edward T.H.
See under Banking.

Flaherty, St. J.A.
Slaughter and May, London (0171) 600 1200. Qualified 1981. Partner handling general banking and finance work.

Fletcher, Phillip Douglas
Milbank, Tweed, Hadley & McCloy, London (0171) 483-3000. Partner in Corporate and Banking Department (Project Finance Group).

Specialisation: Specialises in the development and financing of major infrastructure projects, including power plants, pipelines, roads and satillites. Has represented parties in relation to projects in Europe, the US, Canada and Asia, including the Birecik Dam, Turkey; Tapada Power Plant, Portugal; the Medway Power Plant, UK; the Centre Energia and Rosen Power Plants, Italy: and IEC cogenecotio projects I44A debt insurance, U.S. Lecturer at conferences and forums (e.g. World Economic Congress, Madrid, and Adam Smith Institute, London) on negotiation of power contracts and project documentation and has written a number of articles on these topics.

Career: Admitted, District of Columbia, California and New York. Has been with *Milbank, Tweed, Hadley & McCloy* since 1983 and was resident in the firm's Hong Kong office in 1987 and 1988.

Personal: Born 16th September 1957. Educated at Georgetown University School of Foreign Service, Fletcher School of Law & Diplomacy (MA, 1983) and the University of California, Berkeley (JD, 1983). Member of Council on Foreign Relations. Fluent in French.

Gossling, Margaret
Clifford Chance, London (0171) 600 1000. Partner. Principal areas are project finance, energy finance and general banking work.

Harrison, Brian W.
Allen & Overy, London (0171) 330 3000. Qualified 1985. Partner 1987. Banking Department. Main area of practice is project finance, acting for lenders and sponsors on large infrastructure projects.

Haslam, Peter
Norton Rose, London (0171) 283 6000. Qualified 1981.

Horsfall Turner, Jonathan
Allen & Overy, London (0171) 330 3000. Qualified 1970. Partner 1973. Banking Department. Main area of practice is banking, restructuring, syndications, bank acquisitions and disposals and project 1inance. Also handles capital markets work. Born 27.11.1945.

Humphrey, Anthony R.
See under Banking.

Johnson, Ian
See under Energy & Utilities.

Kinnersley, Thomas A.
See under Asset Finance & Leasing.

MacRitchie, Kenneth
Milbank, Tweed, Hadley & McCloy, London (0171) 448 3000. Partner in Project Finance Group.

Specialisation: Advising clients in negotiating and structuring commercial agreements for major infrastructure projects. Projects include roads and transport infrastructure; minerals and natural resources; electricity, oil and gas facilities. Recent transactions comprise advising lenders on privatisations including the Electricity industry in Northern Ireland and the coal industry in the U.K and advising on major independent power project financings in the U.K., Europe and Asia including Pego, Portugal; Elcogas, Spain; Isab, Italy and the Uch Project in Pakistan. Clients include U.K. clearing banks, international banks and financial institutions and U.K., U.S. and international project developers. Is a contributor to specialist journals and a regular participant in conferences on project finance, infrastructure financing and privatisation.

Prof. Membership: Law Society, Law Society of Scotland.

Career: Qualified in 1976. Partner at *Clifford Chance* 1991-94. Joined *Milbank, Tweed, Hadley & McCloy* in 1994 as a Partner.

Personal: Born 3rd September 1956. Attended Universities of Glasgow, Aberdeen, Manchester and Oxford. Leisure interests include family, gardening, cycling, tennis, classical music and reading. Lives in Oxford.

McCormick, Roger S.
Freshfields, London (0171) 936 4000. Partner and head of the International Project Finance Group. Has advised on major projects both in the UK and internationally. Born 27.2.1951.

Moroney, David
See under Energy & Utilities.

Phillips, Robert J.
McKenna & Co, London (0171) 606 9000. Partner in Corporate (Utilities) Group.

Specialisation: Principal area of practice is advising on transactions involving private/ public sector participation with particular emphasis on major infrastructure and capital projects. Work covers specialist contract drafting, development with other consultants of a risk profile, and negotiating terms of project documents required for limited recourse financed infrastructure schemes. Major projects include independent power projects in Portugal, Morocco, Malaysia and India; road and/or rail schemes in the U.K., Hungary, Thailand and Portugal and, in particular, advising the Department of Transport on the High Speed Channel Rail Link, a private sector consortium on DBFO highways and a private sector consortium on participation in prison services. Regular speaker at international conferences and has spoken at seminars organised by the World Bank amongst others.

Prof. Membership: Law Society, Major Projects Association.

Career: Partner at *McKenna & Co.* since 1979, including period as Senior Resident Partner in Hong Kong 1983-88. Admitted as a Solicitor, Hong Kong, 1983 and as a Barrister and Solicitor, State of Victoria, Australia, 1986.

Personal: Born 15th May 1947. Lives in Walton-on-Thames, Surrey.

Preece, Andrew D.
Herbert Smith, London (0171) 374 8000. Partner and Head of International Finance and Banking Group and Projects Group.

Specialisation: Has considerable experience in project finance, lease finance and general commercial work, with particular expertise in oil and gas and infrastructure financings, both domestic and international, and in complex lease financing and property financings.

Prof. Membership: Law Society, International Bar Association, UK Energy Lawyers Group, Finance & Leasing Association.

Career: Qualified in 1970. Became a Partner at *Herbert Smith* in 1977.

Personal: Educated at Selwyn College, Cambridge.

Ransome, Clive B.
Linklaters & Paines, London 852 2842 4888. Qualified 1985. Partner 1992. Projects & Project Finance Department. Hong Kong Office. Has worked on a number of major projects, project/ structured financings worldwide.

Roberts, M.J.D.
See under Energy & Utilities.

Salt, Stuart R.
See under Energy & Utilities.

Short, Rodney
Clifford Chance, London (0171) 600 1000. Partner 1982. Projects Group. Acts for sponsors, lenders and/or MLAs in limited recourse financing of infrastructure and industrial/ energy projects.

Simpson, Paul
Clifford Chance, London (0171) 600 1000. Partner. Principal area of practice is corporate and banking law relating to projects and infrastructure work.

Skelton, John M.
Macfarlanes, London (0171) 831 9222. Qualified 1977. Partner 1987. Company, Commercial & Banking Department. Specialises in banking and corporate law.

Soutar, Tim
Clifford Chance, London (Hong Kong (+852 281 00229). Partner 1988. Projects Group. Main area of practice is project work dealing with the commercial and financial aspects of large scale industrial and infrastructure projects, primarily in the power and energy sectors. Born 26.9.1955.

Stacey, Paul H.
Slaughter and May, London (0171) 600 1200. Qualified 1983. Specialises in project finance and general banking, especially electricity and power generation finance.

Taylor, Michael P.G.
See under Energy & Utilities.

Vickers, Ray
Skadden, Arps, Slate, Meagher & Flom, London (0171) 248 9929.

Vinter, Graham D.
See under Banking.

Voge, Bill
Latham & Watkins, London (0171) 374 4444.

Weber, David H.
Linklaters & Paines, London (0171) 606 7080. Qualified 1978. Partner in the Project and Project Finance Department.

Woolf, Fiona
See under Energy & Utilities.

Wyman, Chris
Clifford Chance, London (0171) 600 1000. Partner. Main area of practice is project financing in the power, infrastructure and natural resources sectors.

McLean, James A.
See under Intellectual Property.

Stoneham, Michael P.
See under Banking.

EDITORIAL POLICY

Our policy is to identify leading practitioners entirely on merit. It is not possible to buy a place in our biographical lists: inclusion is based on a practitioner's expertise and professional reputation. The same applies to the lists of recommended law-firms and sets of chambers.

Enormous effort has been invested by our ten-strong research team (mainly solicitors and barristers) in canvassing recommendations and identifying leaders. We are confident in the overall accuracy of the results. However, mistakes and omissions are inevitable, and if readers have any suggestions regarding listings or rankings we should be very pleased to hear from them.

The lists will be revised on the basis of fresh research every year.

MEDIA & ENTERTAINMENT

LONDON

There is an increasing tendency for firms with media and entertainment clients to offer a full range of services to every market sector. Of these firms, *Denton Hall* emerges as the leading practice with *Harbottle & Lewis* ranking a close second.

LEADING FIRMS – LONDON – OVERALL EXPERTISE	
DENTON HALL	
HARBOTTLE & LEWIS	
OLSWANG	RICHARDS BUTLER
THE SIMKINS PARTNERSHIP	

Other highly recommended firms include *Olswang*, *Richards Butler* and *The Simkins Partnership*.

HIGHLY REGARDED – LONDON – OVERALL EXPERTISE	
S J BERWIN & CO	BERWIN LEIGHTON
BIDDLE & CO	CAMPBELL HOOPER
CLINTONS	DAVENPORT LYONS
D J FREEMAN	GOULDENS
HAMLIN SLOWE	LEE & THOMPSON
MANCHES & CO	MARRIOTT HARRISON
MISHCON DE REYA	RUSSELLS
SHERIDANS	SIMONS MUIRHEAD & BURTON
TARLO LYONS	TAYLOR JOYNSON GARRETT
THEODORE GODDARD	
ARNOLD SEGAL	BROWN COOPER
DAVID, WINEMAN	EDMONDS BOWEN & CO
KANAAR & CO	NICHOLAS MORRIS
OSWALD HICKSON COLLIER	PETER CARTER-RUCK & PARTNERS
SCHILLING & LOM	SEDDONS
STEVEN FISHER	TITMUSS SAINER DECHERT

Each sector of the entertainment industry has its leading practices; for this reason they are treated seperately.

FILM

Denton Hall is widely regarded as the pre-eminent firm advising the film industry, with outstanding practitioners in Ken Dearsley (who heads the finance unit), Michael Ridley (commissioning, distribution and co-production) and Adrian Barr-Smith. The firm acts for Hollywood studios (especially Paramount/Viacom), a number of prominent production companies, international distributors and other financing entities.

Close on the heels of *Denton Hall* comes *SJ Berwin & Co, Richards Butler* and *Marriott Harrison,* all of which have excellent reputations in the field. *SJ Berwin*'s leading light is Nigel Palmer who has many years' experience in financing and merchandising. Peter McInerney, formerly at Thames Television, has also been recommended. *Richards Butler* boasts the highly regarded Richard Philips, a film finance specialist who advises banks, distributors and other lending institutions and also lectures on the subject.

Peter Dally, William Hinshelwood, David Norris and Frank Bloom at *Marriott Harrison* are all highly experienced practitioners specialising in secured lending, project loans and revolving facilities. The firm also advises major film companies and independents on production and distribution issues.

Other firms highly recommended for film work include *Davenport Lyons, Olswang* and *The Simkins Partnership.*

Davenport Lyons (particularly Leon Morgan) is strong in film finance, the firm representing two major clearing banks and a number of production companies.

LEADING FIRMS – LONDON – FILMS	
DENTON HALL	
S J BERWIN & CO	MARRIOTT HARRISON
RICHARDS BUTLER	
DAVENPORT LYONS	OLSWANG
THE SIMKINS PARTNERSHIP	

Olswang's media unit, comprising five specialist partners, handles an increasing amount of work for major film industry clients. Mark Devereux, who heads the team, is held in high regard.

Nigel Bennett and his team of four at The *Simkins Partnership* are renowned for providing advice on copyright, finance agreements, production contracts and distribution agreements worldwide.

TELEVISION, VIDEO & RADIO

Advice to clients in the broadcasting industry tends to fall into two categories: cable and satellite work, where firms with telecommunications expertise dominate the field, and general broadcasting work (including production, distribution and finance) which is handled by the traditional media firms and particularly those which advise the film industry.

HIGHLY REGARDED – LONDON – TELEVISION & RADIO	
ALLISON & HUMPHREYS	S J BERWIN & CO
CHARLES RUSSELL	CLIFFORD CHANCE
DAVENPORT LYONS	DENTON HALL
GOULDENS	HARBOTTLE & LEWIS
LEE & THOMPSON	MARRIOTT HARRISON
MICHAEL HENRY & Co	OLSWANG
RICHARDS BUTLER	TARLO LYONS

Firms consistently recommended for cable and satellite work include *Allison & Humphreys, Charles Russell* and *Clifford Chance.*

Anthony Ballard at *Allison & Humphreys* specialises in television law, advising on broadcasting, regulatory and policy matters. The firm has been involved in the setting up of satellite programmes since the early 1980's.

Charles Russell handles a broad spectrum of work including advice on interconnection agreements for a number of cable TV companies.

Clifford Chance, in addition to advising on regulatory work, advises on terrestrial broadcasting.

Firms highly recommended for general television work include *Davenport Lyons*: Leon Morgan (named Lawyer of the Year by the Independent Television Association) advises Barclays Bank and the Royal Bank of Scotland, acts for Media Ventures International (owners of Teletext) and Dimbleby Martin Productions and has handled Channel Four's first major commission (Brookside); *Gouldens*, where Christopher Parkinson (also known for radio work) has been recommended; *Harbottle & Lewis*, where Robert Storer and Medwyn Jones advise on finance and production for clients such as Merchant Ivory Productions Ltd; *Lee & Thompson* (particularly Jeremy Gawade); *Marriott Harrison*, where William Hinshelwood and Frank Bloom are experienced in the field of finance; and *Tarlo Lyons* where Judi O'Brien has been recommended.

Michael Henry (formerly of *Nicholson Graham & Jones*) enjoys an excellent reputation in the field. He has recently launched *Michael Henry & Co*, a niche practice advising the BBC, Aardman Animations Ltd, Skyline Film and Television Productions Ltd (producers of major television dramas) in addition to a number of other major film and television clients.

Firms with experience in both aspects (cable and satellite and general broadcasting) include *Denton Hall*, which represents UK Gold, Thames Television and Home Box Office (Adrian Barr-Smith has been recommended for cable and satellite, Michael Ridley for production and distribution and Ken Dearsley for finance); *Olswang*, where David Zeffman handles the corporate and commercial aspects of cable and satellite and Mark Devereux finance and production; and *Richards Butler* which is strong in both finance (Richard Philips is recommended) and cable and satellite, (Stephen Edwards advising on transmission and programme contracts, European regulation, production and distribution).

Practitioners with experience in the video industry include Nigel Palmer at *SJ Berwin & Co*, Ken Dearsley at *Denton Hall* and Judi O'Brien at *Tarlo Lyons*.

THEATRE

Tarlo Lyons and *Barry Shaw* dominate the field. Michael Rose at *Tarlo Lyons* enjoys a national reputation and represents the largest client in the industry: Cameron Mackintosh.

LEADING FIRMS – LONDON – THEATRE	
BARRY SHAW	TARLO LYONS
CAMPBELL HOOPER	HARBOTTLE & LEWIS
THE SIMKINS PARTNERSHIP	

Barry Shaw (formerly of *Wright Webb Syrett*) acts for West End producers, advising on the documentation for plays and musicals such as 'Crazy for You' and 'Grease'.

Other firms with experience in the field include *Campbell Hooper*, where David Wills has been recommended, *Harbottle & Lewis* (and in particular Laurence Harbottle) and *The Simkins Partnership*.

PUBLISHING

Publishing houses generate a substantial amount of legal work including pre-publication libel advice, contract, licensing and copyright. Whilst a great many firms undertake such work, those which have been consistently recommended

HIGHLY REGARDED – LONDON – PUBLISHING	
BIDDLE & CO	DAVENPORT LYONS
DENTON HALL	GOODMAN DERRICK
HARBOTTLE & LEWIS	MANCHES & CO
THE SIMKINS PARTNERSHIP	SIMONS MUIRHEAD & BURTON
TAYLOR JOYNSON GARRETT	

include *Biddle & Co, Davenport Lyons* (David Hooper), *Denton Hall* (in particular, Alan Williams), *Goodman Derrick* (where Robin Perrot has been recommended), *Harbottle & Lewis* (which specialises in video and electronic games), *Manches & Co, Simons Muirhead & Burton* (which advises Harper Collins and Time Out), *Taylor Joynson Garrett* and *The Simkins Partnership* (where Laurence Kaye has been recommended for electronic publishing).

MUSIC

JP Kennedy & Co and *Russells* are the leading music specialists.

Of the two firms, *Russells* is marginally ahead in terms of expertise. Anthony Russell, described as a first class negotiator and litigator, ranks among the most highly recommended practitioners in the field. The firm represents a number of major record companies (most notably Warner), artists and music publishers. *JP Kennedy & Co*, a small niche practice is also highly regarded, the reputation of the firm resting with John Kennedy (described as a rainmaker) who was universally recommended.

LEADING FIRMS – LONDON – MUSIC	
J.P. KENNEDY & CO	RUSSELLS
CLINTONS	EATONS
LEE & THOMPSON	SHERIDANS
S J BERWIN & CO	SEARLES
THE SIMKINS PARTNERSHIP	THEODORE GODDARD

Other firms which have excellent reputations in the field include *Clintons*, where John Cohen has been recommended for recording, publishing and management, *Eatons* (Michael Eaton is highly regarded for commercial advice, *Lee & Thompson, Sheridans* and *The Simkins Partnership*, which has five partners dealing exclusively with the music industry (Julian Turton is recommended).

Lee & Thompson acts for major record companies including Phonogram, Polydor and Island, independents, artists including Queen, Wet Wet Wet, Elton John and Simply Red, managers, producers, agents and publishers. Robert Lee and Andrew Thompson are both widely regarded as authorities.

Sheridans media unit, headed by the highly respected Howard Jones, represents a number of leading artists in the popular music industry including George Michael, Jason Donovan and Paul McCartney.

Firms also recommended for their expertise include *SJ Berwin & Co, Searles* (which represents independent record companies, recording artists and songwriters including Seal, Jamiroquai and Portishead) and *The Simkins Partnership*.

Paddy Grafton Green of *Theodore Goddard* is regarded as the leading authority on tax issues.

LITIGATION

Litigation represents a substantial portion of the work undertaken by media firms.

The most highly recommended litigators include Anthony Julius at *Mishcon de Reya* who recently represented Stephen Fry in the 'Cell Mates' litigation and the Princess of Wales in the widely publicised case against Bryce Taylor and the Mirror Group, and Razi Mireskandari of *Simons Muirhead & Burton* who represented Bryce Taylor.

Other firms recommended for their expertise in the field include *Campbell Hooper,* where David Wills has recently conducted litigation against Stephen Fry on behalf of the producers of 'Cell Mates', and the Bernard Shaw estate in the 'My Fair Lady' case; *Davenport Lyons* and *Crockers,* where Rupert Grey conducts copyright and moral right infringement work for photographers, photographic libraries and syndication agencies.

LEADING FIRMS – LONDON – LITIGATION	
MISHCON DE REYA	SIMONS MUIRHEAD & BURTON
CAMPBELL HOOPER	CLINTONS
CROCKERS	DAVENPORT LYONS
RUSSELLS	SHERIDANS
STEPHENS INNOCENT	

The leading litigators in the music industry are David Davis, David Landsman and Andrew Sharland (who successfully litigated in major cases on behalf of Stone Roses, Pete Townsend and Sony in the George Michael case) of *Clintons*, Brian Howard of *Russells* and Cyril Glasser of *Sheridans*.

Individual practitioners recommended for their expertise in the field include Mark Stephens of *Stephens Innocent* who is well-known for conducting cases on behalf of personalities in the entertainment field.

LEADING INDIVIDUALS – LONDON		
Robert Allan *Denton Hall*	Frank Bloom *Marriott Harrison*	John M.R. Cohen *Clintons*
Peter Dally *Marriott Harrison*	Ken Dearsley *Denton Hall*	Mark Devereux *Olswang*
Michael C.A. Eaton *Eatons*	Laurence Gilmore *Hamlin Slowe*	P. Grafton Green *Theodore Goddard*
Michael Henry *Michael Henry & Co*	William Hinshelwood *Marriott Harrison*	Medwyn Jones *Harbottle & Lewis*
Howard Jones *Sheridans*	Anthony Julius *Mishcon De Reya*	John P. Kennedy *J.P. Kennedy & Co*
David M. Landsman *Clintons*	R.W. Lee *Lee & Thompson*	Peter B.G. McInerney *S J Berwin & Co*
Razi Mireskandari *Simons Muirhead & Burton*	Leon Morgan *Davenport Lyons*	David J. Norris *Marriott Harrison*
Nigel S. Palmer *S J Berwin & Co*	Richard P.S. Philipps *Richards Butler*	Michael Ridley *Denton Hall*
D. Michael Rose *Tarlo Lyons*	A.D. Russell *Russells*	Barry Shaw *Barry Shaw*
Andrew R. Stinson *Harbottle & Lewis*	Robert A. Storer *Harbottle & Lewis*	Andrew J. Thompson *Lee & Thompson*
R. Kim Walker *Biddle & Co*		
J. Anthony Ballard *Allison & Humphreys*	Adrian Barr-Smith *Denton Hall*	Nigel Bennett *The Simkins Partnership*
David W. Davis *Clintons*	Craig F. Eadie *Frere Cholmeley Bischoff*	Stephen Edwards *Richards Butler*
Lloyd H. Evans *Berwin Leighton*	David T. Franks *The Simkins Partnership*	Jeremy Gawade *Lee & Thompson*
Cyril Glasser *Sheridans*	Rupert C. Grey *Crockers*	G. Laurence Harbottle *Harbottle & Lewis*
David Hooper *Biddle & Co*	Brian K. Howard *Russells*	Laurence M. Kaye *The Simkins Partnership*
Stephen D. Kon *S J Berwin & Co*	David Lester *Taylor Joynson Garrett*	Nicholas Lom *Schilling & Lom*
Paul Mitchell *Taylor Joynson Garrett*	Bernard Nyman *Manches & Co*	Judi O'Brien *Tarlo Lyons*
Christopher Parkinson *Gouldens*	Robin Perrot *Goodman Derrick*	Mark D. Phillips *Harbottle & Lewis*
David Rockberger *Davenport Lyons*	Andrew J. Sharland *Clintons*	Michael Simkins *The Simkins Partnership*
Barry Smith *Richards Butler*	Mark H. Stephens *Stephens Innocent*	Peter F. Stone *Berwin Leighton*
Julian M. Turton *The Simkins Partnership*	M. Westaway *Theodore Goddard*	Alan Williams *Denton Hall*
David Wills *Campbell Hooper*	David Zeffman *Olswang*	

In all the tables the names in each group are listed alphabetically.

SOUTH OF ENGLAND & WALES

In the South East of England, *Eatons*, the renowned music specialists, have a branch office in Dorking. In Chelmsford, *Wollastons* provides advice on recording and publishing contracts and management agreements within the music industry.

Bevan Ashford has a presence in the television industry with three specialists (most notably Gareth Jones) operating from the Bristol office, and one from Plymouth. The firm also advises radio stations.

Manches & Co in Oxford has heightened its profile following the recent merger with *Rubinstein Callingham Polden & Gale*. The firm has considerable experience in the field of publishing representing, among others, Conde Nast.

In Bristol, *Osborne Clarke* has two specialist partners advising a number of independent television and radio stations, newspaper groups and advertising agencies. David Ticehurst is experienced in the field.

HIGHLY REGARDED – SOUTH OF ENGLAND & WALES	
BEVAN ASHFORD *Bristol*	EATONS *Dorking*
EDWARDS GELDARD *Cardiff*	EVERSHEDS *Cardiff*
FOOT & BOWDEN *Plymouth*	MANCHES & CO *Oxford*
OSBORNE CLARKE *Bristol*	WIGGIN AND CO *Cheltenham*
WOLLASTONS *Chelmsford*	

Anthony Jaffa at *Foot & Bowden* in Plymouth, primarily a defamation specialist, provides pre-publication advice to newspaper clients.

Wiggin and Co has three specialists advising on sponsorship, cable and satellite broadcasting agreements and programming rights and other telecommunications issues within the media. The firm also advises on recorded and live production of musical works.

In Wales, *Edwards Geldard* and *Eversheds* (Cardiff) have excellent reputations. Phillip Rees at *Edwards Geldard* is highly experienced in the film and music industries and has cornered a position in the Welsh animation industry.

LEADING INDIVIDUALS – SOUTH OF ENGLAND & WALES
Anthony R. Jaffa   *Foot & Bowden*
D.Gareth Jones   *Bevan Ashford*
Phillip Rees   *Edwards Geldard*
David K. Ticehurst   *Osborne Clarke*

Eversheds represents individual artists and world renowned entertainment organisations in the film and music industries and has recently expanded into publishing.

MIDLANDS & EAST ANGLIA

Media practices in the Midlands tend to be based in Birmingham.

HIGHLY REGARDED – MIDLANDS & EAST ANGLIA	
EDGE & ELLISON *Birmingham*	EVERSHEDS *Norwich*
LEATHES PRIOR *Norwich*	WRAGGE & CO *Birmingham*

Edge & Ellison acts for a number of public and private entertainment groups, venues and production companies, advising on publishing contracts, distribution, licence arrangements and merchandising.

Wragge & Co acts for several independent television and film companies, music companies and design consultancies.

In East Anglia, *Eversheds* (Norwich) has a broad client base including television production companies, radio stations, newspapers and artists.

Leathes Prior has expertise in the music industry, drafting recording contracts and management agreements for promoters and agents.

NORTH

In the North West of England, *Lea & Company* is particularly well known within the music industry, advising record companies, musicians and songwriters. The firm is also active in the publishing field, where it advises publishing houses and journalists. Stephen Lea was highly recommended.

HIGHLY REGARDED – NORTH	
BOOTH & CO. *Leeds*	DIBB LUPTON BROOMHEAD *Leeds*
EVERSHEDS *Manchester*	HART-JACKSON & HALL *Newcastle*
LEA & COMPANY *Stockport*	McCORMICKS *Leeds*
RAMSBOTTOM & CO *Blackburn*	

Eversheds (Manchester) office specialises in film and television work, acting for Granada television on TV rights acquisition and production agreements, videogram and CD agreements and merchandising deals. Other film clients include independent production companies and film financiers. The firm has also established a presence within the music industry.

Ramsbottom & Co in Blackburn have cornered a position in the market in advising circuses and showmen.

In Leeds, *Dibb Lupton Broomhead* provides regional newspapers and a television company with pre-publication advice, whilst the nationally acclaimed Peter McCormick of *McCormicks* advises a number of television and radio stations, newspapers, journalists and entertainers on a broad spectrum of matters including broadcasting legislation, contracts, royalties and copyright.

LEADING INDIVIDUALS – NORTH
Caroline Edwards   *Booth & Co.*
Stephen Lea   *Lea & Co*
Peter D.G. McCormick   *McCormicks*

Caroline Edwards at *Booth & Co* has been recommended for advice in copyright.

Hart-Jackson & Hall in Newcastle is retained by the Musicians Union and the British Actors Equity Association.

SCOTLAND

Dundas & Wilson CS emerges as the leading firm advising the Scottish television industry, with Alayne Swanson held in high regard.

Bell & Scott WS, Henderson Boyd Jackson, Steedman Ramage WS and *Tods Murray WS* are all highly regarded.

HIGHLY REGARDED – SCOTLAND	
BELL & SCOTT WS *Edinburgh*	DUNDAS & WILSON CS *Edinburgh*
HENDERSON BOYD JACKSON *Edinburgh*	STEEDMAN RAMAGE WS *Edinburgh*
TODS MURRAY WS *Edinburgh*	

Bell & Scott WS provides advice on financial matters, hire contracts, and a variety of other legal issues to both the producers of and performers at the Edinburgh Fringe Festival. The firm also advises independent film and television producers and is active in the book and music publishing field.

Andrew Kerr (Secretary to the Edinburgh Festival Fringe Society) and Iain MacDonald have been highly recommended.

Henderson Boyd Jackson has a considerable presence in the music industry advising the Music in Scotland Trust, The Dorian Group Ltd and Baby Records. The firm also represents artists, most notably Simple Minds.

Steedman Ramage WS' media department comprises two specialist partners who advise on the corporate and commercial aspects of the film, television and music industries. Simon Brown (a lecturer in entertainment law and author of texts on the subject) is held in high regard.

Richard Findlay has over 15 years' experience in the fields of dance, film and television and fine art. By providing advice to a substantial number of major entertainment clients *Tods Murray WS* maintains its position at the forefront of media law.

LEADING INDIVIDUALS – SCOTLAND	
Simon T.D. Brown	*Steedman Ramage WS*
Richard M. Findlay	*Tods Murray WS*
Andrew M. Kerr	*Bell & Scott WS*
Iain MacDonald	*Bell & Scott WS*
Alayne Swanson	*Dundas & Wilson CS*

LEADERS IN MEDIA & ENTERTAINMENT

LONDON

Allan, Robert

Denton Hall, London (0171) 242 1212. Partner in Media and Technology Department.

Specialisation: Works with music industry clients on music publishing, recording contracts, "due diligence" reviews of music companies and their assets, music business mergers and acquisitions, video licensing, negotiations with rights bodies and other contractual matters. Also works on the "talent" side of the music business, advising on contractual and other issues. Has been published widely in leading professional journals and the trade press. Has lectured at MIDEM and New Music Seminar in New York.

Prof. Membership: International Association of Entertainment Lawyers (UK Committee Member).

Career: Qualified in 1967. Partner with *Simons Muirhead & Allan* 1973-86. Joined *Denton Hall* as a Partner in 1986.

Personal: Born 4th May 1945. Educated at Xaverian College, Brighton. French speaker. Interests include skiing, clay pigeon shooting and wine tasting.

Ballard, J. Anthony

Allison & Humphreys, London (0171) 570 6000. Partner in Entertainment Department.

Specialisation: Main area of practice covers television and films, including satellite, terrestrial, cable and VOD services. Also handles space, telecommunications and administrative law matters, covering satellite networks and regulatory issues. Frequent speaker at conferences.

Prof. Membership: International Bar Association, Law Society, BLACA, CLIP.

Career: Qualified in 1974, having joined *Allison & Humphreys* in 1971. Became a Partner in 1975.

Personal: Born 21st August 1945. Holds an MA (Cantab) 1964-68. Fellow of Royal Anthropological Institute. Leisure interests include astrophysics and painting. Lives in London and Suffolk.

Barr-Smith, Adrian

See under Sports Law.

Bennett, Nigel

The Simkins Partnership, London (0171) 631 1050. Partner in Media and Entertainment Department.

Specialisation: Main areas of practice cover media finance, production and distribution and alternative dispute resolution. Experience in advising producers, distributors, broadcasters and financiers on copyright, financing agreements, production contracts and distribution arrangements world-wide. Other areas of practice include sport and electronic media work.

Prof. Memberships: Law Society, International Bar Association, American Bar Association, Media Dispute Resolution (Founder Member), Editorial Board of International Media Law, British Academy of Film & Television Arts, Producers Association for Cinema & Television, MCC, Musicians Union.

Career: Qualified in 1970 with *Rubinstein Nash*. Lecturer in contract and commercial law, College of Law, Lancaster Gate (1971-73). Joined *The Simkins Partnership* in 1973; Partner 1975; Joint Managing Partner 1992.

Personal: Born 15th June 1945. Attended Dulwich College 1956-64, Clare College, Cambridge 1964-67. Leisure pursuits include golf, cricket, sailing, walking and the jazz guitar.

Bloom, Frank

Marriott Harrison, London (0171) 209 2000. Qualified 1960. Founding Partner. Media and Entertainment Department. Main area of practice covers all aspects of film, television, cable production, broadcasting, financing and exploitation. Born in 1936.

Cohen, John M.R.

Clintons, London (0171) 379 6080. Partner in Entertainment Department.

Specialisation: Main areas of practice are music, theatre and television, negotiating and advising on contracts in relation to recording, music publishing, management, theatrical production and television production. Cases handled have included Elton John v. Dick James, George Michael v. Sony, Tolhurst v. The Cure, Dave Clark v. The Dominion Theatre and a huge number of contentious contracts.

Prof. Membership: The Law Society.

Career: Qualified 1970. Joined *Clintons* in 1968 and has remained there throughout career, becoming a Partner in 1972.

Personal: Born 14th February 1946. Attended University College London 1964-67. Trustee of Mercury Workshop. Leisure interests include producing musicals. Lives in London.

Dally, Peter

Marriott Harrison, London (0171) 209 2000. Qualified 1980. Partner 1986. Media and Technology Department. Main area of practice is media finance including secured lending, project loans and revolving facilities. Born 21.4.1944.

Davis, David W.

Clintons, London (0171) 379 6080.

Dearsley, Ken

Denton Hall, London (0171) 242 1212. Partner in Media and Technology Department.

Specialisation: Specialises in all aspects of film financing, working with the major studios, other film companies, banks and other lending institutions. Also experienced in television production and distribution, video distribution, "due diligence" reviews in the media industry and copyright matters generally.

Prof. Membership: International Bar Association.

Career: Has been with *Denton Hall* since articles. Qualified in 1974. Became a Partner in 1979.

Personal: Born 25th April 1945. Educated at

William Ellis School and Fitzwilliam College, Cambridge 1965-68 (MA Hons in Economics). Leisure pursuits include tennis.

Devereux, Mark J.

Olswang, London (0171) 208 8888. Partner and Head of Entertainment Media and Communications Group.

Specialisation: Main area of practice is film and television finance, production and distribution. Responsible for all areas of work covered by entertainment, media and communications. Regular contributor to media trade press. Speaker at the Media Business School Television course, and the Media Business School Film Course.

Prof. Memberships: Law Society, State Bar of California.

Career: Qualified in 1981, joining *Simon Olswang & Co* in the same year and becoming a Partner in 1982.

Personal: Born 2nd August 1956. Attended Lycee Francais de Londres 1961-74, then University College London 1975-78. Leisure interests include tennis, skiing, diving and photography. Lives in London.

Eadie, Craig F.

Frere Cholmeley Bischoff, London (0171) 615 8000. Partner in Company & Commercial Department.

Specialisation: Media and communications specialist. On the editorial board of 'Telecommunications & Space Journal'. Author of various articles on media and communications and a contributor to the CBI Guide on doing business in Poland. Regular speaker at media seminars.

Career: Qualified in 1980, having joined *Frere Cholmeley Bischoff* in 1978. Became a Partner in 1986.

Personal: Born in 1955. Educated at Worcester College, Oxford 1973-76 and Aix-Marseilles University 1977-78. Trustee of the Institute of Contemporary British History and Watside Charities. Recreations include bird watching and shooting. Lives in London.

Eaton, Michael C.A.

Eatons, London (0181) 877 9727.

Edwards, Stephen

Richards Butler, London (0171) 247 6555. Qualified 1976. Partner. Specialises in broadcasting, including regulatory, copyright, EC and contractual matters. Advises on all forms of publishing.

Evans, Lloyd H.

Berwin Leighton, London (0171) 623 3144. Partner in Company and Commercial Department.

Specialisation: Principal area of practice is media and communications law. Work includes City based financing of, and tax shelters for film; telecoms, cable and satellite practice and regulation, sponsorship, interactive technology and all aspects of television,

video and theatre. Other areas of practice are international trade law, intellectual property and computer law. Work includes asset finance using brands, computer law, copyright and technology licensing in Europe and the Russian Federation and for "in-out" Japanese commercial transactions. Important matters have included Prudential and Tesco commercial contracts, product liability for major Japanese manufacturers, Telewest Communications product distribution, major South African film tax shelters and film financing with Royal Bank of Canada and Scotiabank. Co-author of 'Entertainment Law Precedents' (Longmans) and 'Remedies for Intellectual Sellers of Goods' (Sweet & Maxwell). Has written a number of articles on Russian Joint Ventures, international competition and copyright. Regular speaker on film finance, competition and copyright issues.

Prof. Membership: Law Society, IBA.

Career: Journalist with Thompson, Camrose and Kemsley Newspapers 1959-64. Group Solicitor, Associated Televison Corporation 1968-79. Joined *Berwin Leighton* as a Partner in 1979.

Personal: Born 3rd February 1941. Educated at Uppingham 1954-59 and The College of Law, Guildford. Interests include shooting, motor racing and underwater photography. Lives in Godalming.

Franks, David T.

The Simkins Partnership, London (0171) 631 1050. Qualified 1973. Partner 1979. Entertainment Department. Avises record companies, music publishers, managers, recording artists and composers.

Gawade, Jeremy

Lee & Thompson, London (0171) 935 4665. Qualified 1982. Partner 1992. Media and Entertainment. Specialises in all aspects of film, TV and sports work. Born 4.4.1955.

Gilmore, Laurence

Hamlin Slowe, London (0171) 629 1209. Qualified 1986. Managing Partner and Head of the Entertainment & Intellectual Property Department. Practice covers all aspects of litigation in these areas. Born 17.4.1959.

Glasser, Cyril

Sheridans, London (0171) 404 0444. Qualified 1967. Managing Partner. Litigation Department. Specialises in commercial litigation, public law and media and entertainment work.

Grafton Green, P.

Theodore Goddard, London (0171) 606 8855. Qualified 1967. Partner 1973. Entertainment Group. Work covers copyright and advice on publishing, production, distribution, concert appearance, sponsorship and merchandise. Born 30.3.1943.

Grey, Rupert C.

See under Defamation.

Harbottle, G. Laurence

Harbottle & Lewis, London (0171) 629 7633. Qualified 1952. Senior Partner 1955-94. Consultant from 1994. Film, television and theatre department. Principal area of practice is theatre related work.

Henry, Michael

Michael Henry & Co, London (0171) 242 7999. Sole Practitioner specialising in media, communications and intellectual property.

Specialisation: Clients include the British Broadcasting Corporation, the British Film Institute, the Council of Europe (France), Teilifis na Gaeilge (Ireland), Sianel Pedwar Cymru S4C (Wales), Comataiah Telebhiseir Gaiahlig (Scotland), Philips Interactive Media International Ltd, Aardman Animations Ltd, Carrington Productions International Ltd, London Films Ltd, Skyline Film and Television Productions Ltd, Tembo Records Ltd and Tring International plc. Publications include 'The Film Industry: A Legal Commercial Analysis' (Longman, 1986), the Entertainment Law Volume (15) of the Encyclopedia of Forms & Precedents (Butterworths, 1990), 'Publishing and Multimedia Law' (Butterworths, 1994) and co-author and editor of 'International Agency and Distribution Agreements' (Butterworths US) and 'Security over Intellectual Property' (Longmans, 1993). Has also had articles published in 'The Times', 'The Independent', 'European Intellectual Property Review', 'European Community Law Review', 'International Media Law', 'Journal of International Banking Law', 'New Law Journal' and 'Screen International' and 'Espace Video Europeen' amongst others. Member of Editorial Board of 'Entertainment Law Review'. Consulting Editor and Principal Contributor for Intellectual Property and Entertainment Law Titles of Butterworth's 'Encyclopaedia of Firms and Precedents.'

Hinshelwood, William

Marriott Harrison, London (0171) 209 2000. Founding Partner of firm in 1986. Media Department.

Specialisation: Main area of practice is film and television production financing and distribution. Acts for a number of prominent production companies (UK and American based) as well as international distributors and other financing entities. Particular bias towards co-productions. Frequent speaker at conferences and seminars.

Prof. Membership: Law Society.

Career: Qualified in 1981, Assistant solicitor after articles with *Denton Hall*. Partner at *Frank Bloom & Co.*, then Founding Partner of *Marriott Harrison Bloom and Norris* (now *Marriott Harrison*) in 1986.

Personal: Attended Exeter University (LLB) 1973-76. Leisure interests include golf, cricket and wine. Lives in Ipswich.

Hooper, David

Biddle & Co, London (0171) 606 9301. Qualified 1977. Partner 1986. Media Department. Work covers defamation, entertainment, copyright, publishing, broadcasting and multimedia.

Howard, Brian K.

Russells, London (0171) 439 8692.

Jones, Medwyn

Harbottle & Lewis, London (0171) 629 7633. Qualified 1980. Partner 1994. Film, television and theatre department. Main areas of practice are television production, financing, distribution, broadcasting, film production and financing. Born 13.9.1955.

Jones, Howard

Sheridans, London (0171) 404 0444. Qualified 1975.

Julius, Anthony

See under Litigation (Commercial).

Kaye, Laurence M.

See under Computer Law & I.T.

Kennedy, John P.

J.P. Kennedy & Co, London (0171) 724 4707. Qualified 1977. Sole Practitioner. Main area of practice is entertainment law, specialising in all aspects of the music business.

Kon, Stephen D.

See under European Union/Competition.

Landsman, David M.

Clintons, London (0171) 379 6080. Partner in Entertainment Department.

Specialisation: Deals with music, TV, video, sport, merchandising, media and leisure work.

Professional Membership: Law Society.

Career: Qualified 1970. Founding partner of *D M Landsman & Co*, which merged with *Clintons* in 1990.

Personal: Born 14th March, 1946. Educated at Haberdashers' Aske's School. Leisure pursuits include music, reading, sport and family. Lives in London.

Lee, R.W.

Lee & Thompson, London (0171) 935 4665. Qualified 1970. Partner 1983. Commercial Department. Principal area of practice covers the music business, also film and general commercial law. Born 18.10.45.

Lester, David

Taylor Joynson Garrett, London (0171) 353 1234. Partner in Intellectual Property Department.

Specialisation: Main area of specialisation is copyright and media law, principally for the music business. Experienced in giving commercial advice, negotiation and drafting of contracts, as well as litigation. Also deals

with EC law, principally advising on the interrelationship between competition law and intellectual property, and EC litigation. Recently acted in the creation of a joint venture between three European collecting Societies. Also acting in the PRS v. U2 case, and for a number of clients as regards implementation in the UK of the EC Term and Rental directives. Joint author of 'Joynson-Hicks on UK Copyright'. Has written many articles and given many lectures and seminars.

Prof. Membership: The International Association of Entertainment Lawyers (Executive Committee).

Career: Qualified in 1976, having joined *Joynson-Hicks* in 1974. Became a Partner in 1981.

Personal: Born in 1951. Educated at Magdalen College School, Northants 1961-69 and Queens College, Cambridge 1970-73. Director of the British Music Information Centre and Early Music Centre. Interests include music and architecture. Lives in London.

Lom, Nicholas

Schilling & Lom, London (0171) 453 2500. Qualified 1982. Senior Partner. Entertainment/Commercial Department. Specialises in film, television, video, music and publishing. Born 29.4.1949.

McInerney, Peter B.G.

S J Berwin & Co, London (0171) 837 2222. Qualified 1982. Partner in the Commercial Department. Specialising in Media and Entertainment law, and in particular film and television production, finance, distribution and sports work.

Mireskandari, Razi

Simons Muirhead & Burton, London (0171) 734 4499. Partner in charge of Civil Litigation Department.

Specialisation: Civil litigation with a media bias, Press Law (including pre publication advice), civil liberties, commercial litigation. Past cases include The Princess of Wales v. Bryce Taylor, Angolan National Oil Co. vs. Lundqvist, Sonia Sutcliffe v. News of the World (Barbara Jones), John Major v. Scallywag Magasine, Salman Rushdie, Potter v. BBC & Mary Whitehouse, Rupert Allason MP v. John Pilger, Kate Adie v. Daily Express. Has done television, radio and press interviews.

Career: Qualified in 1986, having joined *Simons Muirhead & Burton* in 1985. Became a Partner in 1989.

Personal: Born 22nd August 1957. Educated at Sussex University (BA) and Keele University (MA). Govenor of Sudbourne School; Member of the Groucho Club. Lives in London.

Mitchell, Paul

Taylor Joynson Garrett, London (0171) 353 1234. Partner in Intellectual Property Department.

Specialisation: Principal area of practice is entertainment and media law including copyright and related work in various areas of the entertainment and media industry including music, books, films, television and multimedia. Other main area involves company law aspects of the acquisitions and disposals of companies and joint ventures in the entertainment and media industry. Editorial Board Member of 'International Media Law'. Contributes articles to various professional publications and is co-author of Joynson-Hicks on UK Copyright Law. Addresses various conferences on topics related to entertainment and media law.

Prof. Membership: Law Society.

Career: Qualified in 1976 while with *Joynson-Hicks* and became a Partner in 1978.

Personal: Born 2nd November 1951. Attended Canford School 1965-69, then Bristol University 1970-73. Roald Dahl Foundation (Advisory Board Member). Leisure pursuits include family life, sailing and walking. Lives in London.

Morgan, Leon R.

Davenport Lyons, London (0171) 287 5353. Partner in Media and Entertainment Department.

Specialisation: Principal area of practice is media production, finance and distribution generally and television and film production and finance in particular as well as literary and music publishing and multi-media. Also handles taxation related to the above including planning for individuals and production/distribution companies. Helped set up the media lending division of the Royal Bank of Scotland. Other major clients include Barclays Bank plc, Media Ventures International, Cori Film Distributors, The Mersey Television Co. Ltd, Brookside Productions Ltd and many individuals including Phil Redmond, Douglas Adams and Fay Weldon. Is regularly quoted in industry periodicals. Charge-out rate is around £200 per hour (variable).

Prof. Membership: Law Society.

Career: Qualified and joined *Davenport Lyons* in 1964. Became a Partner in 1969.

Personal: Born 3rd July 1939. Educated at Westcliff High School 1951-58. Leisure interests include film, books, art, theatre, music and opera. Lives in Notting Hill, London.

Norris, David J.

Marriott Harrison, London (0171) 209 2000. Qualified 1966. Partner 1986. Multimedia and Entertainment Department. Advises major film companies, broadcasters, independent film producers and directors in all aspects of multimedia and entertainment law. Born 18.3.1939.

Nyman, Bernard

Manches & Co, London (0171) 404 4433. Partner in Intellectual Property Department.

Specialisation: Principal area of practice is publishing (books, magazines, journals, etc), dealing with contracts for all aspects of publishing including electronic publishing, acting for publishers, authors, literary agents and learned societies. Also libel reading (i.e pre-publication advice) and dealing with libel complaints post publication. Other work is general intellectual property including advice on copyright, trade marks and passing off. Also agreements in the entertainment industry generally (music, film, video, multi-media and touring). Author of the copyright section of 'The Encyclopedia of Forms & Precedents' (5th Ed, Vol.21) and various articles in 'Entertainment Law Review'.

Prof. Membership: Law Society.

Career: Qualified in 1979. Partner at *Rubinstein Callingham* from 1983. Became Partner at *Manches & Co* in 1994 when the two firms merged.

Personal: Born 27th February 1954. Educated at Royal Liberty School 1965-72 and Sheffield University 1972-75 (BA in Law). Leisure interests include jazz, film and theatre. Lives in London.

O'Brien, Judi
Tarlo Lyons, London (0171) 405 2000. Qualified 1980. Partner 1994. Entertainment and Multimedia Department. Handles mainly music, television video and comedy work. Also advises on multimedia.

Palmer, Nigel S.
S J Berwin & Co, London (0171) 837 2222. Qualified 1979. Partner 1988. Head of Media and Communications Group. Main area of practice is media and entertainment work, including film financing and production merchandising and video distribution. Born 12.5.1950.

Parkinson, Christopher
Gouldens, London (0171) 583 7777. Qualified 1985. Partner 1990. Media Department. Specialises in film, television, radio and new communication technologies, media and media finance.

Perrot, Robin
See under Defamation.

Philipps, Richard P.S.
Richards Butler, London (0171) 247 6555. Partner in Media Unit.

Specialisation: Specialises almost exclusively in film finance work, acting for banks and other financial institutions, distribution companies and major overseas organisations.

Career: Qualified 1978. Partner at *Richards Butler* since 1985.

Personal: Born 1952. Educated at Queens' College, Cambridge.

Phillips, Mark D.
Harbottle & Lewis, London (0171) 629 7633. Qualified 1986. Partner 1990. Company Commercial Department. Specialises in multimedia and interactive entertainment, and print and electronic publishing.

Ridley, Michael
Denton Hall, London (0171) 242 1212. Partner in Media and Technology Department.

Specialisation: Practice encompasses commissioning, distribution, co-production agreements for films and television, sponsorship agreements, broadcasting regulation, satellite agreements, copyright law, artists' contracts and defamation. Has contributed articles to 'International Media Law', 'The Times', 'Broadcast' and 'Edinburgh International Television Festival Daily'. Has given lectures on the Broadcasting Bill, broadcasting in the EC, copyright and television piracy, television and film production.

Prof. Membership: Law Society, Copinger Society, Royal Television Society.

Career: Qualified in 1980. Rights Manager, National Theatre 1980-81. Senior Solicitor and Company Secretary of London Weekend Television International 1981-89. Joined *Denton Hall* in 1989 and became a Partner in 1990.

Personal: Born 21st October 1955. Educated at Woodhouse Grammar School, Finchley and Durham University 1974-77 (BA in Law). Interests outside the law include music (as singer and listener). Trustee of St Paul's Arts Trust and chairman of Pop Up Theatre Company.

Rockberger, David
Davenport Lyons, London (0171) 287 5353. Partner. Head of Company Commercial Department. Specialises in the commercial aspects of media communications and entertainment work.

Rose, D. Michael
Tarlo Lyons, London (0171) 405 2000. Partner in Company and Commercial Department. Head of Entertainment Unit.

Specialisation: Principal area of practice is theatre and related work (largely producer driven and largely involving stage musicals). Specialist experience commenced in 1977. Also handles copyright disputes, piracy claims and defamation as well as most other aspects of entertainment law, general company and commercial work and charity administration. Is administration trustee of a large charity. Major involvement in contract work (including much overseas licensing) in respect of many stage musicals such as 'Cats', 'The Phantom of The Opera', 'Les Miserables', 'Miss Saigon', 'Five Guys Named Moe', 'Carousel', 'Follies', 'Moby Dick' and 'Oliver'. Experience also in high profile copyright and employment disputes as well as some film and TV work. Major clients include the Cameron Mackintosh Group of Companies and the Mackintosh Foundation. Writes a monthly column in 'The Stage' newspaper on entertainment law. Conference speaker on "legal and business issues in the theatre".

Prof. Membership: Law Society, Charity Law Association.

Career: Qualified in 1958. Partner in *Randall Rose* from 1960 until merger with *Tarlo Lyons* in 1986.

Personal: Born 27th August 1934. Educated at Rugby School 1948-52 and University College, London 1952-55. Chairman since 1985 of Allied Cavendish Properties Ltd (30 shareholders). Trustee of the Mackintosh Foundation since 1988. Leisure pusuits include golf, reading and walking. Lives in London.

Russell, A.D.
Russells, London (0171) 439 8692.

Sharland, Andrew J.
Clintons, London (0171) 379 6080.

Shaw, Barry
Barry Shaw, London (0171) 439 3111. Qualified 1965. Partner 1966. Main area of practice is media and entertainment, including defamation. Born 2.1.1941.

Simkins, Michael
The Simkins Partnership, London (0171) 631 1050. Qualified 1958. Sole practitioner 1963-68. Senior partner since 1968. Practice covers film, television and theatre work.

Smith, Barry
Richards Butler, London (0171) 247 6555. Partner. Media & Entertainment Department. Handles all aspects, especially film and TV finance, production and distribution.

Stephens, Mark H.
See under Defamation.

Stinson, Andrew R.
Harbottle & Lewis, London (0171) 629 7633. Qualified 1981. Partner 1984. Music Department. Work includes advising on music industry agreements. Born 1957.

Stone, Peter F.
See under Company/Commercial.

Storer, Robert A.
Harbottle & Lewis, London (0171) 629 7633. Qualified 1971. Partner 1974. Film, Television and Theatre Department. Main areas of practice are film and television production and finance and copyright issues. Born 29.4.1947.

Thompson, Andrew J.
Lee & Thompson, London (0171) 935 4665. Qualified 1977. Partner 1982. Music Department. Work covers all aspects of media and entertainment law advice to the music business. Born 12.2.1953.

Turton, Julian M.
The Simkins Partnership, London (0171) 631 1050. Partner in Media and Entertainment and Advertising Departments.

Specialisation: Main area of practice is

media and entertainment, with emphasis on the music industry but also including book publishing, television and cable. Other area of practice is advertising and marketing, particularly talent and rights acquisition documentation. Has represented artists, composers, publishers and record companies, acquirers of book publishing businesses and media selling operations, advertising agencies acquiring rights to high-profile celebrities, and has acted as consultant on new technology rights issues to one of the UK's ten largest companies. Editor of 'Neighbouring Rights, Artists, Producers and their Collection Societies' and past contributor to 'Merchandising and Sponsorship' and 'Moral Rights'. Author of articles in International Media Law, Entertainment Law Review and Business Magazine. Has lectured at commercial seminars on music publishing agreements, to the Music Publishers Association on the enforceability of contracts, to a conference organised by the British Association of Concert Agents and International Arts Manager magazine on the subject of new technologies.

Prof. Memberships: General Secretary and Committee Member of the International Association of Entertainment Lawyers; Founder Member of Advertising Law International; BAFTA.

Career: Qualified 1980 and joined *The Simkins Partnership* the same year. Articled at *Trower, Still & Keeling*. Became a Partner in 1985.

Personal: Born 23rd July 1952. Attended Bristol University (1974). Leisure interests include golf, reading, food and Arsenal F.C. Lives in London.

Walker, R. Kim

Biddle & Co, London (0171) 606 9301. Partner in Company/Commercial Department.

Specialisation: Main area of practice is commercial work involving intellectual property, principally as it affects the media and entertainment industry. Work concerns in particular contractual and commercial issues affecting the industry, including acquisitions, joint ventures and the ownership, protection and licensing of copyright, trade marks and other intellectual property rights. Also advises on UK and EC competition law and on computer and information technology law and has written and lectured on multimedia, new technologies and the convergence of rights. Spoke at the 1994 Frankfurt Book Fair seminars on electronic publishing.

Career: Qualified in 1983. Worked at *Freshfields* 1981-5. Joined *Biddle & Co* in 1985, becoming a Partner in 1987. Member of Intellectual Property Sub-committee of the City of London Law Society, IAEL.

Personal: Born 15th July 1957. Attended Shrewsbury School 1971-75 and Christ's College, Cambridge, 1976-79. Leisure interests include golf. Lives in Islington, London.

Westaway, M.

Theodore Goddard, London (0171) 606 8855.

Williams, Alan

Denton Hall, London (0171) 242 1212. Partner in Media and Technology Department.

Specialisation: Work includes copyright, libel, commercial contract, publishing and film, television and theatre. Author of 'Intellectual Property: the New Law'; contributed to Publishing Agreements edited by Charles Clark. Author with Mark Turner of Multimedia Contracts, Rights and Licensing. Lectures to Hawksmere; Book House Trust.

Prof. Membership: Law Society, Law and Copyright Committee of the Publishers Association, Editorial Committee of International Media Law.

Career: Qualified in 1969, having joined *Denton Hall* in 1967. Became a Partner in 1972.

Personal: Born 27th October 1944. Attended Merchant Taylors' School 1957-63, then Exeter University 1963-66. Clubs include MCC, Groucho, Whitefriars and Omar Khyyam. Liveryman of the Worshipful Company of Pewterers. Leisure interests include theatre, music, cricket and walking. Lives in London.

Wills, David

Campbell Hooper, London (0171) 222 9070. Partner in Media and Entertainment Department.

Specialisation: Extensive experience of the law and practice of the theatre. Advises producers, financiers and creative personnel in the West End, on Broadway, off Broadway and all other territories where live theatre is performed. Regularly negotiates production rights, finance agreements, co-production ventures, theatre licences and agreements for the services of creative contributors to theatrical productions. Also deals with the publication, recording and exploitation of music in the UK and overseas. Handles media litigation, e.g., for the George Bernard Shaw estate in the 'My Fair Lady' litigation and for the producers of 'Cell Mates' in the action against Stephen Fry. Represents writers and performers on stage and screen. Occasional contributor to 'The Author' and 'The Stage', and speaker at Theatre Investment Fund Seminars.

Career: Qualified 1967 and became a partner at *Campbell Hooper* in 1970.

Personal: Born 7th February 1942. Educated at Tiffin School 1953-60, and Bristol University 1961-64. Trustee of the Mander Mitchenson Theatre Collection. Lives in London and East Grafton, Wiltshire.

Zeffman, David

Olswang, London (0171) 208 8888. Partner and Joint Head of Entertainment, Media and Communications Group.

Specialisation: Principal area of practice involves commercial and corporate aspects of music, cable, satellite and multimedia businesses. Particular expertise in competition law aspects of entertainment industries. Acted in MMC inquiries into record industry; film distribution; Warner/Chappell and in BPI/MCPS Copyright Tribunal Reference. Frequent contributor to Entertainment Law Review and International Media Law. Regular speaker on topics related to music, satellite, cable and competition law.

Prof. Membership: IBA, IAEL.

Career: Qualified 1983 while with *Frere Cholmeley* and became a Partner in 1989. Appointed Head of Company and Commercial Department, *Frere Cholmeley Bischoff* in 1993. Joined *Simon Olswang & Co* as a Partner in 1994.

Personal: Born 28th February 1958. Attended Haberdashers' Aske's School 1969-76, then Brasenose College, Oxford 1977-80. Lives in London.

REGIONS

Brown, Simon T.D.

Steedman Ramage WS, Edinburgh (0131) 226 3781. Partner in Corporate Department.

Specialisation: Handles general corporate and commercial work, including acquisitions and disposals, corporate finance, general contract work, agency and distribution agreements and EC law. Specialises in media, entertainment and publishing law, involving film and TV production, financing and distribution contracts, publishing contracts, music industry agreements, sponsorship agreements, intellectual property issues and passing off. Has lectured on media and entertainment law for the Law Society of Scotland and the Institute of Chartered Accountants of Scotland and on copyright and contracts for the Scottish Publishers' Association. Currently working on a volume of precedent media contracts, due to be published in 1995. Contributed Scottish section of 'International Agency and Distribution Law' by Matthew Bender.

Prof. Membership: Securities Institute (Full Member), English Law Society's European Group, Law Society of Scotland, Society of Writers to Her Majesty's Signet.

Career: Qualified in 1985. Worked for *Dundas & Wilson CS* in Edinburgh 1983-88. Joined *Steedman Ramage WS* in 1989 and became a Partner in 1990.

Personal: Born 1960. Attended the University of Edinburgh 1978-83. Enjoys golf, football, literature, travel and family life. Lives in Edinburgh.

Edwards, Caroline

Booth & Co., Leeds (0113) 283 2000. Solicitor in Intellectual Property Department.

Specialisation: Handles both contentious

and non-contentious intellectual property, media and entertainment work. Acted in Chanel Ltd v. L'Arome (UK) Ltd 1991. Legal Columnist for 'Networking', a quarterly newsletter for women in the media. Public speaking engagements have included UAE Conferences Paris (1993) and Frankfurt (1995), British Law Week, Milan (1994) and Skillset (1994).

Prof. Membership: Union des Avocats Europeen (UAE) (UK Co-ordinator of Intellectual Property Committee).

Career: Qualified in 1988. Worked at *Biddle & Co* 1986-88 and *Alsop Wilkinson* 1988-91. Joined *Booth & Co* in 1991.

Personal: Born 9th September 1963. Attended University of Cambridge 1982-5 (BA Hons, Law). Leisure interests include football and family. Lives in Huddersfield.

Findlay, Richard M.
Tods Murray WS, Edinburgh (0131) 226 4771. Qualified 1975. Partner. Entertainment law. Advises the independent film and television industry, theatre companies, publishers, writers and artists.

Jaffa, Anthony R.
See under Defamation.

Jones, D.G.
Bevan Ashford, Bristol (0117) 923 0111.

Kerr, Andrew M.
Bell & Scott WS, Edinburgh (0131) 226 6703. Senior Partner.

Specialisation: Main area of practice is media and entertainment work. Secretary to the Edinburgh Festival Fringe Society since its incorporation as a limited company in 1969. Has gained wide experience of media and entertainment problems, charitable companies and trusts through involvement with the Festival Fringe which is the largest Arts Festival in the world. Also has wide experience of timesharing developments and associated problems in Scotland and elsewhere.

Prof. Membership: Clerk to Society of Writers to Her Majesty's Signet since 1983 and member since 1966.

Career: Qualified in 1966 and joined *Bell & Scott WS* in the following year. Became a Partner in 1969 and has been Senior Partner since 1987. Has been Law Agent to the Commissioners of Northern Lighthouses since 1975.

Personal: Born 17th January 1940. Educated at Cambridge University (BA 1961) and Edinburgh University (LLB 1964). Former member of the Scottish Arts Council, having been Chairman of the Drama Committee from 1988 to 1991 and again from 1993 to 1994. Lives in Edinburgh.

Lea, Stephen
Lea & Company, Stockport (0161) 480 6691. Qualified 1979.

MacDonald, Iain
Bell & Scott WS, Edinburgh (0131) 226 6703. Partner in Commercial Department. Managing Partner.

Specialisation: Work includes contract advice and negotiation for independent film and TV producers, joint venture agreements for TV and film production, contract and financial advice for arts and festival organisations, space letting and hire contracts, publishing contracts, musician contracts and intellectual property advice. Also handles general commercial work. Lectures and gives case study seminars.

Prof. Membership: Law Society of Scotland, Producers Association of Cinema and Television (PACT).

Career: Joined *Bell & Scott WS* in 1978, becoming a Partner in 1981.

Personal: Born 20th February 1954. Lives in Edinburgh.

McCormick, Peter D.G.
See under Sports Law.

Rees, Phillip
See under Computer Law & I.T.

Swanson, Alayne
Dundas & Wilson CS, Glasgow (0141) 221 8586. Qualified 1983. Partner 1994. Litigation work includes media and entertainment, intellectual property, contractual disputes, employment and insolvency.

Ticehurst, David K.
See under Employment Law.

CD-ROM EDITION

This edition of the directory is available on a CD-ROM which includes both DOS and Windows versions. It can be loaded onto a network, and works with virtually any IBM compatible PC. The full contents of the printed directory are made available to the computer user who will have the advantage of rapid search, retrieval and cross-referencing.

MEDICAL NEGLIGENCE

LONDON

MAINLY PLAINTIFF

Leigh Day & Co, the leading firm, has Sarah Leigh heading the largest plaintiff medical negligence and medical devices litigation department in London. The firm has a strong support team including environmental health officers, scientists, an experienced nurse and a forensic accountant, which enhances their ability to deal with high-profile complex cases. An excellent client briefing paper sets out for clients how the department works. Russell Levy and Anne Winyard, two specialist partners working alongside Sarah Leigh in the department, have also been highly recommended.

Of the other leading plaintiff firms, *Field Fisher Waterhouse* continue to act for plaintiffs in substantial cases, with a large volume of the work from the Association of Victims of Medical Accidents (AVMA). Paul McNeil, highly recommended for work in this field, is a member of The Law Society Medical Negligence Panel and has settled cases in the last 12 months in excess of £1m, including Sheridan v Greenwich Health Authority and May v Royal Brompton Hospital.

LEADING FIRMS – LONDON – MAINLY PLAINTIFF	
LEIGH DAY & CO	
FIELD FISHER WATERHOUSE	KINGSLEY NAPLEY
EVILL & COLEMAN	PARLETT KENT & CO

Kingsley Napley has increased the strength of their medical negligence unit headed by Christine Marsh with the addition of Julia Cahill, a medically qualified partner who has particular expertise in obstetric negligence and claims on behalf of brain damaged children, general surgery, neurosurgery and arteriovenous malformation.

HIGHLY REGARDED – LONDON – MAINLY PLAINTIFF	
BINDMAN & PARTNERS	PANNONE PRITCHARD ENGLEFIELD
PATTINSON AND BREWER	
THOMAS WATTS & CO	

Evill & Coleman continue to be highly regarded and recommendations indicate that their work is of an even higher quality than last year. The department headed by Terry Lee has been involved in a number of significant cases including damages for Chronic Fatigue Syndrome in excess of £250,000. The firm is also co-ordinating the cortico steriod litigation on behalf of the Legal Aid board for over 200 firms country wide.

Parlett Kent & Co have a strong team dealing with medical negligence litigation, including three partners, two assistant solicitors and three nursing advisors. Four of the team are members of The Law Society specialist medical panel. The group covers all areas of medical negligence litigation including professional negligence claims such as the reported case Gascoigne v Sheriden. The group also covers legal aid, legal fees insurance and private work and specialises in cerebral palsy claims. Magi Young and Caroline Jenkins at the firm have both been recommended for their expertise, the latter having particular interest in gynaecological, oncological and obstetrics cases.

LEADING INDIVIDUALS – LONDON – MAINLY PLAINTIFF	
Sarah Leigh *Leigh Day & Co*	
Terry Lee *Evill & Coleman*	
Russell Levy *Leigh Day & Co*	
Paul McNeil *Field Fisher Waterhouse*	
Anne H. Winyard *Leigh Day & Co*	
Grainne Barton *Pannone Pritchard Englefield*	
Julia Cahill *Kingsley Napley*	
Claire Fazan *Bindman & Partners*	
Elisabeth Jamieson *Pannone Pritchard Englefield*	
Caroline Helen Clare Jenkins *Parlett Kent & Co*	
Christine Marsh *Kingsley Napley*	
Richard A. Vallance *Compton Carr*	
Magi Young *Parlett Kent & Co*	

MAINLY DEFENDANT

Hempsons emerge as the pre-eminent firm with Bertie Leigh held in particularly high regard by his competitors. The team is renowned for its expertise in this field and handles all matters relating to medical and dental negligence. Major clients include Medical Defence Union Ltd, Association of Anaesthetists, British Paediatric Association as well as various Health Authorities and Trusts. Also highly recommended at the firm are Rex Forrester and Zoe Harvey.

LEADING FIRMS – LONDON – MAINLY DEFENDANT	
HEMPSONS	
CAPSTICKS	LE BRASSEUR J TICKLE
BEACHCROFT STANLEYS	

Other leading defendant medical negligence practices are *Le Brasseur J. Tickle, Capsticks* and *Beachcroft Stanleys*. *Le Brasseur J. Tickle* handle a wide range of medical negligence claims, and clients include NHS trusts and health authorities, private hospitals and their insurers and medical defence organisations. Robert Sumerling, Ralph Shipway and Christian Dingwall have all been recommended at the firm for their expertise.

HIGHLY REGARDED – LONDON – MAINLY DEFENDANT	
BERRYMANS	BIRCHAM & CO
BIRD & BIRD	COMPTON CARR
RADCLIFFES CROSSMAN BLOCK	
MERRIMAN WHITE	

The medical negligence team at *Capsticks* is headed by David Mason and has ten specialist partners. The team, which acts for the NHS, has been involved in numerous high profile cases during the last year including Joyce v Wandsworth Health Authority and James v Camberwell Health Authority. Also recommended at the firm are Janice Smith who has a specialisation in obstetrics, cardiology, and orthopaedic related negligence, and Katie Hay who has particular interest in brain damaged baby cases and an expertise in structured settlements.

At *Beachcroft Stanleys* the team acts for health service bodies in defence claims throughout southern England, mainly in the Thames region, including many major teaching hospitals. John Holmes at the firm is particularly highly regarded and has handled many reported cases including Gascoine v Haringey Health Authority and Sion v Hampstead Health Authority. Anthony Yeaman, also recommended for his expertise at the firm, is particularly known for dealing with multi-party litigation, structured settlements and internal NHS inquiries.

LEADING INDIVIDUALS – LONDON – MAINLY DEFENDANT

Bertie Leigh *Hempsons*	
John Holmes *Beachcroft Stanleys*	
Cheryl Blundell *Berrymans*	
Christian Dingwall *Le Brasseur J Tickle*	
Rex Forrester *Hempsons*	
C.J. Zoe Harvey *Hempsons*	
David Mason *Capsticks*	
Andrew E. Parsons *Radcliffes Crossman Block*	
R.R.H. Shipway *Le Brasseur J Tickle*	
Janice Smith *Capsticks*	
David M. Stone *Bird & Bird*	
R.W. Sumerling *Le Brasseur J Tickle*	
Anthony George Yeaman *Beachcroft Stanleys*	

UP AND COMING

Katie Hay *Capsticks*

Anthony Barton, a specialist medical legal practice, offers an independent consultant service to both plaintiffs and defendants. Anthony Barton, the principal, has expertise in medical negligence, pharmaceutical product liability, health service law and medical ethics.

LEADING INDIVIDUALS – LONDON

Anthony Barton (Consultant) *Anthony Barton*

R.W. Sumerling *Le Brasseur J Tickle*

SOUTH EAST

Gadsby Wicks continues to be highly regarded in the field of medical negligence. The firm acts only for plaintiffs, and has particular experience in actions both in the UK and the US. Roger Wicks at the firm is highly repected by his competitors and is the chief assessor for The Law Society Medical Negligence Panel. Gillian Gadsby at the firm is also highly recommended.

Osborne Morris & Morgan also specialises in plaintiff work, and Tom Osborne at the firm has particular experience in head injury and brain accident cases.

LEADING FIRMS – SOUTH EAST – MAINLY PLAINTIFF

GADSBY WICKS *Chelmsford*	**OSBORNE MORRIS & MORGAN** *Leighton Buzzard*

Adrian Desmond at *Boyes Turner & Burrows* deals with many legal aid cases, including cases involving children with brain and spinal injuries and quadraplegic and maximum severity claims.

HIGHLY REGARDED – SOUTH EAST – MAINLY PLAINTIFF

BLAKE LAPTHORN *Fareham*	**BOYES TURNER & BURROWS** *Reading*
HENMANS *Oxford*	**THOMSON SNELL & PASSMORE** *Tunbridge Wells*

LEADING INDIVIDUALS – SOUTH EAST – MAINLY PLAINTIFF

Tom Osborne *Osborne Morris & Morgan*	
Roger Wicks *Gadsby Wicks*	
Adrian Desmond *Boyes Turner & Burrows*	
Gillian Gadsby *Gadsby Wicks*	
Alison McClure *Blake Lapthorn*	

Alison McClure at *Blake Lapthorn* has particular expertise in cases involving cerebral palsy and brain damage claims.

Wansbroughs Willey Hargrave, a firm well known for its defendant medical negligence work, have recently opened an office in Winchester where Tim Wright has been recommended. The team handles medical and clinical negligence cases involving the full range of health care professionals.

HIGHLY REGARDED – SOUTH EAST – MAINLY DEFENDANT

COLE and COLE *Oxford*	**WANSBROUGHS WILLEY HARGRAVE**
BRACHERS *Maidstone*	**MERRIMAN WHITE** *Guildford*

Cole and Cole also specialise in defendant work and act for various health authorities.

LEADING INDIVIDUALS – SOUTH EAST – MAINLY DEFENDANT

Tim L. Wright *Wansbroughs Willey Hargrave*

SOUTH WEST

On the plaintiff side, *Russell Jones & Walker* have a large medical negligence practice headed by Gillian Solly, who has particular experience in dealing with injuries arising from laparoscopic surgery cases. She acted for the plaintiff in one of the first cases of its kind in the UK.

HIGHLY REGARDED – SOUTH WEST – MAINLY PLAINTIFF

BARCAN WOODWARD *Bristol*	**OVER TAYLOR BIGGS** *Exeter*
RUSSELL JONES & WALKER *Bristol*	**TOZERS** *Exeter*
WOOLLCOMBE BEER WATTS *Newton Abbot*	
CHRISTOPHER HARRISON *Truro*	**CROSSE & CROSSE** *Exeter*
VEALE WASBROUGH *Bristol*	**WITHY KING & LEE** *Bath*

In all the tables the names in each group are listed alphabetically.

Over Taylor Biggs is another leading plaintiff-orientated practice in the region where Christopher Over is an AVMA referral solicitor. The firm has particular expertise in children's medical negligence cases and co-ordinated the radiation overdose claims against the Royal Devon & Exeter Hospital.

Other notable plaintiff medical negligence departments include *Barcan Woodward, Tozers* and *Woollcombe Beer Watts,* all of which have an AVMA referral solicitor on the team. Laurence Vick has moved to *Tozers* from *Brindley Twist Tafft & James* in the Midlands and heads the medical negligence group. He is particularly well regarded for dealing with birth and gynaecological injuries, especially Erb palsy litigation. Laurence Vick is also an assessor on The Law Society Medical Negligence Panel, as is Derek Reed at *Woollcombe Beer Watts*. Richard Barcan at *Barcan Woodward* is highly regarded and his workload includes legal aid medical negligence claims.

LEADING INDIVIDUALS – SOUTH WEST – MAINLY PLAINTIFF	
Richard Barcan	*Barcan Woodward*
Adrian Hickman	*Christopher Harrison*
Christopher Over	*Over Taylor Biggs*
Derek S. Reed	*Woollcombe Beer Watts*
Gillian Solly	*Russell Jones & Walker*
Laurence N. Vick	*Tozers*

Adrian Hickman, a well-known medical negligence specialist, moved from *E.David Brain & Co* to *Christopher Harrison & Co* in 1994. He represented the parents in the highly publicised case involving a hypodermic needle inside a newborn baby at Treliske Hospital.

LEADING FIRMS – SOUTH WEST – MAINLY DEFENDANT
BEVAN ASHFORD *Bristol*

Bevan Ashford emerge as pre-eminent for defendant work, acting for over 40 district health authorities including the South Western Regional Health Authority. Jill Broadhead at the firm is renowned for work in this field. The experienced team of lawyers is enhanced by access to leading medical experts in the country for advice. The group undertakes medical negligence work for several trust hospitals both in the South West and beyond, in addition to handling several multi-party claims made against the NHS.

HIGHLY REGARDED – SOUTH WEST – MAINLY DEFENDANT
OSBORNE CLARKE *Bristol*
WANSBROUGHS WILLEY HARGRAVE *Bristol*

LEADING INDIVIDUALS – SOUTH WEST – MAINLY DEFENDANT	
Jill Broadhead	*Bevan Ashford*
Robert I. Johnson	*Osborne Clarke*

Osborne Clarke, also a well known defence firm in the region, act for various trusts including United Bristol Healthcare Trust and Northamptonshire Healthcare Trust. Robert Johnson is particularly well regarded.

HIGHLY REGARDED – SOUTH WEST – BOTH
LYONS DAVIDSON *Bristol*

WALES

On the plaintiff side, *Huttons* and *Smith Llewelyn Partnership* are amongst the most highly regarded. The latter firm undertakes all types of medical negligence, together with inquests, NHS investigations, family health care services and tribunals. Tim Musgrave at *Huttons*, highly regarded by his peers, deals with complaints against GP's and NHS, and birth injuries. He is a member of Spinal Injuries Panel and AVMA.

HIGHLY REGARDED – WALES – MAINLY PLAINTIFF	
EDWARDS GELDARD *Cardiff*	HUGH JAMES JONES & JENKINS *Cardiff*
HUTTONS *Cardiff*	ROBERTSONS *Cardiff*
SMITH LLEWELYN PARTNERSHIP *Swansea*	

LEADING INDIVIDUALS – WALES – MAINLY PLAINTIFF	
Peter Llewellyn	*Smith Llewelyn Partnership*
Huw Llewelyn-Morgan	*Smith Llewelyn Partnership*
Tim Musgrave	*Huttons*

Edwards Geldard and *Hugh James Jones & Jenkins,* are also involved in a substanial amount of plaintiff medical negligence work and *Robertsons* of Cardiff has particular experience in obstretrics cases.

HIGHLY REGARDED – WALES – MAINLY DEFENDANT	
BEVAN ASHFORD *Cardiff*	MORGAN BRUCE *Cardiff*
WALKER SMITH & WAY *Wrexham*	

LEADING INDIVIDUALS – WALES – MAINLY DEFENDANT	
Graham J. Miles	*Morgan Bruce*
Tessa Shellens	*Bevan Ashford*

Bevan Ashford and *Morgan Bruce* maintain the pre-eminent position in this field. The latter has considerable experience acting for NHS trusts and health authorities in Wales in all areas of treatment ranging from damaged teeth to brain-damaged babies. The firm recently gained University Hospital of Wales NHS Trust as a client. Other clients include Mid Glamorgan Health Authority, Bridgend and District NHS Trust and South Glamorgan Health Authority. Notable practitioners include Graham Miles at *Morgan Bruce* and Tessa Shellens at *Bevan Ashford*.

MIDLANDS

Several firms undertake plaintiff medical negligence work in the Midlands. Paul Balen at *Freeth Cartwright Hunt Dickens* has a national reputation for his work in the field. He lectures to medical practitioners on medical negligence law and has published a number of articles on the subject. He is on the editorial board of 'Health Care Risk Report' and is joint editor of the 'Butterworths Personal Injury Litigation Service Bulletin'. He is spokesperson for the Benzodiazepine Solicitors' Steering Committeee, and is currently helping to co-ordinate breast implant claimants, and is also acting for women complaining about the five year contraceptive implant Norplant. He is the only assessor from the Midlands for The Law Society Medical Negligence Specialist Panel.

LEADING FIRMS – MIDLANDS – MAINLY PLAINTIFF

FREETH CARTWRIGHT HUNT DICKINS *Nottingham*

CHALLINORS *Birmingham*

Richard Follis at *Challinor Roberts Cooksey* is highly regarded for plaintiff medical negligence work and mainly deals with legal aid claims. He also lectures to the Birmingham Medico-Legal Society training division.

HIGHLY REGARDED – MIDLANDS – MAINLY PLAINTIFF

ANTHONY COLLINS *Birmingham*	**IRWIN MITCHELL** *Birmingham*
ROBIN THOMPSON & PARTNERS *Birmingham*	**SHAKESPEARES** *Birmingham*
NEWSOME VAUGHAN *Coventry*	

LEADING INDIVIDUALS – MIDLANDS – MAINLY PLAINTIFF

Paul Balen *Freeth Cartwright Hunt Dickins*

Richard T. Follis *Challinors*

Stuart Henderson *Irwin Mitchell,,*

Gary E. Christianson *Shakespeares*

Antony Hall *Anthony Collins*

Stuart Henderson has moved from *Robin Thompson & Partners* to head up a new plaintiff department at *Irwin Mitchell,* set up in January 1995. Stuart Henderson chairs the co-ordinating committee of lawyers in the bone cancer misdiagnosis cases that arose at the Royal Orthopaedic Hospital. He also acts for the women found to have breast tumours on mammograms and who were erroneously informed that they were 'all clear', leading to a review of hundreds of thousands of medical records in the West Midlands.

LEADING FIRMS – MIDLANDS – MAINLY DEFENDANT

THE LEWINGTON PARTNERSHIP *Birmingham*

A high proportion of defendant medical negligence work in the Midlands is undertaken by *The Lewington Partnership,* a niche practice concentrating principally on work for Health Authorities and NHS trusts. The firm was set up by practitoners who were the legal advisers to the West Midlands Regional Health Authority before privatisation in 1993. *Wragge & Co* are also recognised for their defendant medical negligence expertise.

HIGHLY REGARDED – MIDLANDS – MAINLY DEFENDANT

WRAGGE & CO *Birmingham*

EAST ANGLIA

On the plaintiff side, *Cunningham John & Co* is well-known in this field, and Simon John, a partner in the firm, is a frequent lecturer and contributor of articles. His legal expertise is supplemented by his medical background. *Dawbarns* also have an extensive plaintiff practice, and have strong connections with the Association of Victims of Medical Accidents.

HIGHLY REGARDED – EAST ANGLIA – MAINLY PLAINTIFF

CUNNINGHAM JOHN *Thetford*	**DAWBARNS** *Wisbech*
LORIMER LONGHURST & LEES *Cambridge*	**PRETTYS** *Ipswich*

LEADING INDIVIDUALS – EAST ANGLIA – MAINLY PLAINTIFF

Richard Everett Barr *Dawbarns*

Paul Harrington *Lorimer Longhurst & Lees*

Simon G. John *Cunningham, John*

Robert Longhurst *Lorimer Longhurst & Lees*

Mills & Reeve have a well-regarded health care practice which includes a substanial volume of defendant medical negligence cases. Howard Weston at the firm is a well established practitioner and highly regarded by his peers. He is on the NHS legal advisers committee and a regular speaker at conferences and to NHS trusts. Stephen King at the Norwich office has also been recommended for his expertise.

LEADING FIRMS – EAST ANGLIA – MAINLY DEFENDANT

MILLS & REEVE *Norwich*

Scrivenger Seabrook is considered to be a leading defence firm in the region, specialising in medical negligence and NHS law. Both partners have vast experience in the field, and have a large defendant medical case load.

HIGHLY REGARDED – EAST ANGLIA – MAINLY DEFENDANT

SCRIVENGER SEABROOK	
GREENWOODS *Peterborough*	**HANSELL STEVENSON** *Norwich*
HEWITSON BECKE + SHAW *Cambridge*	
EVERSHEDS *Norwich*	

LEADING INDIVIDUALS – EAST ANGLIA – MAINLY DEFENDANT

Stephen King *Mills & Reeve*

Howard W. Weston *Mills & Reeve*

Mark John Scrivenger *Scrivenger Seabrook*

Vicki Seabrook *Scrivenger Seabrook*

NORTH WEST

Alexander Harris is highly regarded nationwide as a plaintiff medical negligence firm. Ann Alexander heads the department and has particular expertise in issues relating to children.

The firm undertakes much legal aid work, including cerebral palsy, obstetrics and gynaecology, and anaesthetics. Prominent cases in the last 12 months have included O'Toole v Meresy Regional Health Authority and Robinson v Salford Health Authority. Howard Hatton heads the team at *Hatton Scates & Horton* where the focus is on individual rather than class actions. In 1993 the team achieved record damages for a hip replacement operation and have had several cases awarded over the £1 million mark in the last 12 months.

LEADING FIRMS – NORTH WEST – MAINLY PLAINTIFF

ALEXANDER HARRIS *Sale*

BETESH FOX & CO	**HATTON SCATES & HORTON**
Manchester	Manchester

PANNONE & PARTNERS *Manchester*

Pannone & Partners have a strong medical team combining legal expertise with medical knowledge. The team has been involved in many prominent cases including Sion v Hampstead HA (1994) and B v Islington HA (1991), a keyhole surgery case. The department is headed by John Kitchingman, who is well known for dealing with maximum severity medical accidents. Also recommended at the firm are Jacinta Peake and Stephen Jones.

Janine Tobias at *Betesh Fox* has been highly recommended for her plaintiff medical negligence expertise. The team has been involved in numerous high profile cases, and won an out-of-court settlement of £410,000 for a 10 year-old girl who received treatment for breathing difficulties at birth which resulted in blindness.

HIGHLY REGARDED – NORTH WEST – MAINLY PLAINTIFF

MAXWELL ENTWISTLE & BYRNE	**RUSSELL JONES & WALKER**
Liverpool	Manchester
BULLOCK WORTHINGTON & JACKSON *Manchester*	**LINDER MYERS** *Manchester*

Other highly regarded plaintiff firms include *Russell, Jones & Walker* and *Maxwell Entwistle & Bryne*. The latter specialises in catastrophic injury claims, particularly brain damaged children actions.

LEADING INDIVIDUALS – NORTH WEST – MAINLY PLAINTIFF

Ann Alexander *Alexander Harris*	
John Michael Kitchingman *Pannone & Partners*	
Paul D. McCarthy *Maxwell Entwistle & Byrne*	
Jacinta Peake *Pannone & Partners*	
Janine A. Tobias *Betesh Fox & Co*	

Howard Hatton *Hatton Scates & Horton*
Stephen L. Jones *Pannone & Partners*

As regards defendant work, *Hempsons* undertake medical and dental negligence on behalf of health authorities, trusts and practitioners. The firm has been involved in leading cases such as Whitehouse v Jordan and Wilsher v Essex Area Health Authority.

LEADING FIRMS – NORTH WEST – MAINLY DEFENDANT

HEMPSONS *Manchester*

Other defendant medical negligence departments in the area with strong reputations include *George Davies & Co, Davies Arnold Cooper, Hill Dickinson Davis Campbell* and *Lace Mawer.* The latter firm defended Staffordshire Health Authority against a class action which was one of the largest of its kind in the UK.

HIGHLY REGARDED – NORTH WEST – MAINLY DEFENDANT

DAVIES ARNOLD COOPER *Manchester*	**GEORGE DAVIES & CO** *Manchester*
HILL DICKINSON DAVIS CAMPBELL Liverpool	**LACE MAWER** *Manchester*

ELLIOTT & CO *Manchester*

LEADING INDIVIDUALS – NORTH WEST – MAINLY DEFENDANT

Anthony Gibbons *Hill Dickinson Davis Campbell*
Frances A. Harrison *Hempsons*
Michael Ryan *Hempsons*

NORTH EAST

On the plaintiff side, *Hay & Kilner* are well regarded. One partner in the team is a member of the National Steering Committee in the Benzodiazepene litigation. The firm recently won an award of £900,000 damages in a case of brain damage at birth. The medical negligence department at *Heptonstalls* has continued to expand over the last 12 months.

HIGHLY REGARDED – NORTH EAST – MAINLY PLAINTIFF

HAY & KILNER *Newcastle-upon-Tyne*	**HEPTONSTALLS** *Goole*
IRWIN MITCHELL *Sheffield*	**STAMP JACKSON & PROCTER** *Hull*
PETER MAUGHAN & CO *Gateshead*	

LEADING INDIVIDUALS – NORTH EAST – MAINLY PLAINTIFF

David Body *Irwin Mitchell,,*
Peter Pescod *Hay & Kilner*

The team receives cases on a Regional Yorkshire/ Humberside basis and has a partner on the AVMA Medical Negligence Referral Panel. *Irwin Mitchell* have a strong team of seven, headed by David Body, which acted in Almond v Leeds Western, the first case with damages for a child of over £1,000,000. *Stamp Jackson & Procter* whose team includes three partners, have been involved in the Myodil group action litigation.

HIGHLY REGARDED – NORTH EAST – MAINLY DEFENDANT

WANSBROUGHS WILLEY HARGRAVE *Leeds*

DICKINSON DEES *Newcastle upon Tyne*	**LE BRASSEUR J TICKLE** *Leeds*

On the defendant side, *Wansbroughs Willey Hargrave* have strengthened their position by taking over the substantial medical negligence practice at *Oxley & Coward.* Diane Hallatt, who heads the team, has acted for a large teaching hospital defending a claim which resulted in a structured settlement of £2.3m and raised interesting issues on quantum due

Diane Hallatt	*Wansbroughs Willey Hargrave*

to the need for 24 hour high dependency care. The group also defended a Health Authority in a Judicial Review case brought by a woman refused IVF treatment on age grounds.

SAMUEL PHILLIPS & CO *Newcastle-upon-Tyne*	SMITH & GRAHAM *Hartlepool*
PATTINSON AND BREWER *York*	

Samuel Phillips & Co, where Barry Speker has an established reputation, acts for both plaintiffs and defendants (including Newcastle Health Authority, Freeman Group of Hospital NHS Trust and Newcastle City Health NHS Trust).

David G.M. Keating	*Smith & Graham*
Barry N. Speker	*Samuel Phillips & Co*

Smith & Graham also deal with medical negligence matters for both the plaintiff and defendant. David Keating has been recommended for his work in this field.

SCOTLAND

SHEPHERD & WEDDERBURN *Edinburgh*	SIMPSON & MARWICK WS *Edinburgh*

Hugh Donald at *Shepherd & Wedderburn WS* and John Griffiths at *Simpson & Marwick WS* have been recommended for their expertise in medical negligence.

ALEX MORISON & CO WS *Edinburgh*	BALFOUR & MANSON - NIGHTINGALE & BELL *Edinburgh*
GILLAM MACKIE *Edinburgh*	

Other firms that undertake medical negligence litigation are *Balfour & Manson- Nightingale & Bell, Gillam Mackie* and *Alex Morrison & Co.*

Hugh R. Donald	*Shepherd & Wedderburn*
John R. Griffiths	*Simpson & Marwick WS*

LONDON

Barton, Anthony
Anthony Barton, London (0171) 700 7348. Qualified 1992. Sole Practitioner 1993. Handles medical negligence, pharmaceutical product liability, coroners' inquests, health service law and medical ethics. Born 3.2.1955.

Barton, Grainne
Pannone Pritchard Englefield, London (0171) 972 9720. Qualified 1989. Partner 1993. Medical Negligence Department. Handles exclusively medical negligence matters. Born 8.10.1963.

Blundell, Cheryl
See under Health Care.

Cahill, Julia
Kingsley Napley, London (0171) 814 1200.

Specialisation: Medically qualified patner specialising in medical negligence litigation. Particular expertise in obstetric neligence and claims on behalf of brain damaged children, general surgery, neurosurgery and arteriovenous malformation. Practice also covers legal negligence involving the pursuit of claims against legal advisers in medical negligence cases. Interesting recent cases include McAllister v. Lewisham and North Southwark Health Authority [1994] MEDLR.

Prof. Membership: Law Society Panel of Specialist Medical Negligence Solicitors; Association of Personal Injury Lawyers; Action for Victims of Medical Accidents Lawyers Panel; Inquest.

Career: DIP Physiotherapy 1976. LL.B 1980. Assistant Director, Action for Victims of Medical Accidents 1984. Private practice since 1989.

Personal: Born 24th December 1953. Lives in Islington, London.

Dingwall, Christian
Le Brasseur J Tickle, London (0171) 836 0099. Partner handling medical negligence and health service work.

Specialisation: Principal area of practice is medical negligence and health service work. Handles a wide range of high value medical negligence and employment liability claims, primarily on behalf of defendants. Important cases include R v. Managers of South Western Hospital ex p. M. Clients include NHS trusts and health authorities, private hospitals and their insurers and medical defence organisations. Has addressed conferences and seminars.

Prof. Membership: Law Society.

Career: Qualified in 1986. Partner at *Le Brasseur J Tickle* since 1988.

Personal: Born 28th December 1959. Educated at Bristol University 1979-82 and the College of Law 1982-84. Leisure activities include reading, fell-walking, gardening, running and cycling. Lives in Raynes Park, London.

Fazan, Claire
Bindman & Partners, London (0171) 833 4433. Partner in charge of Personal Injury and Medical Negligence Department.

Specialisation: Medical negligence litigation on behalf of plaintiffs. Experienced in claims involving all types of injury including extensive experience of claims on behalf of adults and children who have suffered brain damage. Advice under the Legal Aid Scheme. Co-author of "Medical Negligence Litigation: A Practitioners Guide", by Irwin, Fazan & Alfrey [published by LAG].

Prof. Membership: Law Society Medical Negligence Panel.

Career: Qualified in 1985. Joined *Bindman & Partners* in 1987 and became a Partner in 1989.

Personal: Born 21st June 1956. Attended London University (LLB 1983).

Forrester, Rex
Hempsons, London (0171) 836 0011. Senior Assistant Solicitor in Medical and Healthcare Department.

Specialisation: Defendant medical negligence specialist. Advises and represents NHS Hospital Trusts and general practitioners, as well as doctors working in the private sector in relation to litigation resulting from allegations of medical negligence arising from all areas of medical practice. Provides representation and advocacy before professional disciplinary tribunals including the GMC, the NHS Tribunal, and at FHS Appeals. Also represents the interests of doctors at coronal inquests and enquiries. Major clients include the Medical Defence Union Ltd, Brighton Healthcare NHS Trust and Royal Surrey NHS Trust.

Prof. Membership: Solicitors' Association of Higher Court Advocates.

Career: Qualified in New Zealand as a Solicitor/Barrister in 1986. Senior Assistant Solicitor with *Hempsons* since 1988. Qualified in England & Wales as a Solicitor in 1991. Obtained Rights of Audience in the Higher Courts (Civil) in 1994.

Personal: Born 19th September 1962. Educated at Christ's College, Christchurch, New Zealand 1976-80, the University of Canterbury, New Zealand (LL.B 1st Class Hons, 1985) and Gonville & Caius College, Cambridge (LL.M, 1986). Interests include travel, reading and photography. Lives in London.

Harvey, C.J. Zoe

Hempsons, London (0171) 836 0011. Partner in Medical & Healthcare Department.

Specialisation: Principal area of practice is medical and healthcare matters. Handles litigation relating to all areas of hospital and general practice. Advises NHS Health Authorities/Trusts and practitioners on medico-legal matters, including professional disciplinary and tribunal representation. Other main area of practice is personal injury, with particular emphasis on medical and pharmaceutical cases. Major cases include Dr Sidney Gee v. GMC. Major clients include the Medical Defence Union Ltd, South East London Health Authority and Royal Surrey Trust.

Prof. Membership: Law Society, Medico-Legal Society.

Career: Qualified in 1979. Became a Partner at *Hempsons* in 1991.

Personal: Born 16th February 1955. Educated at St. Annes's College Convent, Sanderstead, Surrey 1964-73 and Birmingham University 1973-76. Leisure activities include gardening, swimming and embroidery. Lives in New Malden, Surrey.

Hay, Katie

Capsticks, London (0181) 780 2211. Qualified 1988. Partner 1992. Specialises in medical negligence, especially larger cases and structured settlements. Also advises NHS bodies.

Holmes, John

Beachcroft Stanleys, London (0171) 242 1011. Qualified 1984. Partner 1992. Health Law Department. Principal area of practice is medical negligence. Also gives general advice in clinical issues and staff claims.

Jamieson, Elisabeth

Pannone Pritchard Englefield, London (0171) 972 9720. Qualified 1988. Assistant Solicitor. Medical Negligence Department. Handles exclusively medical negligence work. Born 24.10.1946.

Jenkins, Caroline Helen Clare

Parlett Kent & Co, London (0171) 430 0712/3. Qualified 1980. Partner 1963. Senior Partner. Personal Injury Department. Principal area of practice is medical negligence. Particular interest in gynaecological, oncological and obstetrics cases. Born 5.2.1952.

Lee, Terry

Evill & Coleman, London (0181) 789 9221. Partner in Personal Injury Department.

Specialisation: Main areas of practice are catastrophic injuries, medical negligence, brain damage at birth, head injuries, multiple injuries, fatal accident claims and Court of Protection work. He has been involved in a number of significant actions including Brown v. Merton & Sutton Health Authority; Head v. East Anglian Health Authority; Hall v. Pirie and Lambert v. Devon County Council. Some of the actions he has conducted include cases where damages in excess of £1 million have been awarded, and he has also been instrumental in dealing with a number of cases which involve the formation of a structured settlement. He is an assessor to the Personal Injury Panel, as well as a member of the specialised panel of personal injury solicitors. He is also co-ordinating solicitor involved in a series of cases where victims have allegedly suffered side effects as a result of the use of corticosteriod medication. Author of articles for a legal magazine and a book on injuries of maximum severity (awaiting publication). Lectures extensively at conferences and seminars.

Prof. Membership: Association of Personal Injury Lawyers, AVMA (referral solicitor). Law Society of Hong Kong.

Career: Qualified and joined *Evill & Coleman* in 1972. Became a Partner in 1976.

Personal: Born 14th August 1945. Educated at Wimbledon College. Recreations include golf and tennis. Lives in Esher, Surrey.

Leigh, Sarah

Leigh Day & Co, London (0171) 242 1775. Partner in Medical Negligence Department.

Specialisation: Handles primarily major medical negligence cases involving severe disability and death as well as a few cases involving mental handicap problems (e.g. Re F in 1989 - a leading case on consent in mental handicap). Has spoken at many conferences and seminars and written several articles.

Prof. Membership: AVMA, Justice, APIL (Member of Executive since 1992).

Career: Qualified in 1971. Founder Partner (1974) of *Bindman & Partner*. Left to set up own firm in 1985 (renamed *Leigh Day & Co* in 1988).

Personal: Born 29th July 1942. Attended Keele University 1960-64. Trustee of Immigrants Aid Trust. Campaigner for changes in medical negligence litigation system. Lives in London.

Leigh, Bertie

Hempsons, London (0171) 836 0011. Partner in Medical and Healthcare Department.

Specialisation: Principal area of practice is medical law, with particular interest in cases involving obstetrics, anaesthesia, paediatrics, orthopaedics, neurosurgery and general practice. Other main area of expertise is National Health Service Acts and associated regulations. Has dealt with a number of Court of Appeal cases including Gregory v. Pembrokeshire Health Authority [1989], Hughes v. Waltham Forest Health Authority [1991], Lindsay v. Western Health Board [1992] and Bull & Wakeham v. Devon Health Authority [1993]. Major clients include the Association of Anaesthetists and the British Paediatric Association. Author of chapters in 'Ethics & Obstetrics & Gynaecology' (RCOG 1994) and 'Safe Practice in Obstetrics & Gynaecology' (1994). Lectures regularly to lawyers and doctors.

Prof. Membership: Medico-Legal Society.

Career: Qualified in 1976, having joined *Hempsons* in 1973. Became a Partner in 1977.

Personal: Born 30th August 1946. Educated at St. Christopher School, Letchworth 1960-65 and the University of East Anglia 1966-70. Lives in Clapham.

Levy, Russell

Leigh Day & Co, London (0171) 242 1775. Partner in Medical Negligence Department.

Specialisation: Principal area of practice is plaintiff medical negligence and medical devices (product liability) litigation. Has written numerous articles for various specialist publications and is a regular speaker on medical negligence topics.

Prof. Membership: AVMA, APIL.

Career: Qualified 1984. Joined *Leigh Day & Co* as a Partner in 1991.

Personal: Born 15th March 1956. Lives in London.

Marsh, Christine

Kingsley Napley, London (0171) 814 1200. Partner in Civil Litigation (Medical Negligence) Department.

Specialisation: Handles plaintiff medical negligence. Undertakes Legal Aid work. Emphasis on maximum severity injuries. Has acted in several cases reported in national newspapers. Co-author of 'Fatal Accident Litigation' (Tolley's, 1993). Has lectured and presented seminars.

Prof. Membership: APIL, AVMA, Headway, Spinal Injuries Association, Medico-legal Society.

Career: Qualified 1986. Partner at *Bolt Burdon* 1989-92. Joined *Kingsley Napley* as a Partner in December 1992.

Personal: Born 23rd January 1962. Educated at Royal Latin School, Buckingham 1974-80 and Leicester University 1980-83. Leisure interests include tennis, ski-ing, music and gardening.

Mason, David

Capsticks, London (0181) 780 2211. Partner and Head of Obstetric Litigation Group within Litigation Department.

Specialisation: Principal area of practice is medical negligence with specialisation in obstetrics and neurosurgery cases. Also deals with mental health law. Acted for health authorities in successful defence of a number of reported cases including Rance v. Mid Downs Health Authority; Moore v. Worthing Health Authority, Saad v. Mid Surrey Health Authority, Joyce v. Wandsworth Health Authority, de Martell v. Merton and Sutton Health Authority. Co-author of 'Litigation - A Risk Management Guide to Midwives' and articles on medical law for specialist publications. Regular lecturer on medical law and risk management topics, especially obstetrics-related.

Prof. Membership: Law Society.

Career: Called to Bar 1984. Employed Barrister with *Thomas Watts & Co* 1986-1988. Joined *Capsticks* in 1988 as employed Barrister. Requalified as Solicitor and became a Partner in 1990.

Personal: Born 16th October 1955. Attended Winchester College 1969-73, then Oriel College, Oxford 1974-77 (MA in Experimental Psychology). Honorary Legal Adviser to College of Health. Lives in London.

McNeil, Paul

Field Fisher Waterhouse, London (0171) 481 4841.

Specialisation: Partner in the Litigation Department specialising in medical negligence, personal injury and product liability, acting mainly for plaintiffs. Has particular experience in cases involving head and other serious injuries. Has handled many £1 million cases. Recent cases include Sheridan v. Greenwich Health Authority [1995] (£1 million); May v. Board of Governors of the Royal Brompton Hospital [1995] (£1.5 million structured settlement). Publications include 'International Product Liability' (1993) co-author. Also lectures on various aspects of medical law.

Prof. Membership: Law Society Medical Negligence Panel; Association of Personal Injury Lawyers; AVMA.

Career: Qualified 1983. Assistant solicitor, Amhurst Brown 1983-1985. Assistant solicitor, Taylor Joynson Garrett 1985-1992. Assistant solicitor, Field Fisher Waterhouse 1992-1994. Partner since 1994.

Personal: Educated at All Saints' Comprehensive, Huddersfield 1975-1977 and Sheffield University 1977-1980. Leisure pursuits include tennis, swimming and skiing. Born 26th July 1958. Lives in Putney, London.

Parsons, Andrew E.

Radcliffes Crossman Block, London (0171) 222 7040. Qualified 1987. Partner 1992 (Head of Health Group). Litigation Department. Main area of practice is defendant medical negligence.

Shipway, R.R.H.

Le Brasseur J Tickle, London (0171) 836 0099.

Smith, Janice

Capsticks, London (0181) 780 2211. Qualified 1985. Partner 1991. Litigation Department. Specialises in medical negligence, particularly obstetrics, cardiology, A&E and orthopaedic cases.

Stone, David M.

Bird & Bird, London (0171) 415 6000. Partner. Commercial Litigation Department.

Specialisation: Main area of practice is the health sector, acting for trusts, health authorities and advisory bodies in medical negligence and personal injury claims, employment and defamation matters, risk management, health and admin. law generally. Also handles professional negligence, defamation and general commercial litigation. Regular contributor to health press and speaker at health conferences. Editor of Legal Diagnosis and has organised seminars for the health sector.

Prof. Membership: Law Society, Medico-Legal Society.

Career: Qualified in 1983. Assistant solicitor with *Lee Bolton & Lee* 1983-85. Joined *Bird & Bird* in 1985 and became a Partner in 1990.

Personal: Born 1956. Educated at Christ's Hospital, Horsham 1967-74 and Christ's College, Cambridge 1975-78. (Classics). Lives in London.

Sumerling, R.W.

Le Brasseur J Tickle, London (0171) 836 0099.

Vallance, Richard A.

Compton Carr, London (0171) 831 6981. Partner and Head of Litigation Department.

Specialisation: An important part of his practice is professional negligence. Began medical negligence work in 1978 with cases concerning children suffering deafness as a result of treatment for burns. Dealt with numerous maternity cases in the early 1980's and was in the forefront of the development of medical negligence litigation from then on. Also handles commercial litigation. Acted for two of the plaintiffs in the leading case of Naylor v. Preston Area Health Authority,

1987 2 All ER 353. Has lectured on medical negligence to lawyers, doctors and nurses since about 1984 including LAG/AVMA seminars and conferences and the Law Society 1989 Litigation Conference in Birmingham. Contributed a chapter to Powers and Harris's book 'Medical Negligence' (Butterworths) and has written numerous articles. Appeared on Legal Network TV in 1993.

Prof. Membership: The Law Society and its Committees concerning issues of medical negligence, AVMA & AVMA Lawyers Support Group, APIL Medical Negligence Special Interest Group, Medico-Legal Society.

Career: Qualified in 1970. Joined *Compton Carr* in 1971 and became a Partner in 1972. Assessor of the Law Society Medical Negligence Panel from July 1994.

Personal: Born 26th January 1947. Secondary School Governor. Recreations include squash, tennis, reading, opera and theatre. Lives in Saffron Walden.

Winyard, Anne H.

Leigh Day & Co, London (0171) 242 1775.

Specialisation: Partner and specialist in medical negligence. Acts for plaintiffs. Cases mainly involve serious disablities or death, including both adults and children who have suffered brain damage as a result of medical treatment. Particular interest in obstetrics and haematology. Publications include chapters in both 'Medical Negligence' (Powers & Harris) and 'Safe Practice in Obstetrics and Gynaecology' (Clements). Has also written a number of articles on various aspects of medical negligence. Regular speaker at medico-legal conferences and seminars.

Prof. Membership: AVMA, APIL, ATLA, Law Society.

Career: Qualified 1977. Partner, *Fisher Meredith* 1983-1992. Joined *Leigh Day & Co* as partner in 1992.

Personal: Born 1948. Lives in London.

Yeaman, Anthony George

Beachcroft Stanleys, London (0171) 242 1011. Qualified 1988. Health Law Department. Specialises in medical negligence claims for Health Service bodies. Advises on health service law.

Young, Magi

Parlett Kent & Co, London (0171) 430 0712/3. Partner in Medical Negligence Department.

Specialisation: Main area of practice is medical negligence, acting for plaintiffs in all areas, but particularly obstetrics and psychiatry. AVMA referral solicitor and member of Law Society Medical Negligence panel. Also handles personal injury matters, including claims against local authorities. Recently co-authored a paper (Vincent et al, 1994) published in 'The Lancet' about why patients sue their doctors - the first research of this type in the UK. Lectures on nursing and the law, psychiatric negligence and dealing with distressed clients.

Prof. Membership: Law Society. APIL.

Career: Qualified in 1987. With *Pannone Napier & Pannone Blackburn* 1987-1992, as a Partner from 1991. Joined *Parlett Kent & Co* in 1992 and became a Partner in 1993.

Personal: Born 8th December 1960. Educated at Bristol University (B. Soc. Sci 1982). Recreations include gardening, painting and reading. Lives in Brixton and Crediton.

REGIONS

Alexander, Ann

Alexander Harris, Sale (0161) 969 6779. Managing Partner and Partner in charge of Medical Negligence Department.

Specialisation: Principal area of personal practice is advising on all aspects of medical accidents, particularly cerebral palsy, anaesthetics and cases involving children, although the department of eight solicitors and three nurses deals with all aspects of medical negligence. Acted in O'Toole v. Mersey Regional Health Authority (first self-funded Health Authority structured settlement) and for the families of nine of the victims of Beverly Allitt. Appears regularly on television documentaries on medical negligence issues and lectures on the subject to a variety of audiences including lawyers and doctors.

Prof. Membership: Law Society, APIL, AVMA, ATLA (Member of Executive Committee Birth Trauma Litigation Group), assessor to Law Society Specialist Medical Negligence Panel. Member of Editorial Board of Health Care Risk Report.

Career: Qualified in 1978 and then became co-founder of *Alexander Harris* in May 1989. First practice in this country specialising exclusively in medical negligence and pharmaceutical product liability. The practice has now added a specialist personal injury department.

Personal: Born 5th November 1954. Attended University College, London (LL.B 1974). Lives in Bowdon, Cheshire.

Balen, Paul

See under Personal Injury.

Barcan, Richard

Barcan Woodward, Bristol (0117) 9635237. Qualified 1979. Partner 1985. Specialises in medical negligence and personal injury, acting for plaintiffs (including legal aid).

Barr, Richard Everett

Dawbarns, King's Lynn (01553) 764373. Partner in Personal Injury/Medical Negligence Department. Charge-out rate is approximately £110.00 per hour.

Specialisation: Specialises in medical negligence (particularly vaccine damage) claims. Co-ordinator of Groups C and D in the Opren litigation and national co-ordinator (together with *Freeth Cartwright Hunt Dickins*) for the MMR vaccine damage claims. Co-author of the 'Penguin Guide to the Law' and author of two books for the Consumer Association; columnist (Tales from Practice) for the 'Solicitor's Journal'. Has appeared on television in relation to the Opren and MMR vaccine litigation and is a regular guest on BBC Radio Norfolk's fortnightly legal 'phone-in'.
Professional Membership: Secretary to the APIL Multiparty Special Interest Group; President of the West Norfolk and Kings Lynn Law Society; former Legal Aid Committee member and member of the Law Society's LOMAT committee.

Personal: Born 19th July 1947. Educated at Wisbech Grammar School to 1965, University of Nebraska 1965-66 and Nottingham Regional College, 1968. Member of the Society of Authors. Leisure interests include swimming, neglecting his garden, reading and writing. Lives near Kings Lynn.

Body, David

Irwin Mitchell, incorporating Kershaw Tucker, Sheffield (0114) 276 7777. Partner in Personal Injury Department.

Specialisation: Main area of practice is medical negligence on behalf of plaintiffs. Acted in Maynard v. West Midlands RHA; Davis v. City and Hackney Health Authority; Aboul-Hosn v. Governors of National Hospital for Nervous Diseases and Bolitho v. City and Hackney Health Authority and Hopkins v. McKenzie. Author of chapter on 'The Conduct of Proceedings' to Powers & Harris 'Medical Negligence'. Lectures regularly to both doctors and lawyers. Chair of Medical Negligence Special Interest Group of APIL (1992-1995).

Prof. Membership: APIL, AVMA.

Career: Qualified in 1981. Worked at *Halls* 1981-91, from 1984 as a Partner. Joined *Irwin Mitchell* in 1991 as a Partner.

Personal: Born 1st August 1955. Attended Hereford High School and Corpus Christi College, Oxford (BA Hons, 1976). Leisure interests include taking blurred photographs and waiting for the revival of the Welsh rugby team. Lives in Sheffield.

Broadhead, Jill

Bevan Ashford, Bristol (0117) 923 0111. Partner in Medical Negligence Department.

Specialisation: Has nineteen years experience in the medical negligence field, dealing with a wide variety of cases, particularly obstetric and neuro surgical claims. Actively involved in all the multi-party litigation affecting the NHS. Also has expertise in the law relating to the supervision of registered nursing homes by Health Authorities. Acted in Nash v. Southmead Health Authority, Hall v. Avon Health Authority (Training) and Taylor

v Somerset Health Authority. Lectures widely to managers and clinicians within the NHS.

Prof. Membership: Law Society, Bristol Medico Legal Society.

Career: Qualified in 1978. Joined *Bevan Ashford* in 1976, becoming a Partner in 1986.

Personal: Born 1953. Attended University of Birmingham and St Brandon's School, Clevedon. Church Warden. Chairman of Church Restoration Appeal.

Christianson, Gary E.

Shakespeares, Birmingham (0121) 632 4199. Partner in Litigation Department.

Specialisation: Principal area of practice is medical negligence. Handles plaintiff only work, a substantial part of which is legally aided. Broad experience of all types of medical negligence cases. Also has extensive experience of representation at inquests, including substantial matters of public interest (e.g. Sun Valley poultry fire and M40 minibus crash). Has appeared on local radio programmes concerning medical negligence issues. Member of No.6 Area Legal Aid Committee.

Prof. Membership: Birmingham Medico-Legal Society (Honorary Auditor), Law Society, Birmingham Law Society, Law Society Personal Injury Panel.

Career: Qualified in 1984. Became a Partner at *Shakespeares* in 1988.

Personal: Born 22nd June 1960. Educated at Fakenham Grammar School 1972-78 and Birmingham University 1978-81. Lives in Wolverhampton.

Desmond, Adrian

Boyes Turner & Burrows, Reading (01734) 597711. Partner in Medical Negligence and Personal Injury Group.

Specialisation: Acts for plaintiffs in all types of medical accident cases with special interest in brain injury, spinal injury and child cases. Acted in Cavanagh v. Bristol, Heath v. Berkshire, Taylor v. Somerset, Parry v. N W Surrey and Khan v. Ainslie. Writer of ad hoc articles in the various legal journals on issues related to medical negligence. Regular lecturer on the topic.

Prof. Membership: AVMA (referral solicitor), APIL (secretary medical negligence SIG), SIA, Headway, Patients Association, ATLA.

Career: Qualified and joined *Boyes Turner & Burrows* in 1980. Became a Partner in 1986. Became Medical Negligence Panel Assessor and Deputy Taxing Master SCTO in 1994.

Personal: Born 9th January 1955. Educated at Ratcliffe College 1968-73 and Bristol University 1974-77. Enjoys music and literature. Lives in Henley on Thames.

Donald, Hugh R.

Shepherd & Wedderburn WS, Edinburgh (0131) 228 9900. Chief Executive.

Specialisation: Accredited specialist in medical negligence, representing doctors and dentists in civil claims, enquiries and disciplinary proceedings. Lecturer at a number of conferences on medico-legal subjects. Also aviation representing airline and helicopter operators in both civil claims and accident enquiries.

Career: Qualified in 1975, having joined *Shepherd & Wedderburn WS* in 1973. Became a Partner in 1977. Administrative Head of Litigation Department 1990-94. Appointed Managing Partner in April 1994, and Chief Executive in April 1995.

Personal: Born 5th November 1951. Educated at Edinburgh University. Family Mediator. Leisure interests include gardening, walking and church. Lives in Edinburgh.

Follis, Richard T.

Challinors, Birmingham (0121) 455 6333. Qualified 1981. Partner 1984. Medical Negligence Department. Handles plaintiff only medical negligence with a substantial proportion of legally aided work. Born 25.4.1956.

Gadsby, Gillian

Gadsby Wicks, Chelmsford (01245) 494929. Qualified 1989. Founding Partner 1993. Handles medical negligence and medical product liability work. Born 15.11.1965.

Gibbons, Anthony

Hill Dickinson Davis Campbell, Liverpool (0151) 236 5400. Partner in Health Department.

Specialisation: Principal areas of practice are medical negligence, employment law and NHS advisory work. Handles a large volume of medical negligence cases, particularly brain damage cases of high value. Another significant element of work involves NHS property transactions acting on behalf of major NHS clients in the disposal of surplus property and in particular redundant hospitals. Important cases handled include Booth v. Warrington Health Authority (disclosure of witness statements referred to in experts reports), Ashcroft v. Mersey Regional Health Authority (standard of care of consultants in medical negligence cases) and O'Toole v. Liverpool Health Authority (first self-funded structural settlement case in the medical negligence field). Major clients include North West Regional Health Authority and all NHS trusts in Cheshire and Merseyside. Has given lectures to various NHS clients. Participated as a presenter in Liverpool Law Society course on medical negligence.

Prof. Membership: Law Society.

Career: Qualified in 1972. Former in-house Legal Adviser with Mersey RHA 1980-90. Joined *Hill Dickinson Davis Campbell* as a Partner in 1990.

Personal: Born 10th October 1947. Educated at Xaverian College, Manchester 1959-66 and Nottingham University 1966-69 (Nottingham Co-operative Society Prize 1968, Hill Prize 1969). Leisure pursuits in-

clude food, wine and watching sport. Lives in Chester.

Griffiths, John R.

Simpson & Marwick WS, Edinburgh (0131) 557 1545. Qualified 1971. Partner 1989. Solicitor to the Medical and Dental Defence Union of Scotland. Main areas of practice are medical negligence and employment law. Born 16.9.1944.

Hall, Antony

Anthony Collins, Birmingham (0121) 200 3242. Qualified 1986. Partner and head of Medical Negligence and Personal Injury Department. Specialises in all aspects of both areas.

Hallatt, Diane

Wansbroughs Willey Hargrave, Sheffield (0114) 272 7485. Partner in Health Department.

Specialisation: Specialises in defendant medical negligence and health service related law. Work includes large obstetric claims, class actions, major disasters and regional inquiries into serious untoward incidents. Also has experience of a wide range of health service and public administrative law. Advised Grantham Hospital and the district and regional authorities in the Beverley Allitt case. Was also involved in overseeing the HIV haemophilia litigation and in the Myodil and Benzodiazepine class actions.

Career: Qualified 1980. With Trent Regional Health Authority 1986-89. Partner at *Oxley & Coward* 1989-95 and at *Wansbroughs Willey Hargrave* from February 1995.

Harrington, Paul

Lorimer Longhurst & Lees, Cambridge (01223) 311141 & 358227. Qualified 1983.

Harrison, Frances A.

Hempsons, Manchester (0161) 228 0011. Partner in Medical & Healthcare Department.

Specialisation: Principal area of practice is the law relating to hospitals and general practice. Work includes medico-legal advice to and representation of Health Authorities, NHS Trusts and individual practitioners in medical negligence actions. Also advises on ethics in relation to healthcare and representation at enquiries. Other main areas of practice are defamation and the law relating to children. Major cases include Whitehouse v. Jordan (HL) [1981], Wilsher v. Essex Area Health Authority (HL) [1988] and Naylor v. Preston Area Health Authority (CA) [1987]. Lectures widely and writes for legal journals.

Prof. Membership: Law Society.

Career: Qualified in 1978 and joined *Hempsons*. Became a Partner in 1982.

Personal: Educated at Paddock House Grammar School, Accrington, Lancs and Keele University. Lives in Macclesfield.

Hatton, Howard

Hatton Scates & Horton, Manchester (0161) 833 0020.

Specialisation: Plaintiff practice of medical negligence and personal injury. Specialisations include cerebral palsy, brain damage, paralysis, joint replacement, cancer cases. Record damages achieved for hip replacement operation in 1993. Two cases in excess of £1 million settled in 1994. One of first settlements of case involving damage to bile duct at laparoscopic cholecystectomy - this is a further area of specialist interest.

Prof. Membership: Law Society, APIL, Law Society Personal Injuries Panel.

Career: Qualified in 1975.

Henderson, Stuart

See under Personal Injury.

Hickman, Adrian

Christopher Harrison & Co, Truro (01872) 41408. Personal and Medical Injuries Specialist.

Specialisation: Emphasis on head injury matters. Acted in Hotson v. East Berkshire Health Authority (loss of chance), M v. Plymouth Health Authority (pre-action discovery) and Braybrooke v. Parker (first needs based on structured settlement). Author of articles published in personal and medical injuries law letter, APIL newsletter AVMA journal and Butterworths Personal Injury bulletin. Lectures for Legal Action Group and at the Law Society's Civil Litigation Conference 1993. Appears on national radio and regularly on local TV and radio stations.

Prof. Membership: Association of Personal Injury Lawyers, Referral lawyer for Action for Victims of Medical Accidents.

Career: Although not qualified as a Solicitor, has specialised in personal injury litigation for 26 years and medical injury litigation for 15 years. Joined *Christopher Harrison & Co.* in 1994.

Personal: Born 1st March 1949. Attended High Wycombe School 1965. Founder Member and Chairman of the Headway Cornwall; Chairman of AVMA, Cornwall Lawyers Support Group; Member of the Community Health Council. Leisure interests include golf, bird watching and gardening.

John, Simon G.

Cunningham, John & Co, Thetford (01842) 752401. Qualified 1969. Partner 1972. Head of Personal Injury Department. Specialises in medical negligence, particularly relating to head and spinal injuries.

Johnson, Robert I.

See under Litigation (Commercial).

Jones, Stephen L.

Pannone & Partners, Manchester (0161) 832 3000. Qualified 1986. Partner 1992. Medical Negligence Department. Specialises in plaintiff medical negligence claims. Also advises on mental health law.

Keating, David G.M.

Smith & Graham, Hartlepool (01429) 271651. Partner specialising in medical negligence, health law and personal injury.

Specialisation: Principal area of practice is medical negligence and health law (including mental health). Acts primarily for defendants but also plaintiffs. Other area of practice is personal injury acting primarily for plaintiffs. Member of the Personal Injury Panel and the Mental Health Review Tribunal Panel. Important matters handled the Piper Alpha disaster, Cleveland child abuse inquiry, major claims involving brain damage, severe physical injury and for clients lacking capacity. Clients include a number of health authorities and NHS Trusts as well as the Union of Democratic Mineworkers. Chairman of conferences on mental health and community care issues. Has lectured on medical negligence and mental health.

Prof. Membership: Law Society (Council Member and Chairman of Mental Health Sub-Committee), Legal Action Group, AVMA.

Career: Qualified in 1967. Worked in local government 1966-68. Had own practice in the Solomon Islands and Vanuatu 1969-72. Joined *Smith & Graham* in 1972 and became a Partner in 1974.

Personal: Born 31st January 1943. Educated at University College School 1954-61 and Durham University 1961-64. Governor of Hartlepool 6th Form College. lives in Hartlepool.

King, Stephen

See under Health Care.

Kitchingman, John Michael

Pannone & Partners, Manchester (0161) 832 3000. Partner in Medical Negligence Department.

Specialisation: Specialises in medical negligence litigation. Head of department, dealing with all aspects of medical litigation for victims of medical accidents with emphasis on cases of maximum severity. Handled Rogers v. Dr Hallam and Forman in 1994.

Prof. Membership: Association of Personal Injury Lawyers and Medical Negligence Special Interest Group. Member AVMA referral panel and AVMA North West Steering Committee.

Career: Qualified in 1975. Assistant solicitor *Goldberg,* Blackburn 1975-78. Joined and became partner in *Pannone & Partners* 1978.

Personal: Born 5th August 1950. Educated at Bell Vue Grammar School, Bradford 1961-69. Attended University of Hull 1969-72 (LLB 2.1 Hons), and College of Law, Guildford 1972-3. Leisure pursuits include walking, sailing, birdwatching, and travel. Lives near Altrincham.

Llewellyn, Peter

Smith Llewelyn Partnership, Swansea (01792) 651234.

Llewelyn-Morgan, Huw

Smith Llewelyn Partnership, Swansea (01792) 651234.

Longhurst, Robert

Lorimer Longhurst & Lees, Cambridge (01223) 311141 & 358227. Qualified 1979. Partner 1980. Litigation Department. Specialises in medical negligence actions, particularly birth injuries. Born 23.4.1940.

McCarthy, Paul D.

Maxwell Entwistle & Byrne, Liverpool (0151) 227 4545. Partner 1980. Head of Medical Negligence and Catastrophic Injury Department. Particular interest in claims for compensation for babies brain damaged by negligent mishandling of their birth. Born 10.10.1953.

McClure, Alison

Blake Lapthorn, Fareham (01489) 579990. Partner in Personal & Medical Injuries Litigation Department.

Specialisation: Specialist in personal injury and medical negligence litigation. Panel Solicitor for Action for Victims of Medical Accidents. Member of Law Society Personal Injury Panel. Particular experience in personal injury claims of maximum severity.

Prof. Membership: AVMA, APIL, SIA, Committee Member of Hampshire Law Society (Chairman of Education Committee).

Career: Qualified in 1986, having joined *Blake Lapthorn* in 1984. Became a Partner in 1990.

Personal: Educated at Shelley High School, Huddersfield 1974-80 and Southampton University 1980-83. Governor of Portsmouth Sixth Form College.

Miles, Graham J.

Morgan Bruce, Cardiff (01222) 385385. Qualified 1983. Partner 1989. Health Department. Specialises in medical negligence, acting predominantly for health authorities and NHS Trusts.

Musgrave, Tim

Huttons, Cardiff (01222) 378621. Qualified 1987. Associate. Civil Department. Specialises in medical negligence and personal injury, acting for plaintiffs. Born 1.9.1963.

Osborne, Tom

Osborne Morris & Morgan, Leighton Buzzard (01525) 378177.

Over, Christopher

Over Taylor Biggs, Exeter (01392) 823811. Qualified 1977. Founding Partner. Specialises in medical negligence, particularly catastrophic injuries and birth defects. Born 18.10.1952.

Peake, Jacinta

Pannone & Partners, Manchester (0161) 832 3000.

Pescod, Peter

See under Personal Injury.

Reed, Derek S.

See under Crime: Fraud.

Ryan, Michael

Hempsons, Manchester (0161) 228 0011. Partner in Medical & Healthcare Department.

Specialisation: Specialises in defendant medical and dental negligence (hospital and general practice). Handles tribunal work, representation at disciplinary enquiries and professional bodies, court representation including inquests, judicial review, undertaking the defence of serious criminal charges against doctors and dentists, including advocacy. Acted in various cases involving allegations of manslaughter, obtaining controlled drugs by deception, complex pharmaceutical fraud involving clinical trials, judicial review and employment. Has written widely on medico-legal matters.

Career: Qualified in 1983. Assistant Solicitor at *Gordon Dadds & Co* 1983-85. Joined *Hempsons* in 1985 and became a Partner in 1988.

Personal: Born in 1958. Educated at Ellesmere Port Grammar School and Hull University (LL.B, 1979). Member of Stockport Harriers and the Fell Running Association. Also enjoys rugby and swimming. Lives in Bramhall.

Scrivenger, Mark John

Scrivenger Seabrook, St. Neots (01480) 214900. Founding Partner specialising in medical negligence.

Specialisation: Firm was founded to act in clinical negligence and personal injury cases. Individual specialism is defendant clinical negligence. Acted in Royal College of Nursing v. DHSS [1981] AC 800 (House of Lords - instructing solicitor for the RCN). Acts for four NHS Trusts and 2 Health Authorities. Has lectured for many years on law and nursing and NHS topics, and for the Law Society on practice management.

Career: Qualified, Supreme Court of Victoria 1968 and High Court of Autralia 1976. Qualified in England & Wales 1977. Principal Solicitor, Royal College of Nursing 1977-87. Founded *Scrivenger Seabrook* in 1988.

Personal: Born 27th November 1941. Interests include music and wine. Lives in Hail Weston, Cambridgeshire.

Seabrook, Vicki

Scrivenger Seabrook, St. Neots (01480) 214900. Founding Partner in Litigation firm.

Specialisation: Has specialised in personal

injury since qualification. Later expanded into defendant medical negligence. Acted in Davis v. Barking Havering and Brentwood Health Authority. Clients include NHS healthcare and community Trusts and Health Authorities. Member of Personal Injury and Medical Negligence Panels.

Career: Qualified in 1979. At the *Royal College of Nursing* 1979-85, *Merriman & White* 1985-86, *Beachcroft Stanley* 1986-88 and *Le Brasseurs* 1988-89 before establising *Scrivenger Seabrook*.

Personal: Born 1st April 1954. Educated at Barnet College 1970-72 and Central London Polytechnic 1973-76 (LL.B Hons). Lives in St Neots, Cambs.

Shellens, Tessa

Bevan Ashford, Cardiff (01222) 462562. Partner in Litigation Department.

Specialisation: Main areas of practice are medical negligence and general NHS advisory work. Has 18 years experience of practice in these areas, with extensive knowledge of advising Health Authorities and Trusts in medical negligence claims, as well as general NHS advisory issues. Also deals with public law, giving general advice to other public bodies in Wales on matters of statutory interpretation and judicial review. Lectures extensively on medical and nursing law throughout England and Wales.

Career: Qualified in 1974. Joined *Edward Lewis Bevan Ashford* as a Partner in 1991.

Personal: Born 9th May 1949. Attended Southampton University (BA Hons, History 1970).

Solly, Gillian

Russell Jones & Walker, Bristol (0117) 927 3098. Partner 1986. Specialises in medical negligence and personal injury, particularly laparascopic surgery and brain damaged cases, industrial accidents and diseases.

Speker, Barry N.

Samuel Phillips & Co, Newcastle-upon-Tyne (0191) 232 8451. Senior Partner and Head of Litigation Department.

Specialisation: Principal area of work is medical negligence, personal injury, family and matrimonial including child care and adoption and employment law cases. Legal adviser for Newcastle Health Authority and various NHS trusts, NSPCC Newcastle upon Tyne and Barnardo's North East. Regular lecturer on child care law, mental health law and medical negligence.

Prof. Membership: Law Society (Mental Health and Children Panels), Law Society, Lawyers for Business Users Committee.

Career: Qualified 1971 while with *Leigh Gold & Co.*, then joined *Samuel Phillips & Co.* Became a Partner in 1973 and Senior Partner in 1987. Deputy District Judge. Part time Industrial Tribunal Chairman.

Personal: Born 28th June 1947. Attended Heaton Grammar School and London University. Member of Mensa. Leisure pursuits include golf (Arcot Hall Golf Club), debating and the Times Crossword. Lives in Newcastle upon Tyne.

Tobias, Janine A.

Betesh Fox & Co, Manchester (0161) 832 6131. Qualified 1988. Partner 1993. Head of Medical Negligence Department. 95% of work is medical negligence cases. Deals with all types of medical accidents and cases involving paraplegia, tetraplegia and brain damage. Born 26.7.1964.

Vick, Laurence N.

Tozers, Exeter (01392) 424444. Qualified 1981. Partner 1994. Head of Medical Negligence and Personal Injury Department. Specialises in medical negligence, acting for plaintiffs.

Weston, Howard W.

Mills & Reeve, Cambridge + 44(0)1223 364422. Qualified 1966. Partner 1989. Litigation Department. Principal area of practice is medical negligence litigation. Also deals with general NHS, medical and health care issues.

Wicks, Roger

Gadsby Wicks, Chelmsford (01245) 494929.

Specialisation: Specialises in pharmaceutical and medical products liability claims on behalf of plaintiffs. He is co-ordinating measles vaccine damage cases and was a lead solicitor in connection with the Myodil and Benzodiazepine litigation. Has also litigated claims in relation to Bjork-Shiley heart valves, depo-provera, depomedrone, diethystilbestrol, dymer-x, septrin, copper 7 IUDs, human growth hormone, breast implants, steroids and orthopaedic implants. Chief Assessor to The Law Society's Medical Negligence Specialisation Panel.

Career: Founding partner of *Gadsby Wicks* in 1993.

Prof. Membership: Law Society, Association of Personal Injury Lawyers; Association of Trial Lawyers of American and the Environmental Law Foundation.

Wright, Tim L.

Wansbroughs Willey Hargrave, Winchester (01962) 841444. Partner in Health Department.

Specialisation: Specialises in all aspects of medical negligence and health service law, particularly the Mental Health Act, inquests, clinical trials and ethical matters. Has been involved in the successful defence of many high profile cases including the second NHS structured settlement, treating patients without their consent and withdrawing feeding from a PVS patient.

Career: Qualified 1978. With *Woodford & Ackroyd*, Lymington 1984-86 and Wessex Regional Health Authority 1986-94. Joined *Wansbroughs Willey Hargrave* as a Partner in 1994.

EDITORIAL POLICY

Our policy is to identify leading practitioners entirely on merit. It is not possible to buy a place in our biographical lists: inclusion is based on a practitioner's expertise and professional reputation. The same applies to the lists of recommended law-firms and sets of chambers.

Enormous effort has been invested by our ten-strong research team (mainly solicitors and barristers) in canvassing recommendations and identifying leaders. We are confident in the overall accuracy of the results. However, mistakes and omissions are inevitable, and if readers have any suggestions regarding listings or rankings we should be very pleased to hear from them.

The lists will be revised on the basis of fresh research every year.

MULTIMEDIA

MULTIMEDIA (which combines text, graphics, audio and images and/or moving pictures in a digitised format) is a growing industry and one in which a number of law firms are quickly developing expertise.

LONDON

The firms which have developed this specialism are those with established computer/IT, telecommunications, intellectual property or media departments.

Olswang (the first firm to establish multimedia as a distinct discipline in 1986) emerges as the leading specialist. Acting primarily for content owners and distributors, the multimedia unit draws on the expertise of 24 lawyers from various disciplines (including the highly recommended David Zeffman, Mark Sherwood Edwards and Julian Dickens) to advise on finance, investment, rights of ownership, clearance, licensing and where necessary, litigation.

LEADING FIRMS – LONDON	
OLSWANG	
BIRD & BIRD	**DENTON HALL**
THE SIMKINS PARTNERSHIP	
BIDDLE & CO	**CLIFFORD CHANCE**
DAVENPORT LYONS	**MISHCON DE REYA**
THEODORE GODDARD	

Highly recommended firms include *Bird & Bird, Denton Hall* and *The Simkins Partnership*. Multimedia comprises 10-15% of the revenue at *Bird & Bird*. The firm draws on its existing strengths in the fields of telecommunications (David Kerr is also responsible for co-ordination of multimedia projects), information technology (where Hamish Sandison excels), media (Justin Walkey) and intellectual property (Trevor Cook) to advise hi-technology companies, major institutions and multinationals on a broad (and international) spectrum of multimedia work.

Alan Williams and Nicholas Higham head the multimedia unit at *Denton Hall* which comprises twelve lawyers providing advice to clients such as Macmillan Group and Longman Group on strategic and contractual issues for electronic publishing and CD-Rom, CIC (a joint venture between Paramount and Universal Studios) and Thomson Directories on CD-Rom distribution, and the Copyright Licensing Agency Ltd on a variety of issues.

Laurence Kaye and his team of four at *The Simkins Partnership* are involved in the programming aspects of multimedia (Nigel Stamp acting for software companies) and the delivery side where they draw on their expertise in the field of publishing (acting for Harper Collins and others).

HIGHLY REGARDED – LONDON	
HARBOTTLE & LEWIS	MARRIOTT HARRISON
MICHAEL HENRY & Co	
ALLISON & HUMPHREYS	ALLEN & OVERY
ASHURST MORRIS CRISP	FRERE CHOLMELEY BISCHOFF
GOULDENS	S J BERWIN & CO
HAMLIN SLOWE	BRISTOWS COOKE & CARPMAEL
TAYLOR JOYNSON GARRETT	D J FREEMAN
RICHARDS BUTLER	

Other firms with substantial experience in the field include *Biddle & Co, Clifford Chance, Davenport Lyons, Mishcon de Reya* and *Theodore Goddard*.

Biddle & Co's multimedia department comprises ten specialists who advise clients such as Global Communications, Bertelsmann AG (licensing product to Dorling Kindersley for the CD-rom encyclopaedia) and a number of publishers on copyright, royalties and joint ventures. David Hooper is held in high regard.

Multimedia at *Davenport Lyons* is a multi-disciplinary specialism. Leading light David Rockberger acts for rights owners (especially literary and music clients), producers and venture capitalists. The firm is also strong on the fin- ance side, acting for Barclays Bank and another major clearing house.

Mishcon de Reya (with three specialists) and *Theodore Goddard* are also strong on the financial aspect, advising a number of banks and other lenders/investors within the financial sector. *Theodore Goddard* in addition, has recently advised a rights owning company and newspaper publishers.

Clifford Chance has a core of 20 lawyers (including the highly regarded David Griffiths) who advise on a broad range of matters including publishing, software, broadcasting, banking and retailing.

LEADING INDIVIDUALS – LONDON		
David Zeffman *Olswang*		
Trevor M. Cook *Bird & Bird*	**Julian Dickens** *Olswang*	**David H. Griffiths** *Clifford Chance*
Michael Henry *Michael Henry & Co*	**Nicholas Higham** *Denton Hall*	**David Hooper** *Biddle & Co*
Laurence M. Kaye *The Simkins Partnership*	**David Kerr** *Bird & Bird*	**David Rockberger** *Davenport Lyons*
Hamish R. Sandison *Bird & Bird*	**Mark Sherwood Edwards** *Olswang*	**Nigel Stamp** *The Simkins Partnership*
Justin R.C. Walkey *Bird & Bird*	**Alan Williams** *Denton Hall*	

In all the tables the names in each group are listed alphabetically.

Other firms noted for their expertise in the field include *Allen & Overy, Allison & Humphreys, Ashurst Morris Crisp, SJ Berwin & Co, Bristows Cooke Carpmael, DJ Freeman, Frere Cholmeley Bischoff, Gouldens, Hamlin Slowe, Har-*

bottle & Lewis, Marriott Harrison, Richards Butler, Taylor Joynson Garrett, and *Michael Henry & Co,* where Michael Henry (author of 'Publishing and Multimedia Law') has been recommended.

LONDON

Cook, Trevor M.
See under Intellectual Property.

Dickens, Julian
Olswang, London (0171) 208 8888.

Griffiths, David H.
See under Computer Law & I.T.

Henry, Michael
See under Media & Entertainment.

Higham, Nicholas
See under Telecommunications.

Hooper, David
See under Media & Entertainment.

Kaye, Laurence M.
See under Computer Law & I.T.

Kerr, David
Bird & Bird, London (0171) 415 6000.
Partner in Company Department.

Specialisation: Main area of practice is corporate and commercial work involving deals in the telecommunications, multi-media and information technology sectors. Has extensive experience of major transactions in these

areas, including acquisitions, joint ventures, project finance, privatisation and outsourcing agreements. Frequent speaker at conferences on telecommunications and information technology.

Prof. Membership: Communications Lawyers Association, IBA, Law Society.

Career: Qualified in 1985. Joined *Bird & Bird* in 1985, becoming a Partner in 1987.

Personal: Born 1960. Attended Jesus College, Cambridge (MA Hons, 1982). Lives in London.

Rockberger, David
See under Media & Entertainment.

Sandison, Hamish R.
See under Computer Law & I.T.

Sherwood Edwards, Mark
Olswang, London (0171) 208 8888.

Stamp, Nigel
See under Computer Law & I.T.

Walkey, Justin R.C.
Bird & Bird, London (0171) 415 6000.
Partner in Company Department and member of Sports Group.

Specialisation: In-depth knowledge covers the media, sports and entertainment indus-

tries. Particular expertise includes sports marketing (creation, protection and exploitation of events; sale and purchase of events; constitutional and disciplinary matters; TV, video, film and publishing rights deals; sponsorship; licensing and merchandising) and individual representation (general business management, tax planning, endorsement and appearance contracts). Founder of Sportslink Worldwide. Other area of practice is general corporate and commercial law, both nationally and internationally, primarily in the areas of media and communications to include multimedia, telecommunications, broadcasting, advertising, publishing and promotion.

Prof. Membership: Law Society, Licensing Executives Society.

Career: Qualified in 1984. Joined *Bird & Bird* the same year and became a partner in 1987.

Personal: Born 1957. Attended Sherborne School, then the University of Westminster. Lives in London.

Williams, Alan
See under Media & Entertainment.

Zeffman, David
See under Media & Entertainment.

CD-ROM EDITION

This edition of the directory is available on a CD-ROM which includes both DOS and Windows versions. It can be loaded onto a network, and works with virtually any IBM compatible PC. The full contents of the printed directory are made available to the computer user who will have the advantage of rapid search, retrieval and cross-referencing.

PARLIAMENTARY & PUBLIC AFFAIRS

PARLIAMENTARY and public affairs work covers advice on parliamentary procedure, petitioning against bills, monitoring policy decisions which affect clients' interests and promoting, refining or resisting legislative or regulatory activity.

Firms specialising in this work often have a member of staff who is registered as a parliamentary agent. There are two types of parliamentary agent: those authorised by Roll A to act on behalf of promoters and opponents of private bills and those who obtain temporary authorisation on Roll B to act for a petitioner in opposition to a particular private bill for the life of that bill. Roll A agents will be involved in all aspects of drafting, depositing and steering a bill through both Houses of Parliament while Roll B agents cease to be parliamentary agents once opposition to the bill is at an end.

The number of Roll A agents is limited and they all work for either *Bircham & Co, Rees & Freres, Sharpe Pritchard, Sherwood & Co* and *Vizards.*

LONDON

Bircham & Co operate their Parliamentary agency and public affairs practice under the name of *Dyson Bell Martin.* The firm deals with work in Brussels and Strasbourg as well as in Westminster. It drafts all forms of legislation and is active in presenting clients' submissions at local, national and European levels. Ian McCulloch is very well respected for his expertise in this field. Paul Thompson is also well regarded.

Rees & Freres which operates as the parliamentary and public law practice of *Lee Bolton & Lee* also have a good reputation in this field particularly for their work related to transport. The firm has acted for major railway operators, shipping and ferry companies, port and harbour authorities and national transport undertakers. In addition, the firm has acted for local authorities and multinational oil and pharmaceutical corporations. Joseph Durkin is highly regarded for his parliamentary practice, not least because he has more than twenty years' experience in this area and has been involved in a number of high profile transactions. He was the Government Agent instructed by the Department of Transport for the promotion of the Bill for the Severn Bridges Act 1992. He has also acted as the promoting agent under the Ports Act 1991 for such bodies as the Tees and Hartlepool Port Authority. Peter Lane has experience in this field particularly in relation to transport infrastructure projects where he has acted for the British Railways Board among others.

Sharpe Pritchard is well known for its work for local government. It has been involved in the promotion of the London Local Authorities Act, opposition to the Channel Tunnel Act and legislation over its high speed rail link. Michael Pritchard is a Roll A agent recommended for his experience in this field. He has dealt with the Harbours Act, Transport & Works Act, a number of local authority general powers bills, the Cardiff Bay Barrage Act and petitions for the protection of the Crossrail Bill. He is the author of the

parliamentary section of the 'Encyclopaedia of Forms and Precedents'.

Sherwood & Co the parliamentary practice of *Winckworth & Pemberton,* have a particular reputation for dealing with transport bills. The department specialises in the promotion of and opposition to Private Bills in Parliament and similar legislation including the Scottish Provisional Orders and Orders under the Harbours Act 1964 and the Transport and Works Act 1992. It also deals with charters and bye laws and advises on all forms of primary and secondary legislation. Clients include transport undertakers, utilities, local authorities, port authorities, banks, developers, charities and commercial companies. Alison Gorlov who is a Roll A agent has parliamentary agency as her main area of practice dealing with transport and other infrastructure schemes, private bills and statutory orders.

HIGHLY REGARDED – LONDON – PARLIAMENTARY	
BIRCHAM & CO (DYSON BELL MARTIN)	LEE BOLTON & LEE (REES & FRERES)
SHARPE PRITCHARD	VIZARDS
WINCKWORTH & PEMBERTON (SHERWOOD & CO)	

Vizards has traditionally had at least two Roll A agents and the parliamentary department deals with all aspects of private and public legislation. The firm is increasing its involvement in public policy/lobbying work and has associations with the US firm of *Davis, Hockenburg, Wine, Brown, Koehn & Shors PC* based in Iowa. Ronald Perry has been a Parliamentary Agent since 1971 and was highly recommended to us for his opposition work in this field. He is a contributor to Butterworths' 'Encyclopaedia of Forms and Precedents'.

HIGHLY REGARDED – LONDON – PUBLIC AFFAIRS	
ALLEN & OVERY	CLIFFORD CHANCE
LOVELL WHITE DURRANT	RADCLIFFES CROSSMAN BLOCK

An increasing number of firms, especially those with a strong commercial client base, are beginning to enter public policy work. They advise on political and legislative changes and present the clients interests to government. The process starts at an early stage, before legislative drafting and is complementary to parliamentary agency. However, it is a practice still in the early stages of development.

Radcliffes Crossman Block, based in Westminster, are very much at the forefront in this field. Sir Gerrard Neale a former MP, principally deals with the political positioning of legal or commercial marketing issues affecting national and international companies. The firm also undertakes parliamentary petitioning.

The larger City firms are also developing practices in this area. *Clifford Chance* have a strong Public Policy Group of which Richard Thomas is the director. Dealings are primarily with Whitehall, but the Group has also dealt with Westminster and Brussels. Such work has included drafting amendments to UK parliamentary bills, advice to the private sector on the Private Finance Initiative and providing clients with a weekly EU intelligence service. Richard Thomas also has experience of the public sector as a former Director of Consumer Affairs at the Office of Fair Trading.

Allen & Overy, where Colin Overbury was recommended, is developing a practice in this area, as are *Lovell White Durrant* where David Tench was recommended.

LEADING INDIVIDUALS – LONDON – PARLIAMENTARY

Joseph A. Durkin	*Lee Bolton & Lee (Rees & Freres)*
Alison M.H. Gorlov	*Winckworth & Pemberton (Sherwood & Co)*
Peter R. Lane	*Lee Bolton & Lee (Rees & Freres)*
I.H. McCulloch	*Bircham & Co (Dyson Bell Martin)*
Ronald E. Perry	*Vizards*
Michael Pritchard	*Sharpe Pritchard*
Paul Thompson	*Bircham & Co (Dyson Bell Martin)*

LEADING INDIVIDUALS – LONDON – PUBLIC AFFAIRS

Sir Gerrard Neale	*Radcliffes Crossman Block*
Richard Thomas	*Clifford Chance*
Colin Overbury	*Allen & Overy*
David Tench	*Lovell White Durrant*

LEADERS IN PARLIAMENTARY & PUBLIC AFFAIRS

LONDON

Durkin, Joe Anthony

Rees & Freres, London (0171) 222 5381.

Specialisation: Senior partner and specialist in administrative and public law, railways and tramways, highways and harbours, planning, environmental law and compulsory acquisition. 21 years experience of promoting and opposing legislation on behalf of the Central Government, major public sector transport operators, port authorities, universities and colleges and major national and multinational corporations. Publications include 'Blackstones Guide To The Transport & Works Act 1992' (co-author). Regularly addresses conferences on the parliamentary and legislative process, Royal Charter, harbour law, infrastructure, and Transport & Works projects.

Prof. Membership: Society of Parliamentary Agents (past president). Law Society.

Career: 1961-70 solicitor in general practice in the City. 1970-73 Government parliamentary draftsman with the Office of the Parliamentary Counsel. Partner, Rees & Freres since 1973, senior partner since 1981.

Personal: Educated at Sheffield University (LL.B). Born 2nd January 1938.

Gorlov, Alison M.H.

Winckworth & Pemberton (incorporating Sherwood & Co), London (0171) 222 0441. Qualified 1975. Partner 1978. Parliamentary Department. Specialises in Parliamentary Agency: transport, Private Bills, and statutory orders.

Lane, Peter R.

Rees & Freres, London (0171) 222 5381.

Specialisation: Partner at *Rees & Freres,* the parliamentary arm of *Lee Bolton & Lee,* Parliamentary Agent and specialist in public law, transport and infrastructure, and legislative drafting. Experienced in drafting, promoting and opposing legislation, including that for the construction and operation of transport infrastructure projects on behalf of major public sector transport operators, port authorities, British Ports federation, local authorities, universities and colleges and major national and multinational corporations. Advises on harbour law, infrastructure and transport and works projects. Publications include 'Blackstone's Guide to the Transport & Works Act 1992' (co-author).

Prof. Membership: Society of Parliamentary Agents. Law Society.

Career: 1977-80, barrister, member of Peter Boydell QC's chambers (2 Harcourt Buildings). 1978-80, Lecturer in Laws, Queen Mary College, University of London. 1980-85, Government parliamentary draftsman with the Office of the Parliamentary Counsel. Since 1985 solicitor at Rees & Freres, partner since 1987.

Personal: Educated at Hertford College, Oxford (MA) and University of California, Berkley (LL.M). Born 26th April 1953.

McCulloch, I.H.

Bircham & Co In Association with Dyson Bell Martin, London (0171) 222 8044.

Neale, Sir Gerrard

Radcliffes Crossman Block, London (0171) 222 7040. Partner in Public and Parliamentary Affairs Department.

Specialisation: Principal area of practice involves the political positioning of legal or commercial marketing issues affecting national and international companies or institutions. Advises on strategic and tactical planning of public affairs issues.

Prof. Membership: Law Society, Institute of Directors.

Career: Qualified in 1966. Councillor, Milton Keynes 1973-79 (Mayor 1976-77). Member of Parliament 1979-1992. Joined *Radcliffes & Co* as a Partner in 1991.

Personal: Born 25th June 1941. Attended Bedford School 1948-59. Leisure pursuits include sailing and golf. Lives in London.

Overbury, Colin

See under European Union/Competition.

Perry, Ronald E.

Vizards, London (0171) 405 6302. Partner in Commercial Department.

Specialisation: Principal area of practice is as a Parliamentary Agent. Roll A Agent since 1971. Also deals with commercial property and charities. Contributor to Butterworths' Encyclopaedia of Forms and Precedents.

Prof. Membership: Law Society, Society of Parliamentary Agents, UKELA.

Career: Joined *Vizards* in 1968, qualified in 1970 and became a partner in the same year.

Personal: Born 24th September 1945. Attended King Edward VI Grammar School, Chelmsford 1957-64, then Leeds University 1964-67. Trustee of the Dunhill Medical Trust and of E.15 Acting School. Lives in Wimbledon.

Tench, David

Lovell White Durrant, London (0171) 236 0066.

Thomas, Richard

Clifford Chance, London (0171) 600 1000. Director, Public Policy Group; Principal area of practice is parliamentary and public affairs law. Also handles marketing, advertising and fair trading legislation.

Thompson, Paul

Bircham & Co In Association with Dyson Bell Martin, London (0171) 222 8044.

REGIONS

Pritchard, H. Michael V.

Sharpe Pritchard, (0171) 222 3551. Partner specialising in parliamentary work.

Specialisation: Main area of practice is parliamentary work, drafting legislation and advising on parliamentary procedure and tactics. Also delegated legislation, Orders, etc., under, amongst others, the Harbours Act and Transport & Works Act. Has been involved with numerous local authority general powers bills, the Cardiff Bay Barrage Act and petitions for protection on the Crossrail Bill. Author of Parliamentary title of the 'Encyclopaedia of Forms and Precedents'.

Prof. Membership: Society of Parliamentary Agents, Law Society.

Career: Joined *Sharpe Pritchard* in 1958, qualified in 1963 and became a Partner in 1965.

Personal: Born in 1935. Educated at Charterhouse 1948-53 and Balliol College, Oxford

PARTNERSHIP

LONDON

PROFESSIONAL PARTNERSHIPS
(OTHER THAN MEDICAL)

The leading firms for professional partnerships (excluding the medical profession) include *Bristows Cooke & Carpmael, Eversheds* and *Fox Williams.*

Bristows Cooke & Carpmael acting primarily for accountants and solicitors specialises in partnership agreement drafting, joint ventures, amalgamations, demergers and partnership disputes. The bulk of its work however is in the non-contentious domain.

LEADING FIRMS – LONDON – NON-MEDICAL	
BRISTOWS COOKE & CARPMAEL	
EVERSHEDS	FOX WILLIAMS

Eversheds advises on new partnership agreements, tax matters and partnership disputes. Clients include accountants, actuaries, solicitors, and patent and trade mark agents. *Fox Williams* advises professional firms and individual partners including chartered surveyors, architects, accountants and solicitors on partnership deeds, compliance programmes, insolvent partnerships and problems in connection with partnership moves.

Also highly regarded are *Boodle Hatfield, Finers, Kingsley Napley* and *Wright Son & Pepper. Boodle Hatfield's* strength lies in partnership disputes – advising partners and groups of partners in respect of dissolutions, retirement settlements and attempted dismissals, including injunctive relief. Clients include solicitors, accountants, estate agents and medical practices. *Finers* advise lawyers, accountants and architects on partnership formations and break-ups. It also deals with management, growth and remuneration issues.

HIGHLY REGARDED – LONDON – NON-MEDICAL	
BOODLE HATFIELD	FINERS
KINGSLEY NAPLEY	WRIGHT SON & PEPPER
ALLEN & OVERY	FIELD FISHER WATERHOUSE
HERBERT SMITH	HOWARD KENNEDY
McKENNA & CO	NABARRO NATHANSON
REYNOLDS PORTER CHAMBERLAIN	SLAUGHTER AND MAY

Kingsley Napley acts primarily for the legal and accountancy professions, individuals and small businesses. It handles the tax aspects of partnerships, drafting agreements, litigation and regulatory work (representing accountants and solicitors with disciplinary problems).

Wright Son & Pepper handles a large proportion of partnership disputes for solicitors, whilst its work for accountants consists mainly of drafting and updating partnership deeds. It has substantial experience in voluntary arrangements for solicitors.

Field Fisher Waterhouse has also been recommended. It deals with partnership formations, retirements, taxation, amalgamations, acquisitions, joint ventures and dissolutions. *Allen*

& Overy's partnership group, established two years ago, handles the planning of partnership structures, mergers and acquisitions, financial services, partnership documentation, property issues and dispute resolution. Their clients include accountants, actuaries, architects, chartered surveyors, engineers, fund managers, recruitment consultants and solicitors. The firm recently acted for Binder Hamlyn in their merger with Arthur Anderson.

LEADING INDIVIDUALS – LONDON – NON-MEDICAL	
Ronald D. Fox *Fox Williams*	
John D. Lace *Bristows Cooke & Carpmael*	
John B. Northam *Eversheds*	
Colin McArthur *Field Fisher Waterhouse*	
D.T. Morgan *Wright Son & Pepper*	
Stephen Ralph *Boodle Hatfield*	
Tony Sacker *Kingsley Napley*	
Michael D. Simmons *Finers*	
Christine J. Williams *Fox Williams*	
Nicholas J. Wright *Wright Son & Pepper*	

Leading partnership specialists include Ronnie Fox (*Fox Williams*), John Lace (*Bristows, Cooke & Carpmael*) and John Northam (*Eversheds*).

MEDICAL PARTNERSHIPS

Hempsons, acting for doctors and dentists, has long been in the forefront for medical partnerships. Its widely recognised expertise includes advice on partnership formation, disputes, accession and retirement of partners, changes within the partnership structure and termination. It also advises on regulation and investment matters, payment structure of GPs and associated property matters (particularly GP's cost rent schemes and other surgery development). Currently, they are advising the BMA on policy matters relating to partnerships.

Another practice with an excellent reputation for medical partnerships is *Monier-Williams & Boxalls*, acting primarily for GPs in both contentious and non-contentious matters. Also recommended is *Le Brasseur J Tickle,* particularly for partnership disputes. The firm's substantial partnership experience is primarily due to its strong medical negligence practice.

LEADING FIRMS – LONDON – MEDICAL
HEMPSONS
MONIER–WILLIAMS & BOXALLS
LE BRASSEUR J TICKLE

Leading specialists include Lynne Abbess (*Hempsons*), Simon Barnes (*Hempsons*), Jacqueline Cooper (*Hempsons*) and Andrew Hill (*Monier-Williams & Boxalls*). Also recommended is Richard Sumerling of *Le Brasseur J. Tickle.*

LEADING INDIVIDUALS – LONDON – MEDICAL

LEADING INDIVIDUALS – LONDON – MEDICAL	
Lynne M. Abbess *Hempsons*	
Jacqueline Cooper *Hempsons*	
Simon M. Barnes *Hempsons*	
G. Andrew Hill *Monier–Williams & Boxalls*	
R.W. Sumerling *Le Brasseur J Tickle*	

SOUTH OF ENGLAND

Among the few South East firms specialising in this field, *Clarkson Wright & Jakes* and *Linnells* have been consistently recommended. Both firms' expertise is in medical partnerships, with the former acting primarily for GPs on all non-contentious matters including taxation, whilst the latter advises mainly doctors, dentists and vets.

LEADING FIRMS – SOUTH OF ENGLAND
LINNELLS *Oxford*
CLARKSON WRIGHT & JAKES *Orpington*

Linnells' team consists of a trained mediator with expertise in partnership law. The firm advises on partnership agreements, property acquisition, voluntary arrangements, mergers/demergers, partnership assets, finance and disputes involving property and restraint of trade issues. Other clients include solicitors and accountants.

HIGHLY REGARDED – SOUTH OF ENGLAND	
LESTER ALDRIDGE *Bournemouth*	**MUNDAYS** *Esher*
OSBORNE CLARKE *Bristol*	**SLEE BLACKWELL** *Barnstaple*
TRUMP AND PARTNERS *Bristol*	**VEALE WASBROUGH** *Bristol*
BURGES SALMON *Bristol*	**PAYNE MARSH STILLWELL** *Southampton*
RAWLISON & BUTLER *Crawley*	**RODGERS HORSLEY WHITEMANS** *Guildford*

Other South East firms specialising in this area include *Mundays*, *Payne Marsh & Stillwell* (medical partnership), *Rawlison & Butler* and *Rodgers Horsley Whitemans* (dental partnerships). *Mundays* advises on partnership formation, restructuring, mergers and dissolution, partnership disputes, admission of new partners and the retirement/expulsion of partners.

South West firms with a specialism in this field include *Burges Salmon*, *Lester Aldridge*, *Osborne Clarke*, *Slee Blackwell*, *Trump & Partners* and *Veale Wasbrough*.

Lester Aldridge advises on both contentious and non-contentious aspects of professional partnerships, particularly medical practices. *Slee Blackwell* is one of only a handful of solicitors in the country specialising in partnership and acquisition matters in the veterinary profession.

Trump & Partners handles all aspects of professional partnerships including dispute resolution, insolvent partnership and High Court applications for dissolution. Their clients include solicitors, chartered accountants, surveyors and veterinary and medical practitioners. The firm advised a global

maritime communications company and a consortium of leading racetrack owners on joint venture/partnership matters.

Veale Wasbrough's clients are primarily in the medical sector where it acts for around 50 GP partnerships in relation to their partnership agreements and surgery development, and the practical operations of the rent scheme.

LEADING INDIVIDUALS – SOUTH OF ENGLAND
C. Paddy G. Gregan *Linnells*

MIDLANDS

Firms with strong partnership expertise include *Edge & Ellison* and *Freeth Cartwright Hunt Dickins*. The former's expertise covers funding, formation of partnerships, dissolution, responsibilities and liabilities, and associated tax

HIGHLY REGARDED – MIDLANDS	
EDGE & ELLISON *Birmingham*	**FOSTER BAXTER COOKSEY** *Wolverhampton*
FREETH CARTWRIGHT HUNT DICKINS *Nottingham*	

matters. *Freeth Cartwright Hunt Dickins* advises solicitors and accountants on the full range of partnership issues. Also recommended is *Foster Baxter Cooksey* especially for partnership disputes/litigation.

NORTH

Hill Dickinson Davis Campbell and *Mace & Jones* are among the Northern firms with partnership law expertise. The former advises professional partnerships on the drafting of partnership agreements, taxation, disputes, dissolution and partnership litigation. *Mace & Jones* advises primarily

LEADING FIRMS – NORTH	
HILL DICKINSON DAVIS CAMPBELL *Liverpool*	**MACE & JONES** *Liverpool*

solicitors, accountants and GPs on partnership agreements and specific issues such as restrictive covenant clauses. With regard to solicitors, the firm has been involved in a number of cases where a practice has become insolvent.

HIGHLY REGARDED – NORTH	
CUFF ROBERTS *Liverpool*	**VAUDREYS** *Manchester*
COBBETT LEAK ALMOND *Manchester*	**JONES MAIDMENT WILSON** *Manchester*
KERSHAW ABBOTT *Manchester*	**WEIGHTMAN RUTHERFORDS** *Liverpool*

Other recommended firms include *Cobbett Leak Almond* (medical), *Cuff Roberts*, *Jones Maidment Wilson* (partnership disputes/litigation), *Kershaw Abbott* (partnership disputes), *Vaudreys* (partnership litigation) and *Weightman Rutherfords* which deals with partnership agreements, dissolutions

LEADING INDIVIDUALS – NORTH

Graeme K. Jump	*Mace & Jones*
Michael J. Quinn	*Hill Dickinson Davis Campbell*
Paul Walton	*Hill Dickinson Davis Campbell*
D. Anthony Healey	*Vaudreys*
W. Anthony Twemlow	*Cuff Roberts*

and partnership litigation. *Cuff Roberts* advises on the establishment of new partnerships and the expansion/contraction of existing partnerships including dissolutions.

Individuals known in this field include Graeme Jump (*Mace & Jones*), Michael Quinn (*Hill Dickinson Davis Campbell*) and Paul Walton (*Hill Dickinson Davis Campbell*) (especially for

partnership disputes). Also recommended are Anthony Healey (*Vaudreys*) (partnership litigation) and Anthony Twemlow (*Cuff Roberts*) (non-contentious).

SCOTLAND

Both *Bell & Scott* and *Robson McLean* have some expertise in this field. The former advises on all aspects of partnership agreements and partnership disputes. The latter handles primarily family and professional partnerships.

HIGHLY REGARDED – SCOTLAND

BELL & SCOTT WS *Edinburgh*	**ROBSON McLEAN WS** *Edinburgh*

In all the tables the names in each group are listed alphabetically.

LEADERS IN PARTNERSHIP

LONDON

Abbess, Lynne M.

Hempsons, London (0171) 836 0011. Partner in Professional Services Department.

Specialisation: Principal area of practice is partnership law, encompassing advice on partnership formation, disputes, termination and associated property matters (in particular NHS GP's cost rent schemes and other surgery developments). Acts for doctors, dentists, solicitors, accountants and other non-professional partnerships. Advised the GMSC on policy relating to partnerships and surgery developments affecting all NHS GPs in England and Wales. Author of chapters on partnership in 'The Law And General Practice' and numerous articles in a variety of professional publications. Frequent lecturer on partnership issues inter alia for the British Medical Association.

Prof. Membership: Law Society.

Career: Qualified 1982 while with *Hempsons* and became a Partner in 1985.

Personal: Born 2nd October 1956. Lives in Kensington, London.

Barnes, Simon M.

Hempsons, London (0171) 836 0011. Partner and joint Head of the Professional Services Department.

Specialisation: Principal area of practice is partnership law. Has extensive experience in handling all areas of such work, acting for solicitors, accountants, patent agents, dentists and especially doctors. Advises on partnership formations, disputes, terminations and all property related matters.

Prof. Membership: Law Society.

Career: Qualified in 1966. With *Woodham*

Smith until 1990 (Partner from 1972 and Senior Partner from 1988). Joined *Hempsons* as a Partner in 1990.

Personal: Born 13th December 1939. Educated at Bradfield College, Berkshire 1953-62 and Corpus Christi College, Cambridge 1959-62. School Governor. Leisure pursuits include cricket, fly fishing and reading. Member of the Athenaeum. Lives near Tunbridge Wells, Kent.

Cooper, Jacqueline

Hempsons, London (0171) 836 0011. Partner in Professional Services Department.

Specialisation: Partnership law, acting in both partnership formations and disputes for both professional and non-professional partnerships. Advising also on related property ownership issues.

Prof. Membership: Law Society.

Career: Articled *Matthew Arnold and Baldwin*, Watford. Qualified 1987, solicitor with *Hempsons* and became a Partner in 1992.

Personal: Born 17th April 1962. Lives in London.

Fox, Ronald D.

See under Employment Law.

Hill, G. Andrew

Monier–Williams & Boxalls, London (0171) 405 6195. Qualified 1966. Main area of specialisation is partnership law, particularly for the professions (especially doctors).

Lace, John D.

Bristows Cooke & Carpmael, London (0171) 400 8000. Partner in Company Department.

Specialisation: Main areas of practice are company, corporate finance, partnership and

competition law. Extensive experience in mergers, acquisitions, corporate reorganisations and joint ventures, acting particularly for UK and US corporations. Has advised in relation to many partnership agreements, mergers, demergers and disputes, particularly in the accountancy and legal professions. Also advises corporations and trade associations on competition law.

Prof. Membership: Law Society.

Career: Qualified in 1973 after articles at *Meade-King & Co* in Bristol. Joined *Bristows Cooke & Carpmael* in 1974 and became a Partner in 1978.

Personal: Born 11th September 1947. Educated at Malvern College 1961-66. Enjoys sailing, gardening and photography, and is a member of MCC. Lives in London.

McArthur, Colin

Field Fisher Waterhouse, London (0171) 481 4841. Partner in Company and Commercial Department.

Specialisation: Handles all aspects of corporate and partnership law, including establishment, mergers and acquisitions, sales, retirements, dissolutions and joint ventures. Also deals with commercial contracts. Co-author of 'A Director's Guide - Duties, Liabilities and Company Law' (1990), and contributor to 'A Directors Guide to Accounting and Auditing' (1991).

Prof. Membership: Law Society, I.B.A, Institute of Directors.

Career: Qualified in 1969, having joined *Waterhouse & Co (now Field Fisher Waterhouse)* in 1967. Became a Partner in 1974.

Personal: Born 5th November 1944. Educated at Fettes College 1958-63 and Cambridge University 1963-66. Leisure interests include golf and aphorisms. Lives in London.

Morgan, D.T.
Wright Son & Pepper, London (0171) 242 5473.

Northam, John Barrett
Eversheds, London (0171) 919 4500. Partner in Company and Commercial Department.

Specialisation: Main areas of practice are corporate, partnership and commercial matters, including mergers and acquisitions, partnership agreements, break-up of partnerships and outsourcing by local authorities and other sectors. Major clients include local authorities (e.g. Westminster City Council), accountants, actuaries, solicitors, patent and trade mark agents and other professional firms as well as public companies, including those in the FTSE 100 index (e.g. GEC, Watson & Philip Plc and Robey & Co Plc). Gives external and in-house seminars on partnership, directors duties and supply of goods.

Prof. Membership: City of London Law Society.

Career: Qualified in 1960. Appointed Partner at *Jaques & Lewis* (now *Eversheds*) in 1963. Senior/Managing Partner 1984-92.

Personal: Born 22nd July 1935. Educated at Highgate School 1947-53 and Cambridge University 1954-58. President/ trustee of various local organisations. Leisure interests include golf, theatre and walking. Lives in Hadley Wood, Herts.

Ralph, Stephen
Boodle Hatfield, London (0171) 629 7411. Partner specialising in Commercial Litigation

Specialisation: Main area of practice: commercial litigation. Specialist fields: white collar crime, partnership law, insolvency and arbitration. Since 1985, has been instructed in major internationally-reported fraud-related investigations. Has substantial experience in partnership disputes of solicitors, accountants, advising banks and other lending institutions, partners and groups of partners in respect of dissolutions, retirement settlements, attempted dismissals and bank claims, including injunctive relief. Insolvency work has included acting for major accountancy practitioners and as a practitioner in respect of members' voluntary liquidations. Appointed arbitrator in partnership matters.

Prof. Membership: International Bar Association; Insolvency Practitioners' Association; Insolvency Lawyers Association; Society of Practitioners of Insolvency. Fellow of the Chartered Institute of Arbitrators.

Career: Joined *Payne Hicks Beach* in 1972 becoming senior litigation partner. Joined *Boodle Hatfield* as a senior commercial litigation partner in 1992.

Personal: Born 7th April 1946. BA 1971. Qualified 1975. Post-qualifying diploma in Insolvency Law Administration 1988. (Licensed Insolvency Practitioner). Married, 5 children. Leisure pursuits include tennis, painting and theatre. Lives in London and Oxfordshire.

Sacker, Tony
Kingsley Napley, London (0171) 814 1200. Partner in Partnership Unit.

Specialisation: Main area of practice is partnership law. Over 20 years experience advising and negotiating in this area. Also deals with charities. Writing a book to be called 'Partnership Precedents', to be published by Jordan's Spring 1995.

Prof. Membership: City of London Law Society, Westminster Law Society, Association of Charity Lawyers.

Career: Qualified in 1963. Partner from 1967 at *Egerton Sandler*, which merged with *Kingsley Napley* 1989. Partner at *Kingsley Napley* since 1989. President Westminster Law Society 1987-88.

Personal: Born 2nd March 1940. Educated at Owens School to 1958. Chairperson of the Union of Liberal & Progressive Synagogues. Recreations include doing communal work. Lives in London.

Simmons, Michael D.
Finers, London (0171) 323 4000. Partner in Company and Commercial Department.

Specialisation: Handles general company and commercial work, with particular reference to partnership matters. Deals with partnership formation, growth, management and remuneration issues, consultancy advice, disposal of unproductive partners, partnership disputes and dissolution. Acts for partnerships and for individual partners. Also deals with cross border transactions and other international matters, with particular reference to inward investment into the UK. Has a wide overseas clientele. Author of 'An Anatomy of Professional Practice', published by Gazette Publications, and 'Successful Mergers' published by Waterlows. Also many articles published in UK and overseas law journals. Regular speaker at management and marketing conferences for professionals both at home and abroad. Has appeared many times on television and radio as a legal spokesman on various topics. Standard charge out rate £250 per hour.

Prof. Membership: International Bar Association (Vice Chairman of Committee dealing with Professional Practice and Technology), Law Society, American Bar Association.

Career: Qualified in 1958. First Class Honours in Law Society Final and Clements Inn Prize. National Service Commission in Secretarial Branch Royal Air Force 1959-61. With *Malkin Cullis & Sumption* 1961-90, as a Partner and as Senior Partner from 1964. Joined *Finers* as a Partner in 1990.

Personal: Born 19th May 1933. Educated at

St. Paul's School 1947-52 and Emmanuel College, Cambridge 1952-56 (MA and LLM). Leisure interests include music, (especially jazz), football, cricket, tennis, eating and travelling. Lives in Highgate and Italy.

Sumerling, R.W.
See under Medical Negligence.

Williams, Christine J.
See under Corporate Finance.

Wright, Nicholas J.
Wright Son & Pepper, London (0171) 242 5473. Partner in Commercial Department.

Specialisation: Main area of practice is partnership law. Advises on partnership disputes and dissolutions, including interventions and practice management of other firms. Member of the Solicitors Assistance Scheme. Also deals with banking and commercial matters. Solicitor to UK Banking Institution and to various overseas corporations.

Prof. Membership: Law Society.

Career: Qualified in 1970, having joined *Wright Son & Pepper* in 1960. Became a Partner in 1979.

Personal: Born 2nd February 1943. Educated at Charterhouse 1956-60.

REGIONS

Gregan, C. Paddy G.
Linnells, Oxford (01865) 248607. Qualified 1987. Partner 1990. Company and Commercial Department. Main area of practice is partnership law and finance. Also handles corporate finance and insolvency. Born 23.3.1961.

Healey, D. Anthony
Vaudreys, Manchester (0161) 834 6877.

Jump, Graeme K.
Mace & Jones, Manchester (0161) 236 2244. Partner in Commercial Litigation and Insolvency Department.

Specialisation: Handles a wide range of commercial dispute work including professional negligence. Specialist interests include insolvency, construction law and arbitration.

Prof. Membership: Manchester Law Society (Council Member 1988, President 1991-92); Insolvency Practitioners Association (Council Member 1983); Insolvency Lawyers Association; Founder Member and Honorary Secretary of the Northern Arbitration Association (1990); Associate of the Chartered Institute of Arbitrators since 1987.

Career: Qualified in 1969. Joined *Mace & Jones* in 1971 and became a Partner in 1973. Licensed Insolvency Practitioner since October 1989. Appointed Director of the Solicitors Indemnity Fund Ltd and

Insolvency Assessor to the Law Society's Post Qualification Casework Committee in 1992.

Personal: Born 22nd February 1945. Educated at Wellington School, Bebbington, Wirral and Liverpool Chamber of Commerce (Law Society Exams).

Quinn, Michael J.

Hill Dickinson Davis Campbell, Liverpool (0151) 236 5400. Qualified 1974.

Twemlow, W. Anthony

Cuff Roberts, Liverpool (0151) 227 4181.

Walton, Paul

Hill Dickinson Davis Campbell, Liverpool (0151) 236 5400. Senior Partner of

Firm. Member of Commercial and Insurance Litigation Department.

Specialisation: Principal area of practice is professional negligence acting for insurers of architects, surveyors, engineers, accountants, brokers and other professionals. Also plaintiff work against solicitors and some other professionals and advice to insurers generally. Other main area of practice is partnership, advising on professional partnership disputes. Important cases handled include Liverpool L.R.A.T.I v. Sir Frederick Gibberd & Others (Liverpool R.C. Cathedral litigation); Christian Brothers v. Eagle Star & Stephensons, and Offshore Reinsurers PCI v. Evandale and Others (libel action). Clients include major insurers, reinsurers and underwriters, dioceses and religious orders as well as companies and partnerships.

Prof. Membership: Law Society, Official Referees Solicitors Society, Association of Lawyers for Defence of the Unborn.

Career: Qualified 1969. Became a Partner at *Hill Dickinson Davis Campbell* in 1972, Management Partner in 1989 and Senior Partner in 1994.

Personal: Born 18th May 1945. Educated at Exeter University 1963-66 (Lloyd Parry Prize in Constitutional Law and Bracton Society Prize) and The College of Law, Guildford 1966-67. Member of Council of the Catholic Union; Knight of the Equestrian Order of St Gregory. Activities outside the law include herb growing, philately, antiques, opera, shooting and anti-abortion causes. Lives in Hoghton, near Preston.

EDITORIAL POLICY

Our policy is to identify leading practitioners entirely on merit. It is not possible to buy a place in our biographical lists: inclusion is based on a practitioner's expertise and professional reputation. The same applies to the lists of recommended law-firms and sets of chambers.

Enormous effort has been invested by our ten-strong research team (mainly solicitors and barristers) in canvassing recommendations and identifying leaders. We are confident in the overall accuracy of the results. However, mistakes and omissions are inevitable, and if readers have any suggestions regarding listings or rankings we should be very pleased to hear from them.

The lists will be revised on the basis of fresh research every year.

PENSIONS

LONDON

There has continued to be a widespread increase in the size of pension departments with the large corporate firms tending to be particularly strong in this field. *Lovell White Durrant* and *Linklaters & Paines* have emerged by a narrow margin as being the leading departments in this field. The 16 strong pensions team at *Lovell White Durrant* has a high profile workload, including advising trustees of the pension schemes for the mineworkers, and staff of British Coal and British Rail, on preparation for privatization and providing legal advice on pensions related matters to a wide spectrum of clients. Harriet Dawes, head of the department and highly regarded by her competitors, is currently deputy chair of the Occupational Pensions Board. The group has also continued to advise the Mirror Group on a range of issues relating to its past and present pension arrangements. Other members of the team include Russell Strachan, (who advises on all aspects of pensions law and documentation, both contentious and non-contentious), Derek Simler, John Pearson, Jane Samsworth and Stephen Ito, a rising star at the firm who became a partner in May.

LEADING FIRMS – LONDON	
LINKLATERS & PAINES	LOVELL WHITE DURRANT
NABARRO NATHANSON	SACKER & PARTNERS
SLAUGHTER AND MAY	
ALLEN & OVERY	FRESHFIELDS
ROWE & MAW	TRAVERS SMITH BRAITHWAITE

Linklaters & Paines is described as a strong department which generates its own clients. The team has been involved in the Mirror Group pension scheme and has acted for the Department of Transport in the railway privatisation. Anthony Thurnham at the firm has 21 years of experience in pensions law, and Tim Cox following the 'Barber' case has largely been concentrating on the issues of part-time workers and occupational pension schemes. Ruth Goldman has also been recommended at the firm.

Sacker & Partners are the only niche pensions practice and have an excellent reputation with eight full time pension partners of which Mark Greenlees and Jonathan Seres are especially recommended. Mark Greenlees represented the male beneficiaries in the 'Coloroll' reference to the European Court, and Jonathan Seres who also acted in the 'Coloroll' matter, represented Plessey Company in the court application to approve merger of its pension funds with those of GEC and Siemens. Peter Lester at the firm, has particular expertise in relation to multinational pension provision.

Other firms with highly respected pensions units include *Slaughter and May, Nabarro Nathanson, Rowe & Maw, Travers Smith Braithwaite, Allen & Overy* and *Freshfields*.

John Quarrell at *Nabarro Nathanson* is generally regarded to be the doyen of pension law. In the past twelve months a substantial part of his time has been spent with the other Maxwell Trustees' solicitors in working on the recovery of a large amount of the 'missing' assets. He has also advised the Russian Government on their draft legislation for the governance of Non-State Pension Funds. He heads the large pensions department at the firm, and is the Secretary to the Association of Pensions Lawyers. Also known at the firm for expertise in pensions are Peter Ford and John Murray.

Slaughter and May are particularly strong on establishing, operating and winding up or merging pension schemes of many kinds. They also advise on related taxation issues, the impact of domestic and EC regulations and the treatment of pension fund surpluses and deficits. The team has an excellent reputation, and Phillip Bennett, who is the author of "Pension Fund Surpluses", is particularly well regarded. Also recommended at the firm are Howard Jacobs and Edward Codrington.

Rowe & Maw have five specialist partners in the pensions group of which Stuart James is the present Chairman of the Association of Pensions Lawyers and has served on The Goode Committee. Andrew White in the department is the author of 'Pensions Issues in Mergers and Acquisitions', whilst Anna Kelly is a fellow of the Pensions Management Institute. The team enjoys an extensive blue chip client base.

Paul Stannard who heads the group at *Travers Smith Braithwaite* has established himself as a leading practitioner with his involvement in the Mirror Group Pensions Scheme. The group has a flourishing pensions practice and acted on behalf of the women in the Coloroll case before the European Court. The team, in which Stephanie Smith has been recommended, also acted in the landmark 'Drexel' case concerning trustee's conflicts of interest.

HIGHLY REGARDED – LONDON	
BIDDLE & CO	CLIFFORD CHANCE
NICHOLSON GRAHAM & JONES	
BAKER & McKENZIE	EVERSHEDS
HAMMOND SUDDARDS	HERBERT SMITH
McKENNA & CO	RICHARDS BUTLER
SIMMONS & SIMMONS	
ALSOP WILKINSON	CAMERON MARKBY HEWITT
HAND & CO	LAWRENCE GRAHAM
STEPHENSON HARWOOD	

Allen & Overy has a strong pensions department where Derek Sloan is a well known pensions specialist. The team advises corporate clients on the establishment, administration, reorganisation and winding up of pensions schemes, unapproved pension arrangements for senior executives and pension scheme surpluses and deficits.

At *Freshfields*, Kenneth Dierden, David Pollard and Daniel Schaffer also have established reputations, and advise on establishing and operating pensions schemes, restructuring pension arrangements including merger and winding up schemes, governance issues and dispute resolution. Daniel Schaffer has written articles for various journals including *British Pensions Lawyer.*

Biddle & Co has a seven strong pensions group, including Hugh Arthur, Chris Mullen and Belinda Benney, whose work includes high level merger and reconstruction projects, investment work and complex documentation exercises. The firm also played a leading role in the recent Maxwell 'Global Settlement', acting for the independent trustees to the private company schemes, by which pension fund claims totalling several hundred million pounds were settled.

Ian Pittaway at *Nicholson Graham & Jones* is also highly regarded. Over the last year, he has been involved in advising Life Offices and independent financial advisers on the consequences of the SIB review of personal pensions, as well as seeing a re-surgence in the independant trusteeship of ongoing funds as a pre-emptive measure in response to the member-trustee provisions in the Pensions Bill. Peter Docking and Sarah Tier at the firm are contributor and joint editors of *EC Pensions Law.*

Clifford Chance has a strong team including Nick Sherwin, Chris Johnson and Helen Cox, dealing with all aspects of pensions law. Other firms recommended for pensions expertise were *Baker & Mckenzie, McKenna & Co, Hammond Suddards, Herbert Smith, Eversheds, Richards Butler* and *Simmons & Simmons.*

At *Baker & McKenzie,* Robert West advises on all legal aspects of pensions including trust aspects, litigation, surpluses, sales and purchases, drafting and advice to independent trustees. Work has included acting in 'The Times Pension Fund' litigation.

John Cunliffe and Nigel Moore at *McKenna & Co* have vast experience in pensions law, and both acted in the 'Coloroll' litigation. John Cunliffe is also a regular speaker at national pension conferences and courses.

The pensions department at *Hammond Suddards* advises companies on setting up and operating pensions schemes and pension aspects of corporate transactions. Robin Ellison is a consultant within the department, and is the author of a number of works on pensions law. Other members of the team include Jane Marshall (who handled the pensions aspects of the water privatisation and acted for trustees in one of the first large surplus refunds; £50 million), Peter Silke (who has particular expertise in conflicts, surpluses, independent trusteeship, transactional work, unapproved schemes and termination of schemes) and Andrew Powell (who is a contributor to various journals and co-author of 'Managing a Company Pension Scheme').

John Sabel and Roger Lewis at *Eversheds* have considerable expertise in pension law, the latter handled the pension aspects of the privatisation of the electricity supply industry and British Rail. John Sabel is co-author of 'Tolley's Pension Handbook'.

At *Richards Butler,* Keith Wallace has acted in numerous high profile pensions cases including the mineworkers' pension strike absence (£100 million).

Other notable individuals include Ian Gault at *Herbert Smith,* Michael Cowley at *Stephenson Harwood,* Jonathan Fenton at *Alsop Wilkinson* and Sean Hand at *Hand & Co .*

LEADING INDIVIDUALS – LONDON

John Quarrell *Nabarro Nathanson*

H.G. Arthur *Biddle & Co*	**P.F.J. Bennett** *Slaughter and May*	**Harriet Dawes** *Lovell White Durrant*
Kenneth N. Dierden *Freshfields*	**Mark B. Greenlees** *Sacker & Partners*	**Stuart C. James** *Rowe & Maw*
Ian M. Pittaway *Nicholson Graham & Jones*	**David N. Pollard** *Freshfields*	**Jonathan S.D. Seres** *Sacker & Partners*
Derek S. Sloan *Allen & Overy*	**Paul A.C. Stannard** *Travers Smith Braithwaite*	

Belinda Benney *Biddle & Co*	**Edward A. Codrington** *Slaughter and May*	**Michael J. Cowley** *Stephenson Harwood*
Tim Cox *Linklaters & Paines*	**Helen Cox** *Clifford Chance*	**John M. Cunliffe** *McKenna & Co*
Peter J. Docking *Nicholson Graham & Jones*	**Robin Ellison** *Hammond Suddards*	**Jonathan Fenton** *Alsop Wilkinson*
Peter Ford *Nabarro Nathanson*	**Ian T. Gault** *Herbert Smith*	**Ruth T. Goldman** *Linklaters & Paines*
Sean W. L. Hand *Hand & Co*	**Howard R. Jacobs** *Slaughter and May*	**Chris Johnson** *Clifford Chance*
Anna Kelly *Rowe & Maw*	**C. Peter Lester** *Sacker & Partners*	**Roger Lewis** *Eversheds*
Jane M. Marshall *Hammond Suddards*	**Nigel Moore** *McKenna & Co*	**Chris P. Mullen** *Biddle & Co*
John Murray *Nabarro Nathanson*	**H. John H. Pearson** *Lovell White Durrant*	**Andrew M. Powell** *Hammond Suddards*
John Sabel *Eversheds*	**Jane M. Samsworth** *Lovell White Durrant*	**Daniel Schaffer** *Freshfields*
Nick Sherwin *Clifford Chance*	**Peter D. Silke** *Hammond Suddards*	**Derek Simler** *Lovell White Durrant*
Stephanie Smith *Travers Smith Braithwaite*	**Russell A. Strachan** *Lovell White Durrant*	**A. Tony Thurnham** *Linklaters & Paines*
Sarah Jane Tier *Nicholson Graham & Jones*	**Keith Wallace** *Richards Butler*	**Robert J. West** *Baker & McKenzie*
Andrew G. White *Rowe & Maw*		

UP AND COMING

Stephen Ito *Lovell White Durrant*

In all the tables the names in each group are listed alphabetically.

SOUTH EAST

Clarks and *Blake Lapthorn* retain their high reputation for pensions expertise in the South East. Philip Harwood-Smart at *Blake Lapthorn* specialises in the law relating to independent trustees of pension schemes in both ongoing and insolvency cases. David Clark at *Clarks* handles all aspects

HIGHLY REGARDED – SOUTH EAST		
BLAKE LAPTHORN *Fareham*		CLARKS *Reading*
CRIPPS HARRIES HALL *Tunbridge Wells*		

of pensions work but has particular experience of advising trustees in conflict situations, advising independent trustees appointed under s119 Pensions Act 1993 and of acting as an independent trustee. *Cripps Harries Hall* also has a capability in pensions law and has a department incorporating two specialist partners.

LEADING INDIVIDUALS – SOUTH EAST
David Clark *Clarks*
Philip Harwood-Smart *Blake Lapthorn*

SOUTH WEST & WALES

Burges Salmon and *Osborne Clarke* maintain their pre-eminent positions as leaders. Both have highly experienced teams which undertake work in the pensions field for employers, pension scheme trustees and major companies.

LEADING FIRMS – SOUTH WEST & WALES	
BURGES SALMON *Bristol*	OSBORNE CLARKE *Bristol*

Osborne Clarke have reinforced their already considerable pensions presence with the recruitment of Joachim Steinbech from *Bond Pearce*. The pensions unit is headed by Ralph Whiting who enjoys a national reputation as a pensions lawyer. Besides advising Hanson Plc in the 'Melton Medes' pension litigation, the team has been heavily involved in other litigation covered in the press, including the current 'British Steel' litigation. The firm holds an impressive client list in this area including clients such as Imperial Tobacco Trustees.

HIGHLY REGARDED – SOUTH WEST & WALES	
BEVAN ASHFORD *Bristol*	EVERSHEDS *Cardiff*
LYONS DAVIDSON *Bristol*	
VEALE WASBROUGH *Bristol*	

Burges Salmon's growth in pensions work over the last 12 months has been based on four principal types of service. There has been an increased demand for documentation services from actuaries and pension consultants, which seems to have been reinforced by an apparent trend towards insured schemes becoming self-administered. Secondly, the team has had an increased call for consultancy advice, particularly on aspects of sex equality. The practice has also developed in the area of independent trusteeships where the team have had a number of significant appointments to continuing schemes. The group has also continued to develop

their reputation in the more specialised field of FURBS and other unapproved arrangements. Timothy Illston at the firm devised one of the first FURBS 'packages' on the market. Also recommended at the firm as a rising star for pensions work is Lindsay Brown.

In Wales, *Eversheds* is widely recognised for its specialist expertise covering all aspects of pensions work. Ian Davies heads the pensions side within the employment and pensions department and is the only specialist pensions lawyer in South Wales.

Lyons Davidson has also been recommended for its pensions work dealing with all aspects including remuneration packages.

LEADING INDIVIDUALS – SOUTH WEST & WALES
Ralph S. Whiting *Osborne Clarke*
Timothy M. Illston *Burges Salmon*
Ian H. Davies *Eversheds*
Joachim Steinbech *Osborne Clarke*

UP AND COMING
Lindsay K. Brown *Burges Salmon*

MIDLANDS

Wragge & Co, Eversheds and *Edge & Ellison* all have outstanding reputations for their pensions practice. W*ragge & Co* has one of the largest pensions team in the Midlands headed by Gerald Hingley with nine lawyers engaged exclusively in pensions work. The long established team has an excellent reputation which extends beyond the West Midlands and acts for many major clients in the area including Peugeot Talbot Motor Company PLC, Kalamozoo Computer Group PLC and EMAP PLC. Vivien Cockerill at the firm has been recommended for her pensions expertise, providing pensions advice for both employers and trustees.

LEADING FIRMS – MIDLANDS	
EDGE & ELLISON *Birmingham*	EVERSHEDS *Birmingham*
EVERSHEDS *Derby*	PINSENT CURTIS *Birmingham*
WRAGGE & CO *Birmingham*	

In Birmingham, *Eversheds'* pensions team, headed by Liz Fallon has a solid foundation of pensions clients including Bryant Group Plc. Work during the last 12 months has included pensions aspects of the successful bid by Silvermines Group Plc for Molynx. In the Derby office of *Eversheds*, Giles Orton retains a high profile for his litigation work in the field. Richard Davis, also at the Derby office, is highly regarded for his excellent pensions practice, and has particular expertise in occupational pension schemes. He is current chairman of *Eversheds* National Pensions Group, and Director and Chairman of *Eversheds* Pension Trustees Ltd.

HIGHLY REGARDED – MIDLANDS	
HEWITSON BECKE + SHAW *Northampton*	MARTINEAU JOHNSON *Birmingham*
GARRETT & CO	

Edge & Ellison has expanded its pensions department in the last year and now has nine in the team of which three are partners. The group is headed by Simon Ramshaw and covers pensions work across the spectrum. *Edge & Ellison* has a trustee company which provides independent trusteeships for pension schemes in wind up, and professional and independent trustee services to ongoing schemes.

Other notable firms in the region are *Pinsent Curtis, Hewitson Becke + Shaw* and *Martineau Johnson*. M.J. O'Driscoll at *Pinsent Curtis* has particular emphasis on pension scheme documents and associated matters, and Clare Colacicchi at *Hewitson Becke + Shaw* handles pension and trust work. Trevor Clarke at *Garret & Co* is also known for his expertise.

LEADING INDIVIDUALS – MIDLANDS
Richard G.L. Davis *Eversheds*
Gerald Hingley *Wragge & Co*
M.J. O'Driscoll *Pinsent Curtis*
Giles A.C. Orton *Eversheds*
Simon Ramshaw *Edge & Ellison*
Trevor C. Clarke *Garrett & Co*
Vivien Cockerill *Wragge & Co*
Clare Colacicchi *Hewitson Becke + Shaw*
Liz Fallon *Eversheds*

EAST ANGLIA

Karen Gibb-Davis at *Greenwoods* has been recommended for her expertise in pensions work. The firm is a member of the National Association of Pensions Funds and its legal

HIGHLY REGARDED – EAST ANGLIA
GREENWOODS *Peterborough*
EVERSHEDS *Norwich*

service is supplemented by the presence of a Financial Planning Advisor. *Eversheds* also have experience of a broad range of pensions matters.

LEADING INDIVIDUALS – EAST ANGLIA
Karen Gibb-Davis *Greenwoods*

NORTH WEST

An increasing amount of pensions expertise is available in the North West, and the greater competition has resulted in an even higher standard of work. The most highly recommended firms are *Addleshaw Sons & Latham, Alsop Wilkinson, Dibb Lupton Broomhead* and *Davies Arnold Cooper*. *Alsop Wilkinson*, where Derek Morris enjoys an excellent reputation, covers all aspects of group and individual pension arrangements including funded and unfunded unapproved top-up schemes for high earners. Francis Shackleton at *Addleshaw Sons & Latham* is also renowned for his expertise.

Margaret Cox at *Dibb Lupton Broomhead* moved from the Leeds to the Manchester office which is now able to provide a complete pensions related legal service. She heads a pensions team of three which is part of the Human Resources Law Group – a team which brings together the firm's employment and pensions specialists.

HIGHLY REGARDED – NORTH WEST		
ADDLESHAW SONS & LATHAM *Manchester*	**ALSOP WILKINSON** *Liverpool*	
DAVIES ARNOLD COOPER *Manchester*	**DIBB LUPTON BROOMHEAD** *Manchester*	

Patrick Kennedy is head of pensions at *Davies Arnold Cooper*, Manchester, which offers commercial legal advice on all aspects of pensions. Patrick Kennedy has spoken at various national conferences on the subject, and currently serves on the Committee of the National Association of Pension Funds, Manchester Group, and the Barber Committee of the Association of Pensions Lawyers.

LEADING INDIVIDUALS – NORTH WEST
Margaret E. Cox *Dibb Lupton Broomhead*
D.H. Morris *Alsop Wilkinson*
Francis Shackleton *Addleshaw Sons & Latham*

UP AND COMING
Patrick Kennedy *Davies Arnold Cooper*

NORTH EAST

Dibb Lupton Broomhead maintains a high profile in the area covering the full range of pensions work with an emphasis on structuring pension schemes for corporate clients. Timothy Knight, the head of the pension law group, has earned a national reputation for his expertise, and has particular expertise in acting for employers and trustees concerning occupational pension schemes. Martin Lee at the firm, who is also highly recommended, has particular skill in the complexities of trust law and is trustee of a number of pension funds.

Raymond Ainscoe at *Eversheds* is described as an outstanding individual by his competitors and heads the team in Leeds. He has contributed to numerous journals including *Pensions World* and regularly addresses conferences on the subject. As well as mainstream mergers and acquisitions and documentation work, the team has established expertise in specialist areas such as unapproved schemes and pension litigation, which constitutes a substantial part of its workload. Within the last year, the team has acquired a broad range of new clients including industrial PLC's, trustees seeking independent legal advice and financial services institutions seeking pensions advice.

LEADING FIRMS – NORTH EAST		
DIBB LUPTON BROOMHEAD *Bradford*	**EVERSHEDS** *Leeds*	
HAMMOND SUDDARDS *Leeds*		

Richard Archer, also highly regarded, heads the team at *Hammond Suddards* where the work includes advising companies on setting up and operating pensions schemes and pension elements of corporate transactions.

With the establishment of *Nabarro Nathanson's* Sheffield office in October 1994, the firm now offers a full range of pensions services in the North. The team, which is able to draw on additional expertise in its London office, provides independent trustee and pensioneer trustee services and advice to companies, trustees and individuals on all aspects of pension law, including litigation and preparation of pension documents.

HIGHLY REGARDED – NORTH EAST

BOOTH & CO. *Leeds*	**DICKINSON DEES** *Newcastle upon Tyne*
NABARRO NATHANSON *Doncaster*	**WALKER MORRIS** *Leeds*
GARRETT & CO *Leeds*	**SIMPSON CURTIS** *Leeds*

Other notable pension practices include *Walker Morris, Dickinson Dees* and *Booth & Co.* The latter firm is engaged full-time in corporate pensions work, and over the last twelve months has been advising on internal pension scheme mergers, implementing the equalisation of normal retirement ages for male and female scheme members and advice on admission of part-time workers into company schemes. Neville Peel at the firm is co-author of 'Pensions and Insurance on family breakdown' and has been recommended for his pensions expertise as has Rachel Rawnsley who is a rising star in the field of pension work.

LEADING INDIVIDUALS – NORTH EAST

Raymond Ainscoe *Eversheds*	
J.Richard Archer *Hammond Suddards*	
Timothy Knight *Dibb Lupton Broomhead*	
Martin P.W. Lee *Dibb Lupton Broomhead*	
Neville Peel *Booth & Co.*	

UP AND COMING

Rachel Rawnsley *Booth & Co.*

Dickinson Dees has been involved in advising clients on a wide range of regulatory issues and pensions documentation, working with many major actuarial and pensions offices in the region. The team has also been at the forefront of the campaign on behalf of over 8,000 pensioners in their action over the future of the British Steel Pension Scheme.

SCOTLAND

Firms with highly respected pension teams include *Maclay Murray & Spens, Bishop & Robertson Chalmers, McGrigor Donald, Shepherd & Wedderburn WS* and *W & J Burness WS*.

HIGHLY REGARDED – SCOTLAND

BISHOP AND ROBERTSON CHALMERS *Glasgow*	**MACLAY MURRAY & SPENS** *Glasgow*
W & J BURNESS WS *Edinburgh*	**McGRIGOR DONALD** *Glasgow*
SHEPHERD & WEDDERBURN *Edinburgh*	
DUNDAS & WILSON CS *Edinburgh*	

The pension unit at *Maclay Murray & Spens* headed by Andrew Fleming has four full time pension lawyers, of which Marcus Hellyer and Peter Trotter have been recommended. The department is involved in a £100m pension scheme amalgamation.

Bishop & Robertson Chalmers also have a strong pension group consisting of four lawyers, which Iain Talman heads. The team deals with all aspects of pensions work, with particular expertise in small self-administered schemes and independent trusteeships.

LEADING INDIVIDUALS – SCOTLAND

Andrew S. Fleming *Maclay Murray & Spens*
Ian Gordon *McGrigor Donald*
Andrew N. Holehouse *Shepherd & Wedderburn*
Alister M. Sutherland *W & J Burness WS*
Iain J.S. Talman *Bishop and Robertson Chalmers*
Marcus D. Hellyer *Maclay Murray & Spens*
Margaret Meehan *W & J Burness WS*
Peter A. A. Trotter *Maclay Murray & Spens*

Andrew Holehouse at *Shepherd & Wedderburn WS*, deals with all aspects of pensions, has written various articles for journals and regularly speaks at seminars on pensions law. Other notable practitioners are Ian Gordon at *McGrigor Donald* and Alister Sutherland and Margaret Meehan at *W & J Burness*.

LEADERS IN PENSIONS

LONDON

Arthur, H.G.

Biddle & Co, London (0171) 606 9301. Partner in Pensions Group.

Specialisation: Handles all areas of pensions law, including advice to major plcs, trustees and individuals. Work includes mergers and acquisitions, corporate and business transfers and litigation. Also handles the drafting of complex documentation. Author of numerous articles in specialist pensions publications. Well known speaker at conferences for APL, NAPF, PMI and independently sponsored pensions conferences.

Prof. Membership: Association of Pension Lawyers, National Association of Pensions Funds.

Career: Qualified in 1980. Worked at *Lovell White & King* 1978-84. Joined *Biddle & Co.* in 1984, becoming a Partner in 1985.

Personal: Born 6th November 1955. Attended Cardinal Vaughan Memorial School, London 1967-74, then Magdalene College, Cambridge (Open Scholarship in Classics) 1974-77 (MA Law).

Bennett, P.F.J.

Slaughter and May, London (0171) 600 1200. Qualified 1979. Partner 1986. Pensions and Employment Department. Main area of practice is pensions law. Author of Pension Fund Surpluses, first edition 1989, second edition 1994.

Benney, Belinda

Biddle & Co, London (0171) 606 9301. Qualified 1981. Partner 1991. Pensions Department. Work includes documentation and rule drafting, sex discrimination, revenue limits and severance terms.

Codrington, Edward A.
See under Employee Benefits/Share Scheme.

Cowley, Michael J.
Stephenson Harwood, London (0171) 329 4422. Qualified 1984. Partner 1990. Corporate Department. Main area of practice is pensions law. Member of the Association of Pension Lawyers.

Cox, Tim
Linklaters & Paines, London (0171) 606 7080. Qualified 1987. Joined 1985. Employment and Employee Benefits Department. Work includes drafting pension scheme documentation, and advising on pensions matters generally.

Cox, Helen
Clifford Chance, London (0171) 600 1000. Partner. Principal area of practice is pensions law.

Cunliffe, John M.
McKenna & Co, London (0171) 606 9000. Partner in charge of Employee Benefits Group.

Specialisation: Pensions specialist. Advises employers and trustees of occupational pension schemes and insurance companies. Acted in the cases of Coloroll Pension Trustees v. Russell, and London Regional Transport v. Hatt. Major clients include BAA Plc, Black & Decker, Booker Plc, Campbells Foods Plc, Coca-Cola, Geo. Wimpey, Harrods, House of Fraser, Marley Plc and Siemens Plc. Author of 'The Role of the Pension Fund Trustee' and regular contributor to 'Pensions Management' and other pensions publications. Has appeared on BBC television and radio and is a regular speaker at pension conferences and courses organised by the National Association of Pension Funds, the Pension Management Institute and the Association of Pensions Lawyers. Also at commercial conferences and international pensions conferences in London, Amsterdam, Budapest, Berlin, Copenhagen and Sydney. Formerly part-time law lecturer at Liverpool University.

Prof. Membership: Association of Pensions Lawyers, Law Society, Occupational Pensions Advisory Service (Vice President and Chairman of its Professional Standards Committee), National Association of Pension Funds.

Career: Qualified in 1959. Joined *McKenna & Co* as a Partner in 1987.

Personal: Born 6th March 1935. Educated at Liverpool University (LLB 1957 1st Class Hons) and Oxford University (BCL 1961). Recreations include walking, music, travel and gardening. Lives in Tunbridge Wells.

Dawes, Harriet
Lovell White Durrant, London (0171) 236 0066. Qualified 1978. Partner 1980. Pen-

sions Group. Advice on all aspects of pension law and documentation, including reorganisation of schemes, company sales, surpluses, litigation, equal treatment issues, transfers from schemes and regulatory problems arising from the Financial Services Act and the SIB report.

Dierden, Kenneth N.
Freshfields, London (0171) 936 4000. Partner in Employment, Pensions and Benefits Department.

Specialisation: Work covers all aspects of the establishment and operation of pension schemes (both private and public sector). Experienced in pensions litigation and has wide involvement of the pensions aspects of privatisations. Acts for employers and trustees. Professional Membership: Member of the Main Committee of the Association of Pension Lawyers and a past Chairman of its Legislative and Parliamentary Sub-Committee. Associate of the Institute of Taxation. Books and Articles: Contributor to Tolley's 'Company Law Handbook' and Tolley's 'Director's Handbook'.
Other Relevant Experience: Former lecturer at the College of Law. Regular speaker at pensions conferences.

Career: Qualified in 1977. Lecturer at College of Law 1977/80. Joined Freshfields 1980. Partner 1987.

Personal: Born 1952.

Docking, Peter J.
Nicholson Graham & Jones, London (0171) 628 9151. Partner in Pensions Department.

Specialisation: Principal area of practice is pensions law. Covers all aspects including litigation, sales and purchases, trust law issues and life office matters. Frequent lecturer and contributor to pensions and academic journals. Former Chairman of APL's Education Committee and current member of its International Committee. Contributor to and Joint Editor of 'EC Pensions Law'.

Prof. Membership: Association of Pensions Lawyers, Law Society.

Career: Qualified in 1987 and joined *Nicholson Graham & Jones*. Became a Partner in 1991.

Personal: Born 1st June 1961. Educated at Sutton Manor High School for Boys and the University of Exeter. Leisure activities include mountaineering, climbing, walking, skiing and travel.

Ellison, Robin
Hammond Suddards, London (0171) 628 4767. Consultant in Pensions Department.

Specialisation: Acted in the Maxwell pensions case. Author of a number of works on pensions law, including 'Pensions Law and Practice'. Editor of Pensions Law Reports. Has also published 'Pensions and Divorce', 'The Pension Trustee Handbook' and 'Pensions: Europe and Equality'. Regular broadcaster including frequent contributions

to BBC Radio 4's 'Moneybox'.

Prof. Membership: NAPF, Association of Pensions Lawyers, Law Society.

Career: Qualified in 1973. Fellow in Wolfson College, Cambridge 1975-80, specialising in European Pensions Law. Founded *Ellison Westhorp* in 1980, carrying out exclusively pensions work. Managing Director of Finance for Housing Ltd 1982-87 and Director of Baltic plc 1985-87. Became a Consultant for *Hammond Suddards* in 1994.

Personal: Born 3rd February 1949. Leisure interests include antiquarian books, sailing and walking. Lives in London.

Fenton, Jonathan
Alsop Wilkinson, London (0171) 248 4141. Qualified 1983. Pensions partner, experienced pensions practitioner. Principal co-author 'Tolley's Pensions Handbook'.

Ford, Peter
Nabarro Nathanson, London (0171) 493 9933. Qualified 1988. Partner 1993. Pensions Department. Handles all aspects of pensions law, including company sales and purchases, scheme re-organisations and mergers.

Gault, Ian T.
Herbert Smith, London (0171) 374 8000. Partner and Head of Pensions Group.

Specialisation: Has extensive experience of advising on all aspects of pensions law and practice. Currently on the executive committee of the Pensions Research Accountant's Group and the general purposes committee of the Society of Pensions Consultants.

Prof. Membership: Association of Pensions Lawyers.

Career: Qualified in 1977. Partner at *Herbert Smith* since 1988.

Personal: Educated at Clare College, Cambridge.

Goldman, Ruth T.
Linklaters & Paines, London (0171) 606 7080. Qualified 1985. Partner 1992. Corporate Department. Principal area of practice is employment and employee benefits.

Greenlees, Mark B.
Sacker & Partners, London (0171) 329 6699. Partner in specialist pensions law firm.

Specialisation: All aspects of law relating to occupational pension schemes. Represented the male beneficiaries in the 'Coloroll' reference to the European Court. Acted for vendor in what was then the second largest MBO in UK business history. Regular contributor to pensions periodicals; regular speaker at major conferences and seminars.

Prof. Membership: Association of Pension Lawyers.

Career: Qualified in 1979. Joined *Sacker & Partners* in 1977, becoming a Partner in 1982. Member of the Main Committee of APL 1992-4. Chairman of Legislative and

Parliamentary Committee of APL 1992-4. Chairman of Legislation Committee of SPC 1991-2.

Personal: Born 18th April 1954. Attended Berkhamsted 1964-71 and Oxford University 1972-76. Leisure interests include family, old cars and football. Lives near Berkhamsted.

Hand, Sean W.L.

Hand & Co, London (0171) 329 1525. Qualified 1991. Founding partner 1995. Handles all aspects of pensions law. Born 3.9.1955.

Ito, Stephen

Lovell White Durrant, London (0171) 236 0066.

Jacobs, Howard R.

See under Employment Law.

James, Stuart C.

Rowe & Maw, London (0171) 248 4282. Partner in Pensions Department.

Specialisation: Pensions law and related trust, tax and commercial law matters. Other main area of work is unit trusts and retail financial services. Member of the Pension Law Review Committee 1992-93.

Prof. Memberships: Law Society, Association of Pensions Lawyers (Chairman), Reliance Insurance Group. Fellow, Pensions Management Institute.

Career: Articled with *Rowe & Maw*. Qualified in 1967, then joined *Warren Murton & Co*. 1967-77. Returned to *Rowe & Maw* as a partner in 1977.

Personal: Born 3rd March 1944. Attended Reed's School 1958-62. Lives in Surrey.

Johnson, Chris

Clifford Chance, London (0171) 600 1000. Partner. Principal area of practice is pensions law.

Kelly, Anna

Rowe & Maw, London (0171) 248 4282. Qualified 1985. Partner 1989. Pensions Department. Pensions specialist. Born 15.5.1961.

Lester, C. Peter

Sacker & Partners, London (0171) 329 6699. Pensions only law firm.

Specialisation: Deals with all areas of pensions law with specialist expertise in relation to multinational pension provision. Major clients include BBC and the pension funds of leading companies. Has written articles in technical journals and spoken at conferences.

Prof. Membership: Co-opted Member of Parliamentary Committee of the National Association of Pension Funds.

Career: Qualified in 1968. Partner at *Walker Martineau* 1970-83. Joined *Sacker & Partners* as a Partner in 1983.

Personal: Born in 1944. Educated at Christ's

Hospital 1954-62 and Birmingham University 1962-65 (LL.B). Leisure activities include music, theatre and walking. Lives in Hove.

Lewis, Roger

Eversheds, London (0171) 919 4500. Head of Employment and Pensions Department.

Specialisation: Advises employers and trustees in relation to all aspects of corporate pension arrangements. Handled pension aspects of the privatisation of Electricity Supply Industry and British Rail. Author of occasional articles in specialist pensions journals.

Prof. Membership: Law Society, APL, NAPF

Career: Qualified in 1978. Worked with IBM (Systems Analyst) 1966-68, GEC (various managerial positions) 1968-72 and Commission of the European Communities (DG III, Industry and Technology) 1973-75. Joined *Jaques & Lewis* (now Eversheds) in 1976, becoming a Partner in 1979.

Personal: Born 14th April 1945. Attended UCS 1958-63, then Balliol College, Oxford 1963-66 (MA in Physics). Governor of Hebrew University of Jerusalem. Married with two children. Leisure interests include golf, tennis and theatre. Lives in London.

Marshall, Jane M.

Hammond Suddards, London (0171) 628 4767. Partner in Pensions Department.

Specialisation: Has experience in all areas of pensions law, with particular emphasis on privatisation work, conflicts, drafting and surpluses. Handled the pensions aspects of the water privatisation and acted for trustees in one of the first large surplus refunds (50 million). Occasionally contributes articles to the professional press. Has lectured at various conferences and spoken on radio and TV.

Prof. Membership: Law Society, Association of Pension Lawyers.

Career: Qualified in 1978. Worked abroad after qualifying. Joined *Lovell White & King* in 1980 to specialise in pensions. Became a Partner with *Ellison Westhorp* in 1986 and with *Hammond Suddards* following the merger in 1994.

Personal: Born 17th December 1953. Attended March High School for Girls to 1972, then Dundee University 1972-76 (First Class Honours). Leisure interests include gardening and local history. Mother of four. Lives in Lt. Bromley, near Colchester.

Moore, Nigel

McKenna & Co, London (0171) 606 9000. Partner in Employee Benefits Group.

Specialisation: Main area of practice is pensions. Work includes advising on administration of pension schemes; drafting trust deeds and rules; advising on pension aspects of mergers and acquisitions; advising on mergers of schemes and refunds of surplus; handling litigation in High Court and European Court of Justice and advising on

implementation of equal treatment in pension schemes. Also handles employment law, including drafting service contracts and advising on employment aspects of mergers and acquisitions, enforceability of restrictive covenants, dismissal of senior executives, wrongful dismissal claims and industrial tribunal claims. Drafts rules for and advises on the administration of executive share-save and profit sharing schemes and ESOPs. Acted in Coloroll's application to the European Court. Speaking experience includes NAPF training courses, APL annual conference and commercial conferences.

Prof. Membership: Law Society, City of London Solicitors Company, Association of Pension Lawyers, Share Scheme Lawyers Group, Employment Lawyers Association.

Career: Qualified 1986. Articled at *Radcliffes & Co*. 1984-86. Joined *McKenna & Co*. in 1986.

Personal: Born 13th June 1962. Attended St Albans School 1973-80, Warwick University 1980-83, College of Law Chancery Lane 1983-84 and City of London Polytechnic (MA in Business Law) 1984-86. Leisure interests include golf, football and singing. Lives in Welwyn Garden City.

Mullen, Chris P.

Biddle & Co, London (0171) 606 9301. Partner in Pensions Department.

Specialisation: Advises companies and scheme trustees on all aspects of pensions law, relating principally to occupational pension schemes. Particular interests include "passport" schemes, FURBS, and advising independent trustees (e.g. one of the independent trustees who took over responsibility for the Maxwell pension schemes after Robert Maxwell's death). Clients include Lloyds, Norcros plc, Costain Group plc and the NSPCC. Author of a recent article on 'Contracting Out: A Recipe for Success?' (in the March 1995 issue of *PMI Technical News*). Occasional conference speaker. Also gives in-house and client seminars.

Prof. Membership: APL, City of London Solicitors Company, Pensions Committee of the Institute of Chartered Accountants.

Career: Qualified in 1986 after articles at *Biddle & Co*. Became a Partner in 1990.

Personal: Born 11th September 1960. Educated at Jesus College, Cambridge 1979-82 (BA in Law). Lives in Hertford, Herts.

Murray, John

Nabarro Nathanson, London (0171) 493 9933.

Pearson, H. John H.

Lovell White Durrant, London (0171) 236 0066. Qualified 1971. Partner 1986. Pensions and Employment Group. Advises employers, trustees and others on all aspects of pensions law and documentation.

Pittaway, Ian M.

Nicholson Graham & Jones, London (0171) 628 9151. Partner and Head of Pensions Department.

Specialisation: Covers all aspects of pension law including acting as trustee, arbitrator and expert witness. Joint author of 'EC Pensions Law' and numerous articles and lectures. Former Chairman and Secretary of APL.

Prof. Membership: Law Society, Association of Pensions Lawyers, Justice.

Career: Qualified in 1980 and joined *Nicholson Graham & Jones* in 1981. Became a Partner in 1984. Vice-Chairman of the Solicitors Staff Pension Fund.

Personal: Born 28th July 1956. Attended the University of Hull 1974-77. Leisure interests include gardening, golf, wine and whisky.

Pollard, David N.

Freshfields, London (0171) 936 4000. Partner in Employment, Pensions and Benefits Department.

Specialisation: Partner in an integrated group of over 20 lawyers covering the whole range of pensions, employment and benefits work. Acted for trustees in recent Drexel pension case. Author of 'Employment and Pension Rights in Corporate Insolvency' (Tolley, 1994) and Contributor to Tolley's 'Employment Law' and Tolley's 'Insolvency Law'. Co-Editor Tolley's *Trust Law International* magazine. Co-editor (with partner, Ken Dierden) forthcoming book 'Guide to the Pensions Act 1995'.

Prof. Membership: Association of Pension Lawyers (APL), Industrial Law Society (ILS), Employment Lawyers Association (ELA).

Career: Qualified in 1980. Joined *Freshfields* in 1982, worked at the Singapore office 1984-87 and became a Partner in 1990.

Personal: Born 30th August 1956. Attended St John's College, Cambridge 1974-77.

Powell, Andrew M.

Hammond Suddards, London (0171) 628 4767. Partner in Pensions Unit.

Specialisation: Handles all aspects of pensions work, including inter alia documentation, deal based work, financial products, mergers and other complex advice work. Contributor to Trust Law International, Accountancy Age, Acquisitions Monthly and others. Co-author of 'Managing a Company Pension Scheme'.

Prof. Membership: Law Society, Institute of Directors.

Career: Qualified in 1980. Articled *Granville West Chivers & Morgan.* Then in-house lawyer covering pensions work for DHSS; adviser to OPB, NHS superannuation fund; responsible for pensions work at *Denton Hall Burgin & Warrens,* before becoming a Partner at *Ellison Westhorp* in 1990. Joined *Hammond Suddards* in 1994. Former main committee member of Association of Pen-

sion Lawyers; member of APL investment sub-committee and contact on Maxwell related issues, IPEBLA and Association des Juristes Franco-Britanniques. Director of Trustee Corporation Limited.

Personal: Born 26th January 1955. Attended King Henry School to 1975. Graduated from the University of Wales in 1978; then attended Lancaster Gate College of Law. Lives in Harrow-on-the-Hill.

Quarrell, John

Nabarro Nathanson, London (0171) 493 9933. Qualified 1976. Partner and Head of Pensions Department.

Specialisation: Work covers all aspects relating to occupational and personal pension schemes. Has acted in the Hillsdown Foods, Courage, Imperial Tobacco and Mineworkers cases. Acts for Law Debenture in their capacity as trustee of one of the Maxwell Schemes and has been involved in the substantial recovery. Legal adviser to the team advising the government of the Russian Federation on the laws and regulations to be introduced to govern non-state pension funds. Author of 'Pension Fund Investment' (Butterworths). Co-editor of 'Tolley's International Trust Law'. Consulting editor of the NAPF Pensions Legislation Service. Author of numerous articles and papers and a member of Trust Law Reform Committee. Lectures at home and abroad.

Prof. Membership: Law Society; Pensions Management Institute (elected member); Association of Pensions Lawyers (Secretary).

Sabel, John

Eversheds, London (0171) 919 4500. Partner in Employment and Pensions Group.

Specialisation: Main area of practice is pensions law. Gives advice in relation to privatisation; drafting and interpreting schemes documents; acquisitions and disposals of business and companies; discrimination; employment; tax and litigation. Acted in Roberts v. Tate & Lyle Industries Ltd and in Icarus (Hertford) Ltd v. Driscoll. Co-author of Tolley's Pension Handbook. Author of 'Pensions in the United Kingdom', London Chamber of Commerce and Industry. Occasional speaker at conferences and for Association of Pension Lawyers. Former director of Tate & Lyle Pension Trust Limited.

Prof. Membership: Chartered Institute of Transport, Law Society, Association of Pension Lawyers, Life Assurance Legal Society, Member of the Employment Affairs Committee of London Chamber of Commerce and Industry

Career: Qualified in 1971. Worked with Tate & Lyle plc 1974-86, as Legal Assistant to Deputy Legal Adviser. Moved to *Oppenheimers/ Denton Hall* in 1986, becoming a Partner in 1990, before joining *Jaques & Lewis* (now Eversheds) as a Partner in 1994.

Personal: Born 10th November 1944. Attended Abingdon School, Oxford College of

Technology, then London School of Economics. Leisure interests include family and light reading. Married with three children. Lives in London.

Samsworth, Jane M.

Lovell White Durrant, London (0171) 236 0066. Qualified 1978. Partner 1991. Pensions and Employment Department. Deals with all areas of occupational pension provision advising companies and trustees.

Schaffer, Daniel

Freshfields, London (0171) 936 4000. Senior manager in Employment, Pensions and Benefits Group.

Specialisation: Pensions. Advises on establishing and operating pension schemes (both private and public sector), restructuring pension arrangements including merger and winding up schemes, governance issues and dispute resolution (including litigation). Articles published in Pensions World, British Pension Lawyer, Trust Law International, La Synthèse Financière and L'Argus Des Assurances. Speaker at APL Annual Conference 1993, Warburg's Conferences on French pension reform, and commercial conferences.

Prof. Membership: Association of Pension Lawyers (Member of International Sub-Committee). Trust Law Committee working party on trustee/investment and Financial Law Panel working party on "commercial dealings with trustees".

Career: Joined *Freshfields* in 1988. Part-time tutor in trusts at LSE (1987-88), Merton College, Oxford (1987-90) and Balliol College, Oxford (1988-92).

Personal: Born 13th October 1963. Educated at Haberdashers' Aske's School, Elstree 1971-82, Bristol University 1983-86 (LLB, Simmons Scholar) and Merton College, Oxford 1986-87.(BCL 1st Class). Leisure pursuits include travelling in France, and ski-ing. Fluent in French; working knowledge of Spanish.

Seres, Jonathan S.D.

Sacker & Partners, London (0171) 329 6699. Senior Partner of specialist pensions law firm.

Specialisation: Experienced in all aspects of pension schemes, covering establishment, alteration, merger, booklets, related employment law, Financial Services Act work, common investment funds and investment management and custody agreements. Advises employers, trustees, trade unions and charities. Acted for the Plessey company in court application to approve merger of its Pension Funds with those of GEC and Siemens. Acted in application to the ECJ in the Coloroll matter (*Sacker & Partners* were acting for the four classes of male beneficiaries). Author of 'Pensions: A Practical Guide' (3rd edition 1992, Longman). Appeared as pensions tax expert on Channel 4's City Programme.

Prof. Membership: Association of Pension

Lawyers, National Association of Pension Funds, Society of Pension Consultants, Law Society.

Career: MA (Oxon). Qualified in 1971, having joined *Sacker & Partners* in 1967. Became Partner in 1973 and Senior Partner in 1985. Chairman of the Association of Pension Lawyers 1985-88. Current member of the APL International Sub-Committee. Member of former Government/ Industry Working Party for Personal Pension Schemes.

Personal: Born 13th June 1945. Attended Oxford University (PPE (Hons) 1966). Leisure interests include sailing, history and charities. Lives in London.

Sherwin, Nick
Clifford Chance, London (0171) 600 1000. Partner. Principal area of practice is pensions law.

Silke, Peter D.
Hammond Suddards, London (0171) 628 4767. Partner in Pensions Unit of Corporate Department.

Specialisation: Pensions law specialist. Experienced in all areas of pensions law with particular emphasis on conflicts, surpluses, drafting and independent trusteeship, transactional work, unapproved schemes and termination of schemes. Has been involved in a number of cases relating to surplus issues and has advised on pensions issues connected with water privatisation. Advises trustees of schemes established by major quoted companies within the chemicals/ pharmaceuticals industries on pensions issues and handles a high volume of independent trusteeship work arising from the statutory requirements to appoint independent trustees on insolvency. Co-author of 'Allied Dunbar Capital Taxes and Estate Planning Guide' until 1992. Occasional contributor of articles to professional journals.

Prof. Membership: Association of Pensions Lawyers.

Career: Qualified in 1979. With *Lovell White Durrant* 1986-90, then Partner at *Ellison Westhorp* 1990-94. Became a Partner at *Hammond Suddards* in May 1994 on merger with *Ellison Westhorp*.

Personal: Born 2nd December 1949. Educated at Hasmonean Grammar School, London 1961-66, the University of Cape Town 1967-70 (BA, B.Soc.Sc), Birmingham University (M.Soc.Sc, 1973) and York University (BPhil, 1974). Director of the Trustee Corporation Ltd, Hammond Suddards Pension Trust Ltd and Fiscal Services Ltd. Leisure interests include current affairs, specialised philately and reading. Lives in Stanmore, Middlesex.

Simler, Derek
Lovell White Durrant, London (0171) 236 0066. Qualified 1978. Partner, 1985. Pensions Group. Advises employers and trustees on all aspects of pensions law and documen-

tation. Born 26.1.1940.

Sloan, Derek S.
Allen & Overy, London (0171) 330 3000. Qualified 1971. Partner 1977. Employment and Pensions Department. Work includes establishing, reorganising, merging and terminating pension schemes, advice on insolvencies, funding issues and equal treatment.

Smith, Stephanie
Travers Smith Braithwaite, London (0171) 248 9133 or 696 0998. Partner in Pensions Department.

Specialisation: Handles all aspects of pensions law. Regular public speaker.

Prof. Membership: Association of Pensions Lawyers, Life Assurance Legal Society.

Career: Qualified in 1986. Joined *Travers Smith Braithwaite* in 1993, becoming a Partner in 1994.

Personal: Born 22nd March 1962. Holds an LLB from Queen Mary College, London (1983). Lives in London.

Stannard, Paul A.C.
Travers Smith Braithwaite, London (0171) 248 9133. Partner in Pensions Department.

Specialisation: All aspects of pensions law.

Prof. Membership: Hon. Secretary Association of Pensions Lawyers(1991 - 1994), Fellow of the Pensions Management Institute.

Career: Qualified 1982. Joined *Travers Smith Braithwaite* as a Partner in 1989.

Personal: Born 1957.

Strachan, Russell A.
Lovell White Durrant, London (0171) 236 0066. Qualified 1970. Partner 1975. Employment Group. Advises on all aspects of pensions law and documentation both contentious and non-contentious.

Thurnham, A.Tony
Linklaters & Paines, London (0171) 606 7080. Partner 1983. Employment & Employee Benefits Department. Has 22 years experience in pensions law. Author of numerous articles and regular conference speaker.

Tier, Sarah Jane
Nicholson Graham & Jones, London (0171) 628 9151. Partner in Pensions Department.

Specialisation: Deals with all aspects of pensions law including public sector schemes and privatisation, acting as a trustee and benefit design. Lectures at professional conferences, seminars and workshops. Joint author of 'EC Pensions Law' (Wiley Chancery) and numerous articles in the professional and specialist press.

Prof. Membership: Law Society, Association of Pensions Lawyers, National Association

of Pension Funds.

Career: Qualified in 1984. At *Clyde & Co* 1984-87. Joined *Nicholson Graham & Jones* in 1987 and became a Partner in 1991.

Personal: Born 21st November 1960. Educated at the University of Southampton 1980-83. Interests include reading, walking, wine and Buddhism. Lives in Hampstead, London.

Wallace, Keith
Richards Butler, London (0171) 247 6555. Partner specialising in pensions and professional trusteeship.

Specialisation: Main area of practice covers pensions and professional trusteeship, custodianship and unit trusts. Acted in the mineworkers' pensions strike absence case, Cowan v. Charlesworth (1986), (£100 million); when Bejam employees' benefits were not honoured by a predator (£5 million) in 1990; British Telecom disputed pension 'contribution holiday' (£600 million potential) and formation and authorisation of Britain's first 'Futures' and 'Geared Futures and Options' Unit Trusts 1992-93. Editor of 'Pension Lawyer' and the 'Trust Deed and Rules Checklist'. Pensions Editor of TEN Television Education Video Service.

Prof. Membership: Association of Pension Lawyers (Founding Committee Member), NAPF Investment Committee (Elected Member), Occupational Pensions Advisory Service (Council Member & Chairman of Legal Advice Committee), Association of Corporate Trustees Pension Committee (Deputy Chairman), Holborn Law Society (Vice-President 1983-84).

Career: Qualified in 1971. Partner in *Bird & Bird* 1972-84. Joined *Richards Butler* as a Partner in 1984.

West, Robert J.
Baker & McKenzie, London (0171) 919 1000. Partner in Pensions Department.

Specialisation: Principal area of practice involves advising on all legal aspects of pensions including trust aspects, litigation, surpluses, sales and purchases, drafting and advice to independent trustees. Other main area of work is employee benefits and share schemes. Acted in The Times Pension Fund litigation, the Drexel Pension Scheme litigation and in the sex discrimination case in the European Court, Neath v. Hugh Steeper. Contributor on pensions to Butterworths' Legal Service and author of articles for Pensions World and Pensions Management. Member of Legal Advice Committee of the Occupational Pensions Advisory Service. Addressed many conferences in UK, USA and Canada.

Prof. Membership: Law Society, Association of Pension Lawyers (Member of Legislative and Parliamentary Committee), International Employee Benefits Association (Council Member). Legal Committee of the Occupational Pensions Advisory Service.

Career: Qualified in 1978. Joined *Baker &*

McKenzie in 1982 and became a Partner in 1985.

Personal: Born 1st January 1952. Attended Maidenhead Grammar School 1963-71 and Clare College, Cambridge 1971-74. Leisure pursuits include sports and archaeology. Lives in Wargrave, Berks.

White, Andrew G.

Rowe & Maw, London (0171) 248 4282. Partner in Pensions Department.

Specialisation: All aspects of law relating to company and personal pension schemes. Also handles life insurance, advising insurance companies on life policies and other products. Author of 'Pensions Issues in Mergers and Acquisitions' (Longmans 1993); writes a regular monthly article in PLC Magazine. Frequent speaker at conferences.

Prof. Membership: Law Society, Association of Pension Lawyers.

Career: Qualified 1974. Joined *Rowe & Maw* 1977, becoming a Partner in 1979.

Personal: Born 1st January 1950. Attended Manchester Grammar School 1961-68, then University College, Oxford, 1968-72. Leisure pursuits include reading. Lives in London.

REGIONS

Ainscoe, Raymond

Eversheds, Leeds (0113) 243 0391. Partner in Company Department.

Specialisation: Area of practice is pensions, including trust documentation and advice, litigation, sales and acquisitions, scheme mergers, employment, unapproved schemes and independent trusteeship. Contributed to Pensions World and Pensions Management. Lectured to Leeds Metropolitan University 1994 and 1995. Addressed various APL, NAPF and PMI conferences.

Prof. Memberships: Association of Pensions Lawyers, PMI, Member of Committee of Management of Solicitors Staff Pension Fund.

Career: Qualified in 1980 with *Stephenson Harwood*. Left in 1983 to join *Nicholson Graham & Jones*. Joined *Eversheds Hepworth & Chadwick* in 1985. Partner 1987.

Personal: Born 28th April 1954. Attended Bolton School 1965-72, then St. Catherine's College, Oxford (BA) 1972-75, B.C.L. 1977. Trustee of Yorkshire Spinal Deformity Trust, St. James's Hospital, Leeds. Leisure pursuits include Italian racing motorcycles. Author of 3 books – 'Gilera Road Racers', 'Laverda', 'Benelli Road Racers'. Lives in Ilkley.

Archer, J.Richard

Hammond Suddards, Leeds (0113) 234 3500. Partner in Pensions Unit.

Specialisation: Has been involved in pensions work since the early 1980s. Head of Pensions Unit since 1990. Worked on Max-

well case. Former Head of Private Trust Tax and Probate Department: still handles such work. Writes for the Yorkshire Post. Has addressed several internal and external seminars both for *Hammond Suddards* and as an external speaker. Director of Hammond Suddards Pension Trust Limited and the Trustee Corporation Limited.

Prof. Membership: Association of Pension Lawyers, NAPF, Society of Pension Consultants.

Career: Qualified 1969. Articled at *Kirbys* 1965-69. Assistant at *Wells & Hind* 1969-71, and at *Linklaters & Paines* 1971-75. Joined *Hammond Suddards* in 1975, becoming a Partner in 1977.

Personal: Born 27th March 1943. Attended Rugby School (Scholar) 1956-61, then Cambridge University (Open Scholarship) 1961-64. Charity Organiser. Leisure interests include running, reading and walking. Lives in Ilkley.

Brown, Lindsay K.

Burges Salmon, Bristol (0117) 939 2000. Qualified 1987. Associate since 1991. Main area of practice is pensions, advising employers and trustees.

Clark, David

Clarks, Reading (01734) 585321. Partner in Corporate Department.

Specialisation: Handles all areas of pensions work but has particular experience of advising trustees in conflict situations, advising independent trustees appointed under s119 Pension Schemes Act 1993 and of acting as independent trustee. Also handles corporate work and advises on the pensions aspects of mergers and acquisitions. Acted in Clark v. Hicks (independent trusteeship). Author of articles for insolvency journals on this case. Has spoken at conferences and seminars and has conducted trustee training courses with a major accounting practice. Appeared in a training video for lawyers and accountants.

Prof. Membership: Association of Pension Lawyers.

Career: Qualified in 1983. Admitted as a Solicitor and Barrister in New Zealand in 1979. Worked at *Coward Chance* 1980-84, *Linklaters & Paines* 1984-86 and *British Alcan Aluminium plc* 1986-88. Joined *Clarks* in 1988, becoming a Partner in 1989.

Personal: Born 20th December 1953. Holds an LLB 1978 and MA (Business Law) 1984. Full time father; mediocre golfer. Lives in Maidenhead.

Clarke, Trevor C.

Garrett & Co, Birmingham (0121) 698 9000. Pensions Partner.

Specialisation: Handles all legal aspects of occupational and personal pension schemes including Revenue unapproved schemes. Particular expertise in privatisation work involving statutory schemes (e.g. LGSS) Scheme mergers and wind-ups. General trouble-shooting. Considerable experience in

dealing with Directors small self-administered schemes-acting as pensioneer trustee-dealing with 'hospital cases' and up front commission abuses on earmarked policies. General advice to employers, trustees and members. Acting as a statutory independent trustee in insolvency situations and as independent trustee for ongoing schemes. Dealing with 'exit values' from insurance products particularly deposit administration and with profit deferred annuity contracts-reviewing surrender penalties and market value adjustments. Drafting pension deeds and documents; Vetting or drafting Financial Services Act Investment Management Agreements.

Prof. Membership: Law Society. Full member of the Association of Pension Lawyers (a Founder member) and the 'Over 21 Club'. Associate of the Chartered Insurance Institute (B'ham Institute Prize Winner) and recently elected as a Chartered Insurance Practitioner. Recognised by the Pension Schemes Office as a Pensioneer Trustee.

Career: Life and Pensions Consultant before qualifying as a Solicitor. Served Articles with *Edge & Ellison* and became a Partner in 1988. Joined *Simpson Curtis* as a Partner 1990 but in May 1994 joined with eleven other Solicitors from *Simpson Curtis* and left to set up *Garrett & Co.* in Leeds. Has now transferred to Birmingham to assist with the setting up of Garret & Co's new office there. Has been a full time pensions lawyer for over twelve years.

Personal: Aged 46. Keen sportsman. Ex First Class Rugby (Moseley). Now windsurfs, and is a fanatical skier and mountain biker. Has daughter Alice aged 5.

Cockerill, Vivien

Wragge & Co, Birmingham (0121) 233 1000. Qualified 1987. Partner 1992. Specialist pensions lawyer, providing pensions advice for both employers and trustees.

Colacicchi, Clare

Hewitson Becke + Shaw, Northampton (01604) 233233. Qualified 1983. Partner 1990. Pensions Department. Handles pension and trust work. Member of APL and of the Council of the Society of Trust and Estate Practitioners. Lives near Towcester, Northamptonshire. Born 3.8.1958.

Cox, Margaret E.

Dibb Lupton Broomhead, Manchester (0161) 839 2266. Qualified 1991. Partner 1994. Pensions Department. Handles all aspects of pensions related legal advice.

Davies, Ian H.

Eversheds, Cardiff (01222) 471147. Qualified 1984. Partner 1988. Pensions Unit in Company/Commercial Department. Handles all aspects of establishing and running pension schemes.

Davis, Richard G.L.

Eversheds, Nottingham (0115) 950 6201.

Partner in Pensions Department.

Specialisation: Specialises in occupational pension schemes. Covers documentation, transactional work, scheme mergers, reconstructions and wind ups, insolvency advice and independent trusteeship. Has handled several major scheme mergers - through trustee company over 40 schemes. Current Chairman of Eversheds National Pensions Group. Director and Chairman of Eversheds Pension Trustees Ltd.

Prof. Membership: NAPF; APL; IPEBLA; Law Society; T.A.C.T.(through Trustee Company).

Career: Qualified in 1977. At *Overbury Steward & Eaton* 1978-88. Joined *Eversheds (Wells & Hind)* in 1988 and became a Partner in 1989.

Personal: Born 29th April 1952. Attended Leeds University 1970-73.

Fallon, Liz
Eversheds, Birmingham (0121) 233 2001.

Fleming, Andrew S.
Maclay Murray & Spens, Glasgow (0141) 248 5011. Partner in Corporate Department.
Specialisation: Main area of practice is pensions, including documentation, merger and winding up of schemes, independent legal advice to trustees, surplus and deficit questions in schemes and pensions aspects of sales and purchases of companies. Author of articles in 'Occupational Pensions' and 'Accountants Magazine'. Regular speaker at pensions conferences.

Prof. Membership: Law Society of Scotland, Association of Pension Lawyers (Treasurer).

Career: Tutor in Private Law, University of Glasgow 1976-84. Worked with *Linklaters & Paines* 1986-89. Joined *Maclay Murray & Spens* in 1989 and became a Partner in 1990.

Personal: Born 26th November 1954. Educated at Kelvinside Academy and Glasgow University 1972-75. Narrow gauge railway enthusiast. Lives in Glasgow.

Gibb-Davis, Karen
Greenwoods, Peterborough (01733) 555244. Qualified 1989. Solicitor in Employment and Employee Benefits Department. Main area of practice is pensions, principally for employers, trustees and life assurance companies.

Gordon, Ian
See under Tax (Corporate).

Harwood-Smart, Philip
Blake Lapthorn, Fareham (01489) 579990. Partner in Pensions Department.
Specialisation: Particular expertise in Independent Fund Trusteeship in both ongoing and insolvency cases. Currently 130m funds under custodianship. Also gives general advice to companies and trustees on all pension matters. Author of 'A Practical Guide to Oc-

cupational Pension Schemes', 1992. Individual charge-out rate is £150-175 per hour.

Prof. Membership: Association of Pension Lawyers, National Association of Pension Funds.

Career: Qualified in 1971. Worked at *Herbert Smith* 1968-75. (Associate Partner 1973). In private practice in Haywards Heath and Monmouth 1975-77. Solicitor with *Farrer & Co.* 1977-80, then with *Ashurst Morris Crisp* 1980-92 (Associate Partner 1983, Pensions Partner 1985). Joined *Blake Lapthorn* as a Partner in 1992.

Personal: Born 1944. Attended Eastbourne College and Lancaster University. Sidesman of Winchester Cathedral. Leisure interests include heraldry and genealogy. Lives near Winchester. Married with two children.

Hellyer, Marcus D.
Maclay Murray & Spens, Glasgow (0141) 248 5011. Qualified 1986. Assistant Solicitor. Company Law Department. Specialist in all aspects of pensions law.

Hingley, Gerald
Wragge & Co, Birmingham (0121) 233 1000. Qualified 1970. Partner 1974. Specialist pensions lawyer providing pensions advice for both employers and trustees. Born 2.7.1943.

Holehouse, Andrew N.
Shepherd & Wedderburn WS, Edinburgh (0131) 228 9900. Qualified 1981. Partner 1992. Head of Pensions Group. Deals with all legal aspects of pensions. Also employee share schemes. Born 8.12.1955.

Illston, Timothy M.
Burges Salmon, Bristol (0117) 939 2000. Qualified 1986. Partner 1990. Company and Commercial Department. Main areas of practice are pensions and employee benefits, together with experience in corporate taxation work. Born 6.3.1958.

Kennedy, Patrick
Davies Arnold Cooper, Manchester (0161) 839 8396.

Knight, Timothy
Dibb Lupton Broomhead, Leeds (0113) 243 9301. Partner in Pensions Department.
Specialisation: Principal area of practice is pensions law. Extensive experience in this area with a particular emphasis on acting for employers and trustees concerning occupational pension schemes. Also has company/commercial experience.

Prof. Membership: Association of Pension Lawyers (Member of Legislative and Parliamentary Committee).

Career: Computer analyst with Rolls Royce 1966-71. Qualified in 1974 while with *Bell's* in Farnham. Joined *Dibb Lupton Broomhead* in 1976 and became a Partner in 1977.

Personal: Born 14th January 1948. Attended

Ampleforth College 1961-65, then Worcester College Oxford 1966-69. Leisure pursuits include photography, music and musical instruments. Lives in Pateley Bridge.

Lee, Martin P.W.
Dibb Lupton Broomhead, Sheffield 0114 272 0202. Qualified 1966. Partner in the Pensions Group. A leading practitioner in pensions law in the South Yorkshire area since the early 1980s. 24.5.1939.

Meehan, Margaret
W & J Burness WS, Edinburgh (0131) 226 2561. Qualified 1990. Assistant in Pensions Unit. Main areas of practice are pensions law and employee benefit arrangements.

Morris, D.H.
Alsop Wilkinson, Liverpool (0151) 227 3060.

O'Driscoll, M.J.
Pinsent Curtis, Birmingham (0121) 200 1050. Partner in Tax and Pensions Department.
Specialisation: Main area of practice is pensions, with particular emphasis on pension scheme documents and associated matters.

Prof. Memberships: Law Society, Association of Pension Lawyers.

Career: Qualified in 1961, after joining *Pinsent & Co* as an articled clerk in 1958. Became Partner in 1967.

Personal: Born 28th September 1935. Attended St. Philips Grammar School, Birmingham 1946-53, then Oxford University 1955-58. Leisure pursuits include television.

Orton, Giles A.C.
Eversheds, Nottingham (0115) 950 6201. Partner in Commercial Litigation Department.
Specialisation: Main area of practice is pensions litigation, conducting disputes over pension schemes, particularly regarding surplus and winding up. Other area of practice is employment: industrial tribunals, wrongful dismissal and restrictive covenants. Acted in Falconer v. Aslef and NUR (1985), Imperial Tobacco (1990) and Mirror Group Pension Scheme. Author of numerous articles on pensions law. Has addressed a wide range of seminars and conferences, also making TV and radio appearances.
Professional Membership: Association of Pension Lawyers.

Career: Qualified in 1983. Worked at *Broomheads* from 1981, becoming an Associate in 1986. Joined *Eversheds Wells & Hind* in 1987, Associate 1988 and Partner in 1989.

Personal: Born 18th August 1959. Attended King Edward VII School, Sheffield 1970-77; The Queen's College, Oxford (Hastings Exhibition) 1977-80 and Chester College of Law 1980-81. Derby City Councillor 1988-92.

Peel, Neville

Booth & Co., Leeds (0113) 283 2000. Partner in Pensions Department.

Specialisation: Advises corporate clients and trustees regarding all aspects of ongoing pension schemes. Complete service to insolvency practitioners including independent statutory trusteeships. Co-author of 'Pensions and Insurance on Family Breakdown' and 'Pension Schemes Act 1993'.

Prof. Membership: Association of Pension Lawyers, National Association of Pension Schemes.

Career: Qualified in 1967. Previous employment: CEGB, Midlands HQ 1967; Chairman's Staff. CIBA UK 1967-69; Group Secretary, James Neill Holdings plc 1969-90; Executive Director, James Neill Holdings plc 1983-90. Joined *Booth & Co.* as a Partner in 1990.

Personal: Born 27th May 1940. Educated at Wolverhampton Grammar School, and Manchester University (1959-63). Freeman of the Cutlers Company. Member of the Council of the University of Sheffield; and its finance, investment and commercial operations committees. Chairman of the trustees of the University's pension scheme for non-academic staff. Founder trustee of the Sheffield Marathon. Lives in Sheffield.

Ramshaw, Simon

Edge & Ellison, Birmingham (0121) 200 2001. Partner in Pensions Department.

Specialisation: Main area of practice is pensions, covering documentation, transactional work, scheme mergers, reconstructions and wind-ups, insolvency advice and independent trusteeship. Has handled several major scheme mergers; is independent trustee to schemes run by a national clothing company, two quoted public companies and a professional practice which is a world leader in its field. Author of various articles for publications issued by pension consultancies, and of a variety of easy-to-read Technical Guides issued by the firm. Regular lecturer for Professional Associations and pension consultancies. Organiser of and speaker at various trustee training courses.

Prof. Memberships: NAPF, APL, IPEBLA, Law Society.

Career: Qualified 1981, working at *Robert*

Muckle from 1979 to 1983. Then joined *Edge & Ellison*, becoming a Partner in 1986.

Personal: Born 28th January 1958. Attended Newcastle upon Tyne University, 1975-78. Member of the *Edge & Ellison* Main Board, Chief Executive of Trustee Company. Active member of local Church. Keen photographer, blues aficionado and guitar player. Lives in Birmingham.

Rawnsley, Rachel

Booth & Co., Leeds (0113) 283 2000. Solicitor in Pensions Department.

Specialisation: Advises corporate clients and trustees on all aspects of ongoing pension schemes. Provides a complete service to insolvency practitiioners including advising on independent statutory trusteeships. Co-author of 'The Pension Schemes Act 1993' (Sweet & Maxwell).

Prof. Membership: Association of Pensions Lawyers, National Association of Pension Schemes.

Career: Qualified with *Allen & Overy* in 1989. Joined *Booth & Co* in January 1993.

Personal: Born in February 1965. Educated at Cambridge University 1983-86 (MA in Law). Lives in Ilkley.

Shackleton, Francis

Addleshaw Sons & Latham, Manchester (0161) 832 5994. Partner in Pensions and Private Client Department.

Specialisation: Main area of practice is pensions law, handling takeovers and mergers, scheme amalgamations, formation of schemes, documentation, compliance and trusteeship matters. Also deals with a range of private client matters including tax planning, trusts, probate and charities. Has presented seminars. Trustee of several funds.

Prof. Membership: Association of Pension Lawyers, National Association of Pension Funds.

Career: Joined *Addleshaw Sons & Latham* in 1963. Qualified in 1965 and became a Partner in 1969.

Personal: Born 2nd February 1940. Attended Stowe School 1953-58, then St. Johns College, Cambridge 1959-62. Governor of Manchester High School for Girls. Lives in Rochdale.

Steinbech, Joachim

Osborne Clarke, Bristol (0117) 923 0220.

Sutherland, Alister M.

W & J Burness WS, Edinburgh 0141 248 4933. Qualified 1959. Partner in the private client department specialising in tax and trusts work. Frequently writes and lectures on this area of law. Born 11.7.1934.

Talman, Iain J.S.

Bishop and Robertson Chalmers, Glasgow (0141) 248 4672. Partner in Business Law Division (Pensions Unit).

Specialisation: Accredited by The Law Society of Scotland as a specialist in pensions law. All aspects of pensions law and practice including pensioneer trusteeships, independent trusteeships through directorship of Mitre Pensions Ltd. Acted in Mirror Group Pensions and Lilley Group & Clydesdale Group independent trusteeships cases. Author and speaker.

Prof. Membership: Law Society of Scotland, Association of Pension Lawyers, Association of Pensioneer Trustees, Pensions Management Institute, Actuarial Society of Glasgow (Life and Pensions Group).

Career: Qualified in 1976. Partner in 1978. Immediate Past Chairman, Scottish Group of Association of Pension Lawyers, PMI Working Group on Pensions and Divorce, Convener of Law Society Pensions Accreditation Panel, Convener of Law Society Working Party on Pensions Bill.

Personal: Born 18th July 1952. Leisure interests include movies, people and travel.

Trotter, Peter A.A.

Maclay Murray & Spens, Glasgow (0141) 248 5011. Associate, 1994. Company Department. Principal area is pensions and employee benefits. Born 20.5.1960.

Whiting, Ralph S.

Osborne Clarke, Bristol (0117) 923 0220. Qualified 1965. Partner 1989. Commercial Department. Main areas of practice are pensions and commercial law: has been advising in these fields since 1968. Born 1.6.1938.

PERSONAL INJURY

LONDON

MAINLY PLAINTIFF
Russell Jones & Walker is renowned for its plaintiff personal injury practice. The team has been strengthened with the addition of Andrew Dismore, the leading personal injury specialist, who has moved from *Robin Thompson & Partners* this year. Andrew Dismore has a strong record for his work for trade unions and their members. Also highly regarded at the firm are Ian Walker and Fraser Whitehead. Ian Walker was the lead solicitor in the Kings Cross Fire cases and specialises in personal injury disaster litigation.

Pattinson and Brewer have a large specialist plaintiff personal injury team with considerable experience, headed by Frances McCarthy. The team undertakes both trade union and private cases and has been involved in many high profile cases including The Marchioness and Bowbell case and industrial disease cases. The firm is also heading cases on Repetitive Strain Injury (RSI) against B.T. and Harvest Poultry.

HIGHLY REGARDED – LONDON – MAINLY PLAINTIFF	
ROWLEY ASHWORTH	
EVANS BUTLER WADE	FIELD FISHER WATERHOUSE
G.L. HOCKFIELD & CO	HODGE JONES & ALLEN
LAWFORD & CO	PANNONE PRITCHARD ENGLEFIELD
O.H. PARSONS & PARTNERS	STEPHENS INNOCENT
STEWARTS	
ANTHONY GOLD, LERMAN & MUIRHEAD	BINDMAN & PARTNERS
EVILL & COLEMAN	GLAZER DELMAR
POWELL SPENCER & PARTNERS	PRINCE EVANS
REID MINTY	SIMMONDS CHURCH SMILES
STEGGLES PALMER	

Leigh Day & Co continue to have an excellent reputation for personal injury work on behalf of individual plaintiffs, including environmental personal injury claims such as the claims over the death and illness of workers at a South African mercury processing plant and a Namibian Uranium mine which Richard Meeran at the firm is spear-heading. The companies concerned are sufficiently connected with the UK for the claims to be mounted here. Geraldine McCool at the firm specialises in aviation claims for plaintiffs against the Ministry of Defence.

Brian Thompson & Partners and *Robin Thompson & Partners* act on behalf of trade unions, and have strong reputations for plaintiff personal injury work.

Other highly recommended plaintiff personal injury specialists include Roger Goodier at *Rowley Ashworth*.

LEADING INDIVIDUALS – LONDON – MAINLY PLAINTIFF
Andrew Dismore *Russell Jones & Walker*
Frances McCarthy *Pattinson and Brewer*
Ian J. Walker *Russell Jones & Walker*
Roger Goodier *Rowley Ashworth*
Geraldine M. McCool *Leigh Day & Co*
Fraser Whitehead *Russell Jones & Walker*
Patrick Allen *Hodge Jones & Allen*
Martyn Day *Leigh Day & Co*
Richard Meeran *Leigh Day & Co*
Rodney Nelson-Jones *Field Fisher Waterhouse*
Caroline Pinfold *Field Fisher Waterhouse*
Nicola Solomon *Stephens Innocent*
Douglas Stewart *Stewarts*
Peter Woods *Stephens Innocent*

MAINLY DEFENDANT
On the defendant side, *Davies Arnold Cooper* emerge as the pre-eminent firm with *McKenna & Co* a close second. The strong department at *Davies Arnold Cooper* handle all types of claims for defendants and their insurers. The

LEADING FIRMS – LONDON – MAINLY DEFENDANT
DAVIES ARNOLD COOPER
McKENNA & CO

team also undertakes claims in foreign jurisdictions and claims arising abroad but brought before the English courts.

HIGHLY REGARDED – LONDON – MAINLY DEFENDANT	
BEACHCROFT STANLEYS	BERRYMANS
HEMPSONS	KENNEDYS
LAWRENCE GRAHAM	LE BRASSEUR J TICKLE
THEODORE GODDARD	L. WATMORE & CO
L. BINGHAM & CO	EDWARD LEWIS
ELLIOTT & CO	GREGORY, ROWCLIFFE & MILNERS
HEXTALL, ERSKINE	JARVIS & BANNISTER
VIZARDS	WANSBROUGHS WILLEY HARGRAVE
WEDLAKE SAINT	

David Rogers at the firm is particularly well known for his expertise on disease and industrial cancer. The group has substantial involvement in multi party claims as does *McKenna & Co* where Ian Dodds-Smith heads the healthcare team. The team is also well known for product liability work.

PLAINTIFF & DEFENDANT

Of firms which are highly regarded for their personal injury work on behalf of plaintiffs and defendants, Martin Howe at *Howe & Co* has been recommended.

SOUTH EAST

MAINLY PLAINTIFF

Osborne Morris & Morgan, a niche firm specialising in personal injury and medical negligence matters, is well regarded for its work acting on behalf of plaintiffs.

MAINLY DEFENDANT

On the defendant side, *A.E. Wyeth & Co, Cole and Cole* and *Kennedys* are highly recommended. *Kennedys'* specialist personal injury unit headed by David Scrutton, handles all types of litigation with a special emphasis on industrial diseases, including asbestos-related, asthma, VWF, RSI and deafness.

At *A.E. Wyeth & Co*, Maurice Nichols and Brian Williams have been recommended, the latter having particular

expertise in asbestosis, noise induced hearing loss and work-related upper limb disorder claims. *Cole and Cole* act for major insurance companies and Ian Tenquist at the firm has a recognised capability in the field.

PLAINTIFF & DEFENDANT

Penningtons, a firm with a number of offices in the South East, acts for both plaintiffs and defendants. Christopher Mather, a partner at the firm, chaired the Steering Committee of claims arising out of the Clapham Rail disaster and was also on the committee dealing with the Severn Tunnel rail accident. *Amery-Parkes* has a large department, which handles motor-related claims. Clients include the Automobile

Association. Alan Hughes at the firm is co-author of 'The Guidelines for the Assessment of General Damages in Personal Injury'. *Shoosmiths & Harrison* also have a large personal injury department handling an extensive volume of road traffic and industrial accident claims. *Warner Goodman & Streat* who act for plaintiffs and defendants, cover all aspects with an emphasis on multi disaster claims. Eddie Voller has been recommended for his expertise.

In all the tables the names in each group are listed alphabetically.

SOUTH WEST

MAINLY PLAINTIFF

The regional offices of specialist trade union firms *Russell, Jones & Walker* and *Robin Thompson & Partners* continue to maintain their high profile in plaintiff personal injury work and are undeniably at the forefront in this field.

HIGHLY REGARDED – SOUTH WEST – MAINLY PLAINTIFF	
ROBIN THOMPSON & PARTNERS *Bristol*	RUSSELL JONES & WALKER *Bristol*
BATTENS *Yeovil*	BISHOP LONGBOTHAM & BAGNALL *Trowbridge*
BOBBETTS MACKAN *Bristol*	FAULKNERS *Frome*
OVER TAYLOR BIGGS *Exeter*	PARDOES *Bridgwater*
PATTINSON AND BREWER *Bristol*	ROWLEY ASHWORTH *Exeter*
SLEE BLACKWELL *Barnstaple*	TOZERS *Exeter*
TRUMP AND PARTNERS *Bristol*	

The latter firm covers the whole spread of industries, public services, finance and NHS, specialising in serious injuries, asbestos related claims, and increasingly, RSI. The Bristol office of *Russell Jones & Walker* has developed a particular specialisation in accidents in heavy industry, especially the steel industry, and industrial disease cases.

LEADING INDIVIDUALS – SOUTH WEST – MAINLY PLAINTIFF
Jane Dexter *Russell Jones & Walker*
Christine Dodgson *Rowley Ashworth*
A. Herbert *Robin Thompson & Partners*
D.R. Louw *Russell Jones & Walker*

MAINLY DEFENDANT

On the defence side, *Cartwrights* has a long-established reputation in handling respiratory diseases, RSI and deafness. The team has been involved in numerous RSI cases including the High Court case of 'Moran v South Wales Argus'. *Macfarlane Guy* acts for a number of major UK

HIGHLY REGARDED – SOUTH WEST – MAINLY DEFENDANT	
BEVAN ASHFORD *Bristol*	CARTWRIGHTS *Bristol*
FRANK & CAFFIN *Truro*	MACFARLANE GUY *Bath*
SANSBURY HILL *Bristol*	WANSBROUGHS WILLEY HARGRAVE *Bristol*
WOOD AWDRY WANSBROUGHS *Devizes*	
FORD SIMEY DAW ROBERTS *Exeter*	

insurance companies in cases involving road traffic accidents, employers and public liability. The firm undertakes a wide range of litigation, including cases involving catastrophic brain and spine injuries, repetitive strain injury, noise induced hearing loss, structured settlements and post traumatic stress disorder. *Wansbroughs Willey Hargrave* handles all types of employers' and public liability and road traffic litigation. The firm acted in the 50 car multi-fatality incident on the M4, involving eight multi-party

LEADING INDIVIDUALS – SOUTH WEST – MAINLY DEFENDANT
Paul Roger Davies *Sansbury Hill*
Kenneth Gibson *Wansbroughs Willey Hargrave*
Michael Guy *Macfarlane Guy*
Robert John Hams *Wood Awdry Wansbroughs*
David Francis Vernalls *Cartwrights*

consolidated actions valued at several millions of pounds. *Frank & Caffin*, also recommended for its defendant work, act for a number of insurers including General Accident and Zurich Municipal.

PLAINTIFF & DEFENDANT

Townsends handles a large volume of personal injury cases for both plaintiffs and defendants. The firm continues to have a national reputation in asbestosis and serious head injury cases for plaintiffs. The team has been involved in a number of publicised cases including winning compensation of £165,000 for a British Rail widow following the asbestos-linked death of her husband.

HIGHLY REGARDED – SOUTH WEST – BOTH	
BOND PEARCE *Plymouth*	BOYCE HATTON *Torquay*
LYONS DAVIDSON *Bristol*	NASH SOLICITORS *Plymouth*
STEPHENS & SCOWN *Exeter*	TOWNSENDS *Swindon*
AMERY–PARKES *Bristol*	BENNETT METCALFE *Bristol*
CROSSE & CROSSE *Exeter*	DAVIES AND PARTNERS *Gloucester*
KIRBY SIMCOX *Bristol*	STONES *Exeter*
TAYNTONS *Gloucester*	TROBRIDGES *Plymouth*
VEALE WASBROUGH *Bristol*	VEITCH PENNY *Exeter*
WOLFERSTANS *Plymouth*	WOOLLCOMBE BEER WATTS *Newton Abbot*

Further west, *Bond Pearce* is highly regarded for its plaintiff and defendant personal injury practice. The team has a particularly strong reputation in the field of industrial disease and occupational health.

Stephens & Scown emerge in Cornwall as a prominent personal injury practice and has been involved in the Myodil and Benzodiazepine actions.

LEADING INDIVIDUALS – SOUTH WEST – BOTH
Byron Carron *Townsends*
Brigitte H. Chandler *Townsends*
Jonathan Cooper *Bond Pearce*
Bernard V. Rowe *Lyons Davidson*

Lyons Davidson's injury claims service acts for plaintiffs and defendants in personal injury claims ranging from road traffic claims to sensory loss, limbs and spinal injuries. The firm is a member of the Motor Accident Solicitors' Society (MASS). Bernard Rowe, who is a member of the Law Society's Personal Injury Panel, has been recommended at the firm.

WALES

MAINLY PLAINTIFF

On the plaintiff side, *Robin Thompson & Partners* are highly regarded and particularly well known for industrial disease litigation. *Leo Abse & Cohen* also has a strong plaintiff

HIGHLY REGARDED – WALES – MAINLY PLAINTIFF	
HUTTONS *Cardiff*	LEO ABSE & COHEN *Cardiff*
ROBIN THOMPSON & PARTNERS *Cardiff*	

personal injury team and major clients include TGWU, GMB and BIFU. The team has been involved in numerous recent important cases including the Severn Tunnel train crash and continue to handle many asbestosis and industrial deafness claims. *Huttons* has also been recommended and is a member of APIL and the Spinal Injuries Association.

LEADING INDIVIDUALS – WALES – MAINLY PLAINTIFF	
Roger Bent *Robin Thompson & Partners*	
J. Cenric Clement-Evans *Leo Abse & Cohen*	
Ian Hopkins *Leo Abse & Cohen*	
Timothy L. Jones *Leo Abse & Cohen*	
Robin Williams *Leo Abse & Cohen*	

MAINLY DEFENDANT

Among the defendant insurer practices in personal injury work, *Hugh James Jones & Jenkins* and *Morgan Bruce* remain the two major firms in South Wales. Both have considerable experience in road traffic and factory accidents. In addition, *Morgan Bruce* is developing a particular expertise in industrial disease claims such as deafness, RSI, asbestosis and other respiratory diseases.

HIGHLY REGARDED – WALES – MAINLY DEFENDANT	
DOLMANS *Cardiff*	EVERSHEDS *Cardiff*
HOWARD PALSER GROSSMAN HERMER & PARTNERS *Cardiff*	HUGH JAMES JONES & JENKINS *Cardiff*
MORGAN BRUCE *Cardiff*	
BEVAN ASHFORD *Cardiff*	

Dolmans, a smaller Cardiff practice, is also well regarded and is perceived to be more active in the market place than in previous years. This year saw the merger of two Cardiff firms, *Grossman Hermer Seligman* and *Howard Palser & Partners.* The firm, now known as *Howard Palser Grossman Hermer & Partners,* has a large defendant personal injury department acting for major clients including Eagle Star,

LEADING INDIVIDUALS – WALES – MAINLY DEFENDANT	
Gareth J. Williams *Hugh James Jones & Jenkins*	
Simon J. Cradick *Morgan Bruce*	
C. Roger Cradick *Morgan Bruce*	
Ian B. Hermer *Howard Palser Grossman Hermer & Partners*	
Russel J.A. Jenkins *Hugh James Jones & Jenkins*	
Michael L.N. Jones *Hugh James Jones & Jenkins*	
Hugh M. Price *Morgan Bruce*	

Sun Alliance International, General Accident and Commercial Union. *Eversheds,* act for numerous insurance companies, and work handled includes road fatalities and industrial accidents.

PLAINTIFF & DEFENDANT

HIGHLY REGARDED – WALES – BOTH	
DOUGLAS JONES & MERCER *Swansea*	GRAHAM EVANS & PARTNERS *Swansea*
LOOSEMORES *Cardiff*	
ROBERTSONS *Cardiff*	WALKER SMITH & WAY *Wrexham*

Among those who act on behalf of plaintiffs and defendants, *Loosemores* and *Douglas Jones & Mercer* have been particularly recommended. The department at *Loosemores* handles all types of personal injury and motor claims and acts for legal expense insurers and RAC appointed solicitors.

LEADING INDIVIDUALS – WALES – BOTH	
Brian Lewis *Graham Evans & Partners*	
Jeremy B. Wolfe *Douglas Jones & Mercer*	

MIDLANDS

MAINLY PLAINTIFF

The leading plaintiff personal injury firms are considered to be *Robin Thompson & Partners, Rowley Ashworth* and *Russell Jones & Walker. Robin Thompson & Partners* cover all aspects and have a specialist catastrophic injury unit.

LEADING FIRMS – MIDLANDS – MAINLY PLAINTIFF	
ROBIN THOMPSON & PARTNERS *Birmingham*	ROWLEY ASHWORTH *Birmingham*
RUSSELL JONES & WALKER *Birmingham*	

Rowley Ashworth handle personal injury compensation claims on behalf of trade unions, and their clients include AEEU, GMB, CWU and USDAW. *Russell Jones & Walker* also cover a wide range of plaintiff personal injury work including compensation for industrial injury, disasters, road

HIGHLY REGARDED – MIDLANDS – MAINLY PLAINTIFF	
FREETH CARTWRIGHT HUNT DICKINS *Nottingham*	HUNTSMANS *Nottingham*
IRWIN MITCHELL *Birmingham*	
ALFRED SEVIER & SONS *Derby*	ANTHONY COLLINS *Birmingham*
CHALLINOR ROBERTS COOKSEY *Cradley Heath*	DAVIS BLANK FURNISS *Glossop*
ELLIOT MATHER SMITH *Chesterfield*	HIGGS & SONS *Brierley Hill*
NELSONS *Nottingham*	

traffic accidents and disease and disablement. Stuart Henderson, a leading plaintiff lawyer, has moved from *Robin Thompson & Partners* to head up a new plaintiff department at *Irwin Mitchell,* set up in January 1995. Stuart Henderson handled the Leung case which attracted a record £3.4 million damages.

LEADING INDIVIDUALS – MIDLANDS	
	– MAINLY PLAINTIFF
Sarah Goodman *Robin Thompson & Partners*	
Stuart Henderson *Irwin Mitchell,,*	
John McKeown *Rowley Ashworth*	
Paul Balen *Freeth Cartwright Hunt Dickins*	
P. King *Robin Thompson & Partners*	
David Prain *Rowley Ashworth*	
Jeffry Zindani *Russell Jones & Walker*	

MAINLY DEFENDANT

On the defence side, the most highly recommended firms are *William Hatton* and *Buller Jeffries*. *William Hatton* is a niche defendant personal injury practice and has a strong reputation for conducting disease litigation, including RSI, deafness and asbestosis. Timothy Perry at the firm is particularly highly regarded, as is Derek Adamson at *Buller Jeffries*.

LEADING FIRMS – MIDLANDS – MAINLY DEFENDANT	
BULLER JEFFRIES	**WILLIAM HATTON** *Dudley*
Birmingham	

Of the other firms highly regarded, *Cartwright & Lewis,* with its large personal injury department, has particular emphasis on industrial diseases, RTA and public liability. *Everatt & Co,* a specialist personal injury practice, acts for major insurance companies in both employers' liability and road traffic claims. *Chapman Everatt & Co* is also a specialist personal injury practice solely handling insurance funded defendant work.

HIGHLY REGARDED – MIDLANDS	
	– MAINLY DEFENDANT
BROWNE JACOBSON *Nottingham*	**CARTWRIGHT & LEWIS** *Birmingham*
CHAPMAN EVERATT & CO	**EKING MANNING** *Nottingham*
Wolverhampton	
EVERATT & CO *Evesham*	
KEELY SMITH & JOBSON *Lichfield*	**SHAKESPEARES** *Birmingham*
WANSBROUGHS WILLEY HARGRAVE	**WILLCOX LANE CLUTTERBUCK**
Birmingham	*Birmingham*

Other firms recommended for their expertise are *Browne Jacobson* and *Eking Manning* .

LEADING INDIVIDUALS – MIDLANDS	
	– MAINLY DEFENDANT
Derek P. Adamson *Buller Jeffries*	
Timothy Perry *William Hatton*	
Catherine Arkell *Everatt & Co*	
Richard Chapman *Chapman Everatt & Co*	
Allan Everatt *Chapman Everatt & Co*	
Geoffrey J. Lewis *Buller Jeffries*	
Neville Radcliffe *Browne Jacobson*	
Brian Roberts *Cartwright & Lewis*	

PLAINTIFF & DEFENDANT

HIGHLY REGARDED – MIDLANDS – BOTH	
BERRYMAN & CO *Nottingham*	**GEORGE GREEN & CO** *Warley*
NEWSOME VAUGHAN *Coventry*	
ACTONS *Nottingham*	**AMERY–PARKES** *Birmingham*
FLINT, BISHOP & BARNETT *Derby*	**LANGLEYS** *Lincoln*
ROTHERAS *Nottingham*	**ROWLEY DICKINSON** *Birmingham*
SHOOSMITHS & HARRISON *Northampton*	

Of the firms acting on behalf of claimants and insurers, *Berryman & Co* and *Newsome Vaughan* have been highly recommended. Nigel Dace at *George Green & Co* is known for handling road traffic accident (RTA) and industrial disease litigation.

LEADING INDIVIDUALS – MIDLANDS – BOTH
Nigel H. Dace *George Green & Co*

EAST ANGLIA

MAINLY PLAINTIFF

Much of the region's plaintiff work is done by London based trade union firms such as *Robin Thompson & Partners*, although *Ward Gethin* has a large and respected plaintiff practice. The firm acts on behalf of trade unions and deals mainly with factory and road traffic accidents. The department also deals with an increasing amount of RSI work.

HIGHLY REGARDED – EAST ANGLIA	
	– MAINLY PLAINTIFF
WARD GETHIN *King's Lynn*	
DAWBARNS *Wisbech*	**LEATHES PRIOR** *Norwich*
METCALFE COPEMAN & PETTEFAR *Wisbech*	

MAINLY DEFENDANT

On the defence side, *Mills & Reeve* maintain a strong reputation for this area of work. *Eversheds* has increased the volume of defendant personal injury work over the year and has a strong team fully committed to personal injury practice. *Prettys* also has a strong defendant personal injury practice, specialising in industrial disease and RSI.

HIGHLY REGARDED – EAST ANGLIA	
	– MAINLY DEFENDANT
EVERSHEDS *Norwich*	**MILLS & REEVE** *Norwich*
PRETTYS *Ipswich*	
MERRICKS *Ipswich*	

PLAINTIFF & DEFENDANT

Firms undertaking work for plaintiffs and defendants in the region are listed separately.

HIGHLY REGARDED – EAST ANGLIA – BOTH	
BIRKETTS *Ipswich*	**BUCKLE MELLOWS** *Peterborough*
CUNNINGHAM, JOHN *Thetford*	**GREENWOODS** *Peterborough*
TAYLOR VINTERS *Cambridge*	

In all the tables the names in each group are listed alphabetically.

NORTH WEST

MAINLY PLAINTIFF

Among those firms acting for plaintiffs, *John Pickering & Partners* is particularly well known. This niche practice handles all types of personal injury claims with particular emphasis in industrial diseases, most notably asbestosis. John Pickering at the firm has been highly recommended in this field. *Brian Thompson & Partners* has an established reputation in handling claims of accidents in the workplace, RTA and occupational diseases ranging from asbestosis to cancer. *Whittles* also specialises in industrial accidents and disease litigation.

HIGHLY REGARDED – NORTH WEST – MAINLY PLAINTIFF	
ALEXANDER HARRIS *Sale*	BRIAN THOMPSON & PARTNERS *Liverpool*
BULLOCK WORTHINGTON & JACKSON *Manchester*	COLEMANS *Manchester*
GOLDSMITH WILLIAMS *Liverpool*	JOHN PICKERING & PARTNERS *Oldham*
LINDER MYERS *Manchester*	MACE & JONES *Liverpool*
PANNONE & PARTNERS *Manchester*	WHITTLES *Manchester*
DAVIS BLANK FURNISS *Manchester*	DONN & CO *Manchester*
JACKSON & CANTER *Liverpool*	RAMSBOTTOM & CO *Blackburn*
ROWLANDS *Manchester*	RUSSELL JONES & WALKER *Manchester*
WALKER SMITH & WAY *Chester*	

Pannone & Partners has a strong team which acts for numerous trade unions and motor organisations. The department covers all personal injury claims ranging from minor RTAs to international disaster litigation. Frank Patterson, who heads the group, is frequently involved in the legal aftermath of high profile disasters such as the Zeebrugge and Manchester Airport tragedies. *Alexander Harris,* a niche practice, handles catastrophic personal injury and multi-party litigation. The firm is a member of the Personal Injury Accident helpline and also recently broke new ground in structured settlements.

LEADING INDIVIDUALS – NORTH WEST – MAINLY PLAINTIFF	
Frank P. Patterson *Pannone & Partners*	
John Pickering *John Pickering & Partners*	

Other prominent plaintiff firms include *Linder Myers, Goldsmith Williams, Colemans* and *Mace & Jones.* The latter firm has been involved in the Hillsborough Steering Committee set up after the tragedy at the football stadium. *Bullock Worthington & Jackson* acts for trade union members and has particular expertise in back injury caused by lifting. The firm obtained record damages in such a case for a nurse injured whilst lifting a patient.

MAINLY DEFENDANT

On the defendant side, *Lace Mawer* has an established reputation with John Henthorn held in high regard for his work in this area. The team handles all aspects including road traffic accidents, public liability, liability of utilities, and employers' liability. Diseases covered include deafness, work-related upper limb disorders and claims arising from environmental factors. Anthony Wilson at *Hill Dickinson Davis Campbell* has an excellent reputation in the field as

HIGHLY REGARDED – NORTH WEST – MAINLY DEFENDANT	
DAVIES ARNOLD COOPER *Manchester*	HILL DICKINSON DAVIS CAMPBELL *Liverpool*
JAMES CHAPMAN & CO *Manchester*	LACE MAWER *Manchester*
PERCY HUGHES & ROBERTS *Birkenhead*	WEIGHTMAN RUTHERFORDS *Liverpool*
ELLIOTT & CO *Manchester*	HALLIWELL LANDAU *Manchester*
PEASEGOOD WALKER *Manchester*	

does Kevin Finnigan at *James Chapman & Co* who is especially well known for his expertise in brain damage cases. *Weightman Rutherfords* acts for insurance companies and handles a large volume of occupational disease work. *Davies Arnold Cooper* has a dedicated team handling employers' liability claims, motor claims and occupational diseases. *Percy Hughes & Roberts* also have a strong defendant personal injury practice and acts for a number of major insurers.

LEADING INDIVIDUALS – NORTH WEST – MAINLY DEFENDANT	
Kevin P. Finnigan *James Chapman & Co*	
John L. Henthorn *Lace Mawer*	
Anthony E. Wilson *Hill Dickinson Davis Campbell*	

PLAINTIFF & DEFENDANT

Of the firms acting equally on behalf of claimants and insurers *Paul Rooney & Co* is a leading firm in industrial diseases and serious injuries. Work undertaken by the firm this year has included RSI, industrial asthma and mucous membrane cases. *Abson Hall* and *Blackhurst Parker & Yates* also have established reputations in this area of work. Also recommended is *Perkins & Co.*

HIGHLY REGARDED – NORTH WEST – BOTH	
ABSON HALL *Stockport*	BLACKHURST PARKER & YATES *Preston*
PAUL ROONEY & CO *Liverpool*	PERKINS & CO *Manchester*
BETESH FOX & CO *Manchester*	BURNETTS *Carlisle*
ROWLEY DICKINSON *Manchester*	SILVERBECK RYMER *Liverpool*

NORTH EAST

MAINLY PLAINTIFF

Brian Thompson & Partners, which has strong trade union connections, has substantial experience in workplace injuries, RTA cases and occupational diseases. *Marrons* is also well regarded for trade union sponsored personal injury claims. Stephen Porteus and Patrick Murphy at the firm have been highly recommended.

LEADING FIRMS – NORTH EAST	
	– MAINLY PLAINTIFF
ALLAN HENDERSON BEECHAM & PEACOCK Newcastle	BRIAN THOMPSON & PARTNERS Leeds
BRIAN THOMPSON & PARTNERS Newcastle	MARRONS Newcastle

Patrick Murphy has particular expertise in asbestosis and similar diseases and Stephen Porteus handles all aspects of plaintiff personal injury work, including a large volume of RSI cases. *Allan Henderson Beecham & Peacock* has a growing reputation in the area of plaintiff personal injury. *Watson Burton* handles all types of accidents, particularly mining cases.

HIGHLY REGARDED – NORTH EAST	
	– MAINLY PLAINTIFF
IRWIN MITCHELL Sheffield	WATSON BURTON Newcastle
ARCHERS Stockton-on-Tees	T.I. CLOUGH & CO Bradford
EATON SMITH & DOWNEY Huddersfield	GRAHAM & ROSEN Hull
HARROWELL SHAFTOE York	HENRY HYAMS & CO Leeds
MINCOFF SCIENCE & GOLD Newcastle	PATTINSON AND BREWER York
ROBIN THOMPSON & PARTNERS Hull	ROWLEY ASHWORTH Leeds
RUSSELL JONES & WALKER Leeds	

Irwin Mitchell has an excellent reputation for its plaintiff work and was involved in Bird v Hussain, a case highlighted as one of the most important personal injury cases. John Pickering heads the team and has been highly recommended for his work. He achieved damages of £925,000 for a man paralysed by an anaesthetic during a routine operation and is also a member of the Steering Committee on British Coal VWF cases. Michael Napier at the firm is also highly recommended and is president of the Association of Personal Injury Lawyers.

LEADING INDIVIDUALS – NORTH EAST	
	– MAINLY PLAINTIFF
Patrick Murphy Marrons	
Michael Napier Irwin Mitchell	
Stephen Porteus Marrons	
Roger Maddocks Brian Thompson & Partners	
Norman Peacock Allan Henderson Beecham & Peacock	
John Pickering Irwin Mitchell	

MAINLY DEFENDANT

On the defendant side, *Sinton & Co* emerge as the pre-eminent firm with Jim Dias at the firm held in particularly high regard by his peers. David Dobbin and David Raw at the firm also have outstanding reputations. The firm undertakes employers' liability claims, (including industrial diseases),

LEADING FIRMS – NORTH EAST	
	– MAINLY DEFENDANT
SINTON & CO Newcastle	

public liability and road traffic accident claims. Clients include Commercial Union, Norwich Union and Eagle Star. *Crutes* covers the whole range of work mainly on behalf of insurance companies, health authorities and NHS trusts. David Drewe at the firm is particularly well known for his expertise. *Dibb Lupton Broomhead* has gained William Evans, a personal injury specialist, from *Irwin Mitchell*. William Evans is based at the Leeds branch whilst Peter Anson, also renowned for his expertise, is based at the Sheffield office. *Hammond Suddards* has considerable experience in handling multi-defendant claims, disease claims, deafness litigation, and an increasing number of RSI claims.

HIGHLY REGARDED – NORTH EAST	
	– MAINLY DEFENDANT
CRUTES Newcastle	DEAS MALLEN SOUTER Newcastle
DIBB LUPTON BROOMHEAD Leeds, Sheffield	HAMMOND SUDDARDS Leeds
JACKSONS Middlesbrough	NABARRO NATHANSON Doncaster
WANSBROUGHS WILLEY HARGRAVE Leeds	
PHILIP HAMER & CO Hull	ROLLIT FARRELL & BLADON Hull
SMITH & GRAHAM Hartlepool	WHITTLES Leeds

The entire range of insurers' liability work is within the scope of this department, and clients include ICI. *Nabarro Nathanson,* where Stephen Daykin has been highly recommended, handles a significant amount of industrial disease cases. *Wansbroughs Willey Hargraves* maintains its national reputation for defendant personal injury work, acting for a large number of insurance companies. The firm's caseload includes motor, employers' and public liability work and increasingly claims relating to diseases and the environment. Other prominent defendant firms include *Deas Mallen Sauter, Jacksons, Philip Hamer & Co, Smith & Graham,* and *Whittles.*

LEADING INDIVIDUALS – NORTH EAST	
	– MAINLY DEFENDANT
James C. Dias Sinton & Co	
Peter Anson Dibb Lupton Broomhead	
Stephen Daykin Nabarro Nathanson	
David R. Dobbin Sinton & Co	
David M. Drewe Crutes	
William A. Evans Dibb Lupton Broomhead	
Samuel G. Hotchin Wansbroughs Willey Hargrave	
David G. Raw Sinton & Co	

MAINLY PLAINTIFF & DEFENDANT

Of firms undertaking plaintiff and defendant work, *Hay & Kilner* acts for a number of household name insurers and a

HIGHLY REGARDED – NORTH EAST – BOTH	
HAY & KILNER Newcastle-	LINSLEY & MORTIMER Newcastle
HARTLEY & WORSTENHOLME Castleford	LEE & PRIESTLEY Bradford
LUPTON FAWCETT Leeds	SAMUEL PHILLIPS & CO Newcastle
STAMP JACKSON & PROCTER Hull	

major trade union. The team acted in a fatal road accident claim which settled at £725,000. *Linsley & Mortimore,* who have an established reputation in the field, act for a number of well known insurance companies .

LEADING INDIVIDUALS – NORTH EAST – BOTH

Peter Pescod *Hay & Kilner*	
Alun C. Williams *Hay & Kilner*	

SCOTLAND

MAINLY PURSUER

Robin Thompson & Partners has a very strong reputation in Scotland for pursuer representation, in particular for their work in relation to industrial diseases. *Balfour & Manson – Nightingale & Bell WS* are especially known for handling head and spinal injuries, Alfred Tyler has a strong reputation in this field. Drummond Miller undertakes spinal injuries on behalf of pursuers.

HIGHLY REGARDED – SCOTLAND – MAINLY PURSUER

BALFOUR & MANSON – NIGHTINGALE BELL WS *Edinburgh*	**BURNSIDE KEMP FRASER** *Aberdeen*
DRUMMOND MILLER WS *Edinburgh*	**THE FRANK LEFEVRE PRACTICE** *Aberdeen*
HUGHES DOWDALL *Glasgow*	**ROBIN THOMPSON & PARTNERS** *Edinburgh*
ROBSON McLEAN WS *Edinburgh*	
ALLAN McDOUGALL *Edinburgh*	**DIGBY BROWN & CO** *Glasgow*

A substantial proportion of this work emanates from the firm's close connections with trade unions. The firm also undertakes multi-party actions, and Grant McCulloch at the firm is well regarded.

LEADING INDIVIDUALS – SCOTLAND – MAINLY PURSUER

Andrew G. McCulloch *Drummond Miller WS*
David M. Burnside *Burnside Kemp Fraser*
Frank H. Lefevre *The Frank Lefevre Practice*
Alfred J. Tyler *Balfour & Manson – Nightingale & Bell WS*

MAINLY DEFENDER

With regard to defenders, *Simpson & Marwick WS* has an excellent reputation and acts for major insurance companies

HIGHLY REGARDED – SCOTLAND – MAINLY DEFENDER

DUNDAS & WILSON CS *Edinburgh*	**HAMILTON BURNS & MOORE** *Glasgow*
PAULL & WILLIAMSONS *Aberdeen*	**SIMPSON & MARWICK WS** *Edinburgh*
WILSON CHALMERS & HENDRY *Glasgow*	

in Scotland and England. James Tierney at *Paull & Williamsons* is also well regarded for his defender work, as is Neil Cochran at *Dundas & Wilson CS.*

LEADING INDIVIDUALS – SCOTLAND – MAINLY DEFENDER

M. Peter Anderson *Simpson & Marwick WS*
J. Neil Cochran *Dundas & Wilson CS*
George K. Moore *Hamilton Burns & Moore*
James K. Tierney *Paull & Williamsons*

PURSUER & DEFENDER

Of firms acting for both pursuers and defenders, *Biggard Baille & Gifford* represents a major employer liability insurer and has recently been awarded the contract for British Rail's litigation work in Scotland, which will include a

HIGHLY REGARDED – SCOTLAND – BOTH

BIGGART BAILLIE & GIFFORD *Glasgow*	**BRODIES WS** *Edinburgh*
DOWNIE AITON & Co *Glasgow*	**GILLAM MACKIE** *Edinburgh*

substantial amount of personal injury cases. *Brodies,* too, acts for both pursuers and defenders and offers specialist advice in paraplegia cases.

NORTHERN IRELAND

The majority of firms in Northern Ireland carry out personal injury work. Indeed this area accounts for at least one quarter of the total workload of the firms mentioned below. The larger firms are equipped to deal with volume work on behalf of insurers, trade unions and public authorities.

HIGHLY REGARDED – NORTHERN IRELAND – BOTH

CARSON & McDOWELL *Belfast*	**O'REILLY STEWART** *Belfast*

Most firms tend to specialise in acting for either plaintiffs or defendants, although some practices work in both spheres. *O'Reilly Stewart,* which has strong trade union connections, enjoys an excellent reputation for its plaintiff work, although it is one of the few firms to devote equal resources to both plaintiff (Paul Meehan) and defence (Brian Stewart) cases.

HIGHLY REGARDED – NORTHERN IRELAND – MAINLY PLAINTIFF

S.J. DIAMOND & SON *Belfast*	**P.A. DUFFY & CO** *Dungannon*
C & J BLACK *Belfast*	**CLEAVER FULTON & RANKIN** *Belfast*
MILLAR SHEARER & BLACK *Cookstown*	

Fifty per cent of *S. J. Diamond & Sons'* work is based in this field: they act for two trade unions and undertake road traffic and criminal injuries claims, as well as some defendant work. Their leading specialist is Maurice Diamond. *P. A. Duffy & Co* are also well known for their work on behalf of plaintiffs.

HIGHLY REGARDED – NORTHERN IRELAND – MAINLY DEFENDANT

HARRISON, LEITCH & LOGAN *Belfast*	**C & H JEFFERSON** *Belfast*
JOHN McKEE & SON *Belfast*	**JOHNSONS** *Belfast*
McKINTY & WRIGHT *Belfast*	**TUGHAN & CO** *Belfast*
BABINGTON & CROASDAILE *Londonderry*	

In all the tables the names in each group are listed alphabetically.

C & H Jefferson are recognised as the leading firm acting for defendants on the basis of the volume and range of their insurance caseload. Ian Jefferson and Derek Taylor at the latter firm act for leading UK composite insurers, foreign-based insurance companies and Lloyd's syndicates. Also highly regarded is Leonard Edgar at *John McKee & Son* who carries out defence work for insurers and public transport companies relating to product liability and road traffic claims. At *McKinty & Wright* Paul Johnston and John Cross

are well respected, while *Tughan & Co* also have considerable expertise in defence litigation. Other highly regarded firms include *Harrison Leitch & Logan*, and *Johnsons* where Paul Tweed is well known.

LEADING INDIVIDUALS – NORTHERN IRELAND – MAINLY DEFENDANT

John Cross	*McKinty & Wright*
Leonard A. Edgar	*John McKee & Son*
H.L. Ian Jefferson	*C & H Jefferson*
Paul J. Johnston	*McKinty & Wright*
Brian J. Stewart	*O'Reilly Stewart*
Derek T. Taylor	*C & H Jefferson*
Paul Tweed	*Johnsons*

LEADING INDIVIDUALS – NORTHERN IRELAND – MAINLY PLAINTIFF

W. Maurice Diamond	*S.J. Diamond & Son*
Paul Meehan	*O'Reilly Stewart*

LEADERS IN PERSONAL INJURY

LONDON

Allen, Patrick
Hodge Jones & Allen, London (0171) 482 1974. Qualified 1977.

Bruffell, Martin
Berrymans, London (0171) 638 2811.

Day, Martyn
See under Environmental Law.

Dismore, Andrew
Russell Jones & Walker, London (0171) 837 2808. Partner.

Specialisation: Main area of practice is personal injury. Pioneered a new head of damages- loss of congenial employment. Also dealt with some of the early pension loss cases. Successfully fought a pensions loss case to the House of Lords (Smoker and LFCDA) and has dealt with several Court of Appeal matters. Also dealt with some of the early post traumatic stress cases, including the highest ever award for this. Organised the representation of clients at the 93 day public inquiry into the King's Cross disaster. Handles the only medical negligence case ever involving a specialist form of cancer treatment, which led to a major review of procedure. Presently acting in judicial review proceedings before the Court of Appeal, on behalf of 11 unions and the TUC against the Home Secretary challenging the new criminal injuries scheme. Publications have included a paper to the APIL conference 1990 on damages for loss of congenial employment; an APIL preliminary response to the Law Commission 1992; an APIL response to Law Commission on structured settlements 1993; a *Kemp & Kemp* article on analysis of Congenial Employment cases 1993; VCCR briefing on criminal injuries compensation proposals 1994; and various internal Thompsons' publications.

Prof. Membership: Law Society Personal Injury Panel Member and Assessor, APIL (Chair of Damages Special Interest Group, Member of Executive Committee), Law Society Working Party on Law Commission Investigation on Damages, Association of Trial Lawyers of America, Society of Labour Lawyers, Member of Users Committee of Majors and City of London Court.

Career: Qualified in 1980. Worked at General Municipal Workers Union as Education Officer 1976-78. Joined *Robin Thompson & Partners* in 1978, becoming a Partner in 1983.

Personal: Born 2nd September 1954. Attended Bridlington Grammar School, Warwick University, London University and Guildford College of Law. Member of Labour Party, and member of Westminster City Council since 1982. Chief Whip of Labour Group 1982-90, Environment Spokesperson 1983-7, Arts Spokesperson since 1990 and leader since 1990. Speaks French, Greek and German. Leisure interests include travel, Greece, opera and the Arts. Lives in London.

Dodds-Smith, Ian C.
See under Product Liability.

Goodier, Roger
Rowley Ashworth, London (0181) 543 2277. Partner in Personal Injury Department.

Specialisation: Main area of practice is personal injury (mainly trade union supported). Secretary of the Association of Personal Injury Lawyers since 1992.

Prof. Membership: Law Society, Association of Personal Injury Lawyers, Law Society's Personal Injury Panel Member.

Career: Qualified in 1970. Has worked at *Rowley Ashworth* 1963-4, 1968-71 and since 1972, becoming a Partner in 1974.

Personal: Born 7th September 1944. Graduated from Sheffield University 1964-67 LL.B (Hons). Lives in Teddington, Middlesex.

Howe, Martin
Howe & Co, London (0181) 840 4688. Qualified 1983. Founding and Senior Partner 1991. Firm specialises in personal injury and medical negligence.

Kelleher, J.R.
Theodore Goddard, London (0171) 606 8855. Qualified 1978.

McCarthy, Frances
Pattinson and Brewer, London (0171) 405 3033. Qualified 1981. Partner 1985. Personal Injury Department.

Specialisation: Main area of practice is accidents at work and occupational disease claims. Also handles medical negligence and other areas of personal injury. Has handled successful appeals to the European Court of Justice and the question of equal treatment matters of social ssecurity. Co-author of 'Know How for Personal Injury Lawyers'. Regular lecturer for Legal Action Group and other bodies.

Prof. Membership: Law Society, Association of Trial Lawyers of America, Environmental Law Foundation.

Career: Qualified 1981. Joined *Pattinson and Brewer* in 1979 and became a partner in 1985.

McCool, Geraldine M.
Leigh Day & Co, London (0171) 242 1775. Qualified 1985. Partner in the Personal Injury Department specialising in plaintiff actions stemming fom aviation and automobile crashes. Involved in the civil actions following the Lockerbie disaster. Also handles product liability cases particularly in relation to defective medical devices. Qualified 1983. Born 20.4.1961.

Meeran, Richard
Leigh Day & Co, London (0171) 242 1775.

Nelson-Jones, Rodney

Field Fisher Waterhouse, London (0171) 481 4841. Partner in charge of Personal Injury Litigation Department.

Specialisation: Personal injury work includes asbestosis, aviation and road accidents. Also handles medical negligence work. Cases have included the M1 Air Crash (Steering Committee Member), Bryce v. Swan Hunter Group (Asbestosis), and Pendergast v. Sam & Dee (medical negligence). Co-author of 'Product Liability- The New Law Under the Consumer Protection Act 1987', 'Medical Negligence Case Law' (1990) and 'Personal Injury Limitation Law' (1994). Contributor to 'Structured Settlements- A Practical Guide' and 'Butterworths Personal Injury Litigation Service'.

Prof. Membership: Law Society.

Career: Qualified in 1975. Worked at *Prothero & Prothero* 1973-77 and *L Bingham & Co* 1977-83. Joined *Field Fisher Waterhouse* in 1983.

Pearl, Simon

See under Product Liability.

Pinfold, Caroline

Field Fisher Waterhouse, London (0171) 481 4841. Partner in Personal Injury Department.

Specialisation: Main areas of practice are asbestosis, RSI and road accident claims. Acted in Mulry v. William Kenyon & Son Ltd, Rule v Atlas Stone, Causabon-Vincent v. London Electricity PLC and others. Contributed a chapter to 'Personal Injury Claims in the County Court; Practice & Procedure'.

Prof. Membership: A.P.I.L.

Career: Qualified in 1983 and joined *Field Fisher Waterhouse* in the following year. Became a Partner in 1989.

Personal: Born in 1955. Educated at Glenlola Collegiate School and Kings College, London (BA 1977). Enjoys films, reading, music and family life. Lives in London.

Rogers, David

Davies Arnold Cooper, London (0171) 936 2222. Qualified 1975. Partner 1979. Common Law Department. Main area of practice is personal injury litigation, with emphasis on disease and industrial cancer. Handles multi-jurisdictional claims and claims arising in the US and Far East. Born 1.5.1947.

Solomon, Nicola

Stephens Innocent, London (0171) 353 2000. Partner and Head of Litigation Department.

Specialisation: Work includes personal injury, employment, media and intellectual property. Co-author of Pritchard and Solomon 'Personal Injury Litigation'; contributor to 'Know How for Personal Injury Lawyers'; writes regular personal injury update column in Solicitors Journal, and regular column in

Author magazine; Book Review Editor of J.P.I.L.; author of numerous articles on personal injury and media law. Personal Injury Panel Member.

Stewart, Douglas

Stewarts, London (0171) 242 6462. Qualified 1969. Senior Partner 1989. Consultant 1994. Civil Litigation Department. Main areas of practice are personal injury compensation and product liability claims.

Thomas, Margaret Anne Monro

Davies Arnold Cooper, London (0171) 936 2222. Qualified 1977. Common Law Department. Principal area of practice is asbestos related personal injury and defence of health and safety prosecutions.

Walker, Ian J.

Russell Jones & Walker, London (0171) 837 2808. Senior Partner in Personal Injury Department.

Specialisation: Has specialised in plaintiff personal injury since 1975. Acted in the then largest CICB award in 1988. Also the then-largest ever court fatal award (920,000) in 1991. Lead solicitor in the Kings Cross fire cases. Co-Author of 'Tribunal Practice and procedure 1985', 'Know-How for Personal Injury Lawyers 1993', and Editor in Chief of the 'Journal of Personal Injury Litigation'. Regular lecturer for IBC, Euroforum, Hawksmere and others. Assessor for Law Society PI Panel. Member of Executive Committee of Association of Personal Injury Lawyers. Co-chair, International Section of Association of Trial Lawyers of America.

Prof. Membership: Association of Personal Injury Lawyers, Association of Trial Lawyers of America, Law Society, Holborn Law Society, Medico-Legal Society, Association of Plaintiff Lawyers of Australia.

Career: Qualified in 1974. Joined *Russell Jones & Walker* in 1968, becoming a Partner in 1977.

Personal: Born 15th April 1950. Attended Whitgift School 1961-68. Governor of two independent schools. Leisure interests include music, golf, gardening, mountain biking and walking. Lives in Caterham, Surrey.

Watmore, Leslie

L. Watmore & Co, London (0171) 430 1512. Qualified 1957. Senior Partner 1976. Litigation Department. Main area of practice is insurance litigation, covering personal injury actions.

Whitehead, Fraser

Russell Jones & Walker, London (0171) 837 2808. Partner and Co-Ordinator of Personal Injury Department.

Specialisation: Main areas of practice are personal injury, Trade Union and employment work. Undertakes legal work on behalf of Trades Unions and their members, including industrial accidents and disease,

workplace environment issues, Health and Safety law, employment and trade disputes, the law relating to ballots and constitutional law. Also undertakes employment law work on behalf of private individuals and voluntary bodies. Has handled several House of Lords and ECJ cases of significance to collective labour law. Frequently addresses conferences and occasionally writes articles.

Prof. Membership: APIL, PIP, ATLA, LSLA, I of ER, Law Society, Holborn Law Society (President). Executive Committee Society of Labour Lawyers.

Career: Joined *Russell Jones & Walker* and qualified in 1975. Became a Partner in 1978.

Personal: Born 14th December 1950. Educated at Pocklington School, Yorkshire 1962-69 and Sheffield University 1969-72. Awarded a Diploma in EEC law from the University of London in 1992. On the Management Committee of the Mary Ward Law Centre, Trustee of the Child Accident Prevention Trust. Leisure time is devoted to his family. Lives in London.

Woods, Peter

Stephens Innocent, London (0171) 353 2000. Partner in Litigation Department.

Specialisation: Main areas of practice are personal injury (including sports injuries) and medical negligence. Has been instructed by various individuals and Trade Unions specialising in work related upper limb disorders (RSI) from keyboard use. Also handles employment, industrial relations, pensions and insolvency law. Has extensive involvement in acting for Trade Union's employees and pensioners. Acted in British Coal v. British Coal Staff Superannuation Scheme; National Mineworkers & others v. British Coal Corporation and President of the Board of Trade (pit closure decision); and BCCI (SA) in Liquidation. Currently commissioned to publish a handbook on RSI litigation. Has addressed numerous seminars and conferences including TUC and APIL.

Prof. Membership: Personal Injury Panel of Law Society.

Career: Qualified in 1984. Barrister and Solicitor in New Zealand 1985; Solicitor in England 1992. Joined *Stephens Innocent* in 1991, becoming a Partner in 1994. Former Law Centre Convenor and Chairman.

Personal: Born 3rd April 1961. Attended University of Canterbury, New Zealand 1979-84 (LLB, BSc). Leisure interests include kayaking, paragliding, skiing, scuba-diving and cricket. Lives in London.

Adamson, Derek Paul
Buller Jeffries, Birmingham (0121) 212 2620. Qualified 1981. Partner 1985. Civil Litigation Department. Main area of practice is personal injury, including employers liability and motor claims. Also insurance company litigation. Born 20.10.1956.

Anderson, M.Peter
See under Litigation (Commercial).

Anson, Peter
Dibb Lupton Broomhead, Sheffield (0114) 2760351. Qualified 1976. Partner 1990. Head of Insurance Litigation Department. Main areas of practice are defendant personal injury and construction plant hire claims.

Arkell, Catherine
Everatt & Company, Evesham (01386) 47191. Senior Partner in Litigation Department.

Specialisation: Acts for defendant insurers in a variety of personal injury claims. Has dealt with serious road traffic claims including paraplegia, head injury, etc, and many disease cases including large volume deafness, asbestos-related, RSI, and hand/arm vibration claims. Has also dealt with large (over £1 million) fire-related claims for insurers. Recent important cases include Rastin v British Steel Plc [1994] (for successful appellant defendants) and Heal v Garringtons Ltd (for defendant's insurers). Contributed to a chapter in 'Hand-arm vibration: A Comprehensive Guide for Occupational Health Professionals' (ed. Pelmear, Taylor & Wasserman).

Prof. Membership: Law Society.

Career: Qualified in 1979. Became a partner in *Everatt & Co* in 1980. Now Senior Partner.

Personal: Born 8th November 1954. Educated at Westwood's Grammar School and Bristol University 1973-76. Hon. Legal Advisor to Wychavon Citizen's Advice Bureau.

Balen, Paul
Freeth Cartwright Hunt Dickins, Nottingham (0115) 9369369. Partner in Civil Litigation Department.

Specialisation: Main areas of practice are personal injury, medical negligence and product liability. Acts in claims for compensation arising from accidents of all types, co-ordination of group actions and medical negligence claims. Also handles environmental claims. Acted in Benzodiazipine litigation and the Nottingham District Heating cases. Joint editor of Butterworths PILS bulletin. Lecturer on medico-legal matters to doctors and lawyers. Writes a local newspaper column on legal topics and is a Radio Nottingham phone-in 'Legal Eagle'.

Prof. Membership: Law Society (Personal Injury Specialist Panel and medical negligence

specialist panel assessor) APIL, AVMA, ATLA, ELF.

Career: Joined *Freeth Cartwright* in 1975. Qualified in 1977. Partner 1980.

Personal: Born 25th February 1952. Attended Nottingham High School 1960-71, then Cambridge University 1971-74. Member of Nottinghamshire Medico-Legal Society. Member of Law Society Working Party on Group Actions.

Bent, Roger
Robin Thompson & Partners, Cardiff (01222) 484136. Partner.

Specialisation: Main area of practice has been personal injuries litigation since admission. Acted in Williams v. Compair Maxam (unfair selection for redundancy) and Thomas v. NUM (South Wales Area) 1985.

Prof. Membership: Law Society, Cardiff Law Society, APIL, ATLA (American Trial Lawyers).

Career: Qualified in 1967. Joined *Robin Thompson & Partners* in 1971, becoming a Partner in 1974. Managing Partner of the Cardiff Office since 1985.

Personal: Born 24th March 1942. Attended Calday Grange Grammar School 1953-60 and King's College, London 1960-64. Leisure interests include cycling, tennis, walking, music and literature. Lives in Cardiff.

Burnside, David M.
See under Employment Law.

Carron, Byron
Townsends, Swindon (01793) 410800. Partner and Head of Personal Injury Department.

Specialisation: Main area of practice is head injuries and spinal injuries, where damages are usually not less than £100,000 and can be in excess of £1 million. Also handles other injury cases including RTA or industrial accidents. Both plaintiff and defendant work. Has appeared frequently on local TV and radio.

Prof. Membership: Law Society, Gloucestershire and Wiltshire Law Society, APIL, Personal Injury Panel, Headway (National Bath & Swindon Groups).

Career: Qualified in 1965. Joined *Townsends* in 1959, becoming a Partner in 1966. Former Chairman of North Wilts Legal Association, Former County Councillor. Vice Chairman of Wilts County Council. Chairman of Finance Committee of WCC, President of Swindon Rotary Club.

Personal: Born 18th March 1942. Attended High School, Swindon and The College, Swindon. Leisure interests include gardening, walking and music. Lives in Swindon.

Chandler, Brigitte H.
Townsends, Swindon (01793) 410800. Partner in Personal Injury Department.

Specialisation: Main areas of practice are industrial injury and industrial disease, including lifting accidents, dangerous machinery, deafness and particularly claims involving inhalation of dangerous dust and fumes. Wide experience of asbestos claims in every field of work. Has considerable media experience including TV and radio appearances.

Prof. Membership: Law Society, Gloucestershire and Wiltshire Law Society.

Career: Qualified in 1977. Joined *Townsends* in 1977, becoming a Partner in 1981.

Personal: Born 13th January 1952. Attended Aylesbury High School 1963-70. Manchester University (Upper Second class degree). Leisure interests include theatre, travel and tennis. Lives in Swindon.

Chapman, Richard
Chapman Everatt & Co, Wolverhampton (01902) 717700. Qualified 1970. Specialises in defendant personal injury. Acts exclusively for insurers and has no private clients.

Clement-Evans, J. Cenric
Leo Abse & Cohen, Cardiff (01222) 383252. Partner in Trade Union Legal Service Department.

Specialisation: Specialises in plaintiff personal injury claims. Work covers fatal accident cases, industrial and other accidents including severe injuries, group deafness and group RSI litigation against a number of employers and other industrial diseases (e.g. dermatitis). Acts for the TGWU, GMB and private clients.

Prof. Membership: Law Society, APIL, Law Society PI Panel.

Career: Qualified in 1986. With *Globe Wareing Cropper*, Liverpool 1984-88. Joined *Leo Abse & Cohen* in 1988 and became a Partner in March 1992.

Personal: Born 22nd August 1962. Educated at Liverpool College 1970-80, University College of Wales, Aberystwyth 1980-83 and the College of Law, Chester 1983-84. Member of Executive Committee of Drama Association of Wales. Secretary of Now & Then Theatre Co. Interests include drama (especially experimental), theatre, cinema, golf and fitness exercise. Lives in Cardiff.

Cochran, J. Neil
See under Professional Negligence.

Cooper, Jonathan
Bond Pearce, Plymouth (01752) 266633. Qualified 1984. Partner 1989. Personal Injury and Occupational Health Division. Personal injury litigation specialising in industrial disease claims.

Cradick, Simon J.
Morgan Bruce, Cardiff (01222) 385385. Qualified 1984. Partner 1988. Insurance Department. Specialises in insurance litigation, covering all areas of personal injury work.

Cradick, C. Roger
See under Professional Negligence.

Cross, John
McKinty & Wright, Belfast (01232) 246751.

Dace, Nigel Howard
George Green & Co, Warley (01384) 410410.

Specialisation: Partner specialising in personal injury work including motor, employers liability, public liability, and professional and medical negligence claims. His practice also covers subsidence and other property claims. Acts for both plaintiffs and defendants, including major insurance companies and Lloyd's syndicates, at both High Court and County Court level. Very considerable experience of cases involving paraplegic and tetraplegic damage, brain damage and cerebral palsy. Has lectured on behalf of Birmingham Law Society and Worcester Law Society on 'The Practice and Procedure in Personal Injury Claims'.

Prof. Membership: Law Society Personal Injury Panel; Law Society Accident Line; Birmingham Medico-Legal Society.

Career: Qualified 1973. Trained in London. Partner with *George Green & Co* since 1982.

Personal: Educated at Shrewsbury School 1963-67 and Liverpool University 1967-70. Leisure pursuits include playing golf, tennis and bridge, watching most sports, particularly football, and also theatre and opera. Born 6th September 1949. Lives in Stourbridge.

Davies, Paul Roger
Sansbury Hill, Bristol (0117) 9265341.

Daykin, Stephen
Nabarro Nathanson, Doncaster (01302) 344455. Qualified 1974. Partner 1990. Personal Injury Litigation Department. Specialises in industrial disease, employers liability, public liability and health and safety.

Dexter, Jane
Russell Jones & Walker, Bristol (0117) 927 3098.

Diamond, William M.
S.J. Diamond & Son, Belfast (01232) 243726.

Dias, James Curry
Sinton & Co, Newcastle upon Tyne (0191) 281 5211. Qualified 1972. Partner 1974. Personal Injury Department. Principal area of practice is personal injury work, mainly acting for defendants. Also handles medical negligence. Born 18.7.1948.

Dobbin, David R.
Sinton & Co, Newcastle upon Tyne (0191) 281 5211. Qualified 1969. Partner 1972. Litigation Department. Specialises in personal injury, industrial diseases, employment and taxi law.

Dodgson, Christine
Rowley Ashworth, Exeter (01392) 211731. Qualified 1975. Partner 1978. Personal injury Litigation Department. Deals exclusively with plaintiff work.

Drewe, David M.
Crutes, Newcastle-upon-Tyne (0191) 281 5811. Qualified 1981. Partner 1986. Litigation Department. Main areas of practice are personal injury and professional negligence.

Edgar, Leonard A.
John McKee & Son, Belfast (01232) 232303.

Evans, William A.
Dibb Lupton Broomhead, Leeds (0113) 243 9301. Qualified 1986. Partner 1994. Insurance Group. Handles all types of defendant injury work for insurers particularly chest disease cases.

Everatt, Allan
Chapman Everatt & Co, Wolverhampton (01902) 717700. Qualified 1970. Specialises in defendant personal injury. Acts exclusively for insurers and has no private clients.

Finnigan, Kevin P.
James Chapman & Co, Manchester (0161) 236 7772.

Gibson, Kenneth
Wansbroughs Willey Hargrave, Bristol (0117) 926 8981. Qualified 1962.

Goodman, Sarah
Robin Thompson & Partners, Birmingham (0121) 236 7944. Qualified 1980. Partner 1983. Main area of practice is personal injury and medical negligence. Also handles employment work.

Guy, Michael
Macfarlane Guy, Bath (01225) 333800. Partner specialising in defendant personal injury litigation.

Specialisation: Predominantly employers' liability and major motor claims, Industrial disease (especially RSI). Successfully defended one of the first keyboard RSI cases. Writes articles for circulation within client base of insurers. Has experience of addressing external conferences and seminars with insurers and major insureds.

Career: Trained with *Wansbroughs Willey Hargrave* 1974-77. Qualified in 1976. Practised with *Sansbury Hill & Co.* 1977-84, as a Partner from 1980. Set up *Macfarlane Guy* in 1984. Assessor for the Law Society's Specialist Personal Injury Panel.

Personal: Born 15th October 1949. Educated at Bristol University 1968-71. Leisure time is devoted to family life. Lives in Bath.

Hams, Robert John
Wood Awdry Wansbroughs, Devizes (01380) 723611. Qualified 1978. Partner 1990. Insurance Litigation Department. Main area of practice is defendant personal injury litigation.

Henderson, Stuart
Irwin Mitchell, incorporating Kershaw Tucker, Birmingham (0121) 212 1828. Partner in Personal Injury Department.

Specialisation: Particular emphasis on major injury, fatal accident claims (such as Clay v. Pooler [reported]) and medical negligence. Heads firm's Plaintiff Personal Injury Department in Birmingham. Acted in the Leung case, a 3.4 million record award in personal injury cases in the UK. Chairperson of the Co-ordinating Committee of Lawyers in the Royal Orthopaedic Hospital Bone Cancer Misdiagnosis cases; brought to a conclusion the last Thalidomide case. Has extensive media experience and lectures in-house and externally.

Prof. Membership: APIL, Law Society.

Career: Qualified in 1992. Joined *Robin Thompson & Partners* in 1979, becoming a Partner in 1992. Partner in *Irwin Mitchell* from January 1995.

Personal: Born 20th February 1958. Attended UCE Birmingham. Leisure interests include tennis, cinema, art, opera and the music of Van Morrison.

Henthorn, John L.
Lace Mawer, Manchester (0161) 236 2002. Partner in Civil Litigation Department.

Specialisation: Main area of practice involves acting for a number of major insurance companies dealing with substantial employers' liability (both accident and disease) claims, public liability and motor claims. Other main area of work involves acting for employers on all aspects of employment law. Lectures and addresses seminars on both civil litigation and employment law.

Prof. Membership: Law Society, Liverpool Law Society, Employment Lawyers' Association.

Career: Qualified in 1970 while at *Lace Mawer* and became a Partner in 1972. Deputy District Judge since September 1992.

Personal: Born 5th August 1946. Attended Brasenose College, Oxford 1964-67, B.A. (Oxon). Governor, Home Farm Trust (national charity providing full time residential accommodation to adults with learning difficulties). Leisure pursuits include golf (member of the Royal Birkdale Golf Club), tennis, music and bridge. Married with three sons. Lives in Aughton, Ormskirk, Lancashire.

Herbert, A.
Robin Thompson & Partners, Bristol (0117) 941 1606.

Hermer, Ian B.

Howard Palser Grossman Hermer & Partners, Cardiff (01222) 452770. Qualified 1959. Partner 1959-95. Consultant from 1.5.1995. Principal area of practice is employers and public liability.

Hopkins, Ian

Leo Abse & Cohen, Cardiff (01222) 383252. Partner in Litigation Department.

Specialisation: Personal injury litigation specialist. Member of Law Society PI Panel and Scheme contact for Law Society's Accident Line. Handles large personal injury claims for both plaintiffs and defendants including a substantial case load of industrial disease claims (particularly occupational asthma and asbestosis). Clients include Trades Unions, Insurance companies and the general public. Supervisor in Legal Aid Board Franchised Legal Aid Department. Member of Steering Committee for Severn Tunnel train crash.

Prof. Membership: Law Society.

Career: Qualified in 1987. Became a Partner at *Leo Abse & Cohen* in 1990.

Personal: Born 20th August 1961. Educated at Aberdare Grammar School and Kingston University 1979-82. Lives in Aberdare.

Hotchin, Samuel G.

Wansbroughs Willey Hargrave, Leeds (0113) 244 1151. Partner in General Insurance Department.

Specialisation: Principal area of practice is personal injury, advising on high value employers', public and product liability. Also deals with fraud (Specialised Loss Unit) including investigation, recovery and litigation in arson and financial fraud cases, as well as advising on insurers' liabilities to the indemnified.

Career: Qualified and joined *Wansbroughs Willey Hargrave* in 1979. Became a Partner in 1982. Head of the firm's Specialised Loss Unit since 1992.

Hughes, D.A.K.

Amery–Parkes, Basingstoke. Qualified 1961. Senior Litigation Partner. Specialises in personal injury, general.

Jefferson, H.L. Ian

C & H Jefferson, Belfast (01232) 329545.

Jenkins, Russel J.A.

Hugh James Jones & Jenkins, Cardiff (01222) 224871. Qualified 1969. Partner in the Litigation department specialising in defendant personal injury work.

Johnston, Paul J.

McKinty & Wright, Belfast (01232) 246751.

Jones, Timothy L.

Leo Abse & Cohen, Cardiff (01222) 383252. Associate in Trade Union Personal Injury Department.

Specialisation: Principal area of practice is plaintiff personal injury claims, principally employers' liability claims including RTA, industrial disease (especially industrial asthma), RSI, dermatitis, fatal accident claims, factory accidents and personal injury claims by sportsmen. Has handled personal injury claims by professional sportsmen and leading amateurs. Also deals with Inheritance Act cases. Major clients include national trade unions (TGWU and GMB).

Prof. Membership: Law Society and member of Law Society Personal Injury Panel.

Career: Qualified in 1991. Became an associate at *Leo Abse & Cohen* in 1995.

Personal: Born 4th August 1964. Educated at the University College of Wales, Aberystwyth 1983-86. Spare time interests include environmental protection. Lives in Cardiff.

Jones, Michael L.N.

See under Construction & Civil Eng..

King, P.

Robin Thompson & Partners, Nottingham.

Lefevre, Frank H.

See under Employment Law.

Lewis, Brian

Graham Evans & Partners, Swansea (01792) 655822. Qualified 1967. Senior Partner 1985. Personal Injury Department. Acts for defendants in insurance related litigation.

Lewis, Geoffrey John

Buller Jeffries, Birmingham (0121) 212 2620. Qualified 1973. Partner 1979. Principal area of practice is personal injury and insurance related litigation.

Louw, D.R.

Russell Jones & Walker, Bristol (0117) 927 3098.

Maddocks, Roger

Brian Thompson & Partners, Newcastle-upon-Tyne (0191) 261 5341. Qualified 1980. Partner 1985. Specialises in personal injury litigation. Also employment law matters.

Mather, Christopher

Penningtons, . Consultant in Litigation Department.

Specialisation: Main area of practice is personal injury, handling claims of utmost severity for both defendants and plaintiffs. Also handles admiralty work, mainly dry, and employment law, especially for groups of employees. Chairman of the Steering committees for both the Clapham and the Severn Tunnel rail crashes. Formerly spokesman for Hampshire Law Society involving considerable media involvement. Higher Courts (All Proceedings) Qualification, April 1994. Panel Solicitor Spinal Injuries Association.

Prof. Membership: AVMA, Committee Member of Solicitors Association, Higher Courts Advocates. Member of the Law Society Personal Injury Panel.

Career: Qualified in 1973. Joined *Penningtons* in 1994. Assistant Recorder since 1991. Until recently, member of Hampshire and Isle of Wight Valuation Tribunal and Chairman of Hampshire Law Society Public Relations Committee.

Personal: Born 20th June 1947. Attended Ellesmere College and College of Law. Leisure interests include a small holding. Lives in Romsey, Hants.

McCulloch, Andrew Grant

Drummond Miller WS, Edinburgh (0131) 226 5151. Partner in Litigation Department.

Specialisation: Main area of practice is personal injury, covering all areas of Court of Session reparation including complex medical negligence. Also handles matrimonial work, undertaking only large cases involving complex financial issues. Acted in Ross v. Lord Advocate, Latter v. Latter and Docherty (O'Briens Curator) v. British Steel. Part of Tranquilliser Addiction Solicitors Group. Chairman, Scottish Solicitors Myodil Group. Convened several seminars on family law. Solicitor-Advocate (civil).

Prof. Membership: AVMA, APIL, Law Society of Scotland, Society of Solicitors in the Supreme Courts.

Career: Qualified in 1976. Joined *Drummond Miller* in 1974, becoming a Partner in 1979.

Personal: Born 10th February 1952. Attended Glasgow Academy, then Edinburgh University 1969-74 (LLB, BSc). Temporary Sheriff. Child Support Appeal Chairman. Council Member of Law Society of Scotland. Leisure interests include golf, cricket and opera. Lives in Edinburgh.

McKeown, John

Rowley Ashworth, Birmingham (0121) 233 1831. Qualified 1972. Partner 1975. Plaintiff Personal Injury Department. Specialises in industrial injuries. Acts for a variety of Trade Unions, in particular the TGWU, AEEU and USDAW. The majority of cases dealt with are factory accidents and industry related diseases.

Meehan, Paul

O'Reilly Stewart, Belfast (01232) 322512.

Moore, George K.

Hamilton Burns & Moore, Glasgow (0141) 353 2121. Qualified 1971. Founding Partner 1972. Specialises in personal injury work. Qualified as a solicitor advocate with rights of audience in the Court of Session.

Murphy, Patrick

Marrons, Newcastle upon Tyne (0191) 281 1304. Qualified 1979. Partner 1979. Main area of practice is asbestos related diseases.

Cases have included mesothelioma, lung cancer, asbestosis, pleural thickening and pleural plaques.

Napier, Michael

Irwin Mitchell, incorporating Kershaw Tucker, Sheffield (0114) 276 7777. Senior partner specialising in personal injury.

Specialisation: Personal injury law specialist (plaintiff), latterly via associated firm *Pannone Napier* and concentrating on group personal injury and product liability claims such as Practolol (Eraldin), Opren, and Dalkon Shield IUD. Also major involvement in claims arising from disasters such as Land's End tragedy, Manchester air crash, sinking of the Herald of Free Enterprise, Marchioness disaster, King's Cross fire, Piper Alpha explosion and many others, usually in a leading capacity. Other major non-personal injury cases include X v. United Kingdom (human rights for mental patients, ECHR), Barber v. Guardian Royal Exchange (equal pension rights, ECJ), Michael Foot v. Boundary Commission (electoral constituencies), Blackburn v. Newcastle Health Authority (medical negligence) and Dickinson v. Jones Alexander (professional negligence). Author of 'Recovering Compensation for Psychiatric Injury' (Blackstone 1995), 'Psychiatrist & Lawyer- Total Incompatability?', 'The Medical & Legal Response to Post Traumatic Stress Disorder', 'European Perspectives for Practitioners' and 'Group Litigation- past present and future'. Consultant Editor of Personal & Medical Injuries Law Letter and The Litigator. Has addressed numerous lectures and chaired 19 seminars.

Prof. Membership: Law Society (Council Member); Association of Personal Injury Lawyers (President); Association of Trial Lawyers of America (Member of Governing Board); Visiting Professor and Chairman of Centre of Advanced Litigation at Nottingham Trent University; Chairman of Rampton Hospital Advisory Committee; Member of Mental Health Act Commission 1983-92; Past President of South Yorkshire Medico-Legal Society; Trustee of Pitsmoor Citizens Advice Bureau; Freeman of Cutlers Company, Sheffield.

Career: Qualified in 1970. Articled at *Moss Toone & Deane* 1968-70. Worked with *WH Thompson* 1970-72, before joining *Irwin Mitchell* in 1972. Partner from 1973.

Personal: Born 11th June 1946. Attended Loughborough Grammar School and Manchester University. Leisure interests include family, peace and quiet in Norfolk and sport. Lives in Sheffield.

Nichols, Maurice P.

A.E. Wyeth & Co, Dartford (01322) 297000. Partner in Insurance Litigation Department.

Specialisation: Has extensive experience in civil litigation, primarily on behalf of the insurance industry. Is retained by a number of leading insurers to deal with personal injury claims (including the negotiation of struc-

tured settlements), fire claims, product liability (including engineering, motor industry, printing, food industry, ink and paint), building and construction, road traffic, policy disputes, disasters and industrial disease claims (asthma, deafness, RSI, general respiratory and white finger). Work includes advising on and drafting of policies and UK/USA cross border litigation. Acted in Morris v. Ford Motor Company and West v. Bucks County Council (1984). Charge out rate is £100 per hour (plus care and attention).

Prof. Membership: Law Society, New York Bar Association, Forum of insurance Lawyers (President), Holborn and Kent Law Societies, Union Internationale des Avocats.

Career: Qualified in 1974 while at *A.E. Wyeth & Co*. Became a partner in 1976. Admitted as Attorney in New York 1990.

Personal: Born 6th July 1950. Educated at Merchant Taylors School, Middlesex, the University of Birmingham and the College of Law, Guilford. Lives in Battle, East Sussex.

Patterson, Frank P.

Pannone & Partners, Manchester (0161) 832 3000. Head of Personal Injury Litigation.

Specialisation: All areas of personal injury litigation, acting exclusively on behalf of plaintiffs. Handles in particular industrial accidents and industrial disease claims on behalf of trade union clients. Also deals in product liability and aviation claims, including those involving litigation in the United States. Deals with maximum severity damages actions on behalf of plaintiffs with spinal injuries and those with brain damage.

Prof. Membership: Member of the Law Society's Personal Injury Specialist Panel, member of APIL, member of The Association of Trial Lawyers in America (ATLA).

Career: Qualified in 1986, having served articles with *Pannone & Partners*. Became a partner in 1990, and head of personal Injury Litigation in 1993.

Personal: Born 6th December 1959. Attended Barrow-in-Furness Grammar School and The University of Manchester - graduating in 1983.

Peacock, Norman

Allan Henderson Beecham & Peacock, Newcastle-upon-Tyne (0191) 232 3048. Qualified 1974.

Perry, Timothy

William Hatton, Dudley (01384) 211211. Partner since 1981. Civil Litigation Department. Handles defendant insurance and personal injury litigation.

Pescod, Peter

Hay & Kilner, Newcastle-upon-Tyne (0191) 232 8345. Partner in Litigation Department.

Specialisation: Main area of practice is personal injury, acting primarily for major insurers in all types of accident/ disease

claims. Also acts for health service bodies in defence of medical negligence claims. Handles professional negligence work relating to surveyors, accountants, insurance brokers and architects. Has lectured on medical negligence and special damages.

Prof. Membership: Law Society, Personal Injury Panel, Vice-President of FOIL (Forum of Insurance Lawyers). Chairman of Medical Service Committee.

Career: Joined *Hay-Kilner* in 1973. Qualified in 1975 and became a Partner in 1976.

Personal: Born 29th June 1951. Educated at Queen Elizabeth Grammar, Darlington 1962-69 and Newcastle University 1969-72. Chairman of Legal Aid Sub-Committee 1986-89. Chairman of Governors, Ovingham Middle School. Leisure pursuits include history, politics, landscape gardening, architecture and auction sales. Lives in Ovington.

Pickering, John

John Pickering & Partners, Oldham (0161) 633 6667.

Pickering, John

Irwin Mitchell, incorporating Kershaw Tucker, Sheffield (0114) 276 7777. Partner and Head of Personal Injury Department (Sheffield, Leeds and Birghmingham).

Specialisation: Personal injury specialist with a particular interest in medical negligence and catastrophic injury cases (brain injury and spinal injury). Also deals with other types of personal injury and associated professional negligence actions. Important recent cases include Hepworth v. Kerr and Bird v. Hussain. Member of Steering Committee on British Coal VWF cases. Member of the Law Society's Working Party on Structured Settlements. Member of the Brain Injury and Spinal Cord Injury Special Interest Groups within APIL. Experienced lecturer and author of articles for legal journals (*Law Society's Gazette*, *APIL Newsletter*, etc). Charge-out rate is 120-150 per hour.

Prof. Membership: APIL (Member of Executive Committee), ATLA, TLPJ, Law Society, Headway Spinal Injuries Association, AVMA, Justice.

Career: Qualified in 1979 after articles at *Irwin Mitchell*. Became a Partner in the following year. Member of Management Committee.

Personal: Born 23rd July 1955. Educated at Manchester University (LL.B Hons, 1976). Member of the Hospital Advisory Board at Thornbury Hospital. Past President of South Yorkshire Medico-Legal Society. Leisure interests include theatre, squash, golf and motor racing. Lives in Sheffield.

Porteus, Stephen

Marrons, Newcastle upon Tyne (0191) 281 1304.

Prain, David

Rowley Ashworth, Wolverhampton

(01902) 771551. Qualified 1973. Partner, 1976. Personal Injury Litigation Department. Has specialised in personal injury work since 1980.

Price, Hugh M.

Morgan Bruce, Cardiff (01222) 385385. Qualified 1975. Partner 1978. Head of Insurance Department. Main areas of practice are personal injury and professional negligence.

Radcliffe, Neville

Browne Jacobson, Nottingham (0115) 950 0055. Partner in Litigation Department.

Specialisation: Main area of practice is civil litigation, with the emphasis on personal injury litigation, libel and slander, professional indemnity claims and medical negligence. Acts principally for defendant insurance companies. Also acts for plaintiffs. Deals mainly with major claims, claims of maximum severity and other associated heavy personal injury and fatal accident claims. Experienced in effecting structured settlements on behalf of plaintiffs and defendants. Published articles on structured settlements, personal injury law and practice and risk management.

Prof. Membership: Law Society Personal Injury Panel, F.O.I.L.

Career: Articled with *Southern, Ritchie & Southern* in Burnley, then on qualifying joined *Browne Jacobson*. Became a Partner in 1961 and Senior Partner in 1990-1995. Accredited C.E.D.R. Mediator.

Personal: Born 21st August 1932. Attended The Grammar School, Colne, then Manchester University. Chairman of the Ethical Committee of the General Hospital, Highbury Hospital and University Hospital, Nottingham and former Chairman of the Risk Management Committee, University Hospital, Nottingham and No. 10 (East Midlands) Legal Aid Area. Deputy Chairman and Director of Nottingham Law School and Member of Executive Committee, Portland College. Leisure pursuits include fell walking, sport, gardening, travel, music, literature and art. Lives in Nottingham.

Raw, David G.

Sinton & Co, Newcastle upon Tyne (0191) 281 5211. Qualified 1966. Partner 1968. Litigation Department. Specialises in personal injury matters. Also general civil litigation.

Roberts, Brian

Cartwright & Lewis, Birmingham (0121) 426 4171. Partner in charge of Commercial and Liability Department.

Specialisation: Main areas of practice are employers liability and public liability personal injury litigation. Acts on behalf of five major insurance companies, mainly in the areas of industrial disease and catastrophic injuries. Also handles insurance law, advising on matters of policy cover and defending fraudulent claims. Has conducted, or is conducting, claims in respect of humidifier fever,

bladder cancer, asbestosis, WRULD and respiratory diseases.

Prof. Membership: Law Society.

Career: Qualified in 1963. Joined *Cartwright & Lewis* in 1966, becoming a Partner in 1968. Deputy District Judge since 1983.

Personal: Born 25th August 1937. Attended Borrowcon School 1948-55, then Wednesbury Technical College 1955-57. Interests include Christianity; family; music and gardening. Lives in Dormston.

Rowe, Bernard V.

Lyons Davidson, Bristol (0117) 929 7151. Partner and Head of Personal Injury and Insurance.

Specialisation: Principal area of practice is personal injury litigation with emphasis on road traffic accidents. Heads a department of 78 personnel, handling personal injury and road traffic litigation throughout the South West for plaintiffs and defendants. Has been involved in numerous substantial personal injury cases, including structured settlements. Experienced lecturer (e.g. Anglo-French Brain Injury Conference in Paris, 1994). Has made television appearances and attended parliamentary meetings for the Motor Accident Solicitors Society in relation to windscreen insurance discs and the Small Claims Court.

Prof. Membership: Motor Accident Solicitors Society (Chairman 1992-94), Legal Aid Appeal Committtee Member, Law Society, Bristol Law Society (Past Council Member and Training Chairman).

Career: Qualified in 1976. Partner at *Ivesow Jarratt* in Hull from 1977. Joined *Lyons Davidson* in 1986 and became a Partner in 1987. Managing Partner 1992-94.

Personal: Born 21st December 1951. Educated at Watford Grammar School 1963-70 and Hull University 1970-73 (BA, Politics and Law). Leisure pursuits include driving. Lives in Bristol.

Scrutton, David T.

Kennedys, Brentwood.

Stewart, Brian J.

See under Product Liability.

Taylor, Derek T.

C & H Jefferson, Belfast (01232) 329545.

Tenquist, I.R.

Cole and Cole, Oxford (01865) 791122. Qualified 1984. Partner specialising in public liability and personal injury work.

Tierney, James K.

See under Employment Law.

Tweed, Paul

See under Defamation.

Tyler, Alfred J.

Balfour & Manson, Edinburgh (0131) 225

8291. Qualified 1975. Partner 1978. Litigation Department. Principal areas of practice are personal injury (including medical negligence) and aviation.

Vernalls, David Francis

Cartwrights, Bristol (0117) 929 3601. Partner in Insurance Department.

Specialisation: Main area of practice is insurance work involving employers liability. Deals with all aspects of employers liability, including a large number of industrial disease cases. Particular specialisations are deafness and respiratory disease claims, limitation of actions, striking out actions for want of prosecution and failure to comply with the RSC. Acted in Cook v. Square D Ltd; Gilbert v. Lanes Storage & Removals Ltd; Gitsham v. CH Pearce & Sons Ltd; Price v. Dannimac Ltd and Beese v. Brosnan Plant and Excavation Contractors Ltd, all heard in the Court of Appeal. Co-ordinator for deafness cases throughout the country for a major employers liability insurance company. Has lectured to a number of insurance companies on industrial disease, limitation and changes in the rules of the High Court and County Court.

Prof. Membership: Law Society.

Career: Qualified in 1968. Joined *Cartwrights* in 1969 and became a Partner in 1972. Member of Bristol Civil Courts Users Committee.

Personal: Born 23rd September 1941. Educated at Caerphilly Grammar School 1953-60, then Balliol College, Oxford 1960-63. Leisure pursuits include theatre, reading, swimming and tennis. Lives in Bristol.

Voller, Edward

Warner Goodman & Streat, Fareham (01329) 288121.

Williams, Alun C.

Hay & Kilner, Newcastle-upon-Tyne (0191) 232 8345. Partner in Personal Injury Department.

Specialisation: Has specialised in personal injury work for plaintiffs and defendants since 1979. Also handles health and safety and road traffic work.

Prof. Membership: Personal Injury Panel, FOIL.

Career: Qualified in 1979. Joined *Hay & Kilner* in 1977, becoming a Partner in 1982.

Personal: Born 7th August 1955. Attended Newcastle University 1973-76. Leisure interests include military history, football, reading and music. Lives in Newcastle-upon-Tyne.

Williams, Gareth J.

Hugh James Jones & Jenkins, Cardiff (01222) 224871. Qualified 1976. Partner 1978. Litigation Department. Handles mainly personal injury litigation for insurers. Has acted for insurers for almost 20 years and undertaken the usual range of personal injury work. Also deals with commercial litigation acting for a number of local companies.

Williams, Robin

Leo Abse & Cohen, Cardiff (01222) 383252. Partner in Litigation Department.

Specialisation: Principal area of practice covers personal injury claims, employment and Trade Union law. Advises BIFU, GMB and TGWU, various insurance companies, business and private clients. Acts in industrial disease cases including asbestosis, deafness, asthma, RSI and dermatitis. Also handles fatal accident claims, employment injunctions and has extensive experience of all complaints to the Industrial Tribunal including mass dismissal claims, sex discrimination cases, transfer regulations disputes. Has acted in general Chancery and Commercial cases, particularly contested probate actions, winding up petitions and bancruptcy. Lectures on personal injury, employment and Trade Union Law.

Prof. Membership: Law Society, APIL, Personal Injury Panel.

Career: Qualified in 1980 while with *Leo Abse & Cohen* and became a Partner in 1985.

Personal: Born 15th October 1955. Attended Glanafan Comprehensive School 1966-74 and London School of Economics 1974-77. School Governor. Leisure pursuits include sport (rugby, soccer and badminton), theatre, art, cinema, modern music and reading. Lives in Cardiff.

Williams, Brian

A.E. Wyeth & Co, Dartford (01322) 297000. Qualified 1965. Partner, 1965. Insurance Litigation Department. Principal area is personal injury work. Also product liability and professional indemnity claims.

Wilson, Anthony E.

Hill Dickinson Davis Campbell, Liverpool (0151) 236 5400. Partner in Insurance Litigation Department.

Specialisation: Main area of practice is defendant personal injury work and professional indemnity cases. Acts on behalf of insurers in road traffic, employers and public liability claims with special interest in serious injury cases. Involved in professional indemnity work for consulting engineers, surveyors and veterinary surgeons. Handled the industrial dispute at Cammell Laird Shipbuilders in 1984, where the strikers had been imprisoned: successfully defended the actions before the Court of Appeal. Lectures to insurers on personal injury claims.

Prof. Membership: Law Society, Liverpool Law Society and FOIL.

Career: Qualified in 1977. Joined *Hill Dickinson Davis Campbell* in 1977, becoming a Partner in 1981. Head of Insurance Litigation Department 1992-94. Appointed Managing Partner in 1994.

Personal: Born 23rd December 1951. Attended St Francis Xaviers Grammar School 1963-70, Nottingham University 1970-73

and Chester College of Law 1973-74. Leisure interests include hockey, skiing, tennis, golf, collecting antiques and water colours and enjoying fine wines. Lives in Liverpool.

Wolfe, Jeremy B.

Douglas Jones & Mercer, Swansea (01792) 650000.

Specialisation: Has acted for insurers for almost 20 years in the usual range of personal injury work including local authority related claims, lifting accidents, R.S.I. and asbestosis claims.

Prof. Membership: Law Society, Forum of Insurance Lawyers, Member of the Law Society Personal Injury Panel.

Career: Joined *Douglas-Jones & Mercer* in 1976 and qualified in 1978. Became a Partner in 1982.

Personal: Born 29 April 1954. Attended Redditch County High School and obtained London University (External) LL.B in 1975. Leisure pursuits include sport (particularly cricket and fishing).

Zindani, Jeffry

Russell Jones & Walker, Birmingham (0121) 643 6800. Qualified 1989. Partner 1992. Personal Injury and Medical Negligence Department. Undertakes trade union and private client work. Also deals with employment law.

FIRMS OF ACCOUNTANTS

Accountants specialising in litigation support are listed in the accountants' A-Z, with details of the services they offer to solicitors, from forensic accounting to intellectual property or business valuations. This section is found immediately after the main solicitors' A-Z.

PLANNING

LONDON

The three most highly recommended planning firms are *Berwin Leighton*, *Clifford Chance* and *Norton Rose*.

LEADING FIRMS – LONDON	
BERWIN LEIGHTON	CLIFFORD CHANCE
NORTON ROSE	
S J BERWIN & CO	HERBERT SMITH
DENTON HALL	LINKLATERS & PAINES
McKENNA & CO	

Berwin Leighton's planning department, containing amongst others, Nicholas Taylor, Geoffrey Crighton, Timothy Pugh and Ian Trehearne is noted for its strength in depth. The firm has an enviable client list including AMEC, Blue Circle, BAA, British Gas, English Partnerships, Tesco and Property Holdings (the Government's property arm) and has recently handled the public inquiry into the first privately funded toll road motorway scheme in the UK.

The planning unit at *Clifford Chance* comprises seven specialists, three of whom are partners. Best known for their corporate work, Brian Hall and Tony Ward operate mainly as a support unit for the firm's corporate clientele.

Brian Greenwood at *Norton Rose* represents institutions such as English Heritage, Eastern Electricity (on the proposal for a new power station in King's Lynn), Castle Cement Ltd (on a proposed quarry site in Lancashire) and Spitalfields Development Group on the redevelopment of the former Spitalfields market.

Other firms with leading planning departments include *S.J.Berwin & Co, Denton Hall, Herbert Smith, Linklaters & Paines* and *McKenna & Co.*

S.J.Berwin & Co's planning department boasts London's most consistently recommended planning specialist, Patricia Thomas, who not only advises on issues relating to development projects on a national scale, but also contributes to leading planning texts.

Despite the loss of Geoffrey Searle, *Denton Hall* retains a fairly high profile. The planning unit is now headed by Helen Norris who advises Sainsburys, Marks & Spencer, Ladbrokes, Equitable Life, Barclays Bank, Co-operative Retail Services (on Channel Tunnel and Cross Rail Project matters) and Brighton Health Care NHS Trust.

HIGHLY REGARDED – LONDON	
EVERSHEDS	FRESHFIELDS
GOULDENS	NABARRO NATHANSON
SIMMONS & SIMMONS	SLAUGHTER AND MAY
TITMUSS SAINER DECHERT	
ALLEN & OVERY	ALSOP WILKINSON
ASHURST MORRIS CRISP	CAMERON MARKBY HEWITT
DAVIES ARNOLD COOPER	D J FREEMAN
FARRER & CO	FORSYTE SAUNDERS KERMAN
FRERE CHOLMELEY BISCHOFF	GEOFFREY SEARLE
HAMMOND SUDDARDS	LAWRENCE GRAHAM
LOVELL WHITE DURRANT	MACFARLANES
NICHOLSON GRAHAM & JONES	RADCLIFFES CROSSMAN BLOCK
ROWE & MAW	STEPHENSON HARWOOD
TAYLOR JOYNSON GARRETT	THEODORE GODDARD
WILDE SAPTE	
PENNINGTONS	

LEADING INDIVIDUALS – LONDON		
Ian C. Gatenby *McKenna & Co*	Brian J. Greenwood *Norton Rose*	Patricia E. Thomas *S J Berwin & Co*
David M.J. Brock *Herbert Smith*	David Cooper *Gouldens*	Geoffrey Crighton *Berwin Leighton*
Michael D. Cunliffe *Ashurst Morris Crisp*	Martin Edwards *Titmuss Sainer Dechert*	D.F. Evans *Theodore Goddard*
Brian Hall *Clifford Chance*	Garry Hart *Herbert Smith*	David Hawkins *Nabarro Nathanson*
Tony B. Kitson *McKenna & Co*	Richard Max *D J Freeman*	Helen Norris *Denton Hall*
Timothy J. Pugh *Berwin Leighton*	Steven J. Scates *Nicholson Graham & Jones*	Geoffrey Searle *Geoffrey Searle*
Nicholas Taylor *Berwin Leighton*	Ian Trehearne *Berwin Leighton*	
Rod Ainsworth *Eversheds*	Sandra Banks *Denton Hall*	John Bosworth *Ashurst Morris Crisp*
N.A.P. Cheshire *Turner Kenneth Brown*	Michael Gallimore *Lovell White Durrant*	John Garbutt *Nicholson Graham & Jones*
Gary Graves *Nabarro Nathanson*	Richard Hillebron *Slaughter and May*	Norna Hughes *Nabarro Nathanson*
William Innes *Ashurst Morris Crisp*	Raymond K. Jackson *Linklaters & Paines*	Barry S. Jeeps *Stephenson Harwood*
Robert Lewis *Freshfields*	Ian Mackay *McKenna & Co*	Laurence Messer *Davies Arnold Cooper*
Teige O'Donovan *Farrer & Co*	Peter Purton *Norton Rose*	John Qualtrough *Simmons & Simmons*
Michael Redman *Clifford Chance*	Christopher Rees *Davies Arnold Cooper*	Paul Shadarevian *Norton Rose*
Roger Sherlock *Nabarro Nathanson*	Brian Smith *Wilde Sapte*	Peter Stevens *Jeffrey Green Russell*
Anne Tideswell *Rowe & Maw*	Angela Turner *Gouldens*	Tony Ward *Clifford Chance*
Martin Wells *Stephenson Harwood*		

In all the tables the names in each group are listed alphabetically.

The planning unit at *Herbert Smith*, headed by Garry Hart, numbers four specialist partners who undertake a variety of work for public and private sector clients. The firm has been involved in some of the largest development projects of recent years and is particularly strong in the minerals sector. David Brock has also been highly recommended.

Linklaters & Paines planning unit has recently advised on the redevelopment of the National Opera House and neighbouring properties, represented British Airways on the Terminal 5 inquiry and represented BP as lead objector against the CrossRail Bill.

Ian Gatenby and Tony Kitson of *McKenna & Co* handle a substantial amount of property development, new settlements and town expansion schemes and infrastructure work.

Since leaving *Denton Hall*, Geoffrey Searle has launched his own niche planning practice in London. Acting for both commercial/landowning principals and professionals on a referral system, he tailors his services to the needs of the client, either by providing a strategic overview, negotiating for planning permission or advising on inquiries.

Following Lesley McDonagh's appointment to joint managing partner, *Lovell White Durrant's* planning department has been left in the capable hands of Michael Gallimore.

Other notable practitioners include Michael Cunliffe of *Ashurst Morris Crisp,* who acts for developers and planning authorities, Richard Max of *D J Freeman* who represents retailers, developers and local authorities, David Cooper of *Gouldens* (particularly known for his advocacy skills) and David Hawkins of *Nabarro Nathanson* who handles large scale commercial developments and major public inquiries.

Steven Scates of *Nicholson Graham & Jones,* Douglas Evans of *Theodore Goddard*, and Martin Edwards of *Titmuss Sainer Dechert* are also held in high regard.

SOUTH EAST

Planning practices in the South East tend to revolve around one or two highly respected practitioners such as Robert Hinton of *Griffith Smith* and James Little of *Wollastons* (author of 'Planning Controls and their Enforcement'). *Donne Mileham & Haddock* is an exception to the rule having formed Donne Mileham & Haddock Planning Services, now in its second year, which combines both chartered planning and legal expertise. Anthony Allen heads the team of

HIGHLY REGARDED – SOUTH EAST

BREEZE & WYLES *Hertford*	CLARKS *Reading*
CRIPPS HARRIES HALL *Tunbridge Wells*	DONNE MILEHAM & HADDOCK *Brighton*
E. EDWARDS SON & NOICE	FITZHUGH GATES *Brighton*
GRIFFITH SMITH *Brighton*	PITMANS *Reading*
WOLLASTONS *Chelmsford*	
ARGLES & COURT *Maidstone*	BRACHERS *Maidstone*
DUTTON GREGORY & WILLIAMS *Winchester*	MOORE & BLATCH *Southampton*
SHERRARDS *St. Albans*	

nine, providing a comprehensive service for developers, health care trusts and land owners.

Other notable practitioners include Simon Dimmick at *Clarks* (whose team handles all types of planning appeals, Local Plan and CPO inquiries and tribunal work) and Richard Valentine of *Pitmans* who advises on development strategy, major planning appeals and judicial reviews.

Three further practices worthy of note are *Breeze & Wyles, Cripps Harries Hall* which has recently won a complex enquiry on behalf of the property holding subsidiary of a top ten insurance company, and *Fitzhugh Gates*.

LEADING INDIVIDUALS – SOUTH EAST

Henry Abraham *Brachers*	
Anthony J.R. Allen *Donne Mileham & Haddock*	
Simon Dimmick *Clarks*	
Michael Haynes *E. Edwards Son & Noice*	
Robert Hinton *Griffith Smith*	
A. James Little *Wollastons*	
J. Richard H. Valentine *Pitmans*	

SOUTH WEST

Bevan Ashford, Burges Salmon, Clarke Wilmott & Clarke and *Lawrence Tucketts* have the most highly respected planning practices in Bristol.

Bevan Ashford's planning department specialises in appeals and local enquiries. The team, headed by the highly regarded David Wood, comprises seven specialists (two of whom operate from the Exeter office). Rena Young has been recommended as a rising star.

HIGHLY REGARDED – SOUTH WEST

BEVAN ASHFORD *Bristol*	BURGES SALMON *Bristol*
CLARKE WILLMOTT & CLARKE *Taunton*	LAWRENCE TUCKETTS *Bristol*
BOND PEARCE *Plymouth*	FOOT & BOWDEN *Plymouth*
LESTER ALDRIDGE *Bournemouth*	LYONS DAVIDSON *Bristol*
OSBORNE CLARKE *Bristol*	TOZERS *Exeter*
CARTWRIGHTS *Bristol*	CHARLES RUSSELL *Cheltenham*
DAVIES AND PARTNERS *Gloucester*	

In addition to handling a wide variety of planning work for its property clients, *Burges Salmon* has developed specialist expertise in the planning aspects of telecommunications and windfarm projects. Patrick Robinson, who heads the department of five is the first lawyer in private practice in Bristol to be admitted to both of the country's leading professional town planning bodies.

Clarke Willmott & Clarke covers the entire range of planning issues for a number of well-known industrial, commercial and housing developers. Martin Goodall, Nick Engert and John Houghton (formerly of *Denton Hall*) have considerable experience in conducting appeals, High Court challenges and judicial reviews.

Stephen Pasterfield, Craig Begg and Sue Otty of *Lawrence Tucketts* are all noted for their wide ranging expertise. Primarily known for its work for institutions such as the Bristol

Development Corporation, the firm also advises the minerals and waste industries.

Other firms worthy of note include *Lyons Davidson* (where Kevin Gibbs has been recommended) and *Osborne Clarke* (which has recently heightened its profile with the appointment of Tracey Merrett, described as a 'rising star').

Outside Bristol, *Bond Pearce* emerges as the leading planning practice. The firm has a strong environmental bias with Marcus Trinick being recommended in both areas.

Other firms with planning expertise include *Foot & Bowden* (where William Jones is recommended), *Lester Aldridge* and *Tozers*, chiefly in the guise of Peter McMurtrie.

LEADING INDIVIDUALS – SOUTH WEST

Craig Begg *Lawrence Tucketts*	
Martin Goodall *Clarke Willmott & Clarke*	
John Houghton *Clarke Willmott & Clarke*	
Stephen Pasterfield *Lawrence Tucketts*	
Patrick Robinson *Burges Salmon*	
Marcus Trinick *Bond Pearce*	
David Wood *Bevan Ashford*	
Tony Beard *Tozers*	
Nick Engert *Clarke Willmott & Clarke*	
Kevin Gibbs *Lyons Davidson*	
William Jones *Foot & Bowden*	
Peter M. McMurtrie *Tozers*	
Sue Otty *Lawrence Tucketts*	
Emrys J. Parry *Cartwrights*	

UP AND COMING

Tracey Merrett *Osborne Clarke*
Rena Young *Bevan Ashford*

WALES

Eversheds (Cardiff) has one of the largest planning practices in Wales. Its department, headed by Eric Evans, has considerable experience in all aspects of planning and compulsory

LEADING FIRMS – WALES

EDWARDS GELDARD *Cardiff*	**EVERSHEDS** *Cardiff*
MORGAN BRUCE *Cardiff*	

purchase work and advises clients such as the Cardiff Bay Development Corporation and the Welsh Development Agency (along with *Edwards Geldard* and *Morgan Bruce*), the Land Authority for Wales, and Celtic Energy. The firm has also recently represented Cardiff Wales Airport on an inquiry into a proposed waste site.

HIGHLY REGARDED – WALES

ALAN T. JENKINS & CO	
BEVAN ASHFORD *Cardiff*	**DOLMANS** *Cardiff*
HUGH JAMES JONES & JENKINS *Cardiff*	**LEO ABSE & COHEN** *Cardiff*
UNGOED THOMAS & KING *Carmarthen*	

Other highly respected firms include *Edwards Geldard* and *Morgan Bruce*.

Edwards Geldard has an excellent reputation not only for planning applications and appeal work, but also for the environmental aspects of planning work. Huw Williams is held in high regard.

Peter Burgess of *Morgan Bruce* acts for a number of public sector clients in the region, advising on major infrastructure, engineering and new energy products.

Keith Edwards of *Alan T. Jenkins & Co* is also noted for his planning expertise.

LEADING INDIVIDUALS – WALES

Peter Burgess *Morgan Bruce*
Keith Edwards *Alan T. Jenkins & Co*
Eric C. Evans *Eversheds*
Huw R.C. Williams *Edwards Geldard*

MIDLANDS

The leading planning firms in Birmingham are *Edge & Ellison* and *Eversheds*. Both have considerable experience in planning appeals and inquiries, enforcement actions and compulsory purchase. Martin Damms of *Edge & Ellison* and Peter Battye of *Eversheds* are leaders in the field.

LEADING FIRMS – MIDLANDS

EDGE & ELLISON *Birmingham*	**EVERSHEDS** *Birmingham*

Martin White of *Pinsent Curtis* provides a comprehensive planning service including compulsory purchase, acquisition and development control work.

Other firms with planning expertise include *Dibb Lupton Broomhead*, *Martineau Johnson* and *Wragge & Co*.

HIGHLY REGARDED – MIDLANDS

BROWNE JACOBSON *Nottingham*	**DIBB LUPTON BROOMHEAD** *Birmingham*
MARTINEAU JOHNSON *Birmingham*	**SHOOSMITHS & HARRISON** *Northampton*
WRAGGE & CO *Birmingham*	
MARRON DODDS *Leicester*	**PINSENT CURTIS** *Birmingham*
FREETH CARTWRIGHT HUNT DICKINS *Nottingham*	**KNIGHT & SONS** *Newcastle-under-Lyme*
WALL, JAMES & DAVIES *Stourbridge*	

Outside Birmingham, *Browne Jacobson* and *Shoosmiths & Harrison* were consistently recommended.

Of the smaller firms, *Marron Dodds* (and Peter Marron in particular) has a sound reputation for inquiry and judicial review work.

LEADING INDIVIDUALS – MIDLANDS

Peter G. Battye *Eversheds*
Martin Damms *Edge & Ellison*
Peter Marron *Marron Dodds*
Martin White *Pinsent Curtis*

EAST ANGLIA

Mills & Reeve takes the lion's share of planning work in East Anglia. Beverley Firth has an excellent reputation for appeal, inquiry and judicial review work.

Other firms providing a comprehensive planning service include *Birketts, Eversheds, Hewitson Becke + Shaw, Leathes Prior* and *Steele & Co.*

Felix Bourne of *Birketts* is a highly experienced planning law specialist. As the author of several texts on the subject, he is well equipped to advise on any planning issue.

HIGHLY REGARDED – EAST ANGLIA	
BIRKETTS *Ipswich*	**EVERSHEDS** *Norwich*
HEWITSON BECKE + SHAW *Cambridge*	**LEATHES PRIOR** *Norwich*
STEELE & CO *Norwich*	

The team at *Eversheds* advises a broad client base from individual landowners to major institutions on all issues including agreements, enforcement proceedings and local plan representations.

Hewitson Becke + Shaw's planning department comprises two partners, both of whom are members of the Law Society's Specialist Planning Law Panel and Associates of Royal Town Planning Institute.

LEADING INDIVIDUALS – EAST ANGLIA
Felix J.B. Bourne *Birketts*
Beverley J. Firth *Mills & Reeve*

NORTH WEST

Halliwell Landau maintains its position as the pre-eminent firm in Manchester in planning with Roger Lancaster the most highly recommended practitioner. The firm carries out local plan and UDP inquiries, compulsory purchase work and enforcement proceeding work for major housebuilders, food retailers and manufacturers and development corporations.

LEADING FIRMS – NORTH WEST
HALLIWELL LANDAU *Manchester*

Addleshaw Sons & Latham and *Masons* (John Moritz) are also held in high regard and were consistently recommended for their all-round expertise.

HIGHLY REGARDED – NORTH WEST	
AARON & PARTNERS *Chester*	**ADDLESHAW SONS & LATHAM** *Manchester*
COBBETT LEAK ALMOND *Manchester*	**DAVIES WALLIS FOYSTER** *Liverpool*
MASONS *Manchester*	
ALSOP WILKINSON *Liverpool*	
	BULLIVANT JONES & CO *Liverpool*

In all the tables the names in each group are listed alphabetically.

Simon Carter and Ian Kinloch at *Aaron & Partners* also have considerable experience in the field, having both held posts as senior planning lawyers in local government prior to returning to private practice.

Other firms with strong reputations include *Cobbett Leak Almond*, where Peter Oldham is well respected, and *Davies Wallis Foyster.*

LEADING INDIVIDUALS – NORTH WEST
Roger Lancaster *Halliwell Landau*
Simon Carter *Aaron & Partners*
Ian Kinloch *Aaron & Partners*
John Moritz *Masons*
Peter M.B. Oldham *Cobbett Leak Almond*
Brian Wake *Aaron & Partners*

NORTH EAST

Since it was established in 1994 as the first niche planning practice in the UK, *Peter Wilbraham & Co* has expanded rapidly and now comprises four specialist lawyers. At the time of going to print, the highly respected Roger Suddards (Peter Wilbraham's former colleague at *Hammond Suddards*) was expected to join the firm along with a senior planning solicitor from Leeds City Council. The firm enjoys

LEADING FIRMS – NORTH EAST
PETER WILBRAHAM & CO *Leeds*

a national reputation and advises developers, land owners and public authorities within the region and further afield. By combining a top quality service with fees which are significantly lower than the average commercial firm, *Peter Wilbraham & Co* maintains its position as the pre-eminent planning practice in the North East, and Peter Wilbraham, the doyen of planning law.

HIGHLY REGARDED – NORTH EAST	
BOOTH & CO. *Leeds*	**EVERSHEDS** *Leeds*
HAMMOND SUDDARDS *Leeds*	**NABARRO NATHANSON** *Doncaster*
PINSENT CURTIS	**WALKER MORRIS** *Leeds*
DICKINSON DEES *Newcastle*	**OXLEY & COWARD** *Rotherham*
WARD HADAWAY *Newcastle*	
MINCOFF SCIENCE & GOLD *Newcastle*	

Hammond Suddards maintains its high profile despite the loss of two of their planning specialists to *Peter Wilbraham & Co.* David Goodman is held in particularly high regard.

Other firms with strong planning departments include *Booth & Co,* known for their strong client base of local authorities, developers and institutions, *Eversheds* and *Nabarro Nathanson.*

The planning team at *Eversheds* (Leeds), headed by Paul Winter, not only includes several solicitors who started their career in local government, but also two members of the Law Society's Specialist Planning Law Panel and Legal Associate Members of the Royal Town Planning Institute. Recent work has included major 'flagship' urban regeneration projects and large City Grant projects, including the agreement for one of the largest City Grants ever awarded (£8.3 million).

Nabarro Nathanson has developed a particular specialism in the mineral, water and industrial sectors.

Pinsent Curtis' planning department undertakes a variety of work, the senior specialists advising professional organisations such as the TCPA and RTPI. Amanda Beresford has been recommended.

The planning unit at *Walker Morris* comprises six full-time fee earners (Andrew Williamson has been recommended) and handles a broad spectrum of work across the UK. The firm has a particular reputation for complex out of town development schemes involving land in the green belt.

Other firms consistently recommended include *Dickinson Dees, Oxley & Coward* and *Ward Hadaway* (Malcolm Bell). At *Dickinson Dees* Paul Taylor represents housing developers (including Bellway Homes Ltd) and Hassall Homes Ltd and clients within the mining industry including Coal Contractors Ltd.

SCOTLAND

The larger Scottish firms handle most of the planning work in Scotland.

Brodies WS represents property development companies, national multiple retailers and local authorities. Neil Collar at the firm is highly recommended.

HIGHLY REGARDED – SCOTLAND	
BRODIES WS *Edinburgh*	**W & J BURNESS WS** *Edinburgh*
DUNDAS & WILSON CS *Edinburgh*	**LEDINGHAM CHALMERS** *Aberdeen*
MACLAY MURRAY & SPENS *Glasgow*	**McGRIGOR DONALD** *Glasgow*
SHEPHERD & WEDDERBURN *Edinburgh*	
ARCHIBALD CAMPBELL & HARLEY *Edinburgh*	**BIGGART BAILLIE & GIFFORD** *Glasgow*
BIRD SEMPLE *Glasgow*	**PAULL & WILLIAMSONS** *Aberdeen*
STEEDMAN RAMAGE WS *Edinburgh*	
BRECHIN ROBB *Glasgow*	

Martin Sales of *W & J Burness WS* is regarded as being a highly experienced planning specialist. Particularly known for development work, he has been involved in the Harris Superquarry inquiry, one of the longest running public inquiries in Scotland.

Dundas & Wilson CS undertakes public inquiry work and has particular experience in retail, housing and countryside development. The highly respected Ann Faulds is a regular contributor to 'Scottish Planning & Environmental Law'.

The planning unit at *Ledingham Chalmers* primarily services the commercial property department, but is well respected in its own right. *Maclay Murray & Spens* specialises in industrial, commercial and housing related projects. *McGrigor Donald* (Craig Connal) is particularly known for advice on contentious issues.

Kay McCorquodale of *Shepherd & Wedderburn* advises on all planning issues.

LEADING INDIVIDUALS – NORTH EAST
Peter Wilbraham *Peter Wilbraham & Co*
Amanda Beresford *Pinsent Curtis*
David Goodman *Hammond Suddards*
Roger Suddards *Peter Wilbraham & Co*
Paul A.T. Taylor *Dickinson Dees*
Andrew J. Williamson *Walker Morris*
Paul E.A. Winter *Eversheds*
Malcolm Bell *Ward Hadaway*
Michael Renger *Nabarro Nathanson*
J. Neil Robson *Ward Hadaway*

LEADING INDIVIDUALS – SCOTLAND
Neil Collar *Brodies WS*
R. Craig Connal *McGrigor Donald*
Ann Faulds *Dundas & Wilson CS*
Kay McCorquodale *Shepherd & Wedderburn*
Martin Sales *W & J Burness WS*
Eric Young *Archibald Campbell & Harley*
Jeremy Rowan-Robinson *Paull & Williamsons*
G. Bruce Smith *Paull & Williamsons*

LEADERS IN PLANNING

LONDON

Ainsworth, Rod

Eversheds, London (0171) 919 4500.

Banks, Sandra

Denton Hall, London (0171) 242 1212. Partner in Planning, Environmental Groups and Property Department.

Specialisation: Main areas of practice are development projects and planning appeals.

Has handled a number of major development projects including factories, offices, landfill sites, a proposed scheme for the redevelopment of Herstmonceux Castle, business, research and teaching facilities, golf courses and a major development in East London, involving urban regeneration of 600 acres of largely derelict land. Has acted as advocate before courts and tribunals including public inquiries, prosecutions and civil claims. Also handles statutory and Parliamentary work, particularly transport related and has represented owners affected by recent rail projects, e.g. the Crossrail Bill, and the Channel Tunnel Rail Link. Has lectured for the Law Society and others on public law and judicial review. Author of 'Practical Planning Appeals and Inquiries' for Longman. Examiner for the Joint Examination Board of the Law Society and the Royal Town Planning Institute.

Prof. Membership: Legal Associate Member of the Royal Town Planning Institute, UKELA, Law Society's Planning Panel, Fellow of the Royal Society of Arts.

Bosworth, John

Ashurst Morris Crisp, London (0171) 638 1111. Qualified 1988. Senior Assistant. Planning Department. Main area of practice is planning. Also covers environmental and parliamentary work. Born 19.10.1964.

Brock, David M.J.

See under Environmental Law.

Cheshire, N.A.P.

Nabarro Nathanson, London (0171) 242 6006.

Cooper, David

Gouldens, London (0171) 583 7777. Partner in Planning Department.

Specialisation: Has conducted approximately 800 Planning Inquiries on behalf of such clients as ADT Auctions Group, Hanson Properties Limited, Arlington Securities, P&O Developments, ARC Properties, Tarmac Properties, GRE Properties, British Aerospace, Sally UK, Alton Towers and Group Lotus, the majority of them as Advocate. Has also acted on behalf of groups concerned with the conservation of important buildings in London and the Provinces including SAVE Britain's Heritage, the Covent Garden Resident's Association, the Georgian Society and the Victorian Society. Also handles white collar crime work.

Prof. Membership: Law Society Planning Panel, Legal Associate of the Royal Town Planning Institute.

Career: Qualified in 1967. Gained experience in the planning field with George Wimpey Limited before joining *Gouldens* as a Partner in 1973.

Personal: Born 8th June 1942. Took an LLB(Hons) in 1960. Lives in London SW1.

Crighton, Geoffrey

Berwin Leighton, London (0171) 623 3144. Chartered Town Planner and Associate in Planning & Environment Department.

Specialisation: Planning and environment law specialist involved in retail developments throughout the country and major housing schemes in Southern England.

Career: Background in local government, having worked for Lancashire County Council, Staffordshire County Council and Milton Keynes Development Corporation. Joined *Berwin Leighton* as a Senior Associate in 1980.

Personal: Born in 1943. Educated at the Royal Masonic School (MBA, DipTp, MRTPI).

Cunliffe, Michael D.

Ashurst Morris Crisp, London London (0171) 972 7367. Qualified 1974. Partner 1983. Head of the Planning Group. Principal area of practice is planning law. Legal Associate of the Royal Town Planning Institute and Member of the Law Society's Specialist Planning Panel.

Edwards, Martin

Titmuss Sainer Dechert, London (0171) 583 5353. Partner and Head of Planning and Environment Unit.

Specialisation: Principal areas of practice are planning, environment, highways, local government and C.P.O. work. Handles all aspects of planning and environmental law, including advocacy before inquiries and the courts. Recent matters include prosecution on behalf of a local authority of developers for noise and dust nuisance arising from the construction of the Limehouse Link in the London Docklands, advice and conduct of the defence of a client prosecuted after a major river pollution incident, advice to a client involved in a major dispute with HMIP regarding an authorisation under Part 1 of the Environmental Protection Act and advice on the application of the new Waste Management Licensing Regulations to a client company burning solvent based fuels. Has handled a major redevelopment of over 100 acres of redundant land in Inner London for a mixture of retail, office, leisure and residential uses, including representations to the local planning inquiry and a six week planning appeal inquiry involving policy, highways, conservation area, listed building and design issues. Has also handled a major rating appeal (Clement v Addis) in the Court of Appeal and the House of Lords. Member of the Law Society's Specialist Planning Panel and Legal Associate of the Royal Town Planning Institute. Lectures frequently on a wide range of environmental and planning law issues and writes numerous articles for journals such as *The Estates Gazette* and the *Journal of Planning and Environmental Law*. Member of the Editorial Board of *Land Contamination and Reclamation*. Also runs in-house client and training seminars on environmental law.

Prof. Membership: UK Environmental Law Association, International Bar Association, Worshipful Company of Solicitors, Freeman of the City of London, City of London Law Society (Planning and Environmental Law Sub-Committee).

Career: Qualified in 1981. Became a Partner at *Titmuss Sainer & Webb* (now *Titmuss Sainer Dechert*) in 1992. (Formerly solicitor with Cambridge City Council).

Personal: Educated at the University of Kent at Canterbury (BA Hons, 1978) and De Montfort University, Leicester (MA in Environmental Law, 1994).

Evans, D.F.

Theodore Goddard, London (0171) 606 8855. Qualified 1978. Partner 1990. Property Department. Specialises in planning and environment law. Member of City of London Solicitors Company Planning and Environment Sub-Committee and the Law Society's Specialist Planning Panel. Born 17.1. 1953.

Gallimore, Michael

Lovell White Durrant, London (0171) 236 0066. Qualified 1983. Partner 1988.

Planning and Environmental Department. Advises on major developments and infrastructure projects.

Garbutt, John

See under Environmental Law.

Gatenby, Ian C.

McKenna & Co, London (0171) 606 9000. Partner in Planning Group.

Specialisation: Over 28 years specialist practical experience of town and country planning, environmental and public law matters. Involvement in major projects includes Channel Tunnel, Heathrow Terminals Four and Five, Gatwick North Terminal, Stansted Airport extension, Severn Barrage feasibility studies, various town expansion schemes and Birmingham North Relief Road. Specialist in rating matters, including test cases in the Lands Tribunal and Superior Courts. Also extensive experience in land compensation matters and co-operative schemes between landowners and developers.

Prof. Membership: Law Society Planning Panel, Royal Town Planning Institute (Legal Associate), City of London Law Society (Member of Planning and Environmental Sub-Committee), Land Use Society, Parliamentary Agent (Roll B).

Career: Qualified in 1968 while with *Lovell White & King*. Joined *McKenna & Co* in 1975 and became a Partner in 1977.

Personal: Born 30th June 1942. Attended Exeter College, Oxford. Leisure pursuits include sailing, skiing, English National opera and gardening. Lives in London.

Graves, Gary

Nabarro Nathanson, London (0171) 493 9933. Qualified 1983. Partner 1991. Planning Department. Handles all aspects of planning law. Born 19.1.1958.

Greenwood, Brian J.

Norton Rose, London (0171) 283 6000. Head of Planning and Environmental Law Group.

Specialisation: Main areas of practice cover planning and environmental law. Includes advice on all aspects of planning, advocacy and environmental advice for corporate, banking and property clients. Environmental aspects of project finance, sales and acquisitions, including a number of power station projects, paper mill, car industry acquisition. Current planning instructions include proposed landfill, airport expansion, mineral extraction, office development, retail proposal, petroleum infrastructure. The firm acts as external legal advisor to English Heritage. Lectures frequently on environmental and planning law.

Principal author 'Butterworth's Planning Law Service'. Editor 'Butterworths Planning Law Handbook'. Co-author - 'Environmental Regulation and Economic Growth' (Clarendon Press).

Prof. Membership: Chairman City of

London Law Society's Planning and Environmental Law Sub-Committttee; Law Society Planning and Environmental Law Committee; CBI Environmental Protection Panel; UKELA; Law Society's Specialist Planning Panel.

Career: Qualified 1976 with Westminster City Council. South Yorkshire County Council 1976-78. Senior Solicitor, then Assistant County Solicitor, Kent County Council 1978-82. Chief Solicitor, Bedfordshire County Council 1982-85. Joined *Norton Rose* in 1985, Partner 1988.

Personal: Born 15th April 1950. Attended Forest School, then Southampton University 1969-72. College of Law 1973. Honorary Solicitor to Music Masters' and Mistresses' Association. Fellow of the Royal Society of Arts. Leisure pursuits comprise family and classical music. Lives in Bedford.

Hall, Brian
Clifford Chance, London (0171) 600 1000. Partner. Principal areas of practice are local government, planning and environment work.

Hart, Garry
Herbert Smith, London (0171) 374 8000. Partner and Head of Commercial Property and Planning Department.

Specialisation: Development projects include Coin Street, Victoria Plaza, Lutyens House, Moor House, Broadgate, Kings Cross, Tower Place, the South Bank Centre and Bankside Power Station. Editor of 'Blundell & Dobry' (4th and 5th editions).

Career: Joined *Herbert Smith* in 1962. Qualified in 1965. Partner since 1970.

Personal: Born in 1940. Educated at Northgate Grammar School, Ipswich and University College, London (LL.B). Leisure pursuits include sheep farming in Wales and talking. Lives in London.

Hawkins, David
Nabarro Nathanson, London (0171) 493 9933. Qualified 1967. Partner 1978. Planning department. Work covers town planning, administrative law, compulsory purchase, rating and Parliamentary law. Born 17.10.1941.

Hillebron, Richard
Slaughter and May, London (0171) 600 1200. Qualified 1980. Assistant Solicitor. Litigation Department. Main area of practice is town and country planning. Also handles environmental matters.

Hughes, Norna
Nabarro Nathanson, London (0171) 493 9933. Partner. Planning Department. Handles all aspects, particularly contentious planning work. Also handles Tribunal work.

Innes, William
Ashurst Morris Crisp, London (0171) 638 1111. Qualified 1972. Partner 1988.

Property and Planning Departments. 25 years' experience in public and private sectors and advising developers.

Jackson, Raymond K.
Linklaters & Paines, London (0171) 606 7080. Qualified 1979. Joined 1985. Has extensive experience in both the public and private sectors of all town planning matters.

Jeeps, Barry S.
Stephenson Harwood, London (0171) 329 4422. Qualified 1980. Partner 1989. Head of Town & Country Planning Group. Specialises in town and country planning work. Born 17.3.1958.

Kitson, Tony B.
McKenna & Co, London (0171) 606 9000. Partner in Planning Group.

Specialisation: Advises on the planning aspects of all sizes and types of property development. Has handled numerous appeals involving retail, office, industrial and residential developments, and appears as an advocate at public local inquiries. Experienced in negotiating and drafting Section 106 Agreements and other development agreements. Advises on all aspects of local authority law and administration, capital expenditure restrictions and the local government finance implications of joint venture agreements. Advises on compulsory purchase and compensation, and Transport and Works Act schemes. Has advised NHS Trusts and government departments. Also provides advice and representation on all rating matters. Speaker at seminars on planning and environmental law, local government law and rating reform. Advises on the clean-up of contaminated industrial sites and disposal for redevelopment. Has petitioned Parliament on behalf of land owners and developers affected by the Jubilee Line and light rail schemes, and advised on the planning and works powers aspects of privatisation of the electricity and water industries. Contributor to Solicitors Journal, Law Society's Gazette, Journal of Planning and Environmental Law and *McKenna & Co* publications on planning, highways, compulsory purchase and rating.

Prof. Membership: Law Society, Law Society's Panel of Planning Solicitors. City of London Solicitors Company.

Career: Qualified in 1975. Solicitor, London Borough of Newham 1975-77. Principal Solicitor, London Borough of Islington 1977-85. Head of Legal Services, Dartford Borough Council 1985-88. Joined *McKenna & Co* in 1988, and became a Partner in 1990.

Personal: Born 14th February 1952. Educated at Bancroft's School, Woodford 1963-69 and Warwick University 1969-72. Lives in London.

Lewis, Robert
See under Environmental Law.

Mackay, Ian
McKenna & Co, London (0171) 606 9000. Solicitor specialising in all aspects of town planning and development.

Specialisation: Twenty years' experience as planner and planning solicitor of advising planning authorities, developers and public sector agencies on all aspects of town planning and development. Senior member of the Planning Group of the Property Department with particular experience in preparing for and attending large public inquiries throughout the country, including negotiating and drafting complex planning and highway agreements and other planning obligations. Practice also covers highways law, environmental law and compulsory purchase as well as parliamentary work. Advised the Department of Transport on the Channel Tunnel Rail Link Bill. Major clients include J Sainsbury plc, Tarmac Properties; the Crown Estate, Brixton Estate and Northern Ireland Electricity.

Prof. Membership: Law Society, UK Environmental Law Association, City of London Law Society.

Career: Town planner with several local planning authorities, attaining the position of Deputy County Planning Officer. Qualified as a solicitor in 1984. Solicitor (Head of Planning, Highways and Contracts Legal Department), London Borough of Southwark 1986-88. Joined *McKenna & Co* in 1988.

Max, Richard
D J Freeman, London (0171) 583 4055. Qualified 1988. Assistant Solicitor. Property Department. Specialises in and town and country planning. Covers all areas including planning appeals, listed buildings, judicial review, compulsory purchase and aspects of environmental law. Born 1.9.1963.

Messer, Laurence
Davies Arnold Cooper, London (0171) 936 2222. Qualified 1974. Partner 1989. Property Department. All aspects of commercial property, planning and environmental law. Born 27.5.1949.

Norris, Helen
Denton Hall, London (0171) 242 1212. Partner in Planning, Environment and Property Litigation Group, Property Department.

Specialisation: Head of Planning Group. Work includes retail, commercial, residential, leisure and highways. Inquiries, compulsory purchase orders, planning agreements and general planning advice, particularly strategy advice. Contributor to the Journal of Planning Law. Lectures and gives seminars.

Prof. Membership: City of London Law Society, Planning Sub-Committee; and Law Society.

Career: Qualified in 1978, having articled at Wales Gas 1976-78. Solicitor for Greater London Council 1978-80; worked at *Coward*

Chance 1978-80 and *Lovell White & King* 1984-85. Joined *Oppenheimers* in 1986, and joined *Denton Hall* in 1987. Became an Associate Partner at Oppenheimers in 1987 and a Partner at *Denton Hall* in 1989.

Personal: Born 6th July 1953. Attended Grammar School for Girls, Neath; University College of Wales, Aberystwyth, and University College, London. Leisure interests include rugby and a house in France.

O'Donovan, Teige

Farrer & Co, London (0171) 242 2022. Called to the Bar 1985. Property Department.

Specialisation: Specialises in planning and environmental law. Work includes listed building applications and appeals, parliamentary petitions, compulsory purchase matters and tribunal advocacy.

Prof. Membership: Middle Temple.

Personal: Born 7th January 1961. Educated at Girton College, Cambridge 1979-82, the Polytechnic of Central London and the Inns of Court School of Law. Interests include architectural art.

Pugh, Timothy J.

Berwin Leighton, London (0171) 623 3144. Partner in Planning and Environmental Department.

Specialisation: All aspects of Planning and Environmental Law. Particular areas of planning related expertise: urban regeneration, retail, waste disposal, land reclamation and housing projects; compulsory purchase; highway orders; planning and infrastructure agreements; negotiation and case preparation for promoters of and petitioners against private parliamentary bills. Particular areas of environment-related expertise: contaminated land; waste disposal; environmental impact statements; water law; environmental due diligence; environmental terms and conditions of contract. Member: Planning and Environment Committee of the British Property Federation; Planning and Environment Law-Sub Committee of the City of London Law Society; and IBA's Committee on International Environmental Law. Currently representing British Property Federation and CBI as development industry representative on joint working parties with Department of Transport- reviewing developer highway agreements and procedures.

Prof. Membership: City of London Solicitors Company, IBA, UKELA.

Career: Qualified 1984. Articled at *Donne Mileham & Haddock* 1982-84. Joined *Berwin Leighton* 1984; Partner 1990.

Personal: Born 1959. Duffryn High School, Newport, Gwent; University College, London; and College of Law, Lancaster Gate. Leisure interests include skiing, squash, running and lying under old cars. Lives in Hove.

Purton, Peter

Norton Rose, London (0171) 283 6000.

Qualtrough, John

Simmons & Simmons, London (0171) 628 2020. Partner in Property Department.

Specialisation: Principal area of practice is inquiry work and the negotiation and drafting of planning and infrastructure agreements. Other main area is conditional contracts, options and related development agreements.

Prof. Membership: Law Society; City of London Law Society (Committee member of planning and Environmental Law Sub-Committee).

Career: Qualified 1978. Partner at *Simmons & Simmons* since 1988.

Personal: Born 30th April 1953. Holds a BA (1974).

Redman, Michael

Clifford Chance, London (0171) 600 1000. Solicitor Advocate. Principal area of practice is planning and environment. Also handles rating. Born 3.8.1952

Rees, Christopher

Davies Arnold Cooper, London (0171) 936 2222. Qualified 1979. Partner 1988. Property Department. Particular expertise in housebuilding and town expansion projects. Practice also covers environmental law.

Scates, Steven J.

Nicholson Graham & Jones, London (0171) 628 9151. Partner in Property Department. Joint Head of Planning and Environment Unit.

Specialisation: Practice covers all areas of town and country planning with an emphasis on property development. Experienced advocate. Work includes inquiries (Local Plan, EIP and appeals), judicial review, master plan and planning briefs for site assemblies. Other areas of practice are land assembly, options and conditional contracts, development agreements, consortium and joint venture arrangements, infrastructure and construction procurement. Recent experience has included appointment as consortium lawyer for purchase and development of former British Aerospace site at Kingston-upon-Thames; dealing with appeal against enforcement notices at Brands Hatch race circuit, and the development of Brighton Marina for residential use. Major clients include Barratt South London Ltd, Barratt North London Ltd, Barratt Southern Counties Ltd, UML (Unilever), GTE Corp and Laing Homes Ltd. Speaks frequently at conferences, writes articles and holds press conferences to promote development proposals.

Prof. Membership: Law Society, Environmental Practitioners Group, UK Environmental Law Association.

Career: With Reading Borough Council 1978-85. Qualified in 1985. Partner with *Peter Jacobs & Co* 1985-87 and *Sheridans* 1987-89. Senior Partner of *Scates Rosenblatt* 1989-94. Partner with *Nicholson Graham & Jones* from 1994.

Personal: Born 17th January 1957. Educated at University College, Swansea 1975-78 (BA, Political Theory) and Lancaster Gate College of Law (CPE 1981, LSF 1984). Leisure pursuits include motorcycling, golf and tennis. Lives in Chiswick, W.London.

Searle, Geoffrey

Geoffrey Searle, London (0171) 497 3753. Qualified 1968. Partner 1977. Planning and Environment Group. Main area of practice is town and country planning.

Shadarevian, Paul

Norton Rose, London (0171) 283 6000. Qualified 1984. Partner 1991. Commercial Property and Planning Department. Also practises planning/landuse related enviromental Law.

Sherlock, Roger

Nabarro Nathanson, London (0171) 493 9933. Qualified 1975. Partner 1989. Planning Department. Senior solicitor. Practises town and country planning and rating law. Born 6.4.1950.

Smith, Brian

Wilde Sapte, London (0171) 246 7000. Partner in Property Department. Manager of firm's Commercial Property Group.

Specialisation: Main area of practice is planning and development. Has 17 years post qualification experience in this field, in local government, commerce and private practice. Handles environmental work, dealing principally with land contamination and environmental liability in commercial transactions. Also deals with local government law, compulsory purchase and rating.

Prof. Membership: Member of Law Society Planning Panel, Legal Associate of Royal Town Planning Institute.

Stevens, Peter

Jeffrey Green Russell, London (0171) 499 7020. Partner 1994. Town Planning Department.

Specialisation: Work includes highways and infrastructure, compulsory purchase and compensation, options and contracts. Also handles non-domestic rating and other central and local government issues. Makes regular appearances in the Planning and Property Development programmes of Television Educational Network. Member of Law Society's Planning Panel.

Prof. Membership: Law Society. Legal Associate of RTPI.

Career: Qualified in 1973. Worked at *Lovell White & King* 1971-81 before joining *Denton Hall* in 1981, becoming a Partner in 1988, until 1994, then joined *Jeffrey Green Russell* as a Partner in 1994.

Personal: Born 12th March 1948. Attended Latymer Upper School 1957-67, then Manchester University 1967-70. Leisure interests include squash, test cricket, and a hideaway in rural France. Lives in Wimbledon.

Taylor, Nicholas

Berwin Leighton, London (0171) 623 3144. Partner and Head of Planning and Environment Department.

Specialisation: Principal area of practice covers planning, development, compulsory purchase and highways, including public infrastructure schemes, Parliamentary work and planning policy. Other main area of work is environmental matters, including formulation and implementation of corporate environmental policy, environmental impact assessment, waste and regulatory matters. Involved in major planning and environment cases such as Ludgate development (for Rosehaugh), Bluewater Park (for Blue Circle), White City, factory outlet centres, urban regeneration schemes, and major infrastructure projects both road and rail. Member of CBI land Use Panel and Advisory Committee on Oil Pollution of the Sea. Advises National Development Control Forum. Regular conference speaker on planning and environmental topics.

Prof. Membership: Law Society.

Career: Qualified 1974 while with Dorset County Council. Chief Executives' Departments of Dorset County Council and Avon County Council until 1979. Assistant Secretary to Association of County Councils 1979-83 with responsibility for planning, transportation and national representation with Ministers and Whitehall. Joined *Berwin Leighton* in 1983 and became a Partner in 1984.

Personal: Born March 1949. Attended Fitzmaurice Grammar School, then New College, Oxford. Leisure pursuits include family, theatre, opera, riding, tennis and reading. Lives in Kew.

Thomas, Patricia E.

See under Environmental Law.

Tideswell, Anne

Rowe & Maw, London (0171) 248 4282. Qualified 1987. Senior Assistant Solicitor. Planning Team, Property Department. Work includes highways, compulsory purchase and rating.

Trehearne, Ian

Berwin Leighton, London (0171) 623 3144. Planner and Barrister Planning and Environment Department.

Specialisation: Principal area of work is planning law covering advice and advocacy on development, including retail, commercial housing, utility and waste disposal developments and local plan inquiries. Also environment law advising on contamination liability and threats and European Community matters. Advised on Ludgate development, St. George's Hospital, Hyde Park Corner, Euston Centre, Ebbsfleet Station and development of the Channel Tunnel Rail Link and environmental cases such as Dartford and Welbeck. Numerous conferences and seminars. Lectured at City University 1982-84.

Prof. Membership: Royal Town Planning Institute.

Career: London Borough of Newham, 1972-4, then joined the London Borough of Islington 1974-77. Joined the London Borough of Camden in 1979 and moved to *Berwin Leighton* in 1985. Admitted to Partnership in 1988. Called to the Bar 1980.

Personal: Born 17th May 1950. Attended Durham University 1968-71. Leisure pursuits include sailing, building, books and music. Lives in London.

Turner, Angela

Gouldens, London (0171) 583 7777.

Ward, Tony

Clifford Chance, London (0171) 600 1000. Partner. Also handles commercial property and local and central government matters.

Wells, Martin

Stephenson Harwood, London (0171) 329 4422. Senior Associate in Property Department: Town and Country Planning Group.

Specialisation: Advises on a wide range of town planning and related matters, including agreements, appeals, public inquiries and High Court challenges. Cases have included advising on a series of major developments for the University of Greenwich, Stakis plc, the Godinton Estate, Wimpey Homes, the Bristol Port Company and Wonder World plc, and carrying out a study of public inquiries into waste combustion installations for the Energy Technology Support Unit (Department of Trade and Industry).

Prof. Membership: Law Society's Planning Panel, City of London Law Society's Planning and Environmental Law Sub-Committee, UKELA's Town Planning and EIA Working Party.

Career: Qualified in 1972. Legal Assistant at Luton C. B. C. 1965-1971; Solicitor at St Albans C.C. 1972-73, then Watford B.C. 1973-79; Principal Planning Administrator, Hertsmere B.C. 1979-81 and Solicitor to the Council to 1986; Borough Secretary at Runnymede B.C. 1986-87; Assistant Solicitor with *Denton Hall Burgin & Warrens* 1987-88, joining *Stephenson Harwood* in 1988. Senior Associate in 1989.

Personal: Born 12th September 1944. Holds an LLB (Hons) from Exeter University, 1965. Parochial Church Councillor. Leisure interests include music and travel. Lives in Woking, Surrey.

REGIONS

Abraham, Henry

Brachers, Maidstone (01622) 690691. Qualified 1983. Partner 1994. Planning & Environmental Law Department. Handles all aspects of planning applications and appeals.

Allen, Anthony J.R.

Donne Mileham & Haddock, Lewes (01273) 480205. Partner.

Specialisation: Main area of practice is town planning. Head of Planning and Environmental Law Unit 1976-93, and Partner in charge of DM & H Planning Services since 1993. Also in charge of environmental law unit. Has acted in housing and retail development, health authority and university cases, in cases regarding waste deposit licensing, waste transfer stations, planning and licensing, statutory nuisance prosecutions, objections to a waste power plant and mineral extraction. Author of various articles on planning topics. Recent seminar topics have included Environmental Law- The European Background, The Environmental Protection Act Part 1- Integrated Pollution Control, and Trading in Europe- Environmental Aspects.

Prof. Membership: LMRTPI, International Bar Association, European Environmental Law Sub Committee, Environmental Law Foundation, European Environmental Law Association, British Nordic Lawyers Association, UK Environmental Law Association.

Career: MA (Cantab). Qualified in 1970, having joined *Donne Mileham & Haddock* in 1969. Became a Partner in 1976. Member of the Law Society Planning and Environmental Law Committee.

Battye, Peter G.

Eversheds, Birmingham (0121) 233 2001. Qualified 1967.

Beard, Tony

Tozers, Exeter (01392) 424444. Partner specialising in all matters relating to mobile homes and caravan parks including planning.

Begg, Craig

Lawrence Tucketts, Bristol (0117) 929 5252. Associate, Company Commercial Department.

Specialisation: Specialist adviser to franchisors and franchisees on negotiating and drafting master franchise agreements, distribution and agency transactions. Has broad experience in advising in all types of contract, including waste management and collateral warranties. Lecturer and author of articles in franchising press.

Bell, Malcolm

Ward Hadaway, Newcastle upon Tyne (0191) 261 2651. Planning Consultant.

Specialisation: Rural Planning Consultant to *Ward Hadaway*. He was awarded his PhD for work on the impact of public developments on the countryside and has specialised in the appraisal of rural policy and planning proposals. Rural Development Control matters constitute day to day specialism. Has lectured, written and broadcast widely on countryside topics. Has written for journals such as 'The Journal of Planning and Environmental Law', 'The Planner' and 'Town & Country Planning'. Publications include edited volumes on agriculture and conservation in the hills and uplands and on the potential countryside implications of set-aside and farm extensification policies. Is an expert on access law and gave the 1993 legal paper to the Institute of Public Rights of Way Officers. Has practical experience of both access agreements and access orders. With the NFU and his practice he has worked up practical 'innovative access schemes', for example at Aysgarth Falls in Yorkshire. Has appeared as an expert witness on rural environmental questions at many inquiries and is an external examiner on Lancaster University's Environmental Science and Outdoor Studies course.

Prof. Membership: Royal Town Planning Institute, The Institution of Environmental Sciences, Fellow of the Royal Agricultural Societies, Associate of the Institute of Agricultural Management.

Career: Seconded as first joint research fellow of the Economic and Social Research Council and the Natural Environment Research Council, based at the Institute of Terrestrial Ecology 1985-87. Until September 1989 was Regional Professional Services Executive for the North East Region of the NFU. Previously Head of Countryside Policy at NFU Headquarters. Has also been planning advisor to the National Forest. Currently member of a team studying future locations for lowland forestry in England and Wales.

Personal: Educated at Warwick University (BA in History and Politics, MA in Social History, PhD).

Beresford, Amanda

Pinsent Curtis, Leeds (0113) 244 5000. Partner, Head of Environmental and Planning.

Specialisation: All planning work including retail, leisure, industrial residential and Advocacy at Public Inquiries. Also environmental advice including pollution control, energy, waste, transport, contaminated land and due diligence. Major cases include the new Royal Armouries Museum at Clarence Dock, Leeds and a leisure development including multiscreen cinema. Clients include Local Planning Authorities, major private developers, environmental regulatory bodies and several NHS Trusts. Recognised authoress and speaker at conferences.

Prof. Membership: Member U.K.E.L.A.

Career: Qualified in 1985 becoming a partner at *Pinsent Curtis* in 1992.

Bourne, Felix J.B.

Birketts, Ipswich (01473) 232300. Qualified 1980. Consultant 1994. Property Department. Main areas of practice are planning and environmental work. Born 24.9.1953.

Burgess, Peter

Morgan Bruce, Cardiff (01222) 385385. Qualified 1975. Senior Associate 1990. Head of Planning Group. Principal area of practice is Town and Country planning and land assembly work. Also handles judicial review, public law and property litigation matters. Born 2.5.1950.

Carter, Simon

Aaron & Partners, Chester and Aaron Freedmans. Chester (01244) 315366. Managing Partner and Partner in Planning & Local Government and Property Departments.

Specialisation: Main area of practice is planning, local government and property law. Handles range of planning matters, including advice on applications, appeals, enforcement, agreements, lawful use and development generally, as well as advocacy at planning inquiries and local plans. Also deals with most aspects of local government law, including highways, compulsory purchase, rates and prosecutions. Author of articles on planning and has lectured on planning to RIBA and RICS and other professionals. Property work includes sales and purchases and property development generally.

Prof. Membership: Law Society, Chartered Institute of Arbitrators.

Career: Articled at *Simpson Curtis*. Qualified in 1976 and then worked for several local authorities until rejoining private practice with *Aaron & Partners* in 1986, becoming a Partner in 1987. Currently Managing Partner. Committee member North West branch Chartered Institute of Arbitrators and a Council representative. Director of AD Waste Ltd (Local Authority owned waste disposal company). Member Clwyd Alyn Housing Association.

Personal: Born 1952. Educated at Leeds University. Leisure interests include gardening, choral singing and golf. Lives near Malpas, Cheshire.

Collar, Neil

Brodies WS, Edinburgh (0131) 228 3777. Associate in Planning Department, LLM for research into use of planning issues 1990.

Specialisation: Handles town and country planning matters - planning applications, appeals and inquiries, planning issues in relation to land acquisition and disposal, Local Authority compulsory purchase, roads etc. Wide experience of private and public sector clients and has dealt with recent planning applications for retail developments, Scottish wind farms, the acquisition of golf course and leisure developments and inquiries for a proposed barytes mine. Author of 'Planning', published by W. Green & Son and Sweet & Maxwell (Concise Scots Law Series) and a number of articles in journals. Has a regular planning law column in Greens Property Law Bulletin. Part time tutor at University of Edinburgh and speaker on aspects of planning law at several conferences.

Prof. Membership: Law Society of Scotland, Society for Computers and Law.

Career: Qualified in 1992, having joined *Brodies WS* in 1990.

Personal: Born 31st March 1967. Educated at the University of Glasgow 1984-88 and 1989-90 (LLB and Diploma) and Liverpool University 1988-89 (LLM). Enjoys playing the saxophone, hockey and softball. Lives in Edinburgh.

Connal, R. Craig

See under Employment Law.

Damms, Martin

Edge & Ellison, Birmingham (0121) 200 2001.

Dimmick, Simon

Clarks, Reading (01734) 585321. Specialises in local government and planning law.

Edwards, Keith

Alan T. Jenkins & Co, Carmarthen (01267) 235019.

Engert, Nick

Clarke Willmott & Clarke, Taunton (01823) 337474. Qualified 1973. Partner 1979. Head of Planning and Environment Department. Main areas of practice are town and country planning, compensation and land development. Born 28.9.1948.

Evans, Eric C.

Eversheds, Cardiff (01222) 471147. Qualified 1980. Partner 1992. Commercial Property and Planning Department. Main area of practice is local government and planning. Also compulsory purchase and compensation. Former Chief Officer in local government. 30 years public sector experience. Born 25.11.1945.

Faulds, Ann

Dundas & Wilson CS, Edinburgh (0131) 228 8000. Qualified 1989. Associate Partner 1994. Commercial Property Department. Main area of practice is town and country planning law, as well as roads legislation. Born 24.11.1956.

Firth, Beverley J.

See under Environmental Law.

Gibbs, Kevin

Lyons Davidson, Bristol (0117) 929 7151. Partner and Head of Planning, Environmental and Waste Unit, Property Department. Charge-out rate is £110 per hour.

Specialisation: Main area of practice is planning and property law, including advocacy. Advises on all planning and environmental aspects of large and small scale developments, including advice on structure and local plans, compulsory purchase and compensation, conservation, enforcement, advertising control, waste and regulatory matters, contaminated land liabilities, and abatement notices. Has lectured at the Law Society's Local Government Group and on courses organised by the Bristol Law Society and the Royal Town Planning Institute.

Professional Membership: Member of the Royal Town Planning Institute; member of the Built Environment Committee of the UK Environmental Law Committee; member of the Law Society's Planning Panel. Committee member of South West Group of UK Environmental Lawyers' Association.

Career: Qualified 1990. Local government planner from 1980-84; Principal Legal Officer, London Borough of Camden 1984-88. Joined *Lyons Davidson* in 1988 and became a partner in 1994.

Profile: Born 19.5.1954. Holds a Masters Degree in City and Regional Planning from the University of Cape Town (1980). Leisure activities include tennis and hockey; music and travel. Lives in Bristol.

Goodall, Martin

Clarke Willmott & Clarke, Ruishton (01823) 442266. Qualified 1977. Associate Partner 1990. Planning Law Team. Work includes major housing appeals, major retail proposals and advocacy at public inquiries, including enforcement and listed buildings. Born 26.3.1948.

Goodman, David

Hammond Suddards, Leeds (0113) 234 3500. Partner and Head of Planning Department.

Specialisation: Main area of practice is town and country planning handling all aspects of planning issues relating to development, including retailing, residential, office, mineral extraction, waste disposal and leisure uses. Undertakes advocacy at public inquiries. Also deals with environmental law including environmental assessment and environmentally sensitive developments. Has handled a proposal for an overhead transmission line through Cleveland and North Yorkshire, promotion of clinical waste incinerator proposals, and a proposed regional centre and football stadium in the North East. Author of articles on planning law. Lectures regularly to RTPI and other professional bodies.

Prof. Membership: Law Society, Institute of Waste Management Special Interest Group on Incineration, British Wind Energy Association.

Career: Qualified in 1980. Articled at Surrey County Council 1978-80, then Assistant Solicitor at Oldham Metropolitan B.C 1980-84. Senior Solicitor at Newcastle upon Tyne City Council 1984-88. Joined Hammond Suddards in 1988 and became a Partner in 1991.

Personal: Born 15th October 1955. Educated at the Royal Grammar School, Newcastle upon Tyne 1967-74 and Sheffield University 1974-77. Recreations include sport, gardening and theatre.

Haynes, Michael

E. Edwards Son & Noice, Ilford (0181) 514 9000.

Hinton, Robert

See under Local Government.

Houghton, John

Clarke Willmott & Clarke, Taunton (01823) 337474. Qualified 1973. Partner 1980. Planning and Environment Group. Specialises in all aspects of planning law. Born 1948.

Jones, William

Foot & Bowden, Plymouth (01752) 675000. Qualified 1965. Partner 1972. Corporate Services Department. Also handles public authority law, judicial review and planning appeals.

Kinloch, Ian

Aaron & Partners, Chester (01244) 315366. *and Aaron Freedmans.* Chester (01244) 315366. Partner in Planning, Local Government and Compulsory Purchase Department.

Specialisation: Main area of practice is town and country planning law: all aspects of planning including advocacy and s106 agreements. Also handles local government law, including highways, compulsory purchase, and advice on relations and negotiations with local authorities. Author of articles on planning law and local government topics and has lectured at courses and seminars for AMA, Aston University, SAUS at Bristol University and PTRC.

Prof. Membership: Law Society, Royal Town Planning Institute.

Career: Qualified in 1967. Held various local government appointments. Joined *Aaron & Partners* in 1993, becoming a Partner in 1994.

Personal: Born 1945. LLM BA LMRTPI. Member of Branch Executive Committee of North West and North Wales branch, RTPI. Leisure interests include reading history, music and learning Welsh.

Lancaster, Roger

Halliwell Landau, Manchester (0161) 835 3003. Qualified 1975. Partner 1982. Head of Planning and Environmental Law Department. Specialises in town and country planning, environmental law and compulsory purchase matters, including advocacy at inquiries. Born in 1951.

Little, A. James

Wollastons, Chelmsford (01245) 211211. Qualified 1973. Consultant 1990. Planning Law. Previously a local government officer now sole practitioner in an exclusively planning law firm.

Marron, Peter

Marron Dodds, Leicester (0116) 289 2200. Senior Partner in Planning, Development and Public Law Department.

Specialisation: Has twenty years' experience of contentious town planning, together with associated work advising the development industry. Also handles public law matters, compulsory purchase and judicial review. Has acted in cases ranging from new village schemes, landfill proposals and many other

applications of strategic importance. Has given talks over the years to a number of bodies. Major clients include Ashford Developments, Barratt Homes, Ideal Homes, Beazer Homes, David Wilson Homes, Wilson Bowden Ltd, Ibstock Bricks Plc, Rolls Royce Plc and Hallam Land Management Ltd. Individual charge-out rates are based on £125 per hour, negotiable on the basis of complexity and responsibility.

Prof. Membership: Law Society, Chartered Institute of Arbitrators.

Career: Qualified in 1970. Founded *Marron Dodds* as a Senior Partner in 1978. DOT/RYA Ocean Yacht Master with commercial endorsement. ACIArb 1990. Fellow of the Royal Society of Arts 1995.

Personal: Born 3rd June 1944. Attended Liverpool University (LLB Hons 1966). Leisure interests include the Arts and off-shore sailing. Lives in Uppingham, Rutland.

McCorquodale, Kay

Shepherd & Wedderburn WS, Edinburgh (0131) 228 9900.

McMurtrie, Peter M.

Tozers, Exeter (01392) 424444.

Merrett, Tracey

Osborne Clarke, Bristol (0117) 923 0220.

Moritz, John

Masons, Manchester.

Specialisation: Worked for several years in local government, gaining invaluable experience in planning, roads and environmental matters. Has advised on a number of major development projects in the North West and nationally. Advises in connection with planning enquiries, compulsory purchase and other road inquiries, landfill, clinical waste incineration, negotiations with Water Authorities and privatised water companies and environmental assessments. Advises local authorities and development corporations in connection with development of all types, including all aspects of urban regeneration and contaminated land.

Prof. Membership: Secretary of North West Branch of UK Environmental Law Association. Member of the Law Society's Planning Panel.

Career: Qualified in 1973. Partner at *Lambert Storey* in 1980. Joined *Masons* in 1990 as a Partner.

Personal: Born in Manchester. LLB Manchester University. Interests leisure, travel, theatre, swimming, viewing and appreciating art and architecture.

Oldham, Peter M.B.

Cobbett Leak Almond, Manchester (0161) 833 3333. Qualified 1969. Partner 1973. Has 20 years experience of handling appeals relating to large retail developments, principally food superstores. Born 12.4.1945.

Otty, Sue

Lawrence Tucketts, Bristol (0117) 929 5252. Senior Associate in Planning and Development Group.

Specialisation: Specialises in property, planning and environmental law, particularly urban regeneration projects, quarrying, mineral extraction, landfill, waste management, local plans, listed buildings and other conservation issues. Secretary of South West branch of UKELA.

Parry, Emrys J.

Cartwrights, Bristol (0117) 929 3601. Partner in Commercial Property Section.

Specialisation: Specialises in compulsory purchase and planning. Has acted for a local authority in promotion of CPO for a major town centre redevelopment and Housing Act CPO for and against planning authorities at appeals including settlement of compensation claims, claims against passenger transport executives, development corporations and local authorities. Clients include local authorities, a major port authority and private clients.

Prof. Membership: Fellow of the British Institute of Management; Chairman, City of London BIM Property Group; Member of the Law Society's Planning Panel.

Career: In local government until 1977. Legal advisor with The Land Authority for Wales 1977-86, then *D J Freeman* 1986-93 (Partner from 1987). Joined *Cartwrights* as a Partner in 1993.

Personal: Born in 1945. Holds a BSc (Econ) (Hons degree). Board Member, Surrey Heath Housing Association (Vice-chairman of Finance and Resources Committee). Leisure interests include golf. Resides in Bristol.

Pasterfield, Stephen

Lawrence Tucketts, Bristol (0117) 929 5252. Partner and Head of Planning and Development Group.

Specialisation: Specialises in planning, handling all issues relating to development including mineral extraction, waste disposal, landfill, urban regeneration, retailing, office and residential uses; and environmental law including waste management licensing, contaminated land, nuisance and river pollution. Experienced advocate and lecturer on techniques at inquiries. Author of numerous articles. Member of Law Society's specialist Planning Panel.rous contaminated land cases. Has written numerous articles and lectured at Bristol University on river pollution and technique at inquiries. Member of the Law Society's Planning Panel.

Prof. Membership: Law Society.

Career: Qualified in 1974. Principal Solicitor, Solihull MBC 1976-79. Deputy City Solicitor, Winchester City 1979-1988. Became a Partner at *Lawrence Tucketts* in 1994.

Personal: Born 30th April 1949. Educated at Birkenhead School 1960-67. Leisure pursuits include sports of all kinds, especially golf, fishing and horse racing. Lives in Wrington.

Renger, Michael

Nabarro Nathanson, Doncaster (01302) 344455. Qualified 1980. Partner 1990. Environment Department. Work includes advising inward investors on environmental liability and pollution-related litigation.

Robinson, Patrick

Burges Salmon, Bristol (0117) 939 2000. Qualified 1989. Partner 1995. Planning Unit, Property Litigation Department. Work covers all aspects of the planning system and all aspects of compensation law including references to the Lands Tribunal as well as planning related environmental work and waste management. Born 13.6.1964.

Robson, J. Neil

Ward Hadaway, Newcastle upon Tyne (0191) 261 2651. Qualified 1977.

Rowan-Robinson, Jeremy

Paull & Williamsons, Aberdeen (01224) 621621. Qualified 1966. (England & Wales). Consultant in Planning and Environmental Law. Deals with all areas of both planning and environmental law. Born 29.3.1944.

Sales, Martin

W & J Burness WS, Edinburgh (0131) 226 2561. Partner in Litigation Department.

Specialisation: Main area of practice is planning enquiries and appeals, particularly involving development in environmentally sensitive areas. Also handles construction and engineering law matters.

Career: Joined *W&J Burness WS* in 1983 and became a Partner in 1989.

Personal: Born 26th September 1952. Educated at Edinburgh University (MA Hons 1975; PhD 1980; LLB. 1982). Leisure interests include antiques and antiquities. Lives in Edinburgh.

Smith, G. Bruce

Paull & Williamsons, Aberdeen (01224) 621621. Qualified 1967. Partner 1973. Planning and Environmental Law Department. Work includes advising on planning applications, appeals, enforcement notice appeals, local and structure plans and public inquiries. Born 15.6.1947.

Suddards, Roger

Peter Wilbraham & Co, Leeds (0113) 243 2200. Consultant.

Specialisation: Main area of practice is town planning and listed buildings. Work includes planning inquiries and general advice. Former Commissioner of English Heritage; Member of Historic Buildings and Areas Committee, English Heritage, Author of 'Listed Buildings, the Law and Practice' (3rd ed.); Encyclopaedia of Civil Emergencies; and Bradford Disaster Appeal (2nd ed.); Member of Editorial Board of Journal of Planning Law to 1993. Planning Law consult- ant to the United Nations and to the governments of St Lucia and Mauritius. Acted in the planning of the Arndale Centre in Manchester, Central Station in Manchester, York Development Plan and Trinity Hall, Cambridge. Gives frequent lectures for RTPI; Former member of RTPI Services Ltd; Speaker at the Law Society Joint Planning Conferences, Former Chairman of Bradford Grammar School and pro-chancellor of Bradford University.

Prof. Membership: The Law Society, Royal Town Planning Institute, ISVA (Honorary Fellow).

Career: Qualified in 1952. Partner at *J.R. Phillips, Suddards & Co.* 1952-54. *Last Suddards* 1952-88, from 1960 as Senior Partner. Consultant at *Hammond Suddards* 1988-1995, also Partner at *Johnson Hopps & Suddards.* Member of the Law Society Planning Law Committee 1964-81. Honorary Solicitor to RTPI 1991-95.

Personal: Born 5th June 1930. Attended Bradford Grammar School 1939-47. Formerly Chairman of Bradford Grammar School and pro-chancellor of Bradford University. Leisure interests include theatre, music, reading and travel. Lives in Bradford.

Taylor, Paul A.T.

Dickinson Dees, Newcastle upon Tyne (0191) 261 1911. Qualified 1971. Partner 1983. Planning Department. Work includes preparation of applications, conduct of appeals, enforcement procedures and development plan work. Born 19.8.1947.

Trinick, Marcus

See under Environmental Law.

Valentine, J. Richard H.

Pitmans, Reading (01734) 580224.

Wake, Brian

See under Environmental Law.

White, Martin

Pinsent Curtis, Birmingham (0121) 200 1050. Qualified 1979. Partner 1987. Property Department. Main area of practice is town and country planning.

Wilbraham, Peter

Peter Wilbraham & Co, Leeds (0113) 243 2200. Founding Partner specialising in town and country planning.

Specialisation: Specialist in planning since 1970. Has acted for public and private sector clients, who have been involved in the widest range of development issues. These include residential, retail, commercial, industrial, quarrying, landfill, wind energy, public utility proposals and highway matters. Has given advice on issues related to structure and local plans, unitary development plans, planning applications, appeals and general problems associated with aspects of development control, including the removal of permitted development rights. Work has involved listed buildings, conservation areas, advertisement control and tree preservation orders affecting development areas. Acted for the Countryside Commission opposing quarrying in National Parks and the M3 Winchester bypass; for Tyne and Wear Development Corporation on regeneration issues; for South West Thames Regional Health Authority in the redevelopment of five hospitals; for Kelt Energy Limited regarding a gas-fired electricity generation station; for Evans of Leeds PLC and Yorkshire Water PLC over water treatment works, wind energy proposals and incineration proposals; for Severn Trent Water Limited on sewage treatment works and for Wm. Morrison Supermarkets PLC and J. Sainsbury PLC on various superstore proposals. Speaks regularly at conferences and seminars on planning law. Has conducted seminars or workshops at the Town and Country Planning Summer School; speaks annually at the seminars organised by the Northern and Yorkshire branches of the Royal Town Planning Institute.

Prof. Membership: Law Society- Specialist Planning Panel, Legal Member of RTPI.

Career: Qualified in 1966. Assistant Solicitor with East Riding branch of Yorkshire City Council 1970-73. Partner with *Hammond Suddards* 1973-94. Founded *Peter Wilbraham & Co.* in 1994.

Personal: Born 30th August 1942. Attended Bury Grammar School, Lancashire 1953-61. Leisure interests include opera, reading, walking and the Celtic harp. Lives in Menston, near Ilkley, West Yorkshire.

Williams, Huw R.C.

Edwards Geldard, Cardiff (01222) 238239. Qualified 1978. Partner 1988. Commercial Property Department. Principal area of practice encompasses public, planning and environmental law. Born 4.1.1954.

Williamson, Andrew J.

Walker Morris, Leeds (0113) 283 2500. Partner in Planning and Environment Department.

Specialisation: Handles all aspects of planning law with an emphasis on advocacy at s.78 appeals, local planning inquiries, compulsory purchase order and EIP enforcement. Also handles Lands Tribunal and CPA Licensing and Environmental Protection Act authorisation appeals.

Prof. Membership: Corporate Member of Royal Town Planning Institute, Law Society Planning Panel.

Career: Articled at *Race & Newton* in Burnley 1981-83, then joined *Walker Morris* in 1984 and became a Partner in 1985.

Personal: Born 16th February 1957. Lives in Leeds.

Winter, Paul E.A.

Eversheds, Leeds (0113) 243 0391. Partner in Property Department.

Specialisation: Main areas of practice are planning and environmental law. Experience includes major town centre schemes, large urban regeneration projects and residential development. Enjoys both the advocacy and the negotiation aspects. Particularly handles environmental aspects of property transactions (especially contaminated land), waste management and development. Handled City Challenge projects, and Mixed Leisure and Commercial Development, involving the second largest city grant at the time. Contributed 'Contaminated Land' and 'Planning and the Environment' chapters in College of Law Environmental Law Book. Also, contributed contaminated land chapter of the CCH Environment Manual. Part-time lecturer for College of Law; delivered papers at TCPA seminars on 'Sustainability and the Law' and 'Material Considerations'.

Prof. Membership: Law Society, Town & Country Planning Association. Member of Specialist Planning Panel of the Law Society. Legal Associate of the Royal Town Planning Institute. Notary Public.

Career: Qualified 1976. Joined *Eversheds*

Hepworth & Chadwick as a Partner in 1989. Council Member of the TCPA.

Personal: Born 24th April 1949. Attended Leeds University 1968-72. Leisure interests include music and opera, walking, travelling and reading. Lives in Leeds.

Wood, David

Bevan Ashford, Bristol (0117) 923 0111. Partner in Commercial Property Department.

Specialisation: Main area of practice is planning. Handled local authority planning work in Essex 1972-76; specialised in planning and advocacy at Public Inquiries while a Partner in Bristol. Now Head of Planning at *Bevan Ashford*. Lead Partner on privatisation of Port of Bristol including the environmental issues and parliamentary procedures arising. Author of an article in 'Urban Regeneration'. Wrote planning law section for NHS Estates 'Estate Code' guidance to land transactions by Health Authorities and Trusts. Lectured for NHS Training Authority, University of the West of England, CBI and others.

Prof. Membership: Law Society, UK Environmental Law Association.

Career: Qualified in 1969. Worked at *Hatten, Jewers & Mephan* in Basildon, Essex 1969-76. Partner at *Harris & Harris*, Bristol 1976-88, then Partner at *Bevan Ashford* since 1988.

Personal: Born 7th January 1946. Attended Taunton School, Somerset 1957-62.

Young, Eric

Archibald Campbell & Harley WS, Edinburgh (0131) 220 3000. Qualified 1966. Partner 1992. Commercial Department. Main area of practice is town and country planning law. Also handles compulsory purchase and compensation. Born 21.10.1941.

Young, Rena

Bevan Ashford, Bristol (0117) 923 0111.

PRODUCT LIABILITY

D URING the last decade, there has been a significant growth in product liability legislation. This section has been included to reflect the large number of firms that have developed an expertise for handling this type of work.

LONDON

McKenna & Co and *Davies Arnold Cooper* emerge as the pre-eminent firms for defending product liability claims. *McKenna & Co* has one of the largest defendant product liability departments, incorporating four specialist partners, and acts for a large number of multi-national companies in the healthcare and consumer product fields. The team has been involved in various high profile litigation including that relating to benzodiazepine and intra-uterine contraceptive devices.

DAVIES ARNOLD COOPER	McKENNA & CO

Within the team, Ian Dodds-Smith has established a national reputation for his expertise in pharmaceutical liability, acting for numerous manufacturing companies, and Gary Hickinbottom enjoys an excellent reputation for pharmaceutical liability with particular emphasis on group actions. Mark Tyler in the team handles general product liability litigation including consumer and industry products, as well as pharmaceutical claims.

Christopher Hodges also undertakes general product liability but has particular experience in handling litigation on medical devices claims.

Davies Arnold Cooper has a leading department in the field of product liability, with considerable experience in multi-plaintiff drug and pharmaceutical cases. Simon Pearl and David McIntosh at the firm both have outstanding reputations for their expertise in defending product liability claims in the UK and co-ordinating and monitoring claims on an international scale. The team has particular experience in handling pharmaceutical product liability.

HIGHLY REGARDED – LONDON	
CAMERON MARKBY HEWITT	CLIFFORD CHANCE
FIELD FISHER WATERHOUSE	LEIGH DAY & CO
NORTON ROSE	PANNONE PRITCHARD ENGLEFIELD
SIMMONS & SIMMONS	

Cameron Markby Hewitt cover all types of product liability work, from collapsing cranes, food contamination, component failures and vehicle recalls, to major incidents such as the British Midland accident at Kegworth. The team, headed by Anthony Hobkinson, acts for clients both in the UK and overseas, including manufacturers and service facilities in the aerospace, automotive, consumer goods, electronics, engineering, food and pharmaceutical industries and their liability insurers.

Other firms recommended for their expertise include *Norton Rose,* where Lynn West has been recommended, and *Leigh Day & Co,* which is particularly known for medical devices litigation. Geraldine McCool is well-known in relation to product liability.

Field Fisher Waterhouse where Rodney Nelson-Jones was co-author of 'Product Liability - the New Law under the Consumer Protection Act 1987'.

Pannone Pritchard Englefield has a strong reputation for plaintiff medical and pharmaceutical product liability work and Antony Colman, who specialises in issues of product liability, recently published on the subject of Product Risk Management.

Other notable practices are *Clifford Chance* and *Simmons & Simmons*. The group at *Clifford Chance* has considerable experience in all types of product liability issues relating to the consumer, food, manufacturing and retailing, medical and transport sectors. The team of specialist lawyers, one of whom is a qualified doctor, offers a range of services from defective healthcare products to product contamination taxation. *Simmons & Simmons* is particularly known for multi-plaintiff product liability claims, and has expertise in handling pharmaceutical related matters.

LEADING INDIVIDUALS – LONDON
Ian C. Dodds-Smith *McKenna & Co*
Gary R. Hickinbottom *McKenna & Co*
Christopher J.F. Hodges *McKenna & Co*
David A. McIntosh *Davies Arnold Cooper*
Simon Pearl *Davies Arnold Cooper*
Mark Tyler *McKenna & Co*
Antony Colman *Pannone Pritchard Englefield*
Anthony Hobkinson *Cameron Markby Hewitt*
Geraldine M. McCool *Leigh Day & Co*
Rodney Nelson-Jones *Field Fisher Waterhouse*
Lynn West *Norton Rose*

SOUTH EAST

Gadsby Wicks of Chelmsford offers specialist medical and pharmaceutical product liability advice. Roger Wicks heads the team and has a leading reputation for his work acting for

LEADING FIRMS – SOUTH EAST
GADSBY WICKS *Chelmsford*

plaintiffs. The team has handled various high profile liability claims including Toxic Shock Syndrome, Myodil, Breast Implants and Septrin.

MIDLANDS

In the Midlands *Freeth Cartwright Hunt Dickens* has a niche specialism in plaintiff product liability. Paul Balen at the firm has a national reputation for his expertise, co-ordinating group actions such as Silicone Breast Implants and Benzodiazepine litigation.

NORTH

Alexander Harris has an excellent reputation for pharmaceutical product liability, acting for plaintiffs in the 'Myodil' litigation and also handling the 'Opren' and 'Hillsborough' litigation. Product liability litigation at the firm equals one third of its workload. David Harris at the firm has been recommended for his expertise in the field.

Percy Hughes & Roberts, where Michael Grant heads the department incorporating three specialist partners, acts mainly in relation to construction companies. *Goldsmith*

Williams handled the first generic multi-party action contract in the county awarded by the legal aid board. Nick Roland at the firm undertakes the product liability work.

SCOTLAND

In Scotland *W & J Burness* has expertise in product liability, especially in relation to pharmaceutical liability. Marsali Murray at the firm has handled many of the Scottish Benzodiazepine cases.

NORTHERN IRELAND

O'Reilly Stewart emerge as the leading firm in Northern Ireland with expertise in product liability. Brian Stewart undertakes product liability for the firm and clients include American Home Products, Imperial, Smith Kline Beecham and Mizuno.

In all the tables the names in each group are listed alphabetically.

LEADERS IN PRODUCT LIABILITY

LONDON

Colman, Antony
Pannone Pritchard Englefield, London (0171) 972 9720. Partner in Commercial Litigation Department.

Specialisation: Handles wide variety of product liability disputes, with particular experience acting for manufacturers in international commercial litigation. Fluent German speaker. Author of section on Product Risk Management in Product Liability, Law and Insurance (LLP). Has lectured frequently in England and Germany on product liability and litigation procedure.

Career: Admitted NSW 1980 and England 1986. Partner in *Pannone Pritchard Englefield* since 1986.

Personal: Born 1956 in Sydney. BA and LLB from Sydney University. Leisure pursuits include music, tennis, chess.

Dodds-Smith, Ian C.
McKenna & Co, London (0171) 606 9000. Partner and Head of Healthcare Group.

Specialisation: Main area of practice is healthcare related. Deals with the law relating to pharmaceuticals, medical products and devices and products in the cosmetics and food sectors. Specialist in licensing and related regulatory affairs, and on product liability issues. Also covers product liability generally, and personal injury litigation. Has handled many product liability cases, many multi-claimant and with international elements including hormone pregnancy tests, oral contraceptives, blood products, benzodiazepines, IUCD's and heart valves. Has

dealt with several regulatory cases including R v. Licensing Authority ex parte Scotia. Author of 'Product Liability for Medical Products' in 'Medical Negligence' (Butterworths) and 'Legal Liabilities in Clinical Trials' in 'Early Phase Human Drug Evaluation'. Joint Editor with Sir Abraham Goldberg of 'Pharmaceutical Medicine and the Law' (The Royal College of Physicians, 1991). Author of various articles on regulatory and liability issues. Frequent lecturer in the UK and abroad. Consultant Editor to the Personal and Medical Injuries Law Letter, and to the Regulatory Affairs Journal.

Prof. Membership: Law Society, American Bar Association, Drug Information Association, Fellow of the Royal Society of Medicine.

Career: Joined *McKenna & Co* in 1974 and

qualified in 1976. Became a Partner in 1984. Member of the Royal College of Physicians Working Party on Research at Phase 1 in Healthy Volunteers 1985-86. Member of the Medical Research Council Working Party on legal and ethical issues raised by Research in the Mentally Incapacitated (1988). Temporary Adviser (1987) to W.H.O. on the law relating to clinical trials. Legal adviser to the Clinical Sciences Ethics Committee of the University of London and University College Hospital.

Personal: Born 31st July 1951. Educated at Solihull School and Downing College, Cambridge 1969-72. Recreations include gardening and National Hunt racing. Lives in London.

Hickinbottom, Gary R.
McKenna & Co, London (0171) 606 9000.

Specialisation: Partner in the Healthcare group specialising in product liability work with particular reference to medicines and medicinal products. Also handles trade disputes and public law disputes. Important cases include the Benzodiazepine litigation and the Water Charging litigation. Publications include 'Some Practical Problems of Managing Pharmaceutical Product Liability Litigation (with Christopher Hodges published in 'European Pharma Law Centre Position Paper on Product Liability' May 1992). Has also written numerous articles for professional journals.

Prof. Membership: The Law Society; The City of London Law Society; The Association of Commonwealth Lawyers; The Administrative Law Bar Association; The London Jamaican Capital Case Solicitors' Panel; JUSTICE; The Chartered Institute of Arbitrators (Fellow); The Academy of Experts.

Career: Clerk, *Challinor & Roberts*, Birmingham 1975-1978. Articled clerk, *McKenna & Co* 1979-1981. Assistant solicitor, *McKenna & Co* 1981-1986. Partner, *McKenna & Co* since 1986. Assistant Recorder to the Crown Court (Wales and Chester Circuit). Parking Adjudicator for the Parking Committee for London. Membership of committees includes: The Law Society Working Party on Group Actions (1994-5); the Academy of Experts Working Party on the Royal Commission (1994); Editorial Board, The Litigator; London Welsh Trust and Association Council and Committee of Management (since 1993).

Personal: Educated at Queen Mary's Grammar School, Walsall 1967-1974 and University College, Oxford (BA Hons 1st class) 1975-1978. Part-time lecturer in law at the Polytechnic of Central London (now University of Westminster) 1980-1981, and at University College, Oxford 1987-1989. Member of Queen Mary's Club, Oxford Society, London Welsh Club, London Welsh Male Voice Choir, Glamorgan Cricket Club (Vice-President), Yr Academi Gymreig. Leisure pursuits include choral singing, opera and ballet, sport and alpine walking. Born 22nd December 1955. Lives in Oxted.

Hobkinson, Anthony
Cameron Markby Hewitt, London (0171) 702 2345. Partner and Head of Product Liability Group.

Specialisation: Deals with wide range of product liability and product integrity issues for manufacturers, distributors, maintenance and service organisations, and their insurers. Experience includes dealing with liability claims and recall incidents for the aerospace, automotive, consumer goods, and food and drink industries. Problems handled range from the routine to major incidents such as the British Midland accident at Kegworth in 1989. One of several CMH partners and fee earners specialising in products work. Regularly contributes articles to periodicals and lectures at conferences.

Hodges, Christopher J.F.
McKenna & Co, London (0171) 606 9000.

Specialisation: Main areas of practice are product liability and pharmaceutical, medical device and general product safety and product recall. Editor of 'Product Liability: European Laws and Practice', Chapters in 'Producy Liability: Law and Insurance', 'The Textbook of Pharmaceutical Medicine' and various other books. Author of 1995 European Commission Study on the Product Liabilty Directive.

Prof. Membership: Law Society, CBI Consumer Affairs Committee and Working Parties on Product Liability and General Product Safety, ABHI Council and Legal and Regulatory Committees, Vice-Chairman of Harrow Health District Ethical Committee, Secretary of International Bar Association Committee S on Product Liability and Consumer Affairs.

Career: Worked at *Slaughter and May* and *Clifford Chance* before becoming Partner at *McKenna & Co* in 1990.

Personal: Born 19th March 1954. Educated at King Edward's School, Birmingham. Academical Clerk at New College, Oxford. Founder member and Trustee of 'The Sixteen'.

McCool, Geraldine M.
See under Personal Injury.

McIntosh, David A.
See under Insurance & Reinsurance.

Nelson-Jones, Rodney
See under Personal Injury.

Pearl, Simon
Davies Arnold Cooper, London (0171) 936 2222. Qualified 1977. Partner 1980. Head of Healthcare Unit. Practice mainly involves defending pharmaceutical companies, healthcare professionals and their insurers in medical product liability and negligence actions. Also handles insurance and pharmaceutical regulatory work. Recent high-profile litigation includes acting for the NHS in the HIV Haemophilia case.

Tyler, Mark
See under Health & Safety.

West, Lynn
Norton Rose, London (0171) 283 6000. Qualified 1983. Partner specialising in general commercial and banking litigation. Also handles contentious and non-contentious product liability work.

REGIONS

Balen, Paul
See under Personal Injury.

Grant, Michael
Percy Hughes & Roberts, Birkenhead (0151) 647 6081. Partner specialising in product liability. Clients include Cadbury-Schweppes, Unilever and Pepsi Cola.

Harris, David N.
Alexander Harris, Sale (0161) 969 6779.

Murray, Marsali C.
W & J Burness WS, Edinburgh (0131) 226 2561. Qualified 1986. Partner. Litigation Department. Specialises in employment law and general litigation work. Writer to Her Majesty's Signet.

Roland, N.
Goldsmith Williams, Liverpool (0151) 231 1292. Partner. Head of Serious Injuries Department.

Specialisation: Medical negligence and personal injury high value claims and product liability cases. Has been invoved in numerous product liability cases, especially against pharmaceutical companies. Regular appearances on TV, radio and national newspapers. Writes weekly legal column for local newspaper.

Prof. Membership: Law Society, Member of Liverpool Law Society's Bulletin Editorial Committee, Association of Personal Injury Lawyers, ATLA (American Trial Lawyers), International Bar Association, Personal Injury Panel.

Career: Qualified 1986. Joined *Goldsmith Williams* in 1990 as a Partner.

Stewart, Brian J.
O'Reilly Stewart, Belfast (01232) 322512. Qualified 1980. Partner and head of the Litigation Department. Specialises in product liability defence work, mainly relating to pharmaceuticals. Qualified 1980. Admitted to the Republic of Ireland Roll of Solicitors 1991. Former Chairman of the Belfast Solicitors' Association. Member of the International Association of Defence Council.

Wicks, Roger
See under Medical Negligence.

PROFESSIONAL NEGLIGENCE

LONDON

Firms which have been consistently recommended for their work across the range of professions include *Barlow Lyde & Gilbert, Cameron Markby Hewitt, Reynolds Porter Chamberlain* and *Davies Arnold Cooper.*

LEADING FIRMS – LONDON	
BARLOW LYDE & GILBERT	CAMERON MARKBY HEWITT
DAVIES ARNOLD COOPER	REYNOLDS PORTER CHAMBERLAIN
INCE & CO.	
BERRYMANS	KENNEDYS

Firms recommended in respect of specific professions are:
Solicitors: *Barlow Lyde & Gilbert, Reynolds Porter Chamberlain, Ince & Co* and *Davies Arnold Cooper.*
Accountants: *Barlow Lyde & Gilbert, Cameron Markby Hewitt, Davies Arnold Cooper, Fishburn Boxer, Herbert Smith, McKenna & Co* and *Reynolds Porter Chamberlain.*
Lloyd's related: *Elborne Mitchell* represented all the defendants in the Gooda Walker action. Other highly regarded defendant firms include *Cameron Markby Hewitt, Clifford Chance, Clyde & Co, Davies Arnold Cooper, Herbert Smith, Hextall Erskine, McKenna & Co, Reynolds Porter Chamberlain* and *Barlow Lyde & Gilbert.*
Firms acting on behalf of Lloyd's Names include *Denton Hall, D J Freeman, Elliott & Company, Eversheds, Lawrence Graham, Macfarlanes, More Fisher Brown, Norton Rose, Richards Butler, S.J. Berwin, Taylor Joynson Garrett, Warner Cranston, Wedlake Bell* and *Wilde Sapte.*
Construction related: The following firms have been recommended for their work on behalf of surveyors, architects and engineers and their insurers: *Barlow Lyde & Gilbert, Cameron Markby Hewitt, Reynolds Porter Chamberlain, Davies Arnold Cooper, Berrymans, Kennedys, Beale and Co, Hextall Erskine, McKenna & Co, Fishburn Boxer, Alastair Thompson & Partners* and *Orchard.*
The firms covered in this section act primarily for defendants. Of the leading defendant firms, *Barlow Lyde & Gilbert* has a substantial professional indemnity practice. Well regarded practitioners include David Arthur and Ian Jenkins. The group's workload includes acting for accountants, solicitors, stockbrokers, surveyors, architects, engineers and insurance brokers, and recently the team's professional indemnity work has recently extended into directors' and officers' liability insurance.

HIGHLY REGARDED – LONDON	
BEALE AND CO	CLYDE & CO
ELBORNE MITCHELL	FISHBURN BOXER
HERBERT SMITH	HEXTALL, ERSKINE
HOLMAN, FENWICK & WILLAN	McKENNA & CO
SQUIRE & CO	WILLIAMS DAVIES MELTZER
ALASTAIR THOMSON & PARTNERS	BEACHCROFT STANLEYS
JARVIS & BANNISTER	LOVELL WHITE DURRANT
NICHOLAS FISHER	ORCHARD
PINSENT CURTIS	WANSBROUGHS WILLEY HARGRAVE
S J BERWIN & CO	CLIFFORD CHANCE
D J FREEMAN	EDWARD LEWIS
ELLIOTT & CO	EVERSHEDS
EVERSHEDS	FORSYTE SAUNDERS KERMAN
G.L. HOCKFIELD & CO	LAWRENCE GRAHAM
LEWIS SILKIN	LLOYD COOPER
MACFARLANES	MORE FISHER BROWN
NORTON ROSE	OSMOND GAUNT & ROSE
OSWALD HICKSON COLLIER	REID MINTY
RICHARDS BUTLER	ROSLING KING
ROWE & MAW	SIMMONS & SIMMONS
TAYLOR JOYNSON GARRETT	VIZARDS
WARNER CRANSTON	WEDLAKE BELL
WILDE SAPTE	

Reynolds Porter Chamberlain has an established reputation in the field and acts for many major clients including Allied Dunbar (in the highly publicised case BBL v Eagle Star). The firm has also had strong involvement in the Gooda Walker Syndicate action. Highly respected practitioners at the firm include Paul Nicholas, Simon Greenley and Barney Micklem. *Cameron Markby Hewitt* has an outstanding reputation for professional indemnity work which includes

LEADING INDIVIDUALS – LONDON		
Michael Dobias *Davies Arnold Cooper*	Mark E.M. Elborne *Cameron Markby Hewitt*	Simon K.P.T. Greenley *Reynolds Porter Chamberlain*
Ian D.P. Jenkins *Barlow Lyde & Gilbert*	Paul D. Nicholas *Reynolds Porter Chamberlain*	S.K. Tester *Cameron Markby Hewitt*
Nicholas P.G. Thomas *Kennedys*	Michael H. Wadsworth *Cameron Markby Hewitt*	Stuart G. White *Hextall, Erskine*
David A.D. Arthur *Barlow Lyde & Gilbert*	Martin J. Bakes *Herbert Smith*	Andrew A. Bandurka *Holman, Fenwick & Willan*
Andrea Burns *Orchard*	David A.M. Hartfield *Alastair Thomson & Partners*	Michael J. Lent *Alastair Thomson & Partners*
Peter Maguire *Cameron Markby Hewitt*	David A. McIntosh *Davies Arnold Cooper*	C.T. Micklem *Reynolds Porter Chamberlain*
Michael Payton *Clyde & Co*	P.J.H. Rogan *Ince & Co*	B.A. Schofield *Cameron Markby Hewitt*
Alastair M. Simpson *Alastair Thomson & Partners*	N. Squire *Squire & Co*	Paul Taylor *Berrymans*
Robin Williams *McKenna & Co*		

In all the tables the names in each group are listed alphabetically.

handling work for Lloyd's and directors' and officers' liability. Mark Elborne, Michael Wadsworth and Stephen Tester at the firm have been consistently recommended for their expertise. *Davies Arnold Cooper* also has a solid reputation in the area of professional indemnity and has been instructed in connection with the Lloyd's litigation. Michael Dobias at the firm who heads the litigation department is highly respected in the field.

Other leading firms include *Ince & Co, Berrymans* and *Kennedys. Ince & Co* is particularly well known for professional indemnity work in relation to marine/ shipping law but also has non marine connections. *Berrymans* is recognised as a leader in professional indemnity litigation and the department is one of the largest in the firm, incorporating four partners and a group of assistant solicitors. The department acts for insurers and all professionals including architects, surveyors, accountants, lawyers and stockbrokers. Paul Taylor at the firm is renowned for his expertise, especially in relation to work on behalf of consultant engineers. *Kennedys* is known for its insurance work and also has a strong reputation in the field of professional indemnity. Nicholas Thomas at the firm is particularly well regarded and has particular expertise in professional indemnity within the construction field.

Also highly recommended for professional indemnity work is Stuart White at *Hextall Erskine* who has a particular expertise in construction related work.

SOUTH EAST

Blake Lapthorn handles a substantial volume of professional negligence claims and David Higham at the firm has been recommended. The firm covers all types of professional negligence claims and is on the panel of the Solicitors' Indemnity Fund. *Clyde & Co,* a major international law firm, has a strong reputation for insurance and professional indemnity work and the office at Guildford acts for insurers of accountants, solicitors, architects and other professionals. *Thomson Snell & Passmore* also has a strong department incorporating four partners and acts for insurance companies, defending claims against professional firms.

HIGHLY REGARDED – SOUTH EAST

BLAKE LAPTHORN *Fareham*	CLYDE & CO *Guildford*
CRIPPS HARRIES HALL *Tunbridge Wells*	DONNE MILEHAM & HADDOCK *Brighton*
GRIFFITH SMITH *Brighton*	LIGHTFOOTS *Thame*
THOMSON SNELL & PASSMORE *Tunbridge Wells*	

Other firms recommended for defending in professional negligence claims are *Griffith Smith, Cripps Harries Hall* and *Lightfoots.*

Griffith Smith have acted for The Law Society advising firms of solicitors, whilst *Cripps Harries Hall* (Tunbridge Wells) handles work for The Solicitors Indemnity Fund. Neil Summerfield at *Lightfoots* has been recommended for his expertise in the field and has been involved in a number of high value settlements.

Also recommended for professional negligence work, acting for plaintiffs, is *Donne Mileham & Haddock.* They have been involved in actions against solicitors, accountants, surveyors and other professionals.

LEADING INDIVIDUALS – SOUTH EAST

David R.G. Higham *Blake Lapthorn*	
Neil Summerfield *Lightfoots*	

SOUTH WEST

Wansbroughs Willey Hargrave emerges as the pre-eminent firm for professional negligence practice in the South West. The department headed by Paul Rowe is on the Solicitors Indemnity Fund and acts for various Lloyd's syndicates and numerous major insurance companies. Paul Rowe and Paul Redfern at the firm have both been recommended for their expertise in the field. The firm was involved in forming a European grouping of specialist insurance litigation firms in 14 countries. The group, Insurolaw, provides cross-referrals and training in all insurance matters including professional negligence, personal injury and insurance disputes.

LEADING FIRMS – SOUTH WEST

WANSBROUGHS WILLEY HARGRAVE *Bristol*	
BOND PEARCE *Plymouth*	BURGES SALMON *Bristol*

Bond Pearce and *Burges Salmon* are also well known for their professional negligence practices. Both act for defendants and handle all types of professional negligence cases. Richard Challands and Erik Salomonsen at *Bond Pearce* are well respected by competitors for their expertise.

HIGHLY REGARDED – SOUTH WEST

BEVAN ASHFORD *Bristol*	CAMERON MARKBY HEWITT *Bristol*
HANCOCK & LAWRENCE *Truro*	VEALE WASBROUGH *Bristol*
CARTWRIGHTS *Bristol*	CLARKE WILLMOTT & CLARKE *Taunton*
LESTER ALDRIDGE *Bournemouth*	NASH SOLICITORS *Plymouth*
SANSBURY HILL *Bristol*	TRUMP AND PARTNERS *Bristol*

Other firms with strong reputations include *Cameron Markby Hewitt, Hancock & Lawrence, Bevan Ashford* and *Veale Wasbrough.* The latter undertakes professional negligence work for construction industry professionals such as consulting engineers, architects and surveyors and has a large department consisting of five partners and seven assistant solicitors.

LEADING INDIVIDUALS – SOUTH WEST

Richard Challands *Bond Pearce*	
Paul W.L. Redfern *Wansbroughs Willey Hargrave*	
Paul N.C. Rowe *Wansbroughs Willey Hargrave*	
Erik Salomonsen *Bond Pearce*	

WALES

Morgan Bruce emerges as the leading defendant professional negligence práctice in Wales. The firm acts for all professions and is particularly well known for solicitors' negligence cases, undertaking work for the Solicitors' Indemnity Fund. Richard Hale at the firm has particular expertise in this area. The team also acts for insurers of accountants, surveyors and engineers. Other highly regarded practitioners at the firm include Roger Cradick and Hugh Price.

LEADING FIRMS – WALES
MORGAN BRUCE *Cardiff*

Hugh James Jones & Jenkins is widely respected for its expertise in claims affecting a wide range of professionals, including accountants, insurance brokers and financial advisers. It has particular strength in relation to architects', engineers' and surveyors' negligence which developed from its strong construction practice. Michael Jefferies at the firm has an excellent reputation in the field.

HIGHLY REGARDED – WALES	
EVERSHEDS *Cardiff*	HUGH JAMES JONES & JENKINS *Cardiff*
CARTWRIGHTS ADAMS & BLACK *Cardiff*	CLEMENT JONES *Holywell*
DOLMANS *Cardiff*	EDWARDS GELDARD *Cardiff*
HOWARD PALSER GROSSMAN	HUTTONS *Cardiff*
HERMER & PARTNERS *Cardiff*	
LEO ABSE & COHEN *Cardiff*	
BEVAN ASHFORD *Cardiff*	

Eversheds in Cardiff acts for both defendants and plaintiffs and is especially well known for acting on behalf of barristers and surveyors. On the plaintiff side, the firm acts for banks and finance houses in claims, predominantly against surveyors and solicitors.

Cartwrights Adams & Black has also been recommended for its expertise in professional negligence claims. Other notable practitioners are Jeffrey MacWilkinson at *Dolmans* and George Grossman at the newly merged *Howard Palser Grossman Hermer & Partners*. The latter firm is especially well known for acting on behalf of surveyors and accountants.

LEADING INDIVIDUALS – WALES	
C. Roger Cradick *Morgan Bruce*	
Richard Hale *Morgan Bruce*	
Hugh M. Price *Morgan Bruce*	
George Grossman *Howard Palser Grossman Hermer & Partners*	
Michael G. Jefferies *Hugh James Jones & Jenkins*	
Jeffrey N. MacWilkinson *Dolmans*	
Robert Morgan *Eversheds*	

MIDLANDS

Wansbroughs Willey Hargrave has an excellent reputation in this field. The Birmingham office has three specialist part-ners handling defendant professional negligence work and acts for the Solicitors Indemnity Fund and various Lloyds syndicates.

HIGHLY REGARDED – MIDLANDS	
PINSENT CURTIS *Birmingham*	WANSBOROUGHS WILLEY HARGRAVE *Birmingham*
BROWNE JACOBSON *Nottingham*	FREETH CARTWRIGHT HUNT DICKINS *Nottingham*
NEIL F. JONES & CO *Birmingham*	
EDGE & ELLISON *Birmingham*	EVERSHEDS *Birmingham*
SHAKESPEARES *Birmingham*	WRAGGE & CO *Birmingham*
WRIGHT HASSALL & CO *Leamington Spa*	

Also highly recommended is *Pinsent Curtis* which has an extensive defendant practice acting for professionals and their insurers, and has considerable expertise acting on behalf of solicitors. *Neil F. Jones & Co* has undertaken work in relation to the Lloyd's litigation and has a strong practice in respect of professional negligence actions against construction industry professionals. Also known for professional indemnity work is *Browne Jacobson* which undertakes work for the Solicitors Indemnity Fund and other professionals and their insurers. Also worth noting is *Freeth Cartwright Hunt Dickens* for its plaintiff orientated practice, especially in relation to accountants', surveyors' and solicitors' negligence.

EAST ANGLIA

Mills & Reeve is particularly well known for solicitors' negligence and undertakes work on behalf of the Solicitors Indemnity Fund. It also acts for other professionals, including accountants and surveyors. *Eversheds'* litigation department also deals with professional negligence claims for a wide range of professionals. *Merricks* has been particularly recommended for professional indemnity work in relation to the construction industry and handles a large volume of work in this area. Amongst those firms known for plaintiff professional negligence is *Fosters* in Norwich with a reputation for handling solicitors' negligence.

HIGHLY REGARDED – EAST ANGLIA	
BIRKETTS *Ipswich*	EVERSHEDS *Norwich*
FOSTERS *Norwich*	MERRICKS *Ipswich*
MILLS & REEVE *Norwich*	

NORTH WEST

Of firms well known for their defendant work, *James Chapman & Co* has a strong team incorporating eight partners and covering a wide range of professions including solicitors, barristers, estate agents, surveyors, insurance brokers, accountants, engineers and architects. *Weightman Rutherfords* is also highly regarded and Ron Bradshaw at the firm has an established reputation in the field, handling work for the Solicitors Indemnity Fund and insurers of other professionals.

HIGHLY REGARDED – NORTH WEST	
ELLIOTT & CO *Manchester*	JAMES CHAPMAN & CO *Manchester*
KEOGH RITSON *Bolton*	LINDER MYERS *Manchester*
WEIGHTMAN RUTHERFORDS *Liverpool*	
DAVIES ARNOLD COOPER *Manchester*	DAVIES WALLIS FOYSTER *Liverpool*
HILL DICKINSON DAVIS CAMPBELL *Liverpool*	

Keogh Ritson has a large insurance department in which a large quantity of professional indemnity work is dealt with. *Elliott & Company* also has a strong professional indemnity group handling defence claims involving architects, surveyors, accountants, solicitors, insurance brokers and other professional bodies.

Linder Myers is known for representing plaintiffs against solicitors' negligence.

LEADING INDIVIDUALS – NORTH WEST
R.S Bradshaw *Weightman Rutherfords*

NORTH EAST

Wansbroughs Willey Hargrave has an excellent reputation for defendant work handling cases across all the professions, and is particularly well known for handling claims against solicitors, barristers, accountants, engineers, surveyors and financial advisers. The firm acts for approximately twelve professional indemnity providers and undertakes work for the Solicitors Indemnity Fund.

HIGHLY REGARDED – NORTH EAST	
CRUTES *Newcastle*	HAY & KILNER *Newcastle*
IRWIN MITCHELL *Sheffield*	WALKER MORRIS *Leeds*
WANSBROUGHS WILLEY HARGRAVE *Leeds*	
DIBB LUPTON BROOMHEAD *Bradford*	
WILKINSON MAUGHAN *Newcastle*	

Crutes is also highly regarded for professional negligence litigation. Alan Crutes acts for solicitors, accountants, insurance brokers and surveyors.

Walker Morris also has a fast growing professional indemnity practice handling work across the professions. *Hay & Kilner* acts for both plaintiffs and defendants, particularly accountants, solicitors and surveyors. The firm has been involved in several professional negligence actions in the last twelve months involving multi million pound construction claims. *Irwin Mitchell* also has a professional negligence unit which has a first-rate reputation for plaintiff work. *Dibb Lupton Broomhead* handles professional negligence work for the defendant.

LEADING INDIVIDUALS – NORTH EAST
Alan H. Crute *Crutes*

In all the tables the names in each group are listed alphabetically.

SCOTLAND

In Scotland very few firms specialise in pursuer non-medical negligence. The firms recommended as leaders in the field for professional negligence work focus on defender representation. *Simpson & Marwick* act for leading professionals including architects, surveyors, solicitors, engineers and brokers. Peter Anderson at the firm has a strong reputation

HIGHLY REGARDED – SCOTLAND	
BISHOP AND ROBERTSON CHALMERS *Glasgow*	BRECHIN ROBB *Glasgow*
BRODIES WS *Edinburgh*	DUNDAS & WILSON CS *Edinburgh*
SIMPSON & MARWICK WS *Edinburgh*	
BALFOUR & MANSON *Edinburgh*	BIGGART BAILLIE & GIFFORD *Glasgow*
MACROBERTS *Glasgow*	SHEPHERD & WEDDERBURN *Edinburgh*

in the field and is a panel solicitor on the Solicitors Professional Negligence Scheme. *Dundas & Wilson* also handle a substantial amount of solicitors negligence work and additionally deal with surveyors and accountant claims. *Brechin Robb* undertake similar work, exclusively for defenders, and has expertise in claims against forestry and agricultural consultants. As to claims relating to engineering and construction, *Bishop & Robertson Chalmers* is generally seen as the foremost practice. Also recommended for undertaking pursuer work across the full range of professions is *Brodies*.

LEADING INDIVIDUALS – SCOTLAND
M.Peter Anderson *Simpson & Marwick WS*
Karen Bruce Lockhart *Brodies WS*
J. Neil Cochran *Dundas & Wilson CS*
Neil Douglas *Brechin Robb*
Colin M. MacLeod *Dundas & Wilson CS*
Murray W.A. Shaw *Biggart Baillie & Gifford*
Alfred J. Tyler *Balfour & Manson*
John A. Welsh *Bishop and Robertson Chalmers*
David S. Williamson *Brodies WS*

NORTHERN IRELAND

Carson & McDowell, C & H Jefferson and *McKinty & Wright* are all members of The Law Society of Northern Ireland Panel representing solicitors in cases of alleged negligence. *Cleaver Fulton & Rankin* act for plaintiffs against architects, solicitors and civil engineers. *Tughan & Co* defend claims on behalf of accountants, solicitors and medical practitioners.

HIGHLY REGARDED – NORTHERN IRELAND	
CLEAVER FULTON & RANKIN *Belfast*	C & H JEFFERSON *Belfast*
McKINTY & WRIGHT *Belfast*	TUGHAN & CO *Belfast*
CARSON & McDOWELL *Belfast*	

LEADERS IN PROFESSIONAL NEGLIGENCE

LONDON

Arthur, David A.D.

Barlow Lyde & Gilbert, London (0171) 247 2277. Qualified 1978. Partner 1984. Specialises in accountants and insurance brokers professional negligence. Also insurance and reinsurance litigation.

Bakes, Martin J.

Herbert Smith, London (0171) 374 8000. Partner in Litigation Department (Insurance Section).

Specialisation: Has expertise in a wide range of insurance work, including policy disputes between insureds and insurers, subrogated actions against all types of professionals, local authorities, banks and many others, acting for major UK brokers and their errors and omissions insurers.

Career: Qualifed in 1980. Became a Partner at *Herbert Smith* in 1987.

Personal: Educated at Downing College, Cambridge.

Bandurka, Andrew A.

See under Insurance & Reinsurance.

Burns, Andrea

See under Construction & Civil Eng..

Dobias, Michael

Davies Arnold Cooper, London (0171) 936 2222. Qualified 1975. Partner 1980. Head of Litigation Department. Main areas of practice are commercial and insurance litigation, both domestic and international. Born 28.9.1950.

Elborne, Mark E.M.

See under Insurance & Reinsurance.

Greenley, Simon K.P.T.

See under Insurance & Reinsurance.

Hartfield, David A.M.

Alastair Thomson & Partners, London (0171) 405 4440. Partner specialising in professional negligence, insurance and construction work.

Specialisation: Main area of practice is professional negligence, acting for professional indemnity insurers and their insureds in claims against architects, surveyors, engineers, insurance brokers, accountants and licensed conveyancers. Also handles insurance and construction work, acting for (and occasionally against) insurers in respect of policy disputes and for developers in building and contractual disputes.

Prof. Membership: Law Society.

Career: Qualified in 1972. Joined *Alastair Thomson & Partners* as a Partner in 1984. Previously head of litigation department at *Nabarro Nathanson*.

Jenkins, Ian D.P.

Barlow Lyde & Gilbert, London (0171) 247 2277. Qualified 1971. Senior Partner 1989. Professional indemnity specialist. Non-executive diractor of Crowe Underwriting Agency Ltd since 1991 and R. J. Kiln & Co Ltd since 1993.

Lent, Michael J.

Alastair Thomson & Partners, London (0171) 405 4440. Partner in 1983.

Specialisation: Principal area of practice is professional indemnity insurance litigation, acting for insurers of architects, engineers, surveyors, accountants and insurance brokers. Also advises in relation to building contracts. Was involved in the following cases: Portsea Island Mutual Co-op v. Brashier Associates, Normid Housing Association v. Ralphs & Mansell, Wessex Health Authority v. HLM & others, West Faulkner v. London Borough of Newham.

Prof. Membership: Society of Construction Law, Official Referees Solicitors Association, Law Society.

Career: Qualified in 1978. Joined *Alastair Thomson & Partners* in 1981 and became a Partner in 1983.

Maguire, Peter

Cameron Markby Hewitt, London (0171) 702 2345. Partner in Insurance Group.

Specialisation: Specialises in professional indemnity. Work includes accountants, surveyors and miscellaneous professional indemnity matters, including brokers and pension problems. Important cases handled include Banque Bruxelles Lambert SA v. Eagle Star Insurance Company Limited & Others (acting for John D. Wood Commercial Ltd). Also acting in the defence of claims against Lloyd's auditors by Gooda Walker Names. Major clients include Lloyd's Syndicates and insurance companies. Author of various articles including leading insurance publications including *Corporate Cover* and *Professional Liability Today*.

Career: Qualified and joined *Hewitt Woollacott & Chown* in 1984. Became a Partner at *Cameron Markby Hewitt* in 1989.

Personal: Born 9th December 1957. Educated at Hull University 1976-79. Ardent Charlton Athletic supporter. Lives in Twickenham.

McIntosh, David A.

See under Insurance & Reinsurance.

Micklem, C.T.

Reynolds Porter Chamberlain, London (0171) 242 2877. Partner in Professional Indemnity Litigation Department.

Specialisation: Professional indemnity litigation specialist. Work relates principally to solicitors, barristers and surveyors. Has addressed various professional indemnity

seminars.

Prof. Membership: Law Society.

Career: Qualified in 1974. Became a Partner in 1977.

Nicholas, Paul D.

Reynolds Porter Chamberlain, London (0171) 242 2877. Partner in Insurance and Professional Indemnity department.

Specialisation: Insurance and professional indemnity.

Career: Qualified in 1970, having joined *Reynolds Porter* in 1968. Became a Partner in 1972.

Personal: Born 24th April 1946. Educated at Mill Hill School 1959-63 and Emmanuel College, Cambridge (BA 1967, LLB 1968). Governor of Lockers Park School and Trustee of S.W. Hertfordshire Hospice Charitable Trust.

Payton, Michael

See under Insurance & Reinsurance.

Rogan, P.J.H.

See under Insurance & Reinsurance.

Schofield, B.A.

Cameron Markby Hewitt, London (0171) 702 2345. Partner in Insurance and Reinsurance Department.

Specialisation: Principal area of practice is handling of professional indemnity claims against accountants, actuaries, Lloyd's Agents and insurance brokers, acting for insurers and insured. In addition advising on general insurance and reinsurance matters including advising on policy wording construction.

Prof. Membership: Law Society.

Career: Qualified in 1980 became a partner in *Cameron Markby Hewitt* in 1986.

Personal: Date of Birth: 11th June 1956.

Simpson, Alastair M.

Alastair Thomson & Partners, London (0171) 405 4440.

Squire, N.

Squire & Co, London (0171) 490 3444.

Taylor, Paul

Berrymans, London (0171) 638 2811.

Specialisation: Senior Partner and specialist in professional indemnity and construction law. Practice also covers insurance and reinsurance and environmental law. Acts for several major insurers and many professionals, particularly those involved in the construcion industry. Recent cases include a considerable number of international arbitrations, involving disputes in the Gulf, South Africa and the Far East. Acted for Eastern Counties Leather in its successful defence of the pollution claim brought by the Cambridge Water Authority. Involved in numerous major construction disputes in the UK, including the collapse of the Carsington Dam. Currently handling a large number of High Court actions involving construction disputes and pension transfers. Co-editor of both 'Berryman's Building Claims Cases' and 'Binghams & Berrymans' Motor Claims Cases'. Has written many articles for legal, construction and insurance journals and is currently preparing a new text book on environmental liability in the construction industry. Regularly addresses conferences and seminars both in the UK and abroad.

Prof. Membership: International Association of Defence Lawyers; The Society of Construction Law; The Official Referees' Solicitors Association; associate member of FIDIC.

Career: Qualified 1969. Joined *Berrymans* 1970, partner 1973, senior partner 1991.

Personal: Educated at King's College, London (LL.B) 1963-66. Leisure pursuits include watching football (Crystal Palace and Wimbledon), photography, chess and three ageing sports cars. Born 25th February 1946. Lives in Tunbridge Wells.

Tester, S.K.
Cameron Markby Hewitt, London (0171) 702 2345. Qualified 1981.

Thomas, Nicholas P.G.
Kennedys, London (0171) 638 3688. Partner in Litigation Department.

Specialisation: Principal area of expertise is professional indemnity, particularly in the construction field. Acts for architects, surveyors, engineers and contractors, as well as other professionals such as accountants, brokers and authors (defamation). Also covers insurance work generally, including disputes as to whether insurers should respond and which insurers should respond. Acted in BBL v. John D. Wood and others, and National Trust v. Hayden Young. Author of 'Professional Indemnity Claims (An Architect's Guide)', published by Architect's Press in 1981. Regularly addresses conferences and seminars, particularly for insurers.

Prof. Membership: Member of the Law Society, Fellow of the Chartered Institute of Arbitrators.

Career: Joined *Kennedy's* in 1977 and qualified in 1980. Became a Partner in 1981.

Personal: Born 16th October 1954. Attended Bristol University 1973-76. School Governor. Leisure pursuits include all sports, travel and the arts. Lives near Hitchin, Herts.

Wadsworth, Michael Henry
Cameron Markby Hewitt, London (0171) 702 2345. Head of Insurance Group.

Specialisation: Principal area of practice is professional indemnity work. Also handles all aspects of insurance and reinsurance and general commercial litigation.

Prof. Membership: Law Society, City of London Solicitors Company.

Career: Commenced articles with *Hewitt, Woollacott and Chown* and became a Partner in 1965.

Personal: Born 5th June 1939. Attended Highgate School 1951-57, then St. Edmund Hall, Oxford 1959-62. Freeman of the City of London and Liveryman of the Worshipful Company of Glass Sellers. Leisure pursuits include photography, fell walking, tennis and singing.

White, Stuart G.
Hextall, Erskine & Co, London (0171) 488 1424. Partner in Insurance Litigation Department.

Specialisation: Main area of practice is professional indemnity, principally construction related, for architects and engineers. Also handles general insurance work, covering insurance disputes, policy wordings and general liability litigation. Acted in Investors in Industry v. South Bedfordshire D.C., and is involved in the personal accident insurance claim following the death of Robert Maxwell. Major clients include insurance companies, mutual insurance associations and Lloyd's syndicates. Has given seminars on a range of topics such as architects' liability, product liability and liability for pollution. Individual charge-out rates are £165-£185 per hour.

Prof. Membership: Society of Construction Law, Anglo-German Jurists Association, CEDR.

Career: Qualified in 1984. Joined *Hextall, Erskine & Co* in 1981, becoming a Partner in 1987.

Personal: Born 6th July 1957. Attended the Queen's College Oxford, MA (Hons) 1975-78.

Williams, Robin
McKenna & Co, London (Lloyd's) (0171) 929 1250. Partner in Insurance and Reinsurance Department.

Specialisation: Main area of practice is brokers' errors and omissions. Has acted for many of the leading brokers in both litigation and arbitration. Other area of practice is reinsurance: has handled a wide variety of cases going back to Great Atlantic v. AFIA in 1980. Also Contractors' All Risk and Environmental litigation. Cases have included Sasse, Howden, PCW, Multiguarantee, Rotterdamse and current Lloyd's Names litigation. Author of numerous articles. Has spoken widely at seminars and conferences.

Prof. Membership: Law Society, Associate Member of Lloyd's.

Career: Qualified in 1973. Joined *McKenna & Co* in 1971, becoming a Partner in 1979.

Personal: Born 6th February 1949. Attended Hampton School 1960-67 and University College Oxford MA (Oxon). Leisure interests include football, golf, gardening and family. Lives in Woking, Surrey.

Anderson, M. Peter
See under Litigation (Commercial).

Bradshaw, R.S
Weightman Rutherfords, Liverpool (0151) 227 2601. Partner in Litigation Department.

Specialisation: Main area of practice is professional indemnity on behalf of defendants' insurers particularly Solicitors Indemnity Fund. Also handles commercial litigation and partnership disputes.

Prof. Membership: Law Society, Liverpool Law Society.

Career: Qualified in 1955. Joined *Weightman Rutherfords* as a Partner in 1969. Part time Chairman of Industrial Tribunal.

Personal: Born 30th July 1933. Educated at Liverpool College before articles in Liverpool.

Bruce Lockhart, Karen
See under Medical Negligence.

Challands, Richard
Bond Pearce, Plymouth (01752) 266633. Qualified 1975. Partner 1978. Insurance department specialising in professional indemnity, insurance litigation and product liability. Regularly speaks on the subject of Professional indemnity.

Cochran, J. Neil
Dundas & Wilson CS, Edinburgh (0131) 228 8000. Qualified 1972. Partner 1984. Litigation Department. Acts for insurers of solicitors, advocates, engineers, surveyors and also in fire and personal injury claims.

Cradick, C. Roger
Morgan Bruce, Cardiff (01222) 385385. Qualified 1954. Partner 1963. Insurance Litigation Department. Principal area of practice is professional negligence and personal injury. Also deals with road haulage and passenger service vehicle licensing. Born 6.11.1932.

Crute, Alan H.
Crutes, Newcastle-upon-Tyne (0191) 281 5811. Qualified 1955. Partner 1957. Senior Partner 1979. Main areas of practice are professional negligence and medical negligence.

Douglas, Neil
Brechin Robb, Glasgow (0141) 248 5921.

Grossman, George
Howard Palser Grossman Hermer & Partners, Cardiff (01222) 452770.

Hale, Richard
Morgan Bruce, Cardiff (01222) 385385. Qualified 1971. Partner 1974. Professional Indemnity Department. Particular emphasis on claims against solicitors arising out of non-contentious practice. Born 19.7.1947.

Higham, David R.G.
Blake Lapthorn, Fareham (01489) 579990.

Jefferies, Michael G.
See under Construction & Civil Eng..

MacLeod, Colin M.
Dundas & Wilson CS, Edinburgh (0131) 228 8000. Qualified 1979. Partner 1983. Litigation Department. Acts for insurers in claims against surveyors, solicitors, architects and accountants.

MacWilkinson, Jeffrey N.
Dolmans, Cardiff (01222) 345531. Partner in Litigation Department.

Specialisation: Senior litigation Partner specialising in personal injury and professional negligence. Handles plaintiff work in relation to professional negligence. Remaining litigation work is defendant based which includes employers liability, building cases, and civil actions against the police. Major clients include various insurance companies and local authorities as well as Police authorities.

Prof. Membership: Law Society, Chartered Institute of Arbitrators, FOIL.

Career: Qualified in 1966. Partner with *Dolmans* since 1972. Part time Chairman of Social Security Appeals Tribunal since 1985. Deputy District Judge since 1991.

Personal: Born 10th September 1942. Educated at Penarth Grammar School 1954-60.

Leisure interests include golf. Lives in Cardiff.

Morgan, Robert
Eversheds, Cardiff (01222) 471147.

Price, Hugh M.
See under Personal Injury.

Redfern, Paul W.L.
Wansbroughs Willey Hargrave, Bristol (0117) 926 8981. Partner in Professional Indemnity and Insurance Department.

Specialisation: Principal area of practice is professional indemnity, acting for a wide range of professions including surveyors, architects, accountants, brokers and financial intermediaries. Other main area is Lloyd's litigation and insurance including managing and members agent's disputes, insurance and reinsurance litigation. Also handles disputes for British Institute of Facilities Management members under their insurance scheme.

Prof. Membership: Law Society.

Career: Qualified in 1978, having joined *Wansbroughs Willey Hargrave* in 1976. Became a Partner in 1981. Managing Partner of Bristol office 1989-92. Established the firm's Lloyd's office in 1992.

Rowe, Paul N.C.
Wansbroughs Willey Hargrave, Bristol (0117) 926 8981. Partner in Litigation Department.

Specialisation: Main area of practice is professional negligence. Handles claims for all professions including solicitors, surveyors, accountants, architects, financial intermediaries and insurance brokers.

Career: Qualified in 1970. Joined *Wansbroughs Willey Hargrave* in 1971, becoming a Partner in 1976.

Salomonsen, Erik
Bond Pearce, Plymouth (01752) 266633. Qualified 1975. Partner 1979. Insurance Department. Practice encompasses professional negligence including medical malpractice; general and environmental liability.

Shaw, Murray W.A.
See under Construction & Civil Eng..

Summerfield, N.
Lightfoots, Thame (01844) 212305 or 212574/5.

Tyler, Alfred J.
See under Personal Injury.

Welsh, John A.
See under Construction & Civil Eng..

Williamson, David S.
See under Litigation (Commercial).

INDEXES TO PROFILES

Solicitors' Profiles The index to leading solicitors profiled in the specialist lists is located immediately after the section containing in-house lawyers' profiles. This index also includes heads of company legal departments.

Barristers' Profiles Leading barristers' profiles are indexed within the main Barristers' Index located at the end of the directory. Names of profiled barristers are set in bold type.

PROPERTY (COMMERCIAL)

LONDON

Nabarro Nathanson emerges as the pre-eminent firm with a specialist team of 130 lawyers, 30 of whom are partners (seven are based within the firms provincial offices). The property unit is headed by the highly recommended Geoffrey Lander who has recently suceeded David Bramson, another notable practitioner (now senior partner). The firm

represents institutional developers including Land Securities (the UK's largest developer), Hamersons, Great Portland Estates and British Coal; numerous UK pensions funds including CIN; overseas investors and many corporate tenants including Hanover Property Unit Trust, Lilliput and Swift.

Linklaters & Paines, Freshfields, Berwin Leighton and *S J Berwin & Co* have also been highly recommended.

Robert Finch and David Lloyd at *Linklaters & Paines* advise public and private companies on funding, development, leasing and investment. The property department has handled numerous major transactions in the last twelve months including the sale of 460 public houses at £108 million for Scottish & Newcastle Breweries, the disposal of investment properties to Raglan at £90 million and the letting of 140,000 sq. ft at Canary Wharf to Credit Suisse.

The property department at *Freshfields* is primarily a service unit supporting the corporate department. Geoffrey Le Pard, who heads the property unit is nevertheless highly regarded and was recommended by a number of leading practitioners.

Berwin Leighton's property unit numbers 20 specialist partners dealing primarily with public and private sector acquisition and development, site assembly, pre-letting, development funding and project management, town centre redevelopment and rent sharing, portfolio acquisition, rationalisation and management. The firm has some notable clients which include Tesco, Prudential Property Holdings, British Land, Mercury Asset Management, PDFM, Blue Circle and Legal & General. Lawrance Heller and Philip Bretherton have been recommended.

Commercial property commands 19% of the workload at *S J Berwin & Co*. The firm undertakes a variety of work for clients such as British Land, Ladbrokes, Hilton, Marks & Spencer, Mowlem, Securum, Sunlife and British Aerospace and has recently handled the property aspects of the £16

million acquisition of 75.5% of Swiss Centre Ltd for The British Land Company plc.

Other firms with highly respected commercial property departments include *Ashurst Morris Crisp*, *Clifford Chance*, *D J Freeman*, *Gouldens* and *Titmuss Sainer Dechert*.

Laurence Rutman heads the property department at *Ashurst Morris Crisp* which comprises ten partners including the highly regarded Ian Nisse. The firm represents developers, property companies, pension funds and local/statutory authorities and is particularly known for major schemes, inner city and town centre work.

Clifford Chance's property department, which numbers 20 specialists (including Iain Morpeth, Rupert Hill and Tony Briam), provides a comprehensive service to corporations, institutions, pension funds, local and public authorities and banks. The firm is particularly strong on the international front.

In all the tables the names in each group are listed alphabetically.

The 17 specialists at *D J Freeman* handle development, investment, management and lease work for clients such as Land Securities, Sun Alliance and British Gas. The firm is a member of the British Council of Shopping Centres, the British Property Foundation and the British Council of Offices.

Members of the property department at *Gouldens* advise developers, institutional investors, banks, surveyors and other professionals.

Commercial property work comprises 39% of the caseload

at *Titmuss Sainer Dechert*. Steven Fogel and his team of 13 specialist partners undertake a variety of retail, investment, development, landlord and tenant and rent review work.

Other large firms with expertise in the field include *Cameron Markby Hewitt, Denton Hall, Herbert Smith, Rowe & Maw* and *Simmons & Simmons*.

Highly recommended smaller firms include *Boodle Hatfield, Brecher & Co, Church Adams Tatham, Debenham & Co, Manches & Co, Nicholson Graham & Jones* and *Travers Smith Braithwaite*.

LEADING INDIVIDUALS – LONDON

David Bramson *Nabarro Nathanson*	Philip Bretherton *Berwin Leighton*	Diana Courtney *Denton Hall*
Robert G. Finch *Linklaters & Paines*	Lawrance Heller *Berwin Leighton*	Geoffrey Lander *Nabarro Nathanson*
Geoffrey Le Pard *Freshfields*	David G. Lloyd *Linklaters & Paines*	Simon M.P. MacDonagh *Lovell White Durrant*
R.G. Martin *Cameron Markby Hewitt*	Iain C.S. Morpeth *Clifford Chance*	Laurence D. Rutman *Ashurst Morris Crisp*
Richard A. Woof *Debenham & Co*	David Wright *Nabarro Nathanson*	
Jeffrey Bailey *Linklaters & Paines*	Valerie Brecher *Brecher & Co*	Tony Briam *Clifford Chance*
Nicholas A. Brown *McKenna & Co*	Malcolm H. Brummer *Berwin Leighton*	Alan J. Butler *Simmons & Simmons*
Paul E. Clark *D J Freeman*	John Ronald Fenner *Fenners*	Steven Fogel *Titmuss Sainer Dechert*
Penelope Freer *Freshfields*	Garry Hart *Herbert Smith*	G.J. Hayhurst *Paisner & Co*
Rupert Hill *Clifford Chance*	Robert J. Kidby *Lovell White Durrant*	Timothy Lake *Stepien Lake Gilbert & Paling*
Graham Lust *Nabarro Nathanson*	Louis S. Manches *Manches & Co*	R.C. Nicoll *Richards Butler*
Ian Bertram Nisse *Ashurst Morris Crisp*	John Samson *Nabarro Nathanson*	Hugo Scott *Gouldens*
Michael F. Stancombe *Lovell White Durrant*	Chris Tavener *Herbert Smith*	David Taylor *Berwin Leighton*
G.P. White *Slaughter and May*		

SOUTH EAST

HIGHLY REGARDED – SOUTH EAST

BLAKE LAPTHORN *Fareham*	BOODLE HATFIELD *Southampton*
CHURCH ADAMS TATHAM *Reigate*	COLEMANS *Maidenhead*
B.P. COLLINS & CO *Gerrards Cross*	DEAN WILSON *Brighton*
DENTON HALL *Milton Keynes*	DONNE MILEHAM & HADDOCK *Brighton*
GEORGE IDE, PHILLIPS *Chichester*	HAROLD BENJAMIN *Harrow*
LINNELLS *Oxford*	RAWLISON & BUTLER *Crawley*
THOMAS EGGAR VERRALL BOWLES *Chichester*	THOMSON SNELL & PASSMORE *Tunbridge Wells*
WOLLASTONS *Chelmsford*	
BROOKSTREET DES ROCHES *Witney*	BUSS MURTON *Tunbridge Wells*
CRIPPS HARRIES HALL *Tunbridge Wells*	DALLAS BRETT *Oxford*
ELLISON & CO *Colchester*	ENSOR BYFIELD *Southampton*
GLANVILLES *Portsmouth*	GLENISTERS *Ruislip*
HAWKINS RUSSELL JONES *Hitchin*	HEPHERD WINSTANLEY & PUGH *Southampton*
KENNETH ELLIOTT & ROWE *Romford*	LAYTONS *Hampton Court*
MERRIMAN WHITE *Guildford*	MOORE & BLATCH *Southampton*
PARIS SMITH & RANDALL *Southampton*	PENNINGTONS *Basingstoke*
PICTONS *St. Albans*	SHERWIN OLIVER *Portsmouth*
WILLMETT & CO *Windsor*	

Most of the firms in the South East advise on a wide range of commercial property matters. *Blake Lapthorn, Harold Benjamin & Collins* and *Rawlison & Butler* act for a number of developers advising on the acquisition, development and disposal of residential and industrial estates. *Boodle Hatfield* acts for national organisations and locally based property companies and individuals, and has been involved in large scale retail development and numerous marina developments. *Donne Mileham & Haddock* handles development work, being particularly well known for its retail sector expertise. *Thomas Eggar Verrall Bowles* has substantial experience acting for institutional clients.

Other firms with commercial property expertise include *Church Adams Tatham & Co* which has experience in railway related work, *Colemans, B.P. Collins & Co, Dean Wilson, George Ide, Phillips, Linnells, Thomson Snell & Passmore* and *Wollastons*.

Denton Hall acts for a broad property client base including retailers, housebuilders and local authorities. The firm has also provided all legal services to the Commission for New Towns.

LEADING INDIVIDUALS – SOUTH EAST

Michael David Bailey *Donne Mileham & Haddock*

SOUTH WEST

Commercial property comprises 25% of the workload at *Burges Salmon*. The firm has 12 specialist partners handling a range of insolvency, secured lending, housing association, building society and overseas work. Robin Battersby and Robert Smyth are held in high regard.

LEADING FIRMS – SOUTH WEST	
BURGES SALMON *Bristol*	MICHELMORES *Exeter*
VEALE WASBROUGH *Bristol*	
BEVAN ASHFORD *Bristol*	BOND PEARCE *Plymouth*
EVERSHEDS *Bristol*	LAWRENCE TUCKETTS *Bristol*
OSBORNE CLARKE *Bristol*	

Veale Wasbrough has one of the largest property departments in the South West with 16 solicitors, eight of whom are partners. As well as providing the more traditional property work, the firm has in addition developed niche areas of expertise in central and local government work, pipelines work, VAT and BES schemes and in work relating to the quarrying and waste management industries. Through providing advice to clients such as University of Bristol Property Holdings, Esso Petroleum and Barclays Property Holdings Ltd, they are thought to be a force to be reckoned with nationally; both Tim Smithers and Simon Baker being held in high regard.

HIGHLY REGARDED – SOUTH WEST	
CARTWRIGHTS *Bristol*	CLARKE WILLMOTT & CLARKE *Taunton*
CRAWFORD OWEN *Bristol*	DAVIES AND PARTNERS *Gloucester*
FOOT & BOWDEN *Plymouth*	HANCOCK & LAWRENCE *Truro*
HOOPER & WOLLEN *Torquay*	KITSONS *Torquay*
LESTER ALDRIDGE *Bournemouth*	LYONS DAVIDSON *Bristol*
NALDER & SON *Truro*	PORTER BARTLETT & MAYO *Yeovil*
TOWNSENDS *Swindon*	TRETHOWANS *Salisbury*
TRUMP AND PARTNERS *Bristol*	WITHY KING & LEE *Bath*
WOLFERSTANS *Plymouth*	
BEVIRS *Swindon*	BISHOP LONGBOTHAM & BAGNALL *Trowbridge*
BOYCE HATTON *Torquay*	BRETHERTON PRICE ELGOODS *Cheltenham*
CHARLES RUSSELL *Cheltenham*	DICKINSON MANSER *Poole*
KIRBY SIMCOX *Bristol*	LACEYS *Bournemouth*
LINFORD BROWNS *Exmouth*	STEELE RAYMOND *Bournemouth*
WANSBROUGHS WILLEY HARGRAVE *Bristol*	

Outside Bristol the leading commercial property practice is *Michelmores* closely followed by *Bevan Ashford* and *Bond Pearce*. *Michelmores* act for the largest developers in the South West and are experienced in all areas of development and disposal, including business and retail parks and the funding of such developments. Andrew Maynard and Peter Lowless are both highly recommended.

Bevan Ashford handles property work from all five of its branches in the South West. Andrew Rothwell at the Exeter office is highly recommended. *Bond Pearce* undertakes a broad range of commercial property work and is particularly noted for advice on development and investment issues. David Gunn, who heads the property unit, has written many articles on VAT and collateral warranties in development projects and is a frequent speaker at seminars.

Other recommended firms include *Eversheds, Lawrence Tucketts* and *Osborne Clarke*.

In Bristol, *Eversheds* represents breweries, business park developers and investors and retailers.

Lawrence Tucketts has four fee-earners handling joint venture, development and financial work for retailers, investors and landlords. The firm also acts for a number of trading and distribution companies.

Osborne Clarke, known for its all-round development expertise, has particular experience in the leisure and brewing industries. William Tacey is highly regarded.

WALES

The four large Cardiff commercial firms dominate this area of law. *Edwards Geldard* and *Eversheds* are pre-eminent, but also highly regarded are the specialist teams of *Hugh James Jones & Jenkins* and *Morgan Bruce*.

LEADING FIRMS – WALES	
EDWARDS GELDARD *Cardiff*	EVERSHEDS *Cardiff*
HUGH JAMES JONES & JENKINS *Cardiff*	MORGAN BRUCE *Cardiff*

Edwards Geldard handles development work (from single buildings to town centres), investment and finance, especially forward funding and selling. The firm has a wide client base and has recently advised Citibank, Welsh Water and Wilcon Homes on large property transactions. Rowland Davies, who heads the commercial property unit, also represents the Welsh Development Agency and the Cardiff Bay Development Corporation along with *Eversheds* and *Morgan Bruce*.

The team at *Eversheds* has particular strength in acquisitions and disposals of public sector properties, in secured lending for banks, building societies and brewers. Alan Meredith is highly regarded.

David Lloyd Roberts of *Hugh James Jones & Jenkins* represents both local and national developers and acts on behalf

LEADING INDIVIDUALS – SOUTH WEST		
Simon Baker *Veale Wasbrough*	Robin S. Battersby *Burges Salmon*	David Gunn *Bond Pearce*
Peter Lowless *Michelmores*	Andrew E. Maynard *Michelmores*	Andrew C. Rothwell *Bevan Ashford*
Tim M.D. Smithers *Veale Wasbrough*	Robert J. Smyth *Burges Salmon*	
Timothy J. Davidson *Lyons Davidson*	Martin O. Davies Jones *Crawford Owen*	Graham Alan Forward *Kitsons*
Willam A. Tacey *Osborne Clarke*		

In all the tables the names in each group are listed alphabetically.

of a large number of private clients comprising smaller companies, private investors and professional firms. The firm acts for a large number of housing associations, advising on housing projects involving joint ventures between housing associations, developers and local authorities.

HIGHLY REGARDED – WALES	
BERRY SMITH *Bridgend*	BEVAN ASHFORD *Cardiff*
DOLMANS *Cardiff*	GROSSMAN HERMER SELIGMAN *Cardiff*
BEOR WILSON & LLOYD *Swansea*	FRANCIS & CO *Newport*
HALLINANS *Cardiff*	

Morgan Bruce undertakes acquisition and disposal work for commercial and industrial properties, hotel and licensed premises, development and funding work for commercial schemes and secured commercial lending work.

LEADING INDIVIDUALS – WALES
Rowland Davies *Edwards Geldard*
Robert W. James *Morgan Bruce*
Alan Meredith *Eversheds*
David Lloyd Roberts *Hugh James Jones & Jenkins*

MIDLANDS

The leading commercial property practices in the Midlands are *Eversheds* and *Wragge & Co.*

LEADING FIRMS – MIDLANDS	
EDGE & ELLISON *Birmingham*	EVERSHEDS *Birmingham*
WRAGGE & CO *Birmingham*	

Despite the recession, *Eversheds* in Birmingham have extended their client base and secured a number of major instructions including the acquisition of a £15 million site for Fujitsu Fulcrum Telecommunications Ltd and the sale of

HIGHLY REGARDED – MIDLANDS	
MARTINEAU JOHNSON *Birmingham*	PINSENT CURTIS *Birmingham*
SHOOSMITHS & HARRISON *Northampton*	
BAND HATTON AND CO *Coventry*	BLAKESLEY RICE MACDONALD *Chesterfield*
BLYTHE LIGGINS *Leamington Spa*	DIBB LUPTON BROOMHEAD *Birmingham*
EDWARDS GELDARD *Derby*	FREETH CARTWRIGHT HUNT DICKINS *Nottingham*
HACKING ASHTON *Newcastle-under-Lyme*	HADEN STRETTON SLATER MILLER *Walsall*
HARVEY INGRAM *Leicester*	HATCHER ROGERSON *Shrewsbury*
HEWITSON BECKE + SHAW *Northampton*	HIGGS & SONS *Brierley Hill*
KEELY SMITH & JOBSON *Lichfield*	KNIGHT & SONS *Newcastle-under-Lyme*
LANYON BOWDLER *Shrewsbury*	MANBY & STEWARD *Wolverhampton*
MORTON FISHER *Worcester*	NEEDHAM & JAMES *Stratford upon Avon*
OWSTONS *Leicester*	RIGBEYS *Birmingham*

Allied Carpets to Carpetland, a transaction involving 225 properties, and the flotation of Partco which involved 200 properties. Other clients include P&O Properties Ltd, Bryant Properties and Bass plc. Adrian Bland is held in high

regard. *Eversheds* Nottingham branch also has a substantial property department which handles acquisition and disposal work for owner occupiers and investors and also development work where it has cultivated a specialist service. Clients include National Westminster Bank, Derby Pride, Derby University, 30 Further Education Colleges and a number of NHS Trust Hospitals.

The commercial property department at *Wragge & Co* comprises nine specialist partners who handle a broad spectrum of work. Probably best known for property development, the firm has an enviable client list, having recently represented Wilson Connolly Properties plc in the retail and leisure phases of a large scheme in Taunton, Kingspark Developments Ltd in a £15 million development, St. Modwen Properties plc in the sale of £37 million retail parks and joint venture work and Castlemore Securities in a £20 million deal. The firm has also advised on the redevelopment of nine local authorities and town centres. David Askin has been highly recommended.

Other highly recommended firms include *Hewitson Becke + Shaw, Martineau Johnson, Pinsent Curtis* and *Shoosmiths & Harrison,* whilst *Knight & Sons* is noted for its expertise in mines and minerals.

LEADING INDIVIDUALS – MIDLANDS
David J. Askin *Wragge & Co*
Adrian D. Bland *Eversheds*

EAST ANGLIA

Eversheds, Hewitson Becke + Shaw, Mills & Reeve and *Taylor Vinters* all have excellent reputations in the field.

Eversheds handles a variety of acquisition and disposal work, corporate lending and development from the Ipswich and Norwich offices. The firm also undertakes a substantial amount of work for licensed premises.

Hewitson Becke + Shaw has particular experience in property funding matters and joint venture agreements. It acts for property developers and other substantial organisations based both regionally and nationally, and has expanded over the last year with the appointment of three additional solicitors to operate from its offices in Cambridge, Newmarket and Peterbrough.

HIGHLY REGARDED – EAST ANGLIA	
EVERSHEDS *Norwich*	HEWITSON BECKE + SHAW *Cambridge*
MILLS & REEVE *Norwich*	TAYLOR VINTERS *Cambridge*
GOTELEE & GOLDSMITH *Ipswich*	PRETTYS *Ipswich*
BANKES ASHTON *Bury St. Edmunds*	BIRKETTS *Ipswich*
FEW & KESTER *Cambridge*	GREENLAND HOUCHEN *Norwich*
GREENWOODS *Peterborough*	LEATHES PRIOR *Norwich*
LEEDS DAY *Sandy*	

The commercial property unit at *Mills & Reeve* numbers seven solicitors who handle a broad spectrum of work, and has recently appointed an ex-City lawyer.

Other firms noted for their expertise include *Gotelee & Goldsmith* and *Prettys.*

NORTH WEST

The major Manchester firms: *Addleshaw Sons & Latham, Alsop Wilkinson, Cobbett Leak Almond, Eversheds, Halliwell Landau* and *Slater Heelis* absorb much of the larger work although smaller specialist firms such as *Gorna & Co* and *Field Cunningham & Co* compete very successfully.

Commercial property comprises 23% of the workload at *Addleshaw Sons & Latham.* David Tully heads a team that is particularly known for landlord and tenant, development, secured lending and investment sales and purchases.

LEADING FIRMS – NORTH WEST	
ADDLESHAW SONS & LATHAM *Manchester*	**ALSOP WILKINSON** *Liverpool*
COBBETT LEAK ALMOND *Manchester*	**EVERSHEDS** *Manchester*
HALLIWELL LANDAU *Manchester*	**SLATER HEELIS** *Manchester*
BULLIVANT JONES & CO *Liverpool*	**DAVIES WALLIS FOYSTER** *Liverpool*
FIELD CUNNINGHAM *Manchester*	**GORNA & CO** *Manchester*
WEIGHTMAN RUTHERFORDS *Liverpool*	
BERMANS *Liverpool*	**CUFF ROBERTS** *Liverpool*
LACE MAWER *Manchester*	

Operating from Manchester and Liverpool, *Alsop Wilkinson* has a wide ranging expertise acting for many well known institutional investors, developers and public sector bodies. David Edmundson has been highly recommended.

Cobbett Leak Almond handles development work, judicial review cases and property dealing/trading. The firm's client base largely comes from the leisure industry, hotels, pubs and clubs.

HIGHLY REGARDED – NORTH WEST	
BARKER, BOOTH & EASTWOOD *Blackpool*	**BREMNER SONS** *Liverpool*
HILL DICKINSON DAVIS CAMPBELL *Liverpool*	**JONES MAIDMENT WILSON** *Manchester*
NAPTHEN HOUGHTON CRAVEN *Preston*	**VAUDREYS** *Manchester*
AARON & PARTNERS *Chester*	**BRABNER HOLDEN BANKS WILSON** *Liverpool*
CARTMELL SHEPHERD *Carlisle*	**CHAFFE STREET** *Manchester*
ELLIOTT & CO *Manchester*	**INGHAM CLEGG & CROWTHER** *Preston*
KUIT, STEINART, LEVY *Manchester*	**WACKS CALLER** *Manchester*
WALKER SMITH & WAY *Chester*	

The recent recruitment by *Eversheds* of the principle property partner and his senior assistant from *Davies Arnold Cooper* in Manchester has increased the property team to 17 fee earners, seven of whom are partners. The firm offers a specialist service to housing associations and other public sector clients in addition to the comprehensive service it offers to its broad client base. Recent transactions have included major retail and town centre redevelopment schemes for two North West local authorities, the development of a 60 acre business park for AMEC Developments Ltd and the second phase development at Wirral Leisureland for THI (Bramborough) Limited. John Moody has been highly recommended.

Halliwell Landau is active in all market sectors, advising on acquisitions and disposals, development projects, joint ventures, secured lending and landlord and tenant. The property unit has recently advised on the sale of a Salford Quays development worth over £21 million, and on a £58 million pre-funded development at Great Bridgewater Street for AMEC Developments Ltd. David Stratton has been highly recommended.

Slater Heelis offers a comprehensive service for retail, office, industrial and development transactions. The firm represents a diverse range of clients from banks and investment funds to architects, engineers and surveyors.

Gorna & Co represents a number of nationally known property companies, Friendly Societies and housing associations.

In Liverpool, *Alsop Wilkinson* and *Davies Wallis Foyster* are highly regarded.

Davies Wallis Foyster is involved in development work, brewery work (acting for two national brewers) and receiverships of property in particular. The firm also has expertise in waterfront development. *Bullivant Jones & Company* (Pamela Jones and Michael Stephens have been recommended to us) has an excellent reputation both for general commercial property advice and for its work in relation to retail parks.

Weightman Rutherfords is noted for its experience within the brewery industry. Also highly regarded are *Bermans, Cuff Roberts* and *Lace Mawer.*

LEADING INDIVIDUALS – NORTH WEST
P.H. Ashworth *Field Cunningham*
David Edmundson *Alsop Wilkinson*
Pamela Jones *Bullivant Jones & Co*
John Moody *Eversheds*
Michael P. Stephens *Bullivant Jones & Co*
David Stratton *Halliwell Landau*
David J. Tully *Addleshaw Sons & Latham*

NORTH EAST

Booth & Co and *Eversheds* emerge as the pre-eminent commercial property firms in the North East.

The property unit at *Booth & Co* is headed by John Pike (who has an excellent reputation) and comprises ten specialist partners. The firm has an enviable client base and has advised no less than 40 major institutions in the last 12 months on a variety of transactions including the Granary Wharf and other Leeds redevelopments, the sale of Direct Line House, a large retail development in East Anglia for a local authority, and retail park development work for Stadium Group.

The strengths of *Eversheds* commercial property department traditionally lay in retail work, industrial work, property management and letting and development work within the distribution, commercial and financial sectors. Over the last 12 months however, the team has built up specialist expertise in new fields including the public sector, education, utilities and telecommunications. With clients like Asda, Austin Reed Group, Hammersons, MEPC, NFC, British Waterways Board, Barr Wallace Arnold Trust, National Westminster Bank, Bank of Scotland, and National & Provincial Building Society, the firm maintains its position at the forefront of the commercial property field. Andrew Latchmore is held in high regard by his competitors.

LEADING FIRMS – NORTH EAST	
BOOTH & CO. *Leeds*	**EVERSHEDS** *Leeds*
DIBB LUPTON BROOMHEAD *Bradford*	**DICKINSON DEES** *Newcastle*
ANDREW M. JACKSON *Hull*	**DENISON TILL** *York*
GARRETT & CO *Leeds*	**GOSSCHALKS** *Hull*
NABARRO NATHANSON *Doncaster*	**WALKER MORRIS** *Leeds*

Dibb Lupton Broomhead and *Dickinson Dees* are also highly recommended. Neil McLean at *Dibb Lupton Broomhead* is noted for his expertise in the retail and development fields although the firm also acts for hotels, freeholders, statutory bodies, and institutions.

HIGHLY REGARDED – NORTH EAST	
ATTEY BOWER & JONES *Doncaster*	**FINN, GLEDHILL & CO** *Halifax*
GODLOVE PEARLMAN *Leeds*	**GORDONS WRIGHT & WRIGHT** *Bradford*
HAMMOND SUDDARDS *Leeds*	**IRWIN MITCHELL** *Sheffield*
JACKSONS *Middlesbrough*	**MINCOFF SCIENCE & GOLD** *Newcastle*
OXLEY & COWARD *Rotherham*	**PINSENT CURTIS**
PUNCH ROBSON *Middlesbrough*	**READ HIND STEWART** *Leeds*
ROBERT MUCKLE *Newcastle*	**ROLLIT FARRELL & BLADON** *Hull*
WANSBROUGHS WILLEY HARGRAVE *Leeds*	**WARD HADAWAY** *Newcastle*
WILKINSON MAUGHAN *Newcastle*	
ARCHERS *Stockton-on-Tees*	**ARMITAGE SYKES HALL NORTON** *Huddersfield*
BURY & WALKERS *Barnsley*	**CRANSWICK WATSON** *Leeds*
HARTLEY & WORSTENHOLME *Castleford*	**LATIMER HINKS** *Darlington*
STAMP JACKSON & PROCTER *Hull*	**WATSON BURTON** *Newcastle*

Dickinson Dees covers the full range of work, including development work for institutions and house builders, secured lending and insolvency recovery work, housing associations, commercial leasing and estate management, compulsory purchase orders and other local authority work.

Other firms with good reputations include *Denison Till, Garrett & Co, Gosschalks* (with particular reference to licensed premises), *Nabarro Nathanson, Walker Morris* and *Andrew M. Jackson & Co.*

LEADING INDIVIDUALS – NORTH EAST
Andrew Latchmore *Eversheds*
Neil McLean *Dibb Lupton Broomhead*
John D. Pike *Booth & Co.*
Michael R. Sleath *Garrett & Co*
Timothy P. Tonkin *Booth & Co.*
Ian D. Wilkinson *Andrew M. Jackson*

In all the tables the names in each group are listed alphabetically.

SCOTLAND

The leading commercial property practices in Scotland are *Maclay Murray & Spens, McGrigor Donald* and *Shepherd & Wedderburn WS.*

LEADING FIRMS – SCOTLAND	
MACLAY MURRAY & SPENS *Glasgow*	**McGRIGOR DONALD** *Glasgow*
SHEPHERD & WEDDERBURN *Edinburgh*	
DUNDAS & WILSON CS *Edinburgh*	**STEEDMAN RAMAGE** *Edinburgh*
TODS MURRAY WS *Edinburgh*	
ARCHIBALD CAMPBELL & HARLEY *Edinburgh*	**MILLER SAMUEL & CO** *Glasgow*

The property department of *Maclay Murray & Spens,* containing amongst others Ian Quigley, Malcolm Fleming and Ian Macniven, is noted for its strength in depth, and has been capturing the development and retail marketplaces advising no less than 30 institutions on major transactional work including the acquisition of 230 Rumbelows stores for Escom, the £27 million sale of Kingsgate Retail Park, the £9 million sale of Westfield Industrial Estate, and the lease of the Arnotts (at £15 million) and Grosvenor buildings for Scottish Amicable, securities work for Bank of Scotland totalling £37 million and a joint venture project totalling £70 million.

HIGHLY REGARDED – SCOTLAND	
ALEXANDER STONE & CO *Glasgow*	**BENNETT & ROBERTSON** *Edinburgh*
BIRD SEMPLE *Glasgow*	**BOYDS** *Glasgow*
BRODIES WS *Edinburgh*	**W & J BURNESS WS** *Edinburgh*
DICKSON MINTO WS *Edinburgh*	**DORMAN JEFFREY & CO** *Glasgow*
FYFE IRELAND *Edinburgh*	**LEDINGHAM CHALMERS** *Aberdeen*
LESLIE WOLFSON & CO *Glasgow*	**MACROBERTS** *Glasgow*
PAULL & WILLIAMSONS *Aberdeen*	**SEMPLE FRASER WS** *Glasgow*
THORNTONS WS *Dundee*	
ALEX MORISON & CO WS *Edinburgh*	**ANDERSON STRATHERN WS** *Edinburgh*
BALFOUR & MANSON *Edinburgh*	**BIGGART BAILLIE & GIFFORD** *Glasgow*
BISHOP AND ROBERTSON CHALMERS *Glasgow*	**BLACKADDER REID JOHNSTON** *Dundee*
BORLAND MONTGOMERIE KEYDEN *Glasgow*	**BRECHIN ROBB** *Glasgow*
CAMPBELL SMITH WS *Edinburgh*	**DAVIDSON CHALMERS WS** *Edinburgh*
HENDERSON BOYD JACKSON *Edinburgh*	**MacBRIDE MUNRO & CO** *Glasgow*
TINDAL OATTS *Glasgow*	**WRIGHT, JOHNSTON & MACKENZIE** *Glasgow*

The property unit at *McGrigor Donald's* Glasgow office (the firm also has offices in Edinburgh and London) comprises nine specialist partners and is headed by the highly regarded Kirkland Murdoch. Other respected practitioners within the department include David Bankier, Ron Cole, Thomas Anderson and Donna Stephenson.

Shepherd & Wedderburn WS also has some notable practitioners including the highly esteemed Nicholas Ryden and David Smith.

Robin Garrett at *Steedman Ramage WS* is well known for development work. The firm also has several major clients in the retail sector and has recently handled the £11 million sale of the Braehead retail park and £100k p.a. leases for John Menzies (UK) Ltd and Burton Group.

Other firms with strong commercial property departments include *Dundas & Wilson CS* (Philip Dacker and James Hodge have been highly recommended) and *Tods Murray WS* where William Brown is a notable practitioner.

Archibald Campbell & Harley WS and *Miller Samuel & Co* have also received recommendations.

LEADING INDIVIDUALS – SCOTLAND

Thomas D. Anderson *McGrigor Donald*	**David A. Bankier** *McGrigor Donald*	**William Brown** *Tods Murray WS*
David Cockburn *Archibald Campbell & Harley*	**Iain A. Doran** *Miller Samuel & Co*	**Robin J. Garrett** *Steedman Ramage WS*
James (Hamish) S. Hodge *Dundas & Wilson CS*	**Iain G. Macniven** *Maclay Murray & Spens*	**Kirkland B. Murdoch** *McGrigor Donald*
Ian S. Quigley *Maclay Murray & Spens*	**Nicholas C. Ryden** *Shepherd & Wedderburn*	**David A. Smith** *Shepherd & Wedderburn*
Donna Stephenson *McGrigor Donald*		
Stewart Brymer *Thorntons WS*	**Ron Cole** *McGrigor Donald*	**Philip A. Dacker** *Dundas & Wilson CS*
Malcolm F. Fleming *Maclay Murray & Spens*	**Kenneth S. Gerber** *Leslie Wolfson & Co*	**Brian Linderman** *MacBride Munro & Co*
James Sim Fraser MacGregor *Bennett & Robertson*	**Patricia M. McFarlane** *Bennett & Robertson*	**Lionel D. Most** *Alexander Stone & Co*
David R. Reid *W & J Burness WS*	**Donald G.B. Shaw** *Dundas & Wilson CS*	

NORTHERN IRELAND

Since the ceasefire of 1994 there has been a marked increase in the amount of work in this area, as investment in property – particularly retail and housing developments – in Northern Ireland by foreign companies has risen sharply.

HIGHLY REGARDED – NORTHERN IRELAND

CARSON & McDOWELL *Belfast*	**ELLIOTT DUFFY GARRETT** *Belfast*
JOHNS ELLIOT *Belfast*	**L'ESTRANGE & BRETT** *Belfast*
MILLS SELIG *Belfast*	**TUGHAN & CO** *Belfast*
BABINGTON & CROASDAILE *Londonderry*	**C & J BLACK** *Belfast*
CLEAVER FULTON & RANKIN *Belfast*	**C & H JEFFERSON** *Belfast*
JOHNSONS *Belfast*	**McKINTY & WRIGHT** *Belfast*

Carson & McDowell are a leading firm in this field, dealing especially in commercial developements: Alan Reilly enjoys a strong reputation for his expertise in this area. *Elliott Duffy Garrett* (William Mahood) also have an excellent name in commercial property work, as do *Johns Elliott* and *L'Estrange & Brett*. At *Tughan & Co* Phyllis Agnew and John George Willis are highly regarded. *Mills Selig* are highly regarded in the field.

LEADING INDIVIDUALS – NORTHERN IRELAND

B.E. Phyllis M. Agnew *Tughan & Co*
Laurence Mahood *Elliott Duffy Garrett*
Alan J. Reilly *Carson & McDowell*
John-George Willis *Tughan & Co*

LEADERS IN PROPERTY (COMMERCIAL)

LONDON

Bailey, Jeffrey
Linklaters & Paines, London (0171) 606 7080. Qualified 1975. Partner 1980. Property Department. Acts for overseas clients on inward investment into UK real estate.

Bramson, David
Nabarro Nathanson, London (0171) 493 9933. Qualified 1966. Partner 1970. The firm's current Senior Partner. Main areas of practice include 25 years experience in property finance, institutional investment and development funding.

Brecher, Valerie
Brecher & Co, London (0171) 493 5141.

Bretherton, Philip
Berwin Leighton, London (0171) 623

3144. Partner in Property Department.

Specialisation: Main areas of practice are commercial property and property development.

Prof. Membership: Law Society.

Career: Qualified in 1974. Worked at *Slaughter and May* 1972-78, then *Simmons & Simmons* 1978-94, from 1979 as a Partner. Joined *Berwin Leighton* as a Partner in 1994.

Personal: Born 22nd March 1950. Attended King's School Gloucester 1954-67, then Trinity College Oxford 1968-71. Leisure interests include opera, collecting 78s, tennis, skiing and bridge. Lives in Maidenhead.

Briam, Tony
Clifford Chance, London (0171) 600 1000. Partner. Principal area of practice is local government work. Also deals with property development and investment mat-

ters.

Brown, Nicholas Arthur
McKenna & Co, London (0171) 606 9000. Partner and Head of Property Group.

Specialisation: Handles property development and investment work for national and international property companies, institutions and retailers. Work includes acquisition and disposal of investment portfolios and individual investment properties, disposal of major freehold sites in the City of London, acquisition funding and disposal of office and retail properties and development sites, and leases of all types of commercial property, both completed and in course of construction, and subsequent management of investments. Examples of matters handled are the acquisition of Waterside Park, Bracknell for 1,000,000 square feet of commercial development and 600 homes; acquisition by a Government Department of a new lease of premises in Victoria Street, London SW1 (including major refurbishment); development of a Shopping Centre in Bath and the acquisition, development, letting and disposal of a 180,000 square foot office building at Kings Road, Reading.

Prof. Membership: City of London Law Society/Land Law Committee/Investment Property Forum.

Career: Qualified in 1974 after articles at *McKenna & Co*. Became a Partner of the firm in 1980 and Head of the Property Group in 1991, Solicitor to the Leathersellers' Company.

Personal: Born 21st November 1949. Educated at Bristol University 1968-71 (BA in History, Economics and Politics).

Brummer, Malcolm Howard

Berwin Leighton, London (0171) 623 3144. Partner in Property/Banking Department.

Specialisation: Principal area of specialisation is as adviser in banking transactions relating to property. Acted for County Nat-West/UBS and syndicates of banks on the first financings of the Broadgate development; Bank of America in setting up the first UK mortgage-backed Eurobond issue; Alliance & Leicester on the first building society commercial equity participation mortgage scheme; P & O on the £300 million financing of the Meadowhall retail development outside Sheffield; and all 55 banks led by National Westminster Bank on £1 billion reconstruction and refinancing of Rosehaugh Stanhope Group. Has published articles and spoken at, and chaired, various seminars relating to secured lending transactions.

Prof. Membership: Member Law Society.

Career: Qualified in 1972. Became a Partner in 1975. Head of Property Department 1983-90. Also Chairman of Finance Committee 1988-93, Chairman of Board of Management of firm 1990-4.

Personal: Born 21st March 1948. Educated at Haberdashers Aske's, Elstree 1959-65 and at Downing College, Cambridge 1966-69. Leisure interests include opera and family. Lives in London.

Butler, Alan J.

Simmons & Simmons, London (0171) 628 2020. Partner 1977. Property Department.

Specialisation: Broad-based commercial property practice with emphasis on bank and institutional funding, institutional investment and development financing transactions. Acts for banks, pension funds and property companies in connection with property transactions. Clients past and present include County Nat West, Security Pacific, Chase Manhattan, BNP, Swiss Bank Corporation, Bank of Nova Scotia, Banque Paribas, Mitsubishi Estate Company, DESPA, the Abu Dhabi Investment Authority and some of the UK's largest property companies.

Prof. Membership: Law Society.

Career: Qualified in 1973 while at *Simmons & Simmons* and became a Partner in 1977.

Personal: Born 26th April 1947. Attended St. Edmund Hall, Oxford 1966-69 Lives in Oxshott, Surrey.

Clark, Paul E.

D J Freeman, London (0171) 583 4055. Qualified 1970. Partner 1985. Property Services Department. Specialises in commercial property, including development projects, refurbishment, sales and purchases.

Courtney, Diana

Denton Hall, London (0171) 242 1212. Partner in Commercial Property Department.

Specialisation: Work covers all commercial property law, particularly advice in relation to investment property/ development funding, acting for occupiers of offices, shops and industrial property, landlord and tenant advice (including major disputed rent reviews), harbour property work and corporate support. Has lectured on a wide variety of landlord/ tenant subjects.

Prof. Membership: City Property Association (council member and vice president), British Council for Offices, British Property Federation, Anglo American Real Property Institute.

Career: Qualified in 1961, joining *Oppenheimers* in 1966. That firm joined with *Denton Hall* in 1988. Non-Executive Director of Bradford & Bingley Building Society since 1993, and Vice President of the City Property Association since 1994.

Personal: Born 20th March 1939. Attended Lourdes Mount Convent 1947-55, then the Law Society's School of Law 1957 and 1960. Leisure interests include tennis, gardening and racing. Lives in London.

Fenner, John Ronald

Fenners, London (0171) 430 2200 LDE 256. Senior Partner in Commercial Property and Town Planning Department.

Specialisation: Many years experience of commercial property acquisitions, sales, developments, funding, joint venture agreements, property tax, major lettings and building contract advice, all relating to office, industrial and retail developments, including regional shopping centres. Has handled acquisitions of development sites for a major national food retailer, various PLC's and local authority schemes (town centres). Has represented entrepreneurial and institutional clients and banks, including overseas investors. Expertise in urban Regeneration.

Prof. Membership: Law Society, International Bar Association.

Career: Qualified in 1960. Became a Partner of *Lionel Leighton & Company* in 1962. Founder Partner of *Berwin Leighton* in 1970, Managing Partner 1980-84, Chairman of Partners 1984-90 and a Senior Partner 1990-94. Founder and Senior Partner of *Fenners* in

1994. Chairman of the British Urban Regeneration Association (BURA) 1991-. Chairman British Friends of Israel Philharmonic Orchestra Foundation 1993-.

Personal: Born 7th December 1935. Attended Tonbridge School 1949-53, then University College, London 1953-56. Leisure interests include opera, skiing, tennis, community service and politics. Lives in London.

Finch, Robert G.

Linklaters & Paines, London (0171) 606 7080. Qualified 1969. Property Department. Work, in UK and abroad, includes buying, selling, financing, developing and leasing properties of all types. Clients have included public sector bodies, corporate bodies and investment institutions.

Fogel, Steven

Titmuss Sainer Dechert, London (0171) 583 5353. Partner and Head of Property Department.

Specialisation: Handles all property matters, particularly landlord and tenant. Advises on the structure of property transactions and prepares complex funding and rent review provisions for UK and international investors and occupiers. Also handles arbitration and public sector work. Legal adviser to the British Retail Consortium on property issues and currently the campaign for change to law of privity of contract. Contributor to Encyclopaedia of Form and Precedents; co-author of 'Rent Reviews' (1987); co-author of 'Landlord and Tenant Factbook' (1992), 'Insurance Terrorism and Leases' (1993) and 'Rental Inducements and Fitting Out at Rent Review' (1994). Member of editorial board of 'Journal of Property Finance and Development'.

Prof. Membership: British Council of Shopping Centres, British Council for Offices, Anglo American Property Institute, Investment Property Forum, Lambda Alpha International.

Career: Qualified in 1976. Joined *Cohen and Meyohas*, then *Titmuss Sainer & Webb* (now *Titmuss Sainer Dechert*) in 1974. Became a Partner in 1980, then Trainee Solicitor Recruitment Partner in 1982 and Head of Property Department in 1990.

Personal: Born 16th October 1951. Attended Kings College, London (LLB 1972, LLM 1973). Leisure interests include cycling, jazz, photography and creative writing. Lives in London.

Freer, Penelope

Freshfields, London (0171) 936 4000. Qualified 1973. Partner 1979. Principal ares of practice are corporate property and property finance

Hart, Garry

See under Planning.

Hayhurst, G.J.

Paisner & Co, London (0171) 353 0299.

Heller, Lawrance
Berwin Leighton, London (0171) 623 3144. Partner in Commercial Property Department.

Specialisation: Main area of practice is general commercial property with special emphasis on property development, forward funding and joint venture arrangements. Also handles general commercial law. Recent matters have included the acquisition, development and letting of the Royal Bank of Canada Centre, Queen Victoria Street EC4; the acquisition and other aspects of the refurbishment of 99 City Road, London EC1 for Inmarsat and acting for Development Securities PLC on the development of Shire House and Milton House, Silk Street, London EC2. Clients include PDFM Ltd, St. Martins Property Corporation Ltd, Prudential Assurance Co. Ltd, Legal & General Assurance and the Royal Bank of Canada. Editor of and contributor to Longmans 'Practical Commercial Precedents' and 'Commercial Property Development Precedents'. Frequent contributor to *The Estates Gazette* and other property based journals. Regular contributor to BBC Select/Legal Network Television. Charge-out rate is £260.00 per hour.

Prof. Membership: City of London Law Society Property Sub-Committee.

Career: Qualified in 1959. At *Titmuss Sainer & Webb* 1959-63 (Partner from 1962. Partner at *Leighton & Co* 1963-70. Founder and Senior Partner of *Berwin Leighton* from 1980.

Personal: Born 14th April 1934. Educated at Battersea Grammar School 1945-52 and Sidney Sussex College, Cambridge 1953-56 (Legal Tripos, 1st Class Hons). Trustee of Westminster Association for Youth (Young Offenders Rehabilitation). Leisure activities include reading, writing and pontificating as well as skiing and gardening. Lives in London.

Hill, Rupert
Clifford Chance, London (0171) 600 1000. Partner. Principal area of practice is commercial property work.

Kidby, Robert J.
Lovell White Durrant, London (0171) 236 0066. Qualified 1977. Partner 1986. Handles heavyweight commercial property development, investment, and financing.

Lake, Timothy
Stepien Lake Gilbert & Paling, London (0171) 936 2288.

Lander, Geoffrey
Nabarro Nathanson, London (0171) 493 9933. Qualified 1975. Partner 1980. Head of Property Department. Commercial property specialist. Born 11.1.1951.

Le Pard, Geoffrey
Freshfields, London (0171) 936 4000. Partner in and Head of Property Department.

Specialisation: Handles all aspects of commercial property including landlord and tenant, investment, development, planning and finance.

Career: Qualified in 1981. Joined *Freshfields* in 1981, becoming a Partner in 1987.

Personal: Born 30th November 1956. Attended Purley Grammar School 1968-70, Brockenhurst Grammar School 1970-75, Bristol University 1975-78 and Guildford College of Law 1978-79. Lives in Dulwich.

Lloyd, David G.
Linklaters & Paines, London (0171) 606 7080. Qualified 1962. Partner 1969. Head of Commercial Property Department. Experienced in all aspects of commercial property work. Lecturer, past Chairman Anglo American Real Property Institute.

Lust, Graham
Nabarro Nathanson, London (0171) 493 9933. Qualified 1979. Partner 1980. Property Department. Specialises in commercial property investment, development, funding and joint venture work.

MacDonagh, Simon M.P.
Lovell White Durrant, London (0171) 236 0066. Qualified 1979. Partner 1985. Commercial Property Department. Principal areas of practice are development, development finance and joint ventures. Other main areas are commercial leases, hotels and leisure and health authority work. Born 11.9.1953.

Manches, Louis S.
Manches & Co, London (0171) 404 4433.

Martin, R.G.
Cameron Markby Hewitt, London (0171) 702 2345. Qualified 1976. Partner 1982. Commercial Property Department. Main area of practice is development funding and investment work. Also experienced in Landlord and Tenant matters.

Morpeth, Iain C.S.
Clifford Chance, London (0171) 600 1000. Partner in Commercial Property Department. Handles international and domestic transactions including investment and development projects, property joint ventures, leasing, equity and debt financing, structured and tax based finance.

Nicoll, R.C.
Richards Butler, London (0171) 247 6555.

Nisse, Ian Bertram
Ashurst Morris Crisp, London (0171) 638 1111. Qualified 1980. Partner 1987. Commercial Property Department. Specialises in commercial property, particularly development projects and investment transactions.

Rutman, Laurence David
Ashurst Morris Crisp, London (0171)

638 1111. Qualified 1964. Partner and Head of Property Department since 1974. Engaged in all types of commercial property matters with an emphasis on development work. Born 8.10.1937.

Samson, John
Nabarro Nathanson, London (0171) 493 9933. Qualified 1970. Partner 1972. Property Department. Specialises in commercial property acquisition, development, funding and disposal.

Scott, Hugo
Gouldens, London (0171) 583 7777.

Stancombe, Michael F.
Lovell White Durrant, London (0171) 236 0066. Qualified 1979. Partner. Commercial Property Department. Specialising in institutional investment, development work and joint ventures.

Tavener, Chris
Herbert Smith, London (0171) 374 8000. Partner in Commercial Property Department.

Specialisation: Deals with full range of commercial property work for developer and institutional clients. Also spends a proportion of his time dealing with property litigation including rent review work.

Career: Qualified in 1973 after articles with *Herbert Smith*. Became a Partner of the firm in 1982.

Personal: Born in 1948. Educated at RGS, Guildford and Christ Church, Oxford. Leisure time devoted to golf, skiing, music and family. Resides in London.

Taylor, David
See under Local Government.

White, G.P.
Slaughter and May, London (0171) 600 1200. Qualified 1980. Partner. Commercial Property Department. Specialises in landlord and tenant, secured lending, finance leasing and investment.

Woof, Richard A.
Debenham & Co, London (0171) 581 2471. Partner in Commercial Property Department.

Specialisation: Work includes development of offices, factories, business parks and shopping centres, sales and purchases and property management. Considerable experience, since 1971, of "turnover rent" lettings. Acted in the sale of Knightsbridge Estate and the development of the Lakeside Shopping Centre. Commercial Property Section Editor of the Law Society's Gazette, 1975-93.

Prof. Membership: Law Society.

Career: Qualified in 1963. Worked at *Foot & Bowden* in Plymouth 1963-64. Joined *Debenham & Co.* in 1964, becoming a Partner in 1967 and Senior Partner in 1974.

Personal: Born 14th June 1940. Attended

King's College, Taunton 1954-57. Leisure interests include playing the organ, painting, and quarter horse racing. Lives in Loxhill, Surrey.

Wright, David
Nabarro Nathanson, London (0171) 493 9933. Qualified 1971. Partner in Property Department. Born 17th December 1946.

REGIONS

Agnew, B.E. Phyllis M.
See under Corporate Finance.

Anderson, Thomas D.
McGrigor Donald, Glasgow (0141) 248 6677.

Ashworth, P.H.
Field Cunningham & Co, Manchester (0161) 834 4734.

Askin, David J.
Wragge & Co, Birmingham (0121) 233 1000. Qualified 1970. Partner 1973. Specialises in commercial property development especially town centre redevelopment, offices, retail/business parks and private/public sector joint ventures. Born 3.4.1946.

Bailey, Michael David
Donne Mileham & Haddock, Crawley. Partner in Property Department.

Specialisation: Specialises in commercial property. Work includes handling the development of new sites, construction work, joint ventures, landlord and tenant, sales and purchases of businesses and land transactions for charities. Also handles charity and education law. Also acts for R.C. Diocese of Arundel and Brighton, a large number of schools and colleges, a major magazine and newspaper distributor and pension funds. Publications include 'Young Persons - Trouble with the Law' and numerous study notes. CAB Tutor 1974-84, Sussex University and Brighton College of Technology part time lecturer 1967-80.

Prof. Membership: Law Society, Associate of School of Urban and Regional Studies, Sussex University.

Career: Qualified in 1965. Assistant and partner at *Gates & Co* in Brighton 1966-71. Partner at *Whitley Hughes & Luscombe* Crawley from 1973. Firm merged with *Donne Mileham & Haddock* in 1986.

Personal: Born 2nd August 1942. Educated at Varndean Grammar School, Brighton and College of Law. Leisure interests include old buildings and cars, gardening and walking. Positions held include President Sussex Law Society from 1995, Treasurer/Trustee of the Webb Memorial Trust (an educational charity), member of Legal Aid Area Committee from 1975, Chairman 1990/1. Member Know How Housing Team to Eastern

Europe. Lives in Burgess Hill.

Baker, Simon
Veale Wasbrough, Bristol (0117) 925 2020. Qualified 1971. Partner 1973. Chairman since 1988. Property Services Department and Public Sector Unit. Main areas of work are commercial property, public administrative law and local government. Born 15.4.1945.

Bankier, David A.
McGrigor Donald, Glasgow (0141) 248 6677. Qualified 1970. Partner 1978. Property Department. Main area of practice is commercial property law with emphasis on funding of property developments in enterprise zones, joint ventures and public/private sector initiatives in commercial property. Born 24.3.1949.

Battersby, Robin S.
Burges Salmon, Bristol (0117) 939 2000. Qualified 1968. Partner 1972. Commercial Property Department. Specialises in development work with particular emphasis on option agreements and conditional contracts on behalf of landowners.

Bland, Adrian D.
Eversheds, Birmingham (0121) 233 2001. Qualified 1980.

Brown, William
Tods Murray WS, Edinburgh (0131) 226 4771. Qualified 1955. Senior Partner 1994. Commercial Property Department.

Brymer, Stewart
Thorntons WS, Dundee (01382) 229111. Qualified 1979. Partner 1983. Commercial Department. Specialises in commercial property, especially property development work and leasing.

Cockburn, David
Archibald Campbell & Harley WS, Edinburgh (0131) 220 3000. Partner in Commercial Property Department.

Specialisation: Handles a full range of commercial property matters, including purchases, development, sales, leasing (for both landlords and tenants), funding and security work. Also advises on planning matters. Occasionally contributes book reviews and articles to Law Journal of Law Society of Scotland and Scottish Planning and Environmental Law. Regularly contributes by way of lectures to Law Society Update, Scottish Young Lawyers' Association, Surveyors' bodies, Planning Exchange and Edinburgh University.

Prof. Membership: Society of Writers to HM Signet.

Career: Qualified in 1966. Worked with Glasgow Corporation 1966-67, then *Breeze, Paterson & Chapman* 1967-70. Joined *Archibald Campbell & Harley WS* in 1970, becoming a Partner in 1971.

Personal: Born 4th February 1943. Attended Edinburgh University 1961-1964. Leisure pursuits include sport and reading. Lives in Edinburgh.

Cole, Ron
McGrigor Donald, Glasgow (0141) 248 6677. Qualified 1973. Partner 1977. Commercial Property Department. Specialises in development work, property investment and joint venture arrangements.

Dacker, Philip A.
Dundas & Wilson CS, Edinburgh (0131) 228 8000. Qualified 1972. Partner 1976. Commercial Property Department. Specialises in property finance, development, investment and securitisation.

Davidson, Timothy James
Lyons Davidson, Bristol (0117) 929 7151. Partner in Property Department.

Specialisation: Principal area of practice is property development and investment work. This includes acquisitions and disposals of land for commercial or residential development purposes, planning, highway and drainage agreements, letting, funding and disposal of completed developments. Types of development include offices, retail, shopping centres, business and industrial parks and residential estates. Also handles general commercial conveyancing for a range of business clients and landlord and tenant work. Has been involved in several major town centre retail development schemes and the sale of a portfolio of commercial properties with a value of in excess of £80 million. Clients include several publicly quoted development companies, the UK property division of a major international conglomerate, several local authorities, NHS Trusts and Further Education Colleges.

Prof. Membership: Law Society, Bristol Law Society.

Career: Qualified in 1971. Partner at *Lyons Davidson* since 1972. Under-Sheriff of Bristol.

Personal: Born 27th June 1948. Educated at Downside School (to 1966). Lives in Bristol.

Davies, Rowland
Edwards Geldard, Cardiff (01222) 238239. Qualified 1978. Partner 1981. Commercial Property Department. Born 27.8.1953.

Davies Jones, Martin O.
Crawford Owen, Bristol (0117) 984 9000.

Doran, Iain A.
Miller Samuel & Co, Glasgow (0141) 221 7934. Partner in Commercial Property Department.

Specialisation: Main area of practice is commercial property development, including site assembly, pre-letting, forward and other funding arrangements and sales of investment. Also acts as legal clerk to arbitrators, arbiters and experts regarding legal disputes arising in rent reviews.

Prof. Membership: Law Society of Scotland, The Chartered Institute of Arbitrators.

Career: Qualified in 1981. Joined *Miller Samuel & Co.* in 1982 and became a Partner in 1983.

Personal: Born 6th November 1957. Educated at Edinburgh University 1975-79. Lives in Glasgow.

Edmundson, David

Alsop Wilkinson, Liverpool (0151) 227 3060. Qualified 1966. Managing Partner of Liverpool Office. Work includes major asset finance and pension fund property investments.

Fleming, Malcolm F.

Maclay Murray & Spens, Glasgow (0141) 248 5011. Qualified 1968. Partner. Commercial Property Department. All areas, particularly leases and collateral warranties. Born 15.3.1943.

Forward, Graham Alan

Kitsons, Torquay (01803) 296221. Partner 1975. Company Commercial Department. Specialises in company work including sales and purchases of shares and assets.

Garrett, Robin J.

Steedman Ramage WS, Edinburgh (0131) 226 3781. Partner in Commercial Property Department.

Specialisation: Main area of practice is development work for developers and occupiers, including site assembly, planning, letting and disposals. Also handles general acquisitions, including freehold purchases and assignations of leases. Has lectured and led groups at various seminars.

Prof. Membership: Writer to the Signet.

Career: Qualified in 1983. Joined *Steedman Ramage* in 1982, becoming a Partner in 1987.

Personal: Born 2nd April 1959. Attended Robert Gordons College, Aberdeen 1964-77 and Edinburgh University 1977-82. Leisure interests include sport, reading and travelling. Lives in Edinburgh.

Gerber, Kenneth S.

Leslie Wolfson & Co, Glasgow (0141) 226 4499. Qualified 1978. Partner 1988. Commercial Property Department. Handles investment purchases and sales, leases and development work in this field.

Gunn, David

Bond Pearce, Exeter (01392) 211185. Qualified 1982. Partner 1987. Commercial Property Division. Deals with development, investment and funding. Has particular interest in minerals and waste management.

Hodge, James (Hamish) S.

Dundas & Wilson CS, Edinburgh (0131) 228 8000. Qualified 1966. Qualified 1966.

Partner 1968. Commercial Property Department. Emphasis on investment development, rent review, landlord/tenant matters, acquisition/development of shopping centres and portfolio purchases. Born 30.11.1942.

James, Robert W.

Morgan Bruce, Cardiff (01222) 385385.

Jones, Pamela

Bullivant Jones & Company, Liverpool (0151) 227 5671. Partner in Commercial Conveyancing Department.

Specialisation: Main areas of practice are retail and commercial property.

Prof. Membership: Law Society.

Career: Qualified in 1977. Joined *Bullivant Jones & Company* in 1973, becoming a Partner in 1978.

Personal: Born 7th January 1951. Attended Holyhead Comprehensive 1962-68. Leisure interests include reading and gardening. Lives near Tarporley, Cheshire.

Latchmore, Andrew

Eversheds, Leeds (0113) 243 0391. Partner and Head of Commercial Property Department.

Specialisation: Has a wide range of experience in commercial property development work on retail office and industrial schemes acting for developers, funders, owners and tenants. Also substantial retail shopping centre work, including acting for the landlord developer in acquisitions and development of and extensions and variations to shopping centres and in negotiations to relocate tenants and let completed centres to new tenants. Specialist interest in the education sector. Has acted in a number of development projects for educational establishments and for banks funding such projects. This has included innovative tax driven lease transactions to raise capital. Acted for MEPC plc on a number of schemes including a mixed office retail and hotel development in Leeds, for Hammerson UK Properties plc in the major refurbishment and extension of Freshney Place shopping centre, Grimsby, and for the University of York and P&O Developments in the creation of a joint venture company to develop the York Science Park and the anchor letting of a 100,000 square foot building to Smith & Nephew Research. Has written a several articles for legal journals and has lectured at a number of RICS and *Eversheds* seminars.

Prof. Membership: Law Society, Leeds Law Society (Honorary Secretary 1984-90).

Career: Qualified in 1975. Became a Partner at *Eversheds (then Hepworth & Chadwick)* in 1978.

Personal: Born 9th February 1950. Educated at Oundle School 1963-69 and Leeds University 1970-73. Secretary to Governors of Gateways School 1975-90; Governor 1990-93. Leisure pursuits include golf, tennis, skiing, music and walking. Lives in Leeds.

Linderman, Brian

MacBride Munro & Company, Glasgow (0141) 552 0011. Partner in Commercial Property Department.

Specialisation: Main area of practice is commercial leases, acting for both landlords and tenants. Properties involved have ranged from small shops to large units in shopping centres and high streets, commanding rents of up to 157,000 per annum. Also deals with commercial purchases and sales, commercial securities, acquisition of public houses and restaurants and domestic tenancies. Recently wrote an article for the 'Glasgow and Edinburgh Property Executive' on commercial leases. Co-edited the first two issues of 'Sylabus', the magazine of the Scottish Young Lawyers Association. Has organised a number of commercial conveyancing conferences for the Scottish Young Lawyers Association.

Prof. Membership: Law Society of Scotland, Law Society of England & Wales, Scottish Law Agents Society. Honourary member of the Young Lawyers Division of the American Bar Association.

Career: Qualified in 1981. With *Moncrieff Warren Paterson & Co* in Kirkintilloch office 1981-83. With *MacRoberts* in Glasgow 1983-89. Co-founder of *MacBride Munro & Company* in Glasgow in 1989. Admitted as a solicitor in England and Wales in 1993 and accredited by the Law Society of Scotland as a Specialist in Commercial Leasing. Past President of the Scottish Young Lawyers Association.

Personal: Born 22nd June 1959. Educated at Strathclyde University 1976-79. Lives in Glasgow.

Lowless, Peter

Michelmores, Exeter (01392) 436244. Qualified 1976. Partner 1981. Head of Commercial Property Department. Work includes site assembly, joint ventures, funding, forward sales, pre-let; education and housing association law. Born 11.5.1952.

MacGregor, James Sim Fraser

Bennett & Robertson, Edinburgh (0131) 225 4001. Qualified 1975. Partner 1980. Main area of practice is commercial property. Certified specialist in commercial leasing.

Macniven, Iain G.

Maclay Murray & Spens, Glasgow (0141) 248 5011. Qualified 1979. Partner 1982. Commercial Property Department. Specialises in commercial property in the industrial, office and retail sectors. Born 9.6.1953.

Mahood, Laurence

Elliott Duffy Garrett, Belfast (01232) 245034.

Maynard, Andrew E.

Michelmores, Exeter (01392) 436244.

Qualified 1969. Partner 1970. Commercial Property Department. Represents major property developers and property investors who are involved in the whole range of commercial property projects.

McFarlane, Patricia M.

Bennett & Robertson, Edinburgh (0131) 225 4001. Qualified 1976. Partner 1983. Commercial Department. Specialises in commercial property and leasing. Accredited specialist in commercial leasing.

McLean, Neil

Dibb Lupton Broomhead, Leeds (0113) 243 9301. Qualified 1977. Partner 1981. Commercial Property Department. Principal area of practice covers property development and retail work. Born 16.6.1953.

Meredith, Alan

Eversheds, Cardiff (01222) 471147. Qualified 1976. Partner 1982. Commercial Property Department. Work includes property joint ventures, commercial conveyancing and retail sector conveyancing.

Moody, John

Eversheds, Manchester (0161) 832 6666. Managing Partner and Partner in Commercial Property Department.

Specialisation: Work covers all aspects of commercial property with a particular emphasis on development work. Involved in several high profile residential and commercial developments including the redevelopment of the site of the former Crystal Palace. Contributes articles to professional journals and local press. Lectures at Preston Polytechnic and to professional bodies on property joint ventures.

Prof. Membership: Law Society.

Career: Articled 1973-75 at *Ingham Clegg & Crowther* in Preston and became a Partner in 1980. Joined *Yates Barnes* in 1989, then moved to *Eversheds Alexander Tatham* in 1990. Became Head of Commercial Department in 1990 and Managing Partner in 1993. Member of Board of *Eversheds* Legal Services Ltd.

Personal: Born 19th February 1950. Attended Nottingham High School 1961-69, then Jesus College, Cambridge 1969-72. Leisure pursuits include golf, theatre and overseas travel. Lives in Bowdon, Cheshire.

Most, Lionel D.

Alexander Stone & Co, Glasgow (0141) 332 8611. Qualified 1977. Partner 1983. Commercial Property Department. Specialises in leasing, including commercial leases, assignations, subleases and rent reviews.

Murdoch, Kirkland B.

McGrigor Donald, Glasgow (0141) 248 6677. Qualified 1976. Partner 1982. Commercial Property Department; Head of Property. Handles all aspects of property development and investment. Born 7.3.1955.

Pike, John D.

Booth & Co., Leeds (0113) 283 2000. Head of Commercial Property Department.

Specialisation: Main area of practice is commercial property work, covering development, banking, environmental, investment and joint venture matters. Environmental law experience includes contaminated land remediation, waste and lender risk. Numerous articles in property and environmental journals.

Prof. Membership: Law Society, Solicitors Benevolent Association, Notary Public, UKELA.

Career: Articles at *Booth & Co.* 1969-71. Qualified 1972. Partner 1976. Head of Property Group (includes Commercial Property, Environmental, Construction, Planning and Property Litigation). Formerly firm's Trainee Solicitor Partner and Marketing Partner.

Personal: Born 4th October 1947. Attended Queen Elizabeth Grammar School, Wakefield; Keighley School; Jesus College, Cambridge 1966-69. Governor Moorlands School, Leeds. Member of Council for the Protection of Rural England. Leisure pursuits include Rugby Union, skiing, swimming, walking and gardening. Lives in Wetherby.

Quigley, Ian S.

Maclay Murray & Spens, Edinburgh (0131) 226 5196. Qualified 1972. Partner 1977. Commercial Property Department. Handles all aspects including development and leasing and finance. Also shopping centre developments and property aspects of MBOs. Born 29.11.1946.

Reid, David R.

W & J Burness WS, Edinburgh (0131) 226 2561. Qualified 1962. Chairman 1992. Commercial Propery Department. Specialises in property developments, high street retailing and commercial leases.

Reilly, Alan J.

Carson & McDowell, Belfast (01232) 244951.

Roberts, David Lloyd

Hugh James Jones & Jenkins, Cardiff (01222) 224871. Qualified 1974. Partner 1975. Commercial Property Department. Specialisation in housing association stock transfers and other initiatives. Born 5.6.1949.

Rothwell, Andrew C.

Bevan Ashford, Exeter (01392) 411111. Partner in Commercial Property Department.

Specialisation: Specialises in commercial property. Main areas of practice include commercial and industrial property, planning and development. Has experience in public sector work with Local Authorities and Health Authorities and NHS Trusts.

Career: Qualified in 1980. Employed in various local government posts and with *Vanderpump & Sykes*. Joined *Bevan Ashford* in 1989 and became a partner in 1991.

Personal:

Personal: Born on 1st May 1956. Studied law at the London School of Economics. Leisure interests include farming, football, cricket, golf and squash. Shareholder in Manchester United Plc.

Ryden, Nicholas C.

Shepherd & Wedderburn WS, Edinburgh (0131) 228 9900. Qualified 1976. Partner 1978. Commercial Property Department. Work includes banking and construction. Acted in the Parkhead Forest Shopping Centre development. Born 20.3.1953.

Shaw, Donald G.B.

Dundas & Wilson CS, Edinburgh (0131) 228 8000. Partner in Commercial Property Department.

Specialisation: Commercial property. Handles development, letting, finance, investment, and related construction law. Projects recently include, The Buchanan Centre, Glasgow. Clients include Scottish Widows, Allied Dunbar, British Gas, Tesco, Sun Life, British Aerospace, Mobil, Granada, Hypobank, Tarmac, Abbey Life and ITT London and Edinburgh.

Prof. Membership: The Law Society of Scotland.

Career: Qualified in 1979. Articled *Shepherd & Wedderburn*. Partner *Dundas & Wilson CS* since 1985. Deputy managing partner and head of Commercial Property.

Personal: Born 1956. Educated at Edinburgh Academy to 1973 and Aberdeen Univerity to 1977. Leisure pursuits include music, history, art and psychology. Lives in Edinburgh.

Sleath, Michael R.

Garrett & Co, Leeds (0113) 2441954. Partner in Property Department.

Specialisation: Handles all areas of commercial property, but particularly commercial property development and licensed properties. Spent two years assembling Meadowhall and dealing with its planning and onward disposal.

Prof. Membership: Law Society, Committee Member of Leeds Law Society.

Career: Qualified in 1977. Worked at *Simpson Curtis* 1975-78; Legal Department of Asda Group plc 1978-81; and returned to *Simpson Curtis* in 1981, becoming a Partner in 1982. Joined *Garrett & Co* in 1994 as a Partner.

Personal: Born 6th December 1952. Attended Northampton Grammar, then Southampton University 1971-74. Married with two children aged 14 and 11. Lives in West Yorkshire.

Smith, David A.

Shepherd & Wedderburn WS, Edinburgh (0131) 228 9900. Partner in Commercial Property Department.

Specialisation: Main areas of practice are development projects, leases, collateral warranty documentation and opinion work. Occasional speaker at conferences and seminars.

Prof. Membership: Law Society of Scotland, Society of Writers to the Signet.

Career: Joined *Shepherd & Wedderburn* in 1969. Partner in 1974.

Personal: Born 17th November 1947. Edinburgh University 1966-69. Leisure pursuits include veterans' hockey, golf, hill walking and gardening. Lives in Edinburgh.

Smithers, Tim M.D.

Veale Wasbrough, Bristol (0117) 925 2020. Qualified 1982. Partner 1988. Property Services Department. Practice covers planning, development, landlord and tenant, pipelines, waste management and environmental work. Born 10.9.1958.

Smyth, Robert J.

Burges Salmon, Bristol (0117) 939 2000. Qualified 1979. Partner 1987. Property Department. Main areas of practice are commercial property, environmental law and planning. Born 21.07.1951.

Stephens, Michael P.

Bullivant Jones & Company, Liverpool (0151) 227 5671. Qualified 1981.

Stephenson, Donna

McGrigor Donald, Glasgow (0141) 248 6677.

Stratton, David

Halliwell Landau, Salford (0161) 877 7158. Qualified 1971. Partner 1980. Commercial Property Department. Specialises in commercial conveyancing transactions, particularly major retail and office developments.

Tacey, Willam A.

Osborne Clarke, Bristol (0117) 923 0220. Qualified 1964. Partner 1986. Commercial Property Department. Specialises in development work and the brewery sector. Born 13.10.1939.

Tonkin, Timothy P.

Booth & Co., Leeds (0113) 283 2000. Qualified 1977.

Tully, David J.

Addleshaw Sons & Latham, Manchester (0161) 832 5994. Partner in Property Department.

Specialisation: Principal area of practice covers all aspects of commercial property work. Also acts for landed estates advising on tax schemes. Chairman of Law Society Joint Committee with RICS producing Model Rent Review Clauses 1979-85. Lectured to College of Law on Model Rent Review Clauses.

Prof. Membership: Law Society, Manchester Law Society.

Career: Qualified 1964 while with *Addleshaw Sons & Latham* and became a Partner in 1969. Became the Senior Partner in June 1994.

Personal: Born 12th March 1942. Governor Manchester Grammar School. Vice-President St. James's Club, Manchester. Leisure pursuits include fishing, shooting and golf. Lives in Hale, Cheshire.

Wilkinson, Ian D.

Andrew M. Jackson & Co, Hull (01482) 325242. Partner in Commercial Property Department.

Specialisation: Specialises in out of town retail parks, acting primarily on behalf of tenants. Other area of expertise is pension fund investments.

Career: Joined *Payne & Payne* in 1965. Qualified in 1968. Joined *Andrew M. Jackson* in 1974 and became a Partner in 1975.

Personal: Born 25th June 1944. Attended Beverley Grammar School 1955-62, then Southampton University 1962-65. Enjoys sport, reading and walking. Lives in Beverley.

Willis, John-George

Tughan & Co, Belfast (01232) 553300.

EDITORIAL POLICY

Our policy is to identify leading practitioners entirely on merit. It is not possible to buy a place in our biographical lists: inclusion is based on a practitioner's expertise and professional reputation. The same applies to the lists of recommended law-firms and sets of chambers.

Enormous effort has been invested by our ten-strong research team (mainly solicitors and barristers) in canvassing recommendations and identifying leaders. We are confident in the overall accuracy of the results. However, mistakes and omissions are inevitable, and if readers have any suggestions regarding listings or rankings we should be very pleased to hear from them.

The lists will be revised on the basis of fresh research every year.

SHIPPING & MARITIME LAW

SHIPPING work is categorised as 'wet work', (which includes salvage, collision and total losses) and 'dry' work (charter parties, bills of lading and contractual work). Other related areas include marine insurance, ship finance, cargo work, shipbuilding, commodities, international carriage of goods and specialist work on yachts and marinas.

The Admiralty Solicitors Group is setting up its own arbitration service to cater for both 'dry' work, largely stemming from charter party clauses, and 'wet' work principally arising from salvage agreements. Members of the Group all have a strong 'wet' practice.

Recently, there has been pressure to set up a code of practice for users of the Commercial Court in a bid to maintain London's prominence as a leading shipping centre. Client service and value has improved, both in response to this pressure and also because clients are becoming increasingly sophisticated buyers of legal services. For example, P & I Clubs often wish to run cases instead of merely managing them, selecting specialist lawyers, often from more than one firm.

LONDON

Ince & Co has an excellent reputation in all aspects of shipping, insurance and international trade. Very strong in litigation, and well known for its hull work, it has clients among the world's largest shipping, shipbuilding and trading companies and also the London Insurance Market.

LEADING FIRMS – LONDON

INCE & CO.	
CLYDE & CO	HOLMAN, FENWICK & WILLAN
HILL TAYLOR DICKINSON	RICHARDS BUTLER
SHAW AND CROFT	

Richard Sayer, now the firm's senior partner, has been uniformly recommended. His maritime practice covers admiralty, charter party disputes and purchase litigation. Patrick Griggs, the retiring senior partner, also has a first rate reputation and will continue as a consultant at the firm. Partner, Richard Williams covers chartering and carriage of goods by sea, as well as commodity and insurance disputes. Oliver Weiss, also highly regarded, focuses on international marine trade, including carriage of goods by sea, charter party, bills of lading, sale and purchase and total loss investigations.

Holman, Fenwick & Willan has a strong international practice and is well known for its work for salvors and owners, as well as for litigation. It has a high market share of Lloyd's Form cases. Expertise lies across international shipping trade, insurance and commerce, and Archie Bishop at the firm is regarded as one of the foremost Admiralty law practitioners. His main emphasis is collision, salvage, oil pollution and marine insurance. His colleague Richard Crump, has been recommended as a strong all-rounder. The firm's strength has

increased with the arrival of Michael Donnithorn from *Clifford Chance*. (James Gosling is regarded as an up and coming force in the field.)

Clyde & Co rounds off the triumvirate of market leaders. Particularly well known for its cargo work, the firm is also strong across the shipping and marine insurance sectors, as well as in trade and transport. Michael Payton was highly recommended for his marine insurance expertise and David Hall also has an excellent reputation in this area.

Shaw and Croft is too small to handle the same volume of work as the three firms above. However, it is very well respected and at the forefront of the niche practices. It has expertise in bills of lading, charterparties, cargo claims, collisions, salvage, ship finance, sale and purchase, and ship management. Its familiarity with the insurance market also led to its involvement in the Brinks Matt recovery operation. The imminent retirement of Richard Shaw will have a significant impact. The gap will be filled by Roger Croft, Nicholas Taylor and John Maskell who were all commended.

Richards Butler has a good admiralty practice as well as marine insurance expertise. A strong banking practice also gives them particular strength in ship finance. Graeme Bowtle and Lindsay East at the firm have both been recommended.

Hill Taylor Dickinson has acknowledged capability in international shipping and marine insurance. It acts predominantly for shipowners, underwriters and P & I Clubs in international matters, particularly in the Far East, the Middle East and the USA. Stephen Cropper, Timothy Taylor and Robert Wallis are all recommended.

HIGHLY REGARDED – LONDON

HOLMES HARDINGHAM	NORTON ROSE
SINCLAIR ROCHE & TEMPERLEY	
BENTLEYS, STOKES & LOWLESS	CLIFFORD CHANCE
CONSTANT & CONSTANT	ELBORNE MITCHELL
HERBERT SMITH	INGLEDEW BROWN BENNISON & GARRETT
JACKSON PARTON	LAWRENCE GRAHAM
LOVELL WHITE DURRANT	MIDDLETON POTTS
MORE FISHER BROWN	STEPHENSON HARWOOD
THOMAS COOPER & STIBBARD	WALTONS & MORSE
WATSON, FARLEY & WILLIAMS	WILDE SAPTE
ALSOP WILKINSON	BARLOW LYDE & GILBERT
BERWIN LEIGHTON	BLICK & CO
BRECHER & CO	CRUMP & CO.
DAVIES ARNOLD COOPER	DORMAN HARRIS
EDWIN COE	HUGHES HOOKER
LEWIS MOORE	NICHOLAS FISHER
PENNINGTONS	STALLARDS
STOCKLER CHARITY	SWINNERTON ASHLEY-CLAYDON
WATERSON HICKS	WILLIAMSON & HORROCKS
ZAIWALLA & CO	

Sinclair Roche & Temperley has a well respected shipping practice. Shipping, insurance litigation, asset finance and maritime casualty comprise over 75% of the firm's workload. Charles Foster is highly regarded for international ship finance transactions and Ben Leach has been recommended.

Holmes Hardingham is a niche practice with a growing reputation. Adrian Hardingham and Andrew Messent are both recommended. The firm is also strong in transport.

Norton Rose is particularly strong in ship finance. John Shelton and Sue Wright have good reputations in this area.

Most of the larger firms deal with all aspects of shipping, in particular finance and insurance matters. Pre-eminent among them are *Clifford Chance* (Tony Vlasto has been recommended*), Herbert Smith, Lawrence Graham, Lovell White Durrant, Stephenson Harwood, Watson Farley and Williams* and *Wilde Sapte*.

Nicholas Robinson at *Herbert Smith* is well-known for both wet and dry litigation. *Lawrence Graham* is known for its expertise in insurance. Having acted for the Soviet Merchant Marine during the communist era, the firm now represents most of the successor shipping companies in the CIS. The strength of the *Stephenson Harwood* team, now comprising 35 specialists, will be augmented by the addition of four admiralty and finance partners and four assistants from *Sinclair Roche & Temperley*.

The partners include Robin Slade, who is set to join the department headed by his brother, David, and Mark Russell (six of the firm's admiralty lawyers are qualified mariners). The shipping departments at *Lovell White Durrant*, *Watson Farley & Williams* and *Wilde Sapte*, are particularly known for their insurance and finance work.

Of the leading smaller firms, *Bentleys Stokes & Lowless* has a worldwide client base, particularly from Scandinavia, France, Italy and Greece. *Constant & Constant* has recently expanded its practice to cover finance and insurance and clients include national governments and banks. *Elborne Mitchell*, with particular expertise in insurance, acts for a number of Lloyd's syndicates, whilst *Middleton Potts* is especially known for its shipping-related commodities work. At *More Fisher Brown* all partners handle shipping, insurance and international trade. *Ingledew Brown Bennison & Garrett* is well-known for its expertise with yachts, acting for most of the major yacht underwriters.

David Hebden at *Thomas Cooper & Stibbard* is recommended for both wet and dry aspects. Clients of the firm include foreign governments, major oil companies and financial institutions. *Waltons & Morse* represent, among others, insurance companies from Lloyd's and overseas.

LEADING INDIVIDUALS – LONDON

Richard J. Sayer *Ince & Co*

W. Archie Bishop *Holman, Fenwick & Willan*	**David Hall** *Clyde & Co*	**David G. Hebden** *Thomas Cooper & Stibbard*
Anthony R. Miller *Constant & Constant*	**Richard F. Olsen** *Stephenson Harwood*	**Michael Payton** *Clyde & Co*
Richard Shaw *Shaw and Croft*	**Tony Vlasto** *Clifford Chance*	**O.A.R. Weiss** *Ince & Co*
Richard W. Williams *Ince & Co*		

John Bassindale *Clifford Chance*	**Stuart N. Beare** *Richards Butler*	**Tim Boden** *Holman, Fenwick & Willan*
Nicholas Bourke *Elborne Mitchell*	**Graeme J. Bowtle** *Richards Butler*	**Michael Buckley** *Waltons & Morse*
M. Burch *Bentleys, Stokes & Lowless*	**Philip Bush** *Jackson Parton*	**Margaret Campbell** *Richards Butler*
Martin Chambers *Holmes Hardingham*	**David E. Charity** *Stockler Charity*	**Raymond Clarke** *Elborne Mitchell*
Roger A. Cooper *Lawrence Graham*	**Roger Croft** *Shaw and Croft*	**Stephen Cropper** *Hill Taylor Dickinson*
Richard W. Crump *Holman, Fenwick & Willan*	**Simon R. Curtis** *Watson Farley & Williams*	**C.M. De-La-Rue** *Ince & Co*
Robert K. Dibble *Wilde Sapte*	**Michael G. Donithorn** *Holman, Fenwick & Willan*	**Lindsay T. East** *Richards Butler*
John C. Evans *Hill Taylor Dickinson*	**Ralph Evers** *Clyde & Co*	**Alastair Farley** *Watson Farley & Williams*
Nicholas Fisher *Nicholas Fisher*	**Simon Fletcher** *Clyde & Co*	**Charles Foster** *Sinclair Roche & Temperley*
A.D.G. George *Ince & Co*	**Jeremy S. P. Gibb** *Wilde Sapte*	**James C. Gosling** *Holman, Fenwick & Willan*
T. Gray *Bentleys, Stokes & Lowless*	**P.J.S. Griggs** *Ince & Co*	**Adrian Hardingham** *Holmes Hardingham*
Michael Harrisson *Clyde & Co*	**R. Healey** *Ince & Co*	**E.J.D. Hill** *Ince & Co*
Derek Hodgson *Clyde & Co*	**Andrew Johnson** *Hill Taylor Dickinson*	**Simon J. Latham** *Ince & Co*
Michael D. Lax *Lawrence Graham*	**Ben Leach** *Sinclair Roche & Temperley*	**Steven Lowe** *Stephenson Harwood*
C. David Lucas *Middleton Potts*	**Jonathan S. Lux** *Ince & Co*	**John Maskell** *Shaw and Croft*
Ray Mead *Barlow Lyde & Gilbert*	**Andrew Messent** *Holmes Hardingham*	**Roger H. Miles** *Ingledew Brown Bennison & Garrett*
Justin More *More Fisher Brown*	**Julian A.L. Morgan** *Edwin Coe*	**Peter Morgan** *Clyde & Co*
Christopher R. Potts *Middleton Potts*	**David M. Pullen** *Richards Butler*	**J. Nicholas Robinson** *Herbert Smith*
Anthony Rooth *Clyde & Co*	**Mark A. Russell** *Stephenson Harwood*	**D.M. Sheehan** *Ince & Co*
Peter Shelford *Clyde & Co*	**John H. Shelton** *Norton Rose*	**David L. Slade** *Stephenson Harwood*
Robin Slade *Stephenson Harwood*	**Malcolm Strong** *Ince & Co*	**Nicholas Taylor** *Shaw and Croft*
Timothy Taylor *Hill Taylor Dickinson*	**Andrew D. Taylor** *Richards Butler*	**Clive Thorp** *Clyde & Co*
Robert H. Wallis *Hill Taylor Dickinson*	**W. Ian R. Ward** *Lovell White Durrant*	**Martin A. Watson** *Watson Farley & Williams*
Robert G. Wilson *Holman, Fenwick & Willan*	**Sue Wright** *Norton Rose*	

In all the tables the names in each group are listed alphabetically.

SOUTH EAST

Clyde & Co, in Guildford, is the leading firm in the South East.

LEADING FIRMS – SOUTH EAST

CLYDE & CO *Guildford*

At this office the emphasis of the practice lies in casualty, salvage and collision and cargo claims. Brian Nash is known for his charter party, cargo claims and marine insurance work. He is also involved in actions arising out of trading disputes. Anthony Thomas is highly regarded for his 'dry' shipping litigation knowledge, especially cargo recovery work. He is also involved in a lot of work with a Japanese dimension, and has advised the Estonian government.

HIGHLY REGARDED – SOUTH EAST

DONNE MILEHAM & HADDOCK *Brighton*
GLANVILLES *Portsmouth*
MOWLL & MOWLL *Dover*

Donne Mileham & Haddock, through the expertise of Donald Cullen, is recommended for admiralty and marine insurance. He was a coxswain/crew member of the RNLI for over twenty years.

Glanvilles (Portsmouth) has an acknowledged capability in work including the ownership and use of vessels, admiralty jurisdiction and deaths at sea.

Mowll & Mowll in Dover advise on harbour law.

LEADING INDIVIDUALS – SOUTH EAST

Brian Nash *Clyde & Co*
Anthony Thomas *Clyde & Co*
Benjamin Browne *Clyde & Co*
Donald Cullen *Donne Mileham & Haddock*
Jerry Wheatley *Clyde & Co*

SOUTH WEST

Davies Grant & Horton is recommended as the leading shipping firm in the region. It is highly regarded for work in connection with commercial shipping, the fishing industry and yachts. Nicholas Horton has expertise in all aspects of yachting work including insurance, financing, construction, design, sinking and crewing. He also does some work in commercial shipping and acted for a number of applicants in 'Factortame' (an ECJ case). Jonathan Johnson is recommended for his maritime law and commercial litigation work.

LEADING FIRMS – SOUTH WEST

DAVIES GRANT & HORTON *Plymouth*

Bond Pearce has a shipping practice allied to its insurance department. It is known for work relating to cargo claims, shipowners' liability, salvage and collision.

Foot & Bowden is recommended for work in all aspects of shipping. It has recently opened a London office to cope with

HIGHLY REGARDED – SOUTH WEST

BOND PEARCE *Plymouth*	FOOT & BOWDEN *Plymouth*
HOOPER & WOLLEN *Torquay*	PYE-SMITHS *Salisbury*

a growing level of national and international work.

Hooper & Woollen has a niche speciality in harbour and marina development through the expertise of Nigel Wollen. He has been a co-developer of Torquay marina and also handles some yacht and trawler financing work.

LEADING INDIVIDUALS – SOUTH WEST

Nicholas Horton *Davies Grant & Horton*
Jonathan Johnson *Davies Grant & Horton*
Nigel J. Wollen *Hooper & Wollen*

EAST ANGLIA

Birketts, near Felixstowe, has built a strong practice in shipping. The firm has expertise in areas ranging from finance, salvage and marine insurance, to oil pollution, stowaways

LEADING FIRMS – EAST ANGLIA

BIRKETTS *Ipswich*

and yachting. John Weston at the firm, is a former Merchant Navy deck officer and a member of the Royal Institute of Navigation and the Nautical Institute. Michael Dale, who previously worked for a shipping practice in Germany, is also well regarded.

LEADING INDIVIDUALS – EAST ANGLIA

Michael Dale *Birketts*
John Weston *Birketts*

NORTH WEST

Alsop Wilkinson is involved in all aspects of marine law, including 'wet' and 'dry' litigation, salvage, shipbuilding, finance and insurance. David Mawdsley is known for his contractual negotiations, small print work, bills of lading, and charter party disputes and drafting. Martin Hill has been recommended for his work in insurance coverage, defence and subrogation, whilst Raymond Phillips is strong in the carriage of goods as well as shipbuilding and repair.

LEADING FIRMS – NORTH WEST

ALSOP WILKINSON *Liverpool*	HILL DICKINSON DAVIS CAMPBELL *Liverpool*
LACE MAWER *Manchester*	WEIGHTMAN RUTHERFORDS *Liverpool*

Hill Dickinson Davis Campbell has strong capabilities across the marine spectrum, acting for insurers, underwriters and cargo interests. Peter Jackson has an excellent reputation, especially in the areas of international and national road haulage, cargo recoveries and marine insurance. David

Wareing is respected for his work with P & I Clubs, shipowners, crew claims, cargo claims, salvage, stowaways and drug offences. John Maxwell, also highly regarded, has broad expertise and has been involved in ferry casualties in the Baltic, and work with a Polish dimension.

Weightman Rutherfords is involved in all aspects of 'wet' and 'dry' shipping. It has particular expertise in P & I Clubs, ship repairs, admiralty work, charter party disputes, ship purchase and marine insurance. Ian Evans describes himself as a commercial litigator rather than a shipping lawyer. All his work in commercial litigation commodities, insurance and arbitration has a marine aspect.

Lace Mawer has a good reputation for its contentious work.

LEADING INDIVIDUALS – NORTH WEST	
Ian R. Evans	*Weightman Rutherfords*
Martin G. Hill	*Alsop Wilkinson*
Peter W. Jackson	*Hill Dickinson Davis Campbell*
D.H. Mawdsley	*Alsop Wilkinson*
Raymond J. Phillips	*Alsop Wilkinson*
M. John Maxwell	*Hill Dickinson Davis Campbell*
W. David Wareing	*Hill Dickinson Davis Campbell*

NORTH EAST

Eversheds in Newcastle has a good reputation in all aspects of maritime law. Chris Hilton is particularly recommended. He handles P & I Club work including advice on club rules, as well as collision, salvage and casualty, sale and purchase and shipbuilding. Alex Dowie is well known for his 'dry' shipping work including international trade, insurance and re-insurance, ship finance, sale and purchase.

Rayfield Mills' workload includes charter party, bills of lading, P & I Club work, marine insurance, collision, salvage, sale and purchase and ship finance. (Richard Rayfield is recommended for his work in these areas).

LEADING FIRMS – NORTH EAST	
EVERSHEDS *Newcastle*	**RAYFIELD MILLS** *Newcastle*
ANDREW M. JACKSON *Hull*	**MILLS & CO** *Newcastle*

Mills & Co has the advantage of an association with *Ince & Co,* enabling it to share expertise and facilities. It is particularly known for work in shipbuilding, engineering and repair as well as P & I Club work and marine finance. Geoffrey Mills has an excellent reputation. He was a former Director of Services at British Shipbuilders and his clients include Swan Hunter. Alisdair Brown, who specialises in shipbuilding and engineering, is also well regarded.

The shipping department of *Andrew M. Jackson & Co* deal with all aspects of maritime law including carriage of goods, collision and salvage, fishing and EU law. Silas Taylor is very well regarded as a specialist in maritime casualty. He acted for the salmon farmers following the 'Braer' oil spill.

LEADING INDIVIDUALS – NORTH EAST	
Chris J. Hilton	*Eversheds*
Alistdair Brown	*Mills & Co*
Alex Dowie	*Eversheds*
Geoffrey Mills	*Mills & Co*
Stephen Mills	*Rayfield Mills*
Richard Rayfield	*Rayfield Mills*
Silas W. Taylor	*Andrew M. Jackson*

SCOTLAND

Henderson Boyd Jackson has a strong shipping practice, especially in fishing and off-shore oil industry work. Robert Knox, senior partner in the marine department, and solicitor to the Navy in Scotland since 1964, is highly recommended. James Lowe, a former ship's officer, is recommended for handling a wide range of 'wet' and 'dry' disputes.

LEADING FIRMS – SCOTLAND	
HENDERSON BOYD JACKSON *Edinburgh*	**MACKINNONS** *Aberdeen*
MACLAY MURRAY & SPENS *Glasgow*	

MacKinnons has expertise in commercial shipping, admiralty work and marine litigation, representing Port Authorities, insurers and P & I Clubs. (Keith MacRae is well respected). The firm has formed the Fishing Industry Lawyers Group with *Andrew M. Jackson and Co* (Hull and Grimsby). The group is designed to sponsor co-operation, especially in major marine accidents.

Maclay Murray & Spens also has acknowledged capability in this field, in particular with regard to 'wet' work and cargo claims.

LEADING INDIVIDUALS – SCOTLAND	
Robert Knox	*Henderson Boyd Jackson*
James A.G. Lowe	*Henderson Boyd Jackson*
Keith G. MacRae	*Mackinnons*

In all the tables the names in each group are listed alphabetically.

LONDON

Bassindale, John
See under Commodities.

Beare, Stuart N.
Richards Butler, London (0171) 247 6555. Partner in Shipping Unit.

Specialisation: Specialises in all aspects of shipping law.

Career: Qualified in 1974; partner Richards Butler since 1969; member of Baltic Exchange; supporting member London Maritime Arbitrators' Association; member of the Executive Committee of the British Maritime Law Association and chairman of its Standing Committee on the carriage of goods; titulary member of the Comite Maritime International; Senior Warden of the City of London Solicitors' Company and ex-officio committee member City of London Law Society.

Personal: Born in 1936. Attended Clare College, Cambridge (LL.B, MA).

Bishop, W. Archie
Holman, Fenwick & Willan, London (0171) 488 2300. Senior Partner.

Specialisation: Main area of practice is Admiralty law, with an emphasis on collision, salvage, oil pollution and marine insurance. Legal advisor to International Salvage Union. Contributes a variety of articles to specialised marine publications. Regular speaker at conferences and seminars.

Prof. Membership: Law Society.

Career: Deck officer with P&O Line 1954-60. Joined *Holman Fenwick & Willan* 1960, became a Partner in 1971 and Senior Partner in 1989.

Personal: Born 21st July 1937. Thames Nautical Training College HMS Worcester 1952-54. British First Mates Foreign Going Certificate 1959, Solicitor 1971. Leisure pursuits horse riding, golf, art and music. Lives in Farnham.

Boden, Tim
Holman, Fenwick & Willan, London (0171) 488 2300. Master Mariner 1973. Appointed Senior Manager 1991. Admiralty department. Principal area of practice is salvage.

Bourke, Nicholas
Elborne Mitchell, London (0171) 320 9000. Qualified 1969. Partner 1972. Specialist areas of practice are shipping and marine insurance. Born 1944. Leisure: reading, gardening and his lobster pots. Resides: London.

Bowtle, Graeme J.
Richards Butler, London (0171) 247 6555. Partner in Shipping Department.

Specialisation: He specialises in ship financ-

ing, acting for many UK and European banks advising on financing and security stuctures for the acquisition and leasing of ships, drilling rigs and other capital equipment in the marine industry, and in particular those transactions involving structured export credit financing. He is Chairman of the BMLA Sub-Committee on Off-Shore Mobile Craft.

Career: Joined *Richards Butler* in 1964: qualified as a solicitor in 1966:became a partner in *Richards Butler* in 1972.

Personal: Born 1941. Educated at New College, Oxford (MA).

Buckley, Michael
Waltons & Morse, London (0171) 623 4255.

Burch, M.
Bentleys, Stokes & Lowless, London (0171) 782 0990.

Bush, Philip
Jackson Parton, London (0171) 702 0085. Qualified 1983. Partner 1994. Shipping Litigation Department. Handles all aspects of shipping-related litigation and arbitration.

Campbell, Margaret
Richards Butler, London (0171) 247 6555. Partner in Shipping and Insurance Unit.

Specialisation: Work includes marine and non-marine insurance and reinsurance, maritime disputes in relation to charterparties and bills of lading, and general commercial litigation.

Prof. Membership: Law Society; City of London Solicitors Company.

Career: Articled at *Clyde & Co.* Qualified 1981. At *McHale & Co* to 1983; Joined *Richards Butler* in 1983. Partner since 1989.

Personal: Born 1956. Attended Cheltenham Ladies College then Wadham College, Oxford (MA Hons Jurisprudence). Leisure interests include reading, theatre, tennis and bridge. Lives in London.

Chambers, Martin
Holmes Hardingham, London (0171) 283 0222. Qualified 1976.

Charity, David E.
Stockler Charity, London (0171) 404 6661. Partner in Litigation Department.

Specialisation: Maritime arbitration and litigation. Extensive experience advising shipowners, charterers and protection and indemnity associations and conducting associated litigation. Cases handled include 'The Virgo' (1976), 'The Shackleford' (1978) and 'The Spiliada' (1987). Co-author of 'Legal Aspects of the Gulf War' (1991) and has written numerous articles for legal and shipping periodicals. Lectures regularly at conferences and seminars.

Prof. Memberships: Law Society, Supporting Member of London Maritime Arbitrators Association.

Career: Articled with *Holman Fenwick & Willan* 1964-66, qualified in 1966 and became a Partner in 1972. Left in 1992 to become one of the Founding Partners of niche shipping practice *Stockler Charity*.

Personal: Born in 1941. Attended Kingswood School 1954-60, then London School of Economics 1961-64. Leisure pursuits include mountaineering and music. Lives in Tunbridge Wells.

Clarke, Raymond
Elborne Mitchell, London (0171) 320 9000. Qualified 1976. Partner 1982. Specialist in shipping and marine salvage. Born 1946. Leisure: Private flying, cinema. Resides: Epsom.

Cooper, Roger A.
Lawrence Graham, London (0171) 379 0000. Partner in Shipping Department.

Specialisation: Principal area of practice is admiralty work, including collision, salvage and marine casualties generally.

Prof. Membership: Law Society.

Career: Qualified in 1991. Merchant Navy Deck Officer 1961-69. Shipowners Legal Claims Department 1969-74. In private practice dealing with admiralty matters since 1974. Partner at *Lawrence Graham* since 1983.

Personal: Born 12th June 1944. Lives in Billericay.

Croft, Roger
Shaw and Croft, London (0171) 283 6293. Senior Partner specialising in admiralty law and insurance law.

Specialisation: Principal area of practice is admiralty and insurance law. Work includes collision, salvage, pollution, environmental damage and total loss. Other main area of practice is fraud and money laundering. Acted in the 'Goring' (House of Lords) and 'Mare' (Court of Appeal) cases. Clients include several major shipowners, salvors, insurers and P&I clubs.

Prof. Membership: Law Society, City of London Solicitors Company, Royal Institute of Navigation, Average Adjusters Association, Admiralty Solicitors Group, FRSA, LMAA.

Career: Joined the Royal Navy in 1962. Electronic Engineer from 1967. Qualified in 1978. Senior Partner at *Shaw and Croft* from 1992.

Personal: Born 19th May 1946. Educated at Wallington County Grammar School and London University. Interests include golf, cricket, music and reading.

Cropper, Stephen
Hill Taylor Dickinson, London (0171)

283 9033. Qualified 1974. Partner 1982. Shipping and Insurance Department. Principal area of practice is investigation of marine casualties and insurance coverage.

Crump, Richard W.
Holman, Fenwick & Willan, London (0171) 488 2300. Qualified 1981. Partner 1987. Shipping Litigation Department. Practice encompasses all areas of shipping litigation.

Curtis, Simon R.
Watson Farley & Williams, London (0171) 814 8000. Partner in Litigation Department.

Specialisation: Main area of practice is shipping work. Covers range of maritime litigation matters including shipbuilding, conversion and repair. Includes non-contentious work relating to ship building, i.e. new project development. Author of 'The Law of Shipbuilding Contracts', Lloyd's of London Press. Contributor to 'Force Majeure and Frustration of Contracts' (2nd Edition), Lloyds of London Press. Regular speaker at conferences on maritime law.

Prof. Memberships: London Maritime Arbitrators Association (Supporting Member). Fellow of the Chartered Institute of Arbitrators.

Career: Joined *Ince & Co.* in 1979. Qualified 1982. Left to join *Watson Farley & Williams* in 1984. Partner 1986 in Litigation Department.

Personal: Born 10th November 1955. Attended Jesus College, Oxford BA (Hons) (1st Class) and Bachelor of Civil Law. Leisure pursuits include scuba diving, skiing and fishing. Lives in London.

De-La-Rue, C.M.
Ince & Co, London (0171) 623 2011. Partner 1986. Specialises in marine pollution, litigation and arbitration of marine insurance and charterparty disputes.

Dibble, Robert K.
Wilde Sapte, London (0171) 246 7000. Qualified 1980. Partner 1982. Banking Department. Specialises in shipping finance. Also aircraft, trade and countertrade, general banking and project finance.

Donithorn, Michael G.
Holman, Fenwick & Willan, London (0171) 488 2300. Qualified 1980. Partner 1994. Litgation and Arbitration Department. Princial area of practice is marine litigation.

East, Lindsay T.
Richards Butler, London (0171) 247 6555. Partner. Head of Shipping and Insurance Group.

Specialisation: Main area of practice is shipping and insurance. Acts for owners and charterers direct or through their insurers (P&I and defence clubs) in all contractual disputes, charterparty, bill of lading, MOA, and building contracts. Particular expertise in drafting and advising on club rules. Also handles general marine and non-marine insurance, acting for cargo insurers and reinsurers and war-risk underwriters. Cases have included Antaios, Antares, Antonis P. Lemos and Standard Steamship v. Gann. Speaker at and chairman of various seminars.

Prof. Membership: Baltic Exchange.

Career: Qualified in 1973, having joined *Richards Butler* in 1971. Became a Partner in 1977.

Personal: Born 24th March 1949. Attended Skinners School to 1966, then Worcester College, Oxford 1967-70. Leisure interests include cricket, opera and travel. Lives in Rickmansworth, Herts.

Evans, John C.
Hill Taylor Dickinson, London (0171) 283 9033.

Evers, Ralph
Clyde & Co, London (0171) 623 1244. Qualified 1971.

Farley, Alastair
Watson Farley & Williams, London (0171) 814 8000. Qualified 1971.

Fisher, Nicholas
Nicholas Fisher, London (0171) 709 7203. Partner specialising in commercial shipping litigation, insurance and reinsurance litigation.

Specialisation: Handles commercial shipping litigation, including significant client base in container, reefer and tanker operations. Also insurance and reinsurance litigation involving brokers' PI claims. In insurance and reinsurance matters has acted for the Merrett Names Action Group, brokers in PCW, Feltrim and Multi-Guarantee Extended Warranty litigation and in Hong Kong Borneo v. Pilcher.

Prof. Membership: London Maritime Arbitrators Association (Supporting Member), Baltic Exchange, The City of London Solicitors' Company.

Career: Qualified in 1979. Partner at *Richards Butler* 1984-88. Founding Partner of *More Fisher Brown* 1988-93. Founded *Nicholas Fisher* in May 1993.

Personal: Educated at Glyn Grammar School, Epsom 1965-72, then Clare College, Cambridge 1973-76.

Fletcher, Simon
Clyde & Co, London (0171) 623 1244. Qualified 1971.

Foster, Charles
Sinclair Roche & Temperley, London (0171) 638 9044. Partner specialising in ship and oil rig finance, banking and securities.

George, A.D.G.
Ince & Co, London (0171) 623 2011.

Qualified 1971. Partner 1975. Specialises in international transport and trade with emphasis on cargo and credit/political risk.

Gibb, Jeremy S. P.
Wilde Sapte, London (0171) 246 7000. Qualified 1985. Partner 1992. Banking Department. Specialises in asset finance, especially ships and aircraft. Also handles acquisition finance.

Gosling, James C.
Holman, Fenwick & Willan, London (0171) 488 2300. Qualified 1980. Partner 1988. Admiralty Department. Principal areas of practice are salvage, collision, total loss and wreck removal.

Gray, T.
Bentleys, Stokes & Lowless, London (0171) 782 0990.

Griggs, P.J.S.
Ince & Co, London (0171) 623 2011. Qualified 1963. Partner 1966. Specialises in all aspects of marine law including marine and aviation casualties and general insurance disputes.

Hall, David
Clyde & Co, London (0171) 623 1244. Qualified 1968. Partner 1974. Non-Marine Transit and Insurance Departments. Main area of practice is non-marine carriage of goods, both national and international.

Hardingham, Adrian
See under Transport (Road & Rail).

Harrisson, Michael
Clyde & Co, London (0171) 623 1244. Qualified 1971. Partner 1974. Marine Casualty Department. Work covers salvage, collision, total loss, wreck removal and hull insurance.

Healey, R.
Ince & Co, London (0171) 623 2011. Qualified 1971. Partner 1980. Main area of practice is charterparty, cargo claims, sale of goods and Admiralty work.

Hebden, David G.
Thomas Cooper & Stibbard, London (0171) 481 8851. Senior Partner.

Specialisation: Main area of practice is Admiralty Law. Work includes shipping and maritime law, collision, salvage, shipping safety, rules and regulations, and emergency response team management. Also management adviser to shipping and marine insurance industries. Handles day to day shipping problems, including criminal offences at sea, discipline and passenger ship operations. Edited and prepared Laws of Oleron. Author of numerous articles on shipping matters and safety at sea. Has addressed a variety of conferences and seminars.

Prof. Membership: Law Society, British Maritime Law Association, Admiralty

Solicitors Group, Honourable Company of Master Mariners.

Career: Qualified 1971, having joined *Thomas Cooper & Stibbard* in 1964. Became a Partner in 1973 and Senior Partner in 1992. FG Master's Certificate of Competency 1962; BMLA Committee on Salvage 1992.

Personal: Born 2nd March 1937. Attended Barnard Castle School 1948-52; HMS 'Worcester' 1952-54; School of Navigation, Southampton University 1962-64.

Hill, E.J.D.
Ince & Co, London (0171) 623 2011. Qualified 1969. Partner 1974. Specialises in marine insurance.

Hodgson, Derek
Clyde & Co, London (0171) 623 1244. Qualified 1976. Partner 1981. Shipping and Insurance Department. Lives in London.

Johnson, Andrew
Hill Taylor Dickinson, London (0171) 283 9033. Qualified 1984. Partner 1987. Shipping and Maritime Law Department. Work covers charter parties, bills of lading, collision and salvage and marine insurance.

Latham, Simon J.
Ince & Co, London Int+ (010) 852 877 3221. Qualified 1981. Partner 1987. Based in the Hong Kong office. His main area of practice is Admiralty, charterparty, carriage of goods and insurance.

Lax, Michael D.
Lawrence Graham, London (0171) 379 0000. Partner in Shipping Department.

Specialisation: Deals with a range of shipping and maritime law matters. Work includes international trade litigation and arbitration, charter party disputes, cargo claims, marine insurance disputes, oil pollution claims, ship finance, sale and purchase, and shipbuilding contracts.

Career: Qualified in 1977.

Personal: Born 22nd December 1952. Member of Cannon Sports Club. Lives in Wallington.

Leach, Ben
See under Commodities.

Lowe, Steven
Stephenson Harwood, London (0171) 329 4422. Qualified 1972. Partner 1976. Litigation Department. Principal area of work is shipping, insurance and reinsurance disputes.

Lucas, C. David
See under Commodities.

Lux, Jonathan S.
Ince & Co, London (0171) 623 2011. Qualified 1975. Partner 1983. Handles shipping, international trade and insurance advice.

Maskell, John
Shaw and Croft, London (0171) 283 6293. Qualified 1966. Handles shipping law, with an emphasis on charterparty and Bills of Lading disputes.

Mead, Ray
Barlow Lyde & Gilbert, London (0171) 247 2277. Qualified 1975. Partner 1990. Shipping Department. Work includes shipping and international trade, and general commercial litigation.

Messent, Andrew
See under Transport (Road & Rail).

Miles, Roger H.
Ingledew Brown Bennison & Garrett, London (0171) 702 0802 (Home: (01206) 571927). Partner in Marine Department.

Specialisation: Shipping litigation, and arbitration including admiralty (collisions, salvage), total loss, charterparty, bills of lading, charterer's liability policies, bulk liquid claims, damage to offshore installations and marine insurance. Acts for shipowners (principally, but not exclusively, Greek), P&I clubs and Lloyd's underwriters. Handled the the 'Busiris' and 'Marion' cases (the latter reaching the House of Lords), and the 'Maloja II'. Firm's representative on the Admiralty Solicitors Group. Has given in-house seminars and lectures for shipowning companies.

Prof. Membership: Law Society, Honourable Company of Master Mariners, Supporting Member of LMAA and Association of Average Adjusters.

Career: Worked for BP Tanker Company Ltd as deck officer, 1960-72. Obtained Master's Foreign Going Certificate of Competency. Graduated University of Wales Insitute of Science and Technology with BSc (Hons) Maritime Studies in 1972. Joined *Holman Fenwick & Willan* in 1972, as assistant to the Head of the Admiralty department. Joined *Coward Chance* in 1978, qualifying the same year. Partner with *Stringer Saul & Justice* 1985-86, then with *Wilde Sapte* 1986-89. Moved to *Ingledew Brown Bennison & Garrett* in 1989, becoming a Partner in 1990.

Personal: Born 22nd April 1943. Leisure interests include golf. Lives in Colchester, Essex.

Miller, Anthony R.
Constant & Constant, London (0171) 261 0006. Qualified 1965. Partner. Shipping and Maritime Law Department. Particular expertise in salvage collisions, pollution damage to offshore structures and wreck removal cases. Born 11.1.1942.

More, Justin
More Fisher Brown, London (0171) 247 0438. Founder Partner of firm.

Specialisation: Main area of practice is shipping. Particular emphasis on shipping litigation and arbitration, including claims re-

lating to cargo loss and damage, bills of lading and charterparties, ship sales and casualties. International trade matters also covered, with wide experience of international sale of goods, and litigation and arbitration arising therefrom.

Prof. Memberships: Baltic Exchange, London Maritime Arbitrators Association.

Career: Qualified with *Richards Butler* in 1971, Partner 1976. Left to establish *More Fisher Brown* as a Partner in 1988.

Personal: Born 18th August 1946. Attended Bristol University 1965-68. Leisure pursuits include train-spotting, wine-tasting and 3rd division football. Lives in Hackney, London.

Morgan, Julian A.L.
Edwin Coe, London (0171) 831 7466. Partner in Shipping Group.

Specialisation: Shipping work covers sale and purchase, joint ventures, P and I club work and FD&D work. Also handles arbitration. Editor of 'Shipping Case Cards'. Lectures to P&I clubs on shipping and related topics.

Prof. Memberships: Law Society, London Maritime Arbitrators Association (supporting member), American Bar Association (associate member).

Career: Called to the Bar 1977. Worked at West of England P&I club 1979-85 before joining *Watson Farley & Williams*. Admitted as a solicitor in 1988. Joined *Edwin Coe* as a Partner in 1991.

Personal: Born 28th September 1955. Leisure interests include skiing, swimming, golf and foreign languages. Lives in London W2.

Morgan, Peter
Clyde & Co, London (0171) 623 1244. Qualified 1969. Partner 1973. Shipping Department. Main area of practice is shipping, marine insurance and international trade.

Olsen, Richard F.
Stephenson Harwood, London (0171) 329 4422. Partner in Shipping Department.

Specialisation: Principal area of practice is Admiralty work. Specialist since 1970 in collision, salvage, marine insurance, pollution and shipping accidents generally. Regular conference speaker at, amongst others, the International Bar Association and International Tug and Salvage Convention.

Prof. Membership: International Bar Association, Association of Average Adjusters (Annual Subscriber), London Maritime Arbitrators' Association (Supporting Member), City of London Admiralty Solicitors Group.

Career: Qualified in 1969. Assistant Solicitor with *Constant & Constant* 1970-72. Joined *William A. Crump & Son* in 1974 and became a Partner in 1976. Joined *Stephenson Harwood* as a Partner in 1986. Royal Naval Reserve Officer 1967-87.

Personal: Born 1943. Attended Mill Hill School 1956-61, Worcester College, Oxford 1962-65 and the Scandinavian Institute of

Maritime Law at Oslo University 1972-73. Leisure pursuits include sailing, skiing, photography, wine and reading.

Payton, Michael
See under Insurance & Reinsurance.

Potts, Christopher R.
See under Commodities.

Pullen, David M.
Richards Butler, London (0171) 247 6555. Qualified 1967. Partner 1972. International Trade and Commodities. Main areas of practice are commodity trading disputes and documentary credits.

Robinson, J. Nicholas
Herbert Smith, London (0171) 374 8000. Qualified 1976. Partner 1989. Head of Shipping Litigation Department. Handles 'wet' and 'dry' litigation, injunctive relief and multi-jurisdictional cases.

Rooth, Anthony
Clyde & Co, London (0171) 623 1244. Qualified 1975.

Russell, Mark A.
Stephenson Harwood, London (0171) 329 4422. Qualified 1983. Partner specialising in ship finance, general shipping and offshore work.

Sayer, Richard J.
Ince & Co, London (0171) 623 2011. Partner covering maritime law.

Specialisation: Main areas of practice are admiralty (collision, salvage and other casualties), charter party disputes and sale and purchase litigation. Acted for owners of 'The Braer' following the Shetland disaster in 1993. Also a member of the four-man FERIT (Far East Regional Investigation Team) established by all the major Far East insurance associations to investigate the incidence of maritime fraud in the South China Sea in the 1970s. Gives the annual lecture on salvage to the Richards Hogg International Marine Insurance Course.

Prof. Memberships: Chairman (since 1991) of the City of London Admiralty Solicitors Group (Secretary 1972-91), Chairman of the BMLA Salvage Sub-Committee, member of the Baltic Exchange, supporting member of the Association of Average Adjusters, and of the Maritime Arbitrators Association, member of the Admiralty Court Committee since 1986, and member of the Lloyd's Form Working Party.

Career: Qualified in 1966, having joined *Ince & Co.* in 1962. Became a Partner in 1970. Was admitted in Hong Kong in 1979 and sent five months there opening the firm's Hong Kong office.

Personal: Born 7th May 1943. Attended Fralingham College 1956-61. Governor of two schools, and trustee of United Response, a charity caring for learning disabilities. Lei-

sure interests include golf, cricket and theatre. Married with two sons. Lives in London.

Shaw, Richard
Shaw and Croft, London (0171) 283 6293. Qualified 1966. Partner 1980. Specialises in international maritime law. Work includes contracts of carriage goods by sea, charter parties, salvage and marine insurance. Has contributed to '*Lloyds Maritime and Commercial Law Quarterly*' of which he is a member of the editorial board.

Sheehan, D.M.
Ince & Co, London (0171) 623 2011. Qualified 1978. Partner 1981. Specialises in all aspects of shipping and also construction.

Shelford, Peter
Clyde & Co, London (0171) 623 1244. Qualified 1975. Partner 1979. Deals with contentious shipping and marine insurance matters. Born 20.2.1951.

Shelton, John H.
Norton Rose, London (0171) 283 6000. Qualified 1981. Partner 1987. Shipping Finance Group. Specialises in shipping and other forms of asset finance.

Slade, David L.
Stephenson Harwood, London (0171) 329 4422. Partner and Head of Shipping Department.

Specialisation: Main area of practice is shipping finance, shipbuilding contracts and sale and purchase of ships, acting mainly for banks, ship-owners, shipbuilders and ship-brokers. Also deals with disputes under shipbuilding contracts and sale and purchase contracts.

Prof. Membership: Law Society, Worshipful Company of Shipwrights.

Career: Qualified in 1966. Joined *Stephenson Harwood* as a Partner in 1985.

Personal: Born on 3rd July 1941. Educated at St. Peter's, York 1954-60, then Emmanuel College, Cambridge 1960-63 and 1966. (MA 1966 LLM 1966) Formerly a member of the Territorial Army (Airborne Artillery). Holder of T.D.

Slade, Robin
Stephenson Harwood, London (0171) 329 4422. Qualified 1974. Partner in marine casualty and insurance.

Strong, Malcolm
Ince & Co, London (0171) 623 2011. Qualified 1967. Partner 1970. Specialises in sale and purchase of ships and ship finance.

Taylor, Nicholas
Shaw and Croft, London (0171) 283 6293. Qualified 1976. Partner 1983. Shipping lawyer. Specialises in all aspects of marine law including contract of carriage, charterparty and bills of lading.

Taylor, Timothy
Hill Taylor Dickinson, London (0171) 283 9033. Qualified 1978. Partner 1982. Shipping and Insurance Department. Principal area of work is insurance and shipping litigation.

Taylor, Andrew D.
Richards Butler, London (0171) 247 6555. Partner in Shipping Unit.

Specialisation: Specialises in charter disputes, cargo liabilities, marine insurance, P&I clubs and sale and purchase disputes.

Career: Qualified in 1980. Partner at *Richards Butler* since 1983.

Personal: Born 1952. Educated at Lincoln College, Oxford (MA).

Thorp, Clive
Clyde & Co, London (0171) 623 1244. Qualified 1979. Partner 1982. Shipping Department. Work includes charterparties, commodities, oil, Mareva injunctions and Anton Piller sequestration.

Vlasto, Tony
Clifford Chance, London (0171) 600 1000. Partner. Principal area of practice is shipping law.

Wallis, Robert H.
Hill Taylor Dickinson, London (0171) 283 9033.

Ward, W. Ian R.
Lovell White Durrant, London (0171) 236 0066. Qualified 1976. Partner 1976. Shipping Group. Principal area of practice encompasses all aspects of shipping and marine insurance.

Watson, Martin A.
See under Asset Finance & Leasing.

Weiss, O.A.R.
Ince & Co, London (0171) 623 2011. Qualified 1976. Partner 1984. Main area of practice is international marine trade, including carriage of goods by sea, charterparty, bills of lading, sale and purchase and total loss investigations. Born 7.9.1950.

Williams, Richard W.
Ince & Co, London (0171) 623 2011. Qualified 1973. Partner 1978. Main area of work covers chartering and carriage of goods by sea. Also commodity and insurance disputes. Born 13.6.1948.

Wilson, Robert G.
Holman, Fenwick & Willan, London (0171) 488 2300. Qualified 1977. Partner 1982. Litigation and Arbitration Department. Principal area of practice is shipping and maritime law.

Wright, Sue
Norton Rose, London (0171) 283 6000. Qualified 1988. Partner. Banking Group.

Specialises in asset finance. Handles all types of non-litigious work relating to ship and aviation finance.

REGIONS

Brown, Alistdair

Mills & Co, Newcastle-upon-Tyne (0191) 233 2222. Qualified 1991. Partner 1992. Main areas of practice are engineering, shipbuilding, IPRs, building, computing, commercial litigation and insolvency.

Browne, Benjamin

Clyde & Co, Guildford (01483) 31161. Qualified 1978. Partner 1985. Marine Casualty Department. Work includes oil pollution, salvage, collision, general average and transhipments.

Cullen, Donald

Donne Mileham & Haddock, Brighton (01273) 329833.

Dale, Michael

Birketts, Ipswich (01473) 232300. Qualified 1981. Partner 1993. Shipping and Transportation Department. Work includes charterparty, bills of lading, CIF and FOB, oil and bulk cargoes, cargo shortage investigations and recovery, and marine insurance. Born 10.11.1955.

Dowie, Alex

Eversheds, Newcastle upon Tyne (0191) 261 1661. Qualified 1978. Partner 1991. Shipping and International Trade Department. Work covers contentious/non-contentious 'dry' shipping matters and insurance/reinsurance.

Evans, Ian R.

Weightman Rutherfords, Liverpool (0151) 227 2601. Qualified 1975. Partner 1978. Specialises in international commercial arbitrations involving commodities.

Hill, Martin G.

Alsop Wilkinson, Liverpool (0151) 227 3060. Qualified 1977. Partner 1993. Marine and Insurance Department. Main area of practice is insurance work, including cover subrogation and defence. Born 12.5.1953.

Hilton, Chris J.

Eversheds, Newcastle upon Tyne (0191) 261 1661. Qualified 1975. Partner 1976. Shipping Department. 21 years experience in all aspects of maritime law, both 'wet' and 'dry'. Also covers insurance work. Born 19.1.1950.

Horton, Nicholas

Davies Grant & Horton, Plymouth (01752) 255555. Partner specialising in marine work.

Specialisation: Full legal service to yacht industry - in the UK and internationally;

litigation and commercial contract work; marine insurance; sale and purchase; build and refit contracts, international litigation. Also experienced in more broadly based litigation and contract work.

Memberships: British Marine Industries Federation, Royal Ocean Racing Club.

Career: Qualified 1986. *Ingledew Brown Bennison & Garrett* 1984-88. Co-Founded *Davies Grant & Horton*.

Personal: Born August 1960. Merton College, Oxford 1979-82. Leisure: wine, sailing and family. Lives Plymouth.

Jackson, Peter W.

Hill Dickinson Davis Campbell, Liverpool (0151) 236 5400. Partner in Marine Department.

Specialisation: Main areas of practice are marine, goods in transit and insurance litigation. Work includes cargo claims, for both cargo and liability insurers, particularly international road haulage claims; ship related cargo claims for cargo interests; salvage; and monitoring foreign litigation. Also handles marine insurance work, particularly marine insurance policy interpretation for underwriters. Acted in ICI plc v. MAT transport, ITT v. Birkart, the 'Breydon Merchant' F & W Freight, the 'Los Angeles' and Microfine v. Transferry Shipping. Individual charge-out rate is approximately £120 per hour, inclusive of mark-up.

Prof. Membership: Liverpool Underwriters Association, Manchester Marine Insurance Association, London Maritime Arbitrators Association.

Career: Qualified in 1985, having joined *Hill Dickinson Davis Campbell* in 1983. Became a Partner in 1989.

Personal: Born 3rd April 1961. Attended St Edward's College, Liverpool 1972-79, then Exeter College, Oxford 1979-82. Leisure interests include football (Vice Chairman of South Liverpool FC, former Chairman of Football Supporters Association). Lives in Liverpool.

Johnson, Jonathan

Davies Grant & Horton, Plymouth (01752) 255555. Partner specialising in maritime law.

Specialisation: Has specialised in shipping and maritime law since 1976, with commercial litigation work also handled.

Prof. Membership: LMAA, BMIA.

Career: Qualified in 1976. Worked at *Richards Butler* 1976-92, becoming a Partner in 1980. Left to join *Davies Grant & Horton* in 1992 as a Partner.

Personal: Born 31st March 1951. Attended Nottingham University, taking an LLB in 1972. Lives in Plymouth.

Knox, Robert

Henderson Boyd Jackson WS, Edinburgh (0131) 226 6881. Senior Partner in Marine Department.

Specialisation: 35 years' experience of contentious maritime law matters including salvage, collisions, personal injury, cargo, pollution, and general contractual disputes. Also handles general non-marine litigation. Has been personally involved in most of the notable Scottish maritime cases of the last 35 years including The Braer. Author of articles on marine topics for a variety of publications. Acted as Convener of Law Society of Scotland Conferences on Maritime Law held in 1989 and 1991. Solicitor Member of Scottish Committee under Lord Maxwell to advise on the application to Scotland of the 1982 Civil Jurisdiction and Judgments Act.

Prof. Membership: Law Society of Scotland, Writer to the Signet.

Career: Qualified in 1959. In 1960 joined *Boyd Jameson WS* Edinburgh. Became a Partner of that firm in 1962, and Senior Partner in 1980. Solicitor to MOD (Navy) in Scotland acting in collision cases since 1964 and to MOD (Army) in Scotland since 1980. Solicitor to Department of Trade in Shipping Inquiries since 1964. Upon merger of *Boyd Jameson* with *Henderson Boyd Jackson* in 1993, joined *Henderson Boyd Jackson WS* in 1993 as Senior Marine Department Partner.

Personal: Born 23rd May 1935. Educated at Paisley Grammar School and Glasgow University (MA 1955). Subsequently Manchester University 1956-57 and Edinburgh University 1957-59 (LLB 1959). Honorary Consul for Belgium in Scotland. Leisure pursuits include gardening, photography, foreign travel, music, the arts and railways past and present. Lives in Edinburgh.

Lowe, James A.G.

Henderson Boyd Jackson WS, Edinburgh (0131) 226 6881. Partner in Maritime Department.

Specialisation: Handles admiralty work, including collisions, salvage, charterparty disputes, personal injury claims, insurance disputes, shipbuilding and repair contract disputes and cargo claims. Author of 'Maritime Securities' in the Stair Memorial Encyclopaedia and various articles for the legal, marine and fishing industry press. Has presented papers at Law Society Maritime Law courses and to marine insurers on aspects of the Marine Insurance Act 1906.

Prof. Membership: Law Society of Scotland, Honourable Company of Master Mariners, Writer to the Signet, British Maritime Law Association.

Career: Ship's Officer 1966-1980. Gained Master Mariners Certificate in 1976. Joined *Boyd Jameson WS* and qualified as a Solicitor in 1985. Became a Partner in 1986. Joined *Henderson Boyd Jackson* 1993 upon the merger of *Boyd Jameson* and *Henderson & Jackson*.

Personal: Born 14th April 1949. Educated at Edinburgh University 1980-84. Enjoys golf, shooting and fishing. Lives in Edinburgh.

MacRae, Keith G.

Mackinnons, Aberdeen (01224) 632464. Partner in Maritime and Litigation Department.

Specialisation: Acts for marine insurers, covering hull and machinery and P&I. Has particular experience in fishing vessel insurance and claims. Practice split between hull/admiralty work (collisions, salvage, total loss and casualty investigation) and P&I claims (in particular personal accident/employers liability claims from accidents on oil rigs and ships). Also handles oil pollution cases. Work includes on-site investigation on- and offshore. Has a substantial case load in the Sheriff Court and Court of Session, acting for Defenders in personal injury claims and for Pursuers in ship repair and ship builders negligence claims and contractual disputes. Gave a paper to Law Society of Scotland's Second Maritime Law Seminar. Presents seminars on Marine Insurance to clients.

Career: Qualified in 1982. Joined *Mackinnons* in 1980, becoming a Partner in 1983.

Personal: Born 23rd May 1953. Attended Aberdeen University 1971-76 (MA(Hons)) and 1977-80 (LLB). Honorary Norwegian Consul in Aberdeen; Honorary Danish Vice-Consul in Aberdeen. Leisure interests include football, rock and jazz music and travelling. Lives in Catterline.

Mawdsley, D.H.

Alsop Wilkinson, Liverpool (0151) 227 3060. Qualified 1969. Partner 1973. Marine Department. Deals with shipping (contentious and non-contentious) and carriage by land sea and air. Born 21.5.1945.

Maxwell, M. John

Hill Dickinson Davis Campbell, Liverpool (0151) 236 5400. Qualified 1969. Partner 1967. Marine Department. Specialises in marine and commercial litigation.

Mills, Geoffrey

Mills & Co, Newcastle-upon-Tyne (0191) 233 2222. Senior Partner specialising in shipping law.

Specialisation: Principal area of practice covers shipbuilding and ship repair contracts and disputes; ship finance; chartering, sale and purchase; insurance; and commercial engineering contracts and disputes. Other main area of work is joint ventures and government contracts. Acted on behalf of Swan Hunter in the 'Derbyshire' Formal Investigation.

Prof. Membership: Law Society, Notaries Society.

Career: Qualified 1960. Partner *Ingledew Mark Pybus* 1963-77. Director of Legal Services (Legal Advisor) British Shipbuilders 1978-1986. Returned to previous firm, now renamed *Eversheds Ingledew Wright* until 1993, then established *Mills & Co.* as Senior Partner.

Personal: Born 11th November 1934. Attended Bedford School 1948-52, then Trinity Hall, Cambridge 1953-56. Leisure pursuits include fishing, shooting, gardening and golf. Lives in Riding Mill, Northumberland.

Mills, Stephen

Rayfield Mills, Newcastle-upon-Tyne (0191) 261 2333. Qualified 1980.

Nash, Brian

Clyde & Co, Guildford (01483) 31161. Qualified 1982. Partner 1987. Shipping Litigation Department. Work covers marine casualty, cargo recovery, charterparty disputes, marine insurance and commodity trade disputes. Born 17.5.1957.

Phillips, Raymond J.

Alsop Wilkinson, Liverpool (0151) 227 3060. Qualified 1970. Partner 1974. Litigation Department. Main areas of practice are shipping transport and insurance: carriage of goods by sea, air, rail and road; fire, shipbuilding and repair. Born 10.1.1945.

Rayfield, Richard

Rayfield Mills, Newcastle-upon-Tyne (0191) 261 2333. Qualified 1976. Former seafarer. Founding partner 1993. International shipping practice. Has practised shipping law since 1976, covering many areas.

Taylor, Silas W.

Andrew M. Jackson & Co, Hull (01482) 325242. Partner and Head of Admiralty and Shipping Department.

Specialisation: Main area of practice is marine casualty work. Acts on behalf of all main P&I clubs in collisions, salvage and major personal injury cases. Particular expertise in legal matters relating to the fishing industry. Also deals with disputes in respect of towage, pilotage, shipbuild and repair, etc, and claims under hull and machinery insurance. Acted for salmon farmers following 'Braer' oil spill, and in 'Wilhelmina' and 'Zulfikar' collision in English Channel (6 fatalities). Has spoken on maritime law at conferences arranged by the Nautical Institute. Has contributed articles to 'Lloyd's Maritime and Commercial Law Quarterly', and the Nautical Institute's 'Seaways'.

Prof. Membership: Chartered Institute of Arbitrators, Sea Safety Group, British-Nordic Lawyers Association.

Career: Qualified and joined *Andrew M. Jackson* in 1975. Became a Partner in 1980.

Personal: Born 3rd February 1953. Educated at Bedford Modern School 1964-71 and Hull University 1971-74. Leisure pursuits include fishing, badminton and bowling. Lives in South Cave.

Thomas, Anthony

Clyde & Co, Guildford (01483) 31161. Qualified 1976. Partner 1981. Shipping and Litigation Department. Has considerable experience in litigation in the Commercial Court in London, London Arbitration and proceedings overseas. Born 27.5.1952.

Wareing, W.David

Hill Dickinson Davis Campbell, Liverpool (0151) 236 5400. Qualified 1978.

Weston, John

Birketts, Ipswich (01473) 232300. Qualified 1989. Partner 1993. Shipping Department. Work includes wet and dry shipping, sale and purchase, personal injuries, port authority matters and oil pollution. Born 7.4.1956.

Wheatley, Jerry

Clyde & Co, Guildford (01483) 31161.

Wollen, Nigel J.

See under Trusts & Personal Tax.

SPORTS LAW

To describe sport as an area of law is inaccurate. However, there are a number of practitioners who can be described as sports specialists, having acquired an in-depth knowledge of the sporting industry and the attendant legal issues.

LONDON

Farrer & Co emerges as the pre-eminent firm in this area, chiefly in the guise of Charles Woodhouse who is generally considered to be the doyen of sports law. With over twenty years experience in the field, he is legal adviser to

the Central Council for Physical Recreation, the Commonwealth Games Council for England and numerous other governing bodies, representative bodies and charities. In addition to constitutional and disciplinary work, the firm also advises on doping and sponsorship/licensing agreements.

Other highly recommended firms include *Herbert Smith* and *Townleys.*

Herbert Smith has considerable experience of both contentious and non-contentious sports work, including drafting the constitutions of many governing bodies. The firm also represents players in disciplinary proceedings (especially in relation to drug offences) and advises on the regulation of sporting activities. On the contentious side, the firm has represented the International Amateur Athletic Association, British Judo Association, and acted for Diane Modahl, Butch Reynolds, Katrin Krabbe and John Ngugi in the dop-

ing tribunals. Mark Gay is highly respected.

Townleys, a niche practice, specialises in legal and tax planning, licensing, merchandising and event planning. Steven Townley, considered an expert in all sporting issues, is a leading authority in sponsorship law. Nick Couchman is also recommended.

Other firms with notable sports practices include *Collyer Bristow, Denton Hall, Eversheds* and *Max Bitel, Greene.*

Collyer Bristow's sports unit boasts eminent practitioners such as Philip Stinson and Alan Burdon-Cooper who undertake work for sponsorship and other marketing consultants and agencies, television production companies and governing bodies. The firm is also experienced in equestrian sport, representing a governing body and the owners and organisers of three day events.

Denton Hall advises the FA Premier League in relation to sports rights, contracts and disputes, the Test and County Cricket Board and the World League of American Football on its UK interests. The highly regarded Adrian Barr-Smith is also instructed in connection with the European Football Championships in 1996 and the World Cup in France in 1998.

In all the tables the names in each group are listed alphabetically.

Eversheds offers a comprehensive service including advice on sponsorship and merchandising and the constitutional and commercial aspects of clubs, associations and governing bodies. Catherine Bond (co-author of 'Sports Medicine: Ethics and the Law') is particularly known for advising and litigating in respect of disciplinary procedures, liability in relation to violent play and drugs related tribunals and appeals.

Max Bitel, Greene is best known for representing sporting bodies, although the firm also acts for individuals and for sports events such as the Ryder Cup, the London Marathon and the Wimbledon Championships. Nicholas Bitel is well respected.

Individual practitioners who were particularly highly recommended include Mel Stein at *Finers,* Raj Parker at *Freshfields* and Mel Goldberg at *Portner & Jaskel* who all have sound reputations in the field of professional football, and Peter Crystal at *Memery Crystal* (sponsorship, ticketing, event management and corporate hospitality).

SOUTH EAST

Cripps Harries Hall has established a reputation in equine and field sports. Christopher Hall who heads the team of four, advises the British Equestrian Foundation, the British Equestrian Olympic Fund, the Masters of Fox Hounds Association and the Hackney Horse Society.

HIGHLY REGARDED – SOUTH EAST	
CRIPPS HARRIES HALL *Tunbridge Wells*	MATTHEW McCLOY & P'TNERS *Newbury*
PICKWORTHS *Watford*	WOODFORD & ACKROYD *Southampton*
DONNE MILEHAM & HADDOCK *Brighton*	ENSOR BYFIELD *Southampton*

Matthew McCloy of *Matthew McCloy & Partners* is also known for equine sports and has been recommended for his work for the Newbury Trainers Federation.

Pickworths act for motor racing teams, drivers and organisers.

Keith Wiseman of *Woodford & Ackroyd* acts for soccer and tennis clubs on a range of issues.

LEADING INDIVIDUALS – SOUTH EAST
Christopher Hall *Cripps Harries Hall*
Matthew McCloy *Matthew McCloy & Partners*
Keith St. J. Wiseman *Woodford & Ackroyd*

SOUTH WEST

The most prominent firm in this field is *Wansbroughs Willey Hargrave.* The sports specialists act primarily for rugby, golf and cycling clubs on a range of issues including sponsorship deals, intellectual property and licensing matters, but are also known for stadium defects work.

HIGHLY REGARDED – SOUTH WEST	
DAVID JEACOCK	STONES *Exeter*
VEALE WASBROUGH *Bristol*	WANSBROUGHS WILLEY HARGRAVE *Bristol*

David Jeacock is a niche practice which concentrates mainly on constitutional and drug related issues. The firm is particulary known for its work in the field of athletics, advising the British Athletics league and the Sportshall Athletic Association. David Jeacock is Chairman of Swindon Athletic Club and former Secretary to the British Athletics Federation Drug Advisory Committee.

Veale Wasbrough is noted for its involvement in serious claims arising from sporting injuries, whilst Paul Maxlow-Tomlinson of *Stones* maintains a high profile in the field of skiing; he is the only British legal representative on the International Ski Federation.

LEADING INDIVIDUALS – SOUTH WEST
David Jeacock *David Jeacock*
Paul C. Maxlow-Tomlinson *Stones*

MIDLANDS

The sports unit at *Edge & Ellison* is headed by Richard Alderson and represents a number of sporting bodies including the Football League and the British Athletic Foundation.

HIGHLY REGARDED – MIDLANDS	
EDGE & ELLISON *Birmingham*	GERMAN & SOAR *Nottingham*

John Gardiner at *German & Soar* is particularly known for contentious work, where he litigates over contract disputes, injury claims and coach liability.

LEADING INDIVIDUALS – MIDLANDS
Richard A. Alderson *Edge & Ellison*
John Gardiner *German & Soar*

EAST ANGLIA

Taylor Vinters is one of the few firms in the country with a department that acts exclusively in the area of bloodstock law. Jeremy Richardson at *Taylor Vinters'* Newmarket office is well known within the racing industry, representing trainers, owners, jockeys and breeders amongst others.

HIGHLY REGARDED – EAST ANGLIA	
GREENLAND HOUCHEN *Norwich*	TAYLOR VINTERS *Cambridge*

Trevor Nicholls of *Greenland Houchen* has been recommended for professional football and particularly for his work with Norwich Football Club.

LEADING INDIVIDUALS – EAST ANGLIA
Trevor Nicholls *Greenland Houchen*
Jeremy Richardson *Taylor Vinters*

NORTH

The most highly recommended firms in the North of England are *James Chapman & Co,* and *McCormicks.*

James Chapman & Co enjoys a national reputation in the

field of professional football, advising both players and management. Maurice Watkins is a director of and solicitor for Manchester United PLC and advises the Football Association Premier League, being a member of its working party of four. He is also well known for his work in cricket and basketball and is a committee member of the British Association for Sport and the Law.

LEADING FIRMS – NORTH	
JAMES CHAPMAN & CO Manchester	**McCORMICKS** Leeds
GEORGE DAVIES & CO Manchester	**GORNA & CO** Manchester
WALKER MORRIS Leeds	

Peter McCormick of *McCormicks* is perhaps best described as a sports generalist. He not only advises Leeds United Football Club and a number of sporting bodies within the fields of horse racing, rugby, athletics and cricket, but has an impressive client list of sporting personalities which include Fred Truman, Jenny Pitman and Willy Carson.

HIGHLY REGARDED – NORTH	
BROOKE NORTH AND GOODWIN Leeds	**HALLIWELL LANDAU** Manchester
PANNONE & PARTNERS Manchester	
ZERMANSKY & PARTNERS Leeds	

Other firms which have been recommended for their expertise in professional football include *George Davies & Co* and *Gorna & Co*, the latter acts for the League Managers Association and has also advised Peter Shilton, the former England goalkeeper.

Walker Morris represents a number of sports personalities, managers, agents and representative bodies including the Rugby Football League (where they share the work with *Zermansky & Partners*). Christopher Caisley who heads the sports law group is the Chairman of Bradford Northern Rugby Football Club and a former member of the Rugby Football League's Board of Directors as well as being a member of the British Association for Sport and Law.

LEADING INDIVIDUALS – NORTH	
Peter D.G. McCormick McCormicks	
E. Maurice Watkins James Chapman & Co	
Christopher S. Caisley Walker Morris	
Tony Ensor Weightman Rutherfords	
John E. Hewison George Davies & Co	
Mark A. Hovell George Davies & Co	
Michael Morrison Gorna & Co	
R. Teeman Teeman Levine	

SCOTLAND

There is only one firm in Scotland with a dedicated sports law department: *Harper MacLeod*.

The remainder of the firms listed have one or two individuals with specific interests.

Dorman Jeffrey & Co and *McClure Naismith Anderson & Gardiner* are both actively involved in professional football, the latter firm also advises on the promotion and media coverage of boxing matches.

Henderson Boyd Jackson handles various aspects of sports law, including players injuries, contract disputes, sponsorship and share issues. The firm is currently advising agents on FIFA football regulations.

HIGHLY REGARDED – SCOTLAND	
DORMAN JEFFREY & CO Glasgow	**HARPER MACLEOD** Glasgow
HENDERSON BOYD JACKSON Edinburgh	**McCLURE NAISMITH ANDERSON & GARDINER** Glasgow

In all the tables the names in each group are listed alphabetically.

LEADERS IN SPORTS LAW

LONDON

Bagehot, Richard S.
Field Fisher Waterhouse, London (0171) 481 4841. Partner in Company Department.

Specialisation: Principal area of practice is intellectual property, including copyright, sponsorship, merchandising, publishing and sports law. Other main area is information technology, including multi media and software. Major clients include Ordnance Survey. Author of 'Music Business agreements', 'Sponsorship Endorsement and Merchandising' and 'Sales Promotion and Advertising' (all published by Sweet & Maxwell). Occasional speaker at conferences and seminars.

Career: Qualified and joined *Rubinstein Nash* in 1967. Legal advisor to a major rock and roll band 1973-79. Joined *Field Fisher Waterhouse* as a partner in 1979.

Personal: Born 27th February 1941. Educated at St. Mary's College, Nairobi, Kenya 1950-59. Leisure pursuits include clay pigeon shooting. Lives in Amersham, Bucks.

Barr-Smith, Adrian
Denton Hall, London (0171) 320 6501; Fax: (0171) 320 6693. Partner in Media and Technology Department.

Specialisation: Main area of practice is sport, covering broadcasting contracts, licensing and merchandising, event regulation, official supplier contracts and disciplinary matters. Also covers media finance, including film finance, broadcast and cable TV financing, film production and distribution. Has acted for the FA Premier League, England Rugby Players (Playervision), Test & County Cricket Board, and World League of American Football. Hon. Legal adviser to Sports Aid Foundation. Contributes to 'International Media Law'. Tutor at the Film Business School. Member of the Panel of Arbitrators of the American Film Marketing Association.

Prof. Memberships: Design & Artists Copyright Society (Honorary Secretary), Sports Lawyers Association, IBA, Copinger Society.

Career: Qualified in 1977. Solicitor at *Rubinstein Callingham* 1977-79. Legal Director of Artlaw Services 1980-81. Joined *Denton Hall* in 1982, becoming a Partner in 1986.

Personal: Born 23rd January 1952. Attended Emmanuel College, Cambridge, 1970-73. Chairman of Trustees, Interlink Trust.

Leisure pursuits include cricket, tennis and golf. Lives in London.

Bitel, Nicholas A.

Max Bitel, Greene, London (0171) 354 2767. Partner in Sports and Entertainment Department.

Specialisation: Main area of practice is sports law. Acts for major sports events and sportsmen and women. Well known for acting for events such as the Ryder Cup, the London Marathon and the Wimbledon Championships; Author of articles in, amongst others, Sport and the Law Journal. Addresses sports conferences and seminars and public forums.

Prof. Membership: British Association for Sport and the Law, Law Society.

Career: Qualified in 1983, having joined *Max Bitel, Greene* in 1981. Became a Partner in 1983.

Personal: Born 31st August 1959. Attended St Paul's School, London 1972-76; Davidson College, North Carolina 1976-77, and Manchester University 1977-80. Vice Chairman of Wigan Athletic FC. Director of Kings Head Theatre. Leisure interests include football, cricket and theatre. Lives in London.

Bond, Catherine

Eversheds, London (0171) 919 4500. Assistant Solicitor in Media Department.

Specialisation: Main area of practice is sport. Gives a broad range of advice, including constitutional advice, sponsorship, I.P., tribunals and litigation. Also handles intellectual property law, including trademarks, copyright, and also various media related matters.

Prof. Membership: Committee member, British Association for Sport and the Law.

Career: Qualified in 1993, having joined *Jaques & Lewis* (now Eversheds) in 1991.

Personal: Born 4th January 1968. Attended the Kings High School for Girls, Warwick 1979-86, then Reading University 1987-90. Leisure interests include spectating and competing in various sports.

Bracewell, Julia

Brobeck Hale & Dorr International, London (0171) 638 6688. Qualified 1987. Barrister. Company Commercial Department. Specialises in sport, acting for clubs, organisations and businesses.

Breen, Michael M.G.

Edward Lewis, London (0171) 404 5566.

Specialisation: Company, Commercial and Sports Law. Head of Sports and Entertainment Unit representing sporting personalities, agents and managers on contractual and tax arrangements, sponsorship, merchandising, endorsement, publishing and intellectual property matters. Specialist in all aspects of business and legal management for high profile sports and entertainment personalities including Formula One racing drivers, Premier League football players, Five Na-

tions Rugby Union players, leading international athletes and professional sporting bodies.

Prof. Membership: British Association of Sport and the Law.

Career: Qualified in 1988. Became a Partner in 1989.

Burdon-Cooper, Alan R.

Collyer–Bristow, London (0171) 242 7363.

Specialisation: Partner, based in both the Sport & Entertainment and the Commercial Property Departments. His sport and entertainment practice includes drafting commercial agreements and agency contracts relating to sponsorship, licensing and merchandising. Has drafted and advised on many of the major sponsorship contracts relating to British and European Athletics. His commercial property work covers sales and acquisitions, negotiation of commercial leases, and termination and renewal of leases under the provisions of the Landlord & Tenant Act 1954. Articles include 'Drafting of Package Agency & Sponsorship Contracts at national and continental level' in the International Athletic Foundation Sport & Law Supplement.

Prof. Membership: Executive Committee Member of the Institute of Sports Sponsorship.

Career: Articled at Collyer-Bristow, qualifying in 1968. Partner 1969. Senior Partner 1985-94.

Personal: Educated at Oundle School 1955-61 and Emmanuel College, Cambridge 1961-64. Governor of Rose Bruford College of Speech & Drama. Liveryman of the Worshipful Company of Dyers. Leisure pursuits include music, sport and gardening. Born 27th June 1942. Lives near Hemel Hempstead,

Bynoe, Robin

Eversheds, London (0171) 919 4500. Partner in Intellectual Property Group.

Specialisation: Main area of practice is information technology, including multimedia and media work, including merchandising, sponsorship, film production and distribution, video and other publishing and franchising. Supervises the firm's sports practice, including dealing with sports authorities and sporting litigation. Co-author of the book 'Franchising' (FT Law and Tax: 1995). Author of numerous articles, including for the American Bar Association, Franchise Law Journal, and the Journal of Brand Management. Presents numerous in-house and commercial conferences.

Prof. Membership: British Association of Sport and the Law, EFFIA, IFA.

Career: Qualified in 1973, having joined *Jaques & Co.* (now Eversheds) in 1971. Became a Partner in 1977.

Personal: Born 1st June 1948. Attended Oxford University 1967-70. Founder member of

Felix the Wrestler. Lives in London.

Cornthwaite, Jonathan P.

Wedlake Bell, London (0171) 395 3000. Partner in Intellectual Property and EC Law Department.

Specialisation: Sports law, including broadcasting, media, copyright, trade and service marks, passing off, designs, technology licensing, pharmaceuticals and publishing. Also covers competition law, including restrictive practices, unfair competition, UK and EU competition and anti-trust regulations. Has handled major television contracts for leading sporting associations in tennis and rugby football. Also acts for motor racing clients. Author of 'Marketing Law that Matters'; also publishes updates on sports law.

Prof. Membership: Law Society, Westminster Law Society, Competition Law Association.

Career: Qualified in 1979. Joined *Wedlake Bell* in 1987, becoming a Partner in 1989.

Personal: Born 19th June 1954. Attended St Paul's School and the Universities of Oxford and Cambridge. Leisure interests include history, philately, tennis and languages. Lives in Strawberry Hill, Twickenham.

Couchman, Nicholas

Townleys, London (0171) 251 2505. Partner and Head of Media and Communications Group.

Specialisation: Contract and intellectual property aspects of sports marketing in over 15 sports, including sponsorship contracts, character merchandising, personality endorsement agreements, television production contracts and advertising law. Particular specialism in sports rights piracy, counterfeiting and 'ambush marketing' (prevention and litigation), and advising on advertising and promotions copy. Also involved in development of new sponsorship projects in music, culture and the media. Clients include major sports events (e.g. Rugby World Cup), corporate sponsors (Carlsberg-Tetley, Times Newspapers), sports organisations (the Sports Council) and several communications/sponsorship agencies. Author 'Ambush/Parasitic Marketing and Sport' and numerous trade press articles. Regular lecturer at media law conferences.

Career: Qualified 1990. Partner *Townleys* 1992.

Personal: Born 1965. Attended Devenport High School and Nottingham University. French speaker.

Crystal, Peter M.

Memery Crystal, London (0171) 242 5905. Senior Partner in Corporate/Commercial Department.

Specialisation: Main areas of practice are corporate finance and sports. Advises companies on take-overs, flotations, all capital raising, MBO, MBI and share matters and all sports related matters, including transaction structures, sponsorship and corporate aspects. Handles sports transactions for Wembley plc; acted in David Dein & Phillip Carter v. Football League. Has acted for Charlton Athletic since 1981 and has handled agency and sponsorship arrangements and agreements for a well known boxer with IMG. Examiner with the Law Society in Company Law 1974-78. Parliamentary candidate on three occasions. Conference spokesman on Guinness Case.

Prof. Membership: Law Society, Sports Lawyers Association.

Career: Qualified in 1972. Articled at *Simpson Curtis*. Worked at *Clifford Turner* 1973-78. Founded *Memery Crystal* in 1978.

Personal: Born 7th January 1948. Attended Leeds Grammar School; St Edmund Hall Oxford; College of Law, Lancaster Gate; then McGill University, Montreal. Played rugby and boxed for Oxford, captained Otley RUFC and played for Eastern Canada against Wales at rugby. Leisure interests include all sports, reading and travel. Lives in London.

Eagles, Brian
Hammond Suddards, London (0171) 628 4767. Partner and Head of Media and Entertainment Unit.

Specialisation: Entertainment, media and sports law including film finance, merchandising and sponsorship. Also deals with all intellectual property both contentious and non-contentious. He has specific expertise in arbitration and mediation. An accredited CEDR mediator and an arbitrator for the American Film Marketing Association and the World Intellectual Property Organisation. A founder member of Media Dispute Resolution.

Prof. Membership: International Association of Entertainment Lawyers; Law Society; IBA; Chartered Institute of Arbitrators; CEDR; American Film Marketing Association; WIPO; Media Dispute Resolution.

Career: Qualified 1960. Assistant Solicitor with *J Sanson & Co* from 1960, and became a partner in 1961. Partner with *Herbert Oppenheimer Nathan & Vandyk* (1967-1988). Moved to become Partner and Head of Media and Communications Group at *S J Berwin & Co* in 1988. Joined *Hammond Suddards* as a Partner and Head of its Media and Entertainment Unit in May 1994.

Friend, Michael
Keene Marsland, London (0171) 375 1581.

Gay, Mark
Herbert Smith, London (0171) 374 8000. Partner in Commercial Litigation Department.

Specialisation: Has substantial experience in both the contentious and non-contentious aspects of sports law. Considerable expertise in advising various sporting bodies on constitutional issues.

Career: Qualified in 1988. Became a Partner at *Herbert Smith* in 1995.

Personal: Educated at Lady Margaret Hall, Oxford.

Glynn, Richard I.
Nicholson Graham & Jones, London (0171) 628 9151. Partner in corporate finance and member of the Sports Law Group.

Specialisation: Corporate finance, mergers and acquisitions. Sports Law Group is committed to all aspects of the business of sport including acquisitions and disposals, joint venture agreements, event management, stadium management and construction, corporate structuring, acquisition of rights, sponsorship, licensing, sole agency and merchandising agreements. Established the legal sub-committee for the Institute of Sports Sponsorship and co-prepared their standard legal checklist for sponsors. Advises Government's Sportsmatch Scheme on security for complex awards. Regular part-time lecturer at London Business School for MBA and Sloan programmes on 'Practical Law for Businessmen and Entrepreneurs' with particular bias towards service industries and leisure.
Professional Membership: Alumni Association of London Business School, Association of MBAs, part-time faculty London Business School, Institute of Sports Sponsorship.

Career: Qualified 1989 at *S J Berwin & Co.* Schroders Corporate Finance 1990-1991. Joined *Nicholson Graham & Jones* in 1991. Partner 1995.

Personal: Born 24th July 1964. Married (Lisa). Attended St Edmund Hall, Oxford 1983-1986. Blue 1985. MBA London Business School 1990-1992. Leisure pursuits include all sport, food, antiques and golf. Lives in Hampstead, London.

Goldberg, Mel
Portner & Jaskel, London (0171) 486 7881. Consultant and Head of Sports Division.

Specialisation: Has represented numerous international football players, Olympic Gold medallists and several world champions in boxing, squash, tennis and athletics. Has arranged the transfers of several million pound football players from one club to another, and the transfer of European International footballers to the UK. Drafted the Constitution of the International Squash Players Association (ISPA) and was Vice-Chairman of the British Olympic Travel Association to the Moscow Olympic Games in 1980. Has written several articles for leading sports magazines both in the USA and the UK, and has appeared on several television programmes both in the UK and in the USA. Has spoken on the subject of sports law at seminars and conferences.

Prof. Membership: Sports Lawyers Association (USA) and British Association for Sport & Law (Manchester).

Career: Qualified in 1963. Founded own

firm under the style of *Douglas Goldberg & Co* in 1968 before working in the USA. On his return became a Consultant with *Bird & Bird* in the City before joining *Portner & Jaskel*. Listed in 'Who's Who in the Law'.

Personal: Educated at St. John's College, Cambridge 1957-60 (MA Hons. in Law 1960). Past President of Hampstead Rotary Club. Leisure interests include tennis, squash and swimming. Lives in London. Married, 3 children.

Gregory, Lesley A.
Memery Crystal, London (0171) 242 5905. Qualified 1983.

Henderson, Allan J.
Gouldens, London (0171) 583 7777. Qualified 1986. Partner in the Litigation Department specialising in all aspects of employment and sports law. Born 30.5.1961.

Johns, Michael S.M.
See under Company/Commercial.

Jones, Simon
Freshfields, London (0171) 936 4000. Qualified 1989. Manager of Intellectual Property Department. Handles intellectual property, computer law, telecommunications, sports, media and pharmaceuticals.

Moorhead, Benedict R.K.
Moorhead James, London (0171) 831 8888. Founding Partner and sports law specialist.

Specialisation: More than ten years experience as a specialist in sports law. Advises on a range of sports-related matters including merchandising agreements, sponsorship, doping control issues, sports stadia and sports medecine. Acts for the Sports Council of Great Britain, the Sports Council Trust and other governing bodies, and is legal advisor to various sports clubs and charities. Has written articles on sponsorship in sport. Also lectures.

Prof. Membership: Law Society, Statute Law Society, British Association for Sport and the Law.

Career: Qualified in 1983 while at *Blyth Dutton* and became a Partner of the firm in 1987. Founded *Moorhead James* in 1992.

Personal: Born in 1958. Attended Marlborough College and holds a BA in Law (1981). Chairman of Wellesley House and St Peter's Court Educational Trust. Plays cricket, golf, tennis and ski's. Lives in London and Kent.

Ouin, Charles N.
Lawrence Graham, London (0171) 379 0000.

Specialisation: Partner in the Company and Commercial department specialising in commercial contracts and general corporate work. Practice covers sales of businesses and companies, MBOs, venture capital, corporate restructuring, joint ventures and tenders. Also deals with public sector contracts and externalisations. Advised the Government on the establishment of the National Lottery.

Career: Qualified 1973. Assistant solicitor, Holloway Blount & Duke 1973-76. Partner, Blyth Dutton 1976-92. Partner, Lawrence Graham since 1992. Non-executive director of William Sinclair Holdings Plc.

Personal: Educated at Sherborne School and the College of Law. Leisure pursuits include sailing, fishing, architecture and theatre.

Parker, Raj D.

Freshfields, London (0171) 936 4000. Partner in Litigation Department.

Specialisation: Main area of practice is insurance and reinsurance work, including the Johnson Matthey Bankers insurance claims (1984-1990), Eras environmental impairment liability litigation (1990-1994); claims for brokers; intermediaries and banks on mortgage liability claims; claims against Insurance Ombudsman Bureau; acts for Lloyd's in Central fund and related litigation and enquiries. Contributor to forthcoming Lloyd's of London Press 'Insurance Coverage Disputes' and author of articles. Regular speaker at insurance industry seminars. Also deals with sports law, acting for the Football Association in all advisory and contentious work. Acted in the Hillsborough proceedings, the battle to establish the Premier League, recent disciplinary hearings, sits on working parties.

Prof. Membership: Law Society; Society of Solicitor Advocates.

Career: Attended Bar School (1983). and practised as a barrister until 1985. At the Corporation of Lloyd's for a year 1985-86 on an Inquiry. Joined *Freshfields* in 1986 and became a Partner in 1993.

Personal: Born 19th September 1960. Educated at Christ's College 1972-79 and Southampton University 1979-82. Recreations include sport, music, theatre and ornithology. Lives in London.

Russell, Patrick

Charles Russell, London (0171) 203 5018. Partner in Litigation Department.

Specialisation: Acts for sporting regulatory authorities and clubs in the regulatory and disciplinary field. Experienced in public law, judicial review and restraint of trade, etc. Also handles contentious work related to the London insurance and reinsurance market. Acted in judicial review decisions for the Jockey Club and The Law Society, and in ex parte A.H, Aga Khan, and Swindon Town FC.

Prof. Membership: Law Society, Society of English and American Lawyers.

Career: Joined *Charles Russell* in 1976 and qualified in 1979. Became a Partner in 1980. Director of the Solicitors Indemnity Mutual Insurance Association Ltd.

Personal: Born 11th May 1952. Educated at Ampleforth College 1965-70 and University College, Oxford 1971-74. Recreations include golf, sailing, tennis and motorcycling.

Lives near Towcester, Northants.

Stein, M.A.

Finers, London (0171) 323 4000.

Stinson, Philip

Collyer–Bristow, London (0171) 242 7363. Partner in Sports and Entertainment Department.

Specialisation: The law as it applies to marketing and broadcasting with particular reference to the business of sport. Clients include sponsorship and other marketing consultants and agencies, television production companies, sponsoring and sponsored organisations, governing bodies and organisers of major charitable and other events. Often advises in-house legal departments of sponsoring organisations. Author of articles in British Association for Sport and Law Journal, in 'Spectrum' (Magazine of the Independent Television Commission), and in numerous trade journals. Co-wrote the sponsorship legal check-list published by the Institute of Sports Sponsorship; "Highly Recommended" as a sports law practitioner in Legal Business Magazine, June 1994.

Prof. Membership: British Association for Sport and Law, Legal Sub-Committee of the Institute of Sports Sponsorship.

Career: Articled and qualified with *Richards Butler* 1988-91. Joined *Collyer-Bristow* in 1991. Became an Associate in 1993; partner in 1995.

Personal: Born 16th May 1962. Educated at Marlborough College and Worcester College, Oxford. Enjoys real tennis, football and fine art. Lives in London.

Townley, Stephen

Townleys, London (0171) 251 2505. Partner and Founder.

Specialisation: Main area of practice covers sports marketing. Assists and advises on the creation, management and exploitation of sports marketing rights, including sponsorship, television and merchandising. Has been involved in the Olympic Games, Soccer World Cup, Tour de France, Davis Cup and Rugby World Cup in this capacity. Co-author of 'Sponsorship Sport Art and Leisure', Editor of 'Sports Law and Finance' (bi-monthly international newsletter) and author of approximately 70 articles. Has chaired and/ or presented around 60 international conferences and programmes related to his area of practice. 1995 Townleys appointed official legal rights consultants to GAISF (General Association of International Sports Federations).

Prof. Membership: IBA (former Chairman of Sports Committee), International Committee SLA, ANZLA, Sponsorship Association (Founder), European Sponsorship Consultants Association (Co-founder). 1995 Arbitrator - Court of Arbitration in Sport Switzerland.

Career: Qualified in 1978, having articled at *Ingledew Brown Bennison & Garrett.* Com-

pany Secretary and legal adviser for Hawker Siddley Diesels 1978-79, then in-house counsel to the Societe Monegasque de Promotion Internationale West Nally SA 1979-83. Founded *Townleys* in 1983.

Personal: Born 15th December 1952. Took an LLM in 1975. Leisure interests include basketball, tennis and game fishing. Lives in London and Grosmont.

Vleck (née Ward), Karena G.

Farrer & Co, London (0171) 242 2022. Company/ commercial Department.

Specialisation: Principal area of practice is sports law providing specialist advice for sports governing and representative bodies, individual sports people and sponsors. Disciplinary procedures and rules, sports doping cases, formations and advice on constitutions both corporate and unincorporated, merchandising, sponsorship,representation agreements. Other areas of practice are intellectual property generally, charity law and company and commercial law. Acted for the British Athletic Federation in relation to Diane Modahl's doping offence. Other clients include the Central Council of Physical Recreation, the Professional Boxers Association, the Institute of Professional Sport and the All England Netball Association.

Prof. Membership: British Association for Sport and Law.

Career: Qualified in 1992 after articles at *Farrer & Co.*

Personal: Born 10th March 1967. Educated at Millfield School, Street, Somerset 1983-85 and St John's College, Cambridge 1986-89. Lives in London.

Walkey, Justin R.C.

See under Multimedia.

Woodhouse, Charles F.

Farrer & Co, London (0171) 242 2022. Partner and Head of Commercial Department.

Specialisation: Sports law. Legal adviser to the Central Council of Physical Recreation (CCPR), honorary Legal Adviser to Commonwealth Games Council for England and numerous other sports governing bodies, representative bodies and charities. Has advised on the formation, structure and constitutions of many governing bodies, also on disciplinary procedures and rules, handling sport doping cases, eligibility issues and sponsorship and licensing agreements. Co-author of the Palmer Report 'Amateur Status and Participation in Sport' (1984). Has written and spoken at numerous conferences on sports law topics, including the Law Asia 1993 Conference in Sri Lanka on "The role of the lawyer in sport".

Prof. Membership: Law Society, British Association for Sport and the Law.

Career: Joined *Farrer & Co* in 1964. Qualified 1966, became a Partner in 1969.

Personal: Born 6th June 1941. Attended

Marlborough College, McGill University, Montreal and Peterhouse, Cambridge. Leisure interests include cricket and golf. Chairman, Solicitors Staff Pension Fund (SSPF). Director, Santos Europe Ltd. Chairman, Rank Organisation Pension Trustees Ltd. Trustee, LSA Charitable Trust. President Guildford Cricket Club.

REGIONS

Alderson, Richard A.

Edge & Ellison, Birmingham (0121) 200 2001. Partner in Commercial Department.

Specialisation: Main area of practice is sport administration and associated activities, advising governing bodies on television, sponsorship, discipline and constitutional matters. Also works for industry, covering sport and event sponsorship and broadcast sponsorship. Acts for The Football League and other sports bodies.

Prof. Membership: British Association for Sport and the Law.

Career: Qualified in 1976 with *Edge & Ellison*, becoming a Partner in 1981.

Personal: Born 17th July 1951. Attended Bristol University 1970-73. Trustee of St Giles' Hospice (Special interest: charity shops). Leisure interests include tennis and Aston Villa. Lives in Birmingham.

Caisley, Christopher S.

Walker Morris, Leeds (0113) 283 2500. Partner and Head of Commercial Litigation Department.

Specialisation: Main area of practice is sports law. Work includes contract negotiations and disputes, personality merchandising, licensing agreements, and acting for sports personalities, clubs and associations. Other area of practice is commercial litigation. Cases have involved acting for the RFL in defence of High Court proceedings brought for relief against an alleged unfair restraint of trade by an international rugby player, bringing into question the entire system for the transfer of players between countries; the prosecution of an action by a football league manager against his former Club subsequent to his dismissal; and an application for declaratory relief by a Football League player for release from his Contract. Chairman of Bradford Northern RLFC, creating regular contact with the media. Has delivered seminars on the use of drugs in sport.

Prof. Memberships: The Rugby Football League, The British Association for Sport and the Law.

Career: Qualified in 1978, becoming a Partner in 1979. Member of the *Walker Morris* International Committee; also Practice Development Partner. Former member of the RFL Board of Directors.

Personal: Born 2nd June 1951. Attended Grange Boys Grammar School, Bradford.

Vice-Consul for the Netherlands in West and North Yorkshire. Leisure interests include running, reading and an interest in most sports. Lives in Ilkley, West Yorkshire.

Ensor, Tony

Weightman Rutherfords, Liverpool (0151) 227 2601. Senior Partner in Licensing/ Sports Law Departments.

Specialisation: Main areas of practice are licensing (liquor and gaming), professional indemnity litigation, sports law (including foreign and national transfers of players, royalty agreements, trade marks and libel actions) and planning appeals. Has acted as advocate in numerous licensing applications for substantial developments. Conducted planning appeal for new stand at Liverpool F.C. Clients include the Solicitors Indemnity Fund, General Accident, Liverpool F.C., Tetley Pub Co, Whitbreads, Threshers, Greenalls and Bass Taverns.

Prof. Membership: Liverpool Law Society, Coroners Society.

Career: Qualified in 1961. Partner of *Weightman Rutherfords* since 1963. Senior Partner 1992-95. Deputy Coroner, Liverpool since 1965. Part time Chairman of Industrial Tribunals since 1975. Recorder of the Crown Court since 1982.

Personal: Born 4th November 1936. Educated at Malvern College 1950-55 and Liverpool University 1955-58. Trustee of Empire Theatre, Liverpool. Interests include theatre and golf. Lives in Liverpool.

Gardiner, John

German & Soar, Nottingham (0115) 947 0756. Partner in Litigation Department.

Specialisation: Main area of practice is sports law. Acts for a number of well-known sporting figures. Currently litigating in soccer, rugby league, rugby union and tennis, over contract disputes, injury claims and the liability of the coach for injury suffered. Also handles work regarding advocacy, medical negligence, child care and, recently, education. Author of numerous articles in the local and trade press. Has received his Higher Courts Criminal Proceedings qualification.

Prof. Memberships: Law Society, AVMA, British Association of Sport and the Law, Law Society's Panel of Child Care Specialists.

Career: Qualified 1970 Articled at *Perry Parr & Ford* 1964-69, then joined *Seviers* in Derby until 1971. Joined *German & Soar* in 1971, becoming a Partner in 1973.

Personal: Born 26th April 1946. Attended Becket School, Nottingham. Chairman of Governors of Becket School. Leisure interests include rowing, badminton, walking, cycling and writing. Lives in Beeston, Nottingham.

Hall, Christopher

See under Agriculture & Bloodstock.

Hewison, John E.

George Davies & Co, Manchester (0161) 236 8992. Partner in Commercial Department and Managing Partner.

Specialisation: Principal area of practice is sports law, representing sportsmen (mainly professional footballers) in relation to employment contracts, management agreements, taxation disputes and sponsorship contracts. Also handles general company, commercial and EC law. Director of Lawnet Europe Limited - the European arm of the Lawnet group, of which *George Davies & Co* is a member. Clients include the Professional Footballers Association, PFA Financial Management Ltd and numerous professional footballers. Has also advised the Cricketer's Association. Charge-out rate of 125 per hour.

Prof. Membership: Law Society, British Association of Sport and the Law.

Career: Qualified in 1973. Assistant and then Partner (1978) with *George Davies & Co* since qualification.

Personal: Born 16th November 1948. Educated at Manchester Grammar School 1960-68 and Nottingham University 1968-71 (LL.B). Plays golf and follows most sports, particularly football and cricket. Lives in Lymm, Cheshire.

Hovell, Mark A.

George Davies & Co, Manchester (0161) 236 8992. Qualified 1993. Assistant solicitor in the Commercial Department specialising in sports law. Born 7.1.1968.

Jeacock, David

David Jeacock, Swindon (01793) 854111. Sole principal specialising in sports law.

Specialisation: Main area of practice is sports law, concentrating on constitutional and drug related issues, but including intellectual property issues arising out of sport. Also handles company and commercial matters. Major clients include sports governing bodies. Formerly Secretary to British Athletics Federation Drug Advisory Committee. Currently Legal Adviser to British Athletics League and the Sportshall Athletic Federation.

Prof. Membership: Law Society, British Association for Sport & Law.

Career: Qualified in 1970. Deputy Legal Adviser to Burmah Castrol 1973-81. Group Solicitor to Fisons PLC 1981-83. Established own practice in 1984.

Personal: Born in 1946. Educated at Exeter College, Oxford 1964-67. Chairman, Swindon Athletic Club. Lives in Wootton Bassett.

Maxlow-Tomlinson, Paul C.

Stones, Exeter (01392) 51501. Senior Partner.

Specialisation: Main area of practice concerns skiing and travel accidents. Handling ongoing litigation cases in the UK and

Europe, particularly France, Austria, Switzerland and Italy. 1952 Raced in Army Championships; 1954 raced at Oxford University; 1969 Ski Club of Great Britain Gold Test Holder; 1978-82 Council Member of Ski Club of Great Britain; 1982-87 Chairman of Ski Club of Great Britain; 1982-87 Director of the British Ski Federation; Currently British Representative to Legal and Safety Committee of Federation Internationale de Ski, Switzerland, since 1988. Worked for American Grand Circle Travel Company in Europe 1965-67. Author of articles for the Law Society Gazette, Ski Survey, Travel Trade Gazette, Sport and the Law, Debretts Ski Guide, Lectures on Ski Law and various national, daily, Sunday and evening papers. Broadcasts on Devon Air and BBC Radio Devon, French Radio and BBC TV.

Prof. Membership: The Law Society, Director Omni Juris. (European Legal Network).

Career: Qualified 1971. Joined *Stones* in 1972. Founder member and Chairman of the Oakfield Project (ex-prisoners hostels) 1976-83. Member of Devon Probation Committee 1983-86. Senior Partner 1991.

Personal: Born 24th October 1931. Attended Cranleigh School Surrey, then Trinity College, Dublin 1952-3 and Wadham College, Oxford 1953-6. Governor of Sandroyd School since 1984; Executive Council of British Academy of Forensic Science 1987-90. Member British Academy of Experts 1995. Appointed as Arbitrator for International Court of Arbitration for sport, Lausanne, Switzerland 1995. Leisure interests include fishing, shooting, skiing, water colour painting and music. Lives in Exeter, Devonshire.

McCloy, Matthew

See under Agriculture & Bloodstock.

McCormick, Peter D.G.

McCormicks, Leeds (0113) 246 0622. Senior and Managing Partner.

Specialisation: Main area of practice is sports law, with considerable experience in both contentious and non-contentious aspects. Acts for Leeds United Football Club and other sporting bodies, and also for a number of professional sportsmen. Has expertise in horse racing, particularly matters of disciplinary hearings and appeals: the only British lawyer to have appeared in front of the Jockey Club of Germany. Has never lost a case before the British Jockey Club. Also handles matters relating to rugby, athletics and cricket, with clients including Jenny Pitman, Freddie Trueman, Howard Wilkinson, Gordon Strachan and Lee Chapman. Negotiates contracts for personal benefits, corporate sponsorship and ancillary matters, and deals with litigation cases including defamation of character and complaints relating to broadcasting and the press. Acted in the Leeds United/ Stuttgart UEFA Disciplinary Hearing, as a direct result of which Leeds remained in the competition. Also has twenty years experience of tax investigation and enquiry work, both income tax and VAT, and serious fraud cases. Handles an increasing amount of commercial and commercial litigation work, acting for DFS Furniture Company plc, Iceland Frozen Foods plc, Polypipe plc, KPMG Peat Marwick, The Duke of Edinburgh's Award, Hays plc and others. Has written for the Law Society Gazette and the Yorkshire Post. Awarded the Higher Courts (Criminal Proceedings) Qualification in 1994. Lectures widely. Resident legal expert on Radio Leeds, Yorkshire Television and the Yorkshire Post.

Morrison, Michael

Gorna & Co, Manchester (0161) 832 3651.

Nicholls, Trevor

Greenland Houchen, Norwich (01603) 660744. Qualified 1971. Partner 1972. Specialises in sports law and company law. Has acted for Norwich City F.C. since 1983. Born 2.5.1935.

Richardson, Jeremy

See under Agriculture & Bloodstock.

Teeman, R.

Teeman Levine, Leeds (0113) 245 9344. Founder and currently acting as a consultant in Sports Law. Born 19.11.30.

Watkins, E. Maurice

James Chapman & Co, Manchester (0161) 236 7772. Partner in Commercial Department.

Specialisation: Sports law specialist. Solicitor for Manchester United Football Club since 1976 and, since flotation, Manchester United PLC. Also an adviser to the Football Association Premier League and other Premier League clubs on various matters. Member of the Premier League Legal Working Party. Also solicitor to a number of first-class sportsmen and administrators. Director of Manchester United Football Club plc and Manchester United PLC. Has handled numerous high-value soccer transfers at home and abroad. Represents clubs and players before UEFA and FA Disciplinary bodies and International and League Compensation Tribunals and negotiates TV, sponsorship and advertising contracts. Former lecturer in law at Manchester University. Extensive media experience on football related matters.

Prof. Membership: Chairman of the British Association for Sport and the Law.

Career: Qualified in 1966. Solicitor for the Co-operative Insurance Society 1966-68. Joined *James Chapman & Co* as a Partner in 1968.

Personal: Born 30th November 1941. Educated at Manchester Grammar School 1952-60 and University College, London 1960-65 (LLB and LLM). Secretary of Manchester Homeopathic Clinic and trustee of several charities. Interests include cricket, soccer and tennis. Lives in Stockport.

Wiseman, Keith St. J.

Woodford & Ackroyd, Southampton (01703) 321000. Qualified 1970.

FIRMS OF ACCOUNTANTS

Accountants specialising in litigation support are listed in the accountants' A-Z, with details of the services they offer to solicitors, from forensic accounting to intellectual property or business valuations. This section is found immediately after the main solicitors' A-Z.

TAX (CORPORATE)

TAX expertise in the largest law firms has developed to the extent that counsel are used only for the most intricate tax problems. This expertise in all areas of corporate tax has led to fierce competition with accountancy firms for transaction based tax work.

LONDON

Slaughter and May, Freshfields and *Linklaters & Paines* are the clear leaders. Within this trio, *Slaughter and May* is considered to be marginally ahead of the other two in terms of sheer expertise. Stephen Edge is the pre-eminent corporate tax practitioner, but excellence runs throughout the team that includes James Savory, Howard Nowlan, Graham Airs, Fiona Ferguson and Anthony Beare. Although the firm principally concentrates on finance, investment funds and mergers and acquisitions, the team also provides a general tax advisory service. In addition, the group handles Inland Revenue investigations and other tax disputes, and assists in the development of tax efficient structures for corporate and project finance transactions and innovative capital market instruments and products.

LEADING FIRMS – LONDON	
SLAUGHTER AND MAY	
FRESHFIELDS	LINKLATERS & PAINES
ALLEN & OVERY	CLIFFORD CHANCE

Freshfields' department, containing amongst others Richard Ballard, Francis Sandison, Ben Staveley, Timothy Ling and David Taylor, is noted for its strength in depth. It also boasts a leading up and coming tax lawyer in Sarah Falk. The firm advises on a variety of tax issues for its corporate clients and is respected for its work in the international field.

Linklaters & Paines received an identical rating to *Freshfields,* due in no small measure to the reputations of Malcolm Gammie, Anthony Angel, Michael Hardwick and Nikhil Mehta. Best known for international finance, mergers and acquisitions, projects and privatisations, the firm has recently advised on the tax implications of a number of transactions including the Lloyds Bank/Cheltenham & Gloucester Building Society takeover, Trafalgar House's offer for Northern Electric and Gencor's purchase of Shell's worldwide minerals business. The corporate tax unit has also advised the Department of Transport on the British Rail and Railtrack privatisations.

The tax departments of other firms tend to act as support for their corporate departments. Those most highly recommended for their expertise in this category are *Allen & Overy* and *Clifford Chance.*

Allen & Overy's tax unit numbers five specialist partners together with a support staff. The firm provides a comprehensive business tax advisory service to clients from all sectors. David Lewis and Patrick Mears are especially well thought of.

Clifford Chance has the largest tax department of any law firm with 39 specialists, 13 of whom are partners. Through the combination of specialist knowledge of taxation, litigation and revenue expertise, the tax group has an excellent reputation, Douglas French, Edward Sadler, Michael Ehrlich and Peter Elliott being particularly highly regarded.

Norton Rose, Simmons & Simmons, Travers Smith Braithwaite and *Wilde Sapte* are also well-known for their expertise in the field.

Norton Rose's tax department, in addition to providing corporate support, is renowned for its tax advice in project finance and asset finance. The highly regarded Christopher Norfolk has written a textbook on the subject and is Chair of the Revenue Law Committee of the Law Society. Isla Smith, John Challoner and Louise Higginbottom have also been recommended.

Simmons & Simmons' tax unit handles the full range of strategic tax planning services, disputes and litigation including VAT.

Travers Smith Braithwaite's tax department consists of three full time practitioners dealing exclusively with tax issues for the firm's corporate clients. Alasdair Douglas is well regarded by his competitors.

HIGHLY REGARDED – LONDON	
NORTON ROSE	SIMMONS & SIMMONS
TRAVERS SMITH BRAITHWAITE	WILDE SAPTE
ASHURST MORRIS CRISP	BERWIN LEIGHTON
CAMERON MARKBY HEWITT	CLYDE & CO
FIELD FISHER WATERHOUSE	FOX & GIBBONS
HAMMOND SUDDARDS	HERBERT SMITH
LOVELL WHITE DURRANT	MACFARLANES
MARRIOTT HARRISON	McKENNA & CO
MEMERY CRYSTAL	NABARRO NATHANSON
WATSON, FARLEY & WILLIAMS	
ALSOP WILKINSON	RADCLIFFES CROSSMAN BLOCK
TAYLOR JOYNSON GARRETT	THEODORE GODDARD

Wilde Sapte has an excellent reputation for finance leasing. Russell Jacobs, Michael Ratcliff and Miles Walton have been recommended.

Marriott Harrison, specialising in tax planning work, provides long term strategic advice and is often instructed on a consultancy basis.

LEADING INDIVIDUALS – LONDON

Stephen M. Edge *Slaughter and May*		

Anthony L. Angel *Linklaters & Paines*	**Richard M. Ballard** *Freshfields*	**Alasdair F. Douglas** *Travers Smith Braithwaite*
Malcolm J. Gammie *Linklaters & Paines*	**D. Martin** *Herbert Smith*	**Patrick Mears** *Allen & Overy*
E. Christopher D. Norfolk *Norton Rose*	**Howard M. Nowlan** *Slaughter and May*	**Francis G. Sandison** *Freshfields*
James H. Savory *Slaughter and May*	**Miles Walton** *Wilde Sapte*	

G.J. Airs *Slaughter and May*	**Susan Ball** *Clyde & Co*	**Roger F. Berner** *Freshfields*
Guy C.H. Brannan *Linklaters & Paines*	**Peter Brodigan** *Allen & Overy*	**John Challoner** *Norton Rose*
Simon H.T. Clark *Linklaters & Paines*	**Stephen D. Coleclough** *Simmons & Simmons*	**Anthony C.R. Davis** *Lovell White Durrant*
Nigel J.L. Doran *Macfarlanes*	**Michael Ehrlich** *Clifford Chance*	**Peter Elliott** *Clifford Chance*
Jonathan Elman *Clifford Chance*	**Fiona Ferguson** *Slaughter and May*	**Peter John Fisher** *Lovell White Durrant*
Douglas French *Clifford Chance*	**Paul D. Hale** *Simmons & Simmons*	**Michael J. Hardwick** *Linklaters & Paines*
Louise Higginbottom *Norton Rose*	**Stephen L. Hoyle** *Freshfields*	**Russell Jacobs** *Wilde Sapte*
Ian L. Johnson *Ashurst Morris Crisp*	**Donald C. Kelly** *Lovell White Durrant*	**Peter Kempster FCA** *Nabarro Nathanson*
David E. Lewis *Allen & Overy*	**Timothy A. Ling** *Freshfields*	**Stephen J. Machin** *Ashurst Morris Crisp*
Michael McGowan *Linklaters & Paines*	**Nikhil V. Mehta** *Linklaters & Paines*	**David C. Mullarkey** *Linklaters & Paines*
Peter Nias *Simmons & Simmons*	**Nicholas R. Noble** *Field Fisher Waterhouse*	**John H. Overs** *Berwin Leighton*
Michael Paynter *Marriott Harrison*	**Christopher A.L. Preston** *Watson Farley & Williams*	**Michael Ratcliff** *Wilde Sapte*
George F. Renwick *Slaughter and May*	**Howard Ross** *Clifford Chance*	**Edward Sadler** *Clifford Chance*
Thomas A. Scott *Linklaters & Paines*	**Jeremy J.B. Skinner** *Linklaters & Paines*	**Isla M. Smith** *Norton Rose*
Ben W. Staveley *Freshfields*	**Richard J. Stratton** *Travers Smith Braithwaite*	**D.N. Taylor** *Freshfields*
Michael Thompson *Freshfields*	**John G. Watson** *Ashurst Morris Crisp*	**Oonah A. Whitty** *Watson Farley & Williams*

UP AND COMING

Chris Bates *Norton Rose*	**Anthony Beare** *Slaughter and May*	**Sarah Falk** *Freshfields*
Richard Palmer *Ashurst Morris Crisp*	**Yash Rupal** *Linklaters & Paines*	**Michael J. Wistow** *Clifford Chance*
Neil Woodgate *Wilde Sapte*		

SOUTH, EAST ANGLIA & WALES

In the South East of England, *Rawlison & Butler* and *Thomas Eggar Verrall Bowles* have substantial experience in the field.

In the South West, *Burges Salmon, Osborne Clarke* and *Wiggin and Co* have long been recognised as the principle corporate tax practices.

HIGHLY REGARDED – SOUTH, EAST ANGLIA & WALES

BURGES SALMON *Bristol*	**CLARKE WILLMOTT & CLARKE** *Taunton*
EVERSHEDS *Cardiff*	**LESTER ALDRIDGE** *Bournemouth*
MILLS & REEVE *Norwich*	**OSBORNE CLARKE** *Bristol*
RAWLISON & BUTLER *Crawley*	**THOMAS EGGAR VERRALL BOWLES** *Chichester*
WIGGIN AND CO *Cheltenham*	

Timothy Illston and Harry Wiggin of *Burges Salmon* are well-known for international tax planning and cross-border corporate tax, as is C.R.J. Marlow of *Wiggin and Co* who handles a substantial amount of international tax structuring work for multinational companies.

Osborne Clarke has developed a particular expertise in tax planning and structuring on domestic and cross-border dis-posals, acquisitions, high value management buy-outs, private fund raising and substantial property deals. Philip Moss at the firm is highly respected by his competitors.

Other firms in the South West with substantial tax advisory experience include *Clarke Willmott & Clarke* and *Lester Aldridge.*

In Wales, *Eversheds* (Cardiff) has been recommended for its tax advisory work. Naturally, the majority of the work flows from corporate finance transactions, however, the tax unit additionally covers matters such as retirement relief, advice on offshore trusts and a broad range of tax planning.

Mills & Reeve in Norwich has a reputation for being highly experienced in all aspects of corporate tax work.

LEADING INDIVIDUALS – SOUTH, EAST ANGLIA & WALES

Timothy M. Illston *Burges Salmon*
C.R J. Marlow *Wiggin and Co*
Philip G.S. Moss *Osborne Clarke*
Harry Wiggin *Burges Salmon*

UP AND COMING

Mark Womersley *Osborne Clarke*

In all the tables the names in each group are listed alphabetically.

MIDLANDS

Pinsent Curtis emerges as the pre-eminent corporate tax practice with Julian Tonks and David Pett both recommended as leading tax specialists. The firm has a national reputation for tax planning within the financial, public and private sectors.

LEADING FIRMS – MIDLANDS

EVERSHEDS Birmingham	**PINSENT CURTIS** Birmingham

Eversheds (Birmingham) also has an outstanding reputation, chiefly in the guise of Philip Harrison who advises on tax issues for international corporate transactions and the tax implications of commercial litigation. He also handles tax disputes, employee share incentives and personal tax planning for business clients.

HIGHLY REGARDED – MIDLANDS

EDGE & ELLISON Birmingham	**MARTINEAU JOHNSON** Birmingham
WRAGGE & CO Birmingham	

Other firms recommended for their expertise in the field include *Edge & Ellison, Martineau Johnson* and *Wragge & Co.*

LEADING INDIVIDUALS – MIDLANDS

Philip J. Harrison Eversheds
David Pett Pinsent Curtis
Julian M.J. Tonks Pinsent Curtis

UP AND COMING

Richard J. Burston Eversheds
Lawrence Green Eversheds

NORTH

In the North West, the firms with the strongest reputations for corporate tax work are *Addleshaw Sons & Latham* and *Eversheds* (Manchester).

Addleshaw Sons & Latham's tax unit is headed by the highly respected Brian Armitage and handles a variety of work including company reconstructions, employee share schemes and ESOPS.

HIGHLY REGARDED – NORTH

ADDLESHAW SONS & LATHAM Manchester	**BOOTH & CO.** Leeds
BROOKE NORTH AND GOODWIN Leeds	**DIBB LUPTON BROOMHEAD** Bradford
DICKINSON DEES Newcastle	**EVERSHEDS** Leeds
EVERSHEDS Manchester	**HAMMOND SUDDARDS** Leeds
PINSENT CURTIS Leeds	**WACKS CALLER** Manchester
WALKER MORRIS Leeds	

Eversheds advises on reconstructions, tax structures, employee share schemes and incentives.

The most highly recommended firms in the North East are *Eversheds* (Leeds), *Hammond Suddards* and *Pinsent Curtis.*

Eversheds (Leeds) is strong in employee share schemes, corporate tax planning, VAT and inward investment with Richard Hutchinson being particularly highly regarded.

Hammond Suddards has particular expertise in share scheme advice, employee benefits, ESOPs, profit related

pay schemes and stamp duty reserve tax. Rosamond Marshall Smith has been highly recommended.

Pinsent Curtis' tax unit, headed by Judith Greaves, represents both public sector clients and major listed and private companies. The firm advises on all tax aspects; recent transactions have included the flotations of Parkside International plc and Slimma plc, Prospect Industries' acquisition of Whessoe piping division, the group re-organisation of Spring Ram and a tax structuring plan for Royal Armouries. John Christian has also been recommended.

Other firms with considerable experience in the field include *Dibb Lupton Broomhead* and *Booth & Co.*

LEADING INDIVIDUALS – NORTH

Brian Armitage Addleshaw Sons & Latham
John M.S. Christian Pinsent Curtis
Simon Concannon Walker Morris
Judith A. Greaves Pinsent Curtis
Richard K. Hutchinson Eversheds
Rosamond J. Marshall Smith Hammond Suddards

UP AND COMING

Antony P. Betts Pinsent Curtis
Mark C. Simpson Hammond Suddards

SCOTLAND

The leading firms for corporate tax work include *Brodies WS* (and particularly Isobel d'Inverno), *Maclay Murray & Spens,*

LEADING FIRMS – SCOTLAND

BRODIES WS Edinburgh	**McGRIGOR DONALD** Glasgow
MACLAY MURRAY & SPENS Glasgow	

where Martyn Jones is particularly highly recommended, and *McGrigor Donald* which has a strong team in Ian Gordon, Richard Pincher and Maureen Docherty.

HIGHLY REGARDED – SCOTLAND

W & J BURNESS WS Edinburgh	**DICKSON MINTO WS** Edinburgh
DUNDAS & WILSON CS Edinburgh	**SHEPHERD & WEDDERBURN** Edinburgh

Other highly recommended firms include *W & J Burness WS* (where Simon MacKintosh and Heather Thompson are recommended), *Dundas & Wilson CS* and *Shepherd & Wedderburn* (Robert Bertram).

LEADING INDIVIDUALS – SCOTLAND

Robert D.D. Bertram Shepherd & Wedderburn
Isobel d'Inverno Brodies WS
Ian Gordon McGrigor Donald
Martyn Jones Maclay Murray & Spens
Janet Jones Dickson Minto WS
Simon A. MacKintosh W & J Burness WS
Richard Pincher McGrigor Donald
Heather Thompson W & J Burness WS

UP AND COMING

Maureen Docherty McGrigor Donald

LEADERS IN TAX (CORPORATE)

LONDON

Airs, G.J.
Slaughter and May, London (0171) 600
1200. Qualified 1978. Main area of practice
is corporation tax.

Angel, Anthony L.
Linklaters & Paines, London (0171) 606
7080. Qualified 1978. Partner 1984. Head of
Tax Department. Specialises in capital markets (including derivatives and product
development), structured finance, mergers
and acquisitions and international tax structuring.

Ball, Susan
Clyde & Co, London (0171) 623 1244.
Qualified 1973. Partner and Deputy Head of
Tax Department 1993. Main area of practice
is corporate tax. Also handles taxation of em-
ployees.

Ballard, Richard M.
Freshfields, London (0171) 936 4000.
Qualified 1978. Partner 1984. Head of Tax
Department. Main area of practice is corpo-
rate tax, including capital markets, specialist
finance and corporate finance. Born 1953.

Bates, Chris
Norton Rose, London (0171) 283 6000.
Qualified 1984. Solicitor. Tax Department.
Specialises in all areas of domestic and inter-
national tax planning.

Beare, Anthony
Slaughter and May, London (0171) 600
1200. Qualified 1987.

Berner, Roger F.
Freshfields, London (0171) 832 7195.
Qualified 1976. Partner 1993. Tax Department. Head of International Tax. Also
handles corporate finance work.

Brannan, Guy C.H.
Linklaters & Paines, London (0171) 606
7080. Qualified 1981. Advises on all UK tax
aspects of corporate transactions. Also advises on contentious tax matters, and VAT.

Brodigan, Peter
Allen & Overy, London (0171) 330 3000.

Challoner, John
Norton Rose, London (0171) 283 6000.
Qualified 1977. Partner 1988. Managing
Partner in Commercial Tax Department. Ad-
vises on all aspects of UK commercial tax.

Clark, Simon H.T.
Linklaters & Paines, London (0171) 606
7080. Qualified 1981. Partner 1988. Property
Department. In charge of property tax unit.

Coleclough, Stephen D.
See under VAT/Customs & Excise.

Davis, Anthony C.R.
Lovell White Durrant, London (0171)
236 0066. Qualified 1981. Partner 1986.
Business Tax Department. Specialises in
taxation affecting financial institutions.
Other main area of practice is VAT.

Doran, Nigel J.L.
Macfarlanes, London (0171) 831 9222.
Qualified 1984. Partner 1988. Company,
Commercial and Banking Department. Han-
dles corporate tax in relation to mergers and
acquisitions etc.

Douglas, Alasdair F.
Travers Smith Braithwaite, London
(0171) 248 9133 or 696 0998. Qualified
1977. Partner 1985. Managing Partner 1995.
Head of Corporate Tax Department. Main areas of work are corporate finance, mergers,
acquisitions, reconstructions and Isle of Man
taxation. Born 16.3.1953.

Edge, Stephen M.
Slaughter and May, London (0171) 600
1200. Partner in Corporate Tax Department.

Specialisation: Principal area of practice is
corporate taxation with a particular emphasis
on corporate finance and asset finance. Expertise in financial instruments, cross border
financial transactions and securitisations and
other capital markets work. One of the first
UK tax lawyers to concentrate on tax and
other financial aspects of big ticket leasing
and other asset and major project financings.
Advises mainly UK and US multinationals
and investment banks. Experience of privatisations and Inland Revenue investigations.
Contributes to a number of publications on
corporate tax.

Prof. Membership: Law Society.

Career: Qualified in 1975 while with *Slaughter & May* and became a Partner in 1982.

Personal: Born 29th November 1950. Attended Canon Slade Grammar School,
Bolton 1962-69, then Exeter University
1969-72. Lives in London.

Ehrlich, Michael
Clifford Chance, London (0171) 600
1000. Partner. Principal area of practice is
corporate and financial taxation.

Elliott, Peter
Clifford Chance, London (0171) 600
1000. Partner. Principal area of practice is
corporate and financial taxation including international cross-border structures and
transactions.

Elman, Jonathan
Clifford Chance, London (0171) 600
1000. Partner in Tax Department. Specialises

in tax work.

Falk, Sarah
Freshfields, London (0171) 936 4000.
Partner in Tax Department.

Specialisation: Main area of practice is corporate tax. Work covers corporate tax
planning and corporate finance.

Prof. Membership: Law Society.

Career: Qualified 1986, having joined *Freshfields* in 1984. Became a Partner in 1994.

Personal: Born 1962. Attended Sidney Sussex College, Cambridge, 1980-83.

Ferguson, Fiona
Slaughter and May, London (0171) 600
1200. Qualified 1983. Partner specialising in
corporate tax work.

Fisher, Peter John
Lovell White Durrant, London (0171)
236 0066. Qualified 1982. Partner 1988. Corporate Tax Department. Deals with the UK
tax aspects of mergers and acquisitions and
reorganisations. Also UK property tax.

French, Douglas
Clifford Chance, London (0171) 600
1000. Partner. Principal area of practice is
corporate taxation.

Gammie, Malcolm J.
Linklaters & Paines, London (0171) 606
7080.

Hale, Paul D.
See under VAT/Customs & Excise.

Hardwick, Michael J.
Linklaters & Paines, London (0171) 606
7080. Qualified 1984. Joined 1982. Corporate Tax. Handles tax aspects of mergers,
acquisitions and disposals, flotations, rights
issues and privatisations.

Higginbottom, Louise
Norton Rose, London (0171) 283 6000.
Qualified 1983. Partner 1991. Tax Department. Specialises in corporate tax, covering
corporate finance, asset finance, employees
and investment media.

Hoyle, Stephen L.
Freshfields, London (0171) 936 4000.
Partner 1988. Tax Department. Main area of
practice is corporate tax, principally international cross-border matters.

Personal: Born 17.9.1955. Attended St Catherine's College Oxford 1973-76, Gonville &
Caius College Cambridge, 1976-77, and
Northwestern Law School, Chicago, 1977-
78.

Jacobs, Russell
Wilde Sapte, London (0171) 246 7000.
Partner in Corporate Tax Department.

Specialisation: Main area of practice is banking and finance, including structured finance, capital markets and derivatives. Contributor to Butterworths Finance Bill Handbook, Butterworths Response Report (Foreign Exchange Gains and Losses); and the Tax Journal.

Prof. Membership: Law Society.

Career: Qualified in 1983, with *Slaughter and May*. Left to join *Wilde Sapte* in 1992 as a Partner.

Personal: Born 13th September 1959. Attended University College, London 1979-82. Leisure interests include walking and cycling. Lives in Stanmore, Middlesex.

Johnson, Ian L.
Ashurst Morris Crisp, London (0171) 638 1111. Qualified 1992. Solicitor. Tax Department. Specialises in all aspects of corporate tax and general personal tax and trusts. Born 30.5.1962.

Kelly, Donald C.
Lovell White Durrant, London (0171) 236 0066. Qualified 1980. Partner 1986. Corporate Tax Department. Work includes UK tax aspects of mergers and acquisitions, property tax and oil tax.

Kempster FCA, Peter
Nabarro Nathanson, London (0171) 493 9933.

Lewis, David E.
Allen & Overy, London (0171) 330 3000. Qualified 1976. Partner 1982. Corporate Tax Department. Advises on tax aspects of corporate, banking transactions, corporate reconstructions and mergers etc.

Ling, Timothy A.
Freshfields, London (0171) 936 4000. Qualified 1973. Partner 1977. Corporate Tax Department. Head of Department 1986-91; Member of Revenue Law Committee of Law Society 1982-91.

Machin, Stephen J.
See under Corporate Finance.

Martin, D.
Herbert Smith, London (0171) 374 8000. Qualified 1977. Partner 1986. Company Department. Main area of practice covers taxation matters. Born 11.2.1952. Lives in London.

McGowan, Michael
Linklaters & Paines, London (0171) 606 7080.

Mears, Patrick
Allen & Overy, London (0171) 330 3000. Qualified 1982. Partner 1988. Corporate Tax Department. Work covers all aspects of corporate tax. Born 19.1.1958.

Mehta, Nikhil V.
Linklaters & Paines, London (0171) 606 7080. Qualified 1985. Joined 1983. Corporate Taxation Department and Head of India Business Group. Work includes structured finance, projects and assets and capital markets.

Mullarkey, David C.
Linklaters & Paines, London Int+ 852 842 4888. Qualified 1982. Joined 1982. Work includes investment fund structures, joint ventures and structured finance.

Nias, Peter
Simmons & Simmons, London (0171) 628 2020. Partner in Tax Department.

Specialisation: Main areas of practice are corporate and commercial taxation. Work includes cross border transactions, finance leasing, and structured property transactions.

Prof. Membership: Law Society.

Career: Qualified in 1979. Joined *Simmons & Simmons* in 1976, becoming a Partner in 1982 and Head of Tax Department in 1992. Member of Law Society International Tax Sub-Committee; Member of ICC UK Tax Committee.

Personal: Born 24th November 1953. Attended Manchester University 1973-6. LLB. Leisure interests include family and outdoor life, music and tennis. Lives in Wickham Bishops.

Noble, Nicholas R.
Field Fisher Waterhouse, London (0171) 481 4841. Partner and Head of Business Tax Department.

Specialisation: Practice covers the taxation of UK and international transactions, in particular companies and company reorganisations, securities and transactions in securities. Co-author of 'Butterworths Company Reorganisations: Tax and Tax Planning' and 'Butterworths International Taxation of Financial Instruments and Transactions'. Joint editor of and contributor to 'Butterworths Tax Planning Service'.

Prof. Membership: ATII.

Career: Qualified in 1979 having joined *Field Fisher Waterhouse* in 1977. Became a partner in 1984.

Personal: Born 1st October 1953. Educated at Winchester College and Durham University. Recreations include fencing, walking and reading.

Norfolk, E. Christopher D.
Norton Rose, London (0171) 283 6000. Qualified 1972. Partner 1979. Commercial Tax Department. Work covers tax aspects of mergers and acquisitions, corporate structuring, banking, oil and gas. Born 8.8.1948. Fellow of the Chartered Institute of Taxation.

Nowlan, Howard M.
Slaughter and May, London (0171) 600 1200. Qualified 1970. Joined 1968. Partner

specialising in corporate tax. Main area of practice is general corporate tax, with particular emphasis on corporate restructurings and mergers and acquisitions.

Overs, John H.
Berwin Leighton, London (0171) 623 3144. Qualified 1978. Partner 1981. Tax Department. Principal area of work covers corporate tax and VAT. Born 15.8.1953.

Palmer, Richard
Ashurst Morris Crisp, London (0171) 638 1111. Qualified 1988. Corporate tax specialist, with extensive experience of the tax aspects of UK company acquisitions and disposals.

Paynter, Michael
Marriott Harrison, London (0171) 209 2000. Partner in Corporate Tax Department.

Specialisation: Handles tax planning in relation to one off asset disposals; company acquisitions and disposals; corporate reconstructions and reorganisations, including use of appropriate innovative financial instruments; creation of offshore companies and trusts; shares for employees; relocation of employees throughout the UK; extraction of profits including use of double tax treaties and where applicable minimising national insurance contributions and Inland Revenue Special Office and Enquiry Branch investigations. Author of chapter on taxation in the Institute of Directors guide to relocating employees and of numerous articles in Tolley's Practical Tax and other publications. Has addressed a number of conferences and seminars on taxation matters.

Prof. Membership: Law Society, Institute of Taxation, International Tax Planning Association.

Career: Qualified in 1983. Worked at *Cameron Markby* 1981-89, from 1986 as Partner and Head of Corporate Tax Group. Joined *Marriott Harrison* in 1989 as a Partner and Head of Corporate Tax Department.

Personal: Born in 1957. Attended University College Buckland 1976-79; College of Law, Guildford 1979-80 and Wolfson College, Cambridge 1980-81. Passed Institute of Taxation examinations in 1983. Leisure interests include computers. Lives in Harpenden.

Preston, Christopher A.L.
See under VAT/Customs & Excise.

Ratcliff, Michael
Wilde Sapte, London (0171) 246 7000. Qualified 1982. Partner 1989. Corporate Tax Department. Specialises in corporate tax, acting predominantly for banks.

Renwick, George F.
Slaughter and May, London (0171) 600 1200. Qualified 1966. Joined 1963. Main areas of practice are corporate taxation and partnerships.

Ross, Howard
Clifford Chance, London (0171) 600 1000. Partner. Principal area of practice is tax disputes. Also handles commercial tax, building societies taxation, corporate tax planning and oil and gas taxation.

Rupal, Yash
Linklaters & Paines, London (0171) 606 7080. Qualified 1988. Assistant Solicitor. Tax Department. Particular experience in structured finance/ product development, securitisations and derivatives.

Sadler, Edward
Clifford Chance, London (0171) 600 1000. Partner. Principal area of practice is corporate taxation and equipment leasing.

Sandison, Francis G.
Freshfields, London (0171) 936 4000. Partner in Tax Department.

Specialisation: Main area of practice is corporate tax, including mergers and acquisitions, both domestic and international; corporate reorganisations; tax litigation; and privatisations. Cases have included Collard v. Mining and Industrial Holdings (H.L. 1989), R v. HM Treasury, ex parte Daily Mail and General Trust (ECJ 1988), and Smith Kline Beckman's merger with Beecham. Author of 'Tolley's Profit Sharing' (1978), co-author of 'Whiteman on Income Tax' (3rd edition, 1988) and contributor to 'Simon's Taxes', 'Tolley's Tax Planning' and articles in The Tax Journal. Chairman of the City of London Law Society Revenue Law Sub-Committee, Member of the Law Society's Revenue Law Committee and Chairman of the Corporation Tax Sub-Committee.

Prof. Membership: Law Society, City of London Law Society, Addington Society, Institute for Fiscal Studies.

Career: Qualified in 1974. Assistant Solicitor at *Freshfields* 1974-80, and foreign associate at *Sullivan & Cromwell* in New York in 1977, Partner in *Freshfields'* Tax Department from 1980, and Departmental Managing Partner 1991-1994.

Personal: Born 25th May 1949. Attended Charterhouse 1962-67 and Magdalen College Oxford 1967-71. Leisure interests include fishing, wine and reading. Lives in Churt, Surrey.

Savory, James H.
Slaughter and May, London (0171) 600 1200. Qualified 1978. Partner 1985. Tax Department. Work covers corporate and business tax. Born 5.5.1953.

Scott, Thomas A.
Linklaters & Paines, London (0171) 606 7080. Qualified 1983. Joined 1981. Partner since 1989. Corporate Taxation Department. Handles tax aspects of UK and cross-border M&A. Also oil and gas taxation.

Skinner, Jeremy J.B.
Linklaters & Paines, London (0171) 606 7080. Qualified 1965. Partner 1967. Corporate Department. Specialises in corporate law, reorganisations, capital raising and corporate taxation.

Smith, Isla M.
Norton Rose, London (0171) 283 6000. Qualified 1980. Partner 1985. Taxation Department. Work involves all aspects of corporate tax and particularly financing and corporate restructuring.

Staveley, Ben W.
Freshfields, London (0171) 936 4000. Qualified 1981. Partner in the Tax Department specialising in corporate tax. Associate of the Institute of Taxation.

Stratton, Richard J.
Travers Smith Braithwaite, London (0171) 248 9133 or 696 0998. Partner in Corporate Tax Department.

Specialisation: Handles corporate tax matters. Specialist in funds and investment structures including onshore and offshore funds, limited partnerships, venture capital trusts, buy-out arrangements and property based structures. Advised on a complex reconstruction of a major UK private company into three separate companies which involved the creation of debts between the successor companies, a stock dividend arrangement and the disposal of two successor companies. Has also advised a US software company in connection with the off balance sheet structure for its European operations and generally in relation to off balance sheet structures for UK companies. More recently has advised on financing arrangements which make use of limited partnerships and rollover relief, deep discount securities and disposals of companies with "ACT capacity". In the area of property development has advised a UK operator of nursing homes on its nursing home developments with particular reference to VAT, a listed UK property company on the taxation inplications of a number of its developments and a major Japanese bank on its UK property finance proposals for its clients. Recent articles - Venture Capital Trusts in 'Taxation' magazine.

Prof. Membership: President of London branch of Chartered Institute of Tax (1994-95).

Career: Qualified in 1983. Partner at *Travers Smith Braithwaite* since 1989.

Personal: Born in 1957. Educated at Stockport Grammar School and Cambridge University (MA 1979, LL.M 1980, AT II 1988). Spare time is spent engaged in family pursuits and gardening. Lives in London.

Taylor, D.N.
Freshfields, London (0171) 936 4000. Qualified 1984. Partner 1991. Tax Department. Work covers corporate tax, primarily banking and asset finance.

Thompson, Michael
Freshfields, London (0171) 936 4000. Qualified 1979. Partner 1985. Tax Department. Advises on most UK tax aspects of corporate transactions. Born 18.6.1954.

Walton, Miles
Wilde Sapte, London (0171) 246 7000. Partner in Corporate Tax Department.

Specialisation: Deals with all areas of corporate tax with a particular interest in tax for banks, structured finance, asset finance and corporate funding. Co-author of 'Taxation and Banking' (Sweet & Maxwell). Has written various articles for legal journals and spoken at a number of seminars and conferences on corporate tax.

Prof. Membership: Law Society, Institute of Taxation.

Career: Qualified in 1980. With *Slaughter and May* 1980-83. Joined *Wilde Sapte* in 1983 and became a Partner in 1984.

Personal: Born 15th July 1955. Educated at Ratcliffe College, Leicester 1968-73, Brasenose College, Oxford (MA) 1974-77 and Chester College of Law 1977-78. Leisure interests include saxophone, wine, scuba diving and clocks. Lives in London.

Watson, John G.
Ashurst Morris Crisp, London (0171) 638 1111. Qualified 1984. Partner 1989. Tax Department. Fund work, enterprise zones, venture capital, international tax, VAT, corporate deals and leasing.

Whitty, Oonah A.
Watson Farley & Williams, London (0171) 814 8000. Qualified 1981. Partner 1988. Tax Department. Corporate tax specialist. Work includes structured finance and financial instruments and leasing.

Wistow, Michael J.
Clifford Chance, London (0171) 600 1000. Joined 1988. Solicitor in Tax. Main areas of practice are corporate, financing and property tax.

Woodgate, Neil
Wilde Sapte, London (0171) 246 7000. Assistant Solicitor in Corporate Tax Department.

Specialisation: Practice is concentrated on banks and structured and asset finance. Has written and co-written articles for 'The Tax Journal', 'British Tax Review' and Butterworth's 'Journal of International Banking and Finance Law'.

Prof. Membership: Law Society.

Career: Joined *Wilde Sapte* in 1986. Qualified in November 1988.

Personal: Born 19th August 1963. Educated at The Westgate School, Winchester 1974-79, Price's College, Fareham 1979-81 and University College, London 1981-84 (LL.B) and 1985-86 (LL.M). Leisure interests include opera, eating and drinking and shopping (especially accessorising). Lives in London.

Armitage, Brian

Addleshaw Sons & Latham, Manchester (0161) 832 5994. Associate in Company and Corporate Finance Department.

Specialisation: Principal area of practice is advising on tax aspects of corporate restructuring. Advised 3i offices throughout UK on tax implications of financial deals, especially buyouts. Also deals with employee share schemes and business expansion schemes for private companies. Author of Guide to BES. Contributor to Longmans Practical Tax Planning on Management Buyouts, Butterworths Tax Planning on Purchase of Shares and British Tax Review on the Enterprise Investment Scheme and Venture Capital Trusts. Has lectured EIS, employee share schemes and private company tax planning.

Prof. Membership: Institute of Chartered Accountants, Chartered Institute of Taxation.

Career: Partner in *Robson Rhodes* 1963-70. Local Director and Technical Advisory Director to the 3i Group 1970-92. Joined *Addleshaw Sons & Latham* as Associate in 1992.

Personal: Born 29th April 1937. Leisure pursuits include cycling, rambling and golf. Lives in Manchester.

Bertram, Robert D.D.

Shepherd & Wedderburn WS, Edinburgh (0131) 228 9900. Partner in Corporate Department.

Specialisation: Main areas of practice are company and financial law, taxation (company and employee), VAT and stamp duty. A.T.I.I. qualified since 1970 and member of its Technical Committee 1986-93. Member of the VAT Tribunal 1986-92. Involved in the privatisation of the Scottish Electricity Industry, Insurance and Building Society Demutualisations, and Project Finance (UK Oil & Gas). Author of Memorandum on Floating Charges for the Scottish Law Commission, Companies Act Consolidation Amendments for the Law Commission and 'An Introduction to Stamp Duty' for the Institute of Chartered Accountants. Has given papers to the Institute of Taxation, Institute of Chartered Accountants, Law Society and IBC. Convener, Securities Law Seminar at Edinburgh University.

Prof. Membership: Law Society of Scotland, Institute of Taxation (Technical Committee Member 1986-92).

Career: Qualified in 1969. Law Commissioner (Scotland) 1978-86. VAT Tribunal 1986-92. Joined *Shepherd & Wedderburn WS* in 1992. External Examiner at Edinburgh University.

Personal: Born 6th October 1941. Educated at Edinburgh Academy, Oxford and Edinburgh Universities. Non-executive director of the Weir Group Plc, Glasgow.

Betts, Antony P.

Pinsent Curtis, Leeds (0113) 244 5000.

Burston, Richard John

See under Employee Benefits/Share Scheme.

Christian, John M.S.

Pinsent Curtis, Leeds (0113) 244 5000. Partner in Corporate Tax Department.

Specialisation: Main areas of practice are corporate and property tax. Areas of specialisation include corporate finance, reconstructions and demergers, asset finance, treasury and financing, property taxation, employee incentives, VAT, collective investment schemes and public bodies.

Prof. Membership: VAT Practitioners Group.

Career: Qualified in 1985. Worked at *Freshfields* 1983-89. Joined *Simpson Curtis* in 1990, becoming a Partner in 1991.

Concannon, Simon

Walker Morris, Leeds (0113) 283 2500. Associate in Corporate Department.

Specialisation: Principal area of practice is corporate tax. Work includes acquisitions and disposals, flotations, mergers, takeovers, securitisation, leasing, bank financing, MBO's, employee remuneration schemes and earn outs. Also handles property tax including VAT planning, developments, housing associations, nursing homes, sales and leaseback. Important transactions include the £27 million acquisition of a financial services company financed with a rights issue, a £300 million mortgage book acquisition, a £32 million container leasing, a 1 billion US dollar Spanish/Dutch finance structure, a £40 million lease receivables securitisation, and the establishment of an Enterprise Investment Scheme fund and a restricted share scheme. Major clients include Cattle's (Holdings) PLC, Empire Stores PLC, Kalon Group PLC and the Leeds & Holbeck Building Society.

Career: Qualified in 1990. With *Clifford Chance* 1990-94. Joined *Walker Morris* in 1994 and became an Associate in 1995.

Personal: Born 15th July 1966. Educated at Hertford College, Oxford 1984-87 and the College of Law, Chester 1987-88. On the Professional 100 Club Committee. Leisure activities include hiking and squash. Lives in Ilkley.

d'Inverno, Isobel

Brodies WS, Edinburgh (0131) 228 3777. VAT and Corporate Tax Specialist in Corporate Department.

Specialisation: Main areas of practice are VAT and corporate taxation work. Includes corporate acquisitions, disposals, re-organisations and VAT on commercial and corporate transactions. Has addressed seminar on company re-organisations, as well as lecturing on VAT and corporate work. VAT examiner for Institute of Taxation.

Prof. Membership: Institute of Chartered Accountants (England & Wales), Institute of Taxation, VAT Practitioners Group, Member of Revenue Committee of Law Society of Scotland.

Career: Trained as Chartered Accountant with Ernst & Whinney in London. Practised with Ernst & Young from 1980 and Arthur Young from 1985 as Tax Specialist. Joined *Brodies WS* as VAT and Corporate Tax Specialist in June 1991.

Personal: Born 1st September 1957. Attended St Andrew's University (MA Russian Language and Literature 1979). Gained ACA 1983, then ATII 1984. Lives in Edinburgh.

Docherty, Maureen

McGrigor Donald, Glasgow (0141) 248 6677.

Gordon, Ian

McGrigor Donald, Glasgow (0141) 248 6677. Qualified 1979. Partner 1983. Taxation Department. Main area of practice is employee benefits. Also deals with pensions.

Greaves, Judith A.

Pinsent Curtis, Leeds (0113) 244 5000. Partner in Corporate Tax Unit.

Specialisation: Main area of practice is corporate tax, covering acquisitions and disposals, group reorganisations, financing and property transactions and MBOs. Also handles employee share schemes: approved and unapproved schemes, ESOPs, employee buyouts and international schemes.

Prof. Membership: Share Schemes Lawyers Group.

Career: Qualified 1986 with *Linklaters & Paines*. Joined *Simpson Curtis* in 1988, becoming a Partner in 1991.

Green, Lawrence

Eversheds, Birmingham (0121) 233 2001. Associate in Tax Department.

Specialisation: Deals with the tax aspects of corporate and property transactions, including VAT on property and EIS. Also tax based finance leasing. Charge-out rate is £150 per hour.

Career: Trained with *Evershed & Tomkinson* and qualified in 1988. Associate at *Eversheds* since 1993.

Personal: Born 8th March 1964. Educated at Queen Elizabeth Grammar School, Tamworth 1975-80, Queen Elizabeth Mercian School, Tamworth 1980-82, Trinity Hall Cambridge 1982-85 and Chester Law School 1985-86. Leisure interests include cycling and mountain walking. Lives in Sutton Coldfield.

Harrison, Philip J.

Eversheds, Birmingham (0121) 233 2001. Partner in Tax Department.

Specialisation: Work includes tax aspects of corporate and property transactions, tax disputes, employee taxation and personal tax planning for business clients. Also handles employee share incentives, including revenue approved and unapproved schemes and ESOPs (both onshore and offshore). Responsible for the tax and employee incentive aspects of the privatisation of Harland and Wolff Shipyard in 1989. Acted for the taxpayer in Mairs v. Haughey (arising from the H&W privatisation) up to his victory in the House of Lords in 1993. Author of various articles about the implications of this case, especially the expert commentary in the Tax Journal. Member of the Revenue Law Committee of the Birmingham Law Society.

Prof. Membership: Law Society, Society of Trust and Estate Practitioners.

Career: Qualified in 1986. Articled with *Evershed & Tomkinson* 1984-86. Became an Associate with *Evershed Wells & Hind* in 1989 and a Partner in 1991.

Personal: Born 22nd November 1960. Attended King Edward VI School, Lichfield 1972-79; Emmanuel College, Cambridge 1979-82 (BA 1982, MA 1986) and 1983-84 (LLM); College of Law, Chester 1982-83. Leisure interests include family, reading, walking and old cars. Lives in Lichfield, Staffs.

Hutchinson, Richard K.

Eversheds, Leeds (0113) 243 0391. Partner in Corporate Department.

Specialisation: Main areas of practice are corporate tax, including sale and purchase of companies and businesses, employee share schemes, corporate tax planning, VAT on land and buildings and inward investment into UK. Also handles asset finance, including tax based finance leasing and other forms of tax driven finance, particularly for higher education and housing association sectors. Involved in ESOP following MBO of Leyland DAF vans business. Author of 'ESOs: The Use of Trusts with Employee Share Schemes' (Longman) and various articles.

Prof. Membership: Law Society.

Career: Qualified 1984. Assistant at *Freshfields* 1984-89. Associate at *Pinsent & Co* 1989-91, and Partner 1991-92. Joined *Eversheds, Leeds* as Partner 1992.

Personal: Born 4th June 1957. Educated at Magdalen College, Oxford 1976-79. Leisure interests include 18th century English furniture, fly fishing and gardening. Lives in Harrogate.

Illston, Timothy M.

See under Pensions.

Jones, Martyn

Maclay Murray & Spens, Glasgow (0141) 248 5011. Qualified 1976. Associate

1993. Tax Group. Handles corporate, personal and land taxation matters. Born 31.3.1952.

Jones, Janet

Dickson Minto WS, Edinburgh (0131) 225 4455.

MacKintosh, Simon A.

See under Charities.

Marlow, C.R.J.

Wiggin and Co, Cheltenham (01242) 224114. Partner.

Specialisation: Company and tax matters, for UK and international companies and trusts.

Prof. Membership: Law Society, International Bar Association.

Career: Qualified in 1977. *Lovell White Durrant* 1975-80. Joined *Wiggin & Co* in 1980, becoming a Partner in 1982.

Personal: Born 30th September 1949. Attended Uppingham School 1964-69, and Magdalene College, Cambridge 1970-73. Lives in Amberley, Gloucestershire.

Marshall Smith, Rosamond J.

Hammond Suddards, Leeds (0113) 234 3500. Partner and Head of Tax Department.

Specialisation: Main areas of practice are corporate tax, VAT and employee share schemes. Handles all aspects including Inland Revenue investigations and litigation. Also handles personal tax and offshore trust work, advising private company shareholders on tax planning. Acted in Empire Stores plc's Marketing Gifts VAT case in the European Court. Author of various articles. Speaks on tax matters at seminars.

Prof. Membership: Institute of Indirect Tax Practitioners, Society of Trust and Estate Practitioners.

Career: Qualified in 1983. Worked with *Boodle Hatfield & Co.*, 1981-84, then *Clifford Turner* 1984-87. Joined *Hammond Suddards* in 1987, becoming Head of Tax Department in 1991.

Personal: Born 11th April 1959. Attended Newstead Wood School 1970-77, then Durham University 1977-80 and College of Law 1980-81. Leisure interests include swimming and gardening. Lives in Otley.

Moss, Philip G.S.

Osborne Clarke, Bristol (0117) 923 0220. Qualified 1983. Partner 1991. Tax Department. Has experience in all areas of corporate transactions, structuring deals and reorganisations.

Pett, David

See under Employee Benefits/Share Scheme.

Pincher, Richard

McGrigor Donald, Glasgow (0141) 248 6677. Qualified 1990. Associate 1995. Head of Property Tax and VAT Unit 1993. Work includes planning, consultancy and litigation in all types of businesses.

Simpson, Mark C.

Hammond Suddards, Leeds (0113) 234 3500. Partner in Corporate Tax Department.

Specialisation: Deals with the tax aspects of all types of corporate transaction, including corporate and asset finance and banking matters, employment tax including share schemes, ESOP's and PRP, and VAT with particular reference to property transactions. Also undertakes tax planning for business proprietors (tax mitigation on investment and disposals including MBO's, offshore tax planning, maximising reliefs, etc). Has written articles for various publications including 'Mortgage Finance Gazette' and 'Taxation' and has spoken at a number of conferences and seminars.

Prof. Membership: Law Society, VAT Practitioners Group.

Career: Qualified in 1985. With *Freshfields* until joining *Hammond Suddards* in 1991.

Personal: Born 25th January 1960. Educated at Churston Grammar School, Brixham, Devon 1971-78, Downing College, Cambridge 1978-82 (MA, LL.B) and Chancery Lane Law College 1982-83. Lives in Harrogate.

Thompson, Heather

W & J Burness WS, Edinburgh (0131) 226 2561. Qualified 1986. Partner 1992. Private Client Department. Main areas of practice are private and commercial trusts and taxation.

Tonks, Julian M.J.

Pinsent Curtis, Birmingham (0121) 200 1050. Qualified 1982. Partner 1987. Senior Partner 1994. Main areas of practice are corporate and personal tax. Born 19.4.1953. Lives in Birmingham.

Wiggin, Harry

Burges Salmon, Bristol (0117) 939 2000. Qualified 1965. Partner 1986. Tax Department. Specialises in international tax, double taxation and financial structuring.

Womersley, Mark

Osborne Clarke, Bristol (0117) 923 0220.

TELECOMMUNICATIONS

LONDON

Bird & Bird emerges as the pre-eminent firm specialising in telecommunication work. The highly recommended David Kerr heads the team of nine partners who advise clients such as Energis (on domestic matters), British Telecom and European Bank (financiers for large users and suppliers) on a broad spectrum of work including privatisations, commercial contracts, interconnection licence applications, regulatory work and earth station and satellite space launch contracts. The firm also has substantial experience in cable and satellite broadcasting work. Phillip Dann, one of the partners in the team, was also highly recommended.

Hard on *Bird & Bird*'s heels come *Clifford Chance* and *Coudert Brothers*, both of which have well established departments and an enviable client base.

LEADING FIRMS – LONDON	
BIRD & BIRD	
CLIFFORD CHANCE	COUDERT BROTHERS
ALLISON & HUMPHREYS	ASHURST MORRIS CRISP
FRESHFIELDS	

Clifford Chance's leading lights are Liz Hiester and Christopher Millard who represent NTT (Japan), DBT (Germany), France Telecom, Ameritech and US West (work which is shared with *Coudert Brothers*). The firm has recently lost Tim Schwarz, who, after a nine month secondment to the World Bank in the USA (advising on their worldwide telecommunications network) will join *Simmons & Simmons* (well-known in the domestic field, representing Ninex and General Cable) to develop the international side of their telecommunications practice.

Colin Long at *Coudert Brothers* is widely regarded as the doyen of telecommunications law. In addition to handling a vast array of corporate, commercial and regulatory matters for telecommunication giants such as Mercury, Bell South (overseas) and US West, he also advises on competition law and technology transfers and was instructed in the action by Mercury Communications against Oftel and British Telecom in the commercial court. Michael Rhodes is also held in high regard.

Other leading firms include *Allison & Humphries, Ashurst Morris Crisp* and *Freshfields*.

Within this trio, *Allison & Humphries* are marginally ahead in terms of sheer expertise, with the highly experienced Ted Mercer at the helm advising on the regulatory and commercial aspects of telecommunications systems on a domestic and international scale. The firm acts for numerous UK cable companies and UK and overseas investors and has recently handled the sale of 80% interest in a UK cable franchise holder at a price of $75 million.

Stewart White at *Ashurst Morris Crisp* advises on communications policy and strategy in the UK, European Union, Middle East and Asia and was recently involved in the Telecoms restructuring in Jordan. He has, in addition, carried out extensive work for the European Commission, particularly in relation to satellite advice.

Stephanie Liston at *Freshfields* handles all aspects of telecommunications law including regulation, financing, joint ventures and investment in fixed and mobile telecommunications, including cable for MCI (US) and Southwestern Bell.

Other highly recommended firms include *Denton Hall, Dibb Lupton Broomhead, Linklaters & Paines* and *Olswang*.

Nicholas Higham at *Denton Hall* handles a broad range of telecommunications work and heads the team of three specialists that has recently won a coveted contract to advise the Government of Pakistan on the sale of 26% of shares in the Pakistan Telephone Company estimated at $1.5billion and to review their legal and regulatory framework and establish a regulatory office. The team is also advising Hermes Europe Railtel BV on procurement of equipment, cable and installation services for their trans-European telecommunication network.

David Barrett heads the Information technology and telecommunications unit at *Dibb Lupton Broomhead* that primarily advises on regulatory issues and licensing applications.

Robyn Durie at *Linklaters & Paines* advises on the regulatory aspects of privatisations in the UK, Continental Europe and Asia and represents clients such as Bell South and Bell Canada.

Olswang's telecommunications unit comprises three specialist partners who advise on licence applications, regulatory matters, network build issues and financing for new entrants to the telecoms market. David Zeffman, who specialises in cable and satellite work, is held in high regard.

HIGHLY REGARDED – LONDON	
BAKER & McKENZIE	CHARLES RUSSELL
DENTON HALL	DIBB LUPTON BROOMHEAD
FRERE CHOLMELEY BISCHOFF	HOPKINS & WOOD
LINKLATERS & PAINES	OLSWANG
SIDLEY & AUSTIN	SIMMONS & SIMMONS
ALLEN & OVERY	CAMERON MARKBY HEWITT
KEENE MARSLAND	LOVELL WHITE DURRANT
NORTON ROSE	TUCKER TURNER KINGSLEY WOOD

Baker & McKenzie take a portion of the legal work for Bell Atlantic, AT&T and British Telecom.

Individual practitioners who were particularly highly recommended include Mark Moncreiffe at *Charles Russell* who heads a team of three specialist partners acting primarily for domestic cable television and telecommunications companies and John Edwards at *Sidley & Austin* (formerly of *Clifford Chance*), widely regarded as a leading authority.

LEADING INDIVIDUALS – LONDON

Colin Long *Coudert Brothers*

David Barrett *Dibb Lupton Broomhead*	**Phillip J. Dann** *Bird & Bird*	**Robyn Durie** *Linklaters & Paines*
John Edwards *Sidley & Austin*	**Michael Flint** *Denton Hall*	**Liz Hiester** *Clifford Chance*
Nicholas Higham *Denton Hall*	**Christopher R. Hoyle** *Brobeck Hale & Dorr International*	**David Kerr** *Bird & Bird*
Stephanie Liston *Freshfields*	**Edward P.O. Mercer** *Allison & Humphreys*	**Christopher Millard** *Clifford Chance*
Mark A.C. Moncreiffe *Charles Russell*	**Michael Rhodes** *Coudert Brothers*	**Tim Schwarz** *Simmons & Simmons*
Stewart White *Ashurst Morris Crisp*	**David Zeffman** *Olswang*	

REGIONS

There are relatively few firms in the provinces with expertise in the field of telecommunications.

Those consistently recommended include *Wiggin & Co* in Cheltenham which has an excellent reputation for advising cable and satellite television stations, and *Osborne Clarke* in Bristol where John Watkinson (formerly of *Watkinson & Co*) provides advice on a consultancy basis.

HIGHLY REGARDED – REGIONS

EVERSHEDS *Leeds*	
WIGGINS & CO *Cheltenham*	OSBORNE CLARKE *Bristol*

In all the tables the names in each group are listed alphabetically.

LEADING INDIVIDUALS – REGIONS

Neil Brown *Eversheds*
John Watkinson *Osborne Clarke*

In the North of England, Neil Brown of *Eversheds* (Leeds) heads a small team of specialists providing commercial, licensing, regulatory and interconnection advice to a broad client base. Recent transactions have included advising Bell Cablemedia on their Yorkshire and Northern cable franchise, advising National Westminster Bank plc on the outsourcing of their telecommunications systems nationally and British Waterways on the establishment of Fibreway joint venture with a GEC/Plessey subsidiary.

LEADERS IN TELECOMMUNICATIONS

LONDON

Barrett, David

See under Computer Law & I.T.

Dann, Phillip J.

Bird & Bird, London (0171) 415 6000. Qualified 1979. Joined Bird & Bird in 1991 Barrister 1979. Solicitor and Partner 1992. Company Department. Main area of work is telecommunications, space law, broadcasting and computers. Born 1953.

Durie, Robyn

Linklaters & Paines, London (0171) 606 7080. Qualified 1977. Joined 1987. Main area of practice is telecommunications, especially regulatory aspects of privatisations in UK, Continental Europe and Asia, and regulatory work including licence applications, amendments and advice and telecoms aspects of corporate transactions. Also broadcasting and intellectual property.

Edwards, John

Sidley & Austin, London (0171) 360 3600.

Flint, Michael

Denton Hall, London (0171) 242 1212. Consultant in Media and Technology Department.

Specialisation: Specialises in media and entertainment law, including telecommunications and space law, commercial radio, cable and satellite television, copyright and other related commercial matters. Author of 'A User's Guide to Copyright' (Butterworths, 3rd edition 1990), co-author of 'Intellectual Property: The New Law (Butterworths, 1989) and 'Television by Satellite; Legal Aspects' (ESC, 1987) as well as numerous articles in e.g. *European Intellectual Property Review*, *The Financial Times*, *New Law Journal* and *International Business Lawyer*. Lectures in the UK and internationally on copyright, space law and entertainment related matters.

Prof. Membership: British Screen Advisory Council (Deputy Chairman), Panel of Arbitrators of the Amercian Film Marketing Association, Intellectual Property Institute (Chairman of the Council), International Bar Association, American Bar Association, British Association of Film and Television Arts.

Career: Joined *Denton Hall* in 1951. Qualified in 1956. Became a Partner at *Denton Hall* in 1960. Vice President; Paramount Pictures 1967-70. Head of Film and Television Venture Capital Group, Henry Ansbacher & Co Ltd (1970). Called to the Hong Kong Bar in 1980.

Personal: Born 7th May 1932. Educated at London University. Member of the Variety

Club of Great Britain. Member of the Savile, Hurlingham, Wig & Pen, Lords Taverners, Oxford Sailing Club and Law Society's Art Group. Fellow of the Society of Antiquaries. Vice President of British Archaeological Association. Co-producer of a film with David Puttnam entitled 'Glastonbury Fayre' and executive producer of a film entitled 'Can I Help You' (1980). French speaker.

Hiester, Liz

Clifford Chance, London (0171) 600 1000. Partner. Principal area of practice is telecommunications and related converging industry areas including information technology and broadcasting.

Higham, Nicholas

Denton Hall, London (0171) 242 1212. Partner in Media and Technology.

Specialisation: Main areas of practice are telecommunications and information technology. Work includes regulation, privatisation, outsourcing and software development. Also handles commercial law, including joint ventures, international distribution and licensing. Acted in the privatisation of Lattelelekom and Pakistan Telecom and the outsourcing of the I.T. department of Westminster City Council. Author of 'EC Telecommunications Law' and many articles on regulation, communications and I.T. Regular lecturer on telecommunications and I.T.

Prof. Membership: Associate of Chartered Institute of Patent Agents, International Institute of Communications, Trade Marks Agent, IBA.

Career: Qualified in 1971. Joined *Denton Hall* as a Partner in 1992. Previously an Assistant at *Linklaters & Paines* and a Partner at *SJ Berwin*.

Personal: Born 2nd March 1947. Leisure interests include bridge. Lives in London.

Hoyle, Christopher R.

Brobeck Hale & Dorr International, London (0171) 638 6688. Partner in Commercial Department.

Specialisation: Main areas of practice are telecommunications and information technology work of a non-contentious nature. Work has included acting for ACC in obtaining the first UK international single resale licence and negotiating one of the first operator interconnection agreements with BT and in obtaining a waiver of access deficit charges; also negotiating a global telecommunications outsourcing contract for a major bank, negotiating telecommunications joint ventures, and advising Mercury. Currently working on various global outsourcing agreements for data processing centres and separately, telecommunications services. Work has also included advising satellite service providers in their attempts to gain licenses from the DTI. Has acted for program providers in satellite broadcasting, for General Electric Information Services Co., for World Telecom (charge card telecommunications suppliers), and for TIS (premium rate service providers). Also acted in the Beiersdorf acquisition of the Nivea brand. Has written for Computer Law and Security Report, Computer Law and Practice, International Computer Lawyer, Advanced Information Report, Network Monitor and Computer Weekly. Has spoken at various conferences, including the Henry Stewart conferences and the Society for Computers and Law.

Prof. Memberships: Federal Communications Bar Association, Correspondent Editor of Computer Law and Security Report.

Career: Qualified 1983. Worked at IBM (UK), then *Bird & Bird*, then *Theodore Goddard*, joining *Hopkins & Wood* in November 1991 and becoming a Partner in 1992. Joined *Brobeck Hale and Dorr* in 1995.

Personal: Born 13th October 1959. Holds an LLB (Hons) Cantab, LLM (Hons) Cantab and DIP IPL (London). Leisure interests include rugby and rock climbing. Lives in London.

Kerr, David
See under Multimedia.

Liston, Stephanie
Freshfields, London (0171) 936 4000. Manager in Company Department.

Specialisation: Communications work includes drafting, advising upon and negotiating various communications related contracts and commercial transactions and providing EC and UK regulatory advice in connection with telecommunications and broadcasting activities.

Career: Admitted to the State Bar of Texas 1985. Associate with *Fulbright & Jaworski*, in London; Houston and Texas: 1984-87, and Washington, D.C.: 1987-89. Admitted to the District of Columbia Bar in 1988. Senior Attorney with *MCI Communications Corporation* 1990-92. Joined *Freshfields'* Company Department in February 1992. Qualified in England & Wales in 1994.

Personal: Born 15th March 1958. Educated at The Colorado College (BA in History/Political Science 1980), University of San Diego Law School 1980-82 and University of Notre Dame London Law Centre 1982-83. Received Juris Doctor in June 1983. Attended Trinity Hall, Cambridge University and received LL.M. in English Law (1st Class) in June 1984. Lives in London.

Long, C.

Coudert Brothers, London (0171) 248 3000. Partner in Corporate/Commercial Department.

Specialisation: Main area of practice is the corporate, commercial and regulatory aspects of communications. Also handles competition law and technology transfers. Handled the action by Mercury Communications against Oftel and British Telecom in the commercial court. Author of Telecommunications Law & Practice (1988 - new edition 1995); author of numerous articles, and a regular speaker.

Prof. Memberships: Law Society, International Bar Association, (Joint Chairman Communications Law Committee), Society for Computers and Law.

Career: Qualified in 1970. Joined *Coudert Brothers* in 1990 as a Partner.

Personal: Born 4th June 1946. Attended Epsom College 1959-64, then Bristol University 1964-7. Leisure interests include swimming, skiing, golf and tennis. Lives in London.

Mercer, Edward P.O.

Allison & Humphreys, London (0171) 570 6000. Partner in Telecommunications and Broadcasting Department.

Specialisation: Main area of work covers the regulatory and commercial aspects of running telecommunications systems worldwide. Particular expertise in the regulatory field, interconnect procurement agreements and in relation to the cable industry. Related work covers wayleaves, construction contracts, street works, and media aspects of copyright and I.P. law. Acted for first Telecommunications Operators other than Mercury to have a switched interconnect with BT. Acted in a number of private placements and currently involved in regulatory

aspects of flotation work associated with cable companies in the UK. Contributor to the Law Society Gazette, Annual Media Law Review and trade magazines. Frequent lecturer at seminars on cable and telecommunication issues in the UK and Europe.

Prof. Membership: Law Society, Association of District Secretaries.

Career: Qualified 1980. Head of Legal Section Adur District Council 1980-83, then Borough Solicitor, Rossendale Borough Council 1983-85. Secretary to Cable Authority 1985-89. Joined *Allison & Humphreys* in 1989, becoming a Partner in 1990.

Personal: Born 1st February 1956. Attended King Edward's Five-Ways School 1967-74, then Trinity College, Cambridge 1974-77. Leisure pursuits include clay pigeon shooting, acting and badminton. Churchwarden. Lives in Lewes.

Millard, Christopher
See under Computer Law & I.T.

Moncreiffe, Mark A.C.

Charles Russell, London (0171) 203 5000. Head of Company/Commercial Department, in Media and Telecommunications Group.

Specialisation: Acts principally for cable television and telecommunications companies who have entered and are active in the UK telecommunications market. Has handled the interconnection agreements for a number of cable television companies with British Telecommunications plc and others. Also handles general corporate and corporate finance work including share and asset sales and purchases, joint ventures, shareholder arrangements and financings. Frequent speaker at cable television association seminars.

Prof. Memberships: Law Society.

Career: Qualified in 1978. Joined *Charles Russell* in 1984 and became a Partner in 1985.

Personal: Born 23rd March 1953. Attended Uppingham School 1966-70, Queens' College, Cambridge, 1971-4, and Université Libre de Bruxelles 1974-5. Leisure interests include skiing, shooting and farming.

Rhodes, Michael
See under Computer Law & I.T.

Schwarz, Tim

Simmons & Simmons, London (0171) 628 2020. Partner from March 1996 in Commercial Department.

Specialisation: Telecommunications specialist. Shortly after qualification was seconded to the Legal Department of OFTEL for nine months. Subsequently focused almost exclusively on regulatory, anti-trust and commercial law aspects of the telecommunications sector. Has acted for a large number of new entrants to the UK telecommunications market prior to and following the Duopoly Review and has been involved in a number of major investigations by the European Commission in the telecommunications sector. Has advised officials from the Telecommunications Ministries and PTT's of Albania, Bulgaria, the Czech Republic, Latvia, Lithuania, Poland, Romania and Slovenia, on the ground in these countries, on a wide range of legal and regulatory matters. He has worked on a three month telecommunications project in India and a number of telecommunications network financing projects in Western and Eastern Europe. In June 1995 joined the Legal Department of the World Bank in Washington D.C. for a nine month assignment working on telecommunications projects in which the bank is involved worldwide.

Career: Qualified in October 1989 while at *Clifford Chance*. Left *Clifford Chance* in June 1995 to join the Legal Department of the World Bank in Washington D.C. for a nine month assignment. Joining *Simmons & Simmons* as a Partner in early 1996.

White, Stewart

Ashurst Morris Crisp, London (0171) 638 1111. Partner in Company Department.

Specialisation: Main area of practice is media and telecommunications law. Work covers all aspects of law and regulation of media and communications including policy and strategy in the UK and in relation to the European Union, the Middle East and Asia. Involved in International Cabletel Flotation (October 1993) and drafting the telecommunications law of the Hashemite Kingdom of Jordan and the establishment of an investment/venture capital organisation for telecom on behalf of an international institution. Carried out extensive work for the European Commission, particularly in the satellite sector. Co-author of 'Satellite Communications in Europe'; founding

Consulting Editor: 'EC Telecommunications Law'; editor of Butterworth's Encyclopaedia of Forms and Precedents- volume on Telecommunications. Guest lecturer on telecommunications law at Queen Mary College, London.

Prof. Memberships: International Bar Association, Communication Lawyers Association, Law Society.

Career: Qualified as a Solicitor in Australia in 1976, and in the UK in 1979. Practised in the UK since June 1988. Founding Chairman of LAWASIA Media and Communications Committee 1988-92. Founding Chairman of International Bar Association Communications Law Committee 1990-1994; Member of the Council of the Section on Business Law of the International Bar Association since 1994. Joined *Ashurst Morris Crisp* as Head of Media and Communications Group in 1994.

Personal: Born 23rd July 1951. Leisure pursuits include sailing, opera, horse racing and bridge. Lives in London and Bembridge, Isle of Wight.

Zeffman, David

See under Media & Entertainment.

Brown, A. Neil

Eversheds, Leeds (0113) 243 0391. Partner. Head of Telecoms and Utilities Groups.

Specialisation: Main area of practice is work of a commercial/regulatory nature for clients in Telecoms and Utility industries. Telecoms work ranges from wayleaving and construction through licence, regulatory, and interconnection issues to licensing of programme material. Clients include Energis, Bell Cablemedia, and YTTTV. Also active in the Energy/Utility sector particularly second tier licensing and Joint Ventures. Acts for British Waterways in relation to its Hydro power scheme. Eversheds nationally is active on behalf of 5 of the 12 RECs. Has also advised several major landowners on their relationship with the utilities including BW and Railtrack resulting in National Apparatus Agreements.

Prof. Memberships: International Bar Association (Utilities Committee), Solicitors' European Group.

Career: Joined *Breeze & Wyles*, Hertford 1981. Qualified 1983 and left to join *Watson Burton*, Newcastle. Moved to *Eversheds* in 1986. Partner 1988.

Personal: Born 17th January 1957. Attended Richard Hale, Hertford 1969-77, then Warwick University 1977-80. Leisure pursuits include supporting Newcastle United F.C., performing magic, the theatre and languages (Spanish and French). Lives near Ilkley.

Watkinson, John T.

Watkinson & Co, Chepstow (01291) 627172. Qualified 1986. Principal 1986. Handles European Radio, Telecommunications Law & Regulation, as well as licenses, Interconnect agreements and contracts.

TRANSPORT (ROAD & RAIL)

LONDON

Two firms stand out in London for their transport work, *Holmes Hardingham* and *Clyde & Co. Holmes Hardingham* act for U.K. and overseas underwriters, traders, freight forwarders, hauliers, and insurance recovery agents. Adrian Hardingham has an excellent reputation in all areas. Tim Knight is highly regarded for his transit and international carriage of goods by road (C.M.R.) work in particular. He is an expert on domestic haulage including Road Haulage Association conditions. Andrew Messent has been highly recommended for his work in cargo claims, goods in transit and insurance related work.

LEADING FIRMS – LONDON	
CLYDE & CO	HOLMES HARDINGHAM
HILL DICKINSON DAVIS CAMPBELL	INCE & CO. WALTONS & MORSE
DAVIES ARNOLD COOPER	INGLEDEW BROWN BENNISON & GARRETT

Clyde & Co advises on all aspects of transport and goods in transit, and is particularly well known for its cargo work. David Hall is an expert on non-marine transport, warehousing, freight forwarding, and the movement of freight by land. His principal clients include insurers, freight forwarders and the T.T. Club.

Three other leading firms in this area are *Hill Dickinson Davis Campbell*, *Ince & Co* and *Waltons & Morse*. *Hill Dickinson Davis Campbell* acts for insurance companies, brokers and underwriters, handling disputes and goods in transit law for all sectors of the industry. Julia Marshall has been highly recommended.

Waltons & Morse, although principally known for its shipping and insurance work, has a growing reputation in the transport field, due to the expertise of Ian Charles-Jones and Chris Dunn who are very highly regarded.

Two other firms in the first division of transport firms are *Davies Arnold Cooper* and *Ingledew Brown Bennison & Garrett*. *Davies Arnold Cooper*, where Ken Silk is very well regarded, is known for its work in freight forwarding, carriage of goods contracts, C.M.R. and road and rail claims. *Ingledew Brown Bennison & Garrett* has considerable expertise in all aspects of road haulage, warehousing, freight forwarding, and commercial distribution and transportation agreements.

HIGHLY REGARDED – LONDON	
NORTON ROSE	SIMMONS & SIMMONS
CAMERON MARKBY HEWITT	LAWRENCE JONES
REID MINTY	WEDLAKE SAINT
WRIGHT SON & PEPPER	

Another firm with a strong transport department is *Norton Rose*. It has been involved in high-profile privatisation projects in this sector, acting for finance lessors and for rolling stock lease companies. The firm has also advised the lending banks supporting one of the consortium bids for the Channel Tunnel Rail Link.

LEADING INDIVIDUALS – LONDON	
Ian Charles-Jones	*Waltons & Morse*
David Hall	*Clyde & Co*
Adrian Hardingham	*Holmes Hardingham*
Tim Knight	*Holmes Hardingham*
Julia Marshall	*Hill Dickinson Davis Campbell*
Andrew Messent	*Holmes Hardingham*
Chris Dunn	*Waltons & Morse*
Barry A. Prior	*Wedlake Saint*
Ken Silk	*Davies Arnold Cooper*

A firm that deserves a special mention for its high profile railway work is *Simmons & Simmons*, which acted for Railtrack during the privatisation of British Rail. *Wedlake Saint*, known for its specialist knowledge of road haulage, also handles operator licensing, carriage of goods and passenger claims, and local authority tendering of bus contracts. *Reid Minty* has a niche practice in container leasing. It acted in litigation arising from the second largest container fleet takeover in recent years.

SOUTH EAST

Three individuals stand out in the South East. Robin Cooper at *Hawkins Russell Jones* specialises in road traffic work. The firm also has particular expertise in commercial vehicle regulation. Roland des Voeux Pelly at *Pellys* specialises in transport and drivers' hours cases, and has also been involved in the legal interpretation of EC drivers' hours laws.

HIGHLY REGARDED – SOUTH EAST			
CLYDE & CO *Guildford*		HAWKINS RUSSELL JONES *Hitchin*	
KENNETH ELLIOTT & ROWE *Romford*		PELLYS *Bishop's Stortford*	
CLARKS *Reading*		CRIPPS HARRIES HALL *Tunbridge Wells*	
DONNE MILEHAM & HADDOCK *Brighton*		ELLISON & CO *Colchester*	
GRIFFITH SMITH *Brighton*		MOORE & BLATCH *Southampton*	
SHERWIN OLIVER *Portsmouth*			

Finally, Jim Duckworth, a consultant at *Kenneth Elliott & Rowe* and author of 'Road Transport Law', has expertise in public inquiries, road accident claims, damaged goods claims, the C.M.R. convention and other international goods and transport agreements. His firm set up a transport law department in February.

The leading firm in this region for cargo claims is *Clyde & Co*, which has an excellent reputation for work involving the carriage of goods by road and rail. It is also experienced in insurance and trading conditions advice. Anthony Thomas has been recommended for his cargo work, which includes advice on carriers' liability insurance.

There are several firms in the region with expertise in road haulage work. *Donne Mileham & Haddock*'s work in this area includes carriage of goods and insurance advice. Another firm known for road haulage work is *Cripps Harries Hall*, which has particular expertise in bus and coach insurance work.

Two firms should be mentioned for their work in specialist areas: *Griffith Smith* advises on private hire licensing for fleets of taxis, and *Moore & Blatch* has a good reputation for its work in transport inquiries.

Three other firms recommended generally for experience on road transport and issues connected with the motor industry are *Clarks, Ellison & Co* and *Sherwin Oliver*.

LEADING INDIVIDUALS – SOUTH EAST

Robin Cooper	*Hawkins Russell Jones*
James Duckworth	*Kenneth Elliott & Rowe*
R. des Voeux Pelly	*Pellys*
Anthony Thomas	*Clyde & Co*

SOUTH WEST & WALES

In Bristol, *Cartwrights* provides general commercial advice for a number of transport companies. It handles a significant amount of route licensing and other work for the Road Haulage Association, as well as litigation work for Railtrack. The firm also advises on the insurance aspects of road traffic litigation. Geoffrey Jones has an excellent reputation for his work in these areas.

Another Bristol firm recommended for its work in the road transport industry is *Burges Salmon*. Partner, Richard Wynn-Jones, is highly regarded.

HIGHLY REGARDED – SOUTH WEST & WALES

BURGES SALMON *Bristol*	**CARTWRIGHTS ADAMS & BLACK** *Cardiff*
CARTWRIGHTS *Bristol*	**OVER TAYLOR BIGGS** *Exeter*
BOND PEARCE *Plymouth*	**HUGH JAMES JONES & JENKINS** *Cardiff*

Two other specialist firms in the South West are *Over Taylor Biggs* and *Bond Pearce*. *Over Taylor Biggs*, established in 1993, acts principally for goods vehicles operators. It has been recommended for its planning and transport licensing work, and acts for the R.H.A. and Freight Transport Association. It is also known for its advice on overloading and drivers' hours offences. The founding partner, Christopher Over, is highly regarded. *Bond Pearce* has a good reputation for its cargo claims work.

The leading firm in Wales is Cardiff-based *Cartwrights Adams & Black*. It represents operators of both heavy goods vehicles and public service vehicles, and acts for the R.H.A. and the Freight Transport Association. Geoffrey Williams is respected for his contentious and non-contentious work in this area.

Another Cardiff firm, *Hugh James Jones & Jenkins,* has

been recommended for its transport insurance and licensing expertise.

LEADING INDIVIDUALS – SOUTH WEST & WALES

Geoffrey N. D. Jones	*Cartwrights*
Christopher Over	*Over Taylor Biggs*
Geoffrey Williams	*Cartwrights Adams & Black*
Richard T. Wynn-Jones	*Burges Salmon*

MIDLANDS

The leading firm in the Midlands is Nottingham-based *Rotheras*. It has experience in dealing with cargo claims and all aspects of road haulage work, and handles licensing authority hearings. Peter Rothera has been recommended to us.

HIGHLY REGARDED – MIDLANDS

ROTHERAS *Nottingham*	
CARLESS DAVIES & CO *Halesowen*	**GATELEY WAREING** *Birmingham*

Two other first rate transport firms in the area are *Carless Davies & Co* and *Gately Wareing*. *Carless Davies & Co* is a specialist transport practice with expertise in licensing for road haulage companies. *Gately Wareing* handles all aspects of transport and distribution work.

LEADING INDIVIDUALS – MIDLANDS

Peter I. Rothera	*Rotheras*

EAST ANGLIA

Ipswich firm *Gotelee & Goldsmith* has experience in all aspects of road haulage and licensing work, particularly with regard to public inquiries and coach operations. The firm advises hauliers on British and EC legislation concerning overloading, drivers' hours, tachographs and vehicle maintenance. Jonathan Ripman, who has worked in the haulage industry, has an excellent reputation.

HIGHLY REGARDED – EAST ANGLIA

GOTELEE & GOLDSMITH *Ipswich*	**PRETTYS** *Ipswich*
BIRKETTS *Ipswich*	**HOWES PERCIVAL** *Ipswich*

Another leading firm in the area is *Prettys*. It has a good reputation for its work in connection with bills of lading, booking notes, C.M.R. and freight forwarding disputes. Roland Sharp has been recommended for his work in these areas.

Two other notable firms in the region are *Birketts*, which has experience in intermodal transport disputes arising at Felixstowe and Ipswich docks, and *Howes Percival* which is well regarded for its expertise in operators licensing issues.

LEADING INDIVIDUALS – EAST ANGLIA

Jonathan W. Ripman	*Gotelee & Goldsmith*
Roland Sharp	*Prettys*

In all the tables the names in each group are listed alphabetically.

NORTH WEST

Alsop Wilkinson and *Hill Dickinson Davis Campbell* are the two leading firms in the North West. *Alsop Wilkinson* is strong in all aspects of road and rail transport, warehousing and freight forwarding. Martin Hill was widely recommended for his work in connection with international trading conventions, including C.M.R., Hague and Visby. He also undertakes work for the R.H.A., underwriters and for cargo interests.

LEADING FIRMS – NORTH WEST

ALSOP WILKINSON *Liverpool*	HILL DICKINSON DAVIS CAMPBELL *Liverpool*

Hill Dickinson Davis Campbell's practice covers all aspects of transport and the international carriage of goods, and is orientated towards claims and insurance. It handles C.M.R. claims, international haulage, warehousing, freight forwarding, and a substantial amount of work for the T.T. Club. Peter Jackson is one of the leading practitioners in this field.

Aaron & Partners has a highly regarded specialist transport department dealing with all aspects of transport and the international carriage of goods. It is well known for its work in HGV construction and use, licensing, tacograph offences, and international freight forwarding claims. John Dyne has an excellent reputation for his work in these areas.

HIGHLY REGARDED – NORTH WEST

AARON & PARTNERS *Chester*	J.A. BACKHOUSE & SONS *Blackburn*
BLACKHURST PARKER & YATES *Preston*	JONATHAN S. LAWTON *Manchester*
LACE MAWER *Manchester*	

J.A. Backhouse & Sons has also been recommended and is known for its work in connection with coaches and Heavy Goods Vehicles. It is strong on the contentious side; its recent cases include 'R v Abergaveny Justices ex parte' and 'DPP v Ryan'. John Backhouse is highly respected for his transport work.

Blackhurst Parker & Yates is known for its work in connection with the route licensing of public service vehicles. Michael Waller has been recommended to us.

Two more firms worth mentioning are *Jonathan Lawton* and *Lace Mawer*. Jonathan Lawton, a sole practitioner, runs a niche practice specialising in road traffic law. *Lace Mawer* specialises in all areas of litigation relating to the carriage of

LEADING INDIVIDUALS – NORTH WEST

Martin G. Hill *Alsop Wilkinson*	
Peter W. Jackson *Hill Dickinson Davis Campbell*	
John A. Backhouse *J.A. Backhouse & Sons*	
John Dyne *Aaron & Partners*	
Jonathan Lawton *Jonathan S. Lawton*	
L. Michael C. Waller *Blackhurst Parker & Yates*	

goods by road and the distribution of goods in the United Kingdom and internationally. It has also been recommended for representing operators and their drivers in the Magistrates and Crown Courts and at Traffic Commissioner Enquiries.

NORTH EAST

Eversheds in Leeds has one of the largest transport teams in the country. It has been recommended for its work in road and rail delivery operations, including those of a multimodal and pan-European nature. It also has experience in distribution and warehousing contract negotiation. Jonathan Guest has an excellent reputation for his work in these areas.

LEADING FIRMS – NORTH EAST

EVERSHEDS *Leeds*

Another leading firm in the North East is *Andrew M. Jackson & Co,* which handles insurance, road haulage and C.M.R. work. Dominic Ward has been recommended to us.

HIGHLY REGARDED – NORTH EAST

ANDREW M. JACKSON & CO *Hull*	DICKINSON DEES *Newcastle*
FORD AND WARREN *Leeds*	

Ford & Warren is known for its international transport law expertise, and in particular for its road haulage work. Stephen Kirkbright is strong in this area. Finally, *Dickinson Dees* is experienced in all aspects of road and rail haulage, and is particularly well known for bus and coach related work.

LEADING INDIVIDUALS – NORTH EAST

Jonathan R. Guest *Eversheds*	
Stephen Kirkbright *Ford and Warren*	
Dominic J. Ward *Andrew M. Jackson*	

LEADERS IN TRANSPORT (ROAD & RAIL)

LONDON

Charles-Jones, Ian
Waltons & Morse, London (0171) 623 4255.

Dunn, Chris
Waltons & Morse, London (0171) 623 4255.

Hall, David
Clyde & Co, London (0171) 623 1244. Qualified 1968. Partner 1974. Non-Marine Transit and Insurance Departments. Main area of practice is non-marine carriage of goods, both national and international.

Hardingham, Adrian
Holmes Hardingham, London (0171) 283 0222. Partner in Cargo Claims Department.

Specialisation: Principal area of practice is transport law, encompassing international (CMR) and domestic carriage of goods by road, sea and air. Other main area of work is marine insurance, particularly cargo risks. Major cases handled include Buchanan v. Babco (H.L.) (1978), Silber v. Islander Trucking (1985), ITT v Birkart (1988) and the 'Rewia' (1991). Major clients include UK and overseas underwriters, traders, freight forwarders, hauliers and insurance recovery agents. Contributor of various articles on the CMR Convention in Lloyd's Maritime & Commercial Law Quarterly.

Career: Qualified 1978. Founding Partner of *Holmes Hardingham*.

Personal: Born 12th February 1953. Attended University College, Oxford. Holds private pilot's licence.

Knight, Tim

Holmes Hardingham, London (0171) 283 0222. Partner in Cargo Claims Department.

Specialisation: Main area of practice is carriage of goods by road, covering national and international carriage by road, warehousekeeping, related insurance matters and terms and conditions of business. Also experienced in carriage by sea work, including bill of lading claims.

Career: Joined *Ingledew Brown* in 1986, qualifying in 1988. Joined *Holmes Hardingham* in 1989. Became Partner in 1993.

Personal: Born 17th March 1964. Attended University of Kent 1983-85. Leisure pursuits include golf and squash. Lives in Enfield.

Marshall, Julia

Hill Dickinson Davis Campbell, London (0171) 489 9939. Partner in Marine and Transit Department.

Specialisation: Advice and litigation in the field of insurance (marine and non-marine) and goods in transit inter-modally. Drafts and advises Underwriters on policy wordings and advises merchants and carriers on conditions of trading. Has been involved in a number of leading decisions relating to CMR, most recently (1994) in Cicatiello and others v. Anglo European Shipping Services Ltd and others, which successfully argued the first armed hi-jack defence under CMR Article 17.2.

Prof. Membership: Institute of Arbitrators. Founder of ELLSA (European Lawyers for Land, Sea and Air) a specialist European network ensuring expedient international assistance in shipping transit, insurance and most commercial areas.

Career: Admitted 1977 after first training and working in the medical field. Proprietor of own firm 1981. May 1994 merged with and became partner in *Hill Dickinson Davis Campbell*.

Personal: Lives in Eastbourne; one son. Leisure pursuits include family, friends and as much skiing as possible.

Messent, Andrew

Holmes Hardingham, London (0171) 283 0222. Partner in Cargo Claims Department.

Specialisation: Main area of practice is claims arising from the carriage of goods by sea, road and air, and related insurance issues. Co-author of 'CMR: Contracts for the International Carriage of Goods by Road' (1984, new edition in preparation). Contributor to 'International Carriage of Goods by Road (CMR)' (1987).

Career: Qualified 1975. Worked with *Ingledew Brown* until 1976. Then took up a lecturing post until 1985. Returned to IBBG, becoming a Partner in 1987, and moved to *Holmes Hardingham* as one of the founding Partners in 1989.

Personal: Born 23rd January 1951. Attended Wimbledon College 1961-68, then Gonville & Caius College, Cambridge, 1969-72.

Prior, Barry A.

Wedlake Saint, London (0171) 405 9446. Heads the firm's Transport Law team of 5 fee-earners and para-legals.

Specialisation: Main area of practice is road transport law for goods and passenger vehicles; work covers operators licensing, defence of prosecutions, personal injury (road traffic and employers' liability), contract drafting, and commercial litigation associated with the industry. Also handles carriage of goods and passengers claims, including CMR/ Domestic contracts and local authority tendering bus contracts. Cases have included litigation arising from many major motorway multi-vehicle accidents and public inquiries into operators licenses. Regular contributor to Platform (the UK journal of the CPT), Commercial Motor Magazine and the Journal of the British Association of Removers.

Prof. Membership: Law Society, Chartered Institute of Transport, Freight Transport Association, Confederation of Passenger Transport, Law Society Personal Injury Panel.

Career: Qualified in 1969. Joined *Wedlake Saint* as a Partner in 1985.

Personal: Born 24th October 1943. Attended Lawrence Sheriff School, Rugby 1956-63, then Sheffield University 1963-66. Member of the Chartered Institute of Transport; Council Member of CPT UK. Lives in Reading.

Silk, Ken

Davies Arnold Cooper, London (0171) 936 2222.

REGIONS

Backhouse, John A.

J.A. Backhouse & Sons, Blackburn (01254) 677311. Principal.

Specialisation: Main area of practice is transport law and goods and passenger vehicle licensing. Handles specialist advocacy before licensing authorities and the transport tribunal, Magistrates and Crown Court advocacy and cases in the European Court on drivers hours and tachograph matters. Also handles industrial tribunal and environmental law advocacy and advice. Cases have included a reference from Manchester Crown Court to the European Court on the interpretation of the drivers hours rules. Author of articles on transport and general court work. Has sat as a temporary stipendiary

magistrate.

Cooper, Robin

Hawkins Russell Jones, Hitchin (01462) 451411.

Duckworth, James

Kenneth Elliott & Rowe, Romford (01708) 757575.

Dyne, John

Aaron & Partners, Chester (01244) 315366. Senior Partner in Transport.

Specialisation: 1) Special Types and general haulage
2) Storage and distribution, PSV, licensing, carriage of waste, international carriage of goods (CMR), liens, Construction and Use and drivers hours.

Prof. Membership: Road Haulage Association (YES), Heavy Transport Association (Secretary), Institute of Transport Administration, Institute of WastesManagement, Institute of Road Transport Engineers, Institute of Quarrying, Liverpool Chamber of Commerce Ports and Transport Committee. Chester, North Wales & Ellesmere Port Chamber of Commerce Transport Committee.

Career: Qualified and joined *Aaron & Partners* in 1987. Became a Partner in 1990.

Guest, Jonathan R.

Eversheds, Leeds (0113) 243 0391.

Hill, Martin G.

See under Shipping & Maritime Law.

Jackson, Peter W.

See under Shipping & Maritime Law.

Jones, Geoffrey N. D.

Cartwrights, Bristol (0117) 929 3601.

Specialisation: Senior Partner specialising in employment and industrial relations law, has 24 years experience of all aspects of employment and industrial relations matters in contracts, service agreements and disciplinary procedure; multi-applicant industrial tribunals; TURA in tribunals and commercial transactions, and advice and legal action in relation to industrial action. Also practices transport law and has 25 years experience in relation to all aspects of bus and lorry licensing and related public inquiries, road use public inquiries and judicial review challenges to local authorities. Co-author of 'Basic Planning Law and Practice'.

Personal: Educated at Bristol University 1956-59. Former lecturer at the College of Law. Continuing professional education lecturer for the College of Law. Trustee, Southmead Hospital Research Foundation. Born 5th May 1938. Lives in Bristol.

Kirkbright, Stephen

Ford and Warren, Leeds (0113) 243 6601. Qualified 1968. Partner 1970. Business Law Department. Specialiises in transport, particularly HGV transport, nationally and internationally.

Lawton, Jonathan

Jonathan S. Lawton, Manchester (0161) 236 6552. Sole Practitioner.

Specialisation: Road traffic law specialist since 1972, with particular emphasis on commercial operations. Also handles employment law matters, health and safety, and some environmental work. Regular contributor to a number of trade publications, including Croners. Joint honorary legal adviser to the UK Warehousing Association. Freeman of the City of London. Gives frequent lectures and seminars on road haulage law, health and safety and employment. Has made television appearances and been interviewed for radio.

Prof. Membership: Heavy Transport Association.

Career: Qualified in 1962. Became a sole practitioner, practising as *Jonathan S. Lawton Solicitors* in February 1993.

Personal: Born 18th February 1935. Educated at Uppingham School 1948-53. Spent 2 years in the Army as a National Service Officer, then went to Cambridge University 1956-59. Leisure pursuits include painting, clay pigeon shooting, walking and reading. Lives in Broxton, near Chester.

Over, Christopher

See under Medical Negligence.

Pelly, R. des Voeux

Pellys, Bishop's Stortford (01279) 758080. Senior Partner specialising in transport and drivers hours laws.

Specialisation: Principal area of practice is transport and drivers hours laws. Deals with representations drivers hours cases, legal interpretation of EEC drivers hours laws, operational scheduling, specialised contracts of employment and licensing requirements. Also handles planning, employment and crime. Appears in the Magistrates Court and Crown Court, at Employment Tribunals. Makes appearances and submissions to the traffic commissioners and Transport Appeal Tribunal. Joint author of 'The Practical Guide to Drivers Hours and Records Rules' (to be published in 1994). Has lectured on drivers hours to various regional committees of coach operators associations.

Prof. Membership: Confederation of Passenger Transport UK (formerly Bus and Coach Council)

Career: Qualified in 1967. Established *Pelly's* in 1973. Currently Senior Partner.

Personal: Born 13th February 1943. School Governor. Lives in Stansted.

Ripman, Jonathan W.

Gotelee & Goldsmith, Ipswich (01473) 211121. Head of Commercial Litigation Department.

Specialisation: Main area of practice is road haulage work, including public enquiries, tachographs, overloading, general haulage problems in both Magistrates and Crown Courts, terms of business, trading conditions. Also experienced in debt recovery (computerised debt recovery service), employment advice (especially directors' and senior managers' contracts), environmental law and European legislation. Articles published in Roadway, Motor Transport, Commercial Motor, East Anglian Daily Times and Evening Star.

Prof. Memberships: LawNet, LawNet (Europe)- affiliated to EuroJurist, Suffolk & North Essex Law Society (Press and Public Relations Officer), Public Relations Advisory Board.

Career: Joined *Gotelee & Goldsmith* in 1978. Qualified 1981. Partner 1984. Head of Commercial Litigation Department. Two years working experience in road haulage industry 1976-1978.

Personal: Born 13th June 1953. Attended Rugby School 1966-72, then St. Catharine's College, Cambridge 1973-75. School Governor, Woodbridge School. Chairman P.A.C.T. (Suffolk-based children's charity). Leisure pursuits include walking, sport and family. Lives in Woodbridge, Suffolk.

Rothera, Peter I.

Rotheras, Nottingham (0115) 941 4415.

Sharp, Roland

Prettys, Ipswich (01473) 232121.

Thomas, Anthony

See under Shipping & Maritime Law.

Waller, L. Michael C.

Blackhurst Parker & Yates, Preston (01772) 253601.

Ward, Dominic J.

Andrew M. Jackson & Co, Hull (01482) 325242.

Williams, Geoffrey

Cartwrights Adams & Black, Cardiff (01222) 465959. Qualified 1978. Partner 1980. Litigation Department. Specialises in transport, representing operators of heavy goods and public service vehicles.

Wynn-Jones, Richard T.

See under Corporate Finance.

INDEXES TO PROFILES

Solicitors' Profiles The index to leading solicitors profiled in the specialist lists is located immediately after the section containing in-house lawyers' profiles. This index also includes heads of company legal departments.

Barristers' Profiles Leading barristers' profiles are indexed within the main Barristers' Index located at the end of the directory. Names of profiled barristers are set in bold type.

TRAVEL & TOURISM

T HE travel industry is one of the major growth areas and there are surprisingly few firms offering a specialised service. There is, however, a growing trend of large tour operators recruiting in-house lawyers especially for corporate and general commercial work.

LONDON

TRAVEL & TOURISM (LONDON)

It is widely acknowledged that the two premier firms in this field are *Field Fisher Waterhouse* and *Nicholson Graham & Jones*.

LEADING FIRMS – LONDON	
FIELD FISHER WATERHOUSE	NICHOLSON GRAHAM & JONES

Field Fisher Waterhouse's team consists of three specialists dealing exclusively with this area, two of whom were in the travel industry for more than seven years. Simon Chamberlain was a British Airways legal adviser for 10-12 years. Major clients include Thomas Cook Group Ltd, ATOL and ABTA. It acted for Inspirations in the acquisition of Caledonian Airways from BA . It is experienced in setting up bonding schemes for tour operators (an area in which the firm is particularly active). The firm also handles customer disputes, travel insurance cases, disputes between travel companies and competition related issues.

In the past twelve months, *Nicholson Graham & Jones* has been adopting a global approach to travel and tourism. One of its specialists, Tim Robinson, is on the board of the Pacific and Asia Trade Association (PATA) for which the firm does a fair amount of work. It also acts for the European Tour Operators Association via its Brussels office. In addition to dealing with corporate matters, the firm advises on tour operators' margin schemes, commercial agreements, litigation and regulatory issues. Clients include a number of the largest tour operators and travel agencies.

HIGHLY REGARDED – LONDON	
LANE & PARTNERS	NORTON ROSE
PIPER SMITH & BASHAM	
ROWE & MAW	
BOOTH & BLACKWELL	HERBERT SMITH
PINSENT CURTIS	

Also highly recommended are *Lane & Partners, Norton Rose* and *Piper Smith & Basham. Lane & Partners'* strength lies primarily in regulatory matters representing tour operators and clients before the ABTA committee and CAA respectively. It also handles a fair amount of litigation cases

including the on-going computerised reservation system case where it is acting for a group of five airways.

Norton Rose acts primarily for airlines and their tour operating arms. Other clients includes travel agencies and ferry and cruise operators. The firm's expertise covers package travel regulations and litigation matters.

Clients of *Piper Smith & Basham* include some of the largest tour operators, multiple retail travel agents, trade associations, individual traders and consumers. The firm's specialisation covers the regulation of the travel business, the setting up of travel companies, customer complaints, travel accidents, trading standards issues and commercial agreements between tour operators, agents and overseas suppliers.

Booth & Blackwell act for the International Air Transport Association and for British Airways plc. *Herbert Smith* act for First Choice Holidays plc, the third largest tour operator in the UK, advising on general corporate and corporate finance matters, agreements with retailers, financing, bonding and leasing, property work, disputes with dissatisfied holidaymakers, trading standards disputes and general litigation.

Pinsent Curtis enjoys a strong reputation for its contentious expertise in the travel sector. *Rowe & Maw* have advised recently on several airport privatisations including Biggin Hill and Southend.

LEADING INDIVIDUALS – LONDON	
Cynthia M. Barbor	*Nicholson Graham & Jones*
Peter J. Stewart	*Field Fisher Waterhouse*
Simon Chamberlain	*Field Fisher Waterhouse*
Patrick Farrell	*Norton Rose*
Tim S.H. Robinson	*Nicholson Graham & Jones*
Ian G. Skuse	*Piper Smith & Basham*
Richard Venables	*Lane & Partners*

Individuals with excellent national reputations include Cynthia Barbor at *Nicholson Graham & Jones* and Peter Stewart at *Field Fisher Waterhouse*. The former has over thirteen years experience and has acted for many years for the International Leisure Group. The latter is a fellow of the Institute of Travel & Tourism (ITT) and the co-author of 'A Practical Guide to Package Holiday Law & Contracts'.

Patrick Farrell at *Norton Rose* is highly regarded for his work in the field and acts for air lines and tour operators. At *Lane & Partners* Richard Venables is well known for advising UK-based tour operators, particularly on Air Travel Organisers' Licensing, UK and European legal developments and contractual matters. Ian Skuse at *Piper Smith & Basham* enjoys an excellent reputation for his work on behalf of large tour operators and multiple retail travel agents, as well as smaller travel clients and individual traders.

HOTELS & LEISURE (LONDON)

Among the medium-sized firms, *S J Berwin* has a strong reputation in the domestic market. Its team advises both operators and financial institutions on a variety of transactions including the sale and purchase of restaurants, golf clubs, hotels and sports facilities.

HIGHLY REGARDED – LONDON – HOTELS & LEISURE	
S J BERWIN & CO	CLIFFORD CHANCE
DOUGLAS WIGNALL & CO	FIELD FISHER WATERHOUSE
PAISNER & CO	
DENTON HALL	EVERSHEDS
JOELSON WILSON & CO	NICHOLSON GRAHAM & JONES
SIMMONS & SIMMONS	

Clifford Chance has developed a hotel and leisure group. This cross-departmental group (formed two years ago) with a strong international presence, is believed to be the only one among the large City firms. In addition to its large Asian and French clientele, the firm has a sizeable share of hotel and leisure projects in London. They advise on corporate and asset acquisitions, taxation and financing structures, asset use techniques, corporate finance, MBOs, insolvency, project management arrangements and site acquisition, leasing and disposal. Their clients include owners, operators and financial institutions.

Other well-regarded firms include *Field Fisher Waterhouse*, the niche practice of *Douglas Wignall & Co* and *Paisner & Co*. The former's work involves acquisitions and disposals, joint ventures between hotel owners, developers, financiers, bankers and hotel operators, management agreements, finance arrangements, franchise issues and rescues/reorganisations. They acted recently for a major Scandinavian hotel group in the restructuring of their UK hotels. Other clients include the largest hotel operators in the USA and the British Hospitality Association.

LEADING INDIVIDUALS – LONDON – HOTELS & LEISURE	
Bryan J. Pickup	*S J Berwin & Co*
Andrew Little	*Field Fisher Waterhouse*
Douglas Wignall	*Douglas Wignall & Co*

Douglas Wignall & Co's expertise covers hotel and resort developments in UK, Europe (France, Gibraltar, Portugal, Russia, Spain) and Seychelles, international hotel management contracts, acquisitions and disposal, operational matters and Package Travel/Tour regulations.

Denton Hall's work in the sector has an international emphasis and includes the planning, development, management and marketing of leisure projects.

Eversheds act for a number of major hotel groups, advising on acquisitions and disposals, planning and environmental law, franchising and employment matters. They also act for many of the major casinos in London and for several local authorities in connection with private leisure sector developments.

Joelson Wilson & Co provide a comprehensive service in this area, dealing with acquisitions and disposals, commercial agreements, licensing and planning, employment advice, capital raising and buy-outs and management agreements.

Nicholson Graham & Jones have expertise in the purchase, sale, franchising and development of leisure businesses including hotel groups.

Simmons & Simmons has a sound reputation for their work in the leisure sector. They are frequently involved in cross-border transactions: recently they have acted for Bass plc and the Pedro Domecq wine and spirits group.

Notable individuals include Andrew Little (*Field Fisher Waterhouse*) previously an in-house lawyer for Holiday Inn International for five years, Bryan Pickup (*S J Berwin & Co*) and Douglas Wignall (*Douglas Wignall & Co*).

REGIONS

The Leeds firm, *Mason Bond,* which has a separate travel law department, has an excellent national reputation. It advises tour operators and travel agents in respect of consumer claims, trading standards, booking conditions, supplier contracts, commercial disputes and litigation. Stephen Mason, co-author of Sweet & Maxwell's 'Holiday Law' and editor of the 'Travel Law Journal', has been highly recommended, as has Claire Ingleby. Recent major cases handled include Sargent v Citalia and Lucas v Avro Plc. Stephen Mason is one of a handful of solicitors with High Court (civil) advocacy rights.

LEADING FIRMS – REGIONS	
MASON BOND	*Leeds*
STONES	*Exeter*

Other firms active in this field include *Buss Murton* (Tunbridge Wells), *Eversheds (Middlesbrough) and Stones* (Exeter). *Buss Murton* advises medium- sized travel operators on a range of matters including EU directives and booking conditions.

Eversheds (Middlesbrough) specialises in employment and supplier contracts, the revision of contract conditions, and travel and tourism legislation. It has recently developed a particular expertise in the Unfair Terms and Consumer Contracts Directive. Clients include independent travel agents, cruise companies, middle range and overseas tour operators, coach operators, major plcs and to a limited extent, aggrieved consumers. Melanie Pears is a highly regarded specialist.

HIGHLY REGARDED – REGIONS			
EVERSHEDS	*Newcastle*	TODS MURRAY WS	*Edinburgh*
BUSS MURTON	*Tunbridge Wells*		
BOND PEARCE	*Plymouth*	SHAKESPEARES	*Birmingham*
TOZERS	*Exeter*		

Stones is experienced in handling skiing and travel accidents as well as holiday contractual claims. It is currently involved in litigation cases in the UK, France, Austria, Italy and Switzerland. Noted for his expertise in this field is Paul

Maxlow-Tomlinson who has been the British representative on the Legal and Safety Committee of Federation Internationale de Ski since 1988. *Bond Pearce* of Plymouth also enjoy a sound reputation in the field.

LEADING INDIVIDUALS – REGIONS

Stephen M. Mason *Mason Bond*

Paul C. Maxlow-Tomlinson *Stones*

Melanie Pears *Eversheds*

UP AND COMING

Claire Ingleby *Mason Bond*

In all the tables the names in each group are listed alphabetically.

Tozers are the national legal advisor of the British Holiday Caravan Park Association, handling regulatory and contractual work for them. Birmingham-based firm, *Shakespeares* is one of a handful of solicitors specialising in the canalside business, particularly in relation to waterways law.

In Scotland, *Tods Murray WS* is especially known for advice on timeshare and holiday ownership issues. Major clients include Barratt International Resorts Ltd, Timeshare Council, LSI Group of Companies, RCI Ltd, Global Group of Companies, Nevis Range Development Co and Milton Hotels. The firm handled the establishment of Global Vocation Club and the acquisitions of Kenmore resort and Burnside Park for Global Group of Companies. The firm also advised LSI in establishing the Grand Vacation Club.

LEADERS IN TRAVEL, TOURISM & LEISURE

LONDON

Barbor, Cynthia M.
Nicholson Graham & Jones, London (0171) 628 9151. Partner in Litigation Department and Joint Head Travel and Leisure Law Unit.

Specialisation: Main area of practice is travel and leisure law. Has over fifteen years experience in acting for major UK and international tour operators, travel agents, ground handlers, insurers, hotels, airlines and trade associations in the travel industry advising on substantial litigation, commercial agreements and regulatory issues. Also handles general commercial litigation, including insurance and personal injury actions, breach of contract and negligence. Acted for many years for International Leisure Group, which included ILG Travel and Air Europe. Writes regularly for Travel Trade Gazette and other travel publications. Speaks frequently on travel law at UK and international conferences.

Prof. Memberships: Law Society, Institute of Travel and Tourism, Incentive Travel and Meetings Association.

Career: Qualified 1976. Joined *Piper Smith and Basham* 1981, Partner 1985, Managing Partner 1989. Joined *Nicholson Graham & Jones* as Partner in 1993.

Personal: Born 15th October 1951. Chief leisure interest is playing with her children. Lives in Sutton, Surrey.

Chamberlain, Simon
See under Aviation.

Farrell, Patrick
See under Aviation.

Little, Andrew
Field Fisher Waterhouse, London (0171) 481 4841. Partner specialising in hotels and leisure industry related work.

Specialisation: Main area of practice involves advising clients in the hotel industry. Work includes purchases and sales of hotel and leisure businesses, negotiating hotel management agreements and operating leases, advising on financing of hotels and leisure projects, negotiating joint venture agreements and advising on franchising arrangements. Also advises banks on restructuring schemes for hotels, and in negotiating loan and security documents over hotels. An adviser to the British Hospitality Association. Frequently lectures at seminars and conferences for the hotel industry.

Prof. Membership: Law Society, International Bar Association, Hotel Catering & Institutional Management Association, British Association of Hotel Accountants.

Career: Qualified in 1973. With *Lawrence Graham* 1971-76, then a Partner at *Fox & Gibbons*, Dubai and London 1976-84. Vice President and General Counsel, Holiday Inns International 1985-89. Joined *Field Fisher Waterhouse* as a Partner in 1990.

Personal: Born 25th November 1948. Educated at Uppingham School, Exeter University and Guildford College of Law. Leisure pursuits include sailing, golf, theatre, and travel in India. Lives in London W11.

Pickup, Bryan J.
See under Hotels and leisure.

Robinson, Tim S.H.
Nicholson Graham & Jones, London (0171) 628 9151. Partner in Litigation Department, joint Head Travel and Leisure Law Unit.

Specialisation: Travel, Tourism and Leisure law. Acts for tour operators, travel agents, ground handlers, hotel groups, insurers, airlines and trade associations. Also handles general commercial litigation, libel and media acting for newspaper and magazine publishers, exhibition organisers, insurers and others. Writes regularly for Travel Trade Gazette and all major travel and tourism publications, the national press, appears on national and local radio and TV. Speaks regularly at travel industry conferences and seminars in the UK and worldwide.

Prof. Membership: Law Society, Institute of Travel and Tourism, Media Society, Incentive Travel and Meeting Association, Board Director of Pacific Asia Travel Association UK Chapter, European Tour Operators Association.

Career: Qualified 1977, at *Linklaters & Paines* 1974-79. Joined *Nicholson Graham & Jones* in 1979, becoming a Partner in 1982.

Personal: Born in 1953. Attended St Edmund Hall, Oxford 1971-73. Leisure interests include music, reading and horse riding. Lives in London.

Skuse, Ian G.
Piper Smith & Basham, London (0171) 828 8685. Qualified 1980. Partner 1987. Travel and Tourism Department. For the last 11 years has acted for some of the largest tour operators and multiple retail travel agents, together with smaller travel clients and individual traders.

Stewart, Peter J.
Field Fisher Waterhouse, London (0171) 481 4841. Partner and Head of Travel and Tourism Department.

Specialisation: Practice covers commercial areas (contentious and non-contentious) concerning the travel industry. Non-contentious work includes compliance with package travel regulations, CAA requirements and others, and the organisation and sale of travel arrangements. Contentious work includes disputes with suppliers, other travel companies and customers. Cases handled have included a jurisdictional dispute between

Egypt and England, and an OFT enquiry into the travel industry. Author of 'A Practical Guide to Package Holiday Law and Contracts' (third edition 1993) and regular articles for ITT journal and other trade papers. Regularly lectures for ESC, IBC and ITT at travel industry conferences.

Prof. Membership: IBA, IFTTA, ITT.

Career: Qualified 1982., having joined *Field Fisher Waterhouse* in 1980. Became a Partner in 1985.

Personal: Born 3rd February 1956. Attended Campbell College in Belfast 1969-73, then Pembroke College Cambridge 1974-77. Leisure interests include golf, tennis and music. Lives in Goudhurst, Kent.

Venables, Richard
See under Aviation.

Wignall, Douglas
Douglas Wignall & Co, London (0171) 583 1362. Principal.

Specialisation: Main area of practice is travel and tourism. Work includes hotel and resort developments in UK and Europe, international hotel management contracts, acquisition and disposal of hotels, advising on all aspects of hotel operational matters and advising tour operators. Also handles general commercial law, covering all forms of commercial contracts, franchise, distribution and other agency agreements, and joint venture agreements. Has handled hotel and/or resort projects in most countries in Western Europe, Africa, Middle East and Russia. Major clients include ITT Sheraton Corporation, Securum Hotel Holdings Ltd and Global/ High Point Joint Venture. Has lectured and written articles on hotel management contracts. Individual charge-out rate is £150 per hour.

Prof. Membership: Law Society, International Bar Association, Member of British Middle East Law Council, Member of the Company of Scriveners. Registered with PHARE and TACIS.

Career: Qualified in 1974. Worked in industry for approximately 10 years including

Legal Counsel with Sheraton Management Corporation between 1981-84. Set up *Douglas Wignall & Co* in 1984.

Personal: Born 15th April 1950. Attended Brentwood School 1957-68, Leeds University 1968-71, and Guildford Law College 1971-72. Leisure interests include squash and music; member of Hurlingham Club. Lives in London W6.

REGIONS

Ingleby, Claire
Mason Bond, Leeds (0113) 242 4444. Partner in Travel Law Department.

Specialisation: Main area of work is drafting contractual and other documentation for tour operators. Has drafted booking conditions for many major operators and prepared supplier's contracts, agency agreements, newspaper/ operator contracts for reader offers, promotional agreements and conditions and brochure wording. Also handles litigation on behalf of tour operators, defends consumer claims, deals with Trading Standards enquiries and prosecutions and represents operators before the ABTA Code of Conduct Committee. Provides advice on all areas of law affecting tour operators. Firm acts on behalf of more than 80 tour operators of varying sizes. Also represents travel agents, newspapers and a trade association. Author of a number of articles for the 'Travel Law Journal' and one for 'The Legal Executive'. Has lectured for the University of Northumbria and addressed the annual conference of ABTOF in 1994 and 1995. Conducts in-house seminars for tour operators on a number of subjects.

Prof. Membership: Law Society.

Career: Joined *Mason Bond* on qualification in 1990. Became a Partner in 1994.

Personal: Born 5th December 1965. Exeter University 1984-87. Leisure activities include hill walking. Lives near Skipton, North Yorkshire.

Mason, Stephen M.
Mason Bond, Leeds (0113) 242 4444. Partner in Travel Law Department.

Specialisation: Advises tour operators and travel agents. Work includes defending claims brought by consumers, advocacy, dealing with trading standards departments, conducting seminars, drafting booking conditions and supplier contracts. Also handles commercial aspects of travel law, including commercial disputes and litigation, copyright, trademarks and passing off. Acted in Kemp v. Intasun Holidays Ltd 1987 CA, and in many first instance travel law cases reported in Current Law. Joint Editor of the 'Travel Law Journal'; joint author of 'The EC Directive on Package Travel' and ten other booklets for the University of Northumbria. Has addressed numerous seminars on travel law topics advertised by the University of Northumbria, held at the Institute of Advanced Legal Studies, London; and also the Association of British Tour Operators to France Annual Conference. Higher Courts (Civil Proceedings) Qualification 1994; Joint Author 'Holiday Law' Sweet & Maxwell 1995.

Prof. Membership: Law Society, International Federation of Travel and Tourism Advocates.

Career: Qualified 1974. Senior Partner since 1986.

Personal: Married, 3 children. Attended Bradford Grammar School to 1967, and Cambridge University to 1971. School Governor. Leisure interests include travel, acting and supporting Leeds United FC. Lives in Ilkley, West Yorkshire.

Maxlow-Tomlinson, Paul C.
See under Sports Law.

Pears, Melanie
Eversheds, Middlesbrough (01642) 247456. Qualified 1994. Solicitor in Company/Commercial Department: European/Competition Law Group. Principal area of practice is travel law.

TRUSTS & PERSONAL TAX

LONDON

Withers has one of the largest groups of specialist private client solicitors in the country, with expertise in handling work for the landed gentry and other wealthy individuals. The team of 15 partners has been involved in many high profile cases including 'Hambro v Malborough' where the firm acted for the trustees of the Blenheim estate. They co-ordinated actions brought in Greece, the Cayman Islands and the UK by a client whose father had made a lifetime gift of his shipping empire to the trustees of a Cayman Island trust. *Farrer & Co* has an outstanding reputation in relation to acting for wealthy individuals, offering a full range of services. Henry Boyd Carpenter and Mark Bridges have both been recommended for their expertise.

LEADING FIRMS – LONDON	
ALLEN & OVERY	FARRER & CO
LAWRENCE GRAHAM	MACFARLANES
WITHERS	
BOODLE HATFIELD	CURREY & CO
NORTON ROSE	PAYNE HICKS BEACH

Amongst major City firms, *Allen & Overy* has an established practice advising wealthy individuals, business proprietors and senior directors, trustees, families, national museums, cultural and investment agencies of foreign states, universities, major charities and national and international partnerships. Peter Mimpriss heads the group and is renowned for his expertise, as is his colleague William Norris.

Martyn Gower at *Lawrence Graham* is highly regarded by his peers and set up the STAR group (solicitor tax and revenue) with Richard Moyse at *Boodle Hatfield*. The department at *Lawrence Graham* advises on all UK business, property and personal taxes with an emphasis on strategic international tax issues. The firm also undertakes a large volume of work in administration of trusts and probate and investment advice. Martyn Gowar is particularly well known for his involvement in matters arising from the death of the late Lord Derby and acting for Sir Bernard Ashley and family (the widower of Laura Ashley). *Boodle Hatfield* is involved in similar areas of work and acts for large trusts and estates and for wealthy individuals and families worldwide. The firm has opened an office in Oxford dealing with private client work.

Macfarlanes has a strong team of private client specialists consisting of seven partners which covers all aspects including heritage property, international estate and tax planning. Highly regarded individuals in the team include John Dilger, Michael Hayes and John Rhodes.

Other prominent practices include *Currey & Co, Paynes Hicks Beach* and *Norton Rose. Currey & Co* is a niche private client firm with seven partners. The firm specialises in trusts, taxation, estate planning, property, private

company work, wills and probate, and acts for landed estates and family businesses. The team has been involved in various important cases including the House of Lords case 'Fitzwilliam v IRC'.

Paynes Hicks Beach has a strong private client department of seven partners and two consultants acting on behalf of a wide range of clients from dukes and stately homes to foreign public companies controlled by UK family clients. The team gives advise on numerous areas, calling upon specialist departments as necessary in any particular matter.

Michael Macfadyan at *Norton Rose* is held in high esteem in this field, giving the department at *Norton Rose* a strong name in private client work. The team's work has become increasingly international over the last 12 months advising on all aspects of UK tax planning and off shore trust and tax structures, estate and trust administration and private client property transactions. The firm also advises numerous influential UK private clients.

There are a number of other London firms noted for their private client work including *Speechly Bircham, Frere Cholmeley Bischoff* and *Charles Russell*.

HIGHLY REGARDED – LONDON	
CHARLES RUSSELL	FRERE CHOLMELEY BISCHOFF
LINKLATERS & PAINES	NICHOLSON GRAHAM & JONES
SPEECHLY BIRCHAM	TAYLOR JOYNSON GARRETT
TITMUSS SAINER DECHERT	
ALSOP WILKINSON	BIRCHAM
COLLYER–BRISTOW	DAWSON & CO
FLADGATE FIELDER	GOULDENS
HUNTERS	LEE & PEMBERTONS
NABARRO NATHANSON	PAISNER & CO
RADCLIFFES CROSSMAN BLOCK	ROOKS RIDER
ROWE & MAW	SIMMONS & SIMMONS
STEPHENSON HARWOOD	THEODORE GODDARD
TROWERS & HAMLINS	WEDLAKE BELL
WINCKWORTH & PEMBERTON	
BAILEYS SHAW & GILLETT	CUMBERLAND ELLIS PEIRS
EDWIN COE	FORSYTE SAUNDERS KERMAN
GORDON DADDS	GREGORY, ROWCLIFFE & MILNERS
HOWARD KENNEDY	MANCHES & CO
MAXWELL BATLEY	MAY, MAY & MERRIMANS
PARK NELSON THOMPSON QUARRELL	PETER CARTER-RUCK & PARTNERS
RUSSELL–COOKE, POTTER & CHAPMAN	SIMMONDS CHURCH SMILES
TWEEDIE & PRIDEAUX	WITHAM WELD

The private client team at *Speechly Bircham* handles onshore and offshore work. The team acts for the Vestey offshore trusts and has handled work for the Bhopal Trust and the Open Churches Trust (for Andrew Lloyd Webber). The firm has also designed and marketed a loan plan which enables people with relatively modest estates to minimise inheritance tax in a simple and cost effective way.

Frere Cholmeley Bischoff has a strong team whose work

includes inheritance tax planning, offshore trusts and investment strategies. John Drewitt, who is particularly well regarded at the firm, also acts as a trustee of a number of substantial trusts and landed estates. The department at *Charles Russell,* also renowned for its expertise, includes four specialist partners and handles probate, trust and estate administration, wills, tax and asset planning.

Eliza Mellor at *Nicholson Graham & Jones* is also highly recommended for her expertise in the private client field, dealing with work ranging from UK income, capital gains and inheritance tax advice to structuring international families' estate planning and trust litigation.

LEADING INDIVIDUALS – LONDON

Martyn Gowar *Lawrence Graham*	**Richard M. Moyse** *Boodle Hatfield*	
John F. Avery Jones C.B.E. *Speechly Bircham*	**Michael R. Macfadyen** *Norton Rose*	**Eliza Mellor** *Nicholson Graham & Jones*
William Norris *Allen & Overy*		
David Bowyer *Withers*	**Henry Boyd-Carpenter C.V.O.** *Farrer & Co*	**Mark T. Bridges** *Farrer & Co*
Graham S. Brown *Payne Hicks Beach*	**Michael S.E. Carpenter** *Withers*	**Stephen Cooke** *Withers*
John Dilger *Macfarlanes*	**Robert A. Dolman** *Wedlake Bell*	**John Drewitt** *Frere Cholmeley Bischoff*
Peter Duffield *Withers*	**Michael Hayes** *Macfarlanes*	**Chris M. Jarman** *Payne Hicks Beach*
Richard C. Kirby *Speechly Bircham*	**Ian G. Lewis** *Nabarro Nathanson*	**David Long** *Charles Russell*
Clare M. Maurice *Allen & Overy*	**Peter Mimpriss** *Allen & Overy*	**Robin Paul** *Withers*
Nicholas R.D. Powell *Currey & Co*	**John Rhodes** *Macfarlanes*	**Joseph C. Richardson** *Dawson & Co*
David Robinson *Frere Cholmeley Bischoff*	**A.M.A. Skrine** *Hunters*	**Michael Stanford-Tuck** *Taylor Joynson Garrett*
Brian Stevens *Withers*	**David Tandy** *Titmuss Sainer Dechert*	**Anthony J. Thompson** *Withers*

SOUTH EAST

Many firms in the South East have strong private client practices. Particularly well regarded are *Cripps Harries Hall* and *Thomas Eggar Verrall Bowles*. Both firms have large private client departments offering specialist financial and investment advice. *Thomas Eggar Verrall Bowles*, where Richard Thornely and Robert Ashe have established reputations, advise UK and non-resident clients on the full range of private client services.

Cripps Harries Hall provides a finance and investment services division staffed by specialists from the financial sector, and is able to give advice on various matters such as tax efficient investments. The firm also handles all other aspects of private client practice. Simon Leney is known for his expertise in this field..

Adams & Remers act for landed estates, complex family trusts and wealthy individuals. Recent developments within the firm include the establishment of a French law property department dealing with probate and trusts headed by a French lawyer. The investment management section of the private client department has funds under management approaching the figure of £30,000,000. *Girlings* also has a substantial private client practice in the South East covering all aspects of this work.

Boodle Hatfield has opened an office in Oxford dealing with private client work which is headed by Sue Laing. *George Ide, Phillips* and *Rootes & Alliott* both handle French property transactions, and *Staffurth & Bray* has particular expertise in advising on Spanish property matters .

Other notable firms in the region include *Cole and Cole, Buss Murton* and *Thomson Snell & Passmore* which has a strong department lead by James Krafft.

HIGHLY REGARDED – SOUTH EAST

CRIPPS HARRIES HALL *Tunbridge Wells*	**THOMAS EGGAR VERRALL BOWLES** *Chichester*
ADAMS & REMERS *Lewes*	**BOODLE HATFIELD** *Oxford*
BUSS MURTON *Tunbridge Wells*	**COLE and COLE** *Oxford*
GEORGE IDE, PHILLIPS *Chichester*	**GIRLINGS** *Canterbury*
ROOTES & ALLIOTT *Folkestone*	**STAFFURTH & BRAY** *Bognor Regis*
THOMSON SNELL & PASSMORE *Tunbridge Wells*	
BALDOCKS *Guildford*	**BARLOWS** *Guildford*
BLANDY & BLANDY *Reading*	**BRACHERS** *Maidstone*
BURLEY & GEACH *Petersfield*	**BURSTOWS** *Crawley*
CLARKS *Reading*	**B.P. COLLINS & CO** *Gerrards Cross*
DONNE MILEHAM & HADDOCK *Brighton*	**GRIFFITH SMITH** *Brighton*
HALLETT & CO *Ashford*	**ILIFFES BOOTH BENNETT** *Uxbridge*
LAMPORT BASSITT *Southampton*	**MARSHALL & GALPIN** *Oxford*
MATTHEW ARNOLD & BALDWIN *Watford*	**MAYO & PERKINS** *Eastbourne*
MOORE & BLATCH *Southampton*	**MORRELL PEEL & GAMLEN** *Oxford*
PARIS SMITH & RANDALL *Southampton*	**PICTONS** *St. Albans*
RAWLISON & BUTLER *Crawley*	**SPARLING BENHAM & BROUGH** *Colchester*
STANLEY TEE & CO *Bishop's Stortford*	**STEVENS & BOLTON** *Guildford*
TURBERVILLE WOODBRIDGE *Uxbridge*	**WHITE & BOWKER** *Winchester*
WHITEHEAD MONCKTON *Maidstone*	

In all the tables the names in each group are listed alphabetically.

SOUTH WEST

Of the many firms in the South West offering high quality private client advice, a number stand out for their particular expertise in the field. *Burges Salmon* has a team of four partners of which Neil Porter is particularly well regarded for agriculture related private client work. The firm is renowned for its strength in landed estates (including heritage property) and tax planning, incorporating the use of offshore schemes. *Osborne Clarke*, through years of experience in private client work, has acquired a considerable body of knowledge and expertise in personal investment advice, including portfolio and trust management and is a member of ASIM. John Sharpe at the firm, who is highly regarded, also gives agricultural private client advice.

Bond Pearce has been recommended for its expertise in the area and work undertaken includes wills, tax planning, probate and trusts. The firm is also expanding in the area of overseas probate. Jonathan Nicholson has been particularly highly recommended for his private client work.

Wilsons is known for international tax advice and has built up a substantial practice acting for both UK based clients with offshore interests, and overseas clients with interests in the UK. The firm has also established a financial services unit offering personal investment advice and a portfolio management service, in addition to its existing insurance, life insurance and pension advisory service. *Wilsons* recently gained Peter Fitzgerald from *Fladgate Fielder* to add to the strength of the team. John Emmerson and Mark Lea, also partners at the firm, are both renowned for their expertise, with Mark Lea undertaking specialised international tax cases in the Far East.

Anstey Sargent & Probert has a reputation for general estate and tax planning, landed estates, trusts and settlements as well as trusteeship and attorneyship. Adrian Miller at the

firm is particularly highly regarded and is vice chair of STEP (Society of Trust and Estate Practitioners). Nigel Wollen at *Hooper & Wollen* is a well known specialist in private client work undertaking wills, trusts and estate planning for many of the leading families in the area. Other well respected firms include *Clarke Willmott & Clarke*, *Lester Aldridge* (where Barry Glazier handles corporate and personal tax, and onshore and offshore trusts), *Meade-King* and *Eastleys*.

WALES

The firms listed are well regarded for their private client services, dealing with all facets of private client work including tax planning in relation to trusts, wills and probate.

MIDLANDS

Many firms in the Midlands offer a wide range of tax, estate and wills related services. *Anthony Collins* has particular expertise in handling trusts and wills involving beneficiaries with a disability. *Hewitson Becke + Shaw* also has a significant private client presence in the region and acts for many large landed estates and individuals, a number with an international dimension.

Firms with strong agricultural departments usually give practical tax advice to their private clients, especially large landowners. *Blythe Liggins, R. Gwynne & Sons, Roythorne & Co* and *Tallents Godfrey & Co* are particularly known in this respect.

EAST ANGLIA

Eversheds has a strong reputation in the region for its private capital group set up by Michael Willcox. The team provides a range of private capital services to clients both nationally and internationally and has a particular expertise in international estate and financial planning work.

HIGHLY REGARDED – EAST ANGLIA	
EVERSHEDS *Norwich*	HOOD VORES & ALLWOOD *Dereham*
MILLS & REEVE *Norwich*	OVERBURY STEWARD & EATON *Norwich*
WARD GETHIN *King's Lynn*	
BANKES ASHTON *Bury St. Edmunds*	COZENS–HARDY & JEWSON *Norwich*
GREENE & GREENE *Bury St. Edmunds*	HEWITSON BECKE + SHAW *Cambridge*
PRETTYS *Ipswich*	STEELE & CO *Norwich*

Mills & Reeve draws upon the resources of a large department, with strengths and expertise in tax and estate planning, particularly in relation to its traditional agricultural client base. Other firms with expertise in the area are *Hood Vores & Allwood* and *Overbury Steward & Eaton,* both of which act for large private landowners. *Ward Gethin* in King's Lynn has developed a niche practice acting for the elderly, mainly in relation to financial affairs.

LEADING INDIVIDUALS – EAST ANGLIA
Michael Willcox *Eversheds*

NORTH WEST

Alsop Wilkinson advises both UK and non-resident clients on personal financial affairs, covering tax, financial planning, the establishment of settlements and advice on trusts, capital taxation, succession, wills and estates. *Cobbett Leak Almond* also covers the whole range of private client work and acts for a number of high net worth individuals. The firm is particularly known for its advice to the elderly on private client matters. *Lace Mawer* has an established reputation in the field, focussing particularly on large trust work and offshore trusts, as well as handling all aspects of private client work.

HIGHLY REGARDED – NORTH WEST	
ALSOP WILKINSON *Liverpool*	COBBETT LEAK ALMOND *Manchester*
HALLIWELL LANDAU *Manchester*	LACE MAWER *Manchester*
BIRCH CULLIMORE *Chester*	BRABNER HOLDEN BANKS WILSON *Liverpool*
JONES MAIDMENT WILSON *Manchester*	LEES LLOYD WHITLEY *Liverpool*
ROWLANDS *Manchester*	

Geoffrey Shindler at *Halliwell Landau* is renowned for his expertise in the field. The firm provides advice to senior business executives and wealthy individuals on income and estate planning, the creation of trusts and the administration of investments

LEADING INDIVIDUALS – NORTH WEST
Geoffrey A. Shindler *Halliwell Landau*

NORTH EAST

Eversheds has a department consisting of two specialist partners which covers the main areas of private client practice. The team has substantial experience in inheritance tax planning, wills and administration of estates, agricultural advice and trust administration of over 150 trusts.

Lupton Fawcett also offer a substantial private client service. The firm has full stockbroking facilities and John Eaton, who heads the financial services unit, is an acknowledged expert. He was the founder member of the Association of Solicitor Investment Managers and author of the Midland Bank book on inheritance planning. The firm has specialised in tax, trusts and probate for many years and often creates and manages trusts, acting as trustees if required, as well as dealing with related ancillary aspects .

HIGHLY REGARDED – NORTH EAST	
DICKINSON DEES *Newcastle*	EVERSHEDS *Leeds*
HAMMOND SUDDARDS *Leeds*	LUPTON FAWCETT *Leeds*
ROLLIT FARRELL & BLADON *Hull*	WARD HADAWAY *Newcastle*
WILKINSON MAUGHAN *Newcastle*	
ANDREW M. JACKSON *Hull*	ARMITAGE SYKES HALL NORTON *Huddersfield*
ASKEWS *Redcar*	BOOTH & CO. *Leeds*
GORDONS WRIGHT & WRIGHT *Bradford*	HARROWELL SHAFTOE *York*
IRWIN MITCHELL *Sheffield*	LATIMER HINKS *Darlington*
PINSENT CURTIS *Leeds*	WALKER MORRIS *Leeds*

Dickinson Dees is a commercial firm whose private client department has a national reputation. The firm undertakes all high value private client work, particularly specialising in the affairs of large landowners, wealthy businessmen and entrepreneurs. The work involves complex trust matters and the creation and administration of trusts, as well as the administration of substantial stock market investments and other private client matters. Adrian Gifford heads the firm and is highly regarded for his work in the field, as is his colleague Robert Dickinson. *Hammond Suddards* also undertakes a wide range of private client work for high net worth individuals.

Other notable firms include *Wilkinson Maughan, Rollit Farrell & Bladon* and *Ward Hadaway.*

Rollit Farrell & Bladon provides advice to directors and shareholders in conjunction with corporate transactions, particularly in relation to MBO's, flotations, and a wide range of trusts and estates.

LEADING INDIVIDUALS – NORTH EAST
Robert H. Dickinson *Dickinson Dees*
John C.J. Eaton *Lupton Fawcett*
Adrian C. Gifford *Dickinson Dees*

In all the tables the names in each group are listed alphabetically.

SCOTLAND

Private client work is a substantial area of practice for many Scottish firms, including those firms with a strong commercial foundation. All the firms listed have the capability to deal with a whole range of private client matters. *W & J Burness WS* handle tax and trusts work from both the Edinburgh and Glasgow offices, and *Murray Beith & Murray* particularly deal with work in relation to financial planning and portfolio management. Also well regarded is *Gillespie Macandrew* whose work includes inheritance tax planning, income tax and trust administration.

HIGHLY REGARDED – SCOTLAND

W & J BURNESS WS *Edinburgh*	GILLESPIE MACANDREW WS *Edinburgh*
MURRAY BEITH & MURRAY *Edinburgh*	
ANDERSON STRATHERN *Edinburgh*	BORLAND MONTGOMERIE KEYDEN *Glasgow*
BOYDS *Glasgow*	BRODIES WS *Edinburgh*
CAMPBELL SMITH WS *Edinburgh*	DRUMMOND MILLER WS *Edinburgh*
DUNDAS & WILSON CS *Edinburgh*	JAMES & GEORGE COLLIE *Aberdeen*
KETCHEN & STEVENS WS *Edinburgh*	LEDINGHAM CHALMERS *Aberdeen*
MACLAY MURRAY & SPENS *Glasgow*	McMILLAN KILPATRICK S.S.C. *Ayr*
MITCHELLS ROBERTON *Glasgow*	MORTON FRASER MILLIGAN *Edinburgh*
SHEPHERD & WEDDERBURN *Edinburgh*	STEEDMAN RAMAGE WS *Edinburgh*
TODS MURRAY WS *Edinburgh*	WRIGHT, JOHNSTON & MACKENZIE *Glasgow*

NORTHERN IRELAND

Traditionally, private client matters have accounted for a substantial proportion of the work undertaken by all the firms in Northern Ireland. In recent years, however, this work has to some extent shifted away from the Belfast city centre firms to smaller practices, as the former have carried out more commercial and litigious cases. Despite this the larger firms continue to act for private individuals. Financial services work continues to grow: most firms are now able to channel advice through the Law Society's financial services company, the Law Society (NI) Financial Services Ltd.

HIGHLY REGARDED – NORTHERN IRELAND

C & J BLACK *Belfast*	CLEAVER FULTON & RANKIN *Belfast*
S.J. DIAMOND & SON *Belfast*	ELLIOTT DUFFY GARRETT *Belfast*
HEWITT & GILPIN *Belfast*	JOHNSONS *Belfast*
WILSON NESBITT *Belfast*	

Cleaver Fulton & Rankin complement their commercial practice with a highly regarded private client department. Alastair Rankin, Joy Scott and Peter Rankin carry out trusts, tax, probate and domestic conveyancing work. At *C & J Black*, Elizabeth McCaw is a well known specialist. Herbert McCracken at *Johnsons* enjoys a good reputation in the field, as does Peter Hill at *S J Diamond & Sons*. Gilbert Nesbitt at *Wilson Nesbitt* is highly regarded for his personal tax work.

Other highly thought of firms include *Elliott Duffy Garrett* and *Hewitt & Gilpin*.

LEADING INDIVIDUALS – NORTHERN IRELAND

Alastair J. Rankin	*Cleaver Fulton & Rankin*
Joy D.E.M.A. Scott	*Cleaver Fulton & Rankin*
Elizabeth M. McCaw	*C & J Black*
Herbert L. McCracken	*Johnsons*
Peter A. Hill	*S.J. Diamond & Son*
H.W. Gilbert Nesbitt	*Wilson Nesbitt*
Peter J. Rankin	*Cleaver Fulton & Rankin*

LEADERS IN TRUSTS & PERSONAL TAX

LONDON

Avery Jones C.B.E., John F.
Speechly Bircham, London (0171) 353 3290. Qualified 1966. Partner 1970. Senior Partner 1985. Tax Department. Practice covers tax matters in general, particularly international aspects and VAT.

Bowyer, David
Withers, London (0171) 936 1000. Partner in Private Client Department.

Specialisation: Handles private client matters, including advice to individuals and trustees on tax and trust planning, with particular interest in offshore trusts.

Prof. Membership: Law Society, International Academy of Estate and Trust Law, Star Group.

Career: Qualified in 1965. Partner with *Clifford Turner*, then *Clifford Chance* in Private Client Department from 1968 to 1991. Joined *Withers* as a Partner in October 1991.

Personal: Born 27th August 1940. Educated at Tonbridge School 1954-59 and Trinity Hall, Cambridge 1959-62. Leisure pursuits include golf, tennis, skiing and photography. Lives in Overton, Hampshire.

Boyd-Carpenter C.V.O., Henry
Farrer & Co, London (0171) 242 2022. Partner in Private Client Department.

Specialisation: Main areas of practice are general private client work, wills, settlements, probate, settled land, landed estates and charities.

Prof. Membership: Law Society, Holborn Law Society.

Career: Joined *Farrer & Co* in 1962. Qualified in 1966, became a Partner in 1968. Solicitor to the Duchy of Cornwall 1976-1994.

Personal: Born 11th October 1939. Educated at Charterhouse 1953-58 and Balliol College, Oxford 1959-62. School Governor and Charity Trustee. Enjoys reading, music, hill walking and gardening. Lives in Ascot, Berkshire.

Bridges, Mark T.
Farrer & Co, London (0171) 242 2022. Partner in Private Client Department.

Specialisation: Handles tax and trust matters, particularly for non-domiciled and non-resident individuals.

Prof. Membership: Law Society.

Career: Joined *Farrer & Co* in 1978. Qualified in 1980, became a Partner in 1985.

Personal: Born 25th July 1954. Educated at Cambridge University 1973-77. Special Trustee of Middlesex Hospital, Treasurer of Bach Choir, Council Member of Royal School of Church Music. Recreations include sailing and music. Lives in London.

Brown, Graham S.

Payne Hicks Beach, London (0171) 465 4300. Senior Partner and Head of Tax and Trust department.

Specialisation: Areas of practice include legal and fiscal advice to shareholders and boards of family and other private companies; landed estates and heritage property; international trusts, probates and family property. Charities and educational institutions and French law of property and succession, charities at international conferences in London, Paris, Amsterdam, Munich and Taipei.

Prof. Membership: Institute of Taxation in Ireland; member of Law Society's working party on the Financial Services Act; Holborn Law Society (formerly committee member);International Fiscal Association; Franco-British Lawyers' Association.

Personal: Born in 1944. Educated at Bristol University (LL.B, 1966), the Catholic University of Louvain 1969-70, and King's College, London (LL.M, 1975). Leisure interests include arts, heritage and music. Fellow of the Royal Society of Arts; Liveryman Clockmaker's Company. Member of Arts Club. Lives in Bath.

Carpenter, Michael S.E.

Withers, London (0171) 936 1000. Partner in Private Client Department

Specialisation: Handles tax, trust and estate planning for UK and foreign domiciled clients, with special emphasis on advising trustees in relation to commercial transactions. Also covers charity law and practice, advising leading charities on constitutional and strategic issues. Has lectured at innumerable conferences going back to 1970, on a wide variety of topics. Member of the Advisory Editorial Board of the 'Charity Law and Practice Review'.

Prof. Membership: City of London Law Society, Association of Charity Lawyers.

Career: Qualified in 1967 and was with *Slaughter and May* from then until 1994 (from 1974 as a Partner and from 1991 as Senior Partner in the Trust Department). Joined *Withers* as a Partner in 1994.

Personal: Born 7th October 1942. Educated at Eastbourne College 1956-61 and Bristol University 1961-64. Recreations include golf, hill walking, church and village activities.

Cooke, Stephen

Withers, London (0171) 936 1000. Partner in Private Client Department.

Specialisation: Main area of practice is tax and asset management planning for the private client, both in the UK and offshore. Gave Longmans Seminars on Executors' Appointment, Duties and Taxation (1985 and 1987), Sweet & Maxwell seminars on Capital Transfer Tax (1985), Dealing with Future Growth (1984), Drafting Trust Documents for Tax Efficiency Longman Seminars (1985) and

many others. Contributor to 'Tax Cases Analysis' and co-author of 'Inheritance Tax on Lifetime Gifts' (1987).

Prof. Membership: City of London Law Society, International Fiscal Association.

Career: Qualified in 1971, having articled with *Clay Allison & Clark*, Nottinghamshire. Awarded the Law Society SH Clay prize. Joined *Withers* in 1971; Partner in 1973.

Personal: Born 30th July 1946. Attended Stamford School 1956-64 and Leicester School of Architecture. Vice Chairman of the London Handel Society Ltd. Leisure interests include art and music (baroque), cricket, gardening and tennis. Lives in Well, Basingstoke.

Dilger, John

Macfarlanes, London (0171) 831 9222. Qualified 1961. Partner 1964. Tax & Financial Planning Department. Specialises in trusts and the taxation of individuals and partnerships.

Dolman, Robert A.

Wedlake Bell, London (0171) 395 3000.

Drewitt, John

Frere Cholmeley Bischoff, London (0171) 615 8000.

Duffield, Peter

Withers, London (0171) 936 1000. Partner in Private Client Department.

Specialisation: Main areas of practice are trusts, taxation and estate planning. Head of Trust and Private Client Department at *Travers Smith Braithwaite* to 1992. Handles all aspects of private client practice.

Prof. Membership: Law Society, STAR group.

Career: Qualified in 1961. Partner at *Travers Smith Braithwaite* 1966-92. Non-executive Director of CE Heath plc since 1985.

Personal: Born 30th April 1935. Attended Bancroft's School 1945-53 and St John's College, Oxford 1955-58. Leisure interests include fly fishing. Lives in Eridge.

Gowar, Martyn

Lawrence Graham, London (0171) 379 0000. Partner in Tax Department.

Specialisation: Specialises principally in Private Client Tax, acting for large landed estates, trustees (particularly offshore trusts), and private clients with business interests. Also inter-generational transfers of family businesses and general tax work, income tax, capital gains tax and inheritance tax advice generally, including income tax on structured settlements and tax on insurance policies. Editor of Butterworths Encyclopaedia of Forms and Precedents (Vol. 30 on Partnership) and contributor to Simon's Taxes on the tax and trust treatment of demerger shares issues and enhanced scrip dividends. Has lectured widely over the last 15 years. In the last year has lectured in Bermuda, Jersey and

Guernsey on UK taxation of offshore trusts, to a STEP conference on Demergers and Enhanced Scrip Dividends and on International Tax Planning for European Study Conferences. Also lectured and chaired the session at the International Academy of Estate and Trust Law conference in Edinburgh on Tax Issues for the Emigrant.

Prof. Membership: Law Society; Chartered Institute of Taxation (Associate 1976, Fellow 1981); Association of Corporate Trustees; Executive Council member of International Academy of Estate and Trust Law. Member Addington Society.

Career: Joined *Lawrence Graham* in 1967, qualifying in 1970 and becoming Partner in 1973. Member of numerous revenue law committees including the Tax Committee of the Association of Corporate Trustees (1987 to date) and the Capital Taxes Committee of the Chartered Institute of Taxation. Also Clerk to the Governors of Wellington College and Clerk to the Trustees of the Hamlyn Trust.

Personal: Born 11th July 1946. Educated at King's College School, Wimbledon and Magdalen College, Oxford 1964-67. Lives in Elstead, Surrey and enjoys golf, cricket (President of Elstead Cricket Club), and gardening.

Hayes, Michael

Macfarlanes, London (0171) 831 9222. Qualified 1968. Partner 1974. Head of Tax and Financial Planning Department. Specialies in UK and offshore private client tax and estate planning.

Jarman, Chris M.

Payne Hicks Beach, London (0171) 465 4300. Qualified 1980. Partner 1986. Tax, Trust and Probate Department. Specialises in private client, general taxation, VAT, and property work.

Kirby, Richard C.

Speechly Bircham, London (0171) 353 3290. Partner 1973.

Specialisation: Main area of practice is private client work, handling estate and tax planning for UK and non-UK domiciliaries and trusts. Also charity law and administration. Has written numerous articles for national newspapers and specialist taxation periodicals.

Prof. Membership: Law Society.

Career: Head Private Client and Charity Team 1980. Solicitor Worshipful Company of Pewterers 1981 (Freeman 1991)

Personal: Born 18th September 1946. Educated Sevenoaks School 1960-65 and Jesus College, Oxford 1965-68 MA. Member Council Mental After Care Association 1982 (Hon. Treasurer 1987-). Member Carlton Club. Enjoys reading, theatre and swimming. Lives in Dulwich.

Lewis, Ian G.

Nabarro Nathanson, London (0171) 493

9933. Qualified 1972. Partner 1974. Private Client Department. Handles estate planning and international tax planning for individuals and trusts.

Long, David
Charles Russell, London (0171) 203 5096. Partner in Private Client Department.

Specialisation: Handles trusts, wills, probate, charities and tax law.

Prof. Membership: Law Society, Holborn Law Society (President 1992-93, Chairman Trust Section), Charity Law Association, STEP (Society of Trusts and Estate Practitioners). Member of joint committee of The Law Society with the Court of Protection and Public Trust Office.

Career: Joined Charles Russell in 1972 and became a partner in 1974. Hon. Solicitor Royal Philharmonic Society.

Personal: Born 3rd March 1946. Educated at King Edward's School, Birmingham and Balliol College, Oxford 1964-67. Leisure interests included music, tennis, architecture and gardening.

Macfadyen, Michael R.
Norton Rose, London (0171) 283 6000. Partner in Private Client Department.

Specialisation: Main areas of practice are private client (national and international), tax planning, charities, trusts, probate and Court of Protection.

Prof. Membership: Law Society, City of London Solicitors Company, Society of Estates Practitioners, Charity Lawyers Association.

Career: Qualified in 1966. Joined *Norton Rose* in 1961, becoming a Partner in 1970.

Personal: Born 1943. Attended Marlborough College 1956-61. Leisure interests include golf, cricket and walking. Lives in Henley-on-Thames.

Maurice, Clare M.
Allen & Overy, London (0171) 330 3000. Qualified 1978. Partner 1985. Private Client Department. Specialises in tax planning and advice, Revenue investigations and charities.

Mellor, Eliza
Nicholson Graham & Jones, London (0171) 628 9151. Partner in Tax & Private Client Department.

Specialisation: Has twenty years experience working for UK and overseas-based clients, dealing with work ranging from UK income, capital gains and inheritance tax advice to structuring international families estate planning and trust litigation. Has lectured abroad on the use of trusts.

Prof. Membership: Law Society; Technical & International Committees of STEP; International Academy of Estate & Trust Lawyers. International Tax Planning Association.

Career: Qualified in 1974. Joined *Nicholson Graham & Jones* in 1984 and became a Part-

ner in 1985.

Personal: Educated at City of Worcester Grammar School for Girls 1960-67 and Cambridge University 1968-71. Lives in London.

Mimpriss, Peter
See under Charities.

Moyse, Richard M.
Boodle Hatfield, London (0171) 629 7411. Partner in charge of Private Client/ Tax and Financial Planning Department.

Specialisation: Main areas of practice are tax, trusts and financial planning (with an international emphasis), post-mortem tax planning and probate. Specialist fields are capital taxation, trusts, succession, heritage property, contentious trusts and probates. Experienced in the use of trusts in different jurisdictions for estate planning, asset protection and avoidance of forced heirship situations. Has experience in handling large international trusts with conflicts of law, family disputes and succession problems. Sometime editor of the 'Business Law Encyclopaedia' and Financial Editor of the Law Society's 'Business Gazette'. Has made numerous contributions to professional and in-house publications. Extensive lecturing experience, especially on capital taxation and international tax planning in the UK and abroad, to audiences such as the International Academy of Estate and Trust Law and the International Bar Association.

Prof. Membership: Law Society, International Academy of Estate and Trust Law, International Tax Planning Association, International Bar Association.

Career: With *Lawrence Graham* from 1969-73. Qualified in 1970. Joined *Boodle Hatfield* in 1973 and became a Partner in 1974. Member of the Revenue Law Committee of the Law Society and Chairman of Capital Taxes Sub-Committee. Vice President (Europe) of the International Academy of Estate and Trust Law. Member of the 1994 Principal Private Residence Relief Working Party.

Personal: Born 29th September 1943. Educated at Plymouth College 1948-62, then St. John's College, Oxford 1962-65. Married with four children. Leisure pursuits include travel, cricket, music, genealogy, fly fishing and painting. Lives in London.

Norris, William
Allen & Overy, London (0171) 330 3000. Qualified 1959. Partner 1964. Private Client Department. Main area of practice is family wealth management; also handles educational and other charities work. Born 11.5.1937.

Paul, Robin
Withers, London (0171) 936 1000. Partner in Private Client Department.

Specialisation: Main area of practice is probate and succession. Head of Probate Group, advising executors and beneficiaries on all aspects of probate and post death tax planning,

often with an international element. Also deals with trusts, tax and estate planning and heritage property. Co-author of the Administration of Estates section of 'The Lawyers Factbook' and of 'Practical Will Precedents'. Contributor to various legal journals, including 'The Solicitors Journal', 'The Lawyer' and 'Capital Taxes', as well as to FT Law and Tax, 'Practical Tax Planning with Precedents' and the Succession section of 'Practical Commercial Law'. Has lectured at various conferences on wills and succession, with particular emphasis on international aspects.

Prof. Membership: STEP, Law Society, Westminster Law Society.

Career: Qualified in 1977, having joined *Withers* in 1975. Became a Partner in 1982.

Personal: Born 19th December 1952. Educated at Malvern College, then Brasenose College, Oxford 1971-74. Lives in London.

Powell, Nicholas R.D.
Currey & Co, London (0171) 828 4091. Qualified 1969. Partner 1971. Specialises in private client work, including family trusts, wills, probate, personal tax and property.

Rhodes, John
Macfarlanes, London (0171) 831 9222. Qualified 1970. Partner 1975. Main areas of practice are UK and international trust and tax planning.

Richardson, Joseph C.
Dawson & Co, London (0171) 404 5941. Partner in Private Client Department.

Specialisation: Main area of specialisation is taxation. Covers all areas, particularly capital taxation planning (CGT and IHT) and all aspects of settlements (offshore, variation, etc) and heritage property. Also deals with a range of general private client work for high net worth individuals and families (both old and new money) and some charity work. Acts for a number of major landed estates. Has lectured recently on IHT and agricultural tenancies. Charge-out rate is £180 per hour.

Prof. Membership: Law Society, Society of Trusts and Estates Practitioners.

Career: Qualified in 1974. Partner in *Dawson & Co* since 1976.

Personal: Born 21st October 1949. Educated at St Olave's and St Peter's Schools, York 1959-68, then Durham University 1968-71 (BA in Law). Chairman of School Governors, Inhurst House School Trust Ltd. Former Chairman of Selectors, Squash Racket Association (currently Chairman of Disciplinary Panel). Leisure interests are mainly sporting and include cricket, golf and squash. Lives near Basingstoke, Hants.

Robinson, David
Frere Cholmeley Bischoff, London (0171) 615 8000. Partner in and Head of Private Client Department.

Specialisation: Private client specialist, with particular expertise in estate planning, capital taxation and heritage property.

Prof. Membership: Holborn Law Society and City of London Law Society.

Career: Qualified in 1981. With *Glover & Co* 1982-85. Joined *Frere Cholmeley Bischoff* in 1985 and became a Partner in 1989.

Personal: Born in 1955. Educated at Westminster School and Pembroke College, Cambridge. Leisure interests include collecting books, music, art and travel.

Skrine, A.M.A.
Hunters, London (0171) 412 0050.

Stanford-Tuck, Michael
Taylor Joynson Garrett, London (0171) 353 1234. Partner in Tax and Personal Planning Department.

Specialisation: Principal area of practice is international trust and tax planning, acting for high net worth individuals, mainly those who are non-UK domiciled. Work includes protection of assets, structuring cross-border investments, asset enhancement, diversification and protection. Also deals with domestic private client work, encompassing UK based estate and tax planning, landed estates, heritage property, contentious and non-contentious probate and chancery litigation. Has handled administration of a major multinational estate, principally in Japan, trust restructuring for high net worth families relocating to or investing in the UK and the defence of a high profile UK peer in contentious chancery proceedings under the Settled Land Act 1925. Experienced lecturer and author of various articles.

Prof. Membership: Law Society, City of London Solicitors Company, Freeman of the City of London, Society of Trust and Estate Practitioners, Bermuda Society (Committee Member), Star Group.

Career: Qualified in 1972. With *Lovell White & King* 1972-75. Partner with *Appleby Spurling & Kempe* (Bermuda) 1975-84. Joined *Taylor Joynson Garrett* as a Partner in 1985.

Personal: Born 3rd November 1946. Educated at Radley College 1960-65 and Southampton University 1965-68. Chairman of Parish Council. Leisure activities include golf, gardening, skiing and shooting. Lives in Newbury, Berks.

Stevens, Brian
Withers, London (0171) 936 1000. Partner in Private Client Department.

Specialisation: Main area of practice is trusts and capital tax planning, with particular reference to landed estates.

Prof. Membership: Law Society.

Career: Qualified in 1962. Joined *Withers* in 1970 as a Partner.

Personal: Born 3rd November 1938. Educated at Eton College 1951-57. Enjoys music, field sports and gardening. Lives in Hampshire.

Tandy, David
Titmuss Sainer Dechert, London (0171) 583 5353. Partner and Head of Tax and Private Client Department.

Specialisation: Main area of practice is private client. Specialises in estate planning, trusts and charities. Also handles probate, wills and taxation for trusts and estates.

Prof. Membership: Member of International Bar Association, International Tax Planning Association, Society of Trusts and Estates Practitioners, Association of Charity Lawyers, Solicitors Trusts and Revenue Group.

Career: Qualified in 1975. Joined *Titmuss Sainer & Webb* (now *Titmuss Sainer Dechert*) in 1973, becoming a Partner in 1976 and Head of the Private Client Department in 1984. In 1995 the Tax and Private Client departments merged and David Tandy is now Head of the new department.

Personal: Born in 1944. LLB University of London (external) and City of London College EDO Course (1970). Leisure interests include shooting, opera, fitness and wine. Lives in Crawley.

Thompson, Anthony J.
Withers, London (0171) 936 1000. Partner in Private Client Department.

Specialisation: Main areas of practice are tax planning, asset structuring, trusts and probate. Acted in Hambro & Others v. Marlborough & Others (application under the Settled Land Act for an order to resettle the Blenheim Parliamentary Estates). Clients include proprietors of landed estates, proprietors of businesses (particularly in the property industry) and offshore trustees. Has lectured at IBC conferences and contributed to Television Education Network.

Prof. Membership: Law Society.

Career: Qualified in 1968. Partner of *Withers* since 1970. Head of Private Client Department 1980-87. Managing Partner 1987-93.

Personal: Born 29th May 1943. Educated at Haberdashers Aske's School 1956-60 and Trinity College, Cambridge 1961-65. School Governor (Glenesk School). President of Horsley Cricket Club. Recreations include golf and amateur dramatics. Lives in Guildford.

Turnor, Richard
Allen & Overy, London (0171) 330 3000. Qualified 1980. Partner 1985. Advises partnerships, corporate and professional trustees, wealthy families and charities. Born 15.3.1956.

Way, David
Simmons & Simmons, London (0171) 628 2020. Qualified 1977. Partner 1987. Tax Department. Deals with private client work involving national and international tax and estate planning. Born 13.7.1952.

Whitehouse, Christopher J.
Boodle Hatfield, London (0171) 629 7411. Partner in Tax and Financial Planning Department.

Specialisation: Handles corporate tax, personal tax planning, trusts and wills. Specialist fields are all aspects of asset protection, domicile and residence, offshore tax planning and contentious trust administration. Lecturer on insolvency for the CBI 1986-87. Annual Guest Lecturer for the College of Law on the Wills and Estate Planning course. Also lecturer for the Scottish Law Society, the Institute of Chartered Accountants of England and Wales, at the STEP national and Birmingham conferences 1994-95 and for Butterworths on tax planning for non-domiciliaries and offshore tax planning for UK residents. Author of 'Revenue Law: Principles and Practice' (13th edition - forthcoming), co-author with B.McCutcheon of 'McCutcheon on Inheritance Tax' (3rd edition) and co-author of the section on trusts and settlements in the 'Encyclopedia of Forms & Precedents' (5th edition). Has also had numerous articles published in, for example, *Capital Taxes News*, *Capital Taxes*, *Taxation* and *The Tax Journal*.

Career: Called to the Bar in 1972. Principal lecturer and subsequently reader at the College of Law 1971-87. Joined *Boodle Hatfield* 1987. Qualified as a Solicitor and became partner in 1993.

Personal: Born in 1948. Educated at Wirral Grammar School, Oxford University (BA 1969, BCL 1970) and London University (BA 1979). Leisure interests include football, theatre, walking, reading and art. Lives in London.

Willis, David
Frere Cholmeley Bischoff, London (0171) 615 8000. Qualified 1975. Partner 1978. Private Client Department. Main area of practice is trusts and tax work. Also handles regular case load of family law work. Born 24.10.1945.

Rankin, Alastair J.
Cleaver Fulton & Rankin, Belfast (01232) 243141.

Scott, Joy D.E.M.A.
Cleaver Fulton & Rankin, Belfast (01232) 243141.

McCaw, Elizabeth M.
C & J Black, Belfast (01232) 550060.

McCracken, Herbert L.
Johnsons, Belfast (01232) 240183.

Hill, Peter A.
S.J. Diamond & Son, Belfast (01232) 243726.

Nesbitt, H.W. Gilbert
Wilson Nesbitt, Belfast (01232) 428600. Qualified 1978.

Ash, R.F.
Thomas Eggar Verrall Bowles, Chichester (01243) 786111.

Dickinson, Robert H.
Dickinson Dees, Newcastle upon Tyne (0191) 261 1911.

Eaton, John C.J.
Lupton Fawcett, Leeds (0113) 246 9696. Qualified 1965. Partner 1966. 25 years specialisation in financial services, investment management, trusts and tax planning.

Emmerson, John C.
Wilsons, Salisbury (01722) 412412. Qualified 1967. Partner 1991. Tax Planning Department. Handles UK and international tax planning, trust law and charitable trusts. Born 1937.

FitzGerald, Peter R.
Wilsons, Salisbury (01722) 412412. Qualified 1969. Partner 1995. Farms and Estates Department.

Gifford, Adrian C.
Dickinson Dees, Newcastle upon Tyne (0191) 261 1911. Qualified 1977. Partner 1979. Head of Private Client Department. Specialises in trusts and estate planning. Born 25.11.1946.

Glazier, Barry
Lester Aldridge, Bournemouth (01202) 786161. Partner in Private Client Department.

Specialisation: Corporate and personal tax, particularly for family-owned businesses, as well as landed estates, onshore and offshore trusts, and charities. Appointed Managing Partner in 1994.

Career: Articled Penningtons, London; qualified 1966; solicitor Clifford Turner 1966-1971; partner Lester Aldridge since 1972; president of Dorset Chamber of Commerce and Industry 1992-1993, president Bournemouth & District Law Society 1991-1992; director and company secretary, Dorset Training and Enterprise Council; chairman of Eurolegal; chairman of Hurstpierpoint Lawyers' Society; governor of the Bournemouth & Poole College of Further Education.

Personal: Born 1941; resides Wimborne Minster. Educated at Hurstpierpoint College (1950-1960); St Peter's College, Oxford (1960-1963 BA, 1968 MA Oxon); Notary Public. Recreations include concerts and opera, piano playing, walking, ornithology, gardening.

Krafft, James A.
Thomson Snell & Passmore, Tunbridge Wells (01892) 510000. Partner and Head of Private Client Department.

Specialisation: Main areas of practice are general private client work, personal financial planning, tax planning, wills, settlements, powers of attorney and probate.

Prof. Membership: Law Society and Society of Trust and Estate Practitioners.

Career: Qualified in 1971, Articled and practised in London before joining *Thomson Snell & Passmore* in 1976.

Personal: Born 1st May 1944. Educated at Downside School and St. Catherine's College, Oxford. Leisure interests include tennis, golf, bridge, reading and psychology. Lives in Langton Green, Kent.

Laing, Sue
Boodle Hatfield, Oxford.

Lea, Thomas Mark
Wilsons, Salisbury (01722) 412412. Qualified 1970. Partner 1987. UK and International Tax Planning Department. Specialises in international comparative tax planning. Born 27.4.1944.

Leney, Simon
Cripps Harries Hall, Tunbridge Wells (01892) 515121.

Miller, Adrian W.M.
Anstey Sargent & Probert, Exeter (01392) 411221. Qualified 1975. Partner in charge of Private Client Division. Main areas of practice are personal family and financial planning for individuals and landed estates. Born 7.11.1947.

Nicholson, Jonathan
Bond Pearce, Plymouth (01752) 266633. Qualified 1968. Partner 1985. Private Client Division. Over 20 years experience in wills, probate, trust administration and tax. Also handles charity law.

Porter, John Neil
Burges Salmon, Bristol (0117) 939 2000.

Qualified 1960. Partner 1980. Private Client Department. Handles mainstream private client work, principally for farmers and landowners.

Rankin, Peter J.
See under Company/Commercial.

Sharpe, John W.
Osborne Clarke, Bristol (0117) 923 0220. Qualified 1974. Partner 1980. Tax and Trust Department. Work includes UK and international personal taxation, trusts, wills, succession, probate, agricultural law and landed estates. Born 17.3.1949.

Shindler, Geoffrey A.
Halliwell Landau, Manchester (0161) 835 3003. Qualified 1969. Partner 1986. Trust and Estate Planning Department. Specialises in trusts, personal taxation, and wills and probate. Born 1942.

Thornely, Richard M.G.
Thomas Eggar Verrall Bowles, Horsham (0403) 26924. Partner in Private Client Department.

Specialisation: Main areas of practice are personal tax planning, wills and trusts. Also deals with charities and the affairs of the elderly.

Prof. Membership: Law Society, S.T.E.P.

Career: Qualified in 1978. Joined *Thomas Eggar Verrall Bowles* in 1992 and became a Partner in 1993.

Personal: Born 20th January 1957. Educated at Rugby School 1969-74 and Trinity Hall, Cambridge 1975-78. Governor of Queen Alexandra Hospital Home, Worthing. Recreations include mountaineering and music. Lives in Horsham.

Willcox, Michael
Eversheds, Norwich (01603) 272727. Qualified 1970. Partner in the Private Capital Group. Specialises in international private client matters. Born 13.5.1945.

Wollen, Nigel J.
Hooper & Wollen, Torquay (01803) 213251. Qualified 1969. Commercial and Tax Department. Main areas of practice are shipping and maritime law. Emphasis on development of harbours and marinas.

VAT/CUSTOMS & EXCISE

LONDON

Of the firms specialising in general tax law, a number offer advice in all areas of VAT/Customs & Excise law. The leading VAT firms are *Allen & Overy, Simmons & Simmons, Watson, Farley & Williams* and *Lovell White Durrant* followed by *Freshfields* and *Linklaters & Paines*. The leading firm for Customs & Excise work is *Titmuss Sainer Dechert* followed by *Baker & McKenzie*.

VAT

Allen & Overy leads the field, dispensing VAT advice and planning for all major corporate transactions, property investment and development, banking and financial services, insolvency and internal operations particularly the Single European Market. It also deals with VAT investigations and litigation. In the area of Community Customs Duty, work handled includes tariff classification and anti-dumping duty.

LEADING FIRMS – LONDON — VAT	
ALLEN & OVERY	LOVELL WHITE DURRANT
SIMMONS & SIMMONS	WATSON, FARLEY & WILLIAMS

In the area of Excise duty the firm has advised in relation to liability issues and also harmonisation issues resulting from the implementation of the Single Market. Michael Conlon was recommended as a leading practitioner in VAT law.

Simmons & Simmons, another strong firm in the field of corporate tax generally, are very highly regarded for this work in the field of VAT law. Stephen Coleclough and Paul Hale are the two partners in the corporate tax group dealing primarily in VAT matters. They both have experience of VAT and Customs & Excise litigation, acting for a number of high profile PLC companies, and have been involved in cases such as 'BLP Group Plc v Customs & Excise'.

Watson, Farley & Williams advise on all aspects of VAT law and also undertake Customs matters including appeals to the VAT and Duties Tribunal, investigations and general planning advice. Christopher Preston is very highly regarded in the field of indirect taxation and is credited by a number of solicitors as having been instrumental in the development of VAT law in the 1980's. He is currently Chairperson of The Law Society VAT and Customs Duties Sub-Committee and was a founding member of the VAT Practitioners Group.

Lovell White Durrant provide a sound advisory capability on transactions across the commercial, insolvency, property and financial services sector and deal with related litigation in this context. In the last two years, for example, they have, acted for P&O in the Court of Appeal and Kingfisher in the High Court, successfully appealing against VAT decisions. Anthony Davis along with Greg Sinfield heads the indirect taxes department and both are very highly regarded for their work in this field.

A sole practitioner who deserves a mention is Ann Humphrey. She broke the oligarchy of the big firms when she left *Richards Butler* to set up her own firm specialising solely in VAT law.

Other leading firms in this field include *Freshfields, Linklaters & Paines* and *Speechley Bircham*. *Freshfields* continue to handle all aspects of VAT law and Mark Baldwin of this firm is well thought of. The firm is recovering from the departure of Michael Conlon to *Allen & Overy* in 1993. *Linklaters & Paines* have particular expertise handling VAT on property matters, and Carolyn Taylor is well regarded for her work in this field. *Speechly Bircham* also have a niche emphasis on VAT issues on property transactions where John Avery Jones, who is a part-time VAT and Duties Tribunal Chairman, was recommended for both his VAT and Customs & Excise work.

HIGHLY REGARDED – LONDON — VAT	
ANN L. HUMPHREY	FRESHFIELDS
LINKLATERS & PAINES	SPEECHLY BIRCHAM
ASHURST MORRIS CRISP	CLIFFORD CHANCE
HERBERT SMITH	SLAUGHTER AND MAY

Other firms with experience in the field include *Ashurst Morris Crisp, Clifford Chance, Herbert Smith* and *Slaughter and May*.

CUSTOMS & EXCISE

Titmuss Sainer Dechert are the leading firm for Customs & Excise law. They handle the full range of work in this field dealing with investigation cases, tariff classification, valuation and transfer pricing issues in customs valuation, origin, duty preference, export rebates, agricultural levies, import

LEADING FIRMS – LONDON — CUSTOMS
TITMUSS SAINER DECHERT

and export licensing, anti-dumping duties and international trade disputes. Gavin McFarlane is extremely highly regarded and is arguably the leading national expert in this field. He has a great deal of experience in appearing before the VAT and Duty Tribunal and has conducted cases before the European Court of Justice. He has acted in the largest VAT assessment, tried anonymously in the Court of Appeal under public interest immunity certificates.

Also at *Titmus Sainer Dechert* is Malachy Cornwell-Kelly, who spent five years with the Customs & Excise Department and joined the International Trade and Customs Division of *Titmuss Sainer Dechert* in 1993. He has a great deal of experience before the VAT and Duties Tribunal as well as the European Court.

HIGHLY REGARDED – LONDON — CUSTOMS
BAKER & McKENZIE

In all the tables the names in each group are listed alphabetically.

The other firm specialising in the field of Customs & Excise law is *Baker & McKenzie,* which also undertakes a substantial amount of VAT work. The firm has strong international connections and this is reflected in the foreign work undertaken in this field. They advise multinational companies on practice and procedures relating to customs duties and taxes with a view to maximizing the benefit to be derived from international customs regimes and reliefs. They also deal with enquiries and investigations into compliance and customs and VAT obligations, including negotiations with the Customs Investigation Division.

LEADING INDIVIDUALS – LONDON — CUSTOMS
Stephen D. Coleclough *Simmons & Simmons*
Michael Conlon *Allen & Overy*
Gavin McFarlane *Titmuss Sainer Dechert*
Christopher A.L. Preston *Watson Farley & Williams*
John F. Avery Jones C.B.E. *Speechly Bircham*
Mark Baldwin *Freshfields*
Michael John Cant *Nabarro Nathanson*
Malachy Cornwell-Kelly *Titmuss Sainer Dechert*
Anthony C.R. Davis *Lovell White Durrant*
Paul D. Hale *Simmons & Simmons*
Andrew Hart *Baker & McKenzie*
Ann Humphrey *Ann L. Humphrey*
Stephen Shea *Clifford Chance*
Greg Sinfield *Lovell White Durrant*
Carolyn Taylor *Linklaters & Paines*

Andrew Hart is very well regarded for his expertise in this field. A partner at *Baker & McKenzie* since 1980, his clients include Conner Peripherals, Emerson Electric and Informix. He is the author of the Customs and VAT sections of Sweet & Maxwell's 'Encyclopaedia of Information Technology Law'.

REGIONS

It would be fair to say that no firms outside London specialise in this area of work. However the following firms have experience in this field. *Burges Salmon* in Bristol have dealt

HIGHLY REGARDED – REGIONS		
BURGES SALMON *Bristol*	**HAMMOND SUDDARDS** *Leeds*
McGRIGOR DONALD *Glasgow*	
BOOTH & CO. *Leeds*	**EDGE & ELLISON** *Birmingham*
EVERSHEDS *Birmingham*	**HALLIWELL LANDAU** *Manchester*
PINSENT CURTIS *Birmingham*	**VAUDREYS** *Manchester*

with VAT deferral and avoidance schemes relating to educational establishments and also VAT on business sales. *Hammond Suddards* in Leeds have taken a VAT-related case to the House of Lords. North of the border, the Scottish firm *McGrigor Donald* were recommended for their expertise in VAT law and Richard Pincher of this firm is well regarded.

LEADING INDIVIDUALS – REGIONS
Richard Pincher *McGrigor Donald*

LEADERS IN VAT/CUSTOMS & EXCISE

LONDON

Avery Jones C.B.E., John F.
See under Trusts & Personal Tax.

Baldwin, Mark
Freshfields, London (0171) 936 4000. Assistant Solicitor in Tax Department.

Specialisation: Handles all areas of indirect tax work, principally VAT, but also excise duties and customs duty. Also practices in other tax fields, principally asset/property finance and leasing and insurance. Has written various articles on VAT topics in *VAT Intelligence, VAT Planning, The Tax Journal* and *British Tax Review.* Conference speaker for VAT Intelligence, Henry Stewart Conferences and IIR.

Prof. Membership: Law Society, VAT Practitioners Group.

Career: Qualified in 1987 since when he has been an Assistant Solicitor at *Freshfields.*

Cant, Michael John
Nabarro Nathanson, London (0171) 493 9933. Qualified 1984. Assistant 1988. Corporate Tax Department. Specialises in VAT and stamp duties. Member of VAT Practitioners Group.

Coleclough, Stephen D.
Simmons & Simmons, London (0171) 628 2020. Partner in Corporate Tax Department.

Specialisation: Primarily responsible for VAT. Other principal areas: international tax planning and structuring, capital markets and structured finance, securitisations, corporate finance and M&A work. Acted in BLP Group plc v. Customs & Excise. Tax Consultant to Butterworths Company Law Service. Contributor to Butterworths Encyclopaedia of Forms and Precedents. Author of numerous articles in tax and legal publications throughout Europe. Has lectured around Europe on VAT, international tax issues and M&A work. He is Chairman of the Institute of Taxation Technical Committee, Indirect Taxes Sub Committee, and a member of the Law Society's VAT Technical Committee, the VAT Practitioners Group Technical Committee and the International Bar Association Indirect Taxes Committee.

Prof. Membership: Law Society, VAT Practitioners Group, International Bar Association, Institute of Taxation.

Career: Qualified in 1986. Joined *Simmons & Simmons* in 1987, becoming a Partner in 1991.

Personal: Born 6th April 1962. Attended Sheffield University 1980-83 (LLB). Lives in Harrow. Leisure: heavy metal, Gibson guitars, chutney making and snooker.

Conlon, Michael
Allen & Overy, London (0171) 330 3000. Qualified 1992. Partner 1993. Tax Department. Covers all areas of indirect taxation, including investigations, litigation and expert evidence; and customs and excise duties. Born 26.11.1951.

Cornwell-Kelly, Malachy
Titmuss Sainer Dechert, London (0171) 583 5353. International Trade and Customs Division.

Specialisation: Negotiates and handles disputes with Customs and Excise and IBEA on all VAT, customs and excise duty matters.

Work covers investigation cases, tariff classification, valuation and transfer pricing issues, origin, duty preference, export rebates CAP questions, import and export licensing, anti-dumping duties, and appeals to and appearances before the VAT and Duties Tribunal and the European Court. Cases have included agricultural levy disputes and CAP export refunds, dangerous waste disposal trade, and United Nations trade sanctions. Author of 'European Community Law', 2nd edition, a regular column in The New Law Journal, and articles in Taxation, The Practical Tax Lawyer, The Law Society's Gazette and Exporting Today. Frequent conference speaker.

Prof. Membership: Law Society VAT and Duties Committee, VAT Practitioners Group, Customs Practitioners Group, Law Society representative on Joint Customs Consultative Committee, Hon. Sec. of IFS Tax Law Review Committee.

Career: Qualified in 1971. Worked at Customs and Excise Solicitor's Office 1972-77, then *Richards Butler* 1977-83. Joined the Law Society as Revenue Law Committee Secretary in 1983 before becoming Director of Tax Investigations for the Parliamentary Ombudsman in 1988. Joined *Titmuss Sainer & Webb* (now *Titmuss Sainer Dechert*) in 1993.

Personal: Born 11th May 1947. Attended King's College, London, 1965-68 (LLB), then College of Law, London, 1968-69. Secretary of the Tax Law Review Committee at the Institute for Fiscal Studies, chairman of the VAT and Duties Tribunal and deputy special commissioner. Leisure interests include cider and beer making and collecting Customs memorabilia. Lives in Sevenoaks, Kent.

Davis, Anthony C.R.
See under Tax (Corporate).

Hale, Paul D.
Simmons & Simmons, London (0171) 628 2020. Partner in Corporate Tax Department.

Specialisation: Main area of practice is corporate tax and value added tax. Work includes mergers and acquisitions, stock exchange listings, project finance, structured finance and property transactions. Also handles taxation of collective investment schemes, including unit trusts, investment trusts and offshore funds. Author of various articles.

Prof. Membership: Law Society, City of London Solicitors' Company, VAT Practitioners Group.

Career: Qualified 1985, having joined *Simmons & Simmons* in 1983. Became a Partner in 1990.

Personal: Born 1st August 1959. Attended Winchester College 1973-77, then Worcester College Oxford 1977-81. Leisure interests include family life, gardening and bridge. Lives in Amersham.

Hart, Andrew
Baker & McKenzie, London (0171) 919 1000. Partner in EU, Competition and Trade Law Department.

Specialisation: Principal area of practice is commercial and trade law, notably customs and VAT law. Advises multinational and domestic companies on practice and procedures relating to their business, especially the impact of customs duties, taxes and maximizing benefit to be derived from various customs regimes and reliefs. Assists clients in responding to enquiries and investigations into compliance with customs and VAT obligations, including negotiation and settlement of investigations by the Customs Investigation Division and other parts of H.M. Customs & Excise. Clients include Conner-Peripherals, Emerson Electric, McDonnell Douglas and Informix. Writes Customs Update for Butterworth's monthly *VAT Planning incorporating Customs Duties*. Author of Customs and VAT sections of Sweet & Maxwell's 'Encyclopedia of Information Technology Law'. Has undertaken speaking engagements in the US, UK and India on various aspects of UK and EU trade, tax, customs and VAT law and practice. Charge-out rate is £275-£300 per hour.

Prof. Membership: Law Society (Member of VAT and Duties Sub-Committee of Revenue Law Committee), Customs Practitioners Group (Hon. Secretary).

Career: Qualified in 1972. Partner at *Baker & McKenzie* since 1980.

Personal: Born 2nd August 1947. Educated at Nottingham University 1966-69 (LL.B Hons). Leisure interests include football and squash. Lives in London.

Humphrey, Ann
Ann L. Humphrey, London (0171) 701 3939. Qualified 1977. Founder 1993. Main area of practice is tax planning and advice, particularly VAT. Also international corporate tax and lobbying.

McFarlane, Gavin
Titmuss Sainer Dechert, London (0171) 583 5353. (Bar). Director of International Trade and Customs Division.

Specialisation: International Trade and Customs. Negotiates and handles disputes with Customs and Excise on all VAT, customs and excise duty matters. Work includes all investigations cases, classification, transfer pricing in customs valuation, origin, duty preference, export rebates, agricultural levies, import and export licensing, anti-dumping and international trade disputes, VAT and Duty Tribunal appeals and cases before the European Court of Justice. Acted in the largest ever VAT assessment, tried anonymously in the Court of Appeal under public interest immunity certificates. Author of 'Customs and Excise Law and Practice', 'McFarlanes Customs Law Handbook', 'McFarlane on Customs and Excise Cases', 'The ABC of VAT' and regular features in Importing Today, Lloyds List and New Law Journal. Regular lecturer at conferences and broadcaster.

Prof. Membership: Honourable Society of the Middle Temple (Harmsworth Scholar 1962), Fellow of the Chartered Institute of Taxation, VAT Practitioners Group, Institute of Indirect Taxation, Customs Practitioners Group.

Career: Qualified (Bar) 1962. Practised at the Bar 1962-66. Worked at International Computers Ltd Legal Department 1966-68. Took various appointments in the music industry 1968-72 before joining the Solicitors office, HM Customs and Excise, 1972-89. Joined *Titmuss Sainer & Webb* (now Titmuss Sainer Dechert) in 1989.

Personal: Born in 1936. Took an LLB in Sheffield, 1961; Diploma in EC Law, Brussels, 1966; LLM in Sheffield, 1971; PhD in London, 1976; and attended Ecole Nationale d'Administration, 1976. Governor of Tax Research Unit, King's College, London. Lives in London and Haverfordwest.

Preston, Christopher A.L.
Watson Farley & Williams, London (0171) 814 8000. Partner in Tax Department.

Specialisation: Main area of practice covers VAT and customs duties, including both contentious and non-contentious matters and appearing before the VAT tribunal. Also experienced in leasing and structured finance, company taxation and international tax planning.

Prof. Memberships: Law Society (Member of Revenue Law Committee and Chairman of VAT & Duties Sub-Committee), Institute of Tax, VAT Practitioners Group (Founder Member and Chairman of London Chapter). Fellow of the Institute of Taxation.

Career: Admitted 1975. Joined *Watson, Farley & Williams* as a partner in 1982.

Personal: Born 9th October 1950.

Shea, Stephen
Clifford Chance, London (0171) 600 1000. Partner. Handles corporate taxation including VAT and Customs and Excise work.

Sinfield, Greg
Lovell White Durrant, London (0171) 236 0066. Qualified 1989. Partner 1993. Business Tax Department. Principal area of practice covers VAT and Customs Duty.

Taylor, Carolyn
Linklaters & Paines, London (0171) 606 7080. Qualified 1988. Joined 1988. Principal area of practice is property tax.

REGIONS

Pincher, Richard
See under Tax (Corporate).

HEADS OF COMPANY LEGAL DEPARTMENTS

3i plc

Trinity Park, Bickinhill, Birmingham, B37 7ES Tel: (0171) 928 3131

Goddard, Ian *Manager, Legal Department.* Reports to: UK MD. Lawyers in Dept: 15 Deals with equity and loan investment in UK businesses, including MBO's/MBI's, portfolio management, insolvency and associated areas.
Career: Qualified in 1974. Barrister at 7 Fountain Court, Birmingham 1975-83. Joined 3i in 1984. Has held present position since 1988.

600 Group plc

Witan Court, 284 Witan Gate, Milton Keynes, Buckinghamshire, MK9 1EJ Tel: (0908) 234600

Myers, Alan R. *Group Legal Adviser/ Company Secretary.* Reports to: Group Managing Director. Lawyers in dept: 1. Staff: 1. Percentage of work outsourced: 15-20% (conveyancing, litigation, pensions).
Responsible for co-ordination of all legal matters, overseeing outside lawyers where needed. Work includes provision of company secretarial service, general company/ commercial and intellectual property matters.
Career: Qualified 1972.

Abbey National plc

Genesis House, 301-349 Midsummer Boulevard, Milton Keynes, MK9 2JE Tel: (01908) 348070

Malkin, Gwyn *Head of Legal Services.* Reports to: Company Secretary. Lawyers in Dept: 24. Handles commercial and corporate law matters and management of the legal function. Member of Legal Committee of British Bankers Association.
Career: Qualified 1975. Became Head of Legal Services at Abbey National in July 1992.

ABC International Bank plc

Arab Banking Corporation House, 1-5 Moorgate, London, EC2R 6AB Tel: (0171) 776 4008

Bowen-Jones, David *Corporate Secretary & Legal Counsel.* Reports to: Board and General Manager. Lawyers in dept: 1. Staff: 2. Percentage of work outsourced: 5% (litigation, specialist advice and legal opinions).
Principal areas of work are loan documentation, security, bonding, guarantees, corporate secretarial work, expansion of group, and specialist mandates for corporate clients (e.g. joint ventures). Member of Institute of Directors and Chartered Institute of Bankers.
Career: Called to the Bar, Middle Temple, 1973. Executive in legal and general affairs, Samuel Montagu & Co. Ltd 1976-78. Assistant Manager, Legal Affairs, Allied Arab Bank Ltd 1978-82. Counsel, Legal Affairs, Arab Banking Corporation, Bahrain 1982-85. Executive Director, Corporate Finance, ABC International Ltd 1985-90, then took up current position.

ACC Long Distance UK Ltd.

The Chiswick Centre, 414 Chiswick High Road, London, W4 5TF Tel: (0181) 995 3144

Taylor, Michael J. *Director of Legal and Regulatory Affairs.* Reports to: M.D. Lawyers in dept: 2. Staff: 8. Percentage of work outsourced: 15% (property, litigation, M&A).

Head of legal department with responsibility for UK and European legal and regulatory affairs. Principal areas of work are UK and international regulatory work, European joint ventures, major commercial negotiations and UK and overseas governmental lobbying. Played an active role in the planning and negotiation of first BT/ISR interconnect agreement in the industry and first ISR licence between USA and UK, involving high level contact in UK and US governments. Member of Management Board responsible (with Managing Director and Financial Director) for formulating the company's strategic direction and business planning exercises in UK and Europe. Will address European Telecommunications Forum in 1995. Member of Bar Council, IBA, PITCOM and the European Telecommunications Forum (Brussels).
Career: Called to the Bar 1986 while legal adviser to Kyle Stewart Ltd (Construction). Appointed legal adviser to Pillar Electrical plc (part of the Rio Tinto Zinc Group) in 1988; and Senior Legal Adviser to Mercury Communications Ltd 1990-93.

AGF Holdings (UK) Ltd

41 Botolph Lane, London, EC3R 8DL Tel: (0171) 220 6305

Neal, Roger W. *Corporate Affairs Manager/ Co. Sec..* Reports to: Chief Executive and Main Board. Lawyers in dept: 2. Staff: 5. Percentage of work outsourced: 50% (major litigation, property).
Principal areas of work are insurance law and regulation, corporate and commercial law, distribution, consumer protection law, employment, intellectual property and pensions. Work includes M&As, restructuring and joint ventures; EC distribution and competition; general corporate and commercial; hardware and software development and acquisition; trademarks and servicemarks; consumer credit; data protection; advertising and media; company secretarial; insurance regulation and financial services (IMRO, LAUTRO etc). Has been involved in negotiations with unions, DTI and Irish Dept of Commerce. Member of National Contract Managers' Association and director, Franco-British Lawyers Association.
Career: Articled with *Howes Percival*, Northampton. Qualified 1975, and Partner, *Howes & Co* 1975-78. Group Legal Adviser, Willmot Breeden Holdings Ltd 1978-80 (Rockwell International Group). Assistant Legal Adviser, Digital Equipment Co Ltd 1980-83. With *Hunt & Coombs* 1983-85, then joined Camtec Electronics Ltd. Joined AGF Holdings (UK) Ltd in 1988.

AGIP (UK) Ltd.

Agip House, 10 Ebury Bridge Road, London, SW1W 8PZ Tel: (0171) 344 6000

Shoylekov, Richard *Legal Manager.* Reports to: MD. Lawyers in dept: 3. Staff: 6. Percentage of work outsourced: 10% (litigation, employment, specialist work).
Principal areas of work cover oil and gas agreements relating to operations on the UK continental shelf, joint operating/ development agreements, gas sales agreements and all aspects of oil and gas field operations and maintenance. Also deals with employment law matters, litigation/ dispute resolution, intellectual property matters and competition law. Member of IBA Sections on Energy and Natural Resources law and Business law. Speaker at energy industry conferences on former Soviet Union and MBA courses on contract and project structures.
Career: Qualified 1990 while at *Freshfields*. Joined

British Gas Exploration and Production 1991. Solicitor with *Watson Farley & Williams* 1994-95, then joined AGIP (UK) Limited.

Airtours plc

Parkway Three, Parkway Business Centre, 300 Princess Road, Manchester, M14 7QU Tel: (0161) 232 0066

Burns, David *Group Company Secretary.* Reports to: Group Finance Director. Lawyers in Group: 4. Staff: 2. Percentage of work outsourced: 50% (M&A, aircraft financing and leasing).
Principal work undertaken includes advice and co-ordination of acquisitions and involvement in business and commercial development plans. Ensures compliance with Stock Exchange requirements, provides legal advice to subsidiaries and manages company pension scheme. Recent experience includes work on a hostile bid (1993), merging and creation of Going Places (1993-94) and acquisition of Scandinavia's largest tour operator (1994).
Career: Qualified 1980. With CPS and Prosecuting Solicitors Offices/ County Councils (Suffolk and Cheshire) 1981-87. Head of Legal Services and subsidiary Board Directorships, Airtours plc since 1987 and Group Company Secretary 1994.

Albany Life Assurance Co. Ltd.

Metropolitan House, 3 Darkes Lane, Potters Bar, Hertfordshire, EN6 1AJ Tel: (01707) 669000

Geiringer, Bruno *Legal and Compliance Director.* Reports to M.D. Lawyers in dept: 3. Staff: 8. Qualified 1982. Member of Law Society. Born 29.11.1957. Lives in London.

Albright & Wilson plc

210-222 Hagley Road West, Oldbury, Warley, B68 0NN Tel: (0121) 420 5042

Cree, Andrew *Company Secretary and Solicitor.* Reports to: Financial Director. Lawyers in dept: 2. Staff: 5. Percentage of work outsourced: 25 (litigation/ property/ competition and major transactions/ overseas work/ pensions).
Principal areas of work are acquisitions and disposals, joint ventures, competition, trading work (contracts) and company secretarial. Also involved in litigation and environmental matters.
Career: Qualified 1977. Regional Solicitor, British Coal and Head of Commercial Group 1985-90. Partner, *Nabarro Nathanson* 1990-91. Deputy Group Legal Adviser, BAGS plc 1991-92, then joined Albright & Wilson.

Amalgamated Metal Corporation plc

7th Floor, Adelaide House, London Bridge, London, EC4R 9DP Tel: (0171) 626 4521

Farmer, Derek J. *Company Solicitor.* Reports to: Legal and Administration Director. Lawyers in dept: 2. Percentage of work outsourced: variable (e.g. 75% arbitration/ litigation; 90% real property; 30% m&a work; 5% financial services, banking and computer/software disputes).
Deals primarily with corporate acqusitions and disposals and with commodities and financial services work, particularly legal aspects of the London Metal Exchange (LME); general commodities/ financial futures broking and dealing; compliance and regulatory

matters; related computer and software system purchases; disputes (including LME arbitrations). Also involved with international sale of goods and commercial relations; provision of geographic information systems and services (aerial survey, digital mapping etc); industrial operations; employment and property matters. Co-ordinates and monitors advice from overseas lawyers on international operations. Gives in-house seminars on computer/ IT law and practice and GIS project contracts and subcontracts.

Career: Qualified 1974. Assistant solicitor *Roney & Co.* 1974-79 handling general company/ commercial matters. Joined Amalgamated Metal Corporation plc in 1980.

AMEC plc

Sandiway House, Hartford, Northwich, Cheshire, CW8 2YA Tel: (01606) 883885

Fenwick, John *Head of Group Legal Services.* Reports to: Company Secretary. Lawyers in dept: 4. Staff: 6. Work outsourced: litigation requiring specialist expertise.
Responsible for supervising supply of all legal services to AMEC Group and providing legal services in-house. Assists in UK and overseas tendering (advice on risk, contract conditions etc.) joint venture agreements, claims and disputes. Also selects and monitors performance of external solicitors where required.

Career: Qualified 1973. Articled with *Heald Nickinson* and assistant solicitor until 1976. Head of Group Legal Services, John Laing plc 1976-88, then joined AMEC plc.

Amerada Hess Ltd.

33 Grosvenor Place, London, SW1X 7HY Tel: (0171) 823 2626

Huxtable, Alison *Head of Legal and Commercial.* Reports to: Commercial Director. Lawyers in dept: 6. Negotiators: 4. Staff: 15. Percentage of work outsourced: 10% (litigation, property-related matters).
Responsible for preparation and negotiation of a wide range of substantive legal documentation predominantly in respect of Amerada Hess Limited's operated ventures in the UKCS. Regular contributor to Langham Conferences and University of Dundee petroleum/ mineral law conferences. Member of the Bar, BACFI, European Petroleum Negotiators Group.

Career: Called to the Bar 1983. Legal adviser to GKN plc 1984-85 and to Phillips Petroleum Company 1986-87. Joined Amerada Hess Ltd in 1987 as legal adviser and appointed Manager of Legal and Negotiations Department 1992.

American Express Bank Ltd.

60 Buckingham Palace Road, London, SW1W 0RR Tel: (0171) 583 6666

Sharp, Robert *Managing General Counsel.* Reports to: The General Counsel (New York). Lawyers in UK dept: 4. Staff: 3. Work outsourced: Complicated transactions/ litigation.
Manages the legal requirements of American Express Bank Ltd. for Europe and the Middle East and Asia Pacific (Indian Sub-continent region and the Far East). Principal responsibilities are providing strategic and tactical advice to senior management to assist in the fulfilment of business objectives in compliance with applicable laws and regulatory scenario; securing appropriate legal support for transactions; and managing litigation and assistance with recoveries and "work-outs".

Career: Qualified 1972 while at *Freshfields* and solicitor in company/ commercial department until

1977. Joined General Counsel's Office, American Express Bank Ltd 1977.

Amersham International plc

Amersham Place, Little Chalfont, Amersham, Buckinghamshire, HP7 9NA Tel: (01494) 542500

Allnutt, Robert *Group Legal Adviser.* Reports to: Finance Director. Lawyers in dept: 3. Staff: 6. Percentage of work outsourced: 20% (major corporate, property, litigation).
Responsible for provision of legal advice on general commercial matters, intellectual property and product liability.

Career: Qualified 1979.

Amstrad plc

Brentwood House, 169 Kings Road, Brentwood, Essex, CM14 4EF Tel: (01277) 228888

Hyams, David *Company Secretary and Corporate Lawyer.* Reports to: CEO/ Chairman. Lawyers in dept: 3. Staff: 5. Work outsourced: Property, expert need, major litigation and corporate. Deals with company secretarial, legal, insurance, and government regulatory matters related to electronics, computers, software and telecoms. Has represented Amstrad plc before the EC Parliament (Industry and Social Committee) and on a radio phone in. Member of BACFI, Middle Temple and Bar subscriber.

Career: Qualified 1981. Legal counsel to Ingersoll-Rand Sales Co. Ltd. 1982-86. Corporate lawyer to Amstrad plc since 1986 and Company Secretary since 1992.

ARCO British Ltd

London Square, Cross Lanes, Guildford, Surrey, GU1 1UE Tel: (01483) 292040

Dunkley, Sam H. *Senior Counsel.* Reports to: MD. Lawyers in dept: 4. Staff: 4. Percentage of work outsourced: 10-20% (litigation, conveyancing, financing).
Principal areas of work are oil and gas developments, gas sales and transportation with a focus on southern gas basin developments. Deals with acquisitions and disposals, corporate and asset deals and gas sales to new market players, including generators. Also handles personal injury and other litigation, portfolio rationalisation and asset swaps and provides company secretarial services. Involved in $700m acquisition of Tricentrol in 1988 and acquisition of St. James's Oil & Gas Ltd in 1995. Committee Member of UK Energy Lawyers' Group since 1993 and member of IBA Energy Section.

Career: Qualified 1975. With National Iranian Oil Co 1977-79. Senior Attorney, Amoco 1979-87, then joined Arco British Ltd as Senior Attorney and became Senior Counsel in 1989.

Associated Gas Suppliers Ltd.

59 Markham Street, London, SW3 3NR Tel: (0171) 376 5331

Adams, Peter *Head of Corporate Services.* Reports to: M.D. Lawyers in dept: 2. Staff: 16. Percentage of work outsourced: 10% (litigation, overflow).
Supervises legal affairs, planning, administration and transportation negotiations. Member of Law Society, City of Westminster Law Society and Institute of Petroleum.

Career: Qualified 1971. Assistant legal adviser, Cleveland Petroleum 1971-72 and assistant legal adviser to assistant general counsel, Esso Petroleum Ltd 1972-91. Joined Associated Gas Supplies Ltd as

Head of Legal Affairs in March 1991.

AT&T Istel Ltd.

Highfield House, Headless Cross Drive, Headless Cross, Redditch, Worcestershire, B97 5EQ Tel: (015270 550330

Macfarlane, J.A.C. *Director of Legal Services.* Reports to: Chief Executive. Lawyers in dept: 4. Staff: 9. Percentage of work outsourced: 10% (conveyancing, litigation, some company, corporate finance).
Co-ordinates AT&T Corporation's legal resource in the UK. Work includes advising on commercial contracts with an IT bias (including computer hardware and software licences/contracts, integrated solutions/ facilities management contracts and network services contracts), management of intellectual property rights, real estate transactions, litigation and general corporate activity ranging from mbos to company secretarial functions. Appoints and manages external legal advisers in the UK and overseas.

Career: Qualified 1974. Assistant legal adviser, GKN plc until 1976, then solicitor with *Pinsent & Co*, Birmingham. Group solicitor to the Weir Group plc from 1978 and Company Secretary of Weir Pumps Ltd to 1985, then joined AT&T Istel Ltd in January 1986 as sole legal adviser. Company Secretary from 1990.

WS Atkins Ltd

Woodcote Grove, Ashley Road, Epsom, Surrey, KT18 5BW Tel: (01372) 726140

Foley, Michael Timothy *Legal Director.* Responsible for legal affairs of the consultancy both at home and abroad. Member of BACFI General Committee 1981-87 and Vice Chairman 1986-87 and member of Association of Consulting Engineers (Executive Committee).

Career: Called to the Bar 1970. Previously employed as an engineer by Sir William Halcrow and Partners 1963-68. Senior Engineer, Worcestershire CC 1968-71, then joined the WS Atkins Consultancy as Assistant Legal Adviser, becoming Group Legal Adviser in 1978.

Australia and New Zealand Banking Group Ltd.

Minerva House, Montague Close, London, SE1 9DH Tel: (0171) 378 2121

Campbell, Gareth *Legal Adviser and Company Secretary (UK).* Reports to: Senior General Manager. Lawyers in dept: 2. Staff: 5. Percentage of work outsourced: 5% (litigation).
Provides comprehensive legal advice to the London Board of Directors (ANZ Grindlays Bank plc) and management in respect of the Group's Europe, South Asia and Middle East sector: both strategic (corporate structure, disposals) and transaction-specific (e.g. emerging markets, merchant banking) in the UK; and co-ordinating with lawyers overseas. Company Secretary of ANZ Grindlays Bank plc and all other UK subsidiaries. Money laundering co-ordinator for the sector and reporting officer in the UK.

Career: Qualified 1978 while at *Stephenson Harwood* and assistant solicitor until 1981. Solicitor, National Westminster Bank legal department 1981-88. Partner with *Needham & James* 1988-92, then joined ANZ Bank Ltd as legal adviser and Company Secretary.

Avnet EMG Ltd

Elopak House, Rutherford Close, Meadway, Stevenage, Herts, SG1 2PR Tel: (01438) 751133

Wilson, David *General Outside Counsel (Europe).* Reports to: Senior VP General Counsel. Lawyers in dept: 1. Staff: 2. Percentage of work outsourced: 50% (litigation, some acquisition support and some merger support).
Responsible for M&A and general corporate commercial legal advice backed up by Avnet's New York based legal department. Avnet is a $4 billion US corporation expanding in Europe and Asia primarily by acquisitions.
Career: Qualified 1986, Canada; 1993, England and Wales.

Avon Cosmetics Ltd

Nunn Mills Road, Northampton, Northants, NN1 5PA Tel: (01604) 617216

Jowett, Jonathan *Company Secretary and Solicitor.* Reports to: Vice President - Finance and Legal. Lawyers in dept: 1. Staff: 3.
Percentage of work outsourced: 5% (property and litigation).
Deals with commercial contracts, consumer law, sales and marketing, employment, company and regulatory matters. Member of Cosmetics, Toiletries and Perfumery Association Legal Committee.
Career: Qualified 1989. Associate solicitor *Merritt & Co* 1989-91. Assistant Group Solicitor MTM plc 1991-92, then joined Avon Cosmetics.

Avon Rubber plc

Bath Road, Melksham, Wiltshire, SN12 8AA Tel: (01225) 703101

Fairbairn, P.J. *Group Solicitor.* Reports to: Company Secretary. Lawyers in dept: 2. Staff: 2. Percentage of work outsourced: 10-20% (litigation, except employment; City work and overseas matters).
Main areas of work are contract, property, intellectual property, employment, joint ventures, acquisitions and disposals (share sale and purchase and asset sale and purchase).
Career: Qualified 1976 and in private practice with *Willett, Bullough and Boardman*, Warrington 1973-77. Joined Avon Rubber plc as an assistant solicitor in 1977.

Baker Hughes Ltd.

2nd Floor, Hammersley House, 5-8 Warwick Street, London, W1R 5RA Tel: (0171) 287 6585

Aron, Jeremy *Legal Adviser - Europe, Mid East, Africa.* Reports to: General Counsel in Houston. Lawyers in dept: 1. Staff: 1.
Percentage of work outsourced: 10% (commercial property, EC competition and litigation).
Principal areas of work are commercial and contractual law, employment and intellectual property matters. Advises on and negotiates oilfield contracts, handles international acquisition and disposal work, joint ventures, and company secretarial matters. Responsible for employment law advice in Europe, CIS, Africa and Middle East including representation at Tribunals in UK. Manages outside lawyers on litigation and commercial property work. Gives seminars on contractual/compliance issues within his area of responsibility; and an introduction to employment law for UK Managers and Human Resource department. Member of Employment Law Association.
Career: Qualified 1989 and solicitor with *Winward Fearon & Co* until 1992, then joined Baker Hughes.

Balfour Beatty Ltd.

One Angel Square, Torrens Street, London, EC1V 1SX Tel: (0171) 216 6800

McCormack, Frank D.F.T. *Head of Legal Services and Co. Secretary.* Reports to: Chairman. Lawyers in dept: 1. Staff: 9. Percentage of work outsourced: 45% (litigation, conveyancing, project finance).
Responsible for overseeing all group legal matters. Work includes corporate, finance, secretarial and management aspects. Speaks at seminars, both internal and external on joint venture schemes, bonds and guarantees and corporate structures.
Career: Qualified 1983 while at *Gregory Rowcliffe & Co.* Joined *Bucher Williams and Harrup* 1984, a Partner in 1985, then joined Balfour Beatty Ltd in 1987.

Bank of Ireland

34-36 High Street, Slough, Berkshire, SL1 1ED Tel: (01753) 517777

O'Flanagan, Margaret *Legal Adviser.* Reports to: Chief Executive. Lawyers in dept: 1. Staff: 2. Percentage of work outsourced: 40% (debt recovery, perfecting security, general litigation).
Provides general legal advice to Bank of Ireland on all aspects of the Bank's operations, particularly on banking law, EU law, insolvency and general commercial matters. Also advises on charity law and local government.
Career: Called to the Bar 1981. Legal Adviser to YWCA of Great Britain, then In-house lawyer at Woking BC and the to Corporation of Lloyd's 1986-88 and to the Finance and Leasing Association 1988-90.

Banque Indosuez

122 Leadenhall Street, London, EC3V 4QH Tel: (0171) 971 4000

Garner, Margaret T. *Legal Adviser/Co. Sec/Compliance Officer.* Reports to: Chief Executive. Lawyers in dept: 3. Staff: 5. Percentage of work outsourced: 5% (various types).
Responsible for provision of advice on legal, commercial and structural aspects of the Bank's transactions. Work includes drafting and review of lending and security documentation; advising on taxation, new banking products and investment schemes and funds; advising on operational matters including standard agreements for special products. Involved in takeovers, mergers, acquisitions, disposals, rights issues, share issues and establishment of investment funds. Provides full company secretarial service (Group has in excess of 36 subsidiaries), and ensures compliance with FSA, Bank of England and Companies Acts requirements.
Career: Called to the Bar 1968 and practised as a Barrister at *3 Middle Temple* 1968-74. Legal Advisor to the International Bank Division, William & Glyns Bank Ltd 1974-78; then Legal Advisor, Libra Bank Ltd 1978-82. Manager - Trade Finance, Royal Bank of Canada 1982-85, then joined Banque Indosuez.

Barclays Bank PLC

54 Lombard Street, London, EC3P 3AH Tel: (0171) 699 5000

Trust, Howard B. *Group General Counsel/ Group Secretary.* Reports to: Group Finance Director. Lawyers in dept: 1. Staff: 2.
Provides General Counsel advice to the main Board and Senior Management on legal risk as it affects the Group and its businesses as a whole. Also has role of Legal Director for Barclays de Zoete Wedd Ltd, which conducts Barclays investment banking businesses, heading a team of 8 lawyers and a department of 25 staff in total, advising on the full range of investment banking products and related matters.
Career: Solicitor, *Lovell White & King* 1980-85. Solicitor, Morgan Grenfell 1985-87 and Company Secretary 1987-89. Group Legal Director, BZW since 1989.

Bass plc

20 North Audley Street, London, W1Y 1WE Tel: (0171) 409 1919

Winter, Richard *Head of Group Legal Department.* Reports to: Company Secretary. Lawyers in dept: 4. Staff: 9. Work outsourced: litigation, property.
Principal areas of work are general company/ commercial matters including acquisitions, disposals, trading agreements, general commercial contracts, marketing and intellectual property (particularly trade marks). Regularly liaises with lawyers for Holiday Inn Worldwide (also owned by Bass plc). Addresses internal and external seminars. Member of Commerce and Industry Group and Competition Law Panel of CBI.
Career: Qualified 1973 and assistant solicitor with *Eversheds*, Birmingham until 1975 and between 1978 and 1994 (Partner, 1981; London office 1987). Solicitor with Fisons plc 1975-78. Joined Bass plc in 1994.

Beazer Homes plc

Midland Regional Legal Dept, Beazer House, Hare Street, Bilston, West Midlands, WV14 7DY Tel: (01902) 404832

Hale, Gareth *Regional Solicitor.* Reports to: M.D.s of subsidiary companies. Lawyers in dept: 1. Staff: 4. Percentage of work outsourced: minimal (complex litigation and occasional land acquisitions).
Principal areas of work are land acquisitions and disposals together with ancillary matters (joint ventures, planning agreements etc) for subsidiary companies in Midland region. Also manages plot sales, litigation (including that conducted by external solicitors) and gives general advice on a wide range of issues affecting the day-to-day running of subsidiary companies.
Career: Qualified 1980. Trainee underwriter with General Accident Insurance Company 1971-74. With *Turner Garrett & Co* 1978-82, *Osborne Morris & Morgan* 1982-83, *Wilson & Berry* 1983-84 and *Dennis Berry & Co* 1984-87. Joined Beazer Homes plc in January 1988.

BICC plc

Devonshire House, Mayfair Place, London, W1X 5FH Tel: (0171) 629 6622

Pearson, Christopher *Head of Legal Services.* Reports to: Company Secretary. Lawyers in dept: 1. Staff 1. Percentage of work outsourced: 50% (major corporate acquisitions and disposals, financing and property).
Deals with small acquisitions and disposals, setting up joint ventures (incorporated and unincorporated) worldwide, banking, competition, employment, general corporate and some property development work.
Career: Qualified 1972.

Blenheim Group plc

Blenheim House, 630 Chiswick High Road, London, W4 5BG Tel: (0181) 742 2828

Begg, Peter F.C. *Group Legal Director/Company Secretary.* Reports to: Chairman. Lawyers in dept: 2. Staff: 3. Percentage of work outsourced: 50% (litigation, property, some commercial work).
Responsible for provision of legal and company secretarial services to Blenheim Group plc. An ac-

knowledged authority in the field of mergers and acquisitions. Author of "Corporate Acquisitions and Mergers" (Kluwer Law International).

Career: Articles with *Boodle Hatfield*, then assistant solicitor *Clifford Turner & Co* 1972-76. With RTZ Corporation plc 1976-90. Deputy Legal Adviser, Reed International plc 1990-92, then joined Blenheim Group plc.

Blue Circle Industries plc

84 Eccleston Square, London, SW1V 1PX Tel: (0171) 828 3456

Henchley, Richard *Company Secretary/ Legal Adviser.* Reports to: Chief Executive. Lawyers in dept: 3. Staff: 16.
Responsible for provision of legal and company secretarial services to the Group within the UK, and legal services worldwide (in consultation with overseas subsidiaries). Principal areas of work are matters of competition law, commercial contracts and property. Also involved in dispute resolution and environmental issues. Addressed conference on cost control issues for in-house lawyers in March 1995. Council member and Treasurer of Law Society.

Career: Qualified 1965 while at *Simmons & Simmons*. Solicitor with *Richards Butler* 1966-76. With British American Tobacco Ltd 1967-77; British American Cosmetics Ltd 1977-85 and BAT Industries 1985-89. General Counsel and Company Secretary to Rolls Royce plc 1989-93 and joined Blue Circle Industries plc in 1993.

Boots Company plc

Nottingham, Nottinghamshire, NG2 3AA Tel: (0115) 958 2831

Oliver, Michael John *Principal Legal Adviser.* Reports to: Company Secretary. Lawyers in dept: 12. Staff: 6. Work outsourced: various types.
Principal area of work is company/ commercial, including acquisitions, disposals, mergers, joint ventures, licence development and other commercial contracts and competition law.

Career: Qualified 1981. Army Officer 1969-79, then joined *Brutton & Co* as an articled clerk, becoming assistant solicitor and then partner. Joined The Boots Company PLC in 1987.

BP Chemicals Ltd

Britannic House, 1 Finsbury Circus, London, EC2M 7BA Tel: (0171) 496 5005

Saunders, Colin P. *General Counsel.* Reports to: CEO. Lawyers in dept: 4. Staff: 5. Percentage of work outsourced: 10% (non-routine antitrust matters, intellectual property litigation, local employment and land matters).
Principal areas of work are international commercial matters including supply arrangements, joint ventures and alliances, M&A work, licensing, intellectual property, antitrust and employment. Also responsible for BP Group Patents Department (12 Patent Attourneys, 28 staff).

Career: Qualified 1975 and joined BP Chemicals Ltd. Member of the Group Legal Department of The British Petroleum Company plc 1983-1994.

BP Oil UK Ltd

BP House, Breakspear Way, Hemel Hempstead, Herts, HP2 4UL Tel: (01442) 225367

Mallett, L.E. *Legal Adviser and Company Secretary.* Reports to: CEO. Lawyers in dept: 5. Staff: 12. Percentage of work outsourced: 50% (litigation, conveyancing, planning, debt collection, Scottish work).

Principal areas of work are downstream oil and gas. Work includes advising on product supply/exchange, pipelines, aircraft refuelling, joint ventures, employment, environmental matters, shareholders' agreements and competition law. Also deals with general corporate work including company secretarial. Member of BACFI.

Career: Qualified 1969 as a Barrister. Lawyer with ICL 1970-78, then joined BP to deal with downstream work until 1980, general corporate 1980-89, upstream work 1989-91 and downstream work since 1991.

Bristol & West Building Society

P.O. Box 27, Broad Quay, Bristol, BS99 7AX Tel: (0117) 979 2222

Wood, Alison *Assistant Chief Solicitor.* Reports to: Chief Solicitor. Lawyers in dept: 4. Staff: 2. Percentage of work outsourced: 75% (litigation, commercial, property).
Principal areas of work are commercial property, employment litigation and securitisation work.

Career: Qualified 1988 and in private practice with *Cartwrights*, Bristol before joining Bristol & West Building Society.

Bristol Water Holdings PLC

PO Box 218, Bridgwater Road, Bristol, BS99 7AU Tel: (0117) 966 5881 Ext.2024

Dell, Nicholas John *Company secretary/ solicitor.* Reports to: Executive Chairman. Lawyers in Depart: 1. Staff: 2. Percentage of work outsourced: 5% (employment law, company/ commercial, litigation).
Secretarial and solicitor responsibilites to all companies within the Bristol Water Group, including conveyancing, water law, planning and environmental law, company/ commercial and litigation. Member of Commerce and Industry Group and UK Environmental Lawyers Association.

Career: Qualified 1990. Joined Bristol Water Plc 1990 becoming company secretary and solicitor 1995.

Bristow Helicopters Group Ltd

Redhill Aerodrome, Redhill, Surrey, RH1 5JZ Tel: (01737) 822353

McIntosh, Ian *Legal Director and Company Secretary.* Reports to: Chief Executive. Staff: 2. Percentage of work outsourced: 5% (where specialist expertise required eg international arbitrations and acquisitions).
Sole in-house company lawyer providing legal advice on any matter relating to the Group's activities worldwide (turnover £150m+) together with company secretarial duties. Director of main operating company and a number of the UK companies with key role in formulating and implementing the overall strategic policy of the Group as a whole. Major areas of work are commercial contracts of all types frequently involving overseas clients (including major contract for the purchase of up to 20 civilian helicopters from a foreign manufacturer); litigation; employment issues, pensions, employee share scheme; property and insurance.

Career: Articled with Leeds City Council 1974-77. Company solicitor Rentokil Group plc 1978-85. Group solicitor and legal adviser, Ewbank Preece Group Ltd 1985-88, then took up current position.

Britannic Assurance plc

Moor Green, Moseley, Birmingham, B13 8QF Tel: (0121) 449 4444

East, Anna *Head of Legal Department.* Reports to: Company Secretary. Staff: 2. Percentage of work outsourced: 10% (some litigation, various specialist areas such as pensions).
Principal areas of work are commercial conveyancing and general property work resulting from the company's property investment portfolio and its ownership of 200 separate offices nationwide. Also deals with software contracts, policy document compliance (eg with the Unfair Contract Terms Directive) and general company business including employment issues.

Career: Qualified 1985 while with *Talbots*, Rugby/ Birmingham/ Southam. Assistant solicitor *Eversheds*, Birmingham 1985-88, then took up present position.

British Aerospace Defence Ltd

Lancaster House, PO Box 87, Farnborough Aerospace Centre, Farnborough, Hampshire, GU14 6YU Tel: (01252) 384850

Riley, Philip *Legal Director.* Reports to: Chairman and MD, British Aerospace Defence Ltd. Staff: 1. Work outsourced: commercial, joint ventures, litigation.
Principal areas of work are acquisitions/ disposals, company formations and joint ventures. Also deals with general commercial matters. Member, Law Society Commerce and Industry Group and Solicitors European Group.

Career: Commercial apprentice British Aircraft Corp. Ltd 1968-70 and Sales Finance Manager 1970-75. Qualified as a Solicitor 1978 while with *Linklaters & Paines*. Legal Adviser, Military Aircraft 1978-87 and Head of Legal Services 1987-91. Appointed Legal Director British Aerospace Defence Ltd 1991.

British Coal Pension Schemes

Hobart House, Grosvenor Place, London, SW1X 7AD Tel: (0171) 396 7152

Collins, Julian P. *Company Solicitor.* Reports to: Scheme Trustees. Lawyers in dept: 1.
Responsible for British Coal pension schemes (16 billion in funds) following massive restructuring resulting from sale of the coal industry to private ownership. Works in conjunction with external lawyers. Work includes negotiation of innovative pension scheme structure and provision of practical legal advice to Board members and trustees. Member of Association of Pensions Lawyers and Chairman of Law Society Commerce & Industry Group 1993-94. Has lectured on the role of the in-house lawyer and on the privatisation of the coal industry.

Career: Joined NCB/British Coal in 1965; qualified 1967. Assistant solicitor 1967-73; Head of Industrial Branch 1973-84; Deputy Legal Adviser 1984-88; Solicitor and Legal Adviser 1988-93; and, Solicitor, British Coal Pension Schemes since 1993.

British Gas PLC

Rivermill House, 152 Grosvenor Road, London, SW1V 3JL Tel: (0171) 611 2630

Twiss, Charles *Director of legal services.* Reports to: Chief Executive. Lawyers in Dept: 62. Staff: 10. Percent of work outsourced: 25% (property, litigation).
Legal Adviser to Board and overall responsiblity for the provision of legal services within the company including, corporate finance, employment, commercial and competition law. Frequent conference speaker on in-house legal management issues and privitisation

and competition law. General Editor "Managing quality legal services in Business".

Career: Qualified 1967. Assistant solicitor Street Daunt & Farmiloe 1968-77, assistant legal controller London Borough of Harrow 1977-80, solicitor Board of Eastern Electricity 1980-1985. Joined British Gas Plc 1985.

British Olympic Association

1 Wandsworth Plain, London, SW18 1EH Tel: (0181) 871 2677

Mellstrom, Bruce   *Legal Adviser.*   Reports to: Chief Executive. Lawyers in dept: 1. Staff: 1. Percentage of work outsourced: 50% (litigation, specialist intellectual property, instructing counsel). Has general responsibility for all legal matters which arise, providing general legal advice, and drafting and negotiating commercial contracts. Work includes sponsorship/ merchandising contracts, intellectual property management, general commercial advice, Parliamentary lobbying, constitutional issues, matters concerning drugs in sport and intellectual property infringement. Conducted BOA's appeal to the special commissioners of tax and liaised closely with Government on the Olympic Symbols etc (Protection) Bill currently going through Parliament. Member of British Association for Sport and the Law.

Career: Qualified 1989 while with *Herbert Smith* and assistant solicitor to 1993 in corporate finance and general commercial fields. Took up current position in April 1993.

British Petroleum Company plc

Britannic House, 1 Finsbury Circus, London, EC2M 7BA Tel: (0171) 496 2000

Bevan, Peter B. Pugh   *Group General Counsel.* Reports to: Group Chief Executive. Lawyers in dept: 150 (worldwide). Staff: 10. Percentage of work outsourced: 5-10%
Principal areas of work are mergers and acquisitions, finance and general company/ commercial matters. Member of UK Oil Lawyers Group and Co-chairman of IBA sub-committee.

Career: Qualified 1969 and former solicitor with City firm, then joined BP Group. Appointed Group General Counsel September 1992.

British Railways Board

McMillan House, PO Box 1016, Paddington Station, London, W2 1YG Tel: (0171) 313 1144

Sim, Andrew Fraser   *Solicitor to the Board.* Reports to: The Board. Lawyers in dept: 15. Staff: 32. Percentage of work outsourced: 80% (all types). Responsible for provision and management of legal services and advice to the Board.

Career: Head of Litigation, British Railways Board 1982-93 and Deputy Solicitor 1986-93, then took up present position.

British Steel plc

9 Albert Embankment, London, SE1 7SN Tel: (0171) 735 7654

O'Neill, Margaret   *Director of Legal Services.* Reports to: Chairman/ Chief Executive. Lawyers in dept: 11. Staff: 17.
Reponsible for provision of in-house legal services to British Steel Group and managing external advice where required.

British Telecommunications plc

British Telecom Centre, 81 Newgate Street, London, EC1A 7AJ Tel: (0171) 356 4719

Green, Colin R.   *Secretary and Chief Legal Adviser.* Reports to: Chairman. Lawyers in dept: 65. Staff: 200. Percentage of work outsourced: 25% (property).
Manages one of the largest in-house legal departments in the UK, handling all BT's work (other than property) in the UK and managing legal advice overseas. Handles patent and trade mark matters. Responsible for servicing Britain's largest shareholder base (2.7m shareholders) and an additional department of 55 Company Secretaries and associated staff. Involved in the alliance with US telecomms company MCI and sale of BT's stake in McCaw Cellular Communications Inc. Director, BT Property Ltd, Southgate Developments Ltd, Centre for Dispute Resolution (CEDR) and Trustee of BT Pension Fund. Lectures on management of in-house legal departments and on BT's MBA course on introduction to commercial law.

Career: Qualified 1973 while with *Paisner & Co*, then joined *Clintons* and later became Partner. Joined the Post Office in 1977 to handle privatisation of BT. Director of Commercial Department 1985 and appointed Solicitor and Chief Legal Adviser to BT in August 1989; and Secretary and Chief Legal Adviser 1994.

Moodliar, Nuns   *Legal Services Manager.* Reports to: Divisional Manager. Lawyers in dept: 60. Staff: 7. Percentage of work outsourced: minimal (property and some specialist areas such as Eurobond funding).
Responsible and accountable for the provision of legal services to the Personal and National Business Divisions of BT and managing a team of lawyers to deliver this objective. Current main areas of work are satellite TV contracts, satellite consortia, alliances, international correspondent relationships, consumer and business telecoms contracts. Regularly addresses internal group and team meetings.

Career: Legal Adviser, Sun Life Corporation 1978-87. Called to the Bar 1984. Joined BT as a legal adviser in 1987.

British Vita plc

Oldham Road, Middleton, Manchester, M24 2DB Tel: (0161) 643 1133

Stirzaker, Mark   *Company Solicitor.* Reports to: Chief Executive. Lawyers in dept: 2. Staff: 2. Percentage of work outsourced: 20% (public issues, heavyweight litigation, some M&A).
Principal areas of work are mergers and acquisitions and commercial property. Also provides general commercial advice and deals with intellectual property matters.

Career: Qualified 1980.

Brown & Root (UK) Ltd

Brown & Root House, 150 The Broadway, Wimbledon, London, SW19 1RX Tel: (0181) 544 6583

Henniker-Smith, Ian   *Company Secretary and Solicitor.* Reports to: Chief Executive. Lawyers in dept: 12. Staff: 7. Percentage of work outsourced: 1-5% (property, major litigation).
Responsible for the provision of legal services to all Brown & Root group and affiliated companies in their operations in Europe, Africa and elsewhere. Involved in policy making process and business negotiations such as commercial contracts, M&As, joint venture and association agreements and other commercial agreements of all types. Advises on effect of UK, EC and foreign legislation. Manages legal team and

insurance department. Member of Law Society Commerce and Industry Group.

Career: Qualified 1973 while at *Balmer Son & Ritchie*. Assistant solicitor with Three Rivers District Council 1975-78, then joined Brown & Root Ltd. Became Senior Assistant Solicitor 1980, Head of legal department 1982, Company Secretary 1986 and member of Executive Committee from its inception in 1989.

BTR Plc

Silvertown House, Vincent Square, London, SW1P 2PL Tel: (0171) 848 3848

Williams, Stanley K.   *Group Commercial Attorney.* Reports to: Group chief executive. Lawyers in Depart: 8. Staff: 34. percentage of work outsourced: 20% (litigation, larger corporate transactions, pensions).
Deals with legal services and negotiation of acquisitions and disposals, risk management and insurance, intellectual property, real estate management and International pensions and benefits. Also addresses seminars on risk management and legal compliance and published various booklets relative to above.

Career: Qualified 1969. Public sector legal service 1969-1980, deputy company secretary and solicitor Rowntree Plc 1980-1989. Joined BTR Plc 1989 becoming group commercial attorney in 1993.

Builders' Accident Insurance Ltd

Inigo Place, 31-33 Bedford Street, London, WC2E 9EL Tel: (0171) 836 9885

Sweet, Charles J.   *Head of legal department.* Deals with insurance litigation, employers liability and public liability, in the construction industry.

Career: Qualified 1980. Assistant solicitor 1980-1986. Joined Builders' Accident Insurance Ltd 1986. Member of Commerce and Industry Group. A.C.I.I. 1993.

Bull Information Systems Ltd

Computer House, Great West Road, Brentford, Middlesex, TW8 9DH Tel: (0181) 568 9191

Meyer, Caroline   *Director, Legal Services.* Reports to: Finance Director. Lawyers in dept: 2. Staff: 6. Percentage of work outsourced: minimal (some conveyancing and litigation).
Manages legal department providing full legal and contracts service including employment matters, computer leasing, pensions and a small amount of property work. Largest contract under negotiation valued at £200m. Provided start up advice, legal support and model terms for Facilities Management Division. Co-author of articles on the EEC draft software directive (1990) and speaker at ESC summer conference on interoperable software (1991).

Career: Qualified 1979, while with *Theodore Goddard & Co*, then joined C & J Clark Ltd as assistant legal advisor. Attorney, reporting to UK Legal Counsel, Hewlett Packard Ltd 1984-86; then Assistant Legal Advisor, Wang UK Ltd 1986-88. Joined Research Machines plc in 1988 as Legal Advisor/Company Secretary and took up current position with Bull Information Systems Ltd in June 1993.

H.P. Bulmer Holdings plc

The Cider Mills, Plough Lane, Hereford, Hereford and Worcester, HR4 0LE Tel: (01432) 352000

Stebbings, William   *Group Solicitor.* Reports to: Group Company Secretary. Lawyers in dept: 2. Staff: 1. Percentage of work outsourced: 30% (conveyancing, litigation, major corporate matters).

Principal areas of work are company/commercial, competition law, trade marks and company secretarial matters. Provides legal advice on business acquisitions/disposals and joint ventures (UK and overseas); distribution and supply agreements; agency agreements; sponsorship deals; research and development contracts; confidentiality agreements; and UK and EC competition law. Responsible for management and defence of worldwide trade mark portfolio including registrations and licensing; copyright and designs; employment law advice; property management advice; product labelling; and promotions. Committee member of Law Society Commerce & Industry Group (Midlands). Experienced in preparing and presenting compliance programmes on competition law and trade mark matters.

Career: Qualified 1980.

Bunzl plc

110 Park Street, London, W1Y 3RB Tel: (0171) 495 4950

Hussey, P.N. *Co. Secretary and Group Legal Adviser.* Reports to: Chief Executive. Lawyers in dept: 2. Staff: 4. Percentage of work outsourced: 30% (large corporate transactions, litigation, property).
Provides legal services and advice on company/commercial and general corporate matters, and a full company secretarial service including compliance.

Career: Qualified 1983 while with *Addleshaw Sons & Latham.* Commercial solicitor, Grand Metropolitan Retailing Division 1985-86 and Senior Solicitor, Contract Services Division 1986-87. Company Secretary and Group Legal Adviser, Compass Group 1987-88. Legal Adviser, Bunzl plc 1988-92 and then took up present position.

BUPA

Provident House, 24-27 Essex Street, London, WC2R 3AX Tel: (0171) 353 5212

Newton, Paul *Group Legal Adviser.* Reports to: Company Secretary. Lawyers in dept: 7. Staff: 4. Percentage of work outsourced: 25% (litigation, property, large and complex transactions such as bonds issue).
Principal areas of work cover healthcare, insurance (both life and general), employment, company and commercial, intellectual property and regulatory matters. All legal work has a strong healthcare/ health insurance bias.

Career: Articled at *Medlicott & Benson* 1985-87. Joined BUPA as a solicitor in 1987, becoming Group Legal Manager in 1990.

Cable & Wireless plc

124 Theobalds Road, London, WC1X 8RX Tel: (0171) 315 4668

Wall, Elizabeth *Group Director of Legal Services.* Reports to: Director, Finance. Lawyers in dept: 40 (worldwide).
Has overall professional and functional responsibility for the provision of legal services to the Cable & Wireless Federation of companies worldwide. Regular conference speaker on topics concerning in-house lawyers, in-house practice management and international legal practice. Committee member, Law Society Commerce and Industry Group; Steering Committee Member and Treasurer, American Corporate Counsel Association, European Chapter. Member of IBA and ABA.

Career: Qualified 1972 while with *Sale Lingards & Co,* Manchester. Attachee to the Court of Arbitration, International Chamber of Commerce, Paris 1972-74. Solicitor with Hawker Siddeley Aviation Ltd 1974-77;

then Assistant General Counsel and Assistant Secretary with Itel Corporation, San Francisco. Admitted to the California Bar 1982. Vice President and General Counsel, Clarendon Group, New York 1982-85; then Vice President and Chief Counsel McDonnell Douglas Information Systems International. Took up present position in 1990.

Cadbury Schweppes Plc

Legal Dept, Franklin House, Bournville, Birmingham, B30 2NB Tel: (0121) 625 7000

Keating, Michael *Legal Director, Group Confectionery.* Reports to: Company secretary. Lawyers in Depart: 8. Staff: 6. Percentage of work outsourced: 20% (mainly where local overseas input is required).
Manages legal department and provision of legal services including mergers and acquisitions, commercial contracts, licensing and protection of brands all on worldwide basis.

Career: Qualified 1973. Assistant solicitor Nightingales 1973-1976, member of Group legal department T & N Plc 1977-1984. Joined Cadbury Schweppes Plc 1985.

Camelot Group plc

The National Lottery, Magdalen House, Tolpits Lane, Watford, Herts, WD1 8RN Tel: (01923) 425104

Hampton, Sarah *Group Solicitor.* Lawyers in dept: 4. Staff: 5. Percentage of work outsourced: approx 20% (general commercial, contractual, regulatory).
Original member of team preparing Camelot's bid for the National Lottery. Involved in drafting of application for the licence, formalising shareholder and supplier agreements, preparing constitutional documents, discussions and negotiations with the Director General of the National Lottery and his team, dealings with the European Commission, OFT and trustees of prize monies and their advisers. Principal areas of work are commercial, contractual, competition, intellectual property and regulatory, ensuring compliance with licences to run the National Lottery and promote lotteries. Camelot has a projected turnover of £5 billion for 1995/96, operating through over 30,000 retail outlets.

Career: Qualified 1976 while with *Berwin Leighton* and then assistant solicitor. Assistant solicitor *Taylor Joynson Garrett* 1978-81. Legal Counsel and Company Secretary, Cominco Europe Ltd 1981-88. Senior Solicitor and then Head of Legal Services BICC plc 1988-90. Group Legal Adviser, Heron Corporation to 1990-93. Joined Camelot as a consultant in December 1993 and appointed Group Solicitor in 1994.

Carlton Communications plc

15 St George Street, Hanover Square, London, W1R 9DE Tel: (0171) 499 8050

Abdoo, David *Company Secretary.* Reports to: Finance Director. Lawyers in dept: 2. Staff: 4.
Provides legal and company secretarial services in relation to property, litigation, pensions, insurance, IP/ trade marks, corporate governance, general commercial advice, employment, employee incentive schemes and benefits, and corporate finance matters.

Career: Qualified 1986 while at *Clifford Turner* and assistant solicitor, *Clifford Chance* until joined Carlton Communications plc in 1988.

Cattle's (Holdings) plc

Holtenprice Court, 38 Springfields Way, Anlaby, Hull, HU10 6RR Tel: (01482) 564400

Doherty, Patrick J. *Group Secretary and Solicitor.* Reports to: Finance Director. Lawyers in dept: 1. Staff: 1. Percentage of work outsourced: 50% (company/ commercial, banking, litigation). Principal areas of work are consumer credit, employment matters, property, company secretarial and compliance (statutory and Stock Exchange).

Career: Called to the Bar 1976; admitted as a Solicitor 1992. With Engineering Employers' Association (Yorkshire and Humberside) 1978-79; Armstrong Equipment plc 1979-85; ASD plc 1985-90 and joined Cattle's (Holdings) plc in 1991.

Celltech Group plc

216 Bath Road, Slough, Berkshire, SL1 4EN Tel: (01753) 534655

Slater, John *Director of Legal Services and Co. Sec..* Reports to: Finance Director. Lawyers in dept: 2. Staff: 3. Percentage of work outsourced: 10% (litigation, property, foreign legal matters). Responsible for the provision of legal and company secretarial services. Main areas of work are general commercial matters, intellectual property and corporate affairs.

Career: Qualified as a solicitor 1978.

Chubb Insurance Company of Europe S.A.

The Registry, Royal Mint Court, London, EC3N 4QN Tel: (0171) 867 8686

Collins, Gillian: *General Counsel for Europe.* Reports to: Chairman of Europe, Gen. Counsel Worldwide. Lawyers in dept: 2. Percentage of work outsourced: 50-60% (European issues, matters requiring specialist technical expertise).
Responsible for all legal work undertaken by the company in the nine European countries where Chubb currently has offices. Work includes regulatory compliance, policy wordings, monitoring and implementing EC Regulations/Directives, alternate risk transfer advice, drafting reinsurance agreements, general commercial contracts, investment and media liaison. Is also company secretary. Member of EU Committee of American Chamber of Commerce and Vice Chair of Financial Services Sub Committee in Belgium. Regular speaker at in-house and external seminars.

Career: Admitted as a solicitor to the Supreme Court of New South Wales 1987 and to the Federal Court and High Court of Australia 1988. Solicitor, *Mallesons Stephen Jaques* 1988-91. Joined Chubb Insurance Company of Australia Ltd as Claim Manager/ Corporate Solicitor in 1991 and took up current position in 1993.

Civil Aviation Authority

CAA House, 45-59 Kingsway, London, WC2B 6TE Tel: (0171) 832 5794

Britton, Rupert J. *Secretary and legal adviser.* Reports to: Chairman. Lawyers in Depart: 7. Staff: 25.
Deals with aviation, litigation, prosecution, employment, planning, contracts, EC and public international law. Contributor to Atkins Court Forms; Civil Aviation.

Career: Qualified 1971. Assistant solicitor GLC 1971-1974, chief solicitor mid-Bedfordshire DC 1974-1977, assistant solicitor Corporation of London 1977-1980. Joined Civil Aviation Authority 1980 becoming secretary and legal adviser 1994.

Clyde Petroleum plc

Coddington Court, Coddington, Ledbury, Herefordshire, HR8 1JL Tel: (01531) 640811

Windham, Andrew G.   *Co. Secretary & General Manager (Legal).*   Reports to: Group MD. Lawyers in dept: 3. Staff: 9. Percentage of work outsourced: 10% (financings, option and pension work). Responsible for management of legal aspects of the Group's affairs. Principal area of work involves joint ventures, including acquisitions and disposals (both corporate and asset). Also advises on bank financings, rights issues, benefit schemes and general corporate matters, and provides company secretarial services.

Career: Articled at *Stephenson Harwood* 1972-74 and assistant solicitor 1974-77. Legal Adviser, Westland Aircraft Ltd 1978-81 and Senior Legal Adviser 1982-83, then joined Clyde Petroleum plc. Legal Manager 1983-88; International Manager 1988-89 and then took up present position. Member of Group's Executive Committee since 1994.

Coats Viyella plc

28 Savile Row, London, W1X 2DD Tel: (0171) 734 5321

Dow, Sam   *Company Secretary.*   Reports to: Chairman. Lawyers in dept: 2. Staff: 75. Percentage of work outsourced: 15% (major corporate acquisitions, specialist advice).
Responsible for dealing with all areas affecting corporate holding company and major transactions of subsidiaries.
Career: Qualified 1983. Took up current position in 1986.

Coca-Cola Middle East

Amberley Place, 107-111 Peascod Street, Windsor, Berks, SL4 1TE Tel: (01753) 858446

Kearney, Gregory J.   *Division Counsel.*
Reports to: President. Lawyers in dept: 1. Staff: 1. Percentage of work outsourced: 20% (litigation, foreign law advice).
Deals with general commercial legal matters including licensing, contracts, joint ventures, finance, competition law, trade marks, company law and employment geographically encompassing the Middle East from Morocco to Iran.
Member of IBA and Society of British and American Lawyers.
Career: Qualified 1975. Corporate Attorney, General Binding Corp, Illinois 1975-78. Associate *Cliffe Dekker & Todd*, Johannesburg 1979-81. Division Counsel, Coca-Cola Export Group, Johannesburg 1981-86. Legal Director, National Beverage Services (Pty) Ltd, Johannesburg 1987-88. Division Counsel, Coca-Cola Northwest Europe 1988-93 based in London and took up present position in 1993.

Coca-Cola & Schweppes Beverages Ltd

Charter Place, Uxbridge, Middx, UB8 1EZ Tel: (01895) 231313

Blanks, Hester   *Legal Director/ Company Secretary.*   Reports to: MD. Lawyers in dept: 3. Staff: 3. Percentage of work outsourced: small. Responsible for provision of in-house legal advice and company secretarial services and managing external advisers where necessary.

Collett Dickenson Pearce International Group Ltd

33-34 Soho Square, London, W1V 6DP Tel: (0171) 292 4115

Pullen, David J.D.   *Director and Group Company Secretary.*   Reports to: Chairman. Lawyers in dept: 1. Staff: 1. Percentage of work outsourced: 40% (specialised litigation, property, commercial, intellectual property).
Principal areas of work are company secretarial matters, contracts, employment, property, intellectual property, mergers and acquisitions and joint ventures.
Career: Qualified 1972 while with *Russell-Cooke, Potter & Chapman*, becoming assistant solicitor and then partner. Legal Adviser, Standard Telephone & Cable plc 1975-76 and took up current position in 1976.

Colorvision plc

Perdio House, Woodend Avenue, Speke, Liverpool, L24 9WF Tel: (0151) 448 1515

Millar, Tom A.   *Company Solicitor.*   Reports to: MD. Lawyers in dept: 1. Staff: 2. Percentage of work outsourced: 5% (various types).
Main areas of work are employment matters, consumer law, regulatory issues (such as trading standards), general commercial contracts, and commercial property.
Career: Articled with *Robinson Jarvis & Rolf*, Isle of Wight 1985-87. Assistant solicitor with *Cartmell Shepherd*, Carlisle 1987-88 and with *Walker Smith & Way*, Chester 1988-90. Joined Merseyside Passenger Transport Executive as assistant solicitor 1990, subsequently Head of Legal Section and appointed Solicitor and Secretary to the Executive 1991. Took up current position in 1994.

Commonwealth Development Corporation

One Bessborough Gardens, London, SW1V 2JQ Tel: (0171) 828 4488

Rodmell, Graham A.   *General Counsel.*
Reports to: Chief Executive. Lawyers in dept: 10. Staff: 20. Percentage of work outsourced: 10% (in UK - litigation, pensions, some specialist areas and some investment documentation; and overseas - security for loans and some work where local law applies).
Principal areas of work are managment administration (responsible for corporate secretariat); supervising mainstream investment documentation; loan security arrangements including IPOs; international joint ventures; relations with UK and overseas governments and corporate management contracts. Other areas of work include borrowing, disposals, debt reorganisation (including sovereign) and legal aspects of personnel matters. Has lectured at Institute of Advanced Legal Studies, to Crown Agents and at Bradford University.
Career: Qualified 1959. Variety of local government legal appointments until 1967. With *Simmons & Simmons* 1968-75 and joined CDC in 1976.

Concentric plc

Coleshill Road, Sutton Coldfield, West Midlands, B75 7AZ Tel: (0121) 378 4229

Miles, Roger   *Director and Secretary.*

Consolidated Insurance Group

Ambassador House, Paradise Road, Richmond, Surrey, TW9 1SQ Tel: (0181) 940 8343

Bagley, Richard D.F.   *Head of Legal Services.*
Reports to: Chief Operating Officer. Lawyers in dept: 5. Percentage of work outsourced: 5-10% (litigation and property).
Manages Legal and Customer Relations dept, revising policy and agency documentation, claims complaints handling and litigation; advises on consumer credit and personal finance documentation for finance company clients; manages consumer and media relationships. As Group Money Laundering Officer, drafts and implements group procedures and training. Appoints and manages performance of external lawyers to subsidiaries in Europe.
Career: Qualified 1981 while at *Preston & Redman* and solicitor to 1984. Solicitor, Legal Division Abbey Life Group plc 1984-87. Deputy Head of Legal Services, McCarthy & Stone plc 1987-90. Solicitor and company secretary, the Agricultural Mortgage Corporation plc 1990-94, then took up current position.

Consolidated Financial Insurance

Eaton Road, Enfield, Middx, EN1 1YR Tel: (0181) 367 6000

Basaran, Sandra J.   *Legal Director.*   Reports to: Chairman and CEO. Lawyers in dept: 8. Staff: 5. Percentage of work outsourced: 5% (where specialist expertise required).
Deals with corporate, commercial, compliance and company secretarial matters. Work includes M&As, joint ventures, international operations, wide-ranging corporate and commercial matters and compliance for company's investment business. Member of IBA, Life Assurance Legal Society and Institute of Directors.
Career: Called to the Bar 1984. Legal consultant, Moorgate Group plc 1984-86, then joined present employer. Appointed Legal Director 1989.

Control Data Systems Inc.

3 Roundwood Avenue, Stockley Park, Uxbridge, Middx, UB11 1AG Tel: (0181) 606 3500

Kasolowksy, Reiner   *European General Counsel.*   Reports to: V-P Europe, Middle East, Africa. Lawyers in dept: 3. Staff: 2. Percentage of work outsourced: 30% (commercial leases, trade marks, pensions, litigation and foreign law).
Chief lawyer of the European operation of US based company, responsible for control of all major transactions throughout Europe, and project manager for the largest of these. Main areas of work are high-tech and computer law, mergers and acquisitions, competition law and employment.
Career: Admitted to the Bar as Rechtsanwalt 1976 (Frankfurt/ Main), while with German sales team of Control Data Corp. Member of Executive Management Team, Control Data GmbH 1978-81; Chief Lawyer and Human Resources Management 1982-83 and also Manager of Acquisitions 1983-86. General Counsel and Project Manager for Germany, Italy and the Netherlands 1986-88, then took up current position.

Cordiant plc

83/89 Whitfield Street, London, W1A 4XA Tel: (0171) 436 4000

Howell, Peter Graham   *Company Secretary - General Counsel.*   Reports to: Finance Director. Lawyers in Dept: 1
Percent of work outsourced: 95% (litigation, property,

banking, corporate, copy clearance).
Supervises litigation and choice of lawyers. Deals with employment and contractual issues, insurance and pensions worldwide. Organises all plc Board meetings, prepares agendas, etc, and sits on a number of management committees.
Career: With *Joynson Hicks & Co* 1977-80. Qualified in 1979. Assistant Solicitor, Rank Film Distributors Ltd 1980-84. Assistant Solicitor and (from 1987) Partner at *Davenport Lyons & Co* 1985-89. Company Secretary and (from 1992) Director of Legal and Personnel Services with LWT (Holdings) plc 1989-94. Joined Saatchi & Saatchi in 1994.

Costain Group PLC

111 Westminster Bridge Road, London, SE1 7UE Tel: (0171) 705 8525

Nicoll, Peter *Group Legal Adviser/Company Secretary.* Reports to: Chairman, Chief Executive. Lawyers in dept: 9. Direct reporting staff: 5. Percentage of work outsourced: minimal (Stock Exchange and other specialised work).
Responsible for provision of legal services to the Group and provides a full company secretarial service.
Career: Qualified 1973. With Richard Costain Ltd 1973-76, Tarmac Construction Ltd 1976-80 and then joined Costain Group plc.

Courtaulds plc

50 George Street, London, W1A 2BB Tel: (0171) 612 1000

Miller, R.H. *Head of Legal Services.* Reports to: Company Secretary. Lawyers in dept: 8. Staff: 7. Percentage of work outsourced: 30% (litigation, employment, property).
Manages the provision of legal services for the group worldwide. Principal areas of work are mergers and acquisitions; joint ventures; licensing technology; distribution, agency and sales agreements; supply contracts; general commercial contracts; and litigation management. Presents seminars on acquisitions, due diligence and post acquisition auditing.
Career: Qualified 1969. Group Legal Adviser, Fordham Investment Group 1970-71. Group Legal Adviser, Ralli International 1971-73. Group Legal Adviser and Company Secretary, Bowater plc 1973-90, before taking up present position.

Cowie Group plc

Millfield House, Hylton Road, Sunderland, Tyne and Wear, SR4 7BA Tel: (0191) 514 4122

Applegarth, Chris *Company Solicitor.*
Reports to: Main Board. Lawyers in dept: 1. Staff: 3. Percentage of work outsourced: 15%.
Principal areas of work are company/commercial matters, banking, employment, consumer credit, equipment leasing and securitisation of receivables. Other areas of work are matters involving traffic, property, trade and service marks, and business development generally.
Career: Qualified as a Barrister 1975 and practised at the Bar until 1980. Qualified 1983 as a solicitor and took up present position in 1985.

Dairy Crest Ltd

Dairy Crest House, Portsmouth Road, Surbiton, Surrey, KT6 5QL Tel: (0181) 910 4049

Newton, Roger J. *Company Secretary.*
Reports to: Chief Executive. Lawyers in dept: 2. Staff: 6. Percentage of work outsourced: 60%+ (litigation, conveyancing, pensions, acquisitions).

Main areas of work are compliance; attendance at Board/Executive meetings; provision of first stop legal advice on company/commercial and employment issues; and the administration of insurances, properties and trade marks. Director and Secretary of Pensions Trustee Company. Member of Law Society and ICSA.
Career: Qualified 1973. Legal Adviser, Rolls Royce plc and then with Ciba-Geigy plc. Deputy Secretary, Babcock International plc 1981-85. Group Secretary to Nabisco Group Ltd 1986-89 and to Peek plc 1989-92, then took up current position.

David S. Smith (Holdings) plc

16 Great Peter Street, London, SW1P 2BX Tel: (0171) 222 8855

Glover, Jill *Group Legal Adviser.* Reports to: Corporate Services Director. Lawyers in dept: 2. Staff: 1. Work outsourced: major acquisitions, litigation.
Involved in all areas of company and commercial work involving Group companies, including acquisitions.
Career: Qualified 1985, while with *Beachcroft Stanleys.* Assistant solicitor with *Alsop Wilkinson* 1986-89, then joined *McKenna & Co.* Became Group Legal Adviser to the David S. Smith Group in 1992.

Del Monte Foods International Ltd

Del Monte House, London Road, Staines, Middlesex, TW18 4JD Tel: (01784) 447400

Hunt, Tim J. *Company Secretary & Legal Co-ordinator.* Reports to: Finance Director. Staff: 2. Percentage of work outsourced: 35% (acquisitions, licensing, intellectual property and litigation).
Responsible for provision of in-house legal advice and management of external lawyers. Also provides full company secretarial service, including administration of pensions insurance, IP, quality control incident management.
Career: Articled with *Lawrence Messer & Co* 1964-66, then assistant solicitor with *Freshfields* 1966-70. Joined Ultramar PLC in 1970, holding a variety of legal advisory positions within the group, and company secretary 1983-92. Took up present position in March 1993.

Donelon Tyson plc

Donelon House, Crown Lane, Horwich, Bolton, Lancashire, BL6 5HM Tel: (01204) 699222

Mullen, Nicholas H. *Company Secretary/Group Legal Adviser.* Reports to: Chairman. Lawyers in dept: 1. Percentage of work outsourced: 20% (major litigation, conveyancing).
Advises on and drafts terms of business, acquisition and disposal agreements, development agreements, terms of employment and conducts industrial tribunal work and county court litigation. Also advises on and manages conduct of major litigation, involving construction disputes resolution through litigation/arbitration and preparation of construction claims under contracts. Provides full company secretarial service. Member of the Bar of England and Wales.

Eagle Star Holdings plc

60 St Mary's Axe, London, EC3A 8JQ Tel: (0171) 929 1111

Hitchings, Paul *Group Legal Adviser.* Reports to: Deputy Chairman. Lawyers in dept: 12. Staff: 22. Percentage of work outsourced: 5% (litigation).
Responsible for provision of legal services. Principal areas of work are contentious and non-contentious insurance matters. Other areas of work include company/ commercial, general litigation, acquisitions and disposals and conveyancing. Member of BACFI

and General Council of the Bar.
Career: Qualified as a Barrister 1968 and practised at the Bar until 1972. Various appointments in the engineering industries 1972-84. Director of Legal Services, BL plc/ Rover Group plc 1984-89, then took up current position.

Electronic Data Systems Ltd

4 Roundwood Avenue, Stockley Park, Uxbridge, Middlesex, UB11 1BQ Tel: (0181) 848 8989

Curtis, Mark *Legal Director.* Reports to: MD. Lawyers in dept: 2. Staff: 24. Percentage of work outsourced: 50% (property, litigation, commercial). Responsible for provision of in-house legal services and managing external advisers where required.
Career: Qualified 1981.

ELF Enterprise Caledonia Ltd

Silverburn House, 1 Claymore Drive, Bridge Of Don, Aberdeen, AB23 8GB Tel: (01224) 233200

English, Warwick *Vice President - Legal and Chief Counsel.* Reports to: MD. Lawyers in dept: 6. Staff: 20. Percentage of work outsourced: 5-10% (litigation, major property, major finance).
Principal areas of work are oil and gas licensing, joint venture agreements and commercial contracts of all types. Has addressed various oil industry-oriented conferences.
Career: Qualified 1974. Solicitor with *Moore & Blatch* 1974-78. Controller, IP Oil Services 1978-79. Director, Phoenix Hydrocarbons Ltd 1979-81. Manager, Easco Ltd 1981-83; Manager, Legal Affairs, Enterprise Oil 1983-1987. General Counsel ELF UK plc 1987-92, and took up present position in 1993.

Eli Lilly International

Lilly House, 13 Hanover Square, London, W1R 0PA Tel: (0171) 409 4845

Casady, Timothy J. *Senior Counsel Europe/Middle East/Africa.* Reports to: Deputy General Counsel. Lawyers in dept: 5. Staff: 7. Percentage of work outsourced: 50-75% (M&A, regulatory, environmental, product liability).
Responsible for support and management of legal issues and affairs of Eli Lilly throughout Europe, Middle East and Africa, specialising in commercial transactions and alliances. Principal areas of work are commercial law, EU competition law and regulatory matters. Member IBA, ABA and American Corporate Counsel Association. Has lectured on business law at Indiana University School of Business.
Career: Qualified in Indiana and Minnesota.

Emerson Developments (Holdings) Ltd

Emerson House, Heyes Lane, Alderley Edge, Cheshire, SK9 7LF Tel: (01625) 584531

Burgess, Paul *Snr Solicitor/Executive Comml Director.* Reports to: Chairman. Lawyers in dept: 3. Staff: 3. Percentage of work outsourced: 5-10% (litigation, debt collection).
Runs department responsible for planning law and practice, commercial property work, portfolio management and landlord and tenant work. Reports to Main Boards. Plans advocacy and liaises with Silks on planning inquiries/ local plans; and with external solicitors on outsourced work. On Executive Commercial Division Board (Orbit Developments) and Director of portfolio management company. Has addressed conferences and seminars; and tutors on planning law.
Career: Head of Conveyancing Department in private practice 1983-88.

English China Clays plc

1015 Arlington Business Park, Theale, Reading, Berkshire, RG7 4SA Tel: (01734) 304010

Elliott, Peter *Company Secretary and Solicitor.* Responsible for group wide legal, estates, pensions, insurance and secretariat matters.

Career: Qualified 1977, while with *Linklaters & Paines* and assistant solicitor to 1981, based in London and Brussels. Assistant solicitor and then partner with *Charles Russell & Co* 1982-87. Joined English China Clays plc in 1987 and took up current position in 1991.

Enron Europe

4 Millbank, London, SW1 Tel: (0171) 316 5300

Styles, Peter R. *Vice-President, Corporate Projects.* Reports to: President, Enron Europe. Staff: 3.
Principal areas of work are new and special business ventures. Vice-Chairman, BACFI.

Career: Called to the Bar 1978. Various legal advisory positions within ICI (UK) 1978-84. Regional Legal Counsel, Dow UK, London 1984-88 and Business Development Manager, Dow Europe, Zurich 1989-92. Chief Legal Counsel, Enron Europe, London 1992-94, then took up current position.

Enterprise Oil plc

Grand Buildings, Trafalgar Square, London, WC2N 5EJ Tel: (0171) 925 4000

Gaymer, Vivien *Head of Legal Affairs/Company Secretary.* Reports to: Chairman. Lawyers in dept: 6. Staff: 12. Percentage of work outsourced: variable (conveyancing, litigation, large financings or acquisitions, other specialist work).
Responsible for oil and gas legal work of the group worldwide as well as corporate and statutory work. Council Member of SERL and of IBA, Petroleum and Mineral Law Resources Trust (Trustee) and BACFI. Member of Editorial Advisory Board, International Company and Commercial Law Review.

Career: Called to the Bar 1971. Deputy Chief Clerk Inner London Magistrates Courts 1971-74. Assistant Secretary and Legal Adviser to the Institute of Practitioners in Advertising 1974-75. Counsel, Mobil Oil 1975-84, then took up current position. Appointed company secretary in 1991.

Epson (UK) Ltd

Campus 100, Maylands Avenue, Hemel Hempstead, Hertfordshire, HP2 7TJ Tel: (01442) 61144

Brush, David W. *Head of Legal Affairs.* Reports to: MD. Lawyers in dept: 1. Percentage of work outsourced: 20% (leasehold conveyancing, High Court litigation).
Responsible for all legal issues, company secretarial matters and contract management.

Career: Qualified 1979. Assistant solicitor, London Electricity Board 1979-83. Senior solicitor, Imperial Foods Ltd 1983-86. Assistant Group Secretary, Extel Group plc 1986-87. Company secretary Priest Marians Holdings plc 1988 and then took up current position with Epson (UK) Ltd.

Esselte Ltd

Esselte House, 4 Buckingham Gate, London, SW1E 6JR Tel: (0171) 973 5200

Thomas, Martin *General Counsel.* Reports to: VP Legal (Stockholm). Lawyers in dept: 1. Staff: 1. Percentage of work outsourced: 25% (litigation, conveyancing).
Main areas of work are advising on company/commercial, IP and employment matters. Also company secretary and director. Deals with the full range of commercial agreements and advises on pensions (trustee and administrator of Group UK pension plan). Responsible for property holdings and transactions and personnel matters from contracts of employment to termination. Member of FAST Legal Advisory Group. Assisted in producing Software Publishers' Association Model PC Software Licence Agreement for Europe.

Career: Qualified 1977. Legal Adviser, Lucas Industries Ltd 1977-80. Company Secretary and Legal Adviser, Letraset Ltd 1980-84, then joined Esselte Ltd.

European Gas Turbines Ltd.

P.O. Box 1, Thorngate House, Lincoln, LN2 5DJ Tel: (01522) 583010

Gregory, Bruce D. *Director of Legal Services.* Reports to: M.D. Lawyers in dept: 4. Staff: 7. Percentage of work outsourced: 5-10% (litigation, conveyancing, advice on foreign laws and specialist matters).
Supervises 3 lawyers in UK and responsible for provision of legal service for EGT and its subsidiaries in France, Germany, Netherlands, UK and USA. Principal areas of work involve contracts of sale and purchase, collaboration agreements, licensing, acquisitions and disposals and competition law. Other areas of work include preparation of standard form legal documents, advice on IPRS, insurance and company secretarial duties. Member of the General Council of the Bar and BACFI.

Career: Called to the Bar 1970. Head of legal department for North Sea area, Total Oil Marine Ltd 1971-76. Director, Legal Services (East) for Massey-Ferguson Holdings Ltd 1976-87, then joined European Gas Turbines Ltd.

Exxon Chemical Ltd.

PO Box 122, 4600 Parkway, Fareham, Hampshire, PO15 7AP Tel: (01489) 884400

Atha, Jill *Legal Manager and Company Secretary.* Reports to: Chairman. Lawyers in dept: 2. Staff: 2. Percentage of work outsourced: 10% (specialist transactions such as corporate disposals, Scottish land transactions and merger notifications).
Principal areas of work are contract, competition law, employment and environmental law matters. Drafts and reviews commercial contracts of all types. Provides advice and training on competition law aspects of commercial transactions. Advises on employment issues and handles Tribunal appearances. Advises on health, safety and environment issues generally. Also deals with corporate restructuring, joint ventures and provides full company secretarial service. Advises on overseas business transactions.

Career: Qualified 1982. Worked in local government (Kingston-upon-Thames/ Hammersmith and Fulham) 1982-86, then joined Esso Petroleum Company handling downstream work until 1989, upstream work 1989-91 and Commercial Manager, Distribution 1992. Joined Exxon Chemical Ltd in 1993.

Field Group plc

Misbourne House, Badminton Court, Rectory Way, Church Street, Amersham, Buckinghamshire, HP7 0DD Tel: (01494) 433711

Fitzpatrick, Deborah *Legal Advisor/ Asst. Company Secretary.* Reports to: Finance Director. Lawyers in dept: 1. Percentage of work outsourced: 35% (acquisition work, French and German legal advice, some trade mark work).
Principal areas of work are acquisitions (team leader and manager of outside advisers on two recent major acquisitions), employment, intellectual property, Stock Exchange compliance work, and trade and supply agreements (the latest valued at £6 million). Also deals with insurance, pensions and general contractual matters.

Career: Qualified 1987 while with *Steggles Palmer.* Solicitor, corporate department, *D.J. Freeman* 1987-92.

Ford Credit Europe plc

Jubilee House, The Drive, Brentwood, Essex, CM13 3AR Tel: (01277) 692280

Brackley, Michael John *Director Legal Affairs.* Reports to: M.D. Lawyers in dept: 4. Staff: 7. Percentage of work outsourced: 15 (litigation and public debt).
Principal areas of work cover debt, security, bank of England regulation, Consumer Credit Act, advertising and insolvencies.

Career: Qualified 1974. Previously assistant solicitor with *Lovell White & King* (now *Lovell White Durrant*) and Group solicitor to Garrard & Lofthouse group of companies.

Forward Trust Group Ltd

12 Calthorpe Road, Edgbaston, Birmingham, B15 1QZ Tel: (0121) 455 3737

White, Andrew *Head of Legal Services.* Reports to: Chief Executive. Lawyers in dept: 12. Staff: 16. Percentage of work outsourced: 5% (work relating to jurisdictions other than England and Wales).
Principal areas of work concern the legal aspects of consumer credit. Also deals with matters concerning asset finance and leasing. Member of Legal Sub-Committee, Examination Council and Tuition Sub-Committee of Finance and Leasing Association.

Career: Articled at *Evershed & Tomkinson* 1972-74 and then joined Forward Trust Group.

Gallaher Ltd

Members Hill, Brooklands Road, Weybridge, Surrey, KT13 0QU Tel: (01932) 859777

Devereux, Christopher J. *Corporate Legal Adviser.* Reports to: Group Legal Adviser. Lawyers in dept: 4. Staff: 3.
Responsible for provision of in-house legal service within the Gallaher Group.

Career: Qualified 1975 and in private practice until 1978, then joined Gallaher Ltd, as Assistant Solicitor.

Gan Life Holdings plc

Gan House, Harlow, Essex, CM20 2EW Tel: (01279) 626262

Taylor, Stuart *Group Solicitor and Company Secretary.* Reports to: Corporate Director. Lawyers in dept: 3. Staff: 40. Percentage of work outsourced: 20% (specialist litigation, commercial and corporate).
Responsible for provision of in-house legal advice

and co-ordinating and managing external advisers as appropriate. Principal areas of work are compliance; company secretarial; litigation; insurance law; property; FSA, SIB, PIA and IMRO authorisation and compliance procedures; insurance litigation; restrictive covenants and agency agreements. Also deals with data protection, share options and property management. Treasurer of Life Assurance Legal Society.

Career: Qualified 1981. With Scotland Yard legal department 1981-86 and DPP/CPS 1986-87. Senior Compliance Officer, IMRO 1987-88, then took up present position.

GAN UK plc

Minster House, 12 Arthur Street, London, EC4R 9BJ Tel: (0171) 623 5280

Whitfield-Jones, Rosemary *Company Secretary and Legal Adviser.* Reports to: Chairman and Chief Executive. Lawyers in dept: 1. Staff: 3.
Percentage of work outsourced: 30-40% (litigation, complex matters requiring specialist expertise). Principal areas of work are regulatory and compliance matters (UK, EC and overseas); commercial contracts and policy wordings; management of legal costs and panel of solicitors; and providing general legal advice to Board and Senior Managers. Hon. secretary, British Insurance Law Association.

Career: Qualified 1975. Previous companies worked for: Hertz, Tricentul and Sony. Joined GAN in 1990.

Gartmore plc

Gartmore House, 16-18 Monument Street, London, EC3R 8QQ Tel: (0171) 782 2432

Willoughby, Thomas James *Director.* Reports to: Chairman. Lawyers in dept: 5. Staff: 12. Percentage of work outsourced: 20% (some commercial agreements).
Director responsible for legal/compliance and company secretarial matters.

Career: Qualified 1977. Articled with *Addleshaw Sons & Latham* 1973-76, then assistant solicitor with *Philip Conn & Co* 1977-78. Solicitor with *Allen & Overy* 1978-81, specialising in banking and company/commercial work. Joined Gartmore Investment Management Ltd in 1981 and appointed Director of Gartmore plc on flotation in 1993. Member of Institutional Fund Managers Association Regulation and Taxation Committee. Director of Personal Investment Authority and Chairman of Disciplinary Committee.

GEI International plc

Aspley Hill, Woburn Sands, Milton Keynes, Bedfordshire, MK17 8NW Tel: (01908) 281199

Hare, Richard *Company Secretary.* Reports to: Financial Director. Number of lawyers in dept: 1. Staff: 1. Percentage of work outsourced: 20% (acquisitions/ disposals, litigation, tax).
Main areas of work are commercial, banking, employment, property and compliance. Drafts and advises on sale and purchase contracts, agency and distribution agreements, bank facility agreements, employment contracts etc. Advises on dismissal and redundancy and the sale, purchase and lease of property. Also provides full company secretarial service e.g. compliance, annual report, insurance, pension and personnel matters.

Career: Qualified 1984. Solicitor/Assistant Secretary, Vauxhall Motors 1984-88.

General Accident Life Services Ltd

2 Rougier Street, York, YO1 1HR Tel: (01904) 628982

Graham, Donald. *Legal Services Manager.* Reports to: General Manager. Lawyers in Dept: 5 percent
of work outsourced: 20% (most litigation, more complex company and commercial work).
Principal areas of work are life assurance, pensions, unit trusts and PEP's. Handles a variety of matters supporting the mainstream business activities of the financial services group including regulatory matters. Also company secretary.

Career: Called to the Bar in 1975. Has held current position since January 1992.

Geoffrey E. Macpherson Ltd.

Lenton Lane, Nottingham, NG7 2NT Tel: (01602) 868701

Bowden, Roger Alan *Operations Director/ Company Solicitor.* Lawyers in dept: 1. Staff: 48. Percentage of work outsourced: 10% (foreign litigation and court work).
Responsible for all legal, operational and personnel functions of the company including engineering services, transport and maintenance.

Career: Qualified 1972. Former Partner, *Edge & Ellison*, Leicester.

GKN plc

PO Box 55, Redditch, Worcestershire, B98 0TL Tel: (01527) 517715

Denham, Grey *Head of Group Legal Department.* Reports to: Group Secretary. Lawyers in dept: 12. Staff: 20. Percentage of work outsourced: 10% (commercial property, litigation). Responsible for team of 8 lawyers in Redditch handling mergers, acquisitions, corporate joint ventures, competition law (UK, EU and US), corporate reorganisations and funding exercises, and defence contracts on behalf of GKN worldwide. Experienced in M&A work and joint ventures on five continents. Also responsible for team of 4 lawyers specialising in aerospace/defence contracts based at Westland in Yeovil. Committee member of Society of Motor Manufacturers and Traders.

Career: Qualified as a Barrister 1972. Lecturer in legal philosophy, Leicester Polytechnic 1972-74 and Senior Lecturer in legal philosophy and Constitutional law, Nottingham Law School 1974-76 and 1977-78. Common law pupillage 1976-77, Mid-Oxford circuit. Company Legal Officer, Alfred Herbert Ltd 1978-80, then joined GKN plc.

Glaxo Wellcome plc

Landsdowne House, Berkeley Square, London, W1X 6BQ Tel: (0171) 493 4060

Strachan, Jeremy *Director - Legal and Corporate Affairs.* Executive Director responsible for legal and corporate affairs which include legal services, secretariat, human resources, pensions and certain other central functions. Member of BACFI and the General Council of the Bar.

Career: Qualified Barrister. With the Law Commission 1967-72, then Legal Adviser to the British Steel Corporation. Director of Group Legal and Patent Services, ICL 1983, Group Legal Adviser STC plc 1984 and Director of Legal Affairs 1985. Joined Glaxo in 1986 as Director of Group Legal Services.

Grand Metropolitan plc

20 St James's Square, London, SW1Y 4RR Tel: (0171) 321 6000

Myddelton, Roger *Group Legal Director/ Company Secretary.* Reports to: Group Services Director. Staff: 4.
Functionally responsible for legal and company secretarial matters, and for risk management and insurance, throughout the Group.

Career: Qualified 1966. Assistant solicitor, Rank Xerox 1968-78 (Manager of Legal Services from 1973). Deputy Legal Adviser, Courtaulds plc 1978 and appointed Group Legal Adviser in 1979. Joined Grand Metropolitan in 1988.

Graystone plc

Emerson Court, Alderley Road, Wilmslow, Cheshire, SK9 1NX Tel: (01625) 535353

Yates, John Martyn *Group Secretary/ Solicitor.* Reports to: Executive Chairman. Lawyers in dept: 1. Staff: 1. Percentage of work outsourced: 30% (High Court litigation and larger acquisition transactions). Responsible for full legal and secretarial service provided to 3 listed companies and group of operating companies engaged primarily in engineering activities. Work covers general company, commercial, employment and property matters. Deals with group insurances and risk programme, trustee of group pension scheme and administrator of group property portfolio. Member of Law Society Commerce and Industry Group.

Career: Qualified 1970. Company Secretary/ Solicitor George Dew plc 1971-86. Commercial Manager/ Solicitor National Nuclear Corporation 1986-88. Group Legal Adviser/ Secretary Kemira Ince Ltd 1988-89, then joined British Syphon Industries plc as Group Secretary/ Solicitor prior to its acquisition by Graystone plc.

Group 4 Securitas Ltd

Farncombe House, Broadway, Worcs, WR12 7LJ Tel: (01386) 858585

Dufton, Michael *Group Legal Counsel.* Percentage of work outsourced: 20% (litigation, property).
Principal areas of work are contracts, commercial law, insurance matters, international acquisitions, licensing and joint ventures. Accredited CEDR Mediator. Speaker to in-house lawyers on Nottingham University course.

Career: Qualified 1978. With Wiggins Teape plc 1979-81, The Boots Company plc 1981-85 and then joined Group 4 Securitas Ltd.

Guinness plc

39 Portman Square, London, W1H 0EE Tel: (0171) 486 0288

Mildwaters, Kenneth C. *Director of Legal Services.* Lawyers in dept: 13. Staff: 12. Responsible for the provision of legal services to Guinness plc.

Career: Qualified 1977. Solicitor with *Kott Gunning* until 1979, then joined *Glynn and Glynn* as a Partner. Partner at *Kott Gunning* 1981-85. Solicitor with *Theodore Goddard* 1987-88, Associate 1988-89 and Partner 1989-94. Became Director of Legal Services, Guinness plc in 1994.

Hardy Oil & Gas plc

7th Floor, Commonwealth House, 2 Chalkhill Road, Hammersmith, London, W6 8DW Tel: (0181) 741 7373

Neary, Annemarie *Legal Adviser.* Reports to: General Manager. Lawyers in dept: 1. Percentage of work outsourced: 10% (corporate acquisitions and disposals, Stock Exchange and Companies Acts compliance, some financings).
Responsible for all UK legal work including ventures in Namibia, Pakistan, Libya, Algeria and the Netherlands, principally concerned with oil and gas law. Work includes joint venture operating agreements, asset acquisitions and disposals, licence applications, development agreements, consultancy agreements and general commercial contracts. Also provides general legal advice outside oil and gas area and some company secretarial functions.
Member IBA Section on energy and natural resources law and UK Energy Lawyers' Group. Has lectured on oil and gas law at commercial conferences and Dundee University.
Career: Executive officer, Customs anti-evasion, Dublin 1983-85 and with Department of Energy 1985-88. Qualified as a Barrister-at-Law, 1988. Contracts adviser, Parc Ltd 1988-89, then joined Hardy Oil & Gas plc.

Henry Boot & Sons plc

Banner Cross Hall, Sheffield, South Yorkshire, S11 9PD Tel: (0114) 255 5444

Foster, E.S.S. *Group Solicitor.* Reports to: Group M.D. Lawyers in dept: 5. Staff: 8. Percentage of work outsourced: 40-50% (litigation and property acquisition).
Principal areas of work are legal matters relating to construction and property development. Also advises on litigation, options, landlord and tenant, employment law and joint ventures. Member of Chartered Institute of Arbitrators.
Career: Qualified 1988. Conveyancing manager in private practice 1979-84 and Assistant Group Secretary (Legal) Henry Boot and Sons 1984-88. Became Group Solicitor in 1988.

Heron International plc

Heron House, 19 Marylebone Road, London, NW1 5JL Tel: (0171) 486 4477

Parsons, Neil *Group Solicitor/ Company Secretary.* Reports to: Deputy CEO. Lawyers in dept: 1. Staff: 1. Percentage of work outsourced: 75% (property acquisitions and disposals, corporate finance and litigation).
Principal areas of work are general company and commercial matters, corporate finance and banking. Also handles Group company secretarial work and pension scheme. Advises on litigation, trademark protection, employment and I.T. contracts.
Career: Qualified 1987. Solicitor with *Lawrence James* 1987-89, *Brecher & Co* 1989-90 and *Saunders Sobell* 1990-91, then joined Heron International plc.

Hertz (UK) Ltd

Radnor House, 1272 London Road, Norbury, London, SW16 4XW Tel: (0181) 679 1777

Strachan, Robert *Legal Director and company secretary.* Reports to: Managing Director. lawyers in Dept: 1. Staff: 2. Percentage of work outsourced: 10% (insurance litigation).
Responsible for providing and supervising all legal services to UK group companies, including company/ commercial, marketing/ advertising, commercial property, franchising, competition law, company secretarial, employment and property management. Also ensures compliance with consumer credit, data protection and health and safety regulations.
Career: Qualified 1987. Commercial lawyer Rentokil Ltd 1987-1990. Joined Hertz (UK) Ltd 1990 becoming legal director/ company secretary 1993.

Hewlett-Packard Ltd

Cain Road, Bracknell, Berkshire, RG12 1HN Tel: (01344) 362215

Thompson, Richard D. *Director of Legal Services.* Reports to: Director of Finance and Administration. Lawyers in dept: 7. Staff: 10. Work outsourced: litigation, specialist advice, debt collection, conveyancing.
Responsible for provision and management of all legal services including contracts, litigation, legal advice on competition and general company/ commercial matters. Company secretary for Hewlett-Packard Ltd and its subsidiaries and Chairman of Pensions Trustees.
Career: Qualified 1963 while with *Wragge & Co.* Assistant solicitor, *Oppenheimers* 1965 and partner with *Pearman Smith* 1966-74. Assistant Solicitor/Commercial Manager, British Aerospace 1974-82, then took up current position.

Hillsdown Holdings plc

Hillsdown House, 32 Hampstead High Street, London, NW3 1QD Tel: (0171) 794 0677

Chambers, Martin *Group Legal Adviser/ Company Secretary.* Reports to: Chairman. Lawyers in dept: 1. Staff: 2. Percentage of work outsourced: 50% (acquisitions and disposals, litigation, banking).
Responsible for management and co-ordination of all major legal issues at parent and operating company level, including corporate "Yellow Book" work, intellectual property, M&A, joint ventures, employment, distribution and agency contracts, competition and commercial litigation. Member of Law Society Solicitors' European Group, Commerce and Industry Group and Food Law Group.
Career: Qualified 1975, while at *Clifford Turner.* Assistant solicitor with *McKenna & Co* 1975-77. European Legal Counsel to the Eaton Corporation 1977-83 and Group Legal Controller, Guinness plc 1983-88. Chief of Staff Business and Legal Affairs, House of Fraser Holdings plc 1988-90. European Legal Controller for the Albert Fisher Group plc 1991-93, then joined Hillsdown Holdings.

Hilton International Co

International Court, Units 2-3, Rhodes Way, Watford, Herts, WD2 4WY Tel: (01923) 231333

Chester, J. Geoffrey *Solicitor, General Counsel & Secretary.* Lawyers in dept: 5. Staff: 11. Percentage of work outsourced: 20-30% (foreign jurisdiction matters in company/commercial, property, litigation and trade marks).
Responsible for conduct of legal work for Hilton International throughout the world. Deals with legal work for new hotel developments worldwide and acquisitions, disposals and renegotiation/extension of agreements and leases for existing hotels. Supervises important litigation/arbitration proceedings, drafts and reviews commercial contracts, provides management summaries of complex legal documentation and provides secretarial function. Also responsible for trade and service mark protection of the Hilton name worldwide.
Career: Articled with *Lloyd Raymond Co & Edward Thompson Co.* Qualified 1976. Assistant Solicitor, *Hedleys* 1977-78 and with *Fox Gibbons* 1978-80.

Solicitor, Bodday NDT (Dubai) 1980. Assistant solicitor with National Coal Board 1981-85; then Head of the Company/Commercial section of legal department, Ladbroke Group plc until joined Hilton International Co in 1988 after its acquisition by Ladbroke Group plc.

Hoechst UK Ltd

Hoechst House, Salibury Road, Hounslow, Middx, TW4 6JH Tel: (0181) 754 3406

Davies, W.R. *Director of Legal Affairs.* Reports to: Finance Director. Lawyers in dept: 2. Staff: 6. Percentage of work outsourced: 15% (litigation, property, landlord and tenant, major acquisitions or disposals).
Provides legal and company secretarial services for Hoechst's subsidiary and associated companies in the UK. Work includes commercial agreements, competition law, protection of intellectual property interests and IP licensing, acquisitions and disposals, joint ventures, corporate reconstruction and demergers, employment law, commercial leases and IT agreements. Responsible for insurance and estate departments of Hoechst UK. Manages external advisers and handles company secretarial work. Member of Law Society Commerce and Industry Group, Pharmaceutical Lawyers Group, Licensing Executives Society and Society for Computers and Law.
Career: Qualified 1970. Financial analyst, IBM UK Ltd 1970-72. Solicitor, Smiths Industries plc 1972-75. Lawyer, Continental Oil Company Ltd 1975-79. Joined Hoechst UK Ltd as Head of Legal Department 1979 and appointed Director of Legal Affairs and Company Secretary in 1987.

Hogg Robinson plc

Concorde House, Church Street East, Woking, Surrey, GU21 1DJ Tel: (01483) 730311

Bell, Nigel *Group Solicitor.* Reports to: Group Secretary. Lawyers in dept: 1. Staff: 1. Percentage of work outsourced: 30% (property and litigation).
Provides legal advice to three main trading subsidiaries specialising in travel agency, financial services and freight forwarding. Supervises properties department, handles personnel and employment law, commercial agreements of all types ranging from bank documentation to IP and technology licensing. Monitors new legislation and its potential impact (eg EC Directive on Package Travel); advises on marketing, promotions and consumer law and liaises with external solicitors and trade associations. Also provides full company secretarial service.
Career: Qualified 1977 while with *Maughan & Hall*, Newcastle-upon-Tyne. Solicitor in Legal Department for Laporte Industries plc 1978-83, and Brooke Bond Group plc 1983-86, then joined Hogg Robinson plc.

Hoover European Appliance Group

Pentrebach, Merthyr Tydfil, Mid Glam, CF48 4TU Tel: (01685) 721222

Fallon, Michael *Company Lawyer and Company Secretary.* Reports to: President Candy SPA. Lawyers in dept: 1. Staff: 5. Percentage of work outsourced: 80% (all types).
Principal areas of work cover litigation, commercial contracts, employment, pensions, intellectual property, advertising/ promotions, product liability/ sale of goods and property.
Career: Qualified 1985. With CWS Ltd 1983-86, PHH Europe Ltd 1986-87 and Digital Equipment Ltd 1987-91.

Horserace Totalisator Board

Tote House, 74 Upper Richmond Road, London, SW15 2SU Tel: (0181) 874 6411

Heaton, W.J. *Company Secretary and Solicitor.* Reports to: Chief Executive. Lawyers in dept: 1. Staff: 3. Percentage of work outsourced: 90%

Horserace Betting Levy Board

52 Grosvenor Gardens, London, SW1W 0AU Tel: (0171) 333 0043

Evers, Lucilla *Head of Legal Affairs.* Reports to: Chief Executive. Percentage of work outsourced: 70% (disposal of assets, property transactions, loan security, pensions advice).
Main areas of work are reporting to the Home Office, consulting on legislation and drafting levy schemes. Gives talks on the statutory functions and work of the levy board.
Career: Qualified 1978. In-house lawyer with a property company 1982-85 then solicitor with *Jaques & Lewis* 1985-89 and *McKenna & Co* 1989-1993.

HSBC Holdings plc

10 Lower Thames Street, London, EC3R 6AE Tel: (0171) 260 0926

Carr, Chalmers *General Manager and Group Legal Adviser.* Reports to: Group Chief Executive. Lawyers in dept: 19. Staff: 41.
Responsible for the legal, secretarial, compliance and security functions of the HSBC Holdings Group.
Career: Qualified 1959. Served on the legal staff of several major UK companies including Rolls Royce and GKN. Head of Legal Services, Central Electricity Generating Board in London 1983. Joined HSBC in 1989 as Group Legal Adviser at the then Head Office in Hong Kong.

Ibstock plc

Lutterworth House, Lutterworth, Leicestershire, LE17 4PS Tel: (01455) 553071

Pike, Andrew *Company Secretary and Solicitor.* Reports to: M.D. Lawyers in dept: 1. Staff: 5.
Percentage of work outsourced: 70% (litigation, property and major commercial transactions).
Acts as company secretary to plc and principal UK subsidiary. Provides legal advice at head office and operating company level in UK and overseas. Has a particular involvement in acquisitions/ disposals and major corporate transactions. Company secretarial responsibility includes pensions and group worldwide insurance function, share schemes and general personnel responsibilities.
Career: Qualified 1976. Solicitor with *Barlow Lyde & Gilbert* 1976-78, Thomas Tilling Ltd 1978-79, *Cole & Cole*, Oxford 1979-81. Senior solicitor Costain Group plc 1981-89 and Company Secretary and Solicitor to Alfred McAlpine plc 1989-93.

Iceland Group plc

Second Avenue, Deeside Industrial Park, Deeside, Clywd, CH5 2NW Tel: (01244) 830100

Berry, John *Company Secretary.* Reports to: Finance Director. Lawyers in dept: 2. Staff: 18.
Percentage of work outsourced: 80% (conveyancing, litigation, corporate tax).
Responsible for Group's legal, company secretarial, licensing, pensions and employee benefits, insurance, fire and health and safety, and car fleet functions. Member of BACFI. Has addressed conference on ESOPs.
Qualified as a Barrister 1976. Assistant company

secretary Smith's Industries plc 1973-76. Assistant secretary, The Rank Organisation plc 1976-83. Legal Manager HP Bulmer Holdings plc 1983-85, then joined Iceland plc.

ICI Chemicals & Polymers Ltd

P.O. Box 90, Wilton Centre, Middlesborough, Cleveland, TS90 8JE Tel: (01642) 432167

Kay, John L. *Manager, Legal Services/Co. Secretary.* Reports to: Group Director. Lawyers in dept: 9. Staff: 16. Percentage of work outsourced: 15-20% (litigation, conveyancing and other specialist areas).
Principal areas of work involve commercial agreements relating to the chemical industry, electricity and energy. Also company secretary to Phillips-Imperial Petroleum Ltd., Impkemix Energy Ltd., Belasis Hall Technology Park Ltd., and Teesside Gas Transportation Ltd. Member of Bar Council and BACFI.
Career: Qualified 1973. Practising Barrister in Manchester 1973-77; Legal Adviser ICI Mond Division 1977-78; Legal Assistant ICI Petrochemicals 1978-81. Became Assistant Company Secretary ICI Plant Protection 1981 and Company Secretary of Nobel's Explosives Ltd 1982-88. Legal Services Manager of ICI Chemicals & Polymers since 1988.

ICL

ICL House, Brewhouse Street, (off Putney Bridge Rd), London, SW15 1SW Tel: (0181) 788 7272

Christou, Richard *Director, Commercial and Legal Affairs.* Reports to: Chairman and Chief Executive. Lawyers in dept: 30. Staff: 50 percentage of work outsourced: 10% (litigation and conveyancing).
Responsible for ICL commercial and legal affairs. Principal areas of work involve customer supply contracting, litigation, conveyancing, intellectual property rights and managing external advisors. Also handles commercial policies for the ICL Group, maintaining and up-dating policies for worldwide trade. Author of 'International Agency, Distribution and Licensing Agreements' (Longmans, 1986, 1990 and 1995), 'Boilerplate - Practical Clauses' (Longmans 1990 and 1995) and 'Drafting Commercial Agreements' (Longmans 1993). Lectures on commercial and competition law topics.
Career: Aricled at *Stephenson Harwood.* General Manager and then Director and General Manager of Lanitis Bros Ltd, Cyprus 1970-74. Legal Adviser ITT 1975, and became Legal Adviser and Company Secretary to STC Telecommunications Ltd (ITT's UK telecomms operation) to 1985. Company Secretary and Legal Director, Solaglas (UK) Ltd 1985-87. Rejoined STC plc in 1987 as Director, Commercial and Legal Affairs and moved over to ICL in 1990.

Imperial Chemical Industries plc

Imperial Chemical House, 9 Millbank, London, SW1P 3JF Tel: (0171) 834 4444

White, Victor O. *Group Solicitor, Secretary.* Reports to: Chairman. Lawyers in dept: 10. Staff: 95.
Percentage of work outsourced: 33% (litigation, property and pensions).
Oversees the lawyers in the Group and responsible for provision of legal advice to the ICI Board and all members of the ICI Group. Also provides full company secretarial service.
Career: Qualified 1963. Joined ICI legal department 1965. Appointed Deputy Solicitor 1976, Group Solicitor 1980 and Company Secretary 1992.

Inco Alloys Ltd

Wiggin Works, Holmer Road, Hereford, HR4 9SL Tel: (01432) 276461

Glover, Alastair *Company Secretary and Legal Officer.* Reports to: Director/ General Manager.
Lawyers in dept: 1. Staff: 1. Percentage of work outsourced: 25% (conveyancing and litigation). Principal areas of work are commercial, environmental, employment, agency and distribution matters.
Career: Qualified 1972 while at *Freshfields.* Assistant solicitor 1972-77, then joined Inco Alloys Ltd.

Ingersoll-Rand Sales Co Ltd

PO BOX 2, Chorley New Road, Horwich, Bolton, Lancashire, BL6 6JN Tel: (01204) 690325

Jones, Graham R. *Company Solicitor.* Reports to: Director and Company Secretary. Lawyers in dept: 2. Staff: 2.
Percentage of work outsourced: 10% (property and litigation).
Principal areas of work are commercial contracts, intellectual property, litigation and employment. Deals with disposal and acquisition of property and companies, leases of company property, trade marks, review of major engineering contracts, EEC competition law, agency and distribution agreements.
Career: Qualified 1979. Solicitor, *Silverbeck & Co* 1981-83. With Manchester Ship Canal Ltd 1984-89. Returned to private practice with *Glaisyers* 1990-92 and *Linder Myers* 1992-94.

Institute of Practitioners in Advertising

44 Belgrave Square, London, SW1X 8QS Tel: (0171) 235 7020

Circus, Philip James *Legal Affairs Director/ Legal Adviser.* Lawyers in dept: 1. Percentage of work outsourced: 5% (some contractual, competition law).
Principal area of work is advising members of the IPA and ISP on the law relating to advertising, marketing and sales promotion. This includes consumer protection law, intellectual property, lotteries and competitions law, codes of practice affecting advertising and marketing such as British codes of advertising and sales promotion (ITC and ICSTIS codes etc). Also represents interests of UK advertising agency business in relation to UK and EC legislation and regulation. Regular speaker on regulatory issues affecting advertising industry. Author of monthly members bulletin and occasional papers, and regular lecturer and conference speaker with considerable press, radio and TV experience. Joint founder of Advertising Law Group and Chairman of CBI Consumer Affairs Panel. Member, Committee of Advertising Practice; Board Member of Mail Order Protection Scheme and member of Advertising Advisory Committee of the Independent Television Commission. Author of a number of books on advertising and sales promotion law.
Career: Called to the Bar 1975. Executive Officer, Central Criminal Court 1973-75 and Legal Assistant, CBI 1975-77.

Instituto Bancario San Paolo Di Torino spa

Wren House, 15 Carter Lane, London, EC4V 5SP Tel: (0171) 214 8000

Cunningham, Lorian *Legal Adviser.* Reports to: Head of Legal. Lawyers in dept: 1. Percentage of work outsourced: 10% (property litigation).
Principal areas of work are banking and capital

markets involving loan documentation, ISDA documentation, MTN programme and warrant issues.
Career: Qualified 1993. Articled with *Norton Rose.*

John Laing plc
Page Street, London, NW7 2ER Tel: (0181) 959 3636

Gibson, Graham *Head of Group Legal Services.* Reports to: Deputy Chairman. Lawyers in dept: 7. Staff: 14. Percentage of work outsourced: minimal (plc corporate work, matters requiring specialist expertise).
Principal area of work covers major construction litigation and arbitration arising out of building or civil engineering contracts. Also handles non-contentious construction law and general commercial matters including acquisition, formation and dissolution of companies for the Group.
Career: Qualified 1973 while with *Speechly Mumford & Soames.* Solicitor with *Speechly Bircham* 1973-79, then joined John Laing plc. Head of Group Legal Services since 1988.

John Maunders Group plc
Development House, Crofts Bank Road, Urmston, Manchester, M41 0JS Tel: (0161) 747 6656

Kendall, P.D. *Group Solicitor.* Reports to: Chairman. Lawyers in dept: 2. Staff: 4. Percentage of work outsourced: 5% (litigation).
Main areas of work are planning law and residential development matters.
Member of Law Society Commerce and Industry Group.
Career: Qualified 1973 and in private practice to 1977. Solicitor with Tarmac Ltd 1977-85, then joined John Maunders Group plc.

John Wyeth
Huntercombe Lane South, Taplow, Maidenhead, Berkshire, SL6 0PH Tel: (01628) 604377

Reacher, Paul *Legal Director.* Reports to: MD. Lawyers in dept: 1. Staff: 5.

Johnston Group plc
Johnston House, Hatchlands Road, Redhill, Surrey, RH1 1BG Tel: (01737) 242466

Jordan, Marcus H. *Director and Group Legal Adviser.* Reports to: Group M.D. Lawyers in dept: 1. Staff: 1. Percentage of work outsourced: 30-40% (litigation, property).
Principal areas of work are joint ventures company acquisitions and sales, competition law, sale of goods, agency and distribution agreements, employment law, construction contracts, intellectual property work and general commercial contracts.
Career: Qualified 1981 while with *Joynson-Hicks.* Assistant solicitor with *Reynolds Porter Chamberlain* 1982-83 and with *Richards Butler* 1983-88. Group Legal Adviser, Johnston Group plc from 1989 and Director of Johnston Management Holdings Ltd since 1990. Director Johnston Group plc July 1995.

Josiah Wedgwood & Sons Ltd
Barlaston, Stoke on Trent, Staffs, ST12 9ES Tel: (01782) 282394

Jennings, Wendy Joy *Company secretary.* Reports to: Director of human resources. Lawyers in Depart: 1. Staff: 10. Percentage of work outsourced: 10% (conveyancing, High Court litigation, specialist commercial/ corporate).
Deals with general contract, commercial, trade marks

and other I.P., property management, rates, health and safety, environmental law and compliance, share register, corporate and banking compliance, share schemes, general secretarial and administrative support.
Career: Qualified 1978. Assistant solicitor Lovell, White & King 1978-1979, solicitor Knight & Sons 1979-1982. Joined Wedgwood Group 1982 becoming Company secretary 1987.

Kellogg Company of GB Ltd
The Kellogg Building, Talbot Road, Manchester, M16 0PU Tel: (0161) 869 2204

Heizler, Laurie. *Legal Adviser.* Lawyers in dept: 2. Staff: 1. Work outsourced: litigation, property. Principal areas of work: advertising, intellectual property, litigation, employment and environmental matters.
Career: Called to the Bar 1985. Qualified as a solicitor 1994.

Kerr McGee Oil (UK) plc
75 Davies Street, London, W1Y 1FA Tel: (0171) 872 9700

Baxter, Robin *Senior Legal Adviser/ Asst. Co Secretary.* Reports to: General Counsel. Lawyers in dept: 1. Staff: 4. Percentage of work outsourced: 10% (conveyancing, Admiralty, environmental, litigation and arbitration).
Energy lawyer and negotiator with general management experience. Arranges and provides general legal, commercial and administrative advice and support to management by use of a legal department and outside professional support. Principal area of work covers oil and gas: licences, acquisitions, joint ventures, farm-ins, exploration, transportation, pipelines, offshore loading, terminals, refining and marketing. Negotiates agreements to exploit hydrocarbon production in the UK and overseas. Also supplies company secretarial, contract negotiation and administration and personnel functions. Member of Society of Petroleum Engineers and International Negotiators (Petroleum).
Career: Qualified 1978. In local government 1976-80 (City of Edinburgh). With Occidental Petroleum Caledonia Ltd 1980-84 and Occidental International 1984-86. With Premier Consolidation Oilfields plc until 1987, then joined Kerr McGee Corporation.

Kimberly-Clark Corporation
35 London Road, Reigate, Surey, RH2 9PZ Tel: (01737) 736061

Quaranto, Leonard Anthony *Vice President and Chief Counsel.* Reports to: General Counsel and Senior Vice-President. Lawyers in dept: 4. Staff: 2. Percentage of work outsourced: 25% (litigation, property, assistance on major acquisition or transactions).
Principal areas of work are international corporate/commercial, legal and business transactions in Europe, Africa and Middle East. Work includes advising on acquisitions; direct investment; intellectual property licensing; tax; finance; employment; advertising; product liability; contract drafting; long-term supply agreements; litigation; construction contracts and government tenders; sales representatives, agents and distributors' contracts; packaging, labelling and environmental matters; health care; product registration and sales; and joint ventures.
Career: Admitted to the Bar, District of Columbia (Washington DC) 1977, and State of Missouri 1978. Assistant International Counsel to Ralston Purina Company 1978-80 and to Chrysler Corporation 1980-84.

Kingston Communications (Hull) plc
Telephone House, Carr Lane, Kingston upon Hull, Humbs, HU1 3RE Tel: (01482) 602576

Bailey, John P.C. *Head of Legal and Regulatory Affairs.* Reports to: Managing Director. Lawyers in dept: 2. Staff: 3. Percentage of work outsourced: 10% (property matters, litigation, transactions involving foreign law).
Principal areas of work are telecommunications regulatory affairs and commercial contracts (particularly software licensing). Responsible for drafting and negotiation of interconnection agreements and all Group commercial contracts including licences, joint ventures and distribution agreements. Also provides company secretarial service and is actively involved in Group commercial strategy. Wide experience of joint ventures (including international J.V.s in China and the USA). Member of Communication Lawyers Association and regular speaker at conferences on telecomms regulation.
Career: Qualified 1972. Commercial Contracts Executive, Ernest Scragg Ltd, Macclesfield 1972-74. Solicitor, Nickerson Seed Co Ltd, Lincoln 1974-76. Legal Adviser with GEC Telecommunications, Coventry 1976-78 and with Plessey Business Systems Ltd, Nottingham 1978-89, then took up present position.

Kleeneze Holdings plc
Innovations House, 211 Lower Richmond Road, Richmond, Surrey, TW9 4LN Tel: (0181) 878 9111

Davies, Martin C.O. *Group Legal Adviser.* Reports to: Group Finance Director. Lawyers in dept: 1. Percentage of work outsourced: 25-30% (heavyweight company and most litigation). Principal areas of work are commercial contracts, regulatory work, intellectual property (creation and licensing), employment and joint ventures. Also acts as company secretary to certain group companies.
Career: Qualified 1975, while Legal Adviser with British Leyland. Company Secretary, Arthur Bell & Sons plc 1979-81. Senior Legal Adviser, Thorn EMI plc 1982-85 and Group Legal Adviser to The Plessey Company plc 1985-89, then joined Kleeneze Holdings plc.

Kodak Ltd.
Kodak House, PO Box 66, Station Road, Hemel Hempstead, Hertfordshire, HP1 1JU Tel: (01442) 844413

Fletcher Rogers, Helen S. *Company Secretary/ Legal Director.* Reports to: M.D. Lawyers in dept: 5. Staff: 11. Percentage of work outsourced: 10% (litigation, property, major projects).
Provides advice on legal matters and policy formulation relating to the company's business in the UK and its overseas aoociate companies. Principal areas of work are competition law, general commercial matters and intellectual property. Member of Bar and BACFI. Author of 'Legal Aspects of Microfilm' and Co-author of Butterworths Forms & Precedents 'Patents, Inventions and Designs' (4th Edn).
Career: Called to the Bar 1965. Joined Kodak Ltd in 1967. Manager Legal Department 1981. Company Secretary and Legal Director since 1990 and Co-Ordinator of Legal Services, Europe since 1991.

Kraft Jacobs Suchard Ltd

St George's House, Bayshill Road, Cheltenham, Gloucestershire, GL50 3AE Tel: (01242) 236101

Cash, Christopher K. *Company Secretary/Legal Adviser.* Responsible for provision of legal service concerning commercial contracts, patents, trade marks, company acquisitions and disposals, health and safety, food and consumer law, product liability, licensing, property and estate management, pensions, monopolies and mergers, OFT investigations and corporate compliance on anti-trust and other regulatory and statutory compliance. Member FDF Food Law Panel since 1991.

Career: Articled at *Buss Stone & Co,* Tunbridge Wells. Assistant company secretary, Burroughs Machines Ltd 1969-72. Secretary/assistant secretary Beecham Pharmaceuticals UK/ Research International 1972-77. Company secretary/ Director of Legal Affairs CPC UK Ltd 1977-88, then took up present position.

Ladbroke Group plc

Chancel House, Neasden, London, NW10 2XE Tel: (081) 459 8031

Stevens, Marie *Group Solicitor.* Reports to: Financial Director. Responsible for provision of legal services to Ladbroke Group PLC.

Career: Qualified 1974.

LASMO plc

100 Liverpool Street, London, EC2M 2BB Tel: (0171) 945 4545

Golding, Anthony *Group General Counsel.* Reports to: Chief Executive. Lawyers in dept: 9. Staff: 15. Percentage of work outsourced: 10% (public financing, M&A, property, litigation, some employment).
Principal areas of work are corporate finance and M&As. Work includes takeovers, rights issues, Eurobonds and convertibles, US listing and securities issues and acquisitions and disposals of assets and companies. Member of UK Energy Lawyers Group.

Career: Qualified 1977. With Courtaulds plc 1975-80, The BOC Group plc 1981-85 and then joined LASMO plc.

Legal and General Group plc

L & G House, St Monica's Road, Kingswood, Chadworth, Surrey, KT20 6EU Tel: (0737) 370370

Blake, Liz *Group Legal Adviser.* Reports to: Group Secretary. Lawyers in dept: 2. Staff: 2. Work outsourced: Litigation/major corporate transactions. Advises the recuperation, investment and general insurance business units. Data protection co-ordinator and recuperation money laundering reporting officer.

Career: Called to the Bar 1986. Legal adviser Edasco Ltd 1986-89, then joined Legal & General Group.

Lehman Brothers Ltd

1 Broadgate, London, EC2M 7HA Tel: (0171) 260 2894

Austin, David R. *Senior Legal Counsel and Director.* Lawyers in dept: 5. Staff: 2. Percentage of work outsourced: 20% (litigation, services of underwriters' counsel, occasional specialist advice). Dedicated lawyer for investment banking (including corporate finance, M&A) and primary capital markets (mainly equity and equity-related, but also debt) for Lehman Brothers in London and Europe (also Israel). Advises on all aspects of equity offerings, covering documentation, selling, due diligence and general compliance/ regulatory issues. Advises on UK public takeovers (including hostile ones). Member of Commitment Committee dealing with debt and equity issues. Also advises internal Treasury Department on fundraising through primary debt markets. Familiarity with French, German, Spanish, Italian, Dutch, Russian and Scandinavian languages.

Career: Trainee accountant, Ernst & Young 1981-82. Articled with *Herbert Smith* from 1984; and assistant solicitor 1986-1989, then joined Lehman Brothers.

Littlewoods Organisation plc

100 Old Hall Street, Liverpool, Merseyside, L70 1AB Tel: (0151) 235 2661

Hogarth, Mark J.B. *Head of legal depart/ group comp secret.* Reports to: Group Chief Executive. Lawyers in Depart: 4. Staff: 10. Percentage of work outsourced: 10% (litigation and significant corporate transactions, some property). Deals with company, commercial, contracts, employment, property, trading law, corporate affairs and health and safety.

Career: Qualified 1979. Assistant solicitor Messrs Rudd Freeman & Fisher 1980-1982, solicitor Wimpey Group Services Ltd 1982-1983. Joined The Littlewoods Organisation Group PLC 1983 becoming group company secretary 1990.

Lloyds Chemists plc

Manor Road, Atherstone, Manchester, Warks

Buckell, Stephen *Head of Legal Services.* Reports to: Chairman/Board. Lawyers in dept: 5. Staff: 11. Percentage of work outsourced: 5% (various types).
Responsible for provision of legal services to the plc. Principal areas of work include property, acquisitions and disposals, commercial agreements, regulatory matters (including pharmaceutical), insurance, pensions, and litigation. Current secretary, Lloyds Chemists plc.

Career: Qualified 1974. Solicitor, *Crossman Block* 1978-80. With Augustus Barnett & Son Ltd 1980-82 and joined Lloyds Chemists plc in 1985.

Lockington plc

Wilford Industrial Estate, Rudding Lane, Nottingham, NG11 7EP Tel: (01602) 455544

Walker, Kenneth . Reports to: Chairman. Lawyers in dept: 1. Staff: 6. Percentage of work outsourced: 30% (corporate, corporate finance, High Court litigation).
Principal areas of work are planning, landlord and tenant and conveyancing matters. This involves conduct of planning appeals and inquiries; negotiating, drafting and completing planning obligations, options and agreements; drafting commercial leases and residential tenancy agreements. Also provides Magistrates' Court representation on environmental and enforcement actions, company secretarial administration and some County Court litigation. Member of the Property Consultants' Society.

Career: Qualified 1971. Solicitor with Lowestoft BC 1971-73, then Principal of *Kenneth Walker, Solicitor,* Castle Donington 1973-85. Commercial lawyer Nottinghamshire CC 1986-88, then Group Solicitor/Company Secretary to the Standen Group 1988-91. Principal Solicitor, North East Derbyshire DC 1991-2 and Assistant Company Secretary, Sheriff Holdings plc 1993-94. Local radio broadcaster for 15 years.

Lombard North Central plc

Lombard House, 3 Princes Way, Redhill, Surrey, RH1 1NP Tel: (01737) 774111

Hopkin, Denis W. B. *Head of Legal Services.* Reports to: Director, Treasury and Regulation. Lawyers in dept: 9. Staff: 8. Percentage of work outsourced: 10% (conveyancing, litigation). Has full responsibility for legal policy and the provision of legal services for all activities of this major finance house, including supervision of outside lawyers where appropriate. Principal areas of work are consumer credit; asset financing (including small, medium and big ticket leasing); banking company/commercial and data protection. Monitors new legislation and case reports and advises Board Committees of implications. Deals with major projects as Chairman, Legal Committee, Finance Houses Association and Chairman, Legal Affairs, Eurofinas.

Career: Qualified 1960, while with *Herbert Smith & Co* and assistant solicitor to 1963. Assistant solicitor 1963-65 and Partner 1965-70 with *Waltons Bright & Co.* Joined Lombard North Central plc in 1971 as solicitor in charge of conveyancing, becoming Deputy Head of Legal Services in 1978 and Head of Legal Services in 1980.

London International Group plc

35 New Bridge Street, London, EC4V 6BJ Tel: (0171) 489 1977

Rew, Paul W *Company Secretary.* Reports to: Finance Director. Lawyers in dept: 2. Staff: 8. Percentage of work outsourced: 20% (major acquisitions/ disposals; IP; banking; major corporate plc work such as rights issues; litigation and competition).
Has overall responsibility for company secretarial administration, legal services and corporate affairs (investor relations/ corporate PR) heading a team of 8 at LIG's City headquarters. Work includes advising on acquisitions/disposals, commercial law, trademarks and IP, insurance, litigation and EC law. Is a Council Member of the Anti-Counterfeiting Group and has addressed conferences on brand protection.

Career: Qualified 1975 while at *Clifford Turner.* Solicitor, *McKenna & Co* 1976-77, then spent five years at CPC Europe in Brussels as Assistant Attorney. Manager, Legal and Government Affairs, Europe, for Avon Products Inc in Brussels 1982-85 and then returned to the UK to become Director of Group Legal Services/ Company Secretary Laura Ashley Holdings plc. Joined London International Group plc in January 1993.

London Investment Banking Association

6 Frederick's Place, London, EC2R 8BT Tel: (0171) 796 3606

Matthewson, Neil B. *Director of Legal Services and Secretary.* Responsible for LIBA's work on UK regulation, corporate finance, legal matters and relevant European Community legislation.

Career: Qualified 1963. With United Dominions Trust Ltd 1967-76 (Group Company Secretary 1967-72 and Director UK Finance House subsidiary 1972-76). Main Board Director, International Commodities Clearing House Ltd 1977-88, then joined LIBA.

London Weekend Television Ltd
The London Television Centre, Upper Ground, London, SE1 9LT Tel: (0171) 620 1620

Isaacs, Jane *Controller, Legal Services.*
Reports to: Commercial Director. Percentage of work outsourced: 20% (conduct of litigation). Responsible for ensuring LWT's programmes comply with libel and contempt laws and the codes of regulatory bodies governing the broadcasting industry. Provides legal advice on negotiation and drafting of general commercial contracts of the company and its subsidiaries, such as the London studios. Deputy company secretary to LWT (Holdings), providing company secretarial function to its 45 subsidiaries.
Career: Qualified as a Barrister 1987 and in practice at the Bar until 1989. Assistant Legal Adviser, Civil Aviation Authority 1989, then joined LWT as Assistant Legal Adviser, becoming Group Legal Adviser 1991; Controller, Legal Services 1993 and Deputy Company Secretary 1995.

L'Oreal (UK) Ltd
30 Kensington Church Street, London, W8 4HA Tel: (0171) 938 5716

Munro, Ranald T. I. *Group Legal Adviser/ Company Secretary.* Reports to: M.D. Lawyers in dept: 1. Staff: 2. Percentage of work outsourced: 20% (litigation, trade marks where specialist expertise required).
Principal areas of work are contracts, competition law, EEC law, distribution agreements, cosmetics directives, employment, IPR, marketing, advertising, promotions, data protection, health/safety and pensions. Also deals with joint ventures, acquisitions and disposals and provides all usual company secretarial services. Member of Anti-Counterfeiting Group, Cosmetics, Toiletries, Perfumery Association and Employment Law Bar Association.
Career: Qualified as a Barrister 1985. Crown Prosecutor and acting Senior Crown Prosecutor, CPS 1987-89. Senior Legal Adviser, ICL 1989-94, then joined L'Oreal (UK) Ltd. Qualified Lawyers Transfer Test (Solicitor) 1992.

Louis Dreyfus Trading Ltd
162 Queen Victoria Street, London, EC4V 4DB Tel: (0171) 489 9489

Rookes, Roger *Arbitration Manager.* Handles disputes for Louis Dreyfus Group which are based on English law contracts, principally trade-backed contracts such as GAFTA, FOSFA, RSA, SAL, LCA or LMAA. Advises on disputes based on all other jurisdictions (except USA). FCIArb and Fellow of the Institute of Chartered Shipbrokers.
Career: With Continental (London) Ltd 1974-78, Raphaely Trading (UK) Ltd 1979-83, European Grain & Shipping Ltd 1983-88 and V. Berg & Sons Ltd 1988-90, then joined Louis Dreyfus Trading Ltd.

Lucas Industries PLC
Brueton House, New Road, Solihull, West Midlands, B91 3TX Tel: (0121) 627 6000

Almond, Paul M. *Head of legal department.*
Reports to: Company secretary. Lawyers in Depart: 8. Staff: 12. Percentage of work outsourced: 20% (pensions, corporate finance, contested litigation, overseas work).
Overall responsibility for provision of legal advice to Lucas businesses worldwide (except USA), including International mergers and acquisitions, joint ventures and collaborations, intellectual property and commercial contracts of all types. Also addresses conferences on various topics.

Career: Qualified 1979. Assistant solicitor Foster Baxter Cooksey 1976-1982. Joined Lucas Industries 1982 becoming head of legal department 1989.

M & W PLC
Canberra Road, Nursling, Southampton, Hampshire, SO1 9WB Tel: (01703) 737788

Putnam, Nicholas Stewart *Company Secretary.*
Reports to: Chief Executive. Lawyers in dept: 2. Staff: 1. Percentage of work outsourced: 70% (most conveyancing, debt collection).
Principal areas of work are company secretarial, liquor licensing and conveyancing (new store acquistions/ disposal of surplus sites) for the holding company and its wholly owned subsidiary, Misselbrook & Weston Ltd. Also deals with insurance, health and safety compliance, trading standards and environmental health regulations.
Career: Qualified 1983 while with *Allin & Watts*, Bournemouth. Assistant solicitor with *Williams Thompson*, Highcliffe 1983-87 and Partner with *Letcher & Son*, Verwood 1987-91.

Macmillan Publishers Ltd
4 Little Essex Street, London, WC2R 3LF Tel: (0171) 836 6633

Forsyth, Elizabeth A. *Group Legal Director.*
Reports to: Group Managing Director. Lawyers in dept: 1; Staff: 2. Percentage of work outsourced: 50% (libel, large acquisition work, specialised matters.
Principal areas of work: multimedia, intellectual property law, company and commercial law. Also contractual, employment, corporate planning, trademark and pre-litigious matters.
Additional: Conference and seminar speaker on cross-media matters and intellectual property.
Career: 1987-89: Solicitor, *Linklaters & Paines*; 1989-92: Solicitor, *Clifford Chance*; 1992-94: Group Legal Adviser and Deputy Company Secretary, Pearson plc; 1994: Group Legal Director, Macmillan.

Mallinckrodt Veterinary Ltd
Breakspear Road South, Harefield, Uxbridge, Middlesex, UB9 6LS Tel: (01895) 626000

Wilshere, Stephen *Company Secretary.*
Reports to: Senior Vice President Europe. Lawyers in dept: 2. Staff: 2. Percentage of work outsourced: 5% (litigation, complaints about competitors' advertising, specialist EU competition law advice). Head of legal affairs for Europe for the company and its subsidiaries. Principal areas of work are drafting, advising and negotiating on commercial contracts, R&D agreements, acquisitions and divestments. Also handles property matters, computer hardware and software agreements and advises on employment matters and product liability cases. Member of Law Society Commerce and Industry Group and Solicitors European Group.
Career: Qualified 1983 while with *Ellis & Hancock*, Watford/ Hemel Hempstead. Legal adviser to Kodak Ltd 1986-88.

Marathon Oil UK Ltd
Capital House, 25 Chapel Street, London, NW1 5DQ Tel: (0171) 298 2500

Southworth, John D. *Legal Manager.*
Career: Articled 1972; Burmah Oil 1974-75; Chevron Oil 1975-77; British National Oil Corporation 1977-84; Saxon Oil 1984-86; joined Marathon Oil 1986, Legal Manager since 1992. Member of Law Society Commerce and Industry Group and International Bar Association.

McDonald's Development Co Ltd
178-180 Edgware Road, London, W2 2DS Tel: (0171) 402 6677

Pagni, Marco *European Legal Director.*
Reports to: General Counsel - International. Lawyers in dept: 2. Staff: 3. Percentage of work outsourced: 50% (litigation, major transactional work, specialist legal advice, competition law, mergers-related work).
Principal areas of work are competition, contract, franchising, corporate, corporate finance, employment, mergers and acquisitions in all European countries. Also deals with insolvency, real estate, construction law, intellectual property (mainly trademarks: registration and infringement prosecutions), media and advertising law and regulations. Author of Legal Duties and Obligations section of Kluwer's Company Secretary handbook.
Career: Lecturer in law at Oxford University 1985-87. Called to the Bar 1988. European Counsel, Texas Instruments Inc, based in France 1989-93.

Medical Defence Union
3 Devonshire Place, London, W1N 2EA Tel: (0171) 486 6181

Dewhurst, Charles *Head of Legal Services.*
Reports to: Professional Services Director. Lawyers in dept: 5. Staff: 9.
Principal areas of work are acting in medical and dental negligence cases, providing medico-legal advice and tribunal representation.
Career: Qualified 1978. Partner with *Hempsons* 1979-90 and worked with *Oxley & Coward*, Sheffield 1992-93.

Mercantile & General Reinsurance Co. Plc
Moorfields House, Moorfields, London, EC2Y 9AL Tel: (0171) 628 7070

Kay, Anthony *Legal Officer.* Lawyers in dept: 2. Staff: 2. Percentage of work outsourced: 15% (litigation, arbitrations, overseas corporate).
Main areas of work are reinsurance/ insurance in UK and overseas including regulatory aspects, litigation, arbitration and liquidations, policy wordings, specialised risks, large claims, environmental liabilities, commutations and transfers of business. Company/ commercial work includes branches and subsidiaries, joint ventures, intellectual property, finance and operating leases, investment and banking. Member of British Insurance Law Association, AIDA and Association of British Insurers and London Insurance and Reinsurance Market Association. Conference speaker and author of paper on Pollution and Insurance for AIDA 5th World Congress in Madrid.
Career: Qualified 1970. Joined The Mercantile and General Reinsurance Co plc in 1972 as Assistant Legal Officer. Became Deputy Legal Officer 1981 and Legal Officer 1991.

Merck Sharp & Dohme Ltd
West Hill, Hertford Road, Hoddesdon, Hertfordshire, EN11 9BU Tel: (01992) 467272

Dalby, Marc *Legal Director.* Reports to: MD. Lawyers in dept: 3. Staff: 7. Work outsourced: Litigation, banking.
Deals with the legal aspects of the research, development, production and sale of human and veterinary medicinal products. Work includes pharmaceutical regulatory work, commercial contracts, IP, competition law, advertising and promotional law and regulations. Also deals with corporate law,

construction, planning, landlord and tenant law: co-or-dinating UK aspects of corporate disposals, construction of production and office facilities and overseeing the leasehold portfolio. Member ABPI Legal Affairs Committee.

Career: Qualified 1986 as a Barrister and in private practice until 1988. Lawyer with Lloyd's of London 1988-89, then joined NAPP Pharmaceutical Group as Legal Manager. Joined Merck Sharp & Dohme in 1990.

Mercury Asset Management

33 King William Street, London, EC4R 9AS

Parsloe, John   *Director.* Lawyers in dept: 7.

Mercury Communications Ltd

New Mercury House, 26 Red Lion Square, London, WC1R 4HQ Tel: (0171) 528 2000

Butler, James   *Director of Legal Services/ Co. Sec..*
Reports to: Chief Executive and functional reporting line to Group Director of Legal Services, Cable & Wireless plc. Lawyers in dept: 11. Staff: 18. Some work outsourced mainly: some M&A, employment and litigation.
Responsible for all legal affairs of the company, managing the legal department and providing company secretarial services. Member of the Law Council of the worldwide federal law offices of Cable & Wireless plc, which co-ordinates efforts and develops best practice of the various national legal departments within the Cable & Wireless plc.

Career: Qualified 1973 while with *Freshfields*. Corporate Finance Executive, Baring Brothers & Co Ltd 1977-82. Partner with *Crossman Block* 1982-86, *Barlow Lyde & Gilbert* 1986-88 and *Turner Kenneth Brown* 1989-92. Senior Legal Adviser, Mergers & Acquisitions, Cable & Wireless plc 1992-93, then took up present position.

Mersey Docks And Harbour Company

Maritime Centre, Port of Liverpool, Liverpool, Merseyside, L21 1LA Tel: (0151) 949 6000

Bowley, William John   *Director of Legal Services.* Reports to: M.D. Lawyers in dept: 2. Staff: 6. Percentage of work outsourced: 25% (major corporate, joint venture work, certain litigation).
Responsible for all the Company's legal affairs and aspects of the company secretarial, insurance, claims and share registration sections. Principal areas of work are general company/ commercial matters. Also handles shipping, property and environmental law and advises on litigation. Member of Law Society Commerce and Industry Group.

Career: Articled with *J. Frodsham & Sons*, St. Helens 1971-72 and solicitor 1973-74. Joined The Mersey Docks and Harbour Company in 1974 as an assistant solicitor. Became PA to the MD 1979, Principal assistant solicitor 1981, Company Secretary and Solicitor 1982 and Director of Legal Services 1991.

MFI Furniture Group PLC

Southon House, 333 The Hyde, Edgware Road, London, NW9 6TD Tel: (0181) 200 8000

Thomson, Hamish   *Company sec/ director of legal services.* Reports to: Group finance director. Lawyers in Dept: 1. Staff: 3. Percentage of work outsourced: 98% (almost all areas).
Responsible for management of all Groups legal work, except property. Also deals with all of Groups pension schemes and insurance work.

Career: Qualified 1974. Partner Cripps & Shone Marlow Bucks. Joined MFI in 1991.

Mitsubishi Electric UK Ltd

Travellers Lane, Hatfield, Herts, AL10 HXB Tel: (01707) 276100

Thomlinson, Peter R.   *Company Secretary.*
Reports to: Group MD. Lawyers in Dept: 1 Staff: 2 Percentage of work outsourced: N/A (conveyancing, litigation)

Specialisation: General corporate/commercial law, competition law, compliance, litigation. Also supervising corporate public relations and liaising with other Mitsubishi in-house lawyers.

Prof. Membership: BACFI

Career: Called to the Bar in 1981. Pupillage/practice 1981-83. Legal adviser with Cray Electronics Holdings 1985-89. Joined Mitsubishi Electric UK in 1990 and appointed company secretary in 1991. Called to Northern Ireland Bar 1993.

Monument Oil and Gas plc

80 Petty France, London, SW1H 9EX Tel: (0171) 233 1966

Patrick, Iain   *Commercial Director.* Reports to: MD. Lawyers in dept: 2. Staff: 4. Percentage of work outsourced; 10% (foreign or specialist advice, as required).
Principal areas of work are commercial contracts of all types and the negotiation of acquisitions and disposals. Lectures at conferences. Member of Law Society of Scotland.

Career: Qualified 1980. Lawyer with *McLure Naismith Brodie*, Glasgow 1980-81 and with Britoil plc 1981-83. Commercial Manager, Westar Oil/ Acre Oil 1983-88.

More O' Ferrall plc

33 Golden Square, London, W1R 3PA Tel: (0171) 287 6100

Hall, Peter Arnold   *Director and group company secretary.* Reports to: Chairman/ Chief Executive. Lawyers in Depart: 1. Staff: 1. Percentage of work outsourced: 50% (all litigation, some property, company/ commercial work).
Deals with company/ commercial law, company secretarial services, employment law, property law and competition law. Also responsible for health and safety, insurance, pensions and planning law. Member of The Law Society Commerce and Industry Group, and European Company Lawyers Association.

Career: Qualified 1969. Assistant solicitor Trafalgar House Plc 1969-1971, assistant solicitor Dunlop Ltd 1971-1972, solicitor Miles Laboratories Ltd 1972-1973, solicitor Crest Nicholson Plc 1973-1975, solicitor Mears Bros. Holdings Ltd 1975-1978, Solicitor H.P.Bulmer Holdings Plc 1978-1981. Joined More O'Ferrall Plc 1981 as Director and group company secretary.

Motorola Ltd

110 Bath Road, Slough, Berks, SL1 3SZ Tel: (01753) 500063

Morris, Mike   *Director Law Department.*
Lawyers in dept: 3. Staff: 5.

National Grid Company plc

185 Park Street, London, SE1 9DY Tel: (0171) 620 9000

Smith, Fiona B.   *Group legal advisor.* Reports to: Company secretary. Lawyers in Depart: 8. Staff: 13. Percentage of work outsourced: 50% (specialist areas and overflow work).
Deals with matters pertaining to the electricity industry, generally on commercial, competition, planning and environmental matters.

Career: Qualified 1983. Assistant solicitor Maclay Murray & Spens 1983-1985, Southern Scotland Electricity Board 1985-1988. Joined The National Grid Co Plc 1988 becoming group legal adviser 1992.

National Power PLC

Senator House, 85 Queen Victoria Street, London, EC4V 4DP Tel: (0171) 454 9494

Wheeler, Stuart   *Head of legal Services.*
Reports to: Company. Lawyers in Depart: 17. Staff: 26. Percentage of work outsourced: 20% (major joint venture project work, non core matters).
Deals with oil and gas explorations, gas purchase and sale agreements, major acquisitions and other deals and general departmental supervision. Member of IBA Energy Law Group and European Negotiators Group.

Career: Qualified 1975. Assistant solicitor *Slaughter & May* 1975-1976, Beecham Pharmaceuticals 1976-1979, Amoco 1979-1988, Sun Oil International 1988-1991. Joined National Power 1991 as head of legal services.

National Provincial Building Society

Provincial House, Civic Precinct, Bradford, West Yorks, BD1 1NL Tel: (01274) 733444

Mather, Keith R.   *Group Secretary.* Reports to: Finance Director. Staff: 15.
Deals with Board and subsidiary company administration, including management of Board and Subsidiaries Board Business, building society and relevant company law advice and maintenance of statutory records and returns.

Career: Qualified 1972. Partner in private practice 1974-1977, senior assistant solicitor N & P 1978-1982, Mortgage services Manager N & P 1983-1985 becoming chief solicitor 1985. Appointed group secretary 1988.

Nationwide Building Society

P.O. Box 74, Pipers Way, Swindon, Wilts, SN3 1TB Tel: (01793) 455220

Wilson, Charles R.L.   *Group secretary and solicitor.* Reports to: Chief Executive. Lawyers in Depart: 20. Staff: 6.
Deals with commercial, company, property law and litigation, including commercial agreements, vires issues, acquisitions and disposals, lending practices and procedures, impact of legislation and regulation, deposit taking and banking services. Also responsible for company adminstration.

Career: Qualified 1973. Albert Gard & Ruse solicitors 1968-1975, Geoffrey Stevens & Sabel solicitors 1975-1978, secretary and solicitor HFC Trust 1978-1981, secretary and solicitor AVCO Trust 1981-1983, chief solicitor Abbey National PLC 1983-1992. Joined Nationwide Buiding Society 1992 as group secretary and solicitor.

Newbridge Networks Ltd

Coldra Woods, Chepstow Road, Newport, Gwent, NP6 1JB Tel: (01633) 413600

Woodhead, Christopher F.   *Legal Advisor/ Company Secretary.* Reports to: MD. Lawyers in dept: 1. Staff: 1. Percentage of work outsourced: small (legal support for foreign subsidiaries, property work, debt collecting litigation).
Principal areas of work are general commercial matters, such as drafting and negotiating a wide range of commercial agreements, IPR issues and establishing

and managing legal requirements of foreign subsidiaries. Also provides company secretarial and litigation management services.

Career: Qualified 1979 while at *Moon Beever*. Solicitor, *Kagan Morris* 1979-80. Solicitor *Durnford Ford Hastings* 1981-83. Assistant Legal Advisor Plessey 1984-85. Contracts Manager, Mitel Telecom 1985-86 and Legal Advisor, Plessey 1987-89.

News Group Newspapers Ltd

PO Box 481, Virginia Street, London, E1 9BD Tel: (0171) 782 4000

Crone, Tom *Legal Manager.* Reports to: MD. Lawyers in dept: 6. Staff: 11. Percentage of work outsourced: 30% (litigation).
Provides legal advice on all aspects of newspaper-related law, including libel, copyright, contempt, rights, licensing and contracts. Member of BACFI. Author of 'Law and the Media' (Heinnemann) and various articles in newspapers and magazines. Regular speaker at conferences and seminars.

Career: Called to the Bar 1975 (Gray's Inn).

Newspaper Society

Bloomsbury House, Bloomsbury Square, 74-77 Great Russell Street, London, WC1B 3DA Tel: (0171) 636 7014

Newell, David *Head of Government and Legal Affairs.* Principal areas of work are libel, media law, advertising, legal areas and marketing law, copyright and employment law. Has European, UK Government and Parliamentary lobbying role for the media industry. Member of Fleet Street Lawyers Society; Chairman, European Newspaper Publishers' Association Legal Framework Committee; member, ASA Code of Advertising Practice Review Committee and many other industry and legal bodies. Author of numerous books and articles on legal subjects and extensive experience in speaking at legal and industry seminars.

Career: Articled at *Lawford & Co* 1976-78. Lecturer in law, Leicester University 1978-86. Head of Government and Legal Affairs Department of The Newspaper Society since 1984 and Deputy Director since 1992.

Next PLC

Desford Road, Enderby, Leicester, Leicestershire, LE9 5AT Tel: (0116) 286 6411

Davis, Malcolm Arthur *Commercial conveyancer.* Reports to: Head of Department. lawyers in Depart: 4. Staff: 1. Percentage of work outsourced: 10% (heavyweight company/ commercial work).
Deals with conveyancing work in relation to the company's property portfolio, including freehold sales and acquisitions, new leases and renewals, leasehold disposals and acquisitions, licences relating to the company's premises and other documentation relating to company's properties. Also negotiates and approves acceptable conditions in commercial contracts.

Career: Qualified 1972. Articled clerk 1970-1972, assistant solicitor 1972-1976, partner 1976-1986 with Day, Boot & Pollett, Nottingham. Joined Next PLC as commercial conveyancer 1986.

NFC PLC

66 Chiltern Street, London, W1M 1PR Tel: (0171) 317 0123

Fallowfield, Tim *Corporate legal adviser.* Reports to: Company secretary. Lawyers in Depart: 1. Percentage of work outsourced: 80% (full range of corporate legal work).

Deals with mergers and acquisitions, joint ventures, company law, litigation and contracts. Also manages the legal function in NFC PLC and its subsidiaries in UK, USA and Europe.

Career: Qualified 1990 at Clifford Chance, assistant solicitor Clifford Chance including secondment to Kraft Jacobs Suchard 1993-1994. Joined NFC PLC 1994 as corporate legal adviser.

Nimir Services Ltd

30 Old Burlington Street, London, W1 Tel: (0171) 494 3000

Stewart, James A. *Senior Legal Counsel.* Reports to: CEO. Lawyers in dept: 2. Staff: 2. Percentage of work outsourced: 10-15% (litigation/arbitration, trade marks/IP, pensions, landlord and tenant).
Primary responsibility for a portfolio of international exploration and production licences and new venture issues. Responsible for negotiation, drafting and legal management of production sharing agreements and joint operating agreements for the Nimir Group's interests in Yemen, Romania, Malta, Russia and Azerbaijan and the full range of operations contracting associated with operatorship. Provides full legal advisory, agreement drafting and negotiation service in relation to all other general corporate legal functions, and the direction and management of outside legal counsel as required.

Career: Qualified 1970 while with *Alex Morison & Co*, Edinburgh. Solicitor, *Allan, Black & McCaskie*, Elgin 1971-73. Assistant company secretary, Associated British Foods plc 1973-74. Legal Adviser with Amoco Europe Inc 1975-76 and with CFP/ Total in Paris 1976-82. Senior Legal Adviser to Kuwait Foreign Petroleum Exploration Co 1982-84 and to ELF UK plc 1986-87; then legal consultancy with Santa Fe Offshore Construction Co. Group Legal Adviser and company secretary to SD-Scicon plc 1989-92, then took up present position.

North of England P & I Association Ltd

2-8 Fenkle Street, Newcastle-upon-Tyne, NE1 5DS Tel: (0191) 232 5221

Purvis, Stephen H. *Manager.* Reports to: Managing Directors/ Board. Lawyers in Depart: 4. Staff: 7. Percentage of work outsourced: 10% (shipping litigation and arbitration).
Deals with management of Freight, Demurrage and defence Class of the Association which currently insures 400 ships for legal costs insurance. Editorial Board member of "International Maritime Law" and member of Documentary Committee of the Chamber of Shipping, London and BIMCO, Copenhagen.

Career: Qualified 1984 completing pupillage at 1 Brick Court and 2 Essex Court, London 1985. In-house lawyer with Legal and Special Claims Department of Assuranceforeningen Gard, Norway 1985-1989. Joined the Association 1989 becoming manager in 1992.

Northumbrian Water Ltd

Northumbria House, Regent Centre, Gosforth, Newcastle upon Tyne, Tyne and Wear, NE3 3PX Tel: (0191) 284 3151

Kelly, Paul *Company Solicitor.* Number of lawyers in dept: 7. Percentage of work outsourced: 20% (commercial, planning, heavyweight litigation, employment).
Principal areas of work are environmental law matters, commercial contracts, civil and criminal litigation. Also deals with water and drainage law.

Career: Legal assistant, T. Cowie plc 1982-85 and

Legal Executive/ solicitor to Gateshead MBC 1985-92, then joined Northumbrian Water Ltd.

NORWEB plc

Talbot Road, Manchester, M16 0HQ Tel: (0161) 873 8000

Young, Gavin. *Head of Legal Services.* Reports to: Company Secretary. Lawyers in dept: 5. Staff: 24. Percentage of work outsourced: 5% (major litigation, one-off high value software contract, banking).
Principal areas of work are company/commercial and departmental management. Involved in acquisition of businesses or partnership interests and contract drafting. Supervises litigation, conveyancing, property and insurance sections and advises on regulatory regime of OFFER, OFGAS and OFTEL, plus EU public procurement. Present company turnover £1470m. Member of Law Society Commerce and Industry Group.

Career: Qualified March 1974 while with *Goodswens*, Redcar. Solicitor with Stockton BC 1974-75. Senior Assistant Solicitor, Newcastle-upon-Tyne CC 1975-76 and Assistant Director of Administration 1976-78. Assistant Chief Legal Adviser, British Nuclear Fuels plc 1978-84; and Legal and Contracts Adviser, GPT Ltd 1984-88. Group Legal Adviser, Simon Engineering plc 1988-93 and Company Secretary 1993-94, then joined NORWEB plc.

Nuclear Electric plc

Barnett Way, Barnwood, Gloucester, Gloucestershire, GL4 7RS Tel: (01452) 652851

Mizen, Frances *Corporate Solicitor.* Reports to: Company Secretary. Lawyers in dept: 4. Staff: 5. Percentage of work outsourced: 30% (various types). Principal area of work involves negotiating and drafting commercial contracts of all types.

Career: Articled and assistant solicitor with North Thames Gas Board 1967-71. Solicitor, Central Electricity Generating Board 1972-90, then took up current position.

Ocean Group PLC

Ocean House, The Ring, Bracknell, Berkshire, RG12 1AN Tel: (01344) 302000

Chate, Ian *Group legal adviser/ company secretary.* Reports to: Chief Executive/ Chairman. Lawyers in Depart: 6. Staff: 10. Percentage of work outsourced: 20% (litigation, planning, conveyancing, major M & A transactions).
Responsible for all Group's legal affairs with lawyers in business operating units reporting to him. Also selects and monitors service and fee levels of external legal advisers in UK and abroad and deals with the risk management function of the group. Committee member of Commerce and Industry group and writes articles in Legal Business and In-House Lawyer.

Career: Qualified 1970. Assistant solicitor Stephen Jaques & Stephen, Sydney 1970-1972, solicitor Linklaters & Paines 1972-1975, head of legal depart. Gulf Oil GB Ltd 1975-1977, senior attorney Gulf Oil International 1977-1984, general counsel Texas Eastern North Sea Inc. 1984-1989. Joined Ocean Group PLC as group legal adviser and company secretary 1989.

Olivetti UK Ltd

Olivetti House, PO Box 89, 86-88 Upper Richmond Road, London, SW15 2UR Tel: (0181) 785 6666

Hatfield, Gordon *Company Solicitor.* Reports to: Director Finance & Administration. Lawyers in dept: 1. Staff: 15.

Percentage of work outsourced: 10% (property and litigation).

Responsible for control and direction of all legal matters and provision of company secretarial service. Work includes negotiating/drafting bespoke contracts; developing standard terms and conditions of contract; corporate acquisitions/disposals; acquisition/disposal of freehold/leasehold property; IPRs development, protection and exploitation; employment-related matters; and the control and direction of litigation. Liaises with corporate lawyers in Italy and manages outside legal advisers. Also Manager of General Services Department, involving control and direction of central purchasing function, management of company's property portfolio and administration of company's insurances and pension scheme. Member of Society for Computers & Law; Law Society.

Career: Qualified 1976 while at *Fremont & Co.* Assistant solicitor *Macfarlanes* 1976-77. Joined Associated Oiltools, Inc 1977, becoming Assistant General Counsel 1981 and Legal Counsel, International Operations 1986. Took up present position in 1989.

OMI International plc

1-11 Hay Hill, Berkeley Square, London, W1X 7LF Tel: (0171) 491 2121

Gore, Edward *Company Secretary.* Reports to: Chairman. Lawyers in Dept: 1

Percent of work outsourced: 30 (property, litigation, intellectual property).

Deals with company secretarial work (Board Meetings, Stock Exchange, etc.), insurance, property, pensions, employment and contracts.

Career: Qualified in 1981. At *Linklaters & Paines* 1981-84, *Baileys, Shaw & Gillett* 1986-86 and *Lovell White Durrant* 1986-94. Joined OMI International in March 1994.

OMV (UK) Ltd

14 Ryder Street, London, SW1 6QB Tel: (0171) 333 1600

Goodsir, George Michael Peter *Commercial Director.* Reports to: MD. Lawyers in dept: 1. Staff: 2. Percentage of work outsourced: 5% (occasional overloads).

Responsible for commercial strategy and direction with respect to the company's interests in production, exploration, acquisitions and disposals with a focus on portfolio rationalisation. Full responsibility for legal affairs and company secretarial duties.

Career: Acquisitions Contract Analyst, Cities Service Europe-Africa Petroleum Corp in London 1980-81 and International Acquisitions Representative 1981-83. Legal Counsel, Occidental Oil Inc, London 1983, with Occidental Petroleum (Caledonia) Ltd in Aberdeen 1983-86 and Manager, Law and Contracts 1986-88 and 1990-91. Secretary and Legal Counsel to Internal Board of Inquiry investigating Piper Alpha explosion 1988-90. Chief Counsel with OMV (UK) Ltd 1991-94, then became Commercial Director and Company Secretary.

Oryx UK Energy Company

Charter Place, Vine Street, Uxbridge, Middx, UB8 1EZ. Tel: (0895) 852500

Bostock, John T. *Legal manager.* Reports to: Managing Director.

Deals with upstream oil and gas, joint/ unit operating agreements, gas sales/ transportation agreements, aquisitions and investments. Member of International Bar Association.

Career: Qualified 1973. Total Oil Marine Ltd 1973-1979, Conoco UK Ltd 1979-1988, Albright & Wilson Ltd 1988-1992. Joined Oryx UK Energy Company as

legal manager 1992.

Oscar Faber plc

Marlborough House, Upper Marlborough Road, St Albans, Herts, AL1 3UT Tel: (0181) 784 5784

Paterson, Alec *Company Lawyer and Company Secretary.* Reports to: Chairman. Lawyers in dept: 1. Percentage of work outsourced: 20% (property, financial matters including tax, major reorganisation).

Provides legal advice on construction and engineering law, professional appointments, insurance (especially professional indemnity) and employment matters. Member of BACFI.

Career: Called to the Bar 1958.

P & O Properties Ltd

247 Tottenham Court Road, London, W1P 0HH Tel: (0171) 637 1400

Greenwood, S.R. *Head of Legal Department..* Reports to: Managing Director. Lawyers in Dept: 4 Staff: 8

Percent of work outsourced: variable (litigation). Handles commercial property including disposals and substantial acquisitions, landlord and tenant, mortgaging and small developments. Concentrates mostly on London and the South East, and has handled major single and portfolio sales in the City, West End and throughout the country. Also manages the in-house legal team, liaises with outside solicitors, sits on the Board of P&O Properties and advises the group generally.

Career: Qualified with a City firm in 1981. Assistant solicitor with BICC Plc 1981-84.

Pearson plc

Millbank Tower, Millbank, London, SW1P 4QZ Tel: (0171) 411 2000

Sellors, Jonathan *Group Counsel.* Reports to: Group Chief Executive. Lawyers in dept: 1. Staff: 1. Percentage of work outsourced: 75% (drafting, all litigation).

Principal areas of work are corporate finance, M&As, joint ventures, capital raising, regulatory and competition law work and supervision of litigation. Qualified Barrister, Member of Middle Temple and Association of MBAs.

Career: Pupillage at *Francis Taylor Buildings* 1985-86. With Virgin Records, Business Affairs 1986-89. Joined Pearson plc in 1991.

Penguin Books Ltd

27 Wrights Lane, London, W8 5TZ Tel: (0171) 416 3000

Engle, Cecily *Legal Director.* Reports to: MD. Lawyers in dept: 2.

Director responsible for all legal and company secretarial matters across Penguin UK group of companies. Born 1960.

Peninsular & Oriental Steam Navigation Company

78 Pall Mall, London, SW1Y 5EH Tel: (0171) 930 4343

Gradon, Michael *Group Legal Director.* Reports to: Group Managing Director. Lawyers in Dept: 3

Deals with acquisitions, disposals, joint ventures, financing and other major group matters.

Career: Qualified in 1983. With *Slaughter & May* 1981-86. Became P&O Group Legal Director in 1991.

Pentland Group plc

Pentland Centre, Lakeside, Squires Lane, London, N3 2QL Tel: (081) 346 2600

Kelly, Clive Raisman *General Counsel.* Reports to: Chairman. Lawyers in dept: 3. Staff: 4. Percentage of work outsourced: 20% (specialist and major commercial and taxation matters).

Responsible for in-house legal advice, trademarks and other intellectual property administration, liaising and visiting as necessary outside lawyers and overseas subsidiaries and advisers (particularly in Hong Kong, SE Asia and the USA).

Career: Articled at *Champion & Co.* Solicitor with Mobil Oil Company 1959-60. Solicitor with EMI Ltd 1960-67, Commercial Assistant to Group MD (Overseas) 1967-69 and Commercial Manager (Overseas Division) EMI Music Ltd 1969-70. MD Columbia EMI Greece SA 1970-73 and Manager, International Copyright Division, EMI Music Ltd 1973-75; MD EMI South Africa (Pty) Ltd and Director Thorn EMI Group (SA) 1975-84 Council Member of International Federation of Producers of Phonograms and Videograms representing EMI 1973-86. MD - International, EMI Music Ltd 1984-86. Joined Pentland Group plc in 1987.

Pepe Group plc

Pepe House, 449-451 High Road, London, NW10 2JJ Tel: (0181) 560 8888

Dhanji, Anisa *Director of Legal Affairs.* Reports to: Finance Director. Lawyers in dept: 1. Staff: 2. Work outsourced: primarily trade mark related and corporate finance.

Responsible for all the Group's legal matters with an emphasis on brand protection. Work includes managing worldwide trade mark portfolio, Group anti-counterfeiting programme and all related litigation. Also provides general consumer and commercial advice, negotiates and drafts distribution, licence and other commercial contracts and is involved in transactional work relating to the sale of various subsidiaries. Member of International Trade Marks Association, the International Anti-Counterfeiting Coalition, the UK Anti-Counterfeiting Group and the Intellectual Property Managers' Club.

Career: Articled with *Russell & DuMoulin*, Vancouver 1983-84. Sole practitioner and legal consultant 1984-86, then solicitor with *McKenna & Co* dealing with commercial/ intellectual property law 1987-91. Joined Pepe Group plc in 1992.

Performing Right Society Ltd

Copyright House, 29-33 Berners Street, London, W1P 4AA Tel: (0171) 927 8248

Lowe, Nicholas: *Director, Legal & International Affairs.* Reports to: Chairman. Lawyers in dept: 6. Staff: 30. Work outsourced: Only large, particular cases - computers, competition etc.

Responsible for the provision of legal services, international relations, broadcasting negotiations and administration. Director of Irish Music Rights Organisation Ltd and Composers and Authors Society of Hong Kong Ltd. Has addressed a number of conferences and seminars on copyright and music issues.

Career: Qualified 1977 in England, 1993 in Ireland. Articled clerk and solicitor with *Bristows, Cooke and Carpmael* 1974-82. At *Woodham Smith* 1982-85 (Partner from 1984) and then joined the PRS. Assistant to Director of External Affairs 1985-86, Head of Legal Services 1986-93, Director of Legal Affairs 1993-94 and Director of Legal and International Affairs since 1994.

Performing Right Society Ltd

Copyright House, 29-33 Berners Street, London, W1P 4AA Tel: (0171) 927 8248

Uwemedimo, David *Head of Legal Services.* Reports to: Director of Legal and International Affairs. Lawyers in dept: 6. Staff: 15. Percentage of work outsourced: 5% (specialist employment, IT and competition law work).
Head of Legal Services providing legal advice on any aspect of PRS' affairs involving the laws of intellectual property (especially collective administration of copyright), contract, employment (including representing PRS at industrial tribunals), competition, finance, revenue, defamation and statutory compliance. Negotiates and concludes licensing agreements with major music users around the world, lobbies governments worldwide on copyright reform and liaises with PRS' sister societies. Promotes cause of copyright owners through lectures, conference and media appearances. Gives evidence at Copyright Tribunals.

Career: Called to the Bar 1986. Joined PRS in 1987 as Assistant to the Director of External Affairs. Legal Officer and Secretary of the Music Copyright Reform Group 1988-90 and Deputy Head of Legal Services 1990-93, then took up current position.

PHH Europe PLC

PHH Centre, Windmill Hill, Whitehill Way, Swindon, Wiltshire, SN5 9YT Tel: (01793) 887000

Robson, Andrew J. *Legal Services Director/ comp secretary.* Reports to: General Counsel -PHH Corp USA. Lawyers in Depart: 3. Staff: 4. Percentage of work outsourced: 5% (litigation and specialist tax).
Responsible for all legal advice for European operations. Deals with acquisitons, joint ventures, securitizations, general company and corporate finance, treasury work -swaps, facilities and receivables. Also responsible for tax, treasury, personnel, insurance, purchasing, facilities as Head of Corporate resources. Addresses numerous conferences and court appearances. Member of BACFI.

Career: Qualified 1985. Assistant legal adviser Allied Dunbar 1985-1987, assistant group lawyer PHH Europe PLC 1987-1988 and appointed legal director and company secretary 1988.

Pilkington plc

Prescot Road, St Helens, Merseyside, WA10 3TT Tel: (01744) 28882

Bricknell, David John *Group Legal Adviser/ Co. Secretary.* Reports to: CEO. Lawyers in dept: 5. Staff: 12. Percentage of work outsourced: 50%+ (major litigation, international, large scale acquisitions and divestments, specialist counsel advice).
Manages the provision of legal advice to an international Group (80% of turnover overseas). Principal areas of work are antitrust/ competition law, acquisitions and disposals, UK corporate work, senior level service contracts and related matters, and corporate compliance programmes. The majority of work involves international aspects and the necessary management of external legal resources in a number of jurisdictions.

Career: Qualified 1972 while with *Slaughter & May.* Joined Pilkington plc as Assistant Solicitor 1974 becoming Company Secretary 1980; Manager, Legal Department 1989 and Group Legal Adviser 1992.

Pirelli General plc

Corporate Offices, Leigh Road, Eastleigh, Hants, SO50 9PA Tel: (01703) 644522

Sykes, J.P.N *Group Solicitor.* Reports to : Company secretary. Lawyers in Dept: 2 Percent of work outsourced: 25% (litigation, patents and trade marks).
Specialisation: Principal areas of work are company/commercial law, encompassing all aspects of company law, commercial agreements of various kinds; employment law; property law including purchases/sales of properties and leases.

Career: Qualified 1974. Joined Freshfields 1974-77, Cope Allman International plc 1977- 1984.

Polygram International

8 St James Square, London, EC2Y 5AJ Tel: (0171) 747 4083

Constant, Richard *General Counsel, Polygram Group.*
Career: Qualified in 1978 and joined Polygram Group in 1980. Has held present position since 1990.

Powergen plc

53 New Broad Street, London, EC2M 1JJ Tel: (0171) 826 2742

Jackson, David *Co. Secretary/Director of Legal Services.* Reports to: Chairman/ Corporate Affairs Director. Lawyers in dept: 8 Staff: 14. Percentage of work outsourced: 40% (project work/litigation/M&A/some property and corporate).
Has wide ranging responsibilities of both legal and secretarial nature involved in the creation and management of Powergen as a company separate from the CEGB and subsequently as a "Top 100" company. In particular dealt with vesting and flotation of Powergen, and negotiation of key contracts (eg with British Coal and regional electricity companies). Provides substantial advice on new regulatory environment, including preparation of cases for MMC reference. Substantially involved in business diversification through projects in UK and abroad relating to electricity generation, gas trading and pipelines and gas field ownership. Member of Executive Committee involved with day to day running of the business.

Career: Qualified 1977. Assistant solicitor with *Barlow Lyde & Gilbert* 1977-79 and to the Nestle Company Ltd 1979-81. Assistant Group Legal Adviser to Chloride Group plc 1981-87. Legal Adviser, Matthew Hall plc 1987-89, then took up current position.

Price Waterhouse

Southwark Towers, 32 London Bridge Street, London, SE1 9SU Tel: (0171) 939 2060

Bicheno, Tracey *General Counsel.* Reports to: Director of Operations. Percentage of work outsourced: 25% (commercial, some IP and software licensing).
Responsible for providing corporate legal advice to Partners and Staff throughout the UK firm in connection with their business activities. Work includes advising on contracts, terms of business, joint ventures, term loan and partnership agreements. Also advises on or co-ordinates external advice on employment, property, and libel matters and other issues arising on an ad hoc basis.

Career: Qualified 1985 while at *Norton Rose* and assistant solicitor to 1987. Legal Adviser to Parrish plc 1987-88 and Senior Legal Adviser to Smith New Court plc 1988-91. Director of Legal Services and Associate Director, BIS Group 1991-93, then ran own commercial law practice before joining Price Waterhouse as General Counsel in August 1994.

Procter & Gamble Ltd

Hedley House, St Nicholas Avenue, Gosforth, Newcastle upon Tyne, Tyne and Wear, NE99 1EE Tel: (0191) 279 2000

Downey, Bob *Company Secretary and General Counsel.* Reports to: MD. Lawyers in dept: 3. Staff: 5. Percentage of work outsourced: 5% (heavy litigation, corporate restructuring, commercial conveyancing, housing/staff relocation, acquisitions).
Responsible for legal and company secretarial services to the company and a number of its associated companies and subsidiaries in the UK and Ireland. Member CBI Competition Panel. Member of Law Society Standards and Guidance Committee and Chairman Commerce and Industry Group 1991-92. President Newcastle Law Society 1993.

Career: Qualified 1961. In private practice until 1963 and then joined Procter & Gamble Legal Dept. Company Secretary 1984 and General Counsel 1992.

Luscombe, Celia *Company Sec/ care products solicitor.* Reports to: General Manager. Lawyers in Dept: 3. Staff: 4. Percentage of work outsourced: 20% (construction, property, litigation). Deals with general commercial, competition law, consumer law including product liabilty, employment, corporate including company secretarial, acquisitions and disposals, intellectual property and regulatory issues specific to business. As legal adviser at BOC, international work including acquisitons and joint ventures in Eastern Europe. Member of Associaton of Women Solicitors and CTPA.

Career: Called to Bar 1982, requalified as Solicitor 1986.

Proudfoot Plc

Centenary House, 5 Hill Street, Richmond, Surrey, TW9 1SP Tel: (0181) 940 8454

Switalski, Gillian *General counsel and company secretary.* Reports to: Chief Executive. Lawyers in Depart: 3. Staff: 7. Percentage of work outsourced: 30% (property, employment, foriegn jurisdiction, foreign tax and company).
Responsible for all legal affairs world wide, including management of litigation, new business development, franchising, financial matters and complex contractual negotiations. member of ACCA and Women's lawyer group.

Career: Qualified 1983. Solicitor South Yorkshire County Council 1983-1984, Senior Crown Solicitor CPS 1984-1988, solicitor and legal advisor Quaker Oats Ltd, senior manager of legal department. Sony (UK) Ltd 1990-1991 and general manager 1991-1993. Joined Proudfoot Plc 1993.

Prudential Corporation plc

142 Holborn Bars, London, EC1N 2NH Tel: (0171) 548 3568

Councell, Derek John *Director of Legal Services.* Reports to: Chief Executive. Lawyers in UK Group: 11 Type of work outsourced: Property and litigation.
Heads a small team of commercial lawyers providing legal services to the Corporation and its subsidiaries.

Career: Qualified in 1964. Assistant solicitor at *Coward Chance* 1965-68. Legal Director and Company Secretary at Imperial Foods Ltd 1968-86. UK Legal Adviser to Arthur Young (now Ernst & Young) Chartered Accountants 1986-87. Director of Legal Services at Guinness plc 1987-92. Director of Legal Services at Prudential Corporation plc since March 1992.

Quaker Oats Company

1 Castle Yard, Richmond, Surrey, TW10 6TF Tel: (0181) 332 9990

Singer, David   *Counsel - Quaker Beverages Europe.*   Reports to: Vice President - International Law.
Responsible for legal affairs in Europe and a member of Quaker Beverages Europe Executive Committee.
Career: Qualified in 1988.

RCI Europe Ltd

Kettering Parkway, Kettering, Northants, NN15 6EY Tel: (01536) 310101

Briggs, Martin   *Group Legal Counsel.*   Reports to: Group Finance Director. Lawyers in Dept: 1
Work encompasses timeshare law, EU competition law, travel law, contract, trade marks, trade associations, employment law and litigation. Member of International Bar Association (Secretary of Tourism & Travel Law Committee) and Law Society Commerce & Industry Group. Is on the Editorial Board of and a regular contributor to the *Travel Law Journal.*
Career: Qualified in 1984. With *Rowe & Maw* 1982-85 and 1986-94 (Partner 1989-94). Foreign intern/associate at *Chadbourne & Park,* Attorneys in New York 1985-86. Joined RCI Europe in October 1994.

Reiner Moritz Associates Ltd

46 Great Marlborough Street, London, W1V 1BD Tel: (0171) 439 2637

Carter, Robert Benjamin   *Director of Legal and Business Affairs.*   Reports to: Board of Directors. Lawyers in Dept: 1 Percent of work outsourced: 5% (litigation).
Handles all types of contractual and copyright matters pertaining to the entertainment industry and related negotiation. This includes film and TV production and distribution, music and book publishing, audio record (phonographic) production and distribution, underlying rights clearances, etc.
Career: Qualified in 1979. Assistant solicitor at *Deacons* in Hong Kong 1980-82. Group Solicitor, Associated Communications Corporation plc 1982-84. Head of Legal & Business Affairs, The National Video Corporation 1984-87. Head of Contracts, Thames Television plc (1987-88). Joined Reiner Moritz Associates in 1988.

Renault V.I. United Kingdom Ltd

Boscombe Road, Dunstable, Beds, LU5 4LX Tel: (01582) 471122

Herbert, John   *Legal Adviser.*   Reports to: Finance Director. Lawyers in Dept: 1
Percent of work outsourced: 10% (High court litigation, property).
Main emphasis is on contractual work relating to the sale and distribution of commercial vehicles. Also employment law, including attendance at tribunals.
Career: Qualified and joined Renault as Sole Legal Adviser in 1991

Revlon International Corporation

88 Brook Street, London, W1Y 2BA Tel: (0171) 499 1939

Milne, Ian S.   *International Counsel.*   Reports to: Vice President International Counsel. Lawyers in Dept: 1
Percent of work outsourced: 20% (litigation, minor company secretarial work).
Provides general commercial law advice to Revlon affiliates in Europe, the Middle East and Africa, as well

as handling company secretarial work and providing risk management advice. Member of the Law Society Commerce & Industry Group.
Career: Qualified in 1977. Legal Advisor to Watney, Mann and Truman Ltd 1977-80. Commercial Solicitor, Commercial Union Assurance Co. plc 1980-82. Senior Commercial Solicitor (1982-89) and Group Risk Management Director (1989-93), Grand Metropolitan plc. Joined Revlon in October 1993.

Rexham plc

114 Knightsbridge, London, SW1X 7NN Tel: (0171) 584 7070

Potten, Matthew   *Company Secretary/ Head of Legal Affairs.*   Reports to: Chairman; Chief Executive. Lawyers in dept: 3. Staff: 8. Percentage of work outsourced: variable (medium to large m&a transactions, litigation, conveyancing).
Principal areas of work are company secretarial, commercial legal, insurance, property and personnel matters. Member of Middle Temple.
Career: Qualified as a Barrister 1982. In-house lawyer with Imperial Chemical Industries plc 1983-87, Vickers plc 1987-91 and then joined Bowater plc.

Rialto Homes plc

Bayfordbury, Lower Hatfield Road, Hertford, SG13 8EE Tel: (01992) 823500

Reid, Stephen J. P.   *Group Solicitor.*   Reports to: MD. Staff: 5.
Responsible for provision of legal advice on purchase and sale of land and buildings, planning matters, financial arrangements, commercial and residential leases, company law matters, general commercial contracts, statutory compliance, employment legislation and pension schemes.
Career: Qualified 1981 while with *Daynes Chittock & Back,* Norwich. Solicitor with *Trevor Robinson & Co* 1983-86 and *Taylor Vinters* 1986-89, then joined Rialto Homes plc.

Robert Fleming & Co Ltd

25 Copthall Avenue, London, EC2R 7DR Tel: (0171) 638 5858

Crouch, Christopher   *Legal Director - Group Compliance.*   Reports to: Chief Executive. Lawyers in dept: 2. Staff: 6. Percentage of work outsourced: 30% (litigation, transaction work, intellectual property).
Principal areas of work involve financial services law, IT, compliance matters and commercial contracts of all types. Speaker at Securities Houses Compliance Officers Group conferences and other compliance conferences. Member of BACFI.
Career: Qualified 1980. With Save & Prosper Group 1976-81; Manufacturers Life 1981-86 and Eagle Star 1986-87, then took up present position.

Rothmans International

Denham Place, Denham, Middlesex, UB9 5BL Tel: (01895) 834949

Seddon, James W.   *Legal Director.*   Reports to: Product Services Director. Lawyers in dept: 1. Staff: 2. Percentage of work outsourced: 70% (tobacco related commercial, litigation and legislative issues). Responsible for provision of in-house legal services and management of external lawyers as appropriate. Member of Law Society Commerce and Industry Group.
Career: Qualified 1980. Has been with Rothmans for 12 years, previously Head of Legal Department.

N M Rothschild & Sons Ltd

New Court, St Swithin's Lane, London, EC4P 4DU Tel: (0171) 280 5000

Curtis, Penelope   *Compliance Director.*
Reports to: Chairman. Lawyers in Dept: 2
Is responsible for FSA compliance in the Rothschild Group in the UK and the Channel Islands. Member of the International Bar Association and City of London Solicitor's Company. Member of Commodities Committee, FOA.
Career: Qualified in 1981. With *Freshfields* 1979-87. Joined N M Rothschild in 1987 and became Compliance Director in 1989.

Rust Ltd

3 Shortlands, Hammersmith International Centre, London, W6 8RX Tel: (0181) 563 6358

Morris, Piers   *Solicitor and General Counsel.*
Reports to: President. Lawyers in dept: 1. Staff: 4.
Percentage of work outsourced: 40% (litigation, advice on application of law in foreign jurisdictions). Responsible for advice, drafting and negotiation of international contracts, financial risk assessment, joint ventures, shareholder agreements, technology transfer, bonding and financing, insurances, property and employment matters. Provides secretarial function (UK, Europe, Far East and Australia). Also lectures worldwide to lawyers and senior managers on risk management. Rust Ltd manage the non-USA activities of Rust International, Inc. worldwide.
Career: Qualified 1981 (articles with Grand Metropolitan plc). Solicitor, Burmah Oil plc 1981-84. Solicitor, Crown Agents for Overseas Governments and Administrations 1984-88. Solicitor, Bechtel Ltd 1988-89; then Solicitor/Attorney at Law with Charles Adams & Co, Grand Cayman. Solicitor/ International Counsel, McDermott International Inc 1990-94, then joined Rust Ltd.

J Sainsbury plc

Stamford House, Stamford Street, London, SE1 9LL Tel: (0171) 921 6000

Arnold, Christopher James Timothy   *Senior Legal Adviser.*   Reports to: Head of Legal Services. Lawyers in dept: 6. Staff: 2. Percentage of work outsourced: 10% (litigation).
Principal areas of work are employment law, intellectual property (trade marks, patents and licensing - both contentious and non-contentious), and general commercial matters. Employment work covers litigation and advocacy at industrial tribunals and the Employment Appeal Tribunal. Commercial work includes drafting and reviewing employment and general commercial contracts. Member of Employment Lawyers' Association and CBI Employment Law Panel.
Career: Qualified as a Barrister 1976, and practised at the Bar 1986-87. Employment Law Adviser, CBI 1978-81; then joined J. Sainsbury plc.

Sanofi Winthrop Ltd

Sanofi-Winthrop House, Onslow Street, Guildford, Surrey, GU1 4YS Tel: (01483) 554036

Warnock-Smith, Anthony   *Legal Director and Company Secretary.*   Reports to: MD. Lawyers in dept: 3. Staff: 7. Percentage of work outsourced: 25% (litigation, real property, major transactional).
Principal areas of work are the provision of legal advice and services concerning company/ commercial matters, intellectual property, employment, acquisitions/ disposals, competition, EC law and pharmaceutical regulatory issues. Also provides company secretarial services. Pharmaceutical turnover in

the UK is £160 million. Committee Member, Law Society Commerce and Industry Group; Member of Legal Affairs Committee and Intellectual Property Committee of the Association of the British Pharmaceutical Industry. Hon. Legal Adviser, British Institute of Regulatory Affairs.

Career: Qualified 1971 while with GLC Legal and Parliamentary Department, and assistant solicitor to 1973, then joined legal department of Sterling-Winthrop Group Ltd. Director of Legal Services 1975-82 and Director and Company Secretary 1982-91, then joined Sanofi Winthrop Ltd.

Saur (UK) Ltd

22-30 Sturt Road, Frimley, Camberley, Surrey, GU16 6HZ Tel: (01252) 835031

Stiff, R.G. *Company Solicitor.* Reports to: Managing Director. Lawyers in Dept: 1
Principal areas of work are water and environmental law, conveyancing and litigation. Member of British Institute of Management.
Career: In H.M. Forces until 1977. Assistant Secretary, Tunnel Holdings Ltd 1981-82. Company Secretary, Austin Knight Ltd 1983-87. Qualified as a solicitor in 1988. Solicitor for Mid Southern Water/ SAUR (UK) Ltd since 1988.

Save & Prosper Group Ltd

1 Finsbury Avenue, London, EC2M 2QY Tel: (0171) 588 1717

Bassett, Marilyn L. *Head of Legal Services/Co. Sec..* Reports to: Corporate Services Director. Lawyers in dept: 4. Staff: 7. Percentage of work outsourced: 7% (litigation, specialist advice).
Head of legal services and company secretary, responsible for provision of legal advice and company secretarial functions to group companies. Member of Association of Pension Lawyers and member of Technical Committee, ICSA.
Career: Qualified 1976. Legal adviser, J.H. Rayner & Co Ltd 1976-78, then joined Save & Prosper Group Ltd as legal adviser. Became head of legal services 1988 and company secretary 1993.

Schlumberger Ltd (Geco-Prakla)

Schlumberger House, Buckingham Gate, Gatwick Airport, Gatwick, RH6 0NZ

Keeley, Peter L. *VP, General Counsel & Co. Secretary.* Reports to: Group President and General Counsel, Schlumberger Ltd. Lawyers in dept: 18. Staff: 9.
Directs the legal affairs of Geco-Prakla (the seismic business group of Schlumberger Ltd) including M&As; divestitures; joint ventures, co-operations and agencies; ship construction and purchase agreements; corporate structure, tax and treasury issues; financing; client master service agreements; antitrust challenges and investigations; export control; litigation and disputes; real estate leasing; and issues involving intellectual property, employment and labour law. Involved in business strategy, setting company policy, management training and press relations.
Manages 18 member legal department located in 8 offices around the world.
Career: Law clerk, *Donahue, Ehrmantraut & Montedonico,* Washington DC 1984-85, then Attorney, *Weller, Wheelus & Green* Houston/ Beaumont, Texas 1985-88. Legal Counsel, North America Operations, Wireline & Testing North America, Houston 1988-89; then joined Geco-Prakla as Regional Counsel, Europe-Asia. General Counsel and Co. Secretary in Norway 1990 and Vice President, General Counsel and Co. Secretary Paris/London from 1991.

Schroeders PLC

120 Cheapside, London, EC2V 6DS Tel: (0171) 382 6000

Gaulter, Andrew M. *Company Secretary.* Reports to: Chairman. Lawyers in dept: 2. Staff: 5. Percentage of work outsourced: 50% (company shareholder circulars, complex documentation, foreign legal matters).
Provides full company secretarial service to all UK Group Companies.
Career: Articled with *Beachcrofts* 1974-76, then joined Schroders plc.

Scottish & Newcastle plc

Abbey Brewery, 111 Holyrood Road, Edinburgh, Midlothian, EH8 8YS Tel: (0131) 556 2591

Vellani, H.Andrew S. *Group Legal Adviser.* Lawyers in Dept: 1
Responsible for the provision of legal services to Scottish & Newcastle plc and its subsidiary companies. Most time is spent on major projects. Also deals with notifications and competition law advice, including regulatory advocacy with both domestic and EEC competition authorities, drafting of purchasing, sales, brewing, packaging and distribution contracts. Advises on promotions and sponsorship contracts, competitions, lotteries and trading law generally, food labelling and packaging legislation and the drafting of advertising and promotion contracts. Work also includes drafting of trade mark licensing agreements, advice on the registration and defence of trade marks and other intellectual property rights and identifying and instructing external solicitors.
Career: Called to the Bar in 1981. Became Group Legal Adviser to Scottish and Newcastle in 1986 and Company Secretary Scottish and Newcastle Breweries Ltd in 1990. Also Company Secretary of Coors (UK) Ltd from 1991. Admitted as a solicitor in 1991.

Scottish Nuclear Ltd

3 Redwood Crescent, Peel Park, East Kilbride, Glasgow, Lanarkshire, G74 5PR Tel: (01355) 262000

Armour, Robert M. *Company Secretary.* Reports to: CEO. Lawyers in Dept: 2 Percent of work outsourced: 60% (court, employers liability, conveyancing, major contract advice).
Deals with legal matters, pensions, board services, estates, strategy and insurance.
Career: Assistant solicitor *Wright Johnston & McKenzie,* Edinburgh 1983-85, and Partner 1986-90. Joined Scottish Nuclear as Company Secretary in 1990.

Scottish Television plc

Cowcaddens, Glasgow, Lanarkshire, G2 3PR Tel: (0141) 332 9999

Lawrie, Sheelagh J. *Head of Legal and Business Affairs.* Reports to: Director of Finance. Lawyers in Dept: 3
Percent of work outsourced: 30% (general corporate, specific employment/ copyright).
Handles all company secretarial responsibilities, corporate legal work, employment law, contract, copyright and media law.
Career: Qualified in 1990. In private practice in Glasgow (litigation) for 3 years before joining Scottish Television in 1991 as Business Affairs Executive. Became Company Secretary in June 1994.

Scottish Widows' Fund and Life Assurance Society

P.O. Box 902, 15 Dalkeith Road, Edinburgh, EH16 5BU Tel: (0131) 655 8393

Houston, Thomas B. *Group Legal Adviser and Secretary.* Reports to: Executive Board Director. Lawyers in Dept: 3 Percent of work outsourced: 10% (litigation, commercial conveyancing) 100% outsourced by Property Investment Department.
Principal areas of work are general contractual law, unit trusts, PEP's, life and pensions, investments and banking. Work includes EC legislation, management of litigation, employment law, pensions, debt recovery and insolvency, consumer protection, company secretarial and investments. Chairman of Scots Law Advisory Committee (Assoc. Scottish Life Offices).
Career: Admitted as solicitor and qualified as Notary Public in 1974. In private practice and local government 1974-82. Group Legal Adviser and Deputy Secretary LAS Group, Edinburgh 1982-88. Group Legal Adviser and Secretary to Scottish Widows since 1988 and Secretary of Scottish Widows Bank from 1994.

Secure Trust Group PLC

Royex House, Aldermanbury Square, London, EC2V 7HR Tel: (0171) 600 3831

Kaye, J.R. *Company Secretary.* Reports to: Chairman. Lawyers in Dept: 1 Percent of work outsourced: 50% (acquisitions, banking documentation).
Principal areas of work are company law, property, insurance, employment, secretarial and regulatory. Member of Bar Council and Bar Association for Commerce, Finance & Industry. Member of Chartered Institute of Secretaries (FCIS 1970).
Career: Qualified in 1962. With Limmer & Trinidad Lake Asphalt Co. Ltd 1962-72 (Chief Legal Officer from 1967), then Arbuthnot Latham & Co. Ltd 1973-91 (Secretary, and from 1984 Administration Director). Company Secretary of Secure Trust Group since November 1987.

Securicor Group plc

Sutton Park House, 15 Carshalton Road, Sutton, Surrey, SM1 4LD Tel: (0181) 770 7000

Griffiths, Nigel *Group Legal Director.* Reports to: Group Chief Executive. Lawyers in Dept: 6 Percent of work outsourced: 20% (pensions, litigation, property (part only) mergers and acquisitions (some only)).
Principal areas of work are corporate, company secretarial, stock exchange compliance, mergers and acquisitions, contracts, insurance and general commercial. Visiting Fellow in Commercial Law, University of Essex 1988-91.
Career: Qualified in 1971. Became Legal Adviser to Securicor Group in 1977 and Group Legal Director in 1990.

Securities & Investments Board

2-14 Bunhill Row, London, EC1Y 8RA Tel: (0171) 638 1240

Blair, Michael C. *Head of Policy and Legal Affairs.* Reports to: Chief Executive. Lawyers in dept: 11. Staff: 55. Percentage of work outsourced: 15% (litigation, pensions, property).
Principal areas of work are financial services regulation and commercial law. Treasurer of General Council of the Bar and Member of BACFI. Author of numerous articles on law reform and commercial law and text books on The Sale of Goods Act 1979 (Butterworths 1980) and Financial Services: The New Core Rules (Blackstone Press 1991). Consultant Editor,

Butterworths European Law Service (Banking and Financial Services Title) 1992.

Career: Called to the Bar 1965. Lord Chancellor's Department 1966-87 (including Secretary of the Lord Chancellor's Law Reform Committee 1977-79, concerned with reform of Civil and Criminal Courts 1979-82, Under Secretary 1982-87 and Head of Courts and Legal Services Group 1986-87). Legal Director to the Securities and Investments Board 1987, General Counsel 1991-93 and Head of Policy and Legal Affairs since 1993.

Shell International Petroleum Company Ltd

Shell Centre, London, SE1 7NA Tel: (0171) 934 5166

Shraven, Jacques *Legal Co-ordinator.*
Reports to: Chairman. Lawyers in dept: 45. Staff: 79. Percentage of work outsourced: 30% (litigation, financing, M&A, marine, competition, libel, property). Responsible for co-ordinating legal management, corporate matters and dispute settlement (litigation and ADR) in Shell companies worldwide, providing legal advice to committee of Managing Directors. Deals with U.S. litigation, arbitration law (ICC and UNCITRAL), competition law, IP matters, consumer law, single market issues, telecommunications law and employment matters. Member of Council IBA Scection on Energy and Resources Law. Board Member Energy Law Institute (Leyden University) and Netherlands Association of Commercial Law. Lectures on commercial law and legal management and has written articles on Dutch company law.

Career: Qualified 1968. Joined Shell in The Hague in 1968 as a junior legal adviser. Moved to London office 1975 as Finance Adviser in Group Treasury Department. Senior Corporate Lawyer, Shell Internationale Petroleum Maatschappij, The Hague 1977-82. Area Co-ordinator for Royal Dutch/ Shell companies in Venezuela, Curacao, Mexico and New York 1982, and Chief Executive of Shell companies (Argentina) 1984-88, then took up present position.

Shell U.K. Ltd

Shell Mex House, Strand, London, WC2R 0DX Tel: (0171) 257 1866

Wiseman, Richard *General Counsel and Company Secretary.* Reports to: Chairman and Chief Executive. Lawyers in Dept: 20
Percent of work outsourced: 10% (litigation and major corporate acquisitions and disposals).
Handles mainly company and commercial matters and joint ventures. Shell U.K. Ltd is an integrated oil company with substantial upstream interests in the North Sea as well as two refineries, a complex distribution network and some 2,000 dealer-owned and company-owned filling stations. The Legal Department is responsible for advising all of those businesses and the businesses of its subsidiary, Shell Chemicals U.K. Ltd.

Career: Qualified in 1974 (England) and 1984 (Victoria, Australia). Has held a number of legal posts in various companies in the Royal/Dutch Shell Group, including Shell International Petroleum Limited and the Shell Company of Australia.

Siebe plc

Saxon House, 2/4 Victoria Street, Windsor, Berkshire, SL4 IEN Tel: (01753) 855411

Coles, Richard Paul Atwell *Director of Legal Affairs/ Co. Secretary.* Reports to: Group Finance Director. Lawyers in dept: 1. Staff: 3. Percentage of work outsourced: 90%.
Principal areas of work are the provision of legal

advice on pensions and intellectual property and the provision of company secretarial and administrative services.

Career: Qualified 1968. With British Leyland Motor Corporation Ltd 1968-84. Director of Legal Services, Austin Rover Group Ltd 1984-87 and took up present position 1988.

Siemens Group Services Ltd

Siemens House, Oldbury, Bracknell, Berks, RG12 8FZ Tel: (01344) 396110

Howard, Ian. *Managing Director.* Reports to: Chief Executive Officer, Siemens PLC. Lawyers in Dept: 5
Percent of work outsourced: 20% (large mergers and acquisitions, litigation, pensions).
Responsible for management of a multi-disciplinary corporate services organisation and the direct management of the legal function. Handles mergers and acquisition work if it can effectively be done in-house. Is also Company Secretary of Siemens PLC and a member of executive management. Member of the Institute of Chartered Secretaries and the Association of Pensions Lawyers.

Career: Qualified in 1980. Assistant Legal Adviser 1980-82. Assistant Company Secretary 1982-84. Became Company Secretary of Siemens plc in 1984 and Managing Director of Siemens Group Services Ltd in 1994.

Smith & Nephew plc

2 Temple Place, Victoria Embankment, London, WC2R 3BP Tel: (0171) 836 7922

Parson, Michael G. *Group Company Secretary & Legal Adviser.* Reports to: Chief Executive.
Percent of work outsourced: 100%
Career: Qualified in 1965. Legal Department, Cunard/ Trafalgar House plc 1970-75. Group Legal Director, Mass Transit Corporation, Hong Kong 1975-85. Group Secretary and Legal Adviser, Bowater plc 1987-91. Has held present position since March 1991.

Smith New Court plc

Smith New Court, 20 Farringdon Road, London, EC1M 3NH Tel: (0171) 772 2944

Jolowicz, Philip Leonard *Legal Director.*
Responsible for provision of legal services to the plc.
Career: Qualified 1985 while with *Clifford Chance.* Dealt with corporate finance at Paribas Ltd 1986-92, then took up current position.

SmithKline Beecham

One New Horizons Court, Brentford, Middlesex, TW8 9EP Tel: (0181) 975 2000

Beery, James R *General Counsel and Corporate Secretary.* Reports to: Chief Executive and Chairman. Lawyers in dept: 72. Staff: 230.
Responsible for the management of the legal function and provison of legal advice and support at all levels to SmithKline Beecham.
Career: Associate, *Cleary Gottlieb Steen & Hamilton,* New York 1971-73 and London office 1975-76. Foreign legal consultant to *Nagashima & Ohno* Tokyo 1973-75. Partner with *Erickson & Morrison* (London office) 1977-79 and Managing Partner, *Morrison & Foerster* (London office) 1980-92. Joined SmithKline Beecham in January 1994.

Society of Motor Manufacturers and Traders

Forbes House, Halkin Street, London, SW1X 7DS Tel: (0171) 235 7000

Farley, Peter J. *Chief Legal Adviser.* Reports to: Commercial Director. Lawyers in dept: 2. Staff: 7. Percentage of work outsourced: 5% (EC competition law notifications).
Advises society on all legal matters relating to its business, principally general commercial, competition law, intellectual property and employment. Work includes policy formulation; preparation and drafting of licensing, advertising and sponsorship agreements; MMC and OFT enquiries into the motor industry; preparing submissions on behalf of the motor industry to Parliament and the EC Commission; and monitoring and ensuring adherence to Industry Codes of Practice. Regular speaker at motor industry seminars and occasional appearances on TV and radio. Member of BACFI.

Career: Qualified Barrister, pupillage 1982-85, then Consumer Lawyer, Which? Consumers' Association. General and Legal Manager, City Fine Wine plc 1986-87, then joined SMMT.

Sony Music Entertainment (UK) Ltd

10 Great Marlborough St, London, W1V 6HE Tel: (0171) 911 8306

Sternberg, Jonathan *Senior Counsel - UK and Europe.* Reports to: Chairman and CEO. Lawyers in Dept: 5
Principal areas of work are corporate, contracts, EC, acquisitions, rights, litigation. Pension Fund Trustee. Board Member of Phonographic Performance Ltd and Video Perfomance Ltd. Member of BPI Rights Committee (former Chairman).

Sony United Kingdom Ltd

Sony House, The Heights, Brooklands, Weybridge, Surrey, KT13 0XW Tel: (01932) 816710

Pearl, Jonathan *General Manager Legal Affairs.* Reports to: Company Secretary. Lawyers in Dept: 3
Percent of work outsourced: 10% (litigation, property, specialist services).
Provides company/commercial legal advice for all areas of the company.

Career: Qualified in 1988. With *Bates, Wells & Braithwaite* until 1990. UK Legal Counsel, Apple Computer UK Ltd 1990-93. Has held present position since November 1993.

Southern Electric plc

Southern Electric House, Westacott Way, Littlewick Green, Maidenhead, Berkshire, SL6 3QB Tel: (01628) 822166

Morris, Derek *Company Secretary and Solicitor.* Reports to: Finance Director. Lawyers in dept: 8. Staff: 22. Percentage of work outsourced 1-10% (corporate, City/ M&A, major projects).
Specialises in corporate law and corporate governance. Leads a high profile, pro-active and client focused team providing legal advice and services to the plc and subsidiaries. Responsible for and managed the Prospectus writing and preparation for Stock Exchange Listing for the plc and now maintains statutory registers and advises on sharesave and share option schemes. Advises on commercial projects; share schemes; litigation; sale, purchase and lease of property; maximising property assets and minimising costs; negotiating insurance arrangements; and provides company secretarial service.

Career: Qualified 1969. Solicitor *J.A. Simpson & Coulby* 1969-70 and Senior Partner *J.J. Spencer & Co* 1970-72. Solicitor to Neath Borough Council 1972-78. Deputy Solicitor to Southern Electricity Board 1978-85 and Solicitor to the Board 1985-89, Company Secretary and Solicitor to Southern Electric plc since 1989.

Sphere Drake Insurance Group plc

52-54 Leadenhall Street, London, EC3A 2BJ Tel: (0171) 480 7340

Cook, Neil L. *General Counsel.* Reports to: CEO. Lawyers in dept: 1. Staff: 5. Work outsourced: all litigation and property.
Advises the Main Board on all legal and company secretarial matters, and deals with public issue of equity/debt. Sphere Drake is based in London/Bermuda and listed on the New York Stock Exchange, so much work is US public company in nature. Member of Law Society, American Bar Association and New York Bar.
Career: Qualified as solicitor 1981. Solicitor with Ladbroke Group plc to 1984, then Managing Solicitor for *Manfield & Co* 1984-85 (establishing new London office of UAE-based law firm). Joined Lifetime Corporation 1985 and based in London 1985-86, New York 1986-88 and Boston 1988-93. Admitted to New York Bar 1990. Took up present position in 1994.

Spring Ram Corporation Plc

Euroway House, Roydsdale Way, Euroway Trading Estate, Bradford, West Yorkshire, BD4 6SJ Tel: (01274) 686888

Baxandall, Cathy *Group Company Secretary.* Reports to: Group Finance Director. Lawyers in Dept: 1
Type of work outsourced: Specialist work, e.g. intellectual property, employment, overseas law.
Principal areas of work are compliance, legal, project management, asset protection risk management and employee benefits.
Career: Qualified in 1985. Assistant solicitor with *Clifford Chance* in Brussels, Paris and London 1985-90. Banking specialist (latterly Partner) at $SSimpson Curtis$D, Leeds 1990-94. Became Group Company Secretary of the Spring Ram Corporation in September 1994.

Staveley Industries plc

Staveley House, 11 Dingwall Road, Croydon, Surrey, CR9 3DB Tel: (0181) 688 4404

Armitage, Roderick Donald *Legal Director.*
Reports to: Chief Executive. Lawyers in dept: 1. Staff: 5. Percentage of work outsourced: 25% (acquisition/disposals, intellectual property, property, banking).
Responsible for advising on legal, secretarial, property, insurance, group environmental/ health and safety compliance. Involved in over 30 acquisitions/disposals in US/ UK; contract; intellectual property; and antitrust (OFT/ MMC in UK, Hart Scott Rodino in US).
Career: Qualified Barrister and FCIs Management Trainee/ Contracts Officer, Hawker Siddeley Aviation 1965-68. Contracts Manager, Airborne Display Division, GEC Marconi Avionics 1968-70. HQ Contracts Executive, Standard Telephones & Cables 1970-73 and Deputy Manager, Group Financial Analysis, Vickers plc 1973-79. Joined Staveley Industries in 1979 and became Legal Director in 1989.

Stone & Webster Engineering Ltd

Stone & Webster House, 500 Elder Gate, Central Milton Keynes, MK9 1BA Tel: (01908) 602005

Jackson, Howard *Director and Company Secretary.* Reports to: Managing Director. Lawyers in Dept: 1
Percent of work outsourced: 5-10% (conveyancing, litigation).
Career: Qualified in 1976. Assistant solicitor, Tarmac International 1976-79. Company Secretary, Hawker Siddeley Power Engineering 1979-86. Became Company Secretary of Stone & Webster Engineering in 1986 and a Director of the company in 1992.

Swiss Bank Corporation

1 High Timber Street, London, EC4V 3SB Tel: (0171) 329 0329

Stocks, Neil R. *Executive Director.* Reports to: Chief Executive. Lawyers in Dept: 15. Staff: 20
Percentage of work outsourced: 30% (litigation, corporate finance, some capital markets).
Deals with all legal issues affecting SBC Warburg London, including capital markets, derivatives, commercial banking, corporate finance and private banking. Addresses conferences on areas including insurance needs of the financial services industry, environmental law and derivatives.
Career: Qualified 1978; barrister at law. Head of legal department SBC 1990.

Talisman Energy (UK) Ltd

3rd Floor, 48 Leicester Square, London, WC2H 7LT Tel: (0171) 839 8744

Roberts, Walter R. *Manager, Commercial and Legal.* Reports to: Assistant General Manager. Lawyers in dept: 2. Staff: 1. Percentage of work outsourced: 1% (banking, corporate finance, commercial property).
Member of Management Team in London controlling and/ or supplying legal advice and services relating to all operations based on the London office. Principal areas of work are joint venture negotiations and offshore contracting. Also provides company secretarial service, pensions administration and profit sharing scheme administration.
Career: Qualified 1978 while with *Simmons & Simmons*. Legal Counsel for Phillips Petroleum Co 1980-84, then Crown Counsel with Attorney General, Hong Kong (Commercial Unit of Civil Division). Subsequently Legal Adviser to London & Scottish Marine Oil Energy and Resort Representative for Ski Esprit Ltd. Senior Legal Counsel for Phillips Petroleum Co 1987, then Senior Legal Adviser for London & Scottish Marine Oil plc 1987-90.

Tarmac PLC

Hilton Hall, Essington, Wolverhampton, West Midlands, WV11 2BQ Tel: (01902) 307407

FitzHugh, Dirk *Group Legal Adviser.* Reports to: C.O.O. Type of work outsourced: acquisitions, disposals, rights issues, litigation, conveyancing.
Advises Tarmac PLC on Group matters, co-ordinates Divisional Legal Departments, supervises major issues including acquisitions and disposals.
Career: Qualified 1968. Nicholas Williams & Co 1964-71 becoming partner 1969, John Mowlem & Co Legal Department 1971-73. Joined Tarmac PLC 1973; Group Legal Adviser 1992.

Tate & Lyle

Sugar Quay, Lower Thames Street, London, EC3R 6DQ Tel: (0171) 626 6525

Gibber, Robert *Senior Legal Adviser.* Reports to: Company Secretary. Lawyers in Dept: 3 Staff: 3 Percentage of work outsourced : 20% (major acquisitions, overseas work, litigation, employment).
Specialisation: International acquisitions and joint ventures, stock exchange, corporate compliance and finance. Also corporate transactions in UK, competition law, environmental law, property matters, patents/trade marks and share options. Advises the Group Board and Senior Executives.
Prof. Membership: Law society, International Bar Association
Career: Qualified 1988. Formerly with Wilde Sapte as assistant solicitor (1988-90), then joining Tate & Lyle plc in 1990 and appointed senior legal adviser in 1992.

Taylor Nelson AGB

AGB House, Westgate, London, W5 1UA Tel: (0181) 967 0007

Stobart, John *Group Legal Adviser/ Company Secretary.* Reports to: CEO. Lawyers in dept: 2. Staff: 2. Percentage of work outsourced: 10% (excess work load, property, overseas).
Responsible for legal and regulatory affairs of largest UK market research company with turnover in excess of £61m. Deals with joint ventures/ collaborative arrangements worldwide, product licensing, acquisitions and divestments, yellow book compliance, commercial contracts, data protection registration, property, trade marks, employment, insurance and pensions.
Career: Qualified 1978 while with *Smith Roddam*. Legal adviser, 3i plc 1981-86. Partner with *Fennemores* 1986-89 and Director of Legal Services and Company Secretary to Harland Simon Group plc 1989-92. Joined Taylor Nelson AGB in January 1993.

Wright, Paul *Assistant Legal Adviser.* Lawyers in Dept: 2 Type of work outsourced: Property and litigation.
Principal areas of work are company, commercial, intellectual property and corporate finance matters.
Career: Qualified in 1984. With *Nabarro Nathanson* 1984-87, *Gouldens* 1987-89, *McKenna & Co* 1989-93 and *Sebastian Coleman & Co* (Partner) 1993-94.

Templeton Global Investors Ltd

Saltire Court, 20 Castle Terrace, Edinburgh, EH1 2WH Tel: (0131) 469 4000

Kerr, Gerard W. *Legal Services Manager.* Reports to: General Manager. Lawyers in department: 3 Staff: 8. Percentage of work outsourced: 33% (major/ urgent transactions, second opinions).
Responsible for European operations of Franklin Templeton Group, dealing with policy and strategy of legal department and overall administration of department. Involvement in commercial law, corporate law, corporate finance, compliance, company secretarial work, international legal matters concerning Franklin Templeton Group companies and funds, general legal matters.
Career: Qualifed 1987. Solicitor Ross & Connel W.S. 1987-88, Legal Adviser Imperial Chemical Industries PLC 1988-90, Assistant Company Solicitor Lazard Brothers & Co Limited 1990-91. Joined Templeton 1991.

Texaco Ltd

1 Westferry Circus, Canary Wharf, London, E14 4HA Tel: 0171-719 3000

Codd, David   *Director and Chief Legal Adviser.*
Reports to: Chairman. Lawyers in dept: 8. Staff: 15. Percentage of work outsourced: 33% (real property, litigation, specialist advice).
Work covers exploration and production joint ventures, transportation, distribution and sales, operating/unitisation agreements, transportation and processing agreements, gas sales and all associated legal issues. Advises on all aspects of downstream business including the formation and operation of distribution and sales joint ventures. Also advises with regard to new business development in Eastern Europe and is responsible for all aspects of legal affairs associated with downstream subsidiary company in Poland. Member of UK Oil Lawyers Group and contributor to the UK Oil and Gas Law Manual (Sweet & Maxwell).
Career: Qualified 1979. Senior Legal and Lands Adviser, Burmah Oil 1980-84. Senior Legal Adviser to Britoil plc 1984-88 and to Conoco (UK) Ltd 1988-90.

Thames Television

Broom Road, Teddington, Middx, TW11 9NT Tel: (0181) 614 2854

Tingay, Sarah   *Company secretary.* Reports to: CEO. Lawyers in Dept: 5 Staff: 12 Percent of work outsourced: 10 (corporate investments, litigation, libel) Pearson Television Limited, Teddington - Company secretary and Director of Legal and Business Affairs.
Specialisation: Investments, major production deals, company secretarial matters including negotiations and attending board meetings. Also deals with personnel matters and distribution.
Prof. Membership: Copinger society
Career: Qualified 1980. Joined Thames Television in 1987 as Business Affairs assistant, becoming Company Secretary to Thames TV and Pearson TV in July 1993.

Thames Water plc

14 Cavendish Place, London, W1M 9DJ Tel: (0171) 636 8686

Carsley, Clive   *Group Co. Sec. and Chief Legal Adviser.* Reports to: Chairman. Lawyers in dept: 4. Staff: 12. Percentage of work outsourced: 35% (major corporate transactions and work in foreign jurisdictions). Principal areas of work are company secretarial (250,000 shareholder base) and work on overseas water concession projects. Thames Water plc's overseas contracting and operations capacity is currently being developed to take concessions for the privatisation of water utilities in towns such as Bangkok, Jakarta and Adelaide, so much work involves drafting and negotiation of joint ventures, concession and construction contracts and associated funding packages.
Career: Called to the Bar 1966. Commercial Director, Humphreys & Glasgow Ltd 1972-85. Deputy Secretary and Head of Legal Services, Babcock Industrial plc 1985-87. Group Company Secretary, Carless plc 1987-89, then took up current position.

Miller Group Ltd

Miller House, 18 South Groathill Avenue, Edinburgh, Midlothian, EH4 2LW Tel: (0131) 332 2585

Donaldson, Euan J.   *Company solicitor.*
Reports to: Chief Executive. Lawyers in Depart: 6. staff: 7. Percentage of work outsourced: 50% (litigation/ arbitration, joint venture).
Deals with construction, house building, development and mining interests, particularly all aspects of

contenious and non contenious construction law, advice on construction contracts, consultant's appointments and collateral warranties. Also provides secretarial services to Group Board. Member of Public Service and Commerce Group.
Career: Qualified 1985 with Brownlie, Watson & Beckett, assistant solicitor MacRoberts, Glasgow 1985-1988, associate solicitor Bird,Semple,Fyfe,Ireland 1988-1994. Joined The Miller Group Ltd 1994.

Really Useful Group Ltd

22 Tower Street, London, WC2H 9NS Tel: (0171) 240 0880

Hull, Jonathan   *Legal and Business Affairs Manager.* Reports to: Board of Directors. Lawyers in Dept: 2
Handles legal work relating to theatrical production, theatre management, film and television production, sponsorship, merchandising and music publishing.
Career: Qualified in 1988. Articled at Freshfields. Solicitor in Entertainment Department at *Denton Hall* 1989-91. Joined The Really Useful Group as Legal and Business Affairs Manager in 1991.

Thorn EMI plc

4 Tenterden Street, Hanover Square, London, W1A 2AY Tel: (0171) 355 4848

Smith, George Marsden   *Group Legal Adviser.*
Reports to: Company Secretary. Percentage of work outsourced: 50-60% (major acquisitions/disposals). Manages legal function. Involved in general commercial work; banking and corporate finance transactions including syndicated loans and multi-option facilities; and take-overs, merger work and joint ventures both in the UK and abroad. Advises on IP and IT licensing and capital goods acquisitions. Also provides company secretarial functions. Assisted in the acquisition by the Group of Thames Television and Virgin Music, including successful EC Commission application for merger clearance on the Virgin Music acquisition.
Career: Qualified 1975. Solicitor with *Slaughter & May* 1975-80 and with BOC International Ltd 1980-81. Company Solicitor and Assistant Secretary, British Olivetti Ltd 1981-88, then joined Thorn EMI plc.

Towry Law Group

Baylis House, Stoke Poges Lane, Slough, Berks, SL1 3PB Tel: (01753) 554400

Ainslie, David G.   *Group Compliance Officer.*
Reports to: Group Chief Executive. Lawyers in dept: 2. Work outsourced: property, litigation, Stock Exchange, pensions.
Principal areas of work are monitoring financial services regulations in UK, Europe and the Far East and ensuring compliance by operating companies. Also monitors tax and pensions legislation, handles complaints and liases with external lawyers on negligence claims. Author of article on insurance planning in 'Practical Tax Planning With Precedents' (Longmans). Member, UK Association of Compliance Officers.
Career: Qualified 1972, while with *Dawson & Co.* Joined *Lovell White & King* 1976, Partner 1981. Joined Towry Law Group in 1983, became Technical Services Director in 1989 and took up present position in 1994.

Toyota (GB) Ltd

The Quadrangle, Redhill, Surrey, RH1 1PX Tel: (01737) 768585

Jones, Harry   *Company solicitor/ company secretary.* Reports to: Director of finance and systems. Lawyers in Depart: 1. Staff: 1.
Percentage of work outsourced: 20% (High Court

litigation, trade mark registration, some commercial conveyancing).
Responsible for company secretarial, commercial agreements, competition, advertising, consumer credit and consumer law. Also member of Chartered Institute of Arbitrators and Magistrates Association.
Career: Qualified 1980. Assistant solicitor RAC Motoring Services Ltd 1980-1983, assistant solicitor Streeter Marshall & Wilberforce Jackson 1983-1985, legal adviser Society of Motor Manufacturers & Traders Ltd 1985-1989. Joined Toyota (GB) Ltd as company solicitor 1989.

Trafalgar house plc: Engineering Group

1 Berkeley Street, London, W1A 1BY Tel: (0171) 499 9020

Stanley, James   *Head of Legal Services.*
Reports to: Chief Executive, Legal Director (Trafalgar house plc). Lawyers in dept: 36. Staff: 36. Work outsourced: acquisitions/ divestments, major litigation, specialist advice).
Responsible for the conduct, management and control of all commercial issues and significant disputes involving the engineering group. Work includes project contracts, corporate mergers, joint ventures, acquisitions and divestments worldwide. Provides all legal, commercial and associated services, internally and externally, to businesses within the engineering group. Responsible for insurance and risk management functions and reviews and approves all major tenders (in excess of £30m).
Career: Qualified 1980. With *Keeble Hawson Bridge & Co*, Grimsby 1980-84, then *Ralph C. Yablon, Temple Milnes & Carr* 1984-86. Joined Trafalgar House plc in 1986 as Legal Adviser and Solicitor and took up present position 1988.

Transport Development Group PLC

Windsor House, 50 Victoria Street, London, SW1H 0NR Tel: (0171) 222 7411

Walker, Hazel   *Group Company Lawyer.*
Reports to: Group Chief Executive. Lawyers in department: 1. Staff: 1. Percentage of work outsourced: 25% (property and litigation).
Deals with commercial, corporate, property and employment work, especially commercial contracts, acquisitions and disposals. Addresses and intercompany seminars and previously Cadmus lectures. Member of BACFI.
Career: Qualifed 1982. Practiced at Bar 1982-1985, Lawyer Mercury Communication Ltd, THORN EMI PLC, Wembley PLC. Joined Transport Development Group PLC 1994.

Travelex UK Plc

65 Kingsway, London, WC2B 6TD Tel: (071) 405 7200

Clayton, Darren   *Group company secretary.*
Reports to : Chief executive. Lawyers in Dept: 1 Staff: 1 Percent of work outsourced : 50% (acquisitions, joint ventures, major litigation, specialist tax matters, jurisdictional issues).
Specialisation: Deals with compliance, corporate work including contract matters, company secretarial matters, employment law often with an international aspect.
Prof. Membership: Employment Lawyers Assoc.
Career: Qualified 1990. With Titmuss Sainer & Webb until 1993, then joining Travellers Exchange Corporation plc.

TV3 Broadcasting Group Ltd

TV3 Broadcasting Centre, Horton Road, West Drayton: near Heathrow, Middx, UB7 8JD Tel: (01895) 433338

Warner, Annie *Head of Legal and Business Affairs.* Reports to: President. Lawyers in dept: 2. Staff: 3. Percentage of work outsourced: 10% (litigation, some employment, areas of specialist expertise eg software licensing agreements). Supervises drafting and negotiation of all programme contracts from production contracts to acquisition and presenter agreements. Advises on all legal and associated matters, problem solving, dispute resolution and policy formulation. Advises on compliance with ITC regulation of satellite broadcasts, negotiates music usage licensing and lobbies European Commission re broadcasting directive and proposed changes.
Career: Called to the Bar 1981. Pupil at *1 Paper Buildings* and *4 Gray's Inn Square 1981-85*. Assistant, *Woolf Seddon*, primarily concerned with music industry 1985-86, then Legal and Business Affairs Manager, Virgin Records Ltd 1986-88. Head of Business Affairs, Warner Chappell Music 1988, then joined TV3 Broadcasting Group in 1989.

Unisys Europe-Africa Ltd

Bakers Court, Bakers Road, Uxbridge, Middx, UB8 1RG Tel: (01895) 862108

Sonsino, Victor *General Counsel.* Reports to: President Europe-Africa Division. Lawyers in Dept: 13 percent
of work outsourced: 15% (litigation and property). Deals with commercial, intellectual property, company and employment work.
Career: Partner at *Maughan & Hall* 1972-74. Company Secretary/ Solicitor at Amoco 1974-78. Deputy Legal Director, Texas Instruments 1980-87. Has held present position since December 1987.

United Biscuits (Holdings) plc

Church Road, West Drayton, Middlesex, UB7 7PR Tel: (01895) 432100

Frew, A.D. *Group Company Secretary.*
Reports to: CEO. Lawyers in dept: 5. Staff: 26. Percentage of work outsourced: 50% (property, some M&A and employment, overseas work, specialist areas).
Provides full company secretarial service. Also responsible for legal advice, trade marks and corporate relations.
Career: Variety of legal and commercial positions with ICI Ltd 1970-87 and Company Secretary, ICI Chemicals & Polymers Ltd 1987-93.

United International Pictures

UIP House, 45 Beadon Road, Hammersmith, London, W6 0EG Tel: (0171) 636 1655

Reilly, Brian *Senior Vice President/ General Counsel.* Reports to: President/ CEO. Lawyers in dept: 5. Staff: 8. Work outsourced: litigation, property, competition law.
Head of legal department with responsibility for all legal aspects of the company's operations worldwide. Responsibilities include evaluating and improving intellectual property protection programs, negotiating and drafting international acquisition and sales agreements; and joint venture agreements; international antitrust/trade regulation matters; general commercial agreements including licensing, distribution and agency agreements; employment and pension law matters. Also trains and evaluates legal department staff and manages outside lawyers.
Career: Admitted to Bar of the State of New York

1980. Associate Attorney *Grant, Herrmann, Schwartz & Klinger*, New York 1980-84, then International Attorney for American Home Products Corporation, based in New York, 1984-88. International Counsel for Revlon International Corporation, London, 1988-91 and joined United International Pictures in February 1991.

University of Derby

Kedleston Road, Derby, DE22 1GB Tel: (01332) 622222

Gillis, Richard *Company Secretary.* Reports to: Vice-Chancellor. Lawyers in dept: 1. Staff: 1. Deals with company and commercial work. Also Clerk to the Council. Member of Licensing Executives Society. Secretary to the Justice Report on Perjury.
Career: Qualified 1975. Solicitor Greater London Council 1975-1977, advocate Archer & Wilcock, Nairobi 1977-1980, solicitor Shoosmiths & Harrison 1980-1981, assistant to secretary TI Group plc 1981-1985, secretary ABB Transportation Holdings Ltd (formerly British Rail Engineering Ltd) 1985-1995. Joined University of Derby as company secretary 1995.

Vaux Group Plc

The Brewery, Sunderland, SR1 3AN Tel: (0191) 567 6277

Hodgson, Mark Ian *Company solicitor.*
Reports to: Company secretary. Lawyers in Depart: 3. Staff: 5. Percentage of work outsourced: 10% (mostly brewery free trade secured lending). Deals with conveyancing work in large pub package purchases, hotel acquisitions, including joint venture and management agreements, nursing home acquisitions and developments including under building and lease agreements. Also deals with commercial, landlord and tenant, employment, debt collection and some building disputes.
Career: Qualified 1988. Assistant solicitor Watson Burton 1988-1989. Joined Vaux Group Plc as assistant Solicitor 1989.

Vendome Luxury Group plc

50 Jermyn Street, London, SW1Y 6DL Tel: (0171) 522 8333

Pye, James E.K. *Group Legal Adviser.* Reports to: Deputy Chairman. Lawyers in dept: 3. Staff: 10. Percentage of work outsourced: 40% (corporate and financial work).
Has policy formulation, negotiating and drafting responsibilities in the following business areas: corporate; commercial contracts; employment; litigation; and statutory and legislative compliance and lobbying. Work includes M&A, joint ventures, licensing, distribution and franchising contracts, agencies and consultancies, retail concessions and sponsorship arrangements featuring a number of prestige brands such as Alfred Dunhill, Karl Lagerfeld and Hackett. Director of 31 companies within the Group.
Career: Called to the Bar 1972. Trust Counsellor, N.M. Rothschild & Sons Ltd 1972-75. Company lawyer to The Rembrandt Group, South Africa, advising on IP rights and brand-name support 1975-77 and joined the Vendome Luxury Group in 1978, Group Legal Adviser since 1986.

Vodafone Group Services Ltd

The Courtyard, 2-4 London Road, Newbury, Berkshire, RG13 1JL Tel: (01635) 33251

Humphreys, Hugh *Senior Solicitor (Property).* Reports to: Group Secretary. Lawyers in dept: 4. Staff: 6. Percentage of work outsourced: 1% (some property litigation).

Deals with all conveyancing activities and property legal advice for Group, covering offices, engineering depots and warehouses, telephone switching centres, and extensive infrastructure network of radio base stations (over 2000). Negotiates numerous sharing licences to use other operators' sites and reciprocal arrangements. Also deals with planning and building agreements, development rights, planning appeals and enforcement and application of DTI procedures to compel landowners to provide sites. Author of articles on planning and local government matters and was part-time university lecturer on local government and town planning.
Career: Qualified 1966, articled with Bootle County Borough Council and progressed to Chief Assistant Solicitor (1969) and Assistant County Secretary, Merseyside (1974). Legal Director with Skelmersdale New Town Development Corporation 1976-85.

Wates Building Group Ltd

1260 London Road, Norbury, London, SW16 4EG Tel: (0181) 764 5000

Mackie, William G. *Group Solicitor and Secretary.* Reports to: Group Chief Executive. Lawyers in dept: 1. Staff: 3. Percentage of work outsourced: 70% (major litigation, land acquisition, estate conveyancing).
Principal areas of work involve providing legal services in connection with construction, property, employment and commercial matters. Also provides company secretarial services and advises on banking law, insurances, pensions and property portfolio management. Director of Wates Construction Ltd.
Career: Qualified 1977 while with *Lee Bolton & Lee*. Assistant solicitor, *Winckworth & Pemberton* 1978-79. With Civil Aviation Authority 1979-83; Broseley Estates Ltd 1983-86; then joined Wates Building Group Ltd.

Wellcome plc

Unicorn House, PO Box 129, 160 Euston Road, London, NW1 2BP Tel: (0171) 387 4477

Gledhill, Gissla *Company Secretary.* Reports to: Chief Executive. Lawyers in dept: 12. Staff: 70. Percentage of work outsourced: 20% (complex corporate or commercial, product litigation and intellectual property litigation).
Has management responsibility for commercial legal, intellectual property, regulatory control, insurance and company secretarial functions. Manages department providing an in-house legal service to Wellcome plc and its subsidiaries. The department manages a large portfolio of trade marks and patents worldwide and conducts litigation in conjunction with external lawyers in the relevant jurisdiction. Member of BACFI and British Institute of Management.
Career: Called to the Bar, Lincoln's Inn 1982. Company Secretary, Consolidated Gold Fields 1985-89; with Bass plc 1989-92 and then took up current position.

Whessoe plc

Brinkburn Road, Darlington, County Durham, DL3 6DS Tel: (01325) 381818

Copeland, Gary James *Group Company Secretary & Legal Counsel.* Reports to: Chief Executive. Lawyers in dept: 1. Staff: 3. Percentage of work outsourced: 50% (litigation, large scale corporate and other specialist work such as industrial tribunals).
Responsible for provision of in-house legal advice and company secretarial service to the plc. Also manages outside lawyers where required.
Career: Qualified 1983 while with *Simpson Curtis*, Leeds. Joined MTM plc 1986 becoming Deputy Group

Solicitor 1986, Group Solicitor 1989 and Assistant to the Chief Executive in 1993. Joined *Jacksons*, Middlesbrough 1993 and took up present position in 1994.

Whitbread plc

Brewery, Chiswell Street, London, EC1Y 4SD Tel: (0171) 606 4455

Hampson, Michael D. *Company secretary.* Reports to: Group chief executive. Lawyers in Dept: 4 Staff: 11 Percent of work outsourced: 80% (litigation, property, debt collection, licensing, environmental health and food safety issues.
Specialisation: Advises on company, commercial and competition law.
Career: Qualified 1979. Previously with Grand Metropolitan plc (1985-88). Joined Whitbread plc in 1988 and appointed company secretary in 1991.

William Baird plc

79 Mount Street, London, W1Y 5HT Tel: 0171-409 1785

Alsop, Patricia Mary *Company Secretary/ Group Legal Adviser.* Reports to: Chairman/ CEO. Lawyers in dept: 2. Staff: 2. Percentage of work outsourced: 50% (major corporate/ acquisitions/ disposals/ conveyancing).
Principal areas of work are acquisitions/ disposals; employment-related issues, Stock Exchange/ Companies Act compliance; pensions; and general commercial advice and corporate governance. Involved in active acquisition and disposal programme in recent years to divest of engineering businesses and focus on clothing activities in UK and abroad. Also deals with share option schemes (Executive and savings-related), trademarks and the organisation of corporate events (eg AGM, strategy meetings and management conference). Member of Law Society Commerce and Industry Group and on Pensions Committee of British Clothing Industry Association.
Career: Qualified 1981. Solicitor with *Middleton Potts & Co* 1981-84. Group Legal Adviser, Debenhams plc 1984-86 and joined William Baird plc in 1987.

William M. Mercer Ltd

Dexter House, 2 Royal Mint Court, London, EC3N 4NA Tel: (0171) 488 4949

Brooks, D.M.W. *Company Solicitor.* Reports to: Head of European HR. Lawyers in Dept: 5 Percent of work outsourced: 10%

Principal areas of work are share schemes, offshore trusts, executive pay and executive pensions. Member of the IBA and Institute of Directors. Regular conference speaker on employment issues, share schemes and other topics.

Wilson Bowden plc

Wilson Bowden House, 207 Leicester Road, Ibstock, Leicester, Leicestershire, LE67 6HP Tel: (01530) 260777

Townsend, N.J. *Group Legal Director.* Reports to: Chairman and Chief Executive. Lawyers in Dept: 2 percent of work outsourced: 95%.
Responsible for monitoring and supervision of all major contracts for land acquisition/ sale, troubleshooting, strategic land acquisition and the provision of external services for the group.
Career: Qualified in January 1970. Previously a Partner with *Gardiner & Millhouse* 1976-78, *Marron Townsend* 1978-80, *Nicolas Townsend & Co* 1980-87, *Staunton Townsend* 1987-89 and *Edge & Ellison* 1989-93.

Yamaichi International (Europe) Ltd

Finsbury Court, 111-117 Finsbury Pavement, London, EC2A 1EQ Tel: (0171) 330 8138

Finney, Mark *Executive Director/ head of legal depart.* Reports to: Chief Executive/ Deputy C.E. Lawyers in Depart: 5.
Career: Qualified 1983. Practising Barrister 1984-1986. Joined Yamaichi International (Europe) Ltd 1986 becoming head of legal group within Corporate Finance Department 1989, head of Legal Department 1994.

Yorkshire Building Society

Yorkshire House, Westgate, Bradford, BD1 2AU Tel: (01274) 740740

Faulkner, C. John *Chief Solicitor.* Reports to: General Manager. Lawyers in dept: 9. Staff: 25. Percentage of work outsourced: 33% to 50% (commercial conveyancing; Treasury matters; some civil litigation, particularly professional negligence); negligence and commercial recoveries.
Manages all aspects of provision of legal services to the group both within the department and by external lawyers. Principal areas of work are property and mortgage law, insurance (particularly mortgage indemnity), building society law, financial services law

and commercial matters such as mergers and corporate projects. Also responsible for litigation services and legal computer systems.
Career: Qualified 1977 while with *Booth & Co*, Leeds. Solicitor with *Hartley & Worstenholme* 1981-83 and with *Catteralls*, Wakefield 1983-85, Partner 1985-90. Joined Yorkshire Building Society in December 1990.

Yorkshire-Tyne Tees Television Holdings PLC

The Television Centre, Leeds, West Yorkshire, LS3 1JS Tel: (0113) 243 8283

Coyle, Ralph John *Legal Director/ Company Secretary.* Reports to: Chairman. Lawyers in Department: 3. Staff: 6. Percentage of work outsourced: 20% (litigation, conveyancing, some employment law).
Department provides a general legal and company secretarial service to all members of group, including pensions, intellectual property, corporate, commercial, insurance, general employee benefits and employment law. Also deals with property, house management and health and safety areas.
Career: Qualified 1976. legal adviser/ company secretary Fairey Company Limited 1975-1979, manager legal department Abbey Life Insurance Company 1979-1981, company secretary/ legal adviser Quaker Oats Limited 1981-1985. Joined Yorkshire-Tyne Tees Television Holdings PLC as company secretary/ legal director 1985.

Young & Rubicam Ltd

Greater London House, Hampstead Road, London, NW1 7QP Tel: (0171) 387 9366

Fulton, Kathryn *Chief UK counsel.* Reports to: Group Finance Director. Total number lawyers in Depart: 2. Staff: 4. Percentage of work outsourced: 30% (variety including detailed commercial property work, contract work and all litigation).
Deals with all legal decision making and implementing, including copy clearance issues, drafting client contracts, music and equity issues, employment matters and company secretarial duties.
Career: Qualified 1987. Practising Barrister 1987-1989, Legal Adviser ITV Association 1989-1992 becoming Head of Legal Affairs and Company Secretary 1992-1994. Joined *Young & Rubicam Ltd* 1994 as Chief Legal Counsel (UK).

INDEX TO PROFILES
OF LEADING SOLICITORS AND
HEADS OF LEGAL DEPARTMENTS

This index covers two sets of profiles:
leading solicitors' profiles in the Specialist Lists, and
profiles of Heads of Legal Departments.
The Heads of Legal Departments are
shown in italic.

Solicitors mentioned in more than one
Specialist List will have more than one page
number after their name.
The number in bold type is the one which
refers to their main profile.

INDEX TO PROFILES
LEADING SOLICITORS AND HEADS OF LEGAL DEPARTMENTS

Heads of Legal Departments are shown in italic. Page numbers in bold refer to the main profile entry.

Heads of Legal Departments are shown in italic. Page numbers in bold refer to the main profile entry.

Heads of Legal Departments are shown in italic. Page numbers in bold refer to the main profile entry.

Heads of Legal Departments are shown in italic. Page numbers in bold refer to the main profile entry.

Heads of Legal Departments are shown in italic. Page numbers in bold refer to the main profile entry.

Heads of Legal Departments are shown in italic. Page numbers in bold refer to the main profile entry.

Chambers & Partners'

CHAMBERS & PARTNERS'

DIRECTORY OF THE LEGAL PROFESSION

Solicitors' A–Z

AARON & PARTNERS

GROSVENOR COURT, FOREGATE ST, CHESTER, CH1 1HG
DX: 19990

TEL:	(01244) 315366
FAX:	(01244) 350660

Croesnewydd Hall, Wrexham Technology Park, Wrexham, Clwyd LL13 7YP.

Tel:	(01978) 262900
Fax:	(01978) 262808

THE FIRM: A high profile and highly-motivated commercial law practice with a progressive outlook. It is recognised as being one of the foremost commercial law firms and includes specialised areas of work such as environmental, insolvency, mineral extraction, planning, transport and waste disposal. Problem solvers.

PRINCIPAL AREAS OF WORK:

Commercial Services: All aspects of commercial activity, including acquisition and mergers, corporate finance, insolvency, intellectual property, partnership, contracts, employment and joint ventures.

Mineral Extraction & Environmental Law: Specialised advice on land-won and sea-dredged minerals, coal and aggregates, and also on all Environmental Law matters.

Planning and Local Government: Extensive experience in planning, including advocacy agreements, appeals, enforcement and all local government work.

Private Client: Tax planning (especially IHT), wills, domestic conveyancing and probate.

Transport & the International Carriage of Goods: HGV construction and use, licensing, tachograph offences, international freight forwarding and carriage of goods claims. Solicitors to UKWA and Secretary to HTA.

OTHER AREAS OF WORK: Litigation, employment, commercial property, debt collection, construction, and licensing.

OTHER OFFICES: Associate offices in London and France.

CONTACT PARTNER: Simon Carter	
Number of partners:	11
Assistant solicitors:	9
Other fee-earners:	6

AARON FREEDMANS Grosvenor Court, Foregate St, Chester, CH1 1HG **Tel:** (01244) 313071 **Fax:** (01244) 350660 **DX:** 19990 **Ptnrs:** 18 **Asst Solrs:** 13 **Other Fee-earners:** 7. Construction and engineering law and general commercial legal services. Offices also at Manchester, Wrexham and London. Associated offices: France, Switzerland, Portugal, Bahrain and Hong Kong.

ABBOTT KING & TROEN Holbrook House, 14 Great Queen Street, London, WC2B 5DG **Tel:** (0171) 430 1709 **Fax:** (0171) 831 4441 **DX:** 37957 **Ptnrs:** 7 **Asst Solrs:** 3 **Other Fee-earners:** 1. The firm, the first MNP (Multi-national partnership), provides litigation, property, financial, general commercial and EC-related services for corporate clients.

ABERDEIN CONSIDINE & CO 8 & 9 Bon-Accord Crescent, Aberdeen, Grampian, AB1 2DN **Tel:** (01224) 589589 **Fax:** (01224) 572575 **DX:** 46 Aberdeen **Ptnrs:** 20 **Asst Solrs:** 10 **Other Fee-earners:** 4. A leading North East firm with 11 branch offices. One of the largest property firms in Scotland also with strong criminal, matrimonial and civil law departments.

WORKLOAD			
Convey/real estate	40%	Civil court	20%
Criminal	20%	Commercial	15%

ABSON HALL 30 Greek Street, Stockport, Ches, SK3 8AD **Tel:** (0161) 480 1221 **Fax:** (0161) 480 4246 **DX:** 22603 **Ptnrs:** 11 **Asst Solrs:** 6 **Other Fee-earners:** 11. Best known for matrimonial, commercial property, commercial and personal injury litigation. The practice also includes planning, landlord and tenant, bankruptcy and criminal work.

WORKLOAD			
Litigation/incl injury	30%	Prop/insolvency/licensing	25%
Matrim/family/children	20%	Criminal defence	10%
Commercial litigation	10%	Commercial property	5%

ACTONS

2 KING ST, NOTTINGHAM, NOTTS, NG1 2AX
DX: 10001

TEL: (0115) 947 6635
FAX: (0115) 941 0106

THE FIRM: A well-established firm, Actons undertakes a full range of legal services, specialising in the needs of business and commercial organisations. The firm has particular expertise in insolvency law.

PRINCIPAL AREAS OF WORK:

Company/ Commercial: *(Contact Partner:* C.P. Billyeald). *Work includes:* mergers and acquisitions, corporate finance and security, business structures, partnership law, commercial agreements, EC law.

Commercial Property: *(Contact Partner:* A.J. Forster). *Work includes:* development, insolvency, specialist advice to the leisure industry, landlord and tenant.

Insolvency: *(Contact Partner:* R.F. Leman). *Work includes:* a specialised service for insolvency practitioners and insolvent companies and individuals (potential or actual), refinancing and restructuring, perfecting security and the protection of lender's rights.

Litigation: *(Contact Partner:* G. Gunstone). *Work includes:* general commercial disputes, professional negligence claims, property litigation, industrial tribunal claims.

Personal Injury: *Contact Partner:* P.J. Seymor). *Work includes:* plaintiff and defendant litigation including road traffic accidents, industrial accidents and public liability particularly on behalf of local authorities.

Corporate Crime: *(Contact Partner:* J.C. Britten). *Work includes:* corporate fraud.

Private Client: *(Contact Partner:* A.J. Forster).*Work includes:* residential conveyancing, wills, trusts and estates administration, personal financial and tax planning and family law.

LANGUAGES: French, German, Malay, Arabic.

CONTACT PARTNER: Mr C.P. Billyeald

Number of partners:	10
Assistant solicitors:	10
Other fee-earners:	11

WORKLOAD

Insolvency	25%
Personal injury	22%
Commercial litigation	20%
Company/ commercial	16%
Crime	7%
Residential conveyancing	4%

CONTACTS	
Commercial litigation	Giles Gunstone
Company/ commercial	P. Billyeald, A. Forster
Crime	John Britten
Employment	Giles Gunstone
Insolvency	R. Leman, N. Calthrop-Owen
Matrimonial	Diane Dobney
Personal injury	P. Seymour, Gary Chadwick
Residential conveyancing	Lynn Billyeald
Trusts and probate	Mandy Kelly

ADAM COCHRAN 6 Bon Accord Square, Aberdeen, Grampian, AB9 1XU **Tel:** (01224) 588913 **Fax:** (01224) 581149 **DX:** AB1 Aberdeen **Ptnrs:** 3 **Asst Solrs:** 2 . A family firm of solicitors specialising in all aspects of legal work including estate agency, house purchase, wills, trusts, executries, court work, commercial work and particularly agriculture.

ADAMS & REMERS

TRINITY HOUSE, SCHOOL HILL, LEWES, E. SUSSEX, BN7 2NN
DX: 3100 Lewes 1

TEL: (01273) 480616
FAX: (01273) 480618

THE FIRM: Adams & Remers is one of the UK's oldest firms and prides itself on providing a high quality service for institutional, corporate and private clients. The practice's principle office is an imposing building in the County Town of Lewes - a centre of excellence providing a high degree of expertise under one roof.

PRINCIPAL AREAS OF WORK:

General Description: *Work includes:* company/ commercial law with particular emphasis on banking and building society work and all aspects of general civil litigation. Commercial property work is undertaken for institutions, pension funds, health authorities, landed estates and trusts. Private client work includes estate planning, trusts, probate, investment management and taxation.

CONTACT PARTNER: Mr K.P. Ardagh

Number of partners:	7
Assistant solicitors:	5
Other fee-earners:	26

WORKLOAD	
Private client	50%
Commercial	50%

ADDLESHAW SONS & LATHAM

DENNIS HOUSE, MARSDEN ST, MANCHESTER, M2 1JD
DX: 14301

TEL: (0161) 832 5994
FAX: (0161) 832 2250

THE FIRM: Established in 1873, Addleshaw Sons & Latham is one of the largest and most forward-thinking regional firms and is a dedicated commercial law practice. Addleshaw Sons & Latham is a member of the Norton Rose M5 Group of independent legal practices.

PRINCIPAL AREAS OF WORK:

General Description: One of the best respected commercial practices outside the City, the firm serves corporate clients on both a regional and national basis, and has established EC and international expertise.

Company and Corporate Finance: (*Contact Partner:* Andrew Needham). Transactions handled by this, the largest department, include acquisitions and sales of companies, Stock Exchange listings, corporate finance, takeovers and mergers, and management buyouts.

EC, Competition and Commercial: (*Contact Partner:* Garth Lindrup). A highly specialised unit offering advice on all areas of competition law within the European Community, including joint ventures.

Intellectual Property: (*Contact Partner:* Robert Stoker). Advises on patents, copyrights, designs, trademarks and licensing. The department includes a Trade Mark Agent.

Property: (*Contact Partner:* Diana Craven). A wide range of commercial and residential property transactions, including planning and environmental matters.

Insolvency: (*Contact Partner:* Shân Spencer). Widely acknowledged as the leading insolvency practice in the North West, this department has six licensed insolvency practitioners dealing with corporate restructure and insolvency work.

Banking: (*Contact Partner:* Shaun Rearden). Advises lenders and borrowers on all aspects of banking and finance including syndicated lending, project finance, finance for MBO's, securitisation and consumer credit, the financing of higher and further education policies, housing associations and NHS Trusts.

Commercial and Corporate Litigation: (*Contact Partner:* John Gatenby). All aspects of business disputes dealt with speedily and efficiently, both at home and abroad, including general commercial, property and construction issues.

Employment and Benefits: (*Contact Partner:* Malcolm Pike - Employment. Francis Shackleton - Pensions). As well as providing a full range of services in relation to occupational pension schemes, all aspects of employment law are dealt with (including tax and incentive schemes).

Private Client: (*Contact Partner:* David Tully). Advises individuals and trustees on a wide range of legal matters.

Debt Recovery: (*Contact:* Karl Williams). Specialised debt recovery service dealing with extensive range of commercial and consumer debt.

CONTACT PARTNER: Paul Lee

Number of partners:	37
Assistant solicitors:	54
Other fee-earners:	14

WORKLOAD	
Company and corporate finance	28%
Property	23%
Insolvency/ banking	23%
Litigation	17%
Intellectual property	5%
Pensions/ private	4%

CONTACTS	
Banking	Shaun Rearden
Company/ corporate finance	Andrew Needham
Construction	Huw Baker
Corporate tax	Richard Hayes
Debt recovery	Karl Williams
EC/ competition	Garth Lindrup
Employment	Malcolm Pike
Environmental/ planning	Michael Kenworthy
Insolvency	Shân Spencer
Intellectual property	Robert Stoker
Litigation/ arbitration	John Gatenby
Pensions	Francis Shackleton
Private client	David Tully
Property	Diana Craven

ADIE EVANS & WARNER Pearl Assurance House, 4 Temple Row, Birmingham, W. Midlands, B2 5HW **Tel:** (0121) 236 2680 **Fax:** (0121) 236 8499 **DX:** 13079 **Ptnrs:** 2 **Asst Solrs:** 1 **Other Fee-earners:** 2. The practice is evenly divided between family/ matrimonial and criminal law.

WORKLOAD			
Criminal Law	55%	Family Law	45%

AITKEN NAIRN WS 7 Abercromby Place, Edinburgh, EH3 6LA **Tel:** (0131) 556 6644 **Fax:** (0131) 556 6509 **DX:** 18 Edinburgh **Ptnrs:** 7 **Asst Solrs:** 3 **Other Fee-earners:** 2. Broadly based practice. Work includes pursuer and defender personal injury, commercial property, family law and debt collection. Specialisation in barony law.

WORKLOAD			
Litigation	36%	Private client	32%
Residential property	26%	Commercial property	6%

ALAN J. BAILLIE 96 Commercial Street, Dundee, Tayside, DD1 2AJ **Tel:** (01382) 202444 **Fax:** (01382) 202208. A general practice offering specialist advice on housing association law.

ALAN T. JENKINS & CO 36a King St, Carmarthen, Dyfed, SA31 1BS **Tel:** (01267) 235019 **Fax:** (01267) 236690 **DX:** 51405 Carmarthen **Ptnrs:** 1 **Asst Solrs:** 1 **Other Fee-earners:** 1. A small mixed practice concentrating on criminal work, some commercial work, town and country planning and associated matters.

ALASTAIR THOMSON & PARTNERS

DRAGON COURT, 27-29 MACKLIN STREET, LONDON, WC2B 5LX
DX: 37966 Kingsway

TEL: (0171) 405 4440
FAX: (0171) 405 4350

THE FIRM: Founded in 1947, the firm today is primarily a commercial litigation practice with particular expertise in insurance law and insurance–related litigation.
PRINCIPAL AREAS OF WORK: Although best known for work on behalf of professional indemnity insurers, the firm also handles other types of marine and non-marine insurance and reinsurance matters. It also has particular experience in building disputes, and cases involving the international carriage of goods by road, sea and air.
NATURE OF CLIENTELE: Clients include insurers, insurance brokers, accountants, architects, engineers, surveyors, housing developers and companies involved in manufacturing, transport, tourism and financial services.
FOREIGN CONNECTIONS: The firm has established connections with law firms in the USA, the Far East and Europe, and has a network of agents in Scotland, Northern Ireland, Eire, the Isle of Man and the Channel Islands.

CONTACT PARTNERS: Mr A. Simpson
Mr D. Hartfield

Number of partners:	10
Assistant solicitors:	8
Other fee-earners:	5

WORKLOAD	
Professional indemnity insurance	85%
Building disputes & other non-ins. litigation	10%
Other insurance work (eg goods in transit)	5%

ALEXANDER HARRIS

GORDON COURT, MERSEY ROAD, SALE, CHES, M33 6FX
DX: 19265 Sale 1

TEL: (0161) 969 6779
FAX: (0161) 969 6709

THE FIRM: Established 1989, deals exclusively with plaintiff medical negligence, personal injury, pharmaceutical product liability, disaster work, and related issues.
Lead firm in Myodil litigation, Opren; member of Hillsborough, Shiley Heart Valve, Measles Vaccine, North Staffordshire Radiotherapy, and Birmingham Royal Orthopaedic Cancer Mis-diagnosis steering committees. Special interests include brain damage, anaesthetics, obstetrics and gynaecology, head injury, vaccine damage and radiation damage. Close links with USA.

CONTACT PARTNER: Miss Ann Alexander

Number of partners:	5
Assistant solicitors:	9
Other fee-earners:	6

WORKLOAD	
Plaintiff medical negligence	60%
Pharmaceutical product liability, medical devices and disasters	25%
Plaintiff personal injury	15%

ALEXANDERS EASTON KINCH 203 Temple Chambers, Temple Avenue, London, EC4Y 0DB **Tel:** (0171) 353 6221 **Fax:** (0171) 583 0662 **DX:** 264 **Ptnrs:** 9 **Asst Solrs:** 2 **Other Fee-earners:** 2. Handles tax planning, private client, probate and wills, litigation, conveyancing, agricultural, and some commercial work.

WORKLOAD			
Private client	45%	Litigation	40%
Property	10%	Commercial	5%

ALEXANDER STONE & CO 4 West Regent Street, Glasgow, G2 1RW **Tel:** (0141) 332 8611 **Fax:** (0141) 332 5482 **Ptnrs:** 7 **Asst Solrs:** 2. Broad based practice with emphasis on commercial work. Well-known for commercial property expertise.

ALEX MORISON & CO WS Erskine House, 68 Queen Street, Edinburgh, EH2 4NN **Tel:** (0131) 226 6541 **Fax:** (0131) 226 3156 **DX:** 38 Edinburgh **Ptnrs:** 17 **Asst Solrs:** 10 **Other Fee-earners:** 14. Founded in 1850 the practice has four main departments: commercial and corporate; building and construction; litigation; private client and residential.

WORKLOAD			
Private client	40%	Company/comm/comm prop	30%
Litigation	20%	Construction/ building	10%

ALFRED SEVIER & SONS

8-9 ST MARY'S GATE, DERBY, DERBYS, DE1 3JF
DX: 11506 Derby 1

TEL: (01332) 347611
FAX: (01332) 291364

THE FIRM: The practice was founded by Alfred Sevier over 50 years ago and specialises in personal injury litigation of all types including industrial accidents, road accidents, medical negligence and industrial diseases. There is also a non-contentious department.

CONTACT PARTNER: Mr R.J.R. Sevier

Number of partners:	4
Other fee-earners:	4

ALISTAIR MELDRUM & CO 8-9 Genotin Terrace, Enfield, Middx, EN1 2AF **Tel:** (0181) 367 0064 **Fax:** (0181) 366 8578 **DX:** 90609 Enfield **Ptnrs:** 2 **Asst Solrs:** 1 **Other Fee-earners:** 3. Criminal practice, handling minor to major matters including drug importation, 24 hour police station attendance, legal aid work undertaken.

WORKLOAD			
Criminal law	80%	Family law	20%

ALLAN HENDERSON BEECHAM & PEACOCK 7 Collingwood Street, Newcastle-upon-Tyne, Tyne & Wear, NE1 1JE **Tel:** (0191) 232 3048 **Fax:** (0191) 261 7255 **DX:** 61014 Newcastle **Ptnrs:** 3 **Asst Solrs:** 10 . A general practice dealing in most fields of law. A member of the Assocation of Personal Injury Lawyers.

WORKLOAD			
Personal injury	60%	Family	10%
Crime	10%	Conveyancing	10%

ALLAN JANES 21-23 Easton Street, High Wycombe, Bucks, HP11 1NU **Tel:** (01494) 521301 **Fax:** (01494) 442315 **DX:** 4402 High Wycombe **Ptnrs:** 9 **Asst Solrs:** 5 **Other Fee-earners:** 6. Six departments specialising in company/commercial law, civil litigation, private client, criminal, residential conveyancing and family law.

WORKLOAD			
Commercial/private lit	26%	Commercial prop/company	23%
Crime	16%	Matrimonial/ family	14%
Private client	11%	Residential property	10%

ALLAN McDOUGALL & CO SSC 3 Coates Crescent, Edinburgh, EH3 7AL **Tel:** (0131) 225 2121 **Fax:** (0131) 225 8659 **DX:** 32 Edinburgh **Ptnrs:** 8 **Asst Solrs:** 7 **Other Fee-earners:** 7. The firm has a long history in civil litigation, particularly pursuers personal injury, medical negligence and matrimonial law.

WORKLOAD			
Litigation	62%	Private client	28%
Commercial property	8%	Corporate	2%

ALLEN & FRASER 78 Dean St, London, W1V 6BE **Tel:** (0171) 437 4001 **Fax:** (0171) 439 0650. **DX:** 44714 Soho Square **Ptnrs:** 3 **Asst Solrs:** 1 **Other Fee-earners:** 2. Known for its licensing law expertise and for its conveyancing and litigation departments. One partner is Clerk to the Board of the Green Cloth.

WORKLOAD			
Liquor & entertainment	75%	Domestic/comm convey	15%
Other private client	10%		

ALLEN & OVERY

ONE NEW CHANGE, LONDON, EC4M 9QQ
DX: 73

TEL: (0171) 330 3000
FAX: (0171) 330 9999

THE FIRM: As one of the United Kingdom's leading international law firms, Allen & Overy is a vigorous and forward-looking organisation. It has over 130 partners and more than 1,300 staff working in 15 major business centres on three continents, serving clients wherever there is a need for first class business advice on complex transactions or disputes. Internationally, Allen & Overy has a strategic alliance with two leading continental firms, Gide Loyrette Nouel in France, and Loeff Claeys Verbeke in the Benelux countries.

PRINCIPAL AREAS OF PRACTICE:

Corporate: the firm provides a comprehensive service covering all aspects of company and commercial law including public takeovers, mergers and acquisitons, disposals, Stock Exchange flotations, international equity offerings, joint ventures and strategic alliances, corporate restructuring and management buyouts. Specialist practice groups also deal with privatisations, building societies, energy law, environmental law, insurance, media & communications, financial services, construction, EC & competition, intellectual property and information technology.

Banking: the firm advises financial institutions and borrowers on all types of financing transactions in the UK and overseas including acquisition finance, project finance, trade finance, restructurings including debt for equity swaps and all forms of structured finance, asset finance (including aviation and shipping), securitisations, risk reduction techniques and derivatives and all forms of international finance.

International Capital Markets: the firm adivses in relation to capital markets transactions by issuers from all over the world (including developing countries as well as those with developed economics). These include eurobond issues, euro-equity offerings, equity linked issues, securitisations and derivatives.

Litigation: the firm's litigation and dispute resolution practice deals with all forms of commercial dispute including aviation, banking and finance, commercial fraud and crime, construction, defamation, DTI enquiries, employment, environmental law, EC & competition, information technology, intellectual property, product liability, professional negligence, property, shipping and trade sanctions.

Private Client: the firm's large practice provides comprehensive advice to wealthy individuals, entrepreneurs and senior directors, trustees, families, museums, universities and charities worldwide.

Property: the firm provides a full commercial property service to landowners, institutions, property companies, developers, contractors, investors and banks on areas including building contracts, commercial leases and underlettings, development agreements, housing association law, joint ventures, planning procedures and appeals, redevelopments, short and long term funding and site acquisition.

Taxation: the firm provides a comprehensive corporate tax service including advice on employee benefits and share schemes, and VAT and other indirect taxation.

OVERSEAS OFFICES: Beijing, Brussels, Budapest, Dubai, Frankfurt, Hong Kong, Madrid, Moscow, New York, Paris, Prague, Singapore, Tokyo, and Warsaw.

FOREIGN LANGUAGES: Bulgarian, Cantonese, Czech, Dutch, French, German, Hebrew, Hungarian, Italian, Japanese, Malay, Mandarin, Polish, Portuguese, Punjabi, Russian, Slovak, Spanish, Swahili and Swedish.

SENIOR PARTNER: Bill Tudor John
MANAGING PARTNER: John Rink

UK:	
Number of partners:	136
Assistant solicitors:	342
Other fee-earners:	176
INTERNATIONAL:	
Number of Partners:	26
Assistant Solicitors:	70
Other fee-earners:	36

CONTACTS

Banking	David Morley
Building societies	Peter Holland
Commercial property	Adam Cleal
Communications	Michael Scargill
Construction	John Scriven
Corporate - general	Guy Beringer
Corporate - taxation	Patrick Mears
Derivative products	Jeff Golden
EC and competition law	Mark Friend
Employment, pens. & empl. ben.	Derek Sloan
Energy	Roger Davies
Environmental	Owen Lomas
Financial services	Paul Phillips
Housing associations	David Morley
Information technology	Ian Ferguson
Insurance	Ian Stanley
Intellectual property	Colleen Keck
International capital markets	Richard Sykes
Litigation/emerg. procedures	Robert Hunter
MBO's	Alan Paul
Media & entertainment	Richard Cranfield
Mergers/acquisitions/takeovers	Alan Paul
Pharmaceutical & med. prods.	Robert Strivens
Private clients	Richard Turnor
Privatisation	Peter Holland
Projects & project finance	Graham Vinter
Securitisation	David Krischer

CD-ROM EDITION ON THE INTERNET

This edition of the directory is available on a CD-ROM which includes both DOS and Windows versions. It can be loaded onto a network, and works with virtually any IBM compatible PC. The CD-ROM version offers computer-users the advantage of rapid search, retrieval and cross-referencing. It is also available via the Internet.

ALLISON & HUMPHREYS

EAST INDIA HOUSE, 109-117 MIDDLESEX STREET, LONDON, E1 7JF
DX: 870 City EC3

TEL: (0171) 570 6000
FAX: (0171) 570 6060

THE FIRM: Established in 1967, the firm is a varied commercial practice with areas of specialisation in the commercial field.

PRINCIPAL AREAS OF WORK:

Company/ Commercial/ Corporate Finance: *(Contact Partner:* Charles Humphreys). This growing department provides a comprehensive service in the customary areas, including advice on tax and financial aspects of transactions, to a wide variety of clients, of which a number are engaged in the computer industry. Small company start-ups, employee trusts and share ownership schemes are a particular area of specialisation.

Entertainment/ Telecommunications: *(Contact Partner:* Tony Ballard). This department covers the sphere of entertainment law, both contentious and non-contentious, on an international scale, dealing in particular with copyright law, film and television including cable and satellite broadcasting. Clients range from film and television producers in the UK and abroad to distributors, US studios and a major UK broadcaster.

Litigation: *(Contact Partner:* Stephen Gibbs). The largest department in the firm, and a rapidly expanding area of practice backing up the other departments in the firm and with recent experience in handling substantial commercial disputes in professional negligence, reinsurance and banking.

Property: *(Contact Partner:* Moira Gilmour). The firm undertakes primarily commercial property work.

Private Client: *(Contact Partner:* Michael Croft Baker). The firm advises on probate, wills, trusts and tax planning. It also specialises in immigration work.

Pensions: *(Contact Partner:* Ronald Thom). Work undertaken includes preparation of scheme documents, reorganisations and winding-ups, and pensions aspects of takeovers and mergers.

RECRUITMENT AND TRAINING: The firm aims to take on five trainees annually.

CONTACT PARTNER: Ann Hunt

Number of partners:	14
Assistant solicitors:	16
Other fee-earners:	20

WORKLOAD

Litigation	51%
Company/ commercial	19%
Telecommunications and entertainment	15%
Private client	7%
Pensions	5%
Conveyancing	3%

CONTACTS

Company/ commercial	Charles Humphreys
Entertainment	Tony Ballard
Litigation	Stephen Gibbs
Pensions	Ron Thom
Private client	Michael Croft Baker
Telecommunications	Ted Mercer

ALLISON & HUMPHREYS

ALSOP WILKINSON

6 DOWGATE HILL, LONDON, EC4R 2SS
DX: 799

TEL: (0171) 248 4141
FAX: (0171) 623 8286

India Buildings, Liverpool L2 0NH
DX: 14103

Tel: (0151) 227 3060
Fax: (0151) 236 9208

11 St. James's Square, Manchester M2 6DR
DX: 14329

Tel: (0161) 834 7760
Fax: (0161) 831 7515

THE FIRM: Alsop Wilkinson is now one of the largest firms in the country tracing its history back to 1821 with a major presence in London, Liverpool and Manchester. The firm also has a substantial international client base, served by offices in Hong Kong, New York and Brussels.

PRINCIPAL AREAS OF WORK:

Banking: *(Contact Partners:* Mark Vickers (London), Michael Prince and David Maples (Manchester/Liverpool)). The firm's banking lawyers have expertise in corporate lending (including management buy-outs), property finance, asset finance and leasing, recoveries, enforcement and restructurings, loan portfolio transfers, securitisations, standard form documentation, strategic issues affecting banks and other debt providers and regulatory matters.

CHAIRMAN: Roger Lane-Smith

UK:	
Number of partners:	69
Assistant solicitors:	91
Other fee-earners:	45
INTERNATIONAL:	
Number of Partners:	4
Assistant Solicitors:	15
Other fee-earners:	5

Commercial Litigation and Arbitration: *(Contact Partners:* Paul Gordon-Saker (London), Jim Pinsent (Liverpool), Nigel Kissack (Manchester)). Corporate and personal clients are represented in a broad range of commercial disputes including claims in relation to the sale of goods, actions for negligence and breach of contract, and all aspects of company and shareholder disputes.

Commercial Property: *(Contact Partners:* Richard Parker (London), Roy Beckett (Manchester), Philip Rooney (Liverpool)). The firm has a considerable reputation for its commercial property work and acts for many well-known institutional investors and developers, as well as public sector bodies and substantial public and private companies. Service is provided on all aspects of property transactions including acquisition, development, financing, management and ultimate disposal.

Commodities: *(Contact Partner:* Mark Landale (London)). The firm has substantial experience in legal and commercial aspects of trading in commodity and financial futures and other derivative products.

Construction: *(Contact Partners:* Stephen Haller (London), Jim Pinsent (Liverpool/Manchester)). Work includes dispute resolution (litigation, arbitration and ADR), advice on the production of contractual claims, methods of procurement, contract drafting, appointments for professionals, collateral warranties and performance bonds. The firm also advises on BOT/DBFO schemes, including Public Finance Initiative projects, both in the UK and overseas.

Corporate and Commercial: *(Contact Partners:* Peter Wayte (London) Michael Prince and Tim Hamilton (Manchester/Liverpool)). The firm is particularly well-known for its work in connection with development capital and acts for a number of institutional providers of equity and debt finance in this area as well as management teams.

Other work includes company formations, new issues including Stock Exchange flotations and rights issues, mergers, acquisitions and management buy-outs as well as group reorganisations and re-financing.

Corporate Fraud and Investigations: *(Contact Partners:* Paul Thomas (London), Andrew Harris (Manchester/ Liverpool)). The firm advises on court injunctions, privilege against self-incrimination and sanctions against directors, as well as the means by which monies may be traced into the hands of other parties.

Corporate Taxation: *(Contact Partners:* Hazel Ryan, Nicholas Sanderson (London)). Experience spans the whole range of UK corporate taxation including capital allowances, stamp duty and value added tax. Advice is given on the domestic and international tax aspects of transactions, in particular corporate activities such as mergers, acquisitions, demergers, management buy-outs and buy-ins, financings and tax driven structures.

Employee Benefits: *(Contact Partners:* Derek Morris (Liverpool), Hazel Ryan (London)). The firm advises on various forms of employee incentive schemes for both public and private companies such as share option schemes, phantom bonus schemes, employee share ownership plans, and other employee benefit schemes.

Employment: *(Contact Partners:* Gordon Day (London), David Jacks (Liverpool), Mary Clarke (Manchester)). Positive and practical advice covering all employment-related issues including employment contracts, policies and procedures, business transfers and termination and its consequences.

Environment and Planning: *(Contact Partners:* Tony Leek (London), Andrew Dawson (Manchester/ Liverpool)). Advice is given on the proliferation of environmental and planning-related legislation. The firm's specialists have particular expertise in dealing with issues arising from problematic planning applications, hazardous substances, contaminated land, air and water pollution, waste disposal and health and safety at work.

Immigration: *(Contact Partner:* Mark Landale (London)). The firm has a specialist immigration unit able to give advice on all aspects of United Kingdom immigration law and to obtain visas for both corporate and private clients.

Insolvency: *(Contact Partners:* Michael Stubbs (London), Peter Manning (Manchester/ Liverpool)). The firm advises on liquidations, receiverships, administrations, bankruptcy and voluntary arrangements.

Insurance and Reinsurance: *(Contact Partners:* Steven Blair (New York/London), Neil Ellis (London), Martin Hill (Manchester, Liverpool and London)). The firm's team has substantial experience in the national and international insurance and reinsurance markets. Advice is given to individuals, corporate clients and Lloyd's

WORKLOAD	
Commercial litigation/ insolvency	32%
Corporate, banking and employment	32%
Commercial property/ environmental	18%
Reinsurance/ shipping	9%
Private client	5%
Intellectual property	4%

CONTACTS	
Arbitration	Janet Legrand
Banking	Mark Vickers
Commercial litigation	Paul Gordon-Saker
Commercial property	Richard Parker
Commodities	Mark Landale
Construction	Stephen Haller
Corporate and commercial	Peter Wayte
Corporate fraud, investigation	Paul Thomas
Corporate taxation	Hazel Ryan
Employee benefits	Gordon Day
Employment	Gordon Day
Environment and planning	Tony Leek
Immigration	Mark Landale
Insolvency	Paul Gordon-Saker
Insurance and reinsurance	Steven Blair
IP and computer law	George Godar
Marine	Hugh Dalzell
Pensions	Jonathan Fenton
Private client	Andrew Young

agencies on dispute resolution, litigation, arbitration, policy wording, enforcement of contracts, agency matters, investigations, applications for Lloyd's approval of insurance brokers, Lloyd's members and managing agents' documentation and syndicate outwards reinsurance.

Intellectual Property and Computer Law: *(Contact Partners:* George Godar (London), Nigel Kissack (Manchester), Keith Lewin (Liverpool)). The intellectual property team covers all litigation matters relating to patent, trademark and copyright infringement, passing off claims and all computer related disputes. On the non-contentious side we negotiate and draft commercial licences and agreements involving patents, trademarks, copyright, designs, know-how, publishing ventures, franchising, technology transfer and computer hardware and software as well as advising on all aspects of competition law and restrictive trade practices.

Marine: *(Contact Partners:* Hugh Dalzell (London), Stewart Crowther (Hong Kong), David Mawdsley (Liverpool)). The firm is involved in all legal aspects of the shipping industry, both contentious and non-contentious. Investigations, litigation and arbitration are undertaken relating to collisions, salvage, pollution and offshore energy disputes, insurance, P&I, carriage of goods and passengers by land, sea and air, charterparty and bill of lading disputes, shipbuilding, sale/purchase and repair and claims for personal injuries.

Pensions: *(Contact Partners:* Derek Morris (Liverpool), Jonathan Fenton (London)). Service includes document drafting, advising on changes in legislation and revenue practice, advising trustees on their duties and obligations and employers on their rights and powers, advising members on their entitlements and dealing with the negotiation of contractual pension provisions on corporate transactions, particularly management buy-outs.

Private Client: *(Contact Partners:* Andrew Young (London), Michael Pinfold (Liverpool/ Manchester)). Areas covered include tax and financial planning, the establishment of UK and offshore settlements, and advice on trust law, capital taxation, succession law, charities, immigration, wills and estates and heritage.

OTHER OFFICES: Hong Kong, New York, Brussels.

FOREIGN LANGUAGES: French, Italian, Spanish, German, Russian, Japanese, Mandarin, Cantonese, Hindi, Urdu.

AMERY–PARKES

LAW COURTS CHAMBERS, 33 CHANCERY LANE, LONDON, WC2A 1EN
DX: 162 Lon Chancery Lane WC2

TEL: (0171) 404 7100
FAX: (0171) 404 6588

THE FIRM: Founded in 1892 the firm now has offices in four major centres. Whilst principally known for its personal injury and accident litigation work, the firm also has a large private client practice in all locations, and in London a significant company/ commercial department.

OTHER OFFICES: Basingstoke: *8 Partners. Contact:* S. Slough
Birmingham: *6 Partners. Contact:* D. J. Knowles
Bristol: *2 Partners. Contact:* J. Crocker.

FOREIGN CONNECTIONS: In London the firm has French and Spanish speakers and international work is undertaken. The firm has associated offices in Paris and Dublin.

AGENCY WORK: Agency work is handled in all offices.

CONTACT PARTNER: Mr W. Davis

Number of partners:	24
Assistant solicitors:	9
Other fee-earners:	41

WORKLOAD

Accident claims - recovery/ personal injury	65%
Conveyancing, commercial and domestic	20%
Common law and general litigation	10%
Corporate	5%

FIRMS OF ACCOUNTANTS

Accountants specialising in litigation support are listed in the accountants' A-Z, with details of the services they offer to solicitors, from forensic accounting to intellectual property or business valuations.

AMHURST BROWN COLOMBOTTI

2 DUKE STREET, ST. JAMES'S, LONDON, SW1Y 6BJ
DX: 412

TEL: (0171) 930 2366
FAX: (0171) 930 2250

THE FIRM: Amhurst Brown Colombotti is a medium sized commercial practice with considerable international experience. Clients receive a great deal of personal attention from partners who combine practical business experience with legal skills. Their expertise covers company formations and flotations, cross-border transactions, financial services, taxation, commercial and residential property transactions, trust and private client work, commercial litigation, matrimonial and immigration.

INTERNATIONAL CONNECTIONS: The firm has offices in Italy, Spain, Pakistan and Poland and associates in the United States of America, Russia, India, Denmark and Brazil.

FOREIGN LANGUAGES: French, Italian, Spanish, German, Polish, Russian and Urdu.

CONTACT PARTNER: Paul Amandini

Number of partners:	20
Assistant solicitors:	12
Other fee-earners:	4

ANDERSON FYFE 90 St. Vincent Street, Glasgow, G2 5UB **Tel:** (0141) 248 4381 **Fax:** (0141) 204 1418 **DX:** GW138 **Ptnrs:** 5 **Asst Solrs:** 4 **Other Fee-earners:** 6. A long established private and commercial practice including insolvency and strong litigation and debt recovery departments.

WORKLOAD			
Litigation and recovery	29%	Corp/bus law/insolvency	26%
Private/trust/executry	23%	Comm/domestic convey	22%

ANDERSON STRATHERN WS

48 CASTLE STREET, EDINBURGH, EH2 3LX
DX: 3 Edinburgh

TEL: (0131) 220 2345
FAX: (0131) 226 7788

THE FIRM: Anderson Strathern is one of the largest legal firms in Scotland and traces its origins back over two centuries. A full range of services is provided to all business, institutional and private clients. There are partners in each of the Commercial Property, Litigation and Agricultural departments who are accredited by the Law Society of Scotland as specialist practitioners.

The firm is particularly strong in its property practice, both commercial and rural and has a growing reputation in the corporate field. The Litigation Department is highly regarded in employers' liability and health service law fields and has developed the first dedicated Liability Insurance Unit in Scotland.

The firm has traditionally been a leading practice in private client work and continues to be so and regards private client work as an important and valued area of its practice.

PRINCIPAL AREAS OF WORK:

Commercial Property: (*Contact Partners:* Alan Menzies, David Hunter). *Work includes:* purchase and sale, investment acquisition, leasing, property and development finance, securities, development, planning, building contracts, joint ventures, environmental law, energy/ oil and minerals.

Two partners are Law Society Accredited Specialists in commercial leasing law.

Company/ Commercial: (*Contact Partners:* John Kerr, John Stuart). *Work includes:* acquisitions and mergers, MBOs/ MBIs, development capital, capital raising, business start ups, insolvency, commercial contracts, advice to financial institutions, health contracting and arrangements, intellectual property, EU and competition law, sports law and local government.

Litigation: (*Contact Partners:* Robert Fife, Ruari MacNeill). *Work includes:* liability insurance litigation, medical and health related litigation, debt recoveries, professional liability, property disputes, arbitration, industrial relations and employment law, and commercial litigation.

Two partners are admitted as Solicitor Advocates, one partner is a Law Society Accredited Specialist in medical negligence.

JOINT SENIOR PARTNERS: John W. Blair & Nigel W. Buchanan

Number of partners:	26
Assistant solicitors:	30
Other fee-earners:	40

CONTACTS	
Agricultural/ rural/ sporting	Alasdair Fox
	Robin Stimpson
Commercial property	David Hunter
	Alan Menzies
Company/ commercial	John Kerr, John Stuart
Litigation	Robert Fife, Ruari MacNeill
Private client	John Blair, Robin Watt

Agricultural, Rural, Residential and Sporting Properties: (*Contact Partners:* Alisdair Fox, Robin Stimpson.) *Work includes:* purchase, sale, leasing of all agricultural, rural, residential and sporting properties, estate advice and management, farm partnerships, quotas, use and development of natural resources and forestry.

One partner is a Law Society Accredited Specialist in agricultural law.

Private Client: (*Contact Partners:* John Blair, Robin Watt.) *Work includes:* tax and financial planning, trusts including offshore, investment advice, insurance, wills, charities and heritage.

INTERNATIONAL CONNECTIONS: The firm is a founder member and sole Scottish representative of the Association of European Lawyers with contacts throughout Europe and is also the sole Scottish member of ALFA, one of the oldest and largest association of law firms in the USA.

FOREIGN LANGUAGES: French, German.

ANDERSON MACARTHUR & CO Old Bank of Scotland Buildings, South Beach St, Stornoway, Strathclyde, HS1 2BG **Tel:** (01851) 703356 **Fax:** (01851) 702766 **Ptnrs:** 4 **Asst Solrs:** 1 **Other Fee-earners:** 2. Established early this century the firm has 4 partners operating 3 offices in Stornoway and Portree on the Isle of Skye. Deal with general work and specialise in crofting.

ANDREW M. JACKSON & CO

ESSEX HOUSE, MANOR STREET, HULL, HUMBS, HU1 1XH
DX: 11920

TEL: (01482) 325242
FAX: (01482) 212974

THE FIRM: Established in 1874, Andrew M. Jackson & Co has developed a thriving practice with an excellent reputation for providing an extensive range of specialised legal services to clients throughout the UK and overseas. Widely renowned for its expertise in such areas as fishing and shipping law, the firm has a commercial bias, but also a busy private client portfolio. Its individual departments are supplemented by specialist units in such areas as employment and transport law.

PRINCIPAL AREAS OF WORK:

Company/ Commercial: (*Contact Partner:* Martin Whitehead). *Work includes:* company formations and reconstructions, sales and purchases of share capital and assets, MBOs, corporate finance, insolvency, franchising, agency distribution, intellectual property, equipment leasing and computer software.

Shipping: (*Contact Partner:* Silas Taylor). The department deals with all aspects of maritime law acting for vessel owners, insurers and P&I Clubs on collisions, salvage, pilotage, towage, shipbuilding and ship repair disputes, debt recovery by ship arrest and marine personal injury cases. A large volume of dry case work includes haulage and CMR cases. The firm also acts for fish farmers and was heavily involved in actions following a recent oil spillage disaster. The firm was a founder member of the Fishing Industry Lawyers Group.

Commercial Property: (*Contact Partner:* Ian Davis). The department is broken down into specialist units handling development schemes, retail acquisitions and disposals, property investments, agricultural property and general property work.

Litigation: (*Contact Partner:* David Dunk). The department handles both commercial and general litigation. *Work includes:* construction disputes, landlord and tenant, consumer law, corporate libel, winding-up proceedings, passing-off actions and personal injury. In addition, the department also handles a variety of criminal matters.

Private Client: (*Contact Partner:* Kevin Webster). A busy department handles wills, tax and trusts, residential conveyancing and family and matrimonial matters such as divorce and separation, childcare and financial provision.

OTHER OFFICES: Associated Office: Stanley, Falkland Islands.

CONTACT PARTNER: John Hammersley

Number of partners:	20
Assistant solicitors:	24
Other fee-earners:	15

WORKLOAD	
Commercial property	34%
Litigation	20%
Shipping	15%
Company	11%
Private client	10%
Family	10%

CONTACTS	
Admiralty & shipping	Silas Taylor
Commercial property	Ian Davis
Company/ commercial	Martin Whitehead
Conveyancing	Nick Tyrer
Employment	David Dunk
Family	Andrew Haines
Litigation	David Dunk
Tax & trust	Kevin Webster
Transport	Dominic Ward

ANDREW BRYCE & CO 7 Queen St, Coggleshall, Colchester, Essex, CO6 1UF **Tel:** (01376) 563123 **Fax:** (01376) 563336 **Ptnrs:** 1. Experienced in all aspects of environmental law including waste management, water law, contaminated land, pollution control, planning and environmental assessment, environmental management and due diligence, with related health and safety lobbying and training services.

WORKLOAD	
Environmental law	100%

ANN L. HUMPHREY 279 Camberwell New Road, London, SE5 0TF **Tel:** (0171) 701 3939 **Fax:** (0171) 708 1543 **Ptnrs:** 1. A newly established niche practice with substantial experience in tax planning, particularly VAT.

WORKLOAD			
VAT	60%	Corporate tax	40%

ANNE HALL DICK & CO 60 Bank Street, Kilmarnock, Strathclyde, KA1 1ER **Tel:** (01563) 42797 **Fax:** **DX:** 5 Kilmarnock **Ptnrs:** 3 **Asst Solrs:** 1. Specialist family law practice which also undertakes domestic conveyancing.

WORKLOAD			
Court/ family	66%	Conveyancing & property	23%
Trust and executry	5%	General	5%
Commercial	1%		

ANSTEY SARGENT & PROBERT

4-6 BARNFIELD CRESCENT, EXETER, DEVON, EX1 1RF
DX: 8308

TEL: (01392) 411221
FAX: (01392) 218554

THE FIRM: One of the largest firms in the South West, it is highly regarded for its private client, litigation, matrimonial, property and commercial work. Specialist areas include insolvency, (with two partners qualified as licensed insolvency practitioners), and planning. Conveyancing, wills and litigation work are also carried out at 44 Cowick Street, Exeter. The firm is a member of QLG, a national group of independent law firms.

As part of its expansion programme the firm has opened a third office, located in Plymouth. This will enhance its regional coverage. The firm has also developed sophisticated computer software and systems to ensure quality, speed and efficiency for its clients and innovative credit control and debt collecting services.

CONTACT: Miss C.A. Knight	
Number of partners:	17
Assistant solicitors:	6
Other fee-earners:	14

ANTHONY BARTON 42 Gibson Square, London, N1 0RB **Tel:** (0171) 700 7348 **Fax:** (0171) 700 7379 **Ptnrs:** 1 **Other Fee-earners:** 2. A specialist medical legal practice that offers advice to health authorities, medical institutions, pharmaceutical companies, insurance companies and other law firms.

WORKLOAD	
Medical law	100%

ANTHONY COLLINS Pearl Assurance House, 4 Temple Row, Birmingham, W. Midlands, B2 5HG **Tel:** (0121) 200 3242 **Fax:** (0121) 200 2408 **DX:** 13055 **Ptnrs:** 8 **Asst Solrs:** 19 **Other Fee-earners:** 16. Established in 1973. A general practice ranging from commercial to charity work, and including licensing, housing and local authority matters. Legal aid work is undertaken.

WORKLOAD			
Housing/local government	17%	Commercial property	16%
Business law	13%	Civil litigation	11%
Family law	9%	Criminal litigation	9%

ANTHONY GOLD, LERMAN & MUIRHEAD The Hop Exchange, 24 Southwark Street, London, SE1 1TY **Tel:** (0171) 378 8005 **Fax:** (0171) 378 8025 **DX:** 39915 London Bridge South **Ptnrs:** 6 **Asst Solrs:** 11 **Other Fee-earners:** 10. Established 20 years ago with a substantial private client base. Best known for its litigation practice, with emphasis on property litigation, personal injury and matrimonial work. On Law Society specialist P.I. Panel.

WORKLOAD			
Family	25%	Property litigation	15%
Personal injury	12%	Commercial litigation	10%
Conveyancing/property	10%	Corporate/ commercial	10%

APPLEBY HOPE & MATTHEWS

35 HIGH STREET, NORMANBY, MIDDLESBROUGH, CLEV, TS6 0LE
DX: 60040

TEL: (01642) 440444
FAX: (01642) 440342

THE FIRM: Established originally at Redcar in 1955, Appleby Hope & Matthews is a broadly-based general practice, which undertakes a large volume of legal aid work.

PRINCIPAL AREAS OF WORK: The firm handles a wide variety of legal matters, including company/ commercial work, family and matrimonial law problems, commercial and residential conveyancing, crime, licensing, private client work, child care, personal injury and employment. It has a specialist debt collecting department.

NATURE OF CLIENTELE: Local enterprises, private individuals, and large national companies.

AGENCY WORK: Undertaken in all Middlesbrough courts and for Local Authorities in Middlesbrough and Langbaurgh-on-Tees.

CONTACT PARTNERS:
Mr. A.C.W. Hart/Mr. N. Turvey

Number of partners:	4
Assistant solicitors:	3
Other fee-earners:	2

ARCHERS Barton House, 24 Yarm Road, Stockton-on-Tees, Clev, TS18 3NB **Tel:** (01642) 673431 **Fax:** (01642) 613602 **DX:** 60603 **Ptnrs:** 8 **Asst Solrs:** 6 **Other Fee-earners:** 8. Established 1890 with substantial expertise in company/ commercial and commercial property. Strong litigation department especially personal injury and matrimonial. Established private client department.

WORKLOAD			
Business client	30%	Personal injury	29%
General litigation	9%	Matrimonial	9%
Private client	7%	Domestic conveyancing	6%

ARCHIBALD CAMPBELL & HARLEY WS 37 Queen Street, Edinburgh, EH2 1JX **Tel:** (0131) 220 3000 **Fax:** (0131) 220 2288 **DX:** 181 Edinburgh **Ptnrs:** 18 **Asst Solrs:** 8 **Other Fee-earners:** 8. An established Edinburgh practice best known for its high quality commercial property work. Also experienced in planning law.

WORKLOAD			
Commercial property	43%	Private clients	31%
Litigation	12%	Corporate/ commercial	9%
Planning/ environmental	5%		

ARGLES & COURT

12 MILL STREET, MAIDSTONE, KENT, ME15 6XU
DX: 51965 Maidstone 2

TEL: (01622) 656500
FAX: (01622) 656690

THE FIRM: Argles & Court is one of the principal firms in the South East. With three offices in Kent, a staff of more than 120 and advanced office technology, it has the resources to handle a comprehensive range of legal services. The firm has a strong litigation base and an extensive commercial practice with experienced teams handling commercial property and planning work, commercial litigation and insurance litigation. The firm also has many years experience in acting for private individuals, and personal injury claims form a large part of the practice. Argles & Court is registered with BS5750/ ISO 9001 and is a founder member of Quality Law Group, a national group of law firms all committed to acquiring BS5750/ ISO 9001 accreditation. The firm is a member of the Solicitors Financial Services scheme.

PRINCIPAL AREAS OF WORK:

Commercial Litigation: (*Contact:* Timothy Bignell). Work includes all types of commercial disputes and debt collection.

Insurance Litigation: (*Contact:* Michael Cutler). A large volume of insurance work is handled and also personal injury and professional negligence claims.

Matrimonial Department: (*Contact:* Michael Rowlands). Work includes divorce, separation and child care issues.

Environmental: (*Contact:* Andrew Pawlik). This expanding department handles an increasing volume of work, predominantly litigation relating to landfill sites, environmental health and food safety.

Commercial Property: (*Contact Partner:* Corrie King or Marcel Bradbury). The firm has an extensive property practice, covering the acquisition and disposal of all types of commercial property, development sites, options, building contracts, secured lending and planning matters.

CONTACT PARTNER: Mr R.C. Harris

Number of partners:	16
Assistant solicitors:	3
Other fee-earners:	22

WORKLOAD	
Commercial litigation	46%
Private client	29%
Company/commercial	25%

CONTACTS	
Commercial litigation	Timothy Bignell
Commercial conveyancing	Corrie King
Company/ commercial	Simon Davies
Employment	Jonathan Simmons
Environmental	Andrew Pawlik
Insurance litigation	Michael Cutler
Licensing	Stephen Thomas
Planning	Lynn Gladwell
Private client	Colin Trelfer

Company/ Commercial: (*Contact:* Simon Davies or Raymond Harris). Work includes franchising, corporate taxation, insolvency matters and international business law, company formations, reconstructions, takeovers and partnership advice.

Probate: (*Contact:* John Catterick). A complete service covering wills, trusts, probate, tax and financial planning and investments for elderly clients.

Residential Conveyancing: (*Contact:* Colin Trelfer). This department offers a highly efficient conveyancing service at a competitive price to both individual and institutional clients.

Construction: (*Contact:* Jonathan Simmons). Work includes negotiating and advising on construction contracts and drafting terms of engagement, disputes and all aspects of construction law.

Advocacy: (*Contact:* Stephen Thomas). The department has a team of solicitors with advocacy skills, in particular in licensing, road traffic, child care and criminal matters.

Employment: (*Contact:* Jonathan Simmons). The department deals with all aspects of employment law, including employment particulars and contracts, employee rights and tribunal work.

General Litigation: (*Contact:* Andrew Pawlik). This department handles plaintiff personal injury claims, trade descriptions, medical negligence claims, landlord and tenant litigation and consumer disputes.

OTHER OFFICES: Larkfield, Walderslade.

ARMITAGE SYKES HALL NORTON

72 NEW NORTH RD, HUDDERSFIELD, W. YORKS, HD1 5NW
DX: 711270 Huddersfield 9

TEL: (01484) 538121
FAX: (01484) 518968

THE FIRM: Armitage Sykes Hall Norton is a merger of two of the oldest firms in Huddersfield. The practice offers a range of specialist legal services to both commercial and private clients. Legal aid work is undertaken.

PRINCIPAL AREAS OF WORK:

Company & Commercial: The firm acts for a wide variety of businesses, from sole traders to large companies, and offers advice on matters such as the formation of limited liability companies; the preparation and negotiation of shareholder agreements, joint venture agreements and partnership agreements, company re-constructions, acquisitions and mergers; management buy-outs and buy-ins; EC law; liquidation and receivership; employment contracts; directors' duties and responsibilities; boardroom disputes; intellectual property; preparation and advice on sale and purchase of goods contracts and terms and conditions of trade.

Commercial Property: The department offers a broad range of advice, including: negotiation and preparation of commercial leases; sales and purchases of investment properties; environmental law; planning matters, applications and appeals; property disputes and agricultural holdings.

Litigation: A broad range of litigation is handled by the practice, including: breach of contract; actions for breach of intellectual property rights; disputes in relation to sale of goods contracts and supply of services contracts; landlord and tenant disputes; confidentiality and competition disputes; actions related to breach of trust; insolvency matters; debt collection; employment disputes; divorce and matrimonial disputes; family and child care; matrimonial injunctions; mediation; personal injury claims and medical negligence; criminal defence work and claims to the Criminal Injuries Compensation Board.

Private Client: A comprehensive service is offered to the private client, covering matters such as residential conveyancing; the preparation of wills; administration of estates; inheritance tax; powers of attorney; creation of trusts; tax planning; marriage settlements; offshore trusts and investment advice.

CONTACT PARTNER: Neville Sheard

Number of partners:	8
Assistant solicitors:	7
Other fee-earners:	9

WORKLOAD	
Company/ commercial	45%
Litigation	35%
Private client	20%

CONTACTS	
Banking	Philip Brewer
Civil litigation	Paul Richmond
Commercial property	Alan Crabtree
Company	Robert Turner
Employment	Carol Cook
Matrimonial	Sue Colven
Wills/ trusts	Ashley Iredale

ARNOLD SEGAL

NO. 1 LYTTON COURT, 14 BARTER STREET, LONDON, WC1A 2AH
DX: E-Mail: CIS:10014,535

TEL: (0171) 242 8122
FAX: (0171) 242 1224

THE FIRM: Founded in 1986, Arnold Segal occupies a unique position as a sole practitioner in the fields of computer and information technology law.

NATURE OF CLIENTELE: The firm acts for a wide range of companies and partnerships, both suppliers and users, UK and foreign, in all aspects of computer and related commercial and company law.

FOREIGN CONNECTIONS: The firm has a number of informal but established links with foreign legal practices, particularly in the USA.

ASSOCIATIONS: The firm is now consultant to, and associated with, Rosenblatt.

CONTACT PARTNER: Mr Arnold Segal
Number of partners: 1

WORKLOAD

Computer and information technology	95%
Company/ commercial	5%

ARNOLD THOMSON 205 Watling Street West, Towcester, Northants, NN12 7DA **Tel:** (01327) 350266 **Fax:** (01327) 353567 **DX:** 16932 **Ptnrs:** 2 **Asst Solrs:** 3 . A niche agriculture firm, formed in 1990 to serve the increasingly complex needs of the farming and landowning community.

WORKLOAD

Sale/purch/development	35%	Trusts/ tax and probate	20%
Civil litigation	15%	Agricultural tenancies	15%
Quotas	10%	Partnerships	5%

ASHTON MORTON SLACK 35-47 North Church Street, Sheffield, S. Yorks, S1 2DH **Tel:** (0114) 275 2888 **Fax:** (0114) 270 0029/273 0108 **DX:** 10530 **Ptnrs:** 11 **Asst Solrs:** 5 **Other Fee-earners:** 11. A general practice best known for its commercial, accident claims and domestic conveyancing practice. Caters for a full range of clients including legally-aided individuals.

ASHURST MORRIS CRISP

BROADWALK HOUSE, 5 APPOLD ST, LONDON, EC2A 2HA
DX: 639

TEL: (0171) 638 1111
FAX: (0171) 972 7990

THE FIRM: Established in 1821, Ashursts is a leading commercial law practice based in the City of London. It is an international firm with offices in Brussels, Delhi, Paris and Tokyo as well as connections with major overseas law firms.

PRINCIPAL AREAS OF WORK: The firm comprises five main departments and a number of cross-departmental groups.

Company and Commercial: (*Contact:* Geoffrey Green). Company and commercial law constitutes the greater part of the firm's practice. The department advises on corporate finance, in particular mergers and acquisitions (the firm has been involved in some of Britain's most celebrated bid battles), flotations, leveraged and management buy-outs, corporate restructuring, joint ventures, commercial agreements, privatisations and competition work.

Property and Planning: (*Contact:* Laurence Rutman). The department advises on the acquisition, financing, letting and sale of properties, including town centre developments, major office schemes, industrial and warehouse estates, shopping centres, housing developments and all forms of land assembly; the property aspects of corporate flotations, bids and mergers, secured loans and all aspects of property development and investment, including planning law.

Litigation: (*Contact:* Edward Sparrow). This department advises on contractual disputes, product liability, property, construction and engineering disputes, judicial review, professional negligence, defamation and trade libel, arbitration, proceedings under the Company Acts and employment law. With extensive contacts among law firms overseas, the firm can supervise and conduct foreign litigation, particularly in the United States.

Tax: (*Contact:* Stephen Machin). The tax department's work mirrors the range of activities of other parts of the firm, including advice at the planning stages of major corporate, property or commercial deals, especially in relation to mergers and

SENIOR PARTNER: Andrew Soundy
UK:

Number of partners:	65
Assistant solicitors:	158
Other fee-earners:	57
INTERNATIONAL:	
Number of partners:	5
Assistant solicitors:	8
Foreign qualified lawyers	5
Other fee-earners:	2

WORKLOAD

Company	45%
Property	25%
Litigation	15%
Banking	10%
Tax	5%

acquisitions work, capital reconstructions, management and employee buy-outs. Pensions and employee benefits work form a significant aspect of the department's work, as do VAT and Stamp Duty.

Banking: (*Contact:* Stephen Mostyn-Williams). The firm's banking department advises lenders and borrowers, and advises in the fields of corporate debt, bond issues, acquisitions, project finance, hedging and derivative instruments, forfeiting, securitisations, asset-based finance, management buy-outs and trade and commodity finance.

Ashursts also has a number of specialist groups whose members, derived from the main departments, are specialists in such areas as environmental law (Trevor Adam), intellectual property (Ian Starr), employment and employee benefits (Paul Randall), insurance (Jeremy Hill), construction (Chris Vigrass), energy and major projects (Ian Johnson), information technology (Patrick Karney), competition (Roger Finbow), pensions (Graham Williams), planning (Michael Cunliffe), insolvency (David Kershaw), and media & communications (Stewart White).

OTHER OFFICES: The firm has offices in Brussels, at Avenue Louise 65, 1050 Brussels, Belgium. *Tel:* (32-2) 537 6895 *Fax:* (32-2) 537 4353; in Delhi, at 6 Aurangzeb Road D-202, New Delhi, 110 011 India. *Tel:* (91 11) 301 4054 *Fax:* (91 11) 301 4089; in Paris, at 8 Rue Clément Marot, 75008 Paris, France. *Tel:* (33-1) 4720 0088 *Fax:* (33-1) 4720 0093; and in Tokyo, at Kioicho Building, 8th Floor, 3-12 Kioicho, Chiyoda-ku, Tokyo 102, Japan. *Tel:* (81-3) 5276 5900 *Fax:* (81-3) 5276 5922.

Ashursts is the UK member of Le Club, an international association of major corporate law firms in Europe and the United States, and through this association and other international connections, can offer legal services throughout the world.

FOREIGN LANGUAGES: French, German, Greek, Italian, Japanese, Polish, Russian, Spanish, Malay, Chinese and Turkish.

NATURE OF CLIENTELE: Ashursts currently ranks third among UK law firms for the number of Stock Market clients. The firm's clients operate in areas as diverse as advertising and insurance, brewing and banking, steel and stockbroking.

RECRUITMENT AND TRAINING: As Ashursts grows, each department has vacancies for qualified fee-earners of a high calibre; enquiries to Sally James. The firm intends to recruit approximately 25 trainee solicitors for entry in September 1997. Candidates should have high academic ability, a capacity for hard work, a gregarious personality and a sense of humour. Apply by handwritten letter, with CV and names of referees, to Roger Finbow, preferably by the 31 August 1995.

The firm offers an extensive in-house training programme for trainee solicitors and qualified staff at all levels, comprising lectures and seminars, skills training sessions, language training and time management.

CONTACTS	
Banking/ international finance	
	Stephen Mostyn-Williams
Company/ commercial	Geoffrey Green
Competition law	Roger Finbow
Construction	Christopher Vigrass
EC	Julian Ellison
Employment and pensions	Paul Randall
Energy & major projects	Ian Johnson
Environmental law	Trevor Adams
Environment/ product liability	John Evans
Insolvency and reconstruction	David Kershaw
Insurance	Jeremy Hill
Intellectual property	Ian Starr
Litigation	Edward Sparrow
Management buy-outs	Charlie Geffen
Media and communication	Stewart White
Planning	Michael Cunliffe
Property	Laurence Rutman
Tax	Stephen Machin

ASKEWS

4-6 WEST TERRACE, REDCAR, CLEV, TS10 3BX
DX: 60020

TEL: (01642) 475252
FAX: (01642) 482793

THE FIRM: A general practice established in Cleveland for over 60 years, Askews retains the traditional values of a family practice, whilst using the latest technology and information to provide its mixed clientele with a wide range of legal services. Legal Aid work is undertaken.

PRINCIPAL AREAS OF WORK: The firm is best known for its conveyancing, probate, personal injury litigation, crime, childcare and matrimonial work. Other major areas of work include: landlord and tenant advice, consumer problems, and general commercial matters (including employment law).

OTHER OFFICES: Guisborough and Middlesbrough.

CONTACT PARTNER: Mr D.F. Askew

Number of partners:	12
Assistant solicitors:	7
Other fee-earners:	5

WORKLOAD	
Litigation	30%
Family law	29%
Property and probate	26%
Criminal law	14%
Business law	1%

ATTEY BOWER & JONES 82 Cleveland Street, Doncaster, S. Yorks, DN1 3DR **Tel:** (01302) 340400 **Fax:** (01302) 323710 **DX:** 12558 **Ptnrs:** 16 **Asst Solrs:** 4 **Other Fee-earners:** 35. One of the largest firms in Yorkshire with offices in Doncaster, Mexborough, Rotherham and Thorne. Has a general commercial and family practice.

BABINGTON & CROASDAILE 9 Limavady Road, Waterside, Londonderry, Co. L'derry, BT47 1JV **Tel:** (01504) 49531 **Fax:** (01504) 45785 **Ptnrs:** 5 **Asst Solrs:** 3 **Other Fee-earners:** 2. Personal injury and private client work are particular strengths of this firm. Other work includes commercial property, landlord & tenant, debt collection and crime.

J.A. BACKHOUSE & SONS 23 Wellington St (St. John's), Blackburn, Lancs, BB1 8DE **Tel:** (01254) 677311 **Fax: Ptnrs:** 3 **Other Fee-earners:** 1. A niche practice with expertise in law relating to the transport industry, both HGV and coach/ passenger travel.

WORKLOAD			
Transport bus/coach/haul	50%	Transport licensing	25%
Contract disputes/CMR	10%	Personal injury lit	10%
Emp/health/safety lit	5%		

BAILEYS SHAW & GILLETT

17 QUEEN SQUARE, LONDON, WC1N 3RH
DX: 35704 Bloomsbury

TEL: (0171) 837 5455
FAX: (0171) 837 0071

THE FIRM: Baileys Shaw & Gillett, established in 1798, is broadly structured in four practice areas: litigation, commercial, property and private client/tax; in addition, there is a number of specialist groups dealing with particular areas of the law (see 'Contacts' panel).

The firm adopts a team approach when acting for its clients, with the lead partner assembling a group of lawyers with the requisite skills and experience tailored to individual needs.

NATURE OF CLIENTELE: Bailey Shaw & Gillett's clients include fully listed and other quoted companies, a wide range of private companies, institutions, charities and professional firms, as well as trusts, families and individuals. Amongst the firm's commercial clients is a growing number of UK-based companies operating overseas and foreign companies operating in this country.

FOREIGN CONNECTIONS: Baileys Shaw & Gillett is the UK member of Legalliance EEIG, a grouping of European law firms currently also represented in Belgium, Denmark, France, Germany, The Netherlands, Italy and Spain, with an associate member in Sweden.

In May 1994 Baileys Shaw & Gillett opened an office in Abu Dhabi, from where the firm is well placed to advise companies operating in the UAE and the Gulf States.

Through these formal associations and its well-established connections with other firms and professional contacts worldwide, Baileys Shaw & Gillett is able to offer its clients a comprehensive international service.

RECRUITMENT AND TRAINING: *Trainee Solicitor Recruitment Partner:* Jane Henry. *Assistant Solicitor Recruitment Partner:* Varies according to area of specialisation. The firm operates an induction course for trainees, and there is a structured training programme for all fee-earners.

SENIOR PARTNER: Peter Foster

Number of partners:	23
Assistant solicitors:	16
Other fee-earners:	17

WORKLOAD	
Property	35%
Litigation	33%
Commercial	24%
Private client	8%

CONTACTS	
Commercial	Aubrey Roberts
Construction	Howard Russell
EC/ competition	Laurence Kingswood
Employment	Lesley Smith
Environment	Harbans Chohan
Family	Alan Marco
Immigration	Elspeth Guild
IP/ technology	Don Turner
Litigation	Stephen Dobson
Personal Injury	Kate Teasdale
Private client/ tax	Christopher Lintott
Property	John Gaymer
Property litigation	Jeremy Hudson

BAIRD & CO 2 Park Place, Kirkcaldy, Fife, KY1 1XL **Tel:** (01592) 268608 **Fax:** (01592) 203369 **DX:** 9 Kirkcaldy **Ptnrs:** 11 **Asst Solrs:** 4 **Other Fee-earners:** 2. A general practice handling a wide range of work including family, crime, personal injury and property.

BAKER & McKENZIE

100 NEW BRIDGE STREET, LONDON, EC4V 6JA
DX: 233

TEL: (0171) 919 1000
FAX: (0171) 919 1999

Baker & McKenzie is the world's largest law firm. The London office is a leading City firm with a strong domestic and foreign client base. It provides a full range of business and financial legal services to corporations, financial institutions, governments and entrepreneurs.

THE FIRM: Baker & McKenzie was founded in 1949. The firm has grown by anticipating trade and capital flows around the world. Today Baker & McKenzie has some 50 offices in over 30 jurisdictions. Its strategy is to provide for its clients the best combination of local legal and commercial knowledge and international expertise and resources. The firm is sensitive to the need to provide not only legal excellence but also a user friendly service which is efficient, transparent and value for money. To this end the firm implements a variety of client care and quality management programmes.

Baker & McKenzie is uniquely well placed to blend advice on the law and practice of a number of jurisdictions to help the client achieve its objectives: our lawyers work in national, European and international practice groups in their areas of expertise and receive intensive formal training in English law and practice and foreign work opportunities.

PRINCIPAL AREAS OF WORK: There is considerable expertise in international and domestic banking and finance, cross-border corporate and commercial transactions, privately financed projects, disputes, European Union and competition law, environmental law, intellectual property (particularly computer law), international tax and trust planning, the structuring of multi-national groups, employment law, employee benefits and pension matters, construction and engineering law, pharmaceutical law, commercial property and the legal aspects of lobbying.

Baker & McKenzie aims, above all, to provide commercially orientated advice of the highest quality which adds value to the client's business. The firm looks at the best method of service delivery in each case.

The London office offers "hot line" arrangements and secondments of its lawyers to major clients. As an integral part of its service, the firm offers to its clients regular seminars and workshops, newsletters and bulletins on legal developments, magazines and publications. The firm also offers access to its training and library services and to a number of commercial and legal databases, rapid communication through modem links and electronic mail services to clients.

Enquiries for training contracts should be directed to Joanna Darby. Enquiries from other applicants should be directed to Gary Senior.

OTHER OFFICES: Almaty, Amsterdam, Bangkok, Barcelona, Beijing, Berlin, Bogota, Brasilia, Brussels, Budapest, Buenos Aires, Cairo, Caracas, Chicago, Dallas, Frankfurt, Geneva, Hanoi, Ho Chi Minh City, Hong Kong, Juarez, Kiev, Madrid, Manila, Melbourne, Mexico City, Miami, Milan, Monterrey, Moscow, New York, Palo Alto, Paris, Prague, Rio de Janeiro, Riyadh, Rome, St Petersburg, San Diego, San Francisco, Sao Paulo, Santiago, Singapore, Stockholm, Sydney, Taipei, Tijuana, Tokyo, Toronto, Valencia, Warsaw, Washington DC, Zurich.

CONTACT PARTNER: Nigel Carrington

UK:	
Number of partners:	48
Assistant solicitors:	73
Other fee-earners:	44
INTERNATIONAL:	
Number of Partners:	517
Assistant Solicitors:	1214
Other fee-earners:	687

WORKLOAD	
Corporate/ finance/ EC/ tax/ commercial	47%
Litigation/ construction	23%
Employment/ pensions/ immigration	13%
Intellectual property	10%
Commercial property	7%

CONTACTS	
Central & eastern Europe	Peter Strivens
Commercial	Michael Herington
Commercial property	Michael Smith
Construction	Jeremy Winter
Corporate	Gabriel Fisher
EC, competition and trade	Lynda Martin Alegi
Employee benefits	Michael Ingle
Employment	Fraser Younson
Environment	Tom Handler
Finance	Schuyler Henderson
Immigration	Michael Ingle
Information technology	Harry Small
Insolvency	Nick Pearson
Intellectual property	Don Jerrard
Litigation, ADR, arbitration	David Fraser
Major projects	Tim Steadman
Pensions	Robert West
Securities	Tim Gee/Michael Caro
Swaps and derivatives	Schuyler Henderson
Tax	James macLachlan
Venture Capital	Christopher Bown

BALDOCKS

ST MARY'S HOUSE, 59 QUARRY ST, GUILDFORD, SURREY, GU1 3UD
DX: 2409 Guildford 1

TEL: (01483) 573303
FAX: (01483) 300337

THE FIRM: Established in 1945 Baldocks has expanded from its base as a family firm to provide a comprehensive service to both business and private clients. With a reputation for private client work specialising in wills, trusts, matrimonial, property and civil litigation, the firm has developed its corporate side under its business law unit combined with a strong commercial litigation department.

CONTACT PARTNER: William Smythe

Number of partners:	8
Assistant solicitors:	4
Other fee-earners:	6

PRINCIPAL AREAS OF WORK:
  Company/ Commercial: (*Contact:* William Smythe).
  Commercial Property: (*Contact:* Paul Critchley).
  Residential Conveyancing: (*Contact:* Jack Marriott).
  Commercial Litigation: (*Contact:* Duncan Elson).
  Matrimonial and Child Care: (*Contact:* Richard Middlehurst).
  Tax and Private Client: (*Contact:* David Baldock).
OTHER OFFICES AT: The main office is at Guildford with a further office at Cranleigh.

BALDOCKS
SOLICITORS

BALFOUR & MANSON 58 Frederick Street, Edinburgh, EH2 1LS **Tel:** (0131) 225 8291 **Fax:** (0131) 459 2525 **DX:** 4 Edinburgh **Ptnrs:** 18 **Asst Solrs:** 13 **Other Fee-earners:** 17. A large practice handling a wide range of work for both commercial and private clients. Particularly known for litigation.

WORKLOAD			
Litigation	50%	Private Client	30%
Comm/Commercial prop	20%		

BAND HATTON AND COMPANY

1 COPTHALL HSE, STATION SQUARE, COVENTRY, W. MIDLANDS, CV1 2FY
DX: 11207

TEL: (01203) 632121
FAX: (01203) 229038

THE FIRM: A long-established practice, founded in 1896, Band Hatton offers a high quality legal service to both business and private clients, utilising up-to-date technology and working methods, while maintaining traditional values and a committment to a personal and approachable service. The firm enjoys a strong reputation in the commercial field, in particular for its commercial property work. The litigation practice is expanding rapidly in the areas of commercial, employment and matrimonial law. Band Hatton is a member of LawNet, the Federation of Independent Law Firms, and LawNet Europe, and adheres to the LawNet Quality Management Standard.

CONTACT PARTNER: Mr Philip Costigan

Number of partners:	4
Assistant solicitors:	4
Other fee-earners:	10

BANKES ASHTON

81 GUILDHALL STREET, BURY ST. EDMUNDS, SUFFOLK, IP33 1PZ
DX: 57200

TEL: (01284) 762331
FAX: (01284) 764214

THE FIRM: Based in Bury St. Edmunds since its foundation in 1894, Bankes Ashton is now one of East Anglia's larger firms. With strong roots in the agricultural community, the firm is increasingly commercially orientated and is developing a strong company/ commercial and commercial property practice.

PRINCIPAL AREAS OF WORK:
Agriculture: (*Contact Partner:* Jonathan Long). *Work includes:* agricultural holdings, contract farming, employment, environment and planning, gravel and waste, footpaths, insolvency, setaside, tax planning and freehold conveyancing.
Company/ Commercial: (*Contact Partner:* David Barnes). *Work includes:* company takeovers and reconstructions, USM (AIM) work, financing, partnership, tax, insolvency, agency and distributership agreements, franchising, employment, competition law, pensions, intellectual property, freehold, leasehold and planning law (one fee-earner has LMRTPI qualification).
Litigation: (*Contact Partner:* Mark Merriam). A full commercial and private client service is offered, including arbitrations, industrial tribunals, matrimonial, licensing and computerised debt collection, with a strong personal injury practice.
Private Client: (*Contact Partner:* David Hughes). *Work includes:* estate planning, tax, investment, wills, probate, conveyancing (both in the UK and overseas), mental health and family matters.
Investment Management: (*Contact Partner:* David Hughes). A full investment management service (advisory, discretionary and execution only) including PEP management.

CONTACT PARTNER: David Wybar

Number of partners:	13
Assistant solicitors:	3
Other fee-earners:	10

WORKLOAD	
Commercial (inc commercial property)	32%
Tax planning/ wills/ probate	24%
Commercial litigation	14%
Private client litigation	13%
Agricultural	10%
Residential property	7%

CONTACTS	
Agricultural	Jonathan Long
Commercial conveyancing	Richard Storey
Commercial	David Barnes
	Michael Wood
Computerised debt collection	Diane Wood

OTHER AREAS OF WORK: The firm also handles disaster claims, consumer law, professional negligence and environmental law.

FOREIGN CONNECTIONS: Bankes Ashton is experienced in dealing with European lawyers and EC law. The firm has strong connections with France, Germany and Spain and has French and German-speaking commercial lawyers.

Investment management	Michael FitzRoy
Matrimonial	Tony Niblock
Personal injury	Mark Merriam
Residential conveyancing	Richard Ballam
Tax planning/ wills/ probate	David Hughes

BARCAN WOODWARD 31 North Street, Bedminster, Bristol, BS3 1EN **Tel:** (0117) 9635237 **Fax:** (0117) 9668582 **DX:** 98975 Bedminster (Bristol) **Ptnrs:** 4 **Asst Solrs:** 4 **Other Fee-earners:** 3. Best known for its plaintiff medical negligence, personal injury and family work but also undertakes a range of non-contentious matters including conveyancing and probate.

WORKLOAD			
Conveyancing/ probate	33%	Matrimonial/ child care	33%
Personal injury/med neg	33%		

BARKER, BOOTH & EASTWOOD 346 Lytham Rd, Blackpool, Lancs, FY4 1DW **Tel:** (01253) 348141 **Fax:** (01253) 41032 **DX:** 27651 **Ptnrs:** 7 **Asst Solrs:** 1 **Other Fee-earners:** 5. This partnership has a commercial practice with particular experience in acting for clients in the leisure industry.

WORKLOAD			
Commercial/res property	33%	Lit/crime/welf/pers inj	32%
Matrimonial	25%	Wills/probate/financial	8%

BARLOW LYDE & GILBERT

BEAUFORT HOUSE, 15 ST. BOTOLPH STREET, LONDON, EC3A 7NJ		TEL:	(0171) 247 2277
DX: 155		FAX:	(0171) 782 8500
Suite 893, Lime Street, London EC3M 7DQ		Tel:	(0171) 782 8051
		Fax:	(0171) 782 8053
4001, Gloucester Tower, The Landmark, Central, Hong Kong		Tel:	(00 852) 25264202
Contact Partner: Mr Christopher Sharrock		Fax:	(00 852) 28105994
		Telex:	(0802) 82205

THE FIRM: Barlow Lyde & Gilbert is closely linked with the insurance industry and continues to develop to meet the changing needs of clients in the insurance world. The firm is well-known for its litigation skills both in the insurance and broader commercial sectors.

PRINCIPAL AREAS OF WORK:

Insurance: (*Contact Partner:* Colin Croly). The firm's core insurance practice developed from a foundation of standard classes of business such as Public Liability, Employers' Liability, Personal Injury, Fire and All-Risks/ Business Interruption cver. A substantial Professional Indemnity practice includes acting for accountants, solicitors, stockbrokers, surveyors, architects, engineers and insurance brokers. Experience in professional indemnity work has extended into specialisation in Medical Negligence and Directors' and Officers' Liability Insurance. Barlow Lyde & Gilbert has one of the largest Reinsurance practices in Europe with over 30 specialist lawyers, and is regularly called upon to coordinate arbitration and litigation around the world. It assists with the interpretation or drafting of wordings, the conduct of inspections and the setting-up of run-offs. The Insurance Insolvency Group coordinates the consequences of insolvencies. The Employment Group and the Environmental Group draw together specialists throughout the firm to provide advice on all aspects of these areas of law.

Aviation: (*Contact Partner:* Ian Awford) Although the Aviation insurance practice is well known for its work in air disaster investigation and claims handling it is also a commercial practice handling aircraft acquisition and a wide range of other aerospace matters.

Commercial Litigation: (*Contact Partners:* Eddie Hathaway/ Richard Dedman). The firm's first objective is always to achieve a cost-effective outcome to resolve any dispute. Barlow Lyde & Gilbert's commercial litigation work includes Contractual Disputes, Consumer Law, Corporate Fraud, Defamation, Employment Law, Information Technology, Intellectual Property and Product Liability.

SENIOR PARTNER: Mr Ian D.P. Jenkins
CONTACT PARTNER: Mr Kennen Michel

UK:	
Number of partners:	58
Assistant solicitors:	79
Other fee-earners:	42
INTERNATIONAL:	
Number of partners:	3
Assistant solicitors:	6
Foreign qualified lawyers	4
Other fee-earners:	1

CONTACTS	
Aviation	Ian Awford
Commercial litigation	Eddie Hathaway
	Richard Dedman
Company/ commercial	Anthony Rose
Construction	Robert Oakes/ Richard Dedman
Insurance	Colin Croly
Personal injury	Graham Dickinson
Professional indemnity	David Massa
	David Arthur, Stuart Hall
Property	Malcolm Rogerson
Shipping	Ray Mead

Shipping: *(Contact Partner:* Ray Mead). A full service is provided to shipowners and charterers, P&I clubs, hull and machinery and cargo underwriters and brokers as well as to other organisations and individuals involved in all areas of Admiralty and marine litigation and international trade.

Construction: *(Contact Partners:* Robert Oakes/ Richard Dedman). The firm advises building owners, contractors and professionals on the full spectrum of construction law to both the building and civil engineering sectors of the industry. In contentious matters the firm is experienced in litigation and arbitration and is pro-active in dispute resolution. Further, it provides a full range of non-contentious advice including preparation of contracts, procurement methods and rules, professional appointments, collateral warranties and construction-related insolvency.

Company/ Commercial: *(Contact Partner:* Anthony Rose). The scope of company work covers mergers, acquisitions and disposals, assets sales and purchases including sales by receivers and liquidators, company reconstructions, hivedowns and reductions of capital, flotations, introductions and placings, joint venture agreements and shareholder arrangements, financing techniques including security documentation and use of insurance products. In commercial matters the firm advises on regulatory issues including European Directives; trading agreements embracing agency, distribution and sales agreements; intellectual property licensing and transfer and franchising; competition law, both of the UK and European Community; employment law matters.

Property: *(Contact Partners:* Malcolm Rogerson). The firm is active in all areas of commercial property law, providing clients with the full ambit of property services including such matters as site acquisition and disposal, property development, joint ventures and collateral warranties; property finance, secured lending for banks and institutional funding agreements; property-related insolvency work; town and country planning and environmental law; commercial leases and landlord and tenant advice; property aspects of corporate transactions.

Professional Indemnity: *(Contact Partners:* David Massa/David Arthur/Stuart Hall). Our professional indemnity practice has developed substantially over the past 23 years, with a significant increase in the number of professional, liability actions now being brought in the UK and overseas. As a result, we believe we have the largest professional indemnity practice in Britain, with 50 specialist professional indemnity solicitors in the firm.

Personal Injury: *(Contact Partner:* Graham Dickinson). For many years we have been market leaders in all aspects of insurance litigation. The firm has developed a well recognised expertise in handling a wide range of insurance liability claims and there is tremendous depth of knowledge in Employers Liability, Public Liability and Motor Claims. We investigate and fight cases throughout the UK and have a well established network of expert witness, doctors, Counsel and surveillance teams throughout the country.

OTHER SERVICES: The firm publishes regular journals on insurance, environmental law and employment law. The firm has its own seminar suite and conferences and seminars are arranged on topics of interest to clients. The firm has a 24 hour answering service and the nature of its practice involves disaster claims planning and management. Specialist law libraries are available.

FOREIGN CONNECTIONS: In addition to the established Hong Kong office, Barlow Lyde & Gilbert is supported by a global network of legal correspondents. At any given time the firm is likely to have work involving several foreign jurisdictions, particularly in Europe and North America.

BARLOWS 55-56 Quarry Street, Guildford, Surrey, GU1 3UE **Tel:** (01483) 62901 **Fax:** (01483) 573325 **DX:** 2407 **Ptnrs:** 11 **Asst Solrs:** 13 **Other Fee-earners:** 7. Established 1816. Experienced in commercial law, property, litigation, and wills and probate. Other offices in Godalming and Chertsey.

WORKLOAD			
Gen/commercial lit	28%	Prop (incl comm work)	27%
Probate, trusts and tax	25%	Family litigation	10%
General commercial	10%		

BARNETT ALEXANDER CHART

34-35 DEAN ST, LONDON, W1V 5AP
DX: 44716 Soho Sq.

TEL: (0171) 434 4011
FAX: (0171) 434 1269

THE FIRM: Barnett Alexander Chart is an expanding and progressive firm established over 60 years. The partners are young and dynamic, and have developed a strong company/ commercial and litigation practice. Particular emphasis is placed on specialist skills in niche areas.

MAIN CLIENTS INCLUDE: Companies in the banking and finance, leisure, retail, construction, computer and public sectors.

PRINCIPAL AREAS OF WORK:

Corporate and Financial: The firm is well known for its corporate finance work, in particular venture capital transaction, together with mergers, acquisitions and disposals of companies, management buyins, project finance, share issues and shareholders agreements.

Commercial: The firm have a lending public sector practice in externalisation and outsourcing, advising local authorities, government agencies and suppliers. The firm also advises on CCT, VCT and procurement issues.

Public sector: The firm has a leading public sector practice in externalisation and outsourcing, advising local authorities, government agencies and suppliers. The firm also advises on CCT, VCT and procurement issues.

Sports: The firm advises on all aspects of sports law, including sponsorship, marketing, management of events, representing individuals, agents and managers, TV and media, and all contracted matters.

Commercial property: The specialities of this department include hotel and retail development. Other work includes the acquisition and disposal of commercial property, the ownership and use of business premises including shops, offices, warehouses and factories, rent reviews, planning law, property taxation, environmental issues and the law for estate agency.

Commercial litigation: This department concentrates on work in four main areas:-corporate and financial, insurance, construction and debt and asset recovery. Particular specialisms have been developed in banking litigation, injunctive relief and high volume computerised debt recovery. Other work includes defamation, intellectual property, shareholder and partnership disputes and liquor and gaming licensing.

Employment: The firm is fast becoming one of the leading employment law advisers, dealing with all aspects both contentious and non-contentious. The firm's public sector work means extensive experience of Transfer of Undertakings, which together with all forms of discrimination claims, are the unit's specialities.

Immigration: The firm provides dedicated immigration advice particularly to corporations, including work permits and business applications, concentrating on the Americas and the Pacific basin.

OTHER OFFICES: Hammersmith: (*Contact:* Neil Shestopal); Paris (associate office).

LANGUAGES SPOKEN: French, German, Italian, Greek and Japanese.

RECRUITMENT AND TRAINING: *Contact:* Mrs. Hilary Adair.

SENIOR PARTNER: Edward Marston

Number of partners:	9
Assistant solicitors:	9
Other fee-earners:	6

CONTACTS	
Commercial	Harold Shupak
Commercial litigation	Peter Moody
Commercial property	John Chart
Corporate finance	Anthony Fine
Employment	Ruth Harvey
Immigration	Laura Devine
Public sector	Anthony Fine
Sports	Jeff Rubenstein

Barnett Alexander Chart
SOLICITORS

BARNETT SAMPSON 30B Wimpole Street, London, W1M 7AE **Tel:** (0171) 935 9161 **Fax:** (0171) 935 9272 **DX:** 42740 Oxford Circus N. **Ptnrs:** 3 **Asst Solrs:** 3 **Other Fee-earners:** 4. An effective approach to commercial law, probate, property, family law and litigation including substantial group actions, particularly in the financial services field.

WORKLOAD			
Fin serv/comm lit/admin	80%	Family	8%
Commercial property	5%	Company/ commercial	4%
Private client	3%		

BARRIE WARD & JULIAN GRIFFITHS 5 Clarendon Street, Nottingham, Notts, NG1 5HS **Tel:** (0115) 9412622 **Fax:** (0115) 9240485 **DX:** 10158 **Ptnrs:** 4 **Asst Solrs:** 1 **Other Fee-earners:** 2. A general practice, particularly known for criminal legal aid work, but also strong in family, housing benefit, civil liberties and welfare law.

WORKLOAD			
Criminal law	70%	Family	20%
Convey/wills/probate	10%		

BARRY SHAW 10 Soho Square, London, W1V 6EE **Tel:** (0171) 439 3111 **Fax:** (0171) 494 1455 **Ptnrs:** 1. A general practice, particularly known for criminal legal aid work, but also strong in family, housing benefit, civil liberties and welfare law.

BATES, WELLS & BRAITHWAITE

61 CHARTERHOUSE STREET, LONDON, EC1M 6HA
DX: 46612

TEL: (0171) 251 1122
FAX: (0171) 251 2061

THE FIRM: Bates, Wells & Braithwaite was originally established to meet the needs of smaller business clients, and has subsequently developed a strong reputation for a wide range of litigation and family and matrimonial work, as well as a pre-eminence in charity law.

PRINCIPAL AREAS OF WORK:

Company and Business Law: The department handles a wide range of company/commercial work including take-overs, joint ventures, MBOs, entertainment matters, commercial contracts and tax advice. (*Contact Partner:* Hugh Craig).

Litigation: A strong department handles a wide range of commercial litigation, and has particular expertise in libel, employment, entertainment, social work law, personal injury and medical negligence. The firm is also known for its activities in the vital areas of human rights and civil liberties. (*Contact Partner:* John Trotter).

Charity Law: The department is active across the whole of the voluntary sector and represents some of the best-known national and international charities and foundations. It provides a national advisory service to solicitors and has produced a number of specialist publications. (*Contact Partner:* Andrew Phillips).

Matrimonial and Family Law: A strong department handles highly-involved financial cases, often with complex tax, trust or foreign jurisdiction elements and has considerable experience across the full range of family and matrimonial matters. Frances Hughes is a member of the International Academy of Matrimonial Lawyers and sits on the London Regional Committee of the SFLA. She and Pauline Fowler are accredited mediators with F.M.A. (*Contact Partner:* Frances Hughes).

Property: This recently expanded department handles the full range of commercial property matters including development, purchase of freeholds and leaseholds for occupation and investment, the granting of leases, mortgages and planning advice. (*Contact Partner:* Jennifer Warren).

Immigration and Nationality Law: This department advises both the individual client and large and small corporations, on immigration matters. It also advises on British Nationality Law problems. (*Contact Partner:* Philip Trott).

FOREIGN CONNECTIONS: As early as 1971, the firm was instrumental in establishing the PARLEX Group of European Lawyers. This Group is now represented throughout Europe, is registered as the first European Economic Interest Group, uses English as its common language, and offers an excellent facility through which to transact cross-frontier business.

CONTACT PARTNER: Andrew Phillips

Number of partners:	18
Assistant solicitors:	13
Other fee-earners:	21

WORKLOAD	
Litigation	25%
Charity	20%
Immigration	15%
Family	15%
Company/ commercial	15%
Property	10%

CONTACTS	
Charity law	Andrew Phillips
Company/ commercial	Hugh Craig
Family law	Frances Hughes
Immigration	Philip Trott
Property	Jennifer Warren

BATTENS

CHURCH HOUSE, YEOVIL, SOMERSET, BA20 1HB
DX: 100503

TEL: (01935) 23685
FAX: (01935) 706054

THE FIRM: In addition to being one of the largest firms in the South West, with offices in Somerset, Dorset and Avon, Battens is also one of the oldest firms in the country tracing its roots back to almost 300 years. Its Legal Services Division undertakes a wide range of work based around its strong private client department. It benefits from having Law Society specialist panel members in the areas of child care, personal injury and planning.

CONTACT PARTNER: G.J. Hughes

Number of partners:	22
Assistant solicitors:	10
Other fee-earners:	19

The recent rapid growth of its investment, finance and taxation practice has given rise to the formation of its Personal Finance Division which links together the various specialist departments dealing with investment (including in-house fund management), taxation and assurance. The firm also has a substantial interest in Dryfield Trust PLC an authorised institution under the Bank Act.

BATTENS
— solicitors —

PRINCIPAL AREAS OF WORK:

Agricultural Law: *(Contact:* Melanie Shuldham).

Corporate and Commercial: *(Contact:* Ray Edwards).

Commercial Conveyancing: *(Contact:* Rupert Vaughan).

Domestic Conveyancing: *(Contact:* Michael Blackmore, Chard Office).

Housing Associations: *(Contact:* James Mornement).

Investment: *(Contact:* Richard Gibbons).

Litigation – Family Law and Crime: *(Contact:* Graham Hughes).

Litigation – Commercial and Personal Injury: *(Contact:* Roger Paul).

Marine Division: *(Contact:* Clive Holland, Shaftesbury Office).

Planning: *(Contact:* David Stephens, Sherborne Office).

Probate, Wills and Trusts: *(Contact:* Stuart Allen).

Taxation: *(Contact:* Stuart Allen).

OTHER OFFICES: Bristol, Chard, Crewkerne, Dorchester, Shaftesbury, Sherborne, Taunton, Weymouth.

T.G. BAYNES & SONS 208 Broadway, Bexleyheath, Kent, DA6 7BG **Tel:** (0181) 301 2525 **Fax:** (0181) 304 1475 **DX:** 31801 Bexleyheath **Ptnrs:** 13 **Asst Solrs:** 6 **Other Fee-earners:** 14. A substantial general practice with seven offices in the area. Undertakes a broad range of work.

WORKLOAD			
Res conveyancing	40%	Civil litigation	20%
Probate and trusts	20%	Commercial	10%
Matrimonial and family	10%		

BEACHCROFT STANLEYS

20 FURNIVAL ST, LONDON, EC4A 1BN
DX: 45 Ch.Ln.

TEL: (0171) 242 1011
FAX: (0171) 831 6630

BACKGROUND: Founded in 1762, the firm has grown steadily through amalgamation and mergers into a progressive City practice. As a developing practice, the partners are acutely aware of the need to maintain direct client contact. To this end the firm has developed a management team to ensure that active client involvement is maintained at all times. Continuing investment in information technology enhances the quality of delivery of services and enables the firm to provide clients with additional client services including the provision of statistical case analyses, billing and case reports.

TYPES OF WORK UNDERTAKEN: As well as partnerships and individuals, the firm acts for public and private companies and public bodies including particular specialisations in the insurance, health, water and education sectors.

The firm is organised on a departmental basis (business, litigation, private client and property) with a partner or senior lawyer taking the lead role in co-ordinating all the firm's services for each client. Integrated cross-departmental client work interest groups have also been formed to provide specialist services to the following industry and service sectors: insurance, health, water, environment, construction, retail, advertising, education, employment, tax and charity.

THE BUSINESS DEPARTMENT: The business department deals with commercial arrangements and agreements of all kinds including formation and flotation of companies, acquisitions, disposals, amalgamations, mergers, demergers and management buy-outs, and anti-competitive legislation of both UK and EC origin. The firm is also concerned with a wide range of employment law issues, including unfair dismissals and redundancy claims, equality of opportunity and discrimination claims, and service agreements.

SENIOR PARTNER: A.D. Kennedy

Number of partners:	36
Assistant solicitors:	46
Other fee-earners:	56

WORKLOAD	
Commercial Department	42%
Insurance Department	31%
Health Department	26%

CONTACTS	
Business Department	Nick Hall
Litigation (insurance)	Richard Evans
Litigation (gen.comm. & health)	Trevor Blythe
Private client	George Francis
Property (and planning)	John Phelps

Intellectual property is also a particular area of expertise, both in the acquisition and defence of intellectual rights. The firm has an in-house patent adviser who is a Chartered Patent agent, European Patent Attorney and Registered Trade Mark Agent.

THE PROPERTY DEPARTMENT: The property department provides the full range of property services including property investment and development, property finance and portfolio management, sales, purchases, advice on landlord and tenant matters, lease renewals, possession actions, boundary disputes, acquisitions and disposals, building contracts and management construction contracts and the conduct of planning appeals. The firm is able to offer services to meet all clients' planning requirements by combining specialisations within its planning group (the group members include a barrister and a town planning consultant) with the expertise of the firm's property department.

THE LITIGATION DEPARTMENT: The firm's litigation department is divided into two sections, insurance and general commercial and health. The range of litigation is vast and diverse, ranging from motor and employers' liability claims, personal injuries, product liability, commercial disputes, reinsurance, intellectual property, construction, arbitration and medical negligence.

PRIVATE CLIENT: While the firm is mainly orientated towards the business client, it continues to act for a significant number of private clients providing a comprehensive and co-ordinated range of services, including taxation and financial planning, trust and estate planning and charity law expertise.

ADDITIONAL SERVICES: The firm has a number of specialist bulletins which are available to clients and are disseminated on a periodic basis. The bulletins available are: Health Law, Tax, Intellectual Property News, EU, Planning and Environmental and Insurance Litigation Update.

TRAINING: Applicants for training contracts should apply no later than August 1st, two years prior to the date of commencement of training. A brochure describing training and an application form may be obtained from Dafydd Evans, Director of Training.

CONTACTS: Business Department:Nick Hall
Litigation (Insurance):Richard Evans
Litigation (General Commercial and Health):Trevor Blythe
Private Client:George Francis
Property (and Planning):John Phelps

BEACHCROFT STANLEYS
Solicitors

BEALE AND COMPANY Garrick Hse, 27-32 King St, Covent Garden, London, WC2E 8JD **Tel:** (0171) 240 3474 **Fax:** (0171) 240 9111 **DX:** 51632 Covent Garden **Ptnrs:** 9 **Asst Solrs:** 6 **Other Fee-earners:** 9. Well known for construction law with related corporate and commercial work, and a long-standing private client practice.

BEAUMONTS

| OFFA ST, HEREFORD, HEREFORD & WORCS, HR1 2LJ | TEL: (01432) 352345 |
| DX: 17201 | FAX: (01432) 263708 |

THE FIRM: A member of LAWGROUP UK and A.D.R. Register Ltd., this general practice offers a comprehensive service to business and private clients, with emphasis on agricultural, commercial, wills, probate and conveyancing, together with criminal, matrimonial and civil litigation. Legal aid and agency work undertaken.

Solicitors within the practise are members of the Law Society, Panel in Personal Injury, Mental Health, Child Care and Crime (Duty Solicitor).

Quality commitment is demonstrated by the fact the firm was granted a Legal Aid Franchise on 1 August 1994.

CONTACT PARTNER: Anthony Davies	
Number of partners:	4
Assistant solicitors:	1
Other fee-earners:	5

BEAUMONT AND SON Lloyds Chambers, 1 Portsoken St, London, E1 8AW **Tel:** (0171) 481 3100 **Fax:** (0171) 481 3353 **DX:** 551 **Ptnrs:** 14 **Asst Solrs:** 14 **Other Fee-earners:** 7. Areas of practice include insurance, litigation and commercial matters including financing with a significant although not exclusive aviation emphasis.

WORKLOAD			
Aviation/insurance/lit	65%	Comm leasing/banking/fin	25%
Convey/private client	5%	Marine	5%

BECKMAN & BECKMAN 20 Balcombe St, London, NW1 6NB **Tel:** (0171) 724 1435 **Fax:** (0171) 724 7017 **DX:** 41717 West End **Ptnrs:** 5 **Asst Solrs:** 6 **Other Fee-earners:** 2. A general/ commercial practice but with a team of specialists in family/ matrimonial law including cases of wardship and child abduction.

BEITEN BURKHARDT MITTL & WEGENER 13 Devonshire Square, London, EC2M 4TH **Tel:** (0171) 247 9191 **Fax:** (0171) 247 9192. Beiten Burkhardt Mittl & Wegener is an international law firm with its head office in Munich concentrating on all areas of company and commercial work and related fields.

WORKLOAD			
Corporate/commercial	40%	Corporate tax planning	30%
Commercial litigation	20%	Probate/family/est plan	10%

BELL LAMB & JOYNSON 6 Castle St, Liverpool, Merseyside, L2 0NB **Tel:** (0151) 227 2626 **Fax:** (0151) 227 5937 **DX:** 14110 **Ptnrs:** 16 **Asst Solrs:** 5 **Other Fee-earners:** 8. Best known for its insurance company work dealing with traffic accident claims. Finance company work, licensing and criminal work are other strengths. Has seven Merseyside offices.

BELL & SCOTT WS

16 HILL STREET, EDINBURGH, EH2 3LD
DX: 114 Edinburgh 1

TEL: (0131) 226 6703
FAX: (0131) 226 7602

THE FIRM: Bell & Scott is a broad based commercial firm providing a practical and innovative approach to solving legal problems for its clients.

Located in the city centre the firm is known for its strong commercial property department and has created specialist units to service existing clients and target new clients. The firm is capitalising on its recent European appointment and continued membership of two European and International Associations.

PRINCIPAL AREAS OF WORK:

Commercial: *(Contact:* Simon Guest). Contract, intellectual property, licensing, agency, partnership and general business advice.

Commercial Property: *(Contact:* Bruce Anderson). The firm is recognised for its expertise in acquisition and development work, property investment and joint ventures. Commercial leasing is undertaken for both landlords and tenants; security work is undertaken on behalf of lending institutions and borrowers. Planning appeals and planning advice.

Corporate: *(Contact:* Alex Innes). Acquisition and disposal of companies and businesses, shareholder agreements, joint ventures, takeovers, mergers, management buy-outs, corporate restructuring, insolvencies and receiverships, service contract preparation, negotiation and resolution.

Entertainment/ Media: *(Contact:* Iain MacDonald). The firm provides advice to a broad range of clients across the United Kingdom. Specialist advice in the areas of film, TV, theatre and dance.

Litigation: *(Contact:* Colin Heggie). The department specialises in employment advice primarily on behalf of employers. Construction litigation and commercial litigation. Debt collection for lending institutions. The department is recognised for its expertise in personal injury litigation.

Private Client: *(Contact:* Alan Sharp or Susan Calder). The private client department provides a full range of services for the individual client including personal taxation, trusts, wills and executries. A full residential property service is provided.

FOREIGN LANGUAGES: French, German and Spanish.

INTERNATIONAL CONNECTIONS & ASSOCIATED OFFICES: Member of Omni Juris and Legalink.

MANAGING PARTNER: Mr Iain MacDonald

Number of partners:	9
Assistant solicitors:	7
Other fee-earners:	11

WORKLOAD	
Commercial Property	45%
Private Client	25%
Litigation	15%
Corporate	8%
Other	7%

CONTACTS	
Commercial	Simon Guest
Commercial property	Bruce Anderson
Entertainment/ media	Iain Macdonald

BELTRAMI & CO Royal London House, 93 West Nile Street, Glasgow, G1 2NP **Tel:** (0141) 221 0981 **Fax:** (0141) 332 9892 **Ptnrs:** 4 **Asst Solrs:** 1 . Leading criminal defence practice, specialising in all aspects of defence work, and especially serious cases.

BENNETT METCALFE

48 QUEEN SQUARE, BRISTOL, BS1 4LY
DX: 7835 Bristol

TEL: (0117) 929 0451
FAX: (0117) 929 9551

THE FIRM: Established for over 250 years, Bennett Metcalfe enjoys an excellent reputation for its work on behalf of both commercial and private clients. It is particularly noted for its personal injury and commercial litigation expertise. The firm is a member of LawNet.

CONTACT PARTNER: David Boniface	
Number of partners:	9
Assistant solicitors:	7
Other fee-earners:	6

PRINCIPAL AREAS OF WORK:

Company/ Commercial: *(Contact:* Anthony Forster). *Work includes:* MBOs, banking, acquisitions, taxation, intellectual property and charities.

Commercial Litigation: *(Contact:* Alan Reed). *Work includes:* insolvency, employment, banking, professional negligence, company and partnership disputes and debt recovery.

Agriculture: *(Contact:* Francis Montagu). *Work includes:* taxation advice and property.

Personal Injury: *(Contact:* David Boniface). *Work includes:* defendant work for major insurers, plaintiff work for private clients, industrial injury and disease, motor and medical negligence.

Family: *(Contact:* Lesley Sandiford). *Work includes:* divorce and ancillary relief, custody disputes and mediation.

Property: *(Contact:* Anthony Smith). *Work includes:* a wide range of transactions on behalf of corporate and private clients, development conveyancing and self build projects.

Private Client: *(Contact:* Alison Reed). *Work includes:* trusts, probate (contentious and non-contentious), wills, tax planning and personal finance.

OTHER OFFICES: High Street, Wrington, Bristol BS18 7QB.
Tel: (01934) 862786. *Fax:* (01934) 862404. *(Contact Partner:* Francis Montagu).

LANGUAGES SPOKEN: Bengali (Sylheti), Chinese (Mandarin and Cantonese), French and Spanish.

WORKLOAD	
Personal injury (defendant and plaintiff)	25%
Private client and family	20%
Property	15%
Commercial litigation	15%
Company/ commercial including banking	15%
Agriculture	10%

CONTACTS	
Agriculture	Francis Montagu
Commercial litigation	Alan Reed
Company/ commercial	Anthony Forster
Family	Lesley Sandiford
Personal injury	David Boniface
Private client	Alison Reed
Property	Anthony Smith

BENNETT & ROBERTSON 16 Walker Street, Edinburgh, EH3 7NN **Tel:** (0131) 225 4001 **Fax:** (0131) 225 1107 **Ptnrs:** 16 **Asst Solrs:** 8 **Other Fee-earners:** 5. A commercially based firm advising on all aspects of company/ commercial law including debt collection, insolvency and employment from offices in Edinburgh and Glasgow.

BENNETT TAYLOR TYRRELL

72 NEW CAVENDISH ST, LONDON, W1M 8AU
DX: 42716 Oxford Circus North

TEL: (0171) 323 1100
FAX: (0171) 631 0657

THE FIRM: A West End practice offering services to businesses and the people who run them, institutions, professionals, educational organisations and charities, as well as private individuals. The firm aims to give a personal yet professional service.

CONTACT PARTNER: Eze Silas	
Number of partners:	11
Assistant solicitors:	3
Other fee-earners:	4

PRINCIPAL AREAS OF WORK: The firm deals with a range of private and commercial work including property, litigation, matrimonial law, insolvency law, building and construction matters, employment law, company and commercial matters, intellectual property matters, wills, trusts, probate, estate planning and administration, immigration, charity and education law.

BENTLEYS, STOKES & LOWLESS

BENTLEYS, STOKES & LOWLESS International House, 1 St. Katherine's Way, London, E1 9YL **Tel:** (0171) 782 0990 **Fax:** (0171) 782 0991 **DX:** 1074 **Ptnrs:** 11 **Asst Solrs:** 12 **Other Fee-earners:** 7. A general practice with considerable experience in shipping and insurance.

WORKLOAD		
Shipping	80%	Comp/comm/tax/prop/priv 20%

BEOR WILSON & LLOYD Calvert Hse, Calvert Terrace, Swansea, W. Glam, SA1 6AP **Tel:** (01792) 655178 **Fax:** (01792) 467002 **DX:** 39550 **Ptnrs:** 7 **Asst Solrs:** 3 **Other Fee-earners:** 3. Established over 150 years. A broadly based firm specialising in private client matters, company and commercial property, commercial litigation and personal injury. A member of LawNet.

WORKLOAD			
Civil litigation	26%	Commercial	22%
Probate/ wills	20%	Convey/commercial prop	17%
Family	15%		

BERG & CO Byrom Court, 7 Byrom Street, Manchester, M3 4PF **Tel:** (0161) 833 9211 **Fax:** (0161) 834 5566 **DX:** 14379 **Ptnrs:** 7 **Asst Solrs:** 7 **Other Fee-earners:** 4. Commercial and forward-thinking firm serving the needs of business clients inside and outside the UK.

BERMANS Pioneer Buildings, 65-67 Dale St, Liverpool, Merseyside, L2 2NS **Tel:** (0151) 227 3351 **Fax:** (0151) 236 2107 **DX:** 14116 **Ptnrs:** 12 **Asst Solrs:** 7 **Other Fee-earners:** 27. Bermans has secured a national and international reputation as a leading commercial practice with clients varying from small businesses to multinational corporations.

WORKLOAD			
Company/ commercial	25%	Factoring/invoice disc	21%
Gen commercial lit	20%	Finance leasing	12%
Banking/ insolvency	12%	Security enforcement	10%

BERNARD CHILL & AXTELL The First House, 1a The Avenue, Southampton, Hants, SO17 1AH **Tel:** (01703) 228821 **Fax:** (01703) 211300 **DX:** 38508 Southampton 3 **Ptnrs:** 7 **Asst Solrs:** 2 **Other Fee-earners:** 7. Founded 1937. Medium-sized firm best known for its work in criminal and matrimonial law.

WORKLOAD			
Criminal	25%	Matrimonial/ family	25%
Civil litigation	25%	Convey/comm/comp/prob	20%

BERRY & BERRY (incorporating Vallis & Struthers) 11 Church Rd, Tunbridge Wells, Kent, TN1 1JA **Tel:** (01892) 526344 **Fax:** (01892) 511223 **DX:** 3908 **Ptnrs:** 12 **Asst Solrs:** 4 **Other Fee-earners:** 11. Best known for its litigation practice which includes civil, criminal and divorce work. Also undertakes conveyancing, tax and probate work. Has a large legal aid practice.

WORKLOAD			
Matrimonial & family	25%	Criminal litigation	25%
Civil litigation	20%	Probate	15%
Property	15%		

BERRYMAN & CO

PARK HOUSE, FRIAR LANE, NOTTINGHAM, NOTTS, NG1 6DN
DX: 10004

TEL: (0115) 941 7574
FAX: (0115) 947 3930

OTHER OFFICES: Birmingham (a joint venture with Berrymans of London).

THE FIRM: Established in 1896. This is a firm with a young and forward-thinking partnership. Their commitment and determination have led to considerable recent expansion in each of the firm's various specialist departments, especially the insurance litigation and commercial departments.

PRINCIPAL AREAS OF WORK:

Litigation: Emphasis on Insurance Defendant, Commercial Contracts, Insolvency, Employment and Intellectual Property.

Corporate/Commercial: Including Corporate Finance, Commercial Contracts, Planning, Construction and Development, Commercial Conveyancing and Insolvency.

Advocacy: Crime and Immigration

Private Client: Domestic Conveyancing, Matrimonial, Estate Planning, Wills and Tax Planning

RECRUITMENT AND TRAINING: The firm actively recruits trainee solicitors on a continuing basis who will generally stay with the firm after qualification, due to its continuing need for assistant solicitors.

CONTACT PARTNER: Mr C. Harrington

Number of partners:	13
Assistant solicitors:	12
Other fee-earners:	7

WORKLOAD	
Crime	25%
Property	17%
Insurance - defendant	13%
Other private client	11%
Matrimonial	9%
Company/ commercial - non-contentious (employment/formations etc)	8%
Company/ commercial - litigation (insolvency, etc)	8%
Private client litigation	5%
Personal injury	4%

BERRYMANS

SALISBURY HOUSE, LONDON WALL, LONDON, EC2M 5QN
DX: 33861 Finsbury Sq.

TEL: (0171) 638 2811
FAX: (0171) 920 0361

CONTACT PARTNER: Paul Taylor

Number of partners:	24
Assistant solicitors:	47
Other fee-earners:	15

THE FIRM: is a leading litigation and commercial law practice with strong connections throughout the London insurance market. Berrymans continues to expand having recently established a branch in Dubai to add to its offices in England and associated offices in Europe, the Middle East and Far East. The firm is noted for its experience in litigation and dispute resolution of all types in the UK and abroad and has a growing company/ commercial department.

PRINCIPAL AREAS OF WORK: The firm has specialist departments, with partners supported by teams of assistants, concerned with all aspects of insurance litigation as well as company and commercial, property, private client services and agency work.

Construction: (Paul Taylor, Diana Holtham). Acts on behalf of engineers, architects, contractors and employers in construction and engineering disputes in the UK and abroad and provides a full advisory service.

Personal Injury: (Martin Bruffell, Michael Swan). The department, which is one of the largest in the UK, handles all types of claims arising from motor accidents, accidents at work, industrial disease and all aspects of public and employers' liability.

Professional Indemnity: (Charlotte Capstick, David Wilkinson). Acts for defendants in all professions particularly legal, property and financial.

Insurance/ Reinsurance: (David Wilkinson). All aspects of contentious and non-contentious work in the UK and internationally for insurance companies, re-insurers and retrocessionaires.

Commercial Litigation: (Catherine Hawkins, Peter Fitzpatrick). Specialises in subrogated recovery actions for insurers, particularly including fire, flood, motor, subsidence, fraud and product liability.

Medical Law Service: (Cheryl Blundell, Ian Latimer). Specialises in medical negligence, acts for health authorities, local government and insurance companies.

Environmental Law Service: (Steven Francis). Providing specialist legal advice on environmental issues and has already acted in several leading cases in this field. The department which also undertakes planning and local government work has recently taken on an experienced local government planning lawyer.

Company/Commercial: (Peter Bohm). Provides advice regarding joint ventures, acquisitions and disposals, employment (contentious and non-contentious), computer contracts, purchase agreements and general commercial matters, together with all aspects of commercial conveyancing.

Agency: (Alan West). Representation in the London courts, including a full report of proceedings within 24 hours, used by many regional solicitors.

Private Clients: (Adrian Fothergill). A complete range of legal services including wills, trusts, family law and conveyancing.

NATURE OF CLIENTELE: Major insurance companies, consulting engineers, architects, surveyors, quantity surveyors, accountants, barristers, solicitors, banks, area health authorities, private hospitals, government departments and agencies, local authorities, commercial and private clients.

BRANCH OFFICES: Branch offices in Southampton, Birmingham and Dubai.

FOREIGN CONNECTIONS: Berrymans has an associated Paris practice, Bertagna Gruia Berrymans and also has established associations in Athens, Brussels, Bucharest, Madrid, Dusseldorf, Stuttgart, Singapore, Dubai and Abu Dhabi.

RECRUITMENT AND TRAINING: The firm is always interested in recruiting high-quality lawyers and trainee solicitors who wish to specialise in litigation and commercial dispute resolution. There is a programme of regular in-house seminars and training for both qualified and unqualified staff. Applications should be made to the Personnel Manager.

WORKLOAD	
Personal injury	24%
Construction	23%
Professional indemnity	23%
Insurance and reinsurance	14%
Environmental	5%
Company/ commercial	5%
Medical	3%

CONTACTS	
Commercial litigation	Catherine Hawkins
Commercial	Peter Bohm
	Peter Fitzpatrick
Construction	Diana Holtham
	Paul Taylor
Environmental	Steven Francis
Insurance and reinsurance	David Wilkinson
	Jeremy Benfield
Medical law	Cheryl Blundell
	Ian Latimer
Personal injury	Michael Swan
	Martin Bruffell
Private client	Adrian Fothergill
Professional indemnity	Charlotte Capstick
	David Wilkinson

BERRY, REDMOND & ROBINSON 19 The Boulevard, Weston-su-per-Mare, Avon, BS23 1NR **Tel:** (01934) 619000 **Fax:** (01934) 614148 **DX:** 84015 Weston super Mare **Ptnrs:** 10 **Asst Solrs:** 2 **Other Fee-earners:** 5. Busy general practice with property shops and able to offer a full service to private and commercial clients. Experienced in all litigation work.

BERRY SMITH Brackla House, Brackla Street, Bridgend, M. Glam, CF31 1BZ **Tel:** (01656) 645525 **Fax:** (01656) 645174 **DX:** 38004 Bridgend **Ptnrs:** 6 **Asst Solrs:** 2 **Other Fee-earners:** 3. Known primarily for commercial work, with strong matrimonial, litigation and private client departments.

WORKLOAD			
Litigation	30%	Commercial property	25%
Private/res property	20%	Corporate	20%
Employment	5%		

S J BERWIN & CO

222 GRAYS INN ROAD, LONDON, WC1X 8HB
DX: 255 London

TEL: (0171) 837 2222
FAX: (0171) 833 2860

THE FIRM: Founded in 1982, S J Berwin & Co offers a comprehensive legal service to financial, industrial and commercial clients, both national and international. The firm's rapid growth and success is best explained by its ability to handle complex corporate and commercial transactions coupled with a creative approach to clients' problems, a speedy response and close involvement in their strategic decision-making.

CONTACT PARTNER: Mr David Harrel

Number of partners:	51
Assistant solicitors:	67
Other fee-earners:	44

PRINCIPAL AREAS OF WORK:

Corporate Finance: (*Contact:* Robert Burrow/ Jonathan Metliss/ Jonathan Blake). The firm handles the full range of corporate finance activities including flotations, sales and purchases of both companies and businesses, demergers and reconstructions with a particular emphasis on mergers and acquisitions. Our Venture Capital group, which represents many of the major venture funds in the UK and Europe, deal with management buy-outs and buy-ins, venture and development capital and the structuring of venture capital and investment funds. Members of the Banking group advise both banks and borrowers on all aspects of lending transactions and financial products particularly in relation to derivatives, debt restructuring, acquisition finance and securitisations. Our Securities group advise on securities law and regulation, the establishment and marketing of investment funds and product and transaction documents.

EU & Competition Law: (*Contact:* Stephen Kon). The firm has a strong bias towards Europe and was selected by the CBI to lead its Single Market initiative. Its EU, competition and trade law practice is conducted through the London and Brussels offices and advises on domestic and EU mergers and acquisitions, competition, anti-trust and anti-dumping, regulatory work and judicial review proceedings. The department regularly lobbies the European Commission and appears on behalf of clients in proceedings before the European Court of Justice.

Commercial: (*Contact:* Nigel Palmer). Members of the department advise on, and structure, transactions and ventures covering a broad spectrum of commercial matters, many of which have an international dimension, such as commercial agreements, including distribution, agency, dealerships and franchises and media, entertainment, communication and sport including film production and film financing, TV, video, multimedia, music and theatre, satellite and cable, merchandising and sponsorship.

Tax: (*Contact:* Michael Trask). The department covers national and international taxation issues, from domestic corporate tax and VAT, to the fiscal and financial structuring of international transactions and groups of companies. Tax and estate planning advice for private clients, both UK and foreign, is handled by a specialist team.

Property: (*Contact:* Stephen Willson). The department handles all aspects of commercial property work for a wide range of clients including property companies, developers, banks, retailers and hoteliers. Specialists within the department advise on planning, funding and local government work.

WORKLOAD	
Corporate finance	39%
Property	19%
Litigation	17%
Commercial	12%
EU/ competition	10%
Tax	3%

CONTACTS	
Banking	Gillian Smith
Corporate finance	Robert Burrow
	Jonathan Metliss
Employment	Nicola Walker
EU/ competition	Stephen Kon
Financial services	Charles Abrams
I.P./ trade marks	Ray Black
	John Olsen
Litigation	David Harrel
Media	Nigel Palmer
Planning/ development	Geoff Haley
	Pat Thomas
Property	Stephen Willson
Tax	Michael Trask
Venture capital	Jonathan Blake

S J Berwin & Co

Litigation: (*Contact:* David Harrel). The department handles a wide range of international and commercial litigation including insurance, injunctions, corporate disputes, defamation, professional negligence, licensing, construction and engineering disputes, judicial review, property litigation and arbitration. The firm was one of the first to establish an in-house advocacy capability to take advantage of the recent rules allowing solicitors' rights of audience.

INTER-DEPARTMENTAL GROUPS:

Insolvency: (*Contact:* Jonathan Metliss). The group advises on all aspects of the Insolvency Act, assists in corporate rescues and restructurings, including voluntary arrangements and acts for administrators, administrative receivers and liquidators in relation to asset sales and the administration and winding-up of insolvent companies.

Intellectual Property/Trade Marks: (Contact: Ray Black/John Olsen). A specialist Intellectual Property group undertakes enforcement of patents, copyright, design rights, international trade marks, passing off, breach of confidence, computer law and telecommunications regulation and practice.

Project Finance: (*Contact:* Geoff Haley). A specialist team handles infrastructure projects in the transportation, energy and water areas, on an international basis.

Construction: (*Contact:* Geoff Haley). The firm acts for governments, promoters and contractors on construction and BOOT projects, on an international basis.

Environmental: (*Contact:* Pat Thomas). The group has considerable experience in UK and EU environmental and health and safety matters, including auditing and due diligence surveys.

Leisure: (*Contact:* Bryan Pickup). The group advises both operators and financial institutions in the leisure sector on a wide variety of transactions.

Employment and Pensions: (*Contact:* Nicola Walker). The group advises both employers and employees on all aspects of employment law, ranging from immigration to service contracts, severance packages and restrictive covenant claims. The group also deals with pensions, share options and employee benefit schemes.

Central and Eastern Europe: (*Contact:* Simon McLeod). The firm is a founder member of the CBI's Eastern Europe Initiative with responsibility for the Czech Republic, Slovakia and Hungary and has associations with firms throughout the region. The firm advises both Western and Central and East European clients.

OTHER OFFICES AND FOREIGN CONNECTIONS: The firm has an office in Brussels and is the UK member of Interlaw, an international association of major independent law firms. Through this association and other international connections, S J Berwin & Co can offer legal services throughout the world.

RECRUITMENT AND TRAINING: In order to maintain its commitment to organic growth and development (82% of trainee solicitors remained with it after qualification in September 1993) the firm will recruit up to 15 ambitious, commercially-minded individuals to begin training in September 1996.

EDITORIAL POLICY

In this edition, the lists of specialists include profiles of individual practitioners - solicitors and barristers - who have been recommended most frequently to our researchers. Editorial policy is to identify leading practitioners on merit: it is not possible to buy a place in our biographical lists. Inclusion of a profile in this directory is based solely on expertise and reputation.

Enormous effort has been invested by our ten-strong research team (mainly solicitors and barristers) in canvassing recommendations and identifying leaders. We are confident in the overall accuracy of the results. However, mistakes and misjudgements are inevitable, and if readers have any suggestions regarding our listings we should be very pleased to hear from them.

BERWIN LEIGHTON

ADELAIDE HOUSE, LONDON BRIDGE, LONDON, EC4R 9HA
DX: 92

TEL: (0171) 623 3144
FAX: (0171) 623 4416

THE FIRM: Berwin Leighton is one of the major City firms, offering a comprehensive legal service to a wide range of national and international commercial clients. The firm is divided into five main departments dealing with property, corporate, litigation, financial institutions and taxation work. There is close liaison between specialists in different fields and also with the firm's offices in New York, Brussels and its associated firm in Tokyo. This ensures that fully accountable teams provide a comprehensive service to anticipate and meet every client's requirements.

PRINCIPAL AREAS OF WORK:

Property: *(Contact Partner:* David Rhodes). A large department, which has a leading reputation for its commercial property work both for institutions and entrepreneurs. The department handles the full range of commercial freehold and leasehold property development including secured lending and joint ventures.

Planning and Environment: *(Contact Partner:* Nicholas Taylor). A market leader. All planning and environmental aspects of property development, negotiations with planning authorities and planning appeals are handled.

Construction Law and Litigation: *(Contact Partner:* Michael Gibson). All aspects of construction contracts from inception of a project to its completion and beyond.

Litigation: *(Contact Partner:* Ian Lowe). A strong department which handles all types of commercial litigation and arbitration with particular experience in banking, financial services, insurance, property, building contracts, employment, maritime matters and defamation.

Corporate Finance: *(Contact Partner:* Robert Jones). Mergers and acquisitions, flotations, takeovers, venture capital, joint ventures, reconstructions and insolvency, employment, executive benefits and pensions. Much of the work has an international element.

Banking, Asset Finance and Leasing: *(Contact Partner:* Marc Palley). Domestic and international commercial banking, property lending, project financing, house, club and fully syndicated loans, and film finance.

Commercial and Communications: *(Contact Partner:* Lloyd Evans). The department is pre-eminent in entertainment and communications law dealing with film and television, satellite, cable, video and theatre financing and production, rights, acquisition and franchising; trademarks; distribution; computer hardware and software licensing and intellectual property matters.

International Corporate: *(Contact Partner:* Steven Goodman). International joint ventures in the USA, Japan, Europe (including Eastern Europe and CIS), South Africa and Asia.

EC and Competition Law: *(Contact Partner:* Peter Stone). Merger clearance applications, monopoly investigations, competition law notifications, advice on compliance programmes and specific guidance on the EC and EC law implications for commercial contracts and mergers and acquisitions.

Shipping and Aviation: *(Contact Partner:* Jonathan Kellett). The financing and acquisition of ships and aircraft, new building contracts, charter and pool arrangements, liquidations and mortgage recovery work.

Financial Institutions: *(Contact Partner:* Michael Wilson). Specific expertise in banking and insurance-related matters, with particular emphasis on banker's blanket bond insurance, including professional indemnity matters of a banking and financial nature.

Tax and Trust: *(Contact Partner:* John Overs). Tax, trust and probate matters are dealt with on a national and international basis. The department's work embraces all tax aspects of business transactions including corporation tax, value added tax and stamp duty. It also advises on estate and other tax planning, resident and non-resident trusts, immigration and emigration matters, administration of estates, pensions, wills, tax litigation and negotiations with the Inland Revenue.

NATURE OF CLIENTELE: The firm has a wide UK and international client base which includes central and local government, public and private companies, institutions, banks, insurance companies and professional advisers spread across a range of

CONTACT PARTNER: Bernard Bartlett	
Number of partners:	57
Assistant solicitors:	83
Other fee-earners:	51

WORKLOAD	
Property (including planning)	41%
Company/ commercial (including corporate finance and banking)	28%
Litigation	20%
Financial institutions	6%
Taxation	5%

CONTACTS	
Banking/ asset finance	Marc Palley
	Simon Kildahl
Company/ commercial	Lloyd Evans
	Peter Stone
Construction	Michael Gibson
Corporate finance	Robert Jones
	John Bennett
Employment/ pensions	Robert Eldridge
Environment	Andrew Waite
Insurance/ financial	Michael Wilson
	Andrew Rose
Litigation	Ian Lowe
Planning	Nicholas Taylor
Property	David Rhodes
	David Taylor
Shipping	Jonathan Kellett
Tax (corporate)	John Overs

BERWIN LEIGHTON

industries including retail, property, financial, manufacturing and communications. The firm has specific experience of acting for Scandinavian, Japanese and South African clients both in the UK and overseas.

OTHER OFFICES: *New York:* 135 East 57th Street, New York, NY 10022, USA. *Tel:* (212) 754 5400 *Fax:* (212) 754 5401.
Brussels: Avenue de Tervuren 13B, Tervurenlaan, 1040 Brussels, Belgium. *Tel:* (2) 732 3144 *Fax:* (2) 732 3979.
Tokyo (associated office): Kato Nishida and Hasegawa, 360 Marunouchi Building, 2-4-1 Marunouchi, Chiyoda-ku, Tokyo, Japan.

RECRUITMENT AND TRAINING: Berwin Leighton seeks to recruit around 15 trainee solicitors each year, and provides financial assistance for the professional examinations. The firm also operates a summer placement scheme. A relatively young firm, Berwin Leighton prides itself on its informal working atmosphere and high professional standards, and ideally looks for its trainee solicitors to be of partnership potential.

BETESH FOX & CO 17 Ralli Courts, West Riverside, Manchester, M3 5FT **Tel:** (0161) 832 6131 **Fax:** (0161) 832 8172 **DX:** 14359 **Ptnrs:** 10 **Asst Solrs:** 6 **Other Fee-earners:** 4. This City practice handles company/ commercial, contentious and non-contentious work, criminal law, personal injury, accident and professional negligence (medical), commercial and civil litigation, commercial fraud and forensic services.

WORKLOAD			
Comm/civ lit/insurance	27%	Personal injury/med neg	27%
Fraud/crime/forensic	27%	Company/commercial/prop	18%

BEVAN ASHFORD

35 COLSTON AVENUE, BRISTOL, BS1 4TT	TEL: (0117) 923 0111
DX: 7828 Bristol	FAX: (0117) 929 1865
EXETER: Curzon House, Southernhay West, Exeter, Devon EX4 3LY	Tel: (01392) 411111
DX: 8301 Exeter	Fax: (01392) 50764

THE FIRM: Bevan Ashford is one of the largest regional practices in the country.

It has a network of offices serving clients across the South of England, the Midlands and Wales.

In 1991 Bevan Ashford founded ADVOC, a network of similar independent commercial legal firms extending across 14 European countries – and including MacRoberts in Scotland – which has given real practical experience in European law.

The firm's predominant strengths lie in corporate transactions, commercial property, planning and environmental law, commercial litigation and employment matters, intellectual property and media law.

In addition, some offices have developed particular niches:

Bristol is the largest office in the firm and is well known for its national practice for National Health Service bodies and, consequently, strong departments in the fields of medical litigation, commercial property, planning, environmental law and employment law.

Cardiff has a long established reputation in acting for insurance companies and local businesses.

Exeter is a commercial centre with strong departments in company commercial, commercial litigation, employment law, and defendant insurance work.

Plymouth is the base for the head of the firm's local government unit and is active in media law, planning and environmental law.

Taunton and Tiverton combine a full range of general commercial work, with high quality private client services throughout England and Wales.

Tiverton is the firm's centre of excellence for agricultural law, personal taxation and estate planning.

CONTACT PARTNER:	
Number of partners:	54
Assistant solicitors:	63
Other fee-earners:	64

WORKLOAD	
Litigation	50%
Commercial property	20%
Company/ commercial	15%
Domestic conveyancing	10%
Trust, tax, probate and family	5%

CONTACTS	
Administrative/ public law	Iain Fairbairn
Agriculture and bloodstock	Tim Howells
Company/ comm.	Paul Cooper, Simon Rous
Construction/ civil eng.	Steve Hughes
Corporate finance	Paul Cooper
Defamation	Gareth Jones
Employment	David Widdowson
Environmental	David Wood, Malcolm Iley

The London office provides a contact point and facilities for London and international clients. It is principally served by fee-earners attending from other offices as required.

Bevan Ashford is achieving its ambition to compete successfully in national markets, providing comprehensive commercial services to corporate and public sector clients appreciative of the cost benefits of a regional practice.

OTHER OFFICES:
CARDIFF: Waterloo House, Fitzalan Court, Newport Road, Cardiff CF2 1EL
DX: 33011 Cardiff Tel: (01222) 462562 Fax: (01222) 461388
and at Mutley House, 23 Princess Street, Plymouth, Devon PL1 2EX
DX: 8273 Plymouth 2 Tel: (01752) 256888 Fax: (01752) 256012
41 St. James Street, Taunton, Somerset TA1 1JR
DX:32115 Taunton Tel: (01823) 284444 Fax: (01823) 270869
Gotham House, Tiverton, Devon EX16 6LT
DX: 49002 Tiverton Tel: (01884) 242111 Fax: (01884) 259303

Family/ matrimonial	Paul Barber, David Beadel
Licensing	David Wood
Litigation(comm)	David Widdowson,John Evans
Litigation(property)	Charles Metherell
Local government	Malcolm Iley
Media and entertainment	Gareth Jones
Mental health	Susan Thompson
Personal injury	Paul Barber
Planning	David Wood
Private client	Nick Jarrett-Kerr
	James Pettit
Professional negligence	Andrew Whitefield
Property (commercial)	Iain Fairbairn
	Andrew Rothwell

BEVERIDGE ROSS & PREVEZERS

10 AND 11 NEW STREET, LONDON, EC2M 4TP
DX: CDE 828

TEL: (0171) 626 1533
FAX: (0171) 929 4982

THE FIRM: Established since the early 1980s, Beveridge Ross & Prevezers is a well-regarded City firm, which has attracted, in a relatively short time, a strong corporate, commercial and private client base. The firm is best known for commercial property, company/ commercial, commercial litigation (including insolvency and large debt recoveries), computer law, white collar crime, matrimonial and trade finance work. The firm also has strong overseas connections in Hong Kong, Sweden, Turkey and Africa, as well as the usual European countries. Beveridge Ross & Prevezers has grown on its reputation of being one of the youngest firms in the City, and for being able, as a result of its size, to give a personal and individual service to its clients at partner level.

CONTACT PARTNER: Mark Prevezer

Number of partners:	9
Assistant solicitors:	3
Other fee-earners:	2

BEVIRS 36 Regent Circus, Swindon, Wilts, SN1 1UQ **Tel:** (01793) 532363 **Fax:** (01793) 619585 **DX:** 38618 Swindon 2 **Ptnrs:** 12 **Asst Solrs:** 6 **Other Fee-earners:** 5. A general provincial practice undertaking a full range of legal work including agricultural and commercial. Legally-aided clients and large commercial clients.

WORKLOAD			
Litigation	22%	Conveyancing	21%
Matrimonial	14%		

BEVISS & BECKINGSALE Law Chambers, Silver Street, Axminster, Devon, EX13 5AX **Tel:** (01297) 33233 **Fax:** (01297) 35117 **DX:** 43300 **Ptnrs:** 7 **Asst Solrs:** 3 . Long established firm undertaking a wide range of legal services from five offices in East Devon and South Somerset.

WORKLOAD			
Lit (civ/matrim/crim)	35%	Agricultural/dom convey	33%
Probate	22%	Commercial	10%

INTERNATIONAL SECTION

The international section lists foreign law firms based in London. It also lists the foreign connections of English law firms: their branch offices overseas and the foreign languages spoken at their UK offices.

BIDDLE & CO

1 GRESHAM ST, LONDON, EC2V 7BU
DX: 1008 London

TEL: (0171) 606 9301
FAX: (0171) 606 3305

THE FIRM: Biddle & Co is one of the most prominent of the smaller commercial practices in the City. It has a particularly strong reputation for its Corporate, Pensions and Media practice.

The firm's overriding objective is to provide a high-quality service to its clients at competitive rates. A key feature in the achievement of this objective is to offer clients direct access to partners at all times. This approach is one of Biddle & Co's strengths and distinguishing features. The firm's philosophy, quite simply, is that the hands-on involvement of a partner on all significant assignments guarantees the highest degree of quality and efficiency in meeting the clients' needs. The firm involves suitably experienced assistant solicitors as and when cost-effective for clients, but never to the detriment of the partner/client line of communication.

Membership of LOGOS, which is a group of independent law firms with offices throughout the European Union, enables Biddle & Co to offer a high quality international service to its clients.

PRINCIPAL AREAS OF WORK:

Corporate and Commercial: Substantial corporate transactions continue to form the major part of Biddle & Co's core commercial practice. Corporate transactions in which the firm has recently been actively involved include acting for financial institutions as well as management teams in a number of multi-million pound buy-outs, including one of the largest buy-outs (by capitalisation) of the last few years. The firm advises on all aspects of corporate and commercial law, including public takeovers, listings, mergers and acquisitions and banking.

Litigation: The firm's extensive commercial litigation practice regularly leads to involvement in important and well-publicised proceedings. Recent assignments have included involvement in a leading case on the critical issue of the professional liability of auditors, which was heard by the House of Lords. The firm also represented a national broadcaster in one of the key Contempt of Court cases of recent years.

Pensions: In the pensions field the firm has an outstanding reputation for the depth of its expertise and the quality of its advice across the whole spectrum of pensions law, including negotiations on the pensions aspects of corporate acquisitions and disposals, advice on pensions reconstructions, and insolvency-related work for independent trustees.

Property: The Property Department deals with all matters relating to the ownership, management, development, acquisition and sale of land. It also advises on environmental matters and construction contracts and disputes. The department is involved on a daily basis in the complete range of substantial commercial property transactions.

Media and entertainment: In the media and entertainment field, the firm acts for clients in the film, television, publishing and music industries and is heavily involved in the areas of IT, electronic publishing, multi-media, film and recording contracts and telecommunications. Biddle & Co has acted recently for a number of prominent clients in high-profile defamation cases.

Employment: In the employment field, the firm negotiates and drafts individual service contracts, advises on transfers of undertakings, union consultations, restrictive covenants and Industrial Tribunal claims. It has recently been involved in a leading Court of Appeal case concerning whether "second generation" contracting out is caught by the Transfer of Undertakings Regulations.

Taxation: This department has recently advised various foreign clients on inward investment, devised a number of VAT schemes for clients, represented clients who were subject to Inland Revenue investigations and implemented various employee-related schemes, incuding phantom share schemes and employee share trusts.

Gaming: Biddle & Co deals with all aspects of gaming including casino licensing and lotteries, and liquor licensing.

Food law: Biddle & Co advises on all aspects of food safety, including pre-production advice and labelling and defending clients from prosecutions.

CONTACT PARTNER: Martin Winter

Number of partners:	28
Assistant solicitors:	22
Other fee-earners:	9

WORKLOAD	
Company/ commercial	33%
Litigation	30%
Pensions	25%
Property	12%

CONTACTS	
Construction disputes	David Lancaster
Corporate/commercial	Martin Winter
Employment	Geoff Tyler
Food and drugs law	Julian Harris
Intellectual property	Kim Walker
Litigation	Christopher Winder
Media	David Hooper
Pensions	Hugh Arthur
Personal finance & estates	David Biddle
Property	Peter Watson
Taxation	Desmond O'Connell

BIDDLE & C^O

Personal finance and estates: This department advises on general estate planning, wills and settlements and trusts and probate relating to both UK and foreign assets.

Nature of Clientele: Clients include listed companies, financial institutions, banks, major pension funds, news agencies, newspapers, record, video and television companies, casinos, advertising agencies and publishers.

RECRUITMENT AND TRAINING: The firm's continued expansion and its commitment to the provision of a legal service of the highest quality mean that its recruitment programme is of crucial importance in its overall strategy for growth. Each year, the firm aims to recruit up to six trainee solicitors with the aptitude and potential to contribute to the firm's character and reputation for excellence.

BIGGART BAILLIE & GIFFORD Dalmore House, 310 St. Vincent Street, Glasgow, G2 5QR **Tel:** (0141) 228 8000 **Fax:** (0141) 228 8310 **Ptnrs:** 23 **Asst Solrs:** 35 **Other Fee-earners:** 16. With an office in Edinburgh and many associate offices overseas, the firm offers a wide range of services to predominantly commercial clients.

WORKLOAD			
Commercial property	34%	Corporate	30%
Litigation	23%	Private client	13%

BINDMAN & PARTNERS

275 GRAY'S INN RD, LONDON, WC1X 8QF
DX: 37904 King's Cross

TEL: (0171) 833 4433
FAX: (0171) 837 9792

THE FIRM: Founded in 1974, Bindman & Partners are specialists in civil liberties and human rights issues. The firm has the resources to handle major litigation, and considerable experience and expertise in the following areas. A large amount of legal aid work is handled.

PRINCIPAL AREAS OF WORK:

Defamation and Media Law: (*Contact:* Geoffrey Bindman). Wide experience in representing individuals, newspapers, TV companies and other media organisations.

Immigration and Nationality: (*Contact:* Alison Stanley). Immigration expertise includes work permits, EC, comparative and international migration.

Administrative Law: (*Contact:* Stephen Grosz). *Work includes:* judicial review, environmental protection, discrimination and police powers.

Employment: (*Contact:* Robin Lewis). The firm represents mainly employees, but also some corporations, trade unions, voluntary agencies and pressure groups, on matters including discrimination and equal pay claims.

Crime: (*Contact:* Neil O'May). Work ranges from major fraud cases and serious crimes to minor offences.

Matrimonial: (*Contact:* Felicity Crowther). An extensive matrimonial and family practice includes legally-aided clients.

Children: (*Contact:* Naomi Angell or Katherine Gieve). *Work includes:* wardship, adoption, care proceedings, child abduction, custody and access disputes.

Medical Negligence: (*Contact:* Claire Fazan). The firm has an established expertise in medical negligence and other personal injury cases.

Housing: (*Contact:* Saimo Chahal). The firm handles landlord and tenant law, especially for tenants.

CONTACT PARTNER: Geoffrey Bindman

Number of partners:	12
Assistant solicitors:	4
Other fee-earners:	8

CONTACTS	
Civil litigation	Geoffrey Bindman, Robin Lewis
	Stephen Grosz, Clive Romain
Criminal law	Neil O'May, Adrian Clarke
	Michael Schwarz
	Sharon Persaud
Family law	Felicity Crowther
	Naomi Angell, Katherine Gieve
	Desmond O'Donnell
Housing	Saimo Chahal
Immigration	Alison Stanley, Graham Smith
Medical negligence	Claire Fazan, Jon Nicholson
Personal injury	Claire Fazan, Jon Nicholson

L. BINGHAM & CO 4 Carmelite Street, London, EC4Y 0BN **Tel:** (0171) 583 1660 **Fax:** (0171) 353 5801 **DX:** 0037 Ch.Ln. **Ptnrs:** 3 **Asst Solrs:** 3 **Other Fee-earners:** 2. Known for its expertise in personal injury; also handles property, family/ matrimonial and wills and probate.

BIRCHALL BLACKBURN

1ST FLOOR, CRYSTAL HOUSE, BIRLEY STREET, PRESTON, LANCS, PR1 2AQ
DX: 17101

TEL: (01772) 561663 and 253136
FAX: (01772) 202438

CONTACT PARTNER: Mr J.D. Blackburn

Number of partners:	13
Assistant solicitors:	8
Other fee-earners:	10

THE FIRM: Birchall Blackburn has two main offices in Preston and Manchester, supported by a network of satellite offices in Central and East Lancashire, allowing clients ready access to a comprehensive range of legal services. Founded in 1950 to provide a full range of legal service for corporate, institutional and private clients, Birchall Blackburn is one of the most progressive firms in the North West with a growing reputation within the commercial field. The firm has specialist departments which include commercial and company law, commercial property, commercial and civil litigation, licensing and the leisure sector, family law, corporate and personal insolvency and debt recovery, financial services, international law and private client work. Close partner contact is central within the service which combines commercial awareness and experience with a pragmatic down to earth approach. Legal aid work is also undertaken and the firm are holders of the Legal Aid Franchise.

BIRCHAM & CO IN ASSOCIATION WITH DYSON BELL MARTIN

1 DEAN FARRAR ST, WESTMINSTER, LONDON, SW1H 0DY
DX: 2317 Victoria

TEL: (0171) 222 8044
FAX: (0171) 222 3480

CONTACT PARTNER: John Stephenson

Number of partners:	21
Assistant solicitors:	18
Other fee-earners:	29

WORKLOAD	
Private client/charities	28%
Litigation	25%
Parliamentary/public affairs	20%
Property	17%
Company commercial	10%

THE FIRM: Bircham & Co. was founded in 1834 by Francis Bircham, later to become President of the Law Society. The firm retains a substantial private client and property practice, but has also built on its expertise in the areas of litigation and commercial law, in order to maintain a balance of clientele. It also comprises a leading Parliamentary agency and public affairs practice, under the name Dyson Bell Martin. It has an established reputation for courtesy and integrity and seeks to provide a prompt, integrated service at partner level from all its departments.

PRINCIPAL AREAS OF WORK:

Private Client and Charities: (*Contact:* Simon Weil). The firm has a large private client practice and deals with all aspects of financial planning for the individual, including wills, trusts and, in liaison with the Tax department, personal taxation. Probate administration is also undertaken. The firm also acts for a number of national charities, as well as having expertise in the area of heritage property.

Medico/ Legal and Personal Injury: (*Contact:* Veronica Williams). The firm is particularly strong in this field, embracing both litigious and non-litigious matters. The firm acts on behalf of a number of health authorities in defending medical negligence claims, as well as pursuing actions for plaintiffs. It also acts for a number of private medical institutions and hospitals, providing them with a full range of legal services, as well as specialised advice.

Property: (*Contact:* John Stephenson). Both commercial and private client property work is undertaken by the firm. The commercial group specialises in the areas of retail warehouse development, City property developments, investment portfolios, planning and commercial landlord and tenant work. The private client group carries out high quality residential and agricultural property work (including work for large landed estates in London and outside). The firm is also developing a niche practice in the leasehold reform field.

Litigation: (*Contact:* George Josselyn). Apart from the litigious side of the distinct medico/ legal service, this department deals with a wide range of litigation matters, including building and landlord and tenant disputes, commercial litigation, employment law, copyright and passing-off actions, professional negligence and defamation, debt collection, and all aspects of matrimonial and family law.

Tax: (*Contact:* Michael Wood). The department caters for all aspects of taxation, drawing on the skills of specialists both in corporate and personal taxation. The firm has an established offshore facility for its international tax planning work in the personal and corporate contexts for both UK and overseas clients.

Company/ Commercial: (*Contact:* Ian Adamson). This department offers a full range of services to the commercial client, acting for small, new businesses and multinational companies. In particular, the department deals with company formations, partnership and shareholder agreements, mergers and acquisitions, court schemes, and insolvency and liquidation.

Corporate Finance: (*Contact:* David Goodman or John Turnbull). This unit within the company/ commercial department advises smaller and medium-sized companies on all methods of raising finance including flotations and on MBOs, MBIs and BIMBOs.

Parliamentary/ Public Affairs: (Dyson Bell Martin) (*Contact:* Nick Brown). This side of the firm comprises the parliamentary agency and its associated legislative and public affairs practice. Work is undertaken in Brussels and Strasbourg as well as in Westminster. Besides drafting all forms of legislation, it also presents clients' submissions to, and is active in influencing decision makers at local, national and European levels.

Environment: (*Contact:* Paul Johnson). The firm has particular experience in the areas of pollution, nuisance, health and safety at work, planning and the environmental impact of major transport and other infrastructure schemes. The department acts for both commercial and private clients, and for local authorities and other public bodies and agencies.

NATURE OF CLIENTELE: The firm acts for many substantial public sector and charitable institutions, whilst offering services for commercial clients ranging from new businesses to multinational companies. It also retains a very significant private client practice.

LANGUAGES SPOKEN: French, German, Italian and Spanish.

AGENCY WORK: All types of litigation agency work are undertaken and George Josselyn should be contacted for further information.

FOREIGN CONNECTIONS: Associated offices in Paris, Milan, Brussels and Dublin.

BIRCH CULLIMORE Friars, White Friars, Chester, CH1 1XS **Tel:** (01244) 321066 **Fax:** (01244) 312582 **DX:** 19985 Chester **Ptnrs:** 7 **Other Fee-earners:** 9. A well-established firm known as a general private client practice. Now expanding on the commercial side. Legal aid work undertaken.

WORKLOAD			
Private Client	38%	Res/Commercial convey	29%
Litigation/ Matrimonial	16%	Trust Administration	8%
Ecclesiast/Charity/Agric	8%		

BIRD & BIRD

90 FETTER LANE, LONDON, EC4A 1JP
DX: 119

TEL: (0171) 415 6000
FAX: (0171) 415 6111

THE FIRM: A broadly-based commercial law firm, best known for its intellectual property and technology expertise, particularly in the areas of communications, information technology and technology transfer.

PRINCIPAL AREAS OF WORK:

Brands and Trade Marks: (*5 Partners*). A dedicated brands and trademarks group provides specialist advice on the full range of strategic, contractual and litigation issues associated with this field.

Commercial Litigation: (*5 Partners*). This department undertakes all forms of UK and international commercial disputes including sale of goods, computer disputes, product liability, property litigation, insurance, defamation, professional negligence, employment, shipping, international trade, arbitration and ADR work.

Commercial Property: (*3 Partners*). Comprehensive service in relation to all land transactions including property finance and development for a wide range of companies, organisations and individuals.

Company/Commercial: (*12 Partners*). Full range of legal services including mergers & acquisitions, joint ventures, LBJ's, MBI's and MBO's, restructuring, flotations and the related tax issues.

SENIOR PARTNER: David Harriss

Number of partners:	30
Assistant solicitors:	43
Other fee-earners:	19

WORKLOAD	
Company	40%
Intellectual property	29%
Litigation	15%
Property	13%
Private client	3%

EC: (*2 Partners*). European community law forms an integral part of Bird & Bird's client services. Advice is provided through the Brussels office and concentrates in particular on competition enforcement and legislative developments within each of the firm's specialist sectors.

Employment: (*5 Partners*). Advice on contracts of employment, requirements of UK and EC law, TUPE on outsourcing, mergers & acquisitions, employee incentive schemes, termination and the enforcement of fiduciary duties and contractual obligations by injunction.

Environment: (*2 Partners*). Advice and assistance on waste on land, atmospheric pollution, noise, water, hazardous substances and product liability issues, particularly in relation to mergers & acquisitions and property transactions.

Health: (*4 Partners*). Over 40 years' experience in this field. Comprehensive service handling, amongst other things, medical negligence claims and property matters. The firm advises a wide range of NHS Trusts and other healthcare organisations.

Information Technology: (*10 Partners*). Lawyers with technical backgrounds and in-house IT industry experience provide a full range of advice to IT users and suppliers in the public, private and utilities sectors, on IT procurement, outsourcing, electronic trading and IT disputes.

Intellectual Property: (*8 Partners*). Extensive experience in all aspects of this field, but best known for conducting patent actions and other substantial litigation with a heavy technical content.

Multimedia: (*8 Partners*). Full range of commercial advice including joint ventures and financing; rights acquisition and clearance; publishing; electronic distribution and payment; marketing; telecommunications and broadcasting issues; international issues such as defamation and tax.

Pharmaceuticals: (*6 Partners*). Substantial practice handling a wide range of matters for clients in the pharamaceuticals, biotechnology and medical devices sectors, in particular corporate finance, intellectual property, product liability and regulatory issues.

Sport: (*2 Partners*). Advice and assistance on the full range of sports marketing and administration work with extensive domestic and international transactional experience for governing bodies, rights purchasers, sports businesses, teams and individuals; including UK and EC competition law and tax.

Telecommunications: (*7 Partners*). Substantial practice advising on international infrastructure projects, regulation of the industry, provision of service, use of apparatus, interconnection of systems, and competition law issues.

NATURE OF CLIENTELE: Bird & Bird services a wide spectrum of organisations from multinationals and institutions to smaller companies and private individuals. A significant proportion of their clients are high-technology companies.

RECRUITMENT: *Partner:* Graham Camps. Six trainee solicitors and a number of assistant solicitors are recruited annually. The firm's Law Society accredited training programme is co-ordinated by a university law lecturer.

OTHER OFFICE: 209A Avenue Louise, 1050 Brussels
Tel: (322) 644 3616 *Fax:* (322) 644 2486 *Contact:* Simon Topping.

CONTACTS	
Brands & Trade Marks	Morag Macdonald
Commercial litigation	Graham J.H. Smith
Commercial property	Robert Scott
Company/Commercial	David Byam-Cook
EC	Simon Topping
Employment	Penelope Christie
Environment	Robert Scott
Health	David Stone
Information technology	Hamish Sandison
Intellectual property	Trevor Cook
Multimedia	Rory Graham
Pharmaceuticals	Trevor Cook
Sport	Justin Walkey
Telecommunications	David Kerr

B I R D & B I R D

BIRD SEMPLE 249 West George Street, Glasgow, G2 4RB **Tel:** (0141) 221 7090 **Fax:** (0141) 204 1902 **DX:** 10 Glasgow **Ptnrs:** 13 **Asst Solrs:** 25 **Other Fee-earners:** 6. Broad based practice specialising in all aspects of commercial law. Also has an office in Edinburgh.

CD-ROM EDITION ON THE INTERNET

This edition of the directory is available on a CD-ROM which includes both DOS and Windows versions. It can be loaded onto a network, and works with virtually any IBM compatible PC. The CD-ROM version offers computer-users the advantage of rapid search, retrieval and cross-referencing. It is also available via the Internet.

BIRKETTS

20-32 MUSEUM ST, IPSWICH, SUFFOLK, IP1 1HZ
DX: 3206 Ipswich

TEL: (01473) 232300
FAX: (01473) 230524

THE FIRM: With effect from 1st June 1995 **Birkett Westhorp & Long** demerged to form two separate practices in Suffolk (Ipswich) and Essex (Colchester and Halstead). **Birketts** is the newly independent Ipswich practice. The firm is a member of the North Sea Group of Lawyers.

PRINCIPAL AREAS OF WORK:

Litigation: *(Contact Partner:* David Hallett). Construction, Personal Injuries, Commercial, Debt Collection, ADR.

Property: *(Contact Partner:* Peter Weir). Funding, Development, Agriculture.

Shipping and Transport: *(Contact Partner:* John Weston).

Corporate Law: *(Contact Partner:* Annette Whybrow). Employment, Pensions, Corporate Affairs.

NATURE OF CLIENTELE: Includes major UK insurance companies, locally-based PLCs, farmers, landowners, property developers and construction companies, shippers and hauliers, brewers and small businesses.

CONTACT PARTNER: Bob Wright

Number of partners:	24
Assistant solicitors:	9
Other fee-earners:	24

WORKLOAD	
Other litigation	23%
Personal injury litigation	18%
Private client	15%
Commercial property	15%
Corporate	15%
Domestic property	14%

BIRKETT LONG Essex House, 42 Crouch St, Colchester, Essex, CO3 3HH **Tel:** (01206) 562296 **Fax:** (01206) 572393 **DX:** 3603 Colchester **Ptnrs:** 15 **Asst Solrs:** 2 **Other Fee-earners:** 16.

WORKLOAD			
Lit - private client/PI	23%	Litigation - commercial	23%
Property	21%	Private client	18%
Commercial	10%	Planning	5%

B.M. BIRNBERG & CO 103 Borough High St, London Bridge, London, SE1 1NN **Tel:** (0171) 403 3166 **Fax:** (0171) 378 1856 **DX:** 39903 London Bridge South **Ptnrs:** 2 **Asst Solrs:** 6 **Other Fee-earners:** 6. A general but mainly legal aid practice offering a wide range of services but with an emphasis on civil liberties, criminal defence and police malpractice.

BISHOP AND ROBERTSON CHALMERS

2 BLYTHSWOOD SQUARE, GLASGOW, G2 4AD
DX: 11 Glasgow

TEL: (0141) 248 4672
FAX: (0141) 221 9270

22 Ainslie Place, Edinburgh EH3 6JA
DX: ED215

Tel: (0131) 220 3355
Fax: (0131) 220 3777

THE FIRM: One of the larger firms in Scotland, with offices in Glasgow and Edinburgh this firm has a commercial focus. The non-commercial needs of clients can also be met by the Private Client Division. Employing the latest technology systems and reacting swiftly to commercial, social and legal developments both at home and in Europe, the firm displays a forward-looking approach tailored to its clients' needs.

Bishop and Robertson Chalmers operates in three divisions; business law which has units specialising in corporate, commercial property, pensions, European Community law and environmental law; litigation which has specialist construction law, insolvency and employers/public liability units and private client/trusts.

PRINCIPAL AREAS OF WORK:

Business Law Division: The practice is well known for its work in the corporate law field, including corporate restructuring, take overs, mergers, management buy-outs, and advising banks and insurance companies; intellectual property law; media law; insolvency law; pensions law, including benefit design, establishment of schemes, acquisitions and disposals, insolvency wind-ups, redundancies, trusteeships (advising trustees or providing trustee services either individual or through our company,

CONTACT PARTNER: Mr John A. Welsh

Number of partners:	19
Assistant solicitors:	19
Other fee-earners:	21

CONTACTS	
Commercial property	Helen Stirling (Glasgow)
	James Warnock (Edinburgh)
Corporate	James Millar (Glasgow)
	Rodger Murray (Edinburgh)
Debt recovery	David Whyte (Glasgow)
EC law	Iain Taylor (Glasgow)
Employment	David Whyte (Glasgow)
Environmental	Kenneth Ross (Glasgow)

Mitre Pensions Ltd) and all aspects of general advice in pensions law and practice. Accreditations as specialists have been awarded by The Law Society of Scotland to Russell Lang in insolvency law and Iain Talman in pensions law.

The firm has devoted considerable resources to developing expertise in European Community Law and can offer commercial clients concise assistance on competition law and the effect of environmental legislation. Clients can benefit from the firm's ability to identify legislation in progress and lobby the client's view point, to advise on the effects of legislation as it is implemented and to provide litigation services at the European Court of Justice and the Court of First Instance in Luxembourg.

For commercial property work there is a team with a wealth of practical experience. Among the range of services available are: purchases, sales, leasing, securities, town and country planning, property investment, property development, licensing and environmental advice.

Litigation Division: The division has experience in all fields of litigation whether in Court of Session, Sheriff Court, or the criminal courts. Tom Marshall in the Edinburgh Office is a Solicitor Advocate and is a fellow of the Chartered Institute of Arbiters. Accreditations as specialists by The Law Society of Scotland have been awarded to John Welsh in construction law and as a solicitor mediator, and David Whyte in employment law. The range of services available include: arbitration, contract disputes, construction law, alternative dispute resolution, damage claims, employment law, industrial relations, licensing, matrimonial law, personal and property claims, insolvency, bankruptcy and debt recovery.

Private Client Division: The division covers all aspects of law affecting the individual, including purchase and sale of residential property, wills, inheritance tax planning, trusts, financial management and independent financial and investment advice.

As authorised by Law Society of Scotland, the firm also offers independent financial and investment advice.

OTHER OFFICES: A. Mickevivivaus Street, 14-1, 2004 Vilnius, Lithuania.

FOREIGN LANGUAGES: French, German.

International connections and associated offices: Member of IAG International. Associated offices throughout Western and Eastern Europe, Northern and Central America and Hong Kong.

Insolvency	Russell Lang (Glasgow)
Litigation	Alastair Lockhart (Glasgow)
	Tom Marshall (Edinburgh)
Pensions	Iain Talman (Glasgow)
Private client	Madeleine Thomson (Glasgow)

EDITORIAL POLICY

In this edition, the lists of specialists include profiles of individual practitioners - solicitors and barristers - who have been recommended most frequently to our researchers. Editorial policy is to identify leading practitioners on merit: it is not possible to buy a place in our biographical lists. Inclusion of a profile in this directory is based solely on expertise and reputation.

Enormous effort has been invested by our ten-strong research team (mainly solicitors and barristers) in canvassing recommendations and identifying leaders. We are confident in the overall accuracy of the results. However, mistakes and misjudgements are inevitable, and if readers have any suggestions regarding our listings we should be very pleased to hear from them.

BISHOP LONGBOTHAM & BAGNALL Rodney Hse, 5 Roundstone St, Trowbridge, Wilts, BA14 8DH **Tel:** (01225) 755656 **Fax:** (01225) 753266 **DX:** 43106 **Ptnrs:** 7 **Asst Solrs:** 8 **Other Fee-earners:** 13. General practice best known for its work in commercial property, criminal law, personal injury and family law.

WORKLOAD			
Property	23%	Personal injury	19%
Family/ matrimonial	15%	Company/ commercial	13%
Criminal	9%		

C & J BLACK Linenhall House, 13 Linenhall Street, Belfast, BT2 8AA **Tel:** (01232) 550060 **Fax:** (01232) 234125 **Ptnrs:** 3 **Asst Solrs:** 2 **Other Fee-earners:** 1. The firm has a strong client base of both private and commercial clients. Its partners are familiar with the legal systems of England and Wales, the Republic of Ireland and Belgium, as well as Northern Ireland.

WORKLOAD			
Non-cont comm/company	37%	Private client	35%
Litigation	15%	Other/mainly matrim/emp	13%

BLACKADDER REID JOHNSTON

30-34 REFORM STREET, DUNDEE, TAYSIDE, DD1 1RJ
DX: DD2 Dundee

TEL: (01382) 229222
FAX: (01382) 201132

THE FIRM: Blackadder Reid Johnston has been securely established in the Dundee area for over 170 years. Whilst much has changed during that time, the firm remains committed to quality and a high standard of client care. It is proud of its longstanding reputation in the region and, whilst focusing on the future, it maintains its links with the traditions of the past. As a practical demonstration of its commitment to quality, in 1989 Blackadder Reid Johnston became a founder member of LawGroup UK, the national network of quality legal firms.

PRINCIPAL AREAS OF WORK:

Corporate & Commercial: *(Contact Partner:* Sandy Meiklejohn). The department advises on mergers and acquisitions, management buy-outs, commercial property, the establishment of new businesses (including recruitment and statutory regulations), landlord and tenant matters, employment and licensing.

Litigation: *(Contact Partners:* Wilson McMichael and Lindsay Foulis). Representation is provided in personal injury claims, family law matters, criminal proceedings, commercial litigation, mortgage repossessions, arbitration, insolvency and debt collection. Legal aid is available.

Private Client: *(Contact Partner:* Dennis Young). The firm handles the preparation of wills, the setting up of trusts and curatories, powers of attorney, inheritance tax planning, the winding up of estates and administration of trusts and agricultural law.

Property Services: *(Contact Partners:* Donald Hutcheson and Alistair Grieve). A complete conveyancing and estate agency service is offered to those dealing with residential property. The firm has one of the largest property departments in the Tayside region.

Financial Services: *(Contact Manager:* Keith Thomson). The department assists with mortgages, insurance services, pensions and investments.

OTHER OFFICES:
Property Sales Office: 40 Whitehall Street, Dundee. *Tel:* (01382) 229222.
Financial Services Office: 3 Bank Street, Dundee. *Tel:* (01382) 229222.
138 Albert Street, Stobswell, Dundee. *Tel:* (01382) 452200.
259 Brook Street, Broughty Ferry, Dundee. *Tel:* (01382) 229222.
63 High Street, Monifieth. *Tel:* (01382) 532634.
63 High Street, Carnoustie. *Tel:* (01241) 853240.
11 Bank Street, Kirriemuir, Angus. *Tel:* (01575) 572613.

FOREIGN LANGUAGES: French and German.

CONTACT PARTNER: Mr. Dennis J. Young

Number of partners:	16
Consultants:	2
Assistant solicitors:	14
Other fee-earners:	16

WORKLOAD	
Conveyancing/ estate agency	42%
Private client	26%
Commercial/ corporate	15%
Litigation	9%
Financial services	8%

CONTACTS	
Commercial	W.A. Meiklejohn
Conveyancing	D.H.C. Hutcheson
Corporate	J.P. Clark
Estate agency	A.M. Grieve
Financial services	J.P. Clark
Litigation	W.R.W. McMichael
Private client	D.J. Young

**BLACKADDER
REID
JOHNSTON**

Solicitors & Estate Agents

BLACK GRAF & CO 14-15 College Crescent, Swiss Cottage, London, NW3 5LL **Tel:** (0171) 586 1141 **Fax:** (0171) 586 3721 **DX:** 38853 **Ptnrs:** 5 **Asst Solrs:** 5 . The firm is predominantly a commercial firm providing a comprehensive conveyancing service and civil litigation and probate advice.

BLACKHURST PARKER & YATES

9 Cannon Street, Preston, Lancs, PR1 3QD **Tel:** (01772) 253601 **Fax:** (01772) 202085 **DX:** 17113 Preston 1 **Ptnrs:** 7 **Asst Solrs:** 4 **Other Fee-earners:** 2. A general practice with three offices in Lancashire and a mixed private and commercial clientele. Areas of work include litigation, property and probate. Civil and criminal legal aid work undertaken.

WORKLOAD			
Civil Litigation	30%	Matrimonial & Family	25%
Conveyancing	20%	Probate	10%
Commercial	10%	Criminal	5%

BLAIR ALLISON & CO

Fountain Court, Steelhouse Lane, Birmingham, W. Midlands, B4 6EE **Tel:** (0121) 233 2904 **Fax:** (0121) 236 8913 **DX:** 23534 **Ptnrs:** 3 **Asst Solrs:** 3 **Other Fee-earners:** 1. Concentrates on matrimonial law and conveyancing.

WORKLOAD			
Family Law	90%	Conveyancing	4%
Civil lit incl agency	3%	Probate	3%

BLAIR & BRYDEN

27 Union Street, Greenock, Strathclyde, PA16 8DD **Tel:** (01475) 888777 **Fax:** (01457) 781836 **DX:** 2 Greenock **Ptnrs:** 15 **Asst Solrs:** 13 **Other Fee-earners:** 19. With six other offices the firm is a broadly based general practice. Work includes personal injury, litigation, family, crime and licensing.

WORKLOAD			
Domestic/comm convey	24%	Corporate	17%
Criminal work	15%	Consistorial	15%
Others	10%	Civil/commercial lit	10%

BLAKE LAPTHORN

NEW COURT, 1 BARNES WALLIS ROAD, SEGENSWORTH, FAREHAM, HANTS, PO15 5UA   DX: 45260 Park Gate

TEL: (01489) 579990
FAX: (01489) 579127

THE FIRM: Blake Lapthorn was established in 1869, and has expanded significantly to become one of the UK's largest regional firms, with a particularly successful commercial practice. It is a member of the Law South Group, and is developing extensive links within Europe, particularly in France and Germany.

CONTACT PARTNER: David Russell

Number of partners:	30
Assistant solicitors:	52
Other fee-earners:	33

PRINCIPAL AREAS OF WORK:

Company/ Commercial: (*Contact Partner:* Caroline Williams). The department has particular expertise in the areas of: commercial contracts, acquisitions and disposals, corporate taxation, MBOs, mergers, corporate finance, pensions and insolvency. It also handles franchising, intellectual property, EC, competition, computer contracts, construction contracts, employment matters and licensing. The department also receives instructions from educational establishments and public and local authorities.

Commercial Property: (*Contact Partner:* Chris Taunt). The department specialises in the sale and purchase of freehold and leasehold property, options, the granting and taking of leases and development, funding and joint venture agreements. It can also offer expert planning and environmental advice. The department also undertakes a significant volume of work for national and regional breweries.

Litigation: (*Contact Partner:* David Higham). Blake Lapthorn has one of the largest civil litigation departments outside London which handles a substantial volume of personal injury, medical injury and professional negligence claims. Work also includes all kinds of commercial and construction disputes, pension litigation, transport disputes and white collar crime. It also has a substantial debt collection department.

OTHER AREAS OF WORK: A comprehensive private client service includes a large amount of domestic conveyancing work, wills, trusts and probate, matrimonial work and general financial advice. The firm is a member of The Association of Solicitor Investment Managers (ASIM).

OTHER OFFICES: In addition to a prestigious and purpose-built commercial office, Blake Lapthorn has offices in Portsmouth, Southampton and London.

CONTACTS	
Charity Law	Ray Vincent
Civil litigation	David Higham
Company/ commercial	Caroline Williams
Company/ property	Chris Taunt
Construction	Peter Barber
Criminal law	John Mitchell
Debt collection	Nicholas Poole
Education	Carey Blake
Employment	Max Craft
Environmental/ planning	Colin Barlow
Financial planning	David Collins
Information technology	Charles Matthews
Licensing law	Walter Cha
Pensions law	Philip Harwood Smart
Residential property	Michael Profit
Tax	David Russell

BLAKEMORES Station Tower, Station Square, Coventry, W. Midlands, CV1 2GR **Tel:** (01203) 525858 **Fax:** (01203) 228440 **DX:** 11228 Coventry **Ptnrs:** 13 **Asst Solrs:** 8 **Other Fee-earners:** 15. Deals primarily with company/ commercial work and commercial litigation. Head office in Coventry; branch offices in Ashby-de-la-Zouch, Birmingham, Leamington Spa, Solihull, Stratford and Tetbury.

BLAKESLEY RICE MACDONALD

99 SALTERGATE, CHESTERFIELD, DERBYS, S40 1LD
DX: 12358

TEL: (01246) 203261
FAX: (01246) 271207

THE FIRM: The firm is a product of a merger in 1990 of Blakesley & Rooth (founded in 1935) and Rice MacDonald. It is a progressive firm with strong and respected commercial departments, in addition to being well-known for its private client work, particularly in the matrimonial field.

PRINCIPAL AREAS OF WORK:
Company/ Commercial: 1 Partner. *Contact:* Michael MacDonald
Commercial Property: 2 Partners. *Contact:* Jeremy C. Rice
Commercial Litigation: 1 Partner. *Contact:* Neil A. Brown
Residential Conveyancing: *Contact:* Malcolm A. Smith/ Patrick A. Roome
Probate, Wills, Trusts: 1 Partner. *Contact:* Alan J. Redfern
Personal Injury: 1 Partner. *Contact:* Peter J. McGowan
Family: 2 Partners. *Contact:* Clifford W. Bellamy
Crime/ General Litigation: 1 Partner. *Contact:* Michael Wall

CONTACT PARTNER: Mr. M. MacDonald

Number of partners:	8
Assistant solicitors:	2
Other fee-earners:	4

WORKLOAD	
Company/ commercial	21%
Family	20%
Commercial property	15%
Residential conveyancing	11%
Crime/ general litigation	10%
Commercial litigation	10%
Personal injury	8%
Probate/ wills	5%

BLANDY & BLANDY

1 FRIAR ST, READING, BERKS, RG1 1DA
DX: 4008 Reading

TEL: (01734) 587111
FAX: (01734) 583032

THE FIRM: Founded in 1733, Blandy & Blandy is an old established legal practice, which has a long association with Reading. Despite its longevity, the firm is friendly, approachable and modern in its outlook. Both individual and business clients are provided with a full range of legal services. Legal aid is available in appropriate cases.

PRINCIPAL AREAS OF WORK:
Litigation: The firm has a substantial litigation practice which is divided into three areas:
  Family Law: *Work includes:* divorce, child-care, financial provisions, emergency injunctions, and maintenance disputes. Memberships: Solicitors Family Law Association.
  Civil Litigation: *Work includes:* personal injury claims, building disputes, landlord and tenant problems, debt collection, licensing and inheritance disputes.
  Criminal and Magistrates Courts Litigation: *Work includes:* all criminal matters including motoring offences and mental health work.
Company/ Commercial: *Work includes:* company/ partnership formations, acquisition and sale of companies, corporate insolvency, winding-up and bankruptcy, joint ventures, MBOs, competition law, employment disputes and EC law.
Property: *Work includes:* buying, selling and mortgaging both commercial and residential property, estate development, planning matters and Housing Association work.
Private Client: *Work includes:* wills, trusts, probate, and tax planning.
RECRUITMENT AND TRAINING: The firm attaches great importance to recruitment and training. Applications in writing, together with CV, to Philip D'Arcy.
  The firm are members of Lawgroup UK the national network of high quality independent firms of solicitors.

CONTACT PARTNER: Mr. P.B. D'Arcy

Number of partners:	11
Assistant solicitors:	9
Other fee-earners:	6

WORKLOAD	
Litigation	45%
Company/ commercial	16%
Private client	15%
Conveyancing	12%
Commercial property	12%

CONTACTS	
Child care	Brenda Long
Civil litigation	Philip D'Arcy
Commercial property	Kate Taylor
Commercial litigation	Sue Dowling
Company/ commercial	Philip Tranter
Crime	Tim Hammick
Employment	Richard Griffiths
Family	Andrew Don
Licensing	Sue Dowling
Personal injury	Philip D'Arcy
Private client	David Sutton

BLICK & CO Sophie House, 32-35 Featherstone Street, London, EC1Y 8QX **Tel:** (0171) 253 6250 **Fax:** (0171) 251 3519 **Ptnrs:** 7 **Asst Solrs:** 2 **Other Fee-earners:** 1. General practice specialising in shipping, matrimonial, property, company and criminal law. Legal Aid available.

WORKLOAD			
Shipping	40%	Family law	30%
Company	20%	Commercial/Property lit	10%

BLUNTS

2 KING EDWARD STREET, MACCLESFIELD, CHES, SK10 1AA
DX: 19393

TEL: (01625) 429131
FAX: (01625) 511016

THE FIRM: The firm was founded over 100 years ago in Macclesfield, and in the last ten years has expanded considerably, particularly into computerised debt collection at its Walsall Office.

PRINCIPAL AREAS OF WORK: The firm is strong in commercial and domestic conveyancing, debt collection, matrimonial and personal injury, probate and wills.

AGENCY WORK: Family work and criminal matters, general litigation.
Contact Partners: Nigel Read, Macclesfield *Tel:* (01625) 429131.

OTHER OFFICE: Bridge House, Bridge Street, Walsall - (01922) 36007.

CONTACT PARTNER: Nigel R. Read

Number of partners:	7
Assistant solicitors:	1
Other fee-earners:	4

WORKLOAD	
Debt collection	50%
Commercial and domestic conveyancing	30%
Personal injury & matrimonial	20%
Probate and wills	10%

BLYTHE LIGGINS

EDMUND HOUSE, RUGBY ROAD, LEAMINGTON SPA, WARKS, CV32 6EL
DX: 11872

TEL: (01926) 831231
FAX: (01926) 422607

THE FIRM: Blythe Liggins prides itself on its progressive approach, combining efficiency with professional excellence and strong, clear management. The service is personal and the partners place emphasis on getting to know their clients individually and their businesses. The firm offers expertise in all major areas of the law.

PRINCIPAL AREAS OF WORK:

Company and Commercial: *(Contact Partner:* David Lester). *Work includes:* acquisitions and disposals, company formation and business planning, partnerships, insolvency and debt collection, licensing and competition law.

Commercial Litigation: *(Contact Partner:* Richard Thornton). *Work includes:* High Court and County Court litigation, including employment law, personal injury, insurance, consumer law, intellectual property and building disputes.

Commercial and Residential Property: *(Contact Partner:* Patrick Riley). *Work includes:* town and country planning, commercial and domestic property, purchase and sale advice, and landlord and tenant matters.

Private Client: *(Contact Partner:* Paul Waterworth). *Work includes:* matrimonial and family law, tax and financial planning and pensions, estate planning, and wills, probates and trusts.

NATURE OF CLIENTELE: The firm acts for large companies, multinationals, finance houses, educational establishments, charities, small businesses and private individuals.

OTHER OFFICES: Associated offices in Spain, Portugal, Austria, USA and Scotland.

CONTACT PARTNER: Paul B. Waterworth

Number of partners:	11
Assistant solicitors:	6
Other fee-earners:	8

WORKLOAD	
Litigation	40%
Property	30%
Company & commercial	20%
Private client	10%

CONTACTS	
Civil litigation	Richard Thornton
Commercial property	Patrick Riley
Company/ commercial	David Lester
Domestic property	John Labrum
Employment	Richard Moon
Family litigation	Paul Waterworth
Private client	Donald Hunter

BOBBETTS MACKAN

20A BERKELEY SQUARE, CLIFTON, BRISTOL, BS8 1HP
DX: 7838

TEL: (0117) 929 9001
FAX: (0117) 922 5697

THE FIRM: Established in the 1880s, it is a substantial litigation practice acting both for individual clients and handling agency work for the profession. It has concentrated on developing expert teams within each of its main departments. A member of Law Group UK.

PRINCIPAL AREAS OF WORK: Civil department, family and childcare department, criminal defence department, including Courts Martial, and general practice and conveyancing department.

AGENCY WORK: Civil litigation, including advocacy: *Contact:* Mr. Kevin Wood or Mr. Brian Cox. Criminal defence work, advocacy, advice in police stations: *Contact:* Mr. Tony Miles. Family and Childcare: *Contact:* Sally Mitchell.

CONTACT PARTNER: Mr A. Miles

Number of partners:	5
Assistant solicitors:	13
Other fee-earners:	12

WORKLOAD	
Criminal defence	30%
Civil litigation	30%
Matrimonial, care, children	25%
Non-contentious	15%

BOLITHO WAY 15-18 King's Terrace, Portsmouth, Hants, PO5 3AL **Tel:** (01705) 820747 **Fax:** (01705) 862831 **DX:** 2205 Portsmouth **Ptnrs:** 6 **Asst Solrs:** 1 **Other Fee-earners:** 3. Focusing on litigation and intellectual property, particularly computer software. Provides comprehensive service to business and private clients.

WORKLOAD			
Personal injury	20%	Company/ commercial	17%
Civil/commercial lit	15%	Matrimonial/ family	12%
Private client	9%	Intellectual property	8%

BONAR MACKENZIE WS 9-11 Hill Street, Edinburgh, EH2 3JT **Tel:** (0131) 225 8371 **Fax:** (0131) 225 2048 **DX:** 7 Edinburgh **Ptnrs:** 11 **Asst Solrs:** 4 **Other Fee-earners:** 7. A well-established city centre Edinburgh firm handling a full range of legal services. Particularly known for its expertise in insolvency, debt recovery and property.

BOND PEARCE

BALLARD HOUSE, WEST HOE ROAD, PLYMOUTH, DEVON, PL1 3AE
DX: 8251 Plymouth

TEL: (01752) 266633
FAX: (01752) 225350

THE FIRM: Bond Pearce is a leading regional law firm with offices in two key South West centres, Exeter and Plymouth. Commercially aware, progressive and innovative, the firm is one of the largest in the region. Membership of The Norton Rose M5 Group of independent legal practices enhances the firm's national and international presence with offices spanning the UK, Europe, the Middle East and Far East.

PRINCIPAL AREAS OF WORK:

Company/ Commercial: (*Contact:* Simon Richardson). The department handles a wide range of work including business acquisition, disposal and financing, management buy-outs, company restructuring, mergers, Stock Exchange and USM listings, UK and EC competition, agency, distributor and franchise networks, intellectual property and pensions.

Banking and Insolvency: (*Contact:* Victor Tettmar). The department includes five licensed insolvency practitioners and deals with a wide range of work for banks, building societies and insolvency practitioners.

Property: (*Contact:* David Gunn). The property department concentrates primarily on commercial and industrial property and deals with a wide range of investment, development, management and construction work. The firm has a particularly strong planning and environmental unit comprising five lawyers and has been in the forefront of work relating to alternative energy projects.

Litigation: (*Contact:* Richard Challands). The firm is particularly well known for its work in the fields of commercial litigation, professional indemnity, insurance, product liability, construction law, intellectual property, employment, landlord and tenant, personal injury, marine and debt recovery.

CONTACT PARTNER: Jonathan Trafford

Number of partners:	37
Assistant solicitors:	67
Other fee-earners:	24

WORKLOAD	
Litigation	54%
Company,commercial,banking,insolvency	22%
Property	17%
Private client	7%

CONTACTS	
Banking	Victor Tettmar
Commercial litigation	Simon Richardson
Commercial property	David Gunn
Company/ commercial	Roger Acock
Construction	Michael Ford
Employment	Nikki Duncan
Environment	Marcus Trinick
Family	Wendy Boyce

Private Client: (*Contact:* Jonathan Nicholson). The firm offers a full range of services to the private client which includes wills, probate and trusts, estate administration, personal taxation, inheritance tax planning, pensions, off-shore funds, charities, family law, matrimonial and residential conveyancing.

NATURE OF CLIENTELE: Bond Pearce has a broad client base and provides a full range of legal services for major corporations through to private clients. The firm serves primarily commercial and institutional clients including banks, building societies, insurance companies, public and private companies and educational institutions.

OTHER AREAS OF WORK: Bond Pearce accepts all types of agency work.

FOREIGN LANGUAGES SPOKEN: French, German, Swedish, Italian, Russian.

RECRUITMENT AND TRAINING: The firm's culture places strong emphasis on client care, quality of service, training and the development of new specialisations. It continues to recruit newly qualified solicitors as well as specialists. Around ten trainees are chosen annually and prospects are good; nearly half the present partners were trainees with the firm. Regular training courses are held both in-house and with The Norton Rose M5 Group.

OTHER OFFICES: Darwin House, Southernhay Gardens, Exeter, Devon EX1 1LA. *Tel:* (01392) 211185. *Fax:* (01392) 435543. *DX:* 8321 Exeter.

Insolvency	Hamish Anderson
Insurance	Bettina Rigg
Landlord and tenant	Brian Starks
Litigation	Richard Challands
Pensions	Stephen Williams
Personal injury	Jon Cooper
Private client	Jonathan Nicholson
Shipping	Stephen Hankin
Tax planning	Michael Williams

BOODLE HATFIELD

43 BROOK STREET, LONDON, W1Y 2BL
DX: 53

TEL: (0171) 629 7411
FAX: (0171) 629 2621

THE FIRM: Boodle Hatfield has grown from a property-based firm founded over 250 years ago into a leading Central London commercial practice, with regional offices in Southampton and Oxford. Its main departments are property, corporate services, litigation and tax and financial planning. The firm aims to establish close working relationships with all its clients and to provide clear, practical and expert advice.

PRINCIPAL AREAS OF WORK:

Corporate/ Commercial: The corporate services department offers a comprehensive range of skills relating to mergers and acquisitions, management buyouts, corporate finance, banking, investment agreements, joint ventures and commercial agreements and to intellectual property and information technology. It has particular experience in the leisure, transport and information technology/telecommunications sectors. A specialist Anglo-German practice is headed by a bilingual, dual-qualified English partner; a multi-lingual Belgian lawyer provides advice on EU matters.

Litigation: The department is active in all kinds of substantial commercial matters: particularly in transnational disputes, business crime, banking and computer fraud, insolvency, regulatory and compliance issues, insurance, property litigation and partnership disputes; and in matrimonial and family law.

Property: The department has extensive experience in commercial property work, having been involved in town centre, business park and leisure developments as well as large-scale urban estate transactions and associated landlord and tenant matters. It has planning and construction law capabliity and a growing environmental law practice. It acts for developers, owners, funders and UK-based and international investors.

Tax and financial planning: The department has a recognised expertise in tax planning for large complex estates, private companies and high net worth individuals and families, often in an international context. This includes inheritance, capital gains and income tax planning, advice on VAT, the establishment of overseas trusts and corporate structures, and pensions and charity work.

INTERNATIONAL CONNECTIONS: Much work has an international element, especially in France, Germany, Spain and North America where the firm has well-established associations with prominent firms.

CONTACT PARTNER:

Number of partners:	26
Assistant solicitors:	28
Other fee-earners:	19

CONTACTS	
Anglo-German (London)	Chris Putt
Corporate (London)	Simon Renton
Corporate (Southampton)	Moray Macpherson
Employment (London)	Andrew Drake
Employment (Southampton)	Julian Hamblin
Environment (London)	Edward Sutherland
Litigation (London)	Stephen Ralph
Litigation (Southampton)	Julian Hamblin
Property (London)	Tim Manning
Property (Southampton)	David d'Arcy Hughes
Property (Oxford)	Peter Webber
Tax/financial planning(London)	Richard Moyse
Tax/financial planning(Oxford)	Sue Laing

BOODLE
HATFIELD

RECRUITMENT AND TRAINING: The firm has openings for assistant solicitors in each department. Five trainees are recruited per year; some spend six months on secondment to ICI and Shell International. Send a letter and CV to David Sawyer.

OTHER OFFICES:

Town Quay House, 7 Town Quay, Southampton SO14 2PT. *Tel:* (01703) 332001.

One of the region's leading commercial practices, the Southampton office provides a full range of corporate, property and litigation services.

6 Worcester Street, Oxford OX1 2BX Tel: (01865) 790744

Opened in 1994, the Oxford office specialises presently in tax, trusts and financial planning, wills and probate, and commercial and residential property work. All other services are available on demand.

BOOTH & BLACKWELL 3 and 4 Berners St, London, W1P 4AT

Tel: (0171) 580 9371 **Fax:** (0171) 631 3422 **DX:** 35702 **Ptnrs:** 10 **Asst Solrs:** 4 **Other Fee-earners:** 10. Predominantly a commercial firm handling company/ commercial matters, litigation, insolvency, property and private client.

WORKLOAD			
Litigation	57%	Company/ commercial	21%
Property	12%	Private client	10%

BOOTH & CO.

SOVEREIGN HOUSE, SOUTH PARADE, LEEDS, W. YORKS, LS1 1HQ	TEL: (0113) 283 2000
DX: 12004 Leeds	FAX: (0113) 283 2060

THE FIRM: Booth & Co. is one of the foremost commercial practices in the North and has been serving the business community and private individuals since 1775. It has a total staff of 510 (as at May 1995), and occupies four buildings in Leeds. The firm is a member of the Norton Rose M5 Group of independent regional practices, who pool resources on matters such as recruitment, training and research.

PRINCIPAL AREAS OF WORK:

Company/ Commercial: (*Contact:* Tim Wheldon). The department handles company work of every kind from company start-ups to Stock Exchange listings, management buy-outs, joint ventures, venture capital and mergers and acquisitions. Its specialist teams also handle a range of commercial work including pensions, intellectual property, corporate tax, asset finance, employment, and European Community and competition law.

Banking and Building Society: (*Contact:* Mark Chidley). Recognised as a leader in the banking and building society sectors. Work includes the full range of corporate banking for banks and building societies and for borrowers: syndicated and bilateral secured lending, unsecured lending, preparation of lending, preparation of standard and specific documentation and debt rescheduling. For building societies the firm is particularly strong in regulatory and compliance work, corporate acquisitions and commercial advice for societies.

Commercial property: (*Contact:* John Pike). This is one of the strongest commercial property departments in the country, handling the full range of property development, investment, and institutional work including secured lending and incorporating separate specialist town and country planning, construction, agricultural and property management services units. In addition the environmental unit advises on the environmental issues affecting all property transactions.

Commercial litigation: (*Contact:* Peter Cherry). The department has a large commercial and civil litigation practice covering commercial fraud, contractual disputes, injunctive relief, asset finance, employment, personal injury, construction, insolvency, landlord and tenant. In addition the firm has a separate credit management services department offering an efficient computerised debt recovery service.

Credit management/Mortgage recovery: (*Contact:* Anthony Ruane). The firm deals with mortgage repossession, credit management and debt recovery which include both commercial and consumer debt and mortgage shortfall recovery. The department is totally computerised and is capable of handling many thousands of cases.

CONTACT PARTNER: Mark Jones

Number of partners:	41
Assistant solicitors:	91
Other fee-earners:	91

WORKLOAD	
Banking & building society	21%
Credit management/ mortgage recovery	18%
Commercial property	18%
Company/ commercial	16%
Commercial litigation	14%
Residential property	7%
Private client/ family	6%

CONTACTS	
Asset finance	Lennox Towers
Banking	Mark Chidley
Building society law	Adam Bennett
Commercial litigation	Peter Cherry
Commercial property	John Pike
Company/commercial	Tim Wheldon
Construction	Richard Cockram
Corporate finance	Ian McIntosh
Credit management	Anthony Ruane
EC & competition	Gillian Holding
Employment	Tom Flanagan
Environmental	John Pike
Family	David Salter
Insolvency	William Ballmann

Residential property: (*Contact:* Anthony Ruane). The department is probably the largest in the country and handles all aspects of residential property work from conveyancing to sales in possession, relocation, estate sales, mortgage advances, shared ownership schemes and private sales and purchases.

Private client: (*Contacts:* David Salter, Family: Paul Howell, Trusts and Tax). The department undertakes all types of family law including divorce, separation, children and cohabitants, with an emphasis on high value financial settlements. Specialist advice is available where appropriate, on pensions and insolvencies. The firm also offers a full range of services to the private client which includes trusts, tax planning, charities, off shore planning and National Heritage Property.

Nature of Clientele: Clients include banks, building societies, insurance companies and other financial institutions, public and private companies, central and local government bodies, and private individuals.

FOREIGN CONNECTIONS: The main European languages are spoken, and language training is encouraged. Through the Norton Rose M5 Group, the firm can draw upon resources of offices worldwide.

RECRUITMENT: The firm is always looking for high-calibre qualified staff and had around 15 vacancies for qualified solicitors in 1994. Each year, up to 17 trainee solicitors are recruited. A minimum of a 2:1 degree is preferred, though not necessarily in law. The firm encourages candidates with language or science qualifications to apply. Apply by letter two years in advance, to Gillian Holding, enclosing a CV.

TRAINING: A first-class continuing education training programme is accredited under the Law Society CLE scheme. Regular training courses are held both in-house and with the Norton Rose M5 Group.

Intellectual property	Richard Kempner
Pensions	Neville Peel
Planning	Richard Wheeldon
Residential property	Anthony Ruane
Trusts & tax	Paul Howell

BORLAND MONTGOMERIE KEYDEN Apsley House, 29 Wellington Street, Glasgow, G2 6JA **Tel:** (0141) 221 8004 **Fax:** (0141) 221 8088 **DX:** 55 Glasgow **Ptnrs:** 13 **Asst Solrs:** 8 **Other Fee-earners:** 4. Work includes commercial property work, liquor licensing, agricultural law, shipping law, employment law, environmental law, personal injury, family/ matrimonial law and private client work.

WORKLOAD			
Commercial	35%	Litigation	30%
Trust and executry	30%	Domestic conveyancing	5%

BOWER & BAILEY 12 St. Michael's Street, Oxford, Oxon, OX1 2RU **Tel:** (01865) 249122 **Fax:** (01865) 248414 **DX:** 4315 **Ptnrs:** 17 **Asst Solrs:** 10 **Other Fee-earners:** 6. Commercial work and civil litigation are particular strengths of this firm. Other main areas of work are conveyancing and family law.

WORKLOAD			
Litigation	30%	Corp/business client	30%
Private client	25%	Family	15%

BOWER COTTON & BOWER

36 WHITEFRIARS STREET, LONDON, EC4Y 8BH
DX: 94

TEL: (0171) 353 3040
FAX: (0171) 583 2869

THE FIRM: Founded in 1818, this is a commercially orientated practice with a relatively young partnership. It provides an extensive range of legal services.

PRINCIPAL AREAS OF WORK:

Company and Commercial: (*Contact:* Paul Simms). *Work includes:* all aspects of company/ commercial work such as acquisitions and disposals, joint ventures, corporate tax, company reconstructions, licensing, franchising, aviation and employment. The firm has a large number of overseas based commercial clients. The firm also specialises in energy with special emphasis on the retail petrol industry.

Insolvency: (*Contact:* Guy Vincent). *Work includes:* acting for liquidators, administrative receivers, and in bankruptcies and voluntary arrangements including disposals of insolvency assets and debt recovery.

CONTACT PARTNER: Guy Vincent

Number of partners:	10
Assistant solicitors:	4
Other fee-earners:	5

WORKLOAD	
Commercial conveyancing	30%
Litigation	30%
Private client and others	20%
Company/ commercial	20%

Litigation: (*Contact:* Andrew Couch). *Work includes:* commercial litigation, building disputes, personal injury, professional negligence, debt collection, employment, judicial review, shipping litigation, agency work, property litigation, rent reviews, landlord and tenant disputes, planning appeals and advising arbitrators.

Family: (*Contact:* Andrew Todd). All aspects of family and matrimonial work ranging from divorce (including breakdown of foreign marriages) and separation to child-care and financial provisions.

Property: (*Contact:* Michael Parker). All aspects of commercial property work with particular emphasis on secured lending and including planning, construction, landlord and tenant and commercial conveyancing.

Private Client: (*Contact:* Paul Shaerf). *Work includes:* residential conveyancing, wills, probate, trusts, tax, consumer credit, employment, pensions and immigration.

FOREIGN CONNECTIONS: The firm has established links with Switzerland, Spain, France and the USA.

FOREIGN LANGUAGES: French and Spanish.

RECRUITMENT AND TRAINING: Applications should be addressed to Robert Perrin. The firm provides a full programme of in-house continuing legal education.

CONTACTS	
Company/ commercial	Paul Simms
Family	Andrew Todd
Insolvency	Guy Vincent
Litigation	Andrew Couch
Private client	Paul Shaerf
Property	Michael Parker

BOYCE HATTON 12 Tor Hill Rd, Castle Circus, Torquay, Devon, TQ2 5RB **Tel:** (01803) 295343 **Fax:** (01803) 214876 **DX:** 59000 **Ptnrs:** 9 **Asst Solrs:** 4 **Other Fee-earners:** 14. Known for its commercial property and company departments. Also handles residential conveyancing, litigation, licensing and probate work.

BOYDS

THISTLE HOUSE, 146 WEST REGENT STREET, GLASGOW, G2 2RZ
DX: 120 Glasgow

TEL: (0141) 221 8251
FAX: (0141) 226 4799

THE FIRM: Boyds specialises in corporate and commercial work, with a substantial commercial property practice. The firm also offers comprehensive services to private clients and is a member of Lawyers Associated Worldwide.

PRINCIPAL AREAS OF WORK:

Corporate and Commercial: (*Contact:* Stuart Russell or Fiona Neilson). The firm advises on all aspects of corporate and commercial law including company formations, acquisitions and mergers, agency, distribution and franchise agreements, review of contracts and specialist areas such as intellectual property, employment, banking, venture capital, environmental and entertainment law, EIS schemes and management buy-outs and buy-ins.

Commercial Property: (*Contact:* David Boyce, Denis Rodie, Douglas Lamb or Colin Keenan). The firm advises on all types of commercial property transactions and funding, with particular expertise in retail development work and complex tax-driven property investment transactions. Other specialist areas include security work, licensing, planning and agricultural law, including sporting rights.

Litigation: (*Contact:* Robert Gall or Denise Loney). The firm undertakes a broad range of civil litigation work for both commercial and individual clients, with particular strength in the areas of landlord and tenant, contractual disputes and insolvency.

Private Client: (*Contact:* Neil Rankine). A comprehensive range of services is provided including domestic conveyancing, matrimonial and family work, personal taxation advice, trusts, wills and executry work.

CONTACT PARTNER: Stuart Russell

Number of partners:	9
Assistant solicitors:	6
Other fee-earners:	3

WORKLOAD	
Commercial property development/funding	50%
Litigation	20%
Corporate/ commercial	20%
Private client	10%

CONTACTS	
Commercial property	David Boyce
Corporate	Stuart Russell
Litigation	Robert Gall
Private client	Neil Rankine

BOYES TURNER & BURROWS

10 DUKE ST, READING, BERKS, RG1 4RX
DX: 54741 Reading 2

TEL: (01734) 597711
FAX: (01734) 573257

THE FIRM: Boyes Turner & Burrows is a leading Thames Valley firm. It has a strong commercial emphasis whilst retaining a commitment to private client work (it has a Legal Aid Franchise). Founded in 1887 in Reading it occupies modern air-conditioned offices, is fully computerised and employs over 60 staff. The partnership is young and committed to providing fast, effective advice in all areas.

PRINCIPAL AREAS OF WORK:

Banking and Insolvency: Headed by a LIP the firm acts for all the major insolvency practices as well as clearing banks and other financial institutions in both corporate and personal insolvency and securities work.

Company/Commercial: The firm acts for many substantial businesses based in the Thames Valley including UK subsidiaries of multi–nationals. Advice includes business formation, acquisitions & disposals, partnerships and joint ventures, inward investment and corporate restructuring, general business law advice, commercial and trading agreements including distribution and licensing, competition law, company secretarial work.

Debt Collection: Fully computerised system providing competitive rates and handling bulk recoveries for major trading companies as well as financial institutions.

Employment: Preparation of employment contracts, advice on disciplinary issues, industrial tribunal representation, restraint of trade, wrongful dismissal, sex and race discrimination.

Family: Divorce and separation, financial provision, children, emergency procedures (members of SFLA).

Intellectual Property: Ownership and exploitation of IPR, licensing, IPR disputes, computer contracts (software and hardware), product liability. Clients include engineering, electronics and computer companies as well as software houses.

Litigation: Contract disputes, shareholder and partnership disputes, negligence claims, property disputes, mortgage repossessions, landlord and tenant. Agency work undertaken.

Medical Negligence: A specialist team acts exclusively for the victims of medical accidents (AVMA referral solicitors, members APIL, Headway, etc.)

Personal injury: Work place injuries, road traffic accidents, health and safety advice (members APIL and Accident Line).

Private Client: Wills, trusts, probate, tax and residential conveyancing.

Property: Sales and leases of commercial property, commercial and residential development projects, commercial lending, landlord and tenant.

Planning: Planning advice for property development projects as well as appeals and planning enforcement.

NATURE OF CLIENTELE: The firm acts for a number of major Thames Valley based businesses across a broad spectrum of activity, but with strong connections in the hi-tech, electronics and engineering sectors. It also acts for banks, public authorities as well as start-ups and newly established subsidiaries of foreign parents.

Boyes Turner & Burrows has steadily grown across the whole range of its practice and has doubled its number of lawyers over the past five years. It has a strong commitment to client satisfaction

RECRUITMENT AND TRAINING: The firm restricts the number of trainee solicitors recruited to ensure that the best training is given to those taken on every year. The firm takes its training responsibilities seriously, for both trainee solicitors and assistant solicitors, and operates an in-house training programme. (*Staff Partner:* Adrian Desmond. *Training Partner:* Michael Robinson).

CONTACT PARTNER: William Gornall-King

Number of partners:	11
Assistant solicitors:	9
Other fee-earners:	12

WORKLOAD	
Commercial (incl company/ commercial, IP, banking and insolvency	25%
Medical negligence	20%
Litigation (incl. commercial, employment)	20%
Family	12%
Property - commercial	12%
Residential/ private client (wills, etc.)	11%

CONTACTS	
Banking and insolvency	Chris Branson
Company/ commercial	John Cashin
Debt Collection	Chris Branson
Employment	Jonathan West
Family	Mike Weibel
Intellectual property	Bill Gornall-King
Litigation	Mike Robinson
Medical negligence	Adrian Desmond
Personal injury	Jonathan West
Private client	Angela Johnson
Property	Peter Daniel
Town and country planning	Anthony Cooley

BOYES TURNER & BURROWS
SOLICITORS

BRABNER HOLDEN BANKS WILSON

1 DALE ST, LIVERPOOL, MERSEYSIDE, L2 2ET DX: 14118 Liverpool	TEL: (0151) 236 5821 FAX: (0151) 227 3185
6-8 Chapel Street, Preston PRI 8AW DX: 17118	Tel: (01772) 823921 Fax: (01772) 201418

THE FIRM: Formed in 1990 by the merger of Brabner Holden of Liverpool and Banks Wilson of Preston, the firm can trace its origins to the eighteenth century and is one of the leading northwest practices.

PRINCIPAL AREAS OF WORK:

Corporate: The firm is highly regarded for corporate work and advises on aquisitions, disposals, buy-outs, buy-ins, demergers, venture capital, joint ventures, distributorships, agencies, franchising, computer law and intellectual property.

Commercial and Agricultural Property: Property work includes acquisitions, leases, development and sales. On both local and national levels, the firm has particular expertise in housing association work and acting for local authorities and a number of breweries.

Litigation: The firm has particular expertise in employment law, media and defamation work but also undertakes a wide range of other litigation work including contractual disputes, construction litigation, intellectual property actions, landlord and tenant and competition law. It also provides a computerised debt collection service.

Private Client: The firm has a strong base of high net-worth clients providing tax planning for resident and overseas clients, trust administration, probate and conveyancing and also undertakes charity law work.

NATURE OF CLIENTELE: Throughout the UK the firm acts for public and private companies, local and national institutions, local authorities, housing associations, brewers, newspapers and radio clients.

FOREIGN CONNECTIONS: The firm is a member of Eurolegal.

RECRUITMENT & TRAINING: 3 trainee solicitors are recruited annually, and the firm is fully commited to a comprehensive training programme for all its staff and was the first legal practice on Merseyside to gain the Investor In People award.

CONTACT PARTNER: Lawrence Holden

Number of partners:	16
Assistant solicitors:	19
Other fee-earners:	13

WORKLOAD	
Corporate	24%
Commercial property	22%
Commercial litigation	20%
Probate & trust/ tax planning	18%
Private client property & litigation	16%

CONTACTS	
Commercial property	Keith Housley
	Ross Shine
Commercial litigation	Andy Cross
	Amanda Webster
Corporate	Michael Brabner, Tony Harper
Employment	Andy Cross, Mark Feeny
Housing assocs & charities	Lawrence Holden
Intellectual property	John Schorah
Media & defamation	Mark Manley
Private client	Mark Feeny, George Erdozain

BRABY & WALLER

48-50 ST. JOHN ST, LONDON, EC1M 4DP DX: 87 Ch.Ln.	TEL: (0171) 250 1884 FAX: (0171) 250 1749

THE FIRM: Braby & Waller was founded in the 19th century and developed as a City of London commercial practice with particularly close connections in the building materials, manufacturing, finance and supply industries. The client-base covers industry, institutions, and commercial bodies including major public companies and financial institutions.

PRINCIPAL AREAS OF WORK:

General Description: The practice undertakes commercial work with a particular emphasis on credit, insolvency, debt collection, volume litigation and corporate matters including employment.

Commercial and Property: (*Contact:* Hugh Robertson). The firm is organised so that partners and fee earners with particular expertise are available to provide an integrated service to clients. This flexible approach is well suited to the needs of today's commercial client whether it be in respect of acquisitions, disposals, shareholder disputes, employment or insolvency. The firm offers a full range of legal services relating to property including sale and purchase, leasing, security and relevant litigation.

CONTACT PARTNER: Hugh Robertson

Number of partners:	3
Assistant solicitors:	8
Other fee-earners:	20

Debt Collection: (*Contact:* Barry Hogg). The department is believed to be one of the biggest in the City of London and acts for major international and national manufacturers, distributors, communications providers, lenders and professional firms amongst others.

Litigation and Insolvency: (*Contact:* Pauline Devine). The litigation department deals with all aspects of commercial litigation, including insolvency.

Construction Industry: (*Contact:* Peter Brooker). The firm has undertaken construction law for many years, advising on contracts and handling disputes including international arbitration.

BRACHERS

SOMERFIELD HSE, 59 LONDON RD, MAIDSTONE, KENT, ME16 8JH	TEL: (01622) 690691
DX: 4806	FAX: (01622) 681430
115A Chancery Lane, London WC2A 1PP	Tel: (0171) 404 0111
DX: 374	Fax: (0171) 404 0181

THE FIRM: As one of the larger provincial firms, Brachers has a wide ranging commercial and private client practice. The firm has built up large civil litigation, debt collection and insolvency departments complementing its company/ commercial and planning work. The firm also handles an increasing amount of probate, trust, tax and financial services work, and retains close links with Kent's agricultural community. Recent developments include the opening of a London office and the appointment of a Chief Investment Manager.

CONTACT PARTNER: Mr P.J. Prince

Number of partners:	16
Assistant solicitors:	19
Other fee-earners:	23

BRADLEYS 19 Castle St, Dover, Kent, CT16 1PU **Tel:** (01304) 204080 **Fax:** (01304) 215092 **DX:** 6300 **Ptnrs:** 7 **Asst Solrs:** 2 **Other Fee-earners:** 10. General practice with offices at Stoke House, Church Road, Ashford, Kent TN23 1RH *Tel:* (01233) 624551 *Fax:* (01233) 641030 *DX:* 30201.

WORKLOAD			
Conveyancing	20%	Civil litigation	20%
Matrimonial	20%	Criminal	20%
Probate and trusts	10%	Commercial	10%

BRAIN & BRAIN Addington House, 73 London St, Reading, Berks, RG1 4QB **Tel:** (01734) 581441 **Fax:** (01734) 597875 **DX:** 4005 **Ptnrs:** 17 **Asst Solrs:** 10 **Other Fee-earners:** 13. Brain & Brain is a well established commercially orientated firm, with offices in Reading and Basingstoke.

BRECHER & CO

78 BROOK STREET, LONDON, W1Y 2AD	TEL: (0171) 493 5141
DX: 82955 Mayfair	FAX: (0171) 493 6255

THE FIRM: Brecher & Co was founded as a commercial law firm in the mid 1950s and today is one of the leading practices in the West End of London.

The firm enjoys an established reputation for its high level of legal excellence, commercial flair and commitment to partner-led teams. It has a large spread of corporate, institutional and entrepreneurial clients and handles a broad range of commercial and financial work in all the major disciplines.

Brecher & Co is conscious in the current climate of the need to provide value-for-money service and is happy to discuss fees prior to being awarded a mandate.

PRINCIPAL AREAS OF WORK:

Company/ Commercial: (*Contact:* Ian Green). The firm's company/ commercial department advises clients, ranging from multinational PLCs to individual entrepreneurs, on all manner of commercial transactions including the acquisition and disposal of companies and businesses, mergers, joint ventures, corporate reorganisations and debt restructurings, distribution, agency and franchise agreements, partnership arrangements and the non-contentious aspects of employment law.

CONTACT PARTNER: David Brecher

Number of partners:	25
Assistant solicitors:	13
Other fee-earners:	15

WORKLOAD	
Commercial property	45%
Litigation	25%
Company commercial and banking	23%
Tax trust and probate	5%
Other	2%

Banking and Asset Finance: (*Contact:* Paul Salsbury). The firm's dedicated banking and asset finance department advises lenders and borrowers on structuring and documenting all types of domestic and international finance transactions. In addition, the department handles related restructuring and insolvency matters in liaison with the firm's banking litigation team.

Ongoing advice is provided to banks and financial institutions on the continual changes to the legal and regulatory framework within which they operate, including drafting and updating standard documentation.

A large part of the department's work involves advising on asset-backed lending transactions secured on a variety of assets including real property, ships and aircraft, as well as advising on trade finance and equipment leasing. Where appropriate, this work is undertaken in conjunction with the firm's other departments and specialist units.

Corporate Taxation: (*Contact:* Stuart Davidson). The corporate tax unit is headed by tax expert and former HM Inspector of Taxes, Stuart Davidson. The unit provides essential advice to clients of all departments on the tax implications of their business.

Litigation: (*Contact:* Alan Langleben). The firm handles a wide variety of contentious matters for both corporate and private clients. In addition to its mainstream commercial litigation workload, this department also has substantial experience in the following fields: property (including landlord and tenant), banking, construction, insolvency, consumer credit, professional negligence, employment, intellectual property and matrimonial and family.

Finance Leasing: (*Contact:* Geoff Smith). The firm's leasing unit, under the umbrella of the litigation department, advises on the documentation of finance leasing agreements as well as handling contentious matters. Leasing contracts handled by the unit typically concern office equipment, computers, heavy plant and machinery and haulage equipment.

Property: (*Contact:* Alan Wiseman or Susan Freeman). The firm has a long-established reputation for its services to the commercial property world. It has numerous property contacts, and can often assist projects to fruition by introducing banks and other financiers, or by bringing clients together with other interested parties.

Planning and Environment: (*Contact:* Michael Broughton). The firm's planning unit specialises in all aspects of the law of planning, highways, compulsory purchase and allied matters in conjunction with major developments and including negotiations with local and other authorities and the conduct of inquiries.

The environmental law unit advises on the environmental aspects of planning and commercial transactions. The unit liaises with the banking and asset finance department in advising banking clients of their potential liability as lenders to these transactions.

Private Client: (*Contact:* Norma Simon). The private client department provides a full range of services including advice on charity establishment, trusts and estate management, tax planning and inward and outward investment.

Employment Law: (*Contact:* Alan Langleben). The firm's employment law expertise is drawn principally from two departments: the company/ commercial department handles the drafting and variation of employment contracts, service agreements, restrictive covenants and also advises on employee share option schemes and transfer of undertaking regulations. The Litigation department deals with the contentious side of employment law and also assists the Company/ Commercial team at the drafting stage, casting a litigious eye over documentation before a dispute arises.

Advice is also sought from the corporate tax unit, particularly on the tax aspects of termination payments and taxation of damages.

NATURE OF CLIENTELE: Brecher & Co has a broad client base which includes multinationals, listed and USM companies, banks and other financial institutions, private companies and individuals.

FOREIGN CONNECTIONS: The firm has a formal association with a leading German commercial law firm, as well as maintaining existing links with lawyers in other parts of Europe, and worldwide.

RECRUITMENT: Up to six trainees are recruited annually. Candidates should apply by handwritten letter enclosing CV to the Recruitment Partner.

CONTACTS	
Acquisitions and disposals	Howard Kleiman
Arbitration	Alan Langleben/ Kevin Greene
Asset finance	Paul Salsbury/ Andrew Besser
Aviation finance	Austen Hall
Banking	Paul Salsbury/ Andrew Besser
Charities	Norma Simon
Commercial litigation	Alan Langleben
Commercial property	Alan Wiseman
Commercial contracts	Ian Green
Commercial property	Susan Freeman
Company law/ compliance	Sarah de Gay
Computing	Nicky Snook
Construction	Kevin Greene
Corporate (general)	Ian Green
Corporate restructurings	Ian Green
EC law	Sarah de Gay/ Alan Langleben
Employment (non-contentious)	Sarah de Gay
Environment	Michael Broughton
Equipment leasing	Austen Hall
Estate planning	Graham Scammell
	Norma Simon
Insolvency	Andrew Besser
Intellectual property	Nicky Snook
International trade	Ian Green/ Howard Kleiman
Joint ventures	Ian Green
Landlord & tenant (commercial)	Clive Newham
Landlord & tenant (residential)	Nick Doffman
Lease finance litigation	Geoff Smith
Mergers	Ian Green
Planning	Michael Broughton
Private client	Norma Simon
Probate	Graham Scammell
Professional negligence	Alan Langleben
Project finance	Andrew Besser
	Paul Salsbury
Property development	Alan Wiseman
	Susan Freeman
Property finance	Paul Salsbury/Andrew Besser
Property litigation	Alan Langleben
Public company work	Ian Green
Retail property	Susan Freeman
Shipping finance	Austen Hall
Shopping centres	Susan Freeman
Sports law	Andrew Brecher
Tax (corporate)	Stuart Davidson
Tax (personal)	Norma Simon
Trade finance	Austen Hall
Trusts (UK & overseas)	Norma Simon

BRECHIN ROBB 24 George Square, Glasgow, G2 1EE **Tel:** (0141) 248 5921 **Fax:** (0141) 204 0135 **DX:** 14 Glasgow **Ptnrs:** 7 **Asst Solrs:** 7 **Other Fee-earners:** 5. A primarily corporate and commercial law and litigation practice offering a wide range of services to business clients and private individuals.

WORKLOADS			
Commercial litigation	44%	Commercial property	30%
Private client	14%	Corporate/ commercial	12%

BREEZE & WYLES 114 Fore Street, Hertford, Herts, SG14 1AG **Tel:** (01992) 558411 **Fax:** (01992) 582834 **DX:** 57901 Hertford **Ptnrs:** 9 **Asst Solrs:** 4 **Other Fee-earners:** 6. Best known for commercial and domestic conveyancing, the firm handles litigation (especially personal injury), probate, and particularly planning law. Progressive firm with four offices.

WORKLOADS			
Domestic conveyancing	44%	Litigation - gen/family	29%
Comm/company convey	12%	Probate and trust	11%
Planning	4%		

BREMNER SONS & CORLETT 1 Crosshall Street, Liverpool, Merseyside, L1 6DH **Tel:** (0151) 227 1301 **Fax:** (0151) 227 1300 **DX:** 14119 Liverpool 1 **Ptnrs:** 11 **Asst Solrs:** 2 **Other Fee-earners:** 7. The firm was established nearly 150 years ago, and has a mainly commercial clientele.

BRENDAN KEARNEY KELLY & CO 4 Clarendon Street, Derry, Co. L'derry, BT48 7ET **Tel:** (01504) 266935 **Fax:** (01504) 371845. One of the larger firms outside Belfast, particularly known for its criminal work.

BRETHERTON PRICE ELGOODS 123 Promenade, Cheltenham, Glos, GL50 1NW **Tel:** (01242) 224433 **Fax:** (01242) 574285 **DX:** 7403 **Ptnrs:** 8 **Asst Solrs:** 4 **Other Fee-earners:** 18. Commercially orientated firm with particular emphasis on corporate and commercial property development related work. Office in London.

BRETHERTONS

16 CHURCH ST, RUGBY, WARKS, CV21 3PW	TEL:	(01788) 579579
DX: 11672 Rugby - 1; E-mail:brethertons@cix.compulink.co.uk	FAX:	(01788) 570949
Domestic Property Department: 26 Regent Street, Rugby CV21 2PN	Tel:	(01788) 551611
	Fax:	(01788) 551597
Brethertons Auld and Jardine 18a South Bar, Banbury, Oxfordshire, OX16 9AF DX: 24239 Banbury	Tel: Fax:	(01295) 250999 (01295) 257575

THE FIRM: Brethertons is a firm which can trace its history in Rugby back for over 180 years. Its solid base in the town has provided a springboard for carefully planned expansion: the opening of the dedicated Domestic Property Department at the end of 1992 made Brethertons Rugby's largest firm (a position which it maintains). In mid-1995 the firm expanded into Banbury when the firm acquired the commercial practice of Auld and Jardine. Brethertons attributes its success to its commitment to client care and its imaginative use of technology.

The firm offers a wide range of legal services from both Rugby and Banbury. The firm is a legal aid franchise holder and there is a 24-hour helpline for legal advice.

PRINCIPAL AREAS OF WORK:

Commercial Law: *(Contact Partner:* Cliff Cooper). *Work includes:* commercial property, company formation, contract drafting, financing, employment law, licensing, commercial litigation, landlord and tenant.

Computer Law: *(Contact Partner:* Brian Auld). *Work inlcudes:* sofware licensing, facilities management and outsourcing contracts, IT litigation, competition and European law.

CONTACT PARTNER: Cliff Cooper

Number of partners:	10
Assistant solicitors:	4
Other fee-earners:	12

WORKLOAD	
Commercial	23% .
Civil litigation	23%
Crime	19%
Trusts and probate	13%
Domestic conveyancing	12%
Family	10%

Agriculture: *(Contact Partner:* Paul Smith). *Work includes:* all aspects of agricultural advice, bloodstock, property, milk quotas, tax.

Planning: *(Contact Partner:* Paul Smith). *Work includes:* planning and development advice.

Family Law: *(Contact Partner:* Tony Sutton). *Work includes:* divorce, separation and child care.

Wills & Probate: *(Contact Partner:* Chris Pratt). *Work includes:* wills, trusts, probate, financial advice and tax planning.

Crime: *(Contact Partner:* Rod Ross). *Work includes:* all aspects of criminal defence, Magistrates' Court and Crown Court trials.

Civil Litigation: *(Contact Partner:* Richard Pell). *Work includes:* personal injury and medical negligence, contract and employment disputes, commercial litigation, arbitration and ADR.

Domestic Property: *(Contact Partner:* Alan Hooper). *Work includes:* computerised conveyancing and financial advice.

Debt Recovery: *(Contact Partner:* Richard Pell). *Work includes:* all aspects of domestic and international debt recovery. The firm operates a computerised debt recovery service.

FOREIGN LANGUAGES: French, Spanish and Gujerati.

CONTACTS	
Agriculture/ planning	Paul Smith
Commercial litigation	Richard Pell
	Shaun Jardine
Company/ commercial	Cliff Cooper
	Brian Auld
Computer and IT law	Brian Auld
	Andrew Katz
Crime and road traffic	Rod Ross
Domestic conveyancing	Alan Hooper
Family	Tony Sutton
Pers. injury/ civil lit.	Richard Pell
Trusts and probate	Chris Pratt

BRIAN KOFFMAN & CO Queen's Chambers, 5 John Dalton St, Manchester, M2 6ET **Tel:** (0161) 832 3852 **Fax:** (0161) 833 2547 **Ptnrs:** 2 **Asst Solrs:** 4 **Other Fee-earners:** 5. The firm is best known for criminal law and also handles personal injury and medical negligence matters. It operates the legal aid scheme and a 24 hour emergency service.

WORKLOAD			
Crime	80%	Civil matters	20%

BRIAN THOMPSON & PARTNERS Congress House, Great Russell Street, London, WC1B 3LW **Tel:** (0171) 637 9761 **Fax:** (0171) 637 0000 **Ptnrs:** 54 **Asst Solrs:** 34 **Other Fee-earners:** 55. Known for its expertise in personal injury litigation primarily for trade union members (but also for private and legally aided clients) and also in employment and discrimination law.

BRIDGE MCFARLAND SOLICITORS 8 Abbey Walk, Grimsby, Humbs, DN31 1NB **Tel:** (01472) 348566 **Fax:** (01472) 241528 **DX:** 13507 Grimsby **Ptnrs:** 9. Known for its expertise in personal injury litigation primarily for trade union members (but also for private and legally aided clients) and also in employment and discrimination law.

BRIFFA & CO

BUSINESS DESIGN CENTRE, UPPER ST, ISLINGTON GREEN, LONDON, N1 0QH

TEL: (0171) 288 6003
FAX: (0171) 288 6004

THE FIRM: Briffa & Co is a fast growing and innovative specialist intellectual property practice committed to providing a quality service to clients in this field. The firm is flexible in terms of service, delivery and charging bases.

PRINCIPAL AREAS OF WORK:

Litigation: The firm undertakes a broad range of civil contentious intellectual property work relating to patents, designs, copyright, trade marks, passing off and confidential information, including all emergency applications to the courts in these areas. The firm is also developing a reputation for criminal work in copyright matters acting for both prosecutors and defendants.

Licensing and Commercial: The firm acts for clients in the information technology, health care and publishing industries and provides a competitive, value for money and commercially relevant service.

    The firm is continuing to develop the service it offers to meet the changing needs of clients. In all matters it offers a personal and efficient service.

CONTACT PARTNER: Margaret Briffa

Number of partners:	1
Other fee-earners:	2

WORKLOAD	
Litigation	70%
Licensing and commercial	30%

BRINDLEY TWIST TAFFT & JAMES 3 The Quadrant, Coventry, W. Midlands, CV1 2DY **Tel:** (01203) 631632 **Fax:** (01203) 632828 **Ptnrs:** 11 **Asst Solrs:** 9 **Other Fee-earners:** 13. Other offices: Lowick Gate, Siskin Drive, Coventry CV3 4FJ *Tel:* (01203) 531532 *Fax:* (01203) 301300. Provides comprehensive service to business and private clients.

BRISTOWS COOKE & CARPMAEL

10 LINCOLN'S INN FIELDS, LONDON, WC2A 3BP
DX: 269

TEL: (0171) 400 8000
FAX: (0171) 400 8050

THE FIRM: Bristows Cooke & Carpmael is a specialist commercial practice which has acted for leading science and engineering based industries since 1837. Bristows is pre-eminent in the field of intellectual property law and a leading practice in construction law. It combines these specialist areas with complementary practices in company, commercial, property, charity and environmental law. The firm has very strong international connections, particularly with the USA, Europe and Japan.

PRINCIPAL AREAS OF WORK:

Intellectual Property: *(Contact Partners:* Ian Judge, David Brown). The intellectual property department is one of the largest groups of IP specialists in the UK. Many of the fee-earners have scientific and technical qualifications. The department's work encompasses both 'hard' and 'soft' IP and covers all aspects of litigation and non-contentious advice in relation to patents, trade marks, copyright, designs, passing off and confidential information. This includes IT and computers, multimedia, brands, franchising and biotechnology.

Construction: *(Contact Partner:* James Hudson). The second largest department dealing with Official Referees business, arbitration, ADR and transactional advice for the building and civil engineering industries.

Company/Corporate Finance: *(Contact Partners:* Paul Cooke, William Saunders). This department handles all types of corporate work, including acquisitions and mergers, reorganisations, Stock Exchange, joint ventures, venture capital for high-tech and similar business transactions especially for clients with interests in technology. The firm also undertakes a broad range of non-contentious commercial work including a strong practice in partnership matters (Contact Partner: John Lace).

Competition/ Antitrust: *(Contact Partner:* David Brown). The firm has particular experience in intellectual property cases involving EC competition law and antitrust claims and has been responsible for co-ordinating multi-forum disputes including hearings before the EC Commission and the European Court of Justice. All other aspects of EC and domestic competition law and proceedings before the Restrictive Practices Court are also covered.

Commercial Litigation: *(Contact Partners:* Richard de Ste Croix, Kevin Appleton). All areas of commercial litigation and arbitration are dealt with by this department, including insurance law, disputes arising out of mergers and acquisitions, fraud and employment law.

Commercial Property: *(Contact Partner:* Michael Rowles). This department deals with commercial conveyancing, landlord and tenant (including licensed premises), planning, development and funding work.

Professional Institutions and Learned Societies: *(Contact Partner:* Edward Williams). The firm has a substantial practice in the law relating to such bodies (often charitable), particularly in the science and engineering sectors. Charter and by-law work is a particular speciality.

Environment: *(Contact:* Richard Burnett-Hall). The firm has recently enlarged its environmental group by bringing in Richard Burnett-Hall, a leading specialist and author of a standard textbook.

LANGUAGES SPOKEN: French, German, Italian, Polish, Greek, Arabic.

EXECUTIVE PARTNERS:
Ian Judge and David Brown

Number of partners:	24
Assistant solicitors:	42
Other fee-earners:	21

WORKLOAD

Intellectual property (inc. related EC and anti-trust)	50%
Construction & civil engineering/ commercial litigation	20%
Commercial property	10%
Company/ corporate finance/ commercial	10%
Computer and IT	7%
Charities/ professional institutions/ partnership/ environmental	3%

CONTACTS

Charities	Edward Williams
Commercial litigation	Richard de Ste. Croix
	Kevin Appleton
Commercial property	Michael Rowles
	Alexandra Lethbridge
Company	Paul Cooke
Computers and IT	Philip Westmacott
Construction	James Hudson
Corporate finance	William Saunders
EC and anti-trust litigation	David Brown
Environmental	Richard Burnett-Hall
Intell. prop.: patents	Ian Judge
Intell. prop.: patent	David Brown
Intell. prop.: brands/trademk	Sally Field
	Paul Walsh
Intell. prop.: commercial/comp	Avril Martindale
Intell. prop.: general	Edward Nodder
Partnership	John Lace
Professional institutions	Edward Williams

RECRUITMENT AND TRAINING: Bristows Cooke & Carpmael recruits outstanding trainee solicitors each year. The long-term prospects are excellent; around half the present partners trained with the firm. Although a scientific background is particularly useful in intellectual property, applicants with good degrees in any subject are encouraged to apply. A comprehensive in-house training programme is organised. Some trainees spend three months on secondment to IBM and Gillette. Application forms and a recruitment brochure are available.

BRISTOWS COOKE & CARPMAEL

BROBECK HALE and DORR INTERNATIONAL Veritas House, 125 Finsbury Pavement, London, EC2A 1NQ **Tel:** (0171) 638 6688 **Fax:** (0171) 638 5888. An innovative joint venture, established by two US law firms, Brobeck, Phleger & Harrison and Hale and Dorr. Headquartered in New York, the firm has approximately 700 lawyers in the US and London.

BRODIES WS

15 ATHOLL CRESCENT, EDINBURGH, EH3 8HA
DX: ED10 Edinburgh 1

TEL: (0131) 228 3777
FAX: (0131) 228 3878

THE FIRM: Brodies WS is a large Edinburgh-based firm serving an extensive range of United Kingdom and overseas clients. Advice on all the principal areas of legal practice and an increasing range of specialities is provided to both the business and private community through some 70 qualified solicitors, surveyors and accountants.

The firm maintains active connections with legal firms in London and the provinces. Moreover, membership of Unilaw and Terralex gives the practice access to affiliated offices in most European capitals and throughout the world.

Involvement in the commercial sphere has not impinged upon the partnership's commitment to its traditional clientele, with a fifth of the firm's strength devoted to private client work.

PRINCIPAL AREAS OF WORK:

Corporate Law: *Contact Partner:* Alistair Campbell
Banking & Insolvency: *Contact Partner:* David Guild
Commercial Property: *Contact Partners:* Dale Strachan and Bill Drummond
Litigation: *Contact Partners:* David Walker and Joyce Cullen
Trusts, Executry and Personal Financial Services: *Contact Partners:* Andrew Dalgleish and Hugh Stevens
Rural Property: *Contact Partners:* David Houldsworth and Somerled Notley
Residential Property (and Relocation Services): *Contact Partners:* James Clark and James Henderson
Land and Estate Agency (Management and Sales): *Contact:* Mark Gibson

SPECIALIST SERVICES:

Environmental Law: *Contact Partner:* Charles Smith
Planning Law: *Contact Partner:* David Macartney
Employment Law: *Contact Partner:* Joyce Cullen
Professional Negligence: *Contact Partner:* David Williamson
Privatisation: *Contact Partner:* David Guild
Agriculture: *Contact Partner:* Michael Gascoigne
Corporate Tax & VAT: *Contact:* Isobel d'Inverno
Personal Tax & Accountancy: *Contact:* Bob Page
Local Government: *Contact Partner:* George Taylor
Debt Recovery: *Contact Partner:* David Walker

FOREIGN LANGUAGES: French, German, Italian, Russian, Swedish.

INTERNATIONAL CONNECTIONS & ASSOCIATED OFFICES: Member of Unilaw and Terralex. Associated offices in most European capitals, the USA, South America and the Far East. The firm also has a representative office in Hong Kong.

CONTACT PARTNER: Mr George Taylor

Number of partners:	29
Assistant solicitors:	35
Other fee-earners:	34

WORKLOAD	
Commercial litigation	25%
Commercial property	25%
Private client	15%
Corporate	15%
Rural	12%
Land and estates	8%

CONTACTS	
Banking and insolvency	David Guild
Commercial property	Dale Strachan
	Bill Drummond
Corporate law	Alistair Campbell
Corporate tax and VAT	Isobel d'Inverno
Employment law	William Holligan
Environmental law	Charles Smith
Franchising	Julian Voge
Land and estate agency	Mark Gibson
Licensing	Joyce Cullen
Litigation	David Walker/ Joyce Cullen
Personal tax and accountancy	Bob Page
Planning law	David Macartney
Residential property	James Clark
	James Henderson
Rural property	D. Houldsworth/Somerled Notley
Trust and executry	Andrew Dalgleish
	Hugh Stevens

BROOKE NORTH AND GOODWIN

YORKSHIRE HSE, EAST PARADE, LEEDS, W. YORKS, LS1 5SD
DX: 12005

TEL: (0113) 283 2100
FAX: (0113) 283 3999

THE FIRM: A BS5750 approved practice with a long-standing reputation for handling the national and international affairs of a wide range of commercial concerns. There is an emphasis on UK and international company and commercial work, commercial litigation, insolvency, commercial property and property management, employment, offshore trusts and strategic tax planning and environmental law. Commercial acumen and quality of service are the watchwords of the practice. The firm is a founder member of QLG, a national organisation comprising 13 selected law firms in major UK cities.

OTHER OFFICES: Branch Office: Gibraltar (agency work undertaken).
Tel: (00) 350 70545. *Fax:* (00) 350 70511.
Other Connections: Carter Jones McDonald, Isle of Man.

CONTACT PARTNER: Gordon Watson

Number of partners:	10
Assistant solicitors:	5
Other fee-earners:	6

WORKLOAD	
Insolvency	25%
Tax and trusts	20%
Commercial property	20%
Commercial litigation	20%
Company/ commercial	15%

BROOKSTREET DES ROCHES 1 Des Roches Square, Witan Way, Witney, Oxon, OX8 6BE **Tel:** (01993) 771616 **Fax:** (01993) 779030 **DX:** 40205 Witney **Ptnrs:** 3 **Asst Solrs:** 3 **Other Fee-earners:** 2. Principal area of work is commercial property with a particular specialism in commercial retail. Also handles company work, commercial litigation, conveyancing, probate and matrimonial work. In addition the firm has an expertise in charity law.

WORKLOAD			
Commercial property	60%	Commercial litigation	20%
Company	10%		

R.M. BROUDIE & CO 1-3 Sir Thomas St, Liverpool, Merseyside, L1 8BW **Tel:** (0151) 227 1429 **Fax: DX:** 14248 **Ptnrs:** 2 **Asst Solrs:** 5 **Other Fee-earners:** 12. Civil liberties firm. Large specialist criminal department. It also handles civil litigation, judicial review, and agency work.

WORKLOAD			
Crime	90%	Civ lit/judicial review	10%

BROWN COOPER 7 Southampton Place, London, WC1A 2DR **Tel:** (0171) 404 0422 **Fax:** (0171) 831 9856 **DX:** 35731 Bloomsbury **Ptnrs:** 8 **Asst Solrs:** 6 **Other Fee-earners:** 2. Brown Cooper has a commercial practice concentrating on company work and conveyancing. Commercial litigation is also undertaken.

BROWNE JACOBSON

44 CASTLE GATE, NOTTINGHAM, NOTTS, NG1 7BJ
DX: 10007

TEL: (0115) 950 0055
FAX: (0115) 947 5246

THE FIRM: Browne Jacobson is a substantial commercial and institutional law firm offering a full range of legal services. Already acknowledged as a leading regional practice, the firm has developed a national reputation for the quality of its work and has a growing international presence. It operates from offices in Nottingham and London and has a close association with a Paris firm of avocats, Azema Sells. Browne Jacobson has experienced and enthusiastic teams of specialists offering pragmatic legal advice, dedicated to providing value for money without compromising quality.

PRINCIPAL AREAS OF WORK:
Corporate & Commercial: *Work includes:* all corporate/commercial and corporate finance including flotations and new issues, mergers and acquisition, MBOs/MBIs, venture capital, banking, commercial contracts (including joint ventures, franchising, agency and distribution agreements) corporate tax/pensions, share schemes, employment, intellectual property, information technology; commercial property and landlord & tenant, construction, planning and environment.

CONTACT PARTNER: Mr R.V. Brook

Number of partners:	27
Assistant solicitors:	40
Other fee-earners:	38

WORKLOAD	
Commercial and other litigation	23%
Insurance and personal injury litigation	22%
Professional indemnity	19%
Company commercial	16%
Commercial property	10%
Trust, probate and taxation	5%

Litigation: A founder member of CEDR, the firm seeks innovative alternatives to litigation wherever possible: one of the partners is a trained mediator. Where court action is unavoidable, the firm acts to obtain a speedy resolution of the dispute. *Work includes:* employment disputes including loss of profits from business interruption; personal injury (including sports-related injuries) especially on behalf of defendant insurance companies; professional indemnity claims against solicitors, surveyors, accountants, brokers, architects and engineers; medical negligence; contentious intellectual property matters; insurance litigation; defamation; licensing; trading standards and construction disputes. The firm is also active in local government matters and has also acted for private individuals in judicial review cases.

Private Client: The private client department handles all aspects of personal taxation, trusts, wills, probate and administration as well as residential conveyancing and family and matrimonial law. In addition the firm has specialists in the area of mental health law and is represented on the Law Society's Mental Health Panel. Criminal cases are also undertaken, including legal aid work.

LANGUAGES SPOKEN: French, German, Malay and Spanish.

OTHER OFFICES:
Aldwych House, 81 Aldwych, London WC2B 4HN.
Tel: (0171) 404 1546. *Fax:* (0171) 836 3882.

CONTACTS	
Commercial litigation	Peter Ellis
Commercial property	David Hibbert
Company/ commercial	Andrew Pirie
Corporate finance/banking	Rob Metcalfe
	Peter Hands
Crime	Stephen Burdon
Employment	Edward Benson
Matrimonial/ mental health	David Burdett
Personal injury	Neville Radcliffe
Professional indemnity	Robert Ridgwell
Public and administrative law	Tom Huggon
Taxation	Paul Jenkins

BRUNTON MILLER Herbert House, 22 Herbert Street, Glasgow, G20 6NB
Tel: (0141) 337 1199 **Fax:** (0141) 337 3300 **DX:** GW21 **Ptnrs:** 11 **Asst Solrs:** 3
Other Fee-earners: 4. The firm is well-known for its licensing expertise, and also advises on criminal matters, debt collection and family/ matrimonial law.

WORKLOAD			
Court	45%	Licensing	24%
Conveyancing (domestic)	19%	Convey (comm/corp)	12%

BRUTTON & CO 132 High Street, Portsmouth, Hants, PO1 2HR
Tel: (01705) 812711 **Fax:** (01705) 814833 **DX:** 2206 **Ptnrs:** 11 **Asst Solrs:** 5
Other Fee-earners: 8. Work includes: personal injury, family and matrimonial, commercial property and business, mental health, liquor licensing, general litigation, ecclesiastical and probate.

WORKLOAD			
Litigation	43%	Non-cont private client	29%
Contentious family	14%	Non-cont commercial	14%

BUCKLE MELLOWS 45-51 Priestgate, Peterborough, Cambs, PE1 1LB
Tel: (01733) 68175 **Fax:** (01733) 62064 **DX:** 12312 P'Boro 1 **Ptnrs:** 11 **Asst Solrs:** 7 **Other Fee-earners:** 13. Handles all forms of commercial and company work, personal injury, commercial property, divorce, crime and general litigation.

WORKLOAD			
Conveyancing	25%	Family	25%
Civil litigation	15%	Personal injury	15%
Company and commercial	10%	Probate	10%

BUGGE, ARENTZ-HANSEN & RASMUSSEN (UK) ANS

SUITE 1A, 99 GRESHAM STREET, LONDON, EC2P 2BR

TEL: (0171) 600 0334
FAX: (0171) 600 0335

THE FIRM: Bugge, Arentz-Hansen & Rasmussen is a leading Norwegian firm providing services to corporate clients including banks and other financial institutions, the construction industry and oil companies.

THE LONDON OFFICE: The office provides services to clients in, amongst others, the following areas of law:
Corporate and commercial, including matters pertaining to joint stock companies and other corporations.
Banking and Finance. This includes preparation of documentation, as well as assisting loan applicants in negotiations and examination of loan agreements. Assistance in project financing and adaptation.

CONTACT PARTNER: Terje Sommer	
LAWYERS:	
London:	2
Worldwide:	50

Stock Exchange and securities law, including assistance in connection with Stock Exchange listings and flotations.
Mergers and acquisitions. Corporate and tax advice in connection with takeovers, mergers and generational changes.
Competition law.
Financial Regulations. Assistance is provided concerning establishment conditions and regulatory aspects.
LANGUAGES SPOKEN: Norwegian and other Scandinavian languages, English.
OTHER OFFICE: Oslo.
HEAD OFFICE: Stranden 1, P.O. Box 1524 Vika, N 0117 Oslo, Norway.
Tel: 47 22 830270. *Fax:* 47 22 832275 & 47 22 832275.

BULLER JEFFRIES 36 Bennetts Hill, Birmingham, W. Midlands, B2 5SN **Tel:** (0121) 212 2620 **Fax:** (0121) 212 2210 **DX:** 13051 Birmingham 1 **Ptnrs:** 5 **Asst Solrs:** 11 **Other Fee-earners:** 6. A long-established practice specialising in personal injury work and all aspects of insurance law. Also at Coventry.

WORKLOAD			
Pers inj/insurance lit	95%	Conveyancing/wills/prob	5%

BULLIVANT JONES & COMPANY

STATE HOUSE, 22 DALE ST, LIVERPOOL, MERSEYSIDE, L2 4UR
DX: 14120 Liverpool

TEL: (0151) 227 5671
FAX: (0151) 227 5632

THE FIRM: The firm was established in 1970, and has since come to be held in high regard, particularly in the field of commercial property and property related litigation. It places a high emphasis on quality of service and commitment to retained clients.
PRINCIPAL AREAS OF WORK: The firm deals with all matters relating to commercial property, with a particular emphasis on the retail sector. In addition, it handles property and retail related litigation together with a wide range of employment, commercial and private client work.

CONTACT PARTNER: Pamela Jones

Number of partners:	7
Assistant solicitors:	20
Other fee-earners:	4

BULLOCK WORTHINGTON & JACKSON 1 Booth Street, Manchester, M2 2HA **Tel:** (0161) 833 9771 **Fax:** (0161) 832 0489 **DX:** 14403 **Ptnrs:** 5 **Asst Solrs:** 4 **Other Fee-earners:** 7. Long-established practice handling a large volume of plaintiff personal injury work.

WORKLOAD			
Personal injury/med neg	40%	Priv (probate/trusts/tax)	30%
Domestic/comm prop	10%		

BURD PEARSE 21 Fore St, Okehampton, Devon, EX20 1AJ **Tel:** (01837) 52416 **Fax:** (01837) 54540 **DX:** 82500 **Ptnrs:** 5 **Asst Solrs:** 2 **Other Fee-earners:** 3. Founded in 1805, Burd Pearse has five partners all concentrating on various fields of law. One of the partners, J.P.A. Burnett sits on the Revenue Committee of The Law Society.

FIRMS OF ACCOUNTANTS

Accountants specialising in litigation support are listed in the accountants' A-Z, with details of the services they offer to solicitors, from forensic accounting to intellectual property or business valuations.

BURGES SALMON

NARROW QUAY HOUSE, PRINCE ST, BRISTOL, BS1 4AH
DX: 7829

TEL: (0117) 939 2000
FAX: (0117) 929 4705

THE FIRM: A full service commercial practice, enjoying a reputation as the market leader in agricultural law and undertaking a significant amount of high quality private client work. Burges Salmon derives added value from its membership of the Norton Rose M5 Group.

Burges Salmon is a large single office firm which has added an impressive range of regional, national and internationl clients to its extensive established client list. The firm has expanded considerably in recent years and anticipates substantial future growth. Burges Salmon attributes its success to its commitment to the delivery of the highest quality service in clear and businesslike terms and at a price which represents good value for money. The firm's policy is to recruit and train the best lawyers and to support them with high quality staff and technology.

PRINCIPAL AREAS OF WORK: The firm delivers a full range of services either through it's traditional practice groups or by specialist units according to the needs of each client. These units include: banking and insolvency; building societies; charities; construction and engineering; employment and employee benefits and pensions; environment; financial services; housing associations; minerals and mining; planning; rent review; telecommunications and transport and distribution.

Corporate practice group: *(Contact Partner:* Alan Barr*)* handles a growing number of flotations, Stock Exchange work, a full range of company and corporate finance transactions and all associated UK and EU business law. The expanding international practice of this group extends to inward investment, UK offshore and internationl tax planning and asset protection. The group has a national reputation for unit trust and financial services work and a significant presence in the field of agribusiness.

Commercial property team: *(Contact Partner:* Stuart King*)* handles the full range of property transactions including all aspects of planning, funding, building procurement, management, lettings and construction, engineering and other disputes. It has become involved in a number of prestige schemes and in portfolio acquisitions and disposals for property investors in addition to its flourishing corporate support work.

Banking/insolvency practice: *(Contact Partner:* Guy Stobart*)* deals with all aspects of banking, securities, and investment work and corporate insolvency.

Commercial litigation practice group: *(Contact Partner:* Adrian Llewelyn Evans*)* provides a full litigation service for the firm's business clients with particular expertise in intellectual property, professional negligence, employment, insolvency, white collar crime, insurance and partnership disputes. The team includes experts on arbitration and ADR.

Agricultural practice group: *(Contact Partner:* Peter Williams*)* covers the complete range of UK and EU agricultural law, both contentious and non-contentious and extends to the provision of high quality advocacy services.

Private client group: *(Contact Partner:* Martin Mitchell*)* deals with a wide range of trust and tax issues including the provision of estate and tax planning, heritage preservation, UK and offshore trusts, immigration and emigration, family and matrimonial breakdown, charities, high value residential conveyancing and staff relocation.

RECRUITMENT AND TRAINING: The firm recruits law, non-law and mature graduates, and offers both in-house training and residential courses with the Norton Rose M5 Group. Vacation experience is also available. Apply two years in advance; forms from R.D.Llewellin.

CONTACT PARTNER: Mr S.A. King

Number of partners:	32
Assistant solicitors:	62
Other fee-earners:	23

WORKLOAD	
Property	25%
Corporate	25%
Agriculture	17%
Commercial litigation	13%
Private client	12%
Banking and insolvency	8%

CONTACTS	
Agribusiness	Roger Hawes
	William Neville
Agriculture	Peter Williams
Banking/ insolvency	Guy Stobart
	Peter Williams
Commercial	Richard Wynn-Jones
Commercial litigation	Adrian Llewelyn Evans
Commercial property	Stuart King
Construction	Marcus Harling
Corporate	Alan Barr
Employment	George Dyson
Environment	Robert Smyth
Financial services	Christopher Godfrey
Housing Associations	Stephen McNulty
Intellectual property	Simon Coppen
International	Harry Wiggin
Pensions and corporate tax	Tim Illston
Planning	Patrick Robinson
Private client	Martin Mitchell
Transport and distribution	Richard Wynn-Jones

BURLEY & GEACH 8 Swan St, Petersfield, Hants, GU32 3AE **Tel:** (01730) 262401 **Fax:** (01730) 265182 **DX:** 100402 **Ptnrs:** 8 **Asst Solrs:** 5 **Other Fee-earners:** 6. Specialises in litigation and private client matters. Also handles employment law, agriculture, charities, company/ commercial, licensing and intellectual property. Three other offices.

WORKLOAD			
Conveyancing	28%	Private client	24%
Family	14%	Civil litigation	13%
Crime	10%		

W & J BURNESS WS

16 HOPE STREET, CHARLOTTE SQUARE, EDINBURGH, EH2 4DD
DX: 73 Edinburgh

TEL: (0131) 226 2561
FAX: (0131) 225 2964

THE FIRM: Founded by William and James Burness in the early 19th century, W & J Burness has become one of the largest firms in Scotland, a position which has been attained without resort to amalgamation. The firm is divided into five departments (company, commercial property, civil litigation, residential property and private client) with frequent overlap between departments according to the individual requirements of each case.

PRINCIPAL AREAS OF WORK:

Company: (*Contact Partner:* John Rafferty, Edinburgh, Annette Pairman, Glasgow). Acting for private and public companies, the firm has a depth and range of experience in the commercial field. The firm helps with all aspects of company formation and finance, institutional investment, share issues and Stock Exchange listings, business acquisitions, company sales and management buy-outs, mergers, demergers and the negotiation of commercial contracts. Individual bankruptcy, company liquidation and receivership are dealt with by the specialist insolvency section. A team of banking lawyers assists both lenders and borrowers with matters involving regulatory procedures, finance leasing and oil field related securities. Advice can also be sought on a whole range of energy issues, including mineral, oil and gas law. In addition, business clients can benefit from the firm's expertise in the fields of anti-trust law and EC competition regulations, licensing, intellectual property, pensions and environmental law.

Commercial Property: (*Contact Partner:* David Reid, Edinburgh, David Gibson, Glasgow). The department provides comprehensive advice on all commercial property requirements connected with the sale, acquisition and leasing of business sites and buildings. Developments handled by the firm include shops and shopping centres, offices, businesses and factories.

Litigation: (*Contact Partner:* Dr. Martin Sales, Edinburgh, Shona Maclean, Glasgow). The firm handles civil disputes of every kind whether by negotiation, informal arbitration or through the courts. One partner is a qualified Mediator in Alternative Dispute Resolution. The department will prepare and conduct cases for every forum, including the House of Lords and the European Court. Areas in which consultation is common include: contract (particularly construction and engineering), employment, damages for civil fault (medical and professional negligence, personal injury and financial loss), property (ownership and lease disputes, planning and valuation) and defamation. The firm is equipped to react swiftly to the processes of interim application, whether for interim interdict or judicial review.

Residential Property: (*Contact Partner:* Gordon Murray, Edinburgh). The department markets residential properties for sale, and advises generally on all aspects of sale, acquisition, lease and security over residential property.

Private Client and Financial Planning: (*Contact Partner:* George Menzies, Edinburgh, Alister Sutherland, Glasgow, Donald Caskie, Guernsey). The department offers the private client a range of services in the field of tax planning. These include lifetime gifts, new trusts, tax efficient wills, tax benefits on heritage property and works of art, and the provision of tax shelters, encompassing forestry enterprises and Lloyd's underwriting interests. The Guernsey office provides an offshore trust administration service. The comprehensive private client practice also embraces various aspects of financial administration, agricultural law, and the purchase, sale and lease of estates and sporting rights.

INTERNATIONAL CONNECTIONS & ASSOCIATED OFFICES: Member of TELFA.

FOREIGN LANGUAGES: German, French, Italian.

OTHER OFFICES:
242 West George Street, Glasgow G2 4QY.
Tel: (0141) 248 4933. *Fax:* (0141) 204 1601.
9 The Maze, Berthelot Street, St Peter Port, Guernsey, Channel Islands.
Tel: (01481) 710 867. *Fax:* (01481) 710 578.

MANAGING PARTNER:
Malcolm Strang Steel

UK:	
Number of partners:	27
Assistant solicitors:	26
Other fee-earners:	28
INTERNATIONAL:	
Number of Partners:	1
Other fee-earners:	2

WORKLOAD	
Commercial property	29%
Private client	27%
Corporate/ commercial	22%
Litigation	13%
Residential property	9%

CONTACTS	
Agency franchising	James McLean
Agricultural law	Adam Gillingham
Banking work and insolvency	Malcolm Wood
Charities	Simon Mackintosh
Commercial tax	Heather Thompson
Competition law	James McLean
Construction/civil engineering	Dr Martin Sales
Corporate finance	John Rafferty/ Andrew Sleigh
Corporate reorganisations	John Rafferty
Defamation/ judicial review	Bruce Logan
Defence reparation	Marsali Murray
Employment	Marsali Murray
Environment and planning	Dr Martin Sales
Equipment leasing/ inward invest.	Paul Pia
ESOPS	John Rafferty/ Andrew Sleigh
European law	James McLean
Executry	George Menzies
Housing associations	Gordon Murray
Intellectual property	James McLean
Licensed property/ relocations	David Gifford
Pensions	Margaret Meehan/ A Sutherland
Product liability	Marsali Murray
Public sector/ privatisations	Annette Pairman
Purchase/ sale of businesses	John Rafferty
	Andrew Sleigh
Sports law	Andrew Sleigh
Tax planning	S Mackintosh/ A Sutherland
Trust and financial admin	Hubert Ross
Venture capital investment	Andrew Sleigh
	John Rafferty

BURNETT & REID 15 Golden Square, Aberdeen, Grampian, AB9 1JF
Tel: (01224) 644333 **Fax:** (01224) 632173 **DX:** 19 Aberdeen **Ptnrs:** 10 **Asst Solrs:** 4 **Other Fee-earners:** 9. The firm has particular expertise in landed estate management and is experienced in dealing with agricultural holdings.

WORKLOAD			
Res convey/estate agency	27%	Court work	17%
Trust and executry	14%	Agric/land management	14%
Investment/fin planning	13%	Commercial/ corporate	12%

BURNETTS 6 Victoria Place, Carlisle, Cumbria, CA1 1ES **Tel:** (01228) 20265 **Fax:** (01228) 23299 **DX:** 63005 **Ptnrs:** 17 **Asst Solrs:** 5 **Other Fee-earners:** 11. Best known for matrimonial and commercial property work but also handling a wide range of legal matters including considerable personal injury, litigation and company/ commercial work.

WORKLOAD			
Matrimonial/children	21%	Company and commercial	18%
Personal injury	16%	Civil litigation	16%
Res conveyancing	12%		

BURNSIDE KEMP FRASER 4 Queens Terrace, Aberdeen, Grampian, AB1 1XL **Tel:** (01224) 624602 **Fax:** (01224) 624011 **DX:** 78 Aberdeen **Ptnrs:** 2 **Asst Solrs:** 2 **Other Fee-earners:** 2. Known for its private client litigation work including industrial tribunal representation, personal injury claims and family/ matrimonial work.

BURROUGHS DAY 14 Charlotte St, Bristol, BS1 5PT **Tel:** (0117) 9290333 **Fax:** (0117) 9272342 **DX:** 7825 **Ptnrs:** 12 **Asst Solrs:** 9 **Other Fee-earners:** 12. Origins traceable back to 1829. Best known for commercial, litigation and matrimonial work. Commercial and residential conveyancing are other major areas of practice.

BURSTOWS

8 IFIELD RD, CRAWLEY, W. SUSSEX, RH11 7YY
DX: 57100 Crawley

TEL: (01293) 534734
FAX: (01293) 552544

THE FIRM: Founded 20 years ago, Burstows has grown to a 12 partner firm with its main office in Crawley. The firm retains a strong private client division but has in recent years concentrated on the development of its corporate and commercial work in response to the economic growth of the Crawley/ Gatwick area. Burstows is an affiliate member of the British Franchise Association and a founder member of Eurolegal, a European association of lawyers offering commercial legal services for crossborder transactions. The firm is also one of the founder members of QLG, a national association of 13 law firms with a commitment to quality and has achieved accreditation to ISO 9001. (See also entry for QLG.)

PRINCIPAL AREAS OF WORK:

Corporate: (*Contact:* Caroline Armitage). *Work includes:* company formation, restructuring, mergers and acquisitions, management buy-outs/buy-ins, flotations, corporate finance and company secretarial services.

Commercial: (*Contact:* Don Burstow). *Work includes:* joint ventures, licensing/franchising, options, agency, distributorship, the Financial Services Act, consumer law, banking, debt recovery, computer hardware and software advice, intellectual property patents and copyright.

Travel and Transport: (*Contact:* Michael Butler). Work includes: aviation finance, regulatory advice, tourism/travel and transport industry, and contractual and litigious matters, including EU, Central and Eastern Europe specialisations in livestock transport and aviation regulations respectively.

Commercial Property: (*Contact:* Carol Fletcher). *Work includes:* land acquisition/disposal, commercial leases, planning, estates, development, licensed premises.

Town and Country Planning: (*Contact:* Roger Curtis). *Work includes:* planning advice and assistance for both commercial and private development including major planning appeals and enquiries. (Member of Law Society Planning Panel).

Commercial Litigation: (*Contact:* Tony Burstow). *Work includes:* corporate and commercial litigation, employment matters, injunctions, landlord and tenant, building disputes, debt recovery, international litigation, factoring litigation, liquor licensing, white collar crime.

CONTACT PARTNER: Mr Tony Burstow

Number of partners:	12
Assistant solicitors:	8
Other fee-earners:	17

WORKLOAD	
Litigation - general civil	35%
Corporate & commercial, including employment law	26%
Commercial property, including town & country planning	15%
Private client	13%
Insolvency	11%

CONTACTS	
Commercial property	C Fletcher, G Vernon
	P Bartholomew
Commercial litigation	J Innes
Corporate/ commercial	D G Burstow
	C D Armitage
Debt recovery	L. Hills
Employment law	H Sherrard
Family/ matrimonial	W Ryle, G Jutton
Insolvency	A Clinton, A Taylor

Employment Law: (*Contact:* Harry Sherrard). *Work includes:* contentious and non-contentious aspects from drafting of employment contracts, obtaining injunctions and industrial tribunal work.

Personal Injury: (*Contact:* Lee Hills). *Work includes:* plaintiff and defendant work acting for individuals and insurers.

Insolvency: (*Contact:* Andy Taylor). *Work includes:* both corporate and personal insolvency, acting for individuals, directors, receivers, administrators and liquidators. Appointed solicitors for the Treasury Solicitor on directors' disqualification – licensed insolvency practitioners.

Private Legal Services: (*Contact:* John Innes/Philip Lansberry). *Work includes:* wills, probate, trusts, tax planning, family law and matrimonial, residential conveyancing. (These include relocation and remortgage services, personnel surgeries and advice on civil disputes which are offered to businesses, organisations and their personnel).

OTHER OFFICES: Horsham and Brighton.

RECRUITMENT AND TRAINING: Carol Fletcher.

FOREIGN LANGUAGES: French, German and Dutch.

FOREIGN CONNECTIONS: Founder members of Eurolegal with close contacts in all EC member countries.

Intellectual property	N Ellin
Personal injury	L Hills
Residential conveyancing	T Rodemark
Town & country planning	R M Curtis
Wills, probate & trust	J Francis, P Lansberry

BURT BRILL & CARDENS 30 Old Steyne, Brighton, E. Sussex, BN1 1FL **Tel:** (01273) 604123 **Fax:** (01273) 570837 **DX:** 2709 **Ptnrs:** 6 **Asst Solrs:** 5 **Other Fee-earners:** 9. Has two offices. Best known for its litigation work and its large debt collection service. Work also includes criminal, matrimonial law, probate and property.

WORKLOAD			
Probate & trusts	26%	Property	23%
Priv - matrim/pers inj	20%	Commercial litigation	20%
Company/legal aid/other	11%		

BURTON COPELAND

ROYAL LONDON HSE, 196 DEANSGATE, MANCHESTER, M3 3JW
DX: 14362 Manchester 1

TEL: (0161) 834 7374
FAX: (0161) 835 2904

THE FIRM: Established in 1982 specialising in criminal law, especially commercial fraud. In 1991 the firm opened a thriving London office.

PRINCIPAL AREAS OF WORK: The firm's commercial fraud department, with five experienced former members of the Commercial Fraud Squad, is located in both the Manchester and London offices (*Contact Partner:* Ian Burton). The London office deals almost exclusively with "white collar" crime, such as insider dealing and tax fraud, although general criminal work is undertaken when considered appropriate.

The Manchester office, which also handles a large juvenile and general criminal caseload, complements its commercial fraud work with a wide range of commercial services. The firm provides property and litigation expertise.

FOREIGN LANGUAGES: French, German.

LONDON OFFICE: 51 Lincoln's Inn Fields, London WC2A 3LZ. *Tel:* (0171) 430 2277. *Fax:* (0171) 430 1101. *DX:* 37981 Kingsway.

CONTACT PARTNER: Ian Burton

Number of partners:	15
Assistant solicitors:	15
Other fee-earners:	21

CONTACTS	
Commercial fraud	I.R. Burton
Criminal	M.P. Mackey
Motoring	N. Freeman
Private client	M.C. Mason

BURY & WALKERS Britannic Hse, Regent St, Barnsley, S. Yorks, S70 2EQ **Tel:** (01226) 733533 **Fax:** (01226) 207610 **DX:** 12251 **Ptnrs:** 10 **Asst Solrs:** 10 **Other Fee-earners:** 10. Known for commercial and domestic conveyancing. Other areas of work are matrimonial (including all Children Act proceedings), landlord and tenant, probate and trust, commercial and general litigation.

WORKLOAD			
Lit (incl comm lit)	40%	Property/wills/prob/tax	34%
Commercial	26%		

BUSS MURTON

THE PRIORY, TUNBRIDGE WELLS, KENT, TN1 1JJ
DX: 3913

TEL: (01892) 510222
FAX: (01892) 510333

CONTACT PARTNER: Robert Sedgwick	
Number of partners:	18
Assistant solicitors:	9
Other fee-earners:	21

THE FIRM: The Buss Murton Partnership was formed in 1985 from the merger of two of Kent's oldest firms, and today it combines business experience going back over 250 years with a modern and forward-thinking approach. The firm is a general practice and, whilst family and private client matters remain important areas of work, its company/ commercial and commercial litigation departments have expanded rapidly in recent years.

WORKLOAD	
Private client	26%
Company/ commercial	25%
Personal injury	18%
Property	16%
Litigation	15%

PRINCIPAL AREAS OF WORK:

Company/ Commercial: (*Contact:* Simon Judd). Work covers the full spectrum of business activity including: company law, acquisitions, distributorship agreements, insolvency, franchises, and business leases of all types. A separate section deals with the travel industry. The firm is a founder member of the International Property Lawyers Association.

Property: (*Contact:* Anne Milne). A separate department handling all aspects of commercial and residential property work throughout the UK.

Housing: (*Contact:* Graham Waite). Specialist department which acts for a number of substantial registered housing associations. Also involved with housing associations schemes and associated secured lending.

Personal litigation: (*Contact:* Patrick Palmer). Proceedings have been conducted at every level, as high as the House of Lords and the European Court of Justice. Private litigation includes: breach of contract, employment, personal injury claims, and matrimonial matters. No criminal legal aid work is undertaken. A specialised department handles computerised debt collection and agency work.

Personal Injury: (*Contact:* John Hedley). Handles all types of plaintiff and defendant personal injury and medical negligence work including legal expenses, insurance and union funded matters. Specialist sub-section deals with R.T.A. claims.

Private Client: (*Contact:* The Hon. A.C. Colville). A large private client department which has generated a well-established following, handles all aspects of wills, probate, trusts, estate management and tax planning.

Financial Services: (*Contact:* Geoff Craig). Specialist department advises corporate and private clients on: sources of finance, investments, life assurance, pensions.

Agriculture: (*Contact:* Tim Ball). A separate agricultural department has been formed to service an extensive farming client base. The department covers every aspect of farming including the specialist areas of alternative uses of land, planning law, environmental law and farm sales.

CONTACTS	
Agriculture	Tim Ball
Commercial litigation	Mark Agombar
Company/ commercial	Simon Judd
Debt recovery	Graham Bridgman
Financial services	Geoff Craig
Housing	Graham Waite
Intellectual property	Robert Sedgwick
Matrimonial	Patrick Palmer/ Jackie Judd
Personal injury	John Hedley
Personal litigation	Patrick Palmer
Private client	A. Colville/ J. Toth
Property	Anne Milne

OTHER OFFICES: The main offices at Tunbridge Wells are complemented by smaller offices at Cranbrook, Hawkhurst, Tenterden and Staplehurst.

RECRUITMENT AND TRAINING: The firm recruits two or three trainee solicitors every year. The nature and scope of the matters handled provide an excellent training base. It is policy to retain staff following successful completion of articles. Applications in writing should be addressed to Philip Davis.

BUSSMURTON

BUTCHER & BARLOW 2 Bank Street, Bury, Lancs, BL9 0DL **Tel:** (0161) 764 4062 **Fax:** (0161) 797 2912 **DX:** 20506 **Ptnrs:** 6 **Asst Solrs:** 2 **Other Fee-earners:** 3. One of the oldest established practices in Bury offering a comprehensive service for all personal, business and notarial matters.

BUTCHER BURNS Beaumont House, 47 Mount Pleasant, London, WC1X 0AE **Tel:** (0171) 713 7100 **Fax:** (0171) 713 6121 **DX:** 53328 Clerkenwell **Ptnrs:** 3 **Other Fee-earners:** 3. Broadly based long-established practice comprising expertise in most areas of law with particular emphasis on entertainment and defamation.

CAMERON MARKBY HEWITT

SCEPTRE COURT, 40 TOWER HILL, LONDON, EC3N 4BB
DX: 215 London City EC3

TEL: (0171) 702 2345
FAX: (0171) 702 2303

SENIOR PARTNER: Bill Shelford

Number of partners:	74
Assistant solicitors:	136
Other fee-earners:	96

CONTACTS

Advertising and IT	Guilherme Brafman
Asset finance and leasing	Keith Gregory
Aviation/ product liability	Anthony Hobkinson
Banking	John White
Building/ major projects	Frank Dufficy
Commercial litigation	J. Burnett-Hitchcock
Corporate	Arfon Jones
EC and competition law	Nick Paul
Employment/ employee relations	A. Fincham
Financial Services	Simon Morris
Immigration and nationality	Julia Onslow-Cole
Insolvency	Stephen Foster
Insurance and reinsurance	Clive Brown
Intellectual property	John Armstrong
Oil and gas	Penelope Warne
Pensions	Humphrey Morrison
Planning/ environment	Charles Romney
Property	Richard Goodman
Shipping	Michael Freeman
Taxation	Keith Gregory

Cameron Markby Hewitt is a leading City firm providing a full range of legal services to the financial, insurance, commercial and industrial sectors, both in the UK and overseas. It has offices in Lloyd's of London, Aberdeen, Bristol and Brussels.

THE FIRM: Cameron Markby Hewitt has had a strong City reputation for over two centuries and continues to build on its renowned strengths in banking, corporate finance, insolvency, insurance, litigation and property.

The firm's aim is to achieve pre-eminence in an increasing number of areas. It is already highly regarded in aviation, environment, financial services, immigration and securitisation and is actively strengthening its services in advertising, building and engineering, fraud, information technology, multimedia, oil and gas, pensions, product liability and tax.

TYPES OF WORK UNDERTAKEN: In banking and financial services, the firm acts for a broad range of UK and international clients, including many major clearing, commercial and merchant banks; general insurance, life insurance and reinsurance companies, Lloyd's underwriters, agents and brokers; securities houses and building societies.

Clients also include UK and overseas corporations in areas such as manufacturing, investment, real estate, high-technology, and communications.

The firm handles the full range of corporate work including a substantial amount of Stock Exchange listings and flotations, takeovers, mergers, major reconstructions, regulatory investigations, taxation and employment matters. Clients are also advised on all aspects of EC law.

Other key areas of expertise are in dispute management, alternative dispute resolution, commercial litigation, arbitration, investment/ development, planning and communications.

Overall, the firm has a reputation for high quality advice and creative problem solving and is seen as a leader in its use of information technology.

RECRUITMENT AND TRAINING: Cameron Markby Hewitt takes pride in encouraging individual initiative and success, and trains lawyers in business and management skills, as well as technical excellence. Commitment to staff development is therefore high, with a programme of more than 200 internal workshops and seminars throughout the year. In 1994, Cameron Markby Hewitt became the first City law firm to be accredited as an Investor in People, in recognition of the training of staff to meet clients' needs. This is further acknowledgement of the firms' outstanding commitment to an enlightened business management training programme, having won the National Training Award in 1991. Brochures are available on request.

CAMERON
MARKBY
HEWITT

EDITORIAL POLICY

In this edition, the lists of specialist firms include profiles of individual practitioners - solicitors and barristers - who have been recommended most frequently to our researchers. Editorial policy is to identify leading practitioners on merit: it is not possible to buy a place in our biographical lists. Inclusion of a profile in this directory is based solely on expertise and reputation.

Enormous effort has been invested by our ten-strong research team (mainly solicitors and barristers) in canvassing recommendations and identifying leaders. We are confident in the overall accuracy of the results. However, mistakes and misjudgements are inevitable, and if readers have any suggestions regarding our listings we should be very pleased to hear from them.

CAMERONS

218 STRAND, TEMPLE BAR, LONDON, WC2R 1AZ
DX: 217 Ch.Ln.

TEL: (0171) 353 5572
FAX: (0171) 936 2296

1 Peterborough Road, Harrow, Middx HA1 2YW
DX: 4213 Harrow
Contact: Mr D. Tuft

Tel:(0181) 423 6666
Fax:(0181) 864 4904

2 Henry Street, Bath BA1 1JT
DX: 8016 Bath
Contact:Mr J.V. Beaumont

Tel:(01225) 312121
Fax:(01225) 313513

THE FIRM: Tracing its roots back to the nineteenth century, Camerons has grown in recent years by developing specialised services in response to the increasing complexity of the law. From its offices in the Strand (opposite the Law Courts), Harrow and Bath, the firm provides an extensive range of legal services to business and private clients.

PRINCIPAL AREAS OF WORK: The firm's principal areas of speciality are corporate finance, banking law, company and commercial, utilities and energy law, intellectual property, building and construction law, commercial property, planning and environmental law, commercial litigation and ADR, corporate and personal tax, trusts and church and charities law.

OTHER AREAS OF WORK: Expertise is also available in all aspects of pensions and employment law (acting on behalf of employers and employees), landlord and tenant law, domestic conveyancing, matrimonial, personal injury and Australian law.

FOREIGN CONNECTIONS: The firm has strong connections in Australia, Hong Kong, the People's Republic of China, Singapore, Indonesia and the Russian Federation where it has acted on a number of minerals, exploration, energy industry infrastructure and financial services projects.

CONTACT PARTNER: Mr. L.J. Jackson

Number of partners:	9
Assistant solicitors:	1
Other fee-earners:	8

CONTACTS	
Banking and loans	J.S. Ricks
Church law	J.V. Beaumont
Commercial property/ planning	J.S. Ricks
Commercial litigation/ ADR	D. Sims
Company and commercial	L.J. Jackson
Corporate finance	L.J. Jackson
Employment/ intell. property	P. Ross-Smith
Family law and divorce	I. Lloyd
International joint ventures	L.J. Jackson
Tax and trusts	A.D. Farley

CAMPBELL HOOPER 35 Old Queen St, London, SW1H 1AZ **Tel:** (0171) 222 9070 **Fax:** (0171) 222 5591 **DX:** 2365 Victoria **Ptnrs:** 18 **Asst Solrs:** 7 **Other Fee-earners:** 8. Founded in 1754. Handles a wide variety of work including commercial conveyancing, company/ commercial, entertainment, litigation and private client.

WORKLOAD			
Comm lit (incl constr)	26%	Commercial property	23%
Company	19%	Media	17%
Private client	15%		

CAMPBELL SMITH WS

21 YORK PLACE, EDINBURGH, EH1 3EN
DX: 51 Edinburgh

TEL: (0131) 556 3737
FAX: (0131) 557 4069

THE FIRM: Campbell Smith WS is a broadly-based firm which expanded recently on merging with two smaller legal practices. A range of services is provided for both commercial and private clients, including full estate agency services.

PRINCIPAL AREAS OF WORK:

Commercial: (*Contact:* Neil Ferguson). The firm provides advice on all aspects of commercial law for a range of businesses, from public companies to sole traders. All aspects of commercial property work are undertaken including that relating to agricultural businesses and licenced premises.

Litigation: (*Contact:* John H. Crawford). The firm undertakes civil litigation on behalf of public authorities, commercial clients and private clients, with personal injury litigation a particular strength.

Private Client: (*Contact:* David Henderson or Eric J. Scott). The range of services includes residential conveyancing, matrimonial and family work, taxation advice, trusts, wills, estate administration and executry work.

SENIOR PARTNER: Mr John H. Crawford

Number of partners:	7
Assistant solicitors:	3
Other fee-earners:	5

WORKLOAD	
Property; conveyancing (commercial and domestic)	50%
Court including matrimonial and litigation	30%
Trust	19%
Financial	1%

Estate Agency Services: Full estate agency services are provided including inspections and valuations, preparation of particulars, marketing and viewing arrangements.

Education: *(Contact:* Eric J. Scott). The firm is able to provide particular advice in relation to recorded children with special educational needs.

CAMPBELL SMITH W.S.

CANN & HALLETT Trinity Court, Southernhay East, Exeter, Devon, EX1 1PG **Tel:** (01392) 75295 **Fax:** (01392) 411936 **DX:** 8300 Exeter **Ptnrs:** 3 **Asst Solrs:** 2 **Other Fee-earners:** 6. Civil litigation bias and personal injury work in particular, but also experience in housing association law and practice.

WORKLOAD			
Litigation	46%	Probate	16%
Domestic/other convey	13%	Housing association	12%
Matrimonial	9%	Commercial	4%

CANTER LEVIN & BERG 46-48 Stanley St, Liverpool, Merseyside, L1 6AL **Tel:** (0151) 236 8574/7 **Fax:** (0151) 236 1179 **DX:** 14122 **Ptnrs:** 11 **Asst Solrs:** 12 **Other Fee-earners:** 18. A general practice. Work includes criminal, civil litigation, conveyancing, private client and matrimonial.

WORKLOAD			
Civil litigation (RTA)	60%	Civil lit (other)	17%
Crime	12%	Convey/matrim/prob/comm	11%

CAPSTICKS

GENERAL ACCIDENT BUILDING, 77-83 UPPER RICHMOND ROAD, LONDON, SW15 2TT   DX: 59461

TEL: (0181) 780 2211
FAX: (0181) 780 1141

THE FIRM: Capsticks has been acting for regional and district health authorities since the 1970s and is one of the leaders in hospital and health service law. The firm is well known for its original research into topics of interest to the health care community. The firm's clients include NHS trusts, health authorities, insurance companies, utilities and local government.

PRINCIPAL AREAS OF WORK: The firm offers a high quality of work in the fields of medical malpractice, personal injury, employment and administrative law. It carries out a substantial volume of commercial work for health service clients and, through its associated software company (which is a sizeable undertaking) a unique insight into computer law. The firm's expertise extends to class actions, where recent cases have concerned HIV, benzodiazepines, Myodil, Opren and the contamination of water supplies.

COMPUTER SYSTEMS: The firm's practice management system was recently the winner of an award for "the most outstanding application of information technology to the law in the UK" from the Society of Computers and Law. It is extensively used by the fee-earners and maintains a database of cases which is used for research and quality management. The software was written by the firm's data processing division and is licensed to more than 25 other practices. A version of the software is used by several hospitals in their risk management programmes.

RECRUITMENT AND TRAINING: The firm recruits trainee solicitors and makes grants available for study of the Law Society's qualifying examinations. An upper second or first class degree is required, and training is thorough with early responsibility for the conduct of one's own project or cases. A brochure describing the firm, and opportunities for trainee solicitors and others is available on request from the Partnership Secretary.

CONTACT PARTNER: Mr D. Evans

Number of partners:	12
Assistant solicitors:	15
Other fee-earners:	16

WORKLOAD	
Medical negligence	45%
Commercial and property	20%
Personal injury	20%
Employment	10%
Administrative	5%

CONTACTS	
Administrative	Brian Capstick
Commercial property	Hilary Blackwell
Employment	Peter Edwards
General commercial	Chris Brophy
Medical negligence	David Mason
Personal injury	David Evans

CARLESS DAVIES & CO 140 Stourbridge Road, Halesowen, W. Midlands, B63 3UL **Tel:** (0121) 550 2181 **Fax:** (0121) 550 9954 **DX:** 14506 Halesowen **Ptnrs:** 3. Specialist transport practice with expertise in licensing for road haulage companies.

CARRICK CARR & WRIGHT Norwich House, Savile St, Hull, Humbs, HU1 3ES **Tel:** (01482) 25385 **Fax:** (01482) 27584 **DX:** 11935 **Ptnrs:** 5 **Asst Solrs:** 2 **Other Fee-earners:** 6. Best known for its debt recovery, accident claims, commercial litigation and company/ commercial work. Also handles commercial property, conveyancing, family and private client matters.

CARRICK READ INSOLVENCY

TRAFALGAR HOUSE, 29 PARK PLACE, LEEDS, W. YORKS, LS1 2SP DX: 14085 Leeds	TEL: (0113) 243 2911 FAX: (0113) 244 2863
Norwich House, Saville Street, Hull HU1 3ES DX: 11935 Hull	Tel: (01482) 25385 Fax: (01482) 27584
Salisbury House, London Wall, London EC2 M5PS	Tel: (0171) 216 5560 Fax: (0171) 628 7525

THE FIRM: Carrick Read Insolvency is the merged insolvency departments of Read Hind Stewart, Garwood Devine and Druces and Attlee forming a specialist insolvency practice operating from offices in Hull, Leeds and London. The firm is backed by the combined resources of three offices and more than 140 staff. The partners are all licensed insolvency practitioners and the practice acts on behalf of liquidators, receivers, administrators, trustees and those on both sides of the insolvency procedure.

CONTACT PARTNER: Andrew M. Laycock

Number of partners:	4
Assistant solicitors:	10
Other fee-earners:	7

CARSON & McDOWELL Murray House, Murray Street, Belfast, BT1 6HS **Tel:** (01232) 244951 **Fax:** (01232) 245768 **DX:** 403 NR Belfast **Ptnrs:** 9 **Asst Solrs:** 8 **Other Fee-earners:** 1. Large practice known for its corporate, commercial property and insurance litigation work.

WORKLOAD			
Civil litigation	30%	Commercial property	25%
Company/ commercial	25%		

CARTER HODGE

18 HOGHTON ST, SOUTHPORT, MERSEYSIDE, PR9 0PB DX: 20102	TEL: (01704) 531991 FAX: (01704) 537475

THE FIRM: Tracing its origins from 1889, Carter Hodge is a general practice offering a wide range of services to business and private clients. A commitment to Legal Aid is balanced by a wide and growing range of work for the commercial client.
PRINCIPAL AREAS OF WORK:
Litigation: *Work includes:* High Court work, commercial litigation, contractual disputes, professional negligence (including medical negligence), building disputes, employment, debt recovery, personal injury and crime.
Family: *Work includes:* divorce, ancillary relief, cohabitation, inheritance, injunctions and all types of children cases. Some members of the firm are on The Law Society's Children Panel.
Company/ Commercial: *Work includes:* acquisitions and disposals, shareholder disputes, employment and insolvency.
Property: *Work includes:* the whole range of transactions in the private and public sectors.
Private Client: *Work includes:* wills and trusts, personal taxation, tax planning and asset protection for individuals and business proprietors.
Financial Services: *Work includes:* advice on savings and investments, pensions and mortgages. This firm is regulated by The Law Society in the conduct of Investment Business.
OTHER OFFICES: Ainsdale, Birkdale, Heswall and St. Helens.

CONTACT PARTNER: David A. Byard

Number of partners:	9
Assistant solicitors:	3
Other fee-earners:	8

CONTACTS	
Commercial conveyancing	David Howard
Criminal	Nick Archer
General litigation	John Clark
Matrimonial	Brenda Morley
Probate & trust	David Byard
Residential conveyancing	Stephen Holmes

CARTMELL SHEPHERD Viaduct House, Carlisle, Cumbria, CA3 8EZ **Tel:** (01228) 31561 **Fax:** (01228) 401490 **DX:** 63006 **Ptnrs:** 13 **Asst Solrs:** 14 **Other Fee-earners:** 13. Leading practice in Cumbria with five offices. Broad range of work undertaken: specialises in agriculture, company, crime, matrimonial and private client.

WORKLOAD			
Litigation	33%	Property	25%
Private client	16%	Agriculture	15%
Corporate	11%		

CARTWRIGHT CUNNINGHAM HASELGROVE & CO 282-284 Hoe Street, Walthamstow, London, E17 9QD **Tel:** (0181) 520 1021 **Fax:** (0181) 520 5107 **DX:** 32007 Walthamstow **Ptnrs:** 15 **Asst Solrs:** 8 **Other Fee-earners:** 8. Established over 100 years, the firm has two offices in North East London and the metropolitan Essex area. Handles a wide range of work for its commercial and private clientele.

WORKLOAD			
Domestic conveyancing	21%	Commercial/civil lit	20%
Matrimonial	16%	Crime	14%
PI/ medical negligence	9%	Company/ commercial	8%

CARTWRIGHT & LEWIS 53/55 High St, Harborne, Birmingham, W. Midlands, B17 9NU **Tel:** (0121) 426 4171 **Fax:** (0121) 427 3389 **DX:** 19751 Harborne **Ptnrs:** 14 **Asst Solrs:** 5 **Other Fee-earners:** 8. Medium-sized expanding provincial firm, known principally for commercial litigation. Has one of the largest personal injury departments in the West Midlands.

WORKLOAD			
Personal injury	36%	Property	18%
Commercial litigation	16%	Family	12%
Crime	10%	Probate/ trusts	5%

CARTWRIGHTS

MARSH HOUSE, 11 MARSH ST, BRISTOL, BS99 7BB
DX: 7851 Bristol

TEL: (0117) 929 3601
FAX: (0117) 926 2403

THE FIRM: Cartwrights is recognised as a leading national firm in the fields of transport, leisure and licensing and has one of the largest insurance departments in the South West. The firm is increasingly known for its expertise in property and company commercial work. The influence of EC law on all areas of commercial practice continues to be a growth area for the firm, as is construction and work for public bodies.

PRINCIPAL AREAS OF WORK:

Leisure and Licensing: (*Contact:* Tim Davies. *4 Partners*). A complete nationwide and EC-wide service to clients operating in the food and drink retailing, licensed ·trade, bingo, casino, cinema and leisure sectors including many high street names. A section of the department specialises in food safety and environmental matters.

Commercial: (*Contact:* Chris Mitchell. *6 Partners*). Specialist units deal with commercial property (including planning, compulsory purchase and environment), company/ commercial, commercial litigation, employment, transport, construction, local authorities, regional airports and intellectual property. Lawyers work together as a highly motivated team to meet the needs of a wide range of businesses from start ups to quoted PLCs.

Insurance: (*Contact:* David Vernalls. *4 Partners*). Work includes investigating and handling claims relating to personal injury, property damage, professional negligence, criminal prosecutions under health and safety and road traffic legislation, inquests and public inquiries. To provide the best specialist advice the department is organised into 7 units, each concentrating on a particular area.

Private Client: (*Contact:* Andrew Blair. *3 Partners*). Residential property, matrimonial, civil litigation, personal tax planning and administration of estates.

NATURE OF CLIENTELE: Over 20 FTSE 100 companies including major UK leisure and brewery companies, supermarket chains and insurance companies; an international petrol company; local authorities including regional airports, port authorities; construction companies; computer companies; entrepreneurs; local businesses of all sizes; loss adjusters and self-insuring PLCs; private individuals.

RECRUITMENT: Recruitment of professional staff is dealt with by Christopher Eskell. Applications for articles should be made two years in advance by CV with accompanying handwritten letter. The firm employs five trainee solicitors each year.

FOREIGN CONNECTIONS: Cartwrights has established contacts with law firms in Europe, USA and the Far East. French, German, Welsh, Norwegian spoken.

CONTACT PARTNER: Chris Mitchell

Number of partners:	17
Assistant solicitors:	19
Other fee-earners:	19

WORKLOAD	
Commercial	33%
Insurance	31%
Licensing and leisure	27%
Private	9%

CONTACTS	
Commercial property	Emrys Parry/ Ian Dunn
Commercial litigation	Nigel Puddicombe
Commercial contracts	Nigel Williams
Company/ commercial	Chris Mitchell
Compulsory purchase/planning	Emrys Parry
Construction	Nigel Williams
Domestic conveyancing	Karen Bottomley
Employment	Geoffrey Jones
Food safety, consumer protectn	David Hamilton
Insurance, personal injury	David Vernalls
Licensing and leisure	Tim Davies
Local authorities	Emrys Parry
Private litigation	Andrew Blair
Transport	Geoffrey Jones
Wills, probate	Giselle Davies

CARTWRIGHTS ADAMS & BLACK 36 West Bute St, Cardiff, S. Glam, CF1 5UA **Tel:** (01222) 465959 **Fax:** (01222) 480006 **DX:** 200751 **Ptnrs:** 5 **Asst Solrs:** 1 **Other Fee-earners:** 5. Handles commercial, including admiralty, commercial mortgages and mergers. High Court litigation undertaken and industrial and traffic tribunals. Also domestic conveyancing and probate.

CHAFFE STREET

BROOK HOUSE, 70 SPRING GARDENS, MANCHESTER, M2 2BQ
DX: 14431 Manchester

TEL: (0161) 236 5800
FAX: (0161) 228 6862

THE FIRM: Chaffe Street is a modern and progressive specialist commercial practice which has developed rapidly since its establishment in 1983 to become one of Manchester's major commercial law firms. The firm, which provides a complete range of commercial legal advice to corporate institutional and professional clients throughout the UK and overseas, is highly regarded by the professional community for its uncompromisingly high standards.

PRINCIPAL AREAS OF WORK: The firm provides a full range of specialist commercial legal services; namely company/ commercial work, commercial property and commercially orientated litigation.

The services available include flotations, acquisitions and disposals, mergers, management buy-outs, banking law, venture and investment capital, project and asset financing, corporate finance, insolvency, intellectual property, competition law, employment law, pensions, aircraft, commercial property and environmental law.

CONTACT PARTNER: Mr R.H. Street

Number of partners:	9
Assistant solicitors:	7
Other fee-earners:	7

WORKLOAD	
Company/ commercial	65%
Commercial property	25%
Commercial litigation	10%

CHALLINORS St Chad's House, 215 Hagley Road, Birmingham, W. Midlands, B16 9RG **Tel:** (0121) 455 6333 **Fax:** (0121) 455 6369 **DX:** 707295 Edgbaston **Ptnrs:** 7 **Asst Solrs:** 9 **Other Fee-earners:** 8. Strong civil litigation department with growing reputation for medical negligence and personal injury. Also has experience in matrimonial, criminal, commercial and domestic property matters.

WORKLOAD			
Civil litigation	30%	Matrimonial	22%
Convey/prop - comm/dom	15%	Medical negigence	15%
Criminal	10%	Probate	5%

CHAPMAN EVERATT & CO 5 Shaw Park, Shaw Road, Wolverhampton, W. Midlands, WV10 9LE **Tel:** (01902) 717700 **Fax:** (01902) 717447 **DX:** 708560 Wolverhampton 9 **Ptnrs:** 2 **Asst Solrs:** 5 **Other Fee-earners:** 1. Established in 1992; specialist personal injury/ employers' liability practice handling solely insurance funded defendant work.

WORKLOAD	
Civ lit (insurer funded)	100%

CHARLES LUCAS & MARSHALL 28 Bartholomew St, Newbury, Berks, RG14 5EU **Tel:** (01635) 521212 **Fax:** (01635) 37784 **DX:** 30802 **Ptnrs:** 21 **Asst Solrs:** 7 **Other Fee-earners:** 23. Established over 100 years ago, the firm is now a substantial commercial practice with offices covering a wide area throughout Central Southern England. It also handles private client work.

INTERNATIONAL SECTION

The international section lists foreign law firms based in London. It also lists the foreign connections of English law firms: their branch offices overseas and the foreign languages spoken at their UK offices.

CHARLES RUSSELL

8-10 NEW FETTER LANE, LONDON, EC4A 1RS
DX: 19 London/Chancery Lane

TEL: (0171) 203 5000
FAX: (0171) 203 0200

THE FIRM: Charles Russell is a leading London law practice based in the heart of legal London, with a network of offices in the United Kingdom and associated offices and professional contacts throughout the world. With its origins in the 18th century, the firm has grown rapidly over the last few years.

The firm offers a full range of services to corporate, private and institutional clients, and has become highly regarded for its company/commercial and commercial property advice, in addition to its well-established litigation, private client and family work. At Charles Russell the emphasis is on giving the best practical commercial advice on the basis of teamwork and personal attention.

PRINCIPAL AREAS OF WORK:

Company/ Commercial: (*Contact:* Mark Moncreiffe. *17 Partners*). Deals with work across the whole range of company/ commercial law including flotations, mergers and acquisitions, venture capital financing, institutional funding arrangements, management buy-outs and buy-ins, corporate rescues, business start-ups, insolvency and all aspects of corporate tax. The firm also advises on commercial contracts of all descriptions, employment law, pensions and other employee benefits, partnership law, computer law, entertainment, media and telecommunications law, competition and anti-trust law.

Property: (*Contact:* Richard Crouch. *12 Partners*). Offers a complete service for property owners, occupiers, developers, public health sector bodies and large town centre and business park developments. The team provides a comprehensive commercial conveyancing service and advice on funding, planning and environmental law.

Litigation: (*Contact:* Laurence Watt. *6 Partners*). Deals with the full range of litigation services at all levels, in the United Kingdom and overseas, specialising in commercial litigation including judicial review, insurance and reinsurance, medical negligence, shipping and regulatory work and work for the regulatory authorities.

Family: (*Contact:* Peter George. *5 Partners*). Concerned with all legal matters relating to family relationships, their breakdown, separation, divorce and all issues relating to children. These include financial and property aspects, residence and contact, and child abduction, both in England and abroad.

Private Client: (*Contact:* Ian Lockhart. *4 Partners*). Serves the legal needs of individuals, families, schools, and charitable and other institutions in tax and asset planning, including the preparation of wills, administration of trusts and estates, and personal and corporate taxation.

International: The firm has strong links across the world. It is a founder member of The Association of European Lawyers, a grouping of five leading law firms in the United Kingdom, with contacts throughout Europe and is the only English member of ALFA, the oldest and largest association of law firms in the USA.

LANGUAGES SPOKEN: French, German, Spanish, Italian, Portuguese.

OTHER OFFICES: Lloyd's Building (London), Cheltenham, Guildford and Swindon.

CONTACT PARTNER: John South	
Number of partners:	44
Assistant solicitors:	38
Other fee-earners:	22

WORKLOAD	
Company/ commercial	30%
Property	25%
Litigation	20%
Private client	13%
Family	12%

CONTACTS	
Company/ commercial	Mark Moncreiffe
Family	Peter George
Litigation	Laurence Watt
Private client	Ian Lockhart
Property	Richard Crouch

Charles Russell
SOLICITORS

CHARSLEY HARRISON

RIDING COURT, RIDING COURT ROAD, DATCHET, SLOUGH, BERKS, SL3 9LF
DX: 42267 Slough West

TEL: (01753) 586000
FAX: (01753) 582233

THE FIRM: Formed by the merger in 1973 of two long established and well respected Thames Valley practices, Charsley Harrison is a modern, forward-thinking firm geared to meet the needs of both commercial and private clients. The practice has developed rapidly in recent years to represent a wide range of business clients throughout the UK, the EC, the USA and the Pacific Basin and has established links with commercial lawyers in the major cities of the USA, Australia and throughout

CONTACT PARTNER: Mr P.H. Jones	
Number of partners:	9
Assistant solicitors:	4
Other fee-earners:	9

Europe. Unfettered by the high accommodation and staffing costs of city centre firms the practice is able to ensure a high degree of partner involvement in the day to day matters of clients, and a prompt, efficient and professional service.

Principal Areas of Work:

Company and Commercial: (Contact: Philip Jones). A comprehensive service both domestically and internationally encompassing corporate finance, competition, acquisitions and disposals, mergers, mbo's and joint ventures, distribution and agency agreements, intellectual property rights, taxation, insolvency and employment law matters.

Litigation: (Contact: Simon Cullingworth). All aspects of litigation for both corporate and private clients in the UK and abroad before a wide range of courts and tribunals. Work includes general contractual and commercial disputes, misrepresentation, employment matters, insolvency and banking-related litigation, personal injury, professional negligence and defamation.

Property: (Contact: Simon Doyle). Extensive experience of property transactions including purchase, sale, leasing and mortgaging of commercial and retail property, estate development, planning and environmental advice, licensing, site assembly, joint ventures and agricultural property.

Private Client: (Contact: Giles Shedden). The firm has a long tradition in providing a friendly and efficient service to individuals in all aspects of their private legal affairs. Work includes wills, tax and estate planning, personal and family finance, investment management, pensions, saving schemes and school fees planning, charity law and Court of Protection work. A full service is also provided in relation to matrimonial and family law including childcare and adoption.

OTHER OFFICES: Windsor, Slough and Ascot. Associated firm in the Netherlands.

WORKLOAD	
Company/ commercial	35%
Property	33%
Litigation	18%
Probate/ trust	5%

CONTACTS	
Company/ commercial	Phillip Jones
Litigation	Simon Cullingworth
Probate/ trust	Giles Shedden
Property	Simon Doyle

CHATTERTONS 5 South St, Horncastle, Lincs, LN9 6DS **Tel:** (01507) 522456 **Fax:** (01507) 522445 **DX:** 29501 Horncastle **Ptnrs:** 9 **Asst Solrs:** 7 **Other Fee-earners:** 15. A leading Lincolnshire firm with offices in both Horncastle and Boston. Handles property work, commercial law, agricultural law, planning law, litigation and private client work.

CHRISTIAN FISHER 42 Museum Street, Bloomsbury, London, WC1A 1LY **Tel:** (0171) 831 1750 **Fax:** (0171) 831 1726 **DX:** 35737 Bloomsbury **Ptnrs:** 2 **Asst Solrs:** 2 . The firm undertakes civil liberties work, crime, personal injury (including trades union work), employment, administrative law, housing, medical negligence, and immigration.

CHRISTOPHER HARRISON & CO Godolphin House, 7/8 Cathedral Lane, Truro, Cornwall, TR1 2QS **Tel:** (01872) 41408 **Fax:** (01872) 73848 **DX:** 81212 Truro **Ptnrs:** 1 **Other Fee-earners:** 2. The firm specialises in domestic and commercial conveyancing, matrimonial and family matters, and accident/medical negligence claims.

CHURCH ADAMS TATHAM & CO

FULWOOD HOUSE, FULWOOD PLACE, LONDON, WC1V 6HR	TEL: (0171) 242 0841
DX: 183 Ch. Ln.	FAX: (0171) 831 9609
Chatham Court, Lesbourne Road, Reigate, Surrey RH2 7FN	Tel:(01737) 240111
DX: 30400 Reigate 1	Fax:(01737) 242849

THE FIRM: This is a long-established and expanding commercial firm undertaking a wide variety of work. It specialises in building society and railway property work and has particular expertise in franchising and computer law. It operates from London and Reigate – the offices being equal in size and complement.

CONTACT PARTNER: Mr G.J. Jones	
Number of partners:	17
Assistant solicitors:	10
Other fee-earners:	11

PRINCIPAL AREAS OF WORK:

Commercial Property: (*Fee Earners:* 18). Work includes: retail, office and industrial development, development funding, town planning, portfolio management with associated commercial and agricultural conveyancing, railway related work and landlord and tenant transactions.

Litigation: (*Fee-earners:* 13). The firm conducts a wide variety of largely commercial civil litigation at all levels, as well as family law. The department also handles London cases on an agency basis for over sixty country practices.

Company and Commercial: (*Fee-earners:* 7). Work includes: company formations, acquisitions, demergers and restructuring agreements, joint ventures, computer law including electronic banking, franchising, competition law, telecommunications law, intellectual property, pensions, employment law and associated taxation advice.

Private Client: (*Fee-earners: 5).* Work includes: conveyancing, including relocation schemes, mortgages, wills and probate, trusts, private tax and investment advice.

ASSOCIATE US FIRM: The firm has several American clients and a number of its UK clients have US interests. In order to better serve these clients an association has been formed with Williams, Mullen, Christian and Dobbins who have offices in Washington D.C. and Richmond, Virginia.

WORKLOAD	
Property	45%
Litigation	37%
Company/ commercial	10%
Private client	8%

CONTACTS	
Building society work	Tom McKeown (London)
Commercial litigation	Richard Brown (London)
Commercial property	Michael Weston (London)
	Chris Bell (Reigate)
Company commercial	Brian Haynes (Reigate)
Company sec. services	Philip Krauss (London)
Company/ commercial	Gordon Jones (London)
Private clients	Nicholas Pinks (Reigate)

CHURCH BRUCE HAWKES BRASINGTON & PHILLIPS

51-54 Windmill St, Gravesend, Kent, DA12 1BD **Tel:** (01474) 560361 **Fax:** (01474) 328315 **DX:** 6800 Gravesend **Ptnrs:** 7 **Asst Solrs:** 2 **Other Fee-earners:** 6. Has sizeable litigation and conveyancing departments. Also handles Court of Protection, family/ matrimonial, company/ commercial and probate work.

WORKLOAD			
Personal injury/lit	32%	Commercial/conveyancing	29%
Family	26%	Probate	13%

CLAREMONT SMITH

125 HIGH HOLBORN, LONDON, WC1V 6QF
DX: 372 London Chancery Lane

TEL: (0171) 405 8811
FAX: (0171) 831 0973

CONTACT PARTNER: Roger D. Smith

Number of partners:	10
Assistant solicitors:	3

THE FIRM: The origins of Claremont Smith can be traced back in Central London to February 1814. It is best known for its work in the fields of pensions and commercial property acting as it does in relation to all legal affairs of one of the UK's larger pension funds.

PRINCIPAL AREAS OF WORK: Pensions; commercial property; telecommunications law, European and competition law; the legal aspect of quality standards and harmonisation of standards; commercial litigation; trade associations; personal injury litigation and employment law.

OTHER AREAS OF LAW: Although primarily a niche commercial practice the firm does still retain a private clientele for which it handles domestic property transactions, probate and trust work.

LANGUAGES SPOKEN: French, Spanish, Danish, Swedish, Farsi and Armenian.

CD-ROM EDITION ON THE INTERNET

This edition of the directory is available on a CD-ROM which includes both DOS and Windows versions. It can be loaded onto a network, and works with virtually any IBM compatible PC. The CD-ROM version offers computer-users the advantage of rapid search, retrieval and cross-referencing. It is also available via the Internet.

CLARKE WILLMOTT & CLARKE

6 HAMMET ST, TAUNTON, SOMERSET, TA1 1RG
DX: 32100

TEL: (01823) 337474
FAX: (01823) 259643

MANAGING PARTNER: John Cooper

Number of partners:	39
Assistant solicitors:	20
Other fee-earners:	65

THE FIRM: Clarke Willmott & Clarke is one of the leading firms in the South West. The firm combines close partner contact with commercially aware advice to meet a range of commercial and private needs.

High quality, creative advice is provided promptly and economically through integrated teams of specialists.

The firm's lawyers concentrate on long term commercial benefits and work closely with clients to ensure that these are identified within well managed relationships.

Clients range from major Plcs and multinationals to prominent landowners and farmers. Building societies and insurance companies are also represented alongside associations, institutions and individuals.

PRINCIPAL AREAS OF WORK:

Company/ Commercial: (*Contact:* Robert Hunt (Taunton)). Public and private company and commercial transactions including takeovers, hive-downs, joint ventures, shareholder agreements, restructuring, acquisitions and sales of unincorporated undertakings, commercial and distribution agreements and the associated employment issues.

Commercial Property: (*Contact:* Ian Macaulay (Bristol), Tim Walker (Ruishton Lodge) and Roger Seaton (Yeovil)). Considerable experience in acquisitions, sales, joint ventures, development agreements and landlord and tenant.

Planning: (*Contact:* Nick Engert (Ruishton Lodge)). This expanding team has acquired a national reputation in all matters relating to town and country planning and land development. Advice on planning applications and enforcement notices, Section 106 agreements and representation before Public Inquiries.

Environmental Law: (*Contact:* Tim Hayden (Taunton)). One of the few firms in the South West offering specialisation in both contentious and non-contentious matters. Prosecution and defence work for both statutory bodies and private clients and advice on non-contentious issues particularly contaminated land and waste disposal.

Private Client: (*Contact:* each office). The firm prides itself on the quality and range of services offered to the private client including personal tax planning, asset management, wills, trusts, administration of estates, family, matrimonial and residential conveyancing.

Agriculture: (*Contact:* Richard Morgan (Taunton)). The firm has a long tradition in support of the farming and agricultural community in the South West and is particularly active in the area of agricultural tenancies and milk quotas.

Litigation: (*Contact:* Robert Mortee). A wide range of general commercial litigation including commercial contracts, building disputes, employment disputes, defamation, intellectual property and professional negligence.

Personal Injury: (*Contact:* David Sedgwick (Bristol)). A specialist team which has gained a national reputation for its practical handling of personal injury, medical negligence and other damage claims for both defendant and plaintiff.

Insolvency/ Debt Collection: *Contact:* Stephen Allinson LIP (Taunton) for insolvency or Michael Williamson (Crewkerne) for computerised debt collection.

Licensing: (*Contact:* Tim Hayden (Taunton) or Richard Cornell (Yeovil)). Advice relating to licensed premises, breweries, and individual owners and licensees, betting and gaming, and registered and proprietary clubs.

FOREIGN CONNECTIONS: Clarke Willmott & Clarke has strong links with lawyers and other professionals throughout Europe. Languages spoken include French, German, Spanish, Russian, Italian, Dutch and Cantonese.

RECRUITMENT AND TRAINING: The firm annually recruits 8-12 trainee solicitors. Please contact Felicity Shakespear at the Taunton office.

OTHER OFFICES: The firm's other principal offices in Bristol are (0117) 974 4977; Ruishton Lodge; Taunton (01823) 442266 and Yeovil (01935) 71161/ 23407.

CLARKE WILLMOTT & CLARKE
SOLICITORS

CLARKS

GREAT WESTERN HOUSE, STATION RD, READING, BERKS, RG1 1SX
DX: 54700 Reading 2

TEL: (01734) 585321
FAX: (01734) 604611

THE FIRM: Clarks is a long established firm based in Reading. It is one of the leading commercial practices in the Thames Valley. It operates from a single office, resulting in one of the largest concentrations of solicitors in the South East, outside London. The firm's range and depth of expertise are comparable to those of firms in the major cities.

CLIENT BASE: Clarks' clients include multinational and listed companies operating in many parts of the country, as well as many smaller businesses. The firm also acts for lenders, investors and borrowers in banking and corporate finance transactions. The firm has worked for many years with public sector bodies in various fields.

PRINCIPAL AREAS OF WORK:

Corporate: All corporate matters including public issue work, corporate finance, management buy-outs, mergers and joint ventures. The firm undertakes significant banking and pensions work. A specialist unit undertakes business services and sales for smaller businesses.

Insolvency: Corporate receiverships, liquidations and bankruptcies and business investigations.

Commercial: General commercial business including European law, employment, competition, building and engineering contracts, computer contracts and intellectual property.

Litigation: Disputes relating to commercial contracts, motor law, building and engineering, product liability, debt recovery, employment, property and professional negligence. The firm is a founder member of the Centre for Alternative Dispute Resolution.

Health/ Medical Services: Establishment of NHS Trusts, private sector relationships, property transactions, medico-legal issues, litigation and medical negligence.

Commercial Property and Planning: Sales and leases of commercial and agricultural property, residential and commercial development, mortgages and commercial lending, licensing and landlord and tenant. The firm provides a planning consultancy and handles planning applications and appeals for developers, landowners and local authorities. A specialist unit deals with environmental issues and litigation.

Private Client: Tax planning, wills, estate administration, trusts and residential conveyancing.

INTERNATIONAL CONNECTIONS: Clarks has clients in or with interests in many parts of the world. It is part of a network of law firms in France, Germany and Italy. French, German and Italian are spoken.

TRAINING: There is a strong programme of internal training. Training seminars and programmes are also offered to clients.

CONTACT PARTNER: Richard Lee

Number of partners:	11
Assistant solicitors:	16
Other fee-earners:	10

WORKLOAD	
Commercial litigation	31%
Corporate	24%
Commercial property	20%
Commercial	14%
Residential property and private client	11%

CONTACTS	
Banking	Jane Gunnell
Commercial	Peter James
Commercial litigation	Michael Sippitt
Commercial property	Christopher Ward
Computer	Peter James
Construction	Michael Sippitt
Corporate	Richard Lee
Debt collection	David Rintoul
Employment	Peter James
European	Peter James
Health/medical services	Tom Howell
Insolvency	David Few
Intellectual property	Peter James
Local government	Simon Dimmick
Pensions	David Clark
Planning and environment	Simon Dimmick
Private client	Peter Clark
Residential conveyancing	Mary Robertson

CLARKSON WRIGHT & JAKES

VALIANT HOUSE, 12 KNOLL RISE, ORPINGTON, KENT, BR6 0PG
DX: 31603 Orpington

TEL: (01689) 871621
FAX: (01689) 878537

THE FIRM: Established in 1875, Clarkson Wright & Jakes is a substantial commercial practice whose aim is to offer a personal service tailored to clients' specific needs. The firm undertakes a wide range of legal work, and offers notarial service and the expertise of units specialising in employment, debt collection and French law.

PRINCIPAL AREAS OF WORK fall into three main groups:

COMMERCIAL: *(Contact Partner:* M.A. North).

(1) Company & Commercial *Work includes:* company and business acquisitions and sales, MBOs and MBIs, franchise, agency, distribution and other commercial agreements, conditions of sale, terms of business, partnership, business start ups.

CONTACT PARTNER: Andrew Wright

Number of partners:	4
Assistant solicitors:	7
Other fee-earners:	12

(2) **Employment** *Work includes:* contracts of employment and other employment documentation, claims in the Industrial Tribunals and civil courts for dismissal, discrimination and breach of contract.

(3) **Commercial Property** *Work includes:* acquisition, mortgage and disposal of freehold and leasehold shops, factories and other properties, landlord and tenant matters (including lease renewals and surrenders).

(4) **Commercial Litigation** *Work includes:* company, commercial and partnership disputes, building disputes, landlord and tenant matters, professional negligence, passing off actions and contractual disputes, licensing, debt collection and mortgage repossessions.

PERSONAL INJURY LITIGATION: *(Contact Partner:* L.J. Seldon). *Work includes:* motor, employers' and public liability claims, industrial disease and professional indemnity claims.

PRIVATE CLIENT: *(Contact Partner:* P.J. Giblin). *Work includes:* residential property, wills and trusts, tax planning, enduring powers of attorney, winding-up of estates and executorships, Court of Protection and matrimonial.

FOREIGN LANGUAGES: French, Italian and Spanish.

WORKLOAD	
Private client	25%
Personal injury litigation	20%
Commercial litigation (incl debt collection)	15%
Commercial property	15%
Company/ commercial (including notarial)	15%
Employment	10%

CONTACTS	
Commercial	M.A. North
Personal injury	L.J.A. Seldon
Private client	P.J. Giblin

CLARK & WALLACE 14 Albyn Place, Aberdeen, Grampian, AB9 1RP **Tel:** (01224) 644481 **Fax:** (01224) 635237 **DX:** 8 Aberdeen **Ptnrs:** 11 **Asst Solrs:** 6 **Other Fee-earners:** 2. Concentrates primarily on commercial and corporate work including property work and corporate finance. Also acts for private clients.

CLAUDE HORNBY & COX

35-36 GREAT MARLBOROUGH ST, LONDON, W1V 2JA
DX: 37211 Piccadilly

TEL: (0171) 437 8873
FAX: (0171) 494 3070

THE FIRM: The practice has specialised in criminal law since its foundation. In addition to an extensive criminal litigation service, there is, now, a thriving civil department.

PRINCIPAL AREAS OF WORK:

Crime: All aspects of criminal law are covered; cases range from homicide and corporate fraud on a multi-million pound scale to driving offences and shoplifting; legally aided cases are undertaken; the practice will accept instructions to prosecute privately,or, more commonly, to defend; defences at Courts Martial have been conducted regularly by the partners.

OTHER AREAS OF WORK: General civil litigation in the High Court and the County Court, family law, wills, immigration, personal injury, employment; and, both commercial and domestic conveyancing. The practice offers representation before Professional Disciplinary Tribunals.

CLIENTELE: The firm can provide advice for individuals and small businesses on a wide range of subjects.

RECRUITMENT: Generally two trainee solicitors are recruited each year. Training is given in both the criminal and civil sections of the firm. Applications to the Senior Partner, Christopher Green.

CONTACT PARTNER: Christopher Green

Number of partners:	2
Assistant solicitors:	6
Other fee-earners:	4

WORKLOAD	
Criminal litigation	70%
Civil litigation (High Court & County Court)	10%
Matrimonial	7%
Personal injury	6%
Disciplinary proceedings (prof. bodies)	4%
Conveyancing	3%

CONTACTS	
Civil litigation	Mohammed Mir, Kerrie Dawson
Criminal litigation	Christopher Green
	Richard Hallam
Disciplinary proceedings	Christopher Green

CLAYTONS PO Box 38, 22 Rothesay Rd, Luton, Beds, LU1 1PT **Tel:** (01582) 24501 **Fax:** (01582) 405815 **DX:** 5909 **Ptnrs:** 4 **Asst Solrs:** 3 **Other Fee-earners:** 3. Has a branch office in St. Albans specialising in ecclesiastical and charity law. Handles civil, criminal and matrimonial together with conveyancing (both domestic and commercial), and probate. Legal aid work undertaken.

CLEARY, GOTTLIEB, STEEN & HAMILTON City Place House, 55 Basinghall, London, EC2V 5EH **Tel:** (0171) 614 2200 **Fax:** (0171) 600 1698 **Ptnrs:** 5 **Other Fee-earners:** 17. A leading international firm engaged in the general practice of law in major cities around the world. The London office is primarily involved in international financial work and provides securities law and tax advice on a wide range of transactions to investment banks, commercial banks and other participants in the US and European financial markets.

CLEAVER FULTON & RANKIN

50 BEDFORD STREET, BELFAST, BT2 7FW
DX: 421 NR Belfast

TEL: (01232) 243141
FAX: (01232) 249096

THE FIRM: Cleaver Fulton & Rankin is one of Northern Ireland's foremost legal practices, located in the centre of Belfast with additional offices in Bangor and Armagh. Founded in 1893, the firm has continued the tradition of providing clients with a thorough understanding of the legal context of their undertakings and offers sound and practical advice. In recent years the firm has experienced sustained growth and offers an extensive range of legal services with a special emphasis on litigation, company and commercial activities, work for educational and charitable bodies, public and institutional authorities and all categories of private client work.

PRINCIPAL AREAS OF WORK:

Company and Commercial: (*Contact Partner:* Peter Rankin or Ian Dawson). The whole range of company work is undertaken, including incorporation, take-overs, liquidations and receiverships and company secretarial services.

Commercial Property: (*Contact Partner:* Patrick Cross or Neil Faris). All aspects of acquisition, development and investment. The practice's property lawyers assist clients in all aspects of business start-ups and in lease renewal or rent review.

Litigation: (*Contact Partner:* Patrick O'Driscoll or Paul Spring). The firm has a highly respected reputation for providing experienced and able assistance in litigation matters, including the specialist areas of commercial litigation, employment law, defamation, product liability, licensing, intellectual property and construction law.

Private Client: (*Contact Partner:* Alastair Rankin or Joy Scott). An extensive service to private clients entails giving advice on a variety of legal matters and maintaining close working relationships with other professionals including accountants, stock-brokers and estate agents.

Consultancy: (*Contact Partner:* Neil Faris). The firm has established a team to service the specialised needs of clients in legal consultancy and legal advisory work in Northern Ireland. Training seminars are organised for clients and their employees on the impact of new legislation.

CONTACT PARTNER: Neil C. Faris

Number of partners:	9
Assistant solicitors:	14
Other fee-earners:	8

WORKLOAD	
Commercial property	25%
Litigation	25%
Company/ commercial	25%
Private client	15%
Employment	10%

CLEMENT JONES 49 High Street, Holywell, Clwyd, CH8 7TF **Tel:** (01352) 713353 **Fax:** (01352) 713838 **DX:** 21722 Holywell **Ptnrs:** 9 **Asst Solrs:** 14 **Other Fee-earners:** 29. Clement Jones has a branch network throughout Chester and North Wales and is able to offer specialist legal advice to its private and commercial clients.

FIRMS OF ACCOUNTANTS

Accountants specialising in litigation support are listed in the accountants' A-Z, with details of the services they offer to solicitors, from forensic accounting to intellectual property or business valuations.

CLIFFORD CHANCE

200 ALDERSGATE STREET, LONDON, EC1A 4JJ
DX: 606 London

TEL: (0171) 600 1000
FAX: (0171) 600 5555

Clifford Chance is a multi-jurisdictional law firm providing a full range of legal services from offices in 23 major business and financial centres around the world.

OTHER OFFICES: *Europe:* Amsterdam, Barcelona, Brussels, Budapest, Frankfurt, Madrid, Milan, Moscow, Paris, Prague, Rome, Warsaw; *Asia:* Hanoi, Ho Chi Minh City, Hong Kong, Shanghai, Singapore, Tokyo; *Middle East:* Bahrain, Dubai, Riyadh; *North America:* New York.

LANGUAGES: All known business and commercial languages.

THE FIRM: Clifford Chance provides a comprehensive range of legal services relating to: international and domestic banking and securities, corporate and commercial work, property and construction, litigation and arbitration, property, shipping and taxation.

PRINCIPAL AREAS OF WORK: The firm is organised into a number of broad service areas most of which are divided into smaller working groups. Since there is a frequent need for multi-disciplinary teams, there are no rigid structures.

Corporate and Commercial: The firm is well-known for its corporate work especially mergers and acquisitions, flotations (UK and international), leveraged and management buy-outs, insolvency, insurance, energy, oil and gas and government privatisations. The firm has expertise in UK, EC and ECSC competition law, and handles a wide range of commercial contracts with a strong involvement in information technology, telecommunications, media and the environment, employee share plans, employment and pensions, services relating to patents, designs, trade marks, copyright and trade secrets, and preparation and negotiation of exploitation agreements.

Finance: The firm has one of the foremost international finance practices in the world, acting for a wide range of commercial banks, investment banks and corporations, as well as regulatory agencies, supra-national bodies, governments and government agencies. The firm is noted for its core banking, capital markets, projects and asset finance, securitisation, derivatives and regulatory practices and is a leader in developing new financial techniques.

Litigation: The firm has a major dispute resolution practice which operates worldwide. All types of English and international commercial disputes are undertaken. When disputes cannot be resolved by other means, litigation is undertaken in all courts in England and in other jurisdictions worldwide. Arbitration is undertaken in all major arbitration centres. Other forms of resolution such as mediation and executive tribunal are also handled.

Litigation lawyers also undertake inquiries, insolvency matters and all types of investigation. Groups of litigation lawyers undertake work in many specialist fields across all the firm's areas of work.

Tax: Tax aspects of major corporate and financial transactions including M&A, financings, leasing, financial instruments, property, and fund management, trust planning and administration of estates.

Commercial Property: The firm has a leading commercial property practice handling all varieties of property related transactions whether international or domestic. Clients include individuals, corporations, institutions, pension funds, local and public authorities and banks, whether in the role of investor, developer, landowner, occupier, borrower, funder or lender. Areas of work include investment, development projects, leasing, preletting and shell and core lettings, joint ventures, institutional funding, secured lending, property securitisation, property insolvency and security enforcement, portfolio acquisition, disposal and investigation (often as part of a corporate transaction), town planning and planning inquiries, infrastructure, transport and power projects and construction.

NEW BRIDGE STREET CONSULTANTS: The firm also owns a management consultancy, New Bridge Street Consultants, specialising in cash and share incentives, ESOPs, pensions, personnel management and related areas.

CLIENTELE: The firm's strength comes from aggregation of talents and breadth and depth of specialisations. Clients are therefore offered high standards of legal expertise. They are also offered a close working relationship with their lawyers whose approach

SENIOR PARTNER: Keith Clark	
UK:	
Number of partners:	170
Assistant solicitors:	545
Other fee-earners:	165
INTERNATIONAL:	
Number of Partners:	239
Assistant Solicitors:	886
Other fee-earners:	223

CONTACTS

Advertising and marketing	Richard Thomas
Asset/ project finance	Geoffrey White
Banking	Stuart Popham
Building societies	Howard Ross
	Jonathan Beastall,Nick Jordan
Capital markets	Stephen Roith, Rob Palache
Collective investment schemes	James Barlow
Commodities	Mark Harding, John Bassindale
Company/ commercial	Peter Brooks
Computer law and IT	Christopher Millard
Construction	Alan Elias
Corporate finance	Peter Brooks
Derivatives	Habib Motani, Tim Plews
EC & competition	Jim Wheaton, John Osborne
Employment law	David Reid, Robin Tremaine
	Chris Osman
Energy and utilities	Tony Bankes-Jones
Environmental law	Robin Griffiths
	Christopher Napier
Financial services	Tim Herrington
Hotels & leisure	Teddy Bourne, Martin Richards
Insolvency	Andrew Wilkinson
Insurance and reinsurance	Katherine Coates
	Stephen Lewis, Leon Boshoff
	Terry O' Neill
Int. commercial arbitration	John Beechey
Intellectual property	David Perkins
Litigation (commercial)	Tony Willis
Litigation (property)	Wendy Miller
Local government	Brian Hall
Media & entertainment	Mike Francies
Multimedia	David Griffiths
Pensions	Helen Cox
Planning	Brian Hall
Projects	Tony Bankes-Jones
	Rodney Short, Chris Wyman

is both practical and imaginative. Clients are drawn from many different industries and countries of origin – the firm acts for businesses, financiers and governments throughout the world – and its lawyers accordingly have capabilities in various jurisdictions.

RECRUITMENT: The firm continues to expand and career prospects across a range of legal disciplines are excellent. In 1994, 97 trainee lawyers joined the firm and approximately 92 trainee lawyers are expected to join the firm for the year 1995/6. Candidates may come from the law or other disciplines. The firm seeks those who are good communicators and problem solvers with commercial as well as legal knowledge and understanding. Long-term prospects are excellent. Applications by form (available on request) should be made between August and October, two years in advance, to Alistair Dawson.

Overall, Clifford Chance aims to be forceful and effective in the interests of its clients. The firm sees itself as combining innovation, creativity and commercial awareness with an unstuffy style and an empathy with client problems.

A brochure for clients or for prospective trainee solicitors is available on request.

Property (commercial)	Teddy Bourne
Public international law	Jeremy Carver
Publishing	Michael Smyth
Retail	Michael Howell, Michael Edwards
Shipping & maritime law	Chris Perrin
Tax (corporate)	Douglas French
Telecommunications	Liz Hiester
	Christopher Millard

CLIFFORD CHANCE

CLINTONS

55 DRURY LANE, LONDON, WC2B 5SQ
DX: 40021 Covent Gdn. 1

TEL: (0171) 379 6080
FAX: (0171) 240 9310

THE FIRM: Clintons is widely recognised as one of the foremost firms in the worlds of entertainment, sport and the media. The firm also has expertise in all aspects of commercial and corporate law, bringing a practical, informed approach based on an understanding of individual corporate cultures, designed to maximise opportunities as well as resolve difficulties.

PRINCIPAL AREAS OF WORK:

Media, Entertainment and Sport: The department acts for many well-known personalities and substantial corporate clients such as major record companies. Specialist advice is provided in the businesses of music, video, theatre, television, sponsorship and merchandising, film and publishing and the exploitation of intellectual property rights.

Company/ Commercial and Property: The firm provides all aspects of corporate advice to a large range of commercial organisations including new ventures, business expansion schemes, corporate restructuring, international taxation, liquidations and receiverships. All aspects of property transactions are handled by a strong team led by four partners with a special expertise in secured lending, acting for banking and other lending institutions.

Litigation: A strong team of forceful litigators handle a wide diversity of litigation matters with particular emphasis and expertise in major contractual and copyright disputes in the music, entertainment and sports industries, banking, employment, personal injury and matrimonial matters. The firm also acts in relation to major corporate fraud and related matters.

Credit Collection: The firm has a sophisticated, computer-based credit collection department capable of dealing both with high volume corporate collection and individual case by case matters. Allied to the litigation department, the firm is accordingly able to deal with more complicated issues which regularly arise out of credit collection.

Private Client: Advice on all aspects of personal arrangements such as offshore settlements, wills, probate and trusts, international tax advice and matrimonial finance.

INTERNATIONAL CONNECTIONS: The firm has considerable overseas connections, particularly in the USA, continental Europe, Israel and Ireland and in the Channel Islands, Cayman and the Bahamas.

LANGUAGES SPOKEN: French, Hebrew.

CONTACT PARTNERS: Mr J.M.R. Cohen, Mr D.M. Landsman

Number of partners:	12
Assistant solicitors:	5
Other fee-earners:	5

WORKLOAD	
Litigation/Credit collection	30%
Media/Entertainment & Sport	30%
Company/commercial & Property	25%
Private client	15%

CONTACTS	
Company/commercial & Property	John Cohen
Credit collection	David Landsman
Litigation	Andrew Sharland
Media/Entertainment & Sport	David Landsman
Private client	John Cohen

T.I. CLOUGH & CO Bridge House, 24 Sunbridge Road, Bradford, W. Yorks, BD1 2TD **Tel:** (01274) 734461 **Fax:** (01274) 734307 **DX:** 11706 **Ptnrs:** 4 **Asst Solrs:** 4 **Other Fee-earners:** 8. A specialist litigation practice with large and well developed criminal, matrimonial and civil litigation departments.

WORKLOAD			
Crime	40%	Civil litigation	30%
Matrimonial	20%	Child care	10%

CLYDE & CO

51 EASTCHEAP, LONDON, EC3M 1JP
DX: 1071

TEL: (0171) 623 1244
FAX: (0171) 623 5427

THE FIRM: Clyde & Co is a major international law firm, particularly strong in trade, transport, insurance, reinsurance, corporate and finance matters. The practice is fast growing and has a strong international reputation. Many of the lawyers travel widely on client business, working closely with the Clyde & Co overseas offices and correspondent lawyers. The firm's international business is serviced from offices in London, Guildford, Cardiff and regional offices in the Far East, Middle East, Latin America.

PRINCIPAL AREAS OF WORK:

Shipping and Marine Insurance: (*Contact:* Anthony Thomas). Clyde & Co has an international reputation in this field, acting for shipowners, charterers, shipbuilders, cargo owners and insurers. Areas include salvage and collision, carriage of goods, charterparty disputes, marine insurance, bills of lading, general average, pollution, ship finance, sale and purchase, shipbuilding and ship repair disputes.

Insurance Litigation (non-marine and general): (*Contact:* Michael Payton). The firm advises on insurance policies of all kinds including: E&O, D&O, construction risks, credit and political risks, product liability, specie insurance, bloodstock, financial institutions, transport and aviation.

Insurance (non contentious): (*Contact:* Verner Southey). The firm advises on corporate and business transactions in London and world markets, insurance regulation and insurance products.

Reinsurance: (*Contact:* Nigel Brook). The firm's Reinsurance Team specialise in the drafting and interpretation of reinsurance contracts and the pursuit, defence and resolution of reinsurance claims.

Company Commercial: (*Contact:* Verner Southey). The firm advises on all aspects of corporate finance, banking, commercial property, tax, intellectual property, information technology and pensions.

Commercial & Corporate Litigation: (*Contact:* Jonathan Wood). The firm conducts litigation and arbitration before Courts and tribunals in the UK and worldwide through its overseas offices and correspondent lawyers, regarding disputes arising from banking, commodities, trading, commercial contracts, sale of goods, debt recovery, corporate crime, fraud, professional indemnity, product liability and personal injury.

International Trade & Finance incl. Asset Finance: (*Contact:* Simon Poland/ Andrew Wells). The firm advises a wide range of clients on asset finance, commodities, countertrade and project finance.

Energy: (*Contact:* Peter Felter). The firm represents oil producing and exploration companies, oil traders, refineries and petrochemical producers on all aspects of their operations worldwide. The work includes: joint ventures, exploration and production agreements and statutory regulation.

Employment: (*Contact:* Paul Newdick). The firm advises on terms of employment and employment policies, restrictive covenants, wrongful and unfair dismissal, discrimination cases and termination packages.

Environment: (*Contact:* David Reynolds). Clyde & Co advises companies on the impact of and their exposure to UK, EC and international regulations relating to the environment both onshore and offshore. The firm also has considerable experience in the area of insurance of environmental risks.

EC & Competition Law: (*Contact:* Stuart Macdonald). The firm advises UK and foreign companies on regulation and competition law, state aids, free movement of goods and capital and insurance.

CONTACT PARTNER: Martin Heath

UK:	
Number of partners:	76
Assistant solicitors:	86
Other fee-earners:	86
INTERNATIONAL:	
Number of Partners:	13
Assistant Solicitors:	14
Other fee-earners:	7

WORKLOAD	
Insurance/ reinsurance	30%
Marine	30%
Company, commercial, banking, property	20%
Other commercial litigation	10%
International trade	10%

CONTACTS	
Aviation	Simon Poland/ David Reynolds
Banking	David Page
Commercial litigation	Conrad Walker
	Jonathan Wood
Company/ commercial	Verner Southey
	Jon Rayman
Employment	Paul Newdick/ Chris Duffy
Energy	Peter Felter/ Simon Fletcher
Environment	David Reynolds
Insolvency	Jonathan Wood/ Paul Newdick
Insurance	Verner Southey/David Salt
Medical negligence	John Mitchell
Personal injury	Paul Newdick
Product liability	John Blacker
Professional indemnity	Peter Farthing
Reinsurance	Nigel Brook
Shipping	Tony Thomas/ Simon Poland
Trade	Andrew Wells
Transport	Robert Heanley/ David Hall

Aviation: (*Contact:* Colin Franke). Clyde & Co advises on all areas of corporate and litigious aspects of the aviation industry and its insurers.

Transport: (*Contact:* Michael Parker). Advice is given on issues including carriage of goods, CMR and insurance and trading conditions.

NATURE OF CLIENTELE: Clyde & Co acts for insurance companies, shipping and financial services firms, major oil companies, banks, property developers, public companies and multinationals.

OTHER OFFICES: Guildford, Cardiff, Hong Kong, Singapore, Dubai, São Paulo and Caracas.

ASSOCIATE OFFICES: Paris and St. Petersburg.

COBBETT LEAK ALMOND

SHIP CANAL HOUSE, KING ST, MANCHESTER, M2 4WB
DX: 14374

TEL: (0161) 833 3333
FAX: (0161) 833 3030

THE FIRM: Cobbett Leak Almond is one of the largest firms in the North West and offers a comprehensive range of legal services. The firm is committed to meeting the needs of a wide range of commercial concerns and maintains a substantial private client department. It is particularly well-known for its commercial property and planning work; it also serves most of the major breweries operating in the North West. The practice has established European connections and is a member of Eurolegal.

PRINCIPAL AREAS OF WORK:

Commercial Property: (*Contact Partner:* W.A. Brock). *Work includes:* all types of property-related transactions, including licensed premises, secured lending, development and planning work.

Litigation: (*Contact Partner:* D. Pickering). *Work includes:* High Court and County Court litigation, including emergency injunctions, industrial tribunals, intellectual property, personal injury and motor accident claims, building and construction disputes, possession cases for mortgagees, landlord and tenant, Factories Act and Health and Safety legislation, insurance, consumer credit, debt recovery, defamation, insolvency, and enforcement of security.

Corporate and Commercial: (*Contact Partner:* R.S. Hawes). *Work includes:* company formations, acquisitions and disposals, corporate reorganizations, management buy-outs, joint ventures, flotations on the Stock Exchange, corporate finance and tax, banking, EC law and intellectual property, all kinds of trading agreements, employment law and pensions.

Private Client: (*Contact Partner:* A.D. Sturrock). *Work includes:* wills, probate, trusts and settlements, pensions, domestic and estate conveyancing, family and matrimonial law, all aspects of tax and general financial planning, insurance, tax appeals and share valuations.

Licensing and Leisure Industry: (*Contact Partner:* H.K. Lawson). *Work includes:* licensing applications, finance raising, employment problems and staff contracts, and advice on EC regulations.

NATURE OF CLIENTELE: Clients include companies, partnerships, banks, the retail industry, property developers, farmers, the brewing and leisure industry, private clients and charities.

RECRUITMENT AND TRAINING: The firm recruits at least six trainee solicitors every year. Applications by letter and CV to Mr. S.J. White.

LANGUAGES SPOKEN: French, German, Italian, Spanish.

OTHER OFFICE: Wilmslow.

CONTACT PARTNER: Stephen White

Number of partners:	31
Assistant solicitors:	27
Other fee-earners:	24

WORKLOAD	
Commercial Property	28%
Litigation	28%
Company/ commercial	25%
Trusts and probate	9%
Debt collection	5%
Domestic conveyancing	5%

CONTACTS	
Banking	Robin Higham
Commercial Property	Duncan Brock
Company commercial	Roger Hawes
Construction	Philip Hodson
Corporate finance	Robert Turnbull
Environmental	Simon Jones
Insolvency	Henry Stone
Intellectual property	Robert Roper
Licensing	Hamish Lawson
Litigation	David Pickering
Planning	Peter Oldham
Private client	Alan Sturrock

COFFIN MEW & CLOVER

17 HAMPSHIRE TERRACE, PORTSMOUTH, HANTS, PO1 2PU
DX: 2207

TEL: (01705) 812511
FAX: (01705) 291847

Other Offices: Southampton; Fareham (Commercial Office); Cosham; Fareham (West Street); Gosport; Havant and Leigh Park

THE FIRM: A major regional firm providing a comprehensive service to both the commercial and private sectors through a network of offices in South Hampshire. The practice has a central office in Fareham providing the full range of legal services to business. The city centre offices in Portsmouth and Southampton continue to provide commercial services as well as the full range of private client services provided by allthe branch offices.

PRINCIPAL AREAS OF WORK:

Company/ Commercial: (*Contact Partner:* (01329) 825617, Malcolm Padgett). Commercial services range from the formation of companies and partnerships to commercial contracts, the acquisition and disposal of companies and employment matters; specialisms include consumer finance and insurance; insolvency; educational law; intellectual property; marketing law and commercial support to NHS trusts.

Litigation: (*Contact Partner:* (01329) 825617, Jon Bridges). The firm's expanding litigation department offers a specialist dispute resolution team dealing with a broad range of commercial and insurance litigation and arbitration including company and partnership disputes, professional negligence as well as a fully-computerised debt collection unit.

Commercial property litigation and all aspects of construction law are a specialisation of the department which also maintains a dedicated employment and industrial relations unit.

The firm has a personal injury department (*Contact Partner:* (01329) 825617, Keith Hayward) with a wide range of experience in personal injury claims including employer/ employee liability, road traffic accidents and medical negligence and multi-party disaster claims and other group actions.

Commercial Property: (*Contact Partner:* (01329) 825617, Jennifer Bennett). The firm has considerable experience in commercial and residential property development; specialisms include Institutional work; Housing Associations; health and local authority work; retail planning and development; and educational and Health Service assets.

Private Client: The firm is dedicated to offering advice with personal service on a full range of private client matters and legal aid work is welcomed.

Family: (*Contact Partner:* (01329) 822638, Pauline Johnson). The matrimonial team provides services through the branch network and is particularly noted for its expertise when complex business and property matters may be involved.

Residential Property: (*Contact Partner:* (01705) 523111, Courtney Kenny). The residential property department provides services throughout the branch network, it is managed on an area basis and is one of the largest departments of its kind in the area.

Crime: (*Contact Partner:* (01705) 812511, Bill Meads). The firm has a network of criminal practitioners all of whom undertake legal aid work.

Trust and Probate: (*Contact Partner:* (01329) 822638, Roger Hancock). Specialised practitioners offer advice on wills, administration of estates, enduring power of attorney, Court of Protection and trusts. Partners and fee-earners are specialised in offering advice to the elderly.

CONTACT PARTNER: Mr. David Baker

Number of partners:	22
Assistant solicitors:	12
Other fee-earners:	24

WORKLOAD	
Property	27%
Commercial	23%
Matrimonial/ crime	21%
Litigation	21%
Probate and trust	8%

CONTACTS	
Commercial property	Jennifer Bennett
Commercial litigation	Jon Bridges
Construction law	Huw Morgan
Corporate/ commercial	Malcolm Padgett
Crime	Bill Meads
Employment	Jon Bridges
Family	Pauline Johnson
Housing association	Jennifer Bennett
NHS trusts	Philip Yetman
Personal injury	Keith Hayward
Probate/ trust	Roger Hancock
Residential property	Courtney Kenny

COLE and COLE Buxton Court, 3 West Way, Oxford, Oxon, OX2 0SZ **Tel:** (01865) 791122 **Fax:** (01865) 721367 **DX:** 96200 Oxford West **Ptnrs:** 30 **Asst Solrs:** 33 **Other Fee-earners:** 31. Cole and Cole is a leading regional law firm, with six offices and over 175 lawyers and support staff. It offers a full range of legal services to both business and to private clients.

WORKLOAD			
Commercial litigation	25%	Company/ commercial	23%
Family and crime	20%	Res conveyancing	10%
Commercial property	10%	Probate	8%

COLEMANS 27 Marlow Road, Maidenhead, Berks, SL6 7AE **Tel:** (01628) 31051 **Fax:** (01628) 22106 **DX:** 6405 Maidenhead **Ptnrs:** 5 **Other Fee-earn-ers:** 1. Corporate and private client work. Also handles litigation, company/ commercial and planning.

COLEMANS Elisabeth House, 16 St. Peter's Square, Manchester, M2 3DF **Tel:** (0161) 236 5623 **Fax:** (0161) 228 7509 **DX:** 14380 **Ptnrs:** 7 **Asst Solrs:** 6 **Other Fee-earners:** 10. Established in the early 80's, Colemans is a young forward-thinking commercial firm, practising from offices in Manchester and the West Midlands.

COLES MILLER

44-46 PARKSTONE ROAD, POOLE, DORSET, BH15 2PG	TEL: (01202) 673011
DX: 07609	FAX: (01202) 675868
Forelle House, Marshes End, Upton Road, Poole BH17 7AE	Tel: (01202) 667866
DX: 07609 Poole (Commercial Office)	Fax: (01202) 668262

THE FIRM: Coles Miller is one of the largest practices in the area. As with most forward thinking and efficient firms Coles Miller has specialist lawyers offering advice on a wide range of matters, and has particular strengths in commercial, civil litigation, family and matrimonial law.

PRINCIPAL AREAS OF WORK:

Company and Commercial Services: (*Contact:* Neil Meldrum). The firm undertakes the whole range of company/ commercial work including acquisitions and disposals of businesses and companies, mergers and restructuring, commercial contracts, franchising, agency and distributorship agreements both in the UK and EC countries, intellectual property agreements and the preparation of debentures and other security documentation.

Commercial Litigation: (*Contact:* Mark Clarke). The firm has wide experience and expertise in High Court, Chancery and County Court litigation including intellectual property disputes, employment, licensing, professional negligence, construction, engineering, landlord and tenant and insurance matters. There is a substantial uninsured loss recovery department and a separate debt collection department.

Commercial Property: (*Contact:* Roger Sargologo). All aspects of commercial property work including negotiation of commercial leases of industrial, retail and office premises and all Landlord and Tenant Act implications, industrial retail and office freehold and leasehold development, property, residential estate development, and matters dealing with all security arrangements in respect of property.

Conveyancing: (*Contact:* Roger Leedham or Paul Dyer). All aspects of work relating to residential freehold and leasehold property; the firm advises on mortgages, financial services and tenancy agreements.

Private Client: (*Contact:* David Parfitt). The firm offers a comprehensive service to the private client including drafting and advice on wills, probate, trusts, tax, estate administration and inheritance claims.

Family and Matrimonial: (*Contact:* Sheriff Payne or Judy Armitage). Divorce, child care, financial disputes and all aspects of family breakdowns and disputes between cohabitees.

Civil Litigation: (*Contact:* Sheriff Payne or Jim Richardson). In addition to the range of litigation services offered to the commercial clients, the private litigation department provides a comprehensive service including personal injury and accident claims, contractual disputes and property claims.

Criminal: (*Contact:* Simon Elliott). All Magistrates and Crown Court proceedings.

OTHER OFFICES: Wimborne, Broadstone, Bournemouth and West Moors. These offices deal with all areas of work offered by the firm except the more complex areas of company and commercial work, which is dealt with at the Forelle House office.

RECRUITMENT AND TRAINING: The growth of Coles Miller continues and the firm is always looking for trainee solicitors and qualified and non-qualified staff of the highest calibre.

CONTACT PARTNER: Roger Senior

Number of partners:	13
Assistant solicitors:	10
Other fee-earners:	18

WORKLOAD	
Conveyancing, both residential and company	30%
Family and matrimonial	18%
Probate	16%
Commercial litigation	14%
Commercial property	8%
ULR	8%
Company/ commercial	6%

CONTACTS	
Commercial litigation	Mark Clarke
Commercial property	Roger Sargologo
Company/ commercial	Neil Meldrum
Conveyancing	Roger Leedham
Criminal	Simon Elliott
Family and matrimonial	Sheriff Payne
Private client	David Parfitt

B.P. COLLINS & CO

COLLINS HOUSE, 32-38 STATION RD, GERRARDS CROSS, BUCKS, SL9 8EL
DX: 40256 Gerrards Cross

TEL: (01753) 889995
FAX: (01753) 889851

THE FIRM: B.P. Collins & Co. was established in 1965, and has expanded significantly to become one of the largest and best known legal practices at the London end of the M4/ M40 corridors. At its main office in Gerrards Cross, the emphasis is on commercial work, with particular strengths being company/ commercial work of all types, commercial conveyancing and general commercial litigation.

PRINCIPAL AREAS OF WORK AT GERRARDS CROSS OFFICE:

Commercial Property: (*Contact Partner:* Justin Samuel. *4 Partners*). The property department handles the sale, purchase and leasing of all types of commercial property, including offices, shops, factories, warehouses, hotels and nursing homes. It also deals with landlord and tenant legislation, (residential, business or agricultural) planning matters, and acts for developer clients in relation to residential projects. One partner specialises in agricultural matters.

Company/ Commercial: (*Contact Partner:* David Stanning. *3 Partners*). The activities of the company/ commercial department cover virtually all aspects of business life and include substantial company acquisitions and disposals, management buy-outs, business transfers, shareholders' agreements, agency, distribution and franchise agreements, computer contracts and employment matters. Colin Cork is the specialist insolvency partner.

Litigation: (*Contact Partner:* Nicholas Hallchurch. *3 Partners*). *Work includes:* corporate disputes, contentious information technology matters, matrimonial, building disputes and intellectual property disputes. The firm also has an established reputation for employment law work.

Private Client: (*Contact Partner:* David Wilkinson. *2 Partners*). Conveyancing, probate, wills, trusts and tax planning services are offered to the private client. Members of S.T.E.P.

OTHER OFFICES: Beaconsfield and Chalfont St. Peter.

CONTACT PARTNER: David Stanning

Number of partners:	13
Assistant solicitors:	6
Other fee-earners:	8

WORKLOAD	
Commercial property	35%
Litigation	20%
Company and commercial	20%
Residential conveyancing	10%
Probate, wills, etc	10%
Matrimonial	5%

CONTACTS	
Commercial property	Justin Samuel
Company and commercial	David Stanning
Litigation	Nick Hallchurch
Matrimonial	Sue Andrews
Probate, wills, etc	David Wilkinson
Residential conveyancing	Mike Arundel

COLLYER–BRISTOW

4 BEDFORD ROW, LONDON, WC1R 4DF
DX: 163 Ch.Ln.

TEL: (0171) 242 7363
FAX: (0171) 405 0555

THE FIRM: Collyer-Bristow is an imaginative and innovative firm based in Bedford Row. It was established in 1760 but its environment and approach is progressive and friendly. The firm acts for a wide range of institutional clients, public and private companies, charities, businesses, professional partnerships and private clients. An association with a group of European practices, and membership of Eurolink have assisted in developing continental links; an office in New York has enabled the firm to extend its connections in North America; the Far East is also proving an increasing source of business. The bright modernised offices now contain a professionally run Art Gallery where regular and varied exhibitions are held.

PRINCIPAL AREAS OF WORK:

General Description: The firm has a strong commercial property practice and an expanding corporate and commercial department. The litigation and family law departments have excellent reputations within the profession, the sports sponsorship and entertainment practice is developing, and the firm remains committed to providing a comprehensive personal service for its private clients, both in the UK and offshore.

CONTACT PARTNER: Michael Drake

Number of partners:	16
Assistant solicitors:	10
Other fee-earners:	16

WORKLOAD	
Matrimonial and family	25%
Property (commercial)	25%
Litigation	20%
Private client	13%
Commercial	10%
Sport and entertainment	4%
Property (other)	3%

Company/ Commercial: (*Contact:* Paul Sillis/Roger Woolfe). The department continues to grow and its work includes company formations, mergers, acquisitions, sales, buy-outs, reorganisations and all the related range of contractual and commercial advice, including an expertise in advice to company directors.

Commercial Property: (*Contact:* Roger Woolfe/ Giles Thorman). The department acts for many investment companies, property developers and financial institutions on freehold and leasehold sales and disposals, office development schemes, major shopping centre developments, agricultural matters, planning and other related work. Residential and domestic transactions are also handled.

Litigation: (*Contact:* Matthew Marsh). This strong team has experience in property-related and construction litigation and arbitration, judicial review work, commercial and contractual disputes, intellectual property, professional negligence, personal injury, defamation and employment law, and in representation before professional tribunals. The firm is also developing a shipping litigation practice.

Private Client: (*Contact:* John Saner). This is a long-established department where the work involves tax planning, trusts, financial and investment advice within the UK and offshore, wills and the administration of estates, and charities.

Family: (*Contact:* Jeremy Levison). This is one of the leading matrimonial practices in London. Its reputation extends across the entire range of family work, including divorce, custody and financial disputes, wardship and cohabitation. The department is increasingly involved in international work such as forum-shopping, child abduction and the recognition of decrees.

Employment: (*Contact:* Lucy Elgood). A specialist team handles a wide range of employment and boardroom disputes, industrial tribunal applications, executive service contract advice, and the preparation of employment terms and conditions.

Sports Sponsorship, Marketing & Advertising Law: (*Contact:* Alan Burdon-Cooper/Philip Stinson). The firm has a substantial practice in this field, acting for sponsorship, promotions and merchandising consultancies, advertising and marketing agencies, governing bodies, sponsors, sports photographers and publishers, film and video producers and distributors, and is now moving into personality management.

Entertainment and Creative Arts: (*Contact:* Michael Drake/Philip Stinson). The firm acts for a number of artists, sculptors, writers, musicians, photographers, film-makers, designers, and consultancies in the creative arts.

Agency Work: (*Contact:* Matthew Marsh). The agency litigation department provides a service for more than 100 firms outside the capital and overseas.

RECRUITMENT AND TRAINING: To the young man or woman who does not believe that biggest necessarily means best, the firm offers a refreshing alternative; trainee solicitors work closely with partners on a wide variety of work in a friendly atmosphere – opportunities that only a smaller firm can provide. Applicants should have a good academic background, an assured and lively personality, a positive approach and preferably some computer literacy and linguistic ability. CV and references to Giles Thorman.

CONTACTS	
Company/ commercial	Paul Sillis
	Roger Woolfe
Employment	Lucy Elgood
Family/ matrimonial	Jeremy Levison
Litigation	Matthew Marsh
Private client	John Saner
Property	Roger Woolfe/ Giles Thorman
Sport/ entertainment	Alan Burdon-Cooper
	Philip Stinson

COMPTON CARR 6 Dyers Buildings, Holborn, London, EC1N 2JT **Tel:** (0171) 831 6981 **Fax:** (0171) 831 2069 **Ptnrs:** 8 **Asst Solrs:** 3 **Other Fee-earners:** 5. Handles entertainment, litigation, company/ commercial and property. The firm is particularly known for its work in entertainment and medical negligence.

CONDIES 2 Tay Street, Perth, Tayside, PH1 5LJ **Tel:** (01738) 440088 **Fax:** (01738) 441131 **DX:** 25 Perth **Ptnrs:** 7 **Asst Solrs:** 6 **Other Fee-earners:** 2. General practice. Large volume of property work including agricultural. Also experienced in trust and executry affairs and criminal and civil court work.

WORKLOAD			
Conveyancing	30%	Court work	25%
Private client	18%	Agricultural/estate	12%
Hotel/leisure/licensing	6%	Landlord and tenant	4%

CONFREYS 219 Mackintosh Place, Roath, Cardiff, S. Glam, CF2 4RR **Tel:** (01222) 458080 **Fax:** (01222) 497080 **Ptnrs:** 1. Specialist niche practice in mental health law, particularly in representing individuals before the Mental Health Review Tribunal.

WORKLOAD			
Mental health law	80%	Community care/housing	10%
Welfare benefits law	10%		

CONNELL & CONNELL WS 10 Dublin Street, Edinburgh, EH1 3PR
Tel: (0131) 556 2993 **Fax:** (0131) 557 5542 **DX:** 184 Edinburgh **Ptnrs:** 5 **Asst Solrs:** 2 **Other Fee-earners:** 1. A general practice with recognised agricultural expertise.

CONSTANT & CONSTANT Sea Containers House, 20 Upper Ground, Blackfriars Bridge, London, SE1 9QT **Tel:** (0171) 261 0006 **Fax:** (0171) 401 2161 **DX:** 1067 London **Ptnrs:** 27 **Asst Solrs:** 8 **Other Fee-earners:** 9. Long established firm with an international practice. Expanded its shipping base to include banking, insurance, international trade, property, and general commercial matters.

COODES

8 MARKET STREET, ST. AUSTELL, CORNWALL, PL2 4BB
DX: 81250

TEL: (01726) 75021
FAX: (01726) 69103

CONTACT PARTNER: Mr. J.A. Coode

Number of partners:	9
Assistant solicitors:	4
Other fee-earners:	18

THE FIRM: Founded around 240 years ago, the firm has substantial contacts with the agricultural and commercial community throughout Cornwall.

PRINCIPAL AREAS OF WORK: Commercial and domestic conveyancing; civil litigation; family work; private client and charities; crime; commercial and planning. Within these departments the firm has specialists in employment law; professional negligence; personal injury; agriculture and liquor licensing.

OTHER OFFICES: Truro, Newquay, Liskeard, Launceston and Callington.

COOLE & HADDOCK

5 THE STEYNE, WORTHING, W. SUSSEX, BN11 3DT
DX: 3717 Worthing

TEL: (01903) 213511
FAX: (01903) 237053

SENIOR PARTNER: Frank Haddock

Number of partners:	12
Assistant solicitors:	3
Other fee-earners:	7

THE FIRM: Established in Horsham in 1889 and Worthing in 1960, Coole & Haddock built its reputation initially on an extensive private client base mainly in Sussex. This is now complemented by expanding company, commercial and litigation departments which offer a comprehensive service to businesses over a wider area, including London and overseas. The firm has particular expertise in the motor industry.

Company/commercial/commercial property: *(Contact Partner:* Iain Swalwell at Worthing). *Work includes:* Company formations, partnerships, company sales and acquisitions, joint ventures, secured lending, intellectual property, large scale commercial property conveyancing including commercial and residential property development.

Litigation: *(Contact Partner:* Stephen Loosemore at Worthing). *Work includes:* large scale commercial litigation, specific expertise in consumer credit, employment, landlord and tenant, computerised debt collection, personal injury, property litigation.

Domestic conveyancing: *(Contact Partner:* Peter Graves at Horsham and Paul Burke at Worthing). *Work includes:* residential sales and purchases, landlord and tenant, housing associations.

Agricultural/heritage: *(Contact Partner:* Iain Swalwell at Worthing). the firm offers a comprehensive service to landowners and farmers.

Probate/trusts: *(Contact Partner:* Christine Bennett at Horsham). *Work includes:* wills, probate, trusts, administration of estates.

Charities: *(Contact Partner:* John Lacy at Horsham): a specialist in all aspects of charity law and administration.

Family: *(Contact Partner:* Richard Ager at Horsham): divorce and separation, maintenance, custody and access to children, wardship and adoption. The firm's strong family law team includes representation on the Law Society's Children's Panel, and an accredited mediator.

Criminal: *(Contact Partner:* Nigel Desoutter at Horsham). *Work includes:* all Magistrates' and Crown Court proceedings.
Financial services: *(Contact Partner:* David Hanrahan at Horsham). *Work includes:* tax and investment advice to private and business clients, pensions, insurance, mortgages.

COOPER SONS, HARTLEY & WILLIAMS Woolwich Hse, 61 Mosley Street, Manchester, M2 3HZ **Tel:** (0161) 236 0321 **Fax:** (0161) 228 7767 **Ptnrs:** 11 **Asst Solrs:** 8 **Other Fee-earners:** 4. Other offices at Buxton and Chapel-en-le-Frith. Work includes tax planning, matrimonial, employment and commercial property.

M.W. CORNISH & CO

11 OLD JEWRY, LONDON, EC2R 8DU

TEL: (0171) 600 0910
FAX: (0171) 600 0837

THE FIRM: The firm specialises in financial services work, banking, general corporate, corporate finance and related litigation and acts primarily for banks, securities houses, commodity brokers, venture capitalists, investment banks and fund managers. It seeks to provide a cost effective service by combining the advantages of in-house lawyers (with the majority of fee-earners having worked in-house) with the skills and resources of external advisors.

PRINCIPAL AREAS OF WORK: The firm has particular expertise in the following areas: primary and secondary capital markets including all equity, debt & derivatives products such as stock lending, repo, swaps, OTC options, and FX; commodities trading and documentation issues; corporate finance; asset management, including the establishment of onshore and offshore funds; domestic and international banking; ship, aircraft and project financing; leasing; restructurings and insolvency law; company law; general regulatory and trading issues; and offers litigation, arbitration and ADR services in respect of all the above areas.

FOREIGN CONNECTIONS: The firm has correspondents in all major foreign jurisdictions.

CONTACT PARTNERS: M.W. Cornish
P.D. Astleford

Number of partners:	5
Assistant solicitors:	5
Other fee-earners:	2

WORKLOAD	
Collective investment schemes	25%
Financial services	25%
Corporate finance	20%
Litigation	10%
Asset/ project finance and leasing/ shipping/ banking	10%
Company/ commercial	10%

COUDERT BROTHERS

20 OLD BAILEY, LONDON, EC4M 7JP
DX: 42603 Cheapside 1

TEL: (0171) 248 3000
FAX: (0171) 248 3001/3002

THE FIRM: Coudert Brothers in London is a multi-national partnership of solicitors and registered foreign lawyers. It is part of a global network of offices established in 19 cities in 14 countries. In the London office there are six partners, five of whom are solicitors and one of whom is a US attorney. Coudert Brothers is one global partnership and the London office therefore provides the facilities of a full service London law firm as well as access to the international network of Coudert Brothers.

The offices of Coudert Brothers are established in the major financial centres of the world including offices in the United States, Latin America, the Asian Pacific region and in Europe. The major offices in Europe are established in Paris, London and Brussels; The US offices are established in New York, Washington, Los Angeles, San Francisco and San Jose. In Latin America the firm has an associated office in Mexico City. The Asia Pacific offices are established in Bangkok, Beijing, Ho Chi

CONTACT PARTNER: Mr Steven Beharrell

LAWYERS:	
London:	26
Worldwide:	380

CONTACTS	
Arbitration	Jonathan Clegg
Banking and finance	Hugh Thompson
Corporate finance	Steven Beharrell
Energy	Steven Beharrell
Funds	Alasdair Gordon

Minh City, Hanoi, Hong Kong, Jakarta, Singapore, Sydney and Tokyo. The firm's Moscow office was the first established by a foreign law firm in 1988 and is now one of the largest in Moscow servicing all the states of the former Soviet Union.

LONDON OFFICE: This office specialises in international investment, trade and finance with particular expertise in corporate finance, mergers and acquisitions, joint ventures, euro-securities and international banking law, international tax and trust planning, telecommunications and media law, energy privatisation and infrastructure projects, arbitration and litigation.

Litigation	Jonathan Clegg
Real property	Philip Burroughs
Tax	James Benger
Telecommunications	Colin Long

COURTS & CO

15 WIMPOLE ST, LONDON, W1M 8AP
DX: 42722 Oxford Circus North

TEL: (0171) 637 1651
FAX: (0171) 637 0205

THE FIRM: Courts & Co is a "niche" firm, specialising in company and commercial work. The firm provides an in-depth, personal service to companies and their directors working closely with their business advisers, particularly, their accountants. The firm's policy is to combine the highest level of technical expertise with a close understanding of the client's business and commercial requirements.

PRINCIPAL AREAS OF WORK: A large part of the firm's work consists of advising on the purchase and sale of businesses, corporate mergers and reorganisations, as well as a full range of business and commercial matters including taxation and intellectual property work. The firm handles commercial conveyancing, heavy commercial litigation (including environmental and town and country planning matters), employment work (both litigious and non-litigious) mainly for employers; and estate planning, trusts and probate work.

NATURE OF CLIENTELE: Clients include private and public companies, professional partnerships and individual entrepreneurs in all areas of business; charities and trusts. Much of the firm's work is for overseas clients.

CONTACT PARTNERS: Bill Holmes and Ian Paterson

Number of partners:	4
Assistant solicitors:	5
Other fee-earners:	1

WORKLOAD	
Conveyancing/trusts,wills & probate	35%
Company, commercial and tax	35%
Commercial litigation	30%

CONTACTS	
Company/ commercial	Ian Paterson
Conveyancing/probates & trusts	Bill Holmes
Litigation	Michael Krantz and Frank Ryan

COZENS–HARDY & JEWSON

CASTLE CHAMBERS, OPIE ST, NORWICH, NORFOLK, NR1 3DP
DX: 5214

TEL: (01603) 625231
FAX: (01603) 627160/ 612690

THE FIRM: Cozens-Hardy & Jewson provides a service to both local and national clients. A general practice, it offers a complete range of legal services to both business and private clients, including Legal Aid work under the Franchise Scheme.

PRINCIPAL AREAS OF WORK:

Litigation: (*Contact Partner:* Paul Ayers). A wide range of civil contentious work includes: contractual disputes, personal injury, professional negligence and insurance claims, land disputes, licensing applications, mental health, insolvency and debt collection. Legal aid is available, where appropriate.

Company/ Commercial: (*Contact Partner:* Simon Whipp). All aspects of company and partnership work are handled, including formations and reconstructions, insolvency problems, employment law, intellectual property and computer law, and UK and EC competition law.

Commercial Property: (*Contact Partner:* Jon Skelton).*Work includes:* commercial property transactions of every kind including acquisitions and disposals of industrial units, warehouses, shops, pubs, garages, etc., on behalf of limited companies, partnerships and sole traders. The department also handles matters relating to commercial property development, landlord and tenant law and residential transactions (relocation) for corporate clients and their employees.

CONTACT PARTNER: Mr C.G. Groves

Number of partners:	10
Assistant solicitors:	6
Other fee-earners:	9

WORKLOAD	
Property, Trusts & Estates	40%
Litigation	29%
Matrimonial/ family	20%
Commercial	11%

A QUALITY SERVICE
Approved by The Legal Aid Board

Family/ Matrimonial: (*Contact Partner:* Michael Webb). The firm gives advice on all legal aspects of a marriage or relationship, including divorce, separation, wardship, care and adoption proceedings. One partner is a member of the Children Panel. Legal aid is available, where appropriate.

Property, Trusts and Estates: (*Contact Partner:* Alistair Sursham). *Work includes:* dealing with residential property and property development, landlord and tenant and planning matters, wills, probate, the administration of trusts and estates, Inheritance Act claims, Court of Protection and Powers of Attorney, and personal tax planning advice.

Charities: (*Contact:* Matthew Martin). Formation and administration of charities, dealings with Charity Commission and Housing Corporation over statutory and procedural matters and charities advice generally.

CONTACTS	
Commercial	W.S. Whipp
	J.W. Skelton
Litigation	P.R. Ayers
	J.M.E. Chimes
Matrimonial/ family	M.E. Webb
	I.D. White
Property, trusts and estates	M.T. Martin
	A.J. Sursham

CRANSWICK WATSON 7 Greek Street, Leeds, W. Yorks, LS1 5RR **Tel:** (0113) 245 1541 **Fax:** (0113) 243 1273 **DX:** 12013 **Ptnrs:** 10 **Asst Solrs:** 4 **Other Fee-earners:** 10. A commercial firm specialising in developing owner-managed businesses. Litigation, personal injury and private client matters also handled. Agency work accepted.

WORKLOAD			
Private client	25%	Commercial property	20%
Family/ matrimonial	15%	Commercial litigation	15%
Company/ commercial	15%	Defendant pers injury	10%

CRAWFORD OWEN 43 Queen Square, Bristol, BS1 4QR **Tel:** (0117) 984 9000 **Fax:** (0117) 925 1296 **DX:** 78232 Bristol **Ptnrs:** 3 **Asst Solrs:** 2 . Specialist commercial property practice, property development, management, joint ventures and ancillary commercial work, landlord and tenant.

WORKLOAD	
Commercial property	90%

CRIPPS HARRIES HALL

SEYMOUR HOUSE, 11-13 MOUNT EPHRAIM ROAD, TUNBRIDGE WELLS, KENT, TN1 1EN   DX: 3954 Tunbridge Wells

TEL: (01892) 515121
FAX: (01892) 544878

NATURE OF FIRM: As the largest firm in Kent and one of the largest in the South East, Cripps Harries Hall is able to provide all the services required by a business or institution – both now and in the future. The firm attributes its reputation as a progressive practice largely to an ability to meet clients' requirements precisely. Constructive advice and solutions are delivered to clients in an efficient and friendly manner.

The firm's strong client orientation is particularly evident in its approach to charging. The practice is flexible on how it is remunerated and is always willing to estimate costs or provide details of its charging methodology.

The firm's steady growth has been enhanced by attracting new clients away from London firms of solicitors with a high quality of service at a considerably lower cost.

PRINCIPAL AREAS OF WORK:

Commercial: (*Contact:* Andrew Fermor). *Work includes:* commercial contracts and agreements; commercial property; corporate acquisitions and disposals; EC law; employment; environmental law; franchising; housing associations; insolvency; intellectual property; joint ventures; landlord and tenant; MBOs and MBIs; planning; property development; secured lending.

Litigation: (*Contact:* Charles Broadie). *Work includes:* agency; arbitration; construction disputes; debt collection; employment; environment; insurance; judicial review; landlord and tenant; licensing; medical negligence; mortgage possession; personal injury; professional negligence; property litigation.

Finance and Investment Services: (*Contact:* David Lough).

Private Client Department: (*Contact:* Peter Raymond).

Residential Conveyancing Department: (*Contact:* Phyllida de Salis).

SENIOR PARTNER: Christopher Hall	
Number of partners:	22
Assistant solicitors:	19
Other fee-earners:	40

WORKLOAD	
Commercial	31%
Private client	22%
Finance and investment services	21%
Conveyancing	18%
General litigation	8%

CONTACTS	
Commercial litigation	Charles Broadie
Commercial property	Michael Stevens
Company/ commercial	Andrew Fermor
Construction	Peter Ashford
Debt collection	Gavin Tyler
Employment	Caroline Smedley
Environment	Michael Stevens
Finance and investment	David Lough

NATURE OF CLIENTELE: The firm acts for a very broad base of businesses and institutions. It has attracted a strong client following in financial services, insurance and assurance, property (including developers, property portfolio companies, housing associations and lenders), transport and manufacturing, as well as a key government department and clients in publishing, utilities, leisure and several areas of retailing.

OTHER OFFICES: 6-10 Mount Ephrain Road, Turnbridge Wells (Private Client Department and Finance & Investment Services Division).

FOREIGN CONNECTIONS: Associate firms in Berlin, Frankfurt, Paris, Rotterdam, Munich and Madrid.

RECRUITMENT AND TRAINING: Six trainee solicitors are recruited each year. Applications by letter and CV to Jonathan Denny, Managing Partner.

Housing associations	Michael Ellis
Insolvency	Peter Ashford
Private client	Peter Raymond
Property litigation	Gavin Tyler
Trustees and charities	Simon Leney

CRIPPS HARRIES HALL

Solicitors

CROCKERS

10 GOUGH SQUARE, LONDON, EC4A 3NJ
DX: 52

TEL: (0171) 353 0311
FAX: (0171) 583 1417

THE FIRM: Founded in 1912 the firm's reputation was built in the field of insurance, and this still forms the core of its corporate and commercial work. Its links with insurers have enabled the firm to develop a substantial practice in libel (mainly defendant work), as well as personal injury claims and general litigation. The property department handles both commercial and residential conveyancing. Private clients are welcomed.

PRINCIPAL AREAS OF WORK:

Company/ Commercial: The department handles a broad range of commercial work, including private company sales and acquisitions, joint ventures and employment law, predominantly for clients in the insurance industry.

Litigation: The department's principal areas of activity are defamation, copyright, professional indemnity, employers' liability, personal injury and motoring claims.

Property: The department handles all types of commercial property work including development and landlord and tenant as well as domestic conveyancing.

Private Client: The department deals with trusts, wills, probate, personal tax and related areas of work. The estates of both UK and foreign Lloyd's Names are handled by the department.

NATURE OF CLIENTELE: Insurance companies, Lloyd's Brokers and Underwriting Agents are among the firm's clients, reflecting its historical connection with the insurance industry; it also acts for a major property development company and for some of the larger magazine and book publishers. It is drawing a number of its newer clients from syndication agencies and picture libraries.

CONTACT PARTNER: Richard Hudson

Number of partners:	8
Assistant solicitors:	6
Other fee-earners:	5

CONTACTS	
Company/ commercial	Richard Hudson
Defamation/ copyright	Rupert Grey
Personal injury/ motoring	Peter Norman
Private client	Alan Macfadyen
Property	Simon Kingston

CROFTONS Television Hse, Mount St, Manchester, M2 5FA **Tel:** (0161) 834 4391 **Fax:** (0161) 839 1743 **DX:** 18572 Manchester 7 **Ptnrs:** 5 **Asst Solrs:** 2 **Other Fee-earners:** 2. Established in 19th century. Progressive firm with general practice and substantial volume of commercial work. Also handles housing association work.

WORKLOAD			
Housing associations	50%	Priv (probate/convey/lit)	20%
Commercial litigation	10%	Co-operative societies	10%

CROSSE & CROSSE 14 Southernhay West, Exeter, Devon, EX1 1PL **Tel:** (01392) 58451 **Fax:** (01392) 78938 **DX:** 8313 **Ptnrs:** 10 **Asst Solrs:** 6 **Other Fee-earners:** 10. Established around 1900. Medium-sized firm. Well-known for commercial property, family law and medical negligence. Bias towards litigation work. Strong Law Society connections.

WORKLOAD			
Personal injury/med neg	25%	Matrimonial	20%
Crime	16%	Civ lit (incl emp)	12%
Probate	11%	Domestic conveyancing	9%

CRUMP & CO. St. Clare House, 30/33 Minories, London, EC3N 1DD **Tel:** (0171) 369 9010 **Fax:** (0171) 369 9012 **DX:** 1068 City **Ptnrs:** 2 **Other Fee-earners:** 3. Known for its shipping and marine insurance work. Another office in Hong Kong.

CRUTES 7 Osborne Terrace, Newcastle-upon-Tyne, Tyne & Wear, NE2 1RQ **Tel:** (0191) 281 5811 **Fax:** (0191) 281 3608 **DX:** 62553 Jesmond **Ptnrs:** 21 **Asst Solrs:** 15 **Other Fee-earners:** 18. Has offices also in Newcastle, Carlisle, Sunderland, Middlesbrough. Main areas of work are litigation (particularly personal injury), company/ commercial and private client.

CUFF ROBERTS

100 OLD HALL STREET, LIVERPOOL, MERSEYSIDE, L3 9TD
DX: 14126

TEL: (0151) 227 4181
FAX: (0151) 227 2584

THE FIRM: Cuff Roberts' history spans 130 years. With its roots in Liverpool it is committed to Merseyside. The firm has five major departments: company/ commercial, commercial property, commercial litigation, debt recovery and private client. The firm is a member of QLG and has extensive European contacts. Considerable use is made of information technology.

PRINCIPAL AREAS OF WORK: The firm's expertise in the fields of commercial property, company and insolvency work is widely acknowledged. The commercial litigation department is best known for its special skills in food safety and hygiene, planning law, employment matters, construction law, licensing, and professional negligence. The firm operates a highly sophisticated computerised debt collection system, which enables the debt recovery department to offer one of the most efficient services of this type in the region. Domestic conveyancing, tax planning, trust and probate work are handled in the private client department as is the firm's highly regarded matrimonial and family law practice.

CONTACT PARTNER: P. Smith

Number of partners:	21
Assistant solicitors:	8
Other fee-earners:	14

WORKLOAD	
Private client	28%
Commercial litigation	27%
Commercial property	19%
Company commercial	14%
Debt recovery	12%

CUMBERLAND ELLIS PEIRS

COLUMBIA HSE, 69 ALDWYCH, LONDON, WC2B 4RW
DX: 250 Ch.Ln.

TEL: (0171) 242 0422
FAX: (0171) 831 9081

THE FIRM: Formed in 1989 by a merger of two long-established Central London practices which trace their roots back to the 18th century, the firm has attracted considerable company/ commercial and commercial property work and has a substantial litigation department; it also continues to provide the full range of private client services. The firm's philosophy is to combine high quality advice with a positive, personal service, at reasonable cost.

PRINCIPAL AREAS OF WORK:

Company/ Commercial: A wide variety of work is handled, including takeovers, buy-outs, flotations, and employment law for businesses of all sizes.

Litigation: The firm is active in High Court, County Court and Tribunal work (both commercial and private), including personal injury, landlord and tenant, and debt recovery, and is particularly strong in employment and matrimonial law.

Property: The firm's largest department acts for institutions and companies in a wide variety of commercial property work. A separate section deals with residential conveyancing.

Private Client: The department handles all aspects of a client's personal affairs, including probate, wills, trusts, tax planning and landed estates.

Financial Services: All aspects of independent financial advice, including tax-efficient investments, pension and pre-retirement planning, life assurance, school fees, mortgages and health and income protection.

NATURE OF CLIENTELE: The firm acts for public and private companies, institutions, charities (particularly City Livery companies) and a large number of private individuals.

CONTACT PARTNER: Mr. R. Lester

Number of partners:	15
Assistant solicitors:	3
Other fee-earners:	13

CONTACTS	
Commercial property	Robert Maclean
Company/commercial	Iain Mitchell
Financial services	Colin Studd
Litigation	Neil Turner
Private client	Roger Hollinshead
Residential conveyancing	John Sharman

 CUMBERLAND ELLIS PEIRS
SOLICITORS

CUNNINGHAM, JOHN & CO Fairstead Hse, 7 Bury Rd, Thetford, Norfolk, IP24 3PL **Tel:** (01842) 752401 **Fax:** (01842) 753555 **DX:** 100900 **Ptnrs:** 9 **Asst Solrs:** 6 **Other Fee-earners:** 20. Best known for its personal injury and matrimonial litigation, general commercial and property development, and medical negligence work. Has three offices in Norfolk and Suffolk. Legal aid work handled.

CURREY & CO 21 Buckingham Gate, London, SW1E 6LS **Tel:** (0171) 828 4091 **Fax:** (0171) 828 5049 **DX:** 2300 Victoria **Ptnrs:** 7 **Asst Solrs:** 3 **Other Fee-earners:** 4. A small Westminster firm that undertakes mainly private client work. The firm specialises in trusts (including charities), taxation, estate planning, property, private company work, wills and probate.

WORKLOAD	
Private client	100%

CURRY CH. HAUSMANN POPECK

17A WELBECK WAY, LONDON, W1M 7PD
DX: 9082 West End

TEL: (0171) 224 6633
FAX: (0171) 935 4042

THE FIRM: The firm is a general commercial based practice but has developed particular areas of expertise, including handling work for a large number of overseas clients.

PRINCIPAL AREAS OF WORK:

Company/ Commercial: All aspects of this work are dealt with. The firm has particular experience in the field of international commercial agreements, joint ventures and cross-border transactions and mergers and acquisitions. The firm conducts commercial and corporate litigation including arbitrations and insurance litigations. *(Contact Partners:* Mr G. Hausmann and Mr N. Rivers).

Immigration and Nationality: *(Contact Partner:* Mr G. Hausmann).

Employment Law: The firm acts for both employers and employees in non-contentious and litigious matters. *(Contact Partner:* N. Rivers).

Personal Injury: Mainly plaintiff. Accident and injury claims of all natures, including road traffic and industrial injury claims. *(Contact:* L. Bourke).

Family/ Matrimonial: Expertise in this field includes dealing with domestic adoption orders on international adoptions. *(Contact Partner:* Mr L. Curry).

Property: Both commercial and residential property work undertaken, specialising in advising foreign investors and investment consortiums. All property related licensing. *(Contact:* P. Popeck).

Restitution claims: The firm is the leader in acting for restitution claimants against the German government. *(Contact:* L. Curry).

FOREIGN CONNECTIONS: The firm has associated offices in Berlin, Munich, Paris, Geneva, Palo Alto (California), New York and Tel Aviv.

LANGUAGES: French, German, Hebrew, Hungarian.

OTHER OFFICES: 380 Kenton Road, Kenton, Harrow, Middlesex HA3 8EE. *Tel:* (0181) 907 8896. *Fax:* (0181) 907 7554. *DX:* 47504 Kenton. *(Contact:* P. Popeck).

CONTACT PARTNER: Mr N. Rivers

Number of partners:	5
Assistant solicitors:	3
Other fee-earners:	4

CONTACTS	
Commercial/employment	N. Rivers
Company/commercial	G. Hausmann
Family/matrimonial	L. Curry
Immigration	G. Hausmann
Personal injury litigation	L. Bourke
Property/licensing	P. Popeck

CURTIS, MALLET-PREVOST, COLT & MOSLE

TWO THROGMORTON AVENUE, LONDON, EC2N 2DL

TEL: (0171) 638 7957
FAX: (0171) 638 5512

THE FIRM: Founded in 1830 Curtis, Mallet-Prevost, Colt & Mosle is an international law firm with headquarters in New York and branch offices in Frankfurt, London, Hong Kong, Houston, Mexico City, Newark, Paris, and Washington.

PRINCIPAL AREAS OF WORK: The firm has a strong reputation in the fields of litigation and arbitration, banking and corporate finance, commercial, company, mergers and acquisitions, oil and gas, project finance and international tax.

LANGUAGES: Arabic, English, French, Spanish, German.

CONTACT PARTNER: Mr Bruce B. Palmer

LAWYERS:	
London:	4
Worldwide:	200

CURWENS Refuge Hse, River Front, Southbury Road, Enfield, Middx, EN1 3SZ **Tel:** (0181) 367 1577 **Fax:** (0181) 367 1301 **DX:** 90601 Enfield **Ptnrs:** 13 **Asst Solrs:** 2 **Other Fee-earners:** 9. A full range of work from company/ commercial to criminal undertaken. Other offices in Waltham Abbey, Cheshunt, Hoddesdon and Royston.

M.B. CUTTLE & CO Bridge Street Chambers, 72 Bridge St, Manchester, M3 2RJ **Tel:** (0161) 835 2050 **Fax:** (0161) 831 7986 **Ptnrs:** 6 **Asst Solrs:** 2 **Other Fee-earners:** 12. One of the largest and most experienced criminal firms in Manchester. The firm also handles personal injury, civil litigation, commercial and domestic conveyancing.

WORKLOAD			
Crime	60%	Children/ family	15%
Accident	15%	Employment	5%
Contract	5%		

DABELSTEIN & PASSEHL International House, 1 St. Katherine's Way, London, E1 9UN **Tel:** (0171) 702 4661 **Fax:** (0171) 488 2385 **Ptnrs:** 2 **Asst Solrs:** 2 **Other Fee-earners:** 1. A litigation-based law firm with offices in Hamburg and London. It became a multinational partnership in 1992.

WORKLOAD			
Ship/trans/marine insur	70%	Commercial litigation	10%
Personal injury	10%	Other litigation	5%

DALLAS BRETT

PEMBROKE HOUSE, PEMBROKE ST, OXFORD, OXON, OX1 1BL	TEL: (01865) 791990
DX: 82256 Oxford 2	FAX: (01865) 791772

THE FIRM: Dallas Brett was formed just over 10 years ago, as an exclusively commercial practice, providing high quality legal advice from City-trained staff. It has since made a substantial investment in new technologies to ensure rapid access to information and a fast, effective service to clients.

PRINCIPAL AREAS OF WORK:

Company/ Commercial: (*Contact Partner:* Jonathan Loake). The department regularly handles company takeovers, business acquisitions, MBOs, venture capital schemes, group reorganisations, commercial contracts and employment issues such as pensions, share option and employee incentive schemes. Advice is also given on competition law, including Common Market regulations and controls. Jonathan Loake is Chairman of the Thames Valley Commercial Lawyers' Association.

Intellectual Property: (*Contact Partner:* Hugh Brett). The firm has built up a sizeable intellectual property practice covering confidentiality arrangements, publishing and entertainment agreements and software protection. A separate, computerised department handles trade mark, design and copyright (including US copyright) matters. Hugh Brett is a member of the Intellectual Property Committee of the Law Society and is a recognised expert in this field.

Commercial Property: (*Contact Partner:* Hugh Blaza). Acting for a number of household names, the department deals with all forms of land development, landlord and tenant issues (with particular emphasis on portfolio management in the retail and wholesale sectors), environmental reports and advice, planning appeals and public inquiries.

Commercial Litigation: (*Contact Partner:* Andrew Shaw). Extensive experience in this area covers intellectual property, contractual, building and employment disputes, and the firm has particular expertise in obtaining pre-emptive remedies in the High Court.

Aviation Law: (*Consultant:* Glenvil Smith). *Work includes:* aircraft finance and leasing, the regulation and operation of civil air transport, air charter contracts and conditions of carriage.

CONTACT PARTNER: Hugh Brett

Number of partners:	7
Other fee-earners:	4

WORKLOAD	
Intellectual property	30%
Company and employment	20%
Commercial property and environmental	20%
Litigation	15%
Aviation	5%

CONTACTS	
Aviation	G.P.F. Smith
Commercial property	H.A. Blaza
Company and commercial	J.D. Loake
Environmental and planning	R.A. Smith
Intellectual property	H.M.D. Brett
Litigation	A.W. Shaw

DARBYS Sun Alliance House, 52 New Inn Hall Street, Oxford, Oxon, OX1 2QA **Tel:** (01865) 247294 **Fax:** (01865) 728560 **DX:** 4304 Oxford **Ptnrs:** 11 **Asst Solrs:** 10 **Other Fee-earners:** 11. A general practice established in the 1920s. Handles a comprehensive range of work including conveyancing, litigation, commercial, probate, matrimonial work, child-care, criminal and environmental law.

WORKLOAD			
Planning/res/comm prop	24%	Litigation	23%
Criminal	15%	Matrimonial	14%
Company and commercial	10%	Trusts/ probate	8%

DARLINGTON & PARKINSON 78 Pitshanger Lane, London, W5 1QX **Tel:** (0181) 998 4343 **Fax:** (0181) 566 8285 **DX:** 80257 Acton **Ptnrs:** 7 **Asst Solrs:** 3 **Other Fee-earners:** 6. The firm is a substantial legal aid practice, specialising in criminal, matrimonial, and child-related work.

DAVENPORT LYONS

1 OLD BURLINGTON STREET, LONDON, W1X 2NL
DX: 37233 Piccadilly 1

TEL: (0171) 287 5353
FAX: (0171) 437 8216

SENIOR PARTNER: Leon Morgan	
Number of partners:	12
Assistant solicitors:	13
Other fee-earners:	9

THE FIRM: This thriving central London based firm has been significantly strengthened by its merger in March 1995 with Wright Webb Syrett formerly of Soho Square. The firm has always had an excellent reputation in company and commercial work including a long established entertainment departmnent which it has now combined with Wright Webb Syrett's expertise in litigation.

The firm has wide experience in providing comprehensive legal services to corporate and commercial clients across a broad spectrum of market sectors. Those markets include the media in all its forms (television, radio, film, music, publishing and the newspaper industry) the retail sector, advertising, the hotel, sport and leisure industries, computers and information technology as well as property investment and development. The firm prides itself on an unusual blend of high quality legal expertise and commercial sensitivity to clients' needs. This service is provided with speed and efficiency and at a competitive price. The recent expansion has broadened the firm's experience and expertise but is still recognises the importance to clients of partner attention. There are also close contacts in the international sphere particularly with US and EC businesses and lawyers.

PRINCIPAL AREAS OF WORK:

The firm provides legal services to a wide range of corporate and individual clients but also has expertise in a number of particular specialised fields:

Company and Commercial: *(Contact Partner:* David Rockberger). Advice on formations, reorganisations, acquisitions, venture capital, business start ups, joint ventures and corporate tax planning. The firm is particularly well known for its work for growing companies up to and including Stock Exchange quotations.

Entertainment and Media: *(Contact Partner:* Leon Morgan). The firm's wide experience in these fields is reflected in its client list which includes substantial television companies, banks and other financiers and advertising and media agencies. The firm covers every aspect of the entertainment market and has a wide experience of international issues.

Music and Copyright: *(Contact Partner:* James Ware). The firm has a strong reputation in the UK and United States and acts for many leading music publishing corporations and individual musicians advising on recording contracts, copyright and the problems of performers and artists and the impact of EC legislation.

Litigation: *(Contact Partners:* Jim Mackie, Kevin Bays). Commercial litigation is now a major element of the practice following the merger with Wright Webb Syrett, servicing the firm's corporate and entertainment clients.

Defamation: *(Contact Partners:* Kevin Bays, Philip Conway). The substantial defamation practice of Wright Webb Syrett has been brought to the firm whose clients now include a large number of national newspapers and Private Eye magazine. The firm represents both Plaintiffs and Defendants.

Commercial Property: *(Contact Partner:* Graham Atkins). A strong commercial property department acts for major developers, property investors, lending institutions in a broad range of substantial property and property related matters.

Private Client: *(Contact Partner:* John Burrell). This department provides a full service to private clients, both domestic and overseas, including matrimonial matters, wills, the administration of estates, personal tax, trusts and residential property work.

Sport: *(Contact Partner:* Kevin Bays). The firm has a well established practice advising promoters of sporting events and individual sportsmen in connection with protecting and enhancing reputaion.

Davenport Lyons is a well orgainsed firm able to satisfy the legal requirements of clients from private individuals to the largest of corporations.

DAVID BIGMORE & CO 36 Whitefriars Street, London, EC4Y 8BH **Tel:** (0171) 583 2277 **Fax:** (0171) 583 2288 **Ptnrs:** 1 **Asst Solrs:** 3 . Recently established niche practice specialising in both British and international franchising. Also advises on a broad range of corporate and commercial matters including litigation and property.

WORKLOAD			
Franchising and related	60%	Litigation	20%
Other corp/commercial	15%	Conveyancing	5%

DAVID DU PRÉ & CO

90-92 PARKWAY, REGENTS PARK, LONDON, NW1 7AN
DX: 57070

TEL: (0171) 284 3040
FAX: (0171) 485 1145

THE FIRM: Established in 1991 by David du Pré, a former matrimonial barrister who qualified as a solicitor in 1980 and held senior positions in two leading City firms before setting up his own matrimonial practice. He is a member of the Solicitors Family Law Association, the International Society of Family Law and the Family Mediators Association.

PRINCIPAL AREAS OF WORK: Matrimonial, family and co-habitation law including: separation and parental responsibility agreements, divorce petitions, financial applications including emergency applications and cases where there is an international dimension including child abduction.

CONTACT PARTNER: David du Pré

Number of partners:	1
Assistant solicitors:	1

WORKLOAD	
Family/ matrimonial/ divorce	100%

CONTACTS	
Family/ matrimonial/ divorce	David du Pré

DAVID GRAY & CO 56 Westgate Road, Newcastle upon Tyne, Tyne & Wear, NE1 5XU **Tel:** (0191) 232 9547 **Fax:** (0191) 230 4149 **DX:** 61036 **Ptnrs:** 4 **Asst Solrs:** 10 **Other Fee-earners:** 5. Crime, matrimonial, child care, personal injury litigation, landlord and tenant, employment, welfare rights, mental health, voluntary organisations, conveyancing and immigration work.

WORKLOAD			
Crime	34%	Immigration	15%
Family	15%	Civil	13%
Non-contentious	8%	Housing	7%

DAVID PHILLIPS & PARTNERS 202-268 Stanley Rd, Bootle, Merseyside, L20 3EP **Tel:** (0151) 922 5525 **Fax:** (0151) 922 8298 **DX:** 18806 Bootle **Ptnrs:** 8 **Asst Solrs:** 3 . Best known for crime, conveyancing, litigation and matrimonial. Founded in 1982, and now has seven offices.

DAVID PRICE & CO 5 Great James Street, London, WC1N 3DA **Tel:** (0171) 916 9911 **Fax:** (0171) 916 9910 **Ptnrs:** 1 **Asst Solrs:** 2 . A niche defamation practice with substantial expertise in a broad range of 'media' matters, including libel, copyright and contempt.

WORKLOAD	
Defamation	100%

EDITORIAL POLICY

In this edition, the lists of specialist firms include profiles of individual practitioners - solicitors and barristers - who have been recommended most frequently to our researchers. Editorial policy is to identify leading practitioners on merit: it is not possible to buy a place in our biographical lists. Inclusion of a profile in this directory is based solely on expertise and reputation.

Enormous effort has been invested by our ten-strong research team (mainly solicitors and barristers) in canvassing recommendations and identifying leaders. We are confident in the overall accuracy of the results. However, mistakes and misjudgements are inevitable, and if readers have any suggestions regarding our listings we should be very pleased to hear from them.

DAVID & SNAPE Wyndham House, Wyndham Street, Bridgend, M. Glam, CF31 1EP **Tel:** (01656) 661115 **Fax:** (01656) 660545 **DX:** 38001 Bridgend **Ptnrs:** 7 **Asst Solrs:** 3 . A general practice specialising in a broad range of law including conveyancing, building and construction, agriculture, employment, private client, and matrimonial.

DAVIDSON CHALMERS WS

10 CASTLE TERRACE, EDINBURGH, EH1 2DP
DX: 408 Edinburgh

TEL: (0131) 228 9191
FAX: (0131) 228 9003

THE FIRM: Davidson Chalmers was formed in April 1993 by solicitors having many years of experience between them in commercial law. The firm has invested in the latest technology and management structures to combine fast and efficient service with traditional legal advice.

PRINCIPAL AREAS OF WORK:

Commercial Property: *(Contact Partner:* Gordon Davidson). The firm advises on all aspects of commercial property, including acquisitions and sale, property development, commercial leasing, property finance, secured lending and title certification.

Company/Commercial: *(Contact:* Andrew Chalmers). An expanding department offering advice on a broad range of company and commercial matters including share and asset sale/purchase, partnerships, business start-ups, shareholders agreements and service contracts.

CONTACT PARTNER: Andrew S. Chalmers

Number of partners:	2
Assistant solicitors:	2

WORKLOAD	
Commercial property	80%
Company/Commercial	20%

DAVID TRUEX AND COMPANY

212 STRAND, LONDON, WC2R 1AP
DX: 252 (Ch.Ln)

TEL: (0171) 583 5040
FAX: (0171) 583 5151

THE FIRM: Established in 1990, the work of the firm focuses on Anglo-Australian cross-jurisdictional family law cases. The principal, David Truex, is qualified as a lawyer in both countries, and he and his assistants conduct litigation in both English and Australian jurisdictions. The practice has expanded rapidly since its foundation, a substantial proportion of the work comprising international agency matters for other firms. David Truex also acts as a consultant to English and Australian family lawyers, and is regularly retained as an expert witness in Hague Convention international child abduction cases.

PRINCIPAL AREAS OF WORK:

English family law: The firm undertakes a broad range of work, including matrimonial proceedings concerning children and finance, disputes between co-habitees and the enforcement of foreign orders in England and Wales.

Australian family law: For clients resident in the UK and elsewhere outside of Australia, the firm conducts matrimonial litigation in all registries of the Family Court of Australia, including enforcement of English orders in Australia.

CONTACT PARTNER: David Truex

Number of partners:	1
Assistant solicitors:	2

WORKLOAD	
International family law (including consultancy and agency)	50%
Australian family law ·	25%
English family law	25%

CONTACTS	
Family Law	David Truex

DAVID, WINEMAN Craven House, 121 Kingsway, London, WC2B 6NX **Tel:** (0171) 831 0521 **Fax:** (0171) 831 0731 **DX:** 208 **Ptnrs:** 5 **Asst Solrs:** 1 **Other Fee-earners:** 1. Best known for its entertainment practice specialising in music work. Also handles TV, publishing and libel and has specialist insolvency knowledge.

DAVIES ARNOLD COOPER

6-8 BOUVERIE STREET, LONDON, EC4Y 8DD DX: 172	TEL: (0171) 936 2222 FAX: (0171) 936 2020
60 Fountain Street, Manchester M2 2FE	Tel: (0161) 839 8396 Fax: (0161) 839 8309
Room 991, Lloyd's Building, 1 Lime Street, London EC3M 7HA	Tel: (0171) 283 8658 Fax: (0171) 283 8063

London, Manchester, Brussels, Madrid, Hong Kong and at Lloyd's

THE FIRM: Davies Arnold Cooper offers a comprehensive service to both United Kingdom and international clients. It is well-known for its practical and commercial approach and has pioneered many new legal developments.

SENIOR PARTNER: David A. McIntosh

Number of partners:	50
Assistant solicitors:	99
Other fee-earners:	62

PRINCIPAL AREAS OF WORK:

Banking: *(Contact:* John Nelmes). The firm's banking department advises banks and other financial institutions on funding transactions of all kinds. Secured and unsecured, bilateral, syndicated and "Club" deals, with particular emphasis on acquisition and development finance. It also provides general banking advice for refinancings, restructurings and reschedulings.

Commercial Litigation: *(Contact:* Michael Dobias). DAC is a leading player in commercial litigation, both in the UK and internationally. The firm has been involved in representing defendants in many recent catastrophes, and is well-known for representing leading household names in high-profile product liability litigation. The firm has solid expertise in the professional indemnity area and has also been instructed in connection with the major problems in the London insurance market.

Commercial Fraud: *(Contact:* Nicholas Sinfield). The firm has developed a high profile in handling both financial and physical fraud cases, such as fires. Its specialist Fraud Unit also handles a substantial amount of banking recovery work and other white collar fraud.

Commercial Property: *(Contact:* John Coaton). DAC advises and assists in all aspects of commercial property, including development funding and joint ventures; creation of retail, industrial and residential estates and business parks. The firm acts for investment companies in acquisitions and sales, and is actively involved with both landlords and tenants in the management of their property portfolios.

Construction: *(Contact:* Daniel Gowan). DAC has a construction industry practice which is a significant force in construction and engineering both in the UK and internationally. Expertise includes arbitration and litigation, advice on formation of contracts and procurement matters together with all aspects of construction insurance.

Corporate: *(Contact:* Charles Wander). The firm handles all aspects of public and private company legal matters, both in the United Kingdom and internationally. This includes mergers and acquisitions, management buy-outs and buy-ins, public issues, company formations, corporate finance and banking, competition and anti-trust, formation and review of commercial contracts, corporate and international taxation advice, and employment law.

Crisis Management: *(Contact:* Anne Ware). DAC is a pioneer in the field of crisis management and has worked on major disasters involving pollution, as well as a range of financial and physical events.

Environmental: *(Contact:* Laurence Messer). The firm has been involved in some recent high profile environmental compliance actions. DAC advises organisations in a multitude of areas which are now affected by EU-influenced "green" legislation such as waste disposal, marine, contaminated land, construction and nuisance.

Insolvency: *(Contact:* Nigel Montgomery). The firm's insolvency department handles all aspects of insolvency, in particular receiverships and administrations, and works closely with major accountancy firms and banks on rescues and reorganisations. It has a specialist debt recovery unit which is retained by High Street and commercial banks. The department also specialises in insurance and re-insurance insolvencies and Schemes of Arrangement.

Insurance and Reinsurance: (*Contact:* Kenneth McKenzie). DAC's high-profile insurance practice is one of the largest in the UK. It has a fully-staffed office at Lloyd's and has acted in many of the major cases in the insurance sector over the last decade. There is substantial expertise in the regulatory and corporate areas of insurance.

Intellectual Property: (*Contact:* Michael Cover). The firm provides advice on patents, trademarks, copyright and computer law, as well as competition law and information technology. The intellectual property unit's expertise covers all aspects of intellectual property litigation and has recently been involved in some high-profile piracy programmes.

Licensing: (*Contact:* Anthony Horne, Manchester). The firm handles applications for Justices Licences, Public Entertainment Licences/ Supper Hour Certificates and Gaming Licences for Casinos and Bingo Halls and all allied matters relating to both applications for and objections to all such licences, together with appeals to the Magistrates Court, the Crown Court and the High Court.

Marine and Aviation: (*Contact:* John Parker). The firm provides a comprehensive service to the marine and aviation sectors. Marine cargo claims are a speciality, as is marine insurance.

Pensions: (*Contact:* Michael Fletcher). DAC's specialist pensions unit provides commercial legal advice on all aspects of pensions including employer/ trustee powers, an independent trustee service, a full documentation service, scheme mergers, surplus ownership and pensions litigation.

Personal Injury: (*Contact:* David Rogers). All types of personal injury claims are handled by this department, mainly for Defendants and their insurers. The department also handles personal injury claims proceeding in foreign jurisdictions and claims arising abroad but brought before the English courts. The department provides a wide range of related services for insurers and their commercial clients.

Pharmaceutical and Health Care: (*Contact:* Simon Pearl). A specialised team deals with all areas of medical negligence and pharmaceutical product liability, litigation and regulatory work. In addition, DAC has significant expertise in NHS commercial and contract law.

Planning: (*Contact:* Christopher Rees). DAC's planning unit has dealt with all aspects of planning and compulsory purchase for developers and landowners.

Product Liability: (*Contact:* David McIntosh). DAC has built up an unparalleled depth of experience in defending product liability claims in the United Kingdom and co-ordinating and monitoring claims on an international basis.

OTHER OFFICES: DAC has an established office in Manchester and Hong Kong as well as its European offices in Brussels and Madrid. The firm also has close links with major law firms in all important overseas jurisdictions, especially in the United States and Japan – one of its partners is a fluent Japanese speaker. The firm's Lloyd's office provides an on-the-spot service to the Lloyd's insurance market.

LANGUAGES SPOKEN: French, German, Greek, Italian, Spanish, Russian, Flemish, Gujerati, Punjabi, Urdu, Swedish and Japanese.

RECRUITMENT AND TRAINING: DAC recruits between 12 and 15 trainee solicitors a year. Applications to Nicholas Bradley, in the firm's London office. A 2:1 degree standard is preferred.

INTERNATIONAL SECTION

The international section lists foreign law firms based in London. It also lists the foreign connections of English law firms: their branch offices overseas and the foreign languages spoken at their UK offices.

DAVIES GRANT & HORTON

MAYFLOWER HOUSE, ARMADA WAY, PLYMOUTH, DEVON, PL1 1LD
DX: 8283 Plymouth 2

TEL: (01752) 255555
FAX: (01752) 252202

THE FIRM: Davies Grant & Horton is a specialist practice of City-trained marine lawyers, supplying advice to the national and international shipping and insurance communities at competitive rates.

PRINCIPAL AREAS OF WORK:

Shipping Law: *Work includes:* P & I, FD & D, personal injury and fatal accident defence, shipbuilding litigation, ship sale and purchase, registration and mortgage, and international trade disputes, yachts and pleasurecraft.

OTHER AREAS OF WORK: Commercial and insurance litigation/policy wordings.

CONTACT PARTNER: Johnny Johnson

Number of partners:	4
Assistant solicitors:	5
Other fee-earners:	1

WORKLOAD	
Commercial shipping - dry/wet	50%
Commercial & insurance work (litigation)	25%
Yachts/ super yachts	25%

DAVIES AND PARTNERS

ROWAN HOUSE, BARNETT WAY, BARNWOOD, GLOUCESTER, GLOS, GL4 7RT
DX: 55253

TEL: (01452) 612345
FAX: (01452) 611922

THE FIRM: Davies and Partners is forward-thinking and objective in approach. The firm handles a large amount of commercial property, estate conveyancing, company and commercial, commercial litigation, and secured lending work and has also developed a strong personal injury and medical negligence practice.

PRINCIPAL AREAS OF WORK:

Commercial Property: *(Contact Partner:* Barrie Davies). The firm handles all aspects of development land, from initial site acquisition, to individual unit transfers and ancillary documentation, planning applications and appeals, building contracts and freehold and leasehold matters.

Company/ Commercial: *(Contact Partner:* Thomas Brennan). The firm has extensive experience in the whole range of company and commercial work, including corporate finance, mergers, acquisitions and restructuring, MBOs, publicly-quoted companies, company and partnership formation, joint ventures, shareholders' agreements, banking, financial services and franchising; intellectual property, including international, EC and UK competition implications.

Secured Lending: *(Contact Partner:* Peter Mitchell). The firm acts for a range of commercial lenders, from banks and building societies to insurance companies. *Work includes:* mortgage schemes, banking documents, commercial mortgages, security documents, guarantees and indemnities, deeds of priority and financial services implications.

Commercial Litigation: *(Contact Partner:* Geoffrey Hand). *Work includes:* building contracts, judicial review, landlord and tenant, employment, insurance, professional negligence, public liability, economic torts, corporate insolvency, unlawful trading, licensing and debt collection and banking litigation.

Personal Injury and Medical Negligence: *(Contact Partner:* Robert Ashton). The firm handles extensively both plaintiff and defendant personal injury work. Medical negligence work is plaintiff-orientated. Two fee earners are members of the Law Society Personal Injury Panel.

OTHER AREAS OF WORK: All aspects of corporate and personal tax and financial planning, agricultural law (including land acquisition and disposal, agricultural holdings, grazing agreements, share farming agreements, EC implications and business tenancies) and private client work (including residential conveyancing, re-mortgaging, wills, trusts and estate management, and distribution and winding-up of estates).

OTHER OFFICES: Bristol, Birmingham.

CONTACT PARTNER: Thomas Brennan

Number of partners:	16
Assistant solicitors:	13
Other fee-earners:	6

CONTACTS	
Accident and compensation	Robert Ashton
Commercial property	Peter Mitchell
Commercial litigation	Geoffrey Hand
Company/ commercial	Tom Brennan
Land development	Barrie Davies
Private client	Howard Johnson

DAVIES WALLIS FOYSTER

5 CASTLE STREET, LIVERPOOL, MERSEYSIDE, L2 4XE	TEL: (0151) 236 6226
DX: 14128 Liverpool	FAX: (0151) 236 3088

Harvester House, 37 Peter Street, Manchester M2 5GB	Tel: (0161) 228 3702
DX: 14313 Manchester	Fax: (0161) 835 2407

THE FIRM: Davies Wallis Foyster is a large and progressive commercial law firm committed to technical expertise and high quality service. Its three main commercial divisions are corporate, litigation and property.

PRINCIPAL AREAS OF WORK:

Corporate: The firm handles a broad range of corporate and commercial matters. These include acquisitions and disposals, buy-outs and buy-ins, joint ventures, franchising, finance and banking, venture capital, flotations and capital raising, computer contracts, marketing agreements, intellectual property and European Union law. The department also has a substantial insolvency team. (*Contact:* Manchester – Sue Parker, Liverpool – Mark O'Connor).

Litigation: The department is particularly strong in banking, brewery and asset finance recovery work as well as having a growing reputation for defendant insurance work. Other work includes employment, computerised debt collection, construction law, and intellectual property litigation. The licensing department, acting for clients in the brewing, licensed retailing and entertainment industries, is one of the largest in the UK. (*Contact:* Manchester – Kit Sorrell, Liverpool – Graham Sidlow).

Property: The department has an excellent reputation for development work, secured lending, landlord and tenant law, investment and licensed property. The firm acts for a growing list of national retail multiples and has an expanding planning and environmental practice acting for a number of public sector clients and developers in specialist areas of planning, compulsory purchase and environmental law. (*Contact:* Manchester – Guy Wallis, Liverpool – Andrew Green).

CONTACT PARTNER: Jim Davies

Number of partners:	37
Assistant solicitors:	34
Other fee-earners:	27

WORKLOAD	
Litigation	53%
Corporate	25%
Property	22%

CONTACTS	
Commercial property	Guy Wallis
Corporate	Mark O'Connor
Litigation	Kit Sorrell

DAVIS BLANK FURNISS 90 Deansgate, Manchester, M3 2QJ **Tel:** (0161) 832 3304 **Fax:** (0161) 834 3568 **DX:** 14311 Manchester **Ptnrs:** 10 **Asst Solrs:** 5 **Other Fee-earners:** 7. Established in 1877, the firm has developed into a major commercial and litigation practice over the last twenty years. Retains specialist private client practice.

WORKLOAD			
Commercial conveyancing	15%	Other commercial lit	12%
Bus sales/purchases	12%	Domestic conveyancing	12%
Personal injury lit	10%	Construction litigation	10%

DAWBARNS 1-2 York Row, Wisbech, Cambs, PE13 1EA **Tel:** (01945) 61456 **Fax:** (01945) 61364 **DX:** 41351 **Ptnrs:** 10 **Asst Solrs:** 6 **Other Fee-earners:** 7. A progressive provincial practice, the firm undertakes a wide range of work including specialist family law, personal injury (including medical negligence), company/ commercial departments.

DAWSON & CO

2 NEW SQUARE, LINCOLN'S INN, LONDON, WC2A 3RZ	TEL: (0171) 404 5941
DX: 38 Ch.Ln.	FAX: (0171) 831 6924

THE FIRM: A medium-sized firm which handles a substantial volume of all types of litigation, property and property development, and tax planning work. It also acts for many large agricultural estates with their attendant trust and settled land work, a number of charities and large Housing Associations. Other main areas of work include probate, matrimonial and company and commercial work.

CONTACT PARTNER: Mr K. Wood

Number of partners:	17
Assistant solicitors:	6
Other fee-earners	10

DAWSON CORNWELL & CO 17 Red Lion Square, London, WC1R 4QT **Tel:** (0171) 242 2556 **Fax:** (0171) 831 0478 **DX:** 35725 **Ptnrs:** 8 **Asst Solrs:** 2 **Other Fee-earners:** 1. Leading family practice, with six full-time matrimonial specialists, all members of the SFLA. Also litigation, probate and property.

WORKLOAD			
Family and matrimonial	65%	Conveyancing	10%
Wills/trusts/probate	10%	Litigation	10%

DEAN WILSON

96 CHURCH STREET, BRIGHTON, E. SUSSEX, BN1 1UJ
DX: 2706

TEL: (01273) 327241
FAX: (01273) 770913

THE FIRM: Dean Wilson offers a comprehensive range of services to both commercial and private clients, with particular expertise in relation to property development, employment law and licensing matters. The partners include a former Local Authority Planning Committee Chairman, a Chairman of Industrial Tribunals and an Assistant Recorder.

PRINCIPAL AREAS OF WORK:

Corporate and Commercial: *(Contact Partner:* David Barling). The firm can advise on all aspects of corporate, commercial and financial matters, including company and partnership formation, restructuring, acquisitions and disposals, taxation and insolvency. Expertise is offered in employment law and licensing law relating to pubs, clubs, restaurants and gaming, including casino gaming. A full range of commercial property work is undertaken including estate development, planning work, commercial leasing and commercial conveyancing.

Litigation: *(Contact Partner:* Ian Wilson). A range of civil and criminal litigation is undertaken including civil engineering and construction disputes, marine disputes, personal injury actions, professional negligence actions, employment disputes including applications for restraint of trade and non-competition injunctions, industrial tribunals, landlord and tenant disputes, licensing matters and debt recovery.

Private Client: Private client services include wills, probate, administration of estates, trusts and tax planning *(Contact:* Georgina James), residential conveyancing and leases *(Contact:* Joanna Ward), charity law *(Contact:* Georgina James), family law matters including separation, divorce, welfare of children and property disputes *(Contact:* Linda Wall) and criminal law *(Contact:* Imogen Bell).

CONTACT PARTNER: I.K.R. Wilson

Number of partners:	6
Assistant solicitors:	4
Other fee-earners:	6

WORKLOAD	
Domestic conveyancing/ probate	27%
General litigation	15%
Landlord & tenant	15%
Commercial property	15%
Company/ commercial	10%
Employment	10%
Matrimonial	5%
Planning	3%

DEAS MALLEN SOUTER Eldon Chambers, 23 The Quayside, Newcastle upon Tyne, Tyne & Wear, NE1 3DE **Tel:** (0191) 221 0898 **Fax:** (0191) 232 0930 **Ptnrs:** 5 **Asst Solrs:** 4 **Other Fee-earners:** 1. Civil litigation practice well known for medical negligence, personal injury, commercial litigation and construction.

DE BANDT VAN HECKE & LAGAE Royex House, Aldermanbury Square, London, EC2V 7HR **Tel:** (0171) 600 3608 **Fax:** (0171) 600 1718 **Ptnrs:** 1. A member of the Alliance of European Lawyers, De Brandt, van Hecke & Lagae offers a full range of services to the national and international business community.

WORKLOAD			
Banking and finance	50%	General Corporate	50%

DEBENHAM & CO

20 HANS ROAD, KNIGHTSBRIDGE, LONDON, SW3 1RT
DX: 38150 Knightsbridge

TEL: (0171) 581 2471
FAX: (0171) 584 1783

THE FIRM: Founded by Horace Debenham in 1932, Debenham & Co has been based in Knightsbridge since 1973. Whilst the greater part of work is for clients who develop and invest in property, the firm also acts for a wide range of other clients, with property as the common theme; including acting for property companies, insurance companies, pension funds, housing associations, hotel companies, tour operators, public bodies, architects, retailers, manufacturing companies, residential developers, surveyors, builders and private individuals.

CONTACT PARTNER: Richard Woof

Number of partners:	8
Assistant solicitors:	6
Other fee-earners:	5

PRINCIPAL AREAS OF WORK:

Property Development: *(Contact Partner:* Richard Woof). Funding, joint ventures, site assembly, planning, road closures and compulsory purchase.

Housing Associations: *(Contact Partner:* Nick Lear). Purchases and sales (including special schemes such as shared ownership, rural housing and the Leasehold Scheme for the Elderly), funding and joint ventures.

Residential Development: *(Contact Partner:* Nick Lear). Sales for house-builders including options, joint ventures and special sales schemes.

Litigation: *(Contact Partner:* Nigel Beaumont). Property litigation including possession actions, rent review arbitrations, renewals under the 1954 Act, injunctions, planning appeals, squatter proceedings, property development disputes, restrictive covenants and building disputes.

Property Management: *(Contact Partner:* Richard Woof). Leases (including turnover rents), renewals and general management work, with particular emphasis on shopping centres.

DEBEVOISE & PLIMPTON 1 Creed Court, 5 Ludgate Hill, London, EC4M 7AA **Tel:** (0171) 329 0779 **Fax:** (0171) 329 0860 **Ptnrs:** 3 **Asst Solrs:** 5 . An international firm specialising in corporate law, mergers and acquisitions, and privatisations. Offices in New York, Washington, Los Angeles, Paris, Budapest and Prague.

DEIGHTON GUEDALLA 127 City Road, London, EC1V 1JB **Tel:** (0171) 490 5518 **Fax:** (0171) 490 8518 **DX:** 36613 **Ptnrs:** 2 **Other Fee-earners:** 1. Legal aid practice concentrating on civil liberties litigation including actions against police, immigration, discrimination, inquests, employment and criminal law.

DENISON TILL

CHANCERY HOUSE, 143 HOLGATE ROAD, YORK, N. YORKS, YO2 4DE
DX: 61502 ACOMB

TEL: (01904) 610820
FAX: (01904) 646972

THE FIRM: Denison Till is the largest commercial and private practice in York; it has a rapidly expanding commercial office in Leeds. The firm offers a comprehensive range of legal services to a wide range of businesses, insurers and institutions.

PRINCIPAL AREAS OF WORK:

Company/ Commercial	*(Contact Partner:* Alistair Duncan/ Andrew Lindsay)
Litigation & Arbitration	*(Contact Partner:* Anthony Glaister)
Employment	*(Contact Partner:* Anthony Ridge)
Debt Recovery	*(Contact Partner:* Jonathan Cripwell/ Johanne Spittle)
Commercial Property & Planning	*(Contact Partner:* David Barraclough/ Gordon Gildener)
Construction	*(Contact Partner:* Gareth Hevey/ Anthony Glaister)
Family and Matrimonial	*(Contact Partner:* Mark Hepworth)
Ecclesiastical & Charity Law	*(Contact Partner:* Lionel Lennox)
Agricultural & Bloodstock	*(Contact Partner:* David Grice)
Private Client	*(Contact Partner:* John Goodrich)
Personal Injury	*(Contact Partner:* Toby Conyers-Kelly)

OTHER OFFICES: York and Leeds.

FOREIGN CONNECTIONS: The firm is a member of Lawspan, an international grouping of commercial lawyers. In-house language skills include all the major European languages.

CONTACT PARTNER: Christopher Barton

Number of partners:	15
Assistant solicitors:	5
Other fee-earners:	12

WORKLOAD	
Commercial Litigation	25%
Commercial Property	20%
Company/Commercial	20%
Construction	12%
Private Litigation	11%
Tax, trusts and wills	7%
Residential Property	5%

DENISON
TILL

DENTON HALL

5 CHANCERY LANE, CLIFFORD'S INN, LONDON, EC4A 1BU
DX: 242

TEL: (0171) 242 1212
FAX: (0171) 404 0087

THE FIRM: One of the largest firms in the City, Denton Hall is the result of the merger in 1985 of Denton Hall & Burgin, founded in 1788, and Warrens, founded in 1742. In 1988 the firm was joined by 200 partners and staff from the City firm of Oppenheimers.

Denton Hall provides the full range of legal services required by corporate and commercial clients. The firm has developed a very international client base, with particular strengths in the media/ entertainment/ telecommunication industries, the energy sector, property and retail and financial services.

Internationally, Denton Hall has the most extensive Asian network, with offices in Beijing, Hong Kong, Singapore and Tokyo. The firm also has offices in Brussels and Moscow. Denton Hall is a founder member of the Denton International Group of Law firms, an alliance with Heuking Kühn Kunz Wojtek in Germany, Lind & Cadovius in Denmark, Houthoff in The Netherlands and Lambert Grohmann Kerres & Deissenberger in Austria.

In the UK outside London, the firm's Milton Keynes office, established in 1987, is carrying out an increasing range of property, litigation and commercial work.

PRINCIPAL AREAS OF WORK: The firm's offices are organised into departments and work groups based on the business sectors served and specialist areas of practice.

Denton Hall is a full-service practice serving UK and international corporate clients. The firm is particularly well known in the field of media and telecommunications, project and energy law, commercial property, retail, planning and environmental law, intellectual property, corporate and financial services, and litigation and arbitration. The firm advises in all aspects of corporate and international law, including public issues, mergers and acquisitions, joint ventures, banking, competition tax, insurance, insolvency, corporate fraud, pensions and employment.

OTHER OFFICES: Own offices: Beijing, Brussels, Hong Kong, Los Angeles, Milton Keynes, Moscow, Singapore, Tokyo.
Associated offices: Amsterdam, Berlin, Chemnitz, Copenhagen, Dusseldorf, Frankfurt, Hamburg, Rotterdam, Vienna.

RECRUITMENT AND TRAINING: The firm recruits around 30 trainee solicitors every year. Please apply by letter and CV, two years in advance, to Virginia Glastonbury.

MANAGING PARTNER: Jonathan Tatten

UK:	
Number of partners:	78
Assistant solicitors:	121
Other fee-earners:	110
INTERNATIONAL:	
Number of Partners:	12
Assistant Solicitors:	25
Other fee-earners:	34

CONTACTS	
Banking & financial markets	Anthony Bonsor
Commercial property	Roger Sutcliffe
Company/ commercial	Andrew Daws
Competition & EC	David Aitman
Corporate finance	Tony Grant
Employment & immigration	Stephanie Dale
Energy	David Moroney
Environmental law	John Salter
Insolvency	Michael Steiner
Insurance	Kevin Ryan
Intellectual property	Clive Thorne
Litigation & arbitration	Bob Goldspink
Media & entertainment	Alan Williams
Planning	Helen Norris
Retail	Monica Blake
Tax	Jane Douglas
Telecommunications	Nicholas Higham

DEVONSHIRES

SALISBURY HOUSE, LONDON WALL, LONDON, EC2M 5QY
DX: 33856 Finsbury Square

TEL: (0171) 628 7576
FAX: (0171) 256 7318

THE FIRM: Estalished in 1840 and located in the City, Devonshires provides a wide range of services with particular emphasis on work for housing associations and other non-profit making bodies and to its commercial property clients. The firm acts for more than 90 registered housing associations around England and Wales and has more than doubled in size in the past five years as a result of the increasing amount of housing association work and other property development activities. As well as housing associations, clients include local authorities, the property arm of a pension fund, religious charities and patient hotels. The practice also acts for banks, including merchant banks and building societies and on capital markets issues especially, in relation to public sector funding, negotiating over £300 million of loans for our clients last year alone.

PRINCIPAL AREAS OF WORK: Bulk property transfers, development site conveyancing, shared ownership and Right to Buys, for institutions, development corporations and L.A.s; Planning and Construction Law; Housing Management, repossession, disrepair and CCT; General litigation for institutions and debt collection; Employment Law; Banking and Capital Markets.

SENIOR PARTNER: Julian Roberts
MANAGING PARTNER: Michael Phillips

Number of partners:	16
Other fee-earners:	4

CONTACTS	
Housing Association Finance	Andrew Cowan
Litigation	Mike Gregan
Planning and Construction	Nigel Hardy
Property	Allan Hudson
Religious Charities	John Dodd
Shared Ownership	Michael Phillips

DEWAR HOGAN

46 BOW LANE, CHEAPSIDE, LONDON, EC4M 9HR

TEL: (0171) 329 8846
FAX: (0171) 489 0590

THE FIRM: Dewar Hogan is a practice specialising exclusively in contentious property matters and property litigation relating to commercial and residential property. All of its members were formerly with leading London law firms and have many years of experience in the field. Clients of the practice include property companies, property funds, public authorities, banks and private investors. The practice accepts referrals from other firms of solicitors on a fee sharing basis.

PRINCIPAL AREAS OF WORK: Disputes between landlords and tenants, lenders and borrowers and clients and their professional advisers. The current emphasis is on insolvency related work and professional negligence.

CONTACT PARTNER: Mr R.D. Hogan

Number of partners:	2
Assistant solicitors:	1
Other fee-earners:	1

WORKLOAD	
Property litigation	100%

CONTACTS	
Property litigation	Ronald Hogan, John Cox

S.J. DIAMOND & SON Corry House, 7-19 Royal Avenue, Belfast, BT1 1FB **Tel:** (01232) 243726 **Fax:** (01232) 230651 **Ptnrs:** 3 **Asst Solrs:** 4 . Long established family firm offering a comprehensive service to businesses and individuals. Emphasis on personal injury, debt collection and conveyancing work.

WORKLOAD			
Pers inj incl RTAs/crim	50%	Conveyancing	20%
Debt recov/com & prop lit	15%	Industrial tribunals	5%
Matrimonial/ family	5%	Admin of estates	5%

DIANE HINCH

28 GROSVENOR STREET, LONDON, W1X 9FE

TEL: (0171) 917 9680
FAX: (0171) 917 6002

THE FIRM: Established as a niche practice in United States immigration law, the firm specialises in business-related visas, from non-immigrant working visas to permanent residence 'green card' and US citizenship.

NATURE OF CLIENTELE: Clients include: electronic and engineering companies, entertainment industry, biomedical industry, healthcare professionals, financial services industry.

OTHER OFFICE: California, US.

CONTACT PARTNER: Diane B. Hinch

LAWYERS:	
London:	1
Worldwide:	1

WORKLOAD	
US immigration	100%

EDITORIAL POLICY

In this edition, the lists of specialist firms include profiles of individual practitioners - solicitors and barristers - who have been recommended most frequently to our researchers. Editorial policy is to identify leading practitioners on merit: it is not possible to buy a place in our biographical lists. Inclusion of a profile in this directory is based solely on expertise and reputation.

Enormous effort has been invested by our ten-strong research team (mainly solicitors and barristers) in canvassing recommendations and identifying leaders. We are confident in the overall accuracy of the results. However, mistakes and misjudgements are inevitable, and if readers have any suggestions regarding our listings we should be very pleased to hear from them.

DIBB LUPTON BROOMHEAD

125 LONDON WALL, LONDON, EC2Y 5AE DX: 33866 Finsbury Square	TEL: (0171) 600 0202 FAX: (0171) 600 1650
117 The Headrow, Leeds, W.Yorks. LS1 5JX DX: 12017 Leeds Contact Partner: Mr John Winkworth-Smith	Tel: (0113) 243 9301 Fax: (0113) 245 2632
Carlton House, 18 Albert Square, Manchester M2 5PE DX: 14304 Manchester 1 Contact Partner: Mr Paul Nicholls	Tel: (0161) 839 0202 Fax: (0161) 839 4469
Fountain Precinct, Balm Green, Sheffield S1 1RZ DX: 708580 Sheffield 10 Contact Partner: Mr Paul Firth	Tel: (0114) 272 0202 Fax: (0114) 270 0568
Windsor House, Temple Row, Birmingham B2 5LF DX: 13022 B'ham 1 Contact Partner: Mr Nick Seddon	Tel: (0121) 200 1188 Fax: (0121) 236 9228

THE FIRM: With offices in London, Leeds, Manchester, Sheffield and Birmingham, Dibb Lupton Broomhead is the largest commercial practice not based exclusively in the City and is one of the ten largest in the UK. The firm has substantial corporate, litigation, insolvency, and property departments. It has a national reputation for its intellectual property, technology law, insolvency work and debt collection, and is also firmly established in banking, property development, franchising, environmental law, EC law and construction.

PRINCIPAL AREAS OF WORK:

Commercial: (*31 Partners. Contact Partner:* Andrew Darwin). Work includes: corporate finance, flotations, mergers and acquisitions, management buy-outs, consumer law, competition law, franchising, EC law, pensions, employee share option and incentive schemes, media law, and technology law.

Banking and Corporate Recovery: (*26 Partners. Contact Partner:* Tony Bugg). Work includes: liquidations, receiverships, debt recoveries, bankruptcy, corporate investigations, regulatory advice, lending, funding and syndicates, taking securities, guarantees, trade finance, consumer credit, recoveries, insolvency and lender liability.

Property: (*23 Partners. Contact Partner:* Philip Perry). Work includes: property development, planning, construction, environmental law, and commercial leases.

Litigation: (*24 Partners. Contact Partner:* Andrew Chappell). Work includes: contractual disputes, employment law, insurance, intellectual property, defamation, liquor licensing, and debt recovery.

Insurance: (*14 Partners. Contact Partner:* Kevin McLoughlin). Work includes: personal injury, professional indemnity, reinsurance, commercial claims, aviation.

Human Resources: (*11 Partners. Contact Partner:* Paul Nicholls). Work includes: pensions, service contracts, benefits, redundancy, industrial tribunals, discrimination, restraint of trade.

NATURE OF CLIENTELE: Clients include public and private companies, banks and other financial institutions, public bodies, and insurance companies.

INTERNATIONAL CONNECTIONS: The firm has established contacts with law firms worldwide and can provide expert advice to clients with business interests in overseas jurisdictions.

LANGUAGES SPOKEN: German, French, Spanish, Portuguese, Danish, Turkish, Korean, Swedish, Japanese, Italian, Greek, Hindi, Dutch.

RECRUITMENT AND TRAINING: The firm will recruit approximately 20-25 trainee solicitors in 1996. Applications should be made to Alex Holtum (Sheffield office). A minimum 2(1) degree is welcomed but is not as important as a self-assured personality capable of acquiring the confidence of colleagues and the business community. The firm has a structured training programme comprising both professional and skills training.

CONTACT PARTNER: Mr Philip Perry

Number of partners:	139
Assistant solicitors:	200
Other fee-earners:	167

WORKLOAD

Company/ commercial	19%
Banking and corporate recovery	18%
Litigation	14%
Property	14%
Insurance	12%
Debt recovery	9%
Human resources	6%
Intellectual property	4%
Building societies	4%

CONTACTS

Banking	Michael Burton
Building societies	Andrew Chappell
Company/commercial	Andrew Darwin
Debt collection	Paddy Liningham
Employment	David Bradley
Environmental	Graeme Webber
Insolvency & corp. recovery	Tony Bugg
Insurance	Kevin McLoughlin
Intellectual property	Richard Sutton
Litigation	Neil Micklethwaite
Pensions	Tim Knight
Professional indemnity	David Simon
Property	Philip Perry
Tax	Lynda Finan
Telecommunications	David Barrett
Utilities	Nigel Knowles

DICKINSON DEES

CROSS HOUSE, WESTGATE RD, NEWCASTLE UPON TYNE,
TYNE & WEAR, NE99 1SB   DX: 61191

TEL: (0191) 261 1911
FAX: (0191) 261 5855

THE FIRM: A long-established practice, Dickinson Dees is the largest firm of solicitors in the North East region, with a total staff of over 260. The practice offers both commercial and private client services. Traditionally, the firm has been organised along departmental lines. However, the increasing degree of specialisation within the firm has led to the development of more client-focused work systems. These include the continued growth of teams of lawyers serving the requirements of particular industries and the development of dedicated client teams. Among the specialist services are: development and construction, banking and commercial lending, corporate tax, pensions, employee incentives, public procurement, commercial and EC law (based locally and in Brussels), health sector, environmental and planning, local authority and public sector work, employment, information technology, social housing and agriculture.

PRINCIPAL AREAS OF WORK:

Company & Commercial: *(Contact Partner:* Nigel Bellis). The department is by far the largest in the region in terms of both personnel and the range of services offered. It is active across the whole range of commercial transactions, from contested takeover bids to international joint ventures, and from major insolvency work and information technology projects to the negotiation of power supply contracts. In addition, the firm maintains its commitment to providing smaller businesses with excellent advice at a reasonable cost.

Litigation: *(Contact Partner:* Glenn Calvert). Over recent years the litigation practice has grown more quickly than any other of the firm's work. Specialist advice is offered on all contentious matters, ranging from complex construction law issues, computer contracts and shareholder disputes to debt collection, utilising a computerised debt recovery system. The firm has resources which enables it to respond immediately and effectively when urgent action is required.

Commercial Property: *(Contact Partner:* Neil Braithwaite). The practice advises on all aspects of commercial property, including schemes initiated by regional/governmental institutions, reconstruction work, urban regeneration, PFI projects, estate management, mergers and acquisitions support, insolvency and funding projects, construction law, planning and environmental work.

Private Client: *(Contact Partner:* Adrian Gifford). A comprehensive service is offered, covering all aspects of wills, trusts, probate, investment, tax advice, estate administration, matrimonial advice and residential conveyancing.

INTERNATIONAL CONNECTIONS & ASSOCIATED OFFICES: The firm is a member of the Legal Resources Group and has an associated office in Brussels.

CONTACT PARTNER: Graham Wright

Number of partners:	35
Assistant solicitors:	32
Other fee-earners:	52

WORKLOAD	
Corporate	35%
Property	30%
Private client	20%
Litigation	15%

CONTACTS	
Banking	Gordon Sanderson
Building society law	Jonathan Hewitt
Commercial litigation	James Wilders
Commercial property	Geoff Hockaday
Construction	Simon Lewis
Corporate	Nigel Bellis
Corporate tax	Tony Hennessy
Development	Neil Braithwaite
EC and commercial	Alison Fellows
Employment	Glenn Calvert
Health sector	Andrew Jackson
Insolvency	John Pennie
Intellectual property	Paul Cato
Matrimonial	Lyn Rutherford
Mergers and acquisitions	John Flynn
Pensions	Martin Jenkins
PFI and public procurement	Alison Fellows
Planning	Paul Taylor
Private client	Adrian Gifford

DICKINSON MANSER 5 Parkstone Rd, Poole, Dorset, BH15 2NL **Tel:** (01202) 673071 **Fax:** (01202) 680470 **DX:** 07602 **Ptnrs:** 7 **Asst Solrs:** 5 **Other Fee-earners:** 7. The oldest firm in Poole. Provides a full service to all clients including small businesses, private individuals and PLCs. Members of Law Group (UK) Limited and Solicitors Financial Services.

WORKLOAD			
Litigation	33%	Probate & trusts	33%
Property/ commercial	33%		

DICKSON MINTO WS 11 Walker Street, Edinburgh, EH3 7NE **Tel:** (0131) 225 4455 **Fax:** (0131) 225 2712 **Ptnrs:** 12 **Asst Solrs:** 24 **Other Fee-earners:** 12. The firm concentrates exclusively on corporate work including banking, insolvency and intellectual property. Also in London.

WORKLOAD			
Corporate finance	35%	Company/ commercial	35%
Collective investments	10%	Banking	10%
Commercial property	5%		

DIGBY BROWN & CO The Savoy Tower, 77 Renfrew Street, Glasgow, G2 3BZ **Tel:** (0141) 332 8899 **Fax:** (0141) 332 2920 **Ptnrs:** 6 **Asst Solrs:** 6 **Other Fee-earners:** 7. An established practice specialising in pursuer personal injury work.

WORKLOAD		
Litigation	92%	Convey/trust/executry 8%

DIXON, COLES & GILL Bank House, Burton Street, Wakefield, W. Yorks, WF1 2DA **Tel:** (01924) 373467 **Fax:** (01924) 366234 **DX:** 15030 **Ptnrs:** 2 **Asst Solrs:** 1 **Other Fee-earners:** 1. The firm has been Registrars to the Diocese of Wakefield for many years, and in addition to general private practice, has its own complete property service, including a Chartered Surveyor.

D J FREEMAN

43 FETTER LANE, LONDON, EC4A 1NA
DX: 103

TEL: (0171) 583 4055
FAX: (0171) 353 7377

THE FIRM: The firm, founded in 1952, has an established reputation in commercial property, litigation, corporate and commercial law, insurance and reinsurance, and corporate reconstruction and insolvency. The firm has also achieved an increasingly higher profile in employment and media work. The firm has developed organically rather than through merger, and aims to combine the highest standards of client service with the constant development of the knowledge of the businesses of its clients and the markets in which they operate.

PRINCIPAL AREAS OF WORK:

Property: (*Contact:* Paul Clark). *Work includes:* property development projects, property investment and dealing, new business leases, equity participation mortgages, secured loans, property management, landlord and tenant, property taxation, the property aspects of commercial transactions, foreign investment in UK property, town and country planning and construction matters including collateral warranties. The firm is a member of the British Council of Shopping Centres, the British Property Foundation and the British Council of Offices.

Litigation: (*Contact:* Colin Joseph). *Work includes:* commercial conflicts, construction and property disputes, insolvency, entertainment, libel and media law, professional disciplinary tribunals, DTI enquiries, computer law, intellectual property, and employment.

Company commercial: (*Contact:* Antoinette Jucker). *Work includes:* offers for sale and placings, take-overs and acquisitions, venture capital financing, management buy-outs, insolvency, banking, commercial contracts, copyright, computer contracts and competition law. The department also handles UK and overseas tax planning for corporations and individuals.

Insurance: (*Contact:* David Kendall). *Work includes:* insurance and reinsurance dispute resolution, including arbitration, litigation and ADR, Lloyd's, insurance industry regulation, corporate finance, insurance company insolvency and restructuring, agency, run-off and marine and non-marine claims, including professional indemnity and product and environmental liability claims.

Multi–media: (*Contact:* Tony Leifer). *Work includes:* litigation, copyright, regulatory and other company commercial services to the broadcasting, film, entertainment, publishing, print, IT and communications industries.

INTERNATIONAL CONNECTIONS: The firm has particularly strong connections in Germany through its association with Westphal & Voges of Hamburg and Berlin.

NATURE OF CLIENTELE: The firm represents a wide range of UK and international corporate interests, including property investment, development and construction companies, banks, insurance companies, accountants and other professionals, local and other public authorities, the manufacturing, leisure and media industries, major retailers and professional and trade associations.

CONTACT PARTNER: David Solomon	
Number of partners:	48
Assistant solicitors:	61
Other fee-earners:	25

WORKLOAD	
Property services	38%
Commercial litigation	20%
Insurance services	20%
Company commercial	14%
Multi-media	8%

CONTACTS	
Banking and leasing	Chris Brown
Commercial litigation	Colin Joseph
Company commercial	Antoinette Jucker
Construction	David Johnson
Employment	Jane Moorman
Financial services	Christine Derrett
Insolvency	Alan Magnus
Insurance	David Kendall
Mining and minerals	Alan Magnus
Multi-media	Tony Leifer
Planning	Moira Fraser
Public sector	Ted Totman
Taxation	Chris Comyn

DOBERMAN HORSMAN College Chambers, 92-94 Borough Road, Middlesbrough, Clev, TS1 2HL **Tel:** (01642) 230130 **Fax:** (01642) 230133 **DX:** 60508 **Ptnrs:** 5 **Asst Solrs:** 2 **Other Fee-earners:** 6. Established 1935, a general high street practice with main specialisations in civil litigation of all types and commercial work.

WORKLOAD			
Personal injury/med neg	50%	Comm work/comm prop	20%
Commercial litigation	20%	Others	10%

DODSON HARDING 11 Hammet St, Taunton, Somerset, TA1 1RJ **Tel:** (01823) 331293 **Fax:** (01823) 252161 **DX:** 32111 **Ptnrs:** 11 **Asst Solrs:** 5 **Other Fee-earners:** 12. A well-established firm with both commercial and private clients. Best known for commercial property and general litigation work.

WORKLOAD			
Residential property	28%	Family	24%
Litigation	22%	Private client	15%
Commercial property	11%		

DOLMANS 17 Windsor Place, Cardiff, S. Glam, CF1 4PA **Tel:** (01222) 345531 **Fax:** (01222) 398206 **DX:** 33005 Cardiff **Ptnrs:** 14 **Asst Solrs:** 13 **Other Fee-earners:** 20. Practising in South Wales since 1893 and known for its civil litigation and commercial practice. Also has a substantial insolvency and conveyancing practice.

DONELLY & WALL 2 Donegal Square East, Belfast, BT1 5HB **Tel:** (01232) 233157 **Fax:** (01232) 329743. A firm known for its criminal and civil liberties expertise.

DONN & CO 26 Cross St, Manchester, M2 7AN **Tel:** (0161) 834 3311 **Fax:** (0161) 834 2317 **DX:** 14312 **Ptnrs:** 6 **Asst Solrs:** 5 **Other Fee-earners:** 44. Best known for accident and uninsured loss recovery litigation. Also handles commercial and general litigation. Other work includes insolvency, conveyancing, tax and probate.

WORKLOAD			
Manch - Pers inj/trauma	70%	Droylsden/Moston - Crime	50%
Middleton - Crime	50%	Commercial	30%
Probate/ conveyancing	25%		

DONNELLY NEARY & DONNELLY 1 Downshire Road, Newry, Co. Down, BT34 1ED **Tel:** (01693) 64611 **Fax:** (01693) 67000 **Ptnrs:** 4 **Asst Solrs:** 1 **Other Fee-earners:** 1. The practice is equally divided between private client work and commercial and personal injury litigation. Branch office in Newcastle.

WORKLOAD			
Commercial work	30%	Personal injury	30%
Probate	20%	Company law	10%

DONNE MILEHAM & HADDOCK

FREDERICK PLACE, BRIGHTON, E. SUSSEX, BN1 1AT
DX: 2703

TEL: (01273) 329833
FAX: (01273) 739764

THE FIRM: Donne Mileham & Haddock, founded in 1970 from the amalgamation of three of the best known solicitors' practices in the area, is one of the leading firms in the South East with offices throughout East and West Sussex. The firm has continued to expand and is noted for its expertise in commercial law, with specialist commercial departments, providing a skilled and effective service. It is also a member of Law Europe, an association of law firms with offices in most European countries.

PRINCIPAL AREAS OF WORK:

Company/ Commercial: (*Contact Partner:* Andrew Trotter). An experienced team is equipped to handle a variety of commercial projects including: company/ partnership formations, takeovers, mergers and acquisitions, MBOs, Stock Exchange flotations, franchises, intellectual property work and corporate taxation matters.

Commercial Property: (*Contact Partner:* Michael Bailey). The firm has considerable experience in property development work and Town and Country Planning and the department includes a member of the Town Planning Institute. *Work also includes:* the acquisition, disposal and leasing of commercial property, lease negotiation and renewal and landlord and tenant disputes.

Residential Property: (*Contact Partner:* Trevor Maxim). This department can offer a highly efficient, computerised conveyancing service at a competitive price to both individual and institutional clients.

Litigation and Arbitration: (*Contact Partner:* Tim Aspinall). The firm is well known for its litigation expertise and is skilled in handling particularly large and complicated pieces of work. It has a number of litigation teams dedicated to specific areas of work: commercial litigation, property litigation, information technology disputes, intellectual property, construction, professional negligence, insurance claims and licensing applications. The firm is equally well regarded for its personal injury and matrimonial work and is renowned for its expertise in admiralty law. In addition, foreign litigation matters are handled by a team with practical experience of working abroad.

MANAGING PARTNER: Mr Roger Hartwell

Number of partners:	27
Assistant solicitors:	14
Other fee-earners:	48

CONTACTS

Admiralty and maritime	Michael Bloomfield
Adoption and Child Care	David Stevens
Agricultural law	Marion Wilcock/Sheila Deasey
Charities	Michael Long/Derek Sparrow
Commercial fraud	Tim Aspinall
Commercial litigation	Martin Allen
Commercial prop.	Terry Whitney/ Michael Bailey
Company/comm.	Andrew Trotter/Michael Long
Computer law	Michael Long/Andrew Trotter
Constr./engin.	Susan Batstone/Michael Bailey
Consumer law	Tim Ashdown
Corp. finance	Andrew Trotter/ Derek Sparrow
Criminal law	Ray Blount/ Roger Hartwell
Debt recovery	Richard Drower/ Nigel Marchant
Defamation	Susan Batstone
Ecclesiastical law	Michael Bailey
Employment law	Quintin Barry/ Simon Bellm
Environmental law	Tony Allen

Employment: (*Contact Partner:* Quintin Barry). The firm has extensive experience in acting for employers, employees and TUs on such matters as service contracts, redundancies and unfair dismissals, disciplinary and grievance procedures, pensions and incentive schemes.

Debt Recovery: (*Contact Partner:* Tim Aspinall). This department, led by a member of the Institute of Credit Management, handles over 3500 cases a year for clients, including overseas companies trading within the UK. Substantial investment in technology has enabled us to handle large volumes of work at a competitive price.

PRIVATE CLIENT: (*Contact Partner:* Paul Bennett). The firm's private client service includes personal finance, income tax services, estate planning, wills, trusts and probate.

NATURE OF CLIENTELE: A wide client base includes major companies, institutions, public authorities, business advisors and financial organisations, in addition to a substantial number of private clients.

Estate Development	Michael Bailey
Family law	Susan Ansell/ Mark Smith
Food law	Tony Allen
Franchising	Andrew Trotter/Derek Sparrow
Housing Associations	Nick Warde/Paul Bennett
Insolvency	Michael Long/ L. Westbrook
Intellectual prop.	Michael Long/Derek Sparrow
Licensing & leisure	Michael Bailey/ Ray Blount
Mental health	Roger Hartwell
Nursing and healthcare	Robert Campbell
Personal injury	Simon Bellm/ Michael Coleman
Planning	Tony Allen
Private client	Lynda Capelli/Rod Gentry
Professional neg	Andrew Trotter/Derek Sparrow

DORMAN HARRIS 11 Old Jewry, London, EC2R 8DU **Tel:** (0171) 606 0636 **Fax:** (0171) 606 0639 **Ptnrs:** 2 **Other Fee-earners:** 1. A small specialist shipping, commodity and general commercial litigation practice, acting for P&I Clubs, shipowners, charterers and traders.

DORMAN JEFFREY & CO

MADELEINE SMITH HOUSE, 6-7 BLYTHSWOOD SQUARE, GLASGOW, G2 4AD
DX: 178 Glasgow

TEL: (0141) 221 9880
FAX: (0141) 221 9804

THE FIRM: Established in 1979, Dorman Jeffrey & Co was the first Scottish practice to be dedicated entirely to corporate and commercial law. The firm acts for many prominent national and international organisations, amongst them the principal Scottish banks, leading firms of accountants and other financial institutions. Organised around four principal departments, a range of legal services is on offer to the commercial client.

PRINCIPAL AREAS OF WORK:

Company/ Commercial: (*Contact Partner:* Eric Galbraith). The firm provides support in legal aspects of business management from company formation, funding and growth to acquisition, investment and flotation or sale. Assistance is provided with re-organisations, mergers, management buy-outs and buy-ins, joint ventures, employment contracts and other corporate requirements. The department is also experienced in shipping law, aviation, oil and gas, information technology and intellectual property law. The Corporate Department has a reputation for innovative problem-solving and, in recent years, has been in the forefront of the financing of sports stadia development and other sports and leisure projects.

Insolvency/ Corporate Recovery: (*Contact Partner:* Ian J. Cuthbertson). The firm is one of the largest corporate recovery and insolvency practices in Scotland, acting for the principal accountancy firms in their capacity as receivers, administrators and liquidators, and being involved in many high-profile Scottish cases. Ian Cuthbertson is acknowledged to be one of the leading authorities on insolvency in Scotland.

Commercial Property: (*Contact Partner:* John Gallacher). Clients are assisted with transfer of ownership, funding arrangements, investments, disposal of property assets (in relation to insolvency), heritable and leasehold property, acquisition, sale and leasing of commercial and industrial property, property development and related investment and financing, company relocation, leisure projects and licensed premises. The firm is increasingly involved in advising clients on environmental law matters related to commercial property.

Litigation: (*Contact Partner:* Gillian F. Bryson). The department handles all aspects of commercial litigation including employment law, intellectual property, advertising and media, consumer and product liability, licensing and planning, arbitration, construction law and debt recovery.

SENIOR PARTNER: A. Brian Dorman

Number of partners:	14
Assistant solicitors:	9
Other fee-earners:	7

WORKLOAD	
Corporate recovery and insolvency	37%
Corporate	32%
Commercial property	21%
Litigation	10%

CONTACTS	
Aviation	Teddy Davidson
Banking	Graeme Bruce
Company/ commercial	Brian Dorman
Computer law and IT	Brian Dorman
Corporate finance	Eric Galbraith
Debt recovery	Bill Stark
Employment law	Alan Masson
Energy and utilities	Teddy Davidson
Environmental law	Vincent Brown
Insolvency	Ian Cuthbertson
Intellectual property	Eric Galbraith
Licensing and leisure	Yvonne Brady
Litigation (commercial)	Gillian Bryson
Pensions	Teddy Davidson
Property (commercial)	John Gallacher
Shipping	Teddy Davidson

OTHER OFFICES: 20 Ainslie Place, Edinburgh EH3 6AU. *Tel:* (0131) 225 9999. *Fax:* (0131) 225 1688.
FOREIGN LANGUAGES: French, Portuguese.
INTERNATIONAL CONNECTIONS & ASSOCIATED OFFICES: Strong connections are maintained with North America, France, Germany, Australia, Singapore, New Zealand, Holland, Norway and Finland.

DOUGLAS-JONES & MERCER 147 St. Helens Rd, Swansea, W. Glam, SA1 4DB **Tel:** (01792) 650000 **Fax:** (01792) 458212 **DX:** 39556 **Ptnrs:** 12 **Asst Solrs:** 8 **Other Fee-earners:** 14. One of the largest firms in Swansea. Specialist departments in matrimonial, personal injury, and commercial law. Legal aid work undertaken. Branch offices in Ammanford, Gorseinon, Mumbles, and Morriston.

DOUGLAS WIGNALL & CO 44 Essex Street, Strand, London, WC2R 3JF **Tel:** (0171) 583 1362 **Fax:** (0171) 583 0532 **DX:** 48 (Ch.Ln.) **Ptnrs:** 1. Work includes international hotel and resort developments, international management agreements, hotel acquisitions and disposals, advising tour operators, general commercial law, commercial and residential conveyancing.

WORKLOAD			
Travel & leisure	60%	Commercial/res convey	30%
Other company/comm	10%		

DOWNIE AITON & Co 48 West Regent Street, Glasgow, G2 2QT **Tel:** (0141) 332 7314 **Fax:** (0141) 332 6786 **DX:** 32 Glasgow **Ptnrs:** 8 **Asst Solrs:** 6 **Other Fee-earners:** 8. General practice handling company/ commercial work, civil litigation, conveyancing and criminal matters.

WORKLOAD			
Civil lit/pers injury	35%	Criminal	20%
Convey (domestic/comm)	20%	Company/comm/banking	20%
Sports	5%		

DOWNS

156 HIGH ST, DORKING, SURREY, RH4 1BQ
DX: 57300 Dorking

TEL: (01306) 880110
FAX: (01306) 876577

THE FIRM: Formed by the merger of two prominent Dorking practices, Downs is Dorking's largest firm. In the 1980's a substantial business law capability was developed, which now accounts for over half the firm's fees. The practice is a member of the NEXUS group, and with five notaries is the largest notarial firm in Surrey.
PRINCIPAL AREAS OF WORK:
SERVICES FOR THE BUSINESS CLIENT:
Commercial Property: *(Contact Partners:* Iain MacLeod and Michael Debens).
Company/ Commercial: *(Contact Partner:* Christopher Shipley).
Commercial Litigation: *(Contact Partner:* David Rea).
SERVICES FOR THE PRIVATE CLIENT:
Conveyancing: *(Contact Partner:* Miss S.E. Thomas).
Trusts, Wills, Probate and Tax: *(Contact Partner:* Timothy Hughes).
Matrimonial and Child Care: *(Contact Partner:* Anne Trier).
Accidents and Personal Injury: *(Contact:* James Nunns).
FOREIGN LANGUAGES: Spanish, French and German.
INTERNATIONAL CONNECTIONS: Personal English-speaking contacts throughout Europe and in North America.

ADMINISTRATION PARTNER:
Miss S.E. Thomas

Number of partners:	9
Assistant solicitors:	7
Other fee-earners:	5

DRUCES & ATTLEE Salisbury House, London Wall, London, EC2M 5PS **Tel:** (0171) 638 9271 **Fax:** (0171) 628 7525 **DX:** 33862 Finsbury Sq. **Ptnrs:** 16 **Asst Solrs:** 8 **Other Fee-earners:** 7. Strengths in commercial property, company law, litigation and private client. Development in EC legislation, food/ drink law, construction law, FSA and matrimonial work.

WORKLOAD			
Property	34%	Litigation	22%
Company/ commercial	22%	Private client	22%

DRUMMOND MILLER WS

31-32 MORAY PLACE, EDINBURGH, EH2 6BZ
DX: 104 Edinburgh

TEL: (0131) 226 5151
FAX: (0131) 225 2608

THE FIRM: An Edinburgh-based practice with origins going back to 1780, Drummond Miller WS is one of the oldest firms in Scotland. In keeping with its tradition, a large private client department is maintained in tandem with a comprehensive litigation service. The firm has strength in the fields of personal injury and medical negligence, and offers commercial advice to small and medium-sized businesses.

PRINCIPAL AREAS OF WORK:

Litigation: (*Contact Partner:* Grant McCulloch). A wide range of work is dealt with by this branch of the firm. Acting mostly (but not exclusively) for pursuers, the practice devotes considerable resource to cases of personal injury and medical negligence, including multi-party action groups. A substantial portion of this work emanates from the firm's close connections with trade unions. A partner with the firm (Isabel Anderson, based at Dalkeith), certified by the Law Society as an Employment Law Specialist, provides employment contract advice and negotiation services and prepares cases for tribunals. In addition, the family law division undertakes legal aid cases and handles all aspects of matrimonial breakdown, including child abduction.

Private Client: (*Contact Partner:* Elizabeth Couper). The department assists a considerable number of private clients with trusts, wills, executries, investments and tax planning. In addition a large proportion of local residential conveyancing is undertaken by the firm, with a good Estate Agency back-up.

Criminal Law: (*Contact:* Fiona Moore). The practice handles a substantial number of appeals and summary crime.

OTHER AREAS OF WORK:

Company/ Commercial: (*Contact Partner:* Alasdair Buchanan). The department assists small companies with matters of commercial law and also offers advice in the field of commercial property, including development and licensing.

FOREIGN LANGUAGES: French.

INTERNATIONAL CONNECTIONS AND ASSOCIATED OFFICES: In association with MacPhail & Co, Glasgow.

OTHER OFFICES:
64 South Bridge Street, Bathgate EH48 1TL.
Tel: (01506) 56645. *Fax:* (01506) 52347.
11 White Hart Street, Dalkeith EH22 1AE.
Tel: (0131) 663 9568. *Fax:* (0131) 654 2676.
47 Whytescauseway, Kirkaldy KY1 1XD.
Tel: (01592) 205000. *Fax:* (01592) 206217.
151-155 High Street, Musselburgh EH21 7DD.
Tel: (0131) 665 7393. *Fax:* (0131) 653 6192.
3 Grampian Court, Livingston EH54 6QF.
Tel: (01506) 416703. *Fax:* (01506) 416878.
8 The Loan, Loanhead, Midlothian EH20 9AF.
Tel: (0131) 663 9568. *Fax:* (0131) 440 2265.

SENIOR PARTNER: James I. Wilson SSC

Number of partners:	21
Assistant solicitors:	13
Other fee-earners:	16

WORKLOAD	
Residential conveyancing	24%
Court of Session (divorce/ family and reparation)	22%
Sheriff court (civil)	22%
Trust/ executry	10%
Other	9%
Criminal	7%
Commercial conveyancing/ company	4%
Employment law	2%

CONTACTS	
Company/ commercial	Alasdair Buchanan
Criminal law	Fiona Moore
Employment law	Isabel Anderson
Litigation	A. Grant McCulloch
Private client	E. Ann Couper

P.A. DUFFY & CO Market Square, Dungannon, Co. Tyrone, BT70 1AR **Tel:** (018687) 22102 **Fax:** (018687) 40997 **DX:** 425 NR Belfast **Ptnrs:** 10 **Asst Solrs:** 2 **Other Fee-earners:** 5. Broadly based general practice, with five offices. All aspects of litigation and private client work.

WORKLOAD	
All types	100%

A.H. DUNCOMBE & COMPANY 98 High Street, Thame, Oxon, OX9 3EH **Tel:** (01844) 261026/217444 **Fax:** (01844) 217448 **DX:** 80553 **Ptnrs:** 3 **Asst Solrs:** 1 **Other Fee-earners:** 2. The firm practises exclusively in company and commercial law. It has an established reputation in start-ups including overseas investment into the UK, share sales and business transfers.

DUNDAS & WILSON CS

SALTIRE COURT, 20 CASTLE TERRACE, EDINBURGH, EH1 2EN
DX: 22 Edinburgh

TEL: (0131) 228 8000
FAX: (0131) 228 8888

THE FIRM: Dundas & Wilson is one of the leading corporate and commercial law firms with an established reputation for excellence, which has resulted in expansion from its initial Edinburgh base to Glasgow and more recently to London.

The firm provides a full range of legal services equalled only by the largest law firms in the City. Its main areas of work being handled either within or across four principal operating departments - corporate, commercial property, private clients and litigation, often through specialist groupings created either to serve specific clients, specific market sectors or on the basis of specialist legal knowledge.

Although primarily a Scottish firm, Dundas & Wilson recognises the need for interaction with other legal systems throughout the UK, Europe and beyond, and can facilitate this through the three offices and the many areas of expertise available within the firm.

PRINCIPAL AREAS OF WORK:

Agricultural/ Sporting Property: (*Contact Partner:* Robert Turcan). *Work includes:* purchases, sales, farming partnerships and quotas.

Banking: (*Contact Partners:* Michael Stoneham and Brian Rutherford). *Work includes:* MBO/ MBI and acquisition finance, project/ development finance, structured finance, public sector debt and Scottish securities.

Commercial Litigation: (*Contact Partners:* Neil Cochran and Alayne Swanson). *Work includes:* sale of goods, sale of businesses, company disputes, commercial claims and landlord and tenant claims.

Commercial Property: (*Contact Partners:* Hamish Hodge and John Murray). *Work includes:* finance, development, investment, leisure, property joint ventures, landlord and tenant, sales and purchases.

Company & Commercial: (*Contact Partners:* Maureen Coutts and Chris Campbell). *Work includes:* mergers and acquisitions, MBOs/ MBIs, venture capital, contracts and joint ventures.

Construction: (*Contact Partner:* Alastair Morrison). *Work includes:* defect claims, arbitrations, warranty claims and non-contentious advice on Standard Form and other contracts.

Corporate Finance: (*Contact Partner:* David Hardie). *Work includes:* flotations, rights issues, placings, takeovers and general public company work.

Corporate Financial Services: (*Contact Partners:* James Watt and Chris Athanas). *Work includes:* unit trusts, other collective investment schemes, investment trusts, savings vehicles, building societies, insurance companies, compliance, investment management contracts.

EC & Competition: (*Contact Partner:* Christian Hook). *Work includes:* distribution, licensing and agency, anti-dumping complaints, competition law compliance and notifications and permissions.

Employment: (*Contact Partners:* Euan Macleod and Alayne Swanson). *Work includes:* redundancy, unfair dismissal, discrimination, handbooks, procedures, business transfers, drafting contracts and settlement packages.

Employee Share Schemes/ Benefits: (*Contact Partner:* Donald Cumming). *Work includes:* ESOPs, option and profit sharing schemes and general advice.

Environment: (*Contact Partner:* Ann Faulds and Jon Robertson). *Work includes:* criminal and civil liability and general advice.

Family: (*Contact Partner:* Douglas Connell). *Work includes:* all aspects of family law, financial planning and wills.

Heritage: (*Contact Partner:* Douglas Connell). *Work includes:* National Heritage Schemes.

Insolvency/ Corporate Reconstruction: (*Contact Partners:* Chris Campbell and Laurence Ward). *Work includes:* receiverships, administrations, restructuring, corporate insolvency and personal insolvency.

Insurance Litigation: (*Contact Partners:* Neil Cochran and Colin Macleod). *Work includes:* personal injury, fire, product liability, employers' liability, public liability and road traffic.

MANAGING PARTNER: Philip Dacker	
Number of partners:	35
Assistant solicitors:	69
Other fee-earners:	39

WORKLOAD	
Banking, co/comm, capital mkts, corp. insolvency, fin. services	40%
Commercial property	25%
Private clients	20%
Comm litigation, employment, construction/ civil engineering	15%

CONTACTS	
Banking	M. Stoneham, B. Rutherford
Capital markets	D. Hardie
Commercial property	H. Hodge, J. Murray
Commercial litigation	N. Cochran, A. Swanson
Company/ commercial	M. Coutts, C. Campbell
Construction	A. Morrison
Corporate insolvency	C. Campbell, L. Ward
Employment	E. MacLeod, A. Swanson
Financial services	C. Athanas, P. Mackay
	J. Watt
Private client	R. Blair, R. Turcan
	D. Connell

Intellectual Property: (*Contact Partner:* Lorne Byatt). *Work includes:* copyright, trademark and patent licences, acquisitions, disposals and information technology contracts.

Licensing: (*Contact Partner:* Euan MacLeod). *Work includes:* liquor, betting and gaming.

Media: (*Contact Partner:* Laurence Ward). *Work includes:* production and distribution contracts, copy clearance and broadcasting regulatory advice.

Minerals: (*Contact Partner:* Jon Robertson). *Work includes:* mineral development, leases and agreements.

Pensions: (*Contact Partner:* James Watt). *Work includes:* advice on surpluses, deficits, documentation, Article 119, unapproved schemes, winding-up and mergers and acquisitions.

Private Finance Initiative: (*Contact Partner:* Michael Stoneham). Work includes: road and bridge, railway, airport, property transfer, social work, healthcare, waste collection and disposal, water and sewerage schemes.

Professional Indemnity: (*Contact Partners:* Neil Cochran and Pamela Lyall). *Work includes:* solicitors, doctors, accountants, surveyors, architects and engineers.

Residential Property: (*Contact Partner:* Ian Moffett). *Work includes:* purchases, sales, general advice and relocation schemes.

Tax – Corporate/ Personal: (*Contact Partner:* Ian Clark). *Work includes:* general advice, inheritance tax, VAT and Stamp Duty.

Town & Country Planning: (*Contact Partner:* Jon Robertson). *Work includes:* general advice, appeals and hearings.

Trusts: (*Contact Partner:* Neil Macleod). *Work includes:* UK and overseas trusts, charities.

OTHER OFFICES:
Sutherland House, 149 St. Vincent Street, Glasgow G2 5NW. *Tel:* (0141) 221 8586. *Fax:* (0141) 221 8687.
Boston House, 63/ 64 New Broad Street, London EC2M 1JR. *Tel:* (0171) 256 9191. *Fax:* (0171) 256 6464.

FOREIGN LANGUAGES: German, French, Italian and Spanish spoken.

DUNDONS 261 Lavender Hill, London, SW11 1JD **Tel:** (0171) 228 2277 **Fax:** (0171) 924 2759 **DX:** 58556 **Ptnrs:** 2 **Asst Solrs:** 4 **Other Fee-earners:** 3. Best known for criminal legal aid work, care and wardship, and civil liberties cases.

WORKLOAD			
Criminal defence	60%	Child care/related work	40%

DUTHIE HART & DUTHIE 517-519 Barking Rd, Greengate, Plaistow, London, E13 8PT **Tel:** (0181) 472 0138 **Fax:** (0181) 470 7628 **DX:** 52407 Canning Town **Ptnrs:** 5 **Asst Solrs:** 10 **Other Fee-earners:** 14. A general practice known for criminal work. Deals with commercial conveyancing and company work and matrimonial work.

WORKLOAD			
Criminal litigation	60%	Pers injury/gen common	13%
Matrimonial	12%	Conveyancing	8%
Probate	7%		

DUTTON GREGORY & WILLIAMS Trussell Hse, 23 St. Peter St, Winchester, Hants, SO23 8BT **Tel:** (01962) 844333 **Fax:** (01962) 863582 **DX:** 2515 Winchester **Ptnrs:** 13 **Asst Solrs:** 5 **Other Fee-earners:** 11. A broad-based, commercially-orientated practice. Particular specialisations are company and commercial work, commercial property, planning, construction law and litigation.

WORKLOAD			
Lit incl planning & envir	45%	Residential property	15%
Commercial property	11%	Priv client	10%
Family/ matrimonial	10%	Company/ commercial	9%

EASTLEYS The Manor Office, Victoria St, Paignton, Devon, TQ4 5DW **Tel:** (01803) 559257 **Fax:** (01803) 558625 **DX:** 100603 **Ptnrs:** 10 **Asst Solrs:** 5 **Other Fee-earners:** 9. Medium-sized, go-ahead provincial firm, known largely for its residential and commercial conveyancing, civil and matrimonial litigation, probate, tax and financial advice.

EATONS

22 BLADES COURT, DEODAR RD, PUTNEY, LONDON, SW15 2NU

TEL: (0181) 877 9727
FAX: (0181) 877 9940

THE FIRM: Eatons specialise in all aspects of entertainment work with particular emphasis on legal and commercial advice in connection with music and all related areas such as recording, publishing, video, management, merchandising and television arrangements for a full range of emerging and established artists as well as independent and major companies. The combined qualifications of the partners encompass many years of industry and private practice experience.

OTHER OFFICES: Old Gun Court, North Street, Dorking RH4 1YP.

CONTACT: Julie Saffell

Number of partners:	5
Assistant solicitors:	3
Other fee-earners:	1

EATON SMITH & DOWNEY Britannia Buildings, St. Peter's Street, Huddersfield, W. Yorks, HD1 1BB **Tel:** (01484) 537433 **Fax:** (01484) 545060 **DX:** 712956 **Ptnrs:** 9 **Asst Solrs:** 1 **Other Fee-earners:** 6. Traditional firm, established 1922. Engages in all areas of law including conveyancing (commercial and domestic), company work and litigation.

EDGE & ELLISON

RUTLAND HOUSE, 148 EDMUND ST, BIRMINGHAM, W. MIDLANDS, B3 2JR
DX: 708610

TEL: (0121) 200 2001
FAX: (0121) 200 1991

18-19 Southampton Place, London WC1A 2AJ
DX: 37984 Kingsway
Contact: Simon Gordon

Tel: (0171) 404 4701
Fax: (0171) 831 9152

Regent Court, Regent Street, Leicester LE1 7BR
DX: 17006
Contact: David West

Tel: (0116) 2470123
Fax: (0116) 2470030

THE FIRM: Edge & Ellison is one of the UK's leading law firms; its aim is to focus its combined skills, experience, commitment, personalities, strength in depth and locations to add value to its clients' needs and provide a major firm service at a highly competitive "regional" based cost.

PRINCIPAL AREAS OF WORK:

Asset Finance: A dedicated team advising clients operating in the equipment leasing, hire purchase and finance sectors. Clients include major clearing banks, leasing companies and financial institutions. The firm has specialists in a whole range of asset finance products, from receivables financing, factoring and invoice discounting to all forms of operating and finance leasing in the medium to larger sectors including shipping, aircraft and project finance.

Banking & Insolvency: This department is able to advise on any problems concerning financial transactions, from inception to insolvency and recovery. The department has considerable experience and a well-deserved reputation for providing teams of lawyers tailored to the needs of administrative receivers, administrators and liquidators, banks and finance houses.

Commercial: Advising UK and overseas clients on trading arrangements, agency and distributorship agreements and Financial Services Act implications, as well as the impact of legislation emanating from Brussels. Sponsorship agreements, computer contracts and sports law is also a feature of this department.

Commercial Property: A substantial core department advises on all aspects of commercial property including development, investment, buying, selling and leasing of commercial, retail, industrial, leisure and residential property. The firm also deals with landlord and tenant law including business leases, rent reviews and investment schemes. The firm has specialist planning and construction units.

Competition: As part of the specialist services provided to the firm's clients, the Competition Unit deals with all aspects of UK and EC competition law including dealing with EC Merger Regulation applications, merger references under the Fair

CONTACT PARTNER: Mr Digby Jones

Number of partners:	67
Assistant solicitors:	106
Other fee-earners:	70

WORKLOAD	
Company/ commercial	35%
Commercial property	30%
Litigation	20%
Banking and insolvency	10%
Pensions and trusts	5%

CONTACTS	
Advocacy	Steve Edmonds
Asset finance	Angela Davis
Banking and insolvency	Ian Reaves
	John Sullivan
Commercial	Richard Alderson
Commercial property	David Goldsmith
Competition	Gwyn Williams
Computer law	Caroline Egan
Construction	David Lloyd Jones
Corporate finance	Digby Jones

Trading Act and the impact of competition law on commercial transactions generally. The Unit has recently extended its expertise to the impact of the EC Directives in the area of public procurement and competitive tendering by public authorities.

Computer Law: A team with knowledge of and experience in drafting and negotiating a range of agreements relating to the provision of computer hardware and software and computer-related products and services. Types of agreement produced or advised upon have varied according to clients' requirements but include turnkey agreements, bespoke software agreements, hardware supply or leasing agreements, source code deposit agreements and bureau facilities agreements.

Construction: A dedicated Unit advises on all aspects from contractual arrangements to litigation and dispute resolution. Acting on behalf of developers, contractors, professionals, housing associations, purchasers and tenants the team advises on preparing and drafting terms of professional appointments, terms of warranty agreements for funders, purchasers and tenants and forms of building contracts and amendments to such contracts. The team has special expertise in arbitration and High Court litigation.

Corporate Finance: Advising on Stock Exchange, Take-over Panel and international corporate as well as development capital transactions. Mergers, acquisitions and disposals for both public and private companies, and management buy-outs and buy-ins are very much at the heart of this department.

Debt Recovery: A dedicated credit control unit with the ability to take prompt and efficient action to stop debts becoming bad debts, providing a computerised but personal service to clients, tailored to aid their credit control requirements and to offer a response from initial instruction within one day. The unit also reviews documentation to ensure that terms and conditions of payment are in line with business objectives and enforceable.

Employment: A dedicated employment group is devoted exclusively to employment law and employment-related problems. As well as continually monitoring legislative and judicial changes, the team advises on avoidance of employment problems and the best and most cost-effective way of dealing with them. Members of the team regularly appear at industrial tribunals throughout the country. Much of the team's work includes preparation of terms and conditions through to drafting of complex equal opportunities procedures, executive service agreements and staff handbooks.

Energy & Natural Resources: The firm is a leader in the mining and mineral law sector and acts for several major quarrying companies. Over the years it has developed a widely-based practice in waste disposal and waste management which now extends to the generation of heat and power from waste and other aspects of power generation.

Environmental: Gwyn, who heads up the environmental unit, has been in the front line of advising environmentally sensitive industries for many years. Work includes evaluating liabilities in buying or developing contaminated land; corporate due diligence and advising on warranties and indemnities in relation to mergers and acquisitions; advising on and preparing corporate environmental policies and environmental management systems.

Healthcare: Our Healthcare Group has advised both Trust Hospitals and private hospitals, healthcare and nursing homes, on a variety of matters including sales and purchases, the financing and operation of residential care and nursing homes, regulatory work, employment, employer and employee liability, research and development. We recently acted for the largest provider of healthcare services in America in a merger of four leading private hospitals in London. The value of the assets exceeded £100 million. We also act for clients who supply goods and services to the healthcare sector. Two of our Partners are non-executive directors of Trust Hospitals and another Partner is a director of a Health Authority.

Insurance & Personal Injury: A specialist unit, well known in the insurance market for providing a commercial and quality service principally to insurers, underwriters, authorities, public utilities and other corporate bodies in relation to their litigation. This includes personal injury claims (whether arising from employers, public and motor liability obligations or medical negligence), commercial disputes (including product liability and professional negligence) and policy coverage issues involving non-disclosure, misrepresentation or fraud. In addition, members of the unit advise on issues of health and safety and risk management.

Corporate finance	Chris Rawston
Debt recovery	Charles Darby
Employment	James Retallack
Engineering	Fred Honnor
Environmental	Gwyn Williams
Healthcare	Christian Forgaard
Insurance and P.I.	Robin Humphreys
Intellectual property	Michael Luckman
International	Neil Pearson
Licensing	Andrew Potts
Litigation	Digby Rose
Marketing services	David Mandell
Pensions	Simon Ramshaw
Planning	Martin Damms
Property litigation	Gordon Scott
Public sector	David Hull
Retail	Ian Withers
Sports law	Richard Alderson
Tax	Gregory Morris

Edge & Ellison
S O L I C I T O R S

Intellectual Property: Negotiating, drafting and advising on a variety of agreements relating to the exploitation of intellectual property rights (e.g. licences and assignments of patents and know how, copyright, design or trade marks). The department carries out the due diligence investigations of potential target companies, trade and service mark searches and applications and advice on disputes concerning ownership or infringement of intellectual property rights.

International: The firm is committed to providing clients with the information, advice and assistance they need in doing business around the world, a team advises on specific regulations and directives that affect individual business sectors and commercial agreements. The firm has close associations with like-minded lawyers in Pittsburgh, Atlanta, San Diego and New York, also in Brussels, Paris, Amsterdam, Dusseldorf, Frankfurt, Berlin, Madrid and Milan.

Licensing: Enjoying a long standing national reputation in the licensing field, a dedicated team advises and makes applications on behalf of pub and club owners, breweries, owners of stadia and sponsors of events, also theatres, sports facilities, snooker halls, amusement arcades and casinos. Work undertaken ranges from new licence applications to protection orders and transfers. The team has in depth expertise in the Gaming Acts and dealing with local authorities regarding obtaining and keeping public entertainment licences.

Litigation: No organisation seeks litigation, but sometimes it becomes inevitable. The firm has a strong litigation department accustomed to acting promptly and with authority to resolve disputes where practicable or take and progress or defend proceedings through all courts, where necessary or appropriate. Work includes contract disputes, partnership and shareholder disputes, professional negligence claims, intellectual property litigation and injunctions. The firm acts in the legislative areas of health and safety, environmental law, consumer protections, trade descriptions and consumer credit and has a dynamic advocacy unit.

Marketing & Media Services: The firm acts for the largest marketing services group in the world as well as assisting entertainment and media business managers in theatres, opera and music-based organisations. Advice given includes intellectual property, including agreements covering film production and finance, commissioning of artistes and composers, publishing and recording contracts, distribution or licence arrangements, merchandising, sponsorship and protection of confidential information and rights ownership.

Pensions: The firm has one of the largest teams of pensions lawyers outside London. Although dealing purely with legal issues, the work is wide-ranging – from SSAS facility to dealing with major documentation and scheme restructuring projects. In addition to providing a full pensions legal service, the team also works on a one-off project basis with those clients who already have a detailed and in-depth pension knowledge.

Planning: Work includes all aspects of planning applications, appeals inquiries and Local Plans proceedings and the drafting of deeds relating to planning obligations. The advice given relates to the wider issues including the environmental impact on planning and compulsory purchase proceedings and the acquisition and sale of property generally and the planning team works closely with the firm's environmental unit.

Property Litigation: The team advises on landlord and tenant disputes involving actions, forfeiture and re-entry, exclusion orders, possession and dilapidations claims, breaches of contract, specific performance and residential and service tenancies.

Public Sector: Our team has a wealth of practical experience and understanding of the way local authorities operate and deals regularly with public sector transactions and in-house legal departments. We are aware of the political pressures and are sensitive to the public relations issues which are inherent in such transactions. The highest standards of confidentiality will be adhered to at all times and our advice will never overlook the commercial, political and perception-related influences of the public arena and its constant accent on accountability. We are happy to provide, on request, references from local authorities at Chief Executive level.

Retail: The firm has a specialist team of lawyers who act on a regular basis for retailers of all types and sizes, from listed public companies to family businesses, supermarket chains to corner shops, national charities, breweries, off licences, post offices and newsagents. Work includes negotiating leases, buying and selling premises and businesses, Landlord & Tenant Act renewals and negotiations, rent reviews, dispute resolution, debt recovery, in-store franchising, "original tenant" liability, deeds storage, licensing, employment issues, debt recovery and close liaison with retail agents.

Sports Law: The firm acts for a leading premier division football club, as well as several major sports governing bodies. The team deals with regulatory and disciplinary matters, negotiating contracts with sponsors, television and promotional firms, equipment suppliers, advertising and other commercial activities including intellectual property rights. The firm has direct experience of legislation affecting sports clubs including sports ground licensing and safety procedures. Other commercial aspects include advising sports organisations on membership and constitutional difficulties and assuming the "spokesman" role if required.

FOREIGN CONNECTIONS: The firm enjoys strong long-standing links with like minded firms throughout Europe and the USA.

RECRUITMENT AND TRAINING: The firm has a comprehensive training programme for trainee solicitors and qualified members of staff, many of the courses being run in the purpose built training suite in the Birmingham office. Approximately fifteen trainee solicitors are recruited each year and trainees can serve their articles in any of the firm's offices. If you are interested in exploring opportunities with the firm at trainee or qualified level, please contact Robert Halton, Director of Training and Recruitment.

EDMONDS BOWEN & COMPANY 4 Old Park Lane, London, W1Y 3LJ **Tel:** (0171) 629 8000 **Fax:** (0171) 221 9334/459 6382 **DX:** 37217 Piccadilly **Ptnrs:** 6 **Asst Solrs:** 3 **Other Fee-earners:** 2. The firm handles company/commercial matters specialising in media, entertainment, property and litigation. Private client matters also handled.

EDMONDSON HALL First Floor Offices, 168 High Street, Newmarket, Suffolk, CB8 9AJ **Tel:** (01638) 560556 **Fax:** (01638) 561656 **DX:** 50521 Newmarket **Ptnrs:** 2. Specialises in bloodstock law, acting for owners, trainers, breeders, jockeys, racing charities and others within the racing and breeding industry. Also general equine law expertise.

WORKLOAD			
Bloodstock	65%	General property work	10%
Commercial property	10%	Commercial litigation	10%
Company commercial	5%		

EDWARD FAIL BRADSHAW & WATERSON

402 COMMERCIAL ROAD, STEPNEY, LONDON, E1 0LG
DX: 300701 Tower Hamlets

TEL: (0171) 790 4032
FAX: (0171) 790 2739

THE FIRM: One of the oldest established firms in East London, Edward Fail have had a reputation as specialists in criminal law since the 1920s. A merger in 1961 with the general practice of Bradshaw & Waterson (founded in 1887) brought a wide range of legal services to the firm and the merged practices have over a century of experience of dealing with the family and business problems of the area.

PRINCIPAL AREAS OF WORK: The firm has a particularly strong reputation in the area of criminal law and deals with the whole spectrum of criminal offences, including serious crime, petty crime and white collar fraud. The firm also has thriving departments in family law, litigation and conveyancing.

CONTACT PARTNER: Howard Riddle

Number of partners:	5
Assistant solicitors:	7
Other fee-earners:	10

WORKLOAD	
Criminal	55%
Civil litigation	18%
Family and matrimonial	17%
Non-contentious	10%

EDWARD LEWIS

VERULAM GARDENS, 70 GRAY'S INN ROAD, LONDON, WC1X 8NF
DX: 1027

TEL: (0171) 404 5566
FAX: (0171) 404 2244

THE FIRM: Edward Lewis is a progressive and growing firm which has established a reputation for taking a practical, creative and business orientated approach to the provision of commercial legal advice to domestic and international clients. The firm has strong European connections and provides multilingual legal services to foreign and UK clients.

In all the key areas of specialisation, Edward Lewis provides a highly competitive, cost effective and professional service which is directed towards achieving its clients' commercial objectives. The partners are committed to delivering a high quality, personalised service, which all contemporary, successful businesses now demand and which is reflected in the calibre and range of individuals and organisations which instruct the firm.

The Edward Lewis business philosophy is supported by a commitment to the recruitment and training of like-minded professional and support staff and by ongoing investment in information technology which serves to ensure an effective and efficient service.

PRINCIPAL AREAS OF WORK: Edward Lewis advises the private and public business sectors on matters relating to the key areas of insurance litigation, company and commercial law, commercial litigation and property. Specialists in these main areas will often work together in integrated teams to advise clients on deals and actions which call for expertise across a broad spectrum of the law. All of the firm's partners have developed niche areas of practice and expertise and are able to advise clients who are active in specific business and industry sectors, where lawyers have to combine precise legal advice with the intrinsic understanding and experience of how a particular market sector operates.

The main areas of law on which advice is provided include: insurance litigation; banking and corporate finance; venture capital; personal injury; professional and medical negligence; public and employers' liability; company and commercial law; property - including planning, landlord and tenant, investment, development and residential; professional indemnity; defamation; employment law; intellectual property; sports; trusts; health and safety; construction; insolvency; cross-border transactions and disputes; EC and UK competition law; and inward investment.

The firm acts for some of the most highly respected, successful organisations and individuals across a range of sectors including: the commercial and domestic insurance and reinsurance markets; fashion and haute couture; banking; media and telecommunications; publishing; politicians; retailing; healthcare; sports; property development, management and investment; transport; private trusts; national and international holding groups and trading companies.

During 1995/96, Edward Lewis plans to continue expanding across all areas of its practice through generic growth and through strategic recruitment of other specialist practitioners. Close attention will be given to ensuring that its clients continue to receive the business orientated, professional service for which the firm is recognised.

New client enquiries are welcomed and should be directed to the firm's marketing department in the first instance which will notify the appropriate partners.

CONTACT PARTNER: Philip Langford

Number of partners:	13
Assistant solicitors:	24
Other fee-earners:	18

WORKLOAD

Insurance litigation	58%
Commercial litigation	17%
Company and commercial	13%
Commercial property	12%

CONTACTS

Banking & corporate finance	Julian Fellerman
	Martin Thomas
Commercial litigation	Alexander Carter-Silk
	Brendan Murphy
Commercial prop.	Jeremy Dening, Rob McKellar
Company and commercial	Philip Langford
	Michael Breen
Defamation & employment	Brendan Murphy
Europe	Barry Lewis
Health authority	Julian Fellerman
Insolvency	Martin Thomas
Insurance litigation	Tony Collins
Intellectual property	Alexander Carter-Silk
	Brendan Murphy
Inward investment	Rob McKellar
Landlord and tenant	Jeremy Dening
Personal injury	Tony Collins, Brian Moore
Professional negligence	Tony Collins
	Brendan Murphy
Public & employers'liability	Jeremy Rutter
	Kieron West
Retail	Jeremy Dening, Rob McKellar
Sports law	Michael Breen
Trusts	Alexander Carter-Silk

T.V. EDWARDS 29 Mile End Rd, London, E1 4TP **Tel:** (0171) 791 1050 **Fax:** (0171) 790 5101 **Ptnrs:** 8 **Asst Solrs:** 23 **Other Fee-earners:** 18. The firm deals mainly with criminal, family, housing, civil litigation, and conveyancing work. Legal aid practice.

EDWARDS FRAIS ABRAHAMSON 8 & 9 Myrtle Parade, Liverpool, Merseyside, L7 7EL **Tel:** (0151) 707 1212 **Fax:** (0151) 707 2458 **DX:** 28953 Liverpool 2 **Ptnrs:** 4 **Asst Solrs:** 4 **Other Fee-earners:** 6. Specialities include mental health, actions against the police, immigration, discrimination, housing and welfare benefits. Criminal and family work also undertaken.

EDWARDS GELDARD Dumfries House, Dumfries Place, Cardiff, S. Glam, CF1 4YF **Tel:** (01222) 238239 **Fax:** (01222) 237268 **DX:** 33001 **Ptnrs:** 30 **Asst Solrs:** 31 **Other Fee-earners:** 17. Offices in Cardiff, London, Derby and Monmouth. Specialities include corporate finance, insolvency, intellectual and commercial property, litigation, construction, public and environmental law, European law and employment law.

E. EDWARDS SON & NOICE

9-15 YORK ROAD, ILFORD, ESSEX, IG1 3AD	TEL: (0181) 514 9000
DX: 200850; E-Mail: eesn@link.org	FAX: (0181) 514 9009

233-235 High Street North, East Ham, London E6.	
DX: 4702 East Ham.	
108 High Street North, East Ham, London E6 2HU.	Fax: (0181) 552 1864.

The Asda Centre, Tollgate Road, Beckton, London E6 4JP.	Fax: (0171) 473 0156.

THE FIRM: A progressive firm which has trebled in size in the last ten years. The emphasis is on solving the legal problems of individuals and businesses in the community practically, quickly and at a reasonable cost. A well resourced practice able to compete with City practices. Committed to quality initiatives and developing new clients.

A Legal Aid Franchise has been awarded in all available areas.

PRINCIPAL AREAS OF WORK:

Personal Injury: (Contact: Christopher Crook). Members of the Personal Injury Panel. Legal Aid Franchise. Specialisation in road accident and industrial injury. As plaintiff acting for individuals, a large number of legal expense insurers and trade unions. As defendants for major insurance clients.

Family: (Contact: Rebecca Wigglesworth). A large expanding practice with the emphasis on mediation to solve financial and children issues.

Injunctions: (Contact: Kulbir Bhangu). No appointment needed for injunction service dealing in domestic violence, racial attacks and unlawful eviction.

Crime: (Contact: Barry Linnane). From routine Magistrate Court matters to major fraud, high profile cases.

Commercial Property: (Contact: Charles Newman and Hilary Green). Clients receive a high degree of personal attention from the partners.

Private Client: (Contact: Charles Newman). Defamation, sports and media, conveyancing.

Domestic conveyancing, wills and probate: (Contact: Elizabeth Stopps).

Planning: (Contact: Peter Ivermee).

Licensing: (Contact: Peter Ivermee).

Housing: (Contact: Gordon Turner). Disrepair, homelessness and unlawful eviction.

Medical Negligence: (Contact: Fiona Freedland and Philippa Barton).

Immigration and Nationality: (Contact: Rita Sethi). Refugee, family re-union and work permits.

Civil Actions Against the Police: (Contact: Georgia Miller).

Agency Work: (Contact: David Emmerson).

CONTACT PARTNER: Charles F. Newman

Number of partners:	9
Assistant solicitors:	15
Other fee-earners:	24

WORKLOAD	
Personal injury and negligence	50%
Others	10%
Housing	10%
Crime	10%
Commercial and domestic conveyancing	10%
Family	10%

CONTACTS	
Civil actions against police	G. Miller
Commercial property	Charles Newman
Crime	Barry Linnane
Domestic convey./ probate	Elizabeth Stopps
Family	Rebecca Wigglesworth
Housing	Gordon Turner
Immigration	Rita Sethi
Injunctions	Kulbir Bhangu
Licensing	Peter Ivermee
Medical negligence	Fiona Freedland
Personal injury	Christopher Crook
Planning	Peter Ivermee
Sports and media	Charles Newman
Welfare benefits	Sian Whittaker

EDWIN COE

2 STONE BUILDINGS, LINCOLN'S INN, LONDON, WC2A 3TH
DX: 191 London

TEL: (0171) 831 7466
FAX: (0171) 405 1108

THE FIRM: Edwin Coe is a long-established commercial firm offering a comprehensive service to corporate and individual clients. A number of standard published works on specific areas of the law have been written by partners of the firm.

PRINCIPAL AREAS OF WORK:

Corporate and Commercial: Clients include multinational corporations, proprietors of family businesses, established companies, individuals and entrepreneurs. The firm handles acquisitions, banking work, conditions and terms of trading, directors' responsibilities, disposals, mergers, partnerships, pension rights and placings, and specialises in charity and housing association law.

Litigation: A large proportion of new clients are referrals from accountants, other solicitors and insurance loss assessors. Services offered include arbitration, asset protection and recovery, banking, commercial litigation, factoring, fraud, insurance claims, intellectual property, landlord and tenant protection, professional and disciplinary tribunals and professional negligence claims.

Commercial Property: Clients range from insurance companies and retailers to banks and friendly societies. The services offered include banking security work, property development, landlord and tenant, licensing, mortgages and debentures, planning, investment acquisitions, property portfolios and rent review advice.

Private Client: Specialises in the commercial development and management of the affairs of high net worth individuals and the creation and management of domestic and foreign trusts, charities, estate planning and administration, tax planning and wills.

Insolvency: The firm's insolvency team is headed by two licensed practitioners and has strong connections with banks and major accountants. It gives advice to both corporate and individual clients on all aspects of administration, liquidation and receivership.

Marine and Aviation: The specialist team undertakes contentious and non-contentious work covering all aspects of international trade, and has correspondent lawyers throughout the world.

CONTACT PARTNER: John Tomlins

Number of partners:	19
Assistant solicitors:	8
Other fee-earners:	10

WORKLOAD	
Litigation	23%
Private client	20%
Commercial property	20%
Corporate and commercial	20%
Insolvency	10%
Marine and aviation	7%

CONTACTS	
Commercial Property:	John Tomlins
Corporate and Commercial:	Peter Loose
Insolvency:	Christopher Berry
Litigation:	David Greene
Marine and Aviation:	Julian Morgan
Private Client:	John Shelford

Edwin Coe

SOLICITORS

EKING MANNING 44 The Ropewalk, Nottingham, Notts, NG1 5EL **Tel:** (0115) 953 2532 **Fax:** (0115) 953 2533 **DX:** 10010 **Ptnrs:** 9 **Asst Solrs:** 7 **Other Fee-earners:** 2. Medium-sized firm founded 100 years ago with a practice covering company/ commercial, insolvency and litigation (notably insurance litigation).

WORKLOAD			
Litigation	40%	Property/private client	20%
Company and commercial	20%	Insolvency	20%

ELBORNE MITCHELL

ONE AMERICA SQUARE, CROSSWALL, LONDON, EC3N 2LB
DX: 1063

TEL: (0171) 320 9000
FAX: (0171) 320 9111

THE FIRM: Ever since the firm was founded in 1968, the work of Elborne Mitchell has been firmly focused on shipping, insurance and international trade. The firm is experienced in dealing with issues and problems in these core business sectors, giving commercial advice on business operations as well as handling shipping and insurance claims and litigation. The firm is a forward-looking group of lawyers, ready to give constructive and independent advice to clients worldwide.

PRINCIPAL AREAS OF WORK:

Insurance and Reinsurance (*Fee-earners:* 20). The firm is well-known for its knowledge and experience in a wide range of insurance and reinsurance matters, from the drafting of policies to the investigation of insurance frauds and the litigation of complex disputes in the insurance and reinsurance markets. Insurance claims work includes professional negligence and product liability claims and Lloyd's litigation.

CONTACT PARTNER: Andrew Pincott

Number of partners:	13
Assistant solicitors:	22
Other fee-earners:	9

WORKLOAD	
Insurance & reinsurance	54%
Commercial litigation	16%
Shipping	16%
Company/ commercial	14%

Shipping and International Trade: (*Fee-earners:* 10). Shipping and the specialist area of admiralty law have always formed an important part of the firm's practice. Its experience extends to public investigations under the Merchant Shipping Act as well as to salvages, ship collisions and total loss claims. The firm has a team of lawyers concerned with the import and export of goods and methods of financing their purchase and sale. They can assist with the special problems arising from carriage of goods by air, sea, rail and road, and the firm's work extends to the insurance aspects of international trade.

Commercial Litigation: (*Fee-earners:* 6). Areas of work include litigation and arbitration of disputes concerning commodities and futures contracts, commercial debt recovery, business disputes, commercial defamation and injunctions.

Company/ Commercial: (*Fee-earners:* 8). The firm can assist with the structuring of business operations whether the client is based in the UK or overseas. It advises on the formation of companies and partnerships, and on any questions of DTI requirements, EC competition law, immigration requirements, contracts of employment and tax implications. The firm can also advise on the acquisition and disposal of property for commercial purposes and for housing staff on secondment from overseas. The firm advises on problems arising from the failure and insolvency of commercial undertakings, particularly in the fields of insurance, shipping and international trade.

INTERNATIONAL CONNECTIONS: While the firm does not have offices overseas, it enjoys close professional relations with firms of lawyers in most parts of the world. Advice on foreign law and local conditions can be obtained quickly, and clients' interests abroad are protected by qualified representatives answering directly to Elborne Mitchell.

RECRUITMENT: The firm recruits four trainee solicitors every year. It looks for intelligent and articulate lawyers with a good general education. Applications should be made on application forms available from Michelle Jepson.

CONTACTS	
Commercial	Philip Greig
Commercial litigation	Tim Brentnall
Lloyd's litigation	Tim Akeroyd
Professional negligence	Nigel Faulks
Reinsurance	Andrew Pincott
Shipping	Nicholas Bourke

Elborne Mitchell
SOLICITORS

ELLIOT MATHER SMITH

THE COURTYARD, 49 LOW PAVEMENT, CHESTERFIELD, DERBYS, S40 1PB
DX: 12362 Chesterfield

TEL: (01246) 231288
FAX: (01246) 204081

Westgate House, 1 Chesterfield Road South, Mansfield, Notts. NG18 5NR
DX: 10347 Mansfield

Tel: (01623) 655666
Fax: (01623) 659949

THE FIRM: One of the largest practices in North Notts. and North-East Derbys., Elliot Mather Smith was founded in 1987 by the merger of two long-established firms, Elliot Smith & Co of Mansfield and Mathers of Chesterfield. With 13 partners and almost 100 staff, the firm is able to offer an extensive legal service to both commercial and private clients.

PRINCIPAL AREAS OF WORK:

Civil Litigation: Personal injury and medical negligence, consumer problems, hire purchase/ finance problems, tenancy disputes, employment law, building disputes and boundary disagreements.

Commercial: Company acquisitions/ disposals, commercial disputes, business restructuring, debt collection.

Conveyancing: Buying or selling – domestic or commercial, leasehold, freehold, auctions.

Criminal: Advice at police station.

Family Law: Divorce and separation, custody and maintenance, child care.

Private Client: Wills, probate and trusts.

PARTNERS: J.D. Winson, B.J.M. Mather, P.A.G. Dickinson, J.F.G. Calthrop, A.T. Johnston, R. Page, P.A. Hollyer, R.A. Anderton, S.D. Woodward, R.L. Bashforth, D.P. Coffey, S.R.J. King, J.R. Wilford.

OTHER OFFICES: 75 Saltergate, Chesterfield, Derbyshire. *Tel:* (01246) 231288. Sherwood House, Holt Lane, Matlock, Derbyshire. *Tel:* (01629) 584885. 17B Glumangate, Chesterfield, Derbyshire. *Tel:* (01246) 550101.

PRACTICE MANAGER: John Evans

Number of partners:	15
Assistant solicitors:	5
Other fee-earners:	18

WORKLOAD	
Crime	25%
Civil litigation	24%
Matrimonial	18%
Personal injury	17%
Conveyancing	11%
Commercial	5%

CONTACTS	
Civil litigation	P.A. Hollyer, J.F.G. Calthrop
Commercial	P.A. Hollyer, A.J. Johnson
Conveyancing	R.Page
Crime	B.J. Mather, R.A. Anderton
Matrimonial	S.D. Woodward, J.D. Winson
Personal injury	P.A.G. Dickinson, J. Calthrop

ELLIOTT & COMPANY

CENTURION HOUSE, DEANSGATE, MANCHESTER, M3 3WT
DX: 14346

TEL: (0161) 834 9933
FAX: (0161) 832 3693

8 Breams Building, Fetter Lane, London EC4A 1EA
DX: 355 (Ch.Ln.)
Contact Partner: Anthony Greenwood; Senior Partner: Geoffrey A. Lord

Tel: (0171) 242 1563
Fax: (0171) 831 8134

THE FIRM: An expanding firm, founded in 1968, and now based in Manchester and London, Elliott & Company offers a comprehensive and commercially aware service to its client base, both in the UK and overseas.

PRINCIPAL AREAS OF WORK:

Litigation: (*Contact Partners:* John Groome – Manchester; Anthony Greenwood – London). The firm specialises in contentious work and has particular experience in insurance law, handling work ranging from professional indemnity, employer and public liability cases to fire and disaster claims and foreign claims. A wide variety of commercial litigation is undertaken, including construction disputes, product liability, insolvency work, debt recovery, personal injury claims, criminal prosecutions, matrimonial matters and consumer problems.

Company/ Commercial: (*Contact Partner:* Katharine Mellor – Manchester; Tony Watkins – London). A full range of commercial services is available. *Work includes:* corporate finance matters, mergers and acquisitions, franchising, computer law, aviation law, intellectual property work, licensing matters and employment law.

Property: (*Contact Partner:* Tim Chapman – Manchester; Roger Dubbins – London). *Work includes:* commercial and residential conveyancing and agricultural law. The firm has significant experience in retail property and in the fields of planning and environmental law.

INTERNATIONAL CONNECTIONS: The firm is a founder member of the Euro-American Lawyers Group, which provides instant access to expert advice throughout Europe and America.

CONTACT PARTNER: David S. Walton

Number of partners:	24
Assistant solicitors:	35
Other fee-earners:	18

CONTACTS	
Commercial litigation	Mike Woolley
Commercial property	David Walton
Company commercial	Katharine Mellor
Construction	Mike Woolley
Employment law	Fiona Miller
Environmental	Barry Holland
Insolvency	Mike Woolley
nsurance litigation	Geoff Lord
Intellectual property	Robert Jones
Licensing	Barry Holland
Medical negligence	Julian Holt
Motor litigation	Clare Edwards
Personal injury	John Groome
Private client	Tim Chapman
Professional negligence	John Groome
Property litigation	Mike Woolley

ELLIOTT DUFFY GARRETT 7 Donegall Square East, Belfast, BT1 5HD **Tel:** (01232) 245034 **Fax:** (01232) 241337 **DX:** 400 NR Belfast **Ptnrs:** 7 **Asst Solrs:** 6 **Other Fee-earners:** 4. A corporate practice best known for its commercial property and construction work.

WORKLOAD			
Commercial property	30%	Labour/ employment	20%
Company/ commercial	20%	Commercial litigation	15%
Private client	10%	Insolvency	5%

ELLIS-FERMOR & NEGUS Market Place, Ripley, Derbys, DE5 3BS **Tel:** (01773) 744744 **Fax:** (01773) 570047 **DX:** 16873 Ripley **Ptnrs:** 10 **Asst Solrs:** 6 **Other Fee-earners:** 9. Long established, originally a general practice, now also acting for a wide range of companies.

WORKLOAD			
Convey (res/commercial)	34%	Lit (civil/commercial)	22%
Family	18%	Probate	12%
Other commercial	5%	Crime	5%

ELLIS JONES Sandbourne House, 302 Charminster Road, Bournemouth, Dorset, BH8 9RU **Tel:** (01202) 525333 **Fax:** (01202) 535935 **DX:** 122752 Bournemouth **Ptnrs:** 9 **Asst Solrs:** 1 . Offers a wide range of legal services including a free accident advice service and computerised debt recovery system.

ELLIS MOXON 83 Marsh Street, Hanley, Stoke-on-Trent, Staffs, ST1 5HL **Tel:** (01782) 202424 **Fax:** (01782) 208015 **DX:** 20717 Hanley **Ptnrs:** 8 **Asst Solrs:** 2 **Other Fee-earners:** 3. Specialise in licensing law; also handle a wide range of law, including legal aid, from three offices.

WORKLOAD			
Civil lit/licensing	30%	Domestic convey/probate	22%
Commercial property	15%	Matrimonial/children	15%
Crime	14%		

ELLISON & CO Headgate Court, Head Street, Colchester, Essex, CO1 1NP **Tel:** (01206) 764477 **Fax:** (01206) 764455 **DX:** 3601 Colchester **Ptnrs:** 10 **Asst Solrs:** 4 **Other Fee-earners:** 17. Specialist departments – criminal, company/ commercial, intellectual property, commercial property, private and commercial litigation, tax, trusts and probate, matrimonial and French property law. Branch office in Harwich and West Mersea.

WORKLOAD			
Civil litigation	31%	Conveyancing	30%
Probate	11%	Divorce and custody	10%
Criminal	10%	Commercial	4%

ELLIS WOOD Langdales, New Garden House, 78 Hatton Garden, London, EC1N 8JR **Tel:** (0171) 242 1194 **Fax:** (0171) 831 9480 **DX:** 248 Ch.Ln. **Ptnrs:** 4 **Asst Solrs:** 2 . Handles litigation, charity work, ecclesiastical, probate, conveyancing and company law. Other office in West Wickham.

ENSOR BYFIELD

EQUITY COURT, MILLBROOK ROAD EAST, SOUTHAMPTON, HANTS, SO15 1RJ
DX: 49665 Southampton 2, E-mail 100565-2711 @ compuserve.com

TEL: (01703) 233433
FAX: (01703) 212127

THE FIRM: Ensor Byfield is dedicated to the provision of all types of commercial advice with a particular speciality in the field of defendant insurance litigation.

The firm is committed to becoming pre-eminent in the central South Western sector of England for legal advice and support of local and national companies in all aspects of their commercial activities from start up to the realisation of their objectives. A brochure is available on request.

TYPES OF WORK UNDERTAKEN: The practice is committed to provide a full range of legal services to the business community with the usual range of services to private clients including financial services.

Company/ Commercial: This department carries out a wide range of business including merger, acquisition and disposal and a wide range of contractual advice in the computer, entertainment and sporting fields, together with debt collection, employment matters and general commercial litigation.

Insurance Litigation: This department comprises a larger number of experienced fee-earning staff than any similar department or firm in the Southampton area. Advice is given to a number of insurers in all areas of claims and free training for Insurance Company personnel is offered.

Commercial Property: This department offers considerable experience in most areas of commercial property transactions with particular reference to office, retail and investment properties.

SENIOR PARTNER: John T. Byfield

Number of partners:	8
Assistant solicitors:	6
Other fee-earners:	11

WORKLOAD	
Insurance litigation	45%
Company/ commercial	33%
Commercial property	12%
Commercial litigation	9%
Private client	1%

ERIC ROBINSON & CO 18 West End Rd, Bitterne, Southampton, Hants, SO9 4NJ **Tel:** (01703) 447734 **Fax:** (01703) 446594 **DX:** 52750 Bitterne **Ptnrs:** 12 **Asst Solrs:** 11 **Other Fee-earners:** 24. A Hampshire firm with eight offices, best known for its conveyancing, matrimonial and criminal practice. Legal aid work undertaken.

WORKLOAD			
Property	28%	Family and matrimonial	23%
Crime	20%	Other civil litigation	13%
Pers injury (plaintiff)	8%	Other non-contentious	8%

ERSKINE MacASKILL & CO 4 Gayfield Square, Edinburgh, EH1 3NW **Tel:** (0131) 557 1520 **Fax:** (0131) 557 5970 **DX:** 191 Edinburgh **Ptnrs:** 3 **Asst Solrs:** 4 . Specialist matrimonial and child law practice. Also undertakes conveyancing, judicial review and criminal defence work. Legal aid work accepted.

EVANS BUTLER WADE 165 Greenwich High Road, London, SE10 8JA **Tel:** (0181) 858 8926 **Fax:** **Ptnrs:** 6 **Asst Solrs:** 2 . Specialists in housing association developments and management work, multi-party personal injury work, and family work, especially in relation to same-sex relationships.

EVANS DODD

5 BALFOUR PLACE, MOUNT STREET, LONDON, W1Y 5RG
DX: 44644 Mayfair

TEL: (0171) 491 4729
FAX: (0171) 499 2297

CONTACT PARTNER: Geoffrey Dodd

Number of partners:	6
Other fee-earners:	3

WORKLOAD	
Company/ commercial	50%
Litigation	25%
Property	15%
Taxation	10%

PRINCIPAL AREAS OF WORK:

General Description: Established in 1975 as a commercial practice with a strong international bias.

Company and Commercial: (*Contact:* Geoffrey Dodd). All aspects of company and commercial work including public and private corporate law, acquisitions, new issues, joint ventures, banking and finance, aircraft acquisitions and financing.

Commercial Property: (*Contact:* William Hayes). Commercial property acquisitions, sales, leases and financing. Domestic property work also undertaken.

Litigation: (*Contact:* Jeremy Hershkorn). All types of commercial litigation and disputes.

Taxation: (*Contact:* Ian Shane). Multi-national tax structuring for companies and off-shore tax planning for individuals.

EVERATT & COMPANY 100 High Street, Evesham, Hereford & Worcs, WR11 4EU **Tel:** (01386) 47191 **Fax:** (01386) 48515 **DX:** 16167 **Ptnrs:** 3 **Asst Solrs:** 1 **Other Fee-earners:** 3. A specialist practice acting for major insurance companies in both employers' liability and road traffic claims.

WORKLOAD	
Personal injury	75%

EDITORIAL POLICY

In this edition, the lists of specialist firms include profiles of individual practitioners - solicitors and barristers - who have been recommended most frequently to our researchers. Editorial policy is to identify leading practitioners on merit: it is not possible to buy a place in our biographical lists. Inclusion of a profile in this directory is based solely on expertise and reputation.

Enormous effort has been invested by our ten-strong research team (mainly solicitors and barristers) in canvassing recommendations and identifying leaders. We are confident in the overall accuracy of the results. However, mistakes and misjudgements are inevitable, and if readers have any suggestions regarding our listings we should be very pleased to hear from them.

The lists will be revised on the basis of fresh research every year.

EVERSHEDS

SENATOR HOUSE, 85 QUEEN VICTORIA STREET, LONDON, EC4V 4JL DX: 83 London Chancery Lane WC2	TEL: (0171) 919 4500 FAX: (0171) 919 4919
Birmingham: 10 Newhall Street, Birmingham B3 3LX Managing Partner: Ian Jollie	Tel: (0121) 233 2001 Fax: (0121) 236 1583
Bristol: 11-12 Queen Square, Bristol, Avon BS1 4NT Managing Partner: David Vokes	Tel: (0117) 929 9555 Fax: (0117) 929 2766
Cardiff: Fitzalan House, Fitzalan Road, Cardiff CF2 1XZ Managing Partner: David Vokes	Tel: (01222) 471147 Fax: (01222) 464347
Derby: 11 St. James Court, Friar Gate, Derby DE1 1BT Managing Partner: Bill Whysall	Tel: (01332) 360992 Fax: (01332) 371469
Ipswich: Churchgates House, Cutler Street, Ipswich IP1 1UR Managing Partner: Colin Brown	Tel: (01473) 233433 Fax: (01473) 233666
Jersey: Suite No 2, Seaton House, 17-19 Seaton Place, St Helier, Jersey JE2 3QL Managing Partner: Michael Chamberlayne	Tel: (01534) 37321 Fax: (01534) 38163
Leeds: Cloth Hall Court, Infirmary Street, Leeds LS1 2JB Managing Partner: David Ansbro	Tel: (0113) 243 0391 Fax: (0113) 245 6188
London: Senator House, 85 Quenn Victoria Street, London EC4V 4JL Managing Partner: Peter Scott	Tel: (0171) 919 4500 Fax: (0171) 919 4919
Manchester: London Scottish House, 24 Mount Street, Manchester M2 3DB Managing Partner: John Moody	Tel: (0161) 832 6666 Fax: (0161) 832 5337
Middlesbrough: Permanent House, 91 Albert Road, Middlesbrough TS1 2PA Managing Partner: Nigel Robson	Tel: (01642) 247456 Fax: (01642) 240446
Newcastle: Milburn House, Dean Street, Newcastle-upon-Tyne NE1 1NP Managing Partner: Nigel Robson	Tel: (0191) 261 1661 Fax: (0191) 261 8270
Norwich: Holland Court, The Close, Norwich NR1 4DX Managing Partner: Colin Brown	Tel: (01603) 272727 Fax: (01603) 610535
Nottingham: 14 Fletcher Gate, Nottingham NG1 2FX Managing Partner: Bill Whysall	Tel: (0115) 936 6000 Fax: (0115) 936 6001
INTERNATIONAL OFFICES: *Berlin:* Mommsenstrasse 73, 10629 Berlin Germany Rechtsanw#3altin: Juliane Reineke	Tel: (49) 30 8844900 Fax: (49) 30 88449090
Brussels: 65 Rue Stevin, 1040 Brussels Partner: David Church	Tel: (32) 2 2308058 Fax: (32) 3 2310677

THE FIRM: Eversheds provides a comprehensive service in all aspects of business law from its 12 offices across England and Wales.

PRINCIPAL AREAS OF WORK: Eversheds operates over 30 specialist groups of lawyers with specialist knowledge, in the following business areas:-

Banking	Food
Building Societies	Financial Collapse
Commercial Law	Franchising
Commercial Litigation	House Building
Commercial Property	Insolvency
Competition	Intellectual Property
Computer/ IT	International
Construction	Licensing
Consumer Credit	Partnerships
Corporate	Pensions

NATIONAL MANAGING PARTNER: Peter Cole
CHAIRMAN: Keith James

Number of partners:	268
Assistant solicitors:	415
Other fee-earners:	270

Corporate Tax	Personal Injury
Debt Recovery	Personal Tax & Financial Planning
Defamation	Planning
Education	Public Sector
Employment	Recoveries for Financial Institutions
Entertainment Media and Sports Law	Residential Property Development
Environmental	Residential Property
European Community	Shipping
Family	Trading

EVERSHEDS

NATURE OF CLIENTS: Its client base consists of major national and international public corporations, local and public authorities and private buisnesses of all sizes. In particular, there is a strong concentration of manufacturing industry across all locations.

FOREIGN CONNECTIONS: The firm also has offices in Brussels and Berlin and liaises with firms in and throughout Europe, USA and the Far East.

RECRUITMENT: Eversheds recruits approximately 70 trainee solicitors each year. Apply to any office for a Trainee Solicitors' brochure and application form.

TRAINING: Eversheds has a full-time Director of Training and a well-established programme of in-house training at all levels.

EVERY & PHILLIPS and DUNNINGS The Laurels, 46 New St, Honiton, Devon, EX14 8BZ **Tel:** (01404) 43431 **Fax:** (01404) 45493 **DX:** 48800 **Ptnrs:** 8 **Asst Solrs:** 6 **Other Fee-earners:** 6. In association with Dunnings, the largest firm in Honiton, dating back to 1740. A broadly-based practice offering a comprehensive service, including agricultural work, from five offices in East Devon.

EVILL & COLEMAN 113 Upper Richmond Road, London, SW15 2TL **Tel:** (0181) 789 9221 **Fax:** (0181) 789 7978 **DX:** 59451 **Ptnrs:** 7 **Asst Solrs:** 7 **Other Fee-earners:** 9. Established over 50 years. Best known for its work in personal injury and medical negligence. Also handles litigation, employment and company/ commercial.

WORKLOAD			
Personal injury/med neg	65%	Conveyancing	14%
Litigation	10%	Company and employment	8%
Probate	3%		

FARLEYS 22-27 Richmond Terrace, Blackburn, Lancs, BB1 7AQ **Tel:** (01254) 668844 **Fax:** (01254) 583526 **DX:** 13604 Blackburn 3 **Ptnrs:** 9 **Asst Solrs:** 10 **Other Fee-earners:** 6. General practice handling company/ commercial, domestic/ commercial conveyancing, criminal, civil litigation, matrimonial, childcare, probate and financial services.

WORKLOAD			
Civil litigation	30%	Criminal	20%
Conveyancing & probate	20%	Family	20%
Company	10%		

FARRER & CO

66 LINCOLN'S INN FIELDS, LONDON, WC2A 3LH
DX: 32

TEL: (0171) 242 2022
FAX: (0171) 831 9748

THE FIRM: Founded in 1701, Farrer & Co has been practising in Lincoln's Inn Fields for 200 years. During this time the firm has built up a broad-based practice with a reputation for combining expertise with a high standard of personal service for both private and commercial clients. The firm draws clients from a worldwide base and has links with lawyers in most countries.

PRINCIPAL AREAS OF WORK:

Commercial: (*Contact:* Elizabeth Potter). A full range of commercial work is covered. Specialisations include: media law; employment and pensions; private company acquisitions; intellectual property; banking law; FSA work; Yellow and Blue Book work and a very significant sports law practice.

CONTACT PARTNER: Robert Clinton

Number of partners:	36
Assistant solicitors:	29
Other fee-earners:	24

CONTACTS	
Agriculture	Ivor Dicker
Banking	James Furber, Nigel Bulmer
Charities	Judith Hill

Litigation: (*Contact:* Adrian Parkhouse). Litigation and arbitration for corporate and private clients on a national, European and international basis. Specialisations include: contractual disputes; media law; (particularly defamation and intellectual property, including pre-publication advice, for both publishers and individuals); all aspects of land use and building claims; family disputes arising from marriage breakdown or inheritance claims including divorce, family provision and child related issues; partnership and trust disputes.

Private Client: (*Contact:* Michael Chantler). All personal legal work: capital tax planning; offshore tax planning; Heritage Property; the Art World and its fiscal and commercial aspects; wills and probate; administration of estates and family law in conjunction with the matrimonial section in the Litigation Department. The personal aspects of private company and intellectual property work in association with the Commercial Department; the personal aspects of property and planning work – domestic, agricultural and commercial – in association with the Property Department; charitable institutions and charity law.

Property: (*Contact:* Stephen Blair). Commercial, agricultural, institutional and domestic property work of all types; planning and environmental law; landlord and tenant law; joint ventures; property security work; agricultural law and practice; estate management; property taxation including VAT.

LANGUAGES SPOKEN: French and German.

Civil litigation	Adrian Parkhouse
Commercial litigation	Richard Parry
Commercial property	Raymond Cooper
Company and commercial	James Thorne
Computer contracts	Peter Wienand
Construction litigation	Adrian Parkhouse
Defamation	Robert Clinton
Education	Henry Boyd-Carpenter
Employment	Elizabeth Potter Geof. Richards
Entertainment and media	Robert Clinton
Family/matrl.	Richard Parry, Fiona Shackleton
Housing associations	Colin Riseam
Intellectual property	Peter Wienand
Landlord & tenant	Raymond Cooper
Pensions	Elizabeth Potter
Professional negligence	Richard Parry
Residential conveyancing	Colin Riseam
Sport and leisure	Charles Woodhouse
Tax - trusts and estates	Henry Boyd-Carpenter
Town and country planning	Raymond Cooper

FAULKNERS

ARGYLL HOUSE, BATH STREET, FROME, SOMERSET, BA11 1DP
DX: 43802 Frome

TEL: (01373) 465051
FAX: (01373) 467414

THE FIRM: Established in the early 1900s, Faulkners is a general practice offering a wide range of legal services to both private and commercial clients. Urgent matters are dealt with out of hours and home visits are available to clients experiencing mobility problems. Legal aid work is undertaken. The four offices within the practice are linked by land lines to a computer network, allowing the establishment of specialist departments within the firm as a whole.

PRINCIPAL AREAS OF WORK:

General Description: *Work includes:* company/ commercial, licensing, insolvency, debt collection, agriculture, residential conveyancing, property development, commercial property, employment, planning, consumer disputes, professional negligence, landlord and tenant, property disputes, criminal work, family and matrimonial, wills, probate, trusts and tax. Nicholas Rheinberg, the East Somerset Coroner, is a member of the Law Society's Personal Injury Panel and with two partners and two Assistant Solicitors together with support staff involved in personal injury, this is a particular strength of the firm, as is matrimonial and child care work, with Paul Borsay and Patricia Wayman members of the Law Society's Children Panel. The firm is represented on the Bath and Mendip Police Station Duty schemes.

OTHER OFFICES: Midsomer Norton, Paulton and Radstock, *Tel:* (01761) 417575.

CONTACT PARTNER: N.L. Rheinberg

Number of partners:	8
Assistant solicitors:	5
Other fee-earners:	2

WORKLOAD	
Domestic conveyancing	28%
Civil litigation	22%
Probate and trusts	18%
Matrimonial	15%
Criminal litigation	8%
Company/ commercial	8%
Welfare	1%

FENNEMORES Bouverie House, 200 Silbury Boulevard, Milton Keynes, Bucks, MK9 1LL **Tel:** (01908) 678241 **Fax:** (01908) 665985 **DX:** 84757 Milton Keynes **Ptnrs:** 14 **Asst Solrs:** 21 **Other Fee-earners:** 54. Best known for its commercial practice covering corporate, property, debt recovery and litigation. Also handles private client matters including conveyancing, probate, personal injury and matrimonial.

FENNERS

180 FLEET STREET, LONDON, EC4A 2HD

TEL: (0171) 430 2200 LDE 256
FAX: (0171) 430 2218

THE FIRM: Fenners is a City firm providing high standards of advice and service in company/ commercial, commercial property, town planning, environmental law and residential property development and offers a leading capability in urban regeneration. The firm has a broad client base including public and private companies, banks and other financial institutions.

PRINCIPAL AREAS OF WORK:

Commercial Property: (Contact Partner: John Fenner). Investment acquisitions and disposals, site assembly and development (retail, office and industrial), regional and city centre schemes involving both the public and private sectors, institutional funding and forward sale agreements, commercial lettings for landlords and tenants, building agreements, secured lending for borrowers and lenders.

Corporate and Commercial Law: (Contact Partner: Robert Fenner). Mergers and acquisitions, reconstructions, joint ventures, new issues, corporate finance, venture capital, financial services and regulatory law, commercial agency, franchising, intellectual property, employment law, employee share option schemes.

Environmental Law: (Contact Partner: Susan Guy). Contaminated land, waste management, pollution control and liabilities and EC regulations.

Planning: (Contact Partner: Susan Guy). Redevelopment schemes (both commercial and residential), urban regeneration schemes, planning agreements for infrastructure work, planning gain and use restrictions, planning appeals and inquiries.

Residential Property Development: (Contact Partner: Carole Joseph). Site assembly and acquisition, management schemes, sales, town planning matters, road, sewer and other similar agreements.

Property Finance: (Contact Partner: Jeremy Taylor). Portfolio reconstructions, development finance and property joint venture schemes.

FOREIGN LANGUAGES: French, German, Italian, Japanese.

CONTACT PARTNER: John Fenner

Number of partners:	4
Assistant solicitors:	1

WORKLOAD	
Commercial property	50%
Corporate/ commercial	35%
Residential property	15%

CONTACTS	
Commercial property	John Fenner
Corporate/ commercial	Robert Fenner
Environmental law	Susan Guy
Planning	Susan Guy
Property finance	Jeremy Taylor
Residential property	Carole Joseph

FENWICK ELLIOTT

353 STRAND, LONDON, WC2R 0HS
DX: 178 LDE

TEL: (0171) 956 9354
FAX: (0171) 956 9355

THE FIRM: Fenwick Elliott is a niche commercial law firm with specialist expertise in construction, energy and property law. The firm acts internationally for main contractors and specialist sub-contractors, institutional investors, developers, local authorities, architects, engineers, surveyors and private clients.

PRINCIPAL AREAS OF WORK: The firm handles all legal issues associated with construction and development, both on- and off-shore. Particular emphasis on dispute resolution, including ADR and arbitration, often involving international elements. The firm is uniquely experienced in the preparation of claims and delay analysis.

CONTACT PARTNER: Robert Fenwick Elliott

Number of partners:	5
Assistant solicitors:	6
Other fee-earners:	2

FEW & KESTER Chequers House, 77-81 Newmarket Rd, Cambridge, Cambs, CB5 8EU **Tel:** (01223) 63111 **Fax:** (01223) 323370 **DX:** 5813 **Ptnrs:** 10 **Asst Solrs:** 5 **Other Fee-earners:** 6. A general practice. Has a well-established clientele including private and commercial clients. Acts for several Cambridge colleges.

FIELD CUNNINGHAM & CO St. Johns Court, 70 Quay St, Manchester, M3 3EL **Tel:** (0161) 834 4734 **Fax:** (0161) 834 1772 **DX:** 728855 **Ptnrs:** 3 **Asst Solrs:** 3 **Other Fee-earners:** 10. Best known for its experience in commercial property, estate development, construction industry work, planning and company/ commercial.

FIELD FISHER WATERHOUSE

41 VINE STREET, LONDON, EC3N 2AA
DX: 823 London

TEL: (0171) 481 4841
FAX: (0171) 488 0084

THE FIRM: Field Fisher Waterhouse is a broadly-based commercial practice with a wealth of experience in specialist areas of work, an office in Brussels and strong international connections.

PRINCIPAL AREAS OF WORK:

Banking and Finance: (*Contact:* Jon Fife or John Wilson). Asset financing and leasing, currency and interest swaps, Financial Services Act, international and domestic lending, offshore funds, insolvency and receiverships.

Corporate Finance: (*Contact:* Tim Davies or Nicholas Thompsell). Capital raising and debt financing, M&A, management buy-outs, joint ventures, privatisations and corporate reorganisations.

Commercial Law and Intellectual Property: (*Contact:* Mark Abell or Richard Bagehot). Advertising and sales promotion, IT law, distribution and franchising, entertainment, intellectual property, sponsorship.

Commercial Property: (*Contact:* Howard Coffell or Simon Gibbs). Development planning and financing, secured lending, golf courses and recreational properties, hotels and licensed premises, industrial complexes, office and store developments, pipeline conveyancing, and commercial and residential leasing.

EC and Competition Law: (*Contact:* Ian Barnard or Charles Whiddington). All aspects of EC and UK competition law and of single market regulation.

Litigation: (*Contact:* Mark Lowe or Nicholas Rose). Administrative law, contractual disputes, travel and tourism disputes, construction and development, defamation, EC law, insurance, intellectual property, international trade, professional negligence and discipline. The firm also has a large medical litigation practice covering asbestosis, disaster law, pharmaceutical accidents, medical negligence, product liability, and professional conduct (*Contact:* Rodney Nelson-Jones).

Private Client: (*Contact:* Mark Tod). Tax and financial planning, wills, the administration of estates and trusts, UK and overseas settlements, heritage property.

Tax: (*Contact:* Nicholas Noble or Graeme Nuttall). Tax planning for UK and multinational companies, taxation of financial instruments, employee benefits and share schemes and VAT.

Travel, Tourism and Leisure: (*Contact:* Andrew Little or Peter Stewart). Clients include travel agents and tour operators, hotels, restaurants, caterers and leisure complexes, airlines and other carriers.

OTHER AREAS OF WORK: The firm is also well-known for its work in charity law, employment law, immigration, industrial accident and disease disputes, liquor licensing and professional discipline.

NATURE OF CLIENTELE: The firm acts mainly for banks and other financial institutions, listed and unlisted companies, governments and their agencies, professional partnerships and bodies, trade associations, and entrepreneurs.

FOREIGN CONNECTIONS: The firm has an office in Brussels and has particularly strong connections with other EC countries, China, Japan, Korea, Scandinavia and the USA. Languages spoken fluently include Danish, French, German, Italian, Japanese, Mandarin, Polish, Spanish and Swedish.

RECRUITMENT: The firm has a constant need for quality trainee solicitors and laterals; seminars and other training courses are conducted regularly.

MANAGING PARTNER: John Nelson-Jones

Number of partners:	46
Assistant solicitors:	33
Other fee-earners:	37

WORKLOAD

Company and commercial/ tax	34%
Commercial property	19%
Litigation	18%
Banking and finance	11%
Regulatory	8%
Private client	8%
Licensing	2%

CONTACTS

Banking and finance	Jon Fife
Commercial property	Simon Gibbs
Commercial litigation	Mark Lowe
Construction	Colin McArthur
Corporate finance	Tim Davies
EC and competition law	Ian Barnard
Employment	Tony Fisher
Energy	Howard Coffell
Int. trade and projects	John Wilson
IP/franchising	Mark Abell
IT/Computer	Ranald Robertson
Licensing	Peter Glazebrook
Medical litigation	Rodney Nelson-Jones
Private client	Mark Tod
Regulatory	Paul Honigmann
Tax (corporate)	Nicholas Noble
Travel, tourism and hotels	Peter Stewart

FIELDINGS PORTER Silverwell House, Silverwell Street, Bolton, Lancs, BL1 1PT **Tel:** (01204) 387742 **Fax:** (01204) 362129 **DX:** 24112 **Ptnrs:** 12 **Asst Solrs:** 9 **Other Fee-earners:** 8. Well-established legal practice, with particular strengths in commercial work, litigation and family law. Three offices in Bolton and Blackburn.

FIELD SEYMOUR PARKES 1 London Street, Reading, Berks, RG1 4QW **Tel:** (01734) 391011 **Fax:** (01734) 502704 **DX:** 4001 **Ptnrs:** 11 **Asst Solrs:** 3 **Other Fee-earners:** 12. A general practice handling company/ commercial, litigation, planning, crime, conveyancing and family law.

WORKLOAD			
Civil litigation	22%	Domestic conveyancing	14%
Commercial conveyancing	13%	Probate/wills/trusts	12%
Company/ commercial	10%	Debt collection	9%

FINERS

179 GREAT PORTLAND ST, LONDON, W1N 5FD
DX: 42739

TEL: (0171) 323 4000
FAX: (0171) 580 7069

THE FIRM: This medium-sized commercial firm is young and progressive, both in its thinking and in the way in which it is building its practice. Finers has an acknowledged reputation for handling work of quality and substance in a practical and commercial manner.

PRINCIPAL AREAS OF WORK:

Commercial Property: (*Contact:* Michael Bibring). This is an extremely active department, advising household name clients, developers, investment companies and national retail and restaurant chains in connection with developments, joint ventures, sales, purchases and leases of offices, shops, and industrial premises in the UK and abroad. The firm also advises on planning and licensing matters.

Company and Commercial: (*Contact:* Peter Jay). The department handles all types of public and private company work, including acquisitions, mergers and flotations. It also covers information technology, insolvency, partnership and employment law, and has recognised expertise in entertainment law, advising well-known personalities in the film and sports world on their contracts and copyrights.

Litigation: (*Contact:* Richard Gerstein). Mostly active in the High Court, but also in foreign jurisdictions, and dealing with every kind of dispute from major international commercial contracts to employment disputes, this department has particular interest in construction, defamation, restraint of trade, professional negligence and intellectual property. It also acts as Privy Council agents for Commonwealth appeals.

Commercial Franchise, Inland Revenue & Customs and Excise Investigations: (*Contact:* David Swede). This department advises clients, (including other professional advisers) on claims, disputes and prosecutions by the Revenue and other prosecuting authorities. The department also advises in relation to civil fraud including clients' internal investigations.

Private Client: (*Contact:* Michael Green). This department handles residential property, wills, probate, family matters, immigration, employment, tax and personal finance.

International: (*Contact:* David Swede). The firm is an active member of the International Lawyers Group, and has been making plans to exploit the opportunities which the Single European Market will provide.

RECRUITMENT AND TRAINING: Finers will be recruiting four trainee solicitors each year and offer a package which includes a bonus scheme and health care. Write, enclosing a CV, to Stephen Bernstein.

CONTACT PARTNER: Mr D.S. Swede

Number of partners:	26
Assistant solicitors:	10
Other fee-earners:	7

WORKLOAD	
Property	44%
Litigation	31%
Company/ commercial	24%
Private client	1%

CONTACTS	
Company/ commercial	Peter Jay
Employment	Anthony Barling
Litigation	Richard Gerstein
Matrimonial	Christopher Butler
Personal injury	Leon Marks
Property	Michael Bibring

FINN, GLEDHILL & CO 1-4 Harrison Rd, Halifax, W. Yorks, HX1 2AG **Tel:** (01422) 330000 **Fax:** (01422) 342604 **DX:** 16022 Halifax **Ptnrs:** 7 **Asst Solrs:** 2 **Other Fee-earners:** 5. Founded 1731, and one of the largest firms in Halifax, they have an all-round practice with an emphasis on commercial work.

WORKLOAD			
Comm (prop/fin/company)	35%	Civil lit (comm/other)	18%
Conveyancing	12%	Crime	10%
Divorce and matrimonial	10%	Probate and trust	9%

FISHBURN BOXER

60 STRAND, LONDON, WC2N 5LR
DX: 8 Ch.Ln.

TEL: (0171) 925 2884
FAX: (0171) 486 3256

THE FIRM: Fishburn Boxer is a progressive, medium-sized firm with attractive, centrally located offices in the Strand. The firm has modern computer and database facilities, an extensive library and research resources. The long-term prospects for the firm are sustained growth through recruitment from within.

PRINCIPAL AREAS OF WORK:

General Description: The firm handles substantial High Court litigation, commercial work in insurance and professional indemnity for Lloyd's of London and insurance companies, commercial and residential conveyancing, company and tax work.

Insurance: (*Contact:* Andrew Davies). *Work includes:* all types of insurance and reinsurance disputes, claims, professional indemnity, setting up insurance schemes, drafting policy wordings and undertaking prerisk surveys.

Litigation: (*Contact:* Richard Ellis). *Work includes:* commercial, High Court, building contract disputes, slander and libel, personal injury, employment, and intellectual property.

Company/commercial property: (*Contact:* Michael Bowden). *Work includes:* company formations, acquisitions and disposals of shares and assets, takeover agreements, joint ventures, service agreements, management buy-outs, shareholders' agreements, loan documents and insolvency and property letting and leasing, landlord and tenant.

NATURE OF CLIENTELE: Fishburn Boxer has a wide, primarily corporate, client base. It also acts for individuals in employment, conveyancing, estate and tax planning.

FOREIGN CONNECTIONS: Associated practices in the USA.

LANGUAGES SPOKEN: French, German, Spanish and Russian.

RECRUITMENT AND TRAINING: (*Recruitment Partner:* Christopher Lowney). Trainee solicitors are recruited annually. Regular in-house seminars and training sessions are held for all staff.

CONTACT PARTNER: Richard Ellis

Number of partners:	13
Assistant solicitors:	17
Other fee-earners:	13

WORKLOAD	
Litigation	95%
Corporate and commercial	5%

CONTACTS	
ADR	Alison Wallace
Building	Mark Klint
Commercial litigation	Richard Ellis
Construction	John Cayton
Corporate	Michael Bowden
Employment	Alison Wallace
Insurance & reinsurance	Stephen Leonard
Personal injury	Christopher Lowney
Private client	Michael Bowden
Professional indemnity	Andrew Davis
Property	Michael Bowden

FISHER MEREDITH

2 BINFIELD RD, LONDON, SW4 6TA
DX: 37050

FAMILY & CONVEYANCING

TEL: (0171) 622 4468
FAX: (0171) 498 0415

Tel: (0171) 924 9124
Fax: (0171) 924 9906

THE FIRM: Founded by Eileen Meredith Pembridge and another in 1975, Fisher Meredith now consists of six partners and 56 other staff. It has always been a High Street practice doing a large amount of legal aid work but is departmentalised for increased efficiency and to meet specialisation needs. The firm remains firmly committed to personal litigation and legal aid work and is still expanding. Fisher Meredith now has departments specialising in (a) family work of all types including children's advocacy and domestic violence, (b) a substantial amount of criminal law, (c) actions against the Police (d) mental health work (e) non-contentious work including conveyancing, wills and probate, (f) libel, (g) immigration, (h) welfare benefits and (i) housing law. Eileen Pembridge is the Law Society Council member for London South, member of the Courts & Legal Services Committee and Chair of the Law Society's Family Law Committee. The firm has a franchise in family and crime and has applied for further categories in immigration, welfare benefits and actions against the police.

PRINCIPAL AREAS OF WORK:

Family: (*Contact:* Eileen Pembridge/ Keith Price. *Fee-earners:* 12 including 3 on Children's Panel). Covers divorce, complex ancillary relief, cohabitation, inheritance, injunctions and all types of children's cases.

Crime: (*Contact:* Stephen Hewitt/ Paul Graham. *Fee-earners:* 12). A large and thriving department offering an efficient, careful and caring service.

CONTACT PARTNER:
Ms. Eileen Pembridge

Number of partners:	6
Assistant solicitors:	19
Other fee-earners:	9

WORKLOAD	
Crime	53%
Family	24%
Children	10%
Conveyancing	4%
Actions against police	1%
Wills & probate	1%

Police Cases: (*Contact:* Ian Marsden. *Fee-earners:* 3). An efficient and dedicated service.

Defamation: (*Contact:* Eileen Pembridge. *Fee-earners:* 1). The firm has handled some high profile cases in the past and concentrates on plaintiff work.

Residential and Commercial Conveyancing: (*Contact:* Rosalind Widgery/ June van Eck. *Fee-earners:* 3). A friendly and prompt service from senior solicitors. The department offers a moderately priced fast and efficient service on all aspects of conveyancing and wills and on non-contentious probate.

Mental Health: (*Contact:* Chinyeri Inyama. *Fee-earners:* 2 both on MHRT Panel). A prompt and caring service.

Immigration: (*Contact:* Rosie Brennan/ Smita Bajaria. *Fee-earners:* 3). Offers advice and representation on all aspects.

Housing law: (*Contact:* Stephen Pierce. *Fee-earners:* 2). All aspects of housing law for tenants, other residential occupiers and applicants for housing.

Welfare benefits: (*Contact:* Stephen Pierce. *Fee-earners:* 2). All social security appeals, housing benefit review boards and judicial reviews.

NATURE OF CLIENTELE: The firm's clients are mostly individuals engaged in personal transactions or litigation.

LANGUAGES SPOKEN: French, Spanish, German, Russian and Danish.

AGENCY WORK: Fisher Meredith may accept instructions in its areas of special emphasis.

CHARGES: For legal aid work, the charges are as fixed by the LCD. For private clients, the firm charges £80-£120 per hour, as of early 1995.

CONTACTS	
Children	Nina Hansen
Conveyancing	Ros Widgery
Crime	Stephen Hewitt
Family	Eileen Pembridge
Housing	Stephen Pierce
Immigration	Rosie Brennan
Police actions	Ian Marsden
Welfare benefits	Stephen Pierce
Wills & probate	June Van-Eck

FITZHUGH GATES 3 Pavilion Parade, Brighton, E. Sussex, BN2 1RY **Tel:** (01273) 686811 **Fax:** (01273) 676837 **DX:** 2727 Brighton 1 **Ptnrs:** 8 **Asst Solrs:** 4 **Other Fee-earners:** 9. Established 1806. Substantial experience in domestic and commercial conveyancing. Also undertakes litigation and licensing. One partner is a legal member of the Royal Town Planning Institute and on the Law Society's Planning Panel.

FLADGATE FIELDER

HERON PLACE, 3 GEORGE ST, LONDON, W1H 6AD
DX: 9057 West End

TEL: (0171) 486 9231
FAX: (0171) 935 7358

CONTACT PARTNER: Howard Keen

Number of partners:	32
Assistant solicitors:	19
Other fee-earners:	16

THE FIRM: Fladgate Fielder is a commercially orientated Central London law firm with a pedigree that may be traced back over 200 years. The firm offers legal advice of the highest quality in a non-bureaucratic environment; its clients comprise UK, European, US and Israeli listed companies, UK and Canadian insitutions, major private companies and entrepreneurs.

Pivotal to the firm's success are the following factors; namely its standard of excellence in client service, the calibre of its expertise, its innovative and commercial approach to the solution of problems and the combination of efficiency and cost effectiveness to reach the optimum result.

The firm's Basingstoke office replicates the services offered by its London counterpart with the additional focus on information technology businesses.

PRINCIPAL AREAS OF WORK:

Corporate: Listings and flotations, mergers and acquisitions, venture capital, MBO's, UK and cross border corporate and commercial transactions, employment, immigration, computer and intellectual property law, banking, partnership law and company seceretarial work.

Property: Acquisition and disposal, funding, development investment, secured lending, landlord and tenant, housing association, joint ventures, portfolio management and residential estate conveyancing.

Litigation: General commercial litigation, professional negligence, asset recovery, corporate recovery, landlord and tenant, intellectual property, libel, construction disputes, building and product liability and personal injury cases.

CONTACTS	
Anglo-American	David Shier
Anglo-Far Eastern	Bryan Dowler
Anglo-German	Andrew Kaufman
Anglo-Israeli	Avram Kelman
Corporate	Nicolas Greenstone
Employment	Charles Boundy
Immigration	Philip Barth
Libel	Simon Ekins
Litigation	Paul Leese
Property	Allen Cohen
Tax	Andrew McKenzie
Town Planning	Daniel Drukarz

Tax: All aspects of taxation including corporate and business taxes as well as offshore and international aspects, personal tax planning, wills, probate, charities and land estate matters.

FOREIGN CONNECTIONS: Fladgate Fielder has an expanding international dimension based on multi-lingual, dual qualified lawyers working out of London. The firm has Anglo American, German, Israeli and Far Eastern desks and is able to conduct business in German, French, Spanish, Hebrew, Danish and Thai.

OTHER OFFICES:

Walgate House, 25 Church Street, Basingstoke, Hampshire RG21 7QQ.
Tel: (01256) 463044. *Fax:* (01256) 471600.

FLINT, BISHOP & BARNETT Royal Oak House, Market Place, Derby, Derbys, DE1 2EA **Tel:** (01332) 340211 **Fax:** (01332) 347107 **DX:** 11504 **Ptnrs:** 18 **Asst Solrs:** 8 **Other Fee-earners:** 20. One of the largest firms in Derbyshire having seven offices located through the county and offering a full range of specialist legal services including agency work.

WORKLOAD			
Commercial	34%	Property	27%
Litigation (PI)	22%		

FLYNN & McGETTRICK 24-26 Arthur Street, Belfast, BT1 3EF **Tel:** (01232) 244212 **Fax:** (01232) 236490 **Ptnrs:** 3 **Asst Solrs:** 3 . Known for its criminal and civil liberties work.

FOOT & BOWDEN Foot & Bowden Building, 21 Derry's Cross, Plymouth, Devon, PL1 2SW **Tel:** (01752) 675000 **Fax: DX:** 8227 Plymouth 1 **Ptnrs:** 25 **Asst Solrs:** 15 **Other Fee-earners:** 18. Specialist teams with extensive legal experience and expertise in commercial, conveyancing, planning, shipping, litigation, probate, trust, family and criminal work.

WORKLOAD			
Private client	35%	Commercial	25%
Comm lit/incl shipping	20%	Commercial property	10%
Media	10%		

FORBES & PARTNERS

2-6 WELLINGTON STREET, ST. JOHNS, BLACKBURN, LANCS, BB1 8DD
DX: 17952

TEL: (01254) 54374
FAX: (01254) 52347

THE FIRM: Established over fifty years ago, Forbes & Partners is a general practice with a mixed commercial and private client base. A substantial amount of legal aid work is undertaken.

PRINCIPAL AREAS OF WORK: The practice handles a wide variety of work, including company/ commercial, agriculture, civil and commercial litigation, debt recovery, employment, criminal prosecutions, family and matrimonial work, housing, immigration, licensing, wills, probate and trusts, and financial services.

OTHER OFFICES: Blackburn (3), Accrington (2), Clitheroe and Preston.

CONTACT PARTNER: Peter Scholes

Number of partners:	14
Assistant solicitors:	24
Other fee-earners:	18

WORKLOAD	
Private client	40%
Crime	20%
Insurance litigation	20%
Company and commercial	20%

FORD SIMEY DAW ROBERTS 8 Cathedral Close, Exeter, Devon, EX1 1EW **Tel:** (01392) 74126 **Fax:** (01392) 410933 **DX:** 8316 Exeter **Ptnrs:** 16 **Asst Solrs:** 5 **Other Fee-earners:** 11. Main areas of work include civil and criminal litigation, commercial, conveyancing, family law, and personal injuries work. Specialist Leisure Sector Group acting for hotels, restaurants and clubs.

FORD AND WARREN

WESTGATE POINT, WESTGATE, LEEDS, W. YORKS, LS1 2AX
DX: 12064 Leeds

TEL: (0113) 243 6601
FAX: (0113) 242 0905

CONTACT PARTNER: Keith Hearn

Number of partners:	11
Assistant solicitors:	20
Other fee-earners:	23

THE FIRM: Located in fully computerised modern offices in the heart of Leeds' thriving business community, Ford and Warren is known throughout Yorkshire for its broad range of expertise, including management law, commercial litigation, employment law, education law, commercial property work, investment advice, personal injury, professional negligence and transport and distribution.

PRINCIPAL AREAS OF WORK:

Commercial Litigation: *(Contact Partner:* Stephen Kirkbright). The firm deals with a full range of commercial disputes with particular strength in construction and development and transport and distribution law. Experience incorporates comprehensive knowledge of insurance, intellectual property, product liability and licensing.

Corporate and Commercial: *(Contact Partner:* Peter Reeve). *Work includes:* all aspects of corporate and commercial advice to business clients, alongside commercial contracts, media contracts and tax planning advice.

Transport and Distribution: *(Contact Partner:* Stephen Kirkbright). The firm has an established reputation for national and international transport and distribution law.

Commercial Property and Development: *(Contact Partner:* Edward Brown). The firm has extensive experience working with industrial, commercial and retail property. The department has established strong links with the licensed and leisure industry acting for large brewers and small publicans. Guidance is also offered on all aspects of planning and environmental issues.

Agricultural and Rural Law: *(Contact Partner:* David Wightman). This department works on behalf of rural estates and their management, EC quotas, landlord and tenant relationships and general property matters.

Employment and Industrial Relations: *(Contact Partner:* Keith Hearn). *Work includes:* management and workforce restructuring, Industrial Tribunals, service and contract agreements, health authority work, health and safety regulations, trade union labour relations, competition law, and EU Law and Directives.

Personal Injury: *(Contact Partner:* Blaise Smith). The firm has an established international reputation for personal injury work, having co-ordinated multi-plaintiff litigation in the Zeebrugge, Hillsborough and Bradford fire disasters, and the air disaster at Tenerife. The firm also conducts defendant work.

Insurance: *(Contact Partner:* Nick Collins). This is an expanding department that deals with a wide range of actions from personal injury to product liability for a number of large insurance clients.

Professional Negligence: *(Contact Partner:* Blaise Smith). The firm has extensive experience in medical negligence cases, most notably representing clients through the Myodil drugs litigation.

Insolvency: *(Contact Partner:* Stephen Kirkbright). *Work includes:* all aspects of insolvency work, including issuing proceedings and attending creditors' meetings.

Debt Recovery: *(Contact Partner:* Gary Hodgson). *Work includes:* credit control and debt recovery – High Court and County Court work. This department provides a fully computerised debt recovery system.

Education Law: *(Contact Partner:* Edward Brown). All aspects of law relating to education are comprehensively covered. The firm works closely with independent schools, grant maintained schools and special needs schools.

Charities: *(Contact Partner:* Edward Brown). *Work includes:* all aspects of charity law – from formation through to administration.

Conveyancing and Employee Relocation: *(Contact Manager:* John Robson). This commercially aware department advises on tax and employment law implications of employee relocation; and operates a fully computerised conveyancing system.

Private Client: *(Contact Partner:* Nigel Dixon). The firm offers advice on tax and general financial affairs, family law and residential conveyancing.

NATURE OF CLIENTELE: Clients include private individuals, insurance companies, institutional clients, local and national authorities, other professional advisors, and national and international PLCs.

LANGUAGES SPOKEN: French, German, Spanish.

RECRUITMENT AND TRAINING: Two to three trainee solicitors are recruited annually. Applications to Mr Blaise Smith.

FORSYTE SAUNDERS KERMAN

79 NEW CAVENDISH ST, LONDON, W1M 8AQ
DX: 99 Ln.

TEL: (0171) 637 8566
FAX: (0171) 436 6088

Suite 688 Lloyd's, One Lime Street, London EC3M 7HA
DX 807 London City

Tel: (0171) 327 3388/3399
Fax: (0171) 621 1217

CONTACT PARTNER: Alan Kaufman

Number of partners:	31
Assistant solicitors:	17
Other fee-earners:	20

WORKLOAD

Commercial property	49%
Litigation	31%
Company/ commercial	15%
Private client	5%

CONTACTS

Commercial property	Catherine Diggle
Company/ commercial	Peter Carter
Litigation	Howard Zetter
Private client	Michael Lewis

THE FIRM: Forsyte Saunders Kerman is an independent medium-sized firm, whose spread and depth of commercial work reflects its effective approach and commitment.This is a commitment to understanding and achieving clients' business objectives. This is reflected in the quality of the firm's clients which would be the envy of many larger firms. It is large enough to handle substantial and sophisticated projects, yet small enough to encourage individual development. It makes the same commitment to its training programme and its lawyers. Forsyte Saunders Kerman is particularly highly regarded for its top quality commercial property and corporate work; it has a substantial High Court litigation practice (including a specialist property litigation team and insurance claims team) and an active private client department. The firm is managed on truly corporate lines with a Board headed by a Chairman, Paul Di Biase, and Managing Partner, Alan Kaufman.

PRINCIPAL AREAS OF WORK:

Property: (*Contact:* Catherine Diggle. *14 Partners).* The department handles the whole range of property transactions in the private and public sectors including city centre and other commercial developments, planning, investment acquisitions and disposals, owner/ occupier sales and purchases, retail property transactions and property transactions for the leisure industry. The department includes a unit which specialises in all property transactions required by residential developers and housebuilders.

Company and Commercial: (*Contact:* Peter Carter. *5 Partners).* The department's activities encompass the full range of corporate and commercial work. Clients include quoted and unquoted companies, partnerships and sole proprietors with a special emphasis on entrepreneurial and management-owned businesses. Its main areas of work are corporate finance including acquisitions and disposals of both public and private companies, management buy-outs and buy-ins and all forms of commercial work including intellectual property, media-related agreements, joint ventures and competition. The department also has niche expertise in consumer credit documentation for financial institutions.

Litigation: (*Contact:* Howard Zetter.*9 Partners).* The department is experienced in giving a swift practical service to the business and private client in a way which is sensitive to clients' needs and priorities. It handles a wide range of commercial and civil litigation and is particularly well-known for: property-related disputes, insurance claims, construction actions and arbitrations, inter company and partnership disputes, employment and family work.

Private Client: (*Contact:* Michael Lewis. *2 Partners).* The department advises individuals, trusts and executors in business, professional, or public life including overseas nationals whose United Kingdom interests need to be protected or promoted. It provides a wide range of services relating to tax, wills and trusts and is particularly noted for tax planning and asset protection for wealthy individuals and business proprietors.

RECRUITMENT: Forsyte Saunders Kerman recruits several trainee solicitors every year; it offers excellent training and rapid career progression. Application form and brochure available from Rabinder Chaggar.

ForsyteSaundersKerman

FOSTER BAXTER COOKSEY

7-10 GEORGE STREET, SNOW HILL, WOLVERHAMPTON,
W. MIDLANDS, WV2 4DN   DX: 702433 Wolverhampton 5

TEL: (01902) 311711
FAX: (01902) 311102

THE FIRM: Formed by the merger of four well-established Midlands firms, Foster Baxter Cooksey now has over one hundred staff and serves a broad spectrum of private and business clients. The firm has particular expertise in corporate work, intellectual property and civil litigation.

PRINCIPAL AREAS OF WORK:

Corporate Services: *(Contact Partner:* Robert Brown). Areas on which the firm can advise include setting up new companies and partnerships, business structures, shareholders' agreements, directors' rights, duties and obligations, takeovers and buyouts, re-financing and security documentation, asset acquisition and disposal, computer and data protection law, taxation, VAT and insurance, product liability and franchising. Work also includes patent, copyright, trademarks and other intellectual property rights.

Commercial Property: *(Contact Partner:* Simon Bowdler). The firm covers a range of areas including commercial conveyancing, landlord and tenant law, financing, commercial property development, property investment, residential development, planning and environmental law, property taxation and agricultural property.

Litigation: *(Contact Partner:* Nigel Sellar). The litigation department serves both business and private clients, handling cases which vary from complex injunctions and intellectual property claims to matrimonial and family disputes.

Legal Audits: *(Contact Partner:* David Baxter). The firm's legal audit service can advise on articles of association and shareholders' agreements, partnership agreements, grievance, disciplinary and dismissal procedures, health and safety, trading terms and conditions, supplier contracts, lease agreements, insurance, pension and share option schemes, and security documentation.

Insolvency: *(Contact Partner:* Robert Brown). The insolvency team is headed by a Licensed Practitioner and in addition to providing the full legal back-up for liquidators, receivers and administrators, the firm can also be appointed to act as receivers or liquidators in appropriate cases. The firm has a computerised debt recovery system.

Employment: *(Contact Partner:* Tracy Worthington). The firm has extensive knowledge of employment law and can advise on areas such as employment contracts, disciplinary procedures, unfair and wrongful dismissal, discrimination claims, redundancy, tribunal representation, accident claims and maternity rights.

Private Client: *(Contact Partner:* Ian Fallon). A full service is offered to the private individual and includes residential conveyancing, wills, probate, trusts, estate administration, personal injury and medical negligence claims, employment and family/ matrimonial law.

OTHER OFFICES: Telford and Willenhall.

INTERNATIONAL CONNECTIONS: The firm has close professional connections with law firms in the European Community, and has held seminars on the implications of the single European market for commercial clients and professional associates, and language courses for staff. The firm has formal associates with law firms in Brussels, Milan, Munich and Paris, and informal contacts in several other countries.

RECRUITMENT & TRAINING: The firm recruits three trainee solicitors (with at least a 2.1 degree) each year. Applicants should write to Nigel Sellar, Training Partner, with a full CV.

CONTACT PARTNER: David H.W. Baxter

Number of partners:	14
Assistant solicitors:	8
Other fee-earners:	8

CONTACTS	
Commercial property	Simon Bowdler
Corporate services	Robert Brown
Employment	Tracy Worthington
Insolvency	Robert Brown
Legal audits	David Baxter
Litigation	Nigel Sellar
Private client	Ian Fallon

FOSTERS

60 LONDON STREET, NORWICH, NORFOLK, NR2 1JY
DX: 5225 Norwich-1

TEL: (01603) 620508
FAX: (01603) 624090

MANAGING PARTNER: Andrew Saul

Solicitors:	18
Other fee-earners:	21

WORKLOAD	
Family	31%
PI/ professional negligence	18%
Crime and mental health	17%
Residential property	11%
Commercial litigation	8%
Commercial property	6%
Trusts and probate	4%
General civil litigation	4%
Welfare benefits	1%

CONTACTS	
Civil litigation	Ian Comer
Commercial litigation	Iain Roden
Crime and mental health	Bruce Chilton
Family	Catherine Iliff
Property	Alice Liddle
Trusts and probate	Bryan Blythe
Welfare benefits	David Buchanan

THE FIRM: Established in 1761, but a radical and forward looking practice. Strong regional and growing national reputation.

STRUCTURE: Streamlined corporate structure designed to provide clear career paths and real opportunities for all staff.

STANDARDS: Fierce commitment to providing a first class and cost effective service to all clients. Standards of work published to clients and rigorously applied.

STAFF: Emphasis on quality of staff throughout. All staff closely involved in achieving the firm's goals. Regular in-house training.

CLIENTS: Wide range of private and corporate clients. Special facilities provided for the disabled.

SURGERIES: Free specialist advice surgeries for private and business clients.

AGENCY: Magistrates, Crown, County and High Court instructions regularly undertaken. Specialist assistance available.

AREAS OF WORK: General practice with strong reputation in specialist areas. Recruitment of City of London specialists has enabled Fosters to provide an enviable service.

Family: All areas, emphasis on difficult (including high value) cases, child abduction, international cases etc. Members of Children Panel, Family Mediators Association and SFLA. Largest family department in East Anglia and one of the top departments in England and Wales.

Commercial Litigation: All areas including contractual matters, employment, debt, building disputes, health and safety, etc.

Commercial Property: Wide experience, including developments, tenancy matters, management insolvency, health sector and housing association work.

Crime: Wide range of personal and business offences covered, from minor to most serious. Members of Duty Solicitors and PACE schemes.

Mental Health: Specialist representation, membership of Mental Health Review Tribunal Panel.

Planning: Specialist planning expertise provided both to the public and to local authorities.

Personal Injury: Extensive plaintiff work, membership of Personal Injury Panel. One of the fastest growing departments in the region.

Professional Negligence: Reputation especially for medical and solicitors negligence.

Private Client Trusts and Probate: Special focus upon needs of elderly.

Domestic Property: Strong growth (despite the recession) based upon quality, speed and value.

BRANCH OFFICE: Bungay, Suffolk.

TRAINING: Work experience places for students: apply well in advance. Limited number of future vacancies for trainee and newly qualified solicitors of high calibre.

FOX & GIBBONS

2 OLD BURLINGTON STREET, LONDON, W1X 2QA
DX: 37244

TEL: (0171) 439 8271
FAX: (0171) 734 8843

CONTACT PARTNER: Christopher Dixon

UK:	
Number of partners:	11
Assistant solicitors:	7
Other fee-earners:	11

THE FIRM: Established in 1959, Fox & Gibbons is the longest established British law firm in the Middle East and has the largest number of offices there.

PRINCIPAL AREAS OF WORK:

Company/ Commercial: (*Contact:* Christopher Dixon). *Work includes:* all types of company/ commercial law; joint ventures, agency and distribution agreements, mergers and acquisitions, including MBOs and MBIs (with a special emphasis on cross-border transactions); including listed company ESOPs and all aspects of non-contentious employment law and executive remuneration planning, all aspects of employee share ownership, intellectual property law and EC law both through its own office and through its membership of Euro Advocaten (a formal grouping of European lawyers); and international trade.

Banking and corporate finance: (*Contact:* Richard de Belder (banking), Nigel Frudd (corporate finance)*Work includes:* trade finance, letters of credit, bills of exchange; syndicated loans; sub-participations; derivatives; project financing; asset financing; aircraft and shipping financing; secured lending; fund raising, debt and equity funding and corporate financial reconstructions; general banking matters; formation of branches and subsidiaries of financial institutions.

Property and construction finance: (*Contact:* Robert Sprawson). The department has particular expertise in commercial and residential developments including office and retail centres for U.K.-based and international clients and for the Health Sector and Statutory Undertakings. In addition, it has been involved in the acquisition and management of many substantial country anf sporting estates, agricultural and farming properties, and stud-farming and racing establishments. Construction work includes projects in the U.K. and abroad acting for major domestic and international contractors, employers and professionals and negotiating all forms of construction related documentation.

Dispute resolution: (*Contact:* Rachel Harrap). The services offered include resolution of contentious commercial disputes in the Courts and Tribunals, in commercial arbitrations, both U.K.-based and international, and through alternative dispute resolution including resolution of cross-border transactions, shipping disputes, construction and engineering disputes, insolvency, banking claims, product liability and employment disputes.

Taxation: (*Contact:* Nigel Frudd, Desmond Parte). *work includes:* tax planning in corporate structuring and re-structuring, employee incentive schemes, international tax planning, trusts, wills and inheritance tax planning, VAT advice, taxation issues relating to residence or domicile, tax implications of doing business in the U.K., tax planning for the bloodstock industry, establishment and administration of offshore companies and trusts.

FOREIGN CONNECTIONS: Seven languages spoken by members of the firm, many of whom have worked abroad. The five offices in Dubai, Abu Dhabi, Fujairah and Cairo make it the largest firm in the Middle East of all London law firms. In addition, it is the only London law firm with its own office in Gibraltar. The firm is a member of Euro Advocaten, a formal grouping of lawyers, which has fellow members in Germany, Holland, France, Greece, Italy, Belgium, Luxembourg, Ireland, Spain, Portual, Denmark and Austria. The firm also has associated offices in Kuwait, Lebanon, the Yemen, Saudi Arabia and India.

INTERNATIONAL:	
Number of Partners:	5
Assistant Solicitors:	8
Other fee-earners:	2

WORKLOAD	
Property and construction	40%
Company/ commercial	40%
Dispute resolution	10%
Banking/ corporate finance	8%
Taxation	2%

CONTACTS	
Banking	R de Belder
Company/ commercial	C Dixon
Corporate finance	N Frudd
Dispute resolution	R Harrap
Property and construction	R Sprawson
Taxation	N Frudd, D Parte

FOX WILLIAMS

CITY GATE HOUSE, 39-45 FINSBURY SQUARE, LONDON, EC2A 1UU
DX: 33873 Finsbury Sq.

TEL: (0171) 628 2000
FAX: (0171) 628 2100

THE FIRM: Fox Williams provides the highest quality corporate and commercial legal services coupled with a more personal commitment by the partners to their clients' businesses. Since its formation, the firm's energetic approach and rapid, effective, responsive service have resulted in steady growth in both business and reputation. Fox Williams is particularly well known for its mergers and acquisitions and employment law work. The firm acts for leading companies in the healthcare and food industries.

PRINCIPAL AREAS OF WORK:

Corporate: (*Contact Partner:* Tina Williams). The firm undertakes a wide range of transactional and corporate finance work including public company takeovers and mergers, acquisitions and disposals of private companies and businesses, capital raising transactions, flotations, MBOs and venture capital. General corporate work includes business start-ups, restructuring, conversions from private to public companies, banking and financial services work, insolvency and corporate rescues, and tax.

CONTACT PARTNER: Mr S.L. Sidkin

Number of partners:	11
Assistant solicitors:	14
Other fee-earners:	7

WORKLOAD	
Corporate	31%
Litigation	29%
Employment and partnership	19%
Commercial	12%
Property	9%

Commercial: *(Contact Partner:* Stephen Sidkin). The businesses of UK and international clients benefit from positive and informed commercial advice on distribution and agency agreements, franchising, terms of trading, product liability, data protection legislation and all aspects of the protection and exploitation of intellectual property rights, licensing of technology, computer hardware and software agreements, and UK and EC competition law.

Employment: *(Contact Partner:* Ronnie Fox). Fox Williams is well-known for its expertise in calculating and negotiating payments on termination of employment. Employment lawyers also draft executive service agreements, incentive and share option schemes, as well as dealing with redundancy, unfair dismissal, and the enforceability of restrictive covenants and confidentiality undertakings.

Property: *(Contact Partner:* Bryan Emden). Work undertaken includes dealing with substantial property portfolios involving auctions, sales and leasebacks of retail, office and industrial premises; advising on environmental and planning matters, secured lending, VAT and estate management. Development companies are also advised on site purchase and sale schemes as well as associated joint venture projects.

Litigation: *(Contact Partner:* Lindsay Hill). A strong team handles a broad range of substantial UK and international litigation and arbitration and is committed to achieving fast and commercially effective solutions. Its work includes disputes relating to international trade, financial services, intellectual property, product liability, shareholder and joint venture arrangements, partnership, and commercial property.

OTHER AREAS OF WORK: In addition, considerable experience of acting for local authorities enables the firm to give specialist advice on compulsory and voluntary competitive tendering.

NATURE OF CLIENTELE: Clients range from multinational corporations and major public companies, to family businesses and individual entrepreneurs, and also include banks and other financial institutions, regulatory authorities, local authorities, accountants and other professionals, including overseas lawyers.

CONTACTS	
Commercial	Stephen Sidkin
Corporate	Tina Williams
Employment/ partnership	Ronnie Fox
Litigation	Lindsay Hill
Property	Bryan Emden

FOX WILLIAMS

FOY & CO

PO BOX 111, 63 HALLGATE, DONCASTER, S. YORKS, DN1 3DQ
DX: 12563 Doncaster

TEL: (01302) 327136
FAX: (01302) 367656

CONTACT PARTNER: Mr. S.J. Paramore

Number of partners:	6
Assistant solicitors:	4
Other fee-earners:	16

THE FIRM: Established in 1972 as a broadly based practice the firm has expanded rapidly to become a sizeable firm with offices in South Yorkshire and North Nottinghamshire.

PRINCIPAL AREAS OF WORK:

Property: *(Contact Partner:* Mr W.D.G. Jones). This department has grown considerably over the years and offers advice on all aspects of work involved in commercial and domestic property transactions.

Civil Litigation: *(Contact Partner:* Mr I.P. Sandeman). The firm covers a broad spectrum of work for both its business and private clients. Areas of work include employment law, personal injury, professional negligence and a computerised debt collection operation.

Criminal Litigation: *(Contact Partner:* Mr S.J. Paramore). *Work includes:* both admitted and contested proceedings, motoring offences and police investigations. The firm's advocates all participate in Court Duty Solicitor schemes.

Private Client/ Matrimonial: *(Contact Partner:* Mr A. Firth). These departments deal with all aspects of family law, and all matters dealing with wills and probate and taxation advice.

OTHER OFFICES:
102 Bridge Street, Worksop. *Tel:* (01909) 473560. *Fax:* (01909) 482760.
All Saints Square, Rotherham. *Tel:* (01709) 375561. *Fax:* (01709) 828479.

FRANCIS & CO

11 GOLD TOPS, NEWPORT, GWENT, NP9 4UJ
DX: 33226 Newport

TEL: (01633) 244988
FAX: (01633) 246130

THE FIRM: Francis & Co's head office opened in Newport in 1988 although the origins of the firm date back to the nineteenth century. It is divided into four departments, all of which provide a full legal service to businesses both locally and nationally. As a founder member of LawNet Europe the practice can advise on European matters or, alternatively, place clients in direct contact with another member firm in the appropriate country.

PRINCIPAL AREAS OF WORK:

Company and Commercial: *(Contact Partner:* Graeme Guthrie). The firm acts for various concerns from sole traders to public companies, service and manufacturing industries to professional practices. Work covered includes acquisitions and disposals, venture capital, employment and information technology.

Property (Commercial): *(Contact Partner:* David Kershaw). This department, while undertaking purchases, sales, leases and management, also deals with environmental and planning issues.

Debt Recovery: *(Contact Partner:* Fay Sims). Francis & Co's internal department *Debt Call*, offers a comprehensive service for the recovery of bad debts and advises on credit control procedures.

Litigation: *(Contact Partner:* Owen Thomas). The firm tackles an extensive range of commercial litigation, including property litigation and professional negligence claims.

OTHER OFFICES:
17 Welsh Street, Chepstow, Gwent NP6 5LL.
Oakfield House, Hill Street, Lydney, Glasgow GL15 5HE.

FOREIGN LANGUAGES: French, Italian and German.

CONTACT PARTNER: Mr Graeme Guthrie

Number of partners:	12
Assistant solicitors:	6
Other fee-earners:	12

WORKLOAD	
Company commercial	35%
Debt recovery	26%
Commercial property	20%
Civil litigation and family law	19%

CONTACTS	
Commercial property	David Kershaw
Company/ commercial	Graeme Guthrie
Debt recovery	Fay Sims
Family law	Amanda Wooding
Litigation	Owen Thomas

FRANCIS HANNA & CO Central Chambers, 75-77 May Street, Belfast, BT1 3JL **Tel:** (01232) 243901 **Fax:** (01232) 244215 **DX:** 473NR Belfast 1 **Ptnrs:** 3 **Asst Solrs:** 6 **Other Fee-earners:** 4. A leading company in Belfast with over 60 years experience in the field of personal injury. Considerable experience in property and employment matters, matrimonial issues, wills, road traffic accidents and accidents in the workplace, criminal injury and criminal damage claims.

WORKLOAD		
Litigation/ PI	60%	Property/ commercial 40%

FRANK & CAFFIN Princes House, Princes Street, Truro, Cornwall, TR1 2EY **Tel:** (01872) 73077 **Fax:** (01872) 42458 **DX:** 81201 Truro **Ptnrs:** 5 **Asst Solrs:** 4 **Other Fee-earners:** 5. Best known for its conveyancing and civil litigation, this well-established firm does the whole range of work including legal aid. Regular visits made by staff to the Isles of Scilly.

WORKLOAD		
Civil litigation	37%	Convey/private client 36%
Matrimonial	14%	

FRANKS, CHARLESLY & CO Hulton House, 161-166 Fleet Street, London, EC4A 2DY **Tel:** (0171) 353 1588 **Fax:** (0171) 583 0647 **DX:** 152 **Ptnrs:** 12 **Asst Solrs:** 4 **Other Fee-earners:** 8. The firm's major activities are in the corporate and property fields and cover commercial and residential development, banking, trusts, probate, tax and litigation.

THE FRANK LEFEVRE PRACTICE 70 Carden Place, Aberdeen, Grampian, AB1 1UL **Tel:** (01224) 208208 **Fax:** (01224) 626917 **Ptnrs:** 2 **Asst Solrs:** 1 . Specialist litigation practice, particularly known for employment and personal injury work.

FREEDMAN CHURCH

21 WHITEFRIARS STREET, LONDON, EC4Y 8JJ
DX: 74 Ch.Ln.

TEL: (0171) 353 1330
FAX: (0171) 353 1533

THE FIRM: Freedman Church is a leading specialist firm of construction project industry lawyers based in London. The firm's expertise is based on many years advice on a full range of project work of both a non-contentious and contentious nature in both the domestic and international arena.

PRINCIPAL AREAS OF WORK: Construction, industrial processing, energy and engineering; commercial property and planning; litigation, arbitration and ADR; intellectual property; insolvency; employment and health and safety.

NATURE OF CLIENTELE: The firm's clients include employers, main contractors, utilities sub-contractors, construction professionals, property companies, health bodies and trusts, housing associations, local authorities and government agencies.

OTHER OFFICE: Manchester, Chester.

FOREIGN CONNECTIONS: Bahrain, Hong Kong, Lisbon, Paris.

LANGUAGES SPOKEN: French, German, Italian.

CONTACT PARTNER: Peter Shaw

Number of partners:	12
Assistant solicitors:	5
Other fee-earners:	3

WORKLOAD	
Construction and engineering litigation (domestic)	40%
Construction & engineering energy and property (non-contentious)	30%
Construction and engineering litigation (international)	30%

FREETH CARTWRIGHT HUNT DICKINS

WILLOUGHBY HOUSE, 20 LOW PAVEMENT, NOTTINGHAM, NOTTS, NG1 7EA
DX: 10039 Nottingham

TEL: (0115) 9369369
FAX: (0115) 9369370

THE FIRM: Freeth Cartwright Hunt Dickins is a leading Midlands practice, with offices in Nottingham and Derby. In addition to its local client base, the firm has commercial clients spread widely throughout the UK and internationally.

PRINCIPAL AREAS OF WORK:

Company/ Commercial: *(Contact:* Saul Cambridge). The department advises commercial clients ranging from small and emerging businesses to major public companies, government bodies and local authorities. *Work includes:* acquisitions and disposals, mergers, joint ventures and structuring, corporate finance, marketing, distribution and agency agreements, European Community law, trading terms and general commercial agreements both in the UK and abroad, and corporate taxation.

Commercial Property: *(Contact:* George Taylor). *Work includes:* sale, purchase and lease of premises for the retail, leisure, residential, industrial and office sectors, commercial and residential developments from site acquisition and planning aspects to building leasing and funding agreements, security documentation, consortium arrangements and options. There is a specialised unit dealing with town and country planning and environmental issues.

Commercial Litigation: *(Contact:* Guy Berwick). All aspects of commercial disputes including property and construction matters, breach of contract, arbitrations and planning appeals, and debt recovery.

Insolvency: *(Contact:* Graham Greenfield). The department works with most of the leading insolvency practitioners, dealing with all aspects of individual and corporate insolvency. It also advises on Department of Trade investigations and prosecutions, wrongful trading actions and directors' liability claims.

Intellectual Property: *(Contact:* John Lewis). *Work includes:* services relating to patent, trade marks, copyrights and passing off, and all aspects of agreements and disputes concerning intellectual property.

Employment: *(Contact:* Richard Bullock). *Work includes:* tribunal and court work in connection with unfair and wrongful dismissal, single or multiple redundancies, issues involving equal pay and conditions of employment, discrimination law, health and safety legislation, service contracts, executive benefits and restrictive covenants.

CONTACT PARTNER: Ian Payne

Number of partners:	31
Assistant solicitors:	31
Other fee-earners:	55

WORKLOAD	
Commercial litigation	23%
Personal litigation	20%
Commercial property	17%
Company/ commercial	11%
Residential property	8%
Crime	8%
Family	8%
Private client	5%

CONTACTS	
Administrative/ public law	Richard Beverley
Banking	Jane Goulding
Charities	Nigel Cullen
Company/ commercial	Saul Cambridge
Construction	Graham Greenfield
Housing associations	Gary Reynolds
Immigration	Richard Beverley
Insolvency	Graham Greenfield
Intellectual property	John Lewis
Licensing	Stephen Gelsthorpe
Litigation (commercial)	Guy Berwick
Litigation (property)	David Potter

Personal Litigation: *(Contact:* Paul Balen). *Work includes:* professional negligence, personal injury, housing disputes, divorce, custody, wardship and care proceedings and defence against criminal proceedings.

Private Client: *(Contact:* Nigel Cullen). *Work includes:* wills, probate and administration of estates, powers of attorney, Court of Protection, trusts and personal taxation, residential conveyancing and financial services.

FOREIGN CONNECTIONS: Freeth Cartwright Hunt Dickins is a member of LawNet Europe and has developed specific contacts with lawyers throughout Europe.

RECRUITMENT: The firm remains anxious to recruit high quality lawyers and has places for five to eight trainee solicitors each year. The contact partner is Hugh Young.

Personal injury	Richard Beverley
Planning	Heather Davies
Private client	Nigel Cullen
Professional negligence	Paul Balen
Property (commercial)	George Taylor
Sports	Simon Taylor
Tax (corporate)	Ian Payne

FRERE CHOLMELEY BISCHOFF

4 JOHN CARPENTER STREET, LONDON, EC4Y 0NH
DX: 140 London

TEL: (0171) 615 8000
FAX: (0171) 615 8080

THE FIRM: Frere Cholmeley Bischoff is a major City firm with a strong European presence. It is predominantly a commercial practice with a distinguished client list especially of international companies and institutional investors. The firm is capable of providing pan-European advice to business through its network of offices in Paris, Berlin, Milan, Rome, Monaco and Moscow. The firm also has an office in Dubai.

PRINCIPAL AREAS OF WORK IN LONDON:

General Description: The firm has a bias towards corporate and commercial work, with corporate finance transactions, financial services work, commercial litigation and property forming the core of the business. Frere Cholmeley Bischoff is recognised as one of the leading legal advisers to the UK unit trust industry.

Company/ Commercial: *(Contact:* Julian Walton. *24 Partners).* The largest department within the firm, it has a practical approach to current commercial problems and provides business-orientated advice to clients on all aspects of company and commercial law – corporate finance, major transactional work for listed and non-listed companies, insolvency, taxation, pension and industrial welfare schemes, computer contracts, licensing, intellectual property and UK and EC competition law. Within this department:-

The **financial services group** is a market leader in its field and advises clients on all aspects of financial services law.

The **media, telecommunications and entertainment group** offers a comprehensive range of legal advice to major media companies, international artists and representative bodies. It has extensive experience in both the music, multimedia, cable and satellite television industries.

The **aviation group** advises on all aspects of air law, including issues arising from international traffic rights, route licensing, national and EC regulatory matters, the purchase, lease and funding of aircraft, and the handling of claims.

Litigation: *(Contact:* Alan Jenkins. *10 Partners).* This department, with its strong national and international reputation for commercial litigation and arbitration, acts for clients involved in a wide variety of business sectors, including manufacturing and natural resources, financial services and insurance, property and the media and entertainment industries. Significant areas of practice are professional negligence, arbitration (mainly engineering, construction and insurance), fraud recovery, intellectual property disputes and defamation actions. The firm provides advice on all aspects of employment law and undertakes direct advocacy before industrial tribunals.

Property: *(Contact:* Tony Patterson. *11 Partners).* The property department advises on all aspects of property transactions, including investment funding, development, construction, landlord and tenant matters, secured lending, receivership and property taxation. Due to the wide spread of its clients – investors, developers, lenders, retailers, local and government authorities, landowners and occupiers – the property department is very experienced in the many diverse aspects of today's increasingly

MANAGING PARTNER: Mr S.C. Sugar

UK:	
Number of partners:	59
Assistant solicitors:	97
Other fee-earners:	63
Worldwide fee-earners:	219

WORKLOAD	
Company commercial	32%
Overseas offices	20%
Property	19%
Litigation	19%
Private client	10%

CONTACTS	
Aviation	John Balfour
Banking and insolvency	Antony Thomlinson
Commerce and industry	Julian Walton
Corporate finance	Sheila Fyfe
Employment law and pensions	Jane Richards
Environment	Smita Edwards
Financial services	Richard Millar
Litigation	Nicholas Valner
Media/ telecoms/ entertainment	Craig Eadie
Private client	David Robinson
Property	Tony Patterson
Taxation	Sue Taylor

sophisticated property market. Particular specialisations include public sector projects, planning and environmental law, in which area the firm offers multidisciplinary advice to a variety of clients.

Private Client: (*Contact:* David Robinson. *5 Partners*). The department advises wealthy individuals and trusts, including charities, on their legal and fiancial affairs in the UK and abroad. Will-drafting, probate, tax planning in all its aspects (including the preservation of heritage property) and the administration of UK and off-shore trusts are undertaken, often in collaboration with the firm's Monaco office. A specialised group of family lawyers advises on divorce and separation, resolving disputes over financial matters, the residence of children and (in international cases) questions of jurisdiction.

LANGUAGES: The firm's qualified lawyers are fluent in English, French, German, Italian, Spanish, Russian and Arabic.

RECRUITMENT AND TRAINING: An extensive education and training programme is organised for trainees and qualified staff. Trainees are offered the opportunity of spending part of their articles in the firm's overseas offices. Enquiries to Christopher Lake.

FRESHFIELDS

65 FLEET STREET, LONDON, EC4Y 1HS
DX: 23

TEL: (0171) 936 4000
FAX: (0171) 832 7001

THE FIRM: Freshfields is a leading international law firm with offices in Europe, Asia and New York. It provides legal services under English, French, EC, German, Spanish, Belgian, Russian and other CIS laws, and Hong Kong law. With over 700 lawyers in key business and financial centres around the world, Freshfields is well-placed to meet the needs of companies who require consistently high standards of advice and service.

OTHER OFFICES: Bangkok, Barcelona, Brussels, Frankfurt, Hanoi, Ho Chi Minh City, Hong Kong, Madrid, Moscow, New York, Paris, Singapore, Tokyo.

LANGUAGES: Bulgarian, Cantonese, Danish, Dutch, English, French, German, Greek, Irish, Italian, Japanese, Mandarin, Russian, Spanish.

PRINCIPAL AREAS OF WORK IN LONDON (AND CONTACT PARTNER)

Banking: David Ereira
Capital Markets: Clive Rough
Investment Funds: Anthony McWhirter
Commercial Property: Geoff Le Pard
Construction and Engineering: Sally Roe
Corporate: Anthony Salz
EC, Competition: Nicholas Spearing
Employment, Pensions and Benefits: Peter Jeffcote
Energy: Graham Nicholson
Environment: Paul Bowden
Finance: Simon Hall
Financial Services: Guy Morton
Insolvency: Peter Bloxham
Insurance: Philip Richards
Intellectual Property: Hugh Stubbs
International Arbitration: Nigel Rawding
International Project Finance: Roger McCormick
International Tax: Roger Berner
Litigation: Ian Taylor
Tax: Richard Ballard

SENIOR PARTNER: John Grieves	
UK:	
Number of partners:	109
Assistant solicitors:	289
Other fee-earners:	133
INTERNATIONAL:	
Number of Partners:	44
Assistant Solicitors:	119
Foreign qualified lawyers:	108
Other fee-earners:	40

FURLEY PAGE FIELDING & BARTON 39 St. Margaret's Street, Canterbury, Kent, CT1 2TX **Tel:** (01227) 763939 **Fax:** (01227) 762829 **DX:** 5301 Canterbury **Ptnrs:** 15 **Asst Solrs:** 5 **Other Fee-earners:** 18. Best known for company/ commercial, litigation including personal injury and agricultural law. One of the largest practices in East Kent, serving local businessmen, farmers and private individuals.

WORKLOAD			
Litigation	38%	Trust and estates	25%
Commercial	17%	Res conveyancing	16%
Financial services	1%		

FYFE IRELAND Orchard Brae House, 30 Queensferry Road, Edinburgh, EH4 2HG **Tel:** (0131) 343 2500 **Fax:** (0131) 343 3166 **Ptnrs:** 9 **Asst Solrs:** 18 **Other Fee-earners:** 11. Medium-sized practice with strong company/ commercial background and large private client base. Also in London.

FYNN & PARTNERS

70 RICHMOND HILL, BOURNEMOUTH, DORSET, BH2 6JA
DX: DX 7608 Bournemouth

TEL: (01202) 551991
FAX: (01202) 295403

THE FIRM: Fynn & Partners was formed in 1995 as the demerged Bournemouth office of Penningtons. It contains what was previously the environmental, licensing and planning department of Penningtons, with a national reputation, supported by a commercial property department with extensive expertise in leisure/licensed property matters. The firm generally covers all aspects of company and commercial law, with a growing private client practice.

CONTACT PARTNER: Simon Nightingale

Number of partners:	6
Assistant solicitors:	3
Other fee-earners:	4

GABB & CO 32 Monk St, Abergavenny, Gwent, NP7 5NW **Tel:** (01873) 852432 **Fax:** (01873) 857589 **DX:** 43752 Abergavenny **Ptnrs:** 14 **Asst Solrs:** 5 **Other Fee-earners:** 1. Established in 1760. A general practice best known for company/ commercial, conveyancing, wills, tax, agriculture, planning, probate and litigation.

GADSBY WICKS 35/37 Moulsham Street, Chelmsford, Essex, CM2 OHJ **Tel:** (01245) 494929 **Fax:** (01245) 495347 **DX:** 89707 Chelmsford 2 **Ptnrs:** 2 **Asst Solrs:** 2 **Other Fee-earners:** 3. A niche practice specialising in medical negligence, medical and pharmaceutical product liability and general personal injury work.

WORKLOAD			
Medical negligence	60%	Pharmaceutical product	20%
Personal injury	15%	Commercial litigation	5%

GARETH WOODFINE & PARTNERS 16 St. Cuthberts St, Bedford, Beds, MK40 3JG **Tel:** (01234) 270600 **Fax:** (01234) 210128 **DX:** 5619 **Ptnrs:** 8 **Asst Solrs:** 5 **Other Fee-earners:** 11. A broad general practice with an emphasis on company/ commercial and litigation but with private client departments.

INTERNATIONAL SECTION

The international section lists foreign law firms based in London. It also lists the foreign connections of English law firms: their branch offices overseas and the foreign languages spoken at their UK offices.

GARRETT & CO

7 SURREY STREET, LONDON, WC2R 2NN DX: 127 London Chancery Lane	TEL:	(0171) 344 0344
	FAX:	(0171) 438 2518
London: 7 Surrey Street, London WC2R 2NN	Tel:	(0171) 344 0344
	Fax:	(0171) 438 2518
Leeds: 21 Queen Street, Leeds LS1 2TW	Tel:	(0113) 2441954
	Fax:	(0113) 2416291
Reading: Abbots House, Abbey Street, Reading, Berks RG1 3BD	Tel:	(01734) 490000
	Fax:	(01734) 490049
Manchester: Bank House, 9 Charlotte Street, Manchester M1 4EU	Tel:	(0161) 228 0707
	Fax:	(0161) 228 1926
Birmingham: 1 Victoria Square, Birmingham B1 1BD	Tel:	(0121) 698 9000
	Fax:	(0121) 698 9050

THE FIRM: Garrett & Co specialises in UK business law for companies and organisations based in the UK and overseas. The clients of the firm benefit from partner intensive, cost effective service more usually associated with a small firm together with a depth and breadth of experience provided by lawyers recruited from major practices. The firm has formed a unique association with Arthur Andersen which gives its clients access to an organisation with offices in 72 countries around the world; the resources to advise on complicated, time sensitive transactions; and access to the latest international company research and global economic and legal information.

PRINCIPAL AREAS OF WORK:

Company/ Commercial: (*Contact:* Julia Chain in London, Nick Painter in Leeds, Steve Devlin in Manchester, Paul Finlan in Birmingham or Adrian Phillips in Reading). *Work includes:* sales and acquisitions of companies and businesses, management buy-outs and buy-ins, privatisations, venture capital schemes, flotations, loan agreements, commercial agreements, partnerships, joint ventures, dealerships, franchises, insurance law and insolvency.

Commercial Property: (*Contact:* Keith Barnett in London, Mike Sleath in Leeds, Adrian Watson in Birmingham or Debra Kent in Reading). *Work includes:* purchase and sale of business premises, landlord and tenant matters, commercial and industrial development work, tax issues, property audit, property finance, portfolio acquisition, disposal and management.

Intellectual Property: (*Contact:* Mark Turner in London, Alison Harrington in Reading or Richard Boardman in Leeds). *Work includes:* copyright and designs, patents, trade marks, passing off, trade libel, franchising, merchandising, computer and software issues, disaster recovery, piracy, intellectual property health checks.

Pension and Employment Issues: (*Contact:* Paul McCarthy in London, Paula Cole in Manchester or Trevor Clarke in Leeds). *Work includes:* corporate reorganisations, service contracts, unfair dismissals and redundancy, pension arrangements, share incentive and employee benefit schemes.

Banking and Financial Services: (*Contact:* Richard Parlour in London, Susan Molloy or Karen Jarvis in Leeds). *Work includes:* UK and EU banking and financial services regulation, restructuring of financial institutions, securities and derivatives, payment and clearing systems, capital adequacy and financial market integrity.

FOREIGN CONNECTIONS: Garrett & Co is a member firm of the network of worldwide law firms associated with Arthur Andersen. One of the partners of the firm is resident in Paris where he is also a partner in the firm of S G Archibald.

MANAGING PARTNER: Julia Chain	
Number of partners:	21
Assistant solicitors:	32
Other fee-earners:	10

WORKLOAD	
Company commercial	54%
Intellectual property	22%
Commercial property	15%
Employment (inc compensation & benefits)	9%

GARSTANGS Moat House, 10 Drury Lane, London, WC2B 5RE **Tel:** (0171) 379 0170/1082 **Fax:** (0171) 240 2416 **Ptnrs:** 6 **Asst Solrs:** 3 **Other Fee-earners:** 10. A radical specialist practice with substantial expertise in the field of white-collar crime, ancillary civil and public interest litigation. Office in Bolton.

GASKELL RHYS & OTTO-JONES 29 Park Place, Cardiff, S. Glam,
CF1 3QD **Tel:** (01222) 225591 **Fax:** (01222) 395053 **DX:** 50753 Cardiff 2
Ptnrs: 2 **Asst Solrs:** 1 **Other Fee-earners:** 1. Commercial, licensing, conveyancing, probate and sheriff law.

GATELEY WAREING

EQUITY HOUSE, 7 ROWCHESTER COURT, WHITTALL STREET, BIRMINGHAM,
W. MIDLANDS, B4 6DD   DX: 24904

TEL: (0121) 236 8585
FAX: (0121) 233 1874

THE FIRM: Gateley Wareing is one of the most respected medium-sized firms of solicitors in Birmingham and was formed in 1974 by the merger of two long-established practices. Clients range from small traders to multi-million pound public companies.

PRINCIPAL AREAS OF WORK:

Company/ Commercial: *(Contact Partners:* Michael Ward, Paul Hayward, Andrew Sherlock). Advice is given on company formations, acquisitions and disposals, mergers, management buy-outs, corporate finance, flotations, bank financing and corporate taxation. Company secretarial services are provided. Commercial documents are drafted and a full service relating to transport and distribution is provided.

Litigation: *(Contact Partners:* Michael Gillespie, Brendan McGeever). Business disputes of all types are handled including contract disputes, partnership disputes, professional negligence, intellectual property, landlord and tenant, shareholder disputes, redundancy and unfair dismissal. The department also deals with betting, gaming and liquor licence work and operates a computerised debt collection system.

Property: *(Contact Partners:* Kevin Nagle, Neil Handel). The firm advises on the purchase, sale and leasing of commercial property, land acquisition for residential and commercial development, advice to landlords and tenants, planning and building contract work, mortgages and bridging finance.

Construction Law: *(Contact Partners:* Peter Davies, Andrew Hickman). The firm has a specialist department providing a comprehensive service to all aspects of the construction industry, which includes advising on the appropriate form of contract documentation, dealing with contractual problems and handling disputes, whether by litigation or arbitration if necessary.

Banking and Insolvency: *(Contact Partners:* Brendan McGeever and Eugene Jordan). The firm has a separate department which specialises in banking and insolvency law and related areas of work. *Work includes:* loan facility and security documentation, recoveries and debt restructuring, advising on priority issues and compliance with regulatory requirements. Advice is given to clients on coporate strategy and directors' responsibilities, and insolvency practitioners on such matters as their appointment, the rights of creditors, and the preservation and recovery of assets.

Housing Associations: *(Contact Partners:* Kevin Nagle, Neil Handel). The firm has a particular and established expertise in housing association projects having acted for a substantial number of housing associations for many years.

Private Client and Trusts: *(Contact Partner:* Stephen Gateley). Clients are advised on personal tax and estate planning, will drafting and estate administration, and specialist advice is provided to a range of charitable institutions.

Family Law: *(Contact:* Michael Vale). The firm has a specialist department providing advice on all aspects including potential or actual matrimonial break-ups, issues which amongst others relate to property, children, child abduction, matrimonial problems with an international aspect and inheritance and taxation issues.

NATURE OF CLIENTELE: The firm has specialist expertise in providing services to owner-managed businesses. Other clients include banks, housing associations, venture capitalists, property developers, professional partnerships, charitable institutions and individuals.

RECRUITMENT & TRAINING: Trainee solicitors are taken on yearly. Applications from non-law graduates are welcomed. A curriculum vitae should be sent to Neil Handel.

CONTACT PARTNER: Mr McGeever

Number of partners:	11
Assistant solicitors:	17
Other fee-earners:	10

WORKLOAD

Company/ commercial	24%
Banking and Insolvency	22%
Commercial property/housing associations	18%
Construction	14%
Civil litigation	13%
Family	5%
Trusts and charities	4%

CONTACTS

Banking and Insolvency	Brendan McGeever
	Eugene Jordan
Civil litigation	Michael Gillespie
Commercial property	Kevin Nagle
Company/ commercial	Michael Ward
	Paul Hayward, Andrew Sherlock
Construction	Peter Davies
	Andrew Hickman
Family	Michael Vale
Housing associations	Neil Handel
	Kevin Nagle
Trusts and charities	Stephen Gateley

GEOFFREY SEARLE 32 Centre Point House, St Giles High St, London, WC2H 8LW **Tel:** (0171) 497 3753 **Fax:** (0171) 240 5818 **Ptnrs:** 1. A niche planning practice established in October 1994 to meet the demands of developers, private and public sector land-owners and occupiers for a mature, personal and committed service.

WORKLOAD	
Town/country planning	100%

GEORGE DAVIES & CO Fountain Court, 68 Fountain Street, Manchester, M2 2FB **Tel:** (0161) 236 8992 **Fax:** (0161) 228 0030 **DX:** 14316 Manchester M1 **Ptnrs:** 12 **Asst Solrs:** 5 **Other Fee-earners:** 2. Established 1938. The firm has property, litigation, private client, and company/ commercial departments. Also known for medical negligence and sports law.

GEORGE GREEN & CO

195 HIGH ST, CRADLEY HEATH, WARLEY, W. MIDLANDS, B64 5HW
DX: 20752

TEL: (01384) 410410
FAX: (01384) 634237

THE FIRM: Established in 1897 and based in the heart of the Black Country, George Green & Co. is acknowledged as providing the business community with a real alternative to City firms whilst retaining its commitment to the provision of legal advice to its private clientele. In addition a specialist department is devoted to claims litigation and advises major insurers and Lloyd's underwriters.

CONTACT PARTNER: Neill Robb	
Number of partners:	10
Assistant solicitors:	12
Other fee-earners:	14

PRINCIPAL AREAS OF WORK:

Company/ Commercial: (*Contact Partner:* Richard Cliff or Guy Green). *Work includes:* start-ups, acquisition and mergers, reconstructions, corporate finance, MBOs, flotations, partnerships, commercial agreements, joint ventures and taxation.

Commercial Litigation: (*Contact Partner:* Neil Cutler or Richard Green). *Work includes:* contract disputes, debt collection, employment, intellectual property, building disputes, landlord and tenant, planning disputes, insolvency, defamation, European law and emergency injunctions. The work involves both High Court and County Court actions, in addition to arbitrations and industrial tribunal hearings.

Claims Litigation: (*Contact Partner:* Nigel Dace or Tim Salthouse). *Work includes:* advice to major insurance companies and Lloyd's underwriters on matters relating to insurance law, motor accident claims, accidents at work, agricultural accidents, medical claims, property and occupier's liability, public and employer's liability claims, and health and safety prosecutions.

Property Development/ Planning: (*Contact Partner:* Cheryl Leyser). *Work includes:* acquisitions and disposals of land and buildings, leasing, building and development contracts, taxation, property finance, commercial/ residential estate development and planning.

Private Client: (*Contact Partner:* Neill Robb). *Work includes:* wills, probate, estate planning, trusts, charities, pensions, matrimonial law, domestic conveyancing, personal taxation and general criminal work.

OTHER OFFICES: Halesowen.

FIRMS OF ACCOUNTANTS

Accountants specialising in litigation support are listed in the accountants' A-Z, with details of the services they offer to solicitors, from forensic accounting to intellectual property or business valuations. .

GEORGE IDE, PHILLIPS

LION HOUSE, 79 ST. PANCRAS, CHICHESTER, W. SUSSEX, PO19 4NL DX: 30306 Chichester	TEL: (01243) 786668 FAX: (01243) 787566
BELMONT LODGE, BELMONT STREET, BOGNOR REGIS, W. SUSSEX PO21 1LE DX: 31204 Bognor Regis	TEL: (01243) 829231 FAX: (01243) 825553

THE FIRM: George Ide, Phillips serves the needs of industry, commerce, businesses and private clients.

PRINCIPAL AREAS OF WORK: The firm's main areas of practice cover commercial as well as residential conveyancing, company and commercial work, wills, trusts and probate. It includes also town and country planning, financial services, and a facility to undertake some European conveyancing. All types of litigation are undertaken including criminal and civil litigation, building disputes, medical and other professional negligence, personal injury and matrimonial work. The firm is a member of The Solicitors Financial & Property Services Company in order to provide the financial services.

OTHER OFFICES:
166 Pagham Road, Nyetimber, Bognor Regis, West Sussex. *Tel:* (01243) 265513.

CONTACT PARTNER: Jeffrey Hopkins	
Number of partners:	11
Assistant solicitors:	5
Other fee-earners:	6

WORKLOAD	
Litigation (inc. crime & matrimonial work)	70%
Commercial, probate, trust & conveyancing	30%

GEORGE JONAS & CO Citadel, 190 Corporation Street, Birmingham, W. Midlands, B4 6QD **Tel:** (0121) 212 4111 **Fax:** (0121) 212 1770 **DX:** 13013 **Ptnrs:** 2 **Other Fee-earners:** 6. Categories of work: agency commissions willingly undertaken; criminal, civil and family litigation including wardship and care cases; libel.

GEPP & SONS 58 New London Rd, Chelmsford, Essex, CM2 0PA **Tel:** (01245) 493939 **Fax:** (01245) 493940 **DX:** 3306 **Ptnrs:** 11 **Asst Solrs:** 10 **Other Fee-earners:** 8. General practice handling agriculture, corporate services, criminal, litigation, matrimonial, probate and trust, commercial and residential property and shrievalty.

GERMAN & SOAR Fenchurch House, 12 King St, Nottingham, Notts, NG1 2AZ **Tel:** (0115) 947 0756 **Fax:** (0115) 948 4747 **DX:** 10040 **Ptnrs:** 6 **Asst Solrs:** 2 **Other Fee-earners:** 10. Established in 1936 as a family practice. Best known for conveyancing, matrimonial, crime, personal injury. Also experienced in sports law, child care, medical negligence, defamation and commercial litigation.

GHERSON & CO

22 TUDOR STREET, LONDON, EC4Y 0JJ	TEL: (0171) 355 2282 FAX: (0171) 583 3051

THE FIRM: Established in 1988, this is a specialist practice providing in-depth advice on UK immigration law, British nationality law, and European Union freedom of movement of persons. Roger Gherson and David Webb are two well-known solicitors with many years' experience in the field of immigration law.

PRINCIPAL AREAS OF WORK: Particular expertise in employment and business related immigration (including executive relocation, and the admission of entrepreneurs and investors). In addition to a strong corporate caseload, the firm also deals with: the acquisition of settlement and citizenship; complex nationality issues; family reunion; students and other temporary categories; appeals to Adjudicators and the Immigration Tribunal against the refusal of entry clearance, further leave to remain, threatened deportation, etc; judicial review to the High Court.

CLIENTELE: Wide corporate and private client base including other firms of solicitors.

FOREIGN CONNECTIONS: Extensive links overseas particularly in China (including Hong Kong), South Africa, USA and the Indian Sub-Continent.

CONTACT PARTNERS: Mr R. Gherson and Mr D. Webb	
Number of partners:	2
Assistant solicitors:	1
Other fee-earners:	1

WORKLOAD	
UK immigration/ nationality law/ EU freedom of movement	100%

CONTACTS	
Immigration and nationality	David Webb
	Roger Gherson

GILCHRISTS 44 Great Marlborough Street, London, W1V 1DB **Tel:** (0171) 439 1707 **Fax:** (0171) 439 1942 **DX:** 42735 **Ptnrs:** 1 **Asst Solrs:** 3 **Other Fee-earners:** 2. Known for its criminal law practice. Also handles conveyancing, litigation, and matrimonial law.

GILFEDDER & McINNES 34 Leith Walk, Edinburgh, EH6 5AA **Tel:** (0131) 553 4333 **Fax:** (0131) 555 3712 **Ptnrs:** 6 **Asst Solrs:** 5 **Other Fee-earners:** 2. A small specialist practice concentrating on criminal defence work.

WORKLOAD	
Criminal law	100%

GILL AKASTER Scott Lodge, Milehouse, Plymouth, Devon, PL2 3DD **Tel:** (01752) 500111 **Fax:** (01752) 563403 **DX:** 120026 Plymouth 12 **Ptnrs:** 10 **Asst Solrs:** 4 **Other Fee-earners:** 6. Traditionally a private client practice, with an increasing commercial side. Wide range of work undertaken, including legal aid. Particular knowledge of fisheries law.

WORKLOAD			
Matrimonial & family	32%	Civil litigation	20%
Company & commercial	17%	Residential property	16%
Probate, trusts, tax	10%	Crime	5%

GILLAM MACKIE 7 Albyn Place, Edinburgh, EH2 4NN **Tel:** (0131) 226 6576 **Fax:** (0131) 225 7158 **Ptnrs:** 4 **Asst Solrs:** 1 **Other Fee-earners:** 2. Leading litigation practice specialising in personal injury (pursuer and defender), professional negligence (pursuer) and adoption.

WORKLOAD			
Personal injury lit	70%	Med neg/ind diseases	15%
Road traffic law	5%	Social work law	5%
Adoption	5%		

GILLESPIE MACANDREW WS

31 MELVILLE STREET, EDINBURGH, EH3 7JQ
DX: 113 Edinburgh

TEL: (0131) 225 1677
FAX: (0131) 225 4519

THE FIRM: Gillespie Macandrew WS has a long tradition of advising substantial private and commercial clients and estate/ agricultural landowners, and has strengthened its practice with the recent acquisition of J.C. & A. Steuart WS. The firm are winners of the 1995 TSB/Law Society of Scotland Business of Law Award.

PRINCIPAL AREAS OF WORK:

Commercial Law: *(Contact Partner:* Derek A.J. McCulloch). The firm undertakes all aspects of company/ commercial work including commercial property contracts, land development, commercial lending, joint ventures, construction and civil engineering, employment law, environmental law and licensing. Particular expertise is offered regarding renewable energy projects (wind and hydro) and the fish farming industry.

Private Client: *(Contact Partner:* Simon A. Leslie). The practice maintains a strong private client base, and divides its specialist service into the following areas: wills, trusts and inheritance tax planning; income tax; securities and investment fund management; and executries, curatories and trust administration.

Investment/Fund Management: *(Contact Partner:* Thomas K Murray). Comprehensive range of investment services from full discretionary management to execution only. Brochure and Rate Card available on request.

Agriculture/ Estate: *(Contact Partner:* Randall L. Nicol). The department offers traditional expertise in this area, with emphasis on advice to estate and farm landowners. Areas of expertise include fishing, sporting estates, forestry, mineral exploitation and quotas.

Residential Property: *(Contact Partner:* Barbara Finlayson). This department offers clients a full estate agency, conveyancing and factoring service in respect of domestic properties. The firm has close links with several lending bodies.

Litigation: *(Contact Partner:* Ian Turnbull). Civil litigation undertaken in fields of commercial and property disputes with particular interest in employment and construction matters, debt recovery, and matrimonial.

SENIOR PARTNER: Mr Michael Grey

Number of partners:	10
Assistant solicitors:	9
Other fee-earners:	11

WORKLOAD	
Private client	40%
Commercial client	25%
Agric/estate	20%
Residential/ domestic	10%
Litigation	5%

CONTACTS	
Agriculture/ estate	Randall Nicol
Commercial dept	Derek McCulloch
Investment/ fund management	Thomas Murray
Litigation	Ian Turnbull
Private client	Simon Leslie
Residential property	Barbara Finlayson

GILLESPIE MACANDREW WS

GILMORE LEWIS 54 East Crosscauseway, Edinburgh, EH8 9HD
Tel: (0131) 662 1933 **Fax: Ptnrs:** 2. Specialist family/ matrimonial law practice.
Undertakes legal aid work.

GIRLINGS 3-6 Dane John, Canterbury, Kent, CT1 2UG **Tel:** (01227) 768374
Fax: (01227) 450498 **DX:** 5303 Canterbury **Ptnrs:** 23 **Asst Solrs:** 5 **Other Fee-earners:** 27. A broad based general practice, involved with both private client and commercial work. Has five other offices in Kent.

WORKLOAD			
Lit (incl pers injury)	34%	Priv (probate/convey/etc)	30%
Family and matrimonial	26%	Commercial	10%

GISBY HARRISON Goffs Oak House, Goffs Lane, Goffs Oak, Cheshunt, Herts, EN7 5HG **Tel:** (01707) 872222 **Fax:** (01707) 876484 **DX:** 98302 Caffley **Ptnrs:** 7 **Asst Solrs:** 2 **Other Fee-earners:** 5. The firm now concentrates on commercial work and in particular the litigation department acts for a number of large national companies.

WORKLOAD			
Commercial litigation	30%	Commercial property	25%
Residential property	20%	Company and commercial	20%
Tax, trusts and probate	5%		

GLAISYERS

10 ROWCHESTER COURT, PRINTING HOUSE ST, BIRMINGHAM,
W. MIDLANDS, B4 6DZ   DX: 24933 Birmingham 4

TEL: (0121) 233 2971
FAX: (0121) 236 1534

THE FIRM: The firm specialises in criminal, family law and child care and also handles personal injury, consumer law, debt recovery, general contract, landlord and tenant, conveyancing, trust and probate, estate planning, licensing, mental health, housing law and welfare benefits. Close to all courts. All types of agency work undertaken.

CONTACT PARTNER: Mr Charles Royle

Number of partners:	9
Assistant solicitors:	6
Other fee-earners:	14

GLANVILLES 16 Landport Terrace, Portsmouth, Hants, PO1 2QT
Tel: (01705) 827231 **Fax:** (01705) 753611 **DX:** 2211 **Ptnrs:** 11 **Asst Solrs:** 15 **Other Fee-earners:** 8. Commercial/ domestic property and matrimonial work are particular strengths but all major areas of work covered including company/ commercial, insolvency, trusts and probate, marine law and liquor licensing.

WORKLOAD			
Property	45%	Litigation	25%
Private client	23%	Company and commercial	7%

GLAZER DELMAR 223-229 Rye Lane, Peckham, London, SE15 4TZ
Tel: (0171) 639 8801 **Fax:** (0171) 358 0581 **DX:** 34258 Peckham **Ptnrs:** 4 **Asst Solrs:** 7 **Other Fee-earners:** 7. Best known for handling legal aid work, specialising in personal injury, landlord and tenant, crime, immigration, medical negligence and matrimonial work.

WORKLOAD			
Housing	18%	Personal injury	18%
Immigration	15%	Crime	15%
Wills and probate	10%	Conveyancing	10%

EDITORIAL POLICY

In this edition, the lists of specialist firms include profiles of individual practitioners - solicitors and barristers - who have been recommended most frequently to our researchers. Editorial policy is to identify leading practitioners on merit: it is not possible to buy a place in our biographical lists. Inclusion of a profile in this directory is based solely on expertise and reputation.

Enormous effort has been invested by our ten-strong research team (mainly solicitors and barristers) in canvassing recommendations and identifying leaders. We are confident in the overall accuracy of the results. However, mistakes and misjudgements are inevitable, and if readers have any suggestions regarding our listings we should be very pleased to hear from them.

GLENISTERS Television Hse, 269 Field End Road, Eastcote, Ruislip, Middx, HA4 9LS **Tel:** (0181) 868 4343 **Fax:** (0181) 429 3606 **DX:** 35150 Eastcote **Ptnrs:** 7 **Asst Solrs:** 5 **Other Fee-earners:** 10. A broadly based practice catering for both commercial and private clients. Provides debt collection and personal financial services.

GLOVERS

115 PARK STREET, LONDON, W1Y 4DY
DX: 44438 Marble Arch

TEL: (0171) 629 5121
FAX: (0171) 491 0930

CONTACT PARTNER: Ray Anstis	
Number of partners:	11
Assistant solicitors:	5
Other fee-earners:	4

THE FIRM: Glovers is an established firm which combines the efficiency and quality of service provided by the larger City firms with the warmth and personal attention that only a smaller firm can offer.

PRINCIPAL AREAS OF WORK:

Commercial Property: (*Contact:* Ray Anstis). The firm has always been associated with property development and has been involved in many substantial projects including offices, shops, hotels and industrial premises. Work ranges from advice on building contracts and collateral warranties, project finance, planning negotiations, project management agreements, through to selling and leasing of completed developments.

Company/ Commercial: (*Contact:* Ray Anstis/ Jeremy Simmonds). *Work includes:* company formations, purchases and sales, corporate finance work, joint ventures, employment law and pension matters, marketing agreements, and the drafting of conditions of sale.

Banking & Finance: (*Contact:* Jeremy Simmonds/ Catherine Cava). The firm acts for a number of UK and overseas banks on a wide variety of banking matters, including secured lending and the restructuring of loans and charges.

Litigation: (*Contact:* Tony Bourne/ Edward Vaughan). The department undertakes forceful and structured negotiations, backed where necessary by the vigorous pursuit of remedies provided by litigation. *Work includes:* construction disputes, landlord and tenant matters, commercial disputes, banking cases, aviation law, and insolvency.

Construction: (*Contact:* David Miles). The firm acts for one of the UK's leading construction companies and has wide experience in advising on building contracts, collateral warranties and complex construction disputes. Glovers is one of the four original firms responsible for implementation of ADR practices in this country and has its own ADR unit.

Private Client: (*Contact:* Frances Dewhurst). A comprehensive service is offered to all individuals in all matters relating to wills and personal financial and tax planning. Domestic conveyancing, and UK and offshore trusts, are also handled.

CONTACTS	
Banking	Jeremy Simmonds
Commercial litigation	Anthony Bourne
Commercial property	Ray Anstis
Company/ commercial	Ray Anstis
Construction	David Miles
Private client	Frances Dewhurst

WORKLOAD			
Gen/commercial lit	34%	Family	20%
Res conveyancing	13%	Company/comm convey	12%
Wills and probate	7%	Sundries	6%

GODLOVE PEARLMAN Russell House, 15 St. Pauls Street, Leeds, W. Yorks, LS1 2LZ **Tel:** (0113) 243 3861 **Fax:** (0113) 242 0714 **DX:** 12006 Leeds **Ptnrs:** 12 **Asst Solrs:** 4 **Other Fee-earners:** 6. General practice particularly known for matrimonial, licensing, environmental and commercial litigation work. Also handles company/ commercial, domestic property, and legal aid matters.

GODWIN BREMRIDGE & CLIFTON 12 St. Thomas St, Winchester, Hants, SO23 9HF **Tel:** (01962) 841484 **Fax:** (01962) 841554 **DX:** 2502 **Ptnrs:** 5 **Asst Solrs:** 2 **Other Fee-earners:** 2. Provides a full range of legal services, including commercial, trust and probate, domestic conveyancing and litigation work.

GOLDKORN DAVIES MATHIAS 6 Coptic Street, Bloomsbury, London, WC1A 1NH **Tel:** (0171) 631 1811 **Fax:** (0171) 631 0431 **DX:** 35705 Bloomsbury **Ptnrs:** 4 **Other Fee-earners:** 3. A practice giving a personal service particularly in sports, immigration, probate, licensing and commercial work. Well known for defence of serious fraud and white collar crime.

GOLDSMITH WILLIAMS 42-44 Stanley Street, Liverpool, Merseyside, L1 6AL **Tel:** (0151) 231 1292 **Fax:** (0151) 231 1369 **DX:** 14186 Liverpool **Ptnrs:** 5 **Asst Solrs:** 9 **Other Fee-earners:** 33. A specialist practice with particular expertise in personal injury, industrial disease and product liability actions, and in franchising agreements and litigation.

WORKLOAD			
Prod liability plaintiff	30%	Pers injury (plaintiff)	30%
Non-cont convey/remortg	20%	Misc incl welfare benefit	10%
Matrimonial	10%		

GOODGER AUDEN

2/4 LICHFIELD STREET, BURTON-ON-TRENT, STAFFS, DE14 3RB
DX: 10704

TEL: (01283) 544323
FAX: (01283) 535448

THE FIRM: Founded in 1852, Goodger Auden today offers a wide range of legal services. The firm is particularly noted for its computer law expertise, its longstanding connections with the brewing industry and a rapidly growing international profile. In 1989 the firm was instrumental in forming LAW (Lawyers Associated Worldwide), a network of commercial law firms with offices in over 50 countries in the European Community, Eastern Europe, the Middle East, the Far East, Australia, the Americas and Africa.

PRINCIPAL AREAS OF WORK:

Company/Commercial: *(Contact Partner:* Barry Challender). Clients range from sole proprietors to PLCs. The service includes commercial litigation, employment law, EC law, entertainment law, environmental law, licensing, computer and IT law, franchising, insolvency, debt collection, overseas trading, patents and trademarks, company formations and buy-outs, partnerships and commercial agreements.

Property Law: *(Contact Partner:* Michael Nickson). All property transactions are handled from residential conveyancing to large scale commercial developments with related planning aspects, landlord and tenant, housing law and neighbour disputes. Agricultural matters are also handled.

Computer Law: *(Contact Partner:* Peter Scragg). The firm acts for programmers, software houses, hardware manufacturers, distributors, end users and a considerable number of video games publishers both from Europe and the United States. Advice is offered with regard to software licensing, trading conditions, data protection, intellectual property rights, product liability, maintenance agreements, foreign law, contract disputes and EDI agreements.

Family Law: *(Contact Partner:* Margaret Nickson). A full range of services including adoption, wardship, child care, custody, separation, maintenance and property agreements.

Private Client: *(Contact Partner:* Bill Auden). In addition the firm offers advice on immigration, injunctions, investment, taxation, personal injury, wills, probate, trusts, powers of attorney and off-shore operations.

Criminal Law: *(Contact Partner:* Tony Russell). All aspects are undertaken including advice at police stations, bail, appeals, Crown Court, Juvenile Court and Magistrates' Court cases, motoring offences, private and trading prosecutions. Legal Aid work is undertaken.

FOREIGN LANGUAGES: French, German, Spanish, Gujerati and Hindi.

INTERNATIONAL CONNECTIONS: Apart from worldwide connections through LAW strong working links exist with USA, France, Spain, Portugal, Turkey and the Middle East.

OTHER OFFICES:

London (in Association with Peter T. James & Co, 2 Carlos Place, Mount Street, London W1Y 5AE) and 2-4 Lichfield Street, Burton upon Trent.

CONTACT PARTNER: B.J. Challender

Number of partners:	9
Assistant solicitors:	4
Other fee-earners:	5

CONTACTS	
Company/ commercial	B. Challender
	Michael Nickson
Computer law and IT	Peter Scragg
Crime	Tony Russell
Debt collection	Peter Scragg
Domestic/ commercial property	R. Cundy
	Michael Nickson
Employment	Tony Russell/ Richard Crowe
Family/ matrimonial	R. Crowe
	Michael Nickson
Intellectual property	Peter Scragg
Licensing and leisure	Peter Scragg
Overseas property	Pat Sellors
Personal injury	Peter Scragg/ Richard Crowe
Private client	Bill Auden/ Pat Sellors

GOODMAN DERRICK 90 Fetter Lane, London, EC4A 1EQ **Tel:** (0171) 404 0606 **Fax:** (0171) 831 6407 **DX:** 122 **Ptnrs:** 13 **Asst Solrs:** 11 **Other Fee-earners:** 7. Broad commercial practice, particularly noted for its media work in television, publishing and related industries. Also handles property, litigation, corporate and private client matters.

WORKLOAD			
Media/ litigation	35%	Property	25%
Corporate	25%	General litigation	10%
Charities/priv client	5%		

GOODMAN RAY 450 Kingsland Road, Dalston, London, E8 4AE
Tel: (0171) 254 8855 **Fax:** (0171) 923 4345 **Ptnrs:** 3 **Asst Solrs:** 1 **Other Fee-earners:** 2. Specialist family and criminal law practice. Strong reputation for child-related work. All partners are members of the Law Society Children Panel.

GOODSWENS 145 Albert Road, Middlesbrough, Clev, TS1 2PP **Tel:** (01642) 218444 **Fax:** (01642) 210498 **DX:** 60511 Middlesbrough **Ptnrs:** 6 **Asst Solrs:** 3 **Other Fee-earners:** 6. General practice handling company/ commercial, private client and civil litigation matters with particular expertise in licensing law. Office in Redcar also handles family, probate, personal injury and crime.

GORDON DADDS

80 BROOK STREET, MAYFAIR, LONDON, W1Y 2DD
DX: 131

TEL: (0171) 493 6151
FAX: (0171) 491 1065

CONTACT PARTNER: Douglas Alexiou

Number of partners:	13
Assistant solicitors:	6
Other fee-earners:	2

THE FIRM: Founded in the 1920's, Gordon Dadds offers specialist areas of expertise to clients. Best known for its matrimonial and private client work, it has increased its range of services in other areas particularly in the company/ commercial and private client fields. The firm seeks to provide a comprehensive and efficient service in most aspects of private and commercial law.

PRINCIPAL AREAS OF WORK:

Company and Commercial: (*Contact:* Simon Studd). The department provides a fast and efficient service, providing practical solutions consistent with a client's commercial objective. Areas of expertise include: acquisitions, disposals, banking, EC law, partnerships, refinancing and business expansion schemes.

Family and Matrimonial: (*Contact:* Douglas Alexiou). The firm is recognised as a leader in this area. It combines determination with sensitivity, providing a thorough and cost efficient service, supported by its own specialists in conveyancing, tax, trusts and company law. Partners in this department are members of the Solicitors Family Law Association, the International Academy of Matrimonial Lawyers and the Family Mediators Association.

Litigation: (*Contact:* Hugh Elder). Advising commercial and private clients in the resolution of disputes, the firm's aim is to achieve a constructive and cost effective solution for a client. The department advises on all types of commercial litigation including banking, breach of contract, computer contracts, fraud, passing-off, sale of goods, employment, and negligence.

Private Client: (*Contact:* Roger Peters). A comprehensive service is provided, offering clients advice on the administration of estates and post death tax planning, tax planning for the UK and overseas, charities and wills. Partners are members of the Institute of Estate Practitioners and the Society of Trust and Estate Practitioners.

Property: (*Contact:* Michael Boswell). The property department advises commercial and private clients on a wide range of property-related matters including commercial conveyancing, granting of leases, purchase and sale of residential property, rental agreements, reporting for financial institutions, transfer of property and tax advice related to property.

FOREIGN LANGUAGES: French and Greek.

RECRUITMENT: The firm recruits two high-calibre graduates a year as trainee solicitors. Applications should be received by July, two years before articles commence. Please address applications to the 'Staff Partner'.

WORKLOAD

Family and matrimonial	45%
Family and matrimonial	45%
Private client	22%
Private client	22%
Litigation	20%
Litigation	20%
Property	10%
Property	10%
Company and commercial	3%

CONTACTS

Company and commercial	Simon Studd
Family and matrimonial	Douglas Alexiou
Litigation	Hugh Elder
Private client	Roger Peters
Property	Michael Boswell

GORDON & SMYTH 420 Sauchiehall Street, Glasgow, G2 3JS **Tel:** (0141) 332 5705 **Fax:** (0141) 332 6036. The practice specialises in criminal defence work.

GORDONS WRIGHT & WRIGHT

14 PICCADILLY, BRADFORD, W. YORKS, BD1 3LX
DX: 11716 Bradford

TEL: (01274) 733771
FAX: (01274) 728346

THE FIRM: Gordons Wright & Wright is one of Yorkshire's largest firms. The firm acts for nine PLC clients and a wide range of commercial organisations. Particular strengths are employment, licensing, commercial property, family and housing association work. The firm is also well known for personal injury work, and provides a full range of private client services. Jeremy Mackrell is the Bradford Diocesan Registrar and the Registry is located at the Keighley office.

As a member of LawNet the firm is committed to the LawNet Quality Standard. Through LawNet Europe (Eurojuris) the firm is able to enhance its commercial practice by providing an international service for clients.

OTHER OFFICES:
6-14 Devonshire Street, Keighley, West Yorkshire BD21 2AY.
Tel: (01535) 667731. *Fax:* (01535) 609748. *DX:* 21454 Keighley.
4 Park Road, Bingley, West Yorkshire BD16 4JA.
Tel: (01274) 568347. *Fax:* (01274) 569813. *DX:* 21101 Bingley.

CONTACT PARTNER: Tim Ratcliffe

Number of partners:	20
Assistant solicitors:	16
Other fee-earners:	16

WORKLOAD	
Litigation	24%
Commercial property	24%
Residential property	16%
Private client	15%
Family	11%
Corporate/ commercial	10%

GORNA & CO Virginia House, Cheapside, King St, Manchester, M2 4NB **Tel:** (0161) 832 3651 **Fax:** (0161) 834 8572 **DX:** 14339 **Ptnrs:** 8 **Asst Solrs:** 10 **Other Fee-earners:** 5. Commercial firm: emphasis upon commercial property work-investment, development, planning and litigation; also departments covering wide range of litigation and company/ commercial work.

GOSSCHALKS

QUEENS GARDENS, HULL, HUMBS, HU1 3DZ
DX: 11902 Hull

TEL: (01482) 324252
FAX: (01482) 590290

THE FIRM: Gosschalks is a firm which can trace its roots to the latter part of the 19th century. Over the past ten years however the firm has more than quadrupled in size. The firm is known nationally for its expertise within the licensing field with Les Green, the firm's Senior Partner, enjoying the reputation of one of the country's leading solicitors in this regard. In addition the practice has a large number of partners who are recognised as specialists in their own field and of particular note are those in the commercial conveyancing department (particularly in the conveyancing of licensed premises and work in connection therewith) and the civil litigation department (which acts for a large number of insurance companies as well as acting on behalf of plaintiffs). In addition the firm has a long history of acting for a wide range of corporate and private clients and has developed a substantial proficiency in its company, commercial, family, criminal and private client departments. A legal aid franchise has been granted in five areas.

Recently the firm has moved into substantial new purpose built offices enabling it to provide a more efficient service and enhance the use of modern technology.

PRINCIPAL AREAS OF WORK:

Licensing: *(Contact:* Les Green). Les Green has a national reputation for his ability and knowledge within the licensing field concerning both licensed betting offices and pub/ club licensing. The department acts for a large number of nationally known corporate clients in this regard as well as a large number of private clients.

Commercial Litigation: *(Contact:* Mr R.L. Llewellyn). The department handles the whole range of property transactions in the commercial field for corporate and private clients. Particularly known for its conveyancing of licensed premises, it also has a substantial reputation for its general commercial conveyancing work.

Civil Litigation: *(Contact:* Mr W.M. Barlow/ Mr A.B. Wilkie). Handling a wide range of civil litigation, the department is particularly well known for acting for a large number of nationally known insurance companies. Although a large part of the

CONTACT PARTNER: Mr I.C. Lanch

Number of partners:	19
Assistant solicitors:	13
Other fee-earners:	21

WORKLOAD	
Commercial conveyancing	31%
Civil/ commercial litigation	24%
Family and private client	20%
Company	10%
Crime	8%
Licensing	7%

CONTACTS	
Civil litigation	Mr A.B. Wilkie
Commercial conveyancing	Mr R. Llewellyn
Commercial litigation	Mr A.D. Clark
Company	Mr S.W. Lunt
Crime	Mr W.O. Waddington
Domestic conveyancing	Mr N. Johnson
Employment	Mrs M. Clare Johnson
Family	Mr I.C. Lanch
Licensing	Mr R.L. Green
Probate	Mr H. Williamson

department is defendant based work, it acts for a large number of private clients on a plaintiff basis in all areas of personal injury and also specialises in medical negligence cases.

Family/ Matrimonial: *(Contact:* Mr I.C. Lanch). The department's activities encompass the whole range of disputes within this field. The department acts for clients both on a private and legally-aided basis but with particular regard to the private client and high-value financial settlements.

Company/ Commercial: *(Contact:* Mr S.W. Lunt). The firm handles a whole range of company transactions in the private and public sector. Clients include quoted and unquoted companies, partnerships and sole proprietors. Acquisitions, management buy-outs, commercial contracts and all types of general corporate work are conducted.

Crime: *(Contact:* Mr W.O. Waddington). The work covers a broad spectrum from fraud and drug cases to road traffic and general crime. It is one of the largest departments of its type within the Humberside area.

Private Client: *(Contact:* Mr N. Johnson). A comprehensive service is provided advising both buyers and sellers, landlords and tenants of business and private premises as well as property developers. In addition a full range of services to the private client involving trusts and all aspects of probate work.

Commercial Litigation: *(Contact:* Mr A.D. Clark). The firm has a commercial litigation practice acting for corporate and private clients in all aspects of litigation, many cases being of a substantial nature.

Employment: *(Contact:* Mrs M.C. Johnson). The firm advises both employer and employee with a particular emphasis on representation of the employer, offering immediate advice and representation throughout, up to and including tribunal work.

RECRUITMENT AND TRAINING: The firm places a strong emphasis on the continuing education and training of all its partners, fee earners and support staff. The firm continues to employ three or four trainee solicitors each year. *(Contact:* Mr W.O. Waddington).

GOTELEE & GOLDSMITH

35 & 37 ELM ST, IPSWICH, SUFFOLK, IP1 2AY
DX: 3220 Ipswich

TEL: (01473) 211121
FAX: (01473) 230387

CONTACT PARTNER: Mr. M.G. Sparrow

Number of partners:	14
Assistant solicitors:	6
Other fee-earners:	12

THE FIRM: Dating from the 1880's, Gotelee & Goldsmith is firmly established as one of Suffolk's leading practices and provides a complete range of legal services for both commercial and private clients. Present clients range from local authorities, major companies and partnerships to sole traders and individuals.

Litigation has long been a strength of the firm but as a result of the considerable expansion of the firm's commercial client base Gotelee & Goldsmith is now equally well known for its local authority and commercial work.

The firm is an active member of LawNet and has access to the specialist services of five major London firms, through the LawNet Protocol. It has been instrumental in pioneering the LawNet Quality Standard for LawNet firms and has implemented management standards throughout the practice.

PRINCIPAL AREAS OF WORK:

Company/ Commercial: *(Contact Partners:* Howard Nichols/ Jonathan Rands/ Andrew Hudson). The commercial partners' experience in industry has led to an emphasis in offering commercial solutions. A broad range of company and commercial services includes: company/ partnership formation, MBOs, the acquisition or sale of companies and businesses, corporate finance, tax matters, trading agreements, licensing, company receiverships and liquidations, insolvency work, employment contracts, franchise and intellectual property.

Commercial Litigation: *(Contact Partner:* Jonathan Ripman). Commercial claims and disputes, construction litigation, insurance company litigation, intellectual property and professional negligence. The firm has an established expertise in road haulage and advises hauliers on UK and EU legislation governing overloading, construction and use, drivers' hours, tachographs and vehicle maintenance. Advice is given at public inquiries including cases where the Licensing Authority raises environmental objections. Use of debt collection computer software provides a highly efficient service on volume debt collection for the firm's extensive corporate client base.

Employment Law: *(Contact Partner:* Brian Morron). A team experienced in acting for employers and employees provides a full service for both contentious and non-contentious work covering advice on contracts of employment, discrimination, redundancy and setting up effective procedures. Seminars and legal updates are given regularly to local employer groups and personnel officers.

Pensions: *(Contact Partner:* Andrew Hudson). The firm acts for employees and pension scheme trustees in relation to new and existing schemes and advises on all matters affecting them.

Commercial Property: *(Contact Partner:* Michael Sparrow). The firm has a strong property base with particular expertise in the purchase, sale or leasing of industrial sites, office buildings, commercial and residential development projects, building contracts, joint ventures, planning matters and tax considerations.

Agricultural Services: *(Contact Partner:* Peter Crix). An experienced team advises a substantial number of farming families and agricultural businesses on property law, tax planning, agricultural tenancy law and milk quotas.

Local Authority/ Environmental: *(Contact Partner:* Brian Morron). The firm acts for a number of local authorities and has extensive experience of the administration of and law affecting local authorities. Advice is also given upon compulsory purchase and planning appeals both for and against local authorities, health and safety, pollution, noise and environmental matters.

Civil & Criminal Litigation: *(Contact Partners:* Martin Ward – Family/ Child Care work, Anthony Owen – Civil Litigation, Hugh Rowland – Crime). A full service is offered by an experienced litigation team which has a commitment to both private and Legal Aid work. Services include family law and child care (Children Panel membership), criminal law and civil litigation including personal injury, insurance work (P.I. Panel membership), licensing, computer software licensing.

Private Client: *(Contact Partner:* Peter Crix). The firm acts for families and individuals in matters relating to residential conveyancing, wills, trusts, administration of estates, tax, and caring for the elderly and infirm.

OTHER OFFICES: 6 Church Street, Hadleigh, Suffolk IP7 5DU. *Tel:* (01473) 822102.

FOREIGN LANGUAGES: French and Italian.

INTERNATIONAL CONNECTIONS: As a member of LawNet Europe Gotelee & Goldsmith is associated with over 600 firms throughout Europe.

GOTTESMAN JONES & PARTNERS

ALDWYCH HOUSE, ALDWYCH, LONDON, WC2B 4HN

TEL: (0171) 242 8953
FAX: (0171) 405 0527

THE FIRM: Gottesman Jones & Partners is a firm of US lawyers resident in London and was established in 1970.

PRINCIPAL AREAS OF WORK: • Tax, including US and international tax planning.
• Securities, including sale in Europe of securities of US issuers.
• Mergers and acquisitions, including cross-border acquisitions.
• Joint ventures and investments in US.
• Licence and distribution agreements (mainly cross-border).
• Venture capital. US venture capital investment by European institutional investors.

LANGUAGES SPOKEN: French and Japanese.

CONTACT PARTNER: Grant L. Jones or Joseph A. Consolo

LAWYERS:
London: 4
Worldwide: 4

GOUGHS 28 Church St, Calne, Wilts, SN11 0HX **Tel:** (01249) 812086 **Fax:** (01249) 816378 **DX:** 44800 **Ptnrs:** 12 **Asst Solrs:** 5 **Other Fee-earners:** 4. A well-established firm with five offices in Wiltshire, catering for private and commercial clients.

GOULDENS

22 TUDOR STREET, LONDON, EC4Y 0JJ
DX: 67

TEL: (0171) 583 7777
FAX: (0171) 583 3051

THE FIRM: Gouldens is a leading City firm with a long history of success in commercial and international practice. Besides its main City office, it has offices in Brussels, Jersey and Moscow as well as an associated office in Hong Kong. The firm is divided into the traditional areas of corporate work, tax, property, litigation and private client; there are also multi-disciplinary groups for construction, environment, insolvency, insurance, intellectual property, international work, entertainment and sports.

PRINCIPAL AREAS OF WORK:

Company/ Commercial: (*Contact:* Patrick Burgess). The corporate and banking departments advise, among others, major public companies and institutions on all aspects of commercial activity including corporate finance, banking, mergers and acquisitions, tax, FSA regulatory work, venture capital and management buy-outs, EC and competition law, share options and pension schemes.

Property and Planning: (*Contact:* Hugo Scott). The department advises developers, institutional investors, banks, surveyors, and other professionals on the financing, tax structuring, and implementation of major developments, and every year handles a large number of planning appeals.

Litigation: (*Contact:* Charters Macdonald-Brown). The department deals with a wide variety of domestic and international commercial disputes including construction, defamation, employment, insolvency, insurance, and intellectual property. The insolvency group advises leading practitioners and lenders on all aspects of corporate recovery and insolvency. The insurance practice is primarily professional-indemnity based, advising Lloyd's and other insurers. The intellectual property group advises on all IP matters including patent/ trademark disputes.

International and EC: (*Contact:* Julian Doyle). Besides advice on typical problems of transfer-border matters, the international department is experienced in strategic and political issues of international business and also maintains close relationships with leading lawyers across the world, enabling it to provide first class advice wherever required.

RECRUITMENT AND TRAINING: Gouldens attaches exceptionally high priority to the recruitment and training of its staff. The firm has a unique system of articles for its trainee solicitors and expects to keep all trainees on qualification. The firm is looking for graduates of high academic calibre who will accept the challenge of responsibility, in an atmosphere where flair, originality and enthusiasm are particularly encouraged. Candidates should apply by letter and CV to Ruth Orchard.

CONTACT PARTNER: Hugo Scott

UK:	
Number of partners:	32
Assistant solicitors:	64
Other fee-earners:	40
INTERNATIONAL:	
Number of Partners:	2
Assistant Solicitors:	1
Other fee-earners:	1

CONTACTS

Banking	Tom Budd, James Campbell
Commercial litigation	C. MacDonald Brown
Commercial property	Hugo Scott
Company/ commercial	Patrick Burgess
Construction litigation	Allan Henderson
Corporate finance	Max Thorneycroft
Corporate tax	Patrick Harrison
Corporate reconstruction	Martin Piers
Defamation	Charters MacDonald Brown
EC and competition	Julian Doyle
Employment/ insolvency	Martin Piers
Entertainment and media	Chris Parkinson
Environment	Clare Deanesly
Financial services/unit trusts	Paul Nield
Insurance litigation	Ian Lupson
Intellectual property	Fiona Russell
Private client	Jennet Davies
Professional indemnity	C. MacDonald Brown
Property litigation/ sports	Allan Henderson
Town and country planning	David Cooper

GOWMANS

65 HYDE RD, PAIGNTON, DEVON, TQ4 5BT DX: 100600 Paignton	TEL: (01803) 559934 FAX: (01803) 528351
61 Abbey Road, Torquay, Devon TQ2 5NN (Linked Office) DX: 100600 Paignton	Tel: (01803) 559934 Fax: (01803) 213401

THE FIRM: Gowmans is a long established general practice. The firm has traditionally handled domestic conveyancing, wills and probate, but in recent years has expanded and become more litigation biased, handling a wide range of work. It is committed to legal aid work.

PRINCIPAL AREAS OF WORK:

Civil Litigation: The firm has expertise in handling professional negligence work, including plaintiff medical negligence and plaintiff solicitors' negligence. The firm has close links with CAB and is a member of AVMA. Other work includes plaintiff and defendant personal injury, building disputes, computerised ULR and debt collection, licensing and mental health tribunals.

Family/ Matrimonial: The full range of work is covered. One of the partners is a member of the Children Panel.

Criminal: The firm has a substantial criminal practice, with three members of the local Duty Solicitor schemes.

Private Client: *Work includes:* residential and commercial conveyancing, probate, wills and trusts, and partnerships.

LANGUAGES: French, German, Norwegian.

CONTACT PARTNER:
Mr David Boddam-Whetham

Number of partners:	7
Assistant solicitors:	2
Other fee-earners:	8

CONTACTS	
Civil litigation	David Boddam-Whetham
Conveyancing	Robin Hunton
Criminal	Mervyn Williams
Family	Tony Wood
Private client	Jennifer Donson

GRAHAME STOWE, BATESON 7 Portland St, Leeds, W. Yorks, LS1 3DR **Tel:** (0113) 2468163 **Fax:** (0113) 2426682 **DX:** 12022 **Ptnrs:** 9 **Asst Solrs:** 5 **Other Fee-earners:** 7. A general practice handling all areas of litigation work but with particular emphasis in criminal and mental health and matrimonial law. Has five other offices in Leeds and Wakefield.

WORKLOAD			
Matrimonial	40%	Crime	20%
Conveyancing	15%	Civil litigation	10%
Mental health	10%	Personal injury	5%

GRAHAM EVANS & PARTNERS Moorgate House, 6 Christina Street, Swansea, W. Glam, SA1 4EP **Tel:** (01792) 655822 **Fax:** (01792) 645387 **DX:** 39573 Swansea **Ptnrs:** 10 **Asst Solrs:** 1 **Other Fee-earners:** 9. A general practice specialising in all aspects of family and private client law including criminal, personal injury, matrimonial and conveyancing. Undertakes extensive legal aid work.

GRAHAM & OLDHAM Electric House, Lloyds Avenue, Ipswich, Suffolk, IP1 3HZ **Tel:** (01473) 232425 **Fax:** (01473) 230505 **DX:** 3221 Ipswich **Ptnrs:** 11 **Asst Solrs:** 4 **Other Fee-earners:** 22. Handles litigation, licensing, crime, personal injury, medical negligence, employment, commercial, probate, family and conveyancing. Particular expertise in EC law. French and Dutch spoken.

GRAHAM & ROSEN 8 Parliament St, Hull, Humbs, HU1 2BB **Tel:** (01482) 323123 **Fax:** (01482) 223542 **DX:** 11925 **Ptnrs:** 7 **Asst Solrs:** 3 **Other Fee-earners:** 9. Best known for its matrimonial and personal injury work, the firm also has a growing commercial practice. Legal aid work undertaken.

WORKLOAD			
Matrim/fam & child care	30%	Personal injury	20%
Criminal	17%	Commercial litigation	15%
Conveyancing	11%	Wills, probate	7%

GRANVILLE-WEST High Street Chambers, Newbridge, Newport, Gwent, NP1 4XB **Tel:** (01495) 248611 **Fax:** (01495) 248611 **DX:** 86800 Newbridge **Ptnrs:** 8 **Asst Solrs:** 4 **Other Fee-earners:** 9. A general practice handling crime, matrimonial law, personal injury and conveyancing. Specialist expertise in public law children cases and crime.

WORKLOAD			
Civ lit (incl pers inj)	28%	Family and child care	21%
Crime	18%	Domestic conveyancing	13%
Wills/trusts/prob/tax	10%	Company and commercial	10%

GRAYS Duncombe Place, York, N. Yorks, YO1 2DY **Tel:** (01904) 634771 **Fax:** (01904) 610711 **DX:** 61505 **Ptnrs:** 8 **Asst Solrs:** 1 **Other Fee-earners:** 3. Established 1695. Best known for conveyancing, trust and tax work. Also handles civil litigation, personal injury and probate.

WORKLOAD			
Conveyancing	41%	Trust and probate	40%
Litigation	13%	Private client	6%

GRAYSONS 6 Paradise Square, Sheffield, S. Yorks, S1 1TB **Tel:** (0114) 2729184 **Fax:** (0114) 2768664 **DX:** 10509 **Ptnrs:** 8 **Asst Solrs:** 8 **Other Fee-earners:** 5. Areas of work include matrimonial, crime, civil litigation, domestic conveyancing, company law, employment and probate. Has French and Spanish-speaking partner.

GREATHEAD & WHITELOCK 3-5 Hamilton Terrace, Pembroke, Dyfed, SA71 4DF **Tel:** (01646) 682101 **Fax:** (01646) 621248 **Ptnrs:** 5 **Asst Solrs:** 1 . Known for family law and agricultural law. Also experienced in crime, residential conveyancing, and personal injury work. Has connections in West Germany.

WORKLOAD			
Matrimonial/child care	25%	Civil litigation	20%
Probate	20%	Conveyancing	20%
Criminal and licensing	15%		

GREEN DAVID CONWAY & CO

45 CRAWFORD PLACE, LONDON, W1H 1HX
DX: 41726 Marylebone 1

TEL: (0171) 258 0055
FAX: (0171) 724 0385

THE FIRM: Established in 1972, the firm provides a comprehensive but personal service over a broad range of commercial work to UK and international private, corporate and institutional clients.

The firm has established significant connections in Africa, Asia and the Middle East.

PRINCIPAL AREAS OF WORK:

Corporate and Commercial: (*Contact:* D.P. Conway).
Property: (*Contact:* D.P. Conway or S.R. Sheikh).
Litigation: (*Contact:* D.J. Green).
Hotels & Leisure and Healthcare: (*Contact:* S.R. Sheikh).
Media and Intellectual Property: (*Contact:* D.J. Green or S.R. Sheikh).
Insolvency: (*Contact:* S.R. Sheikh or H. Posener).
Tax and Trusts: (*Contact:* D.J. Green or S.R. Sheikh).

CONTACT PARTNERS: D.J. Green, D.P. Conway, S.R. Sheikh

Number of partners:	7
Assistant solicitors:	4
Other fee-earners:	8

GREENE & GREENE

80 GUILDHALL ST, BURY ST. EDMUNDS, SUFFOLK, IP33 1QB
DX: 57205

TEL: (01284) 762211
FAX: (01284) 705739

NATURE OF FIRM: The firm was founded in the 1890s. It is an independent, medium-size firm giving high quality personal service in general and specialist fields. It serves both private and commercial clients. It is a member of LawNet and as a result its lawyers receive training in-house at City firms. The firm achieves economies of scale and it can access specialist advice from its links with London firms where necessary. The firm has continued a policy of expanding by recruiting senior, high quality solicitors during 1994/5, attracting a new company/commercial partner and three senior assistant solicitors in other areas.

PRINCIPAL AREAS OF WORK:

General Description: All the general legal services required by private and commercial clients. The large litigation section is well known. The commercial/tax work of the firm has acquired a high reputation and is expanding rapidly.

Company/Commercial: A team of solicitors with general and specialist expertise covering most fields (including formations, acquisitions, commercial arrangements/contracts, tax, Stock Exchange, competition Law, intellectual property and venture capital work) for a wide range of businesses, private and public companies.

CONTACT PARTNER: Mr. C.J. Thomson

Number of partners:	7
Assistant solicitors:	5
Other fee-earners:	10

WORKLOAD	
Company/ commercial	29%
Private client	27%
Litigation	26%
Commercial property	10%
Employment	3%

Commercial Property: Commercial conveyancing and development conveyancing; including tax, planning and agriculture.

Litigation: High Court, County Court and Tribunal litigation with particular expertise in commercial litigation and negligence (including medical and other professional negligence) claims. Agency work undertaken.

Private Client: A traditional strength of the firm, which is particularly active in tax planning and trusts work. Also conveyancing, agricultural work, wills/estate planning, immigration and nationality.

Employment Law: Tribunal and agency work undertaken and handled personally.

CONTACTS	
Commercial property	C.J. Thomson
Company/ commercial	D.J. Medcalf
Employment law	I.S. Alston
Litigation	M.R. Kay
Private client	M.D. Batt

GREENLAND HOUCHEN

38 PRINCE OF WALES RD, NORWICH, NORFOLK, NR1 1HZ
DX: 5217 Norwich

TEL: (01603) 660744
FAX: (01603) 610700

THE FIRM: A long established general practice which seeks to offer at its three offices a full range of legal services. The partners include in their clientele builders and developers, housing associations, members of the local farming community and other commercial and corporate enterprises, as well as the private client. All aspects of litigation are undertaken with a significant legal aid element.

CONTACT PARTNER: Trevor Nicholls

Number of partners:	13
Assistant solicitors:	1
Other fee-earners:	4

GREENWOOD KYLE 1 Finkle Street, Kendal, Cumbria, LA9 4AE **Tel:** (01539) 721613 **Fax:** (01539) 726137 **DX:** 63401 Kendall **Ptnrs:** 3 **Asst Solrs:** 2 **Other Fee-earners:** 2. A broadly based practice dealing with all aspects of property, agricultural, matrimonial, criminal and private client law.

WORKLOAD			
Domestic/comm prop	35%	Matrimonial/civil lit	25%
Criminal	25%	Probate	15%

GREENWOODS 30 Priestgate, Peterborough, Cambs, PE1 1JE **Tel:** (01733) 555244 **Fax:** (01733) 347988 **DX:** 12306 **Ptnrs:** 15 **Asst Solrs:** 13 **Other Fee-earners:** 17. A large practice handling company/ commercial, commercial property, construction law, planning, litigation, and probate, tax and trusts.

WORKLOAD			
Lit incl comm/pers inj	52%	Property	16%
Construction law	12%	Company and commercial	12%
Wills/prob/trusts/tax	7%	Pensions	1%

GREEN & CO 2-4 Atkinson Street, Manchester, M3 3BH **Tel:** (0161) 834 8980 **Fax:** (0161) 834 8981 **Ptnrs:** 1 **Asst Solrs:** 2 **Other Fee-earners:** 1. Niche practice particularly known for its expertise in all aspects of law relating to children (childcare and adoption in particular).

GREGORY, ROWCLIFFE & MILNERS

1 BEDFORD ROW, LONDON, WC1R 4BZ
DX: 95

TEL: (0171) 242 0631
FAX: (0171) 242 6652

THE FIRM: Gregory, Rowcliffe & Milners has its roots going back to 1784. It consists of a well established private client, company/ commercial and litigation practice with strongly developed Anglo-German connections, (with fluent German-speakers at all levels throughout the firm); and long standing links with a number of organisations concerned with Anglo-German trade. The merged firm is a founder member of Solon EEIG, a grouping of law firms. The current members are from England and Germany.

PRINCIPAL AREAS OF WORK:

Company/ Commercial: (*Contact:* John Anderson). The department has excellent international links with Europe, especially Germany, the USA and the Far East, and represents national and multi-national concerns, providing practical legal and taxation solutions to business problems and objectives over a broad spectrum of commerce and industry. Particular areas include healthcare, education, and leisure activities.

CONTACT PARTNER: Ms Fenella Pringle

Number of partners:	15
Assistant solicitors:	2
Other fee-earners:	6

WORKLOAD	
Litigation	35%
Company/ commercial	23%
Private client	22%
Property	20%

Litigation: (*Contact:* Christopher Harper). The firm is particularly noted for its experience in at least the following areas: insurance litigation including personal injury, professional indemnity, employers liability and industrial diseases; administrative law including judicial review particularly for institutional clients; general commercial litigation including arbitrations; employment law (acting for employer or employee); international disputes including in particular those with a German aspect; family law including settlement of matrimonial disputes and all litigation aspects of trusts. In addition the firm has a sizeable and well known London Agency practice.

Private Client: (*Contact:* Peter Scott). The firm has expertise in inheritance and tax planning (both resident and offshore) including the preservation of listed buildings and works of art, the creation of charitable trusts, and the administration of estates, often with an international dimension.

Property: (*Contact:* David King). All aspects of commercial, industrial, agricultural, residential and investment conveyancing including estate management, planning and tax planning.

CONTACTS	
Anglo German	Lesley Pendlebury Cox
Company/ commercial	John Anderson
Employment	John Sharpe
Family/ matrimonial	Fenella Pringle
Litigation	Christopher Harper
Private client	Peter Scott
Property	David King

GRIFFITH SMITH 47 Old Steyne, Brighton, E. Sussex, BN1 1NW **Tel:** (01273) 324041 **Fax:** (01273) 203796 **DX:** 2701 Brighton **Ptnrs:** 12 **Asst Solrs:** 4 **Other Fee-earners:** 15. Principal areas of work are company/ commercial, civil litigation, and private client with specialist skills including planning and environmental law and financial services.

WORKLOAD			
Private client	33%	Litigation	33%
Commercial (inc commercial	17%	Res conveyancing	16%
Public law/ planning	1%		

GRIFFITHS ROBERTSON 46 West Street, Reading, Berks, RG1 1TZ **Tel:** (01734) 574018 **Fax:** (01734) 507551 **DX:** 40106 Reading **Ptnrs:** 4 **Asst Solrs:** 3 . An expanding firm committed to providing specialist advice on child care matters, family law, criminal law and mental health work.

GRIGOR & YOUNG 1 North Street, Elgin, Grampian, IV30 1UA **Tel:** (01343) 544077 **Fax:** **Ptnrs:** 6 **Asst Solrs:** 5 **Other Fee-earners:** 2. Sale and purchase of farms, leases of farms, limited partnership leases, factoring land, succession.

WORKLOAD			
Domestic conveyancing	26%	Court related/matrimonial	21%
Executry and trust	16%	Private client/other	14%
Comp/comm/agricultural	14%	Estate agency	9%

GRINDEYS

GLEBE COURT, STOKE-ON-TRENT, STAFFS, ST4 1ET
DX: 21053

TEL: (01782) 46441
FAX: (01782) 416220

THE FIRM: Grindeys was founded 150 years ago, and is now one of the larger firms in Staffordshire. As well as its commitment to private client work, the firm has a thriving commercial practice and a very strong litigation department.

PRINCIPAL AREAS OF WORK:

Company/ Commercial: (*Contact:* Mr P. Godfrey). *Work includes:* company acquisitions and buy-outs; company formations; company restructuring; corporate finance; intellectual property; EC and competition law; franchising and insolvency.

Commercial Property: (*Contact:* Mr A.D. Rushton). All aspects of commercial property work handled. As well as commercial sales, purchases and leases the department handles all aspects of housing sssociation work and the preparation of finance documents for commercial loans.

Litigation: (*Contacts:* Mr J.N.A. Sherratt – Commercial Litigation; Mrs J.C. Mitting – Plaintiff P.I.; Mr N.C. Tizley – Defendant P.I.). *Work includes:* personal injury claims for the plaintiff and several large insurance companies; computerised debt collection; employment law; landlord and tenant; professional negligence; disputes with a technical content and all other aspects of commercial litigation.

CONTACT MANAGING PARTNER:
Mrs J.C. Mitting

Number of partners:	10
Assistant solicitors:	12
Other fee-earners:	14

WORKLOAD	
Litigation	50%
Company and commercial/ litigation	30%
Private client	15%
Domestic conveyancing	5%

Private Client: (*Contacts:* Miss D. Trevitt and Mr D. James). This is an expanding department providing a wide-ranging service. *Work includes:* residential conveyancing, probate and administration of trusts and a large criminal and matrimonial practice. One partner is a member of the Child Care Panel.

RECRUITMENT AND TRAINING: (*Contact:* Mrs J.C. Mitting). The firm recruits three trainee solicitors each year and provides a broad training programme. Applications should be made two years prior to commencement of articles.

OTHER OFFICES:
30A The Strand, Longton, Stoke-on-Trent ST3 2JH *Tel:* (01782) 323933.
157 High Street, Tunstall, Stoke-on-Trent ST6 5EA *Tel:* (01782) 825871.

CONTACTS	
Commercial property	A.D. Rushton
Commercial litigation	J.N.A. Sherratt
Company and commercial	P. Godfrey
Defendant personal injury	N.C. Tizley
Plaintiff personal injury	Mrs J.C. Mitting
Private client	Miss D. Trevitt, D. James
Residential conveyancing	S. Phillips

GROSS & CO.

84 GUILDHALL STREET, BURY ST. EDMUNDS, SUFFOLK, IP33 1PR
DX: 57203

TEL: (01284) 763333
FAX: (01284) 762207

22 Bentinck Street, London W1M 6AB
Contact Partner: Graeme Kirk

Tel: (0171) 935 5541
Fax: (0171) 935 6638

THE FIRM: Established in W. Suffolk for over 150 years, this progressive firm offers a specialist immigration service and has a fast-expanding commercial practice as well as a traditional general practice. The firm has an unusually international clientele, as well as sizeable private companies, small businesses and private clients. It is a member of the NIS Group of Independent Solicitors. The firm has an office in London W1 to service its London and international clients.

PRINCIPAL AREAS OF WORK:

Immigration and Nationality law: The majority of work is in the field of business immigration. Assistance is also given in US and Canadian immigration law, and a consultancy service is offered to other solicitors through the ImmLaw service (brochure available).

Company/ Commercial: Expertise in most areas of commercial practice, including commercial property, for a wide range of business clients.

Litigation: All types of litigation including commercial, civil, matrimonial and legal aid. Agency work undertaken.

Private Client: Conveyancing, wills/ estate planning.

FOREIGN CONNECTIONS: The firm has overseas associate offices in New York, Boston, Philadelphia, Montreal and Johannesburg.

LANGUAGES SPOKEN: French, German and Russian.

CONTACT PARTNER: Graeme Kirk	
Number of partners:	6
Assistant solicitors:	2
Other fee-earners:	9

WORKLOAD	
Residential conveyancing	20%
Wills and probate	15%
Company/ commercial	15%
Civil litigation	12%
Commercial property	10%
Matrimonial	10%
Immigration and nationality law	10%
Employment	8%

GROSSMAN HERMER SELIGMAN 7-8 Park Place, Cardiff, S. Glam, CF1 3YD **Tel:** (01222) 371991 **Fax:** (01222) 222795 **DX:** 50777 Cardiff 2 **Ptnrs:** 9 **Asst Solrs:** 1 **Other Fee-earners:** 5. Work includes company/ commercial, commercial and residential property/ development; civil and commercial litigation. Clients include plcs, and insurance companies.

GULBENKIAN HARRIS ANDONIAN

181 KENSINGTON HIGH STREET, LONDON, W8 6SH
DX: 47204 Kensington

TEL: (0171) 937 1542
FAX: (0171) 938 2059

THE FIRM: Whilst the firm engages in a wide range of commercial work (including litigation) it is best known for its expertise in immigration and nationality law which is undertaken for both commercial and private clients.

PRINCIPAL AREAS OF WORK:

Immigration and Nationality Law: (*Contact Partner:* Bernard Andonian or Peter Wyatt). *Work includes:* nationality applications, all aspects of UK immigration and advice (business and private), refugee and asylum work and obtaining work

CONTACT PARTNER: Paul Gulbenkian	
Number of partners:	10
Assistant solicitors:	2
Other fee-earners:	2

permits. The firm has experience in US immigration, Hong Kong, Middle East, Sri Lanka and South Africa. The firm is a founder member of the European Immigration Lawyers group. The Senior Partner is a part-time Immigration Adjudicator.

Matrimonial and Family law: *(Contact Partner:* Paul Gulbenkian or Bernard Andonian). Comprehensive services are provided including advice on separation, divorce, wardship, custody, adoption and all related financial, property and taxation matters. The senior partner is one of the founder members of the Solicitors Family Law Association.

OTHER AREAS OF WORK: In addition, the firm handles commercial litigation, commercial and domestic property transactions, defamation, intellectual property and probate and trust.

NATURE OF CLIENTELE: A largely international client base including multinationals as well as small to medium sized companies and private individuals.

LANGUAGES SPOKEN: French, Spanish, Danish, Swedish, Farsi, Armenian and Arabic.

WORKLOAD	
Immigration	70%
Matrimonial	20%
General	10%

CONTACTS	
General	Paul Gulbenkian
Immigration	Bernard Andonian
	Peter Wyatt
Matrimonial	Bernard Andonian
	Paul Gulbenkian

R. GWYNNE & SONS Edgbaston Hse, Walker St, Wellington, Shrops, TF1 1HF **Tel:** (01952) 641651 **Fax:** (01952) 247441 **DX:** 23107 **Ptnrs:** 11 **Asst Solrs:** 8 **Other Fee-earners:** 17. One of the largest firms in Shropshire. Extensive agricultural and commercial practice. Large legal aid practice, particularly known for mental health, child-care and crime.

WORKLOAD			
Crime	31%	Civil litigation	19%
Family law	17%	Conveyancing incl agric	15%
Trust and probate	8%	Personal injury/med neg	6%

HACKING ASHTON

BERKELEY COURT, BOROUGH ROAD, NEWCASTLE-UNDER-LYME, STAFFS, ST5 1TT   DX: 20954

TEL: (01782) 715555
FAX: (01782) 715566

THE FIRM: Formed in 1978, Hacking Ashton, provides a comprehensive legal service to commercial clients, with particular expertise in intellectual property and construction matters, and also handles a wide range of private client work. The firm has associated offices in London and Glasgow, as well as extensive foreign connections.

PRINCIPAL AREAS OF WORK:

Company/ Commercial: *(Contact:* Robert Ashton). Advice is offered with regard to company formations, acquisitions, disposals, franchising, take-overs, mergers, joint ventures, capital restructuring and financing, service and consultancy agreements, employment law, agency and distribution agreements, partnership and banking.

Litigation: *(Contact:* Malcolm Hacking). The firm specialises in work with a highly technical content, particularly intellectual property (including patents, trademarks, copyright, licensing, franchising and character merchandising), and building construction conciliation and arbitration. The department also undertakes personal injury cases (including medical negligence) and debt collection services.

International Law: *(Contact:* Robert Ashton). Advice is available on establishing overseas businesses, distributorship and agency agreements, EC legislation, restrictive trade practices legislation, foreign litigation, currency financing and commercial documentation.

Commercial Property: *(Contact:* Tom Gregory). The firm deals with sales and purchases of property, estate development, leasing, landlord and tenant law, mortgages and representation at public enquiries, planning appeals and tribunals.

Agricutural Law: *(Contact:* Tom Gregory). The firm handles all aspects of agricultural law including tenancies, quotas, tax planning and sale/ purchase of land.

Private Client: *(Contact:* Catherine Whittles). The department advises on residential conveyancing, tax planning, family and matrimonial law, wills, trusts and probate.

FOREIGN CONNECTIONS: The firm has established an impressive network of international connections, and is associated with overseas firms with offices in Paris, Milan, Geneva and Hamburg. The firm also supplies legal advice in Eastern Europe, the Far East, the Americas and Africa, with correspondent offices in Holland, New York, Canada, Hong Kong, Tokyo, India, Brazil and Mexico.

CONTACT PARTNER: R.F. Ashton

Number of partners:	8
Assistant solicitors:	2
Other fee-earners:	6

WORKLOAD	
Company/ commercial	30%
Commercial litigation	25%
Commercial property	25%
Private client	20%

CONTACTS	
Agricultural	T.R. Gregory
Commercial	R.F. Ashton
	D. Hall
Commercial property	T.R. Gregory
	C.A. Whittles
	J. Edwards
Company work	D. Hall
	R.F Ashton
Construction	M.R. Hacking
Employment	R.F. Ashton
Personal injury	B. White
Probate/ private client	C.A. Whittles

HADEN STRETTON SLATER MILLER

LEICESTER BUILDINGS, BRIDGE STREET, WALSALL, W. MIDLANDS, WS1 1EL
DX: 12122 Walsall

TEL: (01922) 720000
FAX: (01922) 720023

THE FIRM: One of the largest firms in the West Midlands catering for clients ranging from private individuals to major public companies.

PRINCIPAL AREAS OF WORK:

Company/ Commercial: *(Contact Partner:* David Robinson). A wide range of corporate and commercial advice is available. Work includes acquisitions, disposals, re-organisations, joint ventures, formations, management buy-outs/ buy-ins, restructuring and partnership work.

Property: *(Contact Partner:* Peter Williamson). includes all areas of commercial and agricultural property, environmental and planning law.

Litigation: *(Contact Partner:* Malcolm Griffiths). includes all areas of civil, criminal, personal injury, employment, property disputes, licensing, mental health, lands and agricultural tribunal work.

Family: *(Contact Partner:* Robert Dawson) includes advice on all matrimonial proceedings, separation, maintenance, financial claims, protection orders, adoption, wardship, custody and access.

Private Client: *(Contact Partner:* Stephanie Dean) all aspects of residential conveyancing, trusts and probate are handled.

OTHER OFFICES: Lichfield, Bloxwich, Cannock, Darlaston, Great Barr, Hednesford.

CONTACT PARTNER: David Robinson	
Number of partners:	20
Assistant solicitors:	5
Other fee-earners:	15

WORKLOAD	
Domestic conveyancing	20%
Civil litigation	20%
Family law	20%
Corporate/commercial law	15%
Probate	10%
Criminal law	10%
Environmental and planning law	5%

HALLETT & CO

11 BANK ST, ASHFORD, KENT, TN23 1DA
DX: 30202 Ashford

TEL: (01233) 625711
FAX: (01233) 643841

THE FIRM: Hallett & Co is one of the oldest firms in the county and has a long history of advising local families, businessmen and farmers. It has particular expertise both in agricultural matters, employment and commercial law.

PRINCIPAL AREAS OF WORK:

Property: *Work includes:* freehold and leasehold properties, holiday homes, housing associations, tenancy and lease agreements, compulsory purchase, Town and Country Planning applications and appeals, planning enquiries and general conveyancing work, in particular a substantial amount of estate development work.

Company/ Commercial: *Work includes:* business start-up, franchising, joint ventures, commercial and employment contracts, company acquisition and disposal, and education and the charitable status of private schools.

Commercial Litigation: *Work includes:* employment and redundancy disputes, unfair dismissal, consumer law, partnerships, building disputes, landlord and tenant, licensing applications and appeals, debt recovery and carriage of goods.

Private Client: *Work includes:* matrimonial and family law, personal injury, insurance claims, employment law, criminal law, wills, probate and trusts, tax planning and professional negligence. Legal aid work is undertaken.

Agriculture: *Work includes:* buying and selling agricultural land, planning applications and appeals, quotas and subsidies, company formations and partnerships, share farming agreements, tied cottages and Agricultural Holdings legislation.

OTHER OFFICES: New Romney, Lydd.

FOREIGN LANGUAGES: French.

CONTACT: Mr C.A. McDonald	
Number of partners:	8
Assistant solicitors:	2
Other fee-earners:	12

HALLINANS Portland House, 22 Newport Road, Cardiff, S. Glam, CF2 1TD **Tel:** (01222) 482316 **Fax:** (01222) 498566 **DX:** 33009 Cardiff **Ptnrs:** 8 **Asst Solrs:** 7 **Other Fee-earners:** 8. Long established general practice with city centre offices and branch in Caerphilly.

HALLIWELL LANDAU

ST. JAMES'S COURT, BROWN ST, MANCHESTER, M2 2JF
DX: 14317

TEL: (0161) 835 3003
FAX: (0161) 835 2994

THE FIRM: Established in 1975, Halliwell Landau has grown to become one of Manchester's foremost commercial law firms. "In business for business" is central to the firm's cultural ethos. The firm has an impressive client list consisting of both quoted and private companies, professional and institutional clients and it provides a comprehensive range of commercial legal advice to support their business activities. The partnership has a reputation for combining experience, commercial awareness and a willingness to consider new approaches and ideas. The firm's philosophy of entrepreneurial awareness with close attention to detail and dedication to high professional standards has become the hallmark of its work.

PRINCIPAL AREAS OF WORK: The firm provides a comprehensive range of commercial legal advice categorised under the main headings:

Corporate: Advising on mergers, acquisitions, disposals, management buy-ins and buy-outs, flotations, banking law and corporate finance.

Commercial Property: One of the leading commercial property advisers in the North West advising on a whole range of commercial property issues including the acquisition and disposal of properties, site assembly and negotiation of leases.

Commercial Litigation: All aspects of commercial litigation including property litigation, banking and recovery work, insurance litigation including professional negligence.

Planning and Environmental: One of the most respected planning appeal practices in the country, advising some of the region's top companies and both local and national developers.

Construction and Bonds: Advice on all facets of construction law including bonds and guarantees, which play a crucial role in construction agreements.

Employment Law and Pensions: Advises clients on both contentious and non-contentious aspects of legislation and on establishing and running pension schemes.

Trust and Estate Planning: Advice to senior business executives and individuals of high net worth on income and estate planning, the creation of trusts and administration of investments. Also advises trustees and charities.

Intellectual Property: Advice provided goes well beyond the traditional categories of patents, copyright, trademarks and registered designs to enhance advice on any form of intangible rights.

Insolvency and Corporate Recovery: Principally directed at supporting banks and insolvency practitioners on specialised insolvency matters. Also advice to companies and directors on the legal aspects of restructuring, reorganising and refining.

CONTACT PARTNER: Roger Lancaster

Number of partners:	25
Assistant solicitors:	21
Other fee-earners:	18

WORKLOAD

Commercial litigation, incl. personal injury	24%
Corporate and commercial	21%
Commercial property	21%
Insolvency	13%
Trust and estate planning	8%
Planning and environmental law	6%
Intellectual property	4%
Employment	3%

CONTACTS

Commercial property	David Stratton
Commercial lit/personal injury	Paul Thomas
Corporate & commercial	Clive Garston
	Alec Craig
Employment law & pensions	Stephen Hills
Insolvency/ corporate recovery	Andrew Livesey
Intellectual property	Jonathan Moakes
Planning & environmental law	Roger Lancaster
Trust and estate planning	Geoffrey Shindler

A. HALSALL & CO

47-48 HAMILTON SQUARE, BIRKENHEAD, MERSEYSIDE, L41 5BD
DX: 17853

TEL: (0151) 647 6323
FAX: (0151) 647 9818

THE FIRM: Established over a century ago, A. Halsall & Co traditionally acted for private clients in mainly non-contentious cases. Over the last 50 years the firm has also developed a thriving litigation practice and an increasing volume of commercial work from clients seeking the specialist expertise now offered.

PRINCIPAL AREAS OF WORK: The main areas being developed include liquor licensing, retail property portfolio work and Housing Association matters which are handled on a national basis. Strong links have been formed, particularly over the last 10 years, with a number of Housing Associations and specialist lending departments of banks and building societies operating in the voluntary housing sector. The firm has also developed a significant volume of domestic mortgage repossession work in recent years.

PHILOSOPHY: Its client centered philosophy of delivering a consistently high standard of service at a cost-effective price has ensured a steady growth in instructions from organisations regularly requiring quality legal services.

OTHER OFFICES: Greasby, Hoylake (known as J.P. Almond & Co) and Thingwall.

CONTACT PARTNER: John Barnes

Number of partners:	6
Assistant solicitors:	1
Other fee-earners:	2

CONTACTS

Commercial and retail property	Andrew Almond
Housing assoc/residential dev.	John Barnes
Licensing	Chris Johnson

HAMILTON BURNS & MOORE 13 Bath Street, Glasgow, G2 1HY
Tel: (0141) 353 2121 **Fax:** (0141) 353 2181 **DX:** 47 Glasgow **Ptnrs:** 7 **Asst Solrs:** 2 **Other Fee-earners:** 3. A broadly based general practice with a litigation bias. Work includes personal injury claims, crime, insolvency, debt recovery, corporate law and conveyancing (private and commercial).

HAMLIN SLOWE

ROXBURGHE HOUSE, 273-287 REGENT ST, LONDON, W1A 4SQ
DX: 53803 Oxford Circus North

TEL: (0171) 629 1209
FAX: (0171) 491 2259

THE FIRM: Founded in 1906, this medium-sized firm is the result of the amalgamation of A.E. Hamlin and Co. and Slowes in 1984, and Jacobson Ridley in 1990. The firm undertakes a wide variety of work but has particular experience in property development, landlord and tenant litigation, intellectual property litigation, entertainment and media work, and commercial work.

PRINCIPAL AREAS OF WORK:

Property Services: The firm has a long and established reputation in the fields of acquisition, letting and disposal of shop, office and industrial property, development and finance agreements, planning law, compulsory purchase, landlord and tenant, residential conveyancing, and property taxation.

Litigation Services: The firm is known for the strength of its litigation services, and handles all manner of litigation. *Work includes:* heavy commercial litigation, landlord and tenant disputes, mortgages, planning appeals, debt recovery, matrimonial matters and personal injury claims.

Entertainment and Intellectual Property: The firm has an outstanding reputation in the entertainment sector, particularly in the area of copyright infringement. It handles all aspects of entertainment law for many clients including copyright societies, music publishers, record companies, record producers, composers, authors, entertainers, pop artists and film and video artists.

Secured Lending: Combining all disciplines relating to security over property, this department advises on, and effects security documentation for clients, operates a computerised mortgage recovery service ("MORSE") for secured lenders, litigates to repossession when required, and deals with all aspects of conveyancing flowing from these sources.

Company and Commercial: *Work includes:* the formation, purchase, financing and sale of businesses, companies and partnerships, share and rights issues; public flotations; reorganisations, liquidations, shareholder agreements, joint venture, service and employment agreements, and intellectual property.

Private Client: *Work includes:* personal taxation, including capital gains tax, inheritance tax and all aspects of tax planning both UK and international, the creation and administration of UK trusts, wills, administration of estates, and obtaining Grants of Probate.

CLIENTELE: The firm's clients include 17 public companies and 12 large and well known private companies.

RECRUITMENT AND TRAINING: Hamlin Slowe recruits three or four trainee solicitors annually. The minimum requirement is a 2:2 degree, not necessarily in law. Write enclosing CV to Laurence Gilmore.

CONTACT PARTNER: Anthony Hoffman	
Number of partners:	19
Assistant solicitors:	5
Other fee-earners:	16

WORKLOAD	
Litigation services	34%
Property services	33%
Entertainment/ intellectual property	12%
Company and commerical	10%
Secured lending	7%
Private client	4%

CONTACTS	
Company and commercial	Gordon Oliver
Entertainment and IP	Laurence Gilmore
Litigation	Anthony Hoffman
Private client	Christopher Walker
Property services	Brian Casey
Secured lending	Roy Brown

HAMLIN SLOWE
SOLICITORS

HAMMOND SUDDARDS

2 PARK LANE, LEEDS, W. YORKS, LS3 1ES DX: 26441	TEL: (0113) 234 3500 FAX: (0113) 234 3600
Pennine House, 39-45 Well Street, Bradford BD1 5NL. DX: 11768	Tel: (01274) 734700 Fax: (01274) 307239
Moor House, 119 London Wall, London EC2Y 5ET. DX: FINSBURY SQUARE 33885	Tel: (0171) 448 1000 Fax: (0171) 448 1001
Trinity Court, 16 John Dalton Street, Manchester M60 8HS. DX: 14347 Manchester 1	Tel: (0161) 830 5000 Fax: (0161) 830 5001
Avenue Louise 250, 1050, Brussels.	Tel: (00) 322 627 7676 Fax: (00) 322 627 7686.

THE FIRM: One of the UK's major commercial practices, Hammond Studdards offers comprehensive legal services to a wide range of national and international clients. In addition to its offices in Leeds, London, Manchester and Bradford, the firm has a specialist EC law office in Brussels. The total number of partners and consultants is 57 and total staff over 880.

PRINCIPAL AREAS OF WORK:

Company/Commercial: (*Contact:* Noel Hutton). This is one of the two largest departments in the firm. *Work includes:* acquisitions, mergers, flotations, MBOs/MBIs, corporate finance, overseas acquisitions and joint ventures. The firm has represented some of its public company clients on market flotations on the Stock Exchange and other markets and Business Expansion Scheme share issues. It presently provides corporate services to over 30 listed or USM PLCs and specialist services to many others. In 1994 the firm was noted by Acquisitions Monthly as having handled more private takeovers than any other UK law firm - 80 with a total value of £832m.

Litigation: (*Contact:* John Heller). Work includes: commercial claims and disputes, construction litigation, insurance company litigation, employment disputes, intellectual property, and professional negligence. The firm acts for most leading UK insurance companies and leading building societies.

Commercial Property: (*Contact:* John Beckett, Gary Watson). Work includes: purchases, sales and option agreements, office developments, acquisition and disposal of industrial premises, mineral extraction, quarrying and tipping agreements, negotiations, preparation and renewal of leases, city centre redevelopments and retail park development.

Insolvency/ Corporate Recovery: (*Contact:* Chris Jones). Advice to insolvency practitioners and banks on all aspects of their work as receivers, liquidators, trustees, administrators and supervisors. The firm also advises companies and partnerships experiencing serious financial difficulties. Much of the work is of an international nature.

EC Law, Brussels Office: (*Contact:* Stephen Tupper). A full EC law service including competition law, anti-dumping, merger control, environmental law, existing and proposed legislation and regulations. Advice is given on grants for movement of goods and intellectual property matters.

Tax: (*Contact:* Christopher Haan). Work includes: advice on tax planning at all levels, employee share option schemes, and offshore tax.

Pensions: (*Contact:* Jane Marshall). Work includes: advising companies on setting up and operating pension schemes and pension elements of corporate transactions. With the addition of Ellison Westhorp by merger the firm now has one of the largest pensions departments in the UK.

Employment: (*Contact:* Tim Russell). All aspects of employment advice, including service agreements, compensation packages, redundancies and disputes.

Intellectual Property: (*Contact:* Larry Cohen). All aspects of UK, EC, and overseas intellectual property patents, trade marks and copyright claims and disputes.

CONTACT PARTNERS: Alan Bottomley, John Heller, Noel Hutton, Chris Jones

UK:	
Number of partners:	55
Assistant solicitors:	123
Other fee-earners:	118
INTERNATIONAL:	
Number of Partners:	2
Assistant Solicitors:	4

WORKLOAD	
Litigation (including debt collection)	45%
Corporate	35%
Property and planning	13%
Insolvency and corporate recovery	7%

HAMMOND SUDDARDS
SOLICITORS

Information Technology and Telecommunications: (*Contact:* Richard Kemp/Michael Mahony). An effective leading edge service to suppliers and users of high technology in the public and private sectors. The firm acts for many leading national and international manufacturers, systems integrators and suppliers as well as substantial users. Stephen York heads the I.T. litigation section.

Planning: (*Contact:* David Goodman). *Work includes:* planning applications, planning audits, appeals and advocacy, planning and enforcement, highway orders, compulsory purchase, and advice in relation to listed buildings.

Construction: (*Contact:* Mark Hilton/David Jones). All aspects of construction law-contentious and non-contentious. The firm acts for major organisations both nationally and internationally.

Media and Entertainment: (*Contact:* Brian Eagles). The firm acts for corporate clients handling all aspects of film, music, television sports and publishing work.

Environmental Law: (*Contact:* Mike Shepherd). *Work includes:* all advice on environmental matters, environmental, assessments, wind energy and wind farms, environmental litigation and regulation. Defence against environmental prosecutions.

Management Buy-Outs: (*Contact:* Simon Inman). The firm acts for management teams, banks and venture capital houses in buy-out or buy-in situations.

Banking: (*Contact:* Andrew Knight). All types of banking work both for financial institutions – including the UK clearing banks and leading building societies – and for borrowers, secured and unsecured lending, sophisticated transactions and restructuring.

Building Societies: (*Contact:* Steve Gale). The unit draws on all departments and units to co-ordinate the provision of substantial services for many of the UK's leading building societies.

Debt Collection: (*Contact:* Chris Jones/Simon Stell). Computerised debt recovery department dealing with High Court and County Court matters. Commercial and consumer recovery matters are dealt with.

Mortgage Arrears: (*Contact:* Marlice Stalker). Computerised litigation and conveyancing sections acting for leading building societies.

NATURE OF CLIENTELE: Hammond Suddards acts for public companies and large private companies, banks, building societies, insurance companies and other large organisations and for subsidiaries and divisions of UK and overseas multinationals.

FOREIGN CONNECTIONS: Brussels office: fluent Italian, French, German, Czech, Dutch, Spanish, Portuguese, Russian, Ukrainian, Urdu and Hebrew spoken. The firm has connections throughout the USA and in Canada, Australia, Japan, Middle East, France, Germany, Holland, Spain, Scandinavia and all other EC countries.

RECRUITMENT AND TRAINING: High quality lawyers of all disciplines constantly sought, two years prior to articles required. *Contact:* Helen Kavanagh. The firm has a resident training officer. Awards available.

HAMMOND SUDDARDS

SOLICITORS

EDITORIAL POLICY

In this edition, the lists of specialists include profiles of individual practitioners - solicitors and barristers - who have been recommended most frequently to our researchers. Editorial policy is to identify leading practitioners on merit: it is not possible to buy a place in our biographical lists. Inclusion of a profile in this directory is based solely on expertise and reputation.

Enormous effort has been invested by our ten-strong research team (mainly solicitors and barristers) in canvassing recommendations and identifying leaders. We are confident in the overall accuracy of the results. However, mistakes and misjudgements are inevitable, and if readers have any suggestions regarding our listings we should be very pleased to hear from them.

HANCOCK & LAWRENCE The Old Mansion House, Quay Street, Truro, Cornwall, TR1 2HD **Tel:** (01872) 7233 **Fax:** (01872) 40390 **DX:** 81200 Truro **Ptnrs:** 10 **Asst Solrs:** 3 **Other Fee-earners:** 4. Handles private client and commercial work. Particular strengths are commercial property, agriculture, personal injury, marine, Admiralty and professional indemnity.

HAND & CO

GLADE HOUSE, 52 CARTER LANE, LONDON, EC4V 5EA

TEL: (0171) 329 1525
FAX: (0171) 329 1514

THE FIRM: The firm was established in January this year and is now one of only two specialist pensions law practices in the UK.

PRINCIPAL AREAS OF WORK: Advising employers and trustees on all aspects of Pension Law and documentation including the establishment, management and termination of Occupational Pension Schemes; pensions aspects of company sales and acquisitions; pension litigation.

NATURE OF CLIENTELE: Clients include a range of corporate clients, trade unions, trustees (including independent trustees), other pensions professionals.

CONTACT PARTNER: Sean Hand

Number of partners:	1

HANSELL STEVENSON

13 CATHEDRAL CLOSE, NORWICH, NORFOLK, NR1 4DS
DX: 5204

TEL: (01603) 615731
FAX: (01603) 633585

THE FIRM: Hansell Stevenson is a major Norfolk firm with a thriving corporate and private client practice. It has nine offices throughout the county.

PRINCIPAL AREAS OF WORK: The firm's expertise encompasses company/ commercial work, corporate and personal tax, aviation law, commercial litigation, employment, insolvency, environmental law, licensing and intellectual property. A large and experienced team handles plaintiff personal injury and medical negligence litigation.

NATURE OF CLIENTELE: Major UK airline, general aviation companies, insurance companies, motoring organisations, banks and property companies.

FOREIGN LANGUAGES: Norwegian, French and German spoken.

CONTACT PARTNERSHIP DIRECTOR:
Philip Peaston

Number of partners:	13
Assistant solicitors:	7
Other fee-earners:	22

HARBOTTLE & LEWIS

HANOVER HOUSE, 14 HANOVER SQUARE, LONDON, W1R 0BE
DX: 44617Mayfair. E-mail: hal@CityScape.co.uk

TEL: (0171) 629 7633
FAX: (0171) 493 0451

THE FIRM: Founded by Laurence Harbottle in 1955, Harbottle & Lewis initially acted almost exclusively in the entertainment and media industries. It has subsequently steadily expanded into the wider commercial field, whilst retaining its leading position in the entertainment and media fields.

PRINCIPAL AREAS OF WORK:

General Description: Generally recognised as a leader in the entertainment and media fields, Harbottle & Lewis also has an extensive general commercial practice including property and litigation. The firm is very well known for theatre, music, film and television work, publishing and charitable matters and litigation in these areas. It is active in commercial property and has strong aviation and intellectual property practices.

CONTACT PARTNER: Colin Howes

Number of partners:	14
Consultants:	3
Assistant solicitors:	29
Other fee-earners:	32

Company/ Commercial: (*Contact:* Colin Howes. *4 Partners*). *Work includes:* commercial agreements, take-overs and mergers, demergers, equity and loan financing, partnerships, joint ventures, strategic advice, management buy-outs; employment law; insolvency; competition and anti-trust law; media/IP; trade marks; interactive and multi-media; electronic publishing; telecommunications; IT & property.

Tax/ Trust/ Probate: (*Contact:* Alison Dillon. *1 Partner*). *Work includes:* tax planning for individuals and corporations, pension schemes, revenue and Customs and Excise negotiations, international and double taxation planning for residents and non-residents, trusts, wills, probate and administration of estates, family provision and Court of Protection.

Property: (*Contact:* Alan Patten. *3 Partners*). *Work includes:* property development and investment, acquisition and disposal of investment property, commercial conveyancing and business tenancies, domestic conveyancing, leasehold enfranchisement, tenancy agreements and security of tenure, town and country planning, compulsory purchase and rating.

Litigation: (*Contact:* Michael Bowler. *3 Partners*). *Work includes:* commercial, company and contractual disputes, defamation, property disputes, accident cases, employment disputes, licensing applications, divorce and aviation claims.

Film/ Television/ Theatre: (*Contact:* Robert Storer. *2 Partners*). *Work includes:* film, television, cable, satellite, radio and telecommunications, computers, book and periodical publishing, performing rights, theatrical management, artists, sculptors and designers, copyright and other intellectual property rights, charity formation.

Music: (*Contact:* Andrew Stinson. *2 Partners*). *Work includes:* recording, publishing and management agreements, video agreements, production agreements, merchandising and sponsorship agreements, international record licensing and sub-publishing agreements, tour and producers agreements and distribution agreements.

Aviation: (*Contact:* Frances Butler-Sloss. *2 Partners*). *Work includes:* advice on licensing, bilateral agreements, market access, slot allocation, route frequencies, CRS, travel, state aids, competition and anti-trust, franchising and other alliances and in particular advising on the remedies arising from anti-competitive practices. The firm also advises on aircraft and spare engine acquisition, lease financing, wet leasing and charters, airline insurance and engineering support.

Intellectual Property: (*Contact:* Dinah Nissen. *2 Partners*). *Work includes:* all areas of copyright, trade & service marks (including advice on branding & name protection), anti-counterfeiting, passing off, designs, confidential information & computer related matters. The IP group advises on litigation, commercial dealings and competition issues in relation to these areas under UK & European law. The majority of the work involved is of an international nature.

NATURE OF CLIENTELE: Clients range from individuals to medium-sized quoted companies, probably just under half from or related to the entertainment and media industry and the remainder from general commerce, commercial property development and investment.

WORKLOAD	
Company/ commercial	25%
Commercial litigation	21%
Property	14%
Music	12%
Film, TV, radio, theatre, cable	10%
Aviation	9%
Interactive multimedia/ electronic publishing	6%
Tax	3%

CONTACTS	
Advertising	Andrew Stinson
Aviation	Frances Butler-Sloss
Charities	Laurence Harbottle
Company/ commercial	Colin Howes
Defamation	Gerrard Tyrrell
Employment law	Michael Bowler
Film, TV and Radio	Robert Storer
Immigration	Mark Ainsworth
Insolvency	John Stutter
Intellectual Property	Dinah Nissen
Interactive & Multi-Media	Mark Phillips
Litigation	Michael Bowler
Music	Andrew Stinson
Property	Alan Patten
Sports	Paul Richardson
Tax, trust, probate	Alison Dillon
Telecommunications	Marian Derham
Theatre	Laurence Harbottle

HARDING & ROWE 11 The Strand, Barnstaple, Devon, EX31 1EU **Tel:** (01271) 43026 **Fax:** (01271) 78664 **DX:** 34957 Barnstaple **Ptnrs:** 8 **Asst Solrs:** 3 **Other Fee-earners:** 3. General practice, established in 1790, with three offices in North Devon. Principal area of work is property based with a growing civil and criminal litigation department, probate, licensing, agency and advocacy work.

HARDWICK & COMPANY

PORTERS' PLACE, 33 ST. JOHN STREET, LONDON, EC1M 4AA
DX: 175 Ch.Ln.

TEL: (0171) 490 7788
FAX: (0171) 490 7270

THE FIRM: A young, progressive firm with a growing reputation and following of commercial clients.

PRINCIPAL AREAS OF WORK:

Company/ Commercial: (*Contact:* Charles Ranson). A broad range of corporate and commercial matters, with increasing involvement in the fields of intellectual property and information technology.

Commercial Property: (*Contact:* Nigel Skevington). Emphasis on commercial development and investment work for private and public companies, financial institutions and individual entrepreneurs. All aspects of landlord and tenant work undertaken.

Litigation: (*Contact:* Rhodri James). A wide range of commercial disputes with a particular reputation in the fields of factoring, unit trusts and commodities. Work also includes property litigation, construction and intellectual property.

CONTACT PARTNER: Simon Hardwick

Number of partners:	6
Assistant solicitors:	1

WORKLOAD	
Company/ commercial	33%
Commercial litigation	33%
Commercial property	33%

CONTACTS	
Commercial property	Nigel Skevington
Commercial litigation	Rhodri James
Company/ commercial	Charles Ranson

HAROLD BENJAMIN & COLLINS

HILL HOUSE, 67-71 LOWLANDS ROAD, HARROW, MIDDX, HA1 3EQ
DX: 4243 Harrow 1

TEL: (0181) 422 5678
FAX: (0181) 864 0322

THE FIRM: The firm was established in 1953 and is best known for development and commercial conveyancing and building litigation. The firm is excellently located in central Harrow, an area increasingly convenient for a rapidly expanding base of property and other commercial clients. It has a growing litigation department and a newly established corporate department.

PRINCIPAL AREAS OF WORK: *Work includes:* development, commercial and residential conveyancing, town planning, building and other litigation and company and commercial. The firm also specialises in retail premises, particularly commercial leasehold, acting for both landlords and tenants. Its family and probate departments complement its experienced private client team.

CONTACT PARTNER: Roger Lane

Number of partners:	6
Assistant solicitors:	5
Other fee-earners:	7

WORKLOAD	
Commercial property	50%
Litigation	23%
Private client, family and probate	20%
Corporate	7%

HAROLD G. WALKER & COMPANY Lansdowne House, Christchurch Road, Bournemouth, Dorset, BH1 3JT **Tel:** (01202) 555691 **Fax:** (01202) 294118 **DX:** 7609 **Ptnrs:** 9 **Asst Solrs:** 4 **Other Fee-earners:** 2. Established 1946. Has six offices in Dorset. Handles a full range of work for a clientele ranging from legally-aided individuals to commercial clients.

HAROLD MICHELMORE & CO

15-21 MARKET STREET, NEWTON ABBOT, DEVON, TQ12 2RN
DX: 59103

TEL: (01626) 332266
FAX: (01626) 331700

THE FIRM: Established in 1861, the firm draws its mix of commercial, farming and private clients from the wide catchment area of South Devon and Dartmoor. It has well established contacts with various law firms in the EC, and access to the specialist expertise of a number of West Country firms through the footlink network.

PRINCIPAL AREAS OF WORK: The firm has a wide general practice, but particular expertise in agricultural law, commercial property and civil litigation, especially family and personal injury work.

LANGUAGES SPOKEN: French, German, Dutch and Italian.

RECRUITMENT AND TRAINING: One new trainee solicitor per year; the firm's policy is to ensure personal attention and support. Linguistic ability is particularly encouraged.

CONTACT PARTNER: Christopher Thomas

Number of partners:	6
Assistant solicitors:	3
Other fee-earners:	6

HARPER MACLEOD The Ca' d'oro, 45 Gordon Street, Glasgow, G1 3PE **Tel:** (0141) 221 8888 **Fax:** (0141) 226 4198 **DX:** 86 Glasgow **Ptnrs:** 8 **Asst Solrs:** 10 . The corporate law branch of Ross Harper Murphy WS. Also known for commercial litigation and insolvency.

WORKLOAD			
Commercial litigation	25%	Commercial property	25%
Minerals	15%	Corporate	15%
Local authority	10%	Banking	10%

HARRIS & CARTWRIGHT

WINDSOR CROWN HOUSE, 7 WINDSOR RD, SLOUGH, BERKS, SL1 2DX
DX: 42268 Slough (West)

TEL: (01753) 810710
FAX: (01753) 810720

THE FIRM: Established at the beginning of this century, Harris & Cartwright is a progressive and enlightened firm building on its accumulated knowledge and experience to provide a high quality, responsive and cost-effective service to all its clients.

PRINCIPAL AREAS OF WORK:

Company & Commercial: *(Contact Partner:* Stephen Fuller). A rapidly expanding department assists business clients across the full spectrum of problems faced from start-up to flotation and beyond. Services include commercial conveyancing, business sales, takeovers, mergers and acquisitions; partnership formations and agreements; commercial negotiations; company secretarial and administrative matters; commercial litigation; insolvency and receivership, employment; terms and conditions of sale; service contracts and similar agreements.

Litigation: *(Contact Partner:* Christopher Gooderidge). The firm offers an efficient, cost effective service for the resolution of disputes. A wide range of work encompasses medical negligence (the firm is a member of the AVMA Referral Panel, the APIL Medical Negligence Special Interest Group and the Law Society Medical Negligence Panel), personal injury (the firm is a member of the Law Society Personal Injury Panel), all aspects of criminal law; and family disputes including divorce, maintenance, residence of and contact with children, guardianship, and related financial, property and business issues. A full range of commercial litigation is handled in conjunction with the Commercial Department. The practice has considerable expertise in dealing with High Court, County Court and statutory tribunal litigation.

Private Client: *(Contact Partner:* Dan Walters). The work of the department covers all matters relating to the personal and financial affairs of private clients. Services include computerised residential and commercial conveyancing and advice on planning, development, advice to landlords and tenants of commercial, residential and agricultural property; probate, wills, trusts and estate administration; financial guidance and tax planning; establishment and administration of trusts and charities, and Powers of Attorney; financial services including advice on investment, insurance and pensions.

OTHER OFFICES:
272 High Street, Langley, Slough SL3 8HD. *Tel:* (01753) 548011. *Fax:* (01753) 580931. 67a High Street, Burnham, Slough SL1 7JX. *Tel:* (01628) 663041/2 & 667177/8. *Fax:* (01628) 667898

FOREIGN LANGUAGES: French, German and Swedish.

CONTACT PARTNER: Mr Paul Norris

Number of partners:	6
Assistant solicitors:	8
Other fee-earners:	6

WORKLOAD	
Civil litigation	30%
Criminal litigation	25%
Commercial	25%
Probate and wills	10%
Conveyancing	10%

CONTACTS	
Commercial/ comp.	Stephen Fuller/ Paul Norris
Commercial litigation	Raj Dhokia
Commercial property	Paul Norris
Conveyancing	Dan Walters/ Paul Norris
County court agency	Kent Pattinson
Crime	Mark Moorcraft
Employment	Raj Dhokia
Matrimonial	Kent Pattinson
Medical negligence	Christopher Gooderidge
Personal injury	Kent Pattinson
Wills, probate and tax	Sean Robinson

HARRIS da SILVA

355 CITY ROAD, LONDON, EC1V 1LR
DX: 400208 Finsbury 2

TEL: (0171) 713 0700
FAX: (0171) 713 0731

THE FIRM: Harris da Silva is a young and progressive practice with a marked emphasis on litigation. In that sphere the firm deals with a wide variety of work ranging from debt collection to complex disputes involving foreign parties or more than one jurisdiction. Clients range from multinationals to small private companies with equally divers businesses. The firm also undertakes criminal defence work and a variety of other contentious and non-contentious work for private clients.

LANGUAGES SPOKEN: Portuguese, Spanish and Greek.

AGENCY WORK: Undertaken in all divisions of the High Court and local County Courts.

CONTACT PARTNER: Mr C. da Silva

Number of partners:	3
Assistant solicitors:	1
Other fee-earners:	2

HARRIS & HARRIS 14 Market Place, Wells, Somerset, BA5 2RE **Tel:** (01749) 674747 **Fax:** (01749) 676585 **DX:** 44900 Wells **Ptnrs:** 7 **Asst Solrs:** 2 **Other Fee-earners:** 7. A medium-sized country practice, established approximately 150 years ago. Now concentrates on commercial and family law.

HARRISON, LEITCH & LOGAN 3 Rosemary Street, Belfast, BT1 1QQ **Tel:** (01232) 323843 **Fax:** (01232) 332644 **DX:** 401 NR Belfast **Ptnrs:** 5 **Asst Solrs:** 3 **Other Fee-earners:** 4. Large volume of personal injury litigation undertaken. Other areas include company/ commercial, planning and private client work.

WORKLOAD	
Litigation	75% Conveyancing/commercial 25%

HARRIS ROSENBLATT & KRAMER

26-28 BEDFORD ROW, LONDON, WC1R 4HE
DX: 196

TEL: (0171) 242 3254
FAX: (0171) 831 7475

THE FIRM: A well-established firm that provides a comprehensive service to corporate and individual clients. There has been considerable expansion in recent years through amalgamations and organic growth.

The firm is departmentalised but ad hoc interdisciplinary teams comprising partners and/ or fee-earners are frequently assembled to service the needs of clients in particular transactions.

Harris Rosenblatt & Kramer is a progressive law firm operating in a traditional legal environment and aims to consolidate its recent rapid expansion whilst further developing any emerging niche areas.

PRINCIPAL AREAS OF WORK: The core departments comprise finance, banking and insolvency, company/ commercial, commercial property and commercial/banking litigation. In addition the firm has developed strong niche areas in employment and white-collar crime. Advice is also given on probate, private client and tax matters.

Banking, Finance and Insolvency: The firm has three partners specialising in banking, finance and insolvency including security work, consumer finance, portfolio acquisition and sales, equipment leasing and specialised finance orientated computer contracts. Each of those partners has been "in-house" at major institutions and is able to appreciate and respond to the requirements of the financial institutions that instruct them.

Company/ Commercial: The partners in this department are experienced in all aspects of business law and the scope of their activity includes Stock Exchange and Yellow Book work, venture capital, acquisitions and disposals, joint ventures and commercial agreements of all kinds for both private and public companies.

Commercial Property: In this sector the firm acts for public and private development companies and other investors and lenders as well as on behalf of private clients. Advice is given on the financing of commercial property and on environmental matters. The firm offers general landlord and tenant advice and a property management service.

Commercial Litigation: This department consists of six partners and complements the banking, finance and insolvency department and has a depth of experience in credit finance and banking litigation. Many of its clients are household names. Professional negligence mortgage fraud cases are another area in which the department specialises. There is also a particular expertise in emergency relief.

OTHER AREAS OF WORK: The firm is particularly well known for its employment work where the partner in charge writes and lectures on the subject and is a part-time chairman of industrial tribunals. Additionally the firm has an acknowledged strength in white-collar crime. It is one of the leading law firms involved in the motor and motor finance industries.

INTERNATIONAL CONNECTIONS: The firm is a member of LAWROPE with associated offices in the EC and Switzerland. One of the partners is a US-qualified attorney and another member of the firm is qualified in the Republic of Ireland. The firm has working associations in the United States.

FOREIGN LANGUAGES: Members of the firm speak French, German, Italian and Spanish. A brochure describing the firm's services is available on request.

CONTACT PARTNER: Lionel Rosenblatt

Number of partners:	16
Assistant solicitors:	13
Other fee-earners:	9

WORKLOAD	
Litigation	40%
Commercial conveyancing	20%
Asset finance and banking	20%
Employment	10%
Company/ commercial	10%

CONTACTS	
Asset finance/ banking	Stephen Finch
Commercial conveyancing	Roger Abrahams
Commercial litigation	Lionel Rosenblatt
Company/ commercial	John Harris
Employment	Barry Mordsley
Insolvency	Alison Gaines
Personal injury	Lawrence Kormornick
Private client/ tax	Simon Goldring
White collar crime	Sheldon Leaman

HARROWELL SHAFTOE

1 ST. SAVIOURGATE, YORK, N. YORKS, YO1 2NQ
DX: 61506 York

TEL: (01904) 620331
FAX: (01904) 655855

CONTACT PARTNER: Mark Tempest	
Number of partners:	9
Assistant solicitors:	6
Other fee-earners:	7

WORKLOAD	
Litigation	50%
Private client work	25%
Company commercial work	25%

CONTACTS	
Agency work	Robert Onyett
Commercial property	Kevin Millar
Commercial litigation	John Yeomans
Company/ commercial	Kevin Miller
Family Law	John Reynard
Medical negligence	Mark Tempest
Personal injury	Mark Tempest
Private client	William Miers

THE FIRM: A long established firm with a modern outlook. Harrowell Shaftoe has long acted for companies and family firms in the York, North Yorkshire region. Known particularly for its well established private client practice but with substantial development in recent years in company, commercial and litigation work. The firm is committed to quality and is a member of the national network of quality law firms, Law Group UK.

PRINCIPAL AREAS OF WORK:

General Description: The firm has a strong commercial property practice and an expanding corporate and commercial department. The litigation and family law departments have also developed excellent reputations in recent years. The firm's core business is deeply rooted in private client work and the firm remains committed to providing a comprehensive personal service to all its clients both private and commercial.

Company/ Commercial: (*Contact Partner:* Philip Lewis-Ogden). This department continues to grow and its work includes company mergers, acquisitions, sales, buy-outs, reorganisations, corporate financing and related contractual and commercial advice.

Commercial Property: (*Contact Partner:* Kevin Millar). This department has a strong practice in all areas of commercial property including acting for property developers on freehold/ leasehold sales and disposals and on agricultural matters and other related work.

Commercial litigation: (*Contact Partner:* John Yeomans). This department has a strong civil litigation practice including commercial and contractual disputes, intellectual property, professional negligence, insolvency, construction/ planning and employment law.

International and European Law: (*Contact Partner:* Stefano Lucatello). A new and rapidly developing department dealing with cross border litigation, international distribution/franchise/royalty/licensing agreements, offshore tax and trusts and all aspects of international commercial law.

Private Client: (*Contact Partner:* William Miers). This is a long established department with a wide range of expertise principally in wills, probate and trust work and residential property transactions.

Family Law: (*Contact:* John Reynard). The family department is a particularly busy area of the office with a strong emphasis on divorce and financial disputes, injunctions and child contact and residence problems.

Personal Injury: (*Contact Partner:* Mark Tempest). The firm has a long history of acting in mainly plaintiff personal injury cases including cases of utmost severity and medical negligence. Increasing emphasis on this area of work in recent years has improved the level of specialism available.

Crime: (*Contact partner:* Jackie Knights). The practice operates a busy criminal practice providing representation in the criminal courts throughout the region.

AGENCY WORK: (*Contact:* Robert Onyett). The firm has a thriving agency practice and provides an efficient and cost effective service for firms outside York.

RECRUITMENT AND TRAINING: The firm is committed to recruiting trainees providing a wide variety of experience in a friendly atmosphere. Applicants should have a good academic background and a positive approach. CV and references to Jackie Knights.

LANGUAGES: French, Italian, Spanish and German.

OTHER OFFICES:
Harrowell Shaftoe, Moorgate House, Clifton Moor, York.
Tel: (01904 690111. *Fax:* (01904) 692111.
Harrowell Shaftoe, Westow House, The Village, Haxby, York.
Tel: (01904) 760237. *Fax:* (01904) 761555. *DX:* 61460 Haxby.

HARROWELL SHAFTOE

HART BROWN & CO 66-68 Woodbridge Road, Guildford, Surrey, GU1 4RE **Tel:** (01483) 68267 **Fax:** (01483) 39313 **DX:** 2403 Guildford **Ptnrs:** 19 **Asst Solrs:** 22 **Other Fee-earners:** 24. Other offices in Guildford, Godalming, Cranleigh, Cobham, Farnham and Woking. Offers a complete service on a whole range of legal matters.

WORKLOAD			
Residential property	21%	Family	21%
Civil litigation	19%	Crime	18%
Private client	13%	Commercial (non-cont)	8%

HART-JACKSON & HALL 3a Ridley Place, Newcastle upon Tyne, Tyne & Wear, NE1 8JQ **Tel:** (0191) 232 1987 **Fax:** (0191) 232 0429 **DX:** 61003 **Ptnrs:** 3. Well known for entertainment law. Also handles civil and personal injury litigation, conveyancing, family law, and business law.

WORKLOAD			
Commercial	40%	Litigation	30%
Conveyancing	20%	Family/ Childcare	20%
Wills - probate	10%		

HARTLEY & WORSTENHOLME 20 Bank St, Castleford, W. Yorks, WF10 1JD **Tel:** (01977) 553721 **Fax:** (01977) 603105 **DX:** 700134 Castleford **Ptnrs:** 7 **Asst Solrs:** 8 **Other Fee-earners:** 9. Established 1874. Work includes commercial law, conveyancing, probate, litigation, matrimonial law, medical negligence, crime and advocacy. Other office: South Elmsall.

WORKLOAD			
Lit (civil/matrimonial)	60%	Conveyancing	26%
Probate	10%	Debt	2%
Criminal litigation	2%		

HARTNELL & CO

20 CATHEDRAL YARD, EXETER, DEVON, EX1 1HB
DX: 8388 Exeter

TEL: (01392) 421777
FAX: (01392) 421237

THE FIRM: Hartnell & Co is unusual among firms in the South West in being devoted exclusively to family law. Its principal, Norman Hartnell, has contributed to *Family Law* and is Coordinator of the Family Mediators Association (Devon), and is an accredited FMA mediator.

PRINCIPAL AREAS OF WORK: All types of family and matrimonial work are undertaken. In addition, counselling services are offered by consultant counsellors. Legal aid and private agency work are undertaken in Exeter.

CONTACT PARTNER: Norman Hartnell

Number of partners:	1
Assistant solicitors:	2
Other fee-earners:	1

WORKLOAD	
Family	100%

HARVEY INGRAM 20 New Walk, Leicester, Leics, LE1 6TX **Tel:** (0116) 254 5454 **Fax:** (0116) 2554559 **DX:** 10822 Leicester **Ptnrs:** 16 **Asst Solrs:** 12 **Other Fee-earners:** 18. Has an expanding company and commercial practice whilst retaining a substantial client base.

J. & A. HASTIE SSC 43 York Place, Edinburgh, EH1 3HT **Tel:** (0131) 556 7951 **Fax:** (0131) 558 1596 **DX:** 16 Edinburgh **Ptnrs:** 8 **Asst Solrs:** 5 **Other Fee-earners:** 7. An established general practice with two other offices in Glasgow and Galashiels. Emphasis on licensing including licensed property and personal injury work.

HATCHER ROGERSON 25 Castle Street, Shrewsbury, Shrops, SY1 2DA **Tel:** (01743) 248545 **Fax:** (01743) 242979 **DX:** 19725 **Ptnrs:** 19 **Asst Solrs:** 12 **Other Fee-earners:** 12. Offices in Shrewsbury, Wem and Whitchurch. Specialisations include commercial property, company/ commercial, commercial/ general/ personal injury litigation, probate and crime.

WORKLOAD			
Commercial property	20%	Crime/family/matrim	19%
Gen/commercial lit	19%	Gen/agricultural convey	19%
Comm debt recovery	9%	Company/commercial	9%

HATTON SCATES & HORTON Peel Court, 45 Hardman Street, Manchester, M3 3HA **Tel:** (0161) 833 0020 **Fax:** (0161) 833 4186 **Ptnrs:** 2 **Asst Solrs:** 2. A small firm known for its expertise in plaintiff personal injury with 75% of the work being medical negligence including cases involving injuries of the utmost severity.

WORKLOAD			
Medical negligence	50%	Personal injury	30%
Civil litigation	10%	Housing	5%
Judicial review	5%		

HAWKINS RUSSELL JONES 7-8 Portmill Lane, Hitchin, Herts, SG5 1AS **Tel:** (01462) 451411 **Fax:** (01462) 453169 **DX:** 7100 **Ptnrs:** 16 **Asst Solrs:** 8 **Other Fee-earners:** 18. Established in 1591. Best known for commercial and litigation work, the firm also has experienced financial services (member: Association of Solicitor Investment Managers) and personal injury departments. Legal aid work undertaken.

WORKLOAD			
Litigation	45%	Commercial	19%
Conveyancing	19%	Probate	17%

HAWLEY & RODGERS 19-23 Granby St, Loughborough, Leics, LE11 3DY **Tel:** (01509) 230333 **Fax:** (01509) 239390 **DX:** 19602 **Ptnrs:** 12 **Asst Solrs:** 11 **Other Fee-earners:** 7. A general practice with offices in Leicester and Nottingham as well as Loughborough. Predominantly a private client practice.

HAY & KILNER

30 CLOTH MARKET, NEWCASTLE-UPON-TYNE, TYNE & WEAR, NE1 1EE
DX: 61019 Newcastle upon Tyne

TEL: (0191) 232 8345
FAX: (0191) 221 0514

THE FIRM: Established in 1946, Hay & Kilner is one of the North East's larger law firms with headquarters based in the commercial centre of Newcastle-upon-Tyne with branch offices in Wallsend, Gosforth and Jesmond. The firm is a member of LawNet.

PRINCIPAL AREAS OF WORK:

Company and Commercial: (*Contact:* Colin Dickinson. *Fee-earners:* 11). *Work includes:* company, commercial, takeovers and mergers, management buyouts, investments and securities, banking, building societies, employment, computer contracts, intellectual property, partnership law, licensing and leisure, insolvency, commercial property, leasing, tax, planning and construction.

Litigation: (*Contact:* Peter Pescod. *Fee-earners:* 17). *Work includes:* personal injury, insurance, medical negligence, commercial litigation, employment disputes, landlord and tenant, product liability, professional negligence, building/ construction disputes, debt collection, defamation, criminal law; Alternative Dispute Resolution: Member of the Benzodiazepine Steering Group.

Private Client: (*Contact:* Graeme Trotter. *Fee-earners:* 9). *Work includes:* domestic conveyancing, family and matrimonial, tax, wills, probate and trust.

FOREIGN LANGUAGES: French (A Partner is Consul of Belgium and Luxembourg for the North East).

OTHER OFFICES: Wallsend, Gosforth and Jesmond.

CONTACT PARTNER: Martin Soloman

Number of partners:	16
Assistant solicitors:	13
Other fee-earners:	8

CONTACTS	
Commercial litigation	Martin Soloman
Commercial property	Colin Dickinson
Company/ commercial	Colin Dickinson
Construction	Martin Soloman
Employment	Michael McFetrich
Family law/ private client	Graeme Trotter
Insolvency	Neil Harrold
Medical negligence	Peter Pescod
Personal injury/ insurance	Alun Williams

HEDLEYS

6 BISHOPSMEAD PARADE, EAST HORSLEY, SURREY, KT24 6SR
DX: 46106 Cobham

TEL: (01483) 284567
FAX: (01483) 284817

15 St. Helen's Place, Bishopsgate, London EC3A 6DJ
DX: 598 City
Contact Partner: Colin Jenkins

Tel: (0171) 638 1001
Fax: (0171) 588 7547
Telex: 884644

6 Bishopsmead Parade, East Horsley, Leatherhead, Surrey KT24 6SR
DX: 46106 Cobham
Contact Partner: Judith Gleeson

Tel: (01483) 284567
Fax: (01483) 284817

THE FIRM: Established before 1862, the firm specialises in cross-frontier matters, providing a service for business or private clients who reside in one country and who own assets or have legal opportunities or problems in another country. The approach is to seek fast, practical and cost-effective solutions to clients' problems.

PRINCIPAL AREAS OF WORK:

Business Affairs: *Work includes:* corporate work, commercial property, commercial litigation, debt recovery, international defamation and publishing, drafting service contracts, redundancy, unfair/ wrongful dismissal, timeshare structures.

Number of partners:	4
Assistant solicitors:	5
Other fee-earners:	1

Private Client: *Work includes:* tax and tax planning, trust, inheritance, wills, immigration and nationality, European conveyancing.

OTHER AREAS OF WORK: Services for small and medium European enterprises. The firm is a founder member of EU-LEX, an international group of lawyers, accountants and tax advisers.

FIRM'S PRINCIPALS:

COLIN JENKINS, LL.B. (London); admitted, 1955; Languages: French, reading Portuguese and Spanish. Author *Practical Timeshare and Group Ownership.* Advisory Editor *Agency* and contributor to *Timeshare* Titles of the *Encyclopaedia of Forms and Precedents.* Honorary Treasurer. Portuguese – UK Chamber of Commerce.

ROGER TAYLOR; admitted 1970; Member of the Society of Trust and Estate Practitioners.

JUDITH GLEESON, M.A. (Oxford); admitted, 1981; Language: French; Member of the Industrial Law Society.

DAVID HENSHALL, LL.B. (Southampton); admitted, 1983; Languages: German, reading French; Author: sale of goods works.

FOREIGN CONNECTIONS: Hedleys has associates in France, Germany, Denmark, Portugal, Spain, Austria and Poland and links in other EC countries. The firm works daily in the languages of these countries.

HEMPSONS

33 HENRIETTA STREET, COVENT GARDEN, LONDON, WC2E 8NH
DX: 40008 Covent Garden

TEL: (0171) 836 0011
FAX: (0171) 836 2783

75 Mosley Street, Manchester M2 3HR.
DX: 14319 Manchester 1

Tel: (0161) 228 0011
Fax: (0161) 236 6734

THE FIRM: Hempsons is well-known for its particular expertise in the field of medical and healthcare law, partnership work and charity law. The firm has long provided a comprehensive range of services to the professions and charities; clients include district health authorities, NHS trusts, healthcare organisations, local government and individual professionals.

PRINCIPAL AREAS OF WORK:

Medical Litigation: (Contact Partners: John Taylor and Frances Harrison (Manchester). The firm has long been renowned for its expertise in this field and handles matters relating to medical and dental negligence (all areas of hospital and general practice), plaintiff/defendant personal injury litigation, quantum of damages, class actions, disciplinary cases for professional organisations or their members, codes of professional practice and medical crime.

Healthcare Law: (Contact Partners: Bertie Leigh and Frances Harrison (Manchester). The firm advises a range of healthcare organisations on all aspects of law and ethics, mental health and community care law, administrative law and NHS regulatory law.

Partnership: (Contact Partners: Simon Barnes, Lynne Abbess). This section of the firm advises clients on the creation of partnerships and the drafting of partnership agreements; the accession and retirement of partners; the dissolution of partnerships and partnership disputes.

Commercial Litigation/Defamation: (Contact Partners: Janice Barber, Peter Taylor). Advice in relation to all forms of UK commercial disputes including litigation in respect of employment, insurance, arbitration, ADR work, product liability and sale of goods matters. Defamation work is carried out for local authorities and many substantial commercial undertakings.

Commercial Property: (Contact Partner: Gregor Moss). An expanding department handles commercial, institutional, professional and agricultural property, including acquisitions and developments, grant renewal and termination of leases, rent reviews and the cost rent scheme for general practitioners including funding proposed surgery developments.

SENIOR PARTNER: James Watt

Number of partners:	20
Assistant solicitors:	17
Other fee-earners:	13

WORKLOAD

Medical litigation	35%
Partnership	15%
Healthcare	15%
Commercial litigation/defamation	13%
Commercial property	12%
Charity	10%

CONTACTS

Charity	Michael Stewart
Commercial litigation	Janice Barber
Commercial property	Gregor Moss
Defamation	Peter Taylor
Healthcare	Bertie Leigh (London)
	Frances Harrison (Manchester)
Medical litigation	John Taylor
	Frances Harrison (Manchester)
Partnership	Simon Barnes/Lynne Abbess

Charity Law: (Contact Partner: Michael Stewart). Complete service to charities, large and small, including: formation and restructuring of charities, advice to trustees and management on legal duties and powers, updating constitutions, employment issues, dealings with the Charity Commission and the Inland Revenue, financial and commercial activities, trading subsidiaries; fundraising and appeals; disputed legacies.

HENDERSON BOYD JACKSON WS 19 Ainslie Place, Edinburgh, EH3 6AU **Tel:** (0131) 226 6881 **Fax:** (0131) 225 1103 **DX:** 27 **Ptnrs:** 16 **Asst Solrs:** 7 **Other Fee-earners:** 13. Also at 120 West Regent Street, Glasgow G2 2QD. *Tel:* (0141) 333 9444. *Fax:* (0141) 333 1103. Principal activities: corporate finance, commercial property and maritime law.

WORKLOAD			
Corporate	30%	Litigation	25%
Commercial property	25%	Maritime	10%
Private client	10%		

HENMANS

116 ST. ALDATES, OXFORD, OX1 1HA
DX: 4311 Oxford 1

TEL: (01865) 722181
FAX: (01865) 792376

PRINCIPAL AREAS OF WORK:

Company/Commercial: A full range of corporate expertise is provided, including MBOs, corporate finance and company sales/purchases, extended in recent years into corporate insolvency. Commercial services (contract negotiation, often in a European context, publishing and IT agreements, copyright etc.) are backed by the firm's substantial litigation resources. The emphasis is always on positive, cost effective advice.

Employment: (*Contact:* Colin Henney: see "Leader" entry). Both employer and employee work undertaken including Industrial Tribunal and High/County Court litigation; advice on employment contracts and other industrial relations matters.

Professional negligence: A team of five solicitors in this department acts for some of the main indemnity insurers, including the Solicitors Indemnity Fund.

Personal Injury/ Employers' Liability / Medical/ Negligence: The department has a leading reputation for both plaintiff and defendant work. Most of the major insurance companies are represented. Two partners are on the panel of solicitors recommended by Action for Victims of Medical Accidents.

Agricultural/ Land department: A comprehensive service is provided for farmers and land owners throughout the Midlands and Southern England.

Commercial conveyancing: All aspects of site assembly, funding and disposal. Particular expertise in green field development work; planning.

Probate: Specialist team dealing with all aspects of wills, succession, trusts and tax. Member of the Society of Trust and Estate Practitioners.

Family/ Matrimonial: The department deals in particular with complex financial matters arising from separation and divorce, frequently where there is a family owned business. Members of the Solicitors Family Law Association.

Charities: In addition to administration of charity property, assistance is provided with legal aspects of fund raising, trading subsidiaries etc, to a growing list of national charities as well as long-standing local charity clients.

OTHER OFFICE:
6 Oxford Street, Woodstock OX20 1TW. *Tel:* (01993) 811396. *Fax:* (01993) 813184. *DX:* 53700 Woodstock.

CONTACT PARTNER: Alexandra Houston

Number of partners:	12
Assistant solicitors:	14
Other fee-earners:	9

WORKLOAD	
Professional negligence	20%
Private client	20%
Company/commercial & employment & commercial property	20%
Personal injury and medical negligence	20%
Agricultural law	15%
Charities	5%

CONTACTS	
Agricultural/ land law	Roger Henman
Charity	Alexandra Houston
Commercial property	Jeremy Ramsdale
Company/ commercial	Malcom Sadler
Employment	Colin Henney
Family/ matrimonial	Maureen Clarke
Medical negligence	Anthony Henman
Personal injury	Anthony Henman
Probate/ tax planning	Alexandra Houston
Professional negligence	Francis Dingwall

HENRY HYAMS & CO 7 South Parade, Leeds, W. Yorks, LS1 5QX **Tel:** (0113) 243 2288 **Fax:** (0113) 242 4711 **DX:** 12028 **Ptnrs:** 7 **Asst Solrs:** 5 **Other Fee-earners:** 5. General practice with particular strength in civil litigation, criminal, matrimonial and childcare work. Clientele includes legally-aided individuals as well as private and commercial clients.

WORKLOAD	
Legal Aid/private client	100%

HENRY MILNER & CO

COUNTY HOUSE, 14 HATTON GARDEN, LONDON, EC1N 8AT
DX: 53305 Clerkenwell

TEL: (0171) 831 9944
FAX: (0171) 831 9941

THE FIRM: Henry Milner has specialised exclusively in criminal defence work for 20 years. His practice offers a personal and experienced service, handling serious and complicated criminal cases of all types.

PRINCIPAL AREAS OF WORK: Work handled by the firm includes white collar crime (including VAT fraud), mortgage frauds, drugs importation cases involving Customs and Excise, robbery, kidnapping, burglary and blackmail. Mr Milner also specialises particularly in High Court bail applications. A 24 hour emergency service is available, including attendance at police stations.

CONTACT PARTNER: Mr H. Milner

Number of partners:	1
Other fee-earners:	2

HEPHERD WINSTANLEY & PUGH 22 Kings Park Rd, Southampton, Hants, SO15 2UF **Tel:** (01703) 632211 **Fax:** (01703) 227469 **DX:** 38517 Southampton 3 **Ptnrs:** 14 **Asst Solrs:** 9 **Other Fee-earners:** 14. A well-established firm that provides a range of legal services for both business and private clients. A member of the Quality Law Group.

HEPTONSTALLS

7-13 GLADSTONE TERRACE, GOOLE, HUMBS, DN14 5AH
DX: 28831 Goole

TEL: (01405) 765661
FAX: (01405) 764201

THE FIRM: Heptonstalls has provided a high quality legal service to generations of people in the Goole and Howden areas. The firm aims to ensure that clients receive an efficient, personal and friendly service, whatever their legal needs.

PRINCIPAL AREAS OF WORK:

Commercial: (Contact Partner: Malcolm Walker). Advice on a wide range of business and commercial law, including setting up a business (as sole proprietor, partnership and limited company), debt collection, employment law and insolvency. The firm has extensive experience in advising agricultural businesses on such areas as land law, conservation, agricultural tenancies and other aspects of land management.

Personal Injury and Medical Negligence: (Contact Partner: John Burman). The firm has years of experience in handling accident claims whether from medical treatment, road traffic accidents, industrial disease, criminal injuries, defective products or any other cause. Discussions can be held at home if the client's mobility is affected. John Burman is on the AVMA Medical Negligence Referral Panel and is a member of the Law Society Medical Negligence and Personal Injury Panels.

Private Client: (Contact Partner: Roger Beattie). The firm advises on family and matrimonial law, including welfare benefits; tax and family finance; landlord and tenant disputes and other personal litigation and wills, probate and trusts.

OTHER OFFICES: 1 Vicar Lane, Howden, North Humbs. DN14 7BP. *Tel:* (01430) 430209, and 9-11 Ropergate End, Pontefract, W. Yorks WF8 1JU *Tel:* (01977) 602804.

CONTACT PARTNER: John Burman

Number of partners:	5
Assistant solicitors:	8
Other fee-earners:	14

CONTACTS	
Agriculture	M.G. Walker
Civil Litigation	A.S. Pinchbeck
Commercial	R. Beattie
Criminal	A.S. Pinchbeck
Domestic conveyancing	R. Beattie
Medical negligence	J. Burman
Personal injury	J. Burman
Tax and probate	M.G. Walker
Welfare and family	C. Luckett

HERBERT SMITH

EXCHANGE HOUSE, PRIMROSE STREET, LONDON, EC2A 2HS
DX: 28

TEL: (0171) 374 8000
FAX: (0171) 496 0043

THE FIRM: Herbert Smith is a leading international and City law firm. The firm has its headquarters at Broadgate in the City of London and it has offices in Brussels, Paris, Hong Kong and Singapore. We are currently some 1,000 strong with a total of 500 fee earners including 120 partners.

Herbert Smith offers a broad range of services to commercial, financial, industrial and government clients throughout the world. Herbert Smith has been a City based international practice since its establishment more than a century ago and it has grown without merger. The firm has the experience, the technical resources and the people to undertake large complex transactions at short notice and to complete them quickly and efficiently. We make sure that with clear thinking and a full understanding of the needs of our clients we come up with crisp and practical advice and action.

PRINCIPAL AREAS OF WORK:

Company Department: (*Contact:* Richard Bond). Well known as one of the top company and commercial firms, the firm's corporate lawyers aim to provide a speedy, innovative and cost conscious service, co-ordinating assistance from across the firm where necessary. Areas of activity include corporate finance; international equity offerings; mergers, take-overs and disposals; banking, capital markets and international finance; project and asset finance; competition and EU work; venture capital and MBOs; energy; utilities; aviation, shipping and transport; media and telecommunications; insurance; tax; insolvency; privatisations; investment funds and commercial trusts; employment, pensions and share schemes.

Litigation Department: (*Contact:* Lawrence Collins). The firm has experience before every type of court and tribunal including international arbitration and international tribunals. Areas of activity include commercial disputes; international commercial arbitration; insurance and reinsurance; banking and finance; EU and competition; intellectual property and information technology; fraud; judicial review; professional negligence; shareholder and partnership disputes; construction; defamation and shipping. Several of our solicitors are admitted as High Court advocates.

Property Department: (*Contact:* Garry Hart). The firm's property work includes purchases,sales and lettings of property investments; development projects; all forms of secured lending and property financing; disposals for liquidators, receivers and mortgagees; rating; environmental law; town planning; compensation and other areas involving the public sector, including local government law; rent review arbitrations and investigations of property portfolios.

INTERNATIONAL: Herbert Smith has offices in Brussels, Paris, Hong Kong and Singapore which are an integral part of the firm. The principal contacts at each office are given below. Our overseas offices are staffed both by solicitors from the London office and by lawyers familiar with the local language and business customs.

Brussels: Tel:(00 322) 511 7450 Fax:(00 322) 511 7772 - Stephen Kinsella
Paris: Tel: (00 331) 47 23 91 24 Fax: (00 331) 47 20 92 13 - Neil Brimson
*Hong Kong:*Tel: (00 8522) 8456639 Fax: (00 8522) 8459099 - Tim Bellis
Singapore: Tel:(00 65) 536 7990 Fax:(00 65) 536 7993 - Andrew Calderwood

TECHNOLOGY AND SUPPORT SERVICES: Herbert Smith's extensive and sophisticated legal know-how systems are available to all lawyers in the firm via individual desk terminals. The most up-to-date technology is used throughout the firm and there is an extensive library with further access to computer-based information retrieval services.

RECRUITMENT AND TRAINING: Herbert Smith is always interested in receiving applications from able and energetic candidates with good academic qualifications (whether law or non-law) and enquiry should be made to the graduate recruitment manager. The firm will recruit about 60 trainee solicitors in 1995 to commence training contracts in September 1997 or in March 1998. Application should be made on the firm's application form and sent to the recruitment partner. Herbert Smith also runs student vacation schemes. Applications for these schemes should be made to the graduate recruitment manager.

SENIOR PARTNER: Edward Walker-Arnott

Number of partners:	120
Assistant solicitors:	227
Other fee-earners:	144

CONTACTS

Asset/ project finance	Andrew Preece
Banking	Clive Barnard
Commercial litigation	Lawrence Collin
Commercial property	Garry Hart
Commodities litigation	David Natali
Computer law	Bill Moodie
Construction/ engineering	Michael Davis
Corporate services	Richard Bond
Corporate finance	Caroline Goodall
Corporate Tax	David Martin
Corporate reconstruction	Stephen Barton
Employee benefits	Colin Chamberlain
Employment	John Farr
Energy and utilities	Richard Bond
EU/ competition	Richard Fleck
Insolvency	Philip Carrington
Insurance litigation	David Higgins
Insurance and reinsurance	Marian Pell
Intellectual property	Christopher Tootal
International law/ arbitration	Lawrence Collins
Pensions	Ian Gault
Planning	Garry Hart
Professional negligence	David Natali
Shipping	Nicholas Robinson

HERBERT SMITH

HERBERT WILKES

41 CHURCH ST, BIRMINGHAM, W. MIDLANDS, B3 2RT
DX: 13047

TEL: (0121) 233 4333
FAX: (0121) 233 4546

CONTACT PARTNER: Richard Jaffa

Number of partners:	12
Assistant solicitors:	25
Other fee-earners:	21

THE FIRM: Established over 60 years ago, Herbert Wilkes has developed into a modern commercial practice offering a wide range of legal services to business, industry and private individuals. The firm is a member of LawGroup UK and has recently set-up LAWPOWER, a package of legal services for developing businesses.

PRINCIPAL AREAS OF WORK:

Company and Commercial: *(Contact Partner:* Colin Turner). The department handles all aspects of company formation, acquisitions and disposal, corporate finance, management buy-outs and corporate restructuring.

Litigation: *(Contact Partner:* Nigel Wood). The firm deals with the full range of commercial litigation services including High Court, County Court and matters arising from EC legislation. It also provides a specialised commercial debt collection service. Other work includes commercial contract disputes, personal injury, employment matters and health and safety at work.

Property: *(Contact:* Adele McDermott). The practice undertakes and advises on domestic and commercial conveyancing, property development, shops, offices, factories, leases, planning matters, joint ventures and landlord and tenant matters.

Private Client: *(Contact Partner:* Anna Dunford). The firm offers advice to individuals regarding wills, settlements, probate, inheritance tax, personal taxation and pensions. The firm also provides a service to private clients on matters of employment, personal injury, consumer legislation, family matters and divorce, criminal work and licensing.

NATURE OF CLIENTELE: Business and industrial clients nationally as well as long-standing private clients.

FOREIGN CONNECTIONS: The firm has professional links in the major European cities particularly in relation to property buying in Europe. Links with France and Germany are particularly strong.

OTHER OFFICE: 10 Coleshill Road, Hodge Hill, Birmingham B36 8AA. *Tel:* (0121) 784 8484. *Fax:* (0121) 783 4935 DX:27434.

WORKLOAD

Litigation (including insolvency)	36%
Corporate and commercial	27%
Conveyancing	25%
Tax/ trust/ probate	12%

CONTACTS

Building contracts	Peter Tugwell
Civil litigation	Nigel Wood
Commercial conveyancing	Adele McDermott
Corporate finance	Colin Turner
Corporate/ commercial	Colin Turner
Debt recovery	Kevin Curran
Insolvency	Pamela Statter
Large scale voluntary transfer	Peter Ewin
Local/ public authority	Richard Jaffa
Personal injury	Maxine Kelly
Tax/ trust	Anna Dunford

HERBERT MALLAM GOWERS 126 High St, Oxford, Oxon, OX1 4DG **Tel:** (01865) 244661 **Fax:** (01865) 721263 **DX:** 4321 Oxford **Ptnrs:** 7 **Asst Solrs:** 4 **Other Fee-earners:** 2. Long-established practice undertaking general commercial work, licensing, private client work and agricultural matters.

INTERNATIONAL SECTION

The international section lists foreign law firms based in London. It also lists the foreign connections of English law firms: their branch offices overseas and the foreign languages spoken at their UK offices.

HEWITSON BECKE + SHAW

42 NEWMARKET ROAD, CAMBRIDGE, CAMBS, CB5 8EP DX: 122898 Cambridge 4	TEL: (01223) 461155 FAX: (01223) 316511
7 Spencer Parade, Northampton NN1 5AB MDX: 12401 Northampton Contact Partner: Mr John Shephard	Tel: (01604) 233233 Fax: (01604) 27941
Stuart House, City Road, Peterborough PE1 1QF DX: 12344 Peterborough 1 Contact Partner: Miss Fiona Crawley	Tel: (01733) 897979 Fax: (01733) 898060
53 High Street, Saffron Walden, Essex CB10 1AR DX: 200300 Saffron Walden Contact Partner: Mr David Hollest	Tel: (01799) 522471 Fax: (01799) 524742
90 High Street, Newmarket, Suffolk CB8 8JZ DX: 50504 Newmarket Contact Partner: Mr Ian Whiting	Tel: (01638) 665926 Fax: (01638) 667702

THE FIRM: Hewitson Becke + Shaw traces its origins back to 1865. The firm has an extensive company and commercial practice, and a growing body of public sector clients.

PRINCIPAL AREAS OF WORK:

Commercial Property: *(Contact Partner:* Alan Brett). The firm handles a large volume of commercial property work, from the construction of major commercial and residential developments and science parks to small retail and industrial units. The firm is increasingly used by major concerns abroad, including Hong Kong. *Work includes:* The acquisition, development and letting of all manner of commercial sites. The firm has particular expertise in complex funding mechanisms and joint ventures.

Company/ Commercial: *(Contact Partner:* Jeremy Lincoln). *Work includes:* mergers and acquisitions, company structuring and restructuring, venture and development capital investment, management buy-outs/buy-ins, rights issues, Stock Exchange flotations, European Union and International law, merger control, OFT/ Commission investigations, joint ventures, pensions, employee share option and incentive schemes, partnerships and insolvency. The firm acts for a significant number of public limited companies as well as owner-managed businesses and is doing an increasing amount of UK-related work from an expanded US client base.

Intellectual Property: *(Contact Partner:* Paul Taylor). The firm advises on all aspects of obtaining, exploiting and enforcing intellectual property rights, with particular expertise in computer hardware and software, biotechnology, pharmaceutical, film, music and book publishing industries.

Private Client: *(Contact Partner:* Peter Ewart). *Work includes:* Administration of estates, trusts, tax, wills, enduring powers of attorney, pensions, charities, residential property advice, landed estates, court of protection and matrimonial.

Litigation: *(Contact Partner:* John Shephard). The services are provided through eight groups each consisting of staff dedicated to one of the following areas of specialisation: banking, commercial contract law/ equity, construction, employment, intellectual property, personal injury, crime and family. The firm acts nationally for several major clearing banks.

Employment: *(Contact Partner:* Nick Sayer). *Work includes:* Service contracts, pensions, dismissal, redundancy, compensation for unfair dismissal, profit sharing and share option schemes and general employee benefits. The firm is a member of the Employment Lawyers Association and six members of the firm are individual members of the Association.

Agriculture: *(Contact Partner:* Ian Barnett). *Work includes:* The granting of development options by landowners, joint venture and share farming agreements, farm partnerships, taxation and environmental matters, sales and tenancies and mineral exploitation. The firm has a significant following of landed estates and farming clients.

CONTACT PARTNER: Mr Alan Brett	
Number of partners:	38
Assistant solicitors:	41
Other fee-earners:	47

WORKLOAD	
Litigation	35%
Commercial property	26%
Company/ commercial (corporate)	15%
Private client	14%
Residential property	10%

CONTACTS	
Agriculture	Ian Barnett
Commercial litigation	John Shephard
Commercial property	Peter Cooch
Company/ commercial	Jeremy Lincoln
Construction	Amanda Hughes
Debt control	Steve Martin
Employment	Nick Sayer
Intellectual property	Ian Craig
Planning and environmental	Peter Brady
Private client	Peter Ewart
Property funding	Alan Brett
Residential property	David Sabberton

Bloodstock: *(Contact Partner:* Gillian Pearl). The firm advises on most aspects of bloodstock law with particular emphasis on property transactions and general litigation.

Planning and Environmental: *(Contact Partner:* Peter Brady). *Work includes:* local plan enquiries, advising developers, investors, local authorities, conservation and amenity groups, and individuals. The firm has two members of the Law Society's specialist Planning Panel.

Residential Property: *(Contact Partner:* David Sabberton). *Work includes:* Sales, purchases and mortgages of freehold/ leasehold houses/ flats for private clients and institutions as well as builders and developers.

HEWITT & GILPIN Thomas House, 14-16 James Street South, Belfast, BT2 7GA **Tel:** (01232) 323254 **Fax:** (01232) 331741 **Ptnrs:** 6 **Asst Solrs:** 1 . Established in 1930. Provides a wide range of services to companies, charities and private clients. No criminal work.

HEXTALL, ERSKINE & CO

28 LEMAN STREET, LONDON, E1 8ER
DX: 562 CITY

TEL: (0171) 488 1424
FAX: (0171) 481 0232

CONTACT PARTNER: Neil Thomas

Number of partners:	13
Assistant solicitors:	8
Other fee-earners:	23

WORKLOAD	
Insurance related	75%
Other commercial litigation	10%
Company commercial	5%
Property	5%
Private client	5%

CONTACTS	
Commercial litigation	David Hadfield
Commercial property	Harold Martin
Company comm/private client	Anthony Millson
Employers' & public liability	Neil Thomas
Insurance & reinsurance	John Startin
Motor	Richard Cheveley
Policy wordings	Stuart White
Product liability	John Startin
Professional indemnity	Stuart White
Property risks	Jill Heaton

THE FIRM: A long-established practice – the firm continues to build upon its known expertise in commercial and insurance related civil litigation. Litigation clients include leading UK composites, Lloyd's syndicates, corporations and foreign based companies. The practice also covers the full range of non-contentious work.

PRINCIPAL AREAS OF WORK:

Insurance: *Work includes:* all aspects of litigation including professional indemnity (especially surveyors & valuers, brokers, architects, accountants, barristers, engineers, tour operators, sheriffs, bailiffs, directors and officers), insurance and reinsurance disputes, product liability, employers' liability, motor, contractors' all risks, fire and property, Lloyd's litigation; wordings and general advice.

Commercial Litigation: *Work includes:* employment, construction and general commercial litigation, debt recovery. Founder member of CEDR.

Company Commercial: All aspects of company and commercial law are handled including formation, sale and purchase of companies, flotations, joint ventures, trade disputes and employment matters.

Commercial Property: The department handles funding and acquisitions, joint ventures, planning and tax-related aspects over a wide range of commercial, industrial and residential property.

Private Client: The main areas of expertise are personal tax planning, wills, trusts and estate planning[#] and pension scheme guidance for the self-employed and company directors, matrimonial[*] and residential property.
[#] Member of STEP – Society of Trust & Estate Practitioners.
[*] Member of Solicitors' Family Law Association and Family Mediators Association.

RECRUITMENT & TRAINING: The firm recruits three trainee solicitors a year. Applications by letter and CV to Mr. Andrew McWhirter.

FOREIGN CONNECTIONS: The firm is associated with lawyers in Brussels and Vienna and has contact with many other foreign firms.

HIGGS & SONS 134 High St, Brierley Hill, W. Midlands, DY5 3BG **Tel:** (01384) 76411 **Fax:** (01384) 263339 **DX:** 22751 **Ptnrs:** 17 **Asst Solrs:** 16 **Other Fee-earners:** 13. Established 1875. *Work includes:* company/ commercial, conveyancing, planning, probate, trusts, taxation, employment law, personal injury and all common law matters. The firm has four offices.

HILL BAILEY GROUP Wells House, 15-17 Elmfield Rd, Bromley, Kent, BR1 1QP **Tel:** (0181) 290 1177 **Fax:** (0181) 464 3328 **DX:** 94703 Bromley 3 **Ptnrs:** 6 **Asst Solrs:** 10 **Other Fee-earners:** 26. An established and growing practice with strong corporate, litigation and property departments.

R. & J.M. HILL BROWN & CO 3 Newton Place, Glasgow, G3 7PU **Tel:** (0141) 332 3265 **Fax:** (0141) 332 2613 **DX:** 102 Glasgow **Ptnrs:** 4 **Other Fee-earners:** 2. Small general practice specialising in licensing work for licensed trade and the entertainment industry.

HILL DICKINSON DAVIS CAMPBELL

PEARL ASSURANCE HOUSE, DERBY SQUARE, LIVERPOOL, MERSEYSIDE, L2 9XL DX: 14129

TEL: (0151) 236 5400
FAX: (0151) 236 2175

THE FIRM: Established in 1810, Hill Dickinson Davis Campbell, whilst being one of the largest commercial practices in the North West, benefits from having offices in both Liverpool and London. The firm offers a pragmatic approach and personal attention to clients large and small in both the Liverpool and London offices.

PRINCIPAL AREAS OF WORK:

Company/ Commercial: (*Contact:* Michael Quinn). The firm advises on formation, development, dissolution and taxation of partnerships and companies. Advice is also given on intellectual property, insolvency, entertainment law, MBOs, international trade agreements and UK and EC competition law.

Commercial Property: (*Contact:* David Swaffield). A wide range of services is available to developers, development corporations, pension funds and institutional clients. This department also attends to the complexities of planning law and property-related tax advice.

Construction and Engineering: (*Contact:* David Chinn). A wide range of services, both contentious and non-contentious is provided, including advising on and drafting contracts, warranties, bonds and dealing with the resolution of disputes, arbitration proceedings and Court Actions.

Environmental: (*Contact:* Anne Dobie). Advice on all aspects of environmental law is provided by a team of partners drawing on expertise from all departments in the practice.

Litigation: (*Contact:* Tony Wilson). The firm covers all areas of litigation, and can draw on the expertise of its in-house investigation support team.

Goods in Transit/ Marine Insurance: (*Contact:* Julia Marshall in London and Peter Jackson in Liverpool). The firm acts for insurance companies, brokers and underwriters, handling a wide variety of marine cases, including coverage disputes and goods in transit law acting for all sectors of the industry.

Non-Marine Insurance: (*Contact:* Tony Wilson). A large insurance litigation department acts on behalf of a wide variety of insurance companies, brokers and underwriters.

Personal Injury: (*Contact:* Gordon Anderson for non-marine and David Wareing for marine matters). The firm has a large and highly-regarded personal injury department specialising in defence work.

Professional Negligence: (*Contact:* Paul Walton). The firm has extensive experience in negligence claims against professionals including legal and veterinary practitioners and those in the construction industry.

Health/ Medical Negligence: (*Contact:* Allan Mowat). The firm has one of the UK's largest medico-legal practices acting on behalf of health authorities, NHS trusts and other health service bodies, and defending their medical and other staff.

Shipping: (*Contact:* David Wareing). Hill Dickinson Davis Campbell is the largest regional firm in all areas of shipping, ship finance, fisheries protection etc acting for insurance companies, brokers and underwriters, P&I clubs, defence clubs and all sectors of the industry.

CHAIRMAN: Paul Walton

Number of partners:	34
Assistant solicitors:	31
Other fee-earners:	61

WORKLOAD

Litigation (inc insurance/ construction/ professional negligence)	50%
Shipping	15%
Commercial property, planning and environmental	15%
Company, commercial, pensions, tax, intellectual property	10%
Health/ medical negligence	10%

CONTACTS

Commercial property	David Swaffield
Company/ commercial	Michael Quinn
Construction and engineering	David Chinn
Environmental	Anne Dobie
Goods in transit	Julia Marshall (London)
Health/ medical negligence	Allan Mowat
Litigation	Tony Wilson
Marine insurance	Peter Jackson
Non-marine insurance	Tony Wilson
Pensions	Tony Huber
Personal injury	Gordon Anderson
	David Wareing
Professional negligence	Paul Walton
Shipping	David Wareing

Pensions: (*Contact:* Tony Huber). The firm's pension department is a leader in its field advising companies and trustees on all aspects of pensions including documentation and issues arising from corporate acquisitions, disposals, insolvencies and surpluses.

NATURE OF CLIENTELE: The firm has a large national and international clientele comprising public corporate institutional and private clients.

LANGUAGES SPOKEN: French, German and Welsh.

RECRUITMENT & TRAINING: The firm recruits up to six trainee solicitors annually. The firm was the first licensed to provide medical negligence training in articles.

OTHER OFFICES:

45 Ludgate Hill, London EC4M 7JU. *Tel:* (0171) 214 7900. *Fax:* (0171) 214 7911. *DX:* 98940 Cheapside 2.

HILL TAYLOR DICKINSON

IRONGATE HOUSE, DUKE'S PLACE, LONDON, EC3A 7LP
DX: 550

TEL: (0171) 283 9033
FAX: (0171) 283 1144

THE FIRM: Hill Taylor Dickinson's involvement in shipping and insurance work dates back to 1810. The firm has in recent years expanded to offer other specialist services to clients in all commercial sectors and places particular emphasis on working in collaboration with the client at partner level.

PRINCIPAL AREAS OF WORK:

General Description: Hill Taylor Dickinson, a firm providing a service to the commercial and business world, is highly regarded for its experience in shipping, insurance, corporate and venture finance, personal injury, commercial property, and insolvency.

Shipping and Insurance: *11 Partners.* The practice enjoys a high standing amongst the marine and non-marine insurance community, owners, insurers and P&I Clubs with a strong international flavour. This involves acting for clients in major maritime casualties, disaster litigation, pollution claims and the full range of commercial problems arising out of international trade and transport including insurance and re-insurance.

Corporate: *4 Partners.* The practice has wide experience of evaluating venture capital for newly expanding businesses. It also handles buy-outs and buy-ins, shipping finances and leasing and asset finance.

Insolvency: *3 Partners.* In this area of recent and rapid growth, the firm acts in respect of both corporate and personal insolvency including receiverships, and corporate reconstruction and recovery.

Personal Injury: *1 Partner.* The firm acts mainly for employers, insurers and P&I Clubs in shipping and transport and a wide variety of industries. The practice deals with mass and individual claims. Its work includes preventive and practical advice, including drafting of Accident Reporting documents and procedures/ drafting of relevant contractual clauses, as well as civil and criminal litigation arising in this area.

Commercial Property: *3 Partners.* The practice carries out all manner of general commercial property work, Lloyd's syndicates, merchant banks, financial institutions and employers' associations.

FOREIGN CONNECTIONS: With its longstanding international shipping and insurance connections, the practice has many correspondents and contacts worldwide, in particular in the Greek maritime markets, for which the firm has opened an office in Piraeus, Athens, and in the Far East, with an office in Hong Kong.

RECRUITMENT: (*Contact:* Malcolm Taylor). The firm regularly recruits assistant solicitors and trainees.

CONTACT PARTNER: John Pople

Number of partners:	25
Assistant solicitors:	48
Other fee-earners:	1

WORKLOAD	
Shipping	53%
Insurance	13%
Insolvency	10%
Company/ commercial	10%
Other	6%
Commercial property	6%

CONTACTS	
Commercial property	Peter Albertini
Company/ commercial	Tim Railton
Insolvency	Paul Oughton
Insurance	Tim Taylor
Shipping	Stephen Cropper

HOBSON AUDLEY

7 PILGRIM STREET, LONDON, EC4V 6DR
DX: 401

TEL: (0171) 248 2299
FAX: (0171) 248 0672

CONTACT PARTNER: Gerald Hobson	
Number of partners:	11
Assistant solicitors:	14
Other fee-earners:	4

THE FIRM: An exclusively commercial practice which, although small by City standards, is well regarded and has a broad range of corporate clients, both public and private.

PRINCIPAL AREAS OF WORK:

Company & Commercial: *(Contact Partner:* Max Audley). Company acquisitions and sales, MBOs, development and venture capital finance, company reconstructions and amalgamations, rescues and insolvency procedures, joint ventures and competition law. Stock Exchange and general corporate finance law (ranking amongst much larger firms in the league tables for new issues) and banking. Commercial contracts, including franchising and distribution agreements, computer licensing, copyright, and employment agreements.

Commercial Litigation: *(Contact Partner:* Gerald Hobson). The firm's approach to litigation can best be described as pragmatic seeking a speedy and economic resolution of problems, wherever possible. The department handles banking litigation, building disputes, employment and industrial relations law problems, intellectual property litigation, landlord and tenant disputes, professional negligence claims, defamation, computer litigation, and commercial disputes of all kinds.

Commercial Property: *(Contact Partner:* Godfrey Bruce-Radcliffe). Strong bias towards heavyweight development and finance, both institutional and banking, institutional investment, letting, construction and ancillary matters such planning and other development orientated servcies.

NATURE OF CLIENTELE: Clients come from a wide range of industries including financial and marketing services, publishing, healthcare, banking, energy and natural resources, oil field services, venture capital and manufacturing industries.

G.L. HOCKFIELD & CO 41 Reedworth Street, Kennington Rd, London, SE11 4PQ **Tel:** (0171) 735 0489 **Fax:** (0171) 820 1707 **DX:** 33252 **Ptnrs:** 3 **Asst Solrs:** 3 **Other Fee-earners:** 2. Principal areas of work are claimant personal injury, medical and other professional negligence work; and housing litigation on behalf of both tenants and housing associations.

WORKLOAD			
Housing litigation	40%	Personal injury	36%
Prof neg (incl med neg)	15%	Micellaneous areas	9%

HODGE JONES & ALLEN

148-150 CAMDEN HIGH STREET, LONDON, NW1 0NE
DX: 57050 Camden Town

TEL: (0171) 482 1974
FAX: (0171) 267 3476

CONTACT PARTNER: Henry Hodge	
Number of partners:	9
Assistant solicitors:	11
Other fee-earners:	15

WORKLOAD	
Crime	25%
Family	20%
Housing and landlord and tenant litigation	20%
Personal injury and medical negligence	15%
Employment and general litigation	10%
Non-contentious property	10%

THE FIRM: Hodge Jones & Allen was established in 1977 and has expanded rapidly. It has recently merged with the Kentish Town criminal practice of Wyman and Walters. The firm has a particular reputation for legal aid work and its training scheme for trainee solicitors. Henry Hodge is a legal aid specialist member of the Law Society Council. The firm has been involved in a large number of high profile and leading cases in recent years, notably cases involving racial discrimination and personal injury cases arising from the King's Cross fire and the Marchioness disaster.

PRINCIPAL AREAS OF WORK:

Personal Injury: *(Contact Partner:* Patrick Allen). The PI team acts for plaintiffs only and particularly for those who have been injured in road accidents, pavement tripping, accidents at work and as a result of medical negligence. Patrick Allen, the leader of the team, is a member of the executive committee of the Association of Personal Injury Lawyers. The firm has been involved in major multi-party cases.

Housing: *(Contact Partner:* Charles Pigott). The housing team deals with disrepair, homelessness claims including applications for judicial review, possession cases and all aspects of landlord and tenant work, principally on behalf of tenants.

Racial Discrimination and Employment Unit: *(Contact Partner:* Henry Hodge). This unit deals with all claims for racial discrimination and employment issues in the High Court, the County Court and the Industrial Tribunal.

Family: *(Contact Partner:* Lynn Roberts). The family team covers all aspects of family work. Three members of the team are on the child care panel and three on the Lord Chancellor's Department's Child Abduction Panel. All the solicitors belong to the Solicitor's Family Law Association.

Criminal: *(Contact Partner:* Mark Studdert). The department has greatly expanded due to the merger with Wyman and Walters. The team has solicitors on local police station and court duty solicitor schemes. Representatives are available to attend police stations at all hours. Solicitors can be contacted outside office hours via the emergency phone number (01459) 111192.

OTHER AREAS OF WORK: Comprehensive advice service for housing associations and charities on contractual and employment obligations, conveyancing and probate.

NATURE OF CLIENTELE: The largest group of clients are those who live in the North London area, many of whom are referred by local advice agencies such as the Citizens Advice Bureaux and law centres. The firm receives a small but significant number of clients from all over the country who have been referred as a result of the firm's reputation in various areas. The firm also acts for local authorities and voluntary and statutory authorities.

RECRUITMENT AND TRAINING: The firm runs a structured and popular training scheme for trainee solicitors. The annual intake is presently three. Interviews take place in October for training places for the following September.

CONTACTS	
Complaints against the police	T. Salvidge
Crime	M.Studdert
Discrimination	H. Hodge
Education	W. Backhouse
Employment	C. Pigott
Family and children	Lynn Roberts
General litigation	V. Gambling
Housing litigation	W. Backhouse
Medical negligence	P. Allen
Non-contentious property	C. Pigott
Personal injury	P. Allen

HODKINSONS 42-43 Locks Heath Centre, Locks Heath, Hants, SO3 6DX **Tel:** (01489) 885664 **Fax:** (01489) 579149 **DX:** 45251 Park Gate **Ptnrs:** 1 **Asst Solrs:** 2 **Other Fee-earners:** 4. Modern practice, part of Solent Solicitors Group. Specialists in financial services compliance, fraud investigation and defence with accountant and compliance officer team.

HOLMAN, FENWICK & WILLAN

MARLOW HOUSE, LLOYDS AVENUE, LONDON, EC3N 3AL
DX: 1069 London City EC3

TEL: (0171) 488 2300
FAX: (0171) 481 0316

THE FIRM: Holman, Fenwick & Willan has a global reputation for excellence in maritime and commercial law. The firm's traditional expertise in shipping extends to other sectors, including commercial litigation, insurance, reinsurance, commodities, competition and trade.

The firm has offices in the strategic centres for international trade and shipping, including London, Paris, Piraeus, Hong Kong and Singapore. Holman, Fenwick & Willan is a multinational practice. Its foundations are in English law yet the firm has a comprehensive knowledge of other law and the ability to offer clients the most appropriate jurisdiction. The firm's lawyers include nationals from many countries - a reflection of Holman, Fenwick & Willan's international character. Over 350 partners and staff are responsible for a large and diverse caseload.

As a major litigation practice, Holman, Fenwick & Willan has a number of accredited mediators and solicitor advocates and is commited to offering both advocacy and mediation services. The firm is an active contributor to the work of the London Amirality Solicitors' Group. It is also the founding patron of the European Maritime Law Organisation (EMLO), an EU-wide forum for evaluating the impact of European law on shipping, the marine environment and maritime resources.

PRINCIPAL AREAS OF WORK:

Admiralty: Advice on collisions, salvage, total loss, damage and claims arising from wreck removal, oil and chemical pollution, shipboard fires and jetty contacts.

Marine Litigation: Contractual and tortious claims on behalf of shipowners, charterers, cargo owners, freight forwarders and underwriters.

SENIOR PARTNER: Archie Bishop

Number of partners:	59
Other fee-earners:	157
Total Staff:	345

WORKLOAD	
Shipping (admiralty and marine litigation)	50%
Commercial litigation/international trade	20%
Reinsurance	15%
Corporate/ marine finance and related non-contentious work	15%

CONTACTS	
Admiralty	Archie Bishop
Comm.lit./international trade	Keith Michel
Commercial property	Ian Narbeth
Commodities	Patricia Francies
Corporate and marine finance	Brian Robinson
European and competition law	Philip Wareham

Commercial Litigation and International Trade: Resolution of commercial disputes, particularly in the fields of insurance, international trade and finance.

Insurance and Reinsurance: A comprehensive service spanning all aspects of insurance, reinsurance and retrocessional business on behalf of insurers, cedants, reinsurers and brokers.

Corporate and Marine Finance: Legal, financial and commercial matters concerning the sale, purchase, ownership and worldwide operation of ships and other floating structures and advice on corporate, banking, financial and trading operations in the UK and overseas.

Commodities: Both contentious and non-contentious work arising out of the international sale and purchase of all types of commodities.

Oil, Gas and Energy: The firm handles all aspects of financing agreements, drilling contracts, farm-ins and farm-outs, assignment of licence participation and all related matters, both in the North Sea and elsewhere.

Commercial Property: Advising investors, developers, lenders, owners and tenants on all aspects of commercial and residential property transactions, including planning, construction, financing and property-related litigation.

Personal Injury: The investigation of all types of accident and the settlement of personal injury claims, both in the UK and overseas.

Insolvency and Corporate Litigation: Contentious and advisory work in the fields of company insolvency and financial services legislation for lenders, borrowers, directors and office holders, with particular emphasis on the international aspects.

European and Competition: European law and EC and UK competition law, including maritime law, international trade and transport.

FOREIGN LANGUAGES: Bulgarian, Danish, French, German, Greek, Hungarian, Italian, Russian, Serbo-Croat, Spanish and Swedish.

Insolvency/corp. litigation	Steven Paull
Insurance/reinsurance	John Duff
Marine litigation	George Eddings
Oil, gas and energy	Nicholas Hutton
Personal injury	Alan Walls

HOLMES HARDINGHAM

22-23 GREAT TOWER STREET, LONDON, EC3R 5AQ
DX: 636

TEL: (0171) 283 0222
FAX: (0171) 283 0768

CONTACT PARTNER: Nicholas Walser

Number of partners:	10
Assistant solicitors:	10
Other fee-earners:	7

THE FIRM: Holmes Hardingham provides a full range of maritime and commercial law services and also has expertise in international road transport matters.

PRINCIPAL AREAS OF WORK: The firm focuses on shipping law, with all 10 partners and 15 other fee-earners handling a variety of shipping-related matters including: international trade and carriage of goods, commodity sale disputes, commercial and Admiralty litigation and arbitration, oil and gas exploration, marine insurance, collision and salvage, ship sale, purchase and finance, and yachts and pleasure craft.

HOLMES MACKILLOP 109 Douglas Street, Glasgow, G2 4HB **Tel:** (0141) 221 5232 **Fax:** (0141) 204 0136 **Ptnrs:** 9 **Asst Solrs:** 2 **Other Fee-earners:** 5. An established general practice, acknowledged for its intellectual property expertise.

HOOD VORES & ALLWOOD The Priory, Church St, Dereham, Norfolk, NR19 1DW **Tel:** (01362) 692424 **Fax:** (01362) 698858 **DX:** 45050 **Ptnrs:** 8 **Asst Solrs:** 1 **Other Fee-earners:** 6. General practice. Agency instructions (including legal aid work) accepted.

HOOPER & WOLLEN Carlton Hse, 30 The Terrace, Torquay, Devon, TQ1 1BS **Tel:** (01803) 213251 **Fax:** (01803) 296871 **DX:** 59204 Torquay (2) **Ptnrs:** 9 **Asst Solrs:** 4 **Other Fee-earners:** 11. An old-established practice known for conveyancing, probate, trust and family law; with expanding commercial, company and litigation departments.

HOPKINS & WOOD

2-3 CURSITOR STREET, LONDON, EC4A 1NE
DX: 146

TEL: (0171) 404 0475
FAX: (0171) 430 2358

CONTACT PARTNER: R.C.B. Hopkins

Number of partners:	10
Assistant solicitors:	11
Other fee-earners:	4

THE FIRM: Hopkins & Wood is a first-class City practice, geared to meet the needs of its impressive portfolio of commercial clients. Since its formation in 1982 as a commercial litigation and high technology practice, it has developed into a full-service commercial firm, whose hallmarks are accessibility, responsiveness and quality. Its partners have gained their experience at large City firms or as barristers. A broad range of legal skills is coupled with an international perspective and awareness of business needs. The firm has gained a strong reputation for litigation (where it has been involved in many major cases), for intellectual property and high technology work, particularly involving computers and tele-communications, and for corporate finance, and all types of investment capital work. Hopkins & Wood is regarded as one of the leading up-and-coming commercial firms in London. The firm currently has 10 partners and 15 other fee-earners.

PRINCIPAL AREAS OF WORK:

Commercial Litigation: *(Contact Partner:* R.C.B. Hopkins). Financial, insurance, corporate and commercial work, including asset-freezing injunctions and other pre-trial remedies, claims involving securities, directors' liabilities, banking disputes, insolvency, property and construction disputes, contentious tax and trusts, professional negligence, employment, defamation, consumer disputes and general business claims.

Company/ Commercial: *(Contact Partner:* A.J. Saul). Advice to public and private companies on mergers and acquisitions and new share issues, insolvencies and corporate recovery, financial services and securities law, commercial contracts and joint ventures, employment, intellectual property licensing, competition, EC, franchising and international trade law.

Computers and Communications: *(Contact Partner:* S. Rendell). Hopkins & Wood has a substantial reputation in computers and communications law. The four partners who specialise in this area are drawn from the firm's commercial litigation (contractual disputes), intellectual property (IPR infringement and protection) and company/ commercial (contracts, regulatory and corporate transactions) departments. The firm has extensive experience in this fast-moving area of the law and a genuine understanding of the dynamic of IT industries and market places. *Work includes:* FM, distribution and systems integration agreements, software protection, competition, regulatory and EC law and joint ventures, M&A and financings.

Intellectual Property: *(Contact Partner:* Ian Wood). The department advises on both contentious and non-contentious intellectual property matters including, patens, passing off, trademarks, copyright, designs and confidential information. The technical and scientific background of the department's members ensures high quality advice.

Property: *(Contact Partner:* S.J.J. Smith). Commercial property transactions of every kind, including acquisitions and disposals, property development, landlord and tenant, security documentation, planning and rating. The department also handles residential transactions for corporate clients and their employees and substantial residential matters for private clients.

Tax Planning and Trusts: *(Contact Consultant:* P.B.J. Matthews). Estate and tax planning, often in an international context, including the creation of offshore trusts.

NATURE OF CLIENTELE: Clients include banks and a substantial number of internationally known corporations, particularly in the high technology and telecommunications.

FOREIGN CONNECTIONS: The firm has access to a network of specialist law firms in the USA, the EC and throughout the world.

HORWOOD & JAMES 7 Temple Square, Aylesbury, Bucks, HP20 2QB **Tel:** (01296) 87361 **Fax:** (01296) 27155 **DX:** 4102 **Ptnrs:** 6 **Asst Solrs:** 4 **Other Fee-earners:** 4. Established 1792. A general commercial and family practice in Aylesbury. Acts for the local farming and business community and private individuals.

WORKLOAD			
Family	25%	Private client	20%
Civil litigation	20%	Property	20%
Comp (incl employment)	10%	Others	5%

HOWARD JONES & COMPANY 303 Cotton Exchange Building, Old Hall Street, Liverpool, Merseyside, L3 9LF **Tel:** (0151) 231 1577 **Fax:** (0151) 231 1580 **DX:** 14187 Liverpool 1 **Ptnrs:** 2 **Asst Solrs:** 2 . A niche practice specialising in franchising law with a branch office in Hoylake. Also undertakes conveyancing and litigation.

HOWARD KENNEDY

HARCOURT HOUSE, 19 CAVENDISH SQUARE, LONDON, W1A 2AW
DX: 42748 Oxford Circus North

TEL: (0171) 636 1616
FAX: (0171) 499 6871

CONTACT PARTNER: Trevor J. Newey	
Number of partners:	23
Assistant solicitors:	14
Other fee-earners:	5

WORKLOAD	
Conveyancing	44%
Company/ commercial	26%
Litigation	26%
Private client	4%

CONTACTS	
Company/ commercial	Alan Banes
Construction	Anthony Feldman
International	Anthony Slingsby
Litigation	Craig Emden
Private client	Reginald Glick
Property	Graham Craig

THE FIRM: Established in the mid-1930s, Howard Kennedy is now a well-regarded medium-sized firm. Primarily a commercial practice, the firm is organised into four main departments and has the capability to provide a range of specialist services for its clients, which include public companies, entrepreneurial businesses and private individuals. Following a merger in April 1994 with Slingsby, Farmiloe and Greenfield the firm has substantially enhanced its ability to provide an international service to clients and professional advisers. All major European languages are spoken.

PRINCIPAL AREAS OF WORK:

Company/ Commercial: (*Contact:* Alan Banes). The department deals with a high calibre of corporate and corporate finance work which includes Stock Exchange flotations, public share offerings including those under the Enterprise Investment Scheme, mergers and acquisitions, reconstructions and amalgamations, Stock Exchange Yellow Book and The City Code on Take-Overs and Mergers, venture capital and private equity. The department also has considerable experience of advising on shareholder disputes in conjunction with the litigation department. The department combines a high degree of technical know-how and a personal partner-led service, and is frequently dealing with the large City firms. Commercial services include commercial contracts, employment law, agency, distribution and franchising agreements, share option and incentive schemes, consumer protection legislation, corporate taxation and EC law. All aspects of intellectual property matters are also handled.

Litigation: (*Contact:* Craig Emden). A broad range of disputes is handled, for both commercial and private clients, domestic and international. *Work includes:* commercial arbitration, mediation, ADR, company and partnership disputes, construction, negligence claims, insolvency, landlord and tenant actions, employment problems, intellectual property litigation and debt recovery. Private litigation includes matrimonial problems, family law, personal injury claims and immigration.

Commercial Property: (*Contact:* Michael Dobrin). A strong and experienced department includes six partners who handle large-scale developments and investments. Besides acting for property developers and investors this department acts for several major retail, leisure, restaurant and hotel chains. It has considerable expertise in office, industrial and all other types of property as well as in the related specialities of secured lending, planning, licensing, compulsory purchase, compensation, housing law and tenancy problems. Expertise extends to VAT and other tax-related aspects of property transactions. Clients include several listed companies and many smaller companies in the commercial property field.

Private Client: (*Contact:* Reginald Glick). The firm also offers private legal services. *Work includes:* personal taxation, financial services, estate planning and wills, trusts and probate and charities.

International: (*Contact:* Anthony Slingsby). International clients with business or investment projects in the UK are advised by the firm's multi-lingual team. UK clients with overseas interests or activities have the benefit of a large network of overseas legal correspondents.

HOWARD KENNEDY

s o l i c i t o r s

HOWARD PALSER GROSSMAN HERMER & PARTNERS

The Bonded Warehouse, Atlantic Wharf, Cardiff, S. Glam, CF1 5HD **Tel:** (01222) 452770 **Fax:** (01222) 452328 **DX:** 33064 Cardiff 1 **Ptnrs:** 6 **Asst Solrs:** 10 **Other Fee-earners:** 3. Niche practice specialising in defendant personal injury litigation, employment matters, commercial property, FOIL members. Other offices in Cardiff and Swansea.

WORKLOAD			
Defendant pers injury	60%	Commercial property	20%
Commercial litigation	10%	Employment	5%

HOWARTH GOODMAN

8 King Street, Manchester, M60 8HG **Tel:** (0161) 832 5068 **Fax:** (0161) 833 2917 **DX:** 14308 Manchester 1 **Ptnrs:** 10 **Asst Solrs:** 3 **Other Fee-earners:** 7. A medium-sized firm, specialising in housing associations law and property development.

HOWE & CO

27a Bond Street, Ealing, London, W5 5AS **Tel:** (0181) 840 4688 **Fax:** (0181) 840 7209 **Ptnrs:** 3 **Asst Solrs:** 3 **Other Fee-earners:** 9. The firm specialises in personal injury and medical negligence. It also undertakes conveyancing, commercial and immigration work.

HOWES PERCIVAL

Oxford House, Cliftonville, Northampton, Northants, NN1 5PN **Tel:** (01604) 230400 **Fax:** (01604) 20956 **DX:** 12413 Northampton **Ptnrs:** 31 **Asst Solrs:** 15 **Other Fee-earners:** 32. Major commercial firm in the Midlands. *Work includes:* company/ commercial, tax, commercial property and litigation, agriculture, employment and private client.

HUGHES DOWDALL

216 Bath Street, Glasgow, G2 4HS **Tel:** (0141) 332 5321 **Fax:** (0141) 332 0389 **DX:** 51 Glasgow **Ptnrs:** 6 **Asst Solrs:** 8 **Other Fee-earners:** 6. Particularly known for its personal injury and professional negligence work. The firm has also been involved in major disaster litigation.

WORKLOAD			
Criminal court	50%	Civil litigation	30%
Dom/comm conveyancing	20%		

HUGHES HOOKER

3 ST. MICHAEL'S ALLEY, CORNHILL, LONDON, EC3V 9DS

TEL: (0171) 283 2424
FAX: (0171) 626 1234

THE FIRM: Hughes Hooker is a niche City practice specialising in shipping and maritime law. The firms work and clientele is mainly international and has strong overseas connections, especially in Greece. Partners and fee-earners handle a wide variety of shipping matters including: arbitration and litigation including charterparties, bills of lading, damage of goods cargo damage, sale and purchase and shipbuilding and repair disputes.

CONTACT PARTNER: Mr Jacek Bielecki

Number of partners:	3
Assistant solicitors:	4
Other fee-earners:	2

WORKLOAD	
Shipping and maritime law	95%

CONTACTS	
Shipping	J.M. Bielecki

FIRMS OF ACCOUNTANTS

Accountants specialising in litigation support are listed in the accountants' A-Z, with details of the services they offer to solicitors, from forensic accounting to intellectual property or business valuations.

HUGH JAMES JONES & JENKINS

ARLBEE HOUSE, GREYFRIARS RD, CARDIFF, S. GLAM, CF1 4QB
DX: 33000

TEL: (01222) 224871
FAX: (01222) 388222

NATURE OF FIRM: Hugh James Jones & Jenkins is probably the largest firm in Wales with a UK wide reputation for its commercial and insurance litigation practice and commercial property work. The firm has a rapidly growing commercial practice and has established a reputation for insolvency work.

OTHER OFFICES: In addition to its main Cardiff office, the firm has a network of offices throughout South East Wales to include Merthyr, Treharris, Bargoed, Talbot Green and Blackwood.

PRINCIPAL AREAS OF WORK:

Company & Commercial: This is one of the firm's fastest growing departments with experience in a wide range of matters including business start-ups, venture capital, mergers and management buy-outs; commercial contracts; patents and trademarks; stock exchange work and partnerships. (*Contact:* Mr Ceri Preece).

Commercial Property: The firm acts for Housing for Wales and numerous housing associations, financial institutions, national developers, local authorities and private clients. A full range of property-related matters is covered to include planning work and secured lending. (*Contact:* Mr David Roberts).

Commercial Litigation: The firm has one of the leading provincial litigation practices acting for a large number of national and international insurers and also dealing in construction, employment, insolvency, professional indemnity and general commercial litigation. (*Contact:* Mr Gareth Williams).

Private Client: The firm remains committed to the individual client. Services include plaintiff personal injury claims, family work, conveyancing, wills and probate and criminal defence work. Legal aid work is undertaken. Several of the partners are fluent Welsh-speakers. (*Contact:* Ms Cherry Wright).

FOREIGN CONNECTIONS: The firm acts for international clients as well as those with overseas interests. Associations have been formed with legal practices in Nantes, Madrid, Düsseldorf, Rome, Milan and Naples.

AGENCY: All types of agency work are accepted. (*Contact:* Mr Alun Jones).

RECRUITMENT AND TRAINING: The firm recruits about six trainee solicitors every year. Applications by letter and CV should be made to Mr Matthew Tossell. The firm has a Director of Continuing Education, Ms Cherry Wright, and a well-developed programme of in-house lectures and seminars.
Brochures are available on request.

MANAGING PARTNER: Mr Geoffrey Adams

Number of partners:	36
Assistant solicitors:	31
Other fee-earners:	62

WORKLOAD

Commercial litigation, incl construction, insolvency, insurance	55%
Private client	15%
Commercial property	15%
Company/ commercial	15%

CONTACTS

Agency	Alun Jones
Commercial property	David Roberts
Commercial litigation	Gareth Williams
Company & commercial	Ceri Preece
Private client	Cherry Wright

HUGH JAMES
JONES & JENKINS
SOLICITORS · CYFREITHWYR

HUMPHREYS & CO

14 KING ST, BRISTOL, BS1 4EF
DX: 78239

TEL: (0117) 929 2662
FAX: (0117) 929 2722

PRINCIPAL AREAS OF WORK: Best known in the fields of intellectual property, High Court litigation and reinsurance law. Also company and commercial work, property, construction, entertainment, insolvency, insurance, professional and injury/neglignce cases, negligence and personal injury and competition law. Legal aid work for business people is undertaken.

CONTACT PARTNER: Senior Partner

Number of partners:	4
Assistant solicitors:	8
Other fee-earners:	2

HUMPHRIES KIRK Glebe House, North Street, Wareham, Dorset, BH20 4AN **Tel:** (01929) 552141 **Fax:** (01929) 556701 **DX:** 49700 Wareham **Ptnrs:** 7 **Asst Solrs:** 7 **Other Fee-earners:** 12. Long-established general practice with substantial commercial department. Offices in Wareham, Dorchester, Swanage and the Poole/ Bournemouth area.

HUNT & COOMBS

35 THORPE RD, PETERBOROUGH, CAMBS, PE3 6AG
DX: 12302

TEL: (01733) 65312
FAX: (01733) 52748

THE FIRM: Hunt & Coombs is an eight partner firm practising from Peterborough, with a further office at Oundle, and continues to expand. It is also a member of UNILAW and has a legal aid franchise.

PRINCIPAL AREAS OF LAW: This busy and wide-ranging provincial practice offers specialist advice in the following areas: commercial law, crime, private client (divorce, separation and child care, wills, probate and tax planning), conveyancing (domestic and commercial), personal injury, medical negligence administrative law, education, employment, ecclesiastical, charities and agriculture. Landlord & tenant, insolvency. The practice also operates a separate computerised debt collection system.

OTHER OFFICE:
Oundle: 4 New Street, Oundle, Peterborough PE8 4ED.
Tel: (01832) 273506. *Fax:* (01832) 273404.

PARTNERSHIP SECRETARY: T.R. Warren	
Number of partners:	8
Assistant solicitors:	10
Other fee-earners:	5

WORKLOAD	
Crime/ child care	28%
Litigation/ personal injury	26%
Family	19%
Conveyancing (domestic)	11%
Commercial	9%
Probate/ trust	7%

HUNTERS

9 NEW SQUARE, LINCOLN'S INN, LONDON, WC2A 3QN
DX: 61

TEL: (0171) 412 0050
FAX: (0171) 412 0049

THE FIRM: Although founded in the early 18th century, the firm is a thriving modern partnership, serving a broadly-based private and institutional clientele.

PRINCIPAL AREAS OF WORK:

General Description: The firm has a long-established reputation in private client, charity, banking security, and matrimonial work; and an increasing emphasis on commercial property work, employment, and litigation.

Private Client: (*Contact:* John Kennedy. *7 Partners 3 Asst. Solrs*). *Work includes:* trusts, tax planning, tax returns, heritage and agricultural property, wills and probate, partnerships, private businesses and companies, and conveyancing.

Charities: (*Contact:* Hugh Woodeson. *2 Partners*). *Work includes:* acting for major charities; registrations, schemes, trading arrangements, and housing associations.

Banking Security Work: (*Contact:* Roger Nowell. *2 Partners and an assistant*). *Work includes:* security work for several banks.

Matrimonial: (*Contact:* Hugh Woodeson. *2 Partners*). *Work includes:* all aspects, but particularly cases with a substantial financial element.

Commercial Property: (*Contact:* Roger Nowell. *5 Partners and an assistant*). *Work includes:* acquiring and selling property investments, and business tenancies.

Employment: (*Contact:* Paul Almy. *1 Partner*). *Work includes:* contracts and staff handbooks, unfair and wrongful dismissal, redundancy, service occupancies.

Litigation: (*Contact:* Henry Hood. *1 Partner and an assistant*). *Work includes:* wide range of High Court/ County Court work; breach of contract; landlord and tenant disputes, and enforcement of security.

FOREIGN CONNECTIONS: Close relationship with firms in Australia.

RECRUITMENT AND TRAINING: *Partner:* Roger Nowell. Two trainee solicitors with good degrees are recruited annually. Fortnightly seminars. Wide spread of work and direct client contact.

CONTACT PARTNER: Hugh Woodeson	
Number of partners:	9
Assistant solicitors:	5
Other fee-earners:	5

HUNTSMANS 20 Park Row, Nottingham, Notts, NG1 6GW **Tel:** (0115) 9472038 **Fax:** (0115) 9483489 **DX:** 10018 **Ptnrs:** 4 **Asst Solrs:** 2 **Other Fee-earners:** 4. Established family firm with civil litigation bias. Specialising in accident and occupational personal injuries; also matrimonial, criminal, wills, probate, conveyancing.

HUTTONS 16-18 St Andrews Crescent, Cardiff, S. Glam, CF1 3DD **Tel:** (01222) 378621 **Fax:** (01222) 388450 **DX:** 33065 **Ptnrs:** 2 **Asst Solrs:** 6 **Other Fee-earners:** 5. Handles crime, matrimonial law, litigation and conveyancing. Has another office in Caerphilly.

HYLTON-POTTS

7 CHEVAL PLACE, KNIGHTSBRIDGE, LONDON, SW7 1EW
DX: 38161 Knightsbridge

TEL: (0171) 225 1881
FAX: (0171) 589 4008

CONTACT PARTNER: Rodney Hylton-Potts	
Number of partners:	2
Other fee-earners:	7

THE FIRM: Hylton-Potts has particular expertise in computer law and contracts, intellectual property law, litigation and insolvency.

PRINCIPAL AREAS OF WORK:

Intellectual Property and Computer Law: Copyright, trademarks, patents, registered designs, licensing of software, data protection and computer contracts. Rodney Hylton-Potts is Chairman of the Society of Conservative Lawyers Computer Law Reform Committee. He is also a member of the International Bar Association, American Bar Association, New York Bar Association and Canadian Bar Association.

Company/ Commercial: Directors' liability, insolvency and commercial agreements.

Litigation: Debt collecting, matrimonial cases, landlord and tenant matters, employment, and property and building disputes, including work with an international dimension.

OTHER AREAS OF WORK: Commercial and domestic conveyancing, advice on immigration and emigration, particularly to the USA, including advice on applications for the 'Green Card' work permits and visas.

OTHER OFFICES: New York, Geneva, Aberdeen and Guernsey.

IAIN SMITH & COMPANY

18-20 QUEEN'S ROAD, ABERDEEN, GRAMPIAN, AB1 6YT
DX: 4 Aberdeen

TEL: (01224) 645454
FAX: (01224) 646671/644701

Number of partners:	10
Assistant solicitors:	10
Other fee-earners:	9

WORKLOAD	
Litigation	30%
Corporate/ commercial	25%
Conveyancing - domestic	20%
Insolvency	10%
Conveyancing - commercial	10%
Trusts/ wills and executries	5%

THE FIRM:: Established in 1975, Iain Smith and Co. offers a broad range of legal services to both commercial and private clients. Although based in the North-East of Scotland, the firm regularly acts for international clients and strong connections are maintained with Norway and the USA. In addition, the practice represents a number of fishing associations and regularly advises on EC law.

PRINCIPAL AREAS OF WORK:

Corporate and Business Services: The firm advises large and small businesses, public and private concerns, partnerships, companies and sole traders. Expertise includes fund-raising, venture capital, take-overs, mergers, joint ventures, consortium agreements, management buy-outs and all aspects of commercial property. The department is also well-regarded for its insolvency work – receiverships, liquidations, corporate rescues, security and investment.

Litigation Services: The department undertakes a comprehensive range of litigation, including commercial disputes. In particular, the firm has established a considerable reputation for dealing with divorce, custody actions and various types of compensation claims.

Residential Property: A comprehensive service includes the arrangement of surveys, advice on offer price, negotiation and conclusion of contract. The firm is a member of the Aberdeen Solicitors Property Centre and is an approved legal representative of all major building societies and banks.

CONTACTS	
Commercial	Roy Roxburgh
Conveyancing, dom. & comm	Derek Cameron
Financial services	Martin McGuffie
Litigation	Peter Macari
Trusts/ wills and executries	Robert Gillan

Private Client: The department offers expertise on all aspects of wills, trusts, executries and the administration of estates. In addition, free independent financial advice can be sought on matters relating to insurance, pensions, mortgages and investments.

OTHER OFFICES: 52 Victoria Road, Torry, Aberdeen AB1 3DR. *Tel:* (01224) 878417. Kinear House, 33 Evan Street, Stonehaven AB3 2ET. *Tel:* (01569) 63769.

FOREIGN LANGUAGES: French, German and Spanish.

ILIFFES BOOTH BENNETT

THE MARKET HOUSE, HIGH STREET, UXBRIDGE, MIDDX, UB8 1AQ
DX: 45105 Uxbridge

TEL: (01895) 230941
FAX: (01895) 274352

THE FIRM: Iliffes Booth Bennett was formed in May 1994 by the merger of Iliffes and Booth Bennett. The firm now has offices in Chesham, Hayes, Ingatestone and Slough and runs the only solicitors' property centre in the area. Each member of the firm specialises in a particular field, and as a whole, Iliffes Booth Bennett has the expertise to meet the needs of the local business community and the private client. Legal aid is available where necessary.

PRINCIPAL AREAS OF WORK:

Domestic Conveyancing: *Work includes:* full estate agency service, mortgage and insurance advice, free valuations, freehold or leasehold property and preparation of leases and tenancy agreements.

Commercial Conveyancing: *Work includes:* purchase and sale of retail, commercial and industrial property, property development, lease negotiations and renewals, rent reviews, planning applications and agricultural property.

Company Law: *Work includes:* buying and selling a business, terms and conditions of business, company secretarial services, company formations, agency, franchise and licensing and agreements.

Private Client: *Work includes:* divorce and separation, maintenance, matrimonial property, custody and access to children, care proceedings, wardship and adoption, preparation of wills, probate, estate administration, taxation advice and trusts.

Employment: *Work includes:* unfair dismissal, redundancy, discrimination at work, industrial tribunals, contracts of employment and pensions.

Litigation: *Work includes:* commercial contract disputes, debt recovery, personal injury, neighbour disputes, consumer claims and landlord and tenant disputes.

Criminal Law: *Work includes:* 24 hour emergency cover, attendance at police stations, defence in criminal proceedings, juvenile offences and motoring offences.

OTHER AREAS OF WORK: Liquor licensing, mental health tribunals, Court of Protection and power of attorney.

FOREIGN LANGUAGES: French, Urdu, Punjabi, Gujerati, Hindi, Swahili.

OTHER OFFICES:
The Property Centre, 225 High Street, Uxbridge, Middlesex UB8 1LD.
Tel: (01895) 812222.
135-137 High Street, Slough, Berkshire SL1 1DN. *Tel:* (01753) 516533.
52 Coldharbour Lane, Hayes, Middlesex UB3 3ER. *Tel:* (0181) 573 5213.
The Bury, Church Street, Chesham, Bucks HP5 1JE.
Tel: (01491) 778822.
23 High Street, Ingatestone, Essex CM4 9DU.
Tel: (01277) 354065.
Lovell House, 271 High Street, Uxbridge, Middlesex UB8 1AQ.
Tel: (01895) 230941.

CONTACT PARTNER: Steven Booth

Number of partners:	20
Assistant solicitors:	15
Other fee-earners:	28

WORKLOAD

Commercial, personal injury & civil litigation	18%
Family/ matrimonial	17%
Building, estate development and residential conveyancing	16%
Commercial and agricultural property	16%
Crime	15%
Wills, probate, tax, etc.	9%
Company/ commercial	9%

CONTACTS

Civil litigation	Rosemary Jeffries
Commercial property	Susan Mawson
Commercial litigation	Andrew Olins
Company/ commercial	Ann Hinnigan
Crime	Tom Brownlow
Family	Karen Bennett
Personal injury litigation	Gill Pilling
Residential conveyancing	Martin Silverman
Wills, probate	Gill Murray

INCE & CO.

KNOLLYS HOUSE, 11 BYWARD STREET, LONDON, EC3R 5EN
DX: 1070 City

TEL: (0171) 623 2011
FAX: (0171) 623 3225

THE FIRM: Ince & Co is one of the City of London's long established firms of solicitors, and specialises in international commercial law. It is best known for its work in the shipping and insurance sectors, including litigation when necessary. Clients include some of the world's largest shipping, shipbuilding, trading companies and the London Insurance Market. The firm has branch offices in Hong Kong, Singapore and Piraeus and has a powerful network of correspondents throughout the world's major commercial centres.

PRINCIPAL AREAS OF WORK:

Marine and Aviation: *(Contact Partner:* Richard Sayer). The firm has comprehensive experience of matters relating to shipping and aviation around the world. *Work includes:* cargo claims, maritime and aviation casualties, accident investigations, personal injury, official enquiries, collision, salvage and towage, pollution and wreck removal, shipbuilding disputes, arrest, pilotage and EC law.

Insurance and Reinsurance: *(Contact Partner:* Peter Rogan). Marine, non-marine and aviation, including: hull and cargo, war risks, political and contingency risks, loss of earnings and mortgagees' interest, fire, charterers' and shipowners' liability, construction risks, product liability, facultative and treaty reinsurance, administration of run-off portfolios, P&I Club cover, professional indemnity, insurance regulatory requirements including captives, and policy and treaty wordings.

Commercial International Trade: *(Contact Partner:* Richard Williams). The firm acts in every kind of commercial dispute arising out of international trade and commercial activity. The firm's services include the drafting of a wide-ranging spectrum of contracts, and advising on all manner of commercial issues.

Company: *(Contact Partner:* Nick Gould). Much of the work has an international aspect and ranges from company formation, mergers and acquisitions, financing and joint ventures, to restructuring and insolvency. Advice is also given on ancillary areas such as taxation and employment.

Energy: *(Contact Partner:* David Steward). The group deals with the oil and gas industries, from exploration, production and refining, to transportation and trading, including pollution, construction of pipelines and refineries and insurance.

Property and Construction: *(Contact Partner:* David Sheehan). Property work includes commercial, residential, port installations, rigs and offshore structures, pipeline and storage facilities. The firm handles development work, financing and property management and any property-related disputes.

OTHER OFFICES: Branch offices in Hong Kong, Singapore and a Mediterranean office in Piraeus.

RECRUITMENT & TRAINING: *(Contact Partner:* Oliver Weiss). Ince & Co recruits 7 to 10 trainee solicitors a year. Financial assistance is provided through Law School and the firm operates a summer placement scheme.

CONTACT PARTNER: Richard Sayer

UK:	
Number of partners:	52
Assistant solicitors:	49
Other fee-earners:	44
INTERNATIONAL:	
Number of Partners:	8
Assistant Solicitors:	8
Foreign qualified lawyers	9
Other fee-earners:	5

WORKLOAD	
Insurance/ reinsurance	40%
Shipping & international trade	40%
Company, commercial, property	10%
Professional indemnity	10%

CONTACTS	
Admiralty	Richard Sayer, Chris Beesley
Aviation	Mike Pollen
Cargo	Robin Healey, Anthony George
Charterparties	Richard Williams, Jonathan Lux
Commercial property	Albert Levy
Commodities	Stuart Shepherd
Construction	David Sheehan
Corporate	Nick Gould, David Coupe
EC law	Denys Hickey
Environment and pollution	Colin de le Rue
Insurance & reinsur.	Julian Hill, Peter Rogan
Offshore & ener.	David Steward, Chris Sprague
P&I clubs	Bob Deering
Personal injury	Chris Sprague
Political risk insurance	Anthony George
Professional indemnity	Albert Rogers
Ship finance	Malcolm Strong, Tony Suchy
Shipbuilding	Mike Pollen

CD-ROM EDITION ON THE INTERNET

This edition of the directory is available on a CD-ROM which includes both **DOS** and Windows versions. It can be loaded onto a network, and works with virtually any IBM compatible PC. The CD-ROM version offers computer-users the advantage of rapid search, retrieval and cross-referencing. It is also available via the Internet.

INGHAM CLEGG & CROWTHER Guild Chambers, 4 Winckley Square, Preston, Lancs, PR1 3JJ **Tel:** (01772) 250931 **Fax:** (01772) 823150 **DX:** 17106 Preston 1 **Ptnrs:** 14 **Asst Solrs:** 12 **Other Fee-earners:** 18. A broadly-based commercial and private practice with offices throughout Lancashire.

WORKLOAD		
Priv client	50%	Gen commercial/company 30%
Personal injury claims	20%	Site development convey 10%

INGLEDEW BROWN BENNISON & GARRETT

82-84 FENCHURCH STREET, LONDON, EC3M 4BY
DX: 1073 London City EC3

TEL: (0171) 702 0802
FAX: (0171) 702 0091

THE FIRM: Best-known for shipping law, Ingledew Brown Bennison & Garrett also handles a variety of general legal work from company/ commercial and property matters to matrimonial and private client services.

PRINCIPAL AREAS OF WORK:

Marine: (*Contact:* Martin Sutton). Four partners work in this department which deals with all aspects of shipping law. *Work includes:* **Admiralty:** collision, salvage, total loss, marine fraud and pollution cases; **Cargo claims:** warehousing and forwarding, marine cargo insurance and aviation law; **Marine insurance and re-insurance:**; **Maritime and commercial** matters incluidng charter-party and bill of lading disputes, shipbuilding contracts, ship finance, mortgage and leasing, sale of goods contracts and disputes, off-shore contracts, international collection of marine debts and arbitration; **Yachts** and pleasure craft: purchase, sale and registration, charter agreements, insurance, collision, recovery and salvage.

Company/ Commercial: (*Contact:* Peter Brooks). The department deals with all aspects of corporate law, from formation to liquidation, including financing, tax planning, business expansion schemes, intellectual property, employment law, industrial tribunals, pension and employment incentive schemes, insolvency and Stock Exchange work.

Property, Probate & Trusts: (*Contact:* John Allan). Property work includes commercial, investment, residential and agricultural property and planning. The firm also provides expert tax planning and deals with wills, probate and trusts.

NATURE OF CLIENTELE: Clients include shipowners, P&I clubs, underwriters and insurers, charterers and commodity traders, a number of substantial corporations and institutions and private clients.

CONTACT PARTNER: Mr Martin Sutton

Number of partners:	10
Assistant solicitors:	6
Other fee-earners:	6

WORKLOAD	
Marine and marine insurance and yachts	60%
Commercial property	20%

CONTACTS	
Cargo	Stuart Armstrong
Charities	John Allan
Charterparties	Roger Miles
Commercial property	John Allan
Company/ commercial	Peter Brooks
General litigation	Clive Woolf
Marine	Martin Sutton
Private client	John Allan
Yachts, marine and insurance	Ken Thwaites

IRONSIDES RAY & VIALS

ARNCLIFFE HOUSE, 9 SPENCER PARADE, NORTHAMPTON, NORTHANTS, NN1 5AH   DX: 12402
Contact Partner: P.H. Mair

TEL: (01604) 234800
FAX: (01604) 232624

Macaulay House, 10 Friar Lane, Leicester LE1 5QD
DX: 10827
Contact Partner: J.J.B. Stafford

Tel: (0116) 2515253
Fax: (0116) 2512005

Oakham Office, 76 High Street, Oakham, Leics LE15 6AS
DX: 2835 Oakham
Contact Partner: M. Radcliffe

Tel: (01572) 724 455
Fax: (01572) 756 267

THE FIRM: Ironsides Ray & Vials' three offices provide a broad general service at reasonable cost to both private and commercial clients. In recent years there has been a growing emphasis on commercial work.

Number of partners:	15
Assistant solicitors:	9
Other fee-earners:	11

PRINCIPAL AREAS OF WORK:

Commercial Work: (*Contact Partner:* Jeremy Stafford – Leicester amd Ralph Harris - Northampton). *Work includes:* all elements of business, company and partnership law, employment law, intellectual property, EC law, restrictive practices in trade and employment, road haulage, transport and liquor licensing.

Private Client: (*Contact Partner:* Nigel Jones – Northampton and James Coningsby - Leicester). Family law, from mediation, divorce, custody and access, to division of assets, residential conveyancing, drafting of wills, setting up and administration of trusts, powers of attorney, tax planning and personal financial advice.

Litigation: (*Contact Partner:* Chris McKinney – Leicester and Paul Guppy - Northampton). *Work includes:* disputes between companies, employment law cases, personal injury negligence cases for individuals and corporate clients, including medical negligence, and construction cases.

RECRUITMENT AND TRAINING: Applications should be made to Alan Kiddle at 9 Spencer Parade, Northampton.

WORKLOAD	
Insurance litigation	20%
Company/ commercial	19%
Probate	17%
Conveyancing	15%
Civil litigation	11%
Matrimonial	9%
Liquor Licensing	5%
Other	4%

IRONSIDES RAY & VIALS
SOLICITORS

IRWIN MITCHELL incorporating Kershaw Tudor

ST. PETER'S HOUSE, HARTSHEAD, SHEFFIELD, S. YORKS, S1 2EL
DX: 10513 Sheffield

TEL: (0114) 276 7777
FAX: (0114) 275 3306

THE FIRM: Irwin Mitchell, with offices in Sheffield, Birmingham and Leeds, is particularly known for commercial law, commercial litigation, insurance, family, personal injury and disaster law.

PRINCIPAL AREAS OF WORK:

Corporate Service: Company/ Commercial/ EU: (*Contact:* Kevin Cunningham. *Fee-earners:* 17). Services offered include mergers, buy-outs and acquisitions; formation of companies and partnerships; education and charities; commercial contracts; joint ventures; banking; insolvency; intellectual property; high-tech; licensing; corporate finance and taxation. The EU unit offers guidance on European and International law.

Corporate Service: Commercial Property: (*Contact:* Kevin Docherty. *Fee-earners:* 13). This department covers all areas of property transactions including joint venture agreements, development projects, development funding, building contracts and planning. The department has specialist retail, development and commerical units within it.

Corporate Service: Commercial Litigation: (*Contact:* Peter Wylde. *Fee-earners:* 29). *Work includes:* commercial and financial disputes, intellectual property, insolvency, employment, professional negligence, insurance, sale of goods, product liability, building contracts and property disputes.

Business Crime: (*Contact:* Kevin Robinson. *Fee-earners:* 2). The firm is well-known in this field for handling the Matrix-Churchill 'arms to Iraq' affair, and provides advice also on cirminal law generally.

Insurance: (*Contact:* Joe Simpson. *Fee-earners:* 67). The firm handles both contentious and non-contentious insurance work in the form of advising on policy conditions and insurance litigation, acting for insurers in defending claims particularly in the fields of employers' liability, product liability and public liability. The firm also operates a large legal expenses unit.

Debt Collection and Credit Control: (*Contact:* Peter Wylde. *Fee-earners:* 4). The firm operates a computerised debt collection service. They deal with credit investigations and reports and representation at creditors' meetings.

Personal Injury: (*Contact:* John Pickering. *Fee-earners:* 54). Mainly acting for plaintiffs, the firm has a national and international reputation for personal injury litigation.

Disaster Law: (*Contact:* Michael Napiers). The firm offers a specialist service covering: defective products, adverse drug reactions, large-scale and multiple accidents, and international disasters. Major involvement on claims arising from disasters include: Manchester Air Crash, sinking of "Herald of Free Enterprise", "Marchioness" disaster, King's Cross Fire, "Piper Alpha" explosion, and Land's End tragedy.

CONTACT PARTNER: Michael Napier

Number of partners:	49
Assistant solicitors:	48
Other fee-earners:	127

WORKLOAD	
Corporate services	35%
Plaintiff personal injury litigation	23%
Insurance litigation services	22%
Private client	14%
Police prosecution	6%

CONTACTS	
Business crime	Kevin Robinson
Commercial property	Kevin Docherty
Commercial litigation	Peter Wylde
Company/ commercial	Kevin Cunningham
Corporate services	Michael Jelly
Employment	Barry Warne
Family and matrimonial	Martin Loxley
Insurance	Joe Simpson
Intellectual property	Patrick Somers
Personal injury	John Pickering
Residential conveyancing	Steve Martin
Wills and trusts	Paul Hirst

IRWIN MITCHELL
SOLICITORS
INCORPORATING KERSHAW TUDOR

Private Client Services/ Family Law: (*Contact:* Martin Loxley. *Fee-earners:* 11). The full range of matrimonial and family services is offered.

Private Client Services: Conveyancing: (*Contact:* Graham Loukes. *Fee-earners:* 6). Acting on behalf of private individuals, clearing banks and others, the firm operates a fully computerised conveyancing service with close partner involvement.

Private Client Services: Trust and Probate: (*Contact:* Paul Hirst. *Fee-earners:* 6). The trust and probate team deals with wills, personal taxation, trusts and probate on behalf of private individuals and business clients requiring personal advice for their directors or employees.

NATURE OF CLIENTELE: Clients range from the private individual and the family business to public companies and institutions on a national and international scale.

OTHER OFFICES: Birmingham, Leeds.

FOREIGN CONNECTIONS: Well established links with lawyers in the USA and most other foreign jurisdictions.

ISADORE GOLDMAN 125 High Holborn, London, WC1 6QF **Tel:** (0171) 242 3000 **Fax:** (0171) 242 9160 **DX:** 124 **Ptnrs:** 9 **Asst Solrs:** 4 **Other Fee-earners:** 4. Best known for its insolvency practice. Other areas of work include litigation, company/ commercial and conveyancing.

ISON HARRISON & CO 29 Main St, Garforth, Leeds, W. Yorks, LS25 1DS **Tel:** (0113) 286 1455 **Fax:** (0113) 287 3014 **DX:** 29766 Garforth **Ptnrs:** 7 **Asst Solrs:** 13 **Other Fee-earners:** 18. Known for crime, immigration, family, childcare and general civil work.

JACKSON & CANTER

32 PRINCES ROAD, LIVERPOOL, MERSEYSIDE, L8 1TH
DX: 14156

TEL: (0151) 708 6593
FAX: (0151) 708 5850

THE FIRM: The firm was established 32 years ago and was one of the first firms to open branches in hard-pressed inner city areas, to provide services where people live.

PRINCIPAL AREAS OF WORK:

Criminal Work: (*Contact Partner:* Stephen Rogers). There is a well organised criminal department which already undertakes regular agency work for other practices in the area.

Civil Litigation and Injury Work: (*Contact Partner:* Keith Robinson). Two of the partners are on the Personal Injury Panel. The firm deals with all types of personal injury work including medical negligence and road traffic accident work.

Family Work: (*Contact Partner:* Keith Robinson). Two of the partners are members of the Children Panel. All kinds of divorce work and related family problems are dealt with.

Mental Health: (*Contact Partner:* Christopher Topping). The firm has a Mental Health specialist who is a member of the Mental Health Panel.

Immigration: (*Contact Partner:* Andrew Holroyd). The firm has a wide experience in dealing with immigration and nationality work.

Landlord and Tenant: (*Contact Partner:* Andrew Holroyd). The firm regularly acts for tenants in all kinds of housing work.

HELP FOR THE SMALL BUSINESS: (*Contact Partner:* Andrew Holroyd). The firm aims to give straightforward advice for those starting up new businesses.

OTHER OFFICES: Liverpool City Centre, Garston, Scotland Road and the Dingle.

AGENCY WORK: General litigation in the Liverpool County Court and the District Registry and in the Liverpool City Magistrates' Court.

CONTACT PARTNER: Andrew Holroyd

Number of partners:	6
Assistant solicitors:	5
Other fee-earners:	10

WORKLOAD	
Crime	33%
Civil litigation and personal injury	30%
Family	15%
Housing and landlord & tenant	10%
Immigration	5%
Welfare benefits	5%

CONTACTS	
Civil litigation	Keith Robinson
Criminal	Steve Rogers
Family	Keith Robinson
Housing	Chris Topping
Immigration	Andrew Holroyd
Mental Health	Chris Topping
Small businesses	Andrew Holroyd

JACKSON PARTON

18 MANSELL STREET, LONDON, E1 8AA

TEL: (0171) 702 0085
FAX: (0171) 702 0858

THE FIRM: Jackson Parton is a medium-sized City practice specialising in shipping, insurance and commercial litigation. Several of the partners have previous experience in P&I Club shipping management.

PRINCIPAL AREAS OF WORK: (*Contact Partner:* Nicholas Parton). The firm offers expertise in the full range of P&I and FD&D work, including charter disputes, cargo claims, pollution and general average. Other work includes sale and purchase, shipbuilding, mortgage enforcement disputes, marine insurance matters, commodity disputes, grounding, collision and salvage cases.

FOREIGN LANGUAGES: Arabic, French, Dutch, Greek, Italian, Japanese, Norwegian, Persian (Farsi) and Spanish.

CONTACT PARTNER: Nicholas Parton

Number of partners:	10
Assistant solicitors:	4
Other fee-earners:	4

WORKLOAD	
Commercial shipping: owners, charterers, cargo owners & insurers	80%
Admiralty: collision and salvage	20%

JACKSONS

1-15 QUEEN'S SQUARE, MIDDLESBROUGH, CLEV, TS2 1AL
DX: 60512

TEL: (01642) 244154
FAX: (01642) 217050

THE FIRM: Jacksons is a result of the amalgamation of the firms of Cohen Jackson and Jacksons Monk & Rowe, Clayhills Lucas and Jowett and Goyder. The constituent firms have been established for over a century with an emphasis on commercial work. The firm has a considerable personal injury litigation practice and a large private client base. The firm is currently expanding its Middlesbrough office and sees itself as offering a regional service throughout the North East of England.

PRINCIPAL AREAS OF WORK:
Company and Commercial: (*Contact:* Kevin Fletcher. *6 Partners*).
Litigation: (*Contact:* Nicholas Bosher. *7 Partners*).
Commercial Property: (*Contact:* Julian Lewis. *5 Partners*).
Residential Property: (*Contact:* Geoffrey Skeoch. *3 Partners*).
Private Client: (*Contact:* John Breen. *3 Partners*).
Matrimonial: (*Contact:* Robert Smith. *1 Partner*).
Crime: (*Contact:* Simon Catterall. *1 Partner*).
Tax: (*Contact;* John Breen. *1 Partner*).
Employment: (*Contact:* Kevin Fletcher. *2 Partners*).
Insolvency: (*Contact:* Stephen Wiles).
OTHER OFFICES:
62 Dovecot St, Stockton-on-Tees, Cleveland.
5-7 Conisliffe Road, Darlington, Co. Durham.
AGENCY WORK: Agency work of all types is handled throughout all offices. The contact names are Christopher Gannon in Middlesbrough, Robert Smith in Stockton, and Bill Goyder in Darlington.

CONTACT PARTNER: Keith Varley

Number of partners:	21
Assistant solicitors:	15
Other fee-earners:	18

WORKLOAD	
Personal injury	40%
Private client	22%
Company/ commercial	17%
Commercial litigation	8%
Employment	7%
Miscellaneous	6%

CONTACTS	
ADR	W.A. Goyder
Commercial litigation	J.R. Bloom
Company/ commercial	K.J. Fletcher
Crime	S. Catterall
Domestic conveyancing	G. Skeoch
Employment	K.J. Fletcher
Family	R.C. Smith
Personal injury	N.A. Bosher
Wills/ trusts	J.A. Breen

INTERNATIONAL SECTION

The international section lists foreign law firms based in London. It also lists the foreign connections of English law firms: their branch offices overseas and the foreign languages spoken at their UK offices.

JAMES CHAPMAN & CO

CANADA HSE, 3 CHEPSTOW ST, MANCHESTER, M1 5ER
DX: 14358 Manchester 1

TEL: (0161) 236 7772
FAX: (0161) 228 3658

THE FIRM: James Chapman & Co was established nearly a hundred years ago and is a specialist litigation firm concentrating on insurance and indemnity work for many of the major insurance companies and many other substantial corporate entities. With over forty fee-earners involved solely in this work it is able to put together a team to handle an individual claim or a series of claims.

PRINCIPAL AREAS OF WORK: The firm consists of departments handling insurance and indemnity civil litigation mainly on behalf of defendants. Particular emphasis is given to all aspects of personal injury work and professional indemnity claims on behalf of solicitors, barristers, surveyors, architects, accountants and a broad variety of other professional groups.

The commercial department provides services mainly to small and medium sized clients. These include sales and acquisitions of businesses, advising on corporate structure as well as a wide range of company matters. The firm also acts for a leading Premier League Football Club, its governing body and professional sportsmen.

The conveyancing department deals with a large volume of residential and commercial matters. These involve shops, offices and other business premises, planning and property licensing.

A full service in wills, probate and trusts and related matters is provided by the probate department.

CONTACT PARTNER: John McKenna

Number of partners:	19
Assistant solicitors:	20
Other fee-earners:	9

WORKLOAD	
Defendant insurance/ indemnity	80%
Conveyancing (resdential and commercial) & probate	10%
Company	5%
Plaintiff personal injury	5%

CONTACTS	
Commercial/ conveyancing	Maurice Watkins
Personal injury	Kevin Finnigan
Professional indemnity	John McKenna

JAMES & GEORGE COLLIE 1 East Craibstone Street, Bon Accord Square, Aberdeen, Grampian, AB9 1YH **Tel:** (01224) 581581 **Fax:** (01224) 580119 **DX:** 43 Aberdeen **Ptnrs:** 11 **Asst Solrs:** 10 **Other Fee-earners:** 9. The firm provides advice on corporate/ business services, all aspects of residential property, private client work, civil and criminal litigation.

WORKLOAD			
Domestic conveyancing	37%	Company/ commercial	26%
Litigation	13%	Furnished lets	10%
Wills/trusts/executries	8%	Tax	3%

JANE COKER & PARTNERS Emma House, 214 High Road, London, N15 4NP **Tel:** (0181) 885 1415 **Fax:** (0181) 885 2882 **DX:** 55604 Sth Tottenham **Ptnrs:** 2 **Asst Solrs:** 2 **Other Fee-earners:** 3. Highly regarded for its immigration law practice, children and family work.

JARVIS & BANNISTER

6 & 7 GREAT JAMES STREET, LONDON, WC1N 3DA
DX: 165 (Ch.Ln.)

TEL: (0171) 242 3413
FAX: (0171) 831 6088

3 Gracechurch Street, London EC3V
DX: 854 Lon/ City

Tel: (0171) 626 1222
Fax: (0171) 626 1218

Jarvis & Bannister is an established and thriving firm of specialist insurance and reinsurance solicitors based in Holborn and the City. It is remarkable amongst firms of its size in working for insurers almost exclusively and in its depth and breadth of service.

The firm acts on behalf of both the company and Lloyd's markets with distinct specialisms in product liability, professional indemnity, property damage, construction, fraud, reinsurance, aviation and policy matters. There is a strong defendant personal injury department.

The firm strives to be outward looking and involved with the wider concerns of its client base, an attitude which led the firm to found the annual Insurance and Law Debate.

CONTACT PARTNER: Alan Bannister

Number of partners:	8
Assistant solicitors:	11
Other fee-earners:	4

JARVIS & BANNISTER
SOLICITORS

C & H JEFFERSON 8/9 Donegall Square North, Belfast, BT1 5GN **Tel:** (01232) 329545 **Fax:** (01232) 244644 **DX:** 439 NR.Belfast **Ptnrs:** 7 **Asst Solrs:** 10 **Other Fee-earners:** 5. Founded 1898 and one of the largest and foremost firms in Northern Ireland providing a full range of services to insurance companies, commercial and private clients.

WORKLOAD			
Litigation	70%	Employment law	15%
Commercial law	10%	Priv client/debt recovery	5%

JEFFREY GREEN RUSSELL

56 NEW BOND STREET, LONDON, W1Y 9DG
DX: 44627   Internet: jgr@jgrlaw.co.uk
Worldwide Web Server: http//www.potomac.com/jgr

TEL: (0171) 499 7020
FAX: (0171) 499 2449

THE FIRM: Jeffrey Green Russell is a medium-sized commercial law firm based in Bond Street, London W1.

TECHNOLOGY AND COMMUNICATIONS: The firm has a commitment to technology and human resources development, both of which have made a significant contribution to its success. The firm has a local area network. The file server runs on Novell Netware. Staff at all levels have PCs running Microsoft Windows. Lawyers have Gateway 2000 P90 PCs. These are used for numerous purposes including: internal and external e-mail via the Internet; scheduling (Novell Groupwise); word processing (WordPerfect 6.1); document management and know-how retrieval (Soft Solutions); outward faxing (Intel's Netsatisfaction); spreadsheets (Microsoft Excel 5); Internet research; and to access the Hilderbrandt marketing database, the back-office accounting system and other specialised programs. The firm uses the DPS automatic document assembly and case management system for large scale insurance claims litigation and property sales matters. It incorporates direct e-mail capability to clients. For litigation the firm uses the Open Law document imaging and litigation support package.

CONTACT PARTNER:	Mr C. Whitfield-Jones
Number of partners:	20
Assistant solicitors:	16
Other fee-earners:	10

CONTACTS	
Company/ commercial	Anthony Coles
Insurance litigation	Bryan Lincoln
Leisure & licensing	Julian Skeens
Litigation	Philip Cohen
Pensions/ life insurance	Graham Chrystie
Private client	Philip Harris
Property	Clive Whitfield-Jones

PRINCIPAL AREAS OF WORK:

Company/ Commercial: (*Contact:* Tony Coles). A broad spectrum of services focuses on commercial and financial activity. Corporate work includes formations, mergers, acquisitions, MBOs, joint ventures, re-organisations and share issues. Other areas of expertise are commercial work (including computer contracts), banking and finance, intellectual property and franchising, and corporate taxation.

Litigation: (*Contact:* Philip Cohen). Quick, positive and effective action is the hallmark of this department, which handles general commercial litigation, insurance disputes including professional negligence and product liability, personal injury and legal expenses insurance, property litigation, employment matters, debt collection and insolvency, and commercial fraud including computer and technology-related offences.

Property: (*Contact:* Clive Whitfield-Jones). The department offers a full range of services including planning, development work, property finance, investment, dealing (including portfolio break-ups and auction work) and landlord and tenant law.

Licensing and Leisure: (*Contact:* Julian Skeens). A strong department caters for the special demands of the leisure industry, offering a comprehensive service representing clients in courts throughout the country.The firm deals with bingo, nightclubs and discos, pubs, off licences, restaurants and catering, hotels, cinemas, amusement arcades and gaming.

Pensions and Life Insurance: (*Contact:* Graham Chrystie). Pension clients range from major companies to private companies, trustees and individuals. Emphasis is on problem solving and effective commercial advice often on contentious matters. A wide range of experience especially in international, E.U. and offshore areas gives us the facility to advise on all employee benefit issues and to provide documentation including investment and custodian agreements. The firm has expertise in buying, selling, merging and establishing Life and General Insurance Companies.

Personal Finance: (*Contact:* Philip Harris). The department provides a specialist service dedicated to the protection and enhancement of clients' personal wealth. The range of services includes wills and probate, estate and financial planning, trusts and settlements, administration of estates and overseas tax arrangements.

NATURE OF CLIENTELE: Clients from commerce, finance and industry range from small businesses to multi-national corporations. Activities include banking, finance, technology, leisure, restaurants, the licensed trade, brewers, insurance, airlines and property development.

FOREIGN CONNECTIONS: The firm is a member of ACL International, an association of commercial lawyers worldwide. For further information contact the International Partner, David Judah.

JOELSON WILSON & CO

70 NEW CAVENDISH STREET, LONDON, W1M 8AT

TEL: (0171) 580 5721
FAX: (0171) 580 2251

THE FIRM: Established in 1957, Joelson Wilson & Co provides a personal and individual approach and a highly commercial service to its clients. Particularly known for its strong company/ commercial, commercial litigation and commercial property practice, the firm has established a fast-growing reputation for its specialised leisure/ licensing and employment law work. Value for money is a particular keynote.

PRINCIPAL AREAS OF WORK:

Company/ Commercial: (*Contact:* Paul Wilson/ Sheldon Cordell. *Fee-earners:* 4). Including joint ventures, acquisitions and disposals, capital raisings, intellectual property, information technology and communications, competition law, insolvency, commercial and financial agreements of all kinds and advice on all aspects of company and commercial law, often involving cross-border transactions in Europe and elsewhere.

Employment: (*)Contact:* Claire Davies. *Fee-earners:* 3). All aspects of employment law (contentious and non-contentious) for both employers and employees.

Litigation and Licensing: (*Contact:* David Clifton. *Fee-earners:* 4). Including High Court litigation arising from breaches of commercial agreements, building, property and landlord and tenant litigation, international recovery of debts and defamation; specialists in employment law and gaming, liquor and entertainment licensing.

Property: (*Contact:* Paul Baglee. *Fee-earners:* 2). All aspects of buying, selling and leasing commercial property, joint ventures and development work. Also residential transactions.

FOREIGN CONNECTIONS: The firm is the UK member of European Lawyers Network (EEIG), and as such works closely together with the other member firms which are in Amsterdam, Berlin, Brussels, Frankfurt, and Paris.

CONTACT PARTNER: Paul Wilson

Number of partners:	6
Assistant solicitors:	1
Other fee-earners:	3

WORKLOAD	
Litigation, licensing and employment	40%
Company/ commercial	40%
Property	20%

CONTACTS	
Company/ commercial	Paul Wilson
	Sheldon Cordell
Employment	Claire Davies
Licensing and leisure	David Clifton
Litigation	David Clifton
	Claire Davies
Property	Paul Baglee

JOHN BATTERS AND COMPANY Craigie Hall, 6 Rowan Road, Glasgow, G41 5BS **Tel:** (0141) 427 6884 **Fax:** (0141) 427 7909 **Ptnrs:** 1. Recently established practice specialising in licensing (liquor and gaming) and commercial conveyancing.

JOHN BOYLE The Square, 5 West End, Redruth, Cornwall, TR15 2SB **Tel:** (01209) 213507 **Fax:** (01209) 219470 **Ptnrs:** 2 **Asst Solrs:** 2 **Other Fee-earners:** 3. A niche criminal practice formed in 1986 which handles its own Crown Court advocacy. Mainly legal aid work.

WORKLOAD			
Crime	65%	Personal injury	15%
Matrimonial/ children	15%	Conveyancing	5%

JOHN HODGE & CO 27-31 Boulevard, Weston-super-Mare, Avon, BS23 1NY **Tel:** (01934) 623511 **Fax:** (01934) 418210 **DX:** 8403 **Ptnrs:** 9 **Asst Solrs:** 6 **Other Fee-earners:** 7. A general practice with five offices covering North Somerset, South Avon and Bristol.

JOHN HOWELL & CO 427-431 London Rd, Sheffield, S. Yorks, S2 4HJ **Tel:** (0114) 250 1000 **Fax:** (0114) 250 0656 **DX:** 10584 **Ptnrs:** 12 **Asst Solrs:** 17 **Other Fee-earners:** 11. Best known for crime, matrimonial and conveyancing work. Also has a Spanish property department in association with a firm in Spain.

JOHN McKEE & SON

53 ROYAL AVENUE, BELFAST, BT1 1TH
DX: 470 NR Belfast

TEL: (01232) 232303
FAX: (01232) 230081

THE FIRM: John McKee & Son was established in 1887 and is a well known family firm in the Belfast and North Down areas which, despite its long history, adopts a progressive and modern approach. The firm is best known in the field of litigation, where its personal injury work for insurance companies is particularly well-regarded. The firm has a large commercial practice, and specialises in insolvency, employment work and debt recovery, including mortgage repossession, and consumer credit, acting mainly for corporate clients and insolvency practitioners.

CONTACT PARTNER: Lex Ross

Number of partners:	4
Assistant solicitors:	6
Other fee-earners:	1

JOHN PICKERING & PARTNERS 9 Church Lane, Oldham, Lancs, OL1 3AN **Tel:** (0161) 633 6667 **Fax:** (0161) 626 1671 **DX:** 23616 **Ptnrs:** 2. Niche practice which concentrates almost entirely on personal injury claims (plaintiff-orientated). Specialists in industrial disease compensation.

JOHNS ELLIOT 11 Lombard Street, Belfast, BT1 1RG **Tel:** (01232) 326881 **Fax:** (01232) 248236 **DX:** 419 NR Belfast **Ptnrs:** 7 **Asst Solrs:** 4 **Other Fee-earners:** 4. A commercially orientated firm, also handling private client work. Particular strengths are commercial property and construction litigation and arbitration.

WORKLOAD			
Company/ commercial	45%	Litigation	25%
Probate and tax	15%		

THE JOHNSON PARTNERSHIP Cannon Courtyard, Long Row, Nottingham, Notts, NG1 6JE **Tel:** (0115) 941 9141 **Fax:** (0115) 947 0178 **DX:** 10082 **Ptnrs:** 7 **Asst Solrs:** 3 **Other Fee-earners:** 12. The firm is predominantly a criminal practice and has a wide range of expertise within this field. Matrimonial and child care work is also undertaken.

WORKLOAD			
Criminal	95%	Matrimonial and family	5%

JOHNSONS 36 Arthur Street, Belfast, BT1 4GG **Tel:** (01232) 240183 **Fax:** (01232) 249239 **DX:** 405 NR Belfast **Ptnrs:** 3 **Asst Solrs:** 6 . Long established legal practice in Northern Ireland. Originally a family firm, it has expanded to offer a comprehensive, personal and professional legal service to both commercial and private clients.

JOHNSTON & HERRON George Johnston House, Bank Street, Lochgelly, Fife, KY5 9QN **Tel:** (01592) 780421 **Fax:** (01592) 782726 **Ptnrs:** 2 **Asst Solrs:** 1 **Other Fee-earners:** 3. General practice offering specialist advice on licensing matters.

JOHN GAUNT & PARTNERS Omega Court, 372 Cemetery Road, Sheffield, S. Yorks, S11 8FT **Tel:** (0114) 266 8664 **Fax: Ptnrs:** 3 **Other Fee-earners:** 1. General practice offering specialist advice on licensing matters.

WORKLOAD			
Liquor licensing	40%	Landlord and tenant	20%
Commercial property	20%	Commercial litigation	20%

JONATHAN S. LAWTON 4 Oxford Court, Manchester, M2 3WQ **Tel:** (0161) 236 6552 **Fax:** (0161) 236 8713 **DX:** 18564 Manchester 7 **Ptnrs:** 1 **Asst Solrs:** 1 . Niche practice specialising in road traffic and employment law. Environmental and planning law also handled.

WORKLOAD			
Road traffic comm vehicle 60%		Emp/ind tribunals	35%
Environmental law/other	5%		

JONATHAN STEPHENS & CO Ty Cornel, 11 Castle Parade, Usk, Gwent, NP5 1AA **Tel:** (01291) 673344 **Fax:** (01291) 673575 **DX:** 32552 Usk **Ptnrs:** 1 **Asst Solrs:** 1 . Best known for agricultural work. Also handles probate and conveyancing.

WORKLOAD			
Agricultural law	60%	General practice	40%

JONES AND CASSIDY 220 Ormeau Road, Belfast, BT7 **Tel:** (01232) 642290 **Fax:** (01232) 642297 **Ptnrs:** 2. Specialist employment practice handling the full range of employment work on behalf of private and corporate clients.

WORKLOAD			
Employment	90%	Other incl judic review	10%

JONES MAIDMENT WILSON

5 BYROM STREET, MANCHESTER, M3 4PF
DX: 14372

TEL: (0161) 832 8087
FAX: (0161) 835 3123

THE FIRM: Jones Maidment Wilson is one of the leading North West law practices, which since its foundation in 1977 has established a significant reputation in litigation, criminal, family, company and commercial property and private client work. The practice is committed to an ambitious programme of expansion to ensure its continued development and success in future years.

PRINCIPAL AREAS OF WORK:

Company and Commercial: (*Contact:* Jim Banfi. *Fee-earners:* 8). This rapidly expanding department undertakes all aspects of company and commercial work including site acquisitions and assembly, disposals, takeovers and mergers, banking and finance, partnerships, joint ventures and company formations. The practice has established a particular reputation in relation to superstore developments.

Litigation: (*Contact:* Bill Jones. *Fee-earners:* 8). This department has grown considerably in recent years and covers all types of commercial and private litigation. As with other departments, work is undertaken on a partner-led team basis to ensure quality, service and efficiency.

Crime: (*Contact:* Peter Grogan. *Fee-earners:* 16). The firm has one of the largest crime practices in the North West and a substantial reputation for advocacy in criminal and commercial fraud cases.

Family: (*Contact:* John McGoldrick. *Fee-earners:* 10). This department is now one of the largest of its kind in the North West and five solicitors have now been appointed to the Children Panel. The department caters for all types of children cases including care and adoption cases, divorce, injunctions and matrimonial finance.

Private Client: (*Contact:* Ged Wilson. *Fee-earners:* 8). This department provides advice in respect of all matters in connection with the individual's financial and property affairs including taxation, planning, wills, trusts and probate and residential conveyancing. The practice is also active in the fields of financial services and sales and rentals of City Centre residential property.

OTHER OFFICES: (*Contact:* Paul Walker). Market Place, 20-24 Church Street, Altrincham. *Tel:* (0161) 926 9663. *Fax:* (0161) 926 8331. *DX:* 29104 Altrincham.

CONTACT PARTNER: Bill Jones

Number of partners:	10
Assistant solicitors:	14
Other fee-earners:	52

WORKLOAD	
Litigation/crime	34%
Company/commercial	30%
Family	19%
Private client	17%

CONTACTS	
Company/commercial	Jim Banfi
Crime	Peter Grogan
Family	John McGoldrick
Litigation	Bill Jones
Private client	Ged Wilson

JONES MYERS Pearl Chambers, 22 East Parade, Leeds, W. Yorks, LS1 5BZ **Tel:** (0113) 246 0055 **Fax:** (0113) 246 7446 **DX:** 14080 Leeds Park Square **Ptnrs:** 2 **Asst Solrs:** 1 . An established niche practice dealing in matrimonial and child care work.

WORKLOAD			
Family law and care	85%	Conveyancing	10%
Wills	3%		

JULIAN HOLY 31 Brechin Place, London, SW7 4QD **Tel:** (0171) 370 5443 **Fax:** (0171) 244 7371 **DX:** 35765 South Ken. **Ptnrs:** 12 **Asst Solrs:** 9 **Other Fee-earners:** 8. Best known for its commercial property practice. Also handles commercial litigation and company/ commercial matters.

WORKLOAD			
Commercial property	60%	Litigation	20%
Company/ commercial	10%	Res convey/wills/trusts	5%
Financial services	5%		

KANAAR & CO 6-8 James Street, London, W1M 5HN **Tel:** (0171) 495 6060 **Fax:** (0171) 495 3770 **DX:** 9022 West End **Ptnrs:** 1 **Asst Solrs:** 3 **Other Fee-earners:** 2. A traditional legal practice handling all music industry contracts and litigation.

WORKLOAD			
Contract	30%	Litigation	30%
Commercial/res convey	20%	Copyright	20%

KAUFMAN KRAMER SHEBSON 21 Dorset Square, London, NW1 6QW **Tel:** (0171) 262 4511 **Fax:** (0171) 262 8603 **DX:** 41716 Marylebone 2 **Ptnrs:** 7 **Asst Solrs:** 4 **Other Fee-earners:** 1. Established in 1957 and has continued to grow without mergers. Best known for commercial conveyancing, banking, property-related litigation, and probate.

KEEBLE HAWSON

OLD CATHEDRAL VICARAGE, ST. JAMES' ROW, SHEFFIELD, S. YORKS, S1 1XA
DX: 10527

| TEL: | (0114) 272 2061 |
| FAX: | (0114) 270 0813 |

THE FIRM: Well known for its company and commercial services and commercial property work, particularly in relation to development and construction, and financing. The firm also has an extensive litigation base whose clients include a number of insurance companies and trade union work.

CONTACT PARTNER: Mr J.M. Kilner	
Number of partners:	12
Assistant solicitors:	5
Other fee-earners:	11

KEELY SMITH & JOBSON

28 DAM STREET, LICHFIELD, STAFFS, WS13 6AA
DX: 19005

| TEL: | (01543) 414222 |
| FAX: | (01543) 258469 |

THE FIRM: A commercial law practice specialising in the provision of a wide range of legal services to companies and businesses. The firm is composed predominantly of company and commercial lawyers and provides a level of expertise and service generally expected of large 'City' firms. In addition to company work the firm is involved in commercial property work, employment law, intellectual property law, banking and insolvency and commercial litigation. There are also departments dealing with matrimonial disputes, personal injury claims and trust and probate services. The firm is a member of LawNet and operates the LawNet Quality Standard covering all the relevant parts of BS EN ISO 9000.

RECRUITMENT: The firm is particularly keen to attract high quality trainee solicitors.

CONTACT PARTNER: Mr S.M. Keely	
Number of partners:	10
Assistant solicitors:	11
Other fee-earners:	11

CONTACTS	
Commercial/ company	Tim Jobson
Commercial litigation	Heather Bell, Peter Lax
Property	John Parkes

KEENE MARSLAND 37 Artillery Lane, Bishopsgate, London, E1 7LT **Tel:** (0171) 375 1581 **Fax:** (0171) 375 0318 **DX:** 179 London City **Ptnrs:** 7 **Asst Solrs:** 3 **Other Fee-earners:** 2. A general practice handling commercial work and private client including family law. The firm acts for a number of sporting associations and charities.

J. KEITH PARK & CO Claughton House, 39 Barrow Street, St. Helens, Merseyside, WA10 1RX **Tel:** (01744) 30933 **Fax:** (01744) 451442 **DX:** 19451 **Ptnrs:** 2 **Asst Solrs:** 24 **Other Fee-earners:** 34. A general practice with substantial personal injury and medical negligence departments. Also handles family, crime and commercial litigation.

KELLER PINNEY 7 St Andrews Crescent, Cardiff, S. Glam, CF1 3DA **Tel:** (01222) 221600 **Fax:** (01222) 221900 **Ptnrs:** 2. General practice best known for personal injury, employment, commercial and construction matters.

WORKLOAD			
Construction/civ eng	30%	Personal injury/med neg	30%
Company/ commercial	20%	General litigation	10%
Priv/wills/trusts/convey	10%		

E. & L. KENNEDY 72 High Street, Belfast, BT1 2BE **Tel:** (01232) 232352 **Fax:** (01232) 233118 **Ptnrs:** 3. Best known for the range and volume of its licensing work.

WORKLOAD			
Conveyancing	40%	Litigation	40%
Licensing	20%		

J.P. KENNEDY & CO 42 Southwick St, London, W2 1JQ **Tel:** (0171) 724 4707 **Fax:** (0171) 724 6641 **Ptnrs:** 1 **Asst Solrs:** 2 . Small firm known for its entertainment practice.

WORKLOAD	
Music ind and related	100%

KENNEDYS

LONGBOW HOUSE, 14-20 CHISWELL ST, LONDON, EC1Y 4TY
DX: 46628 Barbican

TEL: (0171) 638 3688
FAX: (0171) 638 2212

THE FIRM: Kennedys is a well established City commercial practice which is particularly well known for its insurance litigation work. The firm has experienced rapid organic growth in recent years and although it is a City practice acting for commercial clients, it still maintains a friendly and informal atmosphere. Kennedys also has a reputation for internationl work, especially in Europe.

PRINCIPAL AREAS OF WORK:

Insurance Litigation: *Work includes:* professional indemnity, (especially architects, surveyors, engineers, accountants, financial intermediaries and medical profession) directors' and officers' liability, product liability, employers' liability, motor (and personal injury generally), contractors' all risks, fire and property, fine art and jewellery, performance bonding and fidelity, political and credit risks and reinsurance.

Commercial Litigation: *Work includes:* banking and finance, international trade, commercial arbitration, goods in transit (including marine cargo), employment, consumer credit and general commercial litigation.

Commercial Property: This department handles a wide range of property transactions including large commercial and leisure developments, development finance and secured lending for institutions.

Company/ Commercial: *Work includes:* sale and purchase of businesses, company formations, reconstructions and amalgamations, partnership joint venture and shareholders' agreements, licensing, distribution and agency agreements, standard conditions of sale and purchase, and employment. Acquisition and formation of insurance companies. Insurance regulatory work, insolvencies and run-offs. The firm handles an increasing volume of work for EU and other international commercial clients.

Construction Law: This thriving department provides a comprehensive service for architects, consultants and developers in relation to building agreements and terms of engagement and on all aspects of the construction industry.

INTERNATIONAL CONNECTIONS: Kennedys has a strong client base in the USA and in Germany and receives an increasing volume of work from French sources. A substantial part of the firm's commercial work is European-based. Many of the firm's personnel are fluent in French, Spanish or German. Italian and Greek are also spoken. The firm has two in-house lawyers qualified respectively in France and Germany.

OTHER OFFICES: Brentwood (*Contact:* David Scrutton). The firm also has associated offices in New York, San Francisco, Paris, Karachi and Hong Kong.

RECRUITMENT AND TRAINING: The firm is always keen to consider high quality candidates from the UK or oversees, including experienced legal executives. Five or six trainee solicitors are recruited each year with the emphasis being on quality rather than quantity, and prospects for career development are excellent. Knowledge of a major European language, especially German, is an advantage but not essential. A programme of continuing education is provided by the Director of Training. Applications for training contracts will be considered at any time, but applicants are advised to apply in July or August by handwritten letter and typed CV to the Personnel Manager, Marcus Franks.

SENIOR PARTNER: Stephen Cantle

Number of partners:	24
Assistant solicitors:	34
Other fee-earners:	49

WORKLOAD	
Insurance litigation	78%
Commercial/shipping litigation	8%
Company/commercial	5%
Construction (non-contentious)	3%
Consumer credit/debt recovery	3%
Commercial property	2%
Employment	1%

CONTACTS	
Commercial/shipping	Jurgen Schulze
Commercial property	Richard Harris
Company/commercial	James Shaw
Construction (contentious)	Nick Thomas
Construction (non-contentious)	Gina Watson
Consumer credit/debt recovery	John Yates (Brentwood)
Employment	Nick Williams
Insurance	Steve Cantle
Medical negligence	Janet Sayers
Personal injury	David Scrutton (Brentwood)
Reinsurance	Nick Williams

Kennedys

KENNETH BUSH & CO 11 New Conduit St, King's Lynn, Norfolk, PE30 1DG **Tel:** (01553) 692233 **Fax:** (01553) 767318 **DX:** 57802 **Ptnrs:** 10 **Asst Solrs:** 4 **Other Fee-earners:** 7. One of the larger firms in the King's Lynn area, known for personal injury claims, employment law and licensing. Has an increasingly commercial clientele.

KENNETH CURTIS & CO 88 Aldridge Road, Perry Barr, Birmingham, W. Midlands, B42 2TP **Tel:** (0121) 356 1161 **Fax:** (0121) 356 2973 **DX:** 21502 **Ptnrs:** 3 **Asst Solrs:** 2 **Other Fee-earners:** 2. Specialise in licensing law; also handle domestic and commercial conveyancing, family, civil litigation, wills, trusts, probate and crime.

KENNETH ELLIOTT & ROWE

162-166 SOUTH STREET, ROMFORD, ESSEX, RM1 1SX
DX: 4602 Romford

TEL: (01708) 757575
FAX: (01708) 766674

THE FIRM: One of the larger law firms in Essex, Kenneth Elliott & Rowe has enjoyed a period of constant expansion despite the recession and in 1993 opened an office in Baker Street to service its increasing Central London and overseas clientele. In addition to providing expert advice on corporate law, the firm conducts a large amount of private client work and has specialist expertise in such areas as insolvency, employment, personal injury, childcare, welfare law and licensing.

PRINCIPAL AREAS OF WORK:

Commercial Property: *(Contact:* Chris Dixon). A high percentage of work is foreign sourced: especially from the People's Republic of China, India, Iran, Bahrain and Indonesia. The firm has extensive experience of acquisitions and disposals whether by estate development or investment enhancement of large commercial industries and office properties, for a number of major clients. The firm also has particular expertise in commercial landlord and tenant litigation.

Private Client: *(Contact:* David Farr). The firm undertakes a large amount of private client work including wills, probate, onshore and offshore trusts and partnership matters.

Company/ Commercial: *(Contact:* Mark Dixon). All aspects of company/ commercial work are handled from corporate insolvency (dealing with liquidators or directors) to employment law (both contentious and non-contentious, for employer or employee), share option schemes, corporate finance and taxation.

Social and Family Law: *(Contact:* Edward Woodcraft). The firm is socially conscious, is franchised by the Legal Aid Board and has members on both the Child Care and Personal Injury Panel of the Law Society. The department incorporates a specialist welfare law section and undertakes a substantial number of plaintiff medical negligence claims.

NATURE OF CLIENTELE: The firm undertakes work for substantial financial institutions, local authorities, public companies, retail chains, commercial and industrial estate developers and overseas investment clients including state owned enterprises. There is a strong link with Gulf countries, particularly Lebanon and also with India and the People's Republic of China.

LANGUAGES: French, German, Greek, Hindi, Gujerati, Russian, Turkish, Punjabi, Cantonese, Mandarin, Urdu, Arabic.

OTHER OFFICES:
109 Baker Street, London W1M 1FE. *Tel:* (0171) 224 0522; *Fax:* (0171) 224 0546. 3 St. Thomas Road, Brentwood, Essex CM14 4DB. *Tel:* (01277) 261900; *Fax:* (01277) 261885.

CONTACT PARTNER: Chris Dixon

Number of partners:	9
Assistant solicitors:	7
Other fee-earners:	14

WORKLOAD	
Common law	40%
Commercial property	15%
Private client	10%
Company/ insolvency	10%
Landlord and tenant	10%
Commercial litigation	10%
Licensing transport	5%

CONTACTS	
Commercial property	Chris Dixon
Commercial litigation	Mark Dixon
Company insolvency	Mark Dixon
Family/ matrimonial	Edward Woodcraft
Licensing	Beverley Hamblin
Private client	David Farr
Transport	Adam Carr

KENNETH ELLIOTT & ROWE

EDITORIAL POLICY

In this edition, the lists of specialists include profiles of individual practitioners - solicitors and barristers - who have been recommended most frequently to our researchers. Editorial policy is to identify leading practitioners on merit: it is not possible to buy a place in our biographical lists. Inclusion of a profile in this directory is based solely on expertise and reputation.

Enormous effort has been invested by our ten-strong research team (mainly solicitors and barristers) in canvassing recommendations and identifying leaders. We are confident in the overall accuracy of the results. However, mistakes and misjudgements are inevitable, and if readers have any suggestions regarding our listings we should be very pleased to hear from them.

KENT JONES and DONE Churchill House, 47 Regent Rd, Stoke-on-Trent, Staffs, ST1 3RQ **Tel:** (01782) 202020 **Fax:** (01782) 202040 **DX:** 20727 Hanley **Ptnrs:** 11 **Asst Solrs:** 15 **Other Fee-earners:** 14. One of the leading corporate and commercial practices in the West Midlands with particular knowledge of management buy-outs and initiation of commercial deals. Clients range from large private businesses to publicly-quoted companies.

KEOGH RITSON

59 CHORLEY NEW RD, BOLTON, LANCS, BL1 4QP
DX: 25851 Bolton 2

TEL: (01204) 32611
FAX: (01204) 362944

THE FIRM: One of the North West's foremost legal practices, Keogh Ritson offers an unparalleled service in the specialist areas of commercial and corporate work, insurance litigation and commercial litigation. The firm is committed to the highest professional standards, and its specialist skills have attracted many major regional and national clients.

PRINCIPAL AREAS OF WORK:

Insurance Litigation: (Contact: Barry Taziker). The firm is one of the country's leading insurance litigation practices, with experience spanning over 25 years. A strong department has extensive expertise in defendant personal injury litigation and industrial disease and deafness claims and all other areas of insurance litigation, dealing with more than 120 cases every week. The quality of service has attracted an excellent calibre of client including most of the UK's largest liability insurers.

Commercial Department: (Contact: Alan J. Robins). By providing creative and practical solutions to a wide range of complex commercial problems, this progressive department has earned an excellent reputation. Work includes acquisitions and disposals, joint ventures, mergers, employment law, intellectual property, all aspects of commercial property and related planning and environmental matters.

Commercial Litigation: (Contact: Stephen J. Gorman). The firm has a strong reputation for a meticulous yet speedy approach covering all aspects of commercial litigation from professional indemnity and building disputes to debt collection and commercial disputes of any nature.

OTHER AREAS OF WORK: The firm also handles private client matters such as trusts, probate, wills, and domestic conveyancing to the same high professional standards as the commercial aspects of the practice.

CONTACT PARTNER: Barry Taiziker

Number of partners:	15
Assistant solicitors:	26
Other fee-earners:	18

WORKLOAD	
Insurance litigation	70%
Company/ commercial work	15%
Commercial litigation	10%
Private client	5%

CONTACTS	
Commercial property	D.W. Johnson
Commercial litigation	S.J. Gorman
Company/ commercial	A.J. Robins, A. Lewis
Employment	A. Lewis
Insurance litigation	B. Taziker, D.R. Tyson
Matrimonial	A.J. Robins
Private client	A.J. Robins, V. Maharaj
Professional indemnity	S.N. McLoughlin

KERSHAW ABBOTT Queen's Chambers, 5 John Dalton Street, Manchester, M2 6FT **Tel:** (0161) 839 0998 **Fax:** (0161) 839 1019 **DX:** 14348 Manchester 1 **Ptnrs:** 3 **Asst Solrs:** 3 **Other Fee-earners:** 2. A newly-established firm handling personal injury work, commercial litigation, employment law, debt recovery, insolvency, partnership law, professional and medical negligence. Agency work undertaken.

WORKLOAD			
Commercial litigation	50%	Personal injury	35%
Debt litigation	15%		

KETCHEN & STEVENS WS 55-57 Queen Street, Edinburgh, EH2 3PA **Tel:** (0131) 226 4081 **Fax:** (0131) 220 1612 **DX:** 61 Edinburgh **Ptnrs:** 9 **Asst Solrs:** 8 **Other Fee-earners:** 5. Corporate and commercial practice including litigation with a strong private client department.

WORKLOAD			
Commercial litigation	25%	Trust/executry/tax	20%
Commercial property	20%	Domestic property	15%
Company/ commercial	10%	Matrimonial	5%

KIDD RAPINET 14 & 15 Craven Street, London, WC2N 5AD **Tel:** (0171) 925 0303 **Fax:** (0171) 925 0334 **DX:** 2 Ch.Ln. **Ptnrs:** 39 **Asst Solrs:** 7 **Other Fee-earners:** 10. Known for conveyancing, litigation, immigration, matrimonial, company/ commercial. Offices in Aylesbury, Basingstoke, Haslemere, High Wycombe, Maidenhead, Reading and Slough.

KIDSTONS & CO 1 Royal Bank Place, Buchanan Street, Glasgow, G1 3AA **Tel:** (0141) 221 6551 **Fax:** (0141) 204 0507 **DX:** 56 Glasgow **Ptnrs:** 8 **Asst Solrs:** 2 **Other Fee-earners:** 5. An established general practice with particular expertise in litigation (employment and personal injury) and property (commercial and domestic).

WORKLOAD			
Lit (incl insolvency)	40%	Taxation & trust	20%
Commercial property	15%	Corporate	15%
Domestic property	10%		

KIMBELL & CO 352 Silbury Court, Silbury Boulevard, Milton Keynes, Bucks, MK9 2HJ **Tel:** (01908) 668555 **Fax:** (01908) 674344 **DX:** 31408 **Ptnrs:** 4 **Asst Solrs:** 6 . The firm accepts work exculsively from the business sector and has a firmly established reputation in the fields of corporate and commercial law, business property and commercial litigation.

KINGSFORD STACEY 14 Old Square, Lincoln's Inn, London, WC2A 3UB **Tel:** (0171) 242 6784 **Fax:** (0171) 831 2915 **DX:** 141 **Ptnrs:** 13 **Asst Solrs:** 11 **Other Fee-earners:** 9. Combines a large litigation and commercial conveyancing base with an expanding company and commercial practice. Branch offices in London, EC1 and Harpenden.

WORKLOAD			
Commercial litigation	47%	Commercial conveyancing	28%
Priv client/res convey	12%	Company commercial	7%
Licensing	6%		

KINGSLEY NAPLEY

KNIGHTS QUARTER, 14 ST JOHN'S LANE, LONDON, EC1M 4AJ
DX: 22 Ch.Ln.

TEL: (0171) 814 1200
FAX: (0171) 490 2288

THE FIRM: The firm was established over 50 years ago by the late Sir David Napley and the late Mr Sidney Kingsley and rapidly gained a reputation for its civil, commercial and criminal litigation practice. It is now one of the foremost firms in this field, with considerable experience in handling complex and weighty cases, often with an international element.

PRINCIPAL AREAS OF WORK:

General Description: The firm is unusual in Central London in being able to provide advice and assistance across a broad field, including criminal litigation. Whilst its contentious work is well known, a significant proportion of the firm's work is derived from commercial conveyancing, company/ commercial, taxation and allied work.

Litigation: (*Contact:* David Speker). The department's work encompasses commercial and civil litigation, professional misconduct, medical negligence, defamation, immigration, employment, personal injury and building and landlord and tenant disputes. With the increasing complexity of cases, very often there are both civil and criminal implications and the department is experienced in handling both aspects. Two of the partners also undertake licensing work.

Crime: (*Contact:* John Clitheroe). The work covers a broad spectrum from corporate fraud to corruption and drug cases, some of it conducted with the assistance of accountants and other professionals. The firm also advises in extradition matters, general crime and road traffic cases, police enquiries, the majority of the work being of a 'white collar' nature. Members of the firm appear regularly before various regulatory and professional bodies, both prosecuting and defending.

Family: (*Contact:* Pamela Collis). The firm is well known for its family and matrimonial work. Cases range from all issues concerning childcare, through to cohabitation and complex financial matters on divorce.

Company/ Commercial: (*Contact:* Tony Sacker). The department advises on joint ventures, partnerships, finance, taxation, flotations, rights issues, takeovers, insolvency and liquidation, and general 'business' issues.

CONTACT PARTNER: Paul Terzeon

Number of partners:	23
Assistant solicitors:	11
Other fee-earners:	4

WORKLOAD	
Criminal litigation	40%
Civil litigation	28%
Property	15%
Family	10%
Company commercial	7%

CONTACTS	
Commercial litigation	David Speker
Company commercial	Tony Sacker
Criminal litigation	John Clitheroe
Family	Pamela Collis
Medical negligence	Christine Marsh
Property	Francis Weaver

Property: (*Contact:* Francis Weaver). All aspects of conveyancing of commercial freehold and leasehold property undertaken, together with a small amount of residential property work.
NATURE OF CLIENTELE: Varied: from large public companies to all types of successful businesses and individuals.
FOREIGN CONNECTIONS: French, German, Greek and Spanish are spoken.
RECRUITMENT: Two trainee solicitors are recruited each year. Prospects for able candidates are excellent.

KIRBY SIMCOX 111-117 Regent Street, Kingswood, Bristol, BS15 2LJ
Tel: (0117) 961 1451 **Fax:** (0117) 935 2327 **DX:** 43350 **Ptnrs:** 8 **Asst Solrs:** 9
Other Fee-earners: 5. A broadly-based general practice with a local and national contentious and commercial bias. Childrens Panel members. 24 hour criminal defence department. Accident line members.

WORKLOAD			
Commercial/conveyancing	39%	Family & childcare	20%
Criminal defence	15%	Personal injury	10%
Probate/ wills	8%		

KIRK JACKSON 97 Chorley Rd, Swinton, Manchester, M27 2AB
Tel: (0161) 794 0431 **Fax:** (0161) 794 4957 **DX:** 28201 **Ptnrs:** 7 **Asst Solrs:** 2
Other Fee-earners: 3. Best known for litigation and company/ commercial work. Growing emphasis on building/ construction litigation and foreign work (has a working association with a German/ Spanish lawyer).

WORKLOAD			
Construction litigation	22%	Insurance litigation	14%
Commercial property	12%	Probate and trusts	10%
Gen commercial lit	10%	Family	10%

KIRKLAND & ELLIS 199 Bishopsgate, London, EC2M 3TY **Tel:** (0171) 814 6682 **Fax:** (0171) 814 6622. The London branch of this international firm offers specialist advice on arbitration and litigation, corporate finance and a broad range of commercial matters.

KITSONS 2 Vaughan Parade, Torquay, Devon, TQ2 5EF **Tel:** (01803) 296221 **Fax:** (01803) 296823 **DX:** 59203 Torquay **Ptnrs:** 10 **Asst Solrs:** 2 **Other Fee-earners:** 11. An expanding practice with three Devon offices. The firm handles a substantial volume of both commercial and private client work, including legal aid.

KNIGHTS 25 High Street, Tunbridge Wells, Kent, TN1 1UT **Tel:** (01892) 537311 **Fax:** (01892) 526141 **DX:** 3919 Tunbridge Wells **Ptnrs:** 2 **Other Fee-earners:** 3. Litigation practice, specialising in country sports and countryside law, defamation, trespass, judicial review and crime. Client base drawn from the whole of the UK.

WORKLOAD			
Civil litigation	80%	Criminal litigation	20%

KNIGHT & SONS The Brampton, Newcastle-under-Lyme, Staffs, ST5 0QW
Tel:(01782) 619225 **Fax:**(01782) 717260 **DX:** 20952 **Ptnrs:** 15 **Asst Solrs:** 13 **Other Fee-earners:** 24 Established in 1767. Work includes company/ commercial work, commercial property, planning, licensing and agriculture. Broad client base.

KNOWLES BENNING 24 West Street, Dunstable, Beds, LU6 1SN
Tel: (01582) 667711 **Fax:** (01582) 666893 **DX:** 57010 Dunstable **Ptnrs:** 11 **Asst Solrs:** 7 **Other Fee-earners:** 9. An established general practice with three offices in Bedfordshire. Accepts legal aid work.

KUIT, STEINART, LEVY & CO 3 St. Mary's Parsonage, Manchester, M3 2RD **Tel:** (0161) 832 3434 **Fax:** (0161) 832 6650 **DX:** 14325 **Ptnrs:** 11 **Asst Solrs:** 6 **Other Fee-earners:** 8. The firm is principally commercial with company, conveyancing and litigation departments and it also specialises in intellectual property, banking, tax planning and Inland Revenue back duty work.

LACE MAWER

KING'S HOUSE, 42 KING ST WEST, MANCHESTER, M3 2NU	TEL: (0161) 236 2002
DX: 14302	FAX: (0161) 832 7956

Castle Chambers, 43 Castle Street, Liverpool L2 9SG	Tel: (0151) 236 2002
DX: 14159 LIX: Liv 007	Fax: (0151) 236 2585
Contact Partner: Gordon Jeffrey	

THE FIRM: The result of a merger in 1988, Lace Mawer is one of the leading commercial and litigation practices outside London and has an impressive history going back over 250 years. A large and progressive firm, it has experienced constant expansion in recent years and has a client base throughout the country and overseas, ranging from top 100 PLCs through a majority of the major insurance companies in the UK to a number of middle sized companies and trusts.

PRINCIPAL AREAS OF WORK: The firm is known for its litigation practice and has particular experience in civil litigation, personal injury, professional negligence, building disputes, product liability and contractual cases.

A variety of company and commercial work is handled with a particular emphasis on international law. A specialist team deals with EC law matters where the expertise is particularly strong. Lace Mawer is a member of the Association of European Lawyers with correspondent English speaking firms in every country in Eastern and Western Europe. The firm has a strong property department handling commercial and agricultural property and planning work.

An environmental law unit has been practising for several years drawing its expertise from all departments.

Corporate pension work and offshore trusts are two specialities within the private client department which also deals with wills, trusts, probate, tax planning and charity law.

CONTACT PARTNER: A.S. Harper

Number of partners:	40
Assistant solicitors:	37
Other fee-earners:	43

CONTACTS

Commercial property	Sandy Chapple Gill
Commercial litigation	Tony Brook
Company/ commercial	Gordon Jeffrey
Construction	Tony Brook
Debt collection	Mark Benson
Employment	John Henthorn
European Union/ competition	Gordon Jeffrey
Family	Nigel Shepherd
Insurance defendant	Stewart Harper
Litigation	Stewart Harper
Private client	David Bishop
Transport	Martin Harrison

LACEYS 5 Poole Road, Bournemouth, Dorset, BH2 5QL **Tel:** (01202) 557256 **Fax:** (01202) 551925 **DX:** 7605 Bournemouth **Ptnrs:** 7 **Asst Solrs:** 3 **Other Fee-earners:** 7. A comprehensive service to private and corporate clients includes property work, litigation and general financial advice. Also at Winton and Parkstone.

LAMB BROOKS Victoria Hse, 39 Winchester St, Basingstoke, Hants, RG21 1EQ **Tel:** (01256) 844888 **Fax:** (01256) 840427 **DX:** 3000 Basingstoke **Ptnrs:** 11 **Asst Solrs:** 3 **Other Fee-earners:** 10. A broadly-based practice serving the local community, with increasing emphasis on commercial work for Basingstoke businesses. Other office in Odiham.

LAMPORT BASSITT

46 THE AVENUE, SOUTHAMPTON, HANTS, SO17 1AX	TEL: (01703) 634931
DX: 38529 Southampton 3	FAX: (01703) 222346

THE FIRM: The firm operates an expanding and predominantly commercial practice, and places particular emphasis on technical ability and the specialisation and training required to achieve and maintain technical skills.

PRINCIPAL AREAS OF WORK:

Commercial: A wide range of corporate, employment, insolvency, planning, property, and gaming and liquor licensing work.

Litigation: The firm is involved in the full range of litigation work including building disputes, commercial contracts, debt collection, employment disputes, intellectual property matters, maritime law, property disputes, professional negligence, and has a very significant personal injury department.

CONTACT PARTNER: Mr S.P. Kelly

Number of partners:	9
Assistant solicitors:	10
Other fee-earners:	10

CONTACTS

Agricultural & comm. property	J.J. Newton
Commercial litigation	G.N. Lightfoot
Company/ commercial	S.P. Kelly
Construction	R.G.B. Solomon

Private Client: Residential property, personal tax, probate, trusts, wills and matrimonial.

NATURE OF CLIENTELE: Quoted and private companies, insurance companies, unions and trade associations.

RECRUITMENT: A minimum of two trainee solicitors is recruited each year. Enquiries to Mr. D.H. Cooksley, Practice Manager.

Employment & Family	M.J. Laycock
Insolvency	S.P. Kelly
Insurance & Personal injury	G.N. Lightfoot
Licensing and leisure	A.J. Lightfoot
Private client	J.E. Excell

LANE & PARTNERS

46/47 BLOOMSBURY SQUARE, LONDON, WC1A 2RU
DX: 37980 Kingsway

TEL: (0171) 242 2626
FAX: (0171) 242 0387

THE FIRM: Lane & Partners was established in 1974 and is a firm with strong international connections. Before joining it a number of the partners worked for leading City firms. Lane & Partners concentrates on providing a partner-led service at competitive rates commercial clients, covering all the main areas of law of relevance to them. It is well-known for its work in the areas of international arbitration, construction, and aviation law.

PRINCIPAL AREAS OF WORK:

Company and Commercial Law: The firm advises clients on all aspects of company and commercial law, including mergers and acquisitions, joint ventures, Stock Exchange requirements, the Financial Services Act, insolvency and employment law and UK and EC competition law.

Intellectual Property: The firm advises in respect of patent, trade mark and copyright matters, including licensing, franchising, merchandising and all aspects of infringement.

Litigation: The firm is active in all aspects of commercial litigation with particular emphasis on actions in the Commercial Court.

Arbitration: The firm has an active international arbitration practice, with particular emphasis on major construction disputes. It is involved in many ICC Court of Arbitration cases in the capacity of legal advisers to a party or with a member of the firm acting as an arbitrator.

Commercial Property: The firm is involved on behalf of commercial clients in all aspects of property work including the acquisition of freehold and leasehold properties for occupation, investment or development, the sale and management of properties, planning law and appeals and environmental law.

Construction: The firm advises on all aspects of construction law, including the negotiation and preparation of construction contracts, the interpretation of the standard forms used by the industry and the preparation and handling of claims.

Aviation and Travel: The firm advises UK and foreign airlines and also tour operators and travel agents, their business being closely linked to the aviation world. Advice is also given on aviation insurance and liability cases and on aircraft acquisition and leasing transactions.

NATURE OF CLIENTELE: As well as acting for UK companies, the firm has a considerable number of foreign clients, particularly Swedish, American and Japanese companies. In size, they range from well-known multinationals to small private companies. Their businesses are equally diverse, stretching from international construction and heavy engineering to cosmetics, computers and tour operating.

FOREIGN CONNECTIONS: Partners in the firm are also members of the New York partnership of Marks & Murase, with associated offices in Washington D.C., Los Angeles, Tokyo, Dusseldorf, Hamburg, Brussels, Milan, Paris, Stockholm, Lahore, Toronto, Mexico City, Seoul, Oslo, Zurich, Geneva and Vienna. The firm is thus in a position to provide a co-ordinated service in more than one jurisdiction.

LANGUAGES SPOKEN: French and Italian.

RECRUITMENT: One trainee solicitor is taken on per annum and the firm anticipates recruiting additional qualified staff.

CONTACT PARTNER: W.S. Morton

Number of partners:	11
Assistant solicitors:	6
Other fee-earners:	2

WORKLOAD	
Litigation and arbitration	35%
Company/ commercial	28%
Property (commercial)	17%
Aviation and travel	9%
Construction	6%
Intellectual property	5%

CONTACTS	
Arbitration	Terence Lane
Aviation & travel	Richard Venables
Company and commercial	Keith Gallon
Conpany and commercial	William Morton
Construction	Terence Lane, Colin Hall
Intellectual property	Michael Varvill
Litigation	Ludovic de Walden
Property	Richard Hardman, Mark Barber

LANGLEYS

34 SILVER ST, LINCOLN, LINCS, LN2 1ES
DX: 11010

TEL: (01522) 531461
FAX: (01522) 510476

Queen's House, Micklegate, York YO1 1JH
DX:61533

Tel:(01904) 610886
Fax:(01904) 611086

THE FIRM: Langleys, a commercial and family practice with a strong emphasis on litigation, celebrated its centenary year in 1990. The firm is best known for its personal injury and commercial/ domestic conveyancing work. The firm offers a "big city service" at competitive rates and has established connections throughout mainland Europe. Specialist services are provided for farmers, builders, developers and those in the professions and retail, wholesale and manufacturing industries.

PRINCIPAL AREAS OF WORK:

Commercial Department: *(Contact Partner:* John Morgan). *Work includes:* sale and acquisition of businesses, joint ventures, mergers, partnerships, formation, the structure and funding of companies, intellectual property work, licensing, insolvency, commercial debt recovery (handled by a specialist department) and product liability cases.

Commercial Property Department: *(Contact Partner:* Michael Williamson). *Work includes:* the sale, acquisition and disposal of commercial premises, planning and leasehold work, also agricultural work.

Insurance Litigation Department: *(Contact Partner:* David Thompson). The firm is noted for its work representing the risks of many principal insurance companies.
 Work includes: personal injury, medical negligence, professional negligence and other industrial, road, air or sea accident claims.

Family and Matrimonial Department: *(Contact Partner:* Mr Philip Cragg).

OTHER AREAS OF WORK: These include employment law, private client work such as tax planning, wills, probate and trusts as well as matrimonial and family work, welfare and criminal matters, particularly commercial crime. Legal aid work is undertaken.

OTHER OFFICE: North Hykeham.

CONTACT PARTNERS: Mr. J.R. Morgan (Lincoln); Mr M.D. Williamson (York)

Number of partners:	9
Assistant solicitors:	10
Other fee-earners:	28

WORKLOAD	
Accident/ ins (defendant)	36%
Accident/ ins (plaintiff)	14%
Domestic conveyancing	14%
Matrimonial	10%
Common law	5%
Surveys and valuations	3%
Agency and miscellaneous	3%
Criminal	3%
Debt collection	3%
Wills etc	3%
Commercial	3%
Commercial conveyancing	2%
Licensing, tax & finance, lettings & rentals	1%

LANGLEY & CO

199 BISHOPSGATE, LONDON, EC2M 3TY

TEL: (0171) 814 6637
FAX: (0171) 814 6604

THE FIRM: Langley & Co was established in 1993 and specialises exclusively in employment law. Its principals are Dale Langley (who was formerly Head of Employment Law at Ashurst Morris Crisp) and Jill Andrew (who was a Partner and Head of Employment Law at Masons and the London Employment Department of Dibb Lupton Broomhead).

 The firm deals with all aspects of employment law for corporate clients including contentious and non-contentious matters and also acts for individuals in employment disputes. It aims to provide a highly personalised and responsive service geared to the needs of clients. It is pleased to offer competitive fee quotations and also has a range of fixed price services including the conduct of and representation at Industrial Tribunals. Other services which the firm currently provides include bespoke employment law training courses for clients and the legal profession.

CONTACT PARTNER: Dale Langley
Jill Andrew

Number of partners:	2
Other fee-earners:	2

WORKLOAD	
Employment	90%
General commercial advice	10%

LANYON BOWDLER 23 Swan Hill, Shrewsbury, Shrops, SY1 1NN **Tel:** (01743) 236400 **Fax:** (01743) 354994 **Ptnrs:** 17 **Asst Solrs:** 12 **Other Fee-earners:** 20. Handles a wide range of property work – commercial, agricultural, residential – and has a general business and family practice.

WORKLOAD			
Civil litigation	26%	Conveyancing	23%
Family/ matrimonial	15%	Criminal	13%
Commercial	10%	Probate	9%

LARCOMES 168 London Rd, North End, Portsmouth, Hants, PO2 9DN **Tel:** (01705) 661531 **Fax:** (01705) 671043 **DX:** 42401 **Ptnrs:** 7 **Asst Solrs:** 5 **Other Fee-earners:** 10. Experienced in conveyancing, litigation, matrimonial and probate. Other office in Waterlooville. Offers free financial services advice and also runs a legal advice clinic.

LATHAM & WATKINS

ONE ANGEL COURT, LONDON, EC2R 7HJ

TEL: (0171) 374 4444
FAX: (0171) 374 4460

THE FIRM: Latham & Watkins is a United States law firm with eight domestic and threeinternational offices. The lawyers in the London office represent a cross-section of the firm's transactional and regulatory expertise and experience. As client needs dictate, lawyers can also call upon the collective expertise of over 600 Latham & Watkins lawyers practising worldwide in countless disciplines encompassing virtually every aspect of business-related law.

THE LONDON OFFICE: The work undertaken by the London office is approximately 20% corporate and 80% finance and real estate.

LANGUAGES SPOKEN: German and Romanian.

OTHER OFFICES: Los Angeles, New York, Chicago, San Diego, Orange County, New Jersey, Washington DC, San Francisco, Hong Kong and Moscow.

CONTACT PARTNER: William Long

LAWYERS:	
London:	7
Worldwide:	600

LATIMER HINKS

5-8 PRIESTGATE, DARLINGTON, CO. DURHAM, DL1 1NL
DX: 60100

TEL: (01325) 381600
FAX: (01325) 381072

THE FIRM: Latimer Hinks acts for a wide range of clients, both corporate and private, from the Yorkshire Dales, South Durham and Teesside. The firm offers a full range of legal services, including company/ commercial, agricultural, property, civil litigation, matrimonial, employment, trusts, probate, tax, road traffic and crime.

AGENCY: Agency work of all kinds is undertaken.

SENIOR PARTNER: Mr R.W. Hinks

Number of partners:	7
Assistant solicitors:	8
Other fee-earners:	12

LAWFORD & CO Watchmaker Court, 65 St. John's Street, London, EC1M 4HQ **Tel:** (0171) 353 5099 **Fax:** (0171) 353 5355 **DX:** 53311Clerkenwell **Ptnrs:** 13 **Asst Solrs:** 15 **Other Fee-earners:** 11. Well-known for employment and personal injury work. Specialises also in aviation, education, immigration/ nationality and family law. Offices in Richmond, Manchester and Nottingham.

LAWGROUP UK

ORBITAL HOUSE, 85 CROYDON ROAD, CATERHAM, SURREY, CR3 6PD
DX: 36806 Caterham

TEL: (01883) 341341
FAX: (01883) 340066

NATURE OF GROUP: LawGroup UK is the national network of quality firms of solicitors. It has 84 member firms at present but is seeking to increase this number to around 90.

LawGroup UK is committed to improving the performance of member firms. Minimum quality standards exist for members. An annual audit is carried out to ensure that high standards are achieved and maintained, based on the Practice Management Standards. In addition, projects assisting with ISO 9001, Investors In People and Legal Aid Franchising are regularly undertaken.

Members also benefit from marketing services, publications and newsletters, training, IT advice and group discount schemes.

MANAGING DIRECTOR: Peter Collier

Number of partners:	775
Other fee-earners:	3175
Total Staff:	4000

LAWRENCE GRAHAM

190 STRAND, LONDON, WC2R 1JN
DX: 39

TEL: (0171) 379 0000
FAX: (0171) 379 6854

THE FIRM: Lawrence Graham is one of the oldest firms of solicitors practising in England and advises on all aspects of English corporate and private client law and European Community law. It is a member of an association of leading European law firms, Associated Business Lawyers in Europe (ABLE), and is associated with a leading US securities and property law firm, Rosenman & Colin. The firm's established shipping practice operates from a separate office in St Mary Axe.

The firm handles all aspects of legal work with particular strengths in:
- corporate law including corporate finance;
- commercial property;
- commercial, insurance, property and shipping litigation; and
- tax planning.

It is also well known for its private client practice.

PRINCIPAL AREAS OF WORK:

Commercial Property: (*Contact:* Michael Duffy/ Paul Kinsella. *14 Partners). Work includes:* all commercial property matters, conveyancing, leaseholds, new developments, business parks and shopping centres, construction and building law, planning, environmental, property finance and securitisation. The firm acts for some of the largest institutional investors in property and some of the most progressive property developers. There is also a local public authority unit which advises on contracting out and externalisation of services including large scale transfers to housing associations.

Company and Commercial: (*Contacts:* Michael Richardson and Charles Wilkinson. *16 Partners).* The department acts for banks, stock brokers and other financial institutions. *Work includes:* corporate finance transactions, flotation and Stock Exchange work, investment fund work, Financial Services Act regulation, banking, pensions, intellectual property and competition law, insolvency and energy law, EC law and many types of commercial contracts, including employment and share option schemes. The department also advises on all aspects of law affecting sporting and leisure industries. The department has a large US client base.

Insurance/ Commercial/ Property Litigation: (*Contact:* Michael Edwards/ Bill Richards/ Penny Francis. *13 Partners). Work includes:* a balance of commercial litigation in conjunction with the company and commercial department, insurance and reinsurance matters including personal injury work, and of property litigation in conjunction with the commercial property department.

Shipping (*Contact:* Gavin Purser/ Roger Cooper. *6 Partners). Work includes:* the full range of maritime law including charterparties, contractual matters, marine insurance, collision and salvage, international law and financing.

Taxation: (*Contact:* Martyn Gowar/ Robert Field. *4 Partners). Work includes:* UK and international taxation advice, employee share schemes and cross-border and other tax efficient structuring of commercial transactions.

Private Client: (*Contact:* Hugh Hamilton. *3 Partners). Work includes:* offshore trusts, estate planning and probate, investment services and asset management, personal litigation, matrimonial and private property work including agricultural work.

Recruitment and Training: Applications for trainee solicitors should be made by letter and CV to Mr. Clive Ince. Training is considered of major importance and in-house training programmes are undertaken. The firm also has a social club and a fitness centre.

CONTACT PARTNER: Martyn Gowar

UK:	
Number of partners:	55
Assistant solicitors:	59
Other fee-earners:	32
INTERNATIONAL:	
Number of Partners:	55
Assistant Solicitors:	63
Other fee-earners:	53

WORKLOAD	
Litigation/ shipping	38%
Commercial property	28%
Company/ commercial	22%
Private client and tax	12%

CONTACTS	
Commercial property	Michael Duffy
Company and commercial	M Richardson
	C Wilkinson
Litigation	Michael Edwards
Private client and tax	Martyn Gowar
Shipping	Gavin Purser and Roger Cooper

LAWRENCE GRAHAM

LAWRENCE JONES

SEA CONTAINERS HOUSE, 20 UPPER GROUND, BLACKFRIARS BRIDGE,
LONDON, SE1 9LH   DX: 44304 Southwark

TEL: (0171) 620 1311
FAX: (0171) 620 0860

THE FIRM: Lawrence Jones is a City firm with an unusually strong international client base particularly based in the Pacific Rim and India. The firm also acts for a wide range of UK clients, from public companies to small businesses. Lawrence Jones offers a traditional personal service linked to a realistic appreciation of its clients' commercial and personal requirements. It is committed to Europe through its membership of Eulex-IPG a European grouping of lawyers, tax consultants and accountants.

PRINCIPAL AREAS OF WORK:

Company: (*Contact:* Nicola Fincham). Work covers the full spectrum of corporate procedure and practice, both nationally and internationally, from incorporation, restructuring, takeovers, mergers, joint ventures and disposals, business expansion schemes and other methods of raising capital, to employment law, directors' liabilities, pension schemes and insolvency work. Advice is also given to foreign companies on developing their businesses in the UK and related relocation of staff including tax and immigration problems.

Commercial, Shipping and Aviation: (*Contact:* Michael Offer). *Work includes:* distribution and agency agreements; cross frontier supply agreements; counter trade arrangements and industrial or commercial projects (including turnkey), within and outside the United Kingdom. The Commercial Department has a broadly-based media practice, concentrating on television. The firm acts for UK and overseas terrestrial and satellite broadcasters and independent television and video producers. The firm deals with production and distribution contracts, all aspects of intellectual property, satellite leasing, cable licensing, regulatory and compliance matters and media-related litigation (*Contact:* Richard Howard).

Lawrence Jones also has expertise in aviation and shipping work specialising in the purchase and leasing (operational and financing) of aircraft (often with the Banking Department) and general aviation work.

Banking: (*Contact:* Lyndsay Brown). Lawrence Jones advises on all aspects of finance and credit, including financial instruments, securities, syndicated loans and swap agreements and trade finance, particularly documentary credit transactions. It has been involved in the incorporation and acquisition of banks for overseas clients and the setting up of branches of overseas banks in London.

Property: (*Contact:* Colin Clark). The firm has a strong commercial property department and is involved in all aspects of the process from initial planning stage to completion, particularly in relation to retail developments and banks. *Work includes:* landlord and tenant matters, funding and mortgaging, planning appeals, licensing and tax considerations, over a wide range of projects from offices, supermarkets, leisure complexes, warehouses and hotels, to commercial and residential estates and investment property.

Litigation: (*Contact:* David Smets). A wide variety of substantial commercial litigation and arbitration is handled at all levels, with many cases involving foreign parties or more than one jurisdiction. *Work includes:* banking cases, international trade and transport disputes, insurance, construction, landlord and tenant matters, intellectual property, personal injury, employment disputes and insolvency work.

Transport: (*Contact:* Michael Kemlo). Lawrence Jones has long had close connections with the transport industry and handles freight forwarding, insurance and cargo claims.

FOREIGN LANGUAGES: French, German, Gujerati, Hindi and Punjabi.

SENIOR PARTNER: Michael Waugh

Number of partners:	12
Assistant solicitors:	7
Other fee-earners:	5

WORKLOAD	
Company/ commercial	37%
Property	29%
Banking	19%
Litigation	15%

CONTACTS	
Aviation	Michael Offer
Banking	Lyndsay Brown
Company/ commercial	Nicola Fincham
Insolvency	Michael Conaghan
Litigation	David Smets
Media	Richard Howard
Property	Michael Waugh

LAWRENCE TUCKETTS

BUSH HOUSE, 72 PRINCE STREET, BRISTOL, BS99 7JZ
DX: 7830 Bristol

TEL: (0117) 929 5252
FAX: (0117) 929 8313

THE FIRM: A progressive, expanding practice, the firm acts as business advisers to a wide variety of clients, corporate and unincorporated, whilst maintaining a strong private client department. Particular strengths are in company and commercial work, litigation, property, planning and environmental banking, litigation and insolvency.

Lawrence Tucketts is the first law firm in the South West to have achieved ISO 9001 (BS5750), the international standard of quality assurance. The firm is a member of Quality Law Group (QLG) and European Law Firm (ELF).

OTHER OFFICES: 1 Bank Road, Kingswood, Bristol.
Tel: (0117) 967 7591. *Fax:* (0117) 935 2991. *DX:* 43357 Kingswood.

FOREIGN LANGUAGES: French, German, Spanish, Italian and Russian.

CONTACT PARTNER: Sir Richard Gaskell

Number of partners:	14
Assistant solicitors:	23
Other fee-earners:	8

WORKLOAD	
Litigation	51%
Commercial property and planning	23%
Commercial and corporate	14%
Private client	12%

LAWSON COPPOCK & HART

18 TIB LANE, CROSS ST, MANCHESTER, M2 4JA
DX: 14370

TEL: (0161) 832 5944
FAX: (0161) 834 4409

THE FIRM: This centrally located firm, one of Manchester's oldest, concentrates on company/ commercial work including European law. Expertise extends to other areas, notably probate, wills, trusts, pensions and commercial property. The firm also specialises in protecting suppliers of consumer goods and provides a debt recovery service. Contentious work includes property, general commercial and specialist trademark and copyright litigation.

CONTACT PARTNER: Mr R. Rawsthorn

Number of partners:	8
Assistant solicitors:	1
Other fee-earners:	3

LAW SOUTH

117B GUILDFORD STREET, CHERTSEY, SURREY, KT16 9AF
DX: 48259 Chertsey

TEL: (01932) 560902
FAX: (01932) 571250

CONTACT: Christina Myers

NATURE OF GROUP: Law South is a group of ten independent law firms, comprising 53 offices, 575 lawyers and 1500 staff, spread throughout the South East of England. Formed in 1988, the Group's major objective is the establishment of inter-firm networks to provide collective resources for training, marketing and pooled legal expertise, thus ensuring a consistently high standard of service throughout the region. To this end, a training programme of legal and management skills is established and specialist groups operate in key areas of law.

All firms within the Group offer the fullest range of services to corporate and private clients.

MEMBER FIRMS:
Barlows: (Guildford and Surrey) 11 partners, 75 staff.
Blake Lapthorn: (Portsmouth, London and Hampshire) 30 partners, 290 staff.
Brachers: (Maidstone & London) 16 partners, 112 staff.
Brain & Brain: (Reading and Basingstoke) 14 partners, 85 staff.
Donne Mileham & Haddock: (Brighton and East Sussex) 31 partners, 235 staff.
Girlings: (Canterbury and East Kent) 24 partners, 120 staff.
Leigh Williams: (Bromley and North Kent) 10 partners, 85 staff.
Thomas Eggar Verrall Bowles: (Chichester, Worthing and West Sussex) 31 partners, 210 staff.
Thomson Snell & Passmore: (Tunbridge Wells and Mid-Kent) 37 partners, 170 staff.
White & Bowker: (Winchester and Hampshire) 16 partners, 95 staff.

LAYTONS

CARMELITE, 50 VICTORIA EMBANKMENT, BLACKFRIARS, LONDON, EC4Y 0LS
DX: 253 Chancery Lane

TEL: (0171) 842 8000
FAX: (0171) 842 8080

WORK UNDERTAKEN: Laytons is a commercial firm with four principal offices. Client-driven, its broad services are reinforced by particular legal fields, including corporate finance; commercial contracts; land development; human resources; intellectual property; construction; commercial litigation and arbitration; insolvency and debt recovery; personal injury; defamation; charities and private client services.

PRINCIPAL OFFICES:
BRISTOL – Saint Bartholomews, Lewins Mead, Bristol BS1 2NH.
Tel: (0117) 929 1626.
HAMPTON COURT – 76 Bridge Road, Hampton Court, East Molesey, Surrey KT8 9HF. Tel: (0181) 941 0622.
MANCHESTER – 22 St. John Street, Manchester M3 4EB.
Tel: (0161) 834 2100.

CONTACT PARTNER: Richard Kennett

Number of partners:	25
Assistant solicitors:	35
Other fee-earners:	21

WORKLOAD	
Company/ commercial	32%
General litigation	18%
Commercial property/ land development	18%
Building litigation	13%
Employment	7%
Insolvency	7%
Other including private client/ trusts	5%

LEA & COMPANY Bank Chambers, Market Place, Stockport, Ches, SK1 1UN **Tel:** (0161) 480 6691 **Fax:** (0161) 480 0904 **DX:** 19651 **Ptnrs:** 1 **Other Fee-earners:** 2. A general practice with particular expertise in entertainment law, but also undertaking company, commercial, litigation and conveyancing work.

WORKLOAD			
Civil litigation	35%	Media and entertainment	30%
Prop (comm/domestic)	25%	Company/ partnership	7%
Others	3%		

LEATHES PRIOR

74 THE CLOSE, NORWICH, NORFOLK, NR1 4DR
DX: 5205 Norwich

TEL: (01603) 610911
FAX: (01603) 610088

THE FIRM: Leathes Prior is a 14 partner firm which has grown from its traditional private client base to establish itself as a broad–based progressive practice, with a commitment to providing a high quality service and with a growing reputation in particular specialist areas.

PRINCIPAL AREAS OF WORK: In addition to the firm's established reputation in the areas of insolvency, franchising, international and personal injury/ insurance law, the other areas of work upon which it puts particular emphasis include company matters, banking, commercial litigation and property, debt recovery, defamation, EC law, overseas property, intellectual property, planning, landlord and tenant, employment law and immigration. The firm also has a legal aid practice with particular emphasis on crime, matrimonial, child care and civil liberties.

The firm has a personal Financial Planning Department enabling it ot offer a range of financial services. It is a member of the Quality Law Group and an affiliate member of the British Franchise Association.

FOREIGN CONNECTIONS: Leathes Prior is a member of the EU-LEX International Practice Group, a network of European law firms with member firms throughout the EC. The firm also has close contact with lawyers in Russia, Eastern Europe, the USA, Australia and the Far East. Languages include French, Flemish, German, Punjabi, Turkish and Dutch.

OTHER OFFICES: Canada House, 4 Grammar School Rd, North Walsham, Norfolk NR28 9JJ.
7 Southampton Place, London WC1A 2DR.

CONTACT PARTNERS: Gavin Wilcock/ Jonathan Chadd

Number of partners:	14
Assistant solicitors:	13
Other fee-earners:	11

CONTACTS	
Charitable trusts	William Riley
Civil liberties/ immigration	Tim Cary
Commercial property	Gavin Wilcock
Corporate/ commercial	Paul Warman
Crime	Trevor Beckford
Employment/ litigation	Martin Plowman
Franchising/ IP	Jonathan Chadd
Insolvency/ banking	Peter Nicholls
International	Jonathan Chadd
Matrimonial/ family	Ros Thickett, Ian Denning
Personal injury/ insurance	Tim Cary
Planning/ environmental	Jonathan Chadd
Private client	William Riley, Trent Hobden

LE BOEUF LAMB GREENE & MACRAE

2 SUFFOLK LANE, LONDON, EC4R 0AT

TEL: (0171) 626 3000
FAX: (0171) 626 2623

THE FIRM: LeBoeuf, Lamb, Greene & MacRae is a multinational partnership affiliated with LeBoeuf, Lamb, Greene & MacRae L.L.P., a United States law firm with over 500 lawyers in 13 domestic and 4 international offices. The lawyers in the London office include English solicitors and U.S. lawyers and represent a cross-section of the firm's clientele in corporate, litigation and regulatory matters. Close coordination is maintained between the lawyers in the London office and those in other LeBoeuf offices so that the full resources of the firm may be called upon to assist clients in virtually every aspect of the law.

CONTACT PARTNERS:
James F. Johnson, 4th and Peter J. Sharp

LAWYERS:	
London:	10
Worldwide:	500

PRINCIPAL AREAS OF WORK:

General Description: The London office principally serves clients in the insurance, banking and energy industries. A full range of legal services, including civil litigation, U.S., U.K. and E.C. insurance regulation, corporate/commercial, project finance, insolvency and banking regulation, are provided.

Insurance and Reinsurance: (*Contact Partners:* James F. Johnson, 4th; Peter J. Sharp). U.S., U.K. and E.C. regulatory and litigation matters of all types.

Civil/Commercial Litigation: (*Contact Partner:* Peter J. Sharp). Litigation, arbitration and alternative dispute resolution of all types, including transnational and in particular U.S./U.K. disputes.

Energy/Utilities/Project Finance: (*Contact Partners:* Alan Jones; Garry Pegg). Electricity, oil and gas transactional and advisory matters; regulatory advice; privatisations and major international project work.

Corporate/Commercial: (*Contact Partners:* Alan Jones; Garry Pegg). Corporate mergers and acquisitions, joint ventures and general corporate finance/commercial advice.

Banking: (*Contact Partners:* Peter J. Sharp; Alan Jones). Litigation and general banking advisory matters.

Insolvency: (*Contact Partners:* James F. Johnson, 4th; Peter J. Sharp). All matters involving insolvencies in the U.S., U.K. and E.C. including in particular insurance insolvency.

Foreign Offices: LeBoeuf, Lamb, Greene & MacRae L.L.P. has offices in the United States in New York, Washington D.C., Albany, Boston, Denver, Harrisburg, Hartford, Jacksonville, Los Angeles, Newark, Pittsburgh, Salt Lake City, San Francisco, and elsewhere in Brussels, Moscow and Almaty together with working arrangements with local lawyers in numerous other jurisdictions.

LE BRASSEUR J TICKLE

DRURY HOUSE, 34-43 RUSSELL STREET, LONDON, WC2B 5HA
DX: 37985 Kingsway

TEL: (0171) 836 0099
FAX: (0171) 831 2215

6-7 Park Place, Leeds LS1 2RU
DX: 14086 Leeds

Tel: (0113) 234 1220
Fax: (0113) 234 1573

THE FIRM: Le Brasseur J Tickle is the merged firm of Le Brasseurs and J Tickle & Co, both well-known for their expertise in health care law, commercial law, commercial property and litigation. Based in London and Leeds, it is a national firm with strong international connections.

CONTACT PARTNER: Robert Sumerling

Number of partners:	28
Assistant solicitors:	19
Other fee-earners:	7

PRINCIPAL AREAS OF WORK:

Health Care Law: *(Contacts:* Stephen Janisch (London) and Nick Rawson (Leeds)). 10 Partners. 35%). Core services include clinical and dental negligence, criminal and regulatory law, class actions, risk management, mental health and community care law, administrative law and NHS estates.

General and Commercial Litigation: *(Contacts:* Simon Dinnick and Alex Leslie. 5 Partners. 25%). *Work includes:* insurance litigation, employment and partnership disputes, injunctions, breach of contract, defamation, intellectual property protection, debt recovery and mortgage repossessions.

Personal Injury Law: *(Contact:* Christian Dingwall. 3 Partners. 5%). Extensive experience of personal injury litigation and quantum of damages with a team of quality litigators available in Leeds and London. Full review and budgeting system.

Commercial Property: *(Contacts:* Keith Mitchell and Michael Thorniley-Walker (Leeds). 5 Partners. 20%). The firm handles buying, selling and mortgaging institutional and other commercial property investments, NHS land transactions, estate management, and all landlord and tenant work.

Commercial and Business Law: *(Contacts:* Michael Scanlan and Geoffrey Sparkes (London) and Stephen Everett (Leeds). 3 Partners. 15%). *Work includes:* NHS Private Financial Initiatives, financial services, revenue law, intellectual and information technology law, company law, EU law, banking, joint ventures, mergers, acquisitions and disposals. Clients include public corporations, friendly societies and listed companies.

LEDINGHAM CHALMERS 1 Golden Square, Aberdeen, Grampian, AB9 1HA **Tel:** (01224) 408408 **Fax:** (01224) 648265 **DX:** 15 Aberdeen **Ptnrs:** 27 **Asst Solrs:** 32 **Other Fee-earners:** 30. One of the leading commercial practices in Aberdeen. Also strong in private client and estate agency work. Other offices in Edinburgh and Inverness.

LEE BOLTON & LEE

1 THE SANCTUARY, WESTMINSTER, LONDON, SW1P 3JT
DX: 2301 Victoria

TEL: (0171) 222 5381
FAX: (0171) 222 7502

THE FIRM: Established at 1 The Sanctuary in 1855, Lee Bolton & Lee is a predominantly private client practice with a rapidly expanding commercial element. The firm offers extensive experience and advice across a wide spectrum of activities and is associated with a firm of solicitors and Parliamentary agents, Rees and Freres, to provide a specialist service in parliamentary, public and administrative law.

PRINCIPAL AREAS OF LAW:

Private Client: *(Contact:* J.G. Ouvry). The firm provides expert advice on a full range of private client matters including domestic conveyancing, personal taxation and individual financial planning, wills, trusts, probate and the administration of estates. In addition, a separate department handles all aspects of family and matrimonial law.

Ecclesiastical, Education and Charities: *(Contact:* P.F.B. Beesley). As well as general advice on ecclesiastical matters and disciplinary proceedings, the firm advises four diocesan bishops as Registrars. In the education sphere, advice is provided on all matters from establishing a new school to day-to-day operational and employment matters. The firm's charity practice is linked but not confined to its educational and ecclesiastical work and covers all aspects of charity creation, registration and administration including trusts, tax and charitable property.

Corporate Services: *(Contact:* A.O.E. Davies/ G.J. Fountain/ M.D.G. Collins). Advice is provided for clients ranging from established organisations to emerging businesses and entrepreneurs on every aspect of commercial life from company formations, reconstructions, mergers, MBOs, joint ventures, Stock Exchange work, employment law and pensions, banking and financial services, and receiverships and insolvencies. A broad range of commercial property funding, planning and development work is handled for banks, institutional clients, investors and developers.

WORKLOAD

Health care	35%
General and commercial litigation	25%
Commercial property	20%
Commercial and business law	15%
Personal injury	5%

CONTACTS

Commercial property	Michael Thorniley-Walker
	Keith Mitchell
Commercial and business law	Michael Scanlan
	Stephen Everett
General and comm. litigation	Simon Dinnick
	Alex Leslie
Health care	Stephen Janisch
Personal injury	Christian Dingwall

LE BRASSEUR J TICKLE
SOLICITORS AND PRIVY COUNCIL AGENTS

WORKLOAD

Priv client/estate agency	35%	Company/ commercial	20%
Commercial property	20%	Litigation	15%
Int prop/licensing/other	5%	Employment	5%

CONTACT PARTNER: P.F.B. Beesley

Number of partners:	14
Assistant solicitors:	11
Other fee-earners:	14

WORKLOAD

Parliamentary and public law (acting as Rees and Freres)	41%
Ecclesiastical/ charity/ education	20%
Company/ commercial (including commercial property)	17%
Private client	14%
Litigation	8%

CONTACTS

Charities	P.F.Beesley, R.J.Harwood
Commercial property	G.J.Fountain
Company/ commercial	A.O.E.Davies
Ecclesiastical	P.F.Beesley, N.J.Richens
Litigation	J.P.Sergeant

Litigation: (*Contact:* J.P. Sergeant). A thriving litigation department handles a range of matters including general commercial contracts, employment disputes, computer litigation, professional and medical negligence, property building and landlord and tenant disputes, defamation, insurance and personal injury claims and marine litigation. The firm has long standing relations with numerous public bodies and has developed a considerable expertise in the area of judicial review proceedings.

Parliamentary	J.A.Durkin
Private client	J.G. Ouvry
Public law	P.R. Lane, M.A.R. Peto
Railway property	J.Taplin

LEE CROWDER 24 Harborne Rd, Edgbaston, Birmingham, W. Midlands, B15 3AD **Tel:** (0121) 456 4477 **Fax:** (0121) 456 4710 **DX:** 23057 **Ptnrs:** 9 **Asst Solrs:** 8 **Other Fee-earners:** 5. Primarily commercial including property, acquisitions and disposals, Stock Exchange work and litigation. Clients include listed PLCs and institutional estate owners.

LEEDS DAY

6 BEDFORD ROAD, SANDY, CAMBS, SG19 1EN
DX: 47801

TEL: (01767) 680251
FAX: (01767) 691775

THE FIRM: Leeds Day is the leading firm in the A1 Ouse Valley area. It has three offices in Cambridgeshire and two in Bedfordshire, and almost 100 staff. Its progressive approach is reflected in the establishment of two strategically-located Commercial Centres, from which most commercial work, including EC law, is handled. The first centre is now well established at Sandy and their second centre has recently opened in Huntingdon.

PRINCIPAL AREAS OF WORK:

Litigation: (*Contact:* Mike Williams – business). (*Contact:* Ron Metcalfe – private). (*Contact:* Robert Davies – personal injury). (*Fee-earners:* 16). A full spectrum of commercial litigation ranges from property matters, landlord and tenant claims, intellectual property and debt collection, to insolvency, product liability and professional negligence work. The construction section handles building disputes and arbitrations. Civil litigation includes personal injury, family and matrimonial work. Legal aid is available where appropriate.

Company/ Commercial: (*Contact:* Peter Mount. *Fee-earners:* 3). An expanding department handles all commercial matters from the formation of a new business to its eventual sale. *Work includes:* partnership agreements, commercial contracts, mitigation of tax, company formation and reconstruction, take-overs and mergers, EC advice, employment issues, intellectual property and competition law.

Private Client: (*Contact:* Helen Wingfield Fee-earners: 8). The firm has a strong private client base and its work includes: wills, probate, trusts, tax planning, immigration, consumer law, Court of Protection and family work.

Commercial Property: (*Contact:* Brian Hall. *Fee-earners:* 8). The department handles a wide range of activities including: the acquisition, disposal and development of all types of property (freehold and leasehold), planning and environmental matters, financing of transactions, industrial estate development and licensed premises.

Domestic Property: (*Contact:* Bruce Elam. *Fee-earners:* 5). Five computerised conveyancing departments handle domestic sales, purchases, mortgages and remortgages in each of the five offices, for private and corporate clients.

OTHER AREAS OF WORK: The firm has traditional connections with the local farming community, handling agricultural matters such as tenancies, tax planning and share farming; and it has experience of ecclesiastical law, acting for the Diocese of Ely and shrievalty law, acting for the Under Sheriff of Bedfordshire.

RECRUITMENT & TRAINING: One trainee solicitor is recruited annually. Apply by letter and CV to Anthony Long at Sandy office.

OTHER OFFICES: Huntingdon, St. Neots, Biggleswade and St. Ives.

CONTACT PARTNER: A.J. Roberts

Number of partners:	11
Assistant solicitors:	8
Other fee-earners:	22

CONTACTS	
Civil litigation	Ron Metcalfe
Commercial litigation	Mike Williams
Commercial property	Brian Hall
Company/ commercial	Peter Mount
Domestic property	Bruce Elam
Private client	Helen Wingfield

LEE & PEMBERTONS

45 PONT ST, LONDON, SW1X 0BX
DX: 38166 Knightsbridge

TEL: (0171) 589 1114
FAX: (0171) 589 0807

THE FIRM: Established in the late 18th century, Lee and Pembertons is a successful Knightsbridge firm, noted for its substantial property and private client work. In recent years the firm has expanded its practice to offer the full range of corporate and commercial legal services. It has established a reputation for providing a partner led personal service to clients, and there is a commitment to client care and quality management at all levels.

PRINCIPAL AREAS OF WORK:

Property: (*Contact:* Damian Greenish). *Work includes:* acquisitions and disposals of commercial, residential and agricultural properties, agricultural tenancies and farming partnerships, landlord and tenant and Rent Act law, property development, construction law, town and country planning and leasehold enfranchisement.

Private Client: (*Contact:* Richard Cant). *Work includes:* creation, administration and termination of all types of trusts (in particular charitable trusts), wills, probate and the administration of estates, financial services and tax planning, Lloyd's memberships, pensions and life insurance.

Commercial: (*Contact:* Richard Roney). *Work includes:* company formations, acquisitions, sales, mergers and liquidations, purchases and financing of businesses and partnerships, oil and gas projects, service agreements, banking, insurance, gaming and clubs, environmental law, EC law and regulations affecting businesses.

Litigation: (*Contact:* Richard Gambrill). *Work includes:* commercial, landlord and tenant, company, building and intellectual property disputes, planning appeals, insolvency, defamation, professional negligence, personal injury, matrimonial and family law; immigration and nationality matters; alternative dispute resolution.

LANGUAGES SPOKEN: French, Italian, Spanish and Cantonese.

RECRUITMENT: Two trainee solicitors are recruited annually. A full training programme is available including in-house video. Applications with CV to Julian Whately.

CONTACT PARTNER: Julian Whately

Number of partners:	18
Assistant solicitors:	13
Other fee-earners:	11

WORKLOAD	
Property	40%
Private client	35%
Litigation	15%
Commercial	10%

CONTACTS	
Commercial	Richard Roney
Litigation	Richard Gambrill
Private client	Richard Cant
Property	Damian Greenish

LEE & PEMBERTONS

LEE & PRIESTLEY

QUEEN ANNE CHAMBERS, 41-43 SUNBRIDGE RD, BRADFORD,
W. YORKS, BD1 2AS   DX: 11724

TEL: (01274) 727757
FAX: (01274) 729538

Offices at Leeds, Pudsey and Yeadon

THE FIRM: Lee & Priestley is a long-established firm offering a wide range of legal services. It is developing a substantial commercial and insolvency practice in addition to its large private client base.

PRINCIPAL AREAS OF WORK:

Company/ Commercial: (*Contact:* Mr B. Copsey. *Fee-earners:* 4). Company law, mergers and acquisitions, corporate finance, shareholder protection, commercial agreements, partnerships.

Commercial Property: (*Contact:* Mr R.J. Sheard. *Fee-earners:* 4). Sales and acquisitions of commercial property, granting and renewal of leases, planning and environmental law, property development, commercial mortgages.

Litigation: (*Contact:* Mr B. Walker. *Fee-earners:* 7). All private and corporate contentious matters, personal injury, professional negligence, product liability, insolvency, debt recovery.

Private Client: (*Contact:* Mr J.R.M. Priestley. *Fee-earners:* 7). Wills, trusts, probate, taxation, matrimonial and family work including childcare.

CHIEF EXECUTIVE: Mr D.C. Gale

Number of partners:	12
Assistant solicitors:	2
Other fee-earners:	21

WORKLOAD	
Corporate/ commercial	27%
Family law	21%
Litigation	20%
Conveyancing	17%
Trusts and probate	12%
Others	3%

LEE & PRIESTLEY
SOLICITORS

LEES LLOYD WHITLEY

CASTLE CHAMBERS, 43 CASTLE STREET, LIVERPOOL, MERSEYSIDE, L2 9TJ DX: 14164 Liverpool	TEL: (0151) 227 3541 FAX: (0151) 227 2460
397 Woodchurch Road, Prenton, Birkenhead, Merseyside L42 8PF DX: 15503 Prenton	Tel: (0151) 608 6337 Fax: (0151) 608 0624
34 Ely Place, Holborn Circus, London EC1N 6TD DX: 345 Chancery Lane, London	Tel: (0171) 404 6663 Fax: (0171) 404 6665
37/39 Wallasey Road, Wallasey, Merseyside L45 4NN DX: 20054 Wallasey	Tel: (0151) 630 1434 Fax: (0151) 638 0728

THE FIRM: One of the leading law firms in the North West of England with a significant presence in London. The firm offers the expertise to represent clients both regionally and nationally, providing the resources of a large firm coupled with personal attention associated with smaller practices.

PRINCIPAL AREAS OF WORK: Company, Property, Private Client, Industrial Relations, Debt Recovery and Agency.

CONTACT PARTNER: Graham Smith	
Number of partners:	12
Assistant solicitors:	4
Other fee-earners:	26

LEE & THOMPSON Green Garden House, St. Christopher's Place, London, W1M 5HD **Tel:** (0171) 935 4665 **Fax:** (0171) 486 2391 **Ptnrs:** 5 **Asst Solrs:** 5 **Other Fee-earners:** 1. Entertainment law firm; expertise in music, TV, film, entertainment, licensing and general media, company commercial law and commercial litigation.

WORKLOAD			
Music (incl music lit)	50%	TV & film	25%
Lit (other than music)	10%	General commercial	10%
Sport	5%		

LEIGH DAY & CO

51 GRAYS INN ROAD, LONDON, WC1X 8PP DX: 1019	TEL: (0171) 242 1775 FAX: (0171) 831 4740

THE FIRM: A leading firm specialising in all aspects of complex personal injury work and multi-party actions.

PRINCIPAL AREAS OF WORK:

Environmental Department: Specialising in claims as a result of exposure to pollution (radiation, chemicals, pesticides, sewage in the sea) together with industrial disease and nuisance claims. Cases include the childhood leukaemia cases around Sellafield, nuisance claims for Docklands residents and cases against the tobacco industry.

Medical Negligence Department: Concentrates on cases involving serious disabilities or death and acts for many children with brain injuries as well as clients with a wide variety of other iatrogenic injuries. Also specialises in medical devices such as artifical heart valves, pacemakers and silicone breast implants.

Accident Litigation Department: This department deals with a full range of personal injury claims including road traffic accidents, accidents at work and product liability claims. There is a special expertise in horse riding accidents, actions against the MOD and aviation disasters.

Planning Department: The department's clients include local authorities and objectors concerning plan making, development control, enforcement and appeals. It undertakes a large number of cases with an environmental aspect.

CONTACT PARTNER: Martyn Day	
Number of partners:	7
Assistant solicitors:	9
Other fee-earners:	14

CONTACTS	
Accident	Geraldine McCool
Environmental	Martyn Day
Medical negligence	Sarah Leigh
Planning	Richard Stein

LEO ABSE & COHEN

40 CHURCHILL WAY, CARDIFF, S. GLAM, CF1 4SS
DX: 33002

TEL: (01222) 383252
FAX: (01222) 345572

THE FIRM: Established in 1952 by Leo Abse and Isaac Cohen. Leo Abse & Cohen is now a progressive and expanding law firm in South Wales offering a comprehensive range of legal services but with particular emphasis on litigation. The firm was awarded a franchise by the Legal Aid Board in 1994 and is a member of LawGroup UK, the national network of independent law firms.

PRINCIPAL AREAS OF WORK:

Personal Injury Litigation: The firm has an outstanding reputation in plaintiff personal injury litigation and acts for three major trade unions in Wales. The department has teams of specialist lawyers and fee-earners who cover all areas of work including employers' liability claims, industrial disease claims, road traffic claims and medical negligence claims. Legal aid work is undertaken.

Insurance Litigation: The department is considered to be one of the best in Wales acting for several institutional clients. This specialist department deals with all aspects of insurance law, in particular employers' and product liability, material loss, personal injury and Road Traffic Act related litigation.

Banking and Commercial Litigation: All aspects of banking-related contentious work and commercial litigation is dealt with including insolvency, debt collection and contractual disputes arising therefrom, tortious matters, property disputes, injunctions and pre-emptive remedies.

Commercial Property: The department is headed by two partners and deals with estate developments, acquisition, management and disposal of property, building contracts, agricultural property, planning, commercial mortgages and secured lending, licensed premises, environmental law, VAT and property, options and landlord and tenant matters.

Company and Commercial: Areas covered include: intellectual property, employment, insurance, pensions, franchising, liquidations, acquisitions and disposals of businesses, venture capital, joint ventures, taxations, MBOs, directorships and partnerships.

Family/ Matrimonial Law: The firm has considerable expertise in all aspects of family matters and is well known for its work in divorce, separation, legal issues arising from cohabitation disputes and in particular child care proceedings. Legal aid work is undertaken.

Criminal Law: All categories of criminal work are handled but the department has particular experience in large criminal matters including commercial fraud. Legal aid work is undertaken.

OTHER AREAS OF WORK: The firm also offers a comprehensive range of general legal services to private clients including residential conveyancing, probate, trusts and tax law.

SENIOR PARTNER: Mr D. Gareth Jones

Number of partners:	12
Assistant solicitors:	24
Other fee-earners:	13

WORKLOAD	
Plaintiff personal injury	51%
Legal aid (crime, matrimonial and family)	20%
Defendant insurance litigation	13%
Commercial (contentious/non-contentious)	12%
Property/ probate	4%

CONTACTS	
Commercial services	Myles Davies
Insurance services	John Sherratt
Legal aid services	Terry Leyshon
Property/ probate	Michael Lawson
Trades union services	Robin Williams
	Ian Hopkins

LEONARD GRAY 72-74 Duke St, Chelmsford, Essex, CM1 1JY **Tel:** (01245) 251411 **Fax:** (01245) 490728 **DX:** 3309 Chelmsford 1 **Ptnrs:** 6 **Asst Solrs:** 2 **Other Fee-earners:** 5. The firm has a general practice covering commercial and domestic conveyancing, civil litigation, matrimonial, and child care and employment law.

WORKLOAD			
Domestic conveyancing	36%	Civil litigation	33%
Matrimonial	18%	Child care	5%
Commercial conveyancing	5%	Employment	3%

FIRMS OF ACCOUNTANTS

Accountants specialising in litigation support are listed in the accountants' A-Z, with details of the services they offer to solicitors, from forensic accounting to intellectual property or business valuations.

LÉONIE COWEN & ASSOCIATES

30 KINGSWOOD AVENUE, QUEENS PARK, LONDON, NW6 6LR

TEL: (0181) 964 4177
FAX: (0181) 964 0311

THE FIRM: The firm specialises in local government law. Before its foundation in 1989 Léonie Cowen spent 15 years in local government. She is an accredited mediator. The firm also has a growing corporate and commercial property law practice.

PRINCIPAL AREAS OF WORK:

Social Services (esp. Community Care): Transfer of residential homes, housing stock and funding for development/refurbishment.

Externalisation/CCT: Consultancy and casework for local authorities and employee groups, blue and white collar CCT/VCT, including public procurement.

Local Authority Companies: New structures, management buy-outs, municipal and cross-border trading, including consideration of the constraints.

Local Government Finance: Authorities' powers and constraints, interest rate swaps litigation.

Employment: All aspects including TUPE and acting in sensitive senior level cases.

Education: Acting for authorities and governing bodies.

Charities: The setting-up and management of charities and other non-profit organisations, including Industrial & Provident Societies.

Corporate: Businesses transfers, joint ventures, shareholders agreements and general advice.

Commercial Property: Acquisition, funding, management and disposal of property for public authorities, housing associations, businesses and investors.

CONTACT PARTNER: Léonie Cowen

Number of partners:	1
Other fee-earners:	1

WORKLOAD	
Local government law	80%
Commercial property	10%
Charities	5%
Corporate	5%

CONTACTS	
Charities	Léonie Cowen/Andrew Riddell
Commercial property	Andrew Riddell
Corporate	Léonie Cowen/Andrew Riddell
Local government law	Léonie Cowen

LESLIE WOLFSON & CO 19 Waterloo Street, Glasgow, G2 6BQ **Tel:** (0141) 226 4499 **Fax:** (0141) 221 6070 **DX:** 106 Glasgow **Ptnrs:** 4 **Asst Solrs:** 3 **Other Fee-earners:** 3. Specialising in all aspects of property including commercial, development, landlord/ tenant, residential. Available for consultations at London address (39 Hill St, W1).

LESTER ALDRIDGE

RUSSELL HOUSE, OXFORD ROAD, BOURNEMOUTH, DORSET, BH8 8EX
DX: 7623 Bournemouth 1

TEL: (01202) 786161
FAX: (01202) 786150

THE FIRM: Lester Aldridge is one of the largest law firms in central Southern England. It is a progressive and innovative practice which has adopted a corporate style management structure. The firm is market led with an emphasis on the development of specialist units offering expert advice on specific aspects of the law from lawyers who are familiar with a particular industry. Lawyers are encouraged and trained to adopt a commercial approach, seeking legal solutions to business problems.

PRINCIPAL AREAS OF WORK:

Company and Commercial: (*Contact:* David Ashplant. *Fee-earners:* 8). *Work includes:* business acquisitions, disposals and joint ventures, commercial contract, intellectual property, trading contracts, international trade, and EC law.

Commercial Litigation: (*Contact:* Paul O'Connor. *Fee-earners:* 10). The firm has a large commercial litigation section with substantial overseas experience including the EC, USA, Switzerland and Belize. *Work includes:* commercial disputes, computer and intellectual property litigation, emergency procedures, shareholder and partnership disputes, arbitration and insolvency.

Commercial Property: (*Contact:* Peter Grose. *Fee-earners:* 10). *Work includes:* residential and commercial estate development, mortgage and leasing of all types of property, planning and environmental law and landlord and tenant. Niche units for marina developments, rest and nursing homes, community care and hotels and licensed premises.

MANAGING PARTNER: Barry Glazier

Number of partners:	30
Assistant solicitors:	26
Other fee-earners:	22

CONTACTS	
Asset finance	Janet Gregory
Banking	Graham Jefferies
Care homes	Peter Grose
Commercial litigation	Paul O'Connor
Commercial property	Peter Grose
Computer law and IT	David Jones
Consumer credit	Pip Giddins
Contested wills	Geoff Thomas
Corporate	David Ashplant
Debt collection	Philip Lunn
EC and international trade	David Ashplant

Employment: (*Contact:* Jeremy Allin. *Fee-earners:* 5). *Work includes:* contracts of employment and service agreements, contract and labour disputes, unfair dismissal and redundancy.

Insolvency: (*Contact:* Malcolm Niekirk. *Fee-earners:* 6). The firm has a strong insolvency team providing a service to insolvency practitioners across the country and banks.

Banking and Asset Finance: (*Contact:* Janet Gregory. *Fee-earners:* 11). The firm has one of the largest Asset Finance Units in the country dealing with small and medium ticket transactions for UK bank owned and independent finance houses. The unit includes specialist litigators and a computerised recovery of goods service. The banking unit advises banks and other lenders on lending and recovery techniques.

Debt Collection: (*Contact:* Philip Lunn. *Fee-earners:* 5). Lester Aldridge offers a highly efficient computerised bulk debt collection service.

Private Client Services: (*Contact:* Ray Brown. *Fee-earners:* 34). Lester Aldridge advises private individuals on personal injury claims, matrimonial and family law. Its tax, trusts and wills section is well-known for its expertise in estate planning including setting up and administering non-resident trusts.

Financial Services: (*Contact:* Piers Hughes. Fee-earners: 5). The firm also advises companies and individuals on investments, pensions and life assurance, and offers discretionary management services.

RECRUITMENT AND TRAINING: The firm recruits at least four trainee solicitors every year. Apply by letter and CV to Norman Dunnington at Russell House, Oxford Road, Bournemouth, BH8 8EX.

FOREIGN CONNECTIONS: The firm has strong links with South Africa. A South African desk services clients wishing to trade with South Africa or vice versa. The firm's existing European links with major law firms in the EC are under-pinned by a number of lawyers fluent in French, Spanish, German and Dutch. The firm is a member of Eurolegal.

OTHER OFFICES: Parkstone, Christchurch.

Employment	Jeremy Allin
Family	Stephen Foster
Financial services	Piers Hughes
FSA compliance	Janet Gregory
Health & safety	Richard Byrne
Hotels & licensed premises	Oonagh McKinney
Insolvency	Malcolm Niekirk
Insurance	Mike Giddins
Intellectual property	David Ashplant
International probate	John Maddocks
International tax planning	Barry Glazier
Landlord and tenant	Peter Boardman
Licensing	Colin Patrick
Marina & leisure development	Jonathan Howe
Medical services	Susan Cowan
Pensions	Ian Mereweather
Personal injury	Karen Thompson
Planning and environment	Roger Woolley
Probate/estate administration	David Parkhouse
Professional indemnity	Paul O'Connor
Residential conveyancing	Tony Roberts
South Africa	Stuart Southgate
Trusts	Barry Glazier
UK tax planning	David Parkhouse

L'ESTRANGE & BRETT

7-9 CHICHESTER STREET, BELFAST, BT1 4JG
DX: 424 NR Belfast

TEL: (01232) 230426
FAX: (01232) 246396

THE FIRM: One of the largest firms in Northern Ireland, L'Estrage & Brett is primarily a commercial firm, with strong national and international links in the British Isles, the rest of Europe and North America.

PRINCIPAL AREAS OF WORK:

Corporate Law: (*Contact Partner:* John Irvine). L'Estrange & Brett acts for a wide range of corporate clients and regularly provides advice on matters such as business start-ups and incorporation, acquisitions and disposals, mergers, joint ventures and share issues. The firm also has a strong presence in the developing corporate finance market and frequently advises clients on regulatory and compliance matters under the Financial Services Act.

Commercial Law: (*Contact Partner:* Richard Gray). Clients are advised on all legal aspects of their business activities, including sales and marketing, distribution, franchising, competition law, intellectual property and computer law.

Commercial Property: (*Contact Partner:* Alan Hewitt). One of the largest departments in the firm, L'Estrange & Brett's commercial property solicitors deal with an extensive range of work, including sales, purchases, tenancies, charges, planning and environmental aspects and property management.

Litigation: (*Contact Partner:* Adam Brett). The main focus of the firm's litigation department is commercial litigation and employment law, and it is regularly involved in IP and construction disputes, in addition to more general commercial work. Advice is also provided on personal injury matters.

CONTACT PARTNER: Alan Hewitt

Number of partners:	7
Assistant solicitors:	9
Other fee-earners:	4

WORKLOAD	
Commercial property	35%
Corporate and commercial law	33%
Litigation (including employment law)	25%
Private client	7%

Banking/ Financial Services: *(Contact Partner:* Brian Henderson). One of the most rapidly developing areas of the practice, the service builds on the firm's close links with large commercial practices in the City of London and Dublin. Work covered includes securitisation, asset and finance leasing and debt rescheduling and reorganisation.

OTHER AREAS OF WORK: The firm can also provide expertise on insolvency and EC law in addition to providing a general private client service.

LEVI & CO 33 St. Pauls Street, Leeds, W. Yorks, LS1 2JJ **Tel:** (0113) 2449931 **Fax:** (0113) 2446789 **DX:** 12033 Leeds **Ptnrs:** 8 **Asst Solrs:** 3 **Other Fee-earners:** 10. Founded 1934. General practice known for its criminal, matrimonial and personal injury litigation. Has extended hours, weekend appointments and makes home visits. Legal aid work undertaken.

LEVY & McRAE 26 St Vincent Street, Glasgow, G2 5RL **Tel:** (0141) 307 2311 **Fax:** (0141) 307 6857 **DX:** 149 Strathclyde **Ptnrs:** 4 **Asst Solrs:** 3 **Other Fee-earners:** 3. The firm has a large criminal and court department dealing with matters such as civil actions and insurance claims. Other specialisms include executries, wills, conveyancing, and a particular expertise in franchising.

THE LEWINGTON PARTNERSHIP Midland House, 132 Hagley Road, Edgbaston, Birmingham, W. Midlands, B16 9NN **Tel:** (0121) 454 4000 **Fax:** (0121) 455 8131 **DX:** 707290 Edgbaston 3 **Ptnrs:** 2 **Asst Solrs:** 16 **Other Fee-earners:** 13. Specialist practice concentrating principally on work for Health Authorities and NHS trusts. The firm undertakes defendant medical negligence and personal injury work, commercial, employment and property matters.

LEWIS MOORE Craven House, 121 Kingsway, London, WC2B 6PA **Tel:** (0171) 831 6300 **Fax:** (0171) 405 4485 **Ptnrs:** 3 **Other Fee-earners:** 3. This firm specialises in marine litigation as well as ship sale and purchase. Also handles commercial property work.

WORKLOAD	
Shipping and commercial 80% Property	20%

EDITORIAL POLICY

In this edition, the lists of specialists include profiles of individual practitioners - solicitors and barristers - who have been recommended most frequently to our researchers. Editorial policy is to identify leading practitioners on merit: it is not possible to buy a place in our biographical lists. Inclusion of a profile in this directory is based solely on expertise and reputation.

Enormous effort has been invested by our ten-strong research team (mainly solicitors and barristers) in canvassing recommendations and identifying leaders. We are confident in the overall accuracy of the results. However, mistakes and misjudgements are inevitable, and if readers have any suggestions regarding our listings we should be very pleased to hear from them.

LEWIS SILKIN

WINDSOR HOUSE, 50 VICTORIA STREET, LONDON, SW1H 0NW
DX: 2321 Victoria

TEL: (0171) 227 8000
FAX: (0171) 222 4633

THE FIRM: Lewis Silkin is a succesful commercial practice, which aims to deliver "service excellence through client care". The firm has grown by developing areas of expertise to meet the needs of a wide range of commercial clients. The principal office is in Westminster with a small office in Farnham.

Today, clients are demanding high quality legal advice, relevant to their situation and business and which offers value for money. To satisfy this need in a practical way, Lewis Silkin has established a number of "business focus groups" which draw on the legal expertise from across the three departments within the firm – corporate, property and litigation. As a result the firm has become increasingly well known for its "marketing services" group which focuses on clients in advertising, sales promotion, direct marketing, design, public relations and media, its "services to lenders" group which provides services for residential institutional lenders and its "housing association" group. Its reputation is developing though other specialist focus goups - "corporate finance", "commercial property", "employment", "insurance" and "intellectual property".

PRINCIPAL AREAS OF WORK:

Corporate Finance: *(Contact:* Clare Grayston). The provides a comprehensive range of corporate finance services including acquisitions and mergers, flotations, takeovers, MBOs, joint ventures, venture capital schemes, restructuring, financing and banking.

Commercial Property: *(Contact:* Len Goodrich). The firm provides a wide range of commercial property services including acquisitions, funding, development and disposals, planning and environmental, specialist services to the retail industry, construction and landlord and tenant work.

Employment: *(Contact:* Mike Burd). The firm advises employers and employees on all contentious and non-contntious aspects of employment contracts, personnel policies and employee benefits.

Housing Associations: *(Contact:* Gillian Bastow). The firm has a reputation for its work with housing associations, and is actively involved with the financing and development programmes of a range of clients.

Insurance: *(Contact:* Dennis Wilkins). The firm handles an increasing number of cases involving the construction and property industry, both residential and commercial, valuers, and professionals in the media and avertising worlds.

Marketing Services: *(Contact:* Stephen Groom). As a leader in the field of advertising law the firm provides a comprehensive service to those involved in advertising, design, PR, sales promotion, media and direct marketing.

Services to Lenders: *(Contact:* Richard Waller). The firm handles conveyancing, repossessions, shortfall recovery, professional negligence work and general corporate and property advice to those involved in residential lending.

Intellectual Property: *(Contact:* Stephen Groom). The work includes advice on all aspects on copyright, trademarks and intellectual property.

Commercial Litigation: *(Contact:* Tom Coates). The department has enjoyed particular success and developed strength in depth to handle a wide range of work.

Corporate: *(Contacts:* Trevor Watkins). The corporate department provides a comprehensive range of commercial expertise to the clients of the firm.

NATURE OF CLIENTELE: The firm acts for corporate clients of all sizes, national and international. It has a particular concentration of clients in marketing services and residential institutional lenders, whilst others are involved in sectors as diverse as publishing, cable and media, fashion, restaurants, housing, healthcare, hi-tech, retail and property development.

FOREIGN CONNECTIONS: Extensive connections in the USA, Italy, Germany, France and Switzerland. The practice enjoys the benefits of exclusive UK membership of the European Advertising Lawyers' Association.

RECRUITMENT AND TRAINING: The organises regular in-house courses on both legal topics and skills training including IT, for partners fee earners and support staff.

OTHER OFFICES: The Farnham office handles property related work, particularly for property developers and mortgage repossession work.

CONTACT PARTNER: Roger Alexander

Number of partners:	26
Assistant solicitors:	35
Other fee-earners:	23

WORKLOAD	
Commercial property	25%
Commercial litigation	20%
Corporate finance / M & A	20%
Insurance	15%
Employment	8%
Intellectual property/ advertising	7%
Other	5%

CONTACTS	
Advertising	Stephen Groom
Commercial litigation	Tom Coates
Commercial property	Len Goodrich
Company/ commercial	Trevor Watkins
Corporate finance/ M & A	Clare Grayston
Employment	Mike Burd
Insurance	Dennis Wilkins
Intellectual property	Stephen Groom
Services to lenders	Richard Waller

LIDDELL ZURBRUGG

15-17 JOCKEY'S FIELDS, LONDON, WC1R 4BW
DX: 0061 Ch.Ln.

TEL: (0171) 404 5641
FAX: (0171) 831 8460

THE FIRM: Liddell Zurbrugg specialises in insurance and personal injury litigation, both on behalf of insurers and private clients within the UK and other European countries. Clients include a number of Lloyd's syndicates and insurance companies, both UK and foreign. Several languages are spoken fluently and the firm has established connections in most European countries with particular emphasis on France, Spain, Portugal, Belgium, Switzerland and Germany. The firm includes a Spanish lawyer whose main area of work consists of personal injury claims in Spain and giving evidence before English Courts in relation to spanish law. In addition, he deals with general litigation, property transactions, child abduction and custody cases.

CONTACT PARTNER:
Michael R.W. Zurbrugg

Number of partners:	3
Other fee-earners:	12

LIGHTFOOTS

THE OLD RED LION, 1-3 HIGH STREET, THAME, OXON, OX9 2BX
DX: 80550 Thame

TEL: (01844) 212305 or 212574/5
FAX: (01844) 214984

THE FIRM: This progressive firm, the first nationally to gain the 'Investors in People' award, provides sound advice on most aspects of English corporate and private client law. It also holds a legal aid franchise.

PRINCIPAL AREAS OF WORK: Commercial services include: company/ commercial, commercial property, employment, tax, property litigation and specialist debt collection, mortgage repossession and professional negligence departments.

Private client work includes wills, probate, trusts, residential conveyancing, other general civil litigation, a solicitors estate agency and specialist personal injury and family law departments.

OTHER OFFICES: Princes Risborough, Bucks.

FOREIGN LANGUAGES SPOKEN: French, Italian.

CONTACT PARTNER: John Miles

Number of partners:	6
Assistant solicitors:	4
Other fee-earners:	13

INVESTOR IN PEOPLE

LINDER MYERS Phoenix House, 45 Cross Street, Manchester, M2 4JF **Tel:** (0161) 832 6972 **Fax:** (0161) 834 0718 **DX:** 14360 **Ptnrs:** 6 **Asst Solrs:** 13 **Other Fee-earners:** 12. This leading litigation practice in the North West with three branches and fast expanding business (contentious and non-contentious) and family departments.

WORKLOAD			
Personal injury	25%	Company/ commercial	25%
General litigation	15%	Medical negligence	13%
Matrimonial	12%	Private client	10%

LINDSAYS WS

11 ATHOLL CRESCENT, EDINBURGH, EH3 8HE
DX: 25 Edinburgh

TEL: (0131) 229 1212
FAX: (0131) 229 5611

THE FIRM: Lindsays is a well-established practice operating from three offices in Edinburgh. Traditionally acting for many landed estates, the firm has expanded the breadth of its services to include commercial property, residential conveyancing, employment law and intellectual property. At the same time the practice maintains particular expertise in matters relating to crofting and heritage trusts. As a member of the QLG legal network the firm is working to achieve IS 9001 accreditation.

PRINCIPAL AREAS OF WORK:

Commercial Property: *(Contact Partner:* David Reith). The firm handles all aspects of commercial property and regularly deals with matters relating to the hotel and retail sectors. This service is complemented by expertise in the field of liquor licensing, especially as regards the hotel industry. The practice is well regarded in

CHAIRMAN: Mr R. John Elliot

Number of partners:	16
Assistant solicitors:	12
Other fee-earners:	17

the field of agricultural law, covering both landed estates and crofting, and advising on sporting rights and mineral extraction. In addition the firm handles the commercial property requirements of major building societies and loan transactions.

Litigation: *(Contact Partner:* Alistair Mackie). The firm offers a specialist service in three areas: employment law, intellectual property (especially in relation to academic institutions) and building contract arbitration. The department also handles damages claims, matrimonial disputes, trust variations and challenges to wills.

Residential Conveyancing: *(Contact Partner:* Robert Arbuthnott). The department assists with all aspects of buying and selling residential property, and is authorised to arrange mortgages and insurance.

Private Client: *(Contact Partner:* Brian Robertson). The firm handles trust and executry administration, investment management, taxation, the establishment of charitable trusts and will preparation.

OTHER AREAS OF WORK:

Company/ Commercial: The department advises on the purchase and sale of businesses, company finance, intellectual property, liquor licensing and matters relating to charitable companies.

NATURE OF CLIENTELE: In addition to the private client, the firm regularly acts for hoteliers, retailers, landed estates, building societies, institutions (academic and financial), charities and heritage trusts.

INTERNATIONAL CONNECTIONS & ASSOCIATED OFFICES: Member of QLG – a network of 13 English and Scottish firms.

OTHER OFFICES:

163a Bruntsfield Place, Edinburgh EH10 4DG. *Tel:* (0131) 228 6993.
77 Main Street, Davidsons Mains, Edinburgh EH4 5AD. *Tel:* (0131) 312 7276.

LINFORD BROWNS Magnolia Hse, Church St, Exmouth, Devon, EX8 1HQ **Tel:** (01395) 264384 **Fax:** (01395) 267643 **DX:** 48851 **Ptnrs:** 5 **Asst Solrs:** 4 **Other Fee-earners:** 3. Departments specialising in conveyancing, commercial work, probate and litigation including specialist tribunals. Agency work undertaken.

WORKLOAD			
Priv client/trusts/prob	30%	Conveyancing	20%
Litigation	20%	Company and commercial	20%

LINKLATERS & PAINES

BARRINGTON HOUSE, 59-67 GRESHAM STREET, LONDON, EC2V 7JA
DX: 10

TEL: (0171) 606 7080
FAX: (0171) 606 5113

Linklaters & Paines is one of the world's largest international law firms, which operates from the UK and major financial centres around the globe.

THE FIRM: Linklaters' development has been in response to the commercial needs of its clients - major corporations, banks, financial institutions and governments. Since its formation over 150 years ago Linklaters has had offices in the heart of the City of London. With the growth in global financial markets, cross-border transactions and project finance, the firm has developed internationally with offices in Brussels, Frankfurt, Moscow, Paris, Hong Kong, Singapore, Tokyo and New York. Linklaters also has a representative office in Washington.

Linklaters aims to achieve preeminence in its chosen areas of practice through a firm-wide commitment to excellence and through the experience, helpfulness and creativity of its people. Its goal is to understand, meet and, wherever possible, exceed the expectations of its clients by delivering a first class service and by continually investing in its people and in the training, know-how and technology necessary to support them.

TYPES OF WORK UNDERTAKEN: Unusually for a City law firm, Linklaters combines core businesses - all of which are leaders in their fields - in corporate, international finance, commercial property and litigation.

SENIOR PARTNER: James Wyness
MANAGING PARTNER: Terence Kyle

Number of partners:	162
Assistant solicitors:	862
Total staff:	1798

WORKLOAD	
Corporate	40%
Litigation	15%
International finance	15%
Commercial property	15%
Tax	8%
Intellectual property	5%
Trusts	2%

The firm's corporate practice is largely concerned with financial and commercial transactions and advice on company matters including share offerings, takeovers and mergers, company reconstructions and privatisations. Specialist groups also advise on UK and offshore investment funds, regulatory compliance, insurance, competition and EC, project and asset finance, corporate recovery and insolvency and employment and employee benefits.

Linklaters is the established world leader in international capital markets work and a leading firm in syndicated bank lending. It serves both corporate and banking clients on securities issues (including under UK, French and other laws), and bank lending as well as structured financings and all categories of derivative products. It also advises on all types of commercial property transactions, including investments, developments and business lettings. The firm has specialists who advise on planning, environmental and local government issues, construction contracts and property investment structures.

The firm's litigation practice encompasses most types of contentious business arising in a financial, commercial or industrial context. As well as court, tribunal and arbitration work, it also handles investigations, document handling and debt recovery.

In addition Linklaters has specialist departments in the fields of intellectual property, technology and communications, tax and trusts.

OTHER OFFICES: Brussels, Frankfurt, Moscow, Paris, Hong Kong, Singapore, Tokyo, New York.

Representative office: Washington

CONTACTS	
Banking	Hadyn Puleston Jones
Commercial property	David Lloyd
Competition/ EC	David Hall
Construction and engineering	Marshall Levine
Corporate	Anthony Cann
Corporate recovery/insolvency	Robert Elliott
Employment & emp. benefits	Tony Thurnham
Environment	Beverley Adam
European business	John Edwards
Financial markets	Paul Nelson
Intellectual property, T&C	Jeremy Brown
International finance & CM	Stephen Edlmann
Investment funds	Paul Harris
Litigation	Brinsley Nicholson
Planning and local government	Ray Jackson
Project and asset finance	Alan Black
Securities	Michael Canby
Tax	Tony Angel
Technology & communications	Jeremy Brown
Trusts	Nigel Reid

LINNELLS

12 KING EDWARD ST, OXFORD, OXON, OX1 4HX
DX: 4312 Oxford 1

TEL: (01865) 248607
FAX: (01865) 728445

THE FIRM: This major provincial firm has been in practice for over 90 years. It remains a broad-based practice, and today has seven offices in Oxon and Bucks. The emphasis is on commercial work, particularly commercial property and commercial litigation. Other areas of strength are company work, intellectual property, taxation and trusts, construction, employment, accident litigation, matrimonial property and agricultural work.

PRINCIPAL AREAS OF WORK:

Commercial Property: *(Contact Partner:* Paddy Gregan). The work of this large department, centred in Oxford and Milton Keynes, includes business and agricultural transactions (both freehold and leasehold), planning, environmental, minerals and quarrying matters, retail, construction and development work. *(Fee-earners:* 12).

Litigation: *(Contact Partner:* Jeremy Irwin-Singer). A founder member of ADR NET, leaders in disputes mediation. A full range of commercial and civil litigation is handled. Services to the commercial client include: employment, insolvency, property and construction disputes, licensing applications and computerised debt collection. Private client work includes: accident claims, consumer and landlord and tenant cases, criminal law, family and child care work and professional and medical negligence. (Legal aid franchise holder). *(Fee-earners:* 21.

Company/ Commercial: *(Contact Partner:* John Deech). Advice is given on all commercial issues ranging from company/ partnership formation, taxation, EC and competition law, mergers, acquisitions and disposals, to employment and aviation law, commercial contracts, insolvency and intellectual property law. *(Fee-earners:* 10).

MANAGING PARTNER: Jeremy Irwin-Singer

Number of partners:	20
Assistant solicitors:	18
Other fee-earners:	16

CONTACTS	
Accident claims/litigation	J.Irwin-Singer
Business affairs/comm. prop.	Paddy Gregan
Company law/employment	John Deech
Criminal advice	Warwick Clarke
Debt collecting/insolvency	Jonathan Lloyd-Jones
European law	Euan Temple
Family cases	Stephen Jackson
Farming	Michael Linnell
Immigration & nationality	Phillip Turpin
Intellectual property	John Deech
Landlord and tenant	Carol Oster
Planning & envi./res. property	Anne Cowell
Probate, trusts, tax and wills	Martyn Ess

Private Client: *(Contact Partner:* Martyn Ess). *Work includes:* residential conveyancing, wills, tax, planning matters, probate and administration of estates, education matters, charitable trusts, welfare, looking after the elderly and infirm. *(Fee-earners:* 11.
NATURE OF CLIENTELE: Clients include many well known public and private companies, two large national retail chains, the nation's leading charity, breweries, motor manufacturers, builders, publishers, agricultural estates, Oxford colleges and Oxford University.

LINSKILLS Harrington House, Harrington Street, Liverpool, Merseyside, L2 9QA **Tel:** (0151) 236 2224 **Fax:** (0151) 236 0151 **DX:** 14215 **Ptnrs:** 1 **Asst Solrs:** 6 **Other Fee-earners:** 14. A highly specialised litigation firm undertaking all aspects of litigation including criminal work.

LINSLEY & MORTIMER

THE SIDE, NEWCASTLE-UPON-TYNE, TYNE & WEAR, NE1 3DD
DX: 61043 Newcastle

TEL: (0191) 232 4192
FAX: (0191) 261 6949

THE FIRM: Established over 45 years ago from a litigation base, the firm in the last 10 years has expanded into commercial and insolvency work. All matters are directly supervised by partners.
PRINCIPAL AREAS OF WORK:
Private Client/ Commercial: *Contact:* Richard Chadeyron.
Personal Injury Litigation: *Contact:* Alan Simpson.
Commercial Litigation, Insolvency & Professional Negligence: *Contact:* Toby Scott.
NATURE OF CLIENTELE: Insurers, adjusters, private companies.

CONTACT PARTNER: Mr T. Scott

Number of partners:	3
Assistant solicitors:	2
Other fee-earners:	2

WORKLOAD	
Civil litigation	80%
Private client	10%
General commercial	10%

LISTER CROFT PARTNERSHIP

VICTORIA CHAMBERS, 40 WOOD STREET, WAKEFIELD, W. YORKS, WF1 2HL
DX: 15010

TEL: (01924) 291010
FAX: (01924) 387404

THE FIRM: The original firm of Lister Croft traces its roots back to just before the turn of the century, and has been joined in the past five years by three other firms to form the Lister Croft Partnership. The practice has over 50 staff and is known for providing a caring service to its extensive and long established client base in West Yorkshire.
PRINCIPAL AREAS OF WORK: The practice undertakes a wide range work through its network of branch offices, including domestic conveyancing, personal taxation, criminal prosecutions, personal injury claims (including disaster cases and medical negligence), probate and Court of Protection work, civil litigation and matrimonial matters. All aspects of commercial property are handled on behalf of many PLC clients.
CLIENTELE: A large private-client base and private and public corporations.
AGENCY: All types of agency work are undertaken. *Contact:* Lee Rogers at Wood St, Wakefield.
RECRUITMENT: The firm recruits 1 trainee solicitors each year. Letter and CV to Alan Benstock, Managing Partner.
OTHER OFFICES:
43 Church Lane, Pudsey, Leeds. *Tel:* (0113) 2570526, *Fax:* (0113) 2393262.
112 New Road Side, Horsforth (as Gibbs Pollard). *Tel:* (0113) 2585781,
Fax: (0113) 2591059.
13 The Grove, Ilkley. *Tel:* (01943) 608429, *Fax:* (01943) 816948.

CONTACT PARTNER: Alan Benstock

Number of partners:	7
Assistant solicitors:	7
Other fee-earners:	6

LLOYD COOPER 7A Grafton Street, London, W1X 3LA **Tel:** (0171) 629 4699 **Fax:** (0171) 355 3796 **DX:** 37208 Piccadilly **Ptnrs:** 4 **Asst Solrs:** 2 **Other Fee-earners:** 2. A commercial practice best known for its work in insurance and commercial litigation, company/ commercial and commercial property.

WORKLOAD			
Insurance/reinsurance lit	50%	Company and commercial	25%
Commercial property	15%	Commercial litigation	10%

THE LOGAN PARTNERSHIP The Shooting Lodge, Guildford Road, Sutton Green, Guildford, Surrey, GU4 7PZ **Tel:** (01483) 235000 **Fax:** (01483) 237004 **DX:** 83171 Guildford 2 **Ptnrs:** 2 **Asst Solrs:** 1 **Other Fee-earners:** 1. Specialist family practice with legal aid element. Other work undertaken includes civil liberties, conveyancing, wills and probate.

WORKLOAD			
Matrimonial	40%	Criminal	20%
Conveyancing	16%	Civil litigation	12%

LOOSEMORES Alliance House, 18-20 High St, Cardiff, S. Glam, CF1 2BP **Tel:** (01222) 224433 **Fax:** (01222) 373275 **DX:** 33008 **Ptnrs:** 10 **Asst Solrs:** 10 **Other Fee-earners:** 6. Has a broad private client base and a fast-growing commercial practice. Handles civil litigation, personal injury, and medical negligence work.

WORKLOAD			
Pers inj/motor claims	38%	Matrimonial	15%
Commercial	10%	Wills and probate	5%
Housing	3%		

LORIMER LONGHURST & LEES Devonshire House, 89 Regent Street, Cambridge, Cambs, CB2 1AW **Tel:** (01223) 311141 & 358227 **Fax:** (01223) 460749 **DX:** 5811 Cambridge **Ptnrs:** 3 **Asst Solrs:** 2 **Other Fee-earners:** 4. A small private client practice with specialising particularly in medical negligence, personal injury, armed forces related claims, child care and mental health cases.

LOUDONS WS 29 St Patrick Square, Edinburgh, EH8 9EY **Tel:** (0131) 662 4193 **Fax:** **Ptnrs:** 2 **Asst Solrs:** 2 **Other Fee-earners:** 2. Specialist practice with very strong reputation for its family law expertise.

WORKLOAD			
Family	85%	Personal injury	10%
Debt recovery	5%		

CD-ROM EDITION ON THE INTERNET

This edition of the directory is available on a CD-ROM which includes both DOS and Windows versions. It can be loaded onto a network, and works with virtually any IBM compatible PC. The CD-ROM version offers computer-users the advantage of rapid search, retrieval and cross-referencing. It is also available via the Internet.

LOVELL WHITE DURRANT

65 HOLBORN VIADUCT, LONDON, EC1A 2DY
DX: 57

TEL: (0171) 236 0066
FAX: (0171) 248 4212

Lovell White Durrant is a leading international law firm, based in the City of London. The breadth of its legal practice and depth of its specialist skills enable it to offer a comprehensive corporate service.

THE FIRM: Lovell White Durrant's pioneering approach to international practice is shown in the history of its expansion overseas - with offices in Brussels (1972), New York (1977), Hong Kong (1982), Paris (1990), Tokyo (1990), Prague (1991), Beijing (1992), Vietnam and Shanghai (associated office) (1994). This commitment to an international network continues, as is shown by the opening of an office in Chicago in spring 1995.

Lovell White Durrant has an excellent reputation for its advice on EC law, helped by the strength of the Brussels office. It is also ideally placed to work with clients who have interests in the emerging economies of Eastern Europe and the Far East. The Prague office continues to grow, as do the Russian and Polish practices, and increasingly the firm is involved in transactions in other parts of Eastern Europe. In the Far East there is a strong demand for the combined service available from the five offices in the region, which work together very closely. The firm's stature in the Far East is shown in its membership of the influential Pacific Rim Advisory Council, an association of major law firms.

PRINCIPAL AREAS OF WORK: Banking and corporate finance are central to Lovell White Durrant's London practice. Mergers and acquisitions, venture capital and management buy-outs are areas of practice much in demand from the firm's international clients, and the capital markets and project finance practices (including DBFO contracts and housing association finance) are growing strongly.

The firm is recognised as a leader in litigation and international commercial arbitration, in property, and in business restructuring and asset recovery (with one of the largest insolvency practices in the UK).

In addition to these core activities, Lovell White Durrant has specialist groups dealing with all aspects of business taxation, pensions and employment law; shipping and international trade; and planning, building and engineering, energy and utilities and environmental law. Insurance, reinsurance and UK competition law are particular strengths, and the intellectual property, information technology and telecommunications practices are expanding fast, as is the work on professional indemnity insurance issues.

Lovell White and Durrant places great emphasis on helping clients to achieve their business objectives by providing legal advice that is both imaginative and commercially aware - an emphasis reflected in the recent launch of its business lobbying service. It is also known for nurturing its working relationships with clients and has consistently achieved in independent research very high ratings for client satisfaction.

RECENT DEVOPMENTS: As part of its continuing international expansion and the development of key practice areas, the firm has made a number of significant recruitments in aviation finance, capital markets, intellectual property and reinsurance, in respect of the London, Prague, Hong Kong and Chicago offices; it has also made five internal appointments to partner (in its EC regulatory law, pensions, intellectual property, and commercial and trade law practices - two of these promotions involving its offices overseas).

FURTHER INFORMATION: A comprehensive list of specialist brochures, client notes and newsletters is available from Shirley Martin. Prospective trainee solicitors should contact Hayley Grant for details of the recruitment programme

CONTACT PARTNER: Lesley MacDonagh

UK:	
Number of partners:	118
Assistant solicitors:	269
Other fee-earners:	201
INTERNATIONAL:	
Number of Partners:	26
Assistant Solicitors:	59
Other fee-earners:	88

CONTACTS

Advertising/ consumer law	Patrick Phillipps
Arbitration/ ADR	Mark Huleatt-James
Banking	John Penson
Capital markets	David Hudd
Commercial	Matthew Hill
Commodities	David Macfarlane
Computers	Quentin Archer
Construction & engineering	Nicholas Gould
Corporate finance/ M & A	Daniel Mace
Cross-border transactions	Don Kelly
EC & Competition	Michael Hutchings
Employee benefits	Matthew Hill
Employment	Andrew Williamson
Energy	Michael Stanger
Entertainment	Michael Golding
Environmental	Michael Gallimore
Financial services	Richard Stones
Franchising	Michael Golding
Fraud & asset recovery	Keith Gaines
Insolvency	Peter Horrocks
Insurance	John Young
Intellectual property	Michael Golding
Litigation	John Trotter
Lloyd's	Christian Wells
MBO/ venture capital	John Kitching
Pensions	Harriet Dawes
Planning	Michael Gallimore
Product liability	Patrick Phillipps
Professional indemnity	John Trotter
Project finance	Gavin McQuater
Property	Robert Kidby
Rating & compulsory purchase	David Hunter
Regulatory investigations	Graham Livingstone
Reinsurance	John Powell
Shipping	Ian Ward
Tax and VAT	Anthony Davis
Telecommmunications	Heather Rowe

LOXLEYS Bishopsgate House, 5-7 Folgate Street, London, E1 6BX **Tel:** (0171) 377 1066 **Fax:** (0171) 377 5004 **DX:** 816 City **Ptnrs:** 5 **Asst Solrs:** 2 **Other Fee-earners:** 5. A general commercial, probate and trust practice, with liquor licensing a speciality. Strong connections with Indian sub-continent. Qualified in-house French, Spanish and Italian lawyers able to advise on EC law.

LUCAS & WYLLYS 5 South Quay, Great Yarmouth, Norfolk, NR30 2QJ **Tel:** (01493) 855555 **Fax:** (01493) 630055 **DX:** 41100 **Ptnrs:** 4 **Asst Solrs:** 4 **Other Fee-earners:** 10. A general practice with specialists in the following fields: matrimonial, commercial, personal injury, criminal, conveyancing and wills and probate.

WORKLOAD			
Conveyancing	24%	Civil	24%
Criminal	21%	Matrimonial	17%
Probate	11%	General	3%

LUMB & MACGILL Prudential Buildings, 11 Ivegate, Bradford, W. Yorks, BD1 1SQ **Tel:** (01274) 730666 **Fax:** (01274) 307736 **Ptnrs:** 6 **Other Fee-earners:** 4. Specialists in criminal, care and licensing work. Legal aid.

WORKLOAD		
Crime	85%	Child care	15%

LUPTON FAWCETT Yorkshire Hse, Greek St, Leeds, W. Yorks, LS1 5SX **Tel:** (0113) 246 9696 **Fax:** (0113) 245 6782 **DX:** 12035 Leeds **Ptnrs:** 16 **Asst Solrs:** 15 **Other Fee-earners:** 38. A well established and broadly based practice. Whilst clients include large Plcs the firm remains equally committed to serving owner managed businesses and private individuals.

WORKLOAD			
Personal injury	24%	Private client	22%
Comp/comm/comm prop	20%	Insolvency	10%
Debt collection	8%	Specialist business	8%

LYON CLARK

DAVIOT HOUSE, LOMBARD STREET WEST, WEST BROMWICH, W. MIDLANDS, B70 8EL DX: 14603	TEL: (0121) 553 3211 FAX: (0121) 553 2079
26 Cape Hill, Smethwick, Warley, West Midlands B66 4RR DX: 22553 Contact Partner: Mr Peter Lugsdin	Tel: (0121) 558 2064 Fax: (0121) 555 5422
2 Compton Road, Wolverhampton, West Midlands WV3 9PJ DX: 16151 Contact Partners: Mr Roger Bishop, Miss Julia Bunting	Tel: (01902) 26263 Fax: (01902) 22116

THE FIRM: Lyon Clark is a long-established but forward looking firm, serving the industrial West Midlands area from three strategically located offices. The firm offers a comprehensive service both to business and to private clients.

PRINCIPAL AREAS OF WORK:

Company/ Commercial: (*Contact Partners:* Mr Roger Jukes at West Bromwich, Mr Peter Lugsdin at Smethwick and Mr Roger Bishop at Wolverhampton). A range of corporate services including acquisitions and disposals; agency and distribution; partnership law; insolvency related advice; employment law and advice to directors. The department also handles advice to financial institutions, including all aspects of secured lending.

Licensing: (*Contact Partners:* Mr Peter Lugsdin at Smethwick, Mr David Prichard at West Bromwich and Mr Roger Bishop at Wolverhampton). The firm operates a specialist licensing department under the management of Mr Don Astley. Gaming licensing is dealt with by Mr David Prichard.

Litigation: (*Contact Partners:* Mr Robin Balmain at West Bromwich, Mr Roger Bishop at Wolverhampton). The firm's litigation department is the largest single department, handling all types of High Court, County Court and criminal litigation, plus industrial and other tribunal matters.

MANAGING PARTNER: Mr Roger Jukes	
Number of partners:	10
Assistant solicitors:	4
Other fee-earners:	11

CONTACTS	
Main contact partners:	
Mr Peter Lugsdin	Smethwick
Mr Roger Bishop	Wolverhampton
Mr Roger Jukes	West Bromwich

Family Law: (*Contact Partners:* Mrs Dympna Howells at West Bromwich; Miss Julia Bunting at Wolverhampton). The firm advises on all aspects of matrimonial and child care law.

Planning and Environment: (*Contact Partner:* Mr David Prichard at West Bromwich). This expanding area of law has prompted the firm to offer specialist advice on the environmental challenge and planning issues.

The firm also provides a comprehensive service in all traditional areas of legal practice not specifically mentioned.

LYONS DAVIDSON

BRIDGE HOUSE, 48-52 BALDWIN ST, BRISTOL, BS1 1QD
DX: 7834

TEL: (0117) 929 7151
FAX: (0117) 927 2679

THE FIRM: One of the larger Bristol firms, Lyons Davidson continues to build upon its established expertise in commercial property, commercial and insurance litigation and company/ commercial work as well as developing other areas of specialism in tune with its clients' needs.

SENIOR PARTNER: Mr Timothy Davidson	
Number of partners:	13
Assistant solicitors:	27
Other fee-earners:	50

PRINCIPAL AREAS OF PRACTICE:

Property: Clients include major companies, developers, investors, banks, financial institutions, retailers and local authorities. The department has a broad depth of experience in both commercial and industrial aspects of all property transactions involving the public and private sectors and has specialist units within the department dealing with environment, waste and high volume estate conveyancing work.

Commercial Development: *Contact:* Timothy Davidson

Residential Development (including acquisition for Social Housing): *Contact:* John Hicks

Planning, Environment and Waste: *Contact:* Kevin Gibbs

Plot acquisition, development and sale: *Contact:* Mary McKenzie

Company/ Commercial: The full range of corporate services is provided including company sales and acquisitions, mangement buy-outs, partnerships, flotations, EC law, intellectual property, banking and securities, receiverships and liquidations. Lyons Davidson Trustee Company, the first of its kind in the country, offers an independent trustee service and works in tandem with the pensions and employment unit.

Company/ Commercial: *Contact:* Richard Squire

Insolvency: *Contact:* Paul Hardman

Computer and IT Law: *Contact:* Richard Squire

Employment and Pensions: *Contact:* George Wilkinson

Independent Trustee Company: *Contact:* George Wilkinson

Intellectual Property: *Contact:* Richard Squire

Patent Work: *Contact:* Richard Squire

Commercial Litigation: All aspects of civil and commercial litigation are undertaken including insolvency, contract and building matters, arbitrations, professional negligence claims, employment law disputes and intellectual property. The department provides specialist advice and representation to the health care sector and has an expanding medical negligence practice. It also operates an advocacy unit and a computerised debt recovery service.

Commercial Claims: *Contact:* Peter Fergie

Property litigation: *Contact:* Martin Bastow

Educational Trust Work: *Contact:* Paul Hardman

Special Education Needs: *Contact:* Jill Bolton

Banking and insolvency: *Contact:* Andrew Breckenridge

Licensing: *Contact:* Mark Savill

Intellectual property: *Contact:* Nigel Montgomery

Construction and Civil Engineering: *Contact:* Peter Fergie

Professional Negligence: *Contact:* Peter Fergie

Arbitration: *Contact:* Martin Bastow

Advocacy: *Contact:* Jo Darlington

Healthcare: *Contact:* Nigel Montgomery

WORKLOAD	
Insurance litigation	40%
Commercial property	18%
Company/ commercial	17%
Commercial litigation	17%
Family	6%
Private client	2%

Insurance Litigation and Injury Claims Service: The department provides expert advice and representation to Plaintiffs (P) and Defendants (D) on all aspects of personal injury claims. There is special emphasis on training and immediate access to specialist knowledge for all of the thirty injury claims fee earners through a highly developed internal network.

Insurance Claims: *Contact:* (P) Bernard Rowe, (D) Trevor Still

Plaintiff Insurance Claims: *Contact:* Bernard Rowe

Road Traffic Accident Claims: *Contact:* Bernard Rowe

Medical Negligence: *Contact:* (P) Jill Bolton, (D) Nigel Montgomery

Occupiers' and Employers' Liability: *Contact:* Trevor Still

Product Liability: *Contact:* Nigel Montgomery

Family: The family department offers a full service on all matrimonial and domestic matters. Work includes all financial aspects of divorce, child care (in particular child abduction), domestic violence, cohabitation and welfare benefits.

Financial Issues: *Contact:* James Myatt

Children & Welfare Benefit Issues: *Contact:* Jane Yelland

Child Abduction: *Contact:* Jill Sage

Private Client: Private client department offers a full service on all matters relating to the individual. Work includes all financial aspects of personal taxation, estate administration and will writing.

Will writing: *Contact:* Bernard Godfrey

Estate Administration: *Contact:* John Grenfell

OTHER OFFICE: Plymouth.

MACARTHUR STEWART 87 High Street, Fort William, Highlands, PH33 6DG **Tel:** (01397) 702455 **Fax:** (01397) 705949 **Ptnrs:** 13 **Asst Solrs:** 8 **Other Fee-earners:** 12. General practice with seven offices in the Highlands. Also offers specialist advice on crofting law.

MacBRIDE MUNRO & COMPANY 15 Ingram Street, Glasgow, G1 1HA **Tel:** (0141) 552 0011 **Fax: Ptnrs:** 4 **Asst Solrs:** 2 . The firm offers a broad range of advice to both commercial and private clients, and specialises in commercial property transactions.

MACDONALD OATES Square House, The Square, Petersfield, Hants, GU32 3HT **Tel:** (01730) 268211 **Fax:** (01730) 261232 **DX:** 100400 **Ptnrs:** 7 **Asst Solrs:** 3 **Other Fee-earners:** 3. The firm offers a broad range of advice to both commercial and private clients, and specialises in commercial property transactions.

MACDONALDS 1 Claremont Terrace, Glasgow, G3 7UQ **Tel:** (0141) 248 6221 **Fax:** (0141) 333 0318 **DX:** 142 Glasgow **Ptnrs:** 8 **Asst Solrs:** 7 **Other Fee-earners:** 7. Predominantly acting for commercial clients, the firm has a broad range of expertise including banking, insolvency, employment, commercial property and debt recovery.

MACE & JONES Drury House, 19 Water Street, Liverpool, Merseyside, L2 0RP **Tel:** (0151) 236 8989 **Fax:** (0151) 227 5010 **DX:** 14166 **Ptnrs:** 15 **Asst Solrs:** 19 **Other Fee-earners:** 19. Mace & Jones is a broadly-based practice with a national reputation for expertise in the field of employment law. Spanish, French and German are spoken.

MACFARLANE GUY 3 Kingsmead Square, Bath, Avon, BA1 2AB **Tel:** (01225) 333800 **Fax:** (01225) 337041 **DX:** 8005 Bath **Ptnrs:** 3 **Asst Solrs:** 6 **Other Fee-earners:** 5. A dynamic specialised firm providing a responsive service tuned to the needs of the business and private client.

WORKLOAD		
Personal injury	40% Commercial	35%
Crime	25%	

MACFARLANES

10 NORWICH STREET, LONDON, EC4A 1BD
DX: 138

TEL: (0171) 831 9222
FAX: (0171) 831 9607

THE FIRM: Macfarlanes is a leading City firm, with an unusually wide range of practice. This, and its emphasis on and investment in training, has helped the firm to recruit the best lawyers who thrive in an environment that the larger City firms cannot offer. Macfarlanes is at the forefront in many practice areas, and is instructed by clients who are recognised as leading participants in many industrial and commercial sectors and appreciate the distinctive benefits that working with a smaller cohesive City firm offers.

Throughout the firm's practice, there is a large element of international involvement. Many of its clients are overseas based or owned, and many of the transactions on which it works extend beyond the UK.

TYPES OF WORK: Macfarlanes has an extensive practice and a strong reputation in the traditional City domain of corporate work. It is placed highly in flotation and management buy-out league tables. It has a strong position also in M&A work, where substantial PLC clients instruct the firm on sale and purchase deals. Other specialist fields of corporate work for which it is well-known include investment funds and financial services; advice, particularly on IP and regulatory matters, for marketing and advertising agencies; and employee benefits.

The firm's banking work includes lending transaction work, funding of acquisitions, provision of senior and subordinated debt, trade finance, property finance, and specialist bank litigation.

Work for the property sector covers all transactions involving the ownership, development, investment in and financing of land. Advice is given on all aspects of commercial property, residential property and agricultural property and acting on enterprise zone matters, with specialist groups providing planning and environmental advice and working for the retail, leisure and health sectors. A significant amount of the firm's work includes landlord and tenant issues acting for both landlords and tenants. It has substantial experience in property-related insolvencies, including LPA receiverships.

Litigation and other dispute resolution procedures are a major part of the firm's practice. Within a wide range of work, the firm acts in leading employment law cases; for insured and insurer, especially in advertising and surveying cases; IP cases and disputes over computer hardware and software; financial services regulatory issues and enquiries; Lloyd's related work; sovereign debt, securities and other banking disputes; judicial review, and a broad range of breach of contract claims.

Macfarlanes is at the forefront in advising private clients and their family trusts, not just domestically but on an international basis. Tax planning, including the creation and administration of trusts, the preparation of wills and the administration of estates are central to this work. The firm forms and advises a large number of charitable companies and trusts. The international element is a very significant part of the private client practice both for UK based families and for many overseas taxpayers who come here for advice on tax and trust law. It is frequently instructed at the request of many of the largest US law firms and private banks for this work. Partners have been appointed by courts in the UK and abroad to be trustees in place of existing trustees.

SENIOR PARTNER: Mr V.E. Treves

UK:	
Number of partners:	48
Assistant solicitors:	62
Other fee-earners:	60
INTERNATIONAL:	
Number of Partners:	1

WORKLOAD	
Company/ commercial	44%
Property	26%
Litigation	17%
Tax and financial planning	13%

CONTACTS	
Acquisitions & disposals	Jonathan Macfarlane
Advertising	William King
Agricultural work	John Moore
Banking	Tony Evans
Company/ commercial	Peter Turnbull
Corporate finance	Robert Sutton
Corporate property work	Chris Field
Employee benefits	Douglas Shugar
Enterprise zone work	Chris Field
Financial services	Bridget Barker
General commercial and I.P.	William King
General development work	Chris Field
Health care	John Moore
Investment funds	Bridget Barker
Lending	Tony Evans
Litigation	Tony Thompson
MBOs/MBIs, financial purchases	Peter Turnbull
Pensions	Douglas Shugar
Planning & environmental work	Jayne Walters
Private Client	Michael Hayes
Property	Chris Field
Residential	John Hornby
Retail work	Richard Reuben

MACKAY SIMON 7 Albyn Place, Edinburgh, EH2 4NG **Tel:** (0131) 220 2900 **Fax:** (0131) 220 3400 **Ptnrs:** 2 **Asst Solrs:** 1 **Other Fee-earners:** 3. The firm specialises in employment law and is regarded as one of the leading employment practices in Scotland.

WORKLOAD	
Employment	100%

MACKENZIE MILLS

76 SHOE LANE, LONDON, EC4A 3JB
DX: 0036 London

TEL: (0171) 583 4884
FAX: (0171) 242 4190

THE FIRM: Mackenzie Mills was founded in 1982 and specialises in banking, commercial and insolvency law and litigation. A substantial part of the firm's work is for Italian clients and most of the fee earners are fluent in Italian as well as English. The firm also has a speciality in Brazilian law matters.

PRINCIPAL AREAS OF WORK:

Banking: *(Contact Partners:* David Mills, Tony Clare; *Consultant:* David McCarthy). Mackenzie Mills is one of the few firms of its size in London providing legal advice to international banks over the whole range of wholesale banking transactions and asset finance. It has strong connections with the Italian banking community and also acts for American, Middle East and Far East financial institutions. *Work includes:* syndicated and conduit loans, structured finance, buyer credits, secured lending and advice on all aspects of domestic and international banking law with asset finance and leasing as a particular speciality.

Company & Commercial: *(Contact Partner:* David Mills/ Anthony Indaimo). The work, predominantly for Italian businesses, includes business start-ups, co-operation agreements (agency, distributorship, joint ventures etc), sale and purchase of companies, protection and exploitation of all forms of intellectual property and media law.

Litigation: *(Contact Partner:* Jeremy Scott/ Virginia Rylatt). The firm has particular expertise in banking, company, insolvency, commercial and financial fraud, intellectual property and real property litigation.

Insolvency: *(Contact Partner:* Christopher Coffin/ Jeremy Scott). Mackenzie Mills is recognised as a leading specialist firm in corporate insolvency matters in England and abroad and has considerable experience in liquidations, administrative and other receiverships and administrations.

Property: *(Contact Partner:* Joy Taylor). *Work includes:* the acquisition of freehold and leasehold business premises, site acquisition and development, secured lending, landlord and tenant matters and disposals of commercial property and other assets. The firm also deals with residential property sales and purchasing, the letting, management and supervision of residential investments and the administrations of other assets in the UK on behalf of overseas clients.

Private Client: *(Contact Partner:* Joy Taylor). Advice is provided on immigration and nationality, trusts, wills and probate, employment law and criminal law.

Corporate Services & International Tax Planning: *(Contact Partner:* David Mills). The firm acts as an incorporation agent and provides full company secretarial and registered office services. Clients are advised on all aspects of international tax planning in Europe and elsewhere.

NATURE OF CLIENTELE: Mackenzie Mills acts for clients, both in the UK and abroad, from many sectors including banking and building societies, communications, entertainment, the media, fashion, marketing and sponsorship and insolvency practitioners.

FOREIGN CONNECTIONS: In addition to the long-standing links with Italy, the firm also acts for clients in America and the Middle East. It has recently acquired a strong Brazilian connection.

LANGUAGES: Italian, French, Spanish, Portuguese.

TRAINING: Trainee solicitors are recruited yearly. Professional staff are usually expected to be fluent in spoken Italian. The firm places emphasis on continuing education, both for professional and technical support staff.

CONTACT PARTNER: Mr D.M.D. Mills

Number of partners:	8
Assistant solicitors:	8
Other fee-earners:	6

WORKLOAD	
Civil litigation	30%
Italian cross-border commercial	15%
Property	15%
Commercial	15%
Banking and finance	15%
Insolvency	10%

CONTACTS	
Banking	D. Mills
Civil litigation	J. Scott, V.Rylatt, C. Coffin
Commercial	D. Mills
Insolvency	J. Scott
Italian commercial law	D. Mills
Property	J. Taylor

MACKINNONS 21 Albert Street, Aberdeen, Grampian, AB9 8DA **Tel:** (01224) 632464 **Fax:** (01224) 632184 **DX:** 34 Aberdeen **Ptnrs:** 7 **Asst Solrs:** 1 **Other Fee-earners:** 3. Specialist shipping practice experienced in all aspects of marine law including insurance, finance and shipping litigation.

MACKINTOSH & WYLIE P.O. Box 31, 23 The Foregate, Kilmarnock, Strathclyde, KA1 1LE **Tel:** (01563) 25104 **Fax:** (01563) 37100 **DX:** 7 Kilmarnock **Ptnrs:** 7 **Asst Solrs:** 2 **Other Fee-earners:** 1. Work includes commercial property, crime, family/ matrimonial, licensing and personal injury work.

MACKRELL TURNER GARRETT

INIGO PLACE, 31 BEDFORD ST, LONDON, WC2E 9EH
DX: 40037 Covent Garden 1

TEL: (0171) 240 0521
FAX: (0171) 240 9457

THE FIRM: Mackrell Turner Garrett is the result of a merger in 1987 between Mackrell & Co. in London and Turner Garrett & Co. in Surrey. The firm was founded in 1845 by John Mackrell who established the John Mackrell Prize for practical legal knowledge. The main areas of work are litigation, company, commercial and property.

PRINCIPAL AREAS OF WORK:

Litigation: Substantial insurance litigation and personal injury department; building and general contract claims, landlord and tenant disputes, defamation and intellectual property, white collar crime, general litigation.

Commercial Property: The firm handles every aspect of property development including site appraisal, planning permission, finance, lease structure and built-in rent reviews.

Residential Development: The firm handles planning, restrictive covenants, easements, options, conditional contracts, road and drainage agreements, and all other aspects of development.

Business Development and Company Law: Concentrating especially on the needs of new and expanding businesses, the firm handles acquisitions, disposals and incorporations, joint ventures and partnerships, overseas trading, employment, banking and finance, pension schemes, taxation and intellectual property.

European Community Law: Specifically anti dumping and competition law.

Private Client Services: *Work includes:* conveyancing, personal tax planning, wills and probate, trust management, matrimonial law.

OTHER OFFICES: Dukes Court, Duke Street, Woking, Surrey GU21 5BH. *Tel:* (01483) 755609. *Fax:* (01483) 755818.
And at Addlestone, Weybridge, Knaphill, West Byfleet and New Haw.

INTERNATIONAL CONNECTIONS: The firm is a founder member of Mackrell International which has a network of offices throughout the world.

FOREIGN LANGUAGES: French, German, Swedish, Danish and Norwegian.

RECRUITMENT & TRAINING: The firm recruits about 3 trainee solicitors annually. Applications by letter and CV to M. John at the London office, or Mr C.J. Appleyard at the Woking office.

CONTACT PARTNERS: Mr J.F.S. Cabot (London), Mr M. Slorick (Woking)

Number of partners:	20
Assistant solicitors:	9
Other fee-earners:	6

WORKLOAD	
Insurance litigation	35%
Commercial litigation	20%
Corporate	15%
Domestic property	10%
Trusts and probate	10%
Commercial property	10%

CONTACTS	
Business dev. & company law	M John
Commercial property	M Green, M Slorick
EC law	M John
Ins. Lit. & personal injury	C Croxton, N Rowley
Litigation	J Cabot, C Appleyard
Matrimonial law	A Green
Private client	C Richardson, M Saviker
Residential development	C Richardson

MACLAY MURRAY & SPENS 151 St. Vincent Street, Glasgow, G2 5NJ **Tel:** (0141) 248 5011 **Fax:** (0141) 248 5819 **DX:** 67 Glasgow **Ptnrs:** 31 **Asst Solrs:** 76 **Other Fee-earners:** 9. A large firm handling a broad range of work for both corporate and private clients. Other offices in Edinburgh, London and Brussels.

WORKLOAD			
Company/ commercial	40%	Commercial property	28%
Litigation	17%	Private client	15%

MACLEOD & MACCALLUM P.O. Box No.4, 28 Queensgate, Inverness, Highlands, IV1 1YN **Tel:** (01463) 239393 **Fax:** (01463) 222 879 **DX:** 12 Inverness **Ptnrs:** 9 **Asst Solrs:** 4 **Other Fee-earners:** 11. Undertakes residential and commercial property work, in addition to providing services with regard to agriculture (especially crofting law), crime, family/ matrimonial work, personal injury, estate agents and housing associations. Independent Financial Advisers.

WORKLOAD			
Dom/res conveyancing	30%	Matrimonial and family	20%
Civil/criminal court	20%	Private client	10%
Comm/development convey	10%		

MACROBERTS

152 BATH STREET, GLASGOW, G2 4TB
DX: GW70

TEL: (0141) 332 9988
FAX: (0141) 332 8886

THE FIRM: MacRoberts is a long-established and prominent firm of corporate and commercial solicitors, with offices in Glasgow, Edinburgh and London, serving the needs of the national and international business community. The firm undertakes a wide range of commercial and private client work, and is particularly well-regarded in the fields of corporate finance (including PFI finance), construction, employment and insolvency. Through its international correspondents both within and outwith the ADVOC network, the firm is able to provide legal advice to its clients throughout the world.

PRINCIPAL AREAS OF WORK:

Corporate Department: (*Contact Partner:* Ian Dickson). The firm advises on all aspects of corporate and commercial law including: incorporations, reorganisations, take-overs and mergers, management buy-outs and joint ventures; loan debenture and equity finance, syndications, consumer credit; flotations, Stock Exchange requirements, new issues, placings and other issues, employee share schemes and pension schemes; receivership, administration, liquidation and bankruptcy; franchising, patents and patent licensing, copyright, trademarks and know-how agreements; partnership agreements; EC law; commercial contracts, including agency distribution and finance agreements; computer contracts; employment and service contracts; entertainment law.

Commercial Property Department: (*Contact Partner:* Laurence M. Fraser). Corporate and private clients are advised on all aspects of heritable and leasehold property matters including: acquisition, sale and leasing of commercial and industrial property; commercial, industrial and housing development, investment and finance; commercial and personal secured loans; environmental law; agricultural law, including forestry; company relocation schemes; timeshare and leisure developments; planning law; licensing law.

Personal Department: (*Contact Partner:* David J.C. MacRobert). The practice offers specialist advice to individuals, trustees and executors in relation to their arrangements in such areas as: tax planning and mitigation; preparation of tax returns; investment advice; establishment and administration of trusts; making of wills; administration of estates; preparation of Powers of Attorney; financial services; acquisition, sale and leasing of estate and domestic property; setting up and administration of curatories.

Litigation Department: (*Contact Partner:* James M. Arnott). The department acts for and advises on all aspects of: civil litigation in both Sheriff Courts and the Court of Session; building and engineering disputes and arbitration; insurance and other commercial litigation; employment law and industrial tribunals; trade union disputes; rating and valuation; planning; professional negligence; liquidation, administration, receivership and bankruptcy; product liability; debt recovery; negotiation and resolution of reparation claims; intellectual property disputes; licensing.

OTHER OFFICES:
27 Melville Street, Edinburgh EH3 7JF. *Tel:* (0131) 226 2552. *Fax:* (0131) 226 2501.
39 Victoria Street, London SW1H 0EE. *Tel:* (0171) 799 2669. *Fax:* (0171) 976 8620.

FOREIGN LANGUAGES: French, German, Greek, Dutch, Italian.

INTERNATIONAL CONNECTIONS & ASSOCIATED OFFICES: Member of ADVOC, an international network of independent lawyers, providing access to legal services throughout Europe.

SENIOR PARTNER: Mr James M. Arnott

Number of partners:	20
Assistant solicitors:	23
Other fee-earners:	18

CONTACTS

Arbitration and litigation	Richard Barrie
	Charles Cowie
Banking	Norman Martin
Commercial property	Laurence Fraser
Company law & corp. finance	Ian Dickson
	Michael Murphy
Construction law	James Arnott
	David Henderson
Employment law	Raymond Williamson
Environmental law	Daniel Gardner
Insolvency	David Flint
Intellectual property	David Flint
Taxation and trusts	David MacRobert

MACROBERTS
SOLICITORS
GLASGOW · EDINBURGH · LONDON

MADDEN & FINUCANE 36 Victoria Square, Belfast, BT1 4QB **Tel:** (01232) 238007 **Fax: Ptnrs:** 2 **Asst Solrs:** 6 **Other Fee-earners:** 14. Well-known criminal and civil liberties practice, which also undertakes judicial review and personal injury work.

WORKLOAD			
General practice	30%	Civil litigation	30%
Criminal	30%	Conveyancing	10%

MAGRATH & CO 52-54 Maddox Street, London, W1R 9PA **Tel:** (0171) 495 3003 **Fax:** (0171) 409 1745 **DX:** 9009 West End **Ptnrs:** 6 **Asst Solrs:** 6 **Other Fee-earners:** 7. Recently-established firm specialising in immigration and corporate fraud work.

WORKLOAD	
36%	30%
15%	10%
6%	3%

MALCOLM LYNCH

VASSALLI HOUSE, 20 CENTRAL ROAD, LEEDS, W. YORKS, LS1 6DE
DX: 12100 Leeds

TEL: (0113) 2429600
FAX: (0113) 2342080

THE FIRM: The firm is a company/ commercial practice and is best known for its work on employee ownership and with the co-operative sector. The firm advises trade unionists and management on ESOPs and profit sharing schemes and has a strong charity and local government clientele. Financial services and banking work is undertaken for "socially responsible" clients. The firm has a positive environment unit which works with renewable energy companies and emerging and established "green" businesses. The firm's two consultants specialise in industrial and provident society law and property law.

LANGUAGES SPOKEN: French and Macedonian.

ASSOCIATED OFFICES: Dublin and Cologne.

CONTACT PARTNER: Malcolm Lynch	
Number of partners:	2
Assistant solicitors:	3
Other fee-earners:	3

WORKLOAD	
Employee share schemes and ESOP's	35%
Charity law including property work	30%
Renewable energy including property work	15%
Commercial litigation and employment law	10%
Corporate finance and social investment	10%

MALKINS Inigo House, 29 Bedford St, Covent Garden, London, WC2E 9ED **Tel:** (0171) 379 3385 **Fax:** (0171) 379 3137 **DX:** 40034 Covent Gdn. 2 **Ptnrs:** 11 **Asst Solrs:** 3 **Other Fee-earners:** 2. Work includes commercial property, corporate work, commercial litigation and private client. Significant overseas connections particularly in the Far East.

MANBY & STEWARD

MANDER HOUSE, MANDER CENTRE, WOLVERHAMPTON,
W. MIDLANDS, WV1 3NE DX: 10403

TEL: (01902) 772711
FAX: (01902) 24321/ 713564

THE FIRM: Established in 1826, Manby & Steward has a strong tradition of working both with private clients and with industry and commerce. The firm has an associate office in Brussels and as a member of LawNet Europe has associates throughout the EC.

PRINCIPAL AREAS OF WORK:

Commercial Litigation: *(Contact Partner:* Clive Williams). *Work includes:* contractual disputes, copyright infringement, consumer protection, debt collection, injunctions, personal injury claims, property disputes, trade descriptions.

Commercial Property: *(Contact Partner:* Kevin Styles). *Work includes:* commercial leases and conveyancing, construction contracts, development schemes and financing, joint ventures, licensed properties, overseas property, rent reviews.

Company and Commercial: *(Contact Partner:* Terry Lipscombe). *Work includes:* acquisition, agency, distribution and franchising agreements, asset leasing, buy-outs, EC competition law, guarantees, hire purchase, intellectual/ industrial property, joint ventures, partnerships, restrictive trade practices, service agreements, takeovers, taxation and venture capital.

Planning Law: *(Contact Partner:* Niall Blackie – Legal Associate of the Royal Town Planning Institute). *Work includes:* advocacy, appeals, compensation, compulsory purchase, development of land, enforcement procedures, listed buildings, public inquiries.

Private Client: *(Contact Partner:* David Shepherd). *Work includes:* accidents and personal injury, adoption, charities, conveyancing, Court of Protection, children, charities, ecclesiastical, family law, health and safety, powers of attorney, residential property, tax planning/ personal finance trusts, wills and probate.

Agricultural: *(Contact Partner:* Steven Corfield). *Work includes:* ADHAC procedures, agricultural, residential tenancies, credit management, farm tenancies, joint ventures, quotas, subsidies, succession and inheritance tax.

MANAGING PARTNER: C.H.G. Williams	
Number of partners:	13
Assistant solicitors:	8
Other fee-earners:	14

WORKLOAD	
Commercial conveyancing	33%
Litigation	25%
Residential conveyancing	19%
Company/ commercial	14%
Private client	9%

CONTACTS	
Agriculture	Stephen Corfield
Commercial litigation	Clive Williams
Commercial property	Kevin Styles
Company/ commercial	Terry Lipscombe
Planning law	Niall Blackie
Private client	David Shepherd

NATURE OF CLIENTELE: The firm acts for a broad range of private clients, businesses and companies, developers, builders and housing associations.

OTHER OFFICES: Telford, Bridgnorth and Brierley Hill.

FOREIGN LANGUAGES: French, Portuguese, Spanish, Hindi and Punjabi.

MANCHES & CO

ALDWYCH HOUSE, 81 ALDWYCH, LONDON, WC2B 4RP
DX: 76

TEL: (0171) 404 4433
FAX: (0171) 430 1133

THE FIRM: Manches & Co is a commercial firm with a well established private client practice.

The firm continues to increase its City-based corporate and commercial work. Since its move to Aldwych in 1990, it has merged with the well respected City firm of Carter Faber, its Aldwych neighbours Asshetons and the well respected Rubinstein Callingham Polden & Gale.

The synergies of these mergers include the development of the specialist sections in banking, insolvency work, housing associations and Intellectual Property as well as greater depth in the other mainstream commercial activities.

The London and Oxford offices are brought together by seamless computer, telephonic and videoconference connections, thereby eliminating the usual disadvantages of dual locations.

The firm's philosophy is to find solutions to the clients' problems professionally, courteously and efficiently. It foresees growth in all of its principal areas of activity.

PRINCIPAL AREAS OF WORK:

Company and Commercial: (*Contact Partner:* Simon Smith). *Work includes:* mergers and acquisitions, company flotations, management buy-outs, reconstructions, joint ventures, partnerships, corporate insolvency, European Community law, competition law, construction, insurance law, banking and financial services.

Property: (*Contact Partner:* Louis Manches). *Work includes:* development, site assembly, planning, building contracts, letting and disposal, joint ventures, funding, investment, housing associations, rent reviews, secured lending and residential property.

Litigation: (*Contact Partner:* James Foster). *Work includes:* contractual disputes, shareholder actions, international disputes, insurance litigation, construction litigation, emergency relief, intellectual property disputes, product liability, insolvency, property disputes, negligence claims, employment, and contentious probate and trusts.

Intellectual Property: (*)Contact Partner:* John Rubinstein) *Work includes:* Advertising, Sales Promotions, Marketing and Trade Description Law, Biotechnology, Computer Law, Copyrights, Film, Television and Entertainment product and services, Multimedia Exploitation, Passing off, Publishing, Defamation and Uk and EC Competition.

Tax: (*Contact Partner:* Stephen Goldstraw). *Work includes:* mergers and acquisitions, joint ventures, flotation planning, profit extraction, leasing, management buy-outs, employee benefits, property tax, VAT planning, stamp duty planning, partnership tax, off-shore trading arrangements, insurance and tax, company pension schemes and tax appeals.

Trusts and Probate: (*Contact Partner:* Julian Hayden). *Work includes:* estate planning, preparation of wills, establishment of trusts, administration of estates and charities.

Family: (*Contact Partner:* Jane Simpson). *Work includes:* divorce, children, financial provision, separation agreements, adoption, guardianship, affiliation proceedings, and jurisdiction crossing.

Employment: (*Contact Partner:* Alasdair Simpson). *Work includes:* executive remuneration and benefits, termination package, staff manual, discrimination policies, unfair and wrongful dismissal claims in the Industrial Tribunal, County and High Court.

CONTACT PARTNER: Mr A.J. Simpson

Number of partners:	40
Assistant solicitors:	41
Other fee-earners:	5

WORKLOAD

Commercial litigation	23%
Corporate	23%
Commercial property	22%
Family law	10%
Housing association	8%
Banking and insolvency	6%
Intellectual property	5%
Tax, wills and trusts	3%

CONTACTS

Banking	Robert Rowan
Commercial property	Louis Manches
Commercial tax	Stephen Goldstraw
Computers	Alistair Wilson
Corporate and commercial	Simon Smith
Employment	Alasdair Simpson
Environment	George Gandy
Family law	Jane Simpson
Housing association	Richard Frost
Insolvency	Charles Gordon
Insurance	Peter Angel
Intellectual property	John Rubinstein
Litigation	James Foster
Private tax and trust	Julian Hayden
Publishing	Bernard Nyman

THE OXFORD OFFICE: Established in 1982, the Oxford office has grown rapidly. It occupies modern premises in the city centre. Like the London office, it has a strong bias towards corporate and commercial work. However, it also deals with private client and litigation work, where the emphasis is on locally based clients. The office takes up to two trainee solicitors each year who have the opportunity to work in the London office.

RECRUITMENT AND TRAINING: There are currently 12 trainee solicitors. The firm's Director of Education and Training has responsibility for directing and monitoring each individual's training, and a programme of regular internal lectures has been evolved to assist in this process. CV's should be sent to Mr. Nigel Brown at the London office or Mr. David Tighe in Oxford.

OFFICE EQUIPMENT: IBM AS400.

MANDER HADLEY & CO 1 The Quadrant, Coventry, W. Midlands, CV1 2DW **Tel:** (01203) 631212 **Fax:** (01203) 633131 **DX:** 11204 **Ptnrs:** 9 **Asst Solrs:** 7 **Other Fee-earners:** 12. A third-generation family practice with a client base of small-to-medium-sized businesses. Best known for civil and criminal litigation, private client, trust, charity and business law.

MAPLES TEESDALE 21 Lincoln's Inn Fields, London, WC2A 3DU **Tel:** (0171) 831 6501 **Fax:** (0171) 405 3867 **DX:** 192 London **Ptnrs:** 11 **Asst Solrs:** 3 **Other Fee-earners:** 8. Eleven-partner firm specialising in commercial property, with a good spread of other work.

THE LAW OFFICES OF MARCUS J. O'LEARY Wyvols Court, Swallowfield, Reading, Berks, RG7 1PY **Tel:** (01734) 880245 **Fax:** (01734) 880360 **Ptnrs:** 1. Recently established practice specialising in all aspects of information technology and intellectual property, with particular expertise in software piracy issues.

WORKLOAD	
IT/intellectual property	100%

MARGARET BENNETT

CHARLTON HOUSE, 5A BLOOMSBURY SQUARE, LONDON, WC1A 2LX
DX: 35740 Bloomsbury 1

TEL: (0171) 404 6465
FAX: (0171) 240 5492

THE FIRM: Established in 1990 and already one of the leading firms in London devoted exclusively to matrimonial law. The principal, Miss Bennett, is a founder member and Vice President of the IAML, Chairman of the Family Law Committee of the International Bar Association and founder of the Intercountry Adoption Lawyers Association. All solicitors within the firm are members of the SFLA.

PRINCIPAL AREAS OF WORK: *Work includes:* prenuptial and separation agreements, divorce, financial settlements, children cases (including child abduction), and cases involving European and jurisdictional issues.

ADDITIONAL AREAS: In-house divorce counselling.

CLIENTELE: Client base includes national and foreign private clients.

FOREIGN CONNECTIONS: Contacts with matrimonial lawyers worldwide.

CONTACT PARTNER: Margaret H. Bennett

Number of partners:	1
Assistant solicitors:	1
Associates	4

WORKLOAD	
Family law	100%

MARGRAVES

OLD COURT CHAMBERS, LLANDRINDOD WELLS, POWYS, LD1 5EY
DX: 200154 Llandrindod

TEL: (01597) 825565
FAX: (01597) 825220

THE FIRM: Margraves has been established as a niche practice specialising in wills, trusts, probate, estate and inheritance tax planning. The principal of the firm, Clive Margrave-Jones, has devoted his professional life to this field as a practitioner, visiting university lecturer and an established author. The area of agricultural law is covered by Christopher Rodgers, the author of numerous texts. Margraves welcomes instructions on a consultancy basis from solicitors, accountants, IFA's and other professions.

CONTACT PARTNER: C. Margrave-Jones

Number of partners:	1
Assistant solicitors:	1
Other fee-earners:	2

MARRIOTT HARRISON

12 GREAT JAMES STREET, LONDON, WC1N 3DR
DX: 0001 Ch.Ln

TEL: (0171) 209 2000
FAX: (0171) 209 2001

THE FIRM: Marriott Harrison was established in 1986 to provide specialised media and commercial services and has expanded since then by the addition of substantial corporate and tax expertise. The firm overwhelmingly comprises City-trained lawyers who are committed to providing a high quality service and standard of professionalism with personal attention to the client's needs. Marriott Harrison represents major corporations and entrepreneurs in a number of business sectors including multi-media, venture capital and manufacturing.

PRINCIPAL AREAS OF WORK:

Corporate: *(Contact:* Jonathan Sweet). All aspects of corporate finance including mergers, acquisitions and disposals; management buy-outs and venture capital; Enterprise Investment Schemes and Venture Capital Funds; corporate restructuring; banking; financial services and insolvency.

Commercial: *(Contact:* Stephen Mullens). All forms of commercial agreements but in particular business asset sales and the restructuring of businesses; the licensing of know-how, technology, software and intellectual property rights; professional appointments for construction projects; distribution and agency; terms of trading; trade finance; product liability; data protection and confidentiality and consultancy.

Media: *(Contact:* William Hinshelwood). The group represents prominent organisations within the multi-media industries including US major studios, cable and satellite channels and MSOs. The work covers a wide range of services including the production, distribution and finance of film, television, video, computer and other software products; cable and satellite broadcasting; regulatory advice and all aspects of copyright law.

Tax: *(Contact:* Michael Paynter). The department advises on a broad range of national and international corporate transactions and commercial activities. It has particular experience in dealing with the affairs of entrepreneurs and their substantial private companies and a reputation for developing innovative structures to meet clients' commercial aims. The department has an established facility for its international tax planning work in corporate and personal contexts for both UK and overseas clients.

Litigation: *(Contact:* Peter Curnock).

Property: *(Contact:* Vivienne Elson).

Experienced commercial partners supporting the litigation and property needs of the firm's clients.

OVERSEAS CONNECTIONS: The firm has strong connections throughout Canada and the United States, Hong Kong, the Middle East, France, Brazil and Eastern Europe. One of the partners is the Secretary of the British Polish Legal Association.

CONTACT PARTNER: Frank Bloom

Number of partners:	18
Assistant solicitors:	6

WORKLOAD	
Media	40%
Tax (corporate)	20%
Corporate/ commercial	20%
Litigation	12%
Property	8%

CONTACTS	
Commercial	Stephen Mullens
Corporate	Jon Sweet
Litigation	Peter Curnock
Media	William Hinshelwood
Property	Vivienne Elson
Tax	Michael Paynter

MARRON DODDS

1 MERIDAN SOUTH, MERIDAN BUSINESS PARK, LEICESTER, LEICS, LE3 2WY
DX: 710910 Leicester Meridian

TEL: (0116) 289 2200
FAX: 0116) 289 3733

24 Friar Lane, Leicester LE1 5RA
DX: 10830 Leicester 1
Contact Partner: Brian Dodds

Tel: (0116) 262 8596
Fax: (0116) 251 8322

31 Friar Lane, Leicester LE1 5RB
DX:10830 Leicester 1
Contact Partner: Vera Stamenkovich

Tel: (0116) 253 8585
Fax: (0116) 253 0212

THE FIRM: Marron Dodds has conveniently re-located its commercial practice a very short distance from Junction 21 of the M1 Motorway. The firm has an established reputation in the areas of planning development and environmental law and specialist advice is provided in all areas of commercial property, company/commercial, com-

CONTACT PARTNER: Peter Marron

Number of partners:	13
Assistant solicitors:	6
Other fee-earners:	14

mercial litigation and employment law. Two buildings have been retained in the city centre. At 24 Friar Lane there is a comprehensive criminal practice providing extensive representation in the local courts and a 24 hour police station service; and at 31 Friar Lane a range of services are provided for the individual client with an emphasis on personal injury litigation, medical negligence, matrimonial disputes, care proceedings, welfare law services for the elderly and those with learning disabilities.

WORKLOAD	
Criminal litigation	40%
Commercial and public law	40%
Civil litigation and matrimonial	20%

MARRONS 58 Jesmond Road, Newcastle upon Tyne, Tyne & Wear, NE2 4PQ **Tel:** (0191) 281 1304 **Fax:** (0191) 212 0080 **DX:** 62555 Jesmond **Ptnrs:** 5 **Other Fee-earners:** 5. Almost exclusively plaintiff personal injury litigators handling industrial accident and disease cases, RTA's, medical negligence and multi-party litigation.

WORKLOAD			
Personal injury	95%	Medical negligence	5%

MARSHALL & GALPIN Vanbrugh House, 20-22 St. Michael's Street, Oxford, Oxon, OX1 2EA **Tel:** (01865) 792300 **Fax:** (01865) 791451 **Ptnrs:** 12 **Asst Solrs:** 10 **Other Fee-earners:** 4. Founded over 200 years ago. Principal areas of work are domestic and commercial conveyancing, probate and trusts, and all forms of litigation. Five branch offices.

MARSH, FERRIMAN & CHEALE Southfield House, 11 Liverpool Gardens, Worthing, W. Sussex, BN11 1SD **Tel:** (01903) 234911 **Fax:** (01903) 207867 **DX:** 3701 **Ptnrs:** 7 **Asst Solrs:** 6 **Other Fee-earners:** 8. Result of a merger: Marsh & Ferriman and Davis, Thomas & Cheale. Best known for litigation, conveyancing and probate. Other offices in Goring-by-Sea, Rustington, Littlehampton and Yapton.

MARSONS SOLICITORS

AMADEUS HOUSE, 33-39 ELMFIELD ROAD, BROMLEY, KENT, BR1 1LT
DX: 121100 Bromley 9

TEL: (0181) 313 1300
FAX: (0181) 466 7920

THE FIRM: Traditional High Street legal services from four Branches, and Mortgage Lenders and Housing Association Client work from the firms superb Head Office in Bromley.

Holders of IS0 9001, Law Society Practice Management Standards and Investors in People Award.

PRINCIPAL AREAS OF WORK:

Mortgage Arrears: Having been at the forefront of this delicate problem area since 1991 the Firm now acts for several top ten lenders. Systems include counselling of defaulters, monitoring of accounts and repossession. On line to major Society clients. A same day service on all accounts.

Repossession Sales: Manned only by Solicitors and very experienced Legal Executives. A very pro-active problem solving and selling division, of properties in possession.

Professional Indemnity: The identification of negligence and fraud is a specialist and rapidly (unfortunately) growing area of legal service. This department staffed only by Solicitors includes a consultant who is an acknowledged and much demanded expert witness.

Social Housing: Established 6 years ago this department has a growing reputation in specialist litigation for Housing Associations and Local Authorities.

Conveyancing: For over 25 years the firm has been known for its strength, efficiency and quality of service in this field of legal work. Even in current difficult times we still process over 3000 domestic conveyancing cases a year.

Matrimonial family and immigration: From the four Branch Offices a sympathetic and sensitive service.

Agency: Attending all Courts in South London and North Kent daily.

CONTACT PARTNER:
Brian Marson, Senior Partner

Number of partners:	6
Assistant solicitors:	4
Other fee-earners:	33

CONTACTS	
Agency	Jennifer White
Commercial litigation	Kevin Lee
Domestic conveyancing	P D Fitz-Hugh
Family	Caroline Landes
Immigration	Y Alli-Balogun
Mortgage arrears	B J Marson
Mortgage sales	B J Marson
Professional negligence	Jennifer White
Social housing	Kevin Lee

MARTIN CUNNINGHAM & CO 286 Claremont Rd, Moss Side, Manchester, M14 4EP **Tel:** (0161) 226 5192 **Fax:** (0161) 226 1620 **Ptnrs:** 2 **Other Fee-earners:** 3. Specialists in criminal defence work, including white collar crime. Legal aid work undertaken. Particular expertise in the area of commercial fraud.

WORKLOAD			
Criminal defence work	95%	Welfare/green form	5%

MARTINEAU JOHNSON

ST. PHILIPS HOUSE, ST. PHILIPS PLACE, BIRMINGHAM, W. MIDLANDS, B3 2PP
DX: 13031

TEL: (0121) 200 3300
FAX: (0121) 200 3330

THE FIRM: Martineau Johnson is one of the larger Birmingham city centre firms. It is a broadly-based practice serving a wide range of commercial, institutional and private clients. Originally founded in 1828, the firm now combines a traditional approach to client/ partner relations with modern drive for specialisation and expertise.

TYPES OF WORK UNDERTAKEN INCLUDE:

Banking: *(Contact:* Ian Baker). Acting for banks in funding and financial reconstruction work.

Charities: *(Contact:* Michael Fea). Formation, financial and administration advice for trustees and beneficiaries.

Commercial Agreements: *(Contact:* David Allison). Joint ventures, franchising and conditions of sale and purchase.

Commercial Litigation: *(Contact:* Andrew Spooner). Civil litigation and arbitration of most kinds are conducted.

Commercial Property: *(Contact:* Barry Sankey). Sales and purchases, leases and option agreements of commercial, industrial, office and investment property, including acting for institutional investors.

Company: *(Contact:* David Allison). Sales and purchases of shares in and assets of limited companies.

Construction & Development: *(Contact:* Michael Shepherd). Sales and purchases and options relating to land for building and building contracts and collateral warranties.

Construction Litigation: *(Contact:* Andrew Spooner). Arbitration and other proceedings arising out of building contracts.

Corporate: *(Contact:* Michael Winwood). There are a number of listed company clients for whom Stock Exchange work is undertaken, as well as for companies going to the market.

Corporate Finance: *(Contact:* Andrew Stilton). Management buy-outs and buy-ins.

Debt: *(Contact:* Brian Aikman). Volume debt collection work of all kinds.

Defamation: *(Contact:* David Cooper). Acting for newspapers and other publishers and companies and individuals in libel and slander cases.

EC & Competition: *(Contact:* Geraldine Tickle). Competition law including merger control, MMC enquiries, EU complaints, pricing, trading conduct and its application to distribution, joint ventures, franchising and licensing.

Ecclesiastical: Hugh Carslake, one of the partners, is Registrar to the Birmingham Diocese.

Education: *(Contact:* Simon Arrowsmith). Retained solicitors to 8 universities and about 15 colleges of further education.

Employment: *(Contact:* Ian Marshall). Advising clients on all aspects, contentious and non-contentious, including discrimination and equal rights.

Environment: *(Contact:* Barry Sankey). Advising clients on all aspects including the impact of environmental law on investment land and security.

Family: *(Contact:* Andrew Spooner). Matrimonial and child law advice to private individuals.

Insolvency: *(Contact:* Ian Baker). Acting for receivers, liquidators and trustees in bankruptcy and for creditors affected by debtors' financial difficulties.

Intellectual Property: *(Contact:* William Barker). Copyright, trade marks, passing off and patent advice for owners and users of such rights.

Licensing: *(Contact:* Andrew Spooner). Obtaining liquor licences and advising on the law in that area.

Pensions: *(Contact:* Paul Mullard). Acting for pension fund trustees in relation to formation and administration.

SENIOR PARTNER: Michael Shepherd

Number of partners:	24
Assistant solicitors:	39
Other fee-earners:	28

WORKLOAD	
Corporate	27%
Property	21%
Litigation	19%
Private client	12%
Intellectual property	8%
Education	7%
Employment and pensions	6%

CONTACTS	
Banking	Ian Baker
Charities	Michael Fea
Commercial agreements	David Allison
Commercial litigation	Andrew Spooner
Commercial property	Barry Sankey
Company	David Allison
Construction & development	Michael Shepherd
Construction litigation	Andrew Spooner
Corporate	Michael Winwood
Corporate finance	Roger Blears/ Andrew Stilton
Debt	Brian Aikman
Defamation	David Cooper
EC and competition	Geraldine Tickle
Ecclesiastical	Hugh Carslake
Education	Simon Arrowsmith
Employment	Ian Marshall
Environment	Brian Aikman
Family	Fiona Hunter-Rioch
Insolvency	Ian Baker
Intellectual property	William Barker
Licensing	Andrew Spooner
Pensions	Paul Mullard
Tax - corporate	Jeremy Martineau
Tax - private	Matthew Hansell
Town and country planning	Barry Sankey
Trusts, settlements and wills	Hugh Carslake

Tax – Corporate: *(Contact:* Jeremy Martineau). Advising business clients on taxation aspects of transactions.

Tax – Private: *(Contact:* Matthew Hansell). Advising private clients on their tax planning and administration of returns.

Town & Country Planning: *(Contact:* Barry Sankey). Advising business and investor clients on law in this area, and its relationship to development transactions and environmental questions.

Trusts, Settlements & Wills: *(Contact:* Hugh Carslake). Advising private clients on personal financial planning and arrangements through the creation of these instruments as well as the administration of estates.

FOREIGN CONNECTIONS: The firm is a member of an international legal association and has fellow member firms with which it enjoys close connections in the major trading centres of the world.

RECRUITMENT & TRAINING: Up to 5 trainee solicitors are recruited annually. Training and prospects are excellent, most of the present partners having served articles with the firm. Application forms are available from Yvonne McGowan, Recruitment & Training Administrator.

MARTINEAU JOHNSON
SOLICITORS

MARTIN-KAYE & PARTNERS

HAZLEDINE HOUSE, CENTRAL SQ, TELFORD CENTRE, TELFORD, SHROPS, TF3 4JL   DX: 28073

TEL: (01952) 291757
FAX: (01952) 291759

MANAGING PARTNER: Andrew J.L. Green	
Number of partners:	8
Assistant solicitors:	3
Other fee-earners:	7

PRINCIPAL AREAS OF WORK:

Company and commercial	Contact: Stuart J. Haynes
Intellectual property	) "
Technology transfer	) "
Franchising	) "
Commercial conveyancing	Contact: Barry Stimpson
Landlord and tenant	Contact: Robert Hughes
Commercial and general litigation	Contact: Graham W. Davies
Debt collection	) "
Personal injury	Contact: Christopher Cann
Probate and trusts	Contact: Roderick M. Kirby
Agricultural and charity law	Contact: S. Brian Williams
Employment law	Contact: Andrew E. Wylde

FOREIGN CONNECTIONS: The firm has extensive experience in business abroad and was a founder member of I.A.G. International, a European Group of professional advisors.

NATURE OF CLIENTELE: A broad base of private and commercial clients, including well known multi national companies. Agency and legal aid work undertaken.

RECRUITMENT AND TRAINING: The firm recruits on a regular basis and provides first-class all round training for trainee solicitors in each of the firms departments. *(Contact:* Mrs M. Maquire).

MARTIN TOLHURST PARTNERSHIP 7 Wrotham Rd, Gravesend, Kent, DA11 0PD **Tel:** (01474) 325531 **Fax:** (01474) 560771 **DX:** 6801 Gravesend **Ptnrs:** 8 **Asst Solrs:** 3   **Other Fee-earners:** 12.   A firm with well-established litigation and commercial conveyancing departments, probate, matrimonial and personal injury litigation.

MASON BOND King Charles House, King Charles Croft, Leeds, W. Yorks, LS1 6LA **Tel:** (0113) 242 4444 **Fax:** (0113) 246 7542 **DX:** 26409 **Ptnrs:** 4 **Asst Solrs:** 1 **Other Fee-earners:** 3.   This young firm has become a leading practice in tour operator, travel and holiday law. Also handles childcare, family and criminal law.

MASON & MOORE DUTTON Kirkton House, 4 Hunter St, Chester, CH1 2AS **Tel:** (01244) 348881 **Fax:** (01244) 315513 **DX:** 22151 **Ptnrs: 6 Asst Solrs: 2 Other Fee-earners:** 1. A general practice known for agriculture, company law, conveyancing, and matrimonial work. Also handles probate, employment law and general litigation.

MASONS

30 AYLESBURY STREET, LONDON, EC1R 0ER
DX: 53313 Clerkenwell

TEL: (0171) 490 4000
FAX: (0171) 490 2545

SENIOR PARTNER: Mr J.M. Bishop

Number of partners:	58
Assistant solicitors:	100
Other fee-earners:	75

THE FIRM: Masons has offices in London, Bristol, Manchester, Leeds, Brussels, Hong Kong and Guangzhou (PRC) and associated offices in the USA, Russia, Kazakhstan, across Scandinavia and in Cairo. The firm works regularly in continental Europe, the Middle East, the Pacific Rim, Africa and the Indian subcontinent. Masons provides a broad range of legal services and is well known for advising the construction, engineering and computer industries. While the firm's main specialities include large scale (often international) dispute resolution and advice on major projects generally, Masons also offers a full range of commercial, legal risk management, tax and financial planning and charity services.

PRINCIPAL AREAS OF WORK:

Construction and Engineering: Masons is involved, in the UK and internationally at every stage of the construction process on projects as diverse as airports, tunnels, motorways, marinas, water systems, reservoirs, hospitals and oil rigs. This can be in the context of joint ventures, BOT schemes or for individual companies. Structuring, negotiating, drafting and advising generally on contracts, associated documentation and project finance are major fields of activity. The firm handles national and international disputes whether in the context of arbitration, litigation or ADR including ICC, LCIA and other institutional and non-institutional arbitration work.

Computer Law: The firm has a strong and experienced team to meet the needs of the computer industry and its users. Work involves resolving a wide range of computer disputes as well as drafting and negotiating agreements for the supply and procurement of software and systems; advising on software development, licensing and distribution; and establishing and protecting rights in technology. Particular specialisms include outsourcing, joint marketing ventures, system supply and procurement, channel distribution, data protection and safety critical systems. Masons' own advanced and distinctive use of information systems gives it particular insight in this area of work.

Commercial Dispute Resolution: Advice is given in relation to commercial disputes in a wide range of areas including construction and engineering, technology, intellectual property, insurance, fraud and general commercial actions. Dispute resolution techniques include the traditional methods of litigation and arbitration and, increasingly, Alternative Dispute Resolution procedures. Masons pioneered the application of information technology to the effective management of complex litigation matters and continues to be at the forefront of such use.

Structured Finance: Masons' Structured Finance Unit advises on the financing requirements and the effective management of both domestic and overseas infrastructure and industrial projects, including those arising from the government's Private Finance Initiative; the financing of ships, aircraft, plant and machinery; cross-border and tax based leasing; sales aid or vendor leasing; Local Authority leasing; vehicle leasing, "big" and "middle" ticket equipment leasing; construction, trade and commercial finance; financial instruments and derivatives; and corporate banking.

Property Litigation: Advice is given on the full range of property disputes and property management, including landlord and tenant matters such as rent reviews, dilapidations and repossessions. This involves acting for a wide range of businesses with extensive and strategically important property portfolios such as those in the leisure and drinks sectors.

CONTACTS

Commercial dispute resolution	
	Neil Biggs, London
	Robert Lewington, Hong Kong
	Adam Harris, Bristol
	Edward Davies, Manchester
Company/Commercial	Russell Booker, London
	Jonathan Cheung, Hong Kong
Computer law	Robert McCallough, London
	Adam Harris, Bristol
	Edward Davis, Manchester
	Shelagh Gaskill, Leeds
Construction & engineering	
	Martin Harman, London
	Iain Black, Hong Kong
	Mark Collingwood, Bristol
	Peter Wood, Manchester
	Keith Hartley, Leeds
Consulting	Richard Susskind, London
Debt recovery	Richard Williams, London
Environmental	Peter Stockdale, London
	Mark Richards, Leeds
	Bonnie Martin, Bristol
	John Moritz, Manchester
EU law	Mark Lane, London
	Barbara Linehan, Brussels
Health & safety	Christopher Dering, London
India	Arun Singh, London
Insolvency	Richard Davis, London
Intellectual property	Stephen Aldred, London
Planning	Peter Stockdale, London
	Bonnie Martin, Bristol
	John Moritz, Manchestrer
Property	Guy Jordan, London

EU Law: A multi-discipline unit co-ordinated from London and Brussels gives advice on the impact of EU law on corporate risk management issues and transactions particularly in those industries or areas of domestic law where the Commission is very active, e.g. construction and engineering, information technology, the environment, health and safety, employment, competition law, and procurement law.

Planning: The firm advises on and prepares inquiries relating to local plans, planning appeals and compulsory purchase. The environmental aspect of planning is an important area of work.

Environmental: Masons' environmental law service assists key business sectors including chemicals, construction and engineering, oil and gas, paper and packaging, water and waste and property development. By drawing upon the skills and experience of all other areas of the firm's expertise it offers a fully integrated approach particularly on risk management.

Health and Safety: Health and safety services extend from assisting in planning for the impact of legislative requirements on business activities through to prosecutions and other contentious matters.

Property: The wide range of services includes: advising on commercial development, acting for banks, contractors, owners and occupiers in the management of portfolios, and handling the sale, purchase and tenancy of agricultural land and property management.

Tax and Financial Planning: Masons offers a comprehensive service covering trusts (UK and overseas), wills, and probate, administration of estates, tax (planning and appeals), financial services, charity (creation and advice), and a full range of property work.

Employment: Masons deals with all legal aspects of employer and employee relations, including employee documentation, industrial tribunal and other employment-based proceedings, the resolution of individual and collective disputes, employee benefits, TUPE related issues and immigration.

Consulting: Masons offers consultancy services in the field of legal risk management, including legal risk audits and dispute pre-emption advice particularly for in-house legal departments. Building on the firm's reputation in using IT, advice is also given on IT strategy, system specification and specialist technologies such as hypertext, imaging and document assembly.

Company/Commercial: The firm advises on mergers and acquisitions; MBOs, corporate finance, restructuring and financings. Drafting and negotiating a wide range of commercial agreements such as joint ventures, partnerships and franchise arrangements is also a major area of work.

India: Masons' India Unit, established in 1987, was the first such unit abroad. It acts for a wide range of international companies doing business in India and Indian companies doing business in the EU. It advises on matters in Delhi, Bombay, Calcutta, Madras and Bangalore. It is involved in applications to Government authorities; BOT/ BOO's in the energy sector and construction and civil engineering; transfer of technology and licensing; acquisitions; collaborations and arbitration and litigation.

Intellectual Property: The firm's intellectual property lawyers advise on and handle disputes and transactions relating to patents, trade marks and copyright and designs, trade secrets and unfair competition across all industry sectors.

Insolvency: Masons acts for insolvency practitioners generally and also advises company management and individuals on insolvency matters.

Debt Recovery: The firm operates a fully computerised debt recovery service covering all stages of the process from correspondence through to court proceedings and enforcement if necessary.

REGIONAL OFFICES: The firm operates on a national basis and serves clients in the regions from offices in Bristol, Manchester and Leeds.

OVERSEAS OFFICES: Masons' Hong Kong office provides an all round commercial service to clients in Hong Kong and other parts of the Far East with particular emphasis on construction and engineering projects, commercial litigation and China-related advice. The firm has an office in Guangzhou, Southern China which offers general commercial advice particularly on joint venture agreements with PRC entities as well as servicing clients in the construction and engineering fields. For details on its Brussels office, please refer to main classification: EU Law. Masons has extensive contacts and associations with law firms and consultants on a worldwide basis.

Property	Beverley Pike, Bristol
	Colin Rowe, Manchester
Property litigation	Bonnie Martin, Bristol
	Anne Molyneux, London
Structured finance	Steven Bond, London
	Steven Janes, Nigel Weiss
Tax & financial planning	Peter Instone, London

MASONS

Solicitors
& Privy Council Agents

RECRUITMENT AND TRAINING: The firm usually recruits 14 trainee solicitors each year. Apply by Masons' application form with covering letter to Richard Laudy, London office.

OTHER OFFICES:
Bristol: *Contact:* Mark Collingwood. *Tel:* (0117) 9226622
Manchester: *Contact:* Peter Wood. *Tel:* (0161) 877 3777
Leeds: *Contact:* Keith Hartley. *Tel:* (0113) 233 8905
Brussels: *Contact:* Barbara Linehan. *Tel:* (32) 2 646 0260
Hong Kong: *Contact:* Iain Black. *Tel:* 2 521 5621
Guangzhou: *Contact:* Jonathan Cheung. *Tel:* 86 20 766 0000

MATTHEW ARNOLD & BALDWIN

PO BOX NO. 101, 20 STATION RD, WATFORD, HERTS, WD1 1HT
DX: 4508 Watford

TEL: (01923) 202020
FAX: (01923) 215050

CONTACT PARTNER: John M. Baldwin

Number of partners:	14
Assistant solicitors:	6
Other fee-earners:	16

THE FIRM: Best known for its commercial work, the firm has grown to be one of the leading commercial practices in the area. Good European connections have been developed. Clients range from private individuals to international groups.

The firm also has a strong reputation for its private client work, with an acknowledged expertise in matrimonial and childcare matters.

PRINCIPAL AREAS OF WORK:

Litigation: (*Contact Partner:* Steven Mills). The firm's large litigation department handles a wide variety of commercial and private work, but has particular expertise in commercial disputes, employment, intellectual property, fraud, banking, personal injury and debt recovery.

Company/ Commercial: (*Contact Partner:* Chris Green). Business clients are well served, with the department providing a comprehensive range of services including acquisitions and disposals, MBO's and MBI's, joint ventures, agency and distribution agreements. It also covers intellectual property and employment matters. The department is particularly used to working with and understanding the needs of legal departments.

Commercial Property: (*Contact Partner:* Richard Hanney). The department has extensive experience of commercial property matters including new developments, large industrial sites, leasehold and freehold acquisitions and disposals, including associated planning and environmental issues. The team has also handled major auctions of large numbers of commercial properties.

Information Technology Law: (*Contact Partner:* Chris Green/ Alan Piper). The firm represents many businesses in this sector and is experienced in drafting agreements for outsourcing and for the sale and distribution and purchasing of rights in technology and both hardware and software products. The firm also acts in disputes involving technology including trade marks and copyright.

Family: (*Contact Partner:* Christine Ramsey). The family department has a substantial expertise in matrimonial and family matters with a particular emphasis on childcare and adoption. One partner is a member of the Childcare Panel and one specialist is a barrister.

Private Client: (*Contact Partner:* Iain Donaldson). The firm offers a comprehensive service covering wills, trusts, tax, probate and residential conveyancing.

WORKLOAD

Commercial and general litigation	27%
Company/ commercial	22%
Residential conveyancing	21%
Family and childcare	14%
Private client	8%
Commercial property	8%

CONTACTS

Commercial/general litigation	Steven Mills
Commercial property	Richard Hanney
Company/commercial	Chris Green
Debt collection	Ian Sankey
Family and childcare	Christine Ramsey
Personal injury	Ian Sankey
Resi. convey. & estate devel.	David Marsden
Wills, trust and probate	Iain Donaldson

MATTHEW McCLOY & PARTNERS Toomer's Wharf, Newbury, Berks, RG14 1DY **Tel:** (01635) 551515 **Fax:** (01635) 550228 **DX:** 30806 **Ptnrs:** 2 **Asst Solrs:** 2 . A general practice dealing with commercial work and litigation. Best known for bloodstock work in this country and abroad.

MAURICE COHEN & CO

309 KENTISH TOWN ROAD, LONDON, NW5 2TJ
DX: 46475 Kentish Town

TEL: (0171) 267 2967
FAX: (0171) 267 0839

THE FIRM: Maurice Cohen & Co is well established in the niche area of immigration law and has rapidly gained repute particularly in the field of political asylum. The firm additionally has substantial expertise in all areas of business immigration and handles all types of immigration work. The firm prides itself on the efficient, professional and personal attention given to all clients.

CONTACT PARTNER: Maurice Cohen

Number of partners:	1
Assistant solicitors:	1
Other fee-earners:	2

MAX BARFORD & CO

16 MOUNT PLEASANT ROAD, TUNBRIDGE WELLS, KENT, TN1 1QU
DX: 3918

TEL: (01892) 539379
FAX: (01892) 521874

THE FIRM: Established in 1977, the firm now occupies offices in Tunbridge Wells and Tonbridge. The senior partner and founder Mr. Barford is a member of the Legal Aid Board No.2 Area Committee. Miss Diana Evans is a member of the Children Panel.

PRINCIPAL AREAS OF WORK:

General Description: Although it is predominantly a litigation practice the firm also has a strong non-contentious section. The litigation work includes criminal, personal injury, negligence, contractual disputes, uninsured loss, debt recovery and all aspects of family work and childcare. The non-contentious section deals with all conveyancing, probate, wills and trusts, administration of estates and company and commercial work. In addition, agency work is undertaken for a number of other firms in the High Court, County Court and Magistrates Court.

NATURE OF CLIENTELE: The firm acts for clients from a variety of sources including private companies, insurance companies and individuals.

RECRUITMENT: One trainee solicitor per year. Applications to Miss D. Evans.

CONTACT PARTNER: Mr M. Barford

Number of partners:	5
Assistant solicitors:	5
Other fee-earners:	3

WORKLOAD	
General litigation	30%
Criminal	24%
Conveyancing	17%
Children work	16%
Personal injury	7%
Other	6%

MAX BITEL, GREENE 1 Canonbury Place, London, N1 2NG **Tel:** (0171) 354 2767 **Fax:** (0171) 226 1210 **DX:** 51852 Highbury **Ptnrs:** 6 **Other Fee-earners:** 3. General commercial practice handling company work, commercial litigation and property, and insolvency. Flourishing sports law practice acting for sporting bodies.

MAXWELL BATLEY

27 CHANCERY LANE, LONDON, WC2A 1PA
DX: 190

TEL: (0171) 405 7888
FAX: (0171) 242 7133

THE FIRM: Founded in 1896, Maxwell Batley is a well established City practice which has developed a reputation for a businesslike approach to the law. It handles large scale city and international transactions for substantial institutions, while remaining committed to providing services also to smaller public companies, private companies and businesses, and private individuals. The firm aims to provide practical, commercially-orientated and sometimes innovative advice, promptly and cost effectively. It attaches particular importance to direct partner involvement.

PRINCIPAL AREAS OF WORK:

Banking: (*Contact Partner:* Fraser McColl). Work includes secured and unsecured lending, advice on regulatory matters and trade finance.

Company/ Commercial: (*Contact Partners:* Ian McIntyre, Fraser McColl). Work includes mergers and acquisitions, loan capital, general commercial advice, compliance, venture capital, MBOs, MBIs, distribution and marketing agreements, licensing software and other copyright material and advice on EC law.

Corporate Finance: (*Contact Partner:* Christopher North). Work undertaken includes flotations and new issues, fund raising and reconstructions.

SENIOR PARTNER: Michael Cassidy

Number of partners:	15
Assistant solicitors:	5
Other fee-earners:	8

WORKLOAD	
Property (commercial)	40%
Company/ commercial	20%
Litigation (property)	12%
Banking	10%
Private client	8%
Litigation (commercial)	8%
Computer law and IT	2%

Litigation: (*Contact Partners:* Philip Knights, Philip Adams). Work undertaken includes in particular proceedings for institutional clients concerning land and commercial property, banking, international commerce, intellectual property disputes and employment problems. The firm also acts as Privy Council agents.

Property: (*Commercial Contact Partner:* Peter Radford, *Residential Contact:* John O'Gorman). The firm is particularly noted for its busy commercial property practice, which deals with all aspects of buying, selling, developing, leasing and financing office and industrial properties (including high-tech and commercial business parks) and retail shops including continuous active management of large scale developments. The department has major institutional clients in the UK, USA, Europe, Japan and Australia. The firm also offers a comprehensive residential conveyancing service, acting both for corporate and private clients.

Trusts, Pensions, Tax & Estates: (*Contact Partner:* Frank O'Shea). The department can advise on corporate and personal tax; private, public and corporate trusts (including charitable trusts), pension schemes, wills, probate and the administration of estates.

FOREIGN LANGUAGES: French, German, Italian, Spanish.

CONTACTS	
Banking	Fraser McColl
Company/ commercial	Ian McIntyre
	Fraser McColl
Corporate finance	Christopher North
Litigation	Philip Knights/ Philip Adams
Property (commercial)	Peter Radford
Property (residential)	John O'Gorman
Tax and estates	Frank O'Shea
Trusts/ pensions	Frank O'Shea

MAXWELL ENTWISTLE & BYRNE 14 Castle Street, Liverpool, Merseyside, L2 0SG **Tel:** (0151) 227 4545 **Fax:** (0151) 227 5468 **DX:** 14192 **Ptnrs:** 10 **Asst Solrs:** 9 **Other Fee-earners:** 21. Has six other offices in Merseyside, Liverpool, Wirral and Southport. Handles commercial law, employment law, conveyancing, personal injury litigation, debt collection, matrimonial and professional negligence.

MAYCOCK'S Broadgate House, 7 Eldon Street, London, EC2M 7LS **Tel:** (0171) 375 0586 **Fax:** (0171) 375 0587 **Ptnrs:** 1 **Other Fee-earners:** 2. A specialist practice founded in 1993 undertaking intellectual property work only and bringing together two partners with extensive experience in the field.

MAY, MAY & MERRIMANS

12 SOUTH SQUARE, GRAY'S INN, LONDON, WC1R 5HH
DX: 225 London

TEL: (0171) 405 8932
FAX: (0171) 831 0011

THE FIRM: Founded in 1786, May, May & Merrimans is best known for its private client work, offering a high-quality personal service to individuals and families, many of whom are the owners of substantial residential and agricultural estates and commercial property. The firm brings the same quality of service to its corporate clients and undertakes a broad range of company and commercial business.

PRINCIPAL AREAS OF WORK:

Trusts & Tax: Specialist advice includes will drafting, the creation and variation of all types of settlements including offshore trusts, structuring through companies and trust management.

Probate: A considerable volume of probate and estate planning work is handled, often involving large estates which may include overseas property.

Litigation: The litigation element of the practice deals with most types of contentious civil law, including landlord and tenant disputes, personal injury claims, matrimonial litigation and general commercial disputes.

Property: A full range of property work is undertaken ranging from new town sites to mineral excavations, office and shop leases, agricultural tenancies, estate sales and substantial domestic conveyancing transactions.

Company and Commercial: The firm can assist in the formation of companies and partnerships, in the acquisition of existing enterprises and in all matters which arise in the course of running a business or private company, including share issues, the drafting of contracts and employment questions.

CONTACT PARTNER: Miss A. Sarkis

Number of partners:	11
Assistant solicitors:	4
Other fee-earners:	2

WORKLOAD	
Private client (tax, trust, probate)	50%
Property (domestic/agricultural/comm.)	30%
Litigation/ matrimonial	15%
Company/ commercial	5%

CONTACTS	
Business/ company	Ms. A. Sarkis
Civil litigation	Ms. S. Gillette
Estate planning/ settlements	C.P. Walsh
Family/ matrimonial	Ms. S. Black
Probate	D.H. Smyth
Property (domestic)	R.P. Taylor
Property (commercial)	S. Schofield
Property (agricultural)	R.L.H. Steen
Wills	A.G. Gostwick

MAYO & PERKINS

20 GILDREDGE RD, EASTBOURNE, E. SUSSEX, BN21 4RP
DX: 6900

TEL: (01323) 730543
FAX: (01323) 737214

THE FIRM: Founded in 1910, Mayo & Perkins is a modern general practice which has particular expertise in litigation, family law, commercial and domestic property, and trust and probate work. The main office is in Eastbourne with branch offices in Hailsham and Hampden Park.

PRINCIPAL AREAS OF WORK:

Litigation: (*Contact Partner:* S. Dodds). Work handled includes commercial litigation, personal injury claims and debt recovery, building disputes, breaches of contract and criminal proceedings, family and child care, employment and housing.

Property: (*Contact Partner:* K.D. Minto). Both residential and commercial conveyancing are undertaken and the firm has established a property sales office.

Company/ Commercial: (*Contact Partner:* P.K. Jelly). A wide variety of work includes company acquisitions and sales, partnership and loan documentation and tax implications.

Private Client: (*Contact Partner:* J.R.M. Clarke). The firm advises on wills, trusts and probate, including probate disputes, financial and tax planning including capital investment, life assurance, pensions and mortgages.

CONTACT PARTNER: Mr. S. Dodds

Number of partners:	11
Assistant solicitors:	4
Other fee-earners:	8

CONTACTS	
Company/ commercial	P.K. Kelly
Litigation	B. Davis
Private client	J.R.M. Clarke
Property	K.D. Minto

McARTHUR STANTON Royal Bank Buildings, 35 High St, Dumbarton, Strathclyde, G82 1LU **Tel:** (01389) 762266 **Fax:** (01389) 742282 **DX:** 590 **Ptnrs:** 7 **Asst Solrs:** 3 . General practice with expertise in licensing. Other offices in Helensburgh, Alexandria and Dalmuir.

McCASH & HUNTER P.O. Box 17, 25 South Methven Street, Perth, Tayside, PH1 5ES **Tel:** (01738) 620451 **Fax:** (01738) 631155 **DX:** 4 Perth **Ptnrs:** 6 **Asst Solrs:** 4 **Other Fee-earners:** 3. Experienced in all aspects of agricultural work including tax and property sales. Other work includes family, employment, conveyancing, estate agency and litigation.

McCLURE NAISMITH ANDERSON & GARDINER

292 ST VINCENT STREET, GLASGOW, G2 5TQ
DX: 64 Glasgow

TEL: (0141) 204 2700
FAX: (0141) 248 3998

THE FIRM: McClure Naismith Anderson & Gardiner is a long established Scottish law firm which has undergone a number of major developments in the last decade – new offices in Glasgow, Edinburgh and London, an expansion in the number of partners and range of specialist services, and in 1989 the taking on of British Coal Corporation's in-house legal department which handles all the legal work in Scotland for British Coal Corporation and the British Coal Pension Funds. The firm regularly handles inward investment, principally from the United States and Japan, utilising the corporate and commercial aspects of the practice and welcomes enquiries from solicitors outwith Scotland.

PRINCIPAL AREAS OF WORK:

Corporate/ Commercial: (*Contact Partner:* Kenneth Chrystie) The firm advises corporate and other business clients on all aspects of commercial law. Specialist advice is offered regarding the following matters: company formation and finance, management buy-outs, mergers & acquisitions, insolvency, banking, licensing and distribution agreements, franchising, intellectual property, sponsorship, computer hardware and software agreements, contracts in the entertainment business, employment issues, competition law and mining contracts. The department's industrial expertise embraces coal mining, bus and rail transport, pharmaceuticals and alcoholic drinks.

SENIOR PARTNER: Gordon W.R. Carlisle

Number of partners:	21
Assistant solicitors:	45
Other fee-earners:	7

CONTACTS	
Commercial property	Michael Brown
Consumer credit	Frank Johnstone
Corporate/ commercial	Kenneth Chrystie
Litigation	Alan Thompson
Private client	Gordon Shearer

McCLURE NAISMITH ANDERSON & GARDINER
————— SOLICITORS —————

Commercial Property: *(Contact Partner:* Michael Brown). The practice handles all aspects of property development work for institutional, corporate and private clients including: site acquisition, leasing and sale; factory, shop and office developments; funding arrangements; building contracts; residential estate work; assured tenancy arrangements; management contracts; joint venture agreements and all ancillary contracts. The firm advises landlords and tenants on all aspects of commercial, agricultural and residential leasing. The department also has a team specialising in environmental law, secured lending, and licensed trade conveyancing.

Litigation: *(Contact Partners:* Alan Thomson, Glasgow and William Walker, Edinburgh). The firm undertakes all types of litigation in all courts, tribunals and inquiries throughout Scotland, including Scotland's Supreme Court, the Court of Session, Edinburgh. It also undertakes ADR and Arbitration. Advice is provided to commercial and private clients on a wide range of problems and disputes. Its principal areas of practice include: asset recovery; construction; employment; family; insolvency; debt recovery and credit control; intellectual property; personal injuries; professional negligence and general insurance; planning; licensing and environment; property.

Consumer Credit: *(Contact Partner:* Frank Johnstone). One of the foremost departments of its kind in Scotland, clients include many of the country's leading finance houses, leasing companies, banks, building societies and credit card companies. The firm also advises the Finance House Association and the Consumer Credit Trade Association and is a member of the Finance & Leasing Association (FLA). The service includes high volume debt recovery, asset recovery, the drafting of credit documentation and advice on current and contemplated legislation.

Private Client: *(Contact Partner:* Gordon Shearer). The practice offers specialist advice on estate planning, wills, trusts, curatories, tax planning, insurance, pensions, investment portfolios and the purchase, sale and leasing of residential property. The firm has acted for major house builders for many years.

OTHER OFFICES:
49 Queen Street, Edinburgh EH2 2NH. *Tel:* (0131) 220 1002. *Fax:* (0131) 220 1003.
12 Masons Avenue, London EC2V 5BT. *Tel:* (0171) 600 5408. *Fax:* (0171) 600 5409.

FOREIGN LANGUAGES: French, Danish.

INTERNATIONAL CONNECTIONS & ASSOCIATED OFFICES: Member of the World Law Group.

McCORMICKS

BRITANNIA CHAMBERS, 4 OXFORD PLACE, LEEDS, W. YORKS, LS1 3AX
DX: 26427

TEL: (0113) 246 0622
FAX: (0113) 246 7488

THE FIRM: McCormicks has expanded by planned organic growth to attain a reputation for expertise in a number of fields and acts for a complete range of clients from private individuals and small businesses, sporting and entertainment personalities, to substantial companies including PLC's, banks, financial institutions and building societies.

Currently, company/ commercial and litigation account for 70% of the fee income, criminal 15% and matrimonial, private client and conveyancing 15%. The practice continues to be one of the leading criminal firms in the country, concentrating on serious crime, major fraud and taxation cases. It also has an international reputation in sports law. Partners hold the Higher Courts Qualification, Membership of the Law Society's Personal Injury Panel and Fellowship of the Chartered Institute of Arbitrators. The practice was one of the first in the country to secure Legal Aid Franchises for both offices.

PRINCIPAL AREAS OF WORK: The firm handles all aspects of company and commercial law (including company formations, acquisitions and sales, flotations, contracts, taxation, employment law, franchising, bankruptcies, liquidations and receiverships, sporting and entertainment law), litigation (High Court and County Court claims), family and matrimonial law, criminal law (Magistrates and Crown Court defendant work), commercial and residential conveyancing, VAT and Inland Revenue investigation work, employment law and European law. The firm has also acquired a

CONTACT PARTNER:
Peter D.G. McCormick

Number of partners:	4
Assistant solicitors:	6
Other fee-earners:	17

WORKLOAD

Company/ commercial and litigation	70%
Matrimonial, private client & conveyancing	15%
Criminal	15%

McCormicks
SOLICITORS

substantial niche reputation in charity law, acting in particular for an international charity connected with the British Royal Family and also in commercial litigation and debt collection acting for the professional indemnity insurer.

FOREIGN CONNECTIONS: Associated offices in France, Germany, Spain, Italy, Portugal and Gibraltar; members of "Eurolink for Lawyers" – fluent French, German, Italian and Spanish spoken.

OTHER OFFICE: Harrogate – Wharfedale House, 37 East Parade, Harrogate, North Yorkshire HG1 5LQ – *Tel:* (01423) 530630 *Fax:* (01423) 530709 *DX:* 11974 Harrogate 1. *Resident Partner:* Geoffrey A. Rogers.

OFFICE EQUIPMENT: Olivetti wp, A.I.M. computerised accounting.

CONTACTS	
Commercial lit	Neil Goodrum, Geoff Rogers
Company/ commercial	Peter McCormick
Family/ matrimonial	Mark Burns/ Geoff Rogers
Media and entertainment law	Peter McCormick
Serious fraud	Neil Goodrum, Geoff Rogers
Sports law	Peter McCormick

McCOURTS 53 George IV Bridge, Edinburgh, EH1 1EJ **Tel:** (0131) 225 6555 **Fax:** (0131) 225 5054 **Ptnrs:** 3 **Asst Solrs:** 4 **Other Fee-earners:** 2. Specialist criminal defence practice, dealing exclusively with criminal matters throughout Scotland.

McGOLDRICK CAIRNS 8 Fulwood Place, Gray's Inn, London, WC1V 6HG **Tel:** (0171) 405 4515 **Fax:** (0171) 405 4474 **Ptnrs:** 3 **Asst Solrs:** 4 **Other Fee-earners:** 14. Best known for insurance litigation, litigation and criminal practice. Offices at Bermondsey, Dartford and Sevenoaks. Legal aid work is undertaken.

WORKLOAD			
Insurance litigation	35%	Crime	23%
Commercial civil lit	15%	General litigation	10%
Commercial conveyancing	10%	Conveyancing	7%

McGRATH & CO 4th Floor, King Edward House, 135a New Street, Birmingham, W. Midlands, B2 4QJ **Tel:** (0121) 643 4121 **Fax:** (0121) 643 1978 **Ptnrs:** 6 **Asst Solrs:** 11 **Other Fee-earners:** 39. A general practice handling immigration, civil litigation, criminal law, personal injury and housing.

McGRIGOR DONALD

PACIFIC HOUSE, 70 WELLINGTON STREET, GLASGOW, G2 6SB
DX: GW 135

TEL: (0141) 248 6677
FAX: (0141) 204 1351

THE FIRM: McGrigor Donald is one of the UK's leading law firms, with offices in Glasgow, Edinburgh, London and through its membership of Legal Resources Group, Brussels. McGrigor Donald is acknowledged as a commercially-oriented practice combining specialist legal expertise with a clear understanding of business problems. It handles the full range of commercial and corporate work, with clients ranging from small businesses to large scale operations involving public utilities and multinationals. An extensive selection of private client services is also on offer. Alongside traditional service areas, specialist units meet clients' needs for authoritative advice on areas of newly emerging legislation and regulation. The firm's London office is an established, full service operation with specialist teams covering banking and finance, corporate law (including corporate recovery and insolvency), property (in association with Morrison Skirrow) and litigation.

A full range of services is available within the following core areas: commercial property, litigation, corporate and commercial law, taxation and trust law.

Specialist services are available through each of the firm's offices and include the following:

Banking: *Contact Partners:* Murdo Maclean, Neil Morrison
Construction Law: *Contact Partner:* Brandon Nolan
Corporate Recovery: *Contact Partner:* Robert Glennie
EC Law: *Contact Partner:* Michael Dean
Employment Law: *Contact Partner:* Jim Young
Environmental Law: *Contact Partner:* Pat Hawthorn
Financial Services: *Contact Partners:* Frank Doran, Kathleen Stewart
Intellectual Property: *Contact Partner:* Shonaig Macpherson
Licensing/ Leisure Services: *Contact Associate:* Audrey Ferrie
Media Law: *Contact Partner:* Eddie MacKechnie
Pensions & Employee Benefits: *Contact Partner:* Ian Gordon
Taxation: *Contact Partner:* Allan Nicolson

MANAGING PARTNER: Niall Scott

Number of partners:	45
Assistant solicitors:	73
Other fee-earners:	33

WORKLOAD	
Property	33%
Company	27%
Litigation	23%
Taxation (including private client)	9%
Banking	8%

CONTACTS	
Asset/ project finance	Murdo Maclean
Charities	Eleanor Kerr
Collective investment schemes	Frank Doran
Company/ commercial	Stephen Cook
Computer law and I.T.	Shonaig Macpherson
Debt collection	Audrey Ferrie
Defamation	Niall Scott
Energy and utilities	Iain Macaulay
Environmental law	Patricia Hawthorn
Financial services	Kathleen Stewart
Franchising	Shonaig Macpherson

Tax-driven Property Schemes: *Contact Partner:* David Bankier
Corporate Finance: *Contact Partner:* Morag McNeill
OTHER OFFICES:
Erskine House, 68-73 Queen Street, Edinburgh EH2 4NF.
Tel: (0131) 226 7777. *Fax:* (0131) 226 7700.
63 Queen Victoria Street, London EC4N 4ST.
Tel: (0171) 329 3299. *Fax:* (0171) 329 4000.
Avenue de Cortenberg 79, 1040 Bruxelles. *Tel:* (012) 732 3600. *Fax:* (012) 734 8793.

Insolvency	Robert Glennie
Intellectual property	Shonaig Macpherson
Litigation (commercial)	James Taylor
Media and entertainment	Eddie MacKechnie
Pensions	Ian Gordon
Planning	Craig Connal
Private client	Allan Nicolson
Tax (corporate)	Ian Gordon

McGUINNESS FINCH 9 Stratford Place, London, W1N 9AE **Tel:** (0171) 493 9593 **Fax:** (0171) 629 2839 **DX:** 9076 West End **Ptnrs:** 8 **Asst Solrs:** 5 **Other Fee-earners:** 2. A commercial practice best known for its work in company/commercial and commercial conveyancing.

WORKLOAD			
Commercial property	75%	Planning	10%
Company/ commercial	10%	Litigation	5%

McKENNA & CO

MITRE HOUSE, 160 ALDERSGATE STREET, LONDON, EC1A 4DD	TEL: (0171) 606 9000
DX: 724	FAX: (0171) 606 9100

908 Lloyd's, One Lime Street, London EC3M 7DQ	Tel: (0171) 929 1250
DX: 724	Fax: (0171) 626 5749

THE FIRM: McKenna & Co is a leading UK and international law firm advising primarily industrial and commercial clients, financial institutions and governments. Based on its substantial business practice in the City of London, it has offices in Brussels, Budapest, Prague, Warsaw, Moscow and Hong Kong, is associated with firms in Germany, Australia and Japan, and can give practical and constructive advice to clients on commercial projects and transactions in the UK and many other countries.

PRINCIPAL AREAS OF WORK: Corporate finance, financial services, banking, capital markets, asset and project finance, tax, mergers and acquisitions, privatisation, company and commercial law; insolvency and corporate recovery; aviation; insurance law (conducted at the Lloyd's office); construction law; property acquisition, finance and development; planning; litigation and arbitration; corporate crime and fraud; trade libel, professional negligence; anti-trust and competition law; European Community law; environmental law; healthcare (both personal injury claims and regulatory) and health and safety at work; employment and pensions law; executive immigration; intellectual property, telecommunications and computer law; product liability; power generation and other infrastructure projects. The firm has a strong reputation for industrial specialisation in construction, energy, water, transport, financial services, pharmaceuticals and medical devices, insurance, utilities, waste management and property development.

NATURE OF CLIENTELE: The firm advises major public and private companies, multi-national businesses, financial institutions and intermediaries, governments and government agencies, statutory undertakings and local authorities. Most of the firm's clients are UK businesses, but equally significant are other European, North American, Japanese and other Asia-Pacific clients. It represents clients in transactions and projects in many countries of the world.

INTERNATIONAL: The firm is active throughout western, central and eastern Europe, the CIS (particularly Russia and Central Asian Republics of Kazakhstan, Uzbekistan, Turkmenistan and Kirgiz), and the Asia-Pacific region. The Brussels office acts as the focus and centre for European Union and European Commission work. In Germany the firm is associated with the firm of Sigle, Loose, Schmidt-Diemitz and Partners, which has offices in Stuttgart, Berlin, Frankfurt, Chemnitz and Leipzig. The firm's own offices in Budapest, Prague, Warsaw and Moscow handle corporate and commercial work of all types, especially inward investment advice for businesses developing their interests in those regions. With close connections with other firms throughout Europe the firm can advise on transactions for business clients throughout Europe, the Baltic states, Scandinavia and the CIS.

MANAGING PARTNER:
Mr R.S. Derry-Evans

UK:	
Number of partners:	63
Assistant solicitors:	103
Other fee-earners:	79
INTERNATIONAL:	
Number of Partners:	8
Assistant Solicitors:	16
Other fee-earners:	12

CONTACTS	
Asia-Pacific	David Renton
Banking and asset finance	A S Ivison
Central Europe	Robert Windmill
CIS	Elena Kirillova
Commercial contracts	J P Thurston
Competition law	R J Taylor
Construction	E A Minogue
Corporate finance	G Billington
Corporate tax	B A R Concanon
Debt rescheduling & recoveries	A S Ivison
Employment	S B Jeffreys
Energy/natural resources	C F Woolf
Environmental law	P M Castle
European Union and EEA law	D R Marks
Financial services	P N Smith
Health and safety	M L Tyler
Healthcare & pharmaceuticals	I C Dodds-Smith
Infrastructure project/finance	R J Phillips
Insolvency	A F Loring

The Hong Kong office, which is operated in association with the major Australian firm of Minter Ellison, is active throughout the Asia-Pacific region covering particularly India, Indonesia, Japan (where the firm has an associated office in Tokyo), Malaysia, The People's Republic of China, Singapore, Taiwan, Thailand and Vietnam as well as Hong Kong itself.

All the firm's international offices are closely integrated, being able to work independently on their local work and to form teams as necessary to handle international projects, with partners from London and the international offices often working together wherever the project demands. Their work in general consists of the firm's principal areas of practice as detailed above. All the offices can work in the relevant local languages as well as English, and a number of the lawyers in London also speak one or more languages in addition to English.

Insurance and reinsurance	R J A Williams
Intellectual property/IT	S K Whybrow
Litigation & dispute resolut'n	A L Marks
M & As and disposals	G Billington
Management & leveraged buyouts	G Billington
Pension schemes	J M Cunliffe
Planning	I C Gatenby
Product liability	C J S Hodges
Property	N A Brown
Utilities	C F Woolf
VAT	B A R Concanon
Waste management	P M Castle
Western Europe	R J Taylor

McKENZIE BELL 19 John St, Sunderland, Tyne & Wear, SR1 1JG **Tel:** (0191) 567 4857 **Fax:** (0191) 510 9347 **DX:** 60719 **Ptnrs:** 7 **Asst Solrs:** 3 **Other Fee-earners:** 7. Known for licensing, conveyancing, crime, Industrial Tribunal work, litigation and company law. Has computerised debt-collection service. Other offices in Washington and Fulwell.

McKINTY & WRIGHT

EAGLE STAR HOUSE, 5-7 UPPER QUEEN STREET, BELFAST, BT1 6FS

TEL: (01232) 246751
FAX: (01232) 231432

THE FIRM: McKinty & Wright is a Belfast-based firm with a client-oriented commercial and litigation practice. Although the firm offers specialist expertise on matters peculiar to Northern Ireland, it has a wide client base outside the province, including international and multi-national companies.

PRINCIPAL AREAS OF WORK: McKinty & Wright offers a wide range of services to the commercial client, from routine advice to insolvency, property and insurance matters. The firm's litigation department has extensive experience in all aspects of commercial litigation, in particular employment, personal injury, licensing and construction law.

Number of partners:	11
Assistant solicitors:	9

CONTACTS	
Commercial property	Ivan Frazer
Company/commercial	Eric Boyd
Litigation	Paul Johnston

McLEAN & STEWART 51/53 High Street, Dunblane, Tayside, FK15 0EG **Tel:** (01786) 823217 **Fax:** (01786) 822575 **DX:** 631 Dunblane **Ptnrs:** 4 **Asst Solrs:** 2 . The firm handles a wide range of work including all aspects of estate agency and agriculture.

McMILLAN KILPATRICK S.S.C. 12 Alloway Place, Ayr, Strathclyde, KA7 2AG **Tel:** (01292) 264696 **Fax:** (01292) 610647 **DX:** 1 Ayr **Ptnrs:** 8 **Asst Solrs:** 1 **Other Fee-earners:** 1. With a strong private client base the firm is active in many areas including trust and probate, employment disputes and family law.

WORKLOAD			
Trust and executry	40%	Conveyancing	40%
Court incl tribunals	15%	Gen incl debt rec/agric	5%

MEADE–KING 24 Orchard Street, Bristol, BS1 5DF **Tel:** (0117) 926 4121 **Fax:** (0117) 929 7578 **DX:** 7812 **Ptnrs:** 8 **Asst Solrs:** 5 **Other Fee-earners:** 6. A long-established firm, with offices in Bristol and Bath. Best known for litigation, company and commercial, conveyancing and insolvency. Has a growing commercial clientele.

MEMERY CRYSTAL

31 SOUTHAMPTON ROW, LONDON, WC1B 5HT
DX: 156 Ch.Ln.

TEL: (0171) 242 5905
FAX: (0171) 242 2058

THE FIRM: Memery Crystal was founded in 1978 in response to the need of modern business for professional advice delivered with commercial insight on tight timescales. The firm has established a strong reputation for developing close and responsive working relationships with business clients and providing high quality advice, tailored to suit commercial objectives.

PRINCIPAL AREAS OF WORK:

Company/ Commercial: (*Contact Partner:* Peter Crystal). The department covers the full spectrum of commercial business, company procedure and practice and work includes purchase and sale of companies and businesses, corporate finance, structural re-organisations and mergers, taxation planning, flotations, Stock Exchange and Takeover Code work, capital raising, joint ventures, employment matters and sports law.

Litigation: (*Contact Partner:* Harvey Rands). The focus is on commercial litigation including company, employment, sale of goods, restraint of trade, landlord & tenant, intellectual property, white collar crime, D.T.I. and regulatory enquiries and litigation support for corporate finance.

Property: (*Contact Partner:* Douglas Robertson). The department is involved in the sale, purchase and development of commercial and residential properties, leases, rent reviews, licences, and property financing and acts for investors and developers with substantial property portfolios and for companies, charities, trusts, institutions and individuals.

NATURE OF CLIENTELE: Listed and private companies, partnerships and overseas businesses.

OFFICE TECHNOLOGY: The firm adopts the same techniques of sophisticated information management utilised by modern business to produce results quickly and cost-effectively.

CONTACT PARTNER: Mr Peter Crystal

Number of partners:	7
Assistant solicitors:	13
Other fee-earners:	10

WORKLOAD	
Company/ commercial	45%
Commercial litigation	28%
Property litigation	17%
Property	10%

CONTACTS	
Commercial litigation	D.H. Rands
	B. Clarke
Company/ commercial	P.M. Crystal
	J.P. Davies
Property	D.L. Robertson
Property litigation	D.D. Pfeiffer

MEMERY CRYSTAL
Solicitors

MERRICKS

8 LION STREET, IPSWICH, SUFFOLK, IP1 1DQ
DX: 3264

TEL: (01473) 231331
FAX: (01473) 230041

207-208 Moulsham Street, Chelmsford, Essex CM2 0LG
DX: 89702 Chelmsford

Tel: (01245) 491414
Fax: (01245) 263829

THE FIRM: Merricks is predominantly a litigation practice with particular expertise in construction and insurance matters, servicing clients throughout the country from its offices in Ipswich and Chelmsford.

PRINCIPAL AREAS OF WORK:

Construction/ Engineering: (*Contact Partner:* Anthony Sheppard). An expert team handles: contractual claims, payment of certificates, liability disputes, contract drafting and interpretation, Duty of Care Warranties, joint venture agreements and insurance claims. In-house quantity surveyors also appraise and prepare the quantum of damages for liability.

Insurance: (*Contact Partner:* Andrew Hunn). Merricks has a long and close relationship with clients in the insurance markets. *Work includes:* a substantial volume of personal injury and industrial disease work, property damage, Contractors' All Risks, professional indemnity, fraudulent claims and policy disputes.

CONTACT PARTNER: Andrew J. Hunn

Number of partners:	7
Assistant solicitors:	11
Other fee-earners:	9

WORKLOAD	
Liability claims (including policy disputes, fraud etc)	35%
Insurance litigation inc. personal injury	35%
Construction	25%
Other	5%

CONTACTS	
Construction	Rupert Cowen
Insurance personal injury	Andrew Hunn
Insurance liability claims	Anthony Sheppard

MERRIMAN WHITE

3 KING'S BENCH WALK, INNER TEMPLE, LONDON, EC4Y 7DJ
DX: 1015

TEL: (0171) 936 2050
FAX: (0171) 583 1783

CONTACT PARTNER:
Raymond St. J. Murphy

Number of partners:	2
Assistant solicitors:	11
Other fee-earners:	6

THE FIRM: A long-established compact City firm with an additional office in Guildford. It undertakes litigation, property and commercial work for business clients of all sizes, including major companies in building and publishing, and offers a range of specialist services for Health Authorities. Also provides a wide spectrum of property, tax, estate and matrimonial services to private clients.

OTHER OFFICES:
Merlaw House, 12 The Mount, Guildford GU2 4HN. *Tel:* (01483) 574466. *Fax:* (01483) 506910. *DX:* 2457.

METCALFE COPEMAN & PETTEFAR 6 York Row, Wisbech, Cambs, PE13 1EF **Tel:** (01945) 64331 **Fax:** (01945) 584767 **DX:** 41350 **Ptnrs:** 10 **Asst Solrs:** 13 **Other Fee-earners:** 4. A broadly-based practice with particular expertise in Sunday trading, health and safety, trading standards, commercial conveyancing, and personal injury work.

MICHELMORES 18 Cathedral Yard, Exeter, Devon, EX1 1HE **Tel:** (01392) 436244 **Fax:** (01392) 215579 **DX:** 8304 **Ptnrs:** 10 **Asst Solrs:** 7 **Other Fee-earners:** 10. Concentrates on commercial conveyancing, company commercial, litigation, ecclesiastical law, trusts and probate, planning and environmental law and private client work.

WORKLOAD			
Trusts/ probate	25%	Litigation	25%
Commercial property	25%	Company/ commercial	15%
Res conveyancing	10%		

MICHAEL HENRY & Co

87 CHANCERY LANE, LONDON, WC2A 1JP
Email: michael@henryco.demon.co.uk

TEL: (0171) 242 7999
FAX: (0171) 242 7998

CONTACT PARTNER: Michael Henry

Number of partners:	1
Assistant solicitors:	2

WORKLOAD	
Media & intellectual property: television	25%
Media & intellectual property: film	25%
Copyright & intellectual property	15%
Multimedia & IT	15%
Publishing	10%
Music	10%

THE FIRM: A new (December 1994) specialist media and intellectual property practice with a distinctive high-quality client base which is active across the entire spectrum of the copyright and intellectual property industries and specifically in the film, television, music, multimedia, communications and publishing sectors.

PRINCIPAL AREAS OF WORK: The firm advises solely in the areas of media, communications and intellectual property on both contentious and non-contentious matters. The firm also provides advice and assistance (on a 'no-poaching' basis) to other UK and international law firms who require assistance on media/intellectual property matters.

INTERNATIONAL SECTION

The international section lists foreign law firms based in London. It also lists the foreign connections of English law firms: their branch offices overseas and the foreign languages spoken at their UK offices.

MIDDLETON POTTS

3 CLOTH ST, BARBICAN, LONDON, EC1A 7LD
DX: 46621

TEL: (0171) 600 2333
FAX: (0171) 600 0108

THE FIRM: Middleton Potts was founded in 1976 by six partners, all of whom until then had been with a well-established City practice. The firm has grown steadily each year. The firm acts for financial, commercial, industrial, shipping, and commodity trading clients from all over the world. In 1987, the firm moved to its present address near the Barbican Arts Centre, where it occupies a new building fully equipped with the latest technology. The firm has three main departments. Where a matter requires the involvement of lawyers from more than one department, the partner responsible for the client will ensure close co-ordination between the departments and provide continuity and a regular point of contact between the client and the firm.

PRINCIPAL AREAS OF WORK:

Company/Commercial: (*Contact:* David Godfrey). This department handles international and domestic banking and financial transactions of all kinds, insurance and reinsurance work, the establishment by foreign entities of branches and subsidiaries in the UK, regulatory, compliance and administrative work, the preparation of standard documentation, acquisitions and disposals of shares and assets, corporate reorganisations, joint ventures, ship sales and purchases, major industrial and commercial projects, tax matters and a very broad spectrum of corporate and general commercial matters (including employment law, pensions law, insolvency and intellectual property work).

Commercial Litigation: (*Contact:* Christopher Potts). The firm's litigation practice is one of the most prominent in the City. Middleton Potts features in law reports on average about once a month. The department handles commercial disputes of all kinds and conducts both High Court litigation and arbitration proceedings under the auspices of various trade associations in the City of London and elsewhere. The main areas of work covered are: shipping and Admiralty, commodities, insurance and reinsurance (both marine and non-marine), technical disputes, foreign arbitrations, and disputes in relation to finance and banking, real property, intellectual property, employment and corporate matters.

Property: (*Contact:* Karin Horsley). The principal areas handled by this department include the acquisition, funding, development and disposal of freehold and leasehold office and residential premises, industrial sites and other commercial property units and portfolios, planning matters, the general management of property interests, and general commercial transactions related to property.

FOREIGN CONNECTIONS: With a very strong international element to the practice, Middleton Potts has developed close contacts with clients, lawyers and other professionals from different jurisdictions throughout the world. Many of its lawyers (amongst whom certain are qualified in other jurisdictions) speak at least one, and some speak several, of the following languages: Italian, French, German, Spanish, Portuguese, Polish and Turkish.

NATURE OF CLIENTELE: Major international banks, financial institutions and insurance companies; property companies; P&I Clubs; shipowners and charterers; commodity trading houses; oil majors and traders; multinational companies; and foreign governments.

RECRUITMENT: The firm places a high priority on the recruitment and training of trainee solicitors and young assistant solicitors whom it considers to be the most important source of potential from which to choose future partners. In order to attract the very highest calibre of candidates available, the firm offers remuneration competitive with the best on offer in the City of London. Applications should be made by letter, accompanied by a full CV, to Mr. J.D. Freeman, Director of Finance and Adminstration.

EDUCATION AND TRAINING: An extensive programme of in-house education and training is available.

SENIOR PARTNER: Christopher Potts

Number of partners:	18
Assistant solicitors:	12
Other fee-earners:	7

WORKLOAD	
Commercial Litigation	50%
Company/Commercial	45%
Property	5%

CONTACTS	
Commercial litigation	Christopher Potts
Company/ commercial	David Godfrey
Property	Karin Horsley

MIDDLETON POTTS
SOLICITORS

MIDDLETON & UPSALL 94 East Street, Warminster, Wilts, BA12 9BG
Tel: (01985) 214444 **Fax:** (01985) 213426 **DX:** 43600 Warminster **Ptnrs:** 10 **Asst
Solrs:** 6 **Other Fee-earners:** 7. A general family practice which also deals with
some commercial work involving private limited companies and the farming community.

MILES PRESTON & CO

ELDON CHAMBERS, 30 FLEET STREET, LONDON, EC4Y 1AA

TEL: (0171) 583 0583
FAX: (0171) 583 0128

THE FIRM: Miles Preston & Co is a specialist matrimonial and family law practice
formed in May 1994, the three founding partners having previously worked together
for over 10 years in a large Central London general practice. The firm deals with all
aspects of matrimonial and family law including divorce and separation, cohabitation
and pre-marriage agreements, all issues relating to children and the full range of
emergency procedures. Many of the cases involve the resolution of complex financial
issues usually concerning substantial assets, some with an international dimension.
The practice aims to adopt a firm, effective and fair approach to the conduct of its
cases and to offer a high quality and cost efficient service to its clients. All its solicitors
are members of the Solicitors' Family Law Association.
FOREIGN: The practice has close contacts with a number of other family lawyers
worldwide. In addition Miles Preston is President of the International Academy of
Matrimonial Lawyers which has as its members 250 prominent international family
lawyers practising in various countries around the world.

CONTACT PARTNER: Miles Preston

Number of partners:	3
Assistant solicitors:	1

WORKLOAD	
Family and matrimonial	90%
Cohabitation/ paternity disputes	10%

CONTACTS	
Cohabitation/ paternity	Julia Stancyzk
Family and matrimonial	Siobhan Readhead

MILLAR SHEARER & BLACK 40 Molesworth Street, Cookstown,
Co. Tyrone, BT80 8PH **Tel:** (016487) 62346 **Fax:** (016487) 66761 **Ptnrs:** 6 **Asst
Solrs:** 2 **Other Fee-earners:** 6. Founded 1906. One of the larger practices outside
Belfast. Wide range of work handled for its commercial and private clientele.

WORKLOAD			
Conveyancing	40%	Litigation	30%
Probate	20%	Commercial	10%

MILLER & CO

75-79 REGENT ST, CAMBRIDGE, CAMBS, CB2 1BE
DX: 5816

TEL: (01223) 66741
FAX: (01223) 460429

PRINCIPAL AREAS OF WORK: Founded in 1893, this forward-looking practice has one
of the largest and most experienced matrimonial departments in Cambridge, dealing
with all legal matters concerning personal relationships, marriage, separation, divorce
and the welfare of children. The firm has solicitor members of the Law Society's
Children Panel, the Solicitors' Family Law Association and Family Mediators'
Association.
OTHER AREAS OF WORK: A comprehensive service for small businesses and private
clients includes: commercial and domestic conveyancing, employment matters, wills,
trusts, probate and welfare law. The firm also handles litigation ranging from
defamation work to computerised debt collection. Legal aid is available and, in
personal injury cases, an initial free consultation is provided through the Accident
Legal Advice Scheme.

CONTACT PARTNER: Rosemary Carter

Number of partners:	4
Assistant solicitors:	7
Other fee-earners:	4

MILLER & COMPANY

COBORN HOUSE, 3 COBORN ROAD, LONDON, E3 2DA

TEL: (0181) 503 0084
FAX: (0181) 519 5520

THE FIRM: A new commercial niche firm, specialising in intellectual property, anti-trust, computer and European law. Proven "Top Ten" City law firm expertise. Affordable and aggressively competitive fees.

Innovative, state-of-the-art, computer and communication systems facilitate effective service delivery. Extensive legal information and library facilities are used by the practice.

Established by Clifford Miller. Eleven years' international & leading City law firm experience. Intellectual property, computer contracts & dispute resolution. Successful European Court anti-trust appeals, Commission anti-trust investigations and High Court intellectual property cases. Author, law journal editor, international lecturer. Bsc. Hon. (Physics), ARCS, electronics and communications.

Vivienne Robinson, solicitor, US attorney (New York Bar), ten years international, leading City & US law firm experience, specialist in European, anti-trust and telecommunications laws. MA (Cambridge), License Spéciale en Droit Européen (Brussels), fluent French.

PRINCIPAL AREAS OF WORK:

EC: Anti-trust investigations, defences, compliance. Merger Control. Notifications, clearances & filings. Imports, pricing, cartels, tying and dumping. Telecommunications/Media. Public procurement. Lobbying.

Intellectual Property: Illegal imitation of products, services, brands, marks. Music, literary, film & software copyright. Performers' rights. Patents, designs. Commercial Agreements, eg. franchising, licensing/technology transfer, merchandising.

Computer Law: Contracts, eg. systems integration, outsourcing, software development, licensing, distribution, escrow. Computer leasing. International software distribution, databases, licensing, parallel import control. Dispute resolution.

CONTACT PARTNER: Clifford Miller
Consultant: Vivienne Robinson

Number of partners:	1
Other fee-earners:	1

CONTACTS	
Computer law	Clifford Miller
EC	Vivienne Robinson
	Clifford Miller
Intellectual property	Clifford Miller

MILLER HENDRY 10 Blackfriars Street, Perth, Tayside, PH1 5NS **Tel:** (01738) 637311 **Fax:** (01738) 638685 **DX:** 21 Perth **Ptnrs:** 15 **Asst Solrs:** 6 **Other Fee-earners:** 7. Medium-size firm with four offices handling a broad range of work including agriculture and forestry, private client and domestic property.

MILLER SAMUEL & CO

RWF HOUSE, 5 RENFIELD STREET, GLASGOW, G2 5EZ
DX: 161 Glasgow

TEL: (0141) 221 7934
FAX: (0141) 221 5376

THE FIRM: Established in 1973, Miller Samuel is a well established city centre firm which provices a comprehensive legal service to commercial clients with particular expertise in property development and leasing. The firm has developed a thriving litigation practice which complements the commercial work including landlord and tenant litigation and employment law. It also handles a substantial amount of debt recovery, personal injury and matrimonial work. Its range of services include all private client fields.

PRINCIPAL AREAS OF WORK:

Commercial Property/ Corporate: (Contact: Iain A. Doran). Corporate property development, commercial leasing, investment, funding, construction, etc., service with specialist rent review arbitration/ expert services. Private company work and general commercial contracts also handled.

Litigation: (Contact: Robert P. Kerr). Contract disputes, employment, debt collection, recovery of possession of heritable property, finance leasing, consumer credit, arbitration, industrial injury claims, road traffic accident claims, matrimonial and food law.

Private Client: (Contact: Michael Samuel). A comprehensive service is provided offering clients advice on the administration of estates, tax planning, charities and wills. This department also deals with the purchase and sale of residential property.

CONTACT PARTNERS: P. Michael Samuel or Iain A. Doran

Number of partners:	10
Assistant solicitors:	2
Other fee-earners:	5

WORKLOAD	
Commercial litigation, employment and reparation	50%
Commercial property and corporate	40%
Personal including residential, conveyancing, wills, trusts	10%

MILLS & CO Milburn House, Dean Street, Newcastle-upon-Tyne, Tyne & Wear, NE1 1LE **Tel:** (0191) 233 2222 **Fax:** (0191) 233 2220 **DX:** 61097 **Ptnrs:** 2 **Asst Solrs:** 1 **Other Fee-earners:** 2. Niche practice known for its expertise in shipping law, ship building, ship repair and ship finance.

MILLS & REEVE

FRANCIS HOUSE, 3-7 REDWELL STREET, NORWICH, NORFOLK, NR2 4TJ DX: 5210	TEL: +44 (0) 1603 660155 FAX: +44 (0) 1603 633027
Francis House, 112 Hills Road, Cambridge CB2 1PH DX: 5802 Senior Partner: Jonathan Barclay, Managing Partner: William Barr	Tel: +44 (0) 223 64422 Fax: +44 (0) 223 355848

THE FIRM: A significant practice in East Anglia, the firm was originally founded on private client and agricultural work, and has now expanded to become a major force in commercial, corporate and contentious work.

PRINCIPAL AREAS OF WORK: The firm is known for its expertise in specialist areas including corporate and commercial law, corporate and personal tax, building and engineering, insurance, charities, private client, banking, education, agriculture and professional negligence as well as its expanding niche practice in servicing purchasers and providers of health care.
The firm is a member of the Norton Rose M5 Group of independent legal practices.

CONTACT PARTNER: Jonathan Barclay

Number of partners:	48
Assistant solicitors:	72
Other fee-earners:	61

MILLS SELIG 20 Callender Street, Belfast, BT1 5BQ **Tel:** (01232) 243878 **Fax:** (01232) 231956 **Ptnrs:** 4 **Asst Solrs:** 3 **Other Fee-earners:** 2. All aspects of company/ commercial work undertaken, with particular strength in acquisitions and disposals, banking, franchising and property matters.

WORKLOAD			
Prop/commercial prop	30%	Lit principally corporate	20%
Corporate/commercial	20%	Employment	10%
Banks/ finance houses	10%		

MINCOFF SCIENCE & GOLD

KENSINGTON HOUSE, 4-6 OSBORNE ROAD, NEWCASTLE-UPON-TYNE, TYNE & WEAR, NE2 2AA DX: 62550	TEL: (0191) 281 6151 FAX: (0191) 281 8069

THE FIRM: The firm was established in 1948 with a strong litigation base. Since then it has developed its commercial department to provide a comprehensive service from a youthful and enthusiastic team adapting modern technology to specialist skills.

PRINCIPAL AREAS OF WORK:

General Description: Commercial property, corporate transactions and litigation represent the principal areas. The firm has also developed sections handling licensing, planning and industrial relations.

NATURE OF CLIENTELE: Clients include private individuals, corporate and institutional bodies, national and local PLCs, local authorities, licensing justices and Police Authorities.

CONTACT PARTNER: Austen Science

Number of partners:	6
Assistant solicitors:	8
Other fee-earners:	7

CONTACTS	
Commercial	H.B. Gold
Licensing and planning	A.D. Science
Matrimonial	M. Smith
Medical negligence/pers injury	T.W. Blewitt

MINTER ELLISON

20 LINCOLN'S INN FIELDS, LONDON, WC2A 3ED	TEL: (0171) 831 7871 FAX: (0171) 404 6722

THE FIRM: A long established Australian firm, Minter Ellison has offices and associated firms in all major commercial centres in Australia serving many of the nation's largest corporations. The firm assists not only Australian businesses expanding overseas but also international enterprises with their Australian ventures. The firm established its London office in 1974, making it the longest established Australian law firm in the UK. The London office provides on-the-spot advice to European companies, financial institutions and private investors on all aspects of Australian

RESIDENT PARTNER: Mr Michael Whalley

LAWYERS:	
London:	3
Worldwide:	530

law. The office also helps to guide Australian clients through the complexities of European business and trade law, including advising on the impact of the major changes occurring in the laws of the European Union. The work of the London office can be divided into three broad areas.

PRINCIPAL AREAS OF WORK:

Australian Law: The London office can give immediate and detailed advice on Australian corporate, commercial, financial and taxation laws, particularly in the following fields: company and takeover laws; regulation of the Australian securities industry; mergers and acquisitions; international finance; legal and tax implications of Australian financial transactions; joint ventures and commercial contracts; establishment of new businesses in Australia; general commercial advice; employment laws and practices; foreign investment in Australia; private client advice; Australian based litigation, arbitration and dispute resolution; intellectual property; and taxation. The firm also offers access to expertise in New Zealand law through its associated firm in New Zealand, Rudd Watts & Stone.

English & European Law: Lawyers in the London office are qualified to practise UK law and have, in total, over 20 years' experience practising in England. They are therefore able to advise the firm's clients who are carrying on business in the UK and other parts of Europe. The main areas of practice are general company and commercial advice, takeovers and acquisitions, banking and finance, commercial contracts, business laws, taxation, financial services, employment law, competition law, the administration of estates, property investment and European Union Community laws. The firm also maintains close contact with specialist advisers in leading English law firms.

International Transactions: As the firm has experience of both English and Australian law and business practice, it can provide comprehensive advice on all implications of international transactions. The London office offers expertise in structuring and negotiating international agreements and has made a significant contribution to the successful implementation of business ventures in both Europe and Australia.

OTHER OFFICES: Sydney, Melbourne, Brisbane, Canberra, Gold Coast, Hong Kong.

ASSOCIATED FIRMS: Adelaide, Perth, Auckland, Wellington, Singapore, Beijing, Jakarta.

WORKLOAD	
Commercial	30%
Corporate	20%
Mergers/ acquisitions	15%
International	10%
Banking	10%
Tax	10%
Other	5%

MISHCON DE REYA

21 SOUTHAMPTON ROW, LONDON, WC1B 5HS
DX: 37954 Kingsway E-mail:mishcon.co.uk

TEL: (0171) 405 3711
FAX: (0171) 404 5982

THE FIRM: Mishcon de Reya is an expanding commercial practice based in Central London. The firm has an excellent reputation for commercial litigation, defamation, entertainment, media and family work. It is increasingly regarded for its corporate and commercial property work and provides legal services to a wide range of clients from FTSE 100 to private companies and from entrepreneurs to private individuals.

Mishcon de Reya was born of a merger between Victor Mishcon & Co and seven partners from Bartletts de Reya which took place in 1988. Over the past year the firm has continued to expand. A team of company-commercial lawyers with a strong international client base has recently joined from Bayer-Rosin. The appointment of Gillian Howard, a well-respected employment law adviser and former barrister, as a consultant has further strengthened the firm;s employment practice.

Although the practice has grown considerably since 1988, it is still compact enough for clients to have direct access to partners. It is large enough to guarantee specialist advice across a wide spectrum.

A leading medium-sized practice run openly by young partners, the firm has an excellent reputation built over many years. It is chaired by John Jackson, chairman of Ladbroke Group plc, a senior business figure with extensive commercial experience whose appointment has been widely regarded as an innovative step in the profession.

PRINCIPAL AREAS OF WORK: The firm's services to corporate clients include:

Company work involving new business start-ups, joint ventures, management buyouts, mergers, acquisitions and Stock Exchange flotations. (*Contact:* Graham Stedman. Fee earners: 19).

CONTACT PARTNER: Anthony Julius

Number of partners:	30
Assistant solicitors:	28
Other fee-earners:	35

WORKLOAD	
Litigation	61%
Company/commercial	18%
Property	12%
Family	6%
Private client	3%

Commercial work including advice on competition law, protection of intellectual property rights, contract negotiation, tax planning, commercial credit terms, trade finance including international trade, immigration, employment and industrial relations issues. (*Contact:* Graham Stedman. Fee earners: as above).

The firm also has a specialist media group to cater for the specific needs of clients in all areas of the media. (*Contact:* Peter Armstrong. Fee earners: 7).

Property advice on leases and lease renewals, rent reviews, landlord and tenant issues, planning, acquisitions, disposals, development and construction work, as well as commercial and high volume residential conveyancing. (*Contacts:* Philip Freedman/Ronald Hooberman. Fee earners: 13).

Litigation expertise and advice on trade finance disputes, bank recoveries, fraud investigations, white collar crime, employment disputes, directors' contracts, minority shareholders actions, intellectual property disputes, defamation and media litigations, insolvencies, insurance disputes, property and construction contracts, partnership disputes, tax investigations and general commercial issues. (*Contact:* Anthony Julius. Fee earners: 39).

The firm's services to private individuals include:

Family work including divorce and separation, cohabitation disputes, property and financial settlements, children's cases, adoption and international child abductions. (*Contact:* Sandra Davis. Fee earners: 6).

Expertise in private client matters such as probate, trust, estate and succession law as well as tax planning and advice. (*Contact:* Christopher Allen. Fee earners: 3).

PRO BONO WORK The firm also provides legal services on a pro bono basis to a number of organisations including: Liberty, London City Ballet, Westminster Foundation for Democracy, Artwork, BIPAC, Board of Deputies of British Jews, IJA, Jamaican Council for Human Rights, Stowe Club for Boys.

RECRUITMENT The firm recruits between six and eight trainee solicitors every year. Competitive salaries are offered. Brochures and application forms are available from Karen Sanig, training partner.

CONTACTS	
Banking litigation	Stephen Davis
Company/ commercial	Graham Stedman
Defamation	Brian Hepworth
Employment	Stephen Reading
Entertainment and media	Peter Armstrong
Family	Sandra Davis
Fraud litigation	Gary Miller
Insolvency	Julie Killip
Litigation	Anthony Julius
Private client	Christopher Allen
Property	Philip Freedman
Tax	Brian Slater

MITCHELLS ROBERTON

GEORGE HOUSE, 36 NORTH HANOVER STREET, GLASGOW, G1 2AD
DX: 77 Glasgow

TEL: (0141) 552 3422
FAX: (0141) 552 2935

THE FIRM: Established for over 250 years, Mitchells Roberton can claim to be the oldest law firm in Glasgow. The practice has a strong private client base and a company/ commercial department which has expertise in a number of niche markets, particularly in relation to banks, building societies and academic institutions.

PRINCIPAL AREAS OF WORK:

Private Client: (*Contact Partner:* Eric H. Webster). Services for the private client include will preparation, executries, trusts, residential conveyancing, powers of attorney, financial and retirement advice, tax planning and insurance. The firm also advises on matters of agricultural law.

Company/ Commercial: (*Contact Partners:* Donald B. Reid and Ian C. Ferguson). The department handles a variety of corporate business. Moreover, clients can benefit from expertise in the fields of banking (securities and litigation), building society law (property loans), insolvency, commercial property and European law. The firm has close connections with educational establishments, assisting with their property and employment concerns, and also in the restructuring of academic institutions towards corporate status.

Litigation: (*Contact Partners:* Andrew M. Donaldson and Craig Dunbar). The department handles family and matrimonial law, separation, insolvency, debt recovery and tribunal work, and specialises in civil engineering contract arbitration.

FOREIGN LANGUAGES: French, German.

INTERNATIONAL CONNECTIONS & ASSOCIATED OFFICES: Member of Scottish Lawyers European Group.

SENIOR PARTNER: Eric H. Webster

Number of partners:	13
Assistant solicitors:	4
Other fee-earners:	9

WORKLOAD	
Trust and executry	46%
Commercial and domestic conveyancing	34%
Court work	8%
Miscellaneous	7%
Other commercial work	5%

CONTACTS	
Commercial conveyancing	D.B. Reid
Court	A.M. Donaldson
Domestic conveyancing	I.C. Ferguson
Other commercial work	D.B. Reid
Trust and executry	E.H. Webster

MONIER–WILLIAMS & BOXALLS 71 Lincoln's Inn Fields, London, WC2A 3JF **Tel:** (0171) 405 6195 **Fax:** (0171) 405 1453 **DX:** 37975 Kingsway **Ptnrs:** 8 **Asst Solrs:** 1 **Other Fee-earners:** 2. The firm is known for wine trade connections (particularly protection of appellations d'origine), commodity arbitrations, employment law, professional partnership and charity work.

WORKLOAD			
Private client	32%	Property	22%
Employment	21%	Wine litigation	10%
Commercial	7%		

MOORE & BLATCH

11 THE AVENUE, SOUTHAMPTON, HANTS, SO17 1XF
DX: 38507 Southampton 3

TEL: (01703) 636311
FAX: (01703) 332205

THE FIRM: Moore & Blatch is one of the major law firms in central Southern England with a commercial office in Southampton and a private client office in Lymington. Particular areas of strength are company, commercial litigation, commercial property, private client work and town planning and estate development.

PRINCIPAL AREAS OF WORK:

Company: (*Contact Partner:* Graham Smith. *Fee-earners:* 3). This department specialises in corporate transactions, including share and business acquisitions, MBOs and public offers. Advice on company law, directors' responsibilities, insolvency, competition and EC law, partnership, employment and commercial matters.

Litigation: (*Contact Partner:* Robert Miles. *Fee-earners:* 8). A range of commercial litigation includes employment matters, health and safety legislation, insolvency work, bank litigation, secured lending realisation, substantial trade disputes, credit control and computerised debt collection. The department incorporates a substantial section specialising in personal injury work insurance claims and public and transport inquiries.

Commercial Property: (*Contact Partner:* Steve Ingram. *Fee-earners:* 6). *Work includes:* the acquisition, disposal and management of commercial property (freehold and leasehold), joint venture schemes, loan security work, mortgage and sheltered housing schemes. The department has particular experience in land development and town planning, dealing with planning appeals and inquiries and providing a consultancy service to local government, landowners and developers.

Town Planning: (*Contact Partner:* John Barrington. *Fee-earners:* 4). *Work includes:* planning agreements, plans and appeal inquiries, judicial reviews for developers, landowners and local authorities.

Private Client: (*Contact Partner:* John Hatchard. *Fee-earners:* 14). The department provides a complete service for private client families. *Work includes:* tax and estate planning, investments, wills, trusts, charitable trusts, probate and retirement finance, family law, general civil litigation and property.

Insurance Department: (*Contact Partner:* David Thompson. *Fee-earners:* 10). The department handles the full range of insurance-related matters including plaintiff and defendant personal injury work, uninsured loss recovery, third party recovery, and also advises on all aspects of insurance law.

Intellectual Property: (Contact Partner: Georgina Richards. *Fee-earners:* 3). The department handles all matters relating to intellectual property rights and undertakes trade mark registrations. *Work includes:* transfer of intellectual property rights, licensing, infringement actions, related contracts including computer software, franchising, agency and distribution.

NATURE OF CLIENTELE: The firm acts for public and private companies, insurance companies, financial institutions, partnerships and individuals.

MANAGING PARTNER: M.J. Caton	
Number of partners:	13
Assistant solicitors:	9
Other fee-earners:	16

CONTACTS	
Commercial property	Steve Ingram
Company	Graham Smith
Insurance	David Thompson
Intellectual property	Georgina Richards
Litigation	Robert Miles
Private client	John Hatchard
Town planning	John Barrington

MOORE & BLATCH
SOLICITORS

MOORHEAD JAMES

21 FLEET STREET, LONDON, EC4Y 1AA

TEL: (0171) 831 8888
FAX: (0171) 936 3635

THE FIRM: Moorhead James is a commercial practice offering a comprehensive range of services to clients ranging from private individuals to multinational businesses.

PRINCIPAL AREAS OF WORK:

Corporate & Commercial: *Work includes:* formations, flotations, corporate restructuring, franchising and licensing, sports and leisure, banking, corporate finance, education, EC law and aviation.

Property: The department advises on all aspects of commercial and residential conveyancing, environmental law, construction and development and oil and gas.

Litigation: This includes High Court and County Court Actions, landlord and tenant and other property disputes, employment matters, debt collection, professional negligence and insolvency.

Private Client: *Work includes:* tax planning, charities, wills and probate.

OVERSEAS ASSOCIATED OFFICES: Frankfurt, Rome, Milan, Paris, Hong Kong, Beijing, Prague, Budapest.

FOREIGN LANGUAGES: French, German, Cantonese.

CONTACT PARTNER: Ben Moorhead	
Number of partners:	4
Assistant solicitors:	1

WORKLOAD	
Company and commercial/ international	50%
Property and secured lending	30%
Litigation, landlord and tenant, employment and immigration	20%

R.C. MOORHOUSE & CO 16-17 East Parade, Leeds, W. Yorks, LS1 2BR **Tel:** (0113) 2443121 **Fax:** (0113) 2431100 **DX:** 12043 **Ptnrs:** 8 **Other Fee-earners:** 13. A general practice dealing particularly with insolvency, debt collection, company, and commercial conveyancing.

MORECROFT URQUHART 8 Dale Street, Liverpool, Merseyside, L2 4TQ **Tel:** (0151) 236 8871 **Fax:** (0151) 236 8109 **DX:** 14142 **Ptnrs:** 14 **Asst Solrs:** 7 **Other Fee-earners:** 13. Morecroft Urquhart has four offices throughout Merseyside and is a member of Law Group UK. The firm's main areas of practice are company commercial, litigation, matrimonial, private client and conveyancing.

MORE FISHER BROWN 1 Norton Folgate, London, E1 6DA **Tel:** (0171) 247 0438 **Fax:** (0171) 247 0649 **Ptnrs:** 7 **Asst Solrs:** 7 **Other Fee-earners:** 1. A medium sized City firm practising exclusively in shipping, insurance/ re-insurance and international trade. Winners of the Queen's Award for Export Achievement 1992.

WORKLOAD			
Shipping	75%	Insurance	15%
International trade	10%		

MORGAN BRUCE

BRADLEY COURT, PARK PLACE, CARDIFF, S. GLAM, CF1 3DP
DX: 33014

TEL: (01222) 385385
FAX: (01222) 385300

Princess House, Princess Way, Swansea SA1 3LJ
DX: 39581

Tel: (01792) 634634
Fax: (01792) 634500

167 Fleet Street, London EC4A 2JB
DX: 261

Tel: (0171) 822 8000
Fax: (0171) 822 8222

THE FIRM: A commercial law firm organised into departments and industry groups providing practical commercial advice to business and the public sector. The firm has specialisms including banking, charities, coal and minerals, commercial litigation, commercial property, company commercial, construction, education, EC law, employment, energy and power generation, environmental, health and medical negligence, health and safety, housing associations, insolvency, insurance, intellectual property, landlord and tenant litigation, pensions, planning, private client, professional negligence, property litigation, public law, sports law and tax.

CHAIRMAN: John Bowen	
Number of partners:	50
Assistant solicitors:	78
Other fee-earners:	22

INTERNATIONAL: The firm is a founder member of the Association of European Lawyers, a group of five leading law firms in the UK with contacts throughout Europe and the rest of the world.

LANGUAGES SPOKEN: Bemba, French, German, Greek, Italian, Mandarin, Spanish, Welsh.

MORGAN LEWIS & BOCKIUS

4 CARLTON GARDENS, PALL MALL, LONDON, SW1Y 5AA
DX: 37224 Piccadilly 1

TEL: (0171) 839 1677
FAX: (0171) 839 3650

THE FIRM: Founded in Philadelphia in 1873, Morgan Lewis & Bockius is one of the oldest and largest law firms in the US. As one of the first major US law firms to develop a multi-city practice, Morgan Lewis & Bockius is a leading international law firm able to draw on a wide diversity of capabilities and substantive experience. As a multi-national partnership the firm has a commitment to utilise technology in order to provide a superior service to clients. E-mail, voice messaging and state-of-the-art data communications enable lawyers throughout the firm to work together pooling resources and talents on single projects despite geographical separation. Many of the firm's lawyers have attained positions of recognition in their respective fields of expertise.

LONDON OFFICE: Established in 1981, the London office specialises in international and cross-border financings and tax planning for corporations and individuals and acts as a focal point for many of the international and cross-border business transactions which are handled by the firm in Europe and the Middle East. Such financing work includes broad expertise in loan, equity and guarantee financings from national and multilateral financing institutions such as the World Bank, the International Finance Corporation, the Overseas Private Investment Corporation, the Export-Import Bank and other such institutions. In January 1994 the London office became a multi-national practice of Registered Foreign Lawyers and Solicitors recognised by The Law Society.

AREAS OF PRACTICE: Worldwide, the firm handles a vast diversity of legal work including antitrust; arbitration and ADR; banking and financial services; bankruptcy and reorganisation law; business and corporate law; construction; customs law; energy; environmental law; executive compensation and employee benefits; food, drug and cosmetics law; foreign direct investment in the US; Government contracts and regulation; immigration; insurance law; intellectual property and technology; international financings and trade; litigation; mergers and acquisitions; personal and private client law; product liability; securities law; trademark and copyright law and transport law. In the UK this includes the full range of English company/ commercial; commercial litigation; property; tax and other ancillary practice areas.

OTHER OFFICES: Philadelphia, Washington, New York, Los Angeles, Miami, Harrisburg, Princeton, Frankfurt, Brussels, Tokyo.

CONTACT PARTNER: Robert Rakison

LAWYERS:	
London:	14
Worldwide:	796

Morgan, Lewis & Bockius

REGISTERED FOREIGN LAWYERS & SOLICITORS

MORRELL PEEL & GAMLEN

1 ST. GILES', OXFORD, OXON, OX1 3JR
DX: 4366 Oxford

TEL: (01865) 242468
FAX: (01865) 724878

Property, Planning, Private Client
Company/Commercial, IP, EC, Litigation

Fax: (01865) 724878
Fax: (01865) 792053

THE FIRM: Morrell Peel & Gamlen offers a quality service to its commercial, institutional and private clients. It has a thriving commercial and intellectual property practice, with particular expertise in the high technology sector, as well as established strengths in a full range of property, private client and litigation work. It has recently made a number of new appointments as part of its policy of continuous growth and development.

CONTACT PARTNER: Christine Reid

Number of partners:	7
Assistant solicitors:	5
Other fee-earners:	4

PRINCIPAL AREAS OF WORK:

Charities: (*Contact Partner:* Alan Poulter). *Work includes:* formation of charities and advice on charitable status and tax, especially in the educational and arts sectors.

Commercial Property: (*Contact Partner:* Richard Bell). *Work includes:* landlord and tenant; agricultural, industrial and commercial property transactions; development contracts and construction law.

Planning: (*Contact Partner:* Richard Bell). *Work includes:* planning advice and applications for business and institutional clients.

Company/ Commercial: (*Contact Partner:* Christine Reid). *Work includes:* formation of companies and businesses; business and share sales and purchases; UK and international commercial contracts and employment.

Computer Law and Information Technology: (*Contact Partner:* Christine Reid). *Work includes:* systems acquisition and software development and licensing on all media.

Intellectual Property: (*Contact Partner:* Jonathan Anelay). *Work includes:* patents and technology transfer; copyright; traditional and electronic publishing and contentious and non-contentious trade mark work.

European Community: (*Contact Partner:* Jonathan Anelay). *Work includes:* competition law; EC-funded collaboration; research and development agreements and applications to the European Commission.

Education: (*Contact Partner:* Jonathan Anelay). *Work includes:* education law, especially for further and higher education institutions and schools.

Private Client: (*Contact Partner:* Nigel Roots). *Work includes:* probate; trusts; tax planning for clients with both national and international asset bases; residential property work and the administration of estates.

Litigation (Commercial): (*Contact Partner:* Cathleen Blackburn). *Work includes:* commercial disputes, intellectual property disputes and domestic tribunals.

Litigation (Property): (*Contact Partner:* Cathleen Blackburn). *Work includes:* all disputes relating to land and buildings and their occupation.

Debt Collection: (*Contact Partner:* Cathleen Blackburn). *Work includes:* debt collection for businesses and institutions.

RECRUITMENT AND TRAINING: The firm employs one trainee solicitor every other year and recruits with the intention that its trainees will become its assistant solicitors and partners of the future. All round ability, initiative and common sense are required, in addition to good academic qualifications. Applications to Christine Reid, in writing, with a typed CV.

WORKLOAD	
Property	25%
Private client	18%
Company and commercial	15%
Computers and IT	15%
Intellectual property	10%
Litigation	7%
Education	5%
Charities	5%

CONTACTS	
Charities	Alan Poulter
Commercial property	Richard Bell
Commercial litigation	Cathleen Blackburn
Company and commercial	Christine Reid
Computer law and IT	Christine Reid
Debt collection	Cathleen Blackburn
Education	Jonathan Anelay
European community	Jonathan Anelay
Intellectual property	Jonathan Anelay
Planning	Richard Bell
Private client	Nigel Roots
Property litigation	Cathleen Blackburn

MORTON FISHER

CARLTON HOUSE, WORCESTER ST, WORCESTER, HEREFORD & WORCS, DY10 1BA   DX: 16301/16302

TEL: (01562) 820181
FAX: (01562) 820066

THE FIRM: Morton Fisher has seven offices covering a wide geographical area throughout Worcestershire. The firm serves the needs of the local community, specialising in company/ commercial work for business, agricultural law, and private client work. The firm handles a substantial amount of litigation, including matrimonial work, property and estate administration. The firm is on the Law Society's Childrens Panel and the Personal Injury Panel. It holds the Legal Aid Franchise.

OTHER OFFICES:
Worcester, Droitwich, Stourport-on-Severn, Bromsgrove, Bewdley, Cleobury Mortimer.

CONTACT PARTNER: Mr T. Morgan

Number of partners:	19
Assistant solicitors:	20
Other fee-earners:	25

WORKLOAD	
Family and matrimonial	40%
Various	20%
Property	20%
Company and commercial	20%

MORTON FRASER MILLIGAN WS

15 & 19 YORK PLACE, EDINBURGH, EH1 3EL
DX: 119 Edinburgh

TEL: (0131) 556 8444
FAX: (0131) 557 3778

CHAIRMAN: Mr John Wightman CBE

Number of partners:	19
Assistant solicitors:	17
Other fee-earners:	33

CONTACTS

Commercial property	Hugh Henderson
Corporate law	Bruce Wood
Litigation	David Stewart
Private client	James Rust

THE FIRM: Morton Fraser Milligan WS is a long-established Edinburgh firm offering a range of commercial services alongside a strong private client practice. It serves a variety of clients including banks, finance companies, the drinks industry and environmental agencies. The firm has a branch office in Brussels, maintains strong overseas connections in Europe, the USA and the Far East, and is a member of Interlaw. The practice has developed an expertise in European Community law and advises clients on the regulatory implications of European legislation. In addition, Morton Fraser Relocation Limited provides a comprehensive relocation service to corporate clients involved in moving employees within the UK and worldwide.

PRINCIPAL AREAS OF WORK:

Corporate Law: (*Contact Partner:* Bruce Wood). The department assists clients in the following areas of law: the formation, administration and reconstruction of companies; flotations; takeovers, mergers, acquisitions and management buy-outs; asset finance; banking law, international trade and corporate finance; EC and competition law; pensions law; shipping; corporate tax planning; partnerships; general commercial advice, including contracts, insolvency, intellectual property and computer law.

Commercial Property: (*Contact Partner:* Hugh Henderson). The firm deals with all aspects of commercial property including acquisition, sale, leasing, development, finance and planning. This is complemented by experience in the specialised areas of environmental law, licensing, equipment leasing, rating and valuation.

Litigation: (*Contact Partner:* David Stewart). The department has expertise in various fields of litigation. The main areas in which the firm operates are: all aspects of commercial litigation, accidents, arbitrations, building contracts, child law, consumer advice, contract disputes, debt collection, employment, family law, insolvency, insurance claims, intellectual property, judicial review, landlord and tenant, licensing, motor offences, planning, public inquiries and tribunals.

Private Client: (*Contact Partner:* James Rust). The firm provides assistance in residential conveyancing, wills, executries, taxation, investment and financial planning. The department also undertakes work relating to agriculture and estates.

OTHER OFFICE:
Commercial Department: 18 York Place, Edinburgh EH1 3EP.
Tel: (0131) 557 9595. *Fax:* (0131) 557 6334.

FOREIGN LANGUAGES: French, German, Spanish.

INTERNATIONAL CONNECTIONS & ASSOCIATED OFFICES: The firm has a branch office at BTE 3 Square de Meeûs 19, 1040, Brussels and is a member of Interlaw. Strong overseas connections are maintained with France, Japan, Korea, Australia, USA, Germany, Norway, Sweden, Italy.

MOSS LATHAM & TOONE
80-81 Woodgate, Loughborough, Leics, LE11 2XE **Tel:** (01509) 217770 **Fax:** (01509) 233698 **DX:** 19605 **Ptnrs:** 7 **Asst Solrs:** 4 **Other Fee-earners:** 10. One of the larger firms in the area, it concentrates on conveyancing, crime and civil litigation. Also known for commercial law and probate work.

MOWLL & MOWLL
34 and 36 Castle Street, Dover, Kent, CT16 1PN **Tel:** (01304) 240250 **Fax:** (01304) 240040 **DX:** 6302 Dover **Ptnrs:** 9 **Asst Solrs:** 2 **Other Fee-earners:** 6. Handles company/ commercial, medical negligence, personal injury, and matrimonial matters. Also advises on harbour law. Branch office in Canterbury.

WORKLOAD			
Commercial	34%	Matrimonial	15%
Conveyancing	15%	Litigation	15%
Probate	15%		

MULLIS & PEAKE
Marshalls Chambers, 80A South Street, Romford, Essex, RM1 1QS **Tel:** (01708) 762326 **Fax:** (01708) 747145 **DX:** 4604 Romford **Ptnrs:** 9 **Asst Solrs:** 2 **Other Fee-earners:** 7. Well known locally for commercial development conveyancing, civil litigation and probate work. The firm also specialises in both gaming and liquor licensing.

MUNDAYS

CROWN HOUSE, CHURCH ROAD, CLAYGATE, ESHER, SURREY, KT10 0LP
DX: 36300

TEL: (01372) 467272
FAX: (01372) 463782

THE FIRM: Mundays is a well-respected firm with a particularly strong commercial practice and a highly regarded franchising team. The firm has developed extensive connections in North America, Africa and throughout Europe, and acts for a wide range of clients from major national and international public companies to small private companies, partnerships and individuals.

PRINCIPAL AREAS OF WORK:

Company/ Commercial: (*Contact Partner:* Peter Munday). All aspects of public and private company work are handled, from formations to mergers, MBOs and insolvency work. General commercial work includes: computer agreements, EC law, licensing, agency, distribution, consumer credit problems, employment law, financial services and tax matters.

Intellectual Property: (*Contact Partner:* Ray Walley). A separate department handles all aspects of copyright, trade marks, design and patents; the firm has particular experience in software licensing.

Franchising & Distribution: (*Contact Partner:* Manzoor G.K. Ishani). The firm has been acting for franchisors since the early 70's and has developed extensive experience of the full range of franchising matters, including the creation of documents for international franchising. Manzoor Ishani is a member of the Legal Committee of the British Franchise Association and the firm was recently reported as being in the top three firms in a national poll.

Property: (*Contact Partner:* Simon Withers). The firm undertakes a complete range of commercial property transactions, involving all aspects of the acquisition and disposal of offices, industrial units, warehouses, hotels, houses and flats. *Work includes:* franchise property schemes, town and country planning, site development and redevelopment, mortgages, property insurance and overseas property investment.

Litigation: (*Contact Partner:* Fiona McAllister). Substantial volume of corporate and litigation is handled. *Work includes:* commercial litigation, personal injury claims, debt collection, landlord and tenant disputes, consumer problems, criminal and licensing matters.

Pharmacies: (*Contact Partner:* Simon Withers). Mundays has specific expertise in the sale and purchase of pharmacy businesses, and related matters.

OTHER AREAS OF WORK: The firm has experienced teams handling wills, probate, trusts, tax, family/ matrimonial matters, Court of Protection, welfare law and immigration work. Partners are members of the Law Society Children Panel and Family Law Association.

FOREIGN CONNECTIONS: Mundays has a presence in Brussels and London, and is a member of Eurolink, and a founder member of the European Franchise Lawyers Group.

SENIOR PARTNER:	Peter J. Munday
Number of partners:	13
Assistant solicitors:	5
Other fee-earners:	7

WORKLOAD	
Company and commercial (including franchising and IP)	35%
Residential property, matrimonial, tax and probate	25%
Commercial property	22%
Commercial litigation	18%

CONTACTS	
Commercial property	Simon Withers
Corporate	Peter Munday
European & international	Manzoor G.K. Ishani
Financial services	Richard A. Powell
Franchising & distribution	Manzoor G.K. Ishani
Intellectual property	Ray D. Walley
Litigation	Fiona McAllister

MUNRO & NOBLE 26 Church Street, Inverness, Highlands, IV1 1HX **Tel:** (01463) 221727 **Fax:** (01463) 225165 **DX:** 15 Inverness **Ptnrs:** 8 **Asst Solrs:** 2 **Other Fee-earners:** 6. General practice handling a broad range of work including agriculture, estate agency, probate and trusts, crime and licensing applications.

MURRAY BEITH & MURRAY WS 39 Castle Street, Edinburgh, EH2 3BH **Tel:** (0131) 225 1200 **Fax:** (0131) 225 4412 **DX:** 40 Edinburgh **Ptnrs:** 11 **Asst Solrs:** 11 **Other Fee-earners:** 25. A member of LawNet, the firm acts for individuals, businesses, financial institutions and public and private trusts, offering a comprehensive range of legal and financial services.

MURRAY & COMPANY 41 Alexandra Road, Wimbledon, London, SW19 7JZ **Tel:** (0181) 944 1335 **Fax:** (0181) 944 2755 **DX:** 300120 Wimbledon Central **Ptnrs:** 2 **Other Fee-earners:** 2. The firm has developed a practice advising companies involved in the manufacture and distribution of food and drink through the LAWSCAN service.

WORKLOAD			
Commercial	60%	Commercial property	40%

MYER WOLFF & MANLEY 15-16 Bowlalley Lane, Hull, Humbs, HU1 1YE **Tel:** (01482) 223693 **Fax:** (01482) 225089 **DX:** 11904 **Ptnrs:** 4 **Asst Solrs:** 2 **Other Fee-earners:** 8. Known for their criminal law, matrimonial and child care work. Represents patients at Mental Health Review Tribunals.

WORKLOAD			
Crime	45%	Personal injury/ claims	15%
Family	14%	Conveyancing/ probate	10%
Unclassified misc	8%	Matrimonial	8%

NABARRO NATHANSON

50 STRATTON ST, LONDON, W1X 6NX DX: 77 London/Chancery Lane WC2	TEL: (0171) 493 9933 FAX: (0171) 629 7900
614 Lloyd's, One Lime Street, London, EC3M 7DQ. DX: 77 London/Chancery Lane WC2	Tel: (0171) 629 6522 Fax: (0171) 621 1898
Abbot's House, Abbey Street, Reading RG1 3BD. DX: 4068 Reading	Tel: (01734) 504700 Fax: (01734) 505640
City Plaza, 2 Pinfold Street, Sheffield, S1 2GU. DX: 10595 Sheffield	Tel: (0114) 278 6666 Fax: (0114) 278 6123
The Lodge, South Parade, Doncaster, DN1 2DQ. DX: 28697 Doncaster-2	Tel: (01302) 344455 Fax: (01302) 738408
12 Marina Court, Castle Street, Hull HU1 1TJ. DX: 11931 Hull	Tel: (01482) 219111 Fax: (01482) 218444
ul. Zlota 44/46, 00-120, Warsaw, Poland.	Tel: (48) 2 622 1750 Fax: (48) 2 622 1742
Dubai World Trade Centre, PO Box 9381, Dubai, United Arab Emirates.	Tel: (9714) 314475 Fax: (9714) 313514
1 Place Madou, Box 34, 1030 Brussels, Belgium.	Tel: (0032) 2 223 1309 Fax: (0032) 2 223 2945
M-1065 Budapest, Révay utca 10, Hungary.	Tel: (361) 269 1144 Fax: (361) 269 1233

NATURE OF FIRM: Nabarro Nathanson is one of the UK's largest commercial practices with offices in London, Reading and the North of England and a growing network of international offices. It has nearly 1000 legal and support staff. All the firm's offices provide a friendly and informal, yet highly professional atmosphere.

PRINCIPAL AREAS OF WORK:

General Description: The firm provides a comprehensive range of legal services covering company and commercial; property; construction; taxation and trusts; EC and competition law; international trade; energy law; banking and finance; insurance; intellectual property; litigation; pensions and employee benefits; insolvency; mining and mineral rights; environmental law; shipping; mergers and acquisitions; international litigation; employment law and trade disputes; and the public sector and planning.

Company/Commercial: (*Contact:* Peter Gorty. *34 Partners*). Work includes general company and commercial matters, mergers and acquisitions, corporate restructuring and partnership matters. The department has teams of lawyers working on corporate finance, energy, venture capital, international transactions, European and competition law, insolvency, media, sports and entertainment and employment law. It also provides company secretarial services.

Banking and Project Finance: (*Contact:* John Belton. *5 Partners*). All aspects of banking work are undertaken but the department has specialist expertise in syndicated lending, capital markets, project finance and distressed debt.

Commercial Property: (*Contact:* Geoffrey Lander. *35 Partners*). The firm has one of the largest commercial property departments among British law firms. It provides advice on property investment and development, portfolio management, property finance and overseas property. There is a separate property litigation department

CONTACT PARTNER: David Bramson

Number of partners:	128
Assistant solicitors:	213
Other fee-earners:	157

CONTACTS	
Banking	John Belton
Company and commercial	Peter Gorty
Construction	Martin Bridgewater
Employment	Patrick Moon
Energy	Robert Tudway
Environment	Tom Symes
Health and community care	Paul Ridout
Health and safety	Gareth Watkins
Insolvency	Michael Prior
Insurance	Jennifer Donohue
Intellectual property	Andrew Inglis
Litigation	Peter Sigler
National Centre for Law in Industry	Richard Holt
Northern offices	Susan McKenna

and the firm's public sector department also has considerable experience advising private sector organisations on matters involving and negotiating with local and central government and other public sector bodies.

Litigation: (*Contact:* Peter Sigler. *21 Partners*). The firm has a practical and forthright approach to litigation. Staff operate in groups, each headed by a partner, to ensure personal service. There are separate teams working on general, commercial, property and international litigation. There are also personal injuries, intellectual property, insolvency, health and community care, European and employment groups. A shipping litigation unit operates from the firm's Lloyd's office.

Construction: (*Contact:* Martin Bridgewater. *8 Partners*). Work includes preparation of tenders, drafting and negotiating construction and related contracts, and resolution of construction disputes. There is also a mining and mineral rights group. The firm undertakes both UK and overseas work.

Tax: (*Contact:* Malcolm Finney. *11 Partners*). The firm combines legal and accountancy expertise to provide tax advice of all descriptions including commercial tax planning, private tax planning, VAT, international taxation, property taxation, share schemes, estate planning and trusts.

Pensions: (*Contact:* John Quarrell. *5 Partners*). The pensions department acts for many major client pension funds and advises on pension schemes and pension products. The firm established Stratton Street Trustees Ltd to act as an independent trustee.

Public Sector: (*Contact:* David Abram. *4 Partners*). The firm advises more than 110 local authorities, several development corporations and many other public sector organisations on town centre and other property development, compulsory purchase, local authority finance and public law.

Intellectual Property: (*Contact:* Andrew Inlgis. *2 Partners*). The firm's IP department handles a variety of contentious and non-contentious work. It has also developed a particular strength in the area of Information Technology law.

Planning: (*Contact:* David Hawkins. *5 Partners*). The Nabarro Nathanson planning department is one of the largest in the country. It advises public and private sector clients on all planning matters including strategic advice and large scale planning enquiries. It also deals with administrative law, compulsory purchase and compensation, rating and infrastructure.

Environment: (*Contact:* Tom Symes. *4 Partners*). Nabarro Nathanson's environment group is one of the largest teams of solicitors handling all aspects of environment law in the UK. The group advises on the implications of new environmental legislation for a wide range of clients including waste management, property and construction companies and the public sector.

Health and Community Care: (*Contact:* Paul Ridout. *2 Partners*). The Health and Community Care group provides advice to NHS Trusts, health authorities and private healthcare providers on all aspects of the law covering this area.

NATURE OF CLIENTELE: The firm's extensive client base includes financial and City institutions; UK and international public and private companies; central, local and overseas governments; nationalised industries; other public bodies and professional practices.

NORTHERN OFFICES: There are 17 partners in the Sheffield, Doncaster and Hull offices. The firm has recently established a National Centre for Law in Industry in its new office in Sheffield. Services offered include environment, employment, pensions, intellectual property, health and safety, personal injury, trade and EC law.

THAMES VALLEY: There are 4 partners in the Reading office serving the needs of companies in the M4 corridor. The practice has built a strong reputation in the area of IT/IP advice as well as for property and company/commercial work, reflecting and providing a "City on your doorstep" service.

FOREIGN CONNECTIONS: The firm has overseas offices in Brussels, Warsaw, Budapest and Dubai and associations with leading firms in most major countries throughout the world. There are resident partners in New York and Paris.

RECRUITMENT AND TRAINING: About 30 trainee solicitors are recruited each year and the firm provides summer student placements. The firm is always keen to hear from high calibre staff with experience at all levels. Written applications should be sent to the Director of Personnel. The Legal Training Office provides a comprehensive and vigorous in-house training programme for all legal staff.

Pensions	John Quarrell
Planning	David Hawkins
Property	Geoffrey Lander
Public sector	David Abram
Shipping	Russel Gardener
Tax	Malcolm Finney
Thames Valley	Rosemary Martin-Jones

NABARRO NATHANSON

NALDER & SON Farley House, Falmouth Rd, Truro, Cornwall, TR1 2AT **Tel:** (01872) 41414 **Fax:** (01872) 42424 **DX:** 81204 **Ptnrs:** 8 **Asst Solrs:** 7 **Other Fee-earners:** 16. A family and commercial practice, with the main Truro office concentrating on company, partnership and business law. Other offices in Falmouth, Newquay and Camborne.

WORKLOAD			
Civil litigation	27%	Private conveyancing	26%
Matrimonial	15%	Company and commercial	12%
Probate and wills	11%		

NAPIER & SONS 1/9 Castle Arcade, Belfast, BT1 5DF **Tel:** (01232) 244602 **Fax:** (01232) 330330 **Ptnrs:** 3 **Asst Solrs:** 3 . Broadly based practice, with particular expertise in insolvency matters.

WORKLOAD			
Insolvency	40%	Defence litigation	40%
Misc inc debt collection	20%		

NAPTHEN HOUGHTON CRAVEN 7 Winckley Square, Preston, Lancs, PR1 3JD **Tel:** (01772) 883883 **Fax:** (01772) 257805 **DX:** 17123 **Ptnrs:** 14 **Asst Solrs:** 2 **Other Fee-earners:** 15. Founded in 1990 with the merger of two of Preston's oldest and most respected firms: Houghton Craven & Dicksons and Napthens.

NASH SOLICITORS Beaumont House, Beaumont Park, Plymouth, Devon, PL4 9BD **Tel:** (01752) 664444 **Fax:** (01752) 667112 **DX:** 8250 Plymouth **Ptnrs:** 8 **Asst Solrs:** 4 **Other Fee-earners:** 4. A modern computerised practice with particular emphasis on personal injury and insurance company litigation, commercial and residential property, and company law.

WORKLOAD			
Civil litigation	65%	Matrimonial	20%
Commercial/res property	8%	Other mainly private	7%

NATHAN, SILMAN

OSPREY HOUSE, 78 WIGMORE ST, LONDON, W1H 9DQ
DX: 9019 WE

TEL: (0171) 935 0898
FAX: (0171) 486 4803

THE FIRM: A commercial practice serving the needs of the established corporate client, the entrepreneur and the individual. The practice style is based on personal, partner-led service, with prompt and accurate advice being enhanced by sound commercial judgement. Best known for its niche retail specialisation, the firm's client base includes market leaders in that sector as well as in the property development and investment and construction industries.

PRINCIPAL AREAS OF WORK: The firm is recognised as having developed a particular expertise in retail property and related work and acts for a number of 'household name' retailers, with specialist seminars on topical issues being held regularly for clients and others. The firm is also known for its commercial property expertise (with a particular emphasis on development and joint-ventures), company/commercial, banking, commercial and property litigation, employment, matrimonial and family law, personal injury, professional and medical negligence, intellectual property and information technology.

CONTACT PARTNER: Michael J. Nathan

Number of partners:	3
Assistant solicitors:	2
Other fee-earners:	2

CONTACTS	
Commercial property	G Silman/M Nathan
Company/commercial	M Nathan/S Lewis
Litigation	Angela Robbins
Retail	G Silman/M Nathan

Nathan, Silman
S O L I C I T O R S

THE NATIONAL SOLICITORS' NETWORK

CONQUEST LEGAL MARKETING, 73 GLOUCESTER ROAD, LONDON, SW7 4SS
DX: 44109 Gloucester Road

TEL: (0171) 244 6422
FAX: (0171) 370 6893

NATURE OF GROUP: The National Solicitors' Network (TNSN) was formed by Conquest Legal Marketing in 1991 to provide institutional, corporate and private clients with legal services of the highest quality.

THE FIRMS: The Network embraces more than 250 independent solicitors' practices with 400 offices spread throughout England and Wales. Member firms range from two partner practices to a 37 partner commercial firm. As the largest solicitors' network in the UK, the Network provides an influential voice for its members. A full-time management and marketing team is based in London and there is a panel of regional representatives.

THE GROUP: The Network generates and distributes substantial levels of profitable work to member firms. Agreements have been formed with building societies, insurance companies, banks, centralised lenders, major employers, an international charity and several NHS trusts. A national County Court agency service was set up

CHAIRMAN/ CEO: Richard Berenson
OPERATIONS: Robin Richard
MEMBERSHIP: Angela Willis

Number of partners:	1627
Other fee-earners:	2734

in 1993 and has delivered significant benefit to participating firms. In addition to the generation of fee-earning work, there is a commitment to practice development and quality initiatives. A full range of services includes quality and training seminars and consultancy, information technology advice, negotiated discounts on professional indemnity top-up premiums and other benefits and discounts including marketing materials, office supplies and printwork services.

THE FUTURE: The Network's representative role is increasing as issues such as competitive tendering, franchising of legal services and the adoption of minimum practice standards become the norm. For more details and an application form please write to the address above.

NEEDHAM & GRANT 14 Lincoln's Inn Fields, London, WC2A 3BP **Tel:** (0171) 242 5866 **Fax:** (0171) 831 8254 **Ptnrs:** 5 **Asst Solrs:** 4 **Other Fee-earners:** 2. Highly regarded specialist intellectual property law practice, with emphasis on patent litigation. Also known for reinsurance litigation and arbitration.

WORKLOAD	
Patents/int property	65%

NEEDHAM & JAMES 25 Meer Street, Stratford upon Avon, Warks, CV37 6QB **Tel:** (01789) 414444 **Fax:** (01789) 296608 **DX:** 16202 **Ptnrs:** 9 **Asst Solrs:** 7 **Other Fee-earners:** 10.

WORKLOAD			
Commercial property	35%	Housing association	20%
Private client	15%	Commercial litigation	15%
Company and commercial	15%		

NEIL F. JONES & CO 3 Broadway, Broad Street, Birmingham, W. Midlands, B15 1BQ **Tel:** (0121) 643 1010 **Fax:** (0121) 643 1969 **DX:** 701215 Edgbaston 4 **Ptnrs:** 5 **Asst Solrs:** 5 **Other Fee-earners:** 4. Established 1980. A niche construction practice, also handling insurance work, intellectual property, commercial litigation and employment.

NEILL CLERK & MURRAY 3 Ardgowan Square, Greenock, Strathclyde, PA16 8NG **Tel:** (01475) 724522 **Fax:** (01475) 784339 **DX:** 7 Greenock **Ptnrs:** 13 **Asst Solrs:** 3 **Other Fee-earners:** 1. A mixed practice particularly experienced in corporate matters. Additional offices in Glasgow, Greenock and Gourock.

NELSON & CO St. Andrew's House, St. Andrew's Street, Leeds, W. Yorks, LS3 1LF **Tel:** (0113) 2436491 **Fax:** (0113) 2420113 **DX:** 12047 Leeds **Ptnrs:** 5 **Asst Solrs:** 4 **Other Fee-earners:** 6. A corporate and private client practice with particular specialisation in personal injury, professional negligence, property litigation and debt recovery.

NELSONS Pennine House, 8 Stanford Street, Nottingham, Notts, NG1 7BQ **Tel:** (0115) 958 6262 **Fax:** (0115) 958 4702 **DX:** 10096 Nottingham **Ptnrs:** 15 **Asst Solrs:** 30 **Other Fee-earners:** 30. Fast growing, modern firm, established in 1983. Combines commercial and civil work with large crime and matrimonial practices.

WORKLOAD			
Crime (incl bus crime)	27%	Litigation	17%
Convey/trust/probate	14%	Matrimonial	13%
Personal injury	11%	Commercial	11%

NEWSOME VAUGHAN

GREYFRIARS HOUSE, GREYFRIARS LANE, COVENTRY,
W. MIDLANDS, CV1 2GW   DX: 18854 Cov.2

TEL: (01203) 633433
FAX: (01203) 256496

THE FIRM: Newsome Vaughan is a general practice which is expanding its civil litigation services whilst maintaining its corporate and private client work.

PRINCIPAL AREAS OF WORK: The firm specialises in personal injury litigation (plaintiff and defendant), medical negligence, mortgage possessions, company/ commercial, commercial property, residential conveyancing, probate, trusts and wills.

OVERSEAS CONNECTIONS: The firm is a member of Law Group International.

CONTACT PARTNER: Rupert Griffiths	
Number of partners:	5
Assistant solicitors:	6
Other fee-earners:	6

NICHOLAS FISHER 9-13 Fenchurch Buildings, London, EC3M 5HR **Tel:** (0171) 709 7203 **Fax:** (0171) 709 7204 **Ptnrs:** 2 **Asst Solrs:** 2 . A small city firm providing specialised services in the areas of shipping, insurance, re-insurance and international trade.

WORKLOAD			
Comm ship/int trade	65%	Prof indemnity/insurance	30%
Shipping/insurance doc	5%		

NICHOLAS MORRIS 70-71 New Bond Street, London, W1Y 9DE **Tel:** (0171) 493 8811 **Fax:** (0171) 491 2094 **Ptnrs:** 3 **Other Fee-earners:** 3. Entertainment lawyers; long-established firm. Experienced practitioners in the law relating to music, records, film, television, theatre, property, partnerships, wills, litigation and business affairs.

NICHOLSON GRAHAM & JONES

25-31 MOORGATE, LONDON, EC2R 6AR
DX: 58

TEL: (0171) 628 9151
FAX: (0171) 638 3102

THE FIRM: Nicholson Graham & Jones was founded in 1858 and has been based in Moorgate, close to the Bank of England, since the early part of this century. The work of the firm is predominantly corporate, financial and commercial and it is well known for its high quality client list. The firm is expanding with a young and active partnership who play a major role in the development of the practice.

PRINCIPAL AREAS OF WORK:

General Description: The firm's business philosophy is to offer the quality and range of service associated with a City law firm with accessible and creative advice based on a high degree of partner input. The growth of the firm and its reputation demonstrates the success of this approach. Nicholson Graham & Jones believes in a close relationship with clients, and a clear understanding of their business activities as a pre-requisite to providing advice that meets their needs and commercial objectives efficently and cost-effectively.

Company and Commercial: (*Contacts:* Michael Johns and Stephen Roberts. 11 Partners). The department advises businesses on all aspects of their corporate and commercial activities, particularly all types of corporate finance and commercial agreements. Specialist cross-departmental units concentrate on banking and finance, construction, corporate rescue, insolvency, mergers and acquisitions, management buy-outs, European law and practice, EC and UK competition, central and local government tendering and privatisation, intellectual property, sport and sponsorship and venture capital.

Litigation: (*Contact:* Tony Walker. 9 Partners). The department has substantial experience of general commercial litigation acting for UK and international clients. Specialist units cover banking and insolvency, employment, travel and leisure. The department is structured to offer clients an immediate and flexible response to obtain urgent injunctions, and will always seek the optimum litigation or alternative strategy including settlement, to match the nature of the dispute and the clients' commercial objectives.

Property: (*Contact:* Richard Smith. 6 Partners). The department provides a comprehensive service enabling clients to finance, develop, occupy and invest in property, effectively and efficiently. Specialist units deal with environment and planning law, the public sector and election law.

Pensions: (*Contact:* Ian Pittaway. 4 Partners). The department acts for a large number of major occupational pension schemes providing a full range of services. It receives referrals from many other professionals and provides a pensions capacity for a number of leading firms of solicitors. It has particular expertise in pension fund litigation and offers an Independent Trustee service. The immigration unit deals with entry clearance, work permits, permanent residency and citizenship for private and corporate clients.

Tax: (IContacts: Michael Jacobs and Eliza Mellor. 4 Partners. Corporate tax advice covers UK and international tax structures for companies and individuals, including taxation of businesses, companies and investments, property, VAT, employee incentives and benefits. Specialist areas are employee share schemes, golden

CONTACT PARTNER: Michael Johns

Number of partners:	34
Assistant solicitors:	32
Other fee-earners:	12

WORKLOAD	
Company and commercial	35%
Litigation	24%
Property	21%
Pensions	12%
Tax	8%

CONTACTS	
Acquisitions & mergers	Michael Johns
Banking & finance	Richard Talbot
Competition	Peter Bond
Construction	David Race
Corporate finance	Richard Herbert
Corporate tax	Michael Jacobs
Elections	Piers Coleman
Environment	John Garbutt
Immigration	Jackie Thompson
Insolvency	Shashi Rajani
Intellectual property	Sarah Kirk
Litigation	Tony Walker
Local government	David Race
Pensions	Ian Pittaway
Planning	Steven Scates
Private client	Eliza Mellor
Property	Richard Smith
Sport & sponsorship	Richard Glynn
Travel & tourism	Tim Robinson

handshakes and redundancy. Clients include public and private companies, individuals, charities and trusts. Private client lawyers act for individuals and families frequently with an international element. They offer strategic advice on income and capital taxes and financial planning and deal with probate and administration of estates. The department has specialist expertise in sophisticated offshore trusts and company structures, often utilising its extensive network of foreign-based tax advisers.

NATURE OF CLIENTELE: The firm acts for corporate and institutional clients of all sizes in a variety of industry sectors as well as public authorities and central and local government. It advises entrepreneurs and private businesses from start-ups to major companies, individuals and families of substance.

FOREIGN CONNECTIONS: *(Contact:* Michael Johns). The firm is a founder member of GlobaLex, an international alliance of independent law firms with offices in the USA, Europe and the Far East with a jointly run office in Brussels. Outside GlobaLex, the firm maintains excellent connections with lawyers and other professionals in all major jurisdictions.

AGENCY WORK: *(Contact:* John Garbutt). Specialist units within the firm often act for other firms of solicitors or accountants who do not have expertise in a particular area or where a conflict of interest arises.

RECRUITMENT & TRAINING: *(Contact:* Gail Harcus). For the trainee solicitor the firm offers a rare combination of early responsibility and involvement with the opportunity to gain first class City experience. The firm seeks people whose ambition is to achieve partnership and contribute fully to the development of the practice. A comprehensive and integrated continuing education programme is provided and the current requirement is 5-6 trainees per year.

NICHOLSON GRAHAM & JONES

NICHOLSONS 23 Alexandra Rd, Lowestoft, Suffolk, NR32 1PP **Tel:** (01502) 562140 **Fax:** (01502) 568814 **DX:** 41204 **Ptnrs:** 11 **Asst Solrs:** 5 **Other Fee-earners:** 6. Long-established firm known for company/ commercial, debt recovery, insolvency, litigation, divorce and conveyancing. Also at Beccles, Loddon, Bungay, and Harleston as Nicholson Cadge & Gilbert.

WORKLOAD			
Civil litigation/agency	27%	Comp/comm/partnership	19%
Divorce/matrim/housing	17%	Probate/trust/wills	12%
Domestic property	12%	Liquidation, bankruptcy	7%

NIGHTINGALES 12 St. John St, Deansgate, Manchester, M3 4DX **Tel:** (0161) 832 6722 **Fax:** (0161) 832 7293 **DX:** 14330 **Ptnrs:** 7. Niche practice particularly known for its expertise in family/ matrimonial law.

NORTON ROSE

KEMPSON HOUSE, PO BOX 570, CAMOMILE STREET, LONDON, EC3A 7AN
DX: 85 London

TEL: (0171) 283 6000
FAX: (0171) 283 6500

Norton Rose is a leading international law firm with its principal office in the City of London. Clients include UK and overseas banks and other financial institutions, international businesses, public and major private companies, government departments and agencies, statutory undertakings, sovereign states and individuals. The 1995 survey 'Financial Lawyers on Lawyers' rated Norton Rose best law firm worldwide for overall quality of service, for understanding the client's business and for technical ability.

The firms's expertise covers the whole range of financial and business activities. It is particularly well known for corporate finance, debt, asset and project finance, banking and capital markets, and company and commercial law. It has leading practices in aviation, construction, energy and natural resources, insurance, and maritime law. It has a major litigation department handling all forms of commercial dispute resolution, and highly regarded commercial property and tax departments.

In addition to its principal office in London, the firm has offices in Bahrain, Brussels, Hong Kong, Moscow, Paris, Piraeus, Prague and Singapore. In England, the firm is a member of The Norton Rose M5 Group, seven independent legal practices which work together regularly on a co-operative basis. The services of the Group are therefore available in the major financial, commercial and industrial centres of the country.

MANAGING PARTNER: R. Birkby

UK:	
Number of partners:	83
Assistant solicitors:	192
Other fee-earners:	115
INTERNATIONAL:	
Number of Partners:	17
Assistant Solicitors:	38
Other fee-earners:	11

WORKLOAD	
Corporate & finance	54%
Commercial & marine litigation	29%
Commmercial property	10%
Taxation	4%
Private client	3%

THE FIRM: Norton Rose is divided into five main departments: corporate and financial, commercial litigation, commercial property and planning, taxation and private client. Superimposed on this departmental structure there is a network of market groups, each one comprising lawyers from different departments, but with a common interest in a particular business sector. The Energy and Natural Resources Group, for instance, combines experience from the corporate and financial, taxation and litigation departments.

PRINCIPAL AREAS OF WORK: The corporate and financial department:(*Contact:* Francis Sumner) is the largest, comprising nearly 150 lawyers. It is divided into two business groups: the corporate finance group (*Contact:* Simon Sackman) and the banking group (*Contact:* Peter Thorne), and advises on a wide range of international and domestic transactions including public and private company mergers and acquisitions and equity issues, privatisations, banking and international debt finance, project, shipping and aviation finance, sovereign debt, inward investment, collective investment media, insolvency, and general commercial work. Separate specialist units have been established within this department to deal with project finance (*Contact:* Michael Taylor), European Union and competition work (*Contact:* John Cook), international securities issues (*Contact:* Gilles Thieffry), intellectual property and telecoms (*Contact:* Richard Barratt) and human resources (*Contact:* Stuart Lippiatt).

The commercial litigation department (*Contact:* Michael Lee) has over 80 lawyers, making it one of the largest litigation departments in the country. The department undertakes commercial and corporate litigation and arbitration with a particularly high proportion of multi-jurisdictional and international disputes. The practice of the department reflects the focus of the firm's business as a whole with strengths in litigation arising from banking, shipping, securities and financial services regulation, insurance/reinsurance, construction, aviation and intellectual property. Within the department there is a specialist arbitration group and the department also actively supports alternative dispute resolution methods. It has a comprehensive programme for training legal staff on evidence, pleadings and advocacy, and has invested heavily in litigation support technology.

The commercial property and planning department (*Contact:* Peter Burrows) has around 40 lawyers. Its work covers all aspects of the commercial property market, particularly planning and environmental law, secured lending, finance leasing, single property and portfolio investments and major property developments in London and throughout England and Wales. It also handles the property aspects of company flotations, share and asset acquisitions, disposals, corporate restructuring and insolvencies. The environmental group advises on the impact of domestic and European environmental regulation.

The taxation department (*Contact:* John Challoner) covers all aspects of UK and international corporate and commercial taxation. The majority of the department's work overlaps with corporate finance and banking, for example in capital markets work, the purchase, sale and flotation of companies, national and international joint ventures, collective investment media and a wide variety of asset financing.

The private client department (*Contact:* Hugh Jackson) advises private clients on tax and estate planning, residential and inward investment property transactions, offshore trusts, international asset protection, charitable trusts, incapacity, national heritage property, wills, probate, estate and trust administration.

As the firm expands it creates excellent career prospects, including opportunities to work overseas both before and after qualification. Norton Rose recruits 50-60 trainee solicitors every year. It encourages graduates of any discipline to apply: personality, determination, intellectual ability, and the ability to get on with others are more highly prized than degree subject matter. The firm has always been a pioneer of training and personal development. It has a training programme dedicated specifically to trainee solicitors. Highly competitive salaries are offered, as well as other benefits including sports club, regular social events, and a staff restaurant. Recruitment brochures and application forms are available from Celia Staples, Head of Personnnel.

CONTACTS	
Banking group	Peter Thorne
Comm.property/planning dept.	Peter Burrows
Commercial litigation dept.	Michael Lee
Corporate & financial dept.	Francis Sumner
Corporate finance group	Simon Sackman
European union and competition	John Cook
Human resources	Stuart Lippiatt
Intellectual property/telecoms	Richard Barratt
International securities	Gilles Thieffry
Private client department	Hugh Jackson
Project finance	Michael Taylor
Taxation department	John Challoner

THE NORTON ROSE M5 GROUP

12 THE PRIORY QUEENSWAY, BIRMINGHAM, W. MIDLANDS, B4 6BS
DX: 13036 Birmingham

TEL: (0121) 233 4950
FAX: (0121) 236 8219

GROUP CHAIRMAN: Tony Kay

The Norton Rose M5 Group is an innovative association of a City of London international firm, and six leading regional firms.

Individually, each firm is a leader in its markets, providing strength and depth across a wide range of practice areas. Together, the firms share an association which strengthens the individual practices and offers new service options to clients.

Close coordination between a City and international firm and a major regional firm, whether on a particular transaction or over the whole range of a client's legal requirements, is, in many cases, an increasingly attractive way of meeting the needs of business in a changing legal market.

The Group framework enables the effective provision of this unique service to clients as international, City and regional expertise is combined to meet specific needs and is then delivered in an efficient and cost-effective way.

Shared professional resourcing, including jointly developed knowhow and training programmes, not only adds to the quality and depth of each firm's resources but also underpins the coordinated provision of services to clients on a joint basis.

THE FIRMS:

Addleshaw Sons & Latham:
Dennis House, Marsden Street, Manchester M2 1JD.
Tel: (0161) 832 5994. *Fax:* (0161) 832 2250.
Contact: Paul Lee.

Bond Pearce:
Ballard House, West Hoe Road, Plymouth PLI 3AE.
Tel: (01752) 266633. *Fax:* (01752) 225350.
and
Darwin House, Southernhay Gardens, Southernhay East, Exeter EX1 1LA.
Tel: (01392) 211185. *Fax:* (01392) 435543.
Contact: Jonathan Trafford.

Booth & Co.:
Sovereign House, PO Box 8, South Parade, Leeds LS1 1HQ.
Tel: (0113) 283 2000. *Fax:* (0113) 283 2060.
Contact: Mark Jones.

Burges Salmon:
Narrow Quay House, Prince Street, Bristol BS1 4AH.
Tel: (0117) 927 6567. *Fax:* (0117) 929 4705.
Contact: Guy Stobart.

Mills & Reeve:
Francis House, 3-7 Redwell Street, Norwich NR2 4TJ.
Tel: (01603) 660155. *Fax:* (01603) 633027.
Contacts: Mark Jeffries
and
Francis House, 112 Hills Road, Cambridge CB2 1PH.
Tel: (01223) 364422. *Fax:* (01223) 355848.
Contact: William Barr.

Norton Rose:
Kempson House, PO Box 570, Camomile Street, London EC3A 7AN
Tel: (0171) 283 6000. *Fax:* (0171) 283 6500. *Telex:* 883652.
Contact: Roger Birkby.
Overseas Offices: Hong Kong, Brussels, Paris, Singapore, Bahrain, Piraeus, Moscow and Prague.

Wragge & Co:
55 Colmore Row, Birmingham B3 2AS.
Tel: (0121) 233 1000. *Fax:* (0121) 214 1099.
Contact: John Crabtree.

OAKLEYS 4 Old Maltongate, Malton, N. Yorks, YO17 0EQ **Tel:** (01653) 600070 **Fax:** (01653) 600049 **DX:** 63700 Malton **Ptnrs:** 2. A small practice particularly known for its expertise in the agricultural industry, estates and bloodstock.

WORKLOAD			
Priv (convey/inheritance)	50%	Lit - criminal/civil	30%
Agric landlord/tenant	20%		

OFFENBACH & CO 60 Great Marlborough Street, London, W1V 2BA **Tel:** (0171) 434 9891 **Fax:** (0171) 734 2575 **DX:** 89260 Soho Square **Ptnrs:** 6 **Asst Solrs:** 3 **Other Fee-earners:** 5. Known for crime including commercial fraud and drug related matters. Also civil litigation, entertainment, property, licensing, company and commercial, family, matrimonial and obscene publications.

WORKLOAD			
Criminal defence	80%	Commercial and civil	20%

OGLETHORPE STURTON & GILLIBRAND 16 Castle Park, Lancaster, Lancs, LA1 1YG **Tel:** (01524) 67171 **Fax:** (01524) 382247 **DX:** 63500 Lancaster **Ptnrs:** 9 **Asst Solrs:** 3 **Other Fee-earners:** 5. Well established family firm, specialising in agricultural property and private client work, together with associated commercial, litigation and criminal practice.

WORKLOAD			
Litigation	24%	Private client	21%
Commercial	20%	Commercial property	15%
Trusts	14%	Agriculture	6%

OLSWANG

90 LONG ACRE, LONDON, WC2E 9TT
DX: 37972 Kingsway

TEL: (0171) 208 8888
FAX: (0171) 208 8800

THE FIRM: Olswang is a highly regarded, multi-disciplinary, commercial law firm which has established a reputation for providing a level and quality of expertise normally associated with the larger City firms especially in the corporate, media, communications, technology and entertainment sectors. The firm acts for an unusually high number of established market-leading companies and institutions throughout the UK, Europe and the USA.

PRINCIPAL AREAS OF WORK: The firm is divided into the four principal groups of Corporate and Commercial; Entertainment, media and communications; Litigation; and Commercial Property. These groups, and many of the firm's individual partners, have been acknowledged in the legal press for the high quality of expertise which they provide in specialist disciplines which include company and commercial law, defamation, multimedia and electronic publishing, film finance and production and advertising. In addition to the firm's main areas of practice, Olswang has developed a number of specialist advisory units to provide multi-disciplinary advice on specific business issues and to those clients operating in new growth markets and industries: in particular, dedicated units have been established which offer expertise in the areas of employment law, cross-border transactions, banking, insolvency, publishing, film and TV co-production, IT, telecommunications and multimedia and electronic publishing.

As a result of its combined expertise in the areas of media and entertainment, IT, telecommunications and multimedia, the firm has an established digital convergence unit to provide legal and business advice on the complex issues which have arisen as a result of the rapid integration of the traditional broadcasting media with IT, computer and telecommunications technology.

The firm's corporate, property and litigation expertise extends to all industry sectors, to quoted and unquoted companies and to both the public and private sectors. Every matter is overseen by an appropriate partner in order to ensure that the professional advice provided to the firm's clients is considered and reviewed at a senior level.

RECRUITMENT & TRAINING: Four to six trainee solicitors are recruited annually. A 2:1 degree and second European language are preferred.

CONTACT PARTNER: Mark Devereux

Number of partners:	20
Assistant solicitors:	21
Other fee-earners:	10

WORKLOAD	
Company/ commercial	33%
Entertainment	27%
Property	20%
Litigation	20%

CONTACTS	
Advertising and marketing	Simon Olswang
Commercial property	David Kustow
Company and commercial	Adrian Bott
Cross-border litigation	Alex Maitland-Hudson
Defamation	Caroline Kean
Employment	Julia Palca
Intellectual property	Caroline Kean
IT and telecommunications	Kim Nicholson
Media and entertainment	Mark Devereux
Multimedia	David Zeffman
Property litigation	Marcus Barclay

OLSWANG

ORCHARD 1 Angel Court, London, EC2R 7HJ **Tel:** (0171) 600 2448 **Fax:** (0171) 600 2449 **Ptnrs:** 7 **Asst Solrs:** 3 **Other Fee-earners:** 3. Orchard was formed in March 1995 following a management buy out of the London office of Bermans. The managing partner is David Orchard, well known in the field of international commercial and insolvency litigation.

WORKLOAD			
Litigation	45%	Company commercial	30%
Property/construction	25%		

O'REILLY STEWART O'Reilly Stewart House, 114-116 Royal Avenue, Belfast, BT1 1DL **Tel:** (01232) 322512 **Fax:** (01232) 323003 **Ptnrs:** 4 **Asst Solrs:** 7 **Other Fee-earners:** 3. Emphasis on personal injury litigation and licensing & leisure work. Agency work undertaken for English firms in company/ commercial matters and defence litigation. Also building society work.

WORKLOAD			
Litigation	50%	Conveyancing	20%
Company/ commercial	20%	Building society work	5%
Licensing & gaming	5%		

ORMEROD WILKINSON MARSHALL 1A Katharine Street, Croydon, Surrey, CR0 1NX **Tel:** (0181) 686 5000 **Fax:** (0181) 688 6289 **DX:** 2619 Croydon **Ptnrs:** 12 **Asst Solrs:** 4 **Other Fee-earners:** 14. Work includes: commercial property, company, computer disputes, commercial litigation, personal injury, employment, matrimonial, child care, conveyancing, wills/ probate and financial services.

OSBORNE CLARKE

30 QUEEN CHARLOTTE ST, BRISTOL, BS99 7QQ	TEL: (0117) 923 0220
DX: 7818 Bristol	FAX: (0117) 927 9209
6-9 Middle Street, London EC1A 7JA	Tel: (0171) 600 0155
DX: 46604 Barbican	Fax: (0171) 726 2772

The last 10 years have seen the emergence of regional UK law firms in direct competition with the major firms in the City of London. In the South of England, Osborne Clarke is widely regarded as the leading regional law firm. It competes directly with the London firms from its offices in Bristol, the City of London and Europe.

THE FIRM: Osborne Clarke has a growing national practice for listed and significant unquoted companies, banks and building societies, government agencies, local authorities, public utilities, pension funds and other institutions.

The firm has very strong European connections, with offices in Barcelona, Brussels, Copenhagen, Frankfurt, Paris and Lyon.

PRINCIPAL AREAS OF WORK: Osborne Clarke has developed expertise in advising the following industrial and commercial sectors: advertising and marketing, agriculture, banking, brewing, building societies, charities, construction, distribution, education, energy and utilities, environmental management, facilities management, financial services and collective investments, health authorities and trusts, housing associations, the insolvency industry, IT, leisure, life offices, manufacturing, media and entertainment, packaging, petrol retailing, the public sector, professional services, real estate, retailing, telecommunications, venture capital and waste disposal.

Company and Commercial: The firm's corporate work includes domestic and international corporate finance and venture capital transactions, MBO's, mergers and acquisitions and capital markets work. The commercial department deals with commercial contracts, intellectual property, European law, competition, franchising, computer and software law, and IT procurement.

Human Resources: The employment and human resources team is one of the largest in the UK with substantial teams in London and in Bristol dealing with employment advice, one of the UK's best-known pensions teams, a team whose specialism is health and safety at work and a full tax service including employee benefits.

Litigation: The firm's litigators specialise in major domestic and international commercial disputes and service the firms's corporate clients in contentious matters. The department is recognised for its banking, insolvency, fraud, media, medical and personal injury work.

Commercial Property: The property department acts for major pension funds, brewing and leisure industry interests, institutions and developers in contentious and non-contentious situations. Their work includes the disposal and acquisition of freehold and leasehold interests in land, planning and environmental concerns, funding and development issues, landlord and tenant, and tax.

Tax and Trust: Osborne Clarke has a tax and trust department which services a strong base of high-net-worth clients, particularly entrepreneurs and landowners. It undertakes international tax planning, trust management, tax compliance work, probate and an investment management service.

Other Offices: Barcelona, Brussels, Copenhagen, Frankfurt, Paris, Lyon

SENIOR PARTNER: Mr R.W. Smerdon

Number of partners:	38
Assistant solicitors:	57
Other fee-earners:	36

WORKLOAD	
Litigation	35%
Company/ commercial	30%
Commercial property	22%
Tax and trusts	13%

OSBORNE MORRIS & MORGAN Banbury House, West Street, Leighton Buzzard, Beds, LU7 7DD **Tel:** (01525) 378177 **Fax:** (01525) 851006 **DX:** 90804 Leighton Buzzard **Ptnrs:** 5 **Asst Solrs:** 1 **Other Fee-earners:** 2. Specialises in personal injury and medical negligence matters. Also in Bletchley.

OSMOND GAUNT & ROSE

WINSTON HOUSE, 349 REGENTS PARK ROAD, FINCHLEY, LONDON, N3 1DH
DX: 57254 Finchley 2

TEL: (0181) 349 0321
FAX: (0181) 346 8605

THE FIRM: Osmond Gaunt & Rose is a general practice with some unusual specialisations and a broad range of clients, ranging from overseas governments to private individuals. Emphasis is on the personal contact between client and partner.

PRINCIPAL AREAS OF WORK: Family law, company/ commercial matters, tax planning, immigration, employment law, diplomatic and commonwealth legal matters and international Privy Council cases, plaintiff personal injury and professional negligence work, commercial litigation, commercial and domestic conveyancing and intellectual property work. A particular specialisation is Anglo/ Swedish family law and tax planning.

OTHER OFFICES: Theba House, 49-50 Hatton Garden, London, EC1N 8YS. *Tel:* (0171) 405 9150. *Fax:* (0171) 405 9048

CONTACT PARTNER: Peter Martin	
Number of partners:	6
Assistant solicitors:	2
Other fee-earners:	5

WORKLOAD	
Matrimonial and family work	23%
Company/commercial (including property)	17%
Trust and probate	17%
Domestic conveyancing	12%
Personal injury & prof. neg. (inc. medical)	10%
Employment	7%

OSWALD GOODIER & CO 10 Chapel St, Preston, Lancs, PR1 8AY **Tel:** (01772) 253841 **Fax:** (01772) 201713 **Ptnrs:** 3 **Other Fee-earners:** 1. A general practice, handling work for religious orders and charities as well as substantial amounts of trust and probate work.

OSWALD HICKSON COLLIER

1 PEMBERTON ROW, FETTER LANE, LONDON, EC4A 3EX
DX: 200 London

TEL: (0171) 583 5333
FAX: (0171) 353 0743

THE FIRM: Oswald Hickson Collier is a long-established City firm with an international reputation for libel, slander, and copyright work. Recently joined by Messrs Elias Freeman, whose speciality areas are immigration, international law and property location worldwide, the firm has long provided a wide range of legal services for commercial clients, in media law (primarily defamation), insurance, property and company and commercial law. The firm is organised into four main departments. These are media law (Paul Davies, Richard Shillito, Nicholas Alway, Jane Anderson, Keith Mathieson and Pamela Cassidy), insurance (Timothy Cox, Miles Tomkins, Richard Osborne and Nicola Savile-Tucker), company and commercial services (Michael Hudson and David Freeman) and property (Diana Cornforth and Christopher Elias).

The firm is always happy to hear from high-calibre assistant solicitors. In addition, the firm usually recruits three trainee solicitors each year.

PRINCIPAL AREAS OF WORK: The Media department offers advice on libel, slander, copyright, passing-off, contempt of court, reporting restrictions, PACE applications, pre-publication and pre-broadcasting advice, and breach of confidence, as well as libel insurance and publishing agreements.

The insurance department deals with Lloyd's insurance and reinsurance disputes between Lloyd's Names and their member's and managing agents. Members of the department also handle work (either in the courts or before arbitrators) in a variety of

SENIOR PARTNER: Paul Davies	
Number of partners:	14
Assistant solicitors:	18
Other fee-earners:	7

WORKLOAD	
Defamation/Media	38%
Insurance	31%
Property	19%
Company/Commercial	12%

OSWALD HICKSON COLLIER
SOLICITORS

other fields, including claims under professional indemnity, errors and omissions and public liability insurance policies, shipping claims, construction disputes and general commercial litigation.

The company and commercial services department offers a full range of services to both corporate and private clients. The department handles the formation of companies and partnerships, joint ventures, takeovers, company reorganisations and amalgamations, corporate finance, flotations, commercial agreements, advice on restrictive trade practice legislation, liquidations and receiverships, pensions, share option and profit share schemes, immigration, taxation advice (both UK and international) and employment law of both a contentious and non-contentious nature.

The property department handles commercial and residential conveyancing and employee re-location throughout the world and has a planning and environmental law unit specialising in the energy industry. It also provides private client services.

Agency work is also undertaken: contact Pamela Cassidy.

The partnership sees itself as an effective and competitive commercial firm, prominent in publishing and insurance law, with a reputation for being firm but fair: a firm which above all prides itself on providing personal service.

OVERBURY STEWARD & EATON

3 UPPER KING ST, NORWICH, NORFOLK, NR3 1RL
DX: 5208 Norwich

TEL: (01603) 610481
FAX: (01603) 632460

THE FIRM: The firm is a member of the LawNet Group. It was established over 200 years ago and specialises in family law, criminal, environmental, debt recovery, financial services and matters involving the licenced trade. It also provides advice in respect of a broad range of other legal matters including commercial property and litigation, tax and probate and personal injury.

CONTACT PARTNER: Mr. B.P.G.V Keane

Number of partners:	7
Assistant solicitors:	6
Other fee-earners:	14

OVER TAYLOR BIGGS 1 Oak Tree Place, Manaton Close, Matford, Exeter, Devon, EX2 8WA **Tel:** (01392) 823811 **Fax:** (01392) 823812 **DX:** 300350 Exeter 5 **Ptnrs:** 3 **Asst Solrs:** 2 **Other Fee-earners:** 3. New firm formed to offer partner only service from business park on outskirts of Exeter. Company commercial, property and litigation work.

WORKLOAD			
Company/ corporate	25%	Commercial property	25%
Transport	20%	Med neg/personal injury	20%
Construction litigation	10%		

OWEN WHITE

SENATE HOUSE, 62-70 BATH RD, SLOUGH, BERKS, SL1 3SR
DX: 3409

TEL: (01753) 536846
FAX: (01753) 691360

THE FIRM: This long-established practice occupies modern offices in the heart of the Thames Valley. It handles work of a predominantly commercial nature and has secured a reputation as one of the leading specialist firms in the area of British and International franchising.

PRINCIPAL AREAS OF WORK:

Franchising and Licensing: (*Contact Partner:* Anton Bates). The department offers practical advice based on many years' experience both in the UK and worldwide. Anton Bates is a recognised specialist and legal adviser to the British Franchise Association, to which the firm is affiliated.

Company/ Commercial: (*Contact Partner:* Jane Masih). The firm advises on all aspects of a company's trading activities including: the setting up of joint ventures, agency and distribution agreements, acquisitions, mergers, MBOs and tax implications. Specialist advice is also available on intellectual property matters, information technology and computer law, employment law, EC and competition law.

Commercial Property and Development: (*Contact Partners:* Paul Van Reyk and Nicholas Barnard). Work ranges from the acquisition and disposal of warehouses, factories, offices and building and development sites, to the sale and purchase of

CONTACT PARTNER: Paul Van Reyk

Number of partners:	5
Assistant solicitors:	7
Other fee-earners:	8

WORKLOAD	
Litigation	50%
Commercial property development	20%
Company/commercial	15%
Franchising/licensing	15%
Environment (included within litigation)	10%

shops and businesses. Every aspect of landlord and tenant is covered. The firm has also gained a reputation in representing major housing associations at all stages of development.

Litigation: (*Contact Partner:* Richard Keen). Owen White has an expanding commercial litigation and insolvency department. The firm's range of experience also includes: industrial relations problems, medical negligence and personal injury claims.

Environmental: (*Contact Partner:* Anton Bates). The firm has experience in environmental litigation in particular relating to toxic waste disposal. It also undertakes environmental audits and planning matters.

OTHER AREAS OF WORK: Private client services focus on: wills, probate, tax planning, residential conveyancing.

CONTACTS	
Commercial property & devel.	Mr P. Van Reyk
	Mr N. Barnard
Company/commercial	Ms J. Masih
Environmental	Mr A. Bates
Franchising and licensing	Mr A. Bates
Litigation	Mr R. Keen

OWSTONS 23 Friar Lane, Leicester, Leics, LE1 5QQ **Tel:** (0116) 2530851 **Fax:** (0116) 2532690 **DX:** 10832 Leicester 1 **Ptnrs:** 10 **Asst Solrs:** 7 **Other Fee-earners:** 14. A city-centre firm with a broad client base. Founded in 1860. Emphasis on company/ commercial work and litigation.

WORKLOAD			
Litigation	32%	Private client	29%
Commercial property	17%	Company/ commercial	17%
Insolvency	5%		

OXLEY & COWARD

34/46 MOORGATE ST, ROTHERHAM, S. YORKS, S60 2HB
DX: 12600 Rotherham

TEL: (01709) 374091
FAX: (01709) 377163

THE FIRM: Oxley & Coward is one of the largest law firms in Rotherham, South Yorkshire, where it has been established for over 200 years. From the foundation of a general practice, advising local businesses and private clients, we have built a firm with a national reputation in three other markets: Information Technology, the National Health Service and local government law and planning. Oxley & Coward is a member of LawGroup UK, a national network of independent law firms and is committed to the Investors in People programme.

PRINCIPAL AREAS OF WORK:

Private Client: The firm is dedicated to providing a full range of services to private clients, including litigation, conveyancing, wills, probate, estate planning, family law and work in the criminal courts.

Commercial Property: Leases, licences, finance, planning advice, development schemes, agricultural property.

Business: Acquisition and disposal of businesses, shareholders agreements, joint ventures, contracts, intellectual property, partnerships, agency and distribution, litigation, licensing of pubs and clubs, employment law.

Health: Commercial property, contracts for services, intellectual property, IT contracts and dispute resolution.

Information Technology: Contracts for outsourcing, systems integration, software development, software licences and maintenance contracts and software distribution. Computer disputes including litigation. Training for suppliers and users on contract drafting and negotiation, dispute resolution, outsourcing.

CONTACT PARTNER: John Yates

Number of partners:	11
Assistant solicitors:	3
Other fee-earners:	8

WORKLOAD	
Private client	35%
Property	29%
Litigation	14%
Health	12%
Company/ commercial	10%

CONTACTS	
Company/ commercial	Rosemary Downs
Health	James Ogley
Litigation	Keith Green
Private client	Henry Everatt
Property	Barry Long

OXLEY & COWARD
········· *solicitors* ·········

PAGAN MACBETH 12 St. Catherine Street, Cupar, Fife, KY15 4HN **Tel:** (01334) 657000 **Fax:** (01334) 55063 **Ptnrs:** 3 **Asst Solrs:** 3 **Other Fee-earners:** 1. Founded in February 1994, the practice specialises in business law and is particularly noted for its insolvency work.

WORKLOAD			
Commercial Property	40%	Corporate	40%
Misc company/partnerships	10%	Insolvency	10%

PAGAN OSBORNE 12 St. Catherine Street, Cupar, Fife, KY15 4HN **Tel:** (01334) 653777 **Fax:** (01334) 55063 **Ptnrs:** 9 **Asst Solrs:** 7 **Other Fee-earners:** 9. An established general practice, advising both commercial and private clients. Particularly well-regarded for licensing work.

PAISNER & CO

BOUVERIE HOUSE, 154 FLEET ST, LONDON, EC4A 2DQ
DX: 198

TEL: (0171) 353 0299
FAX: (0171) 583 8621

THE FIRM: Paisner & Co was established in 1932. The firm undertakes a wide range of commercial work for national and international clients with separate company, litigation, property, employment and pensions, tax and private client departments. Specific leasing, intellectual property, construction, reinsurance and environmental groups have also been established to service clients' expanding needs.

PRINCIPAL AREAS OF WORK:

Company and Commercial: (*Contact:* H.M. Paisner). *Work includes:* takeovers, acquisitions, disposals, reconstructions and mergers of public and private companies; flotations and public offerings; management buy-outs and buy-ins; joint ventures; venture and development capital; EC law; banking and finance; leasing; insolvency; franchising; and all types of commercial contracts.

Tax: (*Contact:* J.S. Schwarz). *Work includes:* UK corporate and partnership tax; VAT; stamp duty; taxation of property transactions; EC and international tax strategy; Customs duties; Inland Revenue and Customs' investigations, claims and appeals.

Employee Benefits: (*Contact:* D.H.J. Cohen). *Work includes:* executive share incentives; all-employee share schemes; employee share ownership plans (ESOPs) and profit related pay.

Employment and Pensions: (*Contact:* S.E. Levinson or N. M. Russell). *Work includes:* employment aspects of acquisitions and sales of businesses; remuneration packages; disciplinary matters; discrimination; service agreements; industrial relations policies; collective disputes; Tribunal and High Court litigation; all aspects relating to occupational pension schemes.

Property: (*Contact:* G.J. Hayhurst). *Work includes:* acquisition and disposal of all types of freehold and leasehold property; leases; development; property financing; debt restructuring; management of commercial property portfolios; property work for charities; building contracts; environment; collateral warranties and construction disputes.

Litigation: (*Contact:* M.S. Polonsky). *Work includes:* commercial, company and partnership disputes; proceedings in foreign jurisdictions; property disputes; intellectual property; commodity trading; defamation; construction; insolvency; banking and computer technology; food safety and environment.

Insurance/ Reinsurance: (*Contact:* J.S. Sacher). *Work includes:* international and UK reinsurance and insurance dispute resolution, arbitration and litigation; formation, acquisition and disposal of insurance companies, brokers, agents and captives; corporate reorganisations; regulatory and compliance work.

Private Client: (*Contact:* M.D. Paisner). *Work includes:* UK tax planning; trusts; domicile; offshore arrangements; wills; probate; litigation in relation to disputed estates and trusts; charity law.

NATURE OF CLIENTELE: Clients include national and international companies across a broad range of sectors, including financial services, leisure, retail and mail order, health, communications, manufacturing, insurance, high technology and property development.

FOREIGN CONNECTIONS: The firm has an office in Brussels and has also established international alliances with lawyers in other jurisdictions. The chief of these alliances are with McDermott, Will & Emery in the United States and UGGC (Uettwiller, Grelon, Gout, Canat & Associés) in Paris and UGLD (Uetwiller Grelon, Lippens Dekeyser & Associés) in Brussels. Through this international network, the firm has ready access to the legal expertise, know how and resources of substantial firms in their own countries.

RECRUITMENT & TRAINING: Annual trainee solicitor intake: 8–10. Summer placement scheme intake: 12–14. Extensive in-house training conducted by solicitors within the firm.

CONTACT PARTNER: H.M. Paisner

Number of partners:	37
Assistant solicitors:	40
Other fee-earners:	23

WORKLOAD	
Company/ commercial	35%
Commercial property	20%
Litigation	20%
Insurance/Reinsurance	10%
Private client	10%
Employment	5%

CONTACTS	
Company and commercial	Stephen Rosefield
	Keith Stella
Construction	Hugh Nicholls
Corporate tax	Jonathan Schwarz
Employment	Stephen Levinson
Environment	Craig Baylis
Insolvency	Stephen Nelson
Insurance/ reinsurance	Jonathan Sacher
Intellectual property	Margaret Tofalides
	Linda Fazzani
Key contact	Harold Paisner
Litigation	Michael Polonsky, David Parkin
Pensions	Norman Russell
Private client	Martin Paisner, Wynne Thomas
Property	Geoff Hayhurst, Tony Shellim
Share schemes	David Cohen

PALMER WHEELDON

DAEDALUS HOUSE, STATION RD, CAMBRIDGE, CAMBS, CB1 2RE
DX: 5807

TEL: (01223) 355933
FAX: (01223) 460266

CONTACT PARTNER: Ian Mather

Number of partners:	7
Assistant solicitors:	8
Other fee-earners:	7

WORKLOAD	
Litigation	42%
Commercial	18%
Commercial property	17%
Domestic property	15%
Private client	8%

THE FIRM: Palmer Wheeldon have grown steadily in recent years. The firm, which is a member of LawNet, is commited to quality and the effective use of Information Technology.

PRINCIPAL AREAS OF WORK:

General Description: The practice undertakes general company/ commercial business, property development and commercial conveyancing for private, corporate and public utility clients; the structuring, sale and acquisition of businesses; and High Court and County Court litigation. Particular areas of experience are employment, child care law, and corporate insolvency.

FOREIGN CONNECTIONS: Palmer Wheeldon is a member of Eurojuris with offices throughout western Europe.

FOREIGN LANGUAGES: French, Polish, German, Dutch, Urdu and Punjabi.

RECRUITMENT: The firm recruits up to two trainee solicitors every year. Apply to Charles Fraser, Recruitment Partner.

AGENCY WORK: Agency work is undertaken in Cambridge County Court and District Registry.

PANNONE & PARTNERS 123 Deansgate, Manchester, M3 2BU **Tel:** (0161) 832 3000 **Fax:** (0161) 834 2067 **DX:** 14314 **Ptnrs:** 29 **Asst Solrs:** 15 **Other Fee-earners:** 24. Leading regional practice well known for its high quality corporate work and strong commercial, litigation and private client departments. Extensive international connections.

WORKLOAD			
Lit (comm/prop)/emp	28%	Personal injury/med neg	25%
Corporate	19%	Priv client/family/matrim	14%
Comm Prop/constr/civ eng	14%		

PANNONE PRITCHARD ENGLEFIELD 14 New St, London, EC2M 4TR **Tel:** (0171) 972 9720 **Fax:** (0171) 972 9722 **DX:** 88 London **Ptnrs:** 27 **Asst Solrs:** 13 **Other Fee-earners:** 12. This City firm has the following specialist departments: Banking; Corporate; Litigation; Commercial Property; Private Client; German; French; Italian; Medical Negligence/PI; Employment; Family.

PARDOES 6-9 King Square, Bridgwater, Somerset, TA6 3DG **Tel:** (01278) 457891 **Fax:** (01278) 429249 **DX:** 80602 **Ptnrs:** 9 **Asst Solrs:** 6 **Other Fee-earners:** 12. A medium-sized West Country practice, established 1938. Work includes private client, agriculture and company/ commercial.

WORKLOAD			
Matrimonial	23%	Commercial litigation	19%
Private client	16%	Personal injury	15%
Domestic property	14%	Commercial property	11%

PARIS SMITH & RANDALL

LANSDOWNE HOUSE, CASTLE LANE, SOUTHAMPTON, HANTS, SO9 2JQ
DX: 2008

TEL: (01703) 635191
FAX: (01703) 631835

CONTACT PARTNER: Malcolm Le Bas

Number of partners:	14
Assistant solicitors:	9
Other fee-earners:	12

WORKLOAD	
Litigation (including employment)	21%
Commercial property	19%
Company and commercial	19%
Private client/ probate/ tax / trusts	15%
Family law	13%
Residential property	13%

THE FIRM: Paris Smith & Randall has been established for 175 years in the centre of Southampton. Particularly noted for its commercial property and company/ commercial services, the firm also has strong litigation, matrimonial and private client teams. The Senior Partner, Philip Ely, was President of the Law Society for the year 1991/ 2.

PRINCIPAL AREAS OF WORK:

Company/ Commercial: (*Contact Partner:* Andrew Heathcock). This department has a particularly high reputation in company and insolvency matters.

Commercial Property: (*Contact Partner:* Mark Howarth). The firm has considerable expertise in the acquisition and sale of all types of commercial property.

Residential Property: (*Contact Partner:* Ian Gordon). All aspects of residential transactions are handled.

Litigation: (*Contact Partner:* Clive Thomson). The firm is particularly strong in commercial and personal injury cases, and handles a wide range of litigation. This department is located opposite the Central Law Courts and undertakes all categories of agency work.

Family/ Matrimonial: (*Contact Partner:* Richard Smith). The firm is well known and respected for its work in divorce, separation, and all aspects of family work. Richard Smith is chairman of the Hampshire Solicitors Family Law Association.

Employment: (*Contact Partner:* Malcolm Ross). The department is involved in representing and advising corporate, statutory, and individual clients on all aspects of employment law.

Private Client: (*Contact Partner:* Crispin Jameson). A broad range of work includes personal estate management, pensions, tax, wills, trusts, probate, financial services, immigration and nationality and general tax planning. Crispin Jameson is Chairman of the Society of Trust and Estate Practitioners (Central Southern Branch).

OTHER OFFICES: 9 College Place, Southampton S015 2YR. *Tel:* (01703) 212131. *Fax:* (01703) 332428. *DX:* 38534 Southampton 3.

CONTACTS	
Commercial property	Mark Howarth
Company and commercial	Andrew Heathcock
Education	Philip Ely
Employment	Malcolm Ross
Family	Richard Smith
Insolvency	Malcolm Le Bas
Litigation	Clive Thomson
Probate/ tax/ trusts	Crispin Jameson
Residential property	Ian Gordon
Town and country planning	Philip Ely

PARKER BULLEN 45 Castle Street, Salisbury, Wilts, SP1 3SS **Tel:** (01722) 412000 **Fax:** (01722) 411822 **DX:** 58001 **Ptnrs:** 8 **Asst Solrs:** 9 **Other Fee-earners:** 7. Medium sized provincial practice. Handles commercial property, company law, litigation (including matrimonial and recovery of secured and unsecured lending), conveyancing, probate and trusts.

PARKINSON WRIGHT Haswell House, St. Nicholas Street, Worcester, Hereford & Worcs, WR1 1UN **Tel:** (01905) 726789 **Fax:** (01905) 21363 **DX:** 716 257 **Ptnrs:** 8 **Asst Solrs:** 8 **Other Fee-earners:** 6. Particularly known for personal injury work, family law, crime, domestic and commercial conveyancing, the firm aims to provide a specialised service at local level.

WORKLOAD			
General litigation	35%	Conveyancing	20%
Family law	20%	Criminal law	15%
Business client work	5%	Wills and probate	5%

PARK NELSON THOMPSON QUARRELL

1 BELL YARD, LONDON, WC2A 2JP
DX: 186 Ch.Ln.

TEL: (0171) 404 4191
FAX: (0171) 405 4266

THE FIRM: Park Nelson Thompson Quarrell was formed by the merger in 1993 of Park Nelson and Thompson Quarrell, both of which date back to the 1800s. The new firm offers a complete range of services, drawing on the expertise of each firm, and has strong connections in Europe.

PRINCIPAL AREAS OF WORK:

Company and Commercial: (*Contact Partner:* Mr T.G. Ford). All aspects handled with a particular expertise in employment law.

Commercial Property: (*Contact Partner:* Mr E.A. O'Keeffe). The practice has particular expertise in handling developments, funding agreements and commercial leases in the retail field. In addition the firm provides expertise in planning and environmental law.

Litigation/ Construction: (*Contact Partner:* Mr J.C. Kings). The firm has experience in contentious and non-contentious construction law and commercial litigation. Other areas of specialisation include landlord and tenant and employment law.

Private Client: (*Contact Partner:* Mr R.J. Fairbairn). The firm provides wills, trusts, probate and family matrimonial advice.

International and European Law: (*Contact Partner:* Mr P.C. Calvert). Advice is provided for French diplomats, French companies establishing branches or subsidiaries in the UK, and UK clients purchasing French property.

AGENCY: Agency work is handled.

FOREIGN CONNECTIONS: The firm has associated offices in Dublin, Paris, Rome and Milan.

CONTACT PARTNER: Mr E.A. O'Keeffe	
Number of partners:	17
Assistant solicitors:	10
Other fee-earners:	8

WORKLOAD	
Commercial property	43%
Litigation and construction	20%
Company and commercial	17%
Private client	10%
General property	8%
International and European	2%

CONTACTS	
Commercial property	Mr E.A. O'Keeffe
Company and commercial	Mr T.G. Ford
General property	Mr J.R. Bishop
International and European	Mr P.C. Calvert
Litigation and construction	Mr J.C. Kings
Private client	Mr R.M. Fairbairn

PARK WOODFINE

1 LURKE ST, BEDFORD, BEDS, MK40 3TN
DX: 5603

TEL: (01234) 364321
FAX: (01234) 262572

THE FIRM: One of Bedfordshire's largest law firms, Park Woodfine has retained a strong private client base whilst developing its commercial portfolio. A member of LawNet and LawNet Europe (which has representation throughout the EC and Scandinavia).

PRINCIPAL AREAS OF WORK: The firm handles all aspects of company/ commercial work with an emphasis on acquisitions and disposals of companies, business assets and trading agreements; commercial litigation; commercial property work, including landlord and tenant matters; debt collection; employment law; personal injury litigation and medical negligence; charities work (particularly relating to the care of the disabled, and arts and education); intellectual property and computer law; and health care matters (acting for six NHS Trusts). All offices deal with private client matters such as conveyancing, wills, trusts, tax, probate and family law.

OTHER OFFICES:
28 Church Street, Rushden, Northamptonshire NN10 9SA.
1 Kings Road, Flitwick, Bedfordshire MK45 2HB.

CONTACT PARTNER: Mr Garry Dannan

Number of partners:	7
Assistant solicitors:	7
Other fee-earners:	12

WORKLOAD	
Litigation	26%
Family	21%
Residential conveyancing	14%
Commercial	13%
Criminal	9%
Commercial conveyancing	6%
Contentious employment	5%
Probate	4%
Financial services	2%

PARLETT KENT & CO Signet House, 49-51 Farringdon Rd, London, EC1M 3JB **Tel:** (0171) 430 0712/3 **Fax:** (0171) 430 1796 **DX:** 53308 Clerkenwell **Ptnrs:** 4 **Asst Solrs:** 2 **Other Fee-earners:** 3. Niche practice with particular expertise in personal injury and medical negligence cases.

WORKLOAD			
Medical negligence	70%	Convey/gen non-cont	10%
Personal injury	10%	Matrimonial	5%
Professional negligence	5%		

PARROTT & COALES 14 Bourbon St, Aylesbury, Bucks, HP20 2RS **Tel:** (01296) 82244 **Fax:** (01296) 433723 **DX:** 4100 Aylesbury **Ptnrs:** 6 **Asst Solrs:** 8 **Other Fee-earners:** 7. Established over 200 years, a broadly based family firm well known for its insolvency practice. Handles agency work.

WORKLOAD			
Other work	29%	Domestic conveyancing	28%
Commercial work	15%	Civil litigation	10%
Matrimonial	9%	Probate	9%

O.H. PARSONS & PARTNERS Sovereign Hse, 212-224 Shaftesbury Avenue, London, WC2H 8PR **Tel:** (0171) 379 7277 **Fax:** (0171) 240 1577 **Ptnrs:** 4 **Asst Solrs:** 4 **Other Fee-earners:** 3. Best known for Trade Union work, personal injury litigation and employment law. Founded 1949.

WORKLOAD			
Personal injury	95%	Employment	3%
Crime/consumer affairs	2%		

PATTINSON AND BREWER

30 GREAT JAMES STREET, LONDON, WC1N 3HA
DX: 394 Ch.Ln.

TEL: (0171) 405 3033
FAX: (0171) 405 7239

THE FIRM: The firm of Pattinson and Brewer was founded in about 1892. It has long been a leading trade union practice, having connections going back to the Taff Vale case in 1901 and the formation of the TGWU in 1921. It has a proud commitment to plaintiff personal injury and disease work, and a well-established reputation in the fields of equal opportunities, and medical and professional negligence. It has also been involved in some of the recent unfortunate "disaster" litigation. The firm has a strong team of general litigators and a very experienced property department.

OTHER OFFICES:
8-12 New Road, Chatham, Kent ME4 4QR. *Contact:* John Couch. *Tel:* (01634) 830080. *Fax:* (01634) 830813. *DX:* 6711.
11 Broad Quay, The Centre, Bristol BS1 4DH. *Contact:* Janet Chidgey. *Tel:* (0117) 9273233. *Fax:* (0117) 9273272. *DX:* 78148.
1 Bridge Street, York YO1 1DD. *Contact:* Kevin Hughes. *Tel:* (01904) 670077. *Fax:* (01904) 655052. *DX:* 62574.

RECRUITMENT: The firm presently recruits three to four trainee solicitors each year, and looks for an interest in plaintiff-orientated work.

CONTACT PARTNER: Mr J. Davies

Number of partners:	16
Assistant solicitors:	10
Other fee-earners:	24

WORKLOAD	
Personal injury	59%
Employment/ labour law	18%
Medical negligence	10%
General litigation	6%
Conveyancing/ commercial	5%
Criminal	2%

PAULL & WILLIAMSONS Investment House, 6 Union Row, Aberdeen, Grampian, AB9 8DQ **Tel:** (01224) 621621 **Fax:** (01224) 640446 **DX:** 35 Aberdeen **Ptnrs:** 24 **Asst Solrs:** 23 **Other Fee-earners:** 7. One of the leading commercial firms in the North East of Scotland. The practice has another office in Edinburgh.

PAUL ROONEY & CO Stanley Court, 19-23 Stanley St, Liverpool, Merseyside, L1 6AA **Tel:** (0151) 227 2851 **Fax:** (0151) 255 0455 **DX:** 14183 **Ptnrs:** 6 **Asst Solrs:** 2 **Other Fee-earners:** 35. Established in 1977, the firm handles crime, civil litigation, conveyancing, personal injury and road traffic accidents.

WORKLOAD			
Traffic accident/pers inj	80%	Crime	10%

PAYNE HICKS BEACH

10 NEW SQUARE, LINCOLN'S INN, LONDON, WC2A 3QG
DX: 40 Ch.Ln.

TEL: (0171) 465 4300
FAX: (0171) 465 4400

THE FIRM: Well-known and respected Inns of Court firm, established in the early eighteenth century. Although the firm draws strength from its long traditions, the character of the firm has been created by the present partners' own chosen specialisations, several of which have been the object of favourable comment in journals recently.

PRINCIPAL AREAS OF WORK: The firm is organised into five departments.

Tax, Trust and Probate: (*Contact:* Graham Brown). These are areas of specialisation for which the firm has a reputation as one of the best in London. The range of work undertaken is wider than traditionally associated with private client work, and extends from heritage and agricultural work and property development taxation, to advising entrepreneurs and senior directors, charities, and to off-shore and continental transactions.

Company/ Commercial: (*Contact:* Guy Green). This department deals with the full range of corporate and business law acting for public and private companies and a range of individual entrepreneurs. The international section deals with many clients and correspondents abroad, and has strong connections both within the European Community and elsewhere, including North America and Japan. *Work includes:* acquisitions and mergers, banking, competition law, employment law, EC law, intellectual property including computers and franchising, management buy-outs, marketing and sale of goods law, new issues and partnership agreements.

Commercial Litigation: (*Contact:* Peter Stockwell/ Richard Butcher). The firm has a strong commercial litigation department handling a broad range of work including commercial disputes requiring urgent injunctive relief, arbitration, intellectual property, commercial, landlord and tenant and town and country planning. There is also particular experience in representing clients before regulatory enquiries. Specialised areas of work include advising clients in yacht racing and design and construction, building contract work, partnership disputes and all other aspects of insolvency for both corporate and individual clients.

Family Law: (*Contact:* D.J. Leverton/ I.F. Airey). This department is well known for its specialisation in all aspects of family law including divorce and separation, adoption, custody and wardship, and financial claims. Personal injury actions are also handled.

Property and Conveyancing: (*Contact:* David Fitzgerald/ Andrew Crawford).
Commercial Property: This section deals with all aspects of property transactions, leases, secured lending, management of investment property, development work including joint ventures and planning agreements.
General and Estate Conveyancing: This section deals with residential conveyancing, farm and forestry transactions, agricultural property and staff loan schemes.

FOREIGN CONNECTIONS: The firm has associates in Paris with a network of other correspondents internationally. Several of the partners conduct legal work in French, German or Danish.

RECRUITMENT AND TRAINING: There are usually two to three vacancies for trainee solicitors every year. The minimum educational requirement is a good degree, but emphasis is placed on personality as well as academic achievements. Applications should be made by letter (with CV and references) to the Recruitment Partner.

SENIOR PARTNER: G.S. Brown

Number of partners:	16
Assistant solicitors:	9
Other fee-earners:	39

WORKLOAD	
Private client	33%
Commercial litigation	13%
Commercial property	12%
Company/ corporate	10%
Tax (commercial, or corporate)	10%
General conveyancing	10%
Matrimonial and family law/ litigation	10%
General, miscellaneous	2%

CONTACTS	
Commercial property	David FitzGerald
Commercial litigation	Peter Stockwell
Company/ commercial	Guy Green
Employment law	Richard Butcher
General conveyancing	Andrew Crawford
Intellectual property	Richard Butcher
Matrimonial	David Leverton
Probate	Alastair Murdie
Tax/ trust	Graham Brown

PAYNE MARSH STILLWELL

6 CARLTON CRESCENT, SOUTHAMPTON, HANTS, SO15 2EY
DX: 38514 Southampton 3

TEL: (01703) 223957
FAX: (01703) 225261

THE FIRM: A small essentially commercial practice but also serving private clients. The firm provides a comprehensive and personal service to small and medium sized businesses.

PRINCIPAL AREAS OF WORK: Commercial litigation, professional negligence, partnership law, trade marks and passing off, business transfers, defamation, individual insolvency, commercial property and employment law.

LANGUAGES: French, Italian and Spanish.

CONTACT PARTNER: Antony Silvestro

Number of partners:	5
Assistant solicitors:	2
Other fee-earners:	2

PEASEGOOD WALKER Bank Chambers, 937-941 Rochdale Road, Manchester, M9 8AE **Tel:** (0161) 205 2772 **Fax:** (0161) 203 4218 **Ptnrs:** 2 **Asst Solrs:** 5 **Other Fee-earners:** 1. An expanding general practice specialising in personal injury/ medical negligence, matrimonial/ family law and Spanish property.

PELLYS

THE OLD MONASTERY, WINDHILL, BISHOP'S STORTFORD, HERTS, CM23 2ND
DX: 50401

TEL: (01279) 758080
FAX: (01279) 657578

THE FIRM: The firm was founded approximately twenty five years ago, and has expanded rapidly since then by adopting a policy of high quality and specialisation by its partners and staff. Importance is placed on the benefits of modern technology, and domestic conveyancing, accounting and time costing are all computerised. Extensive use is made of word processing.

PRINCIPAL AREAS OF WORK: Though a broad-based firm aiming to meet the needs of all its clients both private and corporate, it places a particular emphasis on:

Commercial development and domestic property transactions; corporate and general commercial advice; planning law; matrimonial and serious criminal litigation; bus, coach and transport legislation including tachographs and offences relating thereto; civil Court work including commercial, technical and aviation matters, professional and medical negligence, personal injury and debt collection. One of the partners is a member of the Law Society's Personal Injury Panel.

NATURE OF CLIENTELE: Whilst increasingly the firm is instructed by large corporate clients, it aims to act for all types of clients from the first time buyer or victim of an accident to the international PLC.

CHARGES: The firm recognises that the amount of legal fees which have to be paid can be a substantial concern to many people, and accordingly will discuss charges and rates beforehand, giving estimates where appropriate and tailoring the method of payment to the requirement of the individual client where possible. Advice is given on eligibility for legal aid.

CONTACT PARTNER: Duty Partner

Number of partners:	5
Assistant solicitors:	4
Other fee-earners:	10

CONTACTS	
Civil litigation	Philip Pelly
	Miss Jean Laidler
Commercial conveyancing	Colin Grimwade
Crime	Roland Des Voeux Pelly
Domestic conveyancing	Stephen Roche
Matrimonial	Margaret Porter
	Simon Baldwin-Purry
Probate and tax	Neal Bebbington
Transport & planning	Roland Des Voeux Pelly

CD-ROM EDITION ON THE INTERNET

This edition of the directory is available on a CD-ROM which includes both DOS and Windows versions. It can be loaded onto a network, and works with virtually any IBM compatible PC. The CD-ROM version offers computer-users the advantage of rapid search, retrieval and cross-referencing. It is also available via the Internet.

PENNINGTONS

DASHWOOD HOUSE, 69 OLD BROAD ST, LONDON, EC2M 1PE
DX: 33853 Finsbury Square

TEL: (0171) 457 3000
FAX: (0171) 457 3240

THE FIRM: The major departments of the firm are: corporate, commercial, litigation, property, marine and aviation, private client and matrimonial. Penningtons has particular strengths in the areas of corporate finance, intellectual property, commercial litigation, commercial property, insolvency, family law, marine and aviation, dispute resolution and private client work. Overseas activity includes specialist knowledge of and experience in Italy, France, South Africa, Hong Kong, Malaysia, the USA, Oman, the Russian Federation and the CIS. The firm founded the European Law Group, an association of EU business lawyers and is a member of the Law Society Solicitors European Group. Penningtons has in-house lawyers qualified in several member states of the European Union.

PRINCIPAL AREAS OF WORK: The firm is organised into a number of service areas, most of which operate in smaller working groups. There are also cross-departmental groups operating in specific areas of law and industry sectors such as insolvency and corporate recovery, intellectual property, environmental, ADR, marine, energy, construction, employment, pharmaceuticals and planning.

CORPORATE: (*Contact:* Martin Byatt) The department advises on stockmarket flotations, share issues and other capital raising activities, mergers and acquisitions, management buy-outs, and all aspects of company law.

COMMERCIAL: (*Contact:* Geoffrey Walkley) The department advises on most aspects of commercial law, including intellectual property (where it has particular expertise in publishing, technology transfer, information technology and trade mark registration), distribution, agency and supply, competition law, banking, inward investment and establishment in the UK, immigration and nationality, banking and project finance, joint ventures, company and business acquisitions and disposals, pensions and employees' benefit schemes and tax.

COMMERCIAL LITIGATION: (*Contact:* Paul Hadow) Penningtons acts for clients in all types of business disputes, national and international, including construction and engineering disputes, employment matters, insolvency work, insurance, partnership disputes, personal injury claims, professional indemnity claims, secured lending recoveries, share sale and purchase disputes, trade arbitrations and including all aspects of commercial property and landlord and tenant matters. Members of the department are familiar with ADR techniques in addition to litigation and arbitration.

COMMERCIAL PROPERTY: (*Contact:* John Mathé) The department handles the sale and purchase of freehold and leasehold property including offices, factories, warehouses, agricultural and investment property. It also deals with development schemes, town and country planning, environmental law, construction law and with secured lending and property related banking law.

MARINE AND AVIATION: (*Contact:* Hugh Bryant) All aspects of maritime and aviation law, both contentious and non-contentious are handled. Related insurance and reinsurance topics are also covered. The department has particular expertise in the law of oil pollution, insurance and reinsurance, and in the investigation and handling of major casualties and its representatives are members of the British Maritime Law Association, the Association of Average Adjustors, the London Maritime Arbitrators' Association, the Royal Aeronautical Society, the Royal Institute of Navigation, the Nautical Institute, and the British Institute of International and Comparative Law.

PRIVATE CLIENT: (*Contact:* Lesley Lintott) A wide range of private client services are provided including personal tax planning (including offshore tax planning), wills, trusts and the administration of estates.

MATRIMONIAL: (*Contact:* Susan Philipps) Advice is given on all family law matters including separation, divorce, the welfare of children, child abduction and adoption and property disputes between partners. Specialists within the department are members of the Solicitors Family Law Association and the Family Mediators Association.

EUROPE/INTERNATIONAL: (*Contact:* Roger Loveland) Penningtons founded the European Law Group, an association of EU Business Lawyers. It is a member of the Law Society Solicitors European Group, and has in-house lawyers qualified in several EU

MANAGING PARTNER: David Stedman	
UK:	
Number of partners:	46
Assistant solicitors:	36
Other fee-earners:	53
INTERNATIONAL:	
Number of Partners:	1
Assistant Solicitors:	1
Foreign qualified lawyers	2

WORKLOAD	
Property	27%
Litigation	25%
Corporate	16%
Commercial	16%
Private client	9%
Marine and aviation	4%
Matrimonial	3%

CONTACTS	
ADR	Henry Brown
Agricultural	Michael Fellingham
	Julian Chadwick
Banking	Geoffrey Walkley
Commercial property	John Ewens
	Tom Rossiter, John Mathé
Company and commercial	Franco Bosi
	Robin Peile, Roger Duncan
	Paul Milton, Mark Telfer
Construction	Roger Loveland
Corporate finance	Martin Byatt
Corporate recovery	Colin Hay
Corporate finance	Roger Duncan
Employment	Paul Hadow
Environmental	Peter Allan
Family	Susan Philipps
Insolvency	Colin Hay
Intellectual property	Geoffrey Walkley
Litigation	Jonathan Rouse, Michael Felce
	Tracey Gane, Julian Calnan
Marine and aviation	Hugh Bryant
Matrimonial	Susan Philipps, Helen Goss
Medical negligence	Chris Mather
Natural resources	Martin Byatt
Personal injury	David Raine, Chris Mather
Planning	Roger Bullworthy
Private client	Michael Fellingham

and other jurisdictions. Specialist advice is available on such matters as EU competition law, Italian and French law in addition to which the firm has established business groups focusing on the USA, South Africa, the Far East, Italy and France.

LANGUAGES: French, German, Spanish, Italian, Greek, Urdu, Punjabi, Gujerati, Russian, Chinese, Arabic and Afrikaans.

OTHER OFFICES: Basingstoke, Godalming, Newbury, Paris, Oman and Hong Kong.

Private client	Julian Chadwick
Professional negligence	Chris Mather
Project finance	Patrick Doyle
Relocation/ housing ass'ns	Julian Dickins
Residential property	Andrew Templeman

PEPPER, HAMILTON & SCHEETZ

9 HAYWARDS PLACE, LONDON, EC1R 0EE

TEL: (0171) 628 1122
FAX: (0171) 628 6010

THE FIRM: Pepper, Hamilton & Scheetz has been established for more than a century and has over 250 attorneys, stationed in seven cities throughout the United States, in London and in Moscow, serving clients based in North and South America, Europe, the former Soviet Union and the Far East. The international practice provides the full range of general corporate and trade services.

CONTACT PARTNER: S.J. March

LANGUAGES SPOKEN: French, Russian, Dutch, German, Polish, Ukrainian.

OTHER OFFICES: Philadelphia, New York, Washington DC, Detroit, Wilmington, Harrisburg, Berwyn, Moscow, St. Petersburg, Almaty.

PERCY HUGHES & ROBERTS

19 HAMILTON SQUARE, BIRKENHEAD, MERSEYSIDE, L41 6AY
DX: 17862

TEL: (0151) 647 6081
FAX: (0151) 666 1080

THE FIRM: A general practice established in 1919 with a traditional approach and modern methods. It is best known for its insurance litigation, product liability work particularly in food stuffs, building and construction, professional negligence, solicitors' partnership and disciplinary work. Advocacy forms a regular part of the firm's practice in this area, one partner holding a full Higher Courts Certificate. Its commercial property departmnet has considerable depth of experience in major developments for substantial national, as well as local, builders. Private client services include general litigation, particularly personal injury and medical negligence, and with strength in all family law issues.

CONTACT PARTNERS: Mike Grant	
Number of partners:	9
Assistant solicitors:	6
Other fee-earners:	6

◇◇◇
**PERCY HUGHES
& ROBERTS**
SOLICITORS

PERKINS & COMPANY 1 King Street, Manchester, M2 6AW **Tel:** (0161) 834 7770 **Fax:** (0161) 834 8399 **DX:** 710204 Manchester 3 **Ptnrs:** 5 **Asst Solrs:** 2 **Other Fee-earners:** 2. A growing practice that focuses particularly on commercial litigation, construction, employment, matrimonial and personal injury.

PETER CARTER-RUCK & PARTNERS

75 SHOE LANE, LONDON, EC4A 3BQ
DX: 333 Ch.Ln.

TEL: (0171) 353 5005
FAX: (0171) 353 5553

THE FIRM: Peter Carter-Ruck & Partners is well known for its media expertise and its high-profile defamation practice. The firm maintains a 24 hour, seven days a week service: if advice or assistance is required outside normal office hours call (0171) 353 5005 to obtain the name and telephone number of the duty partner.

PRINCIPAL AREAS OF WORK:

Media and Defamation: (*Contact Partners:* Mr P.F. Carter-Ruck, Mr A. Stephenson, Mr A. Pepper, Ms A-M. Pagett, Mr G. Martin, Mr N. Tait). All aspects of media activity are covered from book, radio, newspaper report and article reading, TV programme clearances for libel, copyright, contempt and passing off and all types of publishing, film and theatrical contract work.

CONTACT PARTNER: Andrew Stephenson	
Number of partners:	17
Assistant solicitors:	6
Other fee-earners:	6

Trust and Commercial: (*Contact Partners:* Mr P.F. Carter-Ruck, Ms A-M. Pagett, Mr C.J. Smith, Mr N. Tait). The firm has experience of all aspects of trust law, company formation and management, both national and international, and taxation, including financial settlements in matrimonial disputes, probate, wills and the administration of estates.

Litigation: (*Contact Partners:* Mr A. Stephenson, Mr A. Pepper, Mr N. Tait, Mr G. Martin). The department has extensive experience in all fields of general commercial and media litigation including employment and intellectual property matters.

OTHER AREAS OF WORK: In addition to providing a full commercial and residential conveyancing service, (*Contact Partner:* Mr C.J. Smith), the firm handles appeals to the Judicial Committee of the Privy Council in its capacity as Privy Council agents.

FOREIGN CONNECTIONS: The firm has appointed agents in over 50 countries which enables it, for example, to provide definitive copyright advice in cases involving international publication.

OTHER OFFICES: Associated offices in Aldershot, Glasgow, Hong Kong, Manchester, Moscow, Munich, Paris, Rome and San Francisco.

WORKLOAD	
Defamation - libel/ slander/ media	81%
Criminal	8%
Trusts/ wills/ probate	4%
General litigation	3%
Conveyancing	2%
Intellectual Property - copyright/ passing off	2%

PETERKINS Burgh House, 7-9 King Street, Aberdeen, Grampian, AB2 3AA **Tel:** (01224) 626300 **Fax:** (01224) 626123 **DX:** 3 Aberdeen **Ptnrs:** 23 **Asst Solrs:** 9 **Other Fee-earners:** 17. A leading Grampian firm best known for its company/ commercial work (especially oil and gas related). Experienced in personal injury pursuer claims.

PETER LIELL 184 Divinity Road, Oxford, Oxon, OX4 1LR **Tel:** (01865) 242176 **Fax:** (01865) 200950 **Ptnrs:** 1. A sole practitioner concentrating almost exclusively on education law including High Court litigation, with or without legal aid.

WORKLOAD	
Education Law	100%

PETER, PETER & WRIGHT 8 Fore Street, Holsworthy, Devon, EX22 6ED **Tel:** (01409) 253262 **Fax:** (01409) 254091 **DX:** 118650 Holsworthy **Ptnrs:** 11 **Asst Solrs:** 2 **Other Fee-earners:** 14. A rural practice, founded in the 18th century. Experienced in agriculture, charity, private client work and capital taxation.

WORKLOAD		
Property based matters	45%	Trust/prob/Court of Protn 28%
Litigation/common	27%	

PETER RICKSON AND PARTNERS

6 WINCKLEY SQUARE, PRESTON, LANCS, PR1 3JJ	TEL: (01772) 556677
DX: 17109 Preston 1	FAX: (01772) 202445

The Stock Exchange Building, 4 Norfolk Street, Manchester M2 1DP	Tel: (0161) 833 3355
DX:14318 Manchester 1	Fax: (0161) 833 1042
Contact Partner: Peter Moore	

Union Chambers, 63 Temple Row, Birmingham B2 5LS	Tel: (0121) 631 3304
DX:13026 Birmingham 1	Fax: (0121) 643 0787
Contact Partner:Keith Lamb	

THE FIRM: The practice is one of the best-known in the North West dealing with insurance litigation. There is also a substantial commercial department. In 1993 a Birmingham office was opened to provide a specialist personal injury service in the Midlands.

PRINCIPAL AREAS OF WORK:

Insurance Litigation: (*Contact Partners:* John Cooper, Preston. Jean Hindmoor, Manchester. Keith Lamb, Birmingham). The firm acts for most of the major insurance companies and is one of the North West's leading specialist practices. The insurance litigation department handles employers' liability, public and product liability and road traffic claims. There is a specialist unit dealing with disease claims. In addition, the department advises extensively on policy interpretation.

CONTACT PARTNER:	Peter Rickson
Number of partners:	15
Assistant solicitors:	10
Other fee-earners:	21

WORKLOAD	
Insurance litigation	60%
Private client and property	15%
Commercial litigation	15%
Company/ commercial	10%

Commercial: *(Contact Partners:* Sean Gibbs, Preston. Peter Moore, Manchester). The commercial department provides comprehensive litigation, corporate and property services. The firm acts for a range of clients, from SME to PLC, both local and national. The department deals with a wide spectrum of commercial matters and offers expertise in substantial commercial litigation, corporate transactions (including property) and intellectual property matters.

CONTACTS	
Additional contacts:	
Company	Manchester office
	Stephen Isherwood
Property	Preston office
	Diane Robertson

PETERS & PETERS

2 HAREWOOD PLACE, HANOVER SQUARE, LONDON, W1R 9HB
DX: 44625

TEL: (0171) 629 7991
FAX: (0171) 499 6792

THE FIRM: Formed in 1938, Peters & Peters is a specialist practice best known as one of the leading firms in the area of white collar crime, both domestic and international. Highly motivated staff work on major cases involving fraud, tax and securities offences, Customs infractions and general financial and regulatory problems. Monty Raphael is the founder and Chair of the Business Crime Committee of the International Bar Association. The firm has a rapidly expanding commercial litigation practice advising on all types of commercial disputes in both domestic and foreign jurisdictions. Its work includes defamation, employment and tracing actions.

OTHER SPECIALISMS INCLUDE: Domestic and international business matters. Covering agency, distribution, franchising, international trade (particularly European Union and North America and intellectual property. Raymond Cannon is prominent in these fields and serves on a number of international committees in the UK and US, delivers papers and writes articles and features. The firm also provides a service to corporate and private clients in commercial conveyancing and conducts agency work in all its specialist areas.

CONTACT PARTNER: Monty Raphael	
Number of partners:	7
Assistant solicitors:	6
Other fee-earners:	10

CONTACTS	
Business crime	Monty Raphael, Keith Oliver
	Julia Balfour-Lynn
	Louise Delahunty, Jo Rickards
Commercial litigation	Monty Rapheal
	Kathryn Garbett, Keith Oliver
	Louise Delahunty
Franchising	Raymond Cannon
Intellectual property	Raymond Cannon

PETER WILBRAHAM & CO Minerva House, East Parade, Leeds, W. Yorks, LS1 5J2 **Tel:** (0113) 243 2200 **Fax:** (0113) 244 9777 **Ptnrs:** 2 **Asst Solrs:** 3 **Other Fee-earners:** 1. Based on 25 years experience, this is a new niche practice specialising in planning and environmental law. It offers a comprehensive service, from advocacy at public inquiries, to private and public sector clients.

WORKLOAD	
Plan/environ/highways	100%

PETTMAN SMITH

79 KNIGHTSBRIDGE, LONDON, SW1X 7RB
DX: 38168 Knightsbridge

TEL: (0171) 235 1288
FAX: (0171) 235 2683

THE FIRM: A modern commercial practice, established in 1982, which has since grown considerably. The firm seeks to provide practical and commercially viable solutions to legal and business problems in a friendly, professional manner. The practice is particularly noted for its work in intellectual property.

PRINCIPAL AREAS OF WORK:

Intellectual Property: *(Contact:* Christopher Rennie-Smith). Both contentious and non-contentious work is handled. Actions include copyright, patents, trademarks, passing-off and counterfeit goods. The firm has particular experience in interlocutory proceedings. Non-contentious work includes software licensing and character merchandising.

Commercial Litigation: *(Contact:* Peter Pitt). A comprehensive service includes commercial fraud, employment disputes and property and building contract litigation.

Commercial Property: *(Contact:* Ann Glaves-Smith). The firm handles development work from acquisition to sale, mortgage and other bank security work.

CONTACT PARTNER: Michael Pettman	
Number of partners:	6
Assistant solicitors:	5
Other fee-earners:	2

WORKLOAD	
Commercial litigation and property	33%
Company and commercial	33%
Intellectual property	33%

Company/ Commercial: (*Contact:* Michael Pettman). *Work includes:* business start-ups and venture capital financing, company formations, acquisitions and mergers, and computer-related work. A significant proportion of this advice is to overseas companies.

Taxation: (*Contact:* Michael Pettman). International tax planning is a particular strength, and immigration and nationality questions are also handled.

NATURE OF CLIENTELE: Clients include major public companies, small businesses and entrepreneurs. There is a substantial client base in America and the Middle East.

CONTACTS	
Commercial litigation	Peter Pitt
Commercial property	Ann Glaves-Smith
	Bernard Lester, Patten Bridge
Company and commercial	Michael Pettman
Intellectual property	Christopher Rennie-Smith

PHILIP CONN & CO

7TH FLOOR, LINCOLN HOUSE, 1 BRAZENNOSE STREET, MANCHESTER, M2 5FJ
DX: 14331

TEL: (0161) 833 9494
FAX: (0161) 834 4540

THE FIRM: Philip Conn & Co was founded in 1975 solely as a commercial practice. It has now established a reputation for having one of the strongest intellectual property law practices outside of London, with four of its six partners having a high degree of specialisation. Clientele ranges from multi-national public companies to medium-sized companies. Some private client, sole inventor work is undertaken. Other specialist areas are company law, including acquisition and disposals, joint venture and competition work. Commercial litigation is extensively practised in support of all areas of work offered.

The partnership, which is expanding, offers a multidisciplinary approach within the following principal areas:-

Intellectual Property: (*Contact:* Ian Morris. *Fee-earners:* 7).
Corporate Services including Competition Law: (*Contact:* Lee Brierley. *Fee-earners:* 6).
Commercial Litigation: (*Contact:* Graeme Orchison or Terry Osborn. *Fee-earners:* 7).
Taxation and Private Client: (*Contact:* Philip Conn. *Fee-earners:* 2).
Commercial Conveyancing: (*Contact:* Philip Taylor. *Fee-earners:* 2).
Employment Tribunal: (*Contact:* Andrew Gibson. *Fee-earners:* 3).

AGENCY: All aspects of agency work are undertaken. No legal aid.

RECRUITMENT: All applications by prospective trainee solicitors should be addressed to Ian Morris. However, the firm's requirements are met to September 1997.

FOREIGN CONNECTIONS: The firm has strong links with lawyers, patent attorneys and firms in the EC, USA and Australia in particular.

CONTACT PARTNER: Ian Morris

Number of partners:	6
Assistant solicitors:	4
Other fee-earners:	3

WORKLOAD	
Intellectual property (contentious and non-contentious)	50%
Commercial litigation	20%
Corporate/ commercial	20%
Commercial convey./employment/other	10%

CONTACTS	
Commercial litigation	G. Orchison, T. Osborn
Commercial conveyancing	P.Taylor
Corporate/ commercial	L.D. Brierley
Defamation	A.I. Morris
Employment	A.P. Gibson
Intellectual property	A.I. Morris

PHILIP JONES, HILLYER & JACKSON

BELL TOWER WALK, CHESTER, CH1 2DY
DX: 22153 Chester Northgate

TEL: (01244) 345551
FAX: (01244) 342824

THE FIRM: An expanding first generation firm dedicated to providing a partner-led service to both commercial and private clients. In addition to its long established departments specialising in crime, family/ matrimonial and private client the firm has rapidly expanding commercial and private litigation, company/ commercial financial services and insolvency departments.

Member of Conquest National Network and Personal Injury and Children Panels. (Regulated by The Law Society in the conduct of investment business.)

PRINCIPAL AREAS OF WORK:

Company/ Commercial: including formation, sale and purchase of companies, partnerships, commercial and intellectual property, farms, finance, employment, franchising and debt collection.

CONTACT PARTNER: Mr K.W. Jackson

Number of partners:	8
Assistant solicitors:	2
Other fee-earners:	5

Litigation: including commercial, contract, consumer, landlord and tenant, licensing and insolvency. The firm has particular expertise in criminal law, personal injury (including medical negligence).

Private Client: including wills, trusts, administration of estates, tax, financial planning, residential property, family matters and matrimonial disputes.

OTHER OFFICES:

9 Hunter Street, Chester CH1 2AQ.

2 Church Road, Bebington, Merseyside L63 7PH.

PHILIP HAMER & CO

9-11 SCALE LANE, HULL, S. YORKS, HU1 1PH

DX: 11933 Hull

TEL: (01482) 326666

FAX: (01482) 324432

THE FIRM: Philip Hamer & Co is one of the fastest growing and most technologically advanced legal firms in the Yorkshire and Humberside region. The firm is committed to quality and is registered by the BSI to the ISO 9000 quality standard. Specialist departments within the firm ensure that the right balance of skills, knowledge and expertise are applied to each project undertaken.

PRINCIPAL AREAS OF WORK:

Accident and Personal Injury: (*Contact:* Jim Wyatt). The firm has an increasing reputation for personal injury work and deals with a wide range of cases including medical negligence and multi-plaintiff action. Five members of the department are on the law society specialist personal injury panel.

Company & Commercial: (*Contact:* Alastair Watt, Paul Worthy). The department has a depth of experience in most areas of commercial work with a client base ranging from small partnerships to public companies. Services offered include: company formations, partnership agreements, business tenancies, sale and purchase of commercial property, mergers and acquisitions, management buy-outs/ management buy-ins, intellectual property, commercial contracts and capital taxes.

Litigation: (*Contact:* Andrew Kingston). The department handles all High Court and County Court disputes relating to the sale and transport of goods, building and construction. In addition the firm offers a computerised debt collection service.

Matrimonial: (*Contact:* Peter Harris). The department is renowned for its expertise in all aspects of this field and have members on the law society Children Panel.

Private Client: (*Contact:* Paul Landau, Tim Booth). The private client department provides domestic and residential conveyancing, wills and probate to the private client.

OTHER OFFICES:

Kings Mews, 1 Frances Street, Doncaster DN1 1JR. *Tel:* (01302) 344929. *Fax:* (01302) 344928.

Victoria House, 143-145 The Headrow, Leeds LS1 5TA. *Tel:* (0113) 2442332. *Fax:* (0113) 2440223.

Philip Hamer Limited, 35 Townhead Street, Sheffield S12EZ. *Tel:* (0114) 2521050. *Fax:* (0114) 2521055

SENIOR PARTNER: Philip Hamer

Number of partners:	6
Assistant solicitors:	18
Other fee-earners:	28

CONTACTS	
Civil litigation	Andrew Kingston
Company and commercial	Alastair Watt
Conveyancing (domestic)	Tim Booth
Matrimonial	Peter Harris
Personal injury	Jim Wyatt
Wills and probate	Paul Landau

PHILIP WOODS & CO Regent House, Heaton Lane, Stockport, Ches, SK4 1BF **Tel:** (0161) 429 6767 **Fax:** (0161) 476 6380 **Ptnrs:** 1. Formerly a partner at Eversheds, Philip Woods is a sole practitioner specialising in contentious and non-contentious intellectual property, technology and computer law.

WORKLOAD
Int prop: cont & non-cont 100%

PICKERING & BUTTERS

19 GREENGATE ST, STAFFORD, STAFFS, ST16 2LU	TEL: (01785) 56361
DX: 14551	FAX: (01785) 211115

Market Square, Rugeley WS15 2BN	Tel: (01889) 582281
DX: 18051	Fax: (01889) 574214
Contact Partner: Martin C. Wallbank	

9 Colehill, Tamworth B79 7HE	Tel: (01827) 54381
DX: 12651	Fax: (01827) 69843
Contact Partner: Graham L. Pegg	

THE FIRM: Pickering & Butters is one of the largest law firms in the Midlands. The firm has a sound management structure and is departmentalised so as to offer its clients an informed specialist service. The firm serves commercial and private clients.

PRINCIPAL AREAS OF WORK:

Company/ Commercial: (*Contact:* Simon P. Atherden, Tamworth). *Work includes:* company formation, acquisitions and sales, restructuring, partnerships, distribution, agency, franchising, manufacturing supply agreements and terms of trading, corporate taxation and financial services.

General Insurance Litigation: (*Contact:* Roger A. Price, Stafford). The firm has extensive experience in personal injury work arising from road and industrial accidents, and product liability. It has a defendant insurers department. It also has a plaintiff department and is experienced in medical negligence litigation.

Property: (*Contact:* David Worrall, Stafford). The firm has experience in site acquisitions, developments and sales of land by builders. Conveyancing, both commercial and residential is an important part of the work of this department. It also deals with leases, tenancies, planning, mortgages and insurance and agricultural law.

Litigation: (*Contact:* Roger A. Price, Stafford). *Work includes:* contract disputes, employment law, computerised debt recovery, consumer law, landlord and tenant.

Family Law: (*Contact:* John C. Trubshaw, Rugeley). *Work includes:* all aspects of family law including divorce, financial and property matters, custody, access, adoption and child care.

Tax, Wills, Trusts: (*Contact:* John S. Copley, Rugeley). *Work includes:* personal tax planning, preparation of wills, administration of estates and trusts.

Criminal Litigation: (*Contact:* S.C. King, Tamworth). *Work includes:* duty solicitor representation, private client and legal aid criminal work, motoring, road haulage work and licensing.

CONTACT PARTNER: Donald J.J. White	
Number of partners:	12
Assistant solicitors:	7
Other fee-earners:	19

EDITORIAL POLICY

In this edition, the lists of specialists include profiles of individual practitioners - solicitors and barristers - who have been recommended most frequently to our researchers. Editorial policy is to identify leading practitioners on merit: it is not possible to buy a place in our biographical lists. Inclusion of a profile in this directory is based solely on expertise and reputation.

Enormous effort has been invested by our ten-strong research team (mainly solicitors and barristers) in canvassing recommendations and identifying leaders. We are confident in the overall accuracy of the results. However, mistakes and misjudgements are inevitable, and if readers have any suggestions regarding our listings we should be very pleased to hear from them.

PICKERING KENYON 23-24 Great James Street, London, WC1N 3EL
Tel: (0171) 404 5522 **Fax:** (0171) 404 0070 **DX:** 218 **Ptnrs:** 7 **Asst Solrs:** 5
Other Fee-earners: 5. With its origins in the 16th century, Pickering Kenyon has developed into a modern commercial, litigation, property and private client practice, offering a quality, individualised service to its clients.

WORKLOAD			
Lit incl insurance/insolv	70%	Company/commercial	15%
Property	12%	Private client	3%

PICKWORTHS

28 STATION ROAD, WATFORD, HERTS, WD1 1EG DX: 51504 Watford 2	TEL: (01923) 227292 FAX: (01923) 236807
6 Victoria Street, St. Albans, Herts. AL1 3JB DX: 6143 St. Albans	Tel: (01727) 844511 Fax: (01727) 844277
37 Marlowes, Hemel Hempstead, Herts. HP1 1LQ DX: 8809 Hemel Hempstead	Tel: (01442) 61731 Fax: (01442) 230356

THE FIRM: Pickworths is a leading Hertfordshire practice. The firm offers a comprehensive range of services to commercial and private clients with particular emphasis on planning matters, sports law and personal injury.

PRINCIPAL AREAS OF WORK:

Company/ Commercial: (*Contact:* Peter Goodman). Advice is provided on all aspects of commercial, financial and business law including the restructuring of companies, shareholders agreements, changes in memorandum and articles of association, acquisitions and disposals, refinancing and management buy-outs. Clients are also assisted with contract discussions, terms and conditions, intellectual property, debt collection, employment contracts and disputes, general office procedures and Health and Safety Regulations. Specialist advice is available on employment matters.

Litigation: (*Contact:* David White). Litigation forms a substantial part of Pickworths business and the firm has a long established reputation in this field. A comprehensive range of commercial litigation services is provided, covering all aspects. *Work includes:* breach of contract, emergency injunctions and relief, personal injury and negligence claims for plaintiffs and insurance companies, insolvency and corporate recovery of business debts.

Commercial Property: (*Contact:* Glenda Ferneyhough). Advice is given on: acquiring 'greenfield' sites, buying and selling hotels, supermarkets, shops etc, commercial leases and the acquisition and letting of residential properties for business expansion schemes.

Planning & The Environment: (*Contact:* David Forbes). The firm has specialist expertise in dealing with local plan enquiries, enforcement notices, established use certificates, submission of planning applications, compensation for compulsory purchase and appeals to the Department of the Environment, using in-house advocates. David Forbes is the author of two published books on planning law.

Advocacy: (*Contact:* Andrew Wheldon). Criminal, County Court and High Court advocacy is undertaken. The firm has an active Road Traffic Department and also deals with liquor licensing, public health and environmental law, town and country planning, trading standards, foods and drugs cases, road haulage etc.

Employment: (*Contact:* Ian Tottman). Comprehensive advice for both employers and employees on resignation, dismissal and redundancy, and representation at Industrial Tribunals. In addition a full service dealing with the drafting and preparation of contracts of employment.

Sports Law: (*Contact:* Peter Goodman). Pickworths is one of the country's leading practices in motor racing, acting for teams, drivers and organisers involved in Formula 1, Formula 3000, Formula 3, Touring Car Championships and various other classes. The firm has also acted for a number of manufacturers of exotic road going cars.

Private Client: (*Contact:* Fabian Wilson/Dawn Harrison). *Work includes:* residential conveyancing, matrimonial/ child care, wills and probate.

CONTACT PARTNER: Mr D. Forbes

Number of partners:	6
Assistant solicitors:	6
Other fee-earners:	5

WORKLOAD	
Litigation	30%
Property/ planning	25%
Commercial/ sports law	20%
Crime	15%
Employment, wills and probate	10%

CONTACTS	
Commercial	P.J. Goodman
Crime	A. Wheldon
Employment	I.T. Tottman
Litigation/ matrimonial	D.R. White
Planning	D.S. Forbes
Property	G. Ferneyhough
Sports law	P.J. Goodman

PICKWORTHS
·SOLICITORS·

PICTONS (incorporating SMEATHMANS)

'KEYSTONE', 60 LONDON RD, ST. ALBANS, HERTS, AL1 1NG DX: 122730	TEL: FAX:	(01727) 840431 (01727) 838066
Bedford: 30-32 Bromham Rd, Bedford, Beds. MK40 2QD DX: 5614	Tel: Fax:	(01234) 273273 (01234) 353110
Luton: Carlton Court, 66 Alma Street, Luton, Beds. LU1 2PI DX: 5921	Tel: Fax:	(01582) 410114 (01582) 402736
Hemel Hempstead: 1 The Waterhouse, Waterhouse Street, Hemel Hempstead, Herts HP1 1ES DX: 8800	Tel: Fax:	(01442) 250111/242441 (01442) 248569
Hemel Hempstead: P.O. Box 1, 10 Queensway, Hemel Hempstead, Herts HP1 1LU DX: 8807	Tel: Fax:	(01442) 250111 (01442) 61840
Stevenage: 13 Town Square, Stevenage, Herts. SG1 1BP DX: 6006	Tel: Fax:	(01438) 350711 (01438) 359255
Watford: 24 The Avenue, Watford, Herts. WD1 3NS DX: 4505	Tel: Fax:	(01923) 237631 (01923) 226135
Milton Keynes: Ashton House, 409 Silbury Boulevard, Central Milton Keynes MK9 2LJ DX: 31411	Tel: Fax:	(01908) 663511 (01908) 661800

THE FIRM: Pictons is a broad-based practice offering a full range of legal services to commercial and private clients. Commercially the emphasis is on small to medium sized private clients and public companies. The private client base is primarily regional. The firm is organised and managed on a departmental basis across its branch network and operates written Quality Assurance Standards.

DEPARTMENTS AND DEPARTMENT HEADS:
Corporate and Commercial: R. Talbot, St Albans.
Litigation: S. Jarvis, Milton Keynes.
Domestic Conveyancing: A.J. Richardson, Hemel Hempstead.
Trusts, Wills and Probate: J.C. Thelwall, Bedford.
Financial Services: N. Caisley, St Albans.
Family: S.C. Garwood, St Albans.
Crime: R.J. Fuller, Watford

PRINCIPAL AREAS OF WORK:
Commercial: The Company and Commercial Department offers a wide range of services including company acquisitions and disposals; asset purchases and sales; management buy-outs and buy-ins; partnership matters; advice and preparation on all forms of commercial agreements including distribution and agency agreements.
   The department offers expertise in the fields of Banking Securities and Insolvency from **Bryan Green** at its St Albans office.
   Growing specialist fields within the department: Computer Law; Corporate Taxation and Trusts (John Thelwall, Bedford); Entertainment/ Sports (Peter Baines, St Albans; Chris Tate, Luton); Planning and Environment (Mike Wills, Bedford); Employment Law (Roger Talbot, St. Albans).
   Richard Hulland, a specialist in Pension Law, practices in association with the firm from Hemel Hampstead office.
Commercial Property: Work includes industrial, office and residential development; the acquisition and disposal of small businesses and retail shops; franchising; all aspects of landlord and tenant work including the grant and renewal of commercial leases and planning.
Commercial Litigation: This Division of the firm's Litigation Department works in close association with the Commercial Department facilitating a full quality service for the firm's commercial clients. There is a computerised debt collection service (*Contact:* David Fagan, St Albans).

PARTNERSHIP CHAIRMAN: David Picton
MANAGING PARTNER: Peter Baines

Number of partners:	30
Assistant solicitors:	25
Other fee-earners:	25

WORKLOAD

Commercial, property and company	22%
Commercial litigation/ personal injury	21%
Crime	20%
Domestic conveyancing	15%
Family	13%
Probate/ trusts/ tax planning	9%

CONTACTS

Company/ commercial	R Talbot
Crime	R J Fuller
Domestic conveyancing	A J Richardson
Family	S C Garwood
Financial services	N Caisley
Litigation	A Abrahams
Trusts, wills & probate	J C Thelwall

PICTONS
INCORPORATING
SMEATHMANS
SOLICITORS • COMMISSIONERS FOR OATHS • NOTARY PUBLIC

Personal Injury: The firm handles a substantial volume of personal injury litigation and medical negligence claims.

Private Client: A full range of services is provided by the Family; Domestic Conveyancing; Criminal; Wills, Trusts and Probate and Financial Services Departments. The Litigation and Criminal Departments accept, through all offices of the firm, agency work at Magistrates and County Courts for other firms.

PINSENT CURTIS

3 COLMORE CIRCUS, BIRMINGHAM, W. MIDLANDS, B4 6BH DX: 703167	TEL: (0121) 200 1050 FAX: (0121) 626 1040
41 Park Square, Leeds, N. Yorkshire LS1 2NS DX: 26440	Tel: (0113) 244 5000 Fax: (0113) 234 8000
Dashwood House, 69 Old Broad Street, London EC2M 1NR DX: CDE 661	Tel: (0171) 418 7000 Fax: (0171) 418 7050

THE FIRM: Pinsent Curtis is the merged firm of Simpson Curtis and Pinsent & Co with offices in Birmingham, Leeds, London and Brussels. The combined listed company client base ranks the firm in the national top ten. In addition, it acts for numerous private companies, financial institutions and public sector bodies.

The firm's five departments are market leaders in a range of fields including corporate finance, tax and pensions, healthcare and public sector externalisation.

PRINCIPAL AREAS OF WORK:

Corporate Department: *(Contact Partners:* Sean Lippell, David Hughes, Alan Farkas) has notable expertise in mergers and acquisitions, flotations, Stock Exchange and takeover work, venture capital, corporate structuring of joint ventures, banking and building societies, insolvency.

Litigation Department: *(Contact Partners:* Kevin Perry, John Browne, Colin Goodier), handles commercial litigation of both a national and international nature and a significant volume of professional indemnity and insurance litigation. Dedicated teams also specialise in intellectual property (including computer contracts), employment and construction law, dealing with both contentious and non-contentious work.

Property Department: *(Contact Partners:* Barry Brice, Negel McClea), deals with a whole range of transactions affecting commercial, industrial, agricultural and residential property. Within the department, specialist units concentrate on particular aspects of property work including property development, planning and environmental law. The firm has particular expertise and depth in dealing with compulsory purchase and planning issues, particularly for statutory and public bodies.

Tax Department: *(Contact Partners:* David Pett, Judith Greaves), is probably the largest of any UK law firm outside the City of London. As well as the more traditional areas of corporate and personal tax law, there is particular expertise in dealing with corporate pension schemes, enterprise zones, employee share option schemes and UK and international trusts.

Commercial Department: *(Contact Partners:* Stephen Chandler, John Pratt), deals with intellectual property, franchising, EC and UK Competition Law, project finance, commercial contracts.

London Office: *(Contact Partner:* Paul Downing), initially specialised in commercial litigation, including professional indemnity and insurance litigation. However, since 1991, following a programme of senior recruitment including five partners from top London law firms, the London office has established a significant corporate finance and building society practice, which operates on a fully integrated basis with the corresponding specialist groups in the firm's Birmingham and Leeds offices.

CONTACT PARTNER: Julian Tonks

Number of partners:	98
Assistant solicitors:	133
Other fee-earners:	70

WORKLOAD

Corporate	37%
Litigation/ corporate recovery	36%
Property	18%
Tax and pensions	9%

CONTACTS

Commercial	Stephen Chandler
Company	Sean Lippell
Litigation	Kevin Perry
Property	Barry Brice
Tax and pensions	David Pett

RECRUITMENT AND TRAINING: The firm provides regular in-house training seminars, and is a member of the Legal Resources Group, a national grouping of major commercial firms, which offers a full programme of seminars and residential courses, covering changes in legislation, key legal issues and broader business skills.

OVERSEAS OFFICES: Brussels.

INTERNATIONAL CONNECTIONS: The firm has strong international connections with leading commercial law firms in all significant jurisdictions throughout the world.

FOREIGN LANGUAGES: Chinese (Cantonese), French, German, Greek, Hindi, Japanese, Mirpury, Punjabi, Spanish, Urdu, Italian, Swedish, Dutch, Ukranian, Hebrew, Welsh and Shona.

PIPER SMITH & BASHAM 31 Warwick Square, London, SW1V 2AF **Tel:** (0171) 828 8685 **Fax:** (0171) 630 6976 **DX:** 110 Ch.Ln. **Ptnrs:** 6 **Asst Solrs:** 2 **Other Fee-earners:** 4. Piper Smith & Basham provides a wide range of legal services covering property and commercial work, travel and tour operating, charities, immigration and white collar crime.

PITMANS

47 CASTLE STREET, READING, BERKS, RG1 7SR
DX: 40102

TEL: (01734) 580224
FAX: (01734) 585097

THE FIRM: Pitmans is one of Thames Valley's leading commercial practices, offering a comprehensive legal service to local, national and international businesses. In recent years the partnership has grown and with it, the breadth of skills and specialisations offered. Pitmans' membership of InterAct Europe 1993 EEIG has proved to be invaluable to the success and growth of the practice.

PRINCIPAL AREAS OF WORK:

Company/ Commercial: (*Contact Partner:* Robin Aird. *Fee-earners:* 12). The company/ commercial department is one of the largest in the South East, outside London. It handles a wide variety of work including company formations, mergers and acquisitions, management buy-outs, institutional investment agreements, trading agreements, employment issues, share option schemes and financial services. It advises overseas clients on questions of location and handles work overseas for British clients. The department also offers specialist reports tailored to the needs of individual clients on developing European law affecting them and is able to review legal frameworks in other countries.

Corporate Security and Insolvency: (*Contact Partner:* Neil Bucknell. *Fee-earners:* 5). A specialist department is dedicated to corporate security and insolvency work.

Intellectual Property: (*Contact Partner:* David Archer. *Fee-earners:* 3). The intellectual property department has gone from strength to strength and acts for a large number of the international computer and software companies both in the Thames Valley and overseas. The department offers a wide range of services both of a contentious and non-contentious nature in the patent, copyright, trademark, know-how and entertainment sectors.

Commercial Property: (*Contact Partner:* Christopher Avery. *Fee-earners:* 12). A significant percentage of Pitmans' work is in the commercial property sector. The firm is renowned for its work in land acquisitions, joint venture arrangements and particularly for its expertise in planning and public enquiries. The department's clients include one of the largest landowners in the country, a number of substantial PLCs, local authorities and health authorities. It also has a department specialising in the sale of new homes for residential developers.

Environmental Law: (*Contact Partner:* Richard Valentine. *Fee-earners:* 2). The environmental law department has integrated well with the existing commercial property, general commercial and planning work. This department offers a wide range of services within this complex area of law with particular emphasis on the new laws developing in the European Community.

CONTACT PARTNER: Christopher Avery

Number of partners:	12
Assistant solicitors:	15
Other fee-earners:	20

WORKLOAD	
Company/ commercial	22%
Property (commercial)	19%
Litigation	18%
Residential development	13%
Intellectual property	12%
Insolvency	7%
Planning and environmental	6%
Private client	3%

CONTACTS	
Commercial property	Christopher Avery
Company commercial	Robin Aird
Environmental	Richard Valentine
Insolvency	Neil Bucknell
Intellectual property	Jeremy Newton
Litigation	Sue O'Brien
Planning	Richard Valentine
Private client	Tony Jones

Litigation: (*Contact Partner:* Susan O'Brien. *Fee-earners:* 9). The litigation department has wide experience in all areas of commercial litigation, especially in the hi-technology, construction and finance industries and in international trade. It regularly works with other departments to provide a team approach for larger litigation matters. A debt collection service is available to clients. Criminal, and matrimonial litigation is not undertaken.

Planning: (*Contact Partner:* Richard Valentine. *Fee-earners:* 2). Nearly all the commercial property partners have specialist knowledge of planning law, and a broad range of expertise covers: development strategy, agreements with Highway and Planning Authorities, major planning appeals and judicial reviews of planning decisions.

OTHER AREAS OF WORK: Pitmans undertakes a substantial amount of other non-contentious business, such as residential conveyancing, trust and probate work, wills, family settlements and personal tax planning.

NATURE OF CLIENTELE: Clients range from large PLCs to newly-established businesses, and from private clients to local public authorities. They are located throughout the country and worldwide. Pitmans is a founder member of an EEIG, with associated law firms in Amsterdam, Brussels, Hamburg, Lisbon, Madrid, Milan, Munich, Paris and Turin.

POPPLESTON ALLEN

12 PILCHER GATE, NOTTINGHAM, NOTTS, NG1 1QE
DX: 10100 Nottingham

TEL: (0115) 953 8500
FAX: (0115) 953 8501

CONTACT PARTNER: Mr Jeremy R. Allen

Number of partners:	2
Assistant solicitors:	1
Other fee-earners:	3

THE FIRM: Established in May 1994 by two nationally-renowned solicitors, Poppleston Allen is a niche practice specialising exclusively in licensing matters. Jeremy Allen and Susanna Poppleston, who together built up the substantial and well-regarded department at Hunt Dickins in Nottingham, have taken the entire licensing team from that firm with them in the move.

PRINCIPAL AREAS OF WORK: Poppleston Allen deals with liquor, public entertainment, and betting and gaming licensing. First class legal expertise is provided from the conception stages of a project through acquisition, regular renewal, upgrading and transfer of licences, to dealing with particular problems at licensed premises.

The firm's client base is wide and not restricted to its immediate area, and its consequent experience of the policies and quirks of licensing authorities covers every county in England and Wales. It offers unrivalled expertise in the niche area of discotheques and clubs, as well as pubs and off-licences.

Poppleston Allen anticipates a continued expansion of its licensing and leisure clients, whilst being able to market the specialist practice to other law firms who themselves lack a dedicated licensing department.

WORKLOAD	
Licensing (liquor, public entertainment, betting and gaming	100%

CONTACTS	
Licensing	J.R. Allen, S. Poppleston

Poppleston Allen
Licensing Solicitors

PORTER BARTLETT & MAYO

CENTRAL HOUSE, CHURCH ST, YEOVIL, SOMERSET, BA20 1HH
DX: 100501

TEL: (01935) 24581
FAX: (01935) 706063

CONTACT PARTNER: Mr. P.F. Moule

Number of partners:	17
Assistant solicitors:	6
Other fee-earners:	26

THE FIRM: Porter Bartlett & Mayo is a long-established and expanding firm with offices in Somerset and Dorset. Separate departments cover almost all aspects of legal work including company and commercial work, commercial and residential property, general litiagation, personal injury, criminal litigation, matrimonial, family and child care, probate, trust and tax, agriculture, planning, licensing, debt collection and insolvency. A member of LawNet. Franchised for Legal Aid.

OTHER OFFICES: Langport, Sherborne, Sturminster Newton and Blandford Forum.

PORTNER & JASKEL 8 Welbeck Way, London, W1M 7PE **Tel:** (0171) 486 7881 **Fax:** (0171) 935 0500 **DX:** 9067 West End **Ptnrs:** 4 **Asst Solrs:** 3 **Other Fee-earners:** 3. Handles commercial property, company/ commercial, commercial litigation, intellectual property, EU/ US competition law, building and construction, franchising, immigration and sports law.

POTHECARY & BARRATT

TALBOT HSE, TALBOT COURT, GRACECHURCH ST, LONDON, EC3V 0BS
DX: 590 City

TEL: (0171) 623 7520
FAX: (0171) 623 9815

THE FIRM: A long-established firm with particular expertise in charity and ecclesiastical law, trusts, commercial property, environmental law and insolvency. It also deals with probate matters and family law.

OTHER OFFICE: White Horse Court, North Street, Bishop's Stortford, Hertfordshire CM23 2LD. *Tel:* (01279) 506421. *Fax:* (01279) 657626. *DX:* 50402 Bishop's Stortford.

CONTACT PARTNER: Mr. D. Mobsby

Number of partners:	9
Assistant solicitors:	7
Other fee-earners:	1

POWELL SPENCER & PARTNERS

290 KILBURN HIGH RD, LONDON, NW6 2DB
DX: 37700

TEL: (0171) 624 8888
FAX: (0171) 328 1221

THE FIRM: Powell Spencer & Partners is one of London's foremost legal aid practices, with a strong reputation for its work in the areas of criminal, family, matrimonial, personal injury, medical negligence and civil liberties litigation. The firm offers a community-based service and has adapted its offices to meet the requirements of clients with disabilities and undertakes home visits.

PRINCIPAL AREAS OF WORK:

Litigation: A specialist range of litigation is undertaken, namely criminal defence, personal injury and medical negligence, child care, family and matrimonial work; welfare benefits advice. *Contact:* Criminal – Greg Powell; Child Care – Mike Tait; Matrimonial and Family – Maria Marshall; Personal Injury and Medical Negligence – John Gillman; Welfare Benefits Advice – Sue Davies.

CONTACT PARTNER: Mr Gregory Powell

Number of partners:	5
Assistant solicitors:	7
Other fee-earners:	15

WORKLOAD	
Criminal defence	60%
Civil family	18%
Personal injury	18%
Welfare benefits	4%

FIRMS OF ACCOUNTANTS

Accountants specialising in litigation support are listed in the accountants' A-Z, with details of the services they offer to solicitors, from forensic accounting to intellectual property or business valuations.

PRETTYS

ELM HOUSE, 25 ELM STREET, IPSWICH, SUFFOLK, IP1 2AD
DX: 3218

TEL: (01473) 232121
FAX: (01473) 230002

THE FIRM: Prettys was founded at the beginning of the century, and is now one of the largest practices in East Anglia. It has a substantial litigation practice, an expanding commercial division and an established private client base. It has closeknit teams which provide fast, quality and cost effective advice. High quality service and client care are priorities, reflected in ISO 9001 accreditation by the BSI in April 1993. The firm has contacts in Europe and elsewhere through its membership of Galexy, represented in twelve European countries, and other worldwide contacts. To assist in providing the service required by its London and international clients, Prettys recently opened a London office.

PRINCIPAL AREAS OF WORK:

Company/Commercial: (*Contact:* David Baylis. *Fee-earners:* 5). Business structure, owner and formation; secured and unsecured lending; acquisition and property finance; banking and insolvency; company law, mergers and acquisitions; financial services and venture capital; trading terms and agreements; intellectual property. Pettys is a member of the British Venture Capital Association.

European: (*Contact:* Stephen Smith. *Fee-earners:* 2). Acquisition of residential and commercial properties in France and related aspects; third party insurance recovery and debt recovery throughout Europe.

Industrial Relations: (*Contact:* Richard Hemmings. *Fee-earners:* 3). Advice on employment relations, industrial conflict, job security and dismissal; also trade union and health and safety at work advice; non-discrimination practices; installation of personnel management systems.

Litigation: (*Contact:* Clive Brynley-Jones. *Fee-earners:* 27). Personal injury, fatal accidents and medical negligence claims; partnership and shareholder disputes; construction and engineering disputes and professional negligence; breach of contract and sale of goods disputes. Prettys acts for many insurers, but still undertakes plaintiff work, in particular medical accident cases.

Maritime and Transport: (*Contact:* Roland Sharp. *Fee-earners:* 4). Bill of lading, booking notes, CMR and freight forwarding disputes; charter party disputes; general insurance, reinsurance, general average and marine insurance disputes; collision, salvage and related marine casualties; CIF and FOB contract disputes; ship arrest and injunctive relief.

Property: (*Contact:* David Clark. *Fee-earners:* 7). Commercial, agricultural and residential acquisitions and disposals; landlord and tenant and portfolio management; planning, environmental law and development; secured lending and finance leasing.

Private Client: (*Contact:* Carol Lockett. *Fee-earners:* 9). Tax planning and property; wills and probate; financial services; matrimonial and child welfare.

CONTACT PARTNER: Jonathan Gorst

Number of partners:	15
Assistant solicitors:	19
Other fee-earners:	20

WORKLOAD

Personal injury/ insurance/ medical	39%
Commercial/ European	38%
Private client	23%

CONTACTS

Agriculture	Toby Pound
Civil litigation	Clive Brynley-Jones
Commercial litigation	Peter Blake
Commercial property	David Clark
Company/ commercial	David Baylis
French law	Stephen Smith
Industrial relations	Richard Hemmings
Private client	Carol Lockett

PRETTYS
SOLICITORS

PRICE & SON 33 Hill Lane, Haverfordwest, Dyfed, SA61 1PS **Tel:** (01437) 765331 **Fax:** (01437) 768663 **DX:** 98279 Haverfordwest **Ptnrs:** 4 **Other Fee-earners:** 2. A broad general practice with particular strength in litigation, matrimonial and agriculture.

WORKLOAD

Civ lit apart from matrim	25%	Domestic conveyancing	20%
Matrimonial litigation	20%	Commercial/agricultural	12%
Probate and wills	10%	Criminal work	7%

PRINCE EVANS

77 UXBRIDGE RD, EALING, LONDON, W5 5ST
DX: 5100 Ealing

TEL: (0181) 567 3477
FAX: (0181) 840 7757

THE FIRM: Prince Evans is a well established, broadly based London practice able to provide practical and specialist advice to both commercial and private clients. The firm has a reputation for a robust and energetic approach.

PRINCIPAL AREAS OF WORK:

Property: The firm handles all matters dealing with residential and commercial property with particular specialisation in the housing association and public sector. The work undertaken includes construction, development and planning advice; financing new initiatives; advising on the buying, selling and management of property including a wide range of landlord and tenant matters.

Commercial Litigation: An expanding area of the firm's practice. *Work includes:* general commercial disputes, construction disputes, property disputes, insolvency, employment, contentious probate and intellectual property.

Personal Injury and Medical Negligence: The firm undertakes work in all aspects of this field with particular emphasis on cases involving major disability, notably spinal and brain injuries.

Private Client: A wide range of work which includes UK tax and financial and estate planning; wills, trusts and probate; pensions; all aspects of matrimonial and family law, child care and criminal law.

Company/ Commercial: The firm has developed considerable expertise, and deals with a variety of company and commercial transactions including company formations, acquisitions and takeovers, lettings and disposals both for occupation and, in particular, for investment companies; service and commercial agreements and partnership matters.

CONTACT PARTNER: Robert Jennings

Number of partners:	10
Assistant solicitors:	22
Other fee-earners:	8

CONTACTS	
Banking	T.E. Morley
Building litigation	R.J. Jennings
Child care	P. Eldin-Taylor
Commercial property	T.E. Morley
Commercial litigation	R.J. Jennings
Commercial conveyancing	S.B. Hammett
Crime	P. Eldin-Taylor
Employment law	R.J. Jennings
Family and matrimonial	S. Sandhar
Housing associations	L.J. Robert
Landlord and tenant	A.M. Harvey
Medical negligence	B. Neill
Personal injury	B. Neill
Probate/ wills	T.B. Lemon
Tax planning	T.B. Lemon

PRYCE & CO incorporated with CROWDY & ROSE 6 East Saint Helen Street, Abingdon, Oxon, OX14 5EW **Tel:** (01235) 523411 **Fax:** (01235) 533283 **DX:** 35853 Abingdon **Ptnrs:** 6 **Asst Solrs:** 5 **Other Fee-earners:** 1. Established 1820s. General practice with particular experience in agricultural, company property and personal injury work. Offices in Wantage, Faringdon & Lechlade.

PULLIG & CO

BRIDEWELL HOUSE, 9 BRIDEWELL PLACE, LONDON, EC4V 6AP
DX: 123 Chancery Lane

TEL: (0171) 353 0505
FAX: (0171) 936 2548

THE FIRM: Formed in 1985, Pullig & Co is a forward thinking law firm which aims to produce results for its sizeable portfolio of business and private clients. The firm has a consultant on Iranian law with niche expertise on the Iranian legal system in areas such as international trade and banking.

PRINCIPAL AREAS OF WORK:

Corporate: (*Contact:* John Pullig). Advice is given on all aspects of setting up, running and expanding a business; company law; international trade and employment.

Licensing and Leisure: (*Contact:* Chris Hepher). The department has an excellent reputation in the fields of liquor and entertainment licensing and acts for national brewers as well as individual pubs and off licences.

Immigration: (*Contact:* Anne Balcomb). The firm provides top quality fast immigration work in all areas including business, visas and work permits.

Debt Recovery: (*Contact:* Stephen Barnett). Acting for both creditors and debtors, this department adopts a very practical approach. A cost-efficient fixed fee system is offered for straightforward debt recovery.

CONTACT PARTNER: John Pullig

Number of partners:	3
Assistant solicitors:	1
Other fee-earners:	5

Litigation: *(Contact:* Michael Rapoport). Most types of commercial litigation are handled by a strong and experienced team, with an increasing niche in fraud investigation.

Commercial Property: *(Contact:* Peter Curtis). All aspects of commercial property work are handled by a department which prides itself on speed and thoroughness, and has wide experience of acting for overseas clients.

OTHER AREAS OF WORK: The firm also provides a full range of private client services, from wills, trust, tax and probate to domestic conveyancing (fixed fees available) and matrimonial and family law.

FOREIGN CONNECTIONS: The firm has an associated office in Tehran and strong connections in France, Gibraltar, Jersey, Malaysia, Poland, Singapore, South Africa, Spain, Switzerland and the USA.

LANGUAGES SPOKEN: Armenian, Farsi, French, Gujarati, Hindi, Maltese, Spanish, Swahili and Turkish.

PUNCH ROBSON 35 Albert Road, Middlesbrough, Clev, TS1 1NU **Tel:** (01642) 230700 **Fax:** (01642) 218923 **DX:** 60501 Middlesbrough **Ptnrs:** 15 **Asst Solrs:** 5 **Other Fee-earners:** 7. Long established Teeside firm. Deals with a broad range of legal matters including family law, employment and commercial property. Increasingly commercial.

PUTSMANS

BRITANNIA HOUSE, 50 GREAT CHARLES STREET, BIRMINGHAM, W. MIDLANDS, B3 2LT   DX: 702312 Birmingham 10

TEL: (0121) 236 9116
FAX: (0121) 236 1731

THE FIRM: Putsmans (formerly Maurice Putsman & Co) provides a broad range of commercial advice to businesses in the West Midlands.It has particular expertise in Commercial Property, Insurance Litigation and Commercial Dispute Resolution. The firm has a rigorous, client-centred approach and an inventive and cost conscious attitude to problem solving.

PRINCIPAL AREAS OF WORK:

Commercial Property: *(Contact:* Anthony Baggott). Site acquisitions and disposals, industrial and residential estate development, leases and property management, planning and environmental issues.

Insurance: *(Contact:* Julia Holden). The firm acts for a number of leading insurance companies, defending a wide variety of claims. It also advises on policy documents, underwriting agreements and other aspects of insurance law. including arbitration/mediation between insurance companies.

Personal Injury/Medical Negligence: *(Contact:* Remmy Baba). All aspects of personal injury including road traffic, factory, product liability, occupiers liability and criminal injuries compensation.

General Commercial: *(Contact:* A. Maurice Putsman). Company formations and acquisitions, agency and distribution agreements, franchising, product liability and health and safety. Legal Healthcheck work is undertaken, reviewing a range of legal issues within a client's business.

Commercial Disputes: *(Contact:* Sarah Ferdinand). Litigation and dispute resolution in relation to contract claims, employment law, property and construction disputes, directors/partners disputes, intellectual property, licensing and debt recovery.

Private Clients: *(Contact:* Geoffrey Morris). Residential conveyancing, wills, probate, family and matrimonial.

FOREIGN CONNECTIONS: EUROLINK - A co-operative network of 100 European law firms.

FOREIGN LANGUAGES SPOKEN: Cantonese, French, German, Italian, Mandarin, Punjabi, Russian, Spanish, Urdu.

OTHER OFFICES: Bank Chambers, 313 High Street, West Bromwich B70 8LV. *(Contact Partner:* Michael Cary (0121) 553 3017).

CONTACT PARTNER: Geoffrey Morris

Number of partners:	10
Assistant solicitors:	8
Other fee-earners:	29

WORKLOAD	
Insurance Litigation	35%
Commercial Property	25%
General Commercial	25%
Private Client	15%

PUTSMANS
SOLICITORS

PYE-SMITHS The Hall, 4 New St, Salisbury, Wilts, SP1 2QJ **Tel:** (01722) 412345 **Fax:** (01722) 412321 **DX:** 58006 **Ptnrs:** 3 **Asst Solrs:** 7 **Other Fee-earners:** 9. A general family and commercial practice which includes crime, marine law and forfeiture proceedings. Legal aid and agency work undertaken. Opposite Law Courts.

WORKLOAD			
Landlord and tenant lit	15%	Family and matrimonial	13%
Others	11%	Conveyancing (domestic)	11%
Wills/trusts/probate	10%	Conveyancing	8%

QUALITY LAW GROUP

10 BENNETTS HILL, BIRMINGHAM, W. MIDLANDS, B2 5RS
DX: 13015 Birmingham 1

TEL: (0121) 643 7084
FAX: (0121) 643 6495

EXECUTIVE DIRECTOR: Amanda Pugh

THE GROUP: QLG is a national group of 14 law firms operating in the main commercial centres throughout the UK.

Established in 1992 the group now has over 200 partners, nearly 350 other fee-earners and 700 support staff and is well placed to meet the requirements of commercial clients on a local, regional and national basis anywhere in the UK.

QLG acts as a source of information and innovation for its member firms and facilitates the exchange of legal expertise and resources, organises joint training and marketing initiatives as well as co-ordinating central purchasing from external suppliers.

THE FIRMS: With clients including major public companies, public authorities and international clients, all firms are committed to delivering a quality, value for money service.

All member firms have achieved or are working towards achieving ISO 9001 accreditation as part of the QLG quality code to help ensure a consistent high level of service for their clients.

Member Firms:

London: *Stoneham Langton & Passmore*
Edinburgh: *Lindsays WS*
Birmingham: *Shakespeares*
Bristol: *Lawrence Tucketts*
Crawley: *Burstows*
Croydon:*Stonehams*
Exeter: *Anstey Sargent & Probert*
Glasgow: *Wright Johnston & Mackenzie*
Leeds: *Brooke North & Goodwin*
Liverpool: *Cuff Roberts*
Maidstone: *Argles & Court*
Newcastle upon Tyne: *Ward Hadaway*
Norwich: *Leathes Prior*
Southampton: *Hepherd Winstanley & Pugh*

A NATIONAL GROUP OF LAW FIRMS

QUIJANO & ASSOCIATES 41 South Audley Street, London, W1Y 5DH **Tel:** (0171) 499 4654 **Fax:** (0171) 495 1433. A Panamanian Law firm with offices in London and Panama City and associated offices in Switzerland and British Virgin Islands.

RABIN LEACOCK LIPMAN 7-10 Chandos Street, London, W1M 9DE **Tel:** (0171) 631 4380 **Fax:** (0171) 637 0560 **DX:** 53806 **Ptnrs:** 15 **Asst Solrs:** 7 **Other Fee-earners:** 2. Expanding commercial practice, with particular strengths in commercial property and planning, and international trade and commodities work. Member of British-Soviet Chamber of Commerce.

RADCLIFFES CROSSMAN BLOCK

5 GREAT COLLEGE STREET, WESTMINSTER, LONDON, SW1P 3SJ
DX: 113 Ch.Ln.

TEL: (0171) 222 7040
FAX: (0171) 222 6208

THE FIRM: The merger of Radcliffes & Co and Crossman Block has brought together a considerable depth of experience and enthusiasm which will enhance the policy of both firms to provide practical and imaginative solutions to clients' problems supported by the best technical advice.

The merger will enable full advantage to be taken of the Company/Commercial skills of both firms with particular expertise in the fields of IT, telecommunications and intellectual property. Involvement in property investment and development and the health care sector will continue to be of particular interest and the strengths in tax, charities and private client work of both Radcliffes & Co and Crossman Block will come together in the new practice.

An existing reputation in the field of public affairs and Government relations will continue helped by the firm's close proximity to the Houses of Parliament.

As with most firms of this size a wide range of work is covered. However, the principal areas of activity are those set out in the list of contacts.

ASSOCIATED OFFICE: Nice (*Contact:* Martyn Thurston).

PROFESSIONAL CONNECTIONS: The firm has strong links with lawyers worldwide, in particular with firms in the USA, Canada, Southern Africa, Germany, Netherlands, Spain and Hong Kong.

Commercial Law Affiliates: Radcliffes Crossman Block is the sole English firm for this US based association of law firms, comprising some 190 independent member firms in 70 jurisdictions. Membership enables the firm to offer advice in most legal jurisdictions through firms which continue to meet CLA's quality assurance programme. (*Contact:* Sir Gerrard Neale.)

Radcliffes Trustee Company SA: A Trust Company established in Geneva in 1974. (*Contact:* Lyddon Simon).

Valcross Trust & Corporate Services Limited: A Trusr Company established in 1987 in Gibraltar (with a subsidiary in the Isle of Man). (*Contact:* Stephen Lewin).

Studio Legale Barberi and Studio Aletti in Milan. (*Contact:* Tim Newsome).

LawNet: The firm is a London representative (with specific reference to public affairs, government relations and judicial review) for the 80 English legal firms comprising this organisation. (*Contact:* Sir Gerrard Neale.)

RECRUITMENT AND TRAINING: The firm has the benefit of assistance from its Consultant Director of Research and Training, Professor Robert Merkin, Bracton Professor of Law at Exeter University. Around five trainee Solicitors are required each year. A recruitment brochure is available on request and application is by CV with letter to the Recruitment Partner.

SENIOR PARTNER: Lyddon Simon
MANAGING PARTNER: Robert Vallings

Number of partners:	38
Assistant solicitors:	31
Other fee-earners:	33

CONTACTS

Banking/financial institutions	Philip Peacock
Charities	Guy Greenhous/Paul Voller
Company/commercial/IP	Robin Baron
Computer law/ IT	Roland Gillott
Corporate finance	Rupert Lescher
Employment	Michael Elks
European Union law	Roland Gillott
Financial services	Philip Maddock
Health sector/medl negligence	Andrew Parsons
Immigration	Tim Newsome
Insurance litigation	Paul Clements
Intellectual property	Philip Peacock
Litigation/judicial review	Michael Elks
Local Government	Charles Farrer
Matrimonial/ family	Roger Cobden-Ramsay
Pensions	Robert O'Donovan
Property litigation	Robert Highmore
Property/ planning	Charles Farrer
Public affairs	Sir Gerrard Neale
Tax & private client	Martyn Thurston
	Stephen Lewin
Telecommunications	Philip Peacock

RAEBURN CHRISTIE & CO 16 Albyn Place, Aberdeen, Grampian, AB9 1PS **Tel:** (01224) 640101 **Fax:** (01224) 638434 **DX:** 2 Aberdeen **Ptnrs:** 12 **Asst Solrs:** 14 **Other Fee-earners:** 8. A leading commercial firm in North East Scotland with particular strength in commercial litigation, employment, commercial property, licensing and private client matters.

WORKLOAD			
Commercial & corporate	40%	Private client	30%
Litigation	30%		

RAKISONS

27 CHANCERY LANE, LONDON, WC2A 1NF
DX: 206 Ch.Ln.

TEL: (0171) 404 5212
FAX: (0171) 831 1926

THE FIRM: Rakisons, founded in 1979, is an English based law firm with an international practice offering a complete legal service for financial, commercial and industrial clients.

PRINCIPAL AREAS OF WORK:

Corporate: Takeovers and mergers; joint ventures and shareholders agreements; reorganisation and restructuring of companies; asset acquisition and disposals; management and leveraged buy-outs; venture capital finance; company formations and establishment of businesses; administration of companies and their subsidiaries; Stock Exchange aspects of share and security transactions; partnerships: formation and dissolution; flotations on the USM; BES circulars; company and partnership disputes. Insolvency related transactions; motor industry.

Commercial: Agency distribution, licensing and franchising agreements; leasing and finance agreements; terms and conditions of trade; service contracts, consultancy agreements and related employment matters; patents, trademarks and other intellectual property matters; computer contracts; corporate funding; banking law; commercial disputes.

Commercial Litigation: Commercial litigation; arbitrations; corporate and partnership litigation; defamation; intellectual property litigation; obtaining and discharge of injunctions; motor industry and transport; insurance and re-insurance litigation; enforcement of security and related banking litigation; employment severance litigation and industrial tribunals; real property and landlord and tenant litigation; commercial debt recovery; Inland Revenue and Customs and Excise Back-Duty Investigations. Insolvency related litigation.

Commercial Property: Commercial industrial and residential development; investment; acquisitions, disposals and leases; dealing; auctions and tenders; funding and security documentation; planning; building contracts; property taxation; landlord and tenant law; portfolio management; motor industry; hotel, leisure and licensed premises; insolvency related transactions; environmental law.

International: International agreements and tax structures; crossborder takeovers, mergers and joint ventures; EC law: competition, right of establishment, freedom of movement and anti-dumping; establishing a business in the UK through a UK subsidiary or a branch of an overseas corporation; appointing UK agents and distributors; settling general terms and conditions of trading for use in UK sales; taking premises in the UK; debt recovery and all other commercial litigation. Cross border insolvency.

Insolvency: Administrative receiverships; receiverships; liquidations; corporate voluntary arrangements; administrations; retention of title claims; sequestrations; advice to directors on e.g. wrongful trading and risks of disqualification; bankruptcy and individual voluntary arrangements.

Gaming and Licensing: Casino licensing; sale and purchase of casinos; investment in casinos; enforcement of gaming debts; bookmakers' permits; justices' on-and off-licences; club and restaurant licences; music and dancing licences.

FOREIGN CONNECTIONS: Languages spoken include Danish, French, German, Hebrew, Italian and Swedish. Rakisons is a founding member of IAG International, an integrated advisory group of independent professional firms who provide quick and easy access to advice from other legal, accountancy and taxation firms throughout Europe. IAG currently has 46 members with 76 offices in 67 cities, in Austria, Belgium, Cyprus, Czech Republic, Denmark, England, Estonia, Finland, France, Germany, Holland, Hungary, Isle of Man, Italy, Jersey, Liechtenstein, Luxembourg, Monaco, Norway, Portugal, Russia, Scotland, Slovakia, Spain, Sweden and Switzerland. Rakisons also has representative offices in Australia, Greece, Hong Kong, Ireland, and the USA.

CONTACT PARTNER:
Mr Anthony Wollenberg

Number of partners:	11
Assistant solicitors:	11
Other fee-earners:	6

CONTACTS

Corporate	Joel Adler
Insolvency	Janet Long
Litigation	Anthony Wollenberg
Property	Paul Manning

RAKISONS
S O L I C I T O R S

RAMSBOTTOM & CO 25-29 Victoria St, Blackburn, Lancs, BB1 6DN **Tel:** (01254) 672222 **Fax:** (01254) 681723 **DX:** 15251 **Ptnrs:** 8 **Asst Solrs:** 5 **Other Fee-earners:** 8. Offices in Darwen and Great Harwood. Best known for personal injuries, conveyancing, immigration law and general litigation. One partner has particular interest in entertainment law as affecting circuses.

RATCLIFFE DUCE & GAMMER 49 & 51 London Street, Reading, Berks, RG1 4PS **Tel:** (01734) 574291 **Fax:** (01734) 393143 **Ptnrs:** 9 **Asst Solrs:** 3 **Other Fee-earners:** 6. Best known for its family/ matrimonial and private client work. Has other offices at Wokingham and Wallingford.

RAWLISON & BUTLER

GRIFFIN HSE, 135 HIGH STREET, CRAWLEY, W. SUSSEX, RH10 1DQ
DX: 120750 Crawley

TEL: (01293) 527744
FAX: (01293) 520202

THE FIRM: Established in Horsham in 1865, Rawlison & Butler is now a leading firm of solicitors in the South East of England, with more than 60 employees and an established and highly-regarded corporate and commercial practice. Whilst the firm has retained its strong private client base, commercial property, commercial litigation and all aspects of mergers and acquisitions and corporate finance are its particular areas of strength. The firm's head office is now located in the major growth area of Crawley, where it is currently celebebrating its tenth anniversary.

PRINCIPAL AREAS OF WORK:

Company/ Commercial: (*Contact Partner:* James H.T. Chatfield). The department advises on all aspects of corporate and commercial law with particular emphasis on domestic and international mergers and acquisitions, corporate finance, management buy-outs and buy-ins, public and private share issues and loan issues, business start-ups, and the structuring of private and public companies and joint ventures. In addition, the firm offers expertise in relation to commercial law, in particular, commercial contracts, licensing and marketing of products and services, computer law, software licensing and marketing, installation and leasing agreements and intellectual property.

Commercial Litigation: (*Contact Partner:* Clive J. Prior). The department is active in a wide range of commercial disputes and arbitration matters, including general contractual and property disputes, construction disputes, employment, personal accident claims, carriage of goods and transport disputes, insurance, licensing and debt collection.

Commercial Property: (*Contact Partner:* Clive J. Prior). The department advises on all areas of commercial property law, but with particular emphasis on property development, funding and joint venture agreements, commercial leases, business and agricultural tenancies, rent reviews and all kinds of property disputes.

International Law: (*Contact Partner:* James H.T. Chatfield). With many clients investing in Europe and in North America, Rawlison & Butler has built up extensive contacts with lawyers in these areas and gives advice on all relevant aspects of international law. French and Spanish are spoken.

Planning Law: (*Contact Partner:* Carlton A.J. Burton). The department advises on a broad range of planning matters including applications and appeals, representations at public enquiries, and negotiating and drafting planning, or planning related documents.

Private Client: (*Contact Partner:* Digby R. Armstrong). The firm undertakes all aspects of private client work, including wills, probate, civil litigation and conveyancing.

OTHER OFFICES: 15 Carfax, Horsham, W. Sussex RH12 1DY. *Tel:* (01403) 252492.

CONTACT PARTNER: Clive Prior

Number of partners:	7
Assistant solicitors:	12
Other fee-earners:	8

WORKLOAD	
Commercial property	33%
Private client	27%
Commercial litigation	20%
Company/ commercial	20%

CONTACTS	
Company/ commercial	James Chatfield
Corporate finance	James Chatfield
Employment	Lydia Jasinski
Litigation (commercial)	Clive Prior
Litigation (property)	Clive Prior
Planning	Carl Burton
Private client	Digby Armstrong
Property (commercial)	Clive Prior
Taxation	Patrick Cannon

RAWLISON AND BUTLER

SOLICITORS

RAYFIELD MILLS 3 Collingwood Street, Newcastle-upon-Tyne, Tyne & Wear, NE1 1JE **Tel:** (0191) 261 2333 **Fax:** (0191) 261 2444 **Ptnrs:** 5 **Asst Solrs:** 4 **Other Fee-earners:** 1. A specialist firm in shipping and maritime law, focusing on shipping-related litigation and arbitration.

WORKLOAD	
Shipping incl lit/arbit	100%

RAYNER, DE WOLFE 31 Southampton Row, London, WC1B 5HJ **Tel:** (0171) 405 1212 **Fax:** (0171) 405 1191 **Ptnrs:** 9 **Asst Solrs:** 6 **Other Fee-earners:** 5. General commercial practice (of an international nature) with emphasis on company work, banking, commercial property and commercial litigation. Active in Eastern Europe.

WORKLOAD			
Commercial litigation	33%	Corporate/ commercial	33%
Property	15%	Private client	10%
Emp/ind relations	5%	Immigration/nationality	4%

READ HIND STEWART

TRAFALGAR HOUSE, 29 PARK PLACE, LEEDS, W. YORKS, LS1 2SP
DX: 14085

TEL: (0113) 2436014
FAX: (0113) 2442863

THE FIRM: Read Hind Stewart was established in 1987 and has now developed into a major practice in the commercial centre of Leeds.

PRINCIPAL AREAS OF WORK: The practice undertakes both commercial and private client work but has particularly strong corporate, commercial property, commercial litigation, employment, probate and trust departments. European law is a specialisation, specifically German law-related matters.

RECRUITMENT: As a developing practice, Read Hind Stewart is continually looking for outstanding candidates. Please contact David Hymas, Managing Partner.

WORKLOAD	
Commercial property	35%
Company/ commercial	25%
Commercial litigation	23%
Employment	9%
Debt recovery	8%

REDFERN & STIGANT 57 Balmoral Road, Gillingham, Kent, ME7 4PA **Tel:** (01634) 575511 **Fax:** (01634) 855152 **DX:** 6607 Gillingham **Ptnrs:** 10 **Asst Solrs:** 1 **Other Fee-earners:** 12. Best known for commercial conveyancing, company and partnership law, and litigation. Substantial experience in probate, child welfare, and criminal law.

REES EDWARDS MADDOX

KING EDWARD HOUSE, NEW STREET, BIRMINGHAM, W. MIDLANDS, B2 4QW
DX: 13052 Birmingham

TEL: (0121) 643 0111
FAX: (0121) 631 2225

THE FIRM: Rees Edwards Maddox, an experienced and progressive practice, places a particular emphasis on company and commercial law. Its diverse clientele includes quoted and private companies, professional and trade partnerships, local authorities and financial institutions throughout the British Isles.

PRINCIPAL AREAS OF WORK:

Company/ Commercial: (*Contact Partner:* Gareth Griffiths). This is the firm's largest department. *Work includes:* corporate finance, acquisitions and sales, flotations, insolvency, "management buy-ins/ outs", licensing, charitable trusts, employment contracts, computer law, intellectual property, company formations and general commercial advice to businesses, companies and individuals.

Commercial Litigation: (*Contact Partner:* Elizabeth Stanger). *Work includes:* contractual disputes, employment and Industrial Tribunal work, copyright and intellectual property, debt recovery, arbitration, personal injury and medical negligence, defamation, property disputes, insurance claims and shareholders, directors and partnership disputes.

CONTACT PARTNER: Gareth Griffiths

Number of partners:	7
Assistant solicitors:	4
Other fee-earners:	4

WORKLOAD	
Commercial litigation	35%
Company/ commercial	25%
Corporate finance	20%
Commercial property	15%
Private client	5%

Commercial Property: (*Contact Partner:* Martin Woodward). *Work includes:* purchases, sales and leases of commercial and industrial property, residential and commercial developments, acquisitions and sales of investment portfolios, property finance, and agricultural land.

The needs of the firm's private clients including domestic conveyancing, trusts, wills and probate are also dealt with by this department.

LANGUAGES: French, German and Spanish.

OVERSEAS: The firm has developed a network of correspondent firms throughout Europe and the rest of the world.

CONTACTS	
Charitable trusts	Susan Mann
Commercial litigation	Elizabeth Stanger
Commercial property	Martin Woodward
Company/ commercial	David Nicholds
Corporate finance	Gareth Griffiths
Personal injury	Hugh Brookes
Private client	Peter Clark
Trusts and probate	Martin Woodward

REES & FRERES 1 The Sanctuary, Westminster, London, SW1P 3JT **Tel:** (0171) 222 5381 **Fax:** (0171) 222 4646 **DX:** 2301 Victoria **Ptnrs:** 14 **Asst Solrs:** 8 **Other Fee-earners:** 7. A leading firm in parliamentary law and transport infrastructure projects. Also handles public law and commercial property matters.

REES PAGE 30-32 Lichfield Street, Wolverhampton, W. Midlands, WV1 1DN **Tel:** (01902) 21263 **Fax:** (01902) 711155 **DX:** 10405 Wolverhampton **Ptnrs:** 11 **Asst Solrs:** 11 **Other Fee-earners:** 13. Long-established general practice now with five offices in the West Midlands. Wolverhampton head office expanding further in 1993.

REID MINTY

19 BOURDON PLACE, BOURDON STREET, MAYFAIR, LONDON, W1X 9HZ
DX: 44615 Mayfair

TEL: (0171) 318 4444
FAX: (0171) 318 4445

THE FIRM: Founded in 1980, the firm is a specialist litigation practice with a growing reputation for handling substantial commercial actions.

PRINCIPAL AREAS OF WORK:

Commercial Litigation: *Work includes:* contractual disputes, intellectual property, banking litigation, container and transport law, Lloyd's recoveries, shareholder and partnership disputes, insolvency, defamation, employment law and injunctions.

Professional Negligence: The firm handles cases concerning solicitors, surveyors and accountants and is a member of a specialist panel.

Personal Injury: *Work includes:* trade union and private plaintiff work, member of specialist panel.

Commercial Property: The full range of work is undertaken.

NATURE OF CLIENTELE: Fully quoted PLCs, banks, substantial multinational corporations, full range of general commercial and private clients, Lloyd's syndicates, investment trusts, trade union and private individuals.

FOREIGN CONNECTIONS: The firm is the only UK member of the European Business Lawyers network.

CONTACT PARTNER: Mr S.J. Moss

Number of partners:	9
Assistant solicitors:	6
Other fee-earners:	8

WORKLOAD	
Commercial litigation	30%
Personal injury	15%
Conveyancing	10%
Professional Negligence	10%
Defamation	10%
Insolvency	10%
Container leasing/ transport	10%
Other	5%

REUMERT & PARTNERS

1 KNIGHTRIDER COURT, LONDON, EC4V 5JP

TEL: (0171) 236 4406
FAX: (0171) 236 4599

THE FIRM: Founded more than one hundred years ago, Reumert & Partners is one of the largest law firms in Denmark. The firm is consulted by a wide range of national and international clients in the fields of industry, trade, transport, insurance and finance.

MANAGING PARTNER: Søren Johansen

LAWYERS:	
London:	1
Worldwide:	43

THE LONDON OFFICE: Reumert & Partners has established a reliable and fast-working network throughout the world, so that qualified assistance in international legal matters can be rendered at short notice. The London office is vital to the efficiency with which the firm provides legal services globally.

MAIN AREAS OF WORK:

Company Acquisitions: company and business acquisitions, mergers, management buy-out, management buy-in, corporate structuring, joint-ventures.

Banking and Finance: the financial sector and its regulation, taking of security, syndications, stock-exchange flotations, project financing, leasing.

Maritime, Aviation and Transportation Law: all legal aspects related to the transport industry, including contracts and liability matters, insurance and financing, sale and purchase, contracts of affreightment, shipbuilding contracts.

Insurance, Tort and Negligence: indemnity, liablity and rights of recourse within all commercial insurance areas, reinsurance, policy drafting and liability questions in contract and tort.

Industrial Property and Competition Law: patents, trademarks, designs and copyrights, marketing rights, competition law and licences, computer law, agency and distributor agreements.

EU Law: impact of Union law and harmonisation measures.

Energy, Environmental Problems, Construction and Property: licences, installations, extraction, production and delivery contracts, building and construction contracts, property investment, environmental legislation.

Bankruptcy and Reorganisation: receiverships, reorganisation, compulsory and voluntary winding-up proceedings.

Litigation and Arbitration: All partners handle litigation and arbitraton cases within their own area of work. The partners act as arbitrators in Denmark and abroad.

OTHER OFFICES: Copenhagen.

WORKLOAD	
Banking and finance	40%
Company commercial	40%
Other	10%
Shipping	10%

REYNOLDS PARRY-JONES & CRAWFORD 10 Easton St, High Wycombe, Bucks, HP11 1NP **Tel:** (01494) 525941 **Fax:** (01494) 530701 **DX:** 4407 **Ptnrs:** 8 **Asst Solrs:** 6 **Other Fee-earners:** 1. Established 121 years, the firm assists both corporate and private clients. *Work includes:* commercial law, residential and commercial conveyancing, litigation, and family law.

REYNOLDS PORTER CHAMBERLAIN

CHICHESTER HOUSE, 278-282 HIGH HOLBORN, LONDON, WC1V 7HA
DX: 81 Chancery Lane

TEL: (0171) 242 2877
FAX: (0171) 242 1431

THE FIRM: Reynolds Porter Chamberlain is one of the country's leading insurance practices, with a particular expertise in professional indemnity litigation but also having strong bases in corporate, commercial and private client work. The firm handles an extensive range of legal matters, forming teams from different areas of practice for particularly complex transactions. The firm is also a founder member of TerraLex, an international association of law firms across 90 jurisdictions.

PRINCIPAL AREAS OF WORK:

Insurance: A major part of the practice is designed to meet the needs of insurance companies and Lloyd's underwriters in both professional negligence cases and other areas of liability insurance. The firm also provides more general insurance market litigation and commercial advice including policy drafting and interpretation. An office at Lloyd's assists in the provision of this advice.

Corporate: The corporate department acts for publicly quoted companies, multinational corporations, private companies, trade associations and partnerships. *Work includes:* acquisitions and mergers, share issues, corporate finance, banking, yellow book work, insolvency, franchise and distribution, information technology, competition law, Financial Services Act and immigration.

Commercial Litigation: *Work includes:* contractual disputes, product liability, agency and franchising, insolvency, personal injury, partnership and property disputes.

CONTACT PARTNER: Mr Tim Anderson

Number of partners:	36
Assistant solicitors:	65
Other fee-earners:	51

WORKLOAD	
Insurance	25%
Professional negligence	25%
Construction	10%
Commercial property	10%
Commercial litigation	10%
Company/ commercial	10%
Private client/ family	5%
Intellectual property	5%

Intellectual Property: Patents, trademarks, designs and copyright disputes and licensing are handled for the professions and for industries ranging from pharmaceutical companies to computing, publishing and entertainment companies.

Employment: *Work includes:* contracts, restrictive covenants, misuse of confidential information and trade secrets, employee benefits, pensions and Industrial Tribunal hearings.

Education: The firm acts for teachers' professional associations, universities and schools and advises on all aspects of education law including the further and higher education sectors.

Tax: *Work includes:* UK and international tax planning, offshore trusts, foundations and corporations and the tax implications of property transactions and investment in the UK.

Property: The property department acts for both publicly quoted property companies and investment funds as well as general trading companies in commercial property transactions. Areas of work include investment, site acquisitions, joint ventures, development, town and country planning and landlord and tenant law.

Construction: *Work includes:* advice on building contracts and related documentation and a substantial amount of arbitration and litigation.

Private Client: The firm offers a considerable range of services to private clients, including financial services, personal taxation, wills, trusts and probate.

Family: *Work includes:* all aspects of matrimonial and family law and the department is well known for its high profile wardship cases for local authorities and the Lord Chancellor's Department.

NATURE OF CLIENTELE: Clients include multinational corporations, publicly quoted companies, private companies, property developers, professional and trade associations, insurance companies, underwriters, private individuals and partnerships.

RECRUITMENT & TRAINING: The firm recruits six trainee solicitors a year and provides financial assistance through CPEs. Apply by letter and send CV to Miss Oenone Grant-Duprez.

CONTACTS	
Commercial litigation	Stephen Mayer
Commercial property	Edward Meerloo
	David Haywood
Company/ commercial	Alan Toulson
Construction	Charles Gardner, Stephen Kirby
Corporate finance	Tim Anderson
Family	Jeffrey Freeman
Insurance	Simon Greenley
Intellectual property	Andrew Hobson
Private client	Colin Russell
Professional negligence	Paul Nicholas
Tax & pensions	Charles Suchett-Kaye

Reynolds Porter Chamberlain

RICHARD BUXTON 40 Clarendon Street, Cambridge, Cambs, CB1 1JX **Tel:** (01223) 328933 **Fax:** (01223) 301308 **Ptnrs:** 1. Specialist environmental lawyer. Mainly water, conservation, env. assessment, and noise work. Contentious and non-contentious. Local authorities, groups, statutory bodies, private clients.

WORKLOAD			
Envir: water related	30%	Environmental: noise	20%
Environ: nature conserv	20%	Envir: planning related	20%

RICHARD C.M. SYKES 4 Halkin St, London, SW1X 7DJ **Tel:** (0171) 235 2508 **Fax:** (0171) 235 5774 **Ptnrs:** 1 **Other Fee-earners:** 1. Specialist defamation practice.

RICHARDS BUTLER

BEAUFORT HOUSE, 15 ST. BOTOLPH ST, LONDON, EC3A 7EE
DX: 1066

TEL: (0171) 247 6555
FAX: (0171) 247 5091

THE FIRM: Established in 1920, Richards Butler is noted for the exceptional variety of its work. It has acknowledged strengths in shipping, insurance, aviation, and entertainment law, in which it has an international prominence. The firm also has substantial company/ commercial, litigation and property departments.

PRINCIPAL AREAS OF WORK:

Admiralty: (*Contact:* R.H.J.P. Harvey). *Work includes:* the taking of evidence and the handling of claims and contracts relating to collision; fire and explosion at sea; general average; salvage, including the conduct of Lloyd's open form salvage arbitration; total loss; towage and wreck removal.

Aviation and Aircraft Finance: (*Contact:* J.F. Sherwood). *Work includes:* banking law; international aircraft, asset, and project financing including asset-based financing; cross border and tax-based leasing; option and full payout finance leases, operating leases and leveraged leasing; asset value, deficiency and residual value guarantees; regulatory matters, liability-related issues and operational aspects affecting the aviation industry.

CONTACT PARTNER: Ken Ollerton	
UK:	
Number of partners:	52
Assistant solicitors:	73
Other fee-earners:	62
INTERNATIONAL:	
Number of Partners:	10
Assistant Solicitors:	30
Other fee-earners:	12

Commercial and EC: (*Contact:* S.T. Sayer). EC and United Kingdom competition law, including monopolies and mergers, investigations, restrictive practices, dumping and state subsidies.

Commercial Litigation: (*Contact:* S.P.M. Skrein). *Work includes:* general contentious commercial matters; proceedings in the High Court and European Court; commercial arbitrations; administrative law; construction disputes and Government and Parliamentary Relations work; hearings before statutory tribunals; financial services regulatory and investigative work; County Court cases and occasional work in the criminal courts.

Construction and Engineering: (*Contact:* R.J. Parker). *Work includes:* drafting of documents, negotiation of contracts, preparation of claims, financing, collateral warranties, resolution of disputes by arbitration, litigation or settlement.

Corporate: (*Contact:* F.J. Donagh). *Work includes:* all aspects of company and partnership law; flotations; take-overs; mergers and monopolies; banking and corporate finance including venture capital LBOs, MBOs and MBIs; EC and United Kingdom competition law; environmental law; patents, trademarks, and other intellectual property rights, including matters relating to technology transfer, computers, pharmaceuticals and biotechnology, Government and Parliamentary Relations work.

Employment: (*Contact:* L.G. Rees). The firm handles all areas of employment and industrial relations law for corporate and individual clients, and undertakes advocacy before industrial tribunals.

Energy: (*Contact:* S.T. Sayer). *Work includes:* licensing and contracting; joint operating agreements and joint ventures; gas supply agreements; project financing; energy transportation and pollution.

Environmental Law: (*Contact:* J.M. Aylwin). *Work includes:* All aspects of United Kingdom and EC environmental law are covered including those relating to compliance, clean-up, environmental protection and issues associated with insurance, share, land and other asset transactions, construction and development, lending and insolvency. Environmental audits can be undertaken.

Finance and Banking: (*Contact:* A.R.M. Morgan). *Work includes:* advising banks and other financial institutions on all aspects of law concerning their businesses, both in their own organisations and in their dealing with others. Transactional work undertaken covers financing, particularly aircraft, ship, film and project.

Hospitals and Health: (*Contact:* C. Arnold). *Work includes:* advisory services and litigation services to hospitals, NHS Trusts, health authorities and other sectors of the health service industry – corporate advice, statutory policies and duties, property transactions, insurance, medical negligence and employment.

Insolvency: (*Contact:* I.M. Fletcher). *Work includes:* all matters infringing upon insolvency law and practice in England, Scotland and internationally; wrongful trading and the position of directors generally.

Insurance and Reinsurance: (*Contact:* M.F. Connoley). The firm advises Trade Associations, Insurers and Reinsurers, Brokers, Lloyd's Syndicate, P & I Clubs and Underwriting Agents on all insurance-related matters.

Intellectual Property and Information Technology: (*Contact:* D. Marchese). Contentious and non-contentious work in relation to protection and exploitation of patents, copyright, trademarks, designs, confidential information and similar rights; computer law, telecommunications, satellites, regulatory work, and broadcasting.

International Trade and Commodities: (*Contact:* D.M. Pullen). All aspects of international sale of goods are dealt with, including documentary credits and customs problems.

Local Government: (*Contact:* J.S. Austin). The firm advises on all aspects of law which are relevant to local authorities, including planning, litigation, property, finance, commercial, employment, pensions, and environmental and public health.

Media and Entertainment: (*Contact:* S. Edwards). *Work includes:* all legal, financial, copyright and contractual aspects of the media industry. The firm also acts for well known personalities engaged in the industry.

Pensions and Unit Trusts: (*Contact:* K. Wallace). The firm offers a comprehensive range of services relating to the pensions and life assurance industries, unit trusts, mutual funds and investor trusts.

WORKLOAD	
Shipping	30%
Commercial litigation	25%
Corporate and commercial	25%
Commercial property	20%

CONTACTS	
Banking and finance	Ian Fletcher
Commercial and EU	Stephen Sayer
Corporate	Frank Donagh
Employment	Tim Archer
Energy	Stephen Sayer
Insurance	Margaret Campbell
International trade	David Pullen
IT and telecommunications	Ken Ollerton
Litigation	Michael Skrein
Media	Stephen Edwards
Pensions	Keith Wallace
Property	Richard Nicoll
Shipping	Lindsay East

Property: (*Contact:* R.C. Nicoll). This department handles transactions and problems involving freehold and leasehold property, especially those of a commercial nature, including Town and Country Planning, construction and civil engineering, development and institutional investment and funding, and domestic conveyancing.

Regulation and Compliance: (*Contact:* A.R.M. Morgan). A comprehensive service in the banking, securities and investment industries, on all aspects of regulation and compliance is provided.

Shipping: (*Contact:* L.T. East). All aspects of the shipping and marine insurance industries, particularly the conduct of court and arbitration proceedings and the preparation of marine documents, are dealt with. *Work includes:* marine litigation, especially charterparty and bills of lading disputes; protection and indemnity and defence clubs; marine insurance and reinsurance claims.

Tax: (*Contact:* L.J. Powell). *Work includes:* tax advice to commercial clients, frequently in connection with transactions handled by other departments, share option schemes, ESOPs and corporate tax.

OTHER OFFICES: Abu Dhabi, Hong Kong, Paris and Brussels.

FOREIGN CONNECTIONS: Richards Butler's reputation is to a large extent based on the firm's international capabilities. Much of the work undertaken in the London office has some foreign element, and the lawyers there – especially those in aviation and shipping – regularly travel the world on client business. The firm has an extensive network of contacts among lawyers in the world's main commercial centres.

RECRUITMENT AND TRAINING: Richards Butler provides practical experience across as wide a spectrum of the law as possible. Articles are divided into four periods of five months and one period of four months, each normally in a different section of the firm. While some of the time is spent in the areas of the practice covering general corporate, litigation and commercial property work, there are opportunities to work in other additional specialised areas such as shipping, media law, or international trade. Trainee solicitors regularly attend courses, seminars and in-house lectures. About 35 trainee solicitors are recruited annually, most of whom remain with the firm after qualifying. A 2:1 degree is preferred, and applicants should send a CV and written letter to Director of Personnel, Hilton Wallace.

P.L. RICHBELL 3 Mill Lane, Broomfield, Chelmsford, Essex, CM1 5BQ **Tel:** (01245) 440500 **Fax:** (01245) 440500 **Ptnrs:** 1. Niche personal injury practice acting for accident victims.

WORKLOAD	
Personal injury lit	100%

RICHMONDS 35 Potter Street, Worksop, Notts, S80 2AG **Tel:** (01909) 474321 **Fax:** (01909) 483852 **DX:** 12202 **Ptnrs:** 9 **Asst Solrs:** 11 **Other Fee-earners:** 10. Regional practice with five offices handling a wide range of work with specialist departments in personal injury, probate, trust, tax and company/ commercial.

RICKERBY JESSOP Ellenborough House, Wellington Street, Cheltenham, Glos, GL50 1YD **Tel:** (01242) 222022 **Fax:** (01242) 518428 **DX:** 7415 Cheltenham **Ptnrs:** 15 **Asst Solrs:** 5 **Other Fee-earners:** 12. One of the largest company/ commercial and private client practices in Cheltenham and Gloucester.

INTERNATIONAL SECTION

The international section lists foreign law firms based in London. It also lists the foreign connections of English law firms: their branch offices overseas and the foreign languages spoken at their UK offices.

RIGBEYS

42-44 WATERLOO STREET, BIRMINGHAM, W. MIDLANDS, B2 5QN
DX: 13030

TEL: (0121) 200 3343
FAX: (0121) 200 3360

THE FIRM: The practice occupies a prestigious office in the centre of Birmingham, being a combination of refurbished late 19th century buildings with a modern office block adjoining. It has acknowledged expertise in corporate finance (particularly of merger and acquisition work in relation to small and medium-sized businesses), property development, and housing association work, combined with a substantial spread of commercial and private clients including several quoted public companies, institutional clients and multiple retailers. The firm also specialises in insolvency and commercial litigation. It has a policy of continual partner-led contact with clients to ensure a close bonded professional relationship.

PRINCIPAL AREAS OF WORK:

Corporate Finance: (*Contact:* D.M. Billings). *Work includes:* mergers and acquisitions; flotations, restructures and joint ventures, particularly small to medium-sized businesses (net profits up to £10m p.a.); banking and securities.

General Commercial: (*Contact:* D.M. Billings and P.T. Harris). *Work includes:* terms of trading, product liability, entertainment and sports law and licensing. The firm represents a number of nationally known sports persons.

Commercial Property: (*Contact:* C.J. Popple and S.D. Denslow). *Work includes:* residential and commercial conveyancing (particularly in retailing) allied to specialist services in planning, landlord and tenant, and joint ventures and general development.

Private Client: (*Contact:* C.J. Popple). *Work includes:* wills, trusts, probate and tax planning.

Insolvency: (*Contact:* P.T. Harris). *Work includes:* receiverships, liquidations, bankruptcy, insolvency arrangements and debt recovery.

Commercial Litigation: (*Contact:* A.N. Ballard). *Work includes:* commercial injunctions, contractual disputes, employment law, intellectual property, professional and medical negligence and personal injury, allied to a specialist debt collecting department.

Housing Associations: (*Contact:* S.D. Denslow). The firm specialises in housing associations (their formation, administration and development), shared ownerships, tenancies and public and private funding of housing schemes.

Legal Aid: Undertaken only in special circumstances.

NATURE OF CLIENTELE: Predominantly small to medium-sized businesses, (particularly 'entrepreneur' led) plus several public companies and institutional clients; multiple retailers, numerous housing associations (including the largest in the West Midlands); property developers and national builders, accountants. The private client department has a large number of clients of high net worth.

RECRUITMENT AND TRAINING: The firm adopts a positive policy towards articles, requiring candidates to be of high academic achievement.

CHARGES: Rigbeys adopts a competitive attitude towards charging, and has a reputation for forming close relationships with clients, giving keen estimates and being prepared to negotiate a variety of different fee structures.

CONTACT PARTNER: D.M. Billings

Number of partners:	5
Assistant solicitors:	10
Other fee-earners:	10

WORKLOAD	
Housing association	30%
Commercial property	25%
Corporate/ commercial	20%
Insolvency	15%
Litigation	10%

ROBERT GORE AND COMPANY 17 Grosvenor Street, London, W1X 9FD **Tel:** (0171) 491 2020 **Fax:** (0171) 499 6123 **DX:** 44624 Mayfair **Ptnrs:** 4 **Other Fee-earners:** 2. Founded in 1972, a general commercial practice, geared to corporate and commercial work, acquisitions, mergers and finance, all aspects of commercial property, and related litigation and taxation.

WORKLOAD			
Corporate/commercial	38%	Property	33%
Litigation	23%	Res/wills/trusts/prob	5%

ROBERT LIZAR 159 Princess Road, Moss Side, Manchester, M14 4RE **Tel:** (0161) 226 2319 **Fax:** (0161) 226 7985 **Ptnrs:** 3 **Other Fee-earners:** 1. Specialist niche practice undertaking criminal, civil liberties and mental health work.

ROBERT MUCKLE

NORHAM HOUSE, 12 NEW BRIDGE STREET WEST, NEWCASTLE-UPON-TYNE,
TYNE & WEAR, NE1 8AS   DX: 61011

TEL: (0191) 232 4402
FAX: (0191) 261 6954

THE FIRM: Robert Muckle primarily works with corporate clients based in the northern region who are competing in both local and worldwide markets. The firm has grown rapidly and is well known for all areas of its corporate legal work including mergers, acquisitions, disposals and management buy-outs, intellectual property, employment, property development, construction and planning, banking law, loan finance, insolvency and commercial litigation. It places great store on understanding the long term objectives of its clients' companies; on providing workable solutions to their problems and on giving a responsive service to fast-moving businesses.

RECRUITMENT AND TRAINING: There is a constant need to recruit talented, qualified staff in all the commercial departments. Applicants should have ambition, commercial awareness, good communication skills both with clients and colleagues and an ability to work as part of a team. Excellent career prospects for the right people. Vacancies: approximately 4 per year. Apply to Ian Gilthorpe, Managing Partner.

CONTACT PARTNER: Ian Gilthorpe

Number of partners:	11
Assistant solicitors:	20
Other fee-earners:	14

WORKLOAD	
Commercial	43%
Litigation	29%
Property	28%

CONTACTS	
Commercial	Hugh Welch
Litigation	Bob Elliott
Property	Jonathan Combe

ROBERTSONS 6 Park Place, Cardiff, S. Glam, CF1 3DP **Tel:** (01222) 237777 **Fax:** (01222) 390996 **DX:** 33039 Cardiff **Ptnrs:** 13 **Asst Solrs:** 3 **Other Fee-earners:** 8. Handles company/ commercial, litigation, property and private client matters. legal aid undertaken. Offices in Caerphilly, Barry and Bridgend.

WORKLOAD			
Legal aid (matrim/crime)	25%	Personal injury	25%
Private client	15%	Commercial property	15%
Company and commercial	10%	Res site development	10%

ROBERTS & RICHARDS

7 BIRCHIN LANE, LOMBARD STREET, LONDON, EC3V 9BY

TEL: (0171) 929 1900
FAX: (0171) 929 4800

THE FIRM: An innovative niche City practice specialising in company, commercial and tax work, Roberts & Richards have considerable expertise in representing modern business practice and techniques. The firm provides clear and incisive advice coupled with a high standard of service, personal attention and a determined approach to achieving each client's specific needs.

PRINCIPAL AREAS OF WORK:

Corporate Finance: Mergers and acquisitions, development capital, management purchases, equity and debt issues and loans.

Company: Share incentives, flotations, ventures and corporate tax.

Commercial: Intangible property, competition law, reorganisations and partnerships.

Business Services: Commercial litigation, dispute resolution, contracts, leases and debt recovery.

City Market Services: Corporate research and analysis, business information.

Personnel: Employment law, employee benefits and incentives, personal and trust taxation, mortgages.

Trust & Corporate Services: International structures, nominee and trustee services, settlements and estate planning.

Financial Services: Members of the Association of Solicitor Investment Managers.

CONTACT PARTNER: Robert Justice

Number of partners:	3
Assistant solicitors:	2
Other fee-earners:	2

CONTACTS	
Commercial	P.J.J. Skeen
Company	R.M. Justice
Financial Services	E.J.B.C. Hendin
Litigation	C.G. Smith
Property	J.F. Bechelet
Trusts and tax	R.M. Justice

ROBINSONS Market Place, Ilkeston, Derbys, DE7 4RQ **Tel:** (0115) 9324101 **Fax:** (0115) 9300042 **DX:** 11544 Derby 1 **Ptnrs:** 12 **Asst Solrs:** 6 **Other Fee-earners:** 12. Robinsons is a substantial East Midlands firm offering a wide range of legal expertise and a sound problem-solving approach.

WORKLOAD			
Private client	31%	Corporate/ commercial	25%
Property	23%	Litigation	21%

ROBIN THOMPSON & PARTNERS Congress House, Great Russell Street, London, WC1B 3LW **Tel:** (0171) 637 9761 **Fax:** (0171) 631 5249 **Ptnrs:** 36 **Asst Solrs:** 39 **Other Fee-earners:** 53. Specialised practice experienced in all aspects of industrial and employment law including equal rights.

ROBIN MORTON SOLICITORS 27 Sandyford Place, Glasgow, G3 7NG **Tel:** (0141) 248 7676 **Fax:** (0141) 226 4722 **DX:** 512231 **Ptnrs:** 1. The firm is well-known for its personal injury work and industrial relations expertise.

WORKLOAD	
Liquor licensing	100%

ROBSON McLEAN WS 28 Abercromby Place, Edinburgh, EH3 6QF **Tel:** (0131) 556 0556 **Fax:** (0131) 556 9939 **DX:** 162 Edinburgh **Ptnrs:** 8 **Asst Solrs:** 9 **Other Fee-earners:** 7. The firm can trace its origins back to the early 19th century and has established expertise in the fields of litigation and private client work.

RODGERS & BURTON

15-17 CHURCH RD, BARNES, LONDON, SW13 9HG
DX: 59702 Barnes

TEL: (0181) 878 4854
FAX: (0181) 876 9874

THE FIRM: The firm was founded in 1837, and originally practised around the City and West End. In the 1960s, its offices in Norfolk Street were demolished, and it moved its headquarters to Barnes, where it occupies spacious accommodation overlooking Barnes Common and Barnes Pond.

PRINCIPAL AREAS OF WORK: Whilst being a general High Street practice, Rodgers & Burton offers certain specialist advice in servicing landlords and Housing Associations. In particular, they offer experience in landlord and tenant litigation, housing association law and finance, disposals and acquisitions of property, lease back financing of acquisitions, shared ownership schemes, planning appeals, construction contracts and disputes.

OTHER AREAS OF WORK: Rodgers and Burton also has fee earners with experience in employment law, and a busy matrimonial department. The firm offers an Agency Service in Wandsworth, West London and Brentford County Court.

CONTACT PARTNER: Andrew Raby

Number of partners:	4
Assistant solicitors:	2
Other fee-earners:	4

WORKLOAD	
Matrimonial	43%
Civil Litigation	41%
Private & Commercial Conveyancing	16%

RODGERS HORSLEY WHITEMANS Castle House, Castle Street, Guildford, Surrey, GU1 3UL **Tel:** (01483) 302000 **Fax:** (01483) 301242 **DX:** 2445 Guildford 1 **Ptnrs:** 3 **Asst Solrs:** 3 **Other Fee-earners:** 1. Best known for company/ commercial work and commercial litigation. Also handles residential and commercial conveyancing and private client work. Expertise in medical/ dental and ecclesiastical law.

RODGERS & HOWE 26-30 Bank Street, Sheffield, S. Yorks, S1 1EA **Tel:** (0114) 272 7242 **Fax:** (0114) 275 5083 **DX:** 10574 Sheffield 1 **Ptnrs:** 7 **Asst Solrs:** 5 **Other Fee-earners:** 3. A general commercial and family practice founded 1800. Expanding in civil litigation and criminal. Office of Diocesan Registrar.

ROGERS & WELLS

CITY TOWER, 20TH FLOOR, 40 BASINGHALL STREET, LONDON, EC2V 5DE

TEL: (0171) 628 0101
FAX: (0171) 638 2008

THE FIRM: For more than a century, Rogers & Wells has been providing clients with creative and effective representation in domestic and international transactions and major litigations. Rogers & Wells serves the world's leading financial institutions, industrial companies and businesses in virtually every sector of the economy as well as individuals and government entities. The firm's international work, comprising nearly half of the practice, spans the globe.

THE LONDON OFFICE: In addition to matters referred from the national offices, the London office concentrates primarily on the areas of:

Finance: *Work involves:* advising foreign clients in raising capital in the US market and US companies in raising capital overseas; participating in global transactions as issuers' and underwriter's counsel; representing major international financial institutions and corporate and government issuers; international fund transactions both US registered and offshore.

CONTACT PARTNER: Mr Daniel Bushner

LAWYERS:	
London:	12
Worldwide:	500

WORKLOAD	
Securities/ corporate	65%
Banking	20%
Funds	15%

Acquisitions: Work covers the full range of legal advice required by foreign clients making acquisitions in the US and abroad and US clients making acquisitions abroad. Service includes counselling on tax, antitrust, ERISA, real estate and environmental and government regulation issues.

Tax: *Work includes:* domestic and international tax considerations for sophisticated mergers and acquisitions, business and investment partnership structuring, securities offerings and other financings and real estate investments; transfer pricing issues for foreign and US clients; taxation of investment partnerships; development of new financial products in the tax-exempt and taxable markets; municipal financings; tax controversy practice.

Intellectual Property: The full range of legal services involving patents, copyrights and trademarks, extending to both corporate transactions for the acquisition of technology and litigation for defence or protection of intellectual property.

International Trade: *Work includes:* representing foreign and US manufacturers, importers and exporters in all phases of antidumping and countervailing duty investigations, other trade investigations and litigation, customs matters, international transactions and government relations.

OTHER OFFICES: New York, Washington DC, Los Angeles, Paris, Frankfurt, Hong Kong.

ROITER ZUCKER 5 Broadhurst Gardens, London, NW6 3QX **Tel:** (0171) 328 9111 **Fax:** (0171) 372 5858 **DX:** 38850 **Ptnrs:** 6 **Asst Solrs:** 2 **Other Fee-earners:** 3. Widely experienced in intellectual property, commercial litigation, company/commercial, international trade and finance, property, pharmaceuticals and the media.

WORKLOAD			
Commercial law	45%	Litigation	15%
Property	15%	Company	10%
Probate	5%	Employment	5%

ROLLIT FARRELL & BLADON

WILBERFORCE COURT, HIGH STREET, HULL, HUMBS, HU1 1YJ
DX: 11901 Hull 1

TEL: (01482) 323239
FAX: (01482) 326239

THE FIRM: One of the top firms in the region, Rollit Farrell & Bladon has a broadly based practice providing a comprehensive legal service to commercial and private clients alike.

PRINCIPAL AREAS OF WORK:

Company/ Commercial: *(Contact Partner:* James Brennand). Areas of expertise include company formations, share issues, fund raising, joint ventures, company acquisitions, disposals and flotations, MBOs, finance and credit agreements, equipment leasing and financing agreements, intellectual property, franchising, competition law, restrictive practices and EU law. The Insolvency Unit *(Contact Partner:* Richard Field) deals with all aspects of corporate reconstruction and individual insolvency.

Commercial Property: *(Contact Partner:* Gillian Mann). The firm offers a comprehensive service, its Planning & Environmental Law Unit *(Contact Partner:* John Downing) co-ordinating the planning process at all stages to ensure a complete development brief. Clients range from house builders and developers, landlords and tenants to PLCs with large property portfolios, and also small businesses which may be acquiring their first property. Housing Associations are advised by the firm's own team of specialists.

Litigation: *(Contact Partner:* Michael Scanlan). The firm handles all types of commercial litigation, including intellectual property disputes, licensing, building contract disputes, debt recovery and professional indemnity but is also committed to Alternative Dispute Resolution. The Employment Unit *(Contact Partner:* Pauline Molyneux) is highly experienced in both contentious and non-contentious work. The Insurance Litigation Unit *(Contact Partner:* Peter Maharry) has recognised expertise in defendant work for major insurance companies.

Private Client: *(Contact Partner:* David Bowes). A full service is provided, ranging from tax planning, wills, estate administration, powers of attorney and Court of Protection work, to residential conveyancing, and advice on matrimonial and domestic disputes, consumer law and work-related problems. The firm is able to offer expert advice to charities *(Contact Partner:* John Lane).

MANAGING PARTNER: Mr Peter Bowes
SENIOR PARTNER: Mr Michael Scanlan

Number of partners:	31
Assistant solicitors:	14
Other fee-earners:	25

WORKLOAD	
Company and Commercial	28%
Commercial litigation and employment	23%
Property	22%
Private Client	13%
Insurance Litigation	10%
Insolvency	4%

CONTACTS	
Commercial Litigation	Michael Scanlan
Company and Commercial	James Brennand
Employment	Pauline Molyneux
Insolvency	Richard Field
Insurance Litigation	Peter Maharry
Planning & Environmental	John Downing
Private Client	David Bowes
Property	Gillian Mann

NATURE OF CLIENTELE: Clients include major PLCs, housebuilding companies, property development groups, food manufacturers and retailers, motor groups, medium and small enterprises, professional partnerships, housing associations, agricultural estates, charities and private individuals.

OTHER OFFICES:
Rowntree Wharf, Navigation Road, York YO1 2XA.
Tel: (01904) 625790. *Fax:* (01904) 625807. *DX:* 61534.
26 & 28 Lairgate, Beverley HU17 8ER.
Tel: (01482) 882278. *Fax:* (01482) 871901. *DX:* 28307.
4 Bondgate, Helmsley YO6 5BS.
Tel: (01439) 770207. *Fax:* (01439) 771650.
38 Newbegin, Hornsea HU18 1AD.
Tel: (01964) 532063. *Fax:* (01964) 533205.

ROOKS RIDER

CHALLONER HOUSE, 19 CLERKENWELL CLOSE, LONDON, EC1R 0RR
DX: 53324 Clerkenwell

TEL: (0171) 490 0774
FAX: (0171) 490 1281

THE FIRM: A former Lincoln's Inn firm now in new offices; founded as a result of a merger between two well-respected, long-established firms, Rooks Rider offers a high quality comprehensive and personal service to business and individual clients in the fields of company/ commercial law, partnerships, joint ventures, commercial and residential property and planning, civil litigation (including employment, construction and professional negligence), probate, matrimonial, and charity law. It has an increasing international practice. The firm prides itself in offering creative advice with a practical approach to achieving the client's ambitions.

PRINCIPAL AREAS OF WORK: Special emphasis is placed on corporate transactions, corporate funding, corporate disagreements, corporate and personal taxation, offshore and onshore trusts, intellectual property matters (patent, copyright and computer-related law) and agricultural tenancies.

RECRUITMENT AND TRAINING: The firm values trainee solicitors as its solicitors of the future, and offers them a thoroughly friendly approach with a comprehensive training. Applications should be made to the Personnel Manager, Ros Ehren.

CONTACT PARTNER: Clare Foinette	
Number of partners:	10
Assistant solicitors:	13
Other fee-earners:	8

ROOTES & ALLIOTT 27 Cheriton Gardens, Folkestone, Kent, CT20 2AR **Tel:** (01303) 851100 **Fax:** (01303) 8511150 **DX:** 4903 **Ptnrs:** 7 **Other Fee-earners:** 6. A large Kent firm with strong conveyancing, probate, litigation, criminal and matrimonial departments. Developing French department. Legal aid and agency work undertaken.

ROSENBLATT

9-13 ST ANDREW STREET, LONDON, EC4A 3AE
DX: 493 London Chancery Lane

TEL: (0171) 955 0880
FAX: (0171) 955 0888

THE FIRM: Formed in 1989. The firm has significant experience of advising all types of business enterprises in various market sectors at different stages of their development, from start-up businesses to mature organisations.

THE PARTNERS:
- Ian Rosenblatt is a litigator/ company lawyer who specialises in contentious company/ commercial work.
- Craig Young specialises in commercial and energy work.
- Neil Sampson is a litigator with significant Far Eastern connections.
- Hilary Pennington-Nellor - a litigator who also specialises in family work.

CONTACT PARTNER: Ian Rosenblatt	
Number of partners:	5
Assistant solicitors:	4
Other fee-earners:	7

CONSULTANT: Peter Kay is a commercial property specialist. Arnold Segal specialises in computer and technology law.

INTERNATIONAL CONNECTIONS & ASSOCIATED OFFICES: Most EEC countries, USA and Hong Kong.

FOREIGN LANGUAGES: French.

ROSLING KING

2-3 HIND COURT, FLEET ST, LONDON, EC4A 3DL
DX: 154

TEL: (0171) 353 2353
FAX: (0171) 583 2035

THE FIRM: Rosling King is a well-established commercial firm, which successfully competes with the larger City practices whilst offering close contact with its clients. It is noted for its expertise in the following principal areas.

PRINCIPAL AREAS OF WORK:

Property: (*Contact:* Malcolm Macfarlane/ Owen Rafferty). *Work includes:*acquisitions and disposals, commercial developments, leases, property management, VAT advice, planning; for institutions, banks, insurance companies, property development and investment companies both quoted and un-quoted.

Commercial Loans: (*Contact:* Owen Rafferty). *Work includes:* funding agreements, loan documentation, mortgages and charges, letters of credit; for banks, building societies and funding institutions.

Company and Commercial: (*Contact:* Graham Clark). *Work includes:* acquisitions and disposals, mergers, MBO's, partnerships, insolvency, employment law, intellectual property, EC and UK competition law; for institutions, public companies and smaller businesses in the UK and abroad.

Commercial Litigation: (*Contact:* Georgina Squire/ Richard Anstey). *Work includes:* general litigation, loss recovery, landlord and tenant matters, repossessions, insolvency, professional negligence, building construction disputes and arbitrations; for institutions, insurance companies, banks, building societies, public companies and smaller businesses.

Insurance: (*Contact:* Georgina Squire/ Annabel Crumley). *Work includes:* insurance and reinsurance litigation and general claims work and contract advice, including professional liability, property and construction, casualty and related matters.

Construction and Environmental Law: (*Contact:* Helen Bright/ Georgina Squire). *Work includes:* all aspects of building contract documentation, professional appointments, warranties, bonds etc. and advice thereon; advice on environmental assessment, liability, and compliance; for institutions, property companies, builders and professionals, landowners and developers.

RECRUITMENT AND TRAINING: The firm currently recruits approximately three trainee solicitors each year. Good academic background essential combined with good communication skills and a great deal of common sense and team spirit. Trainee solicitors are given high degree of involvement and responsibility and prospects after completion of articles are good. Training is part in-house and through external conferences. Candidates should apply with CV to Andrew Hardman.

FOREIGN CONNECTIONS: Practice has associated offices in Düsseldorf and Mönchengladbach, and strong connections with overseas lawyers and accountants and a range of overseas clients.

CONTACT PARTNER: Owen Rafferty
Malcolm Macfarlane

Number of partners:	9
Assistant solicitors:	20
Other fee-earners:	14

WORKLOAD	
Commercial litigation	30%
Commercial property	25%
Insurance/ reinsurance	15%
Construction/ environmental	10%
Commercial loans	10%
Company/ commercial	10%

CONTACTS	
Commercial litigation	G. Squire, A. Crumley
Commercial property	O. Rafferty, M. Macfarlane
Commercial loans	Owen Rafferty
Company Commercial	Graham Clark
Construction/ environmental	Georgina Squire
Insurance/ reinsurance	G. Squire, M.Green

ROSS & CONNEL 10 Viewfield Terrace, Dunfermline, Fife, KY12 7JH **Tel:** (01383) 721156 **Fax:** (01383) 721150 **Ptnrs: 6 Asst Solrs: 1 Other Fee-earners: 1.** An established general practice, offering specialist advice on all aspects of child law.

WORKLOAD			
Litigation	40%	Conveyancing	40%
Commercial/leasing work	20%		

ROSS & CRAIG

SWIFT HOUSE, 12A UPPER BERKELEY STREET, LONDON, W1H 7PE
DX: 44416 Marble Arch

TEL: (0171) 262 3077
FAX: (0171) 724 6427

CONTACT PARTNER: Daniel Polden	
Number of partners:	6
Assistant solicitors:	2
Other fee-earners:	7

PRINCIPAL AREAS OF WORK:

Property: Advising on complex joint ventures, development funding, documentation, planning and taxation. From single purchases and disposals to development funding, portfolio acquisitions, sales and break ups.

Company/ Commercial: Includes the full range of corporate and commercial transactions. Some of the more specialist areas include intellectual property, computer contracts, media and entertainment.

Litigation: Commercial disputes, landlord and tenant litigation and property disputes, employment law, intellectual property, complex personal injury work, professional negligence, insolvency and liquidations. Also well known for its considerable matrimonial expertise.

Environmental Law: The specialist Land Regeneration Unit enjoys high level connections with relevant professionals and government departments. It provides services in a consultancy capacity and as a principal adivser on legal matters in itsfield.

NATURE OF CLIENTELE: Clients range from internationally known companies to small businesses and individuals.

FOREIGN CONNECTIONS: The firm has close links with lawyers in many foreign countries.

ROSS HARPER & MURPHY WS 163 Ingram Street, Glasgow, G1 1DW **Tel:** (0141) 552 6343 **Fax: DX:** 190 Glasgow **Ptnrs:** 14 **Asst Solrs:** 29 **Other Fee-earners:** 26. One of the largest criminal and civil litigation practices in Scotland, specialising in divorce, employment law and personal injury.

WORKLOAD			
Criminal	40%	Civil	35%
Conveyancing	20%	Welfare Rights	5%

ROTHERAS

2 KAYES WALK, STONEY STREET, THE LACE MARKET, NOTTINGHAM, NOTTS, NG1 1PZ   DX: 10028 Nottingham

TEL: (0115) 941 4415
FAX: (0115) 941 0105

CONTACT PARTNER: Mr C.C. Hodson	
Number of partners:	11
Assistant solicitors:	1
Other fee-earners:	11

THE FIRM: Established in 1857, Rotheras has built its reputation upon a quality service to clients and is known particularly for its commercial and litigation work. The firm is organised into specialist departments, each headed by partners who have considerable experience in their particular field. It acts for institutions, trade associations, companies, small businesses and has a thriving private client department.

PRINCIPAL AREAS OF WORK:

Corporate and Commercial: Work includes: company formations, share issues, acquisitions, commercial agreements, employment contracts, intellectual property, commercial property including landlord and tenant, compulsory purchase, leases, town and country planning and environmental law.

Litigation: Civil litigation of all kinds including a significant personal injury department for both plaintiff and defendant clients, including medical negligence with P.I. Panel members; contentious intellectual property matters, employment disputes, contractual disputes including construction. One of the firm's partners is the Deputy Coroner for Nottinghamshire.

This department also includes a specialised Transport section advising clients in connection with operator licensing, traffic prosecutions, insurance related work, carriage of goods and all aspects of road transport.

Private Client Department: Handles all aspects of personal taxation, trusts, wills, probate and administration as well as family and matrimonial law. One of its partners is a member of the Child Care Panel. Criminal cases are also undertaken, including legal aid work.

WORKLOAD	
General litigation (inc PI/ transport/ debt recovery)	50%
Probate, trusts and tax	14%
Family (inc. childcare/ crime)	12%
Company and commercial	9%
Conveyancing, planning & environmental	8%
Other (inc. ecclesiastical/ immigration/ education)	7%

CONTACTS	
Corporate and commercial	Mr C.C. Hodson
Ecclesias./Education	Mr C.C. Hodson
Employment	Mr. A.G. Priest
Family and matrimonial	Miss D.J. Murray
Immigration and nationality	Mr A.G. Priest

OTHER AREAS OF WORK: The firm also offers advice in ecclesiastical matters. One of its partners is the Diocesan Registrar for the Diocese of Southwell. It is also able to advise educational institutions on all aspects of contentious and non-contentious education law.

Litigation/Transport	Mr P.I. Rothera
Personal injury	Mrs J.E. George
Planning and Environment	Mr. S. Smith
Wills, trusts, probate, tax	Mr J.D. Allen

ROUSE & CO

THE ISIS BUILDING, THAMES QUAY, 193 MARSH WALL, DOCKLANDS, LONDON, E14 9SG   DX: 42677 Isle of Dogs

TEL: (0171) 345 8888
FAX: (0171) 512 0880

THE FIRM: Rouse & Co was established in mid-1990 and specialises in the protection and enforcement of intellectual and industrial property rights in the UK and throughout the world.

PRINCIPAL AREAS OF WORK:

Protection & Enforcement: Advice and representation in UK litigation involving patents, trade marks, copyrights, unregistered and registered design rights, passing off and breach of confidence. Design and implementation of regional and/or global enforcement and anti-counterfeiting programmes; Assistance in tackling specific problems in all jurisdictions.

INTERNATIONAL SERVICE: The firm has well established relationships with foreign lawyers and agents in most countries and special expertise in teh Asia–Pacific region and central and eastern Europe. Languages spoken include German, French, Spanish and Mandarin.

NATURE OF CLIENTELE: Most of the firm's clients are multi-national companies.

FEES: Fixed fee rate of £145 per hour (excluding VAT and disbursements) regardless of seniority. Initial consultations are offered free of charge. No charge is made for travel time to and from overseas projects. No marking up of bills for urgency, complexity etc.

CONTACT PARTNER: Mr Peter Rouse

Number of partners:	4
Assistant solicitors:	5
Other fee-earners:	3

WORKLOAD

Intellectual property protection and enforcement	100%

CONTACTS

Intellectual property	Peter Rouse
	Tony Willoughby

ROWE & MAW

20 BLACK FRIARS LANE, LONDON, EC4V 6HD
DX: 93

TEL: (0171) 248 4282
FAX: (0171) 248 2009

THE FIRM: Rowe & Maw is one of the UK's leading law firms, with offices in London, including one at Lloyd's, and in Brussels.

Founded 100 years ago, Rowe & Maw has grown to become one of the top commercial law firms in London. With 60 partners and a legal staff of 180, the Firm is large enough to provide the broad range of services required by our clients, yet is still able to provide an individual, personalised service, led by our partners.

PRINCIPAL AREAS OF WORK: Our main strength has always been in advising companies and businesses across their range of activities, both in their day-to-day business and on special projects. Our client list includes top UK and international companies. However, we are equally familiar with acting for small and medium sized businesses, be they owner-managed or listed entities.

In addition to our mainstream corporate practice which has traditionally focused upon the acquisition and disposal of corporate businesses and divisions, both domestically and internationally, the Firm has a number of other strengths. We are widely acknowledged as one of the top firms in the fields of construction, property, litigation, pensions, insurance, employment, intellectual property, environment and aviation.

A QUALITY SERVICE: Rowe & Maw is committed to providing a top quality service, based upon an understanding of businesses and their commercial requirements.

RECRUITMENT: The firm seeks approximately 20 high-calibre graduates to train with it for articles each year.

CONTACT PARTNER: Richard Powles

UK:	
Number of partners:	62
Assistant solicitors:	86
Other fee-earners:	52
INTERNATIONAL:	
Number of Partners:	1
Assistant Solicitors:	2

WORKLOAD

Corporate	46%
Litigation	28%
Property	17%
Intellectual property	6%
Private client	3%

ROWLANDS

35 FOUNTAIN ST, MANCHESTER, M2 2AF
DX: 14371 Manchester 1

TEL: (0161) 228 1561
FAX: (0161) 228 0984

THE FIRM: One of the largest firms in Manchester, Rowlands traces its roots back to 1885. A general practice, the firm has a network of branch offices throughout Greater Manchester.

PRINCIPAL AREAS OF WORK:

Company/ Commercial & Commercial Property: *(Contact Partner:* Philip A. Bellamy). *Work includes:* advice on formation, acquisition, employment matters and all aspects of commercial property work. Liquor and gaming licences.

Family & Matrimonial: *(Contact Partner:* Sidney Oxley). *Work includes:* specialist advice concerning custody and access, child care, maintenance injunctions and property settlements, affiliation orders and disputes between cohabitees.

Litigation: *(Contact Partner:* Malcolm Horner). *Work includes:* personal injury claims arising from accidents whether at work, on the road or caused by medical or professional negligence; also landlord and tenant disputes, criminal cases and motoring offences, debt recovery and insolvency problems. Legal aid work is undertaken.

Private Client: *(Contact Partner:* Samuel Mocton). *Work includes:* domestic conveyancing, wills, probate, trusts, administration of estates and taxation advice.

OTHER OFFICES: Stockport, Droylsden, Sale, New Moston and Urmston.

CONTACT PARTNER: Ronald Taylor

Number of partners:	16
Assistant solicitors:	24
Other fee-earners:	22

CONTACTS	
Commercial property	Philip A. Bellamy
Company and commercial	Philip A. Bellamy
Family and matrimonial	Sidney Oxley
Litigation	Malcolm Horner
Private client	Samuel Mocton

ROWLEY ASHWORTH

247 THE BROADWAY, WIMBLEDON, LONDON, SW19 1SE
DX: 300003 Wimbledon South

TEL: (0181) 543 2277
FAX: (0181) 543 0143

THE FIRM: Established in 1829, Rowley Ashworth is a specialised partnership known for its particular expertise in the field of employment law and personal injury compensation claims on behalf of trade unions and their members.

PRINCIPAL AREAS OF WORK: The work handled covers claims for personal injury, industrial accidents, traffic accidents and industrial disease. The firm is also experienced in residential and commercial conveyancing, wills and probate.

OTHER OFFICES: Birmingham, Exeter, Wolverhampton and Leeds.

MEMBERSHIPS: London Litigation Solicitors Association; Industrial Law Society. Many fee earners are members of APIL and Law Society P.I. panel.

CONTACT PARTNER: Michael Short

Number of partners:	14
Assistant solicitors:	20
Other fee-earners:	18

CONTACTS	
Conveyancing	Andrew Struthers
Employment & labour law	Michael Short
Personal injury	Roger Goodier
Wills, probate	Andrew Struthers

EDITORIAL POLICY

In this edition, the lists of specialists include profiles of individual practitioners - solicitors and barristers - who have been recommended most frequently to our researchers. Editorial policy is to identify leading practitioners on merit: it is not possible to buy a place in our biographical lists. Inclusion of a profile in this directory is based solely on expertise and reputation.

Enormous effort has been invested by our ten-strong research team (mainly solicitors and barristers) in canvassing recommendations and identifying leaders. We are confident in the overall accuracy of the results. However, mistakes and misjudgements are inevitable, and if readers have any suggestions regarding our listings we should be very pleased to hear from them.

ROWLEY DICKINSON

154 GREAT CHARLES STREET, BIRMINGHAM, W. MIDLANDS, B3 3HN DX: 13018 Birmingham 3	TEL: (0121) 233 2298 FAX: (0121) 236 9155
Halifax House 93-101 Bridge Street, Manchester M3 2GX DX: 14332 M1 Contact Partner: John Coyle	Tel: (0161) 834 4215 Fax: (0161) 834 5153
Waterloo House, 9A Huntingdon Court, Ashby-de-la-Zouch, Leicester LE6 3DU DX: 22660 Ashby-de-la-Zouch	Tel: (01530) 417300 Fax: (01530) 417318

THE FIRM: Rowley Dickinson was formed in 1990 on the merger of two long established firms, Rowley & Blewitts of Manchester and Dickinson Simpson of Birmingham. The firm offers a wide range of legal services to business and private clients and maintains a personal approach.

PRINCIPAL AREAS OF WORK:

Litigation: *(Contact Partner:* Michael Parr). The department deals with all areas of civil law, insurance work, personal injury claims, building disputes, contractual disputes, medical negligence and professional negligence.

Company/ Commercial & Conveyancing: *(Contact Partner:* John Coyle). *Work includes:* tax planning and trusts, company and business law (formations, amalgamations, sales and acquisitions etc.), commercial conveyancing and leasing, employment law and industrial tribunals, intellectual property, site development projects and financial services.

Family Law: *(Contact Partner:* Janet Fleming). Clients are advised on all aspects of divorce, annulment and judicial separation, custody and access, domestic problems between unmarried couples, maintenance, capital and property settlements, injunctions and domestic violence and child abduction.

Probate/ Trust: *(Contact Partner:* Nicholas Gee). Assistance is provided with probate, wills, trusts and settlements, tax considerations, administration of estates and litigation arising from claims for and against estates.

NATURE OF CLIENTELE: Clients include insurance companies and property developers.

CONTACT PARTNER: Kirk Simpson	
Number of partners:	16
Assistant solicitors:	10
Other fee-earners:	10

WORKLOAD	
Personal injury	80%
Commercial and employment	20%

CONTACTS	
Commercial property	John Coyle
Commercial litigation	Michael Parr
Commercial property	Fahmida Ismail
Employment	Michael Parr
Personal injury	Alan Fitzpatrick
	Kirk Simpson

ROYDS TREADWELL 2 Crane Court, Fleet Street, London, EC4A 2BL **Tel:** (0171) 583 2222 **Fax:** (0171) 583 2034 **DX:** 102 **Ptnrs:** 11 **Asst Solrs:** 7 **Other Fee-earners:** 4. Established 1958. A general practice known for commercial and residential conveyancing and litigation. Also handles probate and trust work.

ROYTHORNE & CO

10 PINCHBECK RD, SPALDING, LINCS, PE11 1PZ DX: 26701	TEL: (01775) 724141 FAX: (01775) 725736

THE FIRM: Roythorne & Co has been established in South Lincolnshire for more than 50 years. It has a work force in excess of 100, achieved through internal growth.

Its main office is in Spalding where there are currently 13 partners, and there are a further two partners in the branch at Boston and two at Nottingham.

As such, the firm has become one of the foremost practices in the East Midlands, and has also developed a wide network of contacts, both in the profession and in commerce, extending to the City of London and to the large provincial centres. The firm has now established contacts in the USA and Europe.

PRINCIPAL AREAS OF WORK:

General Description: Although based in a predominantly farming area with strong links in the agricultural community, the firm has a widespread industrial and professional clientele, both commercial and private, involving substantial corporate,

PARTNERSHIP SECRETARY: Mr A.D. McCrindle	
Number of partners:	17
Assistant solicitors:	10
Other fee-earners:	28

commercial property and commercial litigation work. Further main areas of work handled are insolvency and debt collection, uninsured loss recovery, environmental law, corporate and personal tax.

Overall, the firm perceives itself as progressive and forward-looking and foresees strong and continued growth in all areas, particularly in its civil and commercial practice.

RECRUITMENT: Trainee solicitors are recruited as an important part of securing high calibre qualified solicitors and the firm has a good retention record.

OTHER OFFICES:
27 Wide Bargate, Boston, Lincolnshire.
Sherwood Court, 8 The Ropewalk, Nottingham.

WORKLOAD	
Commercial litigation	43%
Commercial property	27%
Tax & Probate	15%
Other property	7%
Company	7%
Insolvency	1%

RUDLINGS & WAKELAM 1 Well Street, Thetford, Norfolk, IP24 2BL **Tel:** (01842) 754151 **Fax:** (01842) 766143 **DX:** 100903 Thetford **Ptnrs:** 5 **Asst Solrs:** 5 **Other Fee-earners:** 7. Well established firm handling company/ commercial, civil litigation, family/ matrimonial (in particular child law), debt collection, probate, conveyancing and agriculture.

RUPERT BEAR & CO

UNION CHAMBERS, 11 WEEKDAY CROSS, NOTTINGHAM, NOTTS, NG1 2GB
DX: 10015

TEL: (0115) 924 3333
FAX: (0115) 924 2255

THE FIRM: Rupert Bear & Co is a firm of solicitors specialising in matrimonial and family law. It was established by Rupert Bear who has been a matrimonial lawyer in Nottingham for 27 years. The firm comprises the former staff and family law practice of Evershed Wells & Hind. Further staff have been appointed, including an experienced counsellor. It also has contacts with accountants, valuers, pension advisors, insurance brokers and other professionals who may be required to assist in resolving financial matters resulting from the breakdown of a relationship.

PRINCIPAL AREAS OF WORK: *Work includes:* cohabitation agreements and pre-marriage arrangements, separation and divorce, the legal status of children and the resolution of any dispute arising in relation to children, and financial arrangements relating to all aspects of family relationships.

CONTACT PARTNER: C. Rupert Bear

Number of partners:	1
Assistant solicitors:	6
Other fee-earners:	1

WORKLOAD	
Matrimonial	93%
Conveyancing	7%

CONTACTS	
Matrimonial	C. Rupert Bear

RUSSEL & AITKEN WS 22 & 24 Stirling Street, Denny, C. Scot, FK6 6AZ **Tel:** (01324) 822194 **Fax:** (01324) 824560 **DX:** 1171 **Ptnrs:** 13 **Asst Solrs:** 9 **Other Fee-earners:** 9. Principal areas of work include family law, child care and crime with particular expertise in mental health and disability matters.

J.W. RUSSELL & CO 11 Lower Mary Street, Newtonards, Co. Down, BT23 4JJ **Tel:** (01247) 814444 **Fax:** (01247) 812782 **Ptnrs:** 4 **Asst Solrs:** 1 **Other Fee-earners:** 4. Private client practice, with additional specialisation in local government, company/ commercial and litigation work.

RUSSELL–COOKE, POTTER & CHAPMAN

11 OLD SQUARE, LINCOLN'S INN, LONDON, WC2A 3TS DX: 112 London	TEL: (0171) 405 6566 FAX: (0171) 831 2565
2 Putney Hill, Putney, London SW15 6AB DX: 59456 Putney	Tel: (0181) 789 9111 Fax: (0181) 780 1194
43 Market Place, Kingston-upon-Thames, Surrey KT1 1ET DX: 31546 Kingston-upon-Thames	Tel: (0181) 546 6111 Fax: (0181) 541 4404

THE FIRM: The firm is a medium-sized practice offering a wide range of legal services from specialist departments.

Commercial Department: *(Contact Partner:* John Gould). Although clients include several listed companies, most clients are medium-sized private companies and professional partnerships. Comprising five solicitors, the department advises on all of the legal issues relevant to business.

Landlord and Tenant: *(Contact Partner:* Stephen Clarke). There are three solicitors in this department which deals with commercial and residential leases for property investors.

Commercial Property: *(Contact Partner:* Peter Dawson). Four solicitors handle substantial property investment dealing and development transactions.

Private Client: *(Contact Partners:* Probate, trusts, wills and capital taxes (Richard Frimston); Personal injury and medical negligence claims (Paul Gardiner); Residential conveyancing (Nigel Coates). The matrimonial department is particularly well-known (Madelaine Parker).

French Property: *(Contact Partner:* Sally Osborn). Based in England dealing with matters relating to France including cross-border litigation and the purchase of French property.

Criminal Law: *(Contact Partner:* Peter Cadman). With a prominent reputation, this department of five solicitors regularly acts in high-profile complex cases dealing with very serious charges. It is also uniquely well-placed to deal with commercial fraud combining access to the resources of a larger firm with thorough experience of the workings of the police, Serious Fraud Office, Customs and Excise, Inland Revenue and the criminal courts from the start of investigations onwards.

CONTACT PARTNER: Michael Maskey

Number of partners:	19
Assistant solicitors:	15
Other fee-earners:	15

WORKLOAD	
Private client	20%
Litigation (PI and property)	20%
Commercial property/ general commercial	20%
Crime	20%
Matrimonial	10%
Domestic conveyancing	10%

CONTACTS	
Commercial	John Gould, Peter Dawson
Criminal law	Peter Cadman
Family and matrimonial	Madelaine Parker
French property	Sally Osborn
Landlord and tenant	Stephen Clarke
Medical neg./personal injury	Paul Gardiner
Probate, trusts, wills and tax	Richard Frimston
Residential conveyancing	Nigel Coates

RUSSELL & HALLMARK 4/5 Sansome Place, Worcester, Hereford & Worcs, WR1 1UQ **Tel:** (01905) 726600 **Fax:** (01905) 613302 **DX:** 716252 **Ptnrs:** 7 **Asst Solrs:** 4 **Other Fee-earners:** 1. Departments covering property, company/ commercial, litigation, public enquiries, personal injury, matrimonial and crime. Also at Malvern: Tel (01684) 892000.

WORKLOAD			
Conveyancing	38%	Civil	17%
Matrimonial	14%	Probate	13%
Commercial	5%	Crime	5%

RUSSELL JONES & WALKER

SWINTON HOUSE, 324 GRAY'S INN ROAD, LONDON, WC1X 8DH DX: 202	TEL: (0171) 837 2808 FAX: (0171) 837 2941

THE FIRM: Russell Jones & Walker, founded in London in the 1920's has grown rapidly in the last 10 years expanding from 40 to over 250 staff and partners and opening regional offices in Leeds, Manchester, Birmingham and Bristol. The firm is able to offer a comprehensive range of services to both institutional and private clients and is particularly respected for its litigation skills.

PRINCIPAL AREAS OF WORK:

Personal Injury: *(Contact Partner:* Ian Walker/ Fraser Whitehead). The firm is regarded as a specialist in personal injury litigation. Sixty-eight fee-earners deal with a wide range of plaintiff personal injury work including compensation for industrial injury, disasters, medical negligence, road traffic accidents, environmental pollution, disease and disablement and criminal assault.

CONTACT PARTNER: John Webber

Number of partners:	30
Assistant solicitors:	35
Other fee-earners:	48

WORKLOAD	
Personal injury	66%
Criminal	13%
Commercial litigation	12%

Employment: *(Contact Partner:* Edward Cooper). A strong team advises on all aspects of employment law including contracts, discrimination and unlawful dismissal.

Criminal Law and Investigations: *(Contact Partner:* Rod Fletcher). All categories of criminal law are handled, with a particular focus on white collar crime and commercial fraud.

Litigation: *(Contact Partner:* Barton Taylor). The commercial department advises on all aspects of commercial and general litigation including professional negligence, libel, defamation, intellectual property and copyright and debt collection.

OTHER AREAS OF WORK: In addition to the areas of work listed above, the firm has specialists in the following areas: commercial and residential conveyancing, landlord and tenant contracts, public and administrative law, official hearings and public inquiries, family and matrimonial law and other private client services including wills, probate and trusts.

OTHER OFFICES: Leeds, Birmingham, Bristol and Manchester.

Employment	5%
Company	2%
Family	2%

CONTACTS	
Commercial litigation	Barton Taylor
Company law	Richard Stanton-Reid
Criminal	Rod Fletcher
Employment	Edward Cooper
Family	James Pirrie
Personal injury	Ian Walker, Fraser Whitehead

RUSSELL & RUSSELL 9-13 Wood Street, Bolton, Lancs, BL1 1EE **Tel:** (01204) 34051 **Fax:** (01204) 389223 **DX:** 24146 Bolton 1 **Ptnrs:** 16 **Asst Solrs:** 11 **Other Fee-earners:** 8. Established in 1887. Best known for crime, conveyancing, personal injury and civil litigation. Has a network of branch offices throughout Greater Manchester and Cheshire.

RUSSELLS

REGENCY HOUSE, 1-4 WARWICK ST, LONDON, W1R 6LJ
DX: 37249 Piccadilly 1

TEL: (0171) 439 8692
FAX: (0171) 494 3582

THE FIRM: Founded by its present senior partner in 1974 Russells is best known for its experience and reputation in the entertainment industry.

PRINCIPAL AREAS OF WORK: Although recognised as one of the leading firms in the entertainment industry, with five commercial partners the firm also advises on general commercial matters. Three litigation partners also handle all types of litigation including breach of copyright, defamation, property disputes and divorce. It is also active in commercial and residential property, wills and probate.

CONTACT PARTNER: Mr. Robert Page	
Number of partners:	8
Assistant solicitors:	3
Other fee-earners:	1

RUSSELLS 13 Bath Street, Glasgow, G2 1HY **Tel:** (041) 332 4176 **Fax:** (041) 332 7908 **Ptnrs:** 3 **Other Fee-earners:** 1. General practice with particular expertise in family law.

RUSTONS & LLOYD Beaufort House, Newmarket, Suffolk, CB8 8NN **Tel:** (01638) 661221 **Fax:** (01638) 661732 **DX:** 50501 **Ptnrs:** 8 **Other Fee-earners:** 11. General practice with conveyancing, matrimonial, litigation, company/ commercial, trusts/ probate/ tax departments, and specialising in bloodstock-related matters.

S. RUTTER & CO

SUITE 420, SALISBURY HOUSE, FINSBURY CIRCUS, LONDON, EC2M 5QQ

TEL: (0171) 628 8641/4
FAX: (0171) 374 8070

THE FIRM: Established in 1931 S. Rutter & Co is best known for its experience and reputation in complex and substantial financial disputes in matrimonial matters. The firm also places special emphasis upon High Court litigation of all types (including commercial litigation, employment, landlord and tenant, personal injury, professional negligence and debt recovery) and general company matters. The practice has a department dealing with commercial and residential conveyancing, wills and probate.

CONTACT PARTNER: C. Delves	
Number of partners:	3
Assistant solicitors:	2
Other fee-earners:	2

SACKER & PARTNERS

29 LUDGATE HILL, LONDON, EC4M 7JQ
DX: 63 Ch.Ln.

TEL: (0171) 329 6699
FAX: (0171) 248 0552

THE FIRM: Sacker & Partners was established in 1966 and is the largest specialist pensions law practice in the UK.

PRINCIPAL AREAS OF WORK: All the fee earners are qualified solicitors and practise exclusively in pensions law (and related areas of employment law). The full range of pensions work is undertaken, including pensions litigation, international aspects of pensions provision, and merger and acquisition work.

NATURE OF CLIENTELE: Clients include leading public listed companies, banks, insurance companies, trade unions, public sector bodies, charities and trustees (including independent trustees).

CONTACT PARTNER: M.B. Greenlees

Number of partners:	8
Assistant solicitors:	4

WORKLOAD	
Pensions	100%

SALANS HERTZFELD & HEILBRONN 103 Mount Street, London, W1Y 5HE **Tel:** (0171) 491 3735 **Fax:** (0171) 408 0843. An international law practice with offices in seven countries providing legal services to companies, financial institutions, governments and international organisations.

WORKLOAD			
Corporate/ commercial	30%	Property/ other	25%
Banking/ finance	20%	Litigation/ arbitration	10%
Tax	10%	Labour	5%

SAMUEL PHILLIPS & CO

86 PILGRIM ST, NEWCASTLE-UPON-TYNE, TYNE & WEAR, NE1 6SR
DX: 61028

TEL: (0191) 232 8451
FAX: (0191) 232 7664

THE FIRM: A long-established firm offering a comprehensive range of legal services to private and business clients. In particular, the firm has many years' experience in medico-legal matters.

PRINCIPAL AREAS OF WORK:

Company and Commercial: *(Contact Partner: Stephen Doberman). Work includes:* partnerships and joint ventures, acquisitions, formations, reconstructions, commercial contracts, intellectual property, advising on funding, tax and insurance requirements, licensing and services to overseas companies.

Property: *(Contact Partner: Stephen Doberman).* The work covers all aspects of commercial and residential property including investment, funding, planning and residential building estates.

Litigation: *(Contact Partner: Barry Speker).* Work dealt with includes: medical negligence, employment, commercial disputes, building contract disputes, debt collection, tribunal representation, crime, immigration and personal injury matters.

OTHER AREAS OF WORK: The firm also deals with all family and matrimonial matters particularly in relation to child care and adoption as well as wills and probate and tax planning, and has a large criminal law department.

CONTACT PARTNER: Barry N. Speker

Number of partners:	4
Assistant solicitors:	8
Other fee-earners:	6

CONTACTS	
Child care	Barry Speker, Robert Gibson
Company/ commercial	Stephen Doberman
Crime	Stuart Grant
Employment	Robert Gibson, Barry Speker
Family law	Barry Speker
Immigration	Barry Speker
Medical negligence	Barry Speker
Personal injury	Robert Gibson
Property	Stephen Doberman

SANSBURY HILL 6 Unity Street, Bristol, BS1 5HH **Tel:** (0117) 9265341 **Fax:** (0117) 9225625 **DX:** 7821 Bristol **Ptnrs:** 3 **Asst Solrs:** 6 **Other Fee-earners:** 6. Specialist civil litigation firm, particularly personal injury, but also professional negligence, criminal, conveyancing and probate.

WORKLOAD			
Civil litigation	80%	Criminal	15%
Non-contentious	5%		

SAUNDERS & CO 413-419 Harrow Road, London, W9 3QJ **Tel:** (0181) 960 5611 **Fax:** (0181) 960 1823 **DX:** 46651 Maida Hill **Ptnrs:** 2 **Asst Solrs:** 5 **Other Fee-earners:** 9. Criminal specialists only – all types of crime covered.

WORKLOAD	
Crime	65%

SCHILLING & LOM Royalty House, 72-74 Dean St, London, W1V 6AE **Tel:** (0171) 453 2500 **Fax:** (0171) 453 2600 **DX:** 89265 Soho Sq 1 **Ptnrs:** 5 **Asst Solrs:** 3 **Other Fee-earners:** 5. Specialist commercial litigation firm with particular strength in defamation, entertainment and media, and sports law.

SCOTT-MONCRIEFF, HARBOUR & SINCLAIR Signet House, 49/51 Farringdon Road, London, EC1M 3JB **Tel:** (0171) 242 4114 **Fax:** (0171) 242 3605 **DX:** 53336 Clerkenwell **Ptnrs:** 3 **Asst Solrs:** 2 **Other Fee-earners:** 1. Specialist practice well-known for its expertise in mental health work. The firm's Greenwich office also handles child care work.

WORKLOAD			
Mental health work	65%	Disability law	20%
Children's work	10%	Court of protection	5%

SCRIVENGER SEABROOK 14 High Street, St. Neots, Cambs, PE19 1BU **Tel:** (01480) 214900 **Fax:** (01480 474833 **DX:** 100315 St Neots **Ptnrs:** 2 **Asst Solrs:** 1 . The firm deals exclusively in personal injury, medical negligence and general healthcare work. A substantial proportion of the practice is defendant based.

WORKLOAD			
Medical negligence	70%	Personal injury	25%

SEARLES The Chapel, 26A Munster Road, London, SW6 4EN **Tel:** (0171) 371 0555 **Fax:** (0171) 371 7722 **Ptnrs:** 3 **Asst Solrs:** 3 . Entertainment and intellectual property specialists in the record, publishing, television, and design industries with strong litigation department advising on commercial matters generally.

WORKLOAD			
Music industry	70%	Film and television	20%
Sponsorship/PR/advert	10%		

SEARS TOOTH 50 Upper Brook Street, London, W1Y 1PG **Tel:** (0171) 499 5599 **Fax:** (0171) 495 2970 **DX:** 44643 Mayfair **Ptnrs:** 6 **Asst Solrs:** 2 . Small West End firm known for matrimonial work. Other areas of practice include licensing and property matters.

WORKLOAD			
Divorce and matrimonial	75%	Convey (commercial/res)	20%
Litigation	5%		

SEDDONS 5 Portman Square, London, W1H 9PS **Tel:** (0171) 486 9681 **Fax:** (0171) 935 5049 **DX:** 9061 West End **Ptnrs:** 11 **Asst Solrs:** 6 **Other Fee-earners:** 7. Strong commercial practice specialising in company/ commercial, commercial property, litigation and private client. Also media, commodities, banking and aviation. Prague office.

WORKLOAD			
Property	30%	Litigation	30%
Company and commercial	30%	Private client	10%

SEDGWICK, DETERT, MORAN & ARNOLD

LLOYDS AVENUE HOUSE, 6 LLOYDS AVENUE, LONDON, EC3N 3AX

TEL: (0171) 929 1829
FAX: (0171) 929 1808

THE FIRM: Sedgwick, Detert, Moran & Arnold is one of America's leading litigation and trial law firms. Founded in 1933, the firm now has more than 230 attorneys with offices in San Francisco, Los Angeles, Orange County, Chicago, New York and Zurich.

LONDON OFFICE This office was opened in London in 1985 and became a multinational partnership in 1992. The multinational partnership offers a wide range of litigation and counselling services with an emphasis on directors and officers, fidelity, commercial, environmental, products liability, insurance and reinsurance law. Other work includes professional negligence, arbitration, employment law, construction and intellectual property law.

CONTACT PARTNER: Adam C. Barker

LAWYERS:	
London:	8
Worldwide:	235

WORKLOAD	
Litigation	100%

SEMPLE FRASER WS 130 St Vincent Street, Glasgow, G2 5HS **Tel:** (0141) 221 3771 **Fax:** (0141) 221 3776 **DX:** 337 Glasgow **Ptnrs:** 7 **Asst Solrs:** 12 **Other Fee-earners:** 4. A medium-sized, specialist commercial, corporate and commercial property practice, handling a range of related work including taxation and litigation.

SENIOR CALVELEY & HARDY 8 Hastings Place, Lytham St. Annes, Lancs, FY8 5NA **Tel:** (01253) 733333 **Fax:** (01253) 794430 **Ptnrs:** 4 **Asst Solrs:** 2 **Other Fee-earners:** 1. Member of N.I.S. Group. Best known for private client services, agricultural and development work. One partner is a member of the Solicitors Family Law Association.

WORKLOAD			
Private client	60%	Litigation	20%
Commercial	20%		

SHACKLOCKS 19 The Ropewalk, Nottingham, Notts, NG1 5DU **Tel:** (0115) 941 0789 **Fax:** (0115) 947 5561 **DX:** 10076 **Ptnrs:** 11 **Asst Solrs:** 4 **Other Fee-earners:** 4. Leading regional practice whose work includes company and commercial, commercial property, litigation, insolvency, debt collection, employment, intellectual property, liquor licensing and EC law.

SHADBOLT & CO

CHATHAM COURT, LESBOURNE ROAD, REIGATE, SURREY, RH2 7LD

TEL: (01737) 226277
FAX: (01737) 226165

THE FIRM: Established in 1991, Shadbolt & Co is a specialist law practice working mostly in the field of major projects and the construction and engineering industries in the United Kingdom and internationally. The firm offers a cost-effective commercial service backed by a high degree of experience. All partners and fee earners have a background of working in large City of London firms and the firm includes lawyers who have both engineering and legal qualifications.

PRINCIPAL AREAS OF WORK:

Construction and Engineering: Shadbolt & Co handles a wide range of contentious and non-contentious work relating to the construction and engineering industries in the UK and abroad. This forms the basis of the firm's specialised practice.

Major Projects: The firm advises a variety of clients on the commercial and legal aspects of major projects including reviewing and drafting contract documentation. It is used to working in collaboration with financial and other advisers on major projects both in the United Kingdom and elsewhere in the world.

Commercial Litigation: The firm's work includes litigation, arbitration and other forms of dispute resolution in relation to international and domestic construction and engineering disputes as well as more general commercial litigation and arbitration.

NATURE OF CLIENTELE: Clients are mainly well-known names in the construction industry. The firm's clientele has a strong international bias and clients come from a variety of countries.

RECRUITMENT AND TRAINING: The firm has an on-going recruitment programme for trainee solicitors and for qualified candidates with particular experience and expertise in the construction and engineering industry. Considerable importance is attached to in-house training and the continuing education programme for its solicitors.

INTERNATIONAL CONNECTIONS & ASSOCIATED OFFICES: The firm's practice has strong connections with Paris and the Far East including Hong Kong and it enjoys excellent working relationships with lawyers from many different countries.

CONTACT PARTNER: Richard Shadbolt

Number of partners:	5
Assistant solicitors:	4
Other fee-earners:	2

WORKLOAD	
Dispute resolution/ litigation	55%
Construction and engineering (non-contentious)	25%
Major projects	20%

CONTACTS	
Construction and engineering	S.H. Delves
Dispute resolution/ litigation	P.L. Sheridan
Major projects	E.J. Jenkins

SHAKESPEARES

10 BENNETTS HILL, BIRMINGHAM, W. MIDLANDS, B2 5RS
DX: 13015

TEL: (0121) 632 4199
FAX: (0121) 643 2257

THE FIRM: For more than 130 years Shakespeares (and its antecedent firms) has handled the affairs of companies, organisations and individuals. Shakespeares is one of Birmingham's larger and broader based firms of solicitors offering a comprehensive service to local, national and international organisations, and individuals. Clients benefit from sound advice, supported by systems and facilities designed to provide a fast, efficient and effective service.

Shakespeares is an innovative firm. For instance, it is a founder member of both QLG, a national association of Solicitors dedicated to quality (the firm is accredited to ISO 9001), and of IAG International, a group of well established firms of lawyers, accountants and tax advisers throughout Europe and internationally. The firm was one of the first to operate its own investment management department and has £35m client funds under investment.

PRINCIPAL AREAS OF WORK:

Company/ Commercial: (*Contact:* Charles J.B. Flint. *Fee-earners:* 12). The aims of Shakespeares are the proper protection of its clients and to ensure that businesses are in the best possible shape to perform and grow. The firm concentrates on making the documentation used in all transactions a clear reflection of the terms which have been negotiated but it also ensures clients understand the legal processes involved in reaching their objectives. Advice extends to company structure, management, mergers, acquisitions and disposals, contracts, finance and all other activities of industry and commerce.

Litigation: (*Contact:* John M. Buckingham. *Fee-earners:* 32). For individuals or businesses who find themselves engaged in a dispute, Shakespeares provide solutions with the least possible inconvenience and disruption. Cases vary from complex commercial matters to personal areas such as matrimonial disputes or criminal proceedings. The advice includes commercial litigation, injunctions and intellectual property rights, construction litigation and professional indemnity claims, debt recovery, personal injury, insurance based litigation, medical negligence, crime, family and matrimonial law, housing, welfare law, consumer credit and all kinds of legal aid work. Employment advice at tribunal, and in the court is a particular specialism for two partners

Property: (*Contact:* Paul R.M. Reading. *Fee-earners:* 12). Shakespeares provides a comprehensive range of property services for business, developers, financial institutions, investors, housing associations and charities, as well as private individuals. Its international network enables it to give advice and assistance on the acquisition and sale of overseas properties. Services include commercial property, development, housing associations, residential and various specialist activities such as planning and licensed premises. The agricultural unit has a nationwide reputation.

Private Client and Investment Management: (*Contact:* Nicholas Q. Grazebrook. *Fee-earners:* 14). Shakespeares Investment Management Department manages 35 million pounds of pounds illustrating the high level of confidence in the firm's abilities. Legal services include probate, wills and trusts. Charities are also assisted by this department.

CONTACT PARTNER: M.J. Hibbs

Number of partners:	22
Assistant solicitors:	24
Other fee-earners:	24

WORKLOAD	
Litigation	54%
Property	16%
Company and commercial	16%
Private client	14%

CONTACTS	
Agriculture	Nigel Davis
Charities	Gary De'Ath
Company and commercial	Jill Kennedy
Construction	Andrew Argyle
Debt collection	Stephen Jones
Education	Paul Pharoah
Employment	Mike Hibbs
Insurance litigation	John Buckingham
Investment management	Graham Engefield
Medical negligence	Gary Christianson
Professional indemnity	Diana Wareing
Property	Paul Reading

SHARMAN & TRETHEWY 1 Harpur St, Bedford, Beds, MK40 1PF **Tel:** (01234) 341171 **Fax:** (01234) 352114 **DX:** 5604 **Ptnrs:** 7 **Asst Solrs:** 8 **Other Fee-earners:** 14. Established 1809. Handles all areas of practice including commercial, conveyancing, probate, civil and criminal litigation. Agency work undertaken.

WORKLOAD			
Litigation	51%	Company/commercial prop	18%
Prob/wills/trusts/tax	17%	Residential conveyancing	14%

SHARPE PRITCHARD

ELIZABETH HOUSE, FULWOOD PLACE, LONDON, WC1V 6HG
DX: 353

TEL: (0171) 405 4600
FAX: (0171) 831 1284

NATURE OF FIRM: A well established practice (founded 1826) in the fields of litigation for the public and private sectors; with conveyancing, trusts, tax and some company and commercial. Also well known parliamentary agents with separate office at Westminster.

PRINCIPAL AREAS OF WORK:

General Description: A general practice with a strong emphasis on litigation for a wide variety of clients; particularly public and local authorities and professional clients. Expanding property department.

Litigation: (*Contact:* Ashley Badcock. *5 Partners*). All areas covered particularly construction, environmental and property related litigation, personal injury including medical negligence; local and public authority related litigation – judicial review; commercial and defamation; employment; insolvency and debt collection; Chancery, child care and family.

Parliamentary: (*Contact:* Michael Pritchard. *2 Partners*. A substantial practice at Westminster office for public and local authorities, promotion and opposition of bills for a variety of clients.

Property and commercial: (*Contact:* Grant Pain. *2 Partners*). A wide variety of property-related work, conveyancing, trusts, tax and some company/ commercial. Expanding development work for local authorities.

Contracts: (*Contact:* Stephen Millen. *2 Partners*). The firm undertakes drafting and negotiation of contracts for works, services and supplies and advises on EU and UK public procurement.

BRANCH OFFICES: 3 Dean Farrar Street, Westminster, SW1. Two partners, five fee earners exclusively practising parliamentary agency work for a wide variety of local and public authorities, corporate clients and other firms of solicitors.

NATURE OF CLIENTELE: Public and local authorities, professional, private and small corporate, housing trusts, charities etc.

FOREIGN CONNECTIONS: Italian and French spoken.

AGENCY WORK: Substantial agency practice in all areas; urgent work undertaken – contact Mr. Richards.

RECRUITMENT AND TRAINING: Three trainee solicitors a year are taken on. They should have good academic qualifications and the ability to work as part of a well-knit team. Applications with a C.V. should be made in September of each year to Ashley Badcock.

CHARGES: On application.

CONTACT PARTNER: Ashley Badcock

Number of partners:	11
Assistant solicitors:	8
Other fee-earners:	12

WORKLOAD	
Civil litigation	60%
Parliamentary	22%
Non-contentious	18%

CONTACTS	
Civil litigation	A. Badcock
Contracts	S. Millen
Parliamentary	M. Pritchard
Property and commercial	G. Pain

SHARP & PARTNERS 6 Weekday Cross, Nottingham, Notts, NG1 2GF **Tel:** (0115) 959 0055 **Fax:** (0115) 9584851 **DX:** 10019 **Ptnrs:** 8 **Asst Solrs:** 7 **Other Fee-earners:** 7. Long established practice with four offices undertaking all areas of work, including commercial law, general civil litigation, childcare, adoption, personal injury and insolvency work.

WORKLOAD			
Conveyancing/property	30%	Family/ matrimonial	25%
Civil/ PI/ employment	20%	Company/ commercial	10%
Probate	10%	Crime	5%

CD-ROM EDITION ON THE INTERNET

This edition of the directory is available on a CD-ROM which includes both DOS and Windows versions. It can be loaded onto a network, and works with virtually any IBM compatible PC. The CD-ROM version offers computer-users the advantage of rapid search, retrieval and cross-referencing. It is also available via the Internet.

SHAW AND CROFT

115 HOUNDSDITCH, LONDON, EC3A 7BU
DX: 824

TEL: (0171) 283 6293
FAX: (0171) 626 3639

THE FIRM: Established in 1980 as a specialist shipping and commercial law practice, the firm has grown steadily in these fields, while developing expertise in the related fields of litigation, insurance and banking law.

PRINCIPAL AREAS OF WORK:

Shipping and Maritime Law: *(Contact Partner:* Roger Croft). The firm handles all aspects of shipping work, including arbitration and litigation involving collisions, salvage, charter parties, bills of lading, cargo damage, pollution, and shipbuilding.

Commodities: *(Contact Partner:* Bob McCunn). Work handled includes international sale of goods (particularly oil, grain and other commodities) together with other international commercial transactions.

Insurance: *(Contact Partner:* Jonathan Kenyon). Litigation and advice on all aspects of the insurance markets in London and abroad, particularly marine insurance, P&I, Brokers E and O, reinsurance.

Ship Finance and Corporate: *(Contact Partner:* Richard Coles). Sale and purchase, finance and registration of ships, yachts and fishing vessels, company acquisitions and disposals, joint ventures, agency and employment law.

NATURE OF CLIENTELE: Shipowners, charterers, P and I Clubs and Insurers, salvage companies, banks, commodity traders, ship managers, shipbuilders, insolvency practitioners, property developers and investors.

FOREIGN CONNECTIONS: The firm has particularly strong connections with France, Greece, N. Africa and the Middle East. Four partners speak French fluently. Others speak Greek, German and Spanish. A worldwide network of correspondent lawyers in all major shipping and commercial centres is actively maintained.

CONTACT PARTNER: Roger Croft

Number of partners:	9
Assistant solicitors:	7
Other fee-earners:	6

CONTACTS

Admirality	Roger Croft
Commercial litigation	Nicholas Taylor
Commercial property	Roger Colton
Commodities	Bob McCunn
Company/Commercial	Richard Coles
Insurance	Jonathan Kenyon
Personal Injury	Hamish Edgar
Ship Finance	Richard Coles
Shipping litigation	Giles de Bertodano

SHEAN DICKSON MERRICK 14-16 High Street, Belfast, BT1 2BS **Tel:** (01232) 326878 **Fax:** (01232) 323473 **Ptnrs:** 4 **Asst Solrs:** 2 **Other Fee-earners:** 2. Experienced in licensing matters, the practice also includes company/ commercial, litigation and private client work.

WORKLOAD			
Private client	40%	Litigation	25%
Liquor licensing	20%	Commercial/ corporate	15%

SHEPHERD & WEDDERBURN WS

SALTIRE COURT, 20 CASTLE TERRACE, EDINBURGH, EH1 2ET
DX: 49 Edinburgh

TEL: (0131) 228 9900
FAX: (0131) 228 1222

THE FIRM: Shepherd & Wedderburn WS is one of the largest law firms in Scotland, with a compliment of 260 people. The firm has a strong commercial reputation and has close connections with financial institutions in both Edinburgh and London and with Scottish industry. The firm also values its traditional links with private clients and has a very well-regarded private client department. The services offered embrace all areas of the law for corporate, business and public sector clients, as well as for families and private individuals.

PRINCIPAL AREAS OF WORK:

Corporate: *(Contact Partner:* Paul Hally). The firm is well known for its corporate work especially acquisitions and mergers, stock exchange listings, financial services, venture capital, capital raising, management buy-outs, privatisation, share incentives, pensions, unit trusts and insolvency. The firm is particularly well-regarded for its stock exchange work ranking 8th amongst all UK firms in a recent KPMG Peat Marwick study by acting in flotations as solicitors to the issue.

Commercial: *(Contact Partner:* James Saunders). The firm handles a wide range of commercial contracts with a strong involvement in information technology, UK and EC competition law and energy law.

CHIEF EXECUTIVE: Mr Hugh Donald

Number of partners:	27
Assistant solicitors:	42
Other fee-earners:	47

SHEPHERD & WEDDERBURN WS

Banking: *(Contact Partner:* Iain Meiklejohn). *Work includes:* syndicated loans, asset and project finance and debt restructuring and refinancing.

Commercial Property: *(Contact Partner:* Patrick Andrews). *Work includes:* site assembly and acquisition, environmental law, town and country planning, building contracts, development funding, investment purchase and leasing, sales and disposals, bank securities, office and retail letting, plant leasing and joint ventures.

Litigation: *(Contact Partner:* Ian MacLeod). *Work includes:* administrative law, aviation law, building and construction disputes, commercial litigation, company/ partnership disputes, debt recovery, employment law, insolvency and receivership, insurance disputes, intellectual property, licensing, matrimonial/ family disputes, personal injury, planning and environmental law, product liability, professional liability and property disputes.

Private Client: *(Contact Partner:* Robin Fulton). *Work includes:* preparation of wills, creation of trusts, setting up partnerships, estate and trust administration, investment advice, life assurance, pensions, taxation returns, tax planning, advice to charities and curatories, purchases and sale of forestry, sporting and agricultural interests and residential property.

FOREIGN LANGUAGES: French, German, Italian, Greek.

SHEPHERD & WEDDERBURN WS

SHEPSTONE & WYLIE (UK)

6TH FLOOR, 21 SOUTHAMPTON ROW, LONDON, WC1B 5HA

TEL: (0171) 831 1977
FAX: (0171) 405 1255

THE FIRM: Shepstone & Wylie is a substantial South African firm of attorneys. It is part of an association called WSF International, which comprises Webber Wentzel Bowens, Shepstone & Wylie and Findlay & Tait, all major South African firms. WSF International is further associated with Maitland & Co. in Europe.

THE LONDON OFFICE: Work undertaken by the London office includes shipping, commodities, banking, corporate and commercial work, corporate finance, transnational tax, business and investment planning, immigration and intellectual property.

LANGUAGES SPOKEN: French, German, Afrikaans.

OTHER AND ASSOCIATED OFFICES:
Shepstone & Wylie: Durban, Pietermaritzburg, Richards Bay.
Webber Wentzel Bowens: Johannesburg, Sandton, Pretoria
Findlay & Tait: Cape Town
Maitland & Co: London, Luxembourg, Geneva, the Isle of Man.

CONTACT PARTNER: John Herholdt

LAWYERS:
London: 6
Worldwide: 250

SHERIDANS

14 RED LION SQUARE, LONDON, WC1R 4QL
DX: 270

TEL: (0171) 404 0444
FAX: (0171) 831 1982

THE FIRM: Sheridans has a substantial international practice, and is particularly noted for its work in all branches of the entertainment, media and communications industries and offers a wide range of litigation services. The firm also has a growing reputation for its work in company/ commercial and property law.

PRINCIPAL AREAS OF WORK:

Entertainment & Media: *(Contact:* Howard Jones). *Work includes:* legal services relating to recording artistes, publishing and record companies, intellectual property, theatre, TV, copyright, merchandising, books, video, the press and related areas.

Litigation: *(Contact:* Cyril Glasser). The department has considerable experience in litigation involving commercial, entertainment, media, computer and public law work; matrimonial and immigration law and some criminal work. It also specialises in defamation cases, obtaining emergency orders and has a Privy Council practice.

CONTACT PARTNER: Cyril Glasser

Number of partners:	12
Assistant solicitors:	7
Other fee-earners:	8

WORKLOAD	
Commercial and other litigation	40%
Entertainment and media	30%
Company/ commercial	15%
Property and planning	15%

Company/ Commercial: (*Contact:* Ian Watson). *Work includes:* the raising of finance, setting up of companies, negotiation of joint ventures, management buy-outs, demergers, acquisitions and disposals, reorganisations, insolvency and employment, intellectual property law, trademarks, copyright, and general commercial work.

Property and Planning: (*Contact:* Peter Jacobs). Work in the commercial sphere includes secured lending, property development, building schemes, property financing, investments and planning. The department also handles residential conveyancing, licensing, wills and probate.

NATURE OF CLIENTELE: The clientele includes major recording artistes and companies, television production companies, classical music composers, publishers; a substantial private client base as well as corporate clients.

FOREIGN CONNECTIONS: The work undertaken in the entertainment, media and communications field, and the commercial field generally, requires extensive overseas contact, with the result that the firm is well-versed in dealing with foreign lawyers and professional advisers.

RECRUITMENT AND TRAINING: The firm recruits three trainee solicitors every year. Applications should be made with a CV and an accompanying letter to Cyril Glasser during August 1995 (for September 1997).

CONTACTS	
Commercial litigation	Cyril Glasser
Company/ commercial	Ian Watson
Computers and IT	Michael Thomas
Entertainment and media	Howard Jones
Matrimonial and immigration	Richard Gifford
Property/ planning/ probate	Peter Jacobs

SHERRARDS

35 MARKET PLACE, ST. ALBANS, HERTS, AL3 5DN
DX: 6100 St. Albans

TEL: (01727) 840271
FAX: (01727) 836775

THE FIRM: Known for its expertise in the fields of commercial, planning and housing association law. A growing reputation for the quality of its services and its innovative approach to problem solving.

PRINCIPAL AREAS OF WORK:

Commercial: *Work includes:* mergers, joint ventures, MBOs, computer law, partnerships and general commercial advice/ agreements.

Litigation: *Work includes:* commercial, employment, matrimonial, personal injury and property litigation.

Planning: The department handles appeals, negotiations and advice on all aspects of planning law.

Housing Associations: Specialist department acting for a number of associations. Wide expertise including consortium development, DIYSO, LOTS and shared ownership conveyancing.

OTHER AREAS OF WORK: The firm offers a wide range of private client and conveyancing services.

CONTACT PARTNER: David Korman

Number of partners:	5
Assistant solicitors:	3
Other fee-earners:	3

WORKLOAD	
Conveyancing	25%
Housing associations	25%
Litigation	17%
Company/ commercial	17%
Planning	8%
Probate	8%

SHERWIN OLIVER

NEW HAMPSHIRE COURT, ST. PAUL'S RD, PORTSMOUTH, HANTS, PO5 4JT
DX: 2268 Portsmouth 1

TEL: (01705) 832200
FAX: (01705) 865884

THE FIRM: Established one hundred years ago, Sherwin Oliver Solicitors is one of the leading practices for commercial law in South Hampshire. The firm is a member of LawNet, an association of 78 independent firms of solicitors throughout Great Britain and Southern Ireland.

PRINCIPAL AREAS OF WORK:

Company/ Commercial: (*Contact Partner:* Nigel S. Craig). The firm can advise on acquisitions, mergers, expansion and restructuring, contracts, conditions of sale and purchase, licensing, franchising, and all aspects of commercial law.

CONTACT PARTNER: Andrew D. Peck or Nigel S. Craig

Number of partners:	9
Assistant solicitors:	11
Other fee-earners:	8

Commercial Property: *(Contact Partner:* Andrew D. Peck). This department specialises in commercial and residential property development work and in particular commercial landlord and tenant matters.

Corporate Recovery: *(Contact Partner:* David C. Oliver). A separate department handles corporate recovery and insolvency. Work includes personal and company insolvency and realisation of assets.

Litigation: *(Contact Partner:* Christopher C. Brockman). All forms of litigation are handled by the firm including landlord and tenant, building disputes, insurance claims, debt recovery and industrial tribunal cases. The firm is actively engaged in Alternative Dispute Resolution and one member of the firm is a deputy district judge and practising arbitrator.

Public Sector: *(Contact Partner:* Andrew D. Peck). This specialist department advises on privatisation of legal services within local health authorities, education and the public sector.

Private Client Litigation: *(Contact Partner:* John J.L. Taylor). All matters relating to matrimonial and civil litigation are dealt with by the firm.

Tax, Trusts & Probate: *(Contact Partner:* David G. Burnham-Slipper). This department deals with wills, probate, trusts and tax planning.

INTERNATIONAL CONNECTIONS: Sherwin Oliver Solicitors is a member of LawNet Europe, providing links with over 650 firms in 19 European countries.

FOREIGN LANGUAGES: French and German.

OTHER OFFICE: The Old Manor House, Wickham Road, Fareham PO16 7AR. *Tel:* (01329) 822611. *Fax:* (01329) 822612. *DX:* 40816 Fareham.

WORKLOAD	
Commercial property	30%
Commercial litigation	25%
Company and commercial	25%
General	10%
Corporate recovery	10%

CONTACTS	
Commercial property	Andrew Peck
Commercial litigation	C. Brockman
Company and commercial	Nigel Craig
Computers/ IP	Nigel Craig
Corporate recovery	David Oliver
Private client litigation	John Taylor
Public sector	Andrew Peck
Tax, trusts and probate	D. Burnham-Slipper

SHIELD & KYD 5 Bank Street, (PO Box 61), Dundee, Tayside, DD1 9LB **Tel:** (01382) 24112 **Fax:** (01382) 200109 **DX:** 17 Dundee **Ptnrs:** 13. General practice with an emphasis upon property (commercial and domestic). Other offices in Edinburgh and Arbroath.

SHINDLER & CO

37-39 EASTCHEAP, LONDON, EC3M 1AY
DX: 669

TEL: (0171) 283 6376
FAX: (0171) 626 5735

THE FIRM: Established in 1935, Shindler & Co is a general practice based in the City.

PRINCIPAL AREAS OF WORK:

Commercial Litigation and Arbitration: Work is both domestic and international and includes construction, marine, intellectual property, professional negligence, employment and shareholders disputes.

Company/ Commercial: The firm is highly responsive to the needs of its clients and often provides strategic business as well as legal advice. *Work includes:* company formations, acquisitions, disposals, MBOs, joint ventures and reconstructions, taxation advice and commercial contracts.

Property: A wide range of property work is undertaken.

Environmental Law: The firm's specialist unit deals with such matters as noise, water and air pollution, planning and conservation, environmental insurance, audits and assessments, carriage of hazardous goods and waste disposal.

Private Client: The firm handles family and matrimonial matters, personal tax, wills, probate and trusts and private client litigation (including personal injury).

INTERNATIONAL CONNECTIONS: Central/ East Europe: the firm has a specialist in Hungarian, Czech and Slovak law, and extensive contacts throughout the area. A partner is currently President of the British Hungarian Lawyers Association.

OTHER OFFICE:
10 North End Road, London NW11 7PW. *Tel:* (0181) 458 0666.

CONTACT PARTNER: H.L. Stone

Number of partners:	6
Assistant solicitors:	3
Other fee-earners:	8

SHOOSMITHS & HARRISON

COMPTON HOUSE, ABINGTON STREET, NORTHAMPTON, NORTHANTS, NN1 2LR DX: 12404	TEL: (01604) 29977 FAX: (01604) 20229
Banbury:52-54 The Green, Banbury, Oxon. OX16 9AB Contact: John Spratt	Tel: (01295) 267971 Fax: (01295) 265620.
Northampton:Compton House, Abington Street, Northampton NN1 2LR Contact: Michael Orton Jones	Tel: (01604) 29977 Fax: (01604) 20229
Northampton:Victoria House, 3 Victoria Street, Northampton NN1 3NR Contact: John Temple	Tel: (01604) 29977 Fax: (01604) 234109
Northampton:City Buildings, Fish Street, Northampton NN1 2AE Contact: Andrew Tubbs	Tel: (01604) 29977 Fax: (01604) 604854
Northampton:County House, 56A/ B Sheep Street, Northampton NN1 2LZ Contact: Michael Murray	Tel: (01604) 29977 Fax: (01604) 601494
Nottingham:22a The Ropewalk, Nottingham NG1 5DT. DX: 10104 Contact: Nigel Haynes	Tel: (0115) 9474645 Fax: (0115) 9475556
Reading:Regents Gate, Crown Street, Reading, Berks RG1 2SN. DX: 4009 Contact: Marshall Leopold	Tel: (01734) 498765 Fax: (01734) 498800
Rugby:Bloxam Court, Corporation Street, Rugby, Warwicks. CV21 2DU. DX: 11686 Contact: Chris Hill	Tel: (01788) 573111 Fax: (01788) 536651
Southampton:Russell House, 1550 Parkway, Solent Business Park, Whiteley, Fareham, Hampshire PO15 7AG. DX: 45254 Parkgate Contact: Sally Norcross-Webb	Tel: (01489) 881010 Fax: (01489) 881000

THE FIRM: A major regional practice, Shoosmiths & Harrison is a successful and growing firm. Staffing levels continue to increase and gross fee income in 1994/95 was £25.2m. The firm now operates from Nottingham, Rugby, Northampton, Banbury, Reading and Southampton.

Comprehensive legal services are provided for both commercial and private clients. The firm is recognised for its particular expertise in insurance litigation, building society, commercial property, company and commercial and town and country planning law. All market sectors are served with a particular emphasis on financial institutions and insurers.

The partnership views the future with considerable optimism. The firm has the critical mass of a major London firm and the lower cost base of a regional firm. The quality of the services they represent is increasingly being recognised by commercial clients. As a further example of its commitment to the highest levels of service, the firm has been awarded ISO 9001 after the audit of the British Standards Institution. The firm is currently the largest UK law firm to receive accreditation.

PRINCIPAL AREAS OF WORK: The following services are offered from each of the offices. Initial enquiries can be directed either to the Unit Head shown below or to the most convenient office.

Business Services Unit: *Contact:*John Temple, Victoria House, Northampton
Corporate Unit: *Contact:*Sally Norcross Webb, Southampton
Commercial Litigation Unit: *Contact:*John Hill, Compton House, Northampton
Environmental Health Unit: *Contact:*Ron Reid, City Buildings, Northampton
Employment & Pensions Unit: *Contact:*Peter Ellis, Compton House, Northampton
Charities Unit: *Contact:*Graham Bennett, Southampton
Marine Unit: *Contact:*Kevin Haven, Southampton
Professional Negligence Unit: *Contact:*Paul Laca, Compton House, Northampton
Insolvency Unit: *Contact:*Neil Bradshaw, Compton House, Northampton
Debt Recovery Unit: *Contact:*Sandra Sheperd, Reading
Commercial Property Unit: *Contact:*Anthony Price, Victoria House, Northampton
Building Services Unit: *Contact:*John Peer, Victoria House, Northampton

CONTACT PARTNER: Mr Graham New	
Number of partners:	62
Assistant solicitors:	81
Other fee-earners:	146

SHOOSMITHS&HARRISON
SOLICITORS

Planning Unit: *Contact:*Nick Goddard, Rugby
Environmental Unit: *Contact:*Ron Reid, City Buildings, Northampton
Defendant Personal Injury: *Contact:*Michael Murray, County House, Northampton
ULR & Plaintiff Personal Injury: *Contact:* John Spencer, Reading
Lending Services Unit: *Contact:*Andrew Tubbs, City Buildings, Northampton
Private Client Unit: *Contact:*Michael Orton-Jones, Compton House, Northampton

SHOOSMITHS&HARRISON
SOLICITORS

SHORT RICHARDSON & FORTH 4 Mosley St, Newcastle upon Tyne, Tyne & Wear, NE1 1SR **Tel:** (0191) 232 0283 **Fax:** (0191) 261 6956 **Ptnrs:** 5 **Asst Solrs:** 2 . A mainly commercial firm best known for employment law and commercial property.

WORKLOAD			
Employment law	35%	Commercial property	22%
Civil litigation	22%	Company and commercial	18%
Private client	3%		

SIDLEY & AUSTIN

ROYAL EXCHANGE, LONDON, EC3V 3LE
DX: 580 London City

TEL: (0171) 360 3600
FAX: (0171) 626 7937

This leading international law firm gives advice in all major areas of commercial activity. Its London practice is comprised principally of English solicitors with particular expertise in banking, structured finance, information industries, taxation, corporate finance and property.

THE FIRM: Sidley & Austin was founded in Chicago in 1866, established in London in 1974 and reconstituted as a multinational partnership last year. It has offices in six centres of commerce across the globe. Clients include many of the world's leading institutions, banks and businesses.

The London practice aims to maintain the firm's tradition of furnishing high quality, cost-effective advice in a collegiate environment. It has adopted a strategy of matching its clients' requirements with customised advice, emphasising long term client relationships.

Lawyers in the office have extensive European practice experience and can assist clients with matters within the European Union and elsewhere. Teams of lawyers are quickly mobilised, and carefully managed, to assist clients wherever their needs arise. The English lawyers are supported by US-qualified lawyers resident in London and in the other offices of the firm and by relationships with leading independent law practices around the world.

TYPES OF WORK UNDERTAKEN: Expertise in banking and structured finance covers such areas as banking regulations, domestic and international lending, single bank and syndicated facilities, project finance and trade finance. Asset securitisation is a particular strength and work in this field is carried out for originators, underwriters, credit enhancers, liquidity banks and credit rating agencies. The London office works closely with lawyers in the firm's US offices in adapting US financing techniques to European and other non-US assets and markets.

The firm's information industries expertise covers all aspects of telecoms, IT, soft IP and media, and includes software development, electronic publishing and satellite services. Extensive knowledge of domestic and international regulations underpins the firm's advice in these matters.

Taxation advice is provided by the London office regarding both domestic and international transactions, including mergers and acquisitions, joint ventures, corporate finance, banking and structured finance, commercial property and asset finance.

Advice on corporate finance and commercial matters includes mergers, acquisitions and takeovers, joint ventures, flotations company formations, inward investment and employment law. The firm's wide-ranging knowledge of the telecommunications, utilities and other regulated industries gives it special expertise concerning the privatisation of state-owned enterprises.

Property and property finance expertise includes debt and equity based financing, development arrangements, acquisitions and disposals and institutional investment work.

Number of resident partners:	6
Assistant solicitors:	14
Other fee-earners:	4

CONTACTS	
American matters	Mark Angelson
Banking and structured finance	Graham Penn
	Howard Waterman
	Sarah Smith
Corporate and commercial	John Edwards
Information industries	John Edwards
Property	Mark Angelson
Tax	Drew Scott

SIDLEY & AUSTIN
SOLICITORS AND REGISTERED FOREIGN LAWYERS

SILKS

BARCLAYS BANK CHAMBERS, 27 BIRMINGHAM ST, OLDBURY, WARLEY,
W. MIDLANDS, B69 4EZ   DX: 20876 Oldbury 2

TEL: (0121) 511 2233
FAX: (0121) 552 6322

48-52 Halesowen Road, Netherton, Dudley, West Midlands DY2 9QB.
DX: 10772 Netherton
Contact Partner: Karen Silk

Tel: (01384) 236101
Fax: (01384) 239779

THE FIRM: Founded by the present senior partner in 1953 Silks have expanded into a practice having substantial company clients including public companies, without losing sight of its original roots in criminal, matrimonial work and domestic conveyancing.

PRINCIPAL AREAS OF WORK:

Criminal: Long established practice defending clients in local Magistrates' Courts and Crown Courts.

PI & Civil Litigation: Broad range of litigation work with recent membership at both offices on Accident Line panel with Partners and support staff specialising in personal injury claims.

Conveyancing: Domestic and Commercial. Sales and purchases of domestic, commercial and industrial properties, leases and tenancy agreements.

Matrimonial/Child Care/Welfare: Members on Children panel regularly representing children and parents in Magistrates' and County Courts. Experienced matrimonial lawyers and trained welfare advisers.

Company and Commercial: Company formations, sales and purchase of companies and businesses, shareholder agreements, service agreements and general commercial advice.

Wills and Probate: Including advice on inheritance tax and planning.

Employment & Licensing: One Partner has twenty years experience representing clients, including a retail plc, in Tribunals throughout the UK and advising on contractual claims and general employment matters.

Crime: *Contact:* T.J. Bytheway. *3 Partners.*

Employment: *Contact:* J.B. Burn. *1 Partner.*

NATURE OF CLIENTELE: Clients include private individuals, small and medium-sized companies, and three PLCs.

AGENCY WORK:

Crime: Contact T.J. Bytheway.
Matrimonial: Contact C.A. Strongman.

LANGUAGES SPOKEN: Hindi, Urdu, Punjabi.

CONTACT PARTNER: Mr.J.B. Burn

Number of partners:	7
Assistant solicitors:	1
Other fee-earners:	10

WORKLOAD	
Criminal	21%
PI & civil litigation	20%
Conveyancing: domestic and commercial	20%
Matrimonial/ child care/ welfare	14%
Company & commercial	13%
Wills & probate	7%
Employment & licensing	5%

CONTACTS	
Commercial property	K A H Jones
Company & commercial	J G Silk
Crime	T J Bytheway
Employment	J B Burn
Litigation	J B Burn
Matrimonial	C A Strongman
Residential property	K A H Jones

SILVERBECK RYMER 7th Floor Martins Building, 4 Water Street, Liverpool, Merseyside, L2 3SX **Tel:** (0151) 236 9594 **Fax:** (0151) 227 1035 **DX:** 14189 Liverpool **Ptnrs:** 5 **Asst Solrs:** 10 **Other Fee-earners:** 40. A corporate and private client practice with particular strength in the area of plaintiff and defendant litigation of all descriptions.

WORKLOAD			
Defendant litigation	40%	Plaintiff litigation	40%
Conveyancing	10%	Criminal	4%
Probate	2%	Employment	2%

FIRMS OF ACCOUNTANTS

Accountants specialising in litigation support are listed in the accountants' A-Z, with details of the services they offer to solicitors, from forensic accounting to intellectual property or business valuations.

THE SIMKINS PARTNERSHIP

45-51 WHITFIELD ST, LONDON, W1P 6AA
DX: 7 Ch.Ln

TEL: (0171) 631 1050
FAX: (0171) 436 2744

THE FIRM: The Simkins Partnership is a commercial law firm providing a wide range of legal services with a particular focus on the media, entertainment, marketing and leisure industries.

The firm was established in 1963, since when its film and music law work has steadily developed to form the core of one of the largest and most broadly-based media practices in Europe. The Simkins Partnership is also a leading firm in related areas such as theatre, television, advertising and marketing, sport, publishing, multimedia and photography.

The firm's various specialist groups are complemented by general departments; the corporate, litigation, property and private client departments act for a wide range of individual and corporate clients, again with an emphasis on media and entertainment.

Great emphasis has always been placed on the firm's network of contacts, both at home and overseas, and the firm maintains close links with relevant trade associations and other industry bodies. The firm is the UK member of Advertising Law International, a worldwide network of law firms specialising in advertising and marketing law, and over the years has assembled a network of contacts with media law firms throughout the world.

PRINCIPAL AREAS OF WORK:

Media and Entertainment: Including film and television production, distribution and finance, cable, video, theatre, music, sport, publishing, multimedia and photography.

Advertising and Marketing: The firm advises major advertisers and many of the largest UK advertising agencies on a wide range of issues including domestic and international copy clearance, regulatory matters and artist and client contracts.

Corporate: The corporate department advises on all types of transaction in its field and has extensive experience in corporate finance and the disposal and acquisition of businesses and companies, particularly in the media and entertainment sector.

Property: The property department is experienced in all types of property work including the management, acquisition and disposal of substantial portfolios.

Litigation: The litigation department undertakes a wide variety of general, mainly commercial, litigation. Particular areas of expertise include litigation in the firm's specialist media and entertainment fields, property litigation and international trade disputes.

Family: The family department is one of the leading practices in its field and advises clients on all aspects of family law. The head of the department is an accredited mediator with the Family Mediators Association.

Private Client: The private client department advises on such matters as wills, trusts, domestic conveyancing and personal taxation. Additionally, there is a substantial volume of immigration and nationality work for both private individuals, performing artists and corporate clients.

MANAGING PARTNERS: Nigel Bennett and Cyrus Fatemi

Number of partners:	22
Assistant solicitors:	18
Other fee-earners:	7

CONTACTS	
Advertising	Charles Swan
Broadcasting	Tim Curtis
Commodities litigation	Dominic Free
Competition	Tony Quick
Corporate	Paul Walker
Employment	Paul Walker
Family	Sara Robinson
Film and video	Nigel Bennett
Immigration	Vanessa Hall-Smith
IT and Telecommunications	Nigel Stamp
Litigation	Charles Artley
Multimedia	Lawrence Kaye
Music	Julian Turton
Photography	Charles Swan
Private client	Adrian Nelson
Property	Cyrus Fatemi
Publishing	Julian Turton
Sport	Nigel Bennett
Theatre	David Franks

THE **Simkins Partnership** SOLICITORS

SIMMONDS CHURCH SMILES

13 BEDFORD ROW, HOLBORN, LONDON, WC1R 4BU
DX: 101 London

TEL: (0171) 242 9971
FAX: (0171) 405 0874

THE FIRM: A respected, medium-size Holborn firm with branches in Tunbridge Wells and (as "Corsellis") in Wandsworth. Founded in 1842, it has a comprehensive practice with a wide client base. The firm has international contacts, particularly in New Zealand, and experience in Privy Council work. Partners of the firm are members of the Law Society's Personal Injury and Medical Negligence Panels.

PRINCIPAL AREAS OF WORK: The firm has a high reputation for its skill and experience, with particular emphasis on company and commercial work (including commercial property), plaintiff personal injury and professional negligence (including medical, dental and solicitors), employment, matrimonial and probate/ trust work.

CONTACT PARTNER: Francis Elkin

Number of partners:	16
Assistant solicitors:	2
Other fee-earners:	7

WORKLOAD	
Civil Litigation and Family	35%
Company/commercial/employment	25%
Property and Environment	20%
Trust, probate and tax	20%

SIMMONS & SIMMONS

21 WILSON STREET, LONDON, EC2M 2TQ
DX: 12

TEL: (0171) 628 2020
FAX: (0171) 628 2070

THE FIRM: As one of the leading City firms, Simmons & Simmons has a broadly-based commercial practice with a strong UK and international client base. The firm was founded in 1896 as a general commercial practice and since then has grown continuously and rapidly.

STRUCTURE OF THE FIRM: The firm has a total staff of 1215 worldwide with overseas offices in Paris, Brussels, Lisbon, Milan, Abu Dabi, Hong Kong, Shanghai and New York. Simmons & Simmons occupies joint offices and collaborates with J&A Garrigues, a leading Spanish law firm, in both Brussels and New York, and also with Feddersen Laule Scherzberg & Ohle Hansen Ewerwahn, a leading German law firm, in Brussels. In Lisbon, Simmons & Simmons has set up a joint venture office in association with J&A Garrigues, Pinheiro Neto & Co., and F. Castelo Branco, Nobre Guedes and P. Rebelo de Sousa and in Milan a joint firm with Studio Avv. Eugenio Grippo.

PRINCIPAL AREAS OF WORK:

Corporate Finance & Company: (*Contacts:* Alan Carr/ William Knight). Legal aspects of every type of corporate transaction, including insolvency work.

Banking & Capital Markets: (*Contacts:* Graham Rowbotham/ David Dickinson). A wide range of banking matters, acting for both lenders and borrowers; also regular advice to investment banks on Eurobond issues, and particular expertise in securitisation.

Financial Services: (*Contacts:* Iain Cullen/ Richard Slater). A full service on all matters relating to the financial services industry, including advice on compliance and regulatory issues and on the establishment and promotion of UK and offshore collective investment vehicles, in particular authorised and unauthorised unit trusts, futures and options funds and property funds.

Taxation: (*Contacts:* Peter Nias/ Stephen Coleclough). A complete range of strategic UK and international tax planning services for corporate and private clients.

Employment & Pensions: (*Contacts:* Janet Gaymer/ Charles Scanlan). The preparation of employment documentation, remuneration packages, individual and collective disputes, occupational health and safety, employee incentive schemes, immigration matters and all forms of occupational pension schemes.

Property & Planning: (*Contacts:* Alan Butler/ Stephen Elvidge). All aspects of acquisition, disposal, funding and commercial exploitation of land and building, local government and planning law, including objections and appeals.

Environmental Law: (*Contact:* Stephen Tromans). All areas of environmental law, including waste management, pollution control, civil and criminal liability, insurance and assisting corporate clients in formulating and implementing compliance strategies.

Development & Construction Law: (*Contact:* Robert Bryan). Project structuring and financing, site acquisition and assembly, development agreements, building contracts, professional appointment, collateral warranties, bonds and guarantees, and dispute resolution.

Commercial Litigation: (*Contacts:* Paul Mitchard/ Philip Vaughan). A wide variety of matters including aviation, arbitration, commodities, defamation, fraud, insurance, landlord & tenant, product liability, professional negligence and shipping.

Intellectual Property: (*Contacts:* Kevin Mooney/ Helen Newman). All areas of intellectual property law, both contentious and non-contentious.

Commercial Law: (*Contacts:* Edwin Godfrey/ Jeremy Sivyer). A wide variety of commercial work, ranging from agency, distribution and licensing agreements to international joint ventures and consortia.

EC/ Competition: (*Contacts:* Peter Freeman/ Martin Smith). EC law of all kinds and EC and UK competition law, including mergers, monopolies and restrictive agreements.

NATURE OF CLIENTELE: Clients range from the largest multinational companies and banks to medium and small businesses, from government departments to individuals.

SENIOR PARTNER: Alan Carr
: Alasdair Neil

UK:	
Number of partners:	115
Assistant solicitors:	206
Other fee-earners:	112
INTERNATIONAL:	
Number of Partners:	21
Assistant Solicitors:	63
Other fee-earners:	52

WORKLOAD	
Litigation	25%
Company/commercial & financial services	23%
Property	16%
Commercial/ intellectual property	15%
Banking and capital markets	10%
Tax	9%
Environmental	2%

CONTACTS	
Banking	Graham Rowbotham
Capital markets	David Dickinson
Collective investment schemes	Iain Cullen
Commodities	Jonathan Melrose
Computer law	Rowan Freeland
Construction	Robert Bryan
Consumer law	Edwin Godfrey
Corporate finance	William Knight
EC & competition	Peter Freeman
Employment	Janet Gaymer
Environmental	Stephen Tromans
Financial services	Richard Slater
Immigration	Hilary Belchak
Insolvency	John Houghton
IP	Kevin Mooney
Litigation (commercial)	Paul Mitchard
Litigation (property)	Carol Hewson
Media	Helen Newman
Pensions	Michael Wyman
Pharmaceuticals	Mark Hodgson
Private client	David Way
Property (commercial)	Alan Butler
Securitisation	Jane Borrows
Tax (corporate)	Stephen Coleclough

RECRUITMENT AND TRAINING: The firm will be recruiting 50 trainee solicitors in 1997. Simmons & Simmons is looking for trainees from law and non-law disciplines who have achieved the minimum qualification of a 2:1 degree and who will make good practical lawyers, able to cope with the most demanding work. A comprehensive training programme, for both trainees and qualified fee-earners, includes in-house lectures on a variety of legal business topics, courses in practical legal skills and residential training weekends.

Applications should be made on the firm's own form available on request from the Graduate Recruitment Department.

SIMMONS & SIMMONS

SIMONS MUIRHEAD & BURTON

50 BROADWICK STREET; SOHO, LONDON, W1V 1FF
DX: 44738 Soho Sq

TEL: (0171) 734 4499
FAX: (0171) 734 3263

THE FIRM: Simons Muirhead & Burton, established in 1972, is a fast growing firm offering a comprehensive range of services in the areas of work set out below. The firm undertakes work for commercial and private clients and operates the legal aid scheme in its areas of speciality. The firm aims to provide a quality service at competitive rates.

PRINCIPAL AREAS OF WORK: The firm's strengths lie in media and entertainment law (particularly in television, theatre and publishing), criminal defence work (including commercial fraud and drug trafficking), civil litigation (all aspects including libel work, intellectual property and commercial disputes), immigration and nationality work (all aspects) and Privy Council applications in civil and criminal cases. The firm also has expertise in company and commercial work, residential and commercial conveyancing, employment law and charity law. The firm has, since its inception, specialised in civil liberties and human rights cases.

Media and Entertainment/ Litigation: (*Contact:* Razi Mireskandari).
Crime: (*Contact:* Anthony Burton).
Immigration and Nationality: (*Contact:* Larry Grant).
Property (Commercial): (*Contact:* David Michaels).
Company/ Commercial/ Employment and Charity: (*Contact:* Simon Goldberg).
Privy Council: (*Contact:* Angela Horne).

AGENCY WORK:
1. The location of the firm enables it to service efficiently cases in the High Court and all central London courts and tribunals.
2. The firm also acts as Privy Council agents.

RECRUITMENT AND TRAINING: One trainee solicitor is recruited each Autumn. Application forms are available from the Recruitment Partner, two years in advance.

CONTACT PARTNER: Anthony Burton

Number of partners:	9
Assistant solicitors:	3
Other fee-earners:	14

CONTACTS	
Civil litigation	R. Mireskandari
Company and commercial	R. Mireskandari
	S.M. Goldberg
Conveyancing	D.M. Michaels
Criminal litigation	A.C. Burton
Criminal litigation	B. Spiro
Immigration	L.A. Grant
Media law	R. Mireskandari, S.M. Goldberg

SIMPSON & MARWICK WS

18 HERIOT ROW, EDINBURGH, EH3 6HS
DX: 161 Edinburgh

TEL: (0131) 557 1545
FAX: (0131) 557 4409

THE FIRM: Simpson & Marwick W.S. is a leading litigation practice which has been involved in several high-profile disaster cases in recent years. A full range of private client, property and commercial services are also offered. The firm has offices in Edinburgh, Glasgow, Aberdeen and Dundee.

PRINCIPAL AREAS OF WORK:
Litigation: The firm has particular expertise in actions involving personal injury (*Contact:* G.S. Keyden), public liability claims (*Contact:* M.M. Wood), professional negligence (*Contact:* M.P. Anderson), major accidents and disasters (*Contact:* D.M.G. Russell), medical negligence (*Contact:* Dr. P. Abernethy), judicial review

CHAIRMAN: M. Peter Anderson

Number of partners:	14
Assistant solicitors:	15
Other fee-earners:	13

(Contact: C.A. Shaw), employment matters *(Contact:* J.R. Griffiths), aviation *(Contact:* M.P. Anderson), debt recovery *(Contact:* G. Moffat), the oil industry *(Contact:* D.M.G. Russell) and the construction industry *(Contact:* A.L. Renton).

Corporate and Commercial: *(Contact:* J.K. Miller or R.D. Loudon). The firm advises clients on acquisitions and disposals of business management buy-outs and company administration. The firm also acts for institutional lenders in the preparation of security documentation. All aspects of commercial property work are undertaken.

Private Client: *(Contact:* J.K. Miller or R.D. Loudon). Services provided include estate planning, will preparation, executry work, conveyancing and marketing of residential property.

OTHER OFFICES:

93 West George Street, Glasgow G2 1PB. *Tel:* (0141) 248 2666. *Fax:* (0141) 248 9590. (Contact : P. Wade)

1 Carden Place, Aberdeen AB1 1UT. *Tel:* (01224) 624924. *Fax:* (01224) 626590. (Contact : J.R.B. Leith)

13 Albert Square, Dundee DD1 1XA. *Tel:* (01382) 200373. *Fax:* (01382) 200370. (Contact : J. MacEachern)

WORKLOAD	
Personal injury	35%
Professional negligence	30%
Commercial litigation	15%
Residential property	10%
Healthcare Law	5%
Commercial	5%

SIMPSON MILLAR 101 Borough High Street, London Bridge, London, SE1 1N6 **Tel:** (0171) 407 0781 **Fax:** (0171) 378 1881 **DX:** 39902 London Bridge South **Ptnrs:** 5 **Asst Solrs:** 9 **Other Fee-earners:** 12. The firm was founded in the early 19th century primarily to serve the legal needs of principal land owners and businesses associated with the River Thames. Main areas of practice are personal injury and employment law.

SINCLAIR ROCHE & TEMPERLEY

BROADWALK HOUSE, 5 APPOLD STREET, LONDON, EC2A 2NN
DX: 1075

TEL: (0171) 638 9044
FAX: (0171) 638 0350/1/4

NATURE OF FIRM: A city firm with an international clientele and practice. Founded in 1934 it initially specialised exclusively in shipping law but, whilst retaining strong maritime links, it has developed a full service international legal practice organised into specialised departments and groups which work together to provide an integrated practical approach to business issues.

In addition to the firm's acknowledged experience and expertise in the Far East and Eastern Europe the firm has established links with the world's major business centres.

PRINCIPAL AREAS OF WORK:

General Description: International commercial law with emphasis on transport, banking, finance, tax, litigation and arbitration work, as well as European Community trade and transport law. There are separate departments for company/commercial, ship, asset and project finance, aviation, commercial and shipping litigation and arbitration, marine insurance and casualties, commercial property and tax. The firm has specialist groups concerned with European Community Law, Environmental Law, Oil and Gas and legal aspects of business in Eastern Europe.

Litigation: *(Contact:* Harvey Williams). Shipping and trade-related litigation, particularly cases listed in the Commercial Court; international trade and commodity arbitration.

Ship, Asset and Project Finance: *(Contact:* George Hodgkinson). International ship finance transactions, including negotiation of shipbuilding contracts, leasing, Eurocurrency finance, swap and hedging arrangements and advice on the structuring of transactions and ship registration.

Company/ Commercial: *(Contact:* Kevin Dean and Richard Thomas). Advice on company law, privatisation, structuring of UK and international joint ventures, investment and privatisation projects in central and eastern Europe and the CIS, mergers and acquisitions, offers for sale and placings on the Stock Exchange, offshore listings and EIS's. Advice is also given on EC competition, customs and anti-dumping matters.

SENIOR PARTNER: John Morris

Number of partners:	45
Assistant solicitors:	60
Other fee-earners:	36

WORKLOAD	
Litigation	39%
Ship and project finance	28%
Marine insurance and casualty	11%
Aviation	9%
Company/commercial	8%
Commercial property	4%
EC	1%

CONTACTS	
Aviation and tax	David Relf
Commercial property	Anthony Hurndall
Company/commercial	Kevin Dean
EC law	Richard Thomas, Alfred Merckx
Litigation	Harvey Williams
Marine insurance and casualty	Nigel Taylor
Ship and project finance	George Hodgkinson

Marine Insurance and Casualty: (*Contact:* Nigel Taylor). Litigation arising from collision and salvage cases, including on-board investigation, conduct of public inquiries and other marine environmental cases throughout the world.

Aviation: (*Contact:* David Relf). Advice on acquisition and financing of aircraft, tax based structuring, corporate finance (including capital markets and the establishment of funds) and general commercial issues affecting the industry, regulatory matters, European Community law, insolvency and enforcement issues, liability claims and insurance law and general litigation.

Commercial Property: (*Contact:* Anthony Hurndall). All aspects of transactions involving commercial freehold and leasehold property: development and investment, secured lending, planning and international property projects.

Tax: (*Contact:* David Relf). Advice to clients on English tax law, particularly corporate taxation together with advice on the tax implications and on structuring of international asset and project finance transactions.

NATURE OF CLIENTELE: Major UK and international banks, international shipping companies and cruise lines, property companies, shipyards, airline companies, commodities traders and other commercial trading companies, insurance companies, underwriters, European Commission and Eastern European organisations and institutions.

FOREIGN CONNECTIONS: Offices in Hong Kong, Singapore, Shanghai, Bucharest (representative) and Hanoi and a presence in Brussels. Correspondents in all major cities.

LANGUAGES SPOKEN: French, German, Spanish, Italian, Romanian, Russian, Dutch, Hungarian, Mandarin, Cantonese, Vietnamese, Swedish and Norwegian.

RECRUITMENT AND TRAINING: Legal Staff Partner: Jeff Morgan. Trainee solicitors will be recruited in 1995, when there will also be vacancies for up to ten assistant solicitors.

Training: In-house seminars are held regularly and the Training Partner organises an extensive programme of continuing education for each department covering legal and non-legal issues. The firm is a member of the consortium of City law firms who jointly teach The Trainee Solicitors' Professional Skills Course modules either in-house or at residential weekends in Cambridge.

SINCLAIR TAYLOR & MARTIN 9 Thorpe Close, Portobello Road, London, W10 5XL **Tel:** (0181) 969 3667 **Fax:** (0181) 969 7044 **DX:** 47601 Ladbroke Grove **Ptnrs:** 2 **Asst Solrs:** 6 **Other Fee-earners:** 2. The firm specialises in legal work for charities, housing associations, not-for-profit organisations and local authorities.

WORKLOAD			
Charities	35%	Commercial	25%
Private client/ convey.	15%	Housing association	15%
Crime	10%		

SINGLETONS

EAGLE HOUSE, 67 BROOKE AVENUE, HARROW, MIDDX, HA2 0ND

TEL: (0181) 864 0835
FAX: (0181) 248 3810

THE FIRM Founded in 1994 by well-known competition/ intellectual property solicitor, Susan Singleton, Singletons provides highly specialised advice on EC/ UK competition law, intellectual property, computer/ IT and commercial and EC law to well known public companies and others at low and fixed prices. Susan Singleton is author of a number of books including *EC Competition Law - A Practical Guide for Companies* (Financial Times 1994) and *Introduction to Competition Law* (Pitman 1992) and *Getting Value from Professional Advisers* (Kogan Page 1993) and editor of *IT Law Today, Trading Law*, Comparative Law of Monopolies and joint editor of *Computer Law and Practice*.

CONTACT: Susan Singleton

Number of partners:	1
Other fee-earners:	1

WORKLOAD	
Commercial law/ EC	30%
Competition law	30%
Intellectual property law	25%
Computer/ IT law	15%

SINTON & CO 32 Portland Terrace, Newcastle upon Tyne, Tyne & Wear, NE2 1SQ **Tel:** (0191) 281 5211 **Fax:** (0191) 281 3675 **DX:** 62551 Jesmond **Ptnrs:** 10 **Asst Solrs:** 5 **Other Fee-earners:** 6. General practice with substantial personal injury, litigation department and expertise in company, conveyancing and matrimonial work.

WORKLOAD		
Pers inj/insurance lit	56%	Convey/family/wills/prob 32%

SLATER HEELIS

71 PRINCESS ST, MANCHESTER, M2 4HL
DX: 14334

TEL: (0161) 228 3781
FAX: (0161) 236 5282

THE FIRM: The firm was founded in 1773 and the city offices occupy modernised Georgian premises in the centre of Manchester. Fee earners have access to computer and word processing networks. The majority of the present partners are under 40.

PRINCIPAL AREAS OF WORK:

General Description: Slater Heelis has been involved in the commercial life of Manchester for over 200 years and is now one of the leading firms in the North West, conducting an extensive commercial practice in the region and nationally on a broad client base.

The firm has a strong all-round team which is friendly but highly professional, handling complex high quality work. The firm has expanded considerably in recent years and further expansion is anticipated in the corporate, property and litigation departments.

Company/Commercial: *(Contact Partner:* Peter Renshaw). The work of this department includes listed and other public company work, mergers, re-organisations, acquisitions and disposals of companies and businesses, management buy-outs and all aspects of legal services to all sizes of businesses.

Commercial Property: *(Contact Partner:* Steve Kinsey). *Work includes:* commercial conveyancing and development, support in relation to corporate and commercial transactions, landlord and tenant, planning and housing association work.

Residential Property: *(Contact Partner:* Jarlath Walsh). General domestic conveyancing.

Litigation: *(Contact Partner:* Kevin Jaquiss). The emphasis is on commercial litigation, involving preparations for trial and injunction applications where necessary in substantial High Court actions. There is a significant employment law and industrial tribunal practice. The firm is also well known for its personal injury litigation.

Private Client: *(Contact Partner:* Nick Shaw). The firm has a significant private client practice dealing with all aspects of family law, wills and tax planning, and all aspects of estates and trusts.

Matrimonial and Family: *(Contact Partner:* Mike Hamlin). The firm has a long-standing reputation in family law, personal injury, and other common law claims.

Banking and Insolvency: *(Contact Partner:* Egan Brooks). The firm handles live banking and recovery work, and acts for liquidators and receivers frequently on major receiverships. Two partners are licensed insolvency practitioners.

AGENCY WORK: All types of agency work are undertaken. *Contact:* Mr. K.F. Jaquiss, litigation partner in the Manchester office.

NATURE OF CLIENTELE: Clients include industrial property PLCs and numerous other business organisations including UK subsidiaries of multinationals. The firm acts as North Regional solicitors to a major clearing bank, as well as for other banks and financial institutions.

OTHER OFFICES: Lloyds Bank Building, 1 Tatton Rd, Sale, Greater Manchester M33 1XR. *Tel:* (0161) 969 3131. *Contact:* Mr. S.A. Kinsey.

RECRUITMENT AND TRAINING: Seven vacancies exist for articles with the firm commencing in 1997. Applicants should possess the academic and personal qualities necessary to deal with the challenging nature of the firm's work, a sense of commitment and the ability to work as part of a team, able to relate quickly to the needs of clients. Trainee solicitors are placed with each partner or senior solicitor to whom

CONTACT PARTNER: Mr Christopher Dunn

Number of partners:	18
Assistant solicitors:	18
Other fee-earners:	9

WORKLOAD	
Litigation	27%
Property	23%
Company/ commercial	20%
Insolvency/ banking	17%
Private client	10%
Employment	3%

CONTACTS	
Banking and insolvency	Egan Brooks
Company/ commercial	Peter Renshaw
Housing association	Mike Gaskell
Litigation	Kevin Jaquiss
Matrimonial/ family	Mike Hamlin
Private client	Nick Shaw
Property (commercial)	Steve Kinsey
Property (domestic)	Jarlath Walsh

they are allocated for periods between four and six months, and after the first placement there is consultation over subsequent placements. The training is largely practical, working on client matters from the outset with instruction in that context. Responsibility is given and supervision exercised according to developing ability. The firm seeks to recruit future solicitors from its trainees. Fifteen of the firm's partners were articled with the firm. Applications should be made by letter to Mr. C.F. Dunn at the Manchester office, and accompanied by a full CV.

SLAUGHTER AND MAY

35 BASINGHALL STREET, LONDON, EC2V 5DB
DX: 11 London City EC2

TEL: (0171) 600 1200
FAX: (0171) 726 0038

THE FIRM: Slaughter and May is one of the leading law firms in the world. It has a diverse corporate, commercial and financial practice with offices in the City of London, Paris, Brussels, Hong Kong, Tokyo and New York. It has a staff of more than 1,200 worldwide.

The firm aims to provide a professional service of the highest quality. It enjoys a high reputation for the technical excellence of its lawyers and their commercial understanding and practical, constructive approach. Clients of the firm include governments, professional firms, commercial companies from all business sectors, financial institutions and other organisations.

Much of the firm's work has an international element, its lawyers travel widely and the firm has long-standing relationships with leading lawyers in many countries.

The firm has a distinctive approach to the practice of law and encourages all its lawyers to gain a wide experience in commercial and financial matters so that they offer not only a depth of legal expertise but also versatility and a breadth of commercial experience.

Lawyers in the City of London office are divided into eight departments of which the largest is the corporate and financial department. It is usual for lawyers from several departments to work closely together on each client matter: at the start of each job the client matter partner will select a team tailored to meet the individual commercial and legal requirements of the assignment.

The work of all lawyers is supported by a team of highly qualified information specialists. There is an extensive library and information service and through its own training department the firm provides first class training and on-going professional development for each of its lawyers.

PRINCIPAL AREAS OF PRACTICE:

Corporate and Financial Department: The corporate and financial department advises on all aspects of corporate, commercial and financial law and transactions including mergers and acquisitions, flotations and other securities offerings, capital markets, banking, project and asset finance, privatisation, building societies and insurance, investment funds, energy and natural resources and insolvency and asset recovery.

A separate financial services unit handles advisory and regulatory work in relation to the capital markets and the securities, banking and insurance industries.

Litigation and Arbitration: The firm's litigation and arbitration practice deals with a wide range of proceedings and disputes including hearings before the High Court, the House of Lords and the Privy Council, domestic and international arbitrations, formal inquiries, investigations and inter-jurisdictional disputes.

Intellectual Property: The department advises on the creation, ownership, development, protection, transfer and licensing of all forms of intellectual property rights, trade marks and patents, including dealing with disputes. Data protection and the legal aspects of the use of computer systems are also part of the department's work.

EC and Competition: The department (which includes the Brussels office) has a major practice in UK and EC competition law, particularly in relation to acquisitions and mergers and joint ventures. Its lawyers co-ordinate the anti-trust aspects of transactions in many jurisidictions, advise on compliance and represent clients in relation to inquiries and investigations by the European Commisssion and the Monopolies and Mergers Commission.

SENIOR PARTNER: Giles Henderson CBE

CONTACT PARTNER: Melvyn Hughes

UK:	
Number of partners:	103
Assistant solicitors:	306
Other fee-earners:	159
INTERNATIONAL:	
Number of Partners:	17
Assistant Solicitors:	21
Other fee-earners:	16

WORKLOAD	
Corporate and financial	63%
Commercial litigation	13%
Property (commercial)	8%
Tax	7%
Pensions and employment	4%
EC and competition law	3%
Intellectual property	2%

CONTACTS	
Asset finance	T.A. Kinnersley
Banking	R. Slater
Capital markets	D.T. Frank
Corporate finance	M. Pescod
EC and competition	M.G.C. Nicholson
Environment	J.D. Rice
Financial services/compliance	J.S. Edge
General corporate/commercial	T.G. Freshwater
Insolvency	J.E.F. Rushworth
Intellectual property	C.J. Hickson
Investment funds	C. Hall
Litigation and arbitration	F.W. Neate
Pensions and employment	E.A. Codrington
Project finance & energy	M.J.D. Roberts
Property	P.J. Langley
Taxation	S.M. Edge

Tax: The firm's tax lawyers advise on the tax aspects of transactions (including many where UK and foreign tax systems interact) develop tax-efficient structures and financial instruments and handle taxation disputes. The department has a reputation for highly constructive and innovative work.

Property: Every kind of English legal work on the ownership, management, development and acquisition and sale of land is dealt with.

Environment: The environment practice deals with the growing demand for specialist advice on environmental law across a broad spectrum.

Pensions and Employment: This department deals with all aspects of pensions and employment law, including employee share and benefit schemes, industrial conflicts, sex discrimination, equal pay problems and the pensions and employment aspects of company acquisitions, disposals and takeovers.

Recruitment and Training: Approximately 75 trainee solicitors are recruited every year. Candidates must have a good academic record. Prospective trainees are paid a maintenance allowance, and tuition and examination fees are covered. Applications with a CV should be sent to Neil Morgan, Head of Personnel. There are vacation schemes for students considering law as a career.

Brussels	P.P. Chappatte
Hong Kong	R.J. Thornhill
New York	T.J.B. Pallister
Paris	P.S. Kett
Tokyo	P.A.S. Grindrod

SLEE BLACKWELL 10 Cross Street, Barnstaple, Devon, EX31 1BA **Tel:** (01271) 72128 **Fax:** (01271) 44885/22505 **DX:** 34952 Barnstaple **Ptnrs:** 10 **Asst Solrs:** 2 **Other Fee-earners:** 12. A commercially based practice. Particularly known for litigation. Has an expanding European client base.

WORKLOAD			
Civil litigation	25%	Commercial	20%
Property	20%	Matrimonial	20%
Probate/ taxation	10%	Criminal	5%

SMITH FORT & SYMONDS

30 GREAT UNDERBANK, STOCKPORT, CHES, SK1 1ND
DX: 19658

TEL: (0161) 480 4043
FAX: (0161) 474 7491

THE FIRM: Smith Fort & Symonds has for over 130 years served a wide range of corporate and individual clients in the Manchester area, nationally and overseas.

PRINCIPAL AREAS OF WORK: The commercial team advises on all aspects of setting up, expansion, acquisition and disposal of business. Also copyright and intellectual property, computer software contracts, commercial litigation, commercial property, landlord and tenant issues and debt collection management.

OTHER AREAS OF WORK: Private client services include personal injury litigation, crime, matrimonial and child care; wills, trusts, probate, tax and estate planning and financial services. Legal aid and agency work is undertaken.

OTHER OFFICES: Manchester, Cheadle Hulme and Poynton.

CONTACT PARTNER: Mr T.J. Dennis

Number of partners:	7
Assistant solicitors:	8
Other fee-earners:	7

WORKLOAD	
Commercial litigation	28%
Personal injury, wills, other litigation	20%
Company/ commercial	18%
Commercial property	14%
Domestic conveyancing	12%
Family	8%

SMITH & GRAHAM Church Square Chambers, Hartlepool, Clev, TS24 7HE **Tel:** (01429) 271651 **Fax:** (01429) 231274 **DX:** 60651 **Ptnrs:** 13 **Asst Solrs:** 7 **Other Fee-earners:** 23. Other offices in Billingham, Durham and Hartlepool. The firm focuses on company/ commercial, Eastern Europe, civil litigation, medical negligence, licensing, leisure, crime, conveyancing, probate and family law. Established in 1888.

WORKLOAD			
Comm/prop/licensing	25%	Crime	20%
PI/medical negligence	20%	Private client	18%
Litigation	14%	Other matters	1%

SMITH LLEWELYN PARTNERSHIP 18 Princess Way, Swansea, W. Glam, SA1 3LW **Tel:** (01792) 651234 **Fax:** (01792) 464726 **DX:** 39552 **Ptnrs:** 6 **Asst Solrs:** 3 **Other Fee-earners:** 7. The firm undertakes a full range of work but is also one of the largest medical negligence practices in South Wales.

THE SMITH PARTNERSHIP

COMMERCIAL CENTRE, COLLEGE CHAMBERS, UTTOXETER ROAD, DERBY, DERBYS, DE22 3WZ   DX: 11528 Derby

TEL: (01332) 296888
FAX: (01332) 382301

THE FIRM: Formed in 1987, the firm has grown rapidly through its pro-active and practical approach to its current size with over 140 staff and offices in Derby, Burton-on-Trent, Swadlincote and Stoke-on-Trent.

PRINCIPAL AREAS OF WORK:

Company/ Commercial: All aspects of company and commercial work including acquisitions and mergers, corporate finance, joint ventures, agency and distribution agreements and EC law.

Commercial Litigation: A full general commercial litigation service is provided, including specialisms in insolvency, banking and debt recovery.

Commercial Property: Dealing with the sale and purchase of property, leasing, development, planning taxation and finance and security issues.

Employment: Advice is available on contracts of employment, procedures is cases of dismissal and redundancy and representation before the Industrial Tribunal or Court.

Criminal: Expert advice on all areas of criminal law is provided from all branch offices of the firm, including a Higher Courts unit and a specialism on matters before court-martials.

Intellectual Property: This unit advises on all aspects of intellectual property rights protection.

Family/ Childcare: Dealing with all areas of family law including divorce, separation and a specific specialism in child care issues with members of the Law Society's Children Panel.

Private Client: A full private client service including residential conveyancing, tax planning, probate, trusts and the writing of wills.

Aviation: A specialist unit advising from the major airline to the independent private flier, the airport operator and the flying school. Providing advice on leasing and finance, CAA Regulations, claims handling, sale and purchase and operator agreements.

Defamation: The department handles defamation cases including media litigation.

RECRUITMENT AND TRAINING: The firm usually has about three trainee solicitors in articles at any one time.

FOREIGN LANGUAGES: French, German, Gaelic.

CONTACT PARTNER: Peter Smith

Number of partners:	10
Assistant solicitors:	18
Other fee-earners:	39

WORKLOAD	
Litigation	62%
General commercial	16%
Domestic property	11%
Matrimonial	11%

CONTACTS	
Aviation	Lesley Dixon
Childcare	Graham Dean
Commercial property	Peter Smith
Commercial litigation	Chris Else
Company/ commercial	Matthew Bradley
Crime	Steve Mann
Defamation	Stephen Chittenden
Employment	Amanda Walton
Intellectual Property	Lesley Dixon
Matrimonial	Stephen Chittenden
Personal injury	Simon Richardson
Probate & wills	Angela Hitchcock

A.E. SMITH & SON

FROME HOUSE, LONDON ROAD, STROUD, GLOS, GL5 2AF
DX: 58801

TEL: (01453) 757444
FAX: (01453) 757586

Nailsworth: Contact Partner: T.J. Mugford

Tel: (01453) 832566
Fax: (01453) 835441

THE FIRM: Founded about 1835 the firm operates from offices in Stroud and Nailsworth.

As well as dealing with a very wide range of commercial and private client work, the firm has particular experience in the fields of agricultural law, trusts and probate, property and estate development, advocacy and education (particularly special educational needs). The firm also has connections with European lawyers.

CONTACT PARTNER: J.C. Bridges

Number of partners:	7
Assistant solicitors:	4
Other fee-earners:	2

WORKLOAD			
Litigation	35%	Probate % trusts	35%
Company & commercial	10%	Conveyancing	10%
Family & matrimonial	10%		

SPARLING BENHAM & BROUGH 3 West Stockwell St, Colchester, Essex, CO1 1HQ **Tel:** (01206) 577767 **Fax:** (01206) 564551 **DX:** 3607 **Ptnrs:** 10 **Asst Solrs:** 3 **Other Fee-earners:** 3. Strong in litigation, and landlord and tenant work. Also has a private client, commercial and agricultural practice. Offices in Manningtree (known as *Cyril Cox & Co*) and in Frinton-on-Sea.

SPEECHLY BIRCHAM

BOUVERIE HOUSE, 154 FLEET ST, LONDON, EC4A 2HX
DX: 54

TEL: (0171) 353 3290
FAX: (0171) 353 4825

THE FIRM: Speechly Bircham was formed in 1974 by the amalgamation of two long-established City practices and has expanded considerably since then. The firm advises some very significant commercial and financial institutions from the UK and abroad – but is by no means a large, impersonal organisation, retaining a friendly and professional atmosphere and guaranteeing individual partner contact whatever the scale of the problem.

PRINCIPAL AREAS OF WORK:

Company/ Commercial: (*Contact Partner:* Mervyn Couve). The practice offers expertise in relation to corporate finance (including new issues and mergers and acquisitions), venture capital and MBOs, banking and finance, financial services (particularly in the field of unit trusts) and related areas such as competition, insurance, IT, telecommunications and intellectual property.

Taxation: (*Contact Partner:* John Avery-Jones). The firm is recognised as a leading authority on taxation law, and advises corporate clients and individuals in the UK and overseas. The senior partner is President of the Institute of Taxation and editor of *The British Tax Review*. The department advises on corporate tax planning, VAT, employee benefits, overseas tax and international trusts.

Employment Law: (*Contact Partner:* Alan Julyan). A highly skilled team deals with all aspects of employment law, including equal opportunities, recruitment, contracts and benefit packages. Alan Julyan is the author of *Service Agreements*, a practitioner's guide to this area of the law and other respected publications in the field of employment law.

Litigation: (*Contact Partner:* Bradley Brown). The department has litigation teams in the following areas: landlord and tenant litigation, construction, commercial (including banking and insolvency) and employment law (including unfair dismissal and trade union disputes).

Commercial Property: (*Contact Partner:* Ken Calcutt). The firm has a strong commercial property department and is recognised as one of London's leading firms in this area. Areas of expertise include acquisition and disposal of properties, funding and investment, administration of retail centres, planning and environmental matters (including pollution control and environmental audits), property related litigation (including licensing) and the department has a thriving construction law team which deals with building contracts, warranties and construction disputes.

Private Client: (*Contact Partner:* Richard Kirby). The firm offers a comprehensive service to the private client, including advice on wills, personal tax planning, probate, charitable trusts and the establishment and administration of both UK and offshore trusts.

NATURE OF CLIENTELE: Clients are principally commercial and financial institutions and industrial companies from the UK and abroad along with some local authorities and other public sector organisations and a range of substantial trusts, charitable bodies and private individuals.

RECRUITMENT & TRAINING: The firm recruits around four trainee solicitors a year, and provides a sound practical and well-structured training programme involving a close working relationship with a partner. Applications by letter and CV to Fiona McLaren.

CONTACT PARTNER: Mervyn Couve

Number of partners:	33
Assistant solicitors:	23
Other fee-earners:	20

WORKLOAD	
Commercial property	30%
Corporate	30%
Litigation	25%
Private client and charity law	15%

CONTACTS	
Charity law	John Ward
Commercial property	Ken Calcutt
Construction	Tim Raper
Corporate	Mervyn Couve
Employment	Alan Julyan
Litigation	Bradley Brown
Pensions	Xenia Frostick
Planning & environment	Brian Convery
Private clients	Richard Kirby
Tax	John Avery Jones

SPEECHLY BIRCHAM
S O L I C I T O R S

SPICKETTS Gelliwastad House, 4 Gelliwastad Rd, Pontypridd, M. Glam, CF37 2AU **Tel:** (01443) 407221 **Fax:** (01443) 485789 **DX:** 44350 **Ptnrs:** 6 **Asst Solrs:** 2 **Other Fee-earners:** 3. Known for conveyancing, litigation, criminal and matrimonial law. Other office in Tonypandy. Founded 150 years ago.

WORKLOAD			
Family law/matrimonial	40%	Litigation	20%
Conveyancing	20%	Criminal	15%
Probate & others	5%		

SPIRO GRECH & CO Clifton House, 8 Four Elms Road, Roath, Cardiff, S. Glam, CF2 1LE **Tel:** (01222) 222255 **Fax:** (01222) 450162 **Ptnrs:** 2 **Asst Solrs:** 2 **Other Fee-earners:** 4. A two partner firm dealing exclusively with all aspects of criminal work.

WORKLOAD	
Criminal	100%

SPRECHER GRIER

HANOVER HOUSE, 73-74 HIGH HOLBORN, LONDON, WC1V 6LS
DX: 0041

TEL: (0171) 831 9027
FAX: (0171) 831 2590

CONTACT PARTNER: David Sprecher	
Number of partners:	4
Assistant solicitors:	4
Other fee-earners:	4

THE FIRM: Sprecher Grier is a highly-motivated commercial law firm founded on the philosophy of providing pro-active, practical and results-oriented advice over a broad spectrum of commercial legal work. The firm has particular expertise in banking, corporate recovery and insolvency work for a client base which includes financial institutions, professional practices and major companies and has established an excellent reputation since its formation in 1984.

PRINCIPAL AREAS OF WORK:

Company/ Commercial: *(Contact:* David Sprecher or Emma Shipp). The department has a strong reputation for handling all forms of acquisitions and disposals including complex reconstructions. *Work includes:* mergers and acquisitions, MBOs, and sales of companies and advice on a wide range of non-contentious matters from employee incentive schemes to banking and security documentation.

Insolvency and Debt Recovery: *(Contact:* Ian Grier). The firm is widely recognised as one of the UK's leading specialists in this area, and operates by combining effective legal advice with practical business action. Work involves advising insolvency practitioners on the technicalities of the law, assisting with liquidations, receiverships or petitions for administration orders and voluntary arrangements. Corporate rescue and restructuring is also an area of expertise. The debt recovery team offers speed and efficiency to obtain the best possible solution for clients.

Commercial Litigation: *(Contact:* Ian Grier). A wide range of contentious business is handled, focusing on the need to achieve a fast and cost-effective result for clients. *Work includes:* banking litigation, building and construction disputes, intellectual property matters (especially design copyright), service contracts, disputes involving employment agencies and recruitment consultants, and property related actions.

Commercial Property: *(Contact:* Lesley Goring). A focus on broad business issues underlies advice on the acquisition and disposal of business premises and development ranging from private housing estates to warehousing schemes and industrial parks.

NATURE OF CLIENTELE: Amongst a wide and diverse clientele the firm has expertise in representing airlines, firms of accountants, employment agencies, computer software houses, design and fashion companies, the pharmaceutical industry and companies involved in contract and design within the construction industry.

SQUIRE & CO 49 St. Johns Square, London, EC1V 4JL **Tel:** (0171) 490 3444 **Fax:** (0171) 250 4087/4115 **DX:** 46617 Barbican **Ptnrs:** 6 **Asst Solrs:** 8 **Other Fee-earners:** 7. Non-marine insurance investigations and litigation; insurance and reinsurance disputes; construction arbitrations; fraud and commercial litigation.

STAFFORD YOUNG JONES

THE OLD RECTORY, 29 MARTIN LANE, LONDON, EC4R 0AU
DX: 176 London

TEL: (0171) 623 9490
FAX: (0171) 929 5704

CONTACT PARTNER: Mr A.D. Strong	
Number of partners:	12
Assistant solicitors:	3
Other fee-earners:	4

THE FIRM: A long established City of London practice dealing with a wide range of corporate and private client work, including all types of property transactions, company/ commercial, personal injury, landlord and tenant and general litigation, insolvency, employment, debt recoveries, probate, trusts, wills and family law. Prospective trainee solicitors should write to Paul Adams, at The Old Rectory, enclosing a CV.

STAFFURTH & BRAY

YORK ROAD CHAMBERS, BOGNOR REGIS, W. SUSSEX, PO21 1LT
DX: 31212

TEL: (01243) 864001
FAX: (01243) 860708

THE FIRM: Founded in 1882, Staffurth & Bray offers a broad range of legal services to both private and business clients, including those requiring Legal Aid.

PRINCIPAL AREAS OF WORK:

General Description: *Work includes:* criminal and civil commercial litigation, property litigation (including landlord and tenant and housing law), personal injury, company, insolvency and debt collection, domestic and commercial conveyancing, mental health, family and matrimonial work, including child care, consumer law, defamation, landlord and tenant, licensing, environment, planning, wills, probate, trusts, tax, receiverships, powers of attorney and all aspects of employment law. The firm advises on foreign property transactions. In particular, it has a Spanish property department with two notaries public fluent in that language.

OTHER AREAS OF WORK: The firm undertakes Legal Aid work and is Franchised. It also deals with agency work in Magistrates and County Courts.

FOREIGN CONNECTIONS: The firm has established links with Spain.

OTHER OFFICES: 85 Aldwick Road, Bognor Regis.

CONTACT PARTNER: Roger Turner

Number of partners:	6
Assistant solicitors:	3
Other fee-earners:	11

WORKLOAD	
Civil litigation	27%
Probate/ wills/ trusts/ tax	26%
Crime/ child care work	21%
Conveyancing	18%
Spanish	8%

STALLARDS

DIANA HOUSE, 33-34 CHISWELL STREET, LONDON, EC1Y 4SE
DX: 46629 Barbican

TEL: (0171) 628 2838
FAX: (0171) 588 8220

THE FIRM: The firm was established in 1975, primarily as a company and commercial firm. Its expertise has now developed to include property, banking, insolvency, shipping, construction, financial services, and regulatory matters and it is therefore well equipped to provide a comprehensive and partner led service to its clients. The consistent high quality of the firm's service is demonstrated by the increasing number and range of retained clients.

PRINCIPAL AREAS OF WORK:

Company and Commercial: *(Contact:* Keith Robinson). All aspects of corporate finance, stock exchange work, flotations, acquisitions and mergers, corporate reconstructions and disposals, venture capital and institutional funding, share schemes, intellectual property, employment, and general commercial advice.

Banking: *(Contact:* Susan Breen).Secured lending, drafting and advising on bank documentation, investigations, enforcement of security and insolvency services.

Property: *(Contact:* Jeremy Orpen-Palmer). Property finance and development work, all kinds of industrial and commercial property transactions, commercial and residential investments for overseas clients, estate management, and work for local authorities.

Litigation: *(Contact:* John Taylor). General commercial, employment, landlord and tenant, banking and debt recovery, personal injury and construction disputes, both in the High Court and County Courts.

Shipping: *(Contact:* Rupert Steer). Advice on contentious and non-contentious matters relating to charterparties, bills of lading, commodities, ship construction and repair, sale, purchase and finance, insurance and re-insurance, stevedoring, salvage, towage and collisions.

CLIENTS INCLUDE: publicly quoted companies, stockbrokers, accountants, banks, insurers, P&I clubs and other financial institutions, private companies across a broad range of industries and services, non-resident companies and individuals, and overseas law firms.

CONTACT PARTNER: Keith Robinson

Number of partners:	5
Assistant solicitors:	7
Other fee-earners:	3

WORKLOAD	
Company and commercial	28%
Commercial litigation	26%
Shipping	24%
Property related work	22%

CONTACTS	
Banking/insolvency	Susan Breen
Company/commercial	Keith Robinson
Litigation	John Taylor
Property	Jeremy Palmer
Shipping/ international trade	Rupert Steer

STAMP JACKSON & PROCTER 5 Parliament Street, Hull, Humbs, HU1 2AZ **Tel:** (01482) 324591 **Fax:** (01482) 224048 **DX:** 11927 **Ptnrs:** 11 **Asst Solrs:** 8 **Other Fee-earners:** 12. Work includes company/ commercial, commercial property, commercial litigation, employment, personal injury and medical negligence.

WORKLOAD			
Med neg/personal injury	35%	Commercial litigation	30%
Company and commercial	30%		

STANLEY TEE & COMPANY

6 HIGH ST, BISHOP'S STORTFORD, HERTS, CM23 2LU
DX: 50404 Bishop's Stortford

TEL: (01279) 755200
FAX: (01279) 758400

THE FIRM: Established over 75 years ago Stanley Tee & Company is a progressive firm, which has expanded rapidly within the last decade. The firm offers a comprehensive range of high quality legal services to its private and commercial clients.

PRINCIPAL AREAS OF WORK:

Company/ Commercial: (*Contact:* Rodney Stock). *Work includes:* all aspects of company and commercial work, mergers and acquisitions, employment, liquor licensing and leisure. The firm is well known for its commercial work, including transactions for insurance companies and PLCs.

Litigation: (*Contact:* David Redfern). *Work includes:* commercial litigation, debt collection, property disputes, criminal law, family and matrimonial law and personal injury.

Property: (*Contact:* Bob Elms). The firm has a substantial property practice. The emphasis is on agricultural and commercial property and major development work.

Private Client: (*Contact:* Richard Tee). This department is noted for its expertise in wills, tax, estate planning, Court of Protection work, trusts and probate, with special emphasis on advice to the firm's substantial agricultural clientele.

CONTACT PARTNER: Rodney E. Stock

Number of partners:	11
Assistant solicitors:	8
Other fee-earners:	5

CONTACTS	
Company/ commercial	Rodney Stock
Litigation	David Redfern
Private client	Richard Tee
Property	Bob Elms

STEEDMAN RAMAGE WS

6 ALVA STREET, EDINBURGH, EH2 4QQ
DX: 95 Edinburgh

TEL: (0131) 226 3781
FAX: (0131) 225 8329

THE FIRM: Established in 1894, Steedman Ramage is one of Scotland's leading commercial practices offering broad experience in all of its departments and is currently best known for the quality of its commercial property services.

PRINCIPAL AREAS OF WORK:

Commercial Property: (*Contact Partner:* Sandy Reid). The department is noted in particular for its involvement in the retail world and specialises in major land developments, all other types of property development, investment and funding, commercial leasing (for landlord and tenant), joint ventures, freehold and leasehold sale and purchase, property related aspects of cross-border corporate or commercial deals, planning, and commercial finance and security work.

Corporate: (*Contact Partner:* Simon Brown). The department has a wide ranging practice with particular experience in management buy-outs, distribution agreements, media and entertainment, insolvency, franchising, sales, acquisitions and mergers, share schemes, intellectual property, joint ventures, publishing and all types of commercial contracts.

Litigation: (*Contact Partner:* Victoria Craig). Practice areas include: commercial litigation generally including contractual disputes, mediation, arbitration, copyright and intellectual property, personal and corporate insolvency, employment and industrial tribunal work, debt recovery, personal injury and medical negligence, defamation, property, planning and environmental law, judicial review, matrimonial law, interdict and reparation.

CONTACT PARTNER: Mr A.N. Reid

Number of partners:	12
Assistant solicitors:	16
Other fee-earners:	10

CONTACTS	
Commercial property	Sandy Reid
Corporate	Simon Brown
Litigation	Victoria Craig
Private client	Richard Austin

SOLICITORS

Private Client Department: *(Contact Partner:* Richard Austin). All types of private client work are undertaken including residential conveyancing, estates and farms, trusts, wills and executries, charities, tax planning and investment.

FOREIGN LANGUAGES: French, German, Italian.

INTERNATIONAL CONNECTIONS & ASSOCIATED OFFICES: Member of International Bar Association, Union Des Avocats Europeen, Union Internationale Des Avocats.

STEEL & SHAMASH 13 Baylis Road, London, SE1 7AA **Tel:** (0171) 633 0333 **Fax: Ptnrs:** 4 **Asst Solrs:** 4 **Other Fee-earners:** 4. The firm is known for its expertise in public and administrative law and electoral law. It also handles criminal, mental health, housing and family matters.

STEELE & CO 2 The Norwich Business Park, Whiting Rd, Norwich, Norfolk, NR4 6DJ **Tel:** (01603) 627107 **Fax:** (01603) 625890 **DX:** 5218 **Ptnrs:** 13 **Asst Solrs:** 6 **Other Fee-earners:** 22. With nine offices throughout East Anglia the firm undertakes a broad range of work including licensing, planning and private client matters.

WORKLOAD			
Commercial	33%	Matrimonial/ criminal	18%
Litigation	17%	Private client/fin	16%
Comm/domestic convey	16%		

STEELE RAYMOND

VANDALE HOUSE, POST OFFICE RD, BOURNEMOUTH, DORSET, BH1 1BX
DX: 7643

TEL: (01202) 294566
FAX: (01202) 552285

THE FIRM: Steele Raymond was formed in 1979 and has expanded rapidly since that date, building up a wide range of business clients both in this country and abroad. The firm advises on all areas of company, commercial and business law, but also has a substantial private client practice.

PRINCIPAL AREAS OF WORK:

General Description: *Work includes:* company and business sales and purchases, company formations and reorganisations, partnership matters, intellectual property, EC law, competition law, commercial contracts (including computer contracts), aviation, commercial property matters, town and country planning, environmental law, insolvency and commercial litigation, personal injury, professional and medical negligence, Education law.

NATURE OF CLIENTELE: The firm advises a wide range of clients including individuals, partnerships, housing associations, higher, further and other educational bodies, insolvency practitioners and private and public companies and insurance companies.

OTHER OFFICES: 31 West St, Wimborne, Dorset BH21 1JT. *Contact:* Mr. John Andrews. All areas of work are undertaken, other than criminal matters.

AGENCY WORK: The firm undertakes work, other than criminal work, on an agency basis – *Contact:* Simon Outten or John Andrews.

RECRUITMENT AND TRAINING: The firm has vacancies for two trainee solicitors and normally has vacancies for specialised staff in various parts of its practice. Strong emphasis is placed on training at all levels.

FOREIGN CONNECTIONS: Increasingly the firm's work involves an overseas element, and strong contacts have been developed with legal firms overseas, especially in other EC countries and North America.

CONTACT PARTNER: Mr W.B. Oliver

Number of partners:	12
Assistant solicitors:	8
Other fee-earners:	5

WORKLOAD	
Company and commercial	35%
Commercial litigation	33%
Commercial property	19%
Private client	13%

CONTACTS	
Aviation/ medical negligence	John Andrews
Commercial litigation	Simon Outten
Commercial property	John Daniels/Bill Oliver
Company & comm.	Paul Longland/David Steele
Education	Bill Oliver
Family	Sue Adams
Insolvency, Landlord & tenant	Julian Fenn
Partnership	John Raymond
Personal injury	John Andrews/Peter Rolph
Private client	Paul Causton
Residential developments	Sue Middleton

STEGGLES PALMER 2 Bedford Row, London, WC1R 4BU **Tel:** (0171) 404 4477 **Fax:** (0171) 430 1300 **DX:** 114 Ch.Ln. **Ptnrs:** 6 **Asst Solrs:** 7 **Other Fee-earners:** 6. Known both for its commercial work in the company/ commercial, litigation and property fields and for its work in the employment, and personal injury fields.

WORKLOAD			
Company & commercial	32%	Personal injury	28%
Property	20%	Commercial litigation	20%

STEPHEN RIMMER & CO Hyde Gardens, Eastbourne, E. Sussex, BN21 4PX **Tel:** (01323) 644222 **Fax:** (01323) 733034 **DX:** 6906 **Ptnrs:** 7 **Asst Solrs:** 5 **Other Fee-earners:** 7. A general broad-based practice handling commercial law, general litigation, matrimonial, probate, and property.

WORKLOAD			
Crime	25%	Conveyancing/property	20%
Matrimonial and family	15%	Civil litigation	10%
Personal injury	10%	Probate and trusts	10%

STEPHENS INNOCENT 21 New Fetter Lane, London, EC4A 1AP **Tel:** (0171) 353 2000 **Fax:** (0171) 353 4443 **Ptnrs:** 5 **Asst Solrs:** 13 **Other Fee-earners:** 6. Specialists in the visual arts, and all aspects of the media including libel, film, TV, publishing and fine art. Also human rights.

STEPHENSON HARWOOD

ONE, ST PAUL'S CHURCHYARD, LONDON, EC4M 8SH
DX: 64

TEL: (0171) 329 4422
FAX: (0171) 606 0822

THE FIRM: Stephenson Harwood is a major international firm with a leading reputation and has been established in the City for over 150 years. It is also in Brussels, Guangzhou, Hong Kong, Kuwait and Madrid and is in association with Fidal, the largest law firm in France. Stephenson Harwood's core areas of practice are Corporate, Banking and Litigation. It has three further departments covering Property, Shipping and Tax and a number of specialist groups enabling the firm to advise on virtually every type of commercial and financial transaction.

SENIOR PARTNER: Anthony Isaacs	
Number of partners:	70
Assistant solicitors:	96
Other fee-earners:	45

AREAS OF PRACTICE:

Banking:	Tony Stockwell
Company and Commercial:	Patrick Rodier
Competition:	Antony Mair
Construction:	Steven Wait
Corporate Finance:	Richard Ufland
Employment:	Kate Brearley
Environment:	David Cuckson
European Community:	Antony Mair
Fraud and Business Crime:	Tony Woodcock
Financial Services:	Andrew Sutch
Insolvency and Asset Recovery:	Geoffrey Woolf
Insurance and Reinsurance:	Michael Wilson
Intellectual Property and Information Technology:	Mark Lewis
Litigation, Arbitration and Dispute Resolution:	Christopher Elwen
Matrimonial and Family:	Jonathan Walsh
Pensions:	Michael Cowley
Private Clients, Trusts and Charities:	Mark Baily
Privatisations/Ports:	Christopher Tite
Probate and Administration of Estates:	Robert Partridge
Property Acquisitions, Sales, Finance and Development:	Colin Mackenzie-Grieve
Property Litigation:	Kenneth Duncan
Ship Finance:	Graham Burns
Shipping:	David Slade
Tax:	John Carrell
Town and Country Planning:	Barry Jeeps

STEPHENSONS 26 Union St, Leigh, Lancs, WN7 1AT **Tel:** (01942) 608942 **Fax:** (01942) 679778 **DX:** 22504 **Ptnrs:** 15 **Asst Solrs:** 11 **Other Fee-earners:** 40. An established general practice with a mixed client base, handling substantial legal aid work. Authorised to represent parties at the Mental Health Review Tribunal and the Children Panel.

STEPHENS & SCOWN

26-28 SOUTHERNHAY EAST, EXETER, DEVON, EX1 1RS
DX: 8305

TEL: (01392) 210700
FAX: (01392) 74010

THE FIRM: Founded in the 1930s, the firm has since become a substantial practice with five offices throughout Cornwall and Devon. The two major offices in St. Austell and Exeter are organised into particular departments; the other offices are general practices. Extensive use is made of word processors and computers, the latter providing support systems in several areas of practice.

The firm was one of the first to be granted a legal aid franchise and is a member of LawGroup. Three solicitors at the Exeter office have been granted rights of advocacy in the High Court.

AGENCY WORK: All types of work undertaken.

CHARGES: Fees are normally charged on an hourly basis. Quotations are given for residential conveyancing but fixed fees can be agreed in advance for certain types of work including debt recovery.

PRINCIPAL AREAS OF WORK:

General Description: The firm offers a wide range of legal services and has a good reputation in a number of areas including company/ commercial, agricultural, planning, mining and minerals, waste disposal, building estate development, personal injury claims, commercial litigation, building and construction law and insolvency. The major areas of expansion are in commercial, agricultural and civil litigation.

Company/ Commercial: A number of partners and assistant solicitors in all offices deal with company and commercial work. The principal offices offer 'Businesslink' – an advice service for small and starter businesses. The range of work includes planning, quarrying, mining and landfill matters.

Property: *Commercial:* General sale and purchase of commercial property, tenancy agreements.

Residential: The branches at St. Austell and Truro offer the advantage of computerised conveyancing. The firm also provides a service for builder/ developers, handling land acquisitions and plot sales with computer support.

Litigation: A strong team in this department whose work includes building and construction disputes, insolvency, employment and industrial relations disputes, landlord and tenant, general civil litigation and personal injury claims. The Truro and Exeter offices operate 'Debtlink', a computerised debt recovery system: all of the offices have access to this system.

Agricultural Law: The firm is one of the leading agricultural practices in the West Country, with a large well established clientele. Work includes litigation, agricultural tenancy law, milk quota regulations, agricultural tax planning, farm conveyancing and pollution claims.

OTHER AREAS OF WORK: Wills and probate (3 partners), family, childcare and matrimonial (5 partners), criminal and licensing (3 partners).

NATURE OF CLIENTELE: The firm has a wide range of clients from major PLCs and institutions to individuals. As well as being a regional practice the firm has clients both nationally and internationally.

LANGUAGES SPOKEN: French, German.

RECRUITMENT: The firm recruits four trainee solicitors each year. There are also annual vacancies for assistant solicitors and executives – either as replacements or as a result of continued expansion.

BRANCH OFFICES:
St. Austell: (8 partners, 8 assistant solicitors, 13 other fee-earners).
Truro: (4 partners, 5 assistant solicitors, 5 other fee-earners).
Liskeard: (1 partner, 2 other fee-earners).
Lostwithiel: (1 partner).

CONTACT PARTNER: Mr Roger Keast

Number of partners:	26
Assistant solicitors:	29
Other fee-earners:	27

WORKLOAD	
Commercial and civil litigation	45%
Commercial (other)	22%
Matrimonial and family	12%
Conveyancing	11%
Crime	5%
Probate and trusts	5%

CONTACTS	
Agriculture	Martin Clayden, Richard Jones
Commercial/ civil litigation	Chris Harper
	Mark Stubbs
Company and commercial	Roger Keast
	Jonathan Church
Conveyancing	Michael Northcott
	Michael Beadel
Crime	Stephen Nunn, John Evans
Matrimonial and family	Peter Payne
	Michael Lowry
Planning	Richard Hull, Ian Lamond
Private client	Alan Williamson, Ian Pawley

STEPIEN LAKE GILBERT & PALING

7 ST. BRIDE STREET, LONDON, EC4A 4AS
DX: 9 London

TEL: (0171) 936 2288
FAX: (0171) 936 2109

THE FIRM: The firm was founded in April 1991 formerly being the property department of one of the oldest firms in the City. The firm's major activities are in the commercial property field and this covers all aspects of commercial and residential development, banking, secured lending, investment and property finance.

NATURE OF CLIENTELE: The firm acts for a number of banks, major commercial and residential developers and a number of UK and overseas investors. The firm also acts for a number of UK property investment funds.

RECRUITMENT AND TRAINING: Recruitment Partner: M.W. Thomas.

CONTACT PARTNER: Mr S. Paul Paling

Number of partners:	5
Assistant solicitors:	3

WORKLOAD	
Commercial property	90%
Corporate (property related)	10%

STEVEN FISHER 19 Cato Street, London, W1H 5HR **Tel:** (0171) 262 3240 **Fax:** (0171) 706 2940 **Ptnrs:** 2 **Asst Solrs:** 1 **Other Fee-earners:** 1. Specialist entertainment law firm, with expertise in music, TV, film and video law and also providing a range of other services including property, probate, wills, trusts, litigation and company/ commercial.

WORKLOAD			
Property	30%	Music and entertainment	30%
Litigation	20%	Company and commercial	10%
Probate/wills/trusts	5%		

STEVENS & BOLTON

1 THE BILLINGS, WALNUT TREE CLOSE, GUILDFORD, SURREY, GU1 4YD
DX: 2423 Guildford 1

TEL: (01483) 302264
FAX: (01483) 302254

THE FIRM: Stevens & Bolton is one of Surrey's largest firms, and is well known for its extensive commercial practice in Guildford. It has experienced litigation and commercial property departments, an established reputation in the field of company law, and is able to combine specialist taxation advice with its other areas of practice. The firm also has a strong private client office in Farnham, which has been particularly successful at attracting business away from City firms.

PRINCIPAL AREAS OF WORK:

Company/ Commercial: (*Contact Partner:* Richard Baxter). The firm has considerable experience in the acquisition and disposal of businesses, MBOs, Stock Exchange transactions, corporate restructurings, venture capital, business expansion schemes and insolvency work. In addition, general commercial work includes: banking, computer and intellectual property law, employment and pensions,energy, franchising, licensing and UK and EC competition law.

Commercial Property and Planning: (*Contact Partner:* Michael Laver). This department is equipped to handle a wide range of freehold and leasehold transactions, including funding and security issues, rent reviews, planning, taxation and environmental matters. The firm also provides a comprehensive service for developers, agricultural clients and residential property matters.

Litigation: (*Contact Partner:* Paul Lambdin). A recently expanded department handles: UK and international contractual disputes, employment problems including tribunal work, personal injury claims, shareholder and partnership disputes, international trade, insolvency and building disputes. A cost effective debt recovery service is provided, and family and child care problems are dealt with by a separate specialist unit.

Private Client: (*Contact Partner:* Nicholas Acomb). The firm has a strong reputation in this area, advice ranging from wills and probate to personal tax planning including UK and offshore trusts. The firm also handles more complex institutional trust work, often for overseas clients. Charity work is also handled by this department.

CLIENTELE: UK and overseas clients include listed public companies, large private companies, partnerships and individuals.

OTHER OFFICES:
5 Castle Street, Farnham, Surrey GU9 7HT. *Tel:* (01252) 725040. *Fax:* (01252) 723501. *DX:* 32800 Farnham.

CONTACT PARTNER: Richard A. Baxter

Number of partners:	12
Assistant solicitors:	5
Other fee-earners:	12

WORKLOAD	
Litigation	30%
Company/ commercial	25%
Commercial property	18%
Private client	12%
Other property	10%
Family/ matrimonial	5%

CONTACTS	
Commercial property	Michael Laver
Commercial litigation	Richard King
Company/ commercial	Richard Baxter
Computer Law	Tudor Alexander
Employment	Paul Lambdin
Energy Law	Michael Combes
Family/ matrimonial	Nicholas Walton-Jones
Insolvency	Paul Lambdin
Personal Injury	Janet Waine
Personal tax & trust	Nicholas Acomb
Planning & environmental	Catherine Davey
Residential property	Andrew Bussy
Wills & probate	Michael Hunter

STEWARTS 63 Lincoln's Inn Fields, London, WC2A 3LW **Tel:** (0171) 242 6462 **Fax:** (0171) 831 6843 **DX:** 369 London **Ptnrs:** 8 **Asst Solrs:** 10 **Other Fee-earners:** 6. A small but broadly based general practice advising on company formations, commercial and distribution agreements, intellectual property, tax planning, partnerships, employment law and personal injury. It also has extensive banking and finance experience.

STEWART & WATSON 59 High Street, Turriff, Grampian, AB5 7EL **Tel:** (01888) 563773 **Fax:** (01888) 563773 ext 32 **Ptnrs:** 7 **Other Fee-earners:** 1. The firm undertakes a broad range of work and is particularly known for its agricultural law expertise.

STIBBE SIMONT MONAHAN DUHOT

66 GRESHAM STREET, LONDON, EC2V 7NH

TEL: (0171) 600 4400
FAX: (0171) 600 4411

THE FIRM: The firm is the result of mergers between Stibbe, Blaisse & De Jong (Amsterdam), Simont & Simont (Brussels) and Monahan & Duhot (Paris) completed in 1991/1992 and now operates as a truly multinational partnership of Dutch, Belgian and French lawyers. The history of the constituent parts of the firm goes back to the beginning of the century. The firm has 85 partners. It is one of the leading law firms in each of its three home jurisdictions.

PRINCIPAL AREAS OF PRACTICE: The firm is a full service law firm with an internationally oriented general commercial practice and special emphasis on mergers and acquisitions, banking, securities, corporate and structured finance, project finance, real estate, telecommunications, intellectual and industrial property, environmental law, administrative law, insolvency, litigation and arbitration; the firm distinguishes itself from many other large law firms in Continental Europe because of its specialised tax practice.

OTHER OFFICES: Principal offices in Amsterdam, Brussels and Paris; branch office in New York.

CONTACT PARTNER: Jaap Willeumier

LAWYERS:
London: 3
Worldwide: 350

WORKLOAD	
Banking, finance and securities	70%
Mergers and acquisitions	25%
Miscellaneous	5%

STITT & CO 4 Paper Buildings, Temple, London, EC4Y 7HA **Tel:** (0171) 583 4834 **Fax:** (0171) 353 6801 **DX:** 1052 **Ptnrs:** 3 **Asst Solrs:** 2. The firm specialises in litigation, particularly Bar-related and sports injury cases.

STOCKLER CHARITY 2-3 Cursitor Street, Chancery Lane, London, EC4A 1NE **Tel:** (0171) 404 6661 **Fax:** (0171) 404 6717 **DX:** 445 London **Ptnrs:** 4 **Asst Solrs:** 2 **Other Fee-earners:** 1. Recently formed niche practice with expertise in all aspects of commercial and marine litigation and arbitration including commodity trading disputes.

STONEHAM LANGTON & PASSMORE 8 Bolton St, Piccadilly, London, W1Y 8AU **Tel:** (0171) 499 8000 **Fax:** (0171) 629 4460 **DX:** 37223 **Ptnrs:** 17 **Asst Solrs:** 8 **Other Fee-earners:** 20. The firm's areas of practice are company/commercial, commercial litigation, property and private client with a considerable international element.

STONE KING & WARDLE

13 QUEEN SQUARE, BATH, AVON, BA1 2HJ
DX: 8001 Bath

TEL: (01225) 337599
FAX: (01225) 335437

THE FIRM: Established in 1785, Stone King & Wardle has a substantial commercial and private client practice in the West Country, where it is well known for its matrimonial and family work. It is also known nationally for its work for religious and educational charities.

NATURE OF CLIENTELE: The firm's work is divided between private clients and, in the commercial sphere, small to medium-sized businesses, schools, religious and other charities, and landed estates.

OTHER OFFICE: 3 Southwick Mews, London W2 2JG.
Tel: (0171) 262 4663 *Fax:* (0171) 402 8434

CONTACT: Steven Greenwood

Number of partners:	8
Assistant solicitors:	7
Other fee-earners:	6

WORKLOAD	
Private client (probate/conveyancing)	28%
Private client litigation	26%
Commercial	22%
Charities and education	16%
Commercial litigation	8%

STONES

NORTHERNHAY PLACE, EXETER, DEVON, EX4 3QQ
DX: 8306 Exeter

TEL: (01392) 51501
FAX: (01392) 57007

THE FIRM: One of the largest practices in Exeter, Stones is divided into three departments, company/ commercial, litigation and private client, with teams drawn from departments as relevant to handle work. Extensive use is made of information technology. A central computer provides support systems throughout the firm with specialised packages for domestic conveyancing, probate, trust and debt collection with networked PCs for fee earners and secretaries.

PRINCIPAL AREAS OF WORK: The firm offers a wide range of legal services and has a particularly strong reputation in commercial litigation, contract disputes, charity law, company/ commercial, insolvency, timeshare and personal injury claims (speciality in international ski law and holiday claims). It has an experienced matrimonial unit with Children Panel members. The private client department offers expertise in personal tax and financial planning and agricultural work. The major areas of expansion are in insolvency, personal injury (in particular travel industry claims), timeshare and commercial contract disputes.

FOREIGN CONNECTIONS: The firm is a founder member of Omni Juris, an EEIG registered in Paris with members in France, Germany, Italy, Belgium, the Netherlands, Spain, Luxembourg and Portugal. Members are shortly expected in Norway, Greece and the USA.

LANGUAGES SPOKEN: French, German, Spanish and Maltese.

MANAGING PARTNER: W.H. Winterbotham

Number of partners:	12
Assistant solicitors:	7
Other fee-earners:	7

CONTACTS	
Commercial property	C Rundle
Company/ commercial	A E C Lloyd
Construction & civil eng.	P M Buechel
Employment	B Courtenay-Stamp
Family	D I Howell-Richardson
Insolvency	A E C Lloyd
Intellectual property	A E C Lloyd
Licensing/ leisure	T H S Bourne
Litigation	B Courtenay-Stamp
Personal injury	B Courtenay-Stamp
Residential property	P Tucker
Wills, trusts, probate, tax	M B Harris

STONES PORTER

26 FARRINGDON STREET, LONDON, EC4A 4AQ
DX: 1056

TEL: (0171) 248 9991
FAX: (0171) 236 4025

THE FIRM: Stones Porter is well known for its company/ commercial, litigation and property work and acts for several major companies and institutions.

PRINCIPAL AREAS OF WORK:

Company/ Commercial: *Work includes:* share and loan issues, venture capital investments, Stock Exchange listings, USM admissions, joint ventures, management buy-outs, share options, pension schemes, corporation tax, capital allowances,

CONTACT PARTNER: Hugh Edmunds

Number of partners:	12
Assistant solicitors:	9
Other fee-earners:	6

partnership agreements and disputes, contracts of employment, terms and conditions of trading, agency agreements, intellectual property, computer agreements, commercial and trade contracts, franchising, EC law, competition law and banking securities.

Property: *Work includes:* planning, development, building contracts, joint ventures, town centre developments, shopping centres, business parks, retail parks, property management and leases.

Litigation: *Work includes:* breach of contract, misrepresentation, professional negligence, intellectual property, employment law, landlord and tenant disputes, building contract disputes, professional indemnity insurance, planning proceedings and disciplinary tribunals.

Insolvency: *Work includes:* receivership, business sales, winding-up, bankruptcy, debt recovery and property possession actions.

Private Client: *Work includes:* tax planning, settlements and trusts, investment advice, life assurance and pensions, foreign domicile and residence, wills and probate, estate administration, Court of Protection and personal insolvency.

NATURE OF CLIENTELE: The firm has considerable experience in acting for banks, institutions, manufacturing and distribution companies, retailers and property developers.

WORKLOAD	
Commercial property	35%
Landlord & tenant/housing assoc.	19%
Insolvency/ realisations/ banking	17%
Commercial litigation	15%
Company/ commercial	9%
Private client	5%

CONTACTS	
Banking/ realisations	Heather Leeson
Commercial property	Guy Palmer
Company/ commercial	James Purves
Franchising	Nina Moran Watson
Housing association	Christopher Smith
Insolvency	Hugh Edmunds
Litigation	Roger Hanson/Christopher Woodruff
Private client	Stephen Gallico

STRINGER SAUL

MARCOL HOUSE, 293 REGENT STREET, LONDON, W1R 7PD
DX: 42701·

TEL: (0171) 631 4048
FAX: (0171) 636 2306

THE FIRM: Stringer Saul is a commercial law firm with a commitment to the provision of a quality service. Listed below are the principal areas of practice with contact names.

PRINCIPAL AREAS OF WORK:
Corporate Finance;
Mergers and Acquisitions: *(Contact:* David Smith).
Asset Finance; Transportation
and Equipment Leasing
(including Aviation): *(Contact:* Philip Saul).
Corporate Advice including:
– Insolvency, reconstruction
and recovery *(Contact:* David Smith).
– Pharmaceuticals; product acquisition and regulatory *(Contact:* John Murphy).
– Company secretarial services *(Contact:* David Smith).
Intellectual Property: *(Contact:* John Murphy).
Banking and Secured Lending: *(Contact:* Martin Ackland).
EC and Other International: *(Contact:* John Murphy).
Taxation: *(Contact:* Paul Yerbury).
Litigation
(including intellectual property, administrative law
and employment): *(Contact:* Diana Sternfeld).
Building Contract Disputes: *(Contact:* Martin Russell).
Commercial Property
(including development
and construction): *(Contact:* Geoffrey Stringer).
Planning Environmental and
Local Government: *(Contact:* Alan Ashley).

FOREIGN CONNECTIONS: Stringer Saul has strong connections with overseas lawyers and accountants and regularly acts for overseas clients.

CONTACT PARTNER: Geoffrey Stringer

Number of partners:	15
Assistant solicitors:	5
Other fee-earners:	2

WORKLOAD	
Company/ commercial	46%
Litigation	32%
Property	19%
Tax	3%

CONTACTS	
Company/ commercial	John Murphy
Litigation	Diana Sternfeld
Property	Geoffrey Stringer
Taxation	Paul Yerbury

STRONACHS 12 Carden Place, Aberdeen, Grampian, AB9 1FW **Tel:** (01224) 643573 **Fax:** (01224) 648217 **DX:** AB 41 **Ptnrs:** 18 **Asst Solrs:** 12 **Other Fee-earners:** 8. One of the larger firms in Aberdeenshire, Stronachs is known for its company/ commercial work and property/ estate agency services. A broad range of private client services are also provided.

WORKLOAD			
Convey/estate agency	30%	Corporate/commercial	30%
Litigation	20%	Private client	20%

STUCHBERY STONE 1 Park Street, Maidenhead, Berks, SL6 1SN **Tel:** (01628) 21141 **Fax:** (01628) 74117 **Ptnrs:** 9 **Asst Solrs:** 7 **Other Fee-earners:** 7. Known for its civil litigation and company/ commercial departments. Also handles wills, probate and conveyancing work. The firm is over 100 years old.

STUDIO LEGALE SUTTI

19 PRINCES ST, LONDON, W1R 7RE

TEL: (0171) 409 1384
FAX: (0171) 409 1384

THE FIRM: Studio Legale Sutti has been established in Milan for about forty years. Having recently merged with the firm of Monti & Partners, the practice offers a comprehensive range of commercial law services. The activity of the newly merged firm is organised across three main departments: commercial and company law, intellectual property and employment.

PRINCIPAL AREAS OF WORK: The London Office operates as a front desk, providing, through also a high speed encrypted link with the Milanese offices, a full range of consultative, advisory and litigation services within the Italian jurisdiction to British law firms and their clients, as well as to local corporations and investors.This service covers the following areas of specialisation: company law and commercial contracts, international contracts, foreign investments, distributorship, agency and franchise arrangements, EC and competition law, banking law, insolvency, product liability, entertainment law, industrial property advice and litigation, industrial models, licence negotiation, technology transfer, advertising law, labour law, employment law, employer's liability, industrial relations and pensions law.

INTERNATIONAL ASSOCIATIONS: The practice is a member of LEGIT (Specialists in Legal Information Technology), INDICAM (Institute for the Protection of Trade Marks), American Chamber of Commerce in Italy, British Chamber of Commerce for Italy, Italian Chamber of Commerce for Great Britain.

MAIN OFFICE: Via Montenapoleone 8, 20121 Milan, Italy. *Tel:* (+ 39 2) 762041 *Fax:* (+ 39 2) 76204 805, 76204 806. *Internet:* sutti@ibm.net

CONTACT LAWYER: Davide Braghini

LAWYERS:	
London:	2
Worldwide:	23

WORKLOAD	
Commercial/ banking	45%
Intellectual property/ competition	35%
Employment	20%

Studio Legale Sutti

STURTIVANT & CO

17 BULSTRODE ST, LONDON, W1M 5FQ

TEL: (0171) 486 9524
FAX: (0171) 224 3164

THE FIRM: Established in 1985, and well-known as a specialist practice which is devoted exclusively to UK immigration law. The principal, Karen Sturtivant, is an active member of various professional associations concerned with Immigration Law and she regularly lectures and gives seminars on this subject.

PRINCIPAL AREAS OF WORK: All types of immigration work undertaken; primarily client representation for work permits, business residence and other residence categories. Also settlement; extension of stay; visitors, studies and temporary stay. Appeals to Adjudicators and Tribunals; Judicial Review and deportation and removal cases.

ADDITIONAL AREAS: Nationality and citizenship problems.

CLIENTELE: Wide corporate and private client base.

FOREIGN CONNECTIONS: Contacts with immigration lawyers in many other jurisdictions.

CONTACT PARTNER:
Miss Karen L. Sturtivant

Number of partners:	1
Assistant solicitors:	1

WORKLOAD	
UK immigration & nationality law & work permits	100%

SUGARÉ & CO 36 Park Square, Leeds, W. Yorks, LS1 2NY **Tel:** (0113) 244 6978 **Fax:** (0113) 245 5708 **Ptnrs:** 3 **Other Fee-earners:** 6. Known for criminal law, matrimonial law, conveyancing and civil ltigation.

SWEPSTONE WALSH 9 Lincoln's Inn Fields, London, WC2A 3BP **Tel:** (0171) 404 1499 **Fax:** (0171) 404 1493 **DX:** 142 **Ptnrs:** 4 **Asst Solrs:** 4 **Other Fee-earners:** 3. Established in the defamation, publishing, entertainment and media fields, Swepstone Walsh is also long established in the commercial property and private client departments.

SWINNERTON ASHLEY-CLAYDON 6 Foster Lane, London, EC2V 6HH **Tel:** (0171) 726 4807 **Fax:** (0171) 600 7303 **Ptnrs:** 1 **Asst Solrs:** 1. A niche practice specialising in dry shipping.

WORKLOAD	
Ship/ins./comm arbit	100%

SYDNEY MITCHELL Cavendish House, 39 Waterloo Street, Birmingham, W. Midlands, B2 5PU **Tel:** (0121) 233 1711 **Fax:** (0121) 200 1513 **DX:** 13054 **Ptnrs:** 10 **Asst Solrs:** 7 **Other Fee-earners:** 19. Best known for company/ commercial, insolvency and uninsured loss recovery work. Also undertakes probate, domestic conveyancing, matrimonial and High Court litigation.

WORKLOAD			
Pers inj/uninsured loss	60%	Company/comm/employ.	15%
Repossession	15%	Matrimonial & crime	5%
Conveyancing	5%		

SYLVESTER & MACKETT Castle House, Castle Street, Trowbridge, Wilts, BA14 8AX **Tel:** (01225) 755621 **Fax:** (01225) 769055/755143 **DX:** 43101 Trowbridge **Ptnrs:** 7 **Other Fee-earners:** 6. Long-established firm specialising in all the principal areas of legal work for family and commercial clients. Known for its criminal and matrimonial practice.

TALLENTS GODFREY & CO 3 Middlegate, Newark-on-Trent, Notts, NG24 1AQ **Tel:** (01636) 71881 **Fax:** (01636) 700148 **DX:** 11801 **Ptnrs:** 10 **Asst Solrs:** 4 **Other Fee-earners:** 12. One of the larger firms in the region. Work includes agriculture, company law, commercial property, civil and criminal litigation, and residential conveyancing.

WORKLOAD			
Litigation	22%	Agriculture/bloodstock	20%
Private client (probate)	17%	Other private incl family	15%
Domestic conveyancing	11%	Commercial conveyancing	10%

EDITORIAL POLICY

In this edition, the lists of specialists include profiles of individual practitioners - solicitors and barristers - who have been recommended most frequently to our researchers. Editorial policy is to identify leading practitioners on merit: it is not possible to buy a place in our biographical lists. Inclusion of a profile in this directory is based solely on expertise and reputation.

Enormous effort has been invested by our ten-strong research team (mainly solicitors and barristers) in canvassing recommendations and identifying leaders. We are confident in the overall accuracy of the results. However, mistakes and misjudgements are inevitable, and if readers have any suggestions regarding our listings we should be very pleased to hear from them.

TANNER & TAYLOR 149 Victoria Road, Aldershot, Hants, GU11 1JH **Tel:** (01252) 316565 **Fax:** (01252) 310792 **DX:** 50113 Aldershot **Ptnrs:** 11 **Asst Solrs:** 5 **Other Fee-earners:** 5. Other offices: Farnborough, Hampshire; Farnham, Surrey. General practice with emphasis on litigation including criminal, Courts Martial, children work (panel member), divorce. Also civil litigation, commercial work, conveyancing and probate.

TARLO LYONS

WATCHMAKER COURT, 33 ST. JOHN'S LANE, LONDON, EC1M 4DB
DX: 53323 Clerkenwell

TEL: (0171) 405 2000
FAX: (0171) 814 9421

THE FIRM: Tarlo Lyons was founded in 1927 as a general practice and undertakes a wide variety of commercial and private client work. The firm has particular expertise in computer and information technology law, entertainment law, specifically live stage, music recording, TV and film, commercial litigation and debt recovery.

PRINCIPAL AREAS OF WORK:

Company/ Commercial: *(Contact Partner:* Geoffrey L. Isaacs). The department has experience in handling acquisitions and disposals, joint venture agreements, employment contracts and other forms of commercial contracts and agreements.

Entertainment: *(Contact Partner:* D. Michael Rose). The firm has recently expanded its department and offers expertise in live stage, music recording, TV and film matters.

Information Technology: *(Contact Partner:* Lawrence S. Phillips). The information technology unit offers specialist advice to all sectors of the IT industry from software houses to manufacturing companies. It is proficient in dealing with the legal complexities of leading edge technology such as the use and implementation of electronic data interchange (paperless trading) and can offer access to international expertise through LEGIT – Legal Specialists in Information Technology Law – a European network of firms specialising in IT and computer law.

Property: *(Contact Partner:* Philip D. Diamond). The department handles a wide range of property transactions, principally commercial property but residential matters are also undertaken.

Litigation: *(Contact Partner:* Ezra E. Schwarz). Litigation accounts for a large proportion of the firm's workload. Partners and staff have particular expertise in Inland Revenue and Customs investigations, copyright disputes, employment law and white collar fraud.

Debt Recovery: *(Contact Partner:* Maurice Martin). The firm operates a dedicated Debt Recovery Unit from premises in Southend and offers a comprehensive, computerised service covering all aspects of routine debt recovery including pre-legal stage letter writing and telephoning as well as issuing proceedings and ensuring that judgments are enforced.

Private Client: *(Contact Partner:* Derek G. Randall). *Work includes:* wills and probate, trusts, taxation advice and immigration applications.

NATURE OF CLIENTELE: Clients are drawn from a wide range of industries and business sectors specifically computing and information technology, entertainment and manufacturing.

CONTACT PARTNER: Nigel McEwen

Number of partners:	15
Assistant solicitors:	4
Other fee-earners:	12

WORKLOAD	
Litigation	42%
Commercial	24%
Property	17%
Information technology	10%
Entertainment	7%

CONTACTS	
Commercial	G L Isaacs
Entertainment	D Michael Rose
Information technology	Lawrence Phillips
Litigation	M Martin
Property	P Diamond

TAYLOR & EMMET Norfolk Row, Sheffield, S. Yorks, S1 1SL **Tel:** (0114) 2766111 **Fax:** (0114) 2756530 **DX:** 10549 **Ptnrs:** 10 **Asst Solrs:** 9 **Other Fee-earners:** 10. Approximately 125 years old. Its practice includes both private client and company/ commercial work. Housing Association matters are a speciality.

TAYLOR JOYNSON GARRETT

CARMELITE, 50 VICTORIA EMBANKMENT, BLACKFRIARS, LONDON, EC4Y 0DX
DX: 41 London

TEL: (0171) 353 1234
FAX: (0171) 936 2666

THE FIRM: Taylor Joynson Garrett, one of the leading UK law firms with offices in the City, Brussels and Bucharest, represents UK and overseas clients of every size and type from major corporations to private individuals.

The firm is committed to offering the experience, resources and expertise necessary to provide for every legal need of its extensive corporate client base. The firm's international connections enable it to represent its clients worldwide. It has an office in Brussels which advises on all aspects of European Community law and is part of an affiliation network comprising Graham & James, the third largest international firm in the US which has over 20 offices worldwide (including affiliate offices in the Far East, Asia, the Middle East and Australia); Deacons, the Hong Kong based law firm; and Haarmann, Hemmelrath & Partner, one of the leading firms in Germany. Taylor Joynson Garrett is also a member of Interlex, a non-exclusive association of law firms in over 20 countries.

A leader in many commercial fields, the firm combines expertise from a number of disciplines across the firm forming specialist practice groups to speed response, explore opportunities and reduce time and expense.

Overall the firm sees itself as an expanding commercial practice which, although broadly based and progressive, retains its strong emphasis on the partner-client relationship by ensuring that everyone within the firm understands his or her clients' business, the commercial environment and the financial pressures under which they operate.

PRINCIPAL AREAS OF WORK:

Commercial: (*Contact:* Tim Eyles. *Fee-earners:* 34). The firm has a highly-regarded corporate finance group dealing with mergers and acquisitions, takeovers, management buy-outs, flotations, BES's and rights issues, and other similar transactions. Also in this department there are groups dealing with tax, energy, employment and employee benefits, environmental and EC law.

Banking: (*Contact:* Mark Fletcher. *Fee-earners:* 21). This group advises a large number of clearing, merchant and foreign banks on all aspects of banking and finance. This group encompasses a corporate recoveries team and a dedicated ship finance team.

Intellectual Property: (*Contact:* Paul Mitchell. *Fee-earners:* 29). One of the most comprehensively skilled IP groups spanning all areas including patents, trademarks, copyright, information technology, franchising and entertainment and media. It is widely acclaimed as one of the leading IP groups in the UK.

Commercial Litigation: (*Contact:* David Greig. *Fee-earners:* 44). The department handles a wide variety of commercial disputes and arbitrations, and specialises, in particular, in banking, employment law, shipping disputes, medical negligence, personal injury, corporate fraud, professional negligence and construction, planning and environmental law.

Commercial Property: (*Contact:* Peter Droop. *Fee-earners:* 23). Offering a full range of services relating to commercial property, the department recognises the different needs of trading companies, developers, finance institutions and both national and international investors. This group incorporates specialist construction and planning, property management and environmental teams.

Tax and Personal Planning: (*Contact:* Martin Goodwin. *Fee-earners:* 22). The firm is unusual amongst City firms in offering the full range of private client services. The department advises individuals, on family and matrimonial matters; tax; wills, trusts and probate; and residential conveyancing.

RECRUITMENT AND TRAINING: Taylor Joynson Garrett view their trainee solicitors as the future assistants and partners of the firm. Under careful supervision they are urged to take responsibility for, and have direct contact with, clients and their concerns from an early stage in their training. Trainee solicitors spend six months in four of the departments and are encouraged to take an active part in the administrative and business side of running a busy legal practice.

CONTACT PARTNER: Richard Pertwee

Number of partners:	64
Assistant solicitors:	85
Other fee-earners:	51

WORKLOAD

Litigation	25%
Company and commercial	23%
Intellectual property	14%
Banking	14%
Commercial property	13%
Tax and personal planning	11%

CONTACTS

Banking and insolvency	Mark Fletcher
Central/Eastern Europe	Richard Pertwee
Commercial litigation	David Greig
Commercial property	Peter Droop
Construction	Neil White
Corporate finance	Declan Tarpey
Corporate/commercial	Tim Eyles
EC/EU	Martin Baker
Employment	Martin Baker/Andrew Granger
Entertainment and media	Paul Mitchell
Environment & planning	Christopher Bell
	Patrick Pennal
Industrial copyright	Richard Price
Information technology	Glyn Morgan
Insurance/reinsurance	Peter Kempe
	Clare Ferguson
Patents and trade marks	Richard Price
Shipping	James Sleightholme
Tax and personal planning	Martin Goodwin

TAYLOR
JOYNSON
GARRETT

TAYLOR NICHOL 3A Station Place, London, N4 2DH **Tel:** (0171) 272 8336 **Fax:** (0171) 281 9148 **DX:** 57453 **Ptnrs:** 2 **Asst Solrs:** 1 **Other Fee-earners:** 2. Known for crime, immigration, civil liberties work and actions against the police. Legal aid work undertaken.

WORKLOAD			
Crime/civil liberties	83%	Immigration	10%
Mental health	7%		

TAYLORS Rawlings House, Exchange Street, Blackburn, Lancs, BB1 7JN **Tel:** (01254) 563333 **Fax:** (01254) 682146 **DX:** 15252 Blackburn **Ptnrs:** 5 **Asst Solrs:** 7 **Other Fee-earners:** 3. Recently established niche firm specialising in commercial law/ litigation and intellectual property. Caters for middle corporate sector and owner managers.

WORKLOAD			
Company and commercial	30%	Commercial litigation	30%
Intellectual property	15%	Commercial property	15%
Employment	10%		

TAYLOR VINTERS Merlin Place, Milton Rd, Cambridge, Cambs, CB4 4DP **Tel:** (01223) 423444 **Fax:** (01223) 423486 **DX:** 5801 **Ptnrs:** 21 **Asst Solrs:** 25 **Other Fee-earners:** 13. Known for its company/ commercial, commercial litigation, EC, agricultural, and bloodstock work. Staff proficient in major European languages. Also at Newmarket.

WORKLOAD			
Comp/comm/comm lit/emp	26%	General litigation	23%
Commercial property	22%	Bloodstock	13%
Private client	11%	Agriculture	5%

TAYLOR WALTON

36-44 ALMA ST, LUTON, BEDS, LU1 2PL
DX: 94853 Luton 2

TEL: (01582) 31161
FAX: (01582) 457900

THE FIRM: A progressive and substantial firm, Taylor Walton offers corporate and private clients a depth and range of expertise and resources that only the larger law firm can offer. 50 legal specialists in dedicated commercial and private business units handle a wide variety and personal work. In-depth expertise, quality of service and flexibility are entrenched in the working methods of the practice. Clear explanations of the law are always a priority.

PRINCIPAL AREAS OF WORK:

Company/ Commercial: (*Contact Partner:* Mr C.O. Borthwick). Work covers everything from basic company formations to substantial high profile company acquisition and disposal work and includes such areas as: licensing, franchising, joint ventures, corporate insolvency and the UK business affairs of overseas companies.

Commercial Property: (*Contact Partner:* Mr M.P. Kelly). The department has specialists dealing with all types of commercial property – whether leasehold or freehold, purchased for investment, trading, occupation or development – including advice on construction contracts, financing and landlord and tenant problems.

Litigation (*Contact Partner:* Mr J.D. Hobson). A wide range of consumer and business disputes handled by the firm includes: major contract and building disputes, intellectual property issues, personal injury and accident claims and family/ matrimonial disputes. Fully computerised debt recovery services are avaliable for the High and County Courts.

Employment: (*Contact Partner:* Mr G.T. Plenderleath). The team is led by an Industrial Tribunal Deputy Chairman, and includes a unit dealing with the relocation of employees. All employer and employee matters are handled.

Private client and Financial Services: (*Contact Partner:* Mr D.M. Fryer). Wills and probate, tax planning and trusts advice is offered and independent investment advice is provided by TW Financial Strategists.

OTHER OFFICES: Harpenden - (01582) 765111 and St Albans - (01727) 845245.

CONTACT PARTNER: David Wilson

Number of partners:	17
Assistant solicitors:	7
Other fee-earners:	5

WORKLOAD	
Litigation/ employment	25%
Residential conveyancing	24%
Company and commercial	20%
Commercial property	18%
Private client	12%
Financial services	1%

CONTACTS	
Commercial property	M.P. Kelly
Company and commercial	C.O. Borthwick
Financial services	D.M. Fryer
Litigation	J.D. Hobson
Private client	D.M. Fryer
Residential conveyancing	T.M. Shillabeer

TAYNTONS

CLARENCE CHAMBERS, 8-12 CLARENCE STREET, GLOUCESTER, GLOS, GL1 1DZ

TEL: (01452) 522047
FAX: (01452) 424659

THE FIRM: Established for over 140 years, Tayntons provides a prompt and integrated service across the departments, whilst maintaining its traditionally strong partner to client contact.

PRINCIPAL AREAS OF WORK:

Company/ Commercial: Offers a full range of services including company formations/ acquisitions, partnership agreements, insolvency, franchising and tax.

Family: Provides specialist advice on all matters relating to child care, family, matrimonial and cohabitation problems.

Litigation: Work includes consumer complaints, commercial disputes, redundancy and unfair dismissal, professional indemnity claims.

Personal Injury: It has the largest practice in Gloucestershire. Deals with all accidents with particular expertise in the recovery of damages. Two partners are members of APIL and of the Personal Injury Panel.

Property: Work includes commercial lending, development agreements, domestic conveyancing, town and country planning.

Private Client: Offers a full range of services including wills, trusts, financial advice and tax planning.

CONTACT PARTNER: Alan Bird

Number of partners:	5
Assistant solicitors:	9
Other fee-earners:	5

WORKLOAD

Personal injury	65%
General litigation	10%
Property/ commercial	10%
Matrimonial	10%
Probate/ wills	5%

CONTACTS

Housing associations	Alan Bird
Personal injury (plaintiff)	Nicola Heales
Personal injury (defendant)	Martin Edden

TEACHER STERN SELBY

37-41 BEDFORD ROW, LONDON, WC1R 4JH
DX: 177 Ch.Ln.

TEL: (0171) 242 3191
FAX: (0171) 242 1156

THE FIRM: Teacher Stern Selby is primarily a commercial firm which favours a close working relationship with its clients and their other professional advisers to ensure that matters are conducted with maximum speed and efficiency.

PRINCIPAL AREAS OF WORK:

Commercial Property: (*Contact Partner:* Stuart Stern). *Work includes:* acquisitions and disposals for developers, investors, landlords and tenants. Secured lending and the drafting of security documentation (acting for banks and building societies) are also handled, as is every aspect of landlord and tenant work. Shopping centres a speciality.

Company/ Commercial: (*Contact Partner:* Roger Selby). The department is active in the corporate sector, handling takeovers, mergers, joint ventures, MBOs and disposals, demergers, reconstructions and asset sales. More generally, the firm deals with employment law, intellectual property licences and confidentiality agreements. The firm has particular experience in computer hardware and software contracts, oil exploration agreements and financing, entertainment law (especially recording and management agreements and publishing law); and in the pharmaceutical industry.

Litigation: (*Contact Partner:* Jack Rabinowicz). Primarily in the commercial field, particularly banking, insolvency and finance house matters, together with commercial property litigation. The firm also specialises in administrative and medical negligence cases, and has a national reputation in the field of education law.

OTHER AREAS OF WORK: The firm gives specialist tax planning advice and has substantial experience in the formation and use of foreign trusts and offshore corporate entities to produce the most efficient tax structure to suit individual circumstances. A full range of private client services from residential conveyancing to wills, trusts, probate and estate administration is also provided.

NATURE OF CLIENTELE: Primarily from the finance, commercial property, corporate and entertainment fields, and also corporate and business clients from Canada and Eastern Europe. The firm also has excellent links with accountants, banks, financial institutions, surveyors and has wide-ranging legal contacts overseas.

LANGUAGES SPOKEN: French, German, Italian, Russian, Chinese (Mandarin), Hebrew, Serbo-Croat, and Spanish.

CONTACT PARTNER: Roger Selby

Number of partners:	11
Assistant solicitors:	9
Other fee-earners:	6

WORKLOAD

Commercial litigation	45%
Commercial property	23%
Company and commercial	14%
Secured lending	10%
Residential conveyancing/ probate	5%
Personal injury/ education/ judicial review	3%

CONTACTS

Commercial property	Stuart Stern, Nigel Fisch
Commercial litigation	Jack Rabinowicz
Computer law	David Teacher
Education	Jack Rabinowicz
Entertainment	Roger Selby
General commercial	Roger Selby
Media companies	David Teacher
Oil and gas	Roger Selby
Secured lending	Phil Berry

TEEMAN LEVINE Aire House, Swinegate, Leeds, W. Yorks, LS1 4AG
Tel: (0113) 245 9344 **Fax:** (0113) 242 5276 **DX:** 12062 **Ptnrs:** 10 **Asst Solrs:** 24
Other Fee-earners: 12. Known for its corporate and commercial work.

WORKLOAD			
Commercial litigation	45%	Corporate/ commercial	35%
Commercial property	12%	Private client	8%

THEODORE GODDARD

150 ALDERSGATE ST, LONDON, EC1A 4EJ
DX: 47 London

TEL: (0171) 606 8855
FAX: (0171) 606 4390

THE FIRM: Theodore Goddard is one of the major City law firms serving the business and financial communities. The firm understands the needs of business and has the depth and breadth of resources required to provide a top quality flexible service.

The firm is international in outlook. It has offices in Brussels and Jersey and is represented in Paris by its associated firm, Klein-Goddard (incorporating the recently merged practices of the firm's Paris office and the French firm of Klein et Associes). Through its alliance with leading US corporate lawyers, Dewey Ballantine, the firm has representation in New York, Washington DC, Los Angeles and Hong Kong. In a joint venture with Dewey Ballantine, the two firms have offices in Warsaw, Prague, Cracow and Budapest. In addition, the firm has a strong and effective network of contacts throughout the rest of the world.

PRINCIPAL AREAS OF WORK:

Corporate Finance: The firm deals with the full range of corporate finance work, including mergers and acquisitions, management buy-outs and buy-ins, demergers, investment capital and new issues, including Stock Exchange flotations.

Banking and Finance: The firm provides commercial banking advice to both banks and borrowers, including advice on securitisation of loans, reconstruction of lending packages, company rescues and reorganisations, capital markets transactions and asset and structured finance transactions.

Tax: The firm deals with all tax issues connected with corporate finance work, including the development of tax-related financial instruments and asset finance packages; international tax planning; the tax aspects of takeovers, corporate reconstructions and demergers, management buy-outs and buy-ins; employee share schemes and other employee benefits; personal tax planning including, together with the firm's Jersey office, the formation and administration of offshore trusts and companies.

Media and Communications: The firm has a leading practice in the media and communications sector, concentrating on music, broadcasting, film, television, theatre, and, centred on its expertise in defamation law, newspapers and publishing; it also advises extensively in the telecommunications and IT sectors. The convergence of businesses and technologies in these industries results in the continuous creation of new and complex legal problems, particularly in relation to intellectual property rights and competition and regulatory issues, which are becoming increasingly pan-European. The firm has a highly successful EC and competition group.

Commercial Litigation: The firm has particular expertise in litigation relating to the banking and securities sector; fraud and asset recovery; contractual disputes; product liability, especially in the pharmaceutical industry; and in arbitration.

Property: The firm deals with all types of property transactions, acting for both public and private sector clients. The emphasis is on commercial and industrial property. Specialist groups handle such areas as public authority work, environmental law, planning and rating, construction and development, funding and investment, secured lending, property and construction litigation, retail and leisure transactions and railways.

Other: The firm has thriving practices in the employment and pensions (both contentious and non-contentious) and private client areas.

NATURE OF CLIENTELE: The client base is international. Clients include major public and private companies, multinational corporations, financial institutions and intermediaries, governments, government agencies and local authorities, as well as individuals.

SENIOR PARTNER: Stuart May

Number of partners:	46
Assistant solicitors:	76
Other fee-earners:	35

WORKLOAD	
Corporate finance/ company	26%
Commercial litigation	19%
Media and communications	17%
Property	16%
Banking/ asset finance	13%
Tax	9%

CONTACTS	
Asset finance/ leasing	Kim Walkling
Aviation	Rory MacCarthy
Banking	Julian Maples
Capital markets	Jayesh Patel
Commercial litigation	John Kelleher
Commercial property	David Wilkinson
Company/ commercial	Peter Kavanagh
Corporate finance	John Clark
Corporate tax	Tim Sanders
EC/ competition	Guy Leigh
Entertainment	Paddy Grafton Green
Environment	Christine Lerry
Insolvency	Jonathan Lewis
Intellectual property	Hamish Porter
IT/ telecommunications	Hamish Porter
Media litigation	Martin Kramer
Planning	Douglas Evans
Private client	Joyce Smyth

RECRUITMENT: The firm recruits around 15 trainee solicitors a year. A good degree (2:1 plus), which may or may not be in law, is necessary. The firm is looking for trainees with confidence, commitment and sound commercial sense. With the firm's international focus, language skills are valuable. There is an extensive, award-winning training and development programme covering all fee earners, from trainees to partners and including personal skills development, commercial management and business development training alongside legal training. The firm recruits with a view to retaining trainees who after qualification will go on to become partners with the firm. Tuition fees and a maintenance allowance are paid by the firm to CPE and LPC. The firm runs a summer placement and open day programme.

Details of summer placements and open days as well as the firm's brochure for training contracts, *Your Career as a City Solicitor*, and application forms, are available from the Personnel Department. Applications should be made to Penny Alison (Miss), Personnel Director.

THM TINSDILLS Chichester House, Broad Street, Hanley, Stoke-on-Trent, Staffs, ST1 4EU **Tel:** (01782) 262031 **Fax:** (01782) 287571 **DX:** 20710 **Ptnrs:** 18 **Asst Solrs:** 7 **Other Fee-earners:** 10. Other offices in Hanley (Property Department), Tunstall and in Leek (as Challinors & Shaw). Known for conveyancing, litigation, company law and matrimonial.

THOMAS COOPER & STIBBARD

52 LEADENHALL STREET, LONDON, EC3A 2DJ
DX: 548

TEL: (0171) 481 8851
FAX: (0171) 480 6097

THE FIRM: Established in Bishopsgate in 1825, Thomas Cooper & Stibbard has been based in Leadenhall Street for over 150 years. The firm has expanded from its original practice of shipping law into other areas of commercial and international law.

PRINCIPAL AREAS OF WORK:
Marine: (*Contact:* D.G. Hebden). The firm handles both 'wet' and 'dry' shipping law, ranging from collisions at sea, salvage and towage, pollution and wreck removal and marine insurance, to charterparty disputes, bills of lading, cargo damage, storage or contamination and shipbuilding and repair disputes.
Business, Finance & Insurance: (*Contact:* S.J. Swabey). The firm deals with a wide range of company/ commercial work including company formation, acquisition and disposal, joint ventures, banking law, ship finances, futures markets, financial services advice and insurance.
Commercial Litigation & International Arbitration: (*Contact:* T.J.R. Goode). The firm handles EC law and references to the European Court and a whole range of contentious matters including commodities, sale of goods, copyright and trademarks, building and civil engineering disputes and employment matters.
Property & Probate: (*Contact:* K.E. Harrison). The firm handles freehold and leasehold commercial and residential projects, including development and financing, the drafting of wills and the administration of estates.
NATURE OF CLIENTELE: Clients include shipowners, charterers, insurance companies, foreign governments and ministries, major oil companies, international traders, banks and financial institutions.

CONTACT PARTNER: T.J.R. Goode

Number of partners:	14
Assistant solicitors:	7
Other fee-earners:	13

WORKLOAD	
Shipping (admiralty, maritime & carriage)	60%
Business, finance & insurance	10%
Personal injury	10%
Commercial lit. & international arbitration	10%

CONTACTS	
Banking	Grant Eldred
Commercial litigation	Stephen Swabey
Company law	Stephen Swabey
Construction	Tim Goode
Environment	Paul Barfield
Insurance	Russell Kelly
Personal injury	John Strange
Property	Kate Harrison
Shipping and maritime law	David Hebden

THOMAS EGGAR VERRALL BOWLES

5 EAST PALLANT, CHICHESTER, W. SUSSEX, PO19 1TS
DX: 30300

TEL: (01243) 786111
FAX: (01243) 775640

THE FIRM: Thomas Eggar Verrall Bowles is now one of the largest firms in the region, having substantial offices in Chichester, Horsham and Worthing.

PRINCIPAL AREAS OF WORK: A strong reputation for private client work, including tax and trust administration services, now complemented by strong commercial divisions which account for approximately 45% of the firm's income. The firm differentiates itself from other firms of solicitors through THESIS, its wholly-owned independent investment company, which has the largest department for a firm of solicitors giving investment advice, in England and Wales, and THESIS Corporate Finance which provides corporate financial advice to the firm's corporate clients.

OTHER OFFICES: Worthing and Horsham.

INTERNATIONAL CONNECTIONS: The firm prides itself on being a founder member of the AVRIO Group of European Law Firms with offices in Belgium, France, Germany, Greece, Luxembourg, Denmark, Scotland, Italy, The Netherlands and Portugal.

RECRUITMENT AND TRAINING: Trainee solicitors are recruited annually and a 2:1 degree, not necessarily in law, is preferred. A detailed CV, including at least one referee, should be sent to Mr John Kittow, the Trainee Solicitors Training Partner, Thomas Eggar Verrall Bowles, 5 East Pallant, Chichester, West Sussex PO19 1TS.

CONTACT PARTNER: Mr C.W. Doman

Number of partners:	31
Assistant solicitors:	16
Other fee-earners:	42

WORKLOAD	
Commercial conveyancing	17%
Financial services (THESIS)	16%
Civil litigation	16%
Probate	15%
Commercial	11%
Residential property	9%
Tax services	5%
Family	5%
Trust administration	4%
Ecclesiastical	2%

THOMAS WATTS & CO 19-21 Kensington Church Street, London, W8 4LT **Tel:** (0171) 937 4353 **Fax:** (0171) 938 4782 **DX:** 47203 Kensington High Street **Ptnrs:** 1 **Asst Solrs:** 2 **Other Fee-earners:** 4. Best known for its medical negligence, personal injury and defamation work but also undertakes probate, conveyancing and commercial matters.

WORKLOAD			
Medical negligence	25%	Conveyancing	20%
Probate	15%	Commercial	10%
Defamation	10%		

THOMPSON SMITH & PUXON 4-5 North Hill, Colchester, Essex, CO1 1EB **Tel:** (01206) 574431 **Fax:** (01206) 563174 **DX:** 3617 Colchester **Ptnrs:** 14 **Asst Solrs:** 5 **Other Fee-earners:** 20. General practice with four offices in N.E. Essex. All types of work undertaken including legal aid and agency.

THOMSON & CO

15-17 CASTLE STREET, CAMBRIDGE, CAMBS, CB3 0AH
DX: 5840

TEL: (01223) 562002
FAX: (01223) 460879

THE FIRM: Established in 1985, this young successful firm offers a broad range of legal services and is widely recognised as a leading advocacy practice. In litigation, the firm places equal emphasis on criminal law, childcare and matrimonial law. It has an expanding and thriving civil practice concentrating on personal injury, general civil litigation and employment law. It obtained a Legal Aid Franchise in January 1995. On the non contentious side, the firm specialises in commercial and domestic conveyancing, wills and probate. The firm also handles most aspects of private client work.

CONTACT PARTNER: Mr Raphael Silver

Number of partners:	7
Assistant solicitors:	3
Other fee-earners:	4

THOMSON SNELL & PASSMORE

3 LONSDALE GARDENS, TUNBRIDGE WELLS, KENT, TN1 1NX
DX: 3914 Tunbridge Wells

TEL: (01892) 510000
FAX: (01892) 549884

THE FIRM: This large, highly-regarded firm is one of the oldest legal practices in the country, tracing its roots back to 1570. It has 37 partners, 146 staff and four offices. A wide-ranging general practice, it is best known for its company/ commercial, commercial property, private client, professional negligence and personal injury work. Thomson Snell & Passmore is a founder member of The Law South Group.

PRINCIPAL AREAS OF WORK:

Company/ Commercial: A wide variety of work is handled by a strong commercial team including company formations, acquisitions and disposals, corporate finance and venture capital, MBOs, mergers and joint ventures, partnership, commercial contracts, insolvency, employment, intellectual property, franchising, EC and general competition law, and corporate tax.

Commercial Property: The department advises institutions, investors and tenants upon all aspects of commercial property including funding and tax implications. It also provides a full service to residential and commercial developers, including land acquisition and options, joint ventures, funding agreements, planning and environmental issues, unit sales/leases and estate management.

The firm also advises farmers and estates on all aspects of land ownership, including agricultural holdings, tax, inheritance, development, environmental legislation and EC regulations.

Litigation: The work of the various departments includes all types of commercial disputes, insolvency, employment claims, intellectual property disputes and property related claims including landlord and tenant, building contracts and possession actions.

The department dealing with personal injury and medical negligence has become a leader in the region and the professional negligence and professional conduct departments have experienced substantial and rapid growth. The family department advises on all areas of matrimonial and other family problems including inheritance claims, cross border disputes and child care.

Private Client: Services include trust formation, wills and probate, tax planning, trust and investment management, charity law, pensions, general insurance services through Thomson & Passmore (Insurance Brokers) Ltd and a full residential property service.

FOREIGN CONNECTIONS: The firm is a founder member of EUROJURIST EEIG with associate offices throughout Europe.

OTHER OFFICES: Tonbridge:Lyons, East St., Kent TN9 1HZ (01732 771411: Graham Kenyon or Guy Durdant-Hollamby): Cranbrook (01580 712478: Graham Kenyon or William Brown): Maidstone (01622 757455: David Harries, Robert Reid, Donald Howson or Richard Chalkley).

CONTACT PARTNER: Jeremy Waddell

Number of partners:	37
Assistant solicitors:	12
Other fee-earners:	19

WORKLOAD

Private client (including Investment Management)	18%
General litigation	16%
Company/ commercial	14%
Commercial property/property dev.	13%
Domestic conveyancing	11%
Professional negligence	9%
Personal injury/medical negligence	8%
Family and matrimonial	8%
Professional conduct	3%

CONTACTS

Agriculture	Gilbert Green
Commercial conveyancing	David White
Commercial litigation	Peter Radula-Scott
Company/ commercial	Jeremy Waddell
Domestic conveyancing	Michael Sugden
Investment management	Jeremy Passmore
Matrimonial/ family	Barbara Wright
PI/ medical negligence	Andrew Watson
Probate and equity	James Krafft
Professional negligence	Trevor May
Professional conduct	Richard Chalkley
Property development	Gilbert Green
Property litigation	Raymond Beard
Tax planning	Jeremy Passmore
Tax returns	Peter Bagwell Purefoy
Trust management	Maurice Dewar

THORNTONS WS Whitehall Chambers, 11 Whitehall Street, Dundee, Tayside, DD1 4AE **Tel:** (01382) 229111 **Fax:** (01382) 221779 **DX:** 21 Dundee **Ptnrs:** 22 **Asst Solrs:** 20 **Other Fee-earners:** 18. A full service practice including commercial, litigation, agricultural, private client and residential property services.

THORPE & CO

17 VALLEY BRIDGE PARADE, SCARBOROUGH, N. YORKS, YO11 2JX
DX: 61811

TEL: (01723) 364321
FAX: (01723) 500459

THE FIRM: Established in 1957, Thorpe & Co is one of the most prominent firms in North Yorkshire and offers a full range of legal services to both town and country, private and commercial clients. The firm is also a member of Law Net, the National Federation of Independent Law Firms.

PRINCIPAL AREAS OF WORK: Include personal injury work, agricultural matters, commercial property, consumer problems, company/ commercial work, criminal matters, debt collection, matrimonial and family affairs, employment law work, residential conveyancing, insurance work, landlord & tenant problems, licensing work, taxation, planning work, trusts, wills and probate work, agency work.

OTHER OFFICES: Filey, Whitby and Malton.

CONTACT PARTNER: Ian Brabbs

Number of partners:	11
Assistant solicitors:	2
Other fee-earners:	6

WORKLOAD	
Domestic conveyancing	40%
Matrimonial	20%
Personal injury	20%
Crime	10%
Wills and probate	10%

THRINGS & LONG

MIDLAND BRIDGE, BATH, AVON, BA1 2HQ
DX: 8002 Bath

TEL: (01225) 448494
FAX: (01225) 319735

THE FIRM: Thrings & Long is an established firm which has developed as a commercial practice whilst retaining a commitment to quality for private clients. Situated close to the centre of Bath with a branch office in Frome the firm encourages specialisation within departments.

PRINCIPAL AREAS OF WORK:

Company: (*Contact Partner:* Jonathan Wyld). The department has wide experience of company acquisitions and sales, business start-ups, company reorganisations, joint ventures, partnerships, intellectual property, charitable companies, insolvency and trading terms and conditions.
   The department has extensive contact with corporate financiers and equity funders.

Commercial Property: (*Contact Partner:* Thomas Sheppard). The commercial property department deals with all types of commercial property acquisition, sales and developments including joint venture agreements and planning and environmental law. It works closely with the firm's in-house planning consultant. Particular experience in French property transactions.

Residential Property: (*Contact Partner:* William Power). Extensive large volume relocation and investment purchases using computer technology.

Litigation: (*Contact Partner:* Stephen Roberts). This department is the largest department at Thrings & Long with experience in all major areas of litigation work. Members of the litigation team work closely with other professionals and its advocates frequently appear in all local Courts and Tribunals. The department is particularly known for commercial and property litigation, employment law, family law and road traffic/ personal injury work.

Agriculture: (*Contact Partner:* Jonathan Cheal). Widely recognised and respected as a specialist department providing extensive advice and representation to farmers and landowners in Avon, Gloucestershire, Wiltshire and Somerset.

Private Client: (*Contact Partner:* Jeremy Thring). Combining the skills of experienced lawyers with an in-house accountant and a financial services specialist and latest technology, the firm remains committed to providing a quality service to the private client.

Charity: (*Contact Partner:* Quentin Elston). For many years the firm has acted for a variety of charitable organisations particularly almshouses, grant making and medical charities and churches. This specialist department seeks to provide practical and cost effective advice on all aspects of charity law and practice, and draws upon the strength of the firms other departments to offer trustees a full legal service.

CONTACT PARTNER: Thomas Sheppard

Number of partners:	12
Assistant solicitors:	16
Other fee-earners:	7

WORKLOAD	
Litigation	28%
Probate, trusts and tax	23%
Conveyancing	17%
Commercial property	11%
Company	9%
Agriculture	7%
Charity	5%

CONTACTS	
Agriculture	Jonathan Cheal
Charity	Quentin Elston
Commercial property	Thomas Sheppard
Company & commercial	Jonathan Wyld
Debt recovery/ credit control	Stephen Roberts
Employment law	Stephen Roberts
	Angus Halden
Family law	Brian Jones
Financial services	Jill Treffry
Litigation	Angus Halden, Stephen Roberts
Probate & trusts	Jeremy Thring
Probate and trusts	Graham Bayliss
Residential property	William Power
Tax	Michael Young

THURSFIELDS 14 Church St, Kidderminster, Hereford & Worcs, DY10 2AJ **Tel:** (01562) 820575 **Fax:** (01562) 66783 **DX:** 16304 **Ptnrs:** 14 **Asst Solrs:** 5 **Other Fee-earners:** 16. Best known for commercial property work and company law. Also undertakes matrimonial, personal injury and criminal legal aid work for private clients.

TILLY BAILEY & IRVINE York Chambers, York Rd, Hartlepool, Clev, TS26 9DP **Tel:** (01429) 264101 **Fax:** (01429) 274796 **DX:** 60650 **Ptnrs:** 13 **Asst Solrs:** 7 **Other Fee-earners:** 17. One of the largest firms on Teesside. Known for company/ commercial, matrimonial and High Court litigation.

WORKLOAD			
Litigation	33%	Trust and probate	18%
Company commercial	17%	Other private client	16%
Family	16%		

TILSTON MACLAURIN 100 West Regent Street, Glasgow, G2 2QB **Tel:** (0141) 332 5666 **Fax:** (0141) 332 6757 **Ptnrs:** 5 **Asst Solrs:** 1 **Other Fee-earners:** 1. An established general practice offering a specialist employment law service.

WORKLOAD			
Litigation	40%	Domestic conveyancing	20%
Commercial	20%	General	10%
Employment law	10%		

TINDAL OATTS

48 ST. VINCENT STREET, GLASGOW, G2 5HS
DX: 96 Glasgow

TEL: (0141) 221 8012
FAX: (0141) 221 7803

THE FIRM: Tindal Oatts is a predominantly commercial practice which also provides a comprehensive range of services to private clients. The firm is the sole Scottish member of InsuroLaw (European Insurance Lawyers Group) and has particular expertise in insurance litigation, employment law and insolvency work.

PRINCIPAL AREAS OF WORK:

Corporate and Commercial: *(Contact:* Sandy Weatherhead OBE). The firm advises on all aspects of corporate and commercial law including company formation, acquisition, restructuring and disposal, management buy-outs, formation of partnerships, franchising, commercial contracts, service contracts, intellectual property law, banking and financial matters. Insolvency law advice is provided for liquidations, receivers and trustees *(Contact:* William Young). The range of commercial property work undertaken includes property development, property investment, leasing (landlord and tenant), acquisitions and disposals, farms and estates, hotels and leisure premises, timeshare, commercial lending and securities *(Contact:* Alan Borthwick).

Litigation: *(Contact:* Bill Speirs). The firm undertakes a wide range of civil and commercial litigation including litigation on behalf of insurers, contractual disputes, product liability actions, licensing, employment disputes, industrial tribunal work, debt recovery, insolvency and corporate recovery work *(Contact:* Dorothy Hatfield).

Private Client: *(Contact:* Susan Lang). A comprehensive service is provided for private clients including residential conveyancing, assured tenancies, family and matrimonial work, personal investments, insurance, tax and financial advice, wills, trusts and executry work.

FOREIGN LANGUAGES: French, German.

INTERNATIONAL CONNECTIONS: Through membership of Insurolaw, the firm has associations with law firms in most European jurisdictions.

CHAIRMAN: Sandy Weatherhead OBE

Number of partners:	8
Assistant solicitors:	9
Other fee-earners:	7

WORKLOAD	
Commercial litigation	36%
Corporate/commercial/commercial property	28%
Private client	22%
Liquidation/ insolvency	14%

CONTACTS	
Commercial property	Alan Borthwick
Corporate/ commercial	Sandy Weatherhead
Litigation	Bill Speirs
Private client	Susan Lang

TITMUSS SAINER DECHERT

2 SERJEANTS' INN, LONDON, EC4Y 1LT
DX: 30 London

TEL: (0171) 583 5353
FAX: (0171) 353 3683

THE FIRM: Titmuss Sainer Dechert is one of the leading City of London firms, with a total complement of 270 lawyers and supporting staff. The firm has a strong international presence through its union with Dechert Price & Rhoads, a large US law firm. The two practices have over 450 lawyers in nine locations: London, Brussels, Paris, New York, Washington DC, Philadelphia, Boston, Princeton and Harrisburg.

NATURE OF CLIENTELE: The firm's clients include substantial UK and international listed and private companies from a wide cross section of industry and commerce.

PRINCIPAL AREAS OF WORK:

Corporate Services: (*Contact:* David Vogel). Core services include flotations, capital issues, transborder and domestic mergers, acquisitions and disposals and corporate reorganisations and recoveries, general corporate and financial advice.

Property: (*Contact:* Steven Fogel). A comprehensive range of property services including commercial, industrial and retail development, investment and dealing. Clients include major retailers, property developers, large corporations, universities and public authorities.

Planning and Construction: (*Contact:* Chris Edwards). Drafting and enforcements of building contracts, collateral warranties, professional appointments, maintenance agreements, insurance and the preparation and handling of claims through negotiation, arbitration or litigation.

Environment: (*Contact:* Martin Edwards). All aspects of environmental law including regulatory matters and enforcement. All aspects of planning including development, plans, compulsory purchases, conservation, highways, infrastructure, rating, plus advocacy at inquiries and other hearings.

Financial Services: (*Contact:* Reg Morton). Specialist compliance advice and corporate finance transactions for clients within the financial services industry.

Insurance and Reinsurance: (*Contact:* Michael Smith). The firm serves Lloyd's and non-Lloyd's insurance and reinsurance clients and deals with mergers and acquisitions in the insurance market, insurance litigation and arbitration and advice upon the Lloyd's Act and Byelaws.

Investigations: (*Contact:* David Byrne). All civil and criminal aspects of corporate fraud, DTI inquiries, SFO investigations, Inland Revenue and Customs &Excise investigations, disciplinary proceedings, insider dealing, investigations by the SRO's, money laundering and compliance.

Banking: (*Contact:* Dick Russell). Transactional support and advice to banks and other institutional lenders, with particular emphasis on corporate and property development finance together with syndication, securitisation, asset finance and distress debt transactions.

Corporate Recovery: (*Contact:* Sally Unwin). Legal support and advice to lenders, insolvency practitioners and borrowers, particularly in connection with corporate rescues, debt rescheduling and workouts.

Commercial Litigation: (*Contact:* Andrew Hearn). Comprehensive commercial litigation services in a broad range of national and international disputes before courts, arbitrators, tribunals and inquiries both in the UK and overseas. The disputes concern areas as diverse as banking, insurance, intellectual property and defamation. Also provide ADR services.

Property Litigation: (*Contact:* Jeremy Grose). All forms of dispute resolution concerning landlord and tenant, lease renewals, rent reviews and possession proceedings including self-help remedies. Advice concerning boundary disputes, easements, rights of light, restrictive covenants, professional negligence relating to property, realisation of security, property related insolvency and disputes arising out of the sale of land.

Commercial Law: (*Contact:* Simon Leonard). Intellectual property, UK and EC competition law, computer law, anti-piracy, product liability, overseas joint ventures, and general commercial contracts. The firm's Intelmark trade mark agency service assists in the management and protection of trade marks, names and logos.

CONTACT PARTNER: Michael Smith

Number of partners:	43
Assistant solicitors:	42
Other fee-earners:	40

WORKLOAD

Property	38%
Corporate	20%
Litigation	18%
Financial and insurance services	11%
Intellectual Property	8%
Tax and private client	5%

CONTACTS

Banking	Dick Russell
Commercial	Simon Leonard
Commercial litigation	Andrew Hearn
Corporate	David Vogel
Corporate Recovery	Sally Unwin
Customs & excise	Gavin McFarlane
Employment & pensions	Georgina Keane
Environment	Martin Edwards
Financial services	Reg Morton
Insurance/ Lloyd's	Michael Smith
Investigatons	David Byrne
Media & IT	Paul Gardner
Planning and construction	Chris Edwards
Property	Steven Fogel
Property litigation	Jeremy Grose
Public sector	Graham McGowan
Tax and private client	David Tandy
Trade marks and patents	Barbara Cookson

Employment and Pensions: (*Contact:* Georgina Keane [Employment] or Jenny Lewis [Pensions]). Acts for employers and individuals on employment disputes, pensions, share option and incentive schemes and service agreements.

Customs, Excise and International Trade Taxation: (*Contact:* Gavin McFarlane). All negotiations and disputes in customs, excise, VAT, and matters arising from international trade taxation, particularly anti-dumping, origin, classification and valuation matters, especially in the area of transfer pricing.

Tax and Private Client: (*Contact:* David Tandy). All aspects of estate planning, both on shore and off shore for domiciles and non domiciles including drafting of wills, settlements, and all aspects of individual personal affairs (except matrimonial). UK and international tax planning of corporate & commercial transactions, tax & VAT planning of UK property transactions, personal tax planning for high net worth individuals, tax litigation.

RECRUITMENT AND TRAINING: Trainee solicitor recruitment is organised to give the fullest attention to individual career development. Andrew Hearn, Chairman of the Trainee Solicitors Recruitment Panel co-ordinates the training programme which embraces the CPD and which is essentially practical, but includes in-house and external seminars and courses in business development and management. *Contact:* Lynn Muncey for trainee solicitor recruitment brochure.

TODS MURRAY WS

66 QUEEN STREET, EDINBURGH, EH2 4NE
DX: 58 Edinburgh

TEL: (0131) 226 4771
FAX: (0131) 225 3676

THE FIRM: Tods Murray WS, based at the heart of Edinburgh's business community, is a major Scottish law firm and has established a strong reputation servicing both private and commercial clients over the past 150 years. It is widely regarded as one of Scotland's leading commercial property law firms and over the last decade has developed a thriving corporate department. More recently it has successfully expanded into growing niche markets such as planning and environmental law, holiday and entertainment law, financial services, banking and securitisation. Membership of the international legal association, Multilaw, has provided the practice with a network of connections throughout the world's commercial centres.

PRINCIPAL AREAS OF WORK:

Commercial Property: (*Contact Partner:* Douglas Moffat). Tods Murray acts for major developers and institutional investors, lenders and retailers. The service covers the following areas: purchases and sales; leasing; property development and funding agreements; commercial lending and the creation and enforcement of securities over all types of property; institutional investment in agricultural and forestry land; financing of commercial property transactions; planning problems; building and other property related contracts. The department has also taken a leading role in the development of securitisation.

Corporate Finance: (*Contact Partner:* Martin Thurston Smith). The firm provides an extensive corporate service, including company formation and finance, the issue of shares, loan stocks and other securities, mergers and acquisitions, reconstructions, management buy-outs, unit trusts, time-share schemes, banking and consumer credit, service and employment contracts, pension schemes, life assurance contracts, share incentive, share option and profit sharing schemes, computer contracts, intellectual property, insolvency and receiverships.

Private Client Services: (*Contact Partner:* David Anderson). The significant expansion of the commercial business of the firm has not been at the expense of its well-established private client base where the importance of continuity and personal service has always been acknowledged. The private client department offers a comprehensive residential property service where a 'one-stop' service covering all aspects of sale and purchase is provided. A specialist team deals with wills, trusts, executries and general financial management for both individuals and trusts.

Litigation: (*Contact Partner:* Michael Simpson). The development of the firm's court department has been in line with that of the commercial business of the firm. The department provides services to both commercial and private clients by repre-

CHAIRMAN OF THE MANAGEMENT BOARD: Mr Charles Abram

Number of partners:	24
Assistant solicitors:	18
Other fee-earners:	17

WORKLOAD	
Commercial property	33%
Corporate	24%
Tax, estates and trusts	15%
Litigation	13%
Residential	8%
Agriculture, estates and forestry	7%

CONTACTS	
AEF	John Fulton
Banking and insolvency	Hamish Patrick
Commercial property	Douglas Moffat
Corporate & commercial	Martin Thurston Smith
Corporate finance	William Simmons
Entertainment law	Richard Findlay
Environmental law	Colin Graham
Leisure and travel	David Dunsire
Litigation	Michael Simpson
Pensions and unit trusts	Martin Thurston Smith
Securitisation	Graham Burnside
Tax, estates and trusts	David McLetchie

senting them in a wide range of civil cases and disputes before courts, tribunals and arbiters. Commercial matters of consultation include building and planning disputes, rating valuation appeals, actions for damages arising out of negligence or breach of contract, debt recovery, licensing applications and disputes relating to commercial property and insolvency. For private clients, the firm acts in contractual disputes, personal injury cases and matters of matrimonial breakdown.

Agriculture, Estates and Forestry: *(Contact Partner:* John Fulton). The practice has traditionally acted for some of Scotland's largest landowners. Partners can advise on all aspects of modern farming and forestry, including government grants and fiscal incentives. Advice can also be provided in relation to country sports, time-share developments and heritage property.

Entertainment Law: *(Contact Partner:* Richard Findlay). The firm looks after the legal requirements of many well known names in the Scottish arts and entertainment industry. A member of the International Association of Entertainment Lawyers, Tods Murray's clients include the Edinburgh Military Tattoo, the Italian and French Film Festivals, Scotland's premier repertory theatre company, festivals of jazz and blues and several independent film production companies.

TOLHURST FISHER Trafalgar Hse, 8 Nelson Street, Southend-on-Sea, Essex, SS1 1EF **Tel:** (01702) 352511 **Fax:** (01702) 348900 **DX:** 2811 **Ptnrs:** 6 **Asst Solrs:** 3 **Other Fee-earners:** 6. Best known for commercial property and company law. Also handles trust and fund management. Recently opened a new commercial office in Chelmsford. Founded 1860.

WORKLOAD			
Commercial	30%	Res conveyancing	23%
Debt collection	18%	Civil litigation	17%
Trust and probate	12%		

TOLLER HALES & COLLCUTT

CASTILIAN CHAMBERS, 2 CASTILIAN STREET, NORTHAMPTON, NORTHANTS, NN1 1JX   DX: 12422

TEL: (01604) 258558
FAX: (01604) 258500

THE FIRM: Established in 1877, Toller Hales & Collcutt is a broadly based provincial practice with four offices in Northamptonshire. It offers a full range of legal services to both commercial and private clients.

PRINCIPAL AREAS OF WORK:

Corporate/ Commercial: *(Contact Partner:* Christopher Pykett). The department undertakes all aspects of company formation, acquisition and disposal, MBOs and MBIs, joint ventures, reconstruction, franchise, agency and distribution agreements, taxation, intellectual property, EC law and insolvency.

Commercial Property: *(Contact Partner:* Andrew Rudkin). The firm offers a wide-ranging property service covering industrial, retail and offices premises, and acquisition, disposal, leasing, landlord and tenant law, building contracts, joint ventures, property taxation (VAT), investment and development work. A specialist Planning Unit deals with all planning issues. Liquor licensing is also included in this department.

Litigation: *(Contact Partner:* John Campbell). The litigation team handles all aspects of commercial and private client litigation. Specialist areas of practice include employment disputes (contracts, redundancy, wrongful dismissal and discrimination), personal injury (five PI Panel Solicitors), professional negligence, construction and insurance.

Family/ Child Care: *(Contact Partner:* David Eastwood). The firm has a substantial specialist unit dealing with all aspects of family disputes.

Private Client: *(Contact Partner:* Barry Rogers). The firm offers a comprehensive service to the private client, including all types of property transfers, wills, trusts, probate and a dedicated financial planning department.

LEGAL AID FRANCHISE: Awarded during 1995 covering crime, personal injury, family, debt, employment and consumer issues.

NATURE OF CLIENTELE: Clients range from insurance companies and P.L.Cs to businesses of all sizes. The firm has a strong private client base and is a member of the Conquest Network.

CONTACT PARTNER: Andrew Rudkin	
Number of partners:	15
Assistant solicitors:	19
Other fee-earners:	25

WORKLOAD	
Litigation	36%
Private Client	28%
Family	24%
Commercial	12%

OTHER OFFICES: Corby, Kettering and Wellingborough.

RECRUITMENT AND TRAINING: The firm expects to take on approximately two trainee solicitors every year and applications should be made on the firm's own application form to Mr Andrew Rudkin.

TOWNLEYS

32 SEKFORDE STREET, LONDON, EC1R 0HH
DX: 53303

TEL: (0171) 251 2505
FAX: (0171) 251 2709

THE FIRM: Townleys is a commercial firm specialising in sports, media and sponsorship law. Established in 1983, Townleys has been at the forefront of developments in the domestic and international sports law field and is now widely regarded both at home and internationally as the pre-eminent specialist English firm in this area.

The firm has particular expertise in legal and tax planning for sports, media and arts clients, sponsorship contracts, licensing, merchandising and event planning, the development and protection of intellectual property rights, international trademark programmes, and broadcasting and communications law and regulations.

Townleys advise on the legal structuring and commercial exploitation of all types of sporting and cultural events which have ranged from the Boat Race and Davis Cup to Asian Football, Australian Tennis, the Rugby World Cup and the Times World Chess Championship. Much of its work is international in flavour and the firm has strong overseas connections and foreign language skills. Clients include international sports governing bodies, major corporate sponsors, sponsorship consultancies, sports television distribution agencies, and advertising and communications agencies.

The firm also undertakes a variety of other commercial work, including commercial and sports litigation, intellectual property law, company law and insolvency.

CONTACT PARTNER: Nicholas Couchman

Number of partners:	5
Assistant solicitors:	3
Other fee-earners:	3

WORKLOAD	
Sports and media	70%
Commercial/ property	20%
Litigation	10%

CONTACTS	
Commercial/ property	Michael Townley
Litigation	Michael Townley, Mark Lake
Sports and media	Nicholas Couchman

TOWNSENDS

42 CRICKLADE STREET, SWINDON, WILTS, SN1 3HD
DX: 6204

TEL: (01793) 410800
FAX: (01793) 616294

THE FIRM: Established in 1814, Townsends has grown steadily and is now the largest law firm in Wiltshire. It is expanding its corporate client base, whilst maintaining high-quality private client services. There is also an emphasis on extending European and foreign connections, and on maintaining high levels of staff training.

PRINCIPAL AREAS OF WORK:

Company/ Commercial: (*Contact:* Brian Jacomb). *Work includes:* business start-ups, agency and distributorship agreements, partnerships and joint ventures, MBOs, takeovers, insolvency, employment law, computer law, consumer credit, bloodstock, taxation and EC law.

Litigation: (*Contact:* Byron Carron). Work includes commercial disputes, personal injury, industrial diseases, construction disputes, licensing, debt recovery, defamation, employment law, insurance claims, landlord and tenant, product liability, professional negligence, and criminal matters.

Property: (*Contact:* Alan Goulding). *Work includes:* agricultural law (including milk quotas), commercial and residential acquisitions, sales and development, leases, planning, construction documentation and mortgages.

Private Client/ Financial Services: (*Contact:* Sir John Sykes). Work includes advice on investments, pensions, inheritance tax planning and a range of private client work, including wills, trusts, powers of attorney and advice to charities.

Family/ Childcare: (*Contact:* Richard Sharp). The firm advises on all aspects of family and childcare law. Members of Children Panel, Family Mediators Association and Swindon Family Law Association.

NEWBURY OFFICE: Also offers the full range of services.

CONTACT PARTNER: Julian George

Number of partners:	23
Assistant solicitors:	12
Other fee-earners:	20

WORKLOAD	
Commercial litigation	24%
Private client and financial services	18%
Personal injury litigation	18%
Residential property and agriculture	14%
Commercial property	14%
Commercial	12%

CONTACTS	
Agriculture	Christopher Goldingham
Commercial	Brian Jacomb
Commercial property	Alan Goulding
Commercial litigation	Michael Nield
Personal injury litigation	Byron Carron
Private client	Sir John Sykes
Residential property	Christopher Goldingham

TOZERS

BROADWALK HOUSE, SOUTHERNHAY WEST, EXETER, DEVON, EX1 1UA
DX: 8322

TEL: (01392) 424444
FAX: (01392) 70517

THE FIRM: Tozers was established in 1785 and is one of the largest law firms in South Devon, expanding rapidly in recent years with new offices in Paignton (1993) and Torquay (1995) and with the move of the Exeter office to new premises in the city centre. The firms offers a successful blend of experience and traditional values on the one hand, and a progressive outlook and a high degree of commercial awareness on the other. It is committed to investing in its staff (and hopes to achieve the Investors in People award) and in computer technology (all six offices are linked on a wide area network and now use windows software exclusively). Specialist teams have been developed to ensure expertise in niche areas and currently the firm has as a number of solicitors the Law Society's specialist panels - Children, Personal Injury, Medical Negligence and Planning.

PRINCIPAL AREAS OF WORK:

Planning & Environmental Law: including Caravan Parks & Mobile Home Law.

Charities & Schools: the specialist team advises religious, educational and other charities as well as schools both in the private and state sectors.

Commercial Lending & Recovery: the firm has advised the banking industry for many years on all aspects of this work.

Commercial & Residential property

Litigation: including employment and industrial relations disputes, property disputes, debt recovery, criminal law and general civil litigation: specialist teams advise on - Family & Childcare; Medical & Personal Injury; Professional Negligence in Financial Services (in particular pensions mis-selling).

Will, Probate, Tax & Trusts: including tax planning and investment management for trusts and individuals.

LANGUAGES SPOKEN: French, Spanish, Japanese, Polish and Italian are available.

AGENCY WORK: All aspects of civil and criminal litigation, licensing and personal searches.

RECRUITMENT & TRAINING: Current policy: two trainee solicitors per year – no vacancies until Autumn 1996.

OTHER OFFICES:

8-10 St Pauls Road, Newton Abbot, Devon TQ12 4PR.
Tel: (01626) 62161. *Fax:* (01626) 55589. *DX:* 59102.
2-4 Orchard Gardens, Teignmouth, Devon TQ14 8DR.
Tel: (01626) 772376. *Fax:* (01626) 770317. *DX:* 82051.
73-75 Abbey Road, Torquay, Devon TQ2 5NN.
Tel: (01803) 291898. *Fax:* (01803) 299293. *Fax:* 59023 Torquay 1.
Sandwell House, 4 Dendy Road, Paignton, Devon TQ4 5BZ.
Tel: (01803) 529101. *Fax:* (01803) 529201. *DX:* 100610.
Strand Chambers, Dawlish, Devon EX7 9EZ.
Tel: (01626) 862323. *Fax:* (01626) 866851. *DX:* 82100.

MANAGING PARTNER: M.M. Brotherton, (01626) 62161

Number of partners:	18
Assistant solicitors:	11
Other fee-earners:	12

WORKLOAD

Litigation	32%
Commercial	30%
Property	21%
Probate	17%

CONTACTS

Charities and schools	Richard King
Children and family	Philip Kidd
Commercial lending & property	Tim Fogarty
Litigation	Peter Edwards
Medical negligence	Laurence Vick
Planning and mobile home law	Tony Beard
Probate	Vernon Clarke

TRAVERS SMITH BRAITHWAITE

10 SNOW HILL, LONDON, EC1A 2AL
DX: 79

TEL:	(0171) 248 9133 or 696 0998
FAX:	(0171) 236 3728 or 696 9747

THE FIRM: Founded more than two centuries ago, Travers Smith Braithwaite has developed into a major commercial law firm with the expertise and capability to advise on a wide range of business activities. Today's clients include regulatory, financial, trade and industrial organisations throughout the UK and from all over the world.

Travers Smith Braithwaite prides itself on not being so large as to have an impersonal atmosphere yet enjoys a quality of work and a range of clients normally associated with larger firms. By resisting rapid growth, the firm has been able to maintain the high standards of service it provides to clients. Small, closely knit and consistent teams of lawyers will provide advice to a client year in year out, ensuring a clear understanding of the client's business and an effective working relationship. Central to the firm's approach is the philosophy that partners should be closely involved in most of the matters undertaken and that delegation should not be automatic but considered in every case in the light of both effectiveness and cost.

PRINCIPAL AREAS OF WORK: The firm's business comprises seven main areas:

Corporate Law: takeovers, mergers and acquisitions, new issues, company law, financial services and regulatory law, capital markets and venture capital.

Commercial Law: business agreements, EU and competition law, intellectual property, information technology, environment, employment law, privatisations and healthcare.

Finance: secured and unsecured lending, finance leasing, acquisition finance, trade and project finance, property finance, banking regulations, rescheduling and insolvency.

Litigation: domestic and international, commercial litigation and arbitration.

Property: acquisition, disposal and development of industrial, retail, office, residential and agricultural property, planning and construction law.

Pensions: establishment, administration and winding up of pension funds and pension litigation.

Tax: domestic and international corporate tax planning, acquisition and structured finance, employee incentive schemes, private client tax planning, settlements and wills.

WORK CONTACTS:

Corporate	–	Christopher Bell
Commercial	–	John Longdon
Competition and EU	–	David Strang
Employment	–	Dorothy Henderson
Environment	–	Christopher Carroll
Finance	–	Graham Wedlake
Financial Services	–	Margaret Chamberlain
Insolvency	–	Jeremy Walsh
Insurance and Reinsurance	–	Stephen Paget-Brown
Litigation	–	John Kingston
Pensions	–	Paul Stannard
Property	–	Robert Harman
Tax	–	Alasdair Douglas
Venture Capital	–	Christopher Hale

FOREIGN CONNECTIONS: The firm enjoys a close working relationship with foreign law firms in the main legal jurisdictions and is a member of a network of European law firms.

FOREIGN LANGUAGES: French, German, Italian, Spanish, Swedish and Polish.

OTHER OFFICE: Travers Smith Braithwaite was the first City firm to open an office in Douglas to represent both Isle of Man and non-Isle of Man based corporate clients in relation to a wide range of business requirements and transactions. As Registered Legal Practitioners practising in the Isle of Man, the firm can advise on both English and Isle of Man law, including the provision of opinions to foreign lawyers as to matters of Isle of Man law. Principal areas of work include company, corporate

CONTACT PARTNER: Alasdair F. Douglas

Number of partners:	40
Assistant solicitors:	70
Other fee-earners:	23

WORKLOAD	
Corporate	29%
Finance	16%
Property	15%
Litigation	15%
Commercial	14%
Tax	6%
Pensions	5%

CONTACTS	
Commercial	John Longdon
Competition and EU law	David Strang
Corporate	Christopher Bell
Employment	Dorothy Henderson
Environment	Christopher Carroll
Finance	Graham Wedlake
Financial services	Margaret Chamberlain
Insolvency	Jeremy Walsh
Insurance/reinsurance	Stephen Paget-Brown
Litigation	John Kingston
Pensions	Paul Stannard
Property	Robert Harman
Tax	Alasdair Douglas
Venture capital	Christopher Hale

finance, financial services, commercial, intellectual property, employment, pensions, EU and competition, insurance, shipping, banking regulations, asset and shipping finance. *Contact:* Michael Pinson: 4 Upper Church Street, Douglas, Isle of Man IM1 1EE *Tel:* (01624) 625515.

RECRUITMENT & TRAINING: Travers Smith Braithwaite continues to develop and is always looking to recruit, at both assistant and trainee level, people of academic excellence and sound judgement who are able to take their careers, but not themselves, seriously. The firm's training philosophy is that skill and expertise are best acquired through practical experience complemented by carefully targeted formal instruction. Great emphasis is placed on ensuring that trainees are actively involved in a broad range of work.

Applications for traineeships should be made in writing to Christopher Carroll enclosing a full CV together with the names and addresses of academic and personal referees.

TRETHOWANS College Chambers, New St, Salisbury, Wilts, SP1 2LY **Tel:** (01722) 412512 **Fax:** (01722) 411300 **DX:** 58004 **Ptnrs:** 12 **Asst Solrs:** 10 **Other Fee-earners:** 15. Expanding provincial firm known for its practice in commercial property, commercial litigation, and general commercial law. Also agricultural law, tax planning, wills, probate and debt recovery.

WORKLOAD			
Property	23%	Fin serv investigation	22%
Company and commercial	20%	Other litigation	18%
Private client	17%		

TROBRIDGES 1 Ford Park Road, Mutley Plain, Plymouth, Devon, PL4 6LY **Tel:** (01752) 664022 **Fax:** (01752) 223761 **DX:** 120154 **Ptnrs:** 3 **Asst Solrs:** 3 **Other Fee-earners:** 4. General practice with a litigation bias, with a particular emphasis on personal injury and family work.

WORKLOAD			
Pers inj lit/civil lit	45%	Conveyancing/commercial	30%
Family	18%	Probate	5%
Crime	1%		

TROWERS & HAMLINS

6 NEW SQUARE, LINCOLN'S INN, LONDON, WC2A 3RP
DX: 31 Ch.Ln.

TEL: (0171) 831 6292
FAX: (0171) 831 8700

THE FIRM: Trowers & Hamlins is a substantial international firm with 44 partners, 57 assistant solicitors and 23 trainee solicitors. Its practice is wide and varied. A leader in the housing law field, the firm is also strong in commercial and litigation disciplines.

PRINCIPAL AREAS OF WORK:

Company and Commercial: (*Contact:* Donald Jones). This expanding area of practice is involved in both UK and international work. The firm advises on commercial agreements of all types; company formation; competition law; corporate finance (including housing and public sector finance); banking; acquisitions and mergers; EIS's; EC law; management buy-outs; offshore company work; partnership agreements and public companies.

Litigation: (*Contact:* John Linwood). The firm deals with nearly all aspects of commercial and property litigation. It has a particularly strong reputation in construction and has a section dealing specifically with all aspects of construction law, handling contentious and non-contentious work. The litigation service includes administrative law and judicial review; banking and financial disputes; building disputes; commercial disputes; copyright and passing-off; defamation; employment law; partnership disputes; and professional negligence.

Property: (*Contact:* Jonathan Adlington). The largest area of the firm's practice encompasses Commercial, Housing, Public Sector, Residential and Estate law. The firm acts major property institutions, companies, banks, developers, housing associations (some 230) and individuals. Housing work includes site acquisitions, shared ownership and other forms of disposal, assured and secure tenancies, partnership schemes with local authorities, and public and private funding of housing schemes. The firm's Public Sector Group has worked with local authorities and housing associations on most of the successful voluntary transfers of local authority housing stock in the UK, and has considerable experience in CCT.

MANAGING PARTNER: Don Moorhouse

UK:	
Number of partners:	38
Assistant solicitors:	46
Other fee-earners:	49

WORKLOAD	
Property (housing, public sector, comm.)	35%
Corporate/ company and commercial	30%
Litigation	20%
Private client	15%

CONTACTS	
Commercial property	Elizabeth McKibbin
Company/ commercial	Jennie Gubbins
Construction	David Mosey
Corporate finance	Ralph Picken
Environmental	Ian Doolittle
Facilities Management	Martin Amison
International	John McHugo
Litigation (commercial)	John Linwood
Litigation (property)	Roger King
Local government	John Clark, Ian Doolittle
Private client	Michael Williamson

Private Client: (*Contact:* Michael Williamson). Advice to individuals with industrial, invested or landed wealth is a traditional part of the firm's practice. The firm's private client lawyers have particular knowledge of tax planning, trusts, life insurance, pensions and domicile and residence law. The firm has a specialist charities group. A tax section advises on all aspects of the firm's work.

OTHER OFFICES: Manchester, Exeter, Dubai, Oman and Abu Dhabi. The firm is also associated with Ann Tan and Associates in Singapore, and has a cooperation arrangement with Winstead Sechrest & Minick P.C. in the USA, and with a Yemeni law firm.

NATURE OF CLIENTELE: *Clients include:* public and private companies, banks, financial institutions, local and central government authorities; housing associations; building contractors and developers, professional associations, insurance companies, partnerships and individuals. The firm has a considerable amount of international work, not only in the Gulf where it has a long-standing presence, but also through its links with Europe and the USA.

LANGUAGES SPOKEN: French, German, Arabic, Spanish, Russian, and Turkish.

RECRUITMENT: The firm takes up to 12 trainee solicitors every year. It is looking for personable candidates with a good academic background and with wide-ranging outside interests. A training officer and librarian assist partners in a comprehensive training programme. Application form available from Elizabeth McKibbin.

TRUMANS 22 Park Row, Nottingham, Notts, NG1 6GX **Tel:** (0115) 941 7275 **Fax:** (0115) 948 4272 **DX:** 10023 **Ptnrs:** 9 **Asst Solrs:** 10 **Other Fee-earners:** 27. A general practice concentrating on private client work with a strong litigation department and a growing commercial department. Also specialise in divorce, child care work and crime.

WORKLOAD			
Civil litigation	40%	Res conveyancing	15%
Crime	15%	Matrimonial	15%
Probate	7%	Debt	5%

TRUMP AND PARTNERS

34 ST. NICHOLAS ST, BRISTOL, BS1 1TS
DX: 7815

TEL: (0117) 929 9901
FAX: (0117) 921 1053

THE FIRM: Trump and Partners has been based in St. Nicholas Street in the commercial heart of Bristol since its creation some 90 years ago.

PRINCIPAL AREAS OF WORK: Half the fee earners in the firm are in the business client department providing a wide range of legal services to corporate and institutional clients.

The private client department is best known for its family law services.

The litigation department provides services to both corporate and private clients as appropriate. The firm holds a Legal Aid Franchise.

Increasingly, the provision of financial services is enhancing the traditional private client services of conveyancing, wills, trust and probate.

Although divided into departments, the firm recognises the need to form teams and in appropriate appropriate cases, expertise from two or more departments is brought together to serve the client.

AGENCY WORK: Agency work is undertaken in all matrimonial and civil courts in Bristol.

RECRUITMENT AND TRAINING: Applications for articles should be submitted in writing with typed CV two years before commencement date, for the attention of Robert Bourns.

CHARGES: Charges are based on hourly rates, which are reviewed annually and which depend on the level of fee earners involved. Where appropriate, a fixed fee can be agreed.

CONTACT PARTNER: Mrs J.E. Hillman

Number of partners:	10
Assistant solicitors:	11
Other fee-earners:	5

WORKLOAD	
Business client	39%
Litigation	27%
Family/ divorce	18%
Private client	14%

CONTACTS	
Civil litigation	Andrew Troup
Commercial property	Nicholas Pritchard
Company commercial	David Simpson
Employment	Robert Bourns
Family/ divorce	David Woodward
Financial services	Erica Thomas
Partnership	Nick Moss
Personal injury/medical	Jo Hillman
Private client	Robert Moody

TUCKERS

35 QUEEN ANNE STREET, LONDON, W1M 9FB DX: 53829 Oxford Circus North	TEL: (0171) 580 1764 FAX: (0171) 637 8738
7 St. John Street, Manchester M3 4DN DX: 18190 Manchester	Tel: (0161) 835 1414 Fax: (0161) 835 1415

THE FIRM: Tuckers Solicitors are a purely criminal law firm with offices located in both the North of England and Central London. The firm acts on behalf of both private and legally-aided clients in all aspects of criminal law from drink driving, road traffic matters to business crime, drugs and murder.

AGENCY WORK: As the offices are staffed 24 hours a day, police station attendance is always available to clients and other firms of solicitors/ accountants requiring assistance for their own clients.

OFFICE EQUIPMENT: Tuckers use the latest computerised systems for file management, billing and administrative control.

FOREIGN CONNECTIONS: The practice has strong connections in France and Germany.

CHARGES: Hourly costs: Private clients – Partner 120. – Assistant 90.

CONTACT PARTNER: Mr. B.M. Tucker

Number of partners:	3
Assistant solicitors:	10
Other fee-earners:	29

WORKLOAD	
Crime (all types)	100%

CONTACTS	
Bus crime/commercial fraud	B. Craig
Crime	Franklin Sinclair (Manchester)
	Barry Tucker

TUCKER TURNER KINGSLEY WOOD & CO

18 BEDFORD ROW, LONDON, WC1R 4EB DX: 220	TEL: (0171) 242 3303 FAX: (0171) 831 1732

THE FIRM: The firm moved to larger offices in Bedford Row on 1st September 1994. It is a medium-sized practice with a solid commercial background and strong international connections. In addition, the firm offers a range of specialised private client services.

PRINCIPAL AREAS OF WORK:

Property: *(Contact Partner:* David Jones). *Work includes:* secured lending, acquisitions and disposals, portfolio restructuring and re-gearing, syndicated investment, environmental audits, securitisation, mortgage portfolio transfers, refurbishment, portfolio management, business tenancies, rent reviews, lease renewals, secured and foreign currency loans, development and professional team arrangements, site assembly, planning and environmental, building construction, civil engineering projects and agricultural property.

Company/ Commercial: *(Contact Partners:* Alec Melville). *Work includes:* mergers and acquisitions, take-overs, joint ventures, venture and development capital, MBOs, flotations, intellectual property, telecommunications, licensing and franchising, employment, building society law, loan documentation, securitisation, consumer credit, insolvency rescue and reconstruction, partnership, hotels and leisure, financial services, taxation and insurance law.

International Services: *(Contact Partner:* Alec Melville). *Work includes:* international finance, cross-border joint ventures, distribution and agency agreements throughout Europe, parallel imports and exports, international arbitration, international real estate, cross-border financial services and international tax planning.

Litigation: *(Contact Partner:* Richard Briggs). *Work includes:* professional negligence, asset preservation and recovery, fraud, intellectual property disputes, commercial disputes, arbitration, breach of contract, company and partnership disputes, insurance and re-insurance claims, personal injury, construction and property disputes, landlord and tenant, employment disputes, defamation, licensing, contentious probate and advocacy.

CONTACT PARTNER: Alec Melville

Number of partners:	6
Assistant solicitors:	5
Other fee-earners:	8

TUCKER TURNER KINGSLEY WOOD & Co
solicitors

Secured Lending and Debt Recovery: *(Contact Partner:* Bob Joyce). *Work includes:* secured lending, building society law and practice, enforcement of mortgagees rights, receiverships, sales in possession, personal covenant recovery, third party post realisation recovery, asset preservation and recovery, standard debt recovery, professional fees recovery and company winding-up and bankruptcy.

Private Client: *(Contact Partners:* David Pearce/ Paul Davis). *Work includes:* wills and estate planning, on and offshore trusts, UK and overseas tax, residential property, investment management, executor services and administration of estates, advocacy and the arrangement of loans for real property purchase.

FOREIGN LANGUAGES SPOKEN: French, German, Spanish & Italian.

INTERNATIONAL CONNECTIONS: The firm maintains strong links with lawyers in Belgium, Holland, Germany, France, Spain, Italy, Australia, USA, South Africa, Hong Kong and Singapore.

Additionally, the firm is a member of Advonet, a group of German Lawyers, with members throughout Europe, and ICEL, a group of Banking Lawyers throughout Europe.

RECRUITMENT AND TRAINING: One/ two trainee solicitors are recruited each year. Apply in November to Paul Davis.

TUGHAN & CO 30 Victoria Street, Belfast, BT1 3GS **Tel:** (01232) 553300 **Fax:** (01232) 231916 **Ptnrs:** 9 **Asst Solrs:** 3 **Other Fee-earners:** 5. Known for its commercial property work, the firm is also highly regarded for its company/ commercial and litigation expertise. private client work.

WORKLOAD			
Lit incl insur/employment	45%	Comp/commercial	40%
Private client	10%		

TURBERVILLE WOODBRIDGE

122 HIGH ST, UXBRIDGE, MIDDX, UB8 1JT
DX: 45116 Uxbridge

TEL: (01895) 259871
FAX: (01895) 273519

THE FIRM: The present firm was constituted in 1983 from a merger of two long-established Uxbridge firms, namely Woodbridge & Sons (founded 1796), and Turberville Smith & Co (founded 1820). The firm has three offices, two in Uxbridge and one in Hillingdon.

PRINCIPAL AREAS OF WORK:

General Description: The firm handles a broad spread of work for commercial, private and legally-aided clients, covering domestic and commercial property; civil, family, employment and personal injury litigation; computerised debt collection; wills, probate, trusts and taxation; licensing; criminal; County Court agency.

CONTACT PARTNER: Mr. Sess Sigré	
Number of partners:	11
Assistant solicitors:	11
Other fee-earners:	9

TURNBULL, SIMSON & STURROCK WS 26 High Street, Jedburgh, Borders, TD8 6AE **Tel:** (01835) 862391 **Fax:** (01835) 862017 **Ptnrs:** 8 **Asst Solrs:** 1 . The firm offers a broad range of services and has particular expertise in relation to agricultural law.

TURNER & CO 107 Fenchurch Street, London, EC3M 5JB **Tel:** (0171) 480 7991 **Fax:** (0171) 481 0939 **Ptnrs:** 3 **Other Fee-earners:** 1. A specialist shipping, commodities and general commercial practice.

TURNERS 1 Poole Rd, Bournemouth, Dorset, BH2 5QQ **Tel:** (01202) 291291 **Fax:** (01202) 553606 **DX:** 7637 **Ptnrs:** 13 **Asst Solrs:** 3 **Other Fee-earners:** 7. Three offices in S.E. Dorset. In addition to an established private client and property practice, the firm has developed a strong commercial and litigation practice.

TWEEDIE & PRIDEAUX

5 LINCOLN'S INN FIELDS, LONDON, WC2A 3BT
DX: 6 Ch.Ln

TEL: (0171) 242 9231
FAX: (0171) 831 1525

THE FIRM: A long established practice. The firm undertakes company and commercial work; commercial conveyancing; private client work including residential conveyancing, wills, trusts and probate; litigation and work for charities.
OTHER OFFICE:
390 London Road, Mitcham, Surrey CR4 4EA.
Tel: (0181) 640 5124. *Fax:* (0181) 640 2695. *DX:* 88151 Mitcham South.
FOREIGN LANGUAGES SPOKEN: French and Spanish.
FOREIGN CONNECTIONS: Zimbabwe.

CONTACT PARTNER: Mr C.R. Skottowe

Number of partners:	7
Assistant solicitors:	4
Other fee-earners:	4

TWITCHEN MUSTERS & KELLY

CLIFFTOWN CHAMBERS, 20 WESTON ROAD, SOUTHEND-ON-SEA,
ESSEX, SS1 1AS   DX: 2821

TEL: (01702) 339222
FAX: (01702) 331563

THE FIRM: Twitchen Musters & Kelly is the result of the merger at the beginning of 1990 between Twitchen and Musters and Robinson Kelly.
PRINCIPAL AREAS OF WORK: A litigation practice, this is one of the most prominent firms in provincial Essex involved in criminal and childcare work. The firm also undertakes substantial personal injury and family law work, and all High Court and County Court litigation, including agency work.
OTHER OFFICES:
Alexandra Chambers, 46 Alexandra Street, *Tel:* (01702) 334222, *Fax:* (01702) 391496, in Southend-on-Sea.

CONTACT PARTNER: Patrick H.A. Musters

Number of partners:	4
Assistant solicitors:	3
Other fee-earners:	9

TYNDALLWOODS 5 Greenfield Crescent, Edgbaston, Birmingham, W. Midlands, B15 3BE **Tel:** (0121) 454 7996 **Fax:** (0121) 624 8401 **DX:** 23502 **Ptnrs:** 10 **Asst Solrs:** 14 **Other Fee-earners:** 18. With four offices in Birmingham, the firm undertakes a wide range of legal aid and private client work.

UNDERWOOD & CO

40 WELBECK ST, LONDON, W1M 8LN
DX: 9074 West End

TEL: (0171) 487 4461
FAX: (0171) 486 8974

THE FIRM: Established in 1845, Underwood & Co specialises in banking and commercial litigation and commercial property work. The firm also has a strong private client connection and undertakes a wide variety of work in this area. The emphasis is on partner involvement and professional expertise at reasonable cost.
PRINCIPAL AREAS OF WORK:
Commercial Litigation: The firm conducts all types of commercial litigation with an emphasis on banking, professional negligence, insolvency, and debt collection.
Commercial and Residential Property: The firm handles all aspects of commercial and residential transactions in relation to freehold and leasehold property including secured lending, the grant and renewal of commercial leases, and the sale and purchase of nursing homes and hotels.
Company/ Commercial: *Work includes:* company formation and restructuring, business assets sale and purchase, licensing, employment law, partnership agreements and commercial contracts, intellectual property and insolvency matters.
Private Client: The firm advises on matters involving administration of estates, wills, probate and personal tax planning work, immigration and work permits and family law.

CONTACT PARTNER: B.W. Dawson

Number of partners:	6
Assistant solicitors:	9
Other fee-earners:	6

WORKLOAD	
Commercial litigation	50%
Commercial and residential property	30%
Private client	10%
Company commercial	10%

UNDERWOODS

1 HOLYWELL HILL, ST. ALBANS, HERTS, AL1 1ER

TEL: (01727) 810800
FAX: (01727) 841293

THE FIRM: Underwoods is a young firm founded in 1991 which specialises in local government matters and civil litigation, in particular employment, personal injury work, administrative and public law. It provides a distinctive and high quality personal service and is recognised as one of the best small firms. Kerry Underwood addresses seminars for the Law Society and the University of Cambridge and appears regularly on radio and television in relation to legal topics. He is a part-time Chairman of Industrial Tribunals and a member of the Law Society's Personal Injury Panel, and a Fellow of The Chartered Institute of Arbitrators.

PRINCIPAL AREAS OF WORK:

Adminstrative/ Public Law: (*Contact:* Kerry Underwood). *Work includes:* judicial review, education, civil liberty matters, discrimination, human rights and considerable local authority work.

Local Government Law: (*Contact:* Robert Males/ Kerry Underwood). *Work includes:* education law, judicial reviews, joint ventures, leasing and funding, transfers of undertakings.

Corporate and Commercial: (*Contact:* Barry Banks). *Work includes:* business start-ups, trading agreements, venture capital, joint venture agreements, insolvency and corporate restructuring, compulsory competitive tendering and transfers of undertakings.

Employment: (*Contact:* Kerry Underwood/ Robert Males). *Work includes:* transfer of undertakings regulations, sex and race discrimination, EU law, Industrial Tribunal and Employment Appeal Tribunal advocacy, redundancy and contract, and severance. Clients include local authorities and major companies and employees.

Litigation: (*Contact:* Kerry Underwood/ Sonya Brown). *Work includes:* personal injury, (Law Society's Personal Injury Panel), medical negligence, building disputes, intellectual property matters, debt recovery and contractual disputes.

Commercial Property: (*Contact:* Robert Males). *Work includes:* sales and acquisitions, leases, landlord and tenant law.

Private Client: (*Contact:* Robert Males/ Sonya Brown). *Work includes:* residential conveyancing, probate, wills and trusts, family and matrimonial law and consumer problems.

CONTACT PARTNER: Mr Kerry Underwood

Number of partners:	1
Assistant solicitors:	2
Other fee-earners:	3

WORKLOAD

Employment	28%
Personal injury	27%
Other	20%
Litigation	15%
Local governt./administrative & public law	10%

CONTACTS

Administrative/ public law	Kerry Underwood
Commercial property	Robert Males
Corporate and commercial	Barry Banks
Employment	Kerry Underwood
	Jennifer O'Dwyer
European law	Jennifer O'Dwyer
Litigation	Kerry Underwood, Sonya Brown
Local government	Robert Males
	Kerry Underwood
Personal injury	Sonya Brown, Kerry Underwood
	Clare Ranger
Private client	Sonya Brown, Robert Males
	Clare Ranger

UNGOED THOMAS & KING 6 Quay St, Carmarthen, Dyfed, SA31 1JT **Tel:** (01267) 237441 **Fax:** (01267) 238317 **DX:** 51400 **Ptnrs:** 6 **Asst Solrs:** 5 **Other Fee-earners:** 1. Established at the beginning of the century, this is a general practice with five other offices in the area.

VALLANCE LICKFOLDS Lincoln House, 300 High Holborn, London, WC1V 7LN **Tel:** (0171) 404 0707 **Fax:** (0171) 404 0031 **DX:** 126 London **Ptnrs:** 8 **Asst Solrs:** 1 **Other Fee-earners:** 2. A general commercial litigation and private client practice with particular emphasis on liquor and entertainment licensing and sporting contracts.

VARLEY HIBBS & CO Kirby House, Little Park St, Coventry, W. Midlands, CV1 2JZ **Tel:** (01203) 631000 **Fax:** (01203) 630808 **DX:** 11214 **Ptnrs:** 11 **Asst Solrs:** 5 **Other Fee-earners:** 9. Established in 1927. Branch office in Leamington Spa. Well known for civil litigation, company and commercial, general litigation and family matters.

WORKLOAD

Civil/commercial lit	24%	Company and commercial	23%
Advocacy	17%	Family	14%
Conveyancing	13%	Probate/miscellaneous	9%

VAUDREYS

13 POLICE STREET, MANCHESTER, M2 7WA
DX: 14341

TEL: (0161) 834 6877
FAX: (0161) 834 2440

THE FIRM: Founded in 1877, Vaudreys is a leading specialist commercial practice, with over 100 years' involvement in the business and commercial life of Manchester. A highly motivated partnership with a modern progressive attitude, the practice ensures close contact with clients and an understanding of their commercial needs. The firm has made a substantial investment in the latest technology.

PRINCIPAL AREAS OF WORK:

Insurance Litigation Department: *(Contact Partner:* Iain Moore). The firm acts for a wide cross-range of UK insurance companies and a number of large corporate concerns regarding their insurance arrangements. *Work includes:* industrial injury and disease cases, on-site investigations of claims and their subsequent valuation, construction and mining litigation, product liability cases and commercial transport operations.

Corporate and Commercial Department: *(Contact Partner:* Paul Brown). The firm offers a comprehensive service to commercial and corporate clients. *Work includes:* mergers, acquisitions, disposals, joint ventures, franchising, licensing, the exploitation and protection of intellectual property and design rights, immigration and employment matters, the full range of company-related services and advice on insolvency matters.

Commercial Litigation Department: *(Contact Partner:* Robert Moss). The firm has a reputation for achieving fast and effective solutions both nationally and internationally. *Work includes:* commercial disputes of all types, including landlord and tenant and property related disputes, construction contracts, employment, insolvency, banking litigation and debt recovery.

Commercial Property Department: *(Contact Partner:* Mark Pattison). *Work includes:* leasing, acquisition and disposal, landlord and tenant matters, complex site compilations or break-ups, development and redevelopment, planning matters and corporate property projects.

International Trade: *(Contact Partner:* Tony Martin). The firm operates throughout Western and Eastern Europe, the USA and the Far East. *Work includes:* the import and export of goods and services, the establishment of agencies, distributorships and businesses, general trading agreements, and joint ventures, the licensing and sale of technology in foreign jurisdictions and shipping matters, including construction contracts, cargo disputes and related marine matters. A French lawyer is employed within the department.

Banking and Financial Services: *(Contact Partner:* Paul Brown). The firm acts as Regional Solicitors to a number of major banks and as advisers to finance house subsidiaries of UK clearing banks. In addition to the full range of banking services, advice is available on specific project financing over assets such as shipping, aircraft, fleet transport and large-scale computer installations.

Private Client Department: *(Contact Partner:* Martyn James). The firm has a long-standing reputation for providing a friendly and efficient service. *Work includes:* wills, probate, tax and estate planning and domestic property transactions.

Family Law: *(Contact Partner:* Robert Moss). *Work includes:* resolution of financial and property disputes, divorce and/or judicial separation proceedings, cohabitation agreements, wardship proceedings and resolutions of all problems relating to children.

RECRUITMENT AND TRAINING: The firm recruits six trainee solicitors each year. Application and CV to Peter Lindsay.

CONTACT PARTNER: Tony Healey

Number of partners:	12
Assistant solicitors:	34
Other fee-earners:	12

WORKLOAD	
Insurance litigation	25%
Commercial property	25%
Commercial litigation	25%
Corporate	20%
Private client	5%

CONTACTS	
Banking	Paul Brown
Computer/ IP	Tony Martin
Construction	Tony Healey
Employment	Tony Healey
Health and safety	Ian Moore
Insurance litigation	Ian Moore
International	Tony Martin
Landlord and tenant	Stephen Birchall
	Mark Pattison
Licensing	Tony Healey
Litigation (commercial)	Robert Moss
Private client	Martyn James

VEALE WASBROUGH

ORCHARD COURT, ORCHARD LANE, BRISTOL, BS1 5DS
DX: 7831; LIX BSL 001

TEL: (0117) 925 2020
FAX: (0117) 925 2025

THE FIRM: Veale Wasbrough is one of the leading commercially-orientated practices in the South-West region with associated offices in 43 leading EU and other European cities. The firm is fully resourced and forward-looking with modern city centre offices; having on-site clients' car parking. The client base consists of high profile organisations such as major clearing banks, building societies, leading accountancy practices, local government authorities, central government departments, insurance companies, retail chain stores, construction companies, public and private utilities, and independent schools. It offers practical and effective advice to exacting professional standards. Overall City quality expertise at rates which reflect lower provincial overheads.

PRINCIPAL AREAS OF WORK:

Central & Local Government: (Simon Baker/Nigel Campbell). Growing national reputation for advising government departments, utilities and local authorities. Particular expertise on regulated procurement, TUPE and CCT issues.

Company/ Commercial: (Nigel Campbell). Specialist advice to well-known public companies, private companies, start-ups and individuals. Particular emphasis on mergers and acquisitions, corporate finance, pensions, employee benefits, intellectual property, medical partnerships, director and shareholder disputes and insolvency.

Construction: (Roger Hoyle). National reputation in construction disputes, building and engineering contracts, professional indemnity insurance and collateral warranties.

Education & Training: (Robert Boyd/Nigel Campbell). Legal services to over 450 schools, Universities, FE Colleges, NSAs, TECs, Examining Boards. Training provided on employment, CCT, regulated procurement, property, health & safety and education.

Employment Law: (Chris Southam). Dedicated, rapidly growing team dealing with national industrial disputes.

Litigation: (Michael Davies). Banking, insurance, commercial disputes, employment, judicial review, computerised debt collection and business fraud, insolvency litigation, partnership disputes and intellectual property.

Personal Injury: (Maureen Harvie). Well regarded department, acts for both plaintiffs and defendants in two distinct work groups. All types of accident, product liability and criminal injury compensation claims covered. Medical negligence unit. Takes many referrals on complex cases from other solicitors.

Private Client: (Mike Rendell). Wills, estate administration, matrimonial disputes, residential conveyancing, remortgages and tax planning.

Property: (Tim Smithers). Acquisition, financing, development, letting and disposal of all types of commercial property. Niche areas of expertise include Pipelines, VAT and BES schemes, and quarrying and waste management industries.

RECRUITMENT AND TRAINING: The firm recruits up to four trainee solicitors each year, who are law or non-law graduates with a good academic record. Applications to Paul Cottam with CV.

SPECIALIST INTERDEPARTMENTAL UNITS: Construction, Education, Employment, Environmental, European, Finance & Banking, Insolvency, Intellectual Property, Medical Negligence, Pensions, Public Authorities, Retail.

CONTACT PARTNER: Derek Bellew

Number of partners:	24
Assistant solicitors:	30
Other fee-earners:	25

WORKLOAD	
Commercial litigation	22%
Personal injury	21%
Private client	20%
Company commercial	19%
Property services	18%

CONTACTS	
Banks & building societies	Simon Pizzey
Commercial litigation	Michael Davies
Company and commercial	Nigel Campbell
Construction law	Roger Hoyle
Corporate relocation	Wayne Thomas
Employment law	Christopher Southam
Environmental law	Tim Smithers
European law	David Worthington
Family/ matrimonial	John Bedford
Insolvency	Gary Philpott
Intellectual property	Rosemary Collins
Joint ventures	Stuart Whitfield
Local authorities	Simon Baker
Medical practices	Derek Bellew
Packing/printing industry	Christopher Southam
Pensions	Derek Bellew
Personal injury	Maureen Harvie
Pipelines	Tim Smithers
Public sector	Nigel Campbell
Regulated procurement	Rosemary Collins
Residential Conveyancing	Mike Rendell
Waste management	Tim Smithers
Wills/probate	Mary McCartney

VEALE WASBROUGH
—— SOLICITORS ——

VEITCH PENNY

1 MANOR COURT, DIX'S FIELD, EXETER, DEVON, EX1 1UP
DX: 8309 Exeter

TEL: (01392) 78381
FAX: (01392) 410247

THE FIRM: Founded over 30 years ago Veitch Penny is a broad based firm offering a wide range of services to private clients and the corporate sectors. Growth has been steady over the past 10 years, and continues.

PRINCIPAL AREAS OF WORK:

Litigation: *(Contact Partner:* Michael Penny). The firm is regarded as a specialist in personal injury litigation work, with one team representing plaintiffs, legal expense insurers and motoring organisations while another concentrates on defendant insurers' work. Compensation injury claims arising from road and workplace accidents, and medical negligence are all catered for. The firm which additionally has a speciality in local government insurance litigation also conducts general litigation within both private and commercial sectors.

Company/ Commercial: *(Contact Partner:* Simon Young). This is a small but growing department offering complete support to the smaller company. Company formation, partnership and employment law and intellectual property are among the areas covered.

Private Client: *(Contact Partner:* Charles Dowell). Private client work remains an essential part of the practice, offering conveyancing, probate and trust, taxation, agricultural property and many other topics.

OTHER OFFICES: Crediton.

CONTACT PARTNER: Mr Michael Penny	
Number of partners:	7
Assistant solicitors:	6
Other fee-earners:	7

WORKLOAD	
Defendant personal injury (insurers and local authorities)	33%
Plaintiff personal injury	33%
Conveyancing/ probate and trust	20%
Commercial	7%
General litigation	7%

VICTOR LISSACK & ROSCOE 8 Bow Street, Covent Garden, London, WC2E 7AJ **Tel:** (0171) 240 2010 **Fax:** (0171) 379 4420 **DX:** 40026 Covent Garden **Ptnrs:** 2 **Asst Solrs:** 2 **Other Fee-earners:** 2. Specialists in white collar and all other crime including extradition and courts martial as well as disciplinary tribunal work.

WORKLOAD			
Criminal law	70%	Priv/debt collect/civ lit	30%

VIZARDS

42 BEDFORD ROW, LONDON, WC1R 4JL
DX: 189

TEL: (0171) 405 6302
FAX: (0171) 405 6248

THE FIRM: Established in 1797, Vizards is particularly noted for its expertise in the fields of insurance law, litigation, property, charities and parliamentary law acting as parliamentary and privy council agents. Over the years it has also developed a substantial commercial practice with a strong international emphasis. The firm recently opened a city office principally for London's insurance community. The firm is formally affiliated to Davis, Hockenberg, Wine, Brown, Koehn & Shors PC. of Des Moines, Iowa, USA and also has associated offices in Paris and Milan.

PRINCIPAL AREAS OF WORK:

Charities: *(Contact Partner:* Christopher D.F. Oldham). Vizards acts for a large national charity and other prominent private charities and has long experience in this particular field. Advice covers the establishing of new charities, the preservation of charitable status and all aspects of the administration of charities.

Commercial: *(Contact Partner:* Ronald E. Perry). This department offers expertise in the areas of commerce and finance to undertakings ranging from family businesses and professional partnerships to large well known corporations both in the UK and abroad. In general terms, the firm provides a complete corporate service.

Commercial Property: *(Contact Partner:* Richard T. Barber). The department deals with many commercial transactions involving housing associations and property developers in the UK and abroad, and it deals with all aspects of planning law.

Construction Law: *(Contact Partner:* Peter G. Knight). Vizards has a well-established association with the construction industry and is able to deal with all matters of a building, architectural or engineering nature in the UK and abroad, including contractual drafting, contractual disputes and arbitration and insurance.

CONTACT PARTNER: Christopher D.F. Oldham	
Number of partners:	20
Assistant solicitors:	19
Other fee-earners:	19

WORKLOAD	
Personal injury	30%
Insurance and reinsurance	25%
Property (commercial)	15%
Construction and civil engineering	10%
Employment	5%
Litigation (commercial)	4%
Company and commercial	3%
Charities	3%
Parliamentary	2%
European community	2%
Family and immigration	1%

Environmental Law: *(Contact Partner:* Susan M.H. Linnell). The development of this new area means that the firm is called upon to act and to advise in matters of health and safety regulation; contaminated land sites; company warranties and assessments. Clients range from the individual to large companies and trusts as well as interest groups.

Insurance and Reinsurance: *(Contact Partner:* Martin R. Staples, Robert M. Harrison). The insurance department is the largest within the firm and is regarded as being one of the leading firms in this field. All areas of insurance law are covered, in particular policy drafting, construction and interpretation; litigation covering product liability and material loss, professional negligence, personal injury, transportation/ highway law and re-insurance. Clients include a wide variety of domestic and foreign insurance companies and Lloyd's syndicates. The firm's new (April 1995) city office has been established principally to serve the London Market (Contact Partner: Robert Harrison).

Litigation: *(Contact Partner:* Danny E. Hockman). A variety of work is handled for both private and corporate clients in domestic and international disputes. The department also advises on debt recovery; mortgage possession; immigration and nationality; family; employment law actions and tribunals and white collar crime.

Parliamentary: *(Contact Partner:* Ronald E. Perry). The firm has traditionally included at least two Roll A Agents and the Parliamentary department deals with all aspects of private and public legislation, including the Transport & Works Act 1992.

Private Client: *(Contact Partner:* Christopher D.F. Oldham). As well as domestic conveyancing, the department advises on trusts, wills, taxation and financial planning, and administration of estates.

FOREIGN CONNECTIONS: *(Contact Partner:* Michael P.D. Ellman). In addition to its affiliation to the largest law firm in Iowa, USA, Vizards was a founder member of the International Grouping of Lawyers in 1980 which now consists of law firms from over 40 different countries. This includes its associated offices in Paris and Milan and enables it to extend its services to the whole of Europe and the USA.

One partner in the firm is also qualified in Scotland and is able to deal with work within the Scottish jurisdiction.

LANGUAGES SPOKEN: Dutch, French, German, Gujerati, Hindi, Italian, Russian, Spanish and Urdu.

CONTACTS	
Charities	C.D.F. Oldham
Commercial litigation	P.G. Knight
Company and commercial	R.E. Perry
Construction	P.G. Knight
Employment	D.E. Hockman
European community	M.P.D. Ellman
Family and immigration	M.P.D. Ellman
Insurance and reinsurance	M.R. Staples
Local authority liabilities	M.R. Whittaker
Parliamentary/ public affairs	R.E. Perry
Personal injury	R.J.S. Foster
Professional negligence	R.M. Harrison
Property	R.T. Barber

VIZARDS
S O L I C I T O R S

WACE MORGAN 2 Belmont, Shrewsbury, Shrops, SY1 1TD **Tel:** (01743) 361451 **Fax:** (01743) 231708 **DX:** 19718 Shrewsbury **Ptnrs:** 8 **Asst Solrs:** 4 **Other Fee-earners:** 5. Established 200 years, specialising in employment, advising consulting engineers, personal injury, matrimonial, childcare, probate, trusts, property and licensing.

WORKLOAD		
Convey (domestic/comm) 33%	Family (matrim and child) 26%	
Probate/trusts/wills 21%	Lit (civ/pers inj/emp) 18%	
Comm (comp/partnership) 2%		

WACKS CALLER

STEAM PACKET HOUSE, 76 CROSS STREET, MANCHESTER, M2 4JU
DX: 14383 Manchester 1

TEL: (0161) 957 8888
FAX: (0161) 957 8899

THE FIRM: Now in its ninth year the firm has undergone major expansion during the last 12 months and has further consolidated its position as a leading specialist firm in the realm of corporate finance/ company/ commercial work. In addition, it has expanded into providing services to Lenders/ Institutions.

PRINCIPAL AREAS OF WORK:

Company/ Commercial: *(Contact:* Arran Wacks). The firm provides vigorous expert advice and assistance for the business community on all types of corporate and commercial transactions including Stock Exchange and Takeover Panel work. It is especially renowned for its skill and pragmatic approach in negotiating merger and acquisition agreements, joint venture agreements and MBO's.

Commercial Litigation: *(Contact:* Liz Cowell). This department was founded five years ago and has grown rapidly by providing an aggressive yet user-friendly service for the commercial client.

CONTACT PARTNER: Arran Wacks

Number of partners:	14
Assistant solicitors:	9
Other fee-earners:	8

WORKLOAD	
Company/ commercial	55%
Litigation	25%
Property	20%

Commercial Property: (*Contact:* Robert Harris). This department handles all commercial property transactions and other property related matters with the emphasis on speed (where required) in addition to skill and experience.

Employment: (*Contact:* Anthony Dempsey). Provides a commercial and practical approach to all employment and related issues for both employers and senior employees.

Customs & Excise: (*Contact:*David Hanman).

Intellectual Property: (*Contact:* Simon Wallwork). This department was founded two years ago and has developed a full capability (both contentious and non-contentious) in this field including the protection and exploitation of inventions, trademarks, copyright works, designs, information technology, trade secrets and know-how.

Lending Support: The firm has an established department providing support and advice to Lenders/ Institutional clients.

CONTACTS	
Banking	Paul Brinepew
Commercial property	Robert Harris
Corporate finance	Martin Caller
Employment	Anthony Dempsey
Gen. company/ commercial	Kevin Philt
Insolvency	Joanne Joyce
Intellectual property	Simon Wallwork
Litigation	Liz Cowe
Recoveries	Geoffrey Smith
Taxation	David Hanman

WAKE SMITH

68 CLARKEHOUSE ROAD, SHEFFIELD, S. YORKS, S10 2LJ
DX: 10534 Sheffield

TEL: (0114) 266 6660
FAX: (0114) 267 1253

THE FIRM: Founded in 1802, Wake Smith is a general commercial practice providing a flexible service to companies and businesses of all sizes, as well as private clients, in the Sheffield area.

PRINCIPAL AREAS OF WORK: The main areas of work are divided into four departments: company and commercial; commercial property; commercial litigation and private client.

The firm has considerable experience in the company/ commercial field, including the sale and purchase of businesses, capital structures and intellectual property rights, providing a service to quoted PLCs and major private companies, and also to smaller companies and partnerships. The firm advises in commercial disputes, insolvency and licensing and has a well developed commercial property department.

In addition, the private client department provides advice on matters such as personal tax, pensions, trusts, property and general litigation.

OTHER OFFICES: City Centre Office - 6 Campo Lane, Sheffield.

CONTACT PARTNER: Mr J.C.V. Hunt	
Number of partners:	13
Assistant solicitors:	5
Other fee-earners:	9

WALKER CHARLESWORTH & FOSTER
26 Park Square, Leeds, W. Yorks, LS1 2PL **Tel:** (0113) 245 3594 **Fax:** (0113) 244 4312 **DX:** 26415 **Ptnrs:** 8 **Asst Solrs:** 3 **Other Fee-earners:** 1. A long-established general practice with a bias toward agricultural work, litigation, and accident claims, domestic conveyancing, probate and tax planning, and company/ commercial.

WORKLOAD			
Housing associations	80%	Conveyancing	10%
Litigation (most areas)	5%	Probate	5%

WALKER LAIRD
9 Gilmour Street, Paisley, Strathclyde, PA1 1DG **Tel:** (0141) 887 5271 **Fax:** (0141) 889 3268 **DX:** 32 Paisley **Ptnrs:** 8 **Asst Solrs:** 2 **Other Fee-earners:** 2. General private client and litigation firm with some commercial work; specialises in employment and family law, including child custody and abduction cases.

WORKLOAD			
Conveyancing	25%	Criminal	25%
Civil litigation	25%	Executries/fin serv/priv	13%
Commercial	12%		

WALKER MARTINEAU
64 Queen Street, London, EC4R 1AD **Tel:** (0171) 236 4232 **Fax:** (0171) 236 2525 **DX:** 553 **Ptnrs:** 12 **Asst Solrs:** 16 **Other Fee-earners:** 8. A progressive medium-sized firm based in the City. A largely commercial practice, the firm also has extensive institutional contacts and experience.

WALKER MORRIS

KINGS COURT, 12 KING STREET, LEEDS, W. YORKS, LS1 2HL
DX: 12051

TEL: (0113) 283 2500
FAX: (0113) 245 9412

THE FIRM: Based in Leeds, Walker Morris is one of the largest commercial law firms in the North providing a full range of legal services to industry and commerce.

PRINCIPAL AREAS OF WORK:

Corporate and Tax: (*Contact:* Peter Smart). The corporate and tax department's work includes corporate finance, public company takeovers and mergers, flotations, pensions, acquisitions and disposals of companies, MBOs and general commercial advice. Banking and insolvency, corporate tax and intellectual property are handled by separate specialist units.

Commercial Property and Planning: (*Contact:* David Duckworth). The commercial property and planning departments deal with all aspects of the acquisition of sites for development including major town centre redevelopments and large scale residential sites, town and country planning and environmental matters, property portfolios for institutional and private investors, commercial lettings and joint ventures.

Commercial Litigation: (*Contact:* Chris Caisley). The commercial litigation department deals with a broad scope of work both within the UK and internationally and before courts, tribunals and arbitrators. It also incorporates a number of dedicated units headed by specialists in the areas of construction law, employment, insurance litigation, property litigation and the contentious aspects of intellectual property law, banking and secured lending and commercial fraud. The firm houses a large corporate debt recovery service utilising advanced and fully integrated systems.

Private Client: The firm has retained a private client department dealing with personal tax strategies, probate and trust administration, and residential conveyancing (*Contact:* Andrew Turnbull), and family law and related issues (*Contact:* Richard Manning).

Additional Areas of Work: The Walker Morris Sports Law Unit acts for sports personalities, clubs and associations working within this industry, and work includes contract negotiations and disputes, personality merchandising and licensing agreements (*Contact:* Chris Caisley). In recent years the firm has developed significant expertise in complex commercial fraud and has established a dedicated unit handling investigation, preventive and defence work in a number of major cases (*Contact:* Derek Duffy). The firm has also created cross-departmental practice groups focused on servicing the firm's clients in the banking, building society (*Contact:* David Duckworth) and housing association (*Contact:* Andrew Hurst) movements. The firm's Public Services Group acts on behalf of local authorities and health organisations (*Contact:* David Duckworth).

NATURE OF CLIENTELE: Clients are drawn from the whole spectrum of commerce and industry including retail, the professions, the service industries, manufacturing, construction and development, high technology, and the financial services industry.

FOREIGN CONNECTIONS: The firm advises on European and EC issues and is the founder member of a European Economic Interest Grouping which provides a network of European law firms sharing a common philosophy and approach.

OFFICE SUPPORT SERVICES: The firm places great emphasis on the fast and accurate production and delivery of documents; its purpose-built offices in Leeds are specially networked to take the most advanced processing and communications systems.

RECRUITMENT AND TRAINING: The firm's year-on-year expansion has resulted in its always having a continuing recruitment policy for motivated young solicitors in all major disciplines. The firm recruits around ten trainee solicitors every year. Discretionary grants are provided.

Career prospects are excellent (most of the partners were articled with the firm). Application forms and recruitment brochures are available from Paul Emmett, recruitment partner. A training scheme is available to keep its lawyers up-to-date, consisting of in-house seminars, external conferences and information updates.

CONTACT PARTNER: Chris Caisley

Number of partners:	26
Assistant solicitors:	50
Other fee-earners:	77

WORKLOAD

Commercial litigation	35%
Commercial property	25%
Company and commercial	20%
Building societies	12%
Private clients	5%
Tax	3%

CONTACTS

Banking and building societies	Philip Mudd
	Roger Limbert
Commercial litigation	Chris Caisley
Commercial property	David Duckworth
Commercial property devt.	Paul Walker
	Mark Tordoff
Construction	Martin Scott
Corporate debt recovery	Chris Gibson
Corporate	Peter Smart
Corporate finance	Paul Emmett, Ian Gilbert
Corporate crime	Derek Duffy
Corporate tax	Simon Concannon
EC and competition	Patrick Cantrill
Employment	David Smedley
Environment	Andrew Williamson
Family	Richard Manning
Health and public services	David Duckworth
Housing associations	Andrew Hurst
Insolvency	Philip Mudd
Insurance litigation	Chris Caisley
Intellectual property	Patrick Cantrill
Licensing	Patrick Whur
Pensions	Andrew Turnbull
Personal injury	Chris Caisley
Private client, trust and tax	Andrew Turnbull
Professional indemnity	Roger Limbert
Property litigation	Andrew Beck
Residential property devt.	Paul Walker
Retail	Richard Innes
Sports law	Chris Caisley
Town and country planning	Andrew Williamson
Trade marks	Patrick Cantrill

WALKER SMITH & WAY

26 NICHOLAS STREET, CHESTER, CH1 2PQ
DX: 19982 Chester 1

TEL: (01244) 321111
FAX: (01244) 327080

THE FIRM: Founded in the early 1800's, Walker Smith & Way is a broad based practice which has shown steady and sustained natural growth. It is now able to offer a comprehensive range of services to a wide range of clients, including trades unions, liability insurers, and a number of major PLCs.

PRINCIPAL AREAS OF WORK:

Litigation: *(Contact Partner:* Mr John Brimelow). The firm is regarded as a specialist in personal injury litigation working for both plaintiffs and defendants, and including medical negligence work. All categories of criminal work are handled with a particular focus on cases involving controlled drugs. All aspects of employment law are dealt with as well as liquor licensing, contractual disputes, and environmental, pollution, and Food Safety Act matters.

Company/ Commercial: *(Contact Partner:* Mr Peter Collins). The firm has a small but growing company and commercial department, embracing company takeovers and management buy-outs for the smaller company, commercial conveyancing, in which field the firm acts for a number of substantial PLCs, and specialist teams deal with the law affecting agriculture and forestry, and pipeline easements.

Private Client: *(Contact Partner:* Mr Roland Dawson). The department concentrates on domestic conveyancing, probate, wills and trusts and has a specialist family and matrimonial team which is highly regarded in the North West of England and North Wales.

RECRUITMENT AND TRAINING: The firm recruits two/ four trainee solicitors each year. Apply to Miss Angela Woods.

OTHER OFFICES: Wrexham and Ellesmere Port.

CONTACT PARTNER: Mr John Brimelow

Number of partners:	23
Assistant solicitors:	17
Other fee-earners:	8

WORKLOAD	
Personal injury	40%
Commercial / domestic property	20%
Private client	17%
Commercial litigation	14%
Licensing/ agriculture	9%

CONTACTS	
Agriculture	P. Collins
Commercial property	G.M.D. Prestt
Commercial litigation	J.F. Ives
Criminal/ licensing	J.H.D. Heath
Domestic property	M. Jessop
Matrimonial	D.L. Hopkins
Medical negligence	D.C. Rudd
Personal injury	J.D. Brimelow
Trusts	R.A. Dawson

WALLACE & PARTNERS

9 GREAT JAMES ST, LONDON, WC1N 3DA
DX: 377

TEL: (0171) 404 4422
FAX: (0171) 831 6850

THE FIRM: Wallace & Partners is a young and thriving central London practice which specialises in business matters, handling work often associated with large City firms.

PRINCIPAL AREAS OF WORK:

Company/ Commercial: *(Contact Partner:* Rex Newman). *Work includes:* Stock Exchange advice, public issues, commercial contracts, venture capital, joint ventures, management buy-outs and buy-ins, mergers and acquisitions, loan arrangements, advice on the responsibilities of directors; shareholder agreements; tax planning, contracts of employment, franchising and general commercial matters.

Litigation: *(Contact Partner:* Simon Serota). The firm is strong in property-related litigation as well as employment, professional negligence, and shareholder and boardroom disputes.

Property: *(Contact Partner:* Adrian Wallace). *Work includes:* development, investment, acquisition and funding, planning and environmental, business leases, rent reviews, estate management and general landlord and tenant work.

Private Client: *(Contact Partner:* Barry Shaw). This department deals with personal financial planning including wills, capital tax advice, trusts and probate.

NATURE OF CLIENTELE: The firm acts for a diverse spread of clients including listed companies, family businesses, entrepreneurs and foreign dignitaries.

FOREIGN CONNECTIONS: Wallace & Partners has developed a network of contacts throughout Europe and provides advice on many aspects of international commerce. One of the partners is a member of the New York Bar.

RECRUITMENT AND TRAINING: Contact Barry Shaw for an application form.

CONTACT PARTNER: Adrian Wallace

Number of partners:	6
Assistant solicitors:	4
Other fee-earners:	4

WALL, JAMES & DAVIES

19 HAGLEY ROAD, STOURBRIDGE, W. MIDLANDS, DY8 1QW
DX: 710678

TEL: (01384) 371622
FAX: (01384) 374057

THE FIRM: Established over 150 years ago, the firm offers a comprehensive service to private and corporate clients, with particular expertise in planning, litigation, matrimonial law and personal tax planning.

PRINCIPAL AREAS OF WORK:

Company/ Commercial: *(Contact Partner:* R. Davies). *Work includes:* acquisitions and disposals, all aspects of private company work, partnerships, commercial law and disputes, and insolvency.

Private Client: *(Contact Partner:* C. Hamlyn). *Work includes:* wills and probate, trusts, powers of attorney and Court of Protection matters, all aspects of personal taxation with particular emphasis on tax planning.

Planning: *(Contact Partner:* J.H. Dolman). *Work includes:* a full specialist planning service including applications and appeals, enforcement appeals, local and structure plans, input and inquiry appearances.

Matrimonial: *(Contact Partner:* J.M. Browne). *Work includes:* divorce and matters ancillary thereto and resolutions of problems relating to children.

Property: *(Contact Partner:* R.W. Kendrick). *Work includes:* commercial and domestic conveyancing, landlord and tenant, and business tenancies.

Civil Litigation: *(Contact Partner:* S.J. Beddow). *Work includes:* commercial litigation, employment law and personal injury claims.

CONTACT PARTNER: Mr. R. Davies

Number of partners:	6
Assistant solicitors:	3
Other fee-earners:	4

WORKLOAD	
Litigation, including matrimonial	33%
Wills, probate, trusts & tax	28%
Property, commercial & residential	18%
Town & country planning	16%
Company/ commercial	5%

WALSH LAWSON 54/ 62 Regent Street, London, W1R 5PJ **Tel:** (0171) 393 9393 **Fax:** (0171) 393 9303 **DX:** 37214 **Ptnrs:** 7 **Asst Solrs:** 3 . A predominantly 'City' practice in the West End handling exclusively company/ commercial and commercial conveyancing.

WORKLOAD			
Company/corp finance	60%	Commercial property	30%
Tax	10%		

WALTONS & MORSE

PLANTATION HOUSE, 31-35 FENCHURCH STREET, LONDON, EC3M 3NN
DX: 1065

TEL: (0171) 623 4255
FAX: (0171) 626 4153

THE FIRM: Waltons & Morse is a long established City firm with an international reputation in the areas of shipping and insurance. The firm has several acknowledged market niches and is organised and prepared for sustained growth in its chosen areas of practice.

PRINCIPAL AREAS OF WORK:

General Description: Historically recognised for shipping and insurance, the firm is also known for its property and corporate work. Whilst concentrating on its core businesses, the firm is nevertheless expanding its involvement in complementary areas, in particular the electricity industry.

NATURE OF CLIENTELE: Lloyd's London and overseas insurance companies, shipping and salvage companies (particularly from Japan, Korea and Australasia), the electricity industry, commercial radio and a major UK clearing bank.

FOREIGN CONNECTIONS: The firm is a member of the Delta Group of European Lawyers EEIG represented in Belgium, Germany and the Netherlands.

BRANCH OFFICES: Also at Suite 642, Lloyd's, Lime Street, London EC3.

MANAGING PARTNER: Michael Brown

Number of partners:	20
Assistant solicitors:	18
Other fee-earners:	16

WORKLOAD	
Shipping and transit	31%
Insurance and reinsurance	29%
Corporate	21%
Commercial property	19%

CONTACTS	
Corporate	Nicholas Traill
Insurance	David Webster
Property	Jeremy Brooks
Shipping	Michael Buckley

WANSBROUGHS WILLEY HARGRAVE

103 TEMPLE STREET, BRISTOL, BS99 7UD DX: 7846	TEL: (0117) 926 8981 FAX: (0117) 929 1582
7 Park Square East, Leeds LS1 2LW DX: 14099 Leeds	Tel: (0113) 244 1151 Fax: (0113) 243 6050
37 Temple Street, Birmingham B2 5DP DX: 13057 Birmingham 1	Tel: (0121) 631 4099 Fax: (0121) 631 3781
34-43 Russell Street, London WC2B 5HA DX: 40044 Covent Garden	Tel: (0171) 497 3262 Fax: (0171) 497 1210
Suite 670 Floor 6, One Lime Street, Lloyd's, London EC3M 7DQ DX: 753 London	Tel: (0171) 327 4447 Fax: (0171) 327 4448
285-289 Glossop Road, Sheffield S10 2HB DX: 709824 Sheffield 16	Tel: (0114) 272 7485 Fax: (0114) 272 8517
1a St. Cross Road, Winchester SO23 9WP DX: 2540 Winchester	Tel: (01962) 841444 Fax: (01962) 843133

THE FIRM: Wansbroughs Willey Hargrave is a national firm operating a network of 7 offices across the country. The firm is a leading provider of legal services to the insurance and health sectors and has an excellent reputation for its range of services to corporate clients.

PRINCIPAL AREAS OF WORK:

Defendant Insurance Litigation including Professional Indemnity: The firm handles a wide range of negligence claims across all professions.

General Liability Risks: The firm has extensive experience in personal injury work, including motor, employer's, public and product liability and is known for its handling of complex arson and financial fraud claims.

Health: The firm handles a high volume of medical negligence cases and advises on health service law and a wide range of general commercial, property and employment matters.

Property: The firm advises on all aspects of development and landlord and tenant matters and is experienced in secured lending and project funding. A specialist construction law team advises on contracts, warranties, negligence claims and disputes.

Company/Commercial: Work includes the full range of corporate transactions and all types of agreements including partnerships, joint ventures, franchising and also intellectual property and computer law.

Commercial Litigation: Work includes all commercial disputes including computerised debt recovery.

Employment: The specialist employment team advises on all aspects of employment law and employment disputes, and is experienced in representing employers at Industrial Tribunals.

Private Client: Work includes trusts, estate administration wills and contested probate and family law. A separate unit advises on the establishment and administration of charities.

SENIOR PARTNER: Robert A. Heslett
CHIEF EXECUTIVE: Christopher A. Charles

Number of partners:	49
Assistant solicitors:	108
Other fee-earners:	53

WORKLOAD	
Defendant Insurance Litigation	38%
General liability risks	32%
Property and construction	11%
Commercial litigation	10%
Company and commercial	6%
Private client	3%

CONTACTS	
Birmingham	Paul Murray
Bristol	John Blackwell
Leeds	Robert Heslett
Lloyd's	Mark Speed
London	Alison MacLennan
Sheffield	Geoff Daunt
Winchester	Nigel Day

WARD GETHIN 11-12 Tuesday Market Place, King's Lynn, Norfolk, PE30 1JT **Tel:** (01553) 773456 **Fax:** (01553) 766857 **DX:** 57813 **Ptnrs:** 14 **Asst Solrs:** 4 **Other Fee-earners:** 10. Specialist departments handle volume litigation, family, commercial, property, probate and Court of Protection, and crime. Two Children and one MHRT Panel members.

WORKLOAD			
Conveyancing	21%	Divorce/separation/family	16%
Probate/ wills	14%	Pers injury (plaintiff)	13%
Crime	12%	Care of the elderly	5%

WARD HADAWAY Alliance Hse, Hood Street, Newcastle upon Tyne, Tyne & Wear, NE1 6LJ **Tel:** (0191) 261 2651 **Fax:** (0191) 232 6928 **DX:** 61265 **Ptnrs:** 21 **Asst Solrs:** 11 **Other Fee-earners:** 26. Progressive commercial practice handling company/ commercial, property, agriculture, planning, environmental, litigation and private client matters.

WORKLOAD			
Litigation	36%	Property	35%
Company & commercial	23%	Private client	6%

J.W. WARD & SON 52 Broad St, Bristol, BS1 2EP **Tel:** (0117) 929 2811 **Fax:** (0117) 929 0686 **DX:** 7824 **Ptnrs:** 7 **Asst Solrs:** 10 **Other Fee-earners:** 6. The firm has a flourishing private client base while also offering a range of specialist services for commercial clients in the South West and nationally.

WARNER CRANSTON

PICKFORDS WHARF, CLINK ST, LONDON, SE1 9DG
DX: 39904 London Bridge South

TEL: (0171) 403 2900
FAX: (0171) 403 4221

THE FIRM: This City firm was founded in 1979 and during its 16 year history has grown from one (the founder, David Warner) to a total workforce of over 100. All partners, and the majority of fee-earners, have come from large City firms or from industry. In 1987, the practice's existing commercial litigation department was augmented by the entire in-house litigation department of Courtaulds Plc. In 1986, the firm moved to its present offices overlooking the Thames on the South side of London Bridge.

The philosophy of the firm has always been that clients of national and international repute can best be served by a small, highly professional and totally committed team of lawyers. The underlying principle is one of big firm expertise, coupled with a very personal service. From its inception, the firm has always had a strong international practice.

The firm has developed a reputation as an alternative law practice to the major City firms.

PRINCIPAL AREAS OF WORK:

General Description: The firm handles contentious and non-contentious work for corporate clients with a strong international bias. The firm has a policy of only undertaking work which falls within its areas of speciality and believes that in those areas its expertise is equal to that of the very large City firms. All areas of the practice are expanding.

Company and Commercial: *6 Partners.* The department handles a mix of public company and large private company work, including mergers and acquisitions, banking, corporate finance, IT and telecommunications work and all aspects of commercial law. Corporate tax and competition advice comes within the ambit of the Company and Commercial Department.

Commercial Property: *1 Partner.* The practice undertakes commercial property work, primarily in connection with commercial transactions including retail, shop, office and greenfield site acquisition and disposal. Commercial property work is also undertaken from the Coventry office.

Litigation: *5 Partners.* Three partners concentrate on commercial and international litigation arising out of a variety of transactions, including commercial and trading contracts, banking and financial operations insolvency as well as Lloyds insurance. The department also handles internal company conflicts and has considerable expertise in the tracing of assets internationally.

The remaining two partners concentrate on construction and technical litigation, acting for contractors, architects, engineers and professional indemnity insurers as well as having ADR expertise.

A recent major development has been the joining as a partner in the department, of an emminent commercial barrister.

Employment: *2 Partners.* The department advises employers on service agreements, remuneration packages, share options and statutory matters including unfair dismissal and trade union laws and handles most industrial tribunal advocacy in-house.

CONTACT PARTNER: Peter Alfandary

Number of partners:	16
Assistant solicitors:	20
Other fee-earners:	14

WORKLOAD	
Company commercial and finance	35%
Commercial litigation	28%
Employment	15%
Property	11%
Construction and arbitration	11%

CONTACTS	
Commercial litigation	Michael Cranston
	Michael Jones
Commercial property	Duncan Edwards
Company/commercial	Ian Fagelson
	Wit Gryko
	Tim Foster
Construction litigation	John Wright
	Nick Speed
Corporate immigration	Peter Alfandary
Employment	David Warner
	David Dalgarno
French Inward Investment	Peter Alfandary
	David Heard
	Edward Miller
Insurance/reinsurance	Patricia Mitchell
Litigation (Coventry)	Larry Coltman
	Michael Dillon Weston

The department also advises senior executives on service contracts and termination of employment. A division of the Employment Department headed up by a third partner deals exclusively in work permits for corporate clients.

WARNER CRANSTON
SOLICITORS

NATURE OF CLIENTELE: Warner Cranston acts for corporate clients, both national and international, including many household names, and both quoted and private companies. The firm also acts for foreign governments, trade associations, chambers of commerce and insurance companies.

FOREIGN CONNECTIONS: The firm has strong corporate and professional links in a number of countries, but in particular the United States and France which together account for approximately one third of the firm's business. The firm has set up a French team designed to service its French corporate clients. Languages other than English are spoken by partners and assistants.

RECRUITMENT AND TRAINING: The firm recruits candidates of the highest calibre and has an active (and continuous) recruitment programme. Considerable importance is attached to in-house training by partners and independent consultants, covering both legal and business skills. Included are regular legal updates as well as sessions on letter writing, negotiating and marketing.

OTHER OFFICES: Coventry: 2 Partners. The office also provides litigation and commercial property services to UK and international clients as well as offering a highly sophisticated national computerised debt recovery service.

WARNER GOODMAN & STREAT 66 West Street, Fareham, Hants, PO16 0JR **Tel:** (01329) 288121 **Fax:** (01329) 822714 **DX:** 40804 **Ptnrs:** 11 **Asst Solrs:** 13 **Other Fee-earners:** 19. Established over 140 years. Six offices in S. Hants. Specialists in personal injury and dealing with full range of private client work. Open about their fee structure.

WORKLOAD			
Court litigation	35%	Family	15%
Probate	15%	Conveyancing	15%
Company/comm/com prop	15%	Criminal	5%

WARREN & ALLEN 24 Low Pavement, Nottingham, Notts, NG1 7ED **Tel:** (0115) 950 7121/ 955 2222 **Fax:** (0115) 948 4649 **DX:** 10030 **Ptnrs:** 11 **Asst Solrs:** 11 **Other Fee-earners:** 9. Criminal/ civil litigation; conveyancing; company/ commercial law; wills and finance; family. Other offices in Ilkeston and Bingham (also Property Shop).

WORKLOAD			
Civil/matrimonial lit	37%	Crime	24%
Conveyancing	14%	Probate, trusts, etc	13%
Commercial	12%		

WATERSON HICKS

14-15 PHILPOT LANE, LONDON, EC3M 8AJ

TEL: (0171) 929 6060
FAX: (0171) 929 3748

THE FIRM: Waterson Hicks is a commercial practice specialising in maritime law and insurance. The firm's work and clientele is largely international. It has associated offices in Zurich and Singapore and has strong overseas connections especially in Greece and the USA. French is spoken in the firm. Clients include major ship owners, oil companies, commodity traders, P&I clubs and insurers for whom both contentious and non-contentious work is done. Insurance work encompasses marine, through transport and Lloyd's related disputes. Shipping work covers commercial and admiralty litigation and sale and purchase. Waterson Hicks also undertakes personal injury litigation, specialising in the area of head injuries.

CONTACT PARTNER: M.J. Wisdom

Number of partners:	4
Assistant solicitors:	3

WORKLOAD	
Shipping and through transport	70%
Personal injury	10%
Insurance	10%
Commercial	10%

L. WATMORE & CO Chancery House, 53/66 Chancery Lane, London, WC2A 1QU **Tel:** (0171) 430 1512 **Fax:** (0171) 405 7382 **DX:** LDE 246 **Ptnrs:** 7 **Asst Solrs:** 5 **Other Fee-earners:** 3. A practice specialising in insurance related litigation, mainly on behalf of insurance companies, with a particular emphasis on personal injury.

WORKLOAD			
Personal injury lit	80%	Other insurance related	15%

WATSON BURTON

20 COLLINGWOOD STREET, NEWCASTLE UPON TYNE, TYNE & WEAR, NE99 1YQ
DX: 61009

TEL: (0191) 232 3101
FAX: (0191) 232 0532

CONTACT PARTNER: Mr. D.C. Foster

Number of partners:	16
Assistant solicitors:	25
Other fee-earners:	49

THE FIRM: Established for over 180 years, and one of the best-known and largest firms in the North of England, Watson Burton offers a service comparable with that of a City firm. It is progressive, forward thinking and young in outlook, with a strong commercial foundation. The role of the firm's Commercial Group, which has three departments handling company commercial, commercial litigation and commercial property, is the cornerstone of the firm's activities. Clients' business is dealt with on a national and international basis.

PRINCIPAL AREAS OF WORK:

Company Commercial: Work handled includes acquisitions and disposals, corporate finance work, UK and EC competition law, insolvency, electricity law, banking and building society matters, trading law, computer law, consumer credit, education law, pension schemes, intellectual property matters and franchising. A legal audit service is available.

Litigation: A variety of contentious matters is handled, including construction disputes, commercial and intellectual property litigation, consumer disputes, employment law problems, licensing, fishery prosecutions and debt recovery.

Commercial Property: The firm acts for well-known retailers, property and construction companies, developers and housing associations in a wide range of matters, including leases, acquisitions, disposals, landlord and tenant advice and planning and environmental law.

Personal Injuries/Trade Unions: The firm undertakes a large volume of personal injury cases with an increasing number of medical negligence claims. The group has active trade union connections.

Private Client: *Work includes:* residential conveyancing, family and matrimonial work, wills, probate, trusts, charities and tax planning.

FOREIGN CONNECTIONS: Watson Burton is a member of Eu-Lex International Practice Group, a network of European law firms with member firms throughout the EC.

WATSON, FARLEY & WILLIAMS

15 APPOLD STREET, LONDON, EC2A 2HB
DX: 530 City

TEL: (0171) 814 8000
FAX: (0171) 814 8141/2

SENIOR PARTNER: Alastair Farley

UK:	
Number of partners:	29
Assistant solicitors:	92
Other fee-earners:	17
INTERNATIONAL:	
Number of Partners:	20
Assistant Solicitors:	24
Other fee-earners:	9

THE FIRM: Watson, Farley & Williams was established in the City of London in 1982 and is now an international commercial law practice with offices in London, Athens, Oslo, Paris, New York, Moscow and Copenhagen. The firm has an excellent reputation in the area of banking and asset financing, particularly ship and aircraft finance, and has a number of other specialist areas. The practice currently has 136 qualified fee earners (including English, French, Russian and New York qualified lawyers), 18 trainees and a total staff of 304.

PRINCIPAL AREAS OF WORK:

Shipping and Ship Finance: *(Contact Partner:* Alastair Farley). Watson, Farley & Williams is best known for its work in shipping and ship finance advising on international ship finance transactions including lease financing, environmental issues, commercial shipping matters such as newbuildings, the sale and purchase of vessels and flagging, and oil and gas exploration and development. Simon Curtis is the author of a recent book on shipbuilding contracts.

Aviation and Aircraft Finance: *(Contact Partner:* Geoffrey Williams). The firm has specialist aviation lawyers who advise on aircraft financing, secured lending, tax-based, tax-leveraged and FSC leasing, the sale and purchase of aircraft, operating leases, aviation regulation and other associated transactions.

Banking and Finance: *(Contact Partner:* Geoffrey Wynne). The banking group deals with all types of domestic and international financings, syndicated and single bank lending and is experienced in project and asset finance. It also advises on general banking matters, restructurings, workouts and insolvencies.

CONTACTS

Aviation and aircraft finance	Geoffrey Williams
Banking	Geoffrey Wynne
Corporate and commercial	Charles Walford
Eastern Europe	Douglas Wardle
EC and competition	Richard Whish
Litigation	Charles Smallwood
Property	Maria Llewellyn
Shipping and ship finance	Alastair Farley
Taxation	Christopher Preston

Corporate and Commercial: *(Contact Partner:* Charles Walford). The corporate lawyers advise on corporate finance matters, acting for both UK and overseas companies. The group also undertakes general corporate and commercial work, including intellectual property, employment and executive immigration.

Litigation: *(Contact Partner:* Charles Smallwood). The litigation team handles a wide range of general commercial litigation and arbitration disputes, with an emphasis upon the maritime, energy and finance sectors, including maritime transportation disputes, enforcement of security and environmental issues.

EC and Competition: *(Contact Partner:* Richard Whish/ Philip Ruttley). The EC group has a particular expertise in competition law and EC maritime law. Richard Whish is one of the senior editors of *Butterworths Competition Law*. The firm also advises on general EC law matters relating to, for example, free provision of services, banking and securities regulation, EC transport policy and EC environmental issues.

Taxation: *(Contact Partner:* Christopher Preston). The tax group deals with all general corporate and commercial tax advice and has a specialist knowledge of tax structuring for financing transactions, shipping and energy taxation, tax litigation and VAT. Christopher Preston is the author of the leading text on VAT.

Property: *(Contact Partner:* Maria Llewellyn). Commercial property matters include acquisitions and disposals of commercial properties, landlord and tenant matters, insolvency work, secured lending and development work, environmental issues and planning.

Central and East Europe: *Contact Partner:* Douglas Wardle). The firm is able to offer its clients a specialist transactions service covering the Central and East European region through a network of local business developers and lawyers in most countries. The firm's lawyers have worked on East European transactions in 12 countries since 1989 and have particular expertise in acquisitions, joint ventures and privatisations.

OVERSEAS OFFICES: Athens, Oslo, Paris, New York, Moscow and Copenhagen.

ASSOCIATED OFFICES: Kingdom of Saudi Arabia: Jeddah, Riyadh.

RECRUITMENT AND TRAINING: The firm is looking for about 12 trainees who are likely to obtain at least a 2:1 degree, not necessarily in law. There is a generous benefits package and the firm provides financial assistance for both the Law Society Finals course and the CPE. New trainees are introduced to the firm with a comprehensive induction course covering legal topics and practical instruction. There is also a full continuing education programme for trainees and solicitors and many trainees spend time in one of the overseas offices to gain some international experience. The firm places an emphasis on training its solicitors to become good all round commercial lawyers before they specialise. For brochure and application form contact Fiona Wood.

EDITORIAL POLICY

In this edition, the lists of specialists include profiles of individual practitioners - solicitors and barristers - who have been recommended most frequently to our researchers. Editorial policy is to identify leading practitioners on merit: it is not possible to buy a place in our biographical lists. Inclusion of a profile in this directory is based solely on expertise and reputation.

Enormous effort has been invested by our ten-strong research team (mainly solicitors and barristers) in canvassing recommendations and identifying leaders. We are confident in the overall accuracy of the results.

WATTERSON TODMAN

107-133 PROMENADE, CHELTENHAM, GLOS, GL50 1PF
DX: 7410 Cheltenham

TEL: (01242) 224422
FAX: (01242) 519381

THE FIRM: This forward-thinking firm combines an old-established practice with a modern high quality service. It is a large general practice with an emphasis on commercial work and a significant number of high calibre business clients. Specialist commercial advice is available in employment law, company, commercial, property and planning matters, with a comprehensive range of private client services.

PRINCIPAL AREAS OF WORK:

Company/ Commercial: (*Contact Partner:* W. John Todman). An experienced team handles all manner of corporate and business matters including: partnership and company formations, corporate reorganisations, MBO's, acquisitions and disposals, distribution and licensing agreements, employment contracts and shareholder agreements.

Litigation: (*Contact Partner:* Nicholas P. Cox). A wide variety of commercial and private client litigation which includes: employment litigation, landlord and tenant, contractual disputes, debt collection (the firm operates a computerised system), insolvency work and property disputes. Other work ranges from traffic offences to divorce, financial claims and personal injury litigation.

Property: (*Contact Partner:* Mark A. Fabian). A full range of commercial, agricultural, institutional and residential property services; planning and environmental law; landlord and tenant; mining and quarrying; estate management, financing and property taxation.

Probate, Trust and Tax: (*Contact Partner:* Nicholas P. Hunt). The firm provides advice on wills, trust creation and administration, tax planning, the administration of estates and financial services.

CONTACT PARTNER: Mr Nicholas P. Hunt	
Number of partners:	6
Assistant solicitors:	5
Other fee-earners:	7

WEDLAKE BELL

16 BEDFORD STREET, COVENT GARDEN, LONDON, WC2E 9HF
DX: 40009 Covent Gdn.

TEL: (0171) 395 3000
FAX: (0171) 836 6117

THE FIRM: Wedlake Bell is a progressive firm based in central London and provides a full range of legal services to financial institutions, corporations and private clients. The firm has considerable overseas connections and maintains an office in Guernsey, where two partners are resident. Its membership of TELFA provides close links with commercial law firms in all the jurisdictions of the European Union. Its size and structure enable the firm to provide a personal service which is responsive to the requirements of the client and has close partner involvement.

In addition to the main departments of company and commercial, banking, commercial litigation, commercial property and private client tax planning, the firm offers specialist advice on competition, construction, employee share schemes and pensions, environment, European Union, food, insolvency, intellectual property, matrimonial, pensions, pharmaceuticals, planning, sports marketing and communications, trust and charities law.

PRINCIPAL AREAS OF WORK:

Corporate and Commercial: (*Contact:* Anthony Gubbins). This department has wide experience in a range of corporate finance and commercial transactions, including acquisitions and disposals of public and private companies and businesses, management buy-outs and buy-ins, flotations and equity issues, corporate reconstructions, joint ventures, European and competition law, employee share schemes and pensions and corporate tax.

Property: (*Contact:* Michael Nicol). All aspects of property ownership, use, management and exchange are handled in this department including development funding and project finance, due diligence for flotations and acquisitions, planning advice and appeals, landlord and tenant issues and environmental law. The department also provides specialist services to non residents relating to UK property matters.

SENIOR PARTNER: Robert Dolman	
UK:	
Number of partners:	31
Assistant solicitors:	25
Other fee-earners:	17
INTERNATIONAL:	
Number of Partners:	2
Assistant Solicitors:	3
Other fee-earners:	2

WORKLOAD	
Property	25%
Corporate/commercial	23%
Litigation	23%
Private client	18%
Intellectual property	6%
Banking	5%

Banking and Insolvency: (*Contacts:* Philip Matthews and Peter Cull). This group operates within the corporate and commercial department handling all types of secured lending, asset financing including ships and aircraft, acquisition finance, money-laundering, debt restructuring and all aspects of corporate insolvency.

Intellectual Property: (*Contact:* Jonathan Cornthwaite). Expertise in this area includes advice on the creation, ownership, protection and use of intellectual property rights, and on distribution, franchise, technology transfer and publishing agreements. The group also has specialist experience in sports merchandising, televising and sponsorship agreements, marketing law, pharmaceutical law, software protection and anti-counterfeiting.

Litigation: (*Contact:* Robert Salter). The department handles a range of contentious matters involving both litigation and arbitration, and covering commercial disputes, judicial review and individual claims. It has specialist expertise in construction, insurance, professional indemnity, employment, banking, landlord and tenant, intellectual property and matrimonial litigation. In conjunction with the private client department it advises and takes action on behalf of Lloyd's names.

Construction: (*Contact:* Suzanne Reeves). The construction operates within the litigation department and advises developers, contractors, sub-contractors, professional consultants and insurers on both contentious and non-contentious matters.

Private Client: (*Contact:* Nigel Goodeve-Docker). The private client work of this department includes capital tax planning, trusts, offshore tax jurisdictions and asset protection, wills and the administration of estates, heritage and agricultural property. The pensions group covers all aspects of establishing and managing pension schemes including those in relation to takeovers and mergers.

Pension and Share Schemes: (*Contact:* Clive Weber). Advice is given to employers, trustees and members on all aspects of occupational pension schemes. The group also advises on the establishment and operation of employee share ownership trusts and option schemes, in addition to which trusutee services are available.

FOREIGN CONNECTIONS: (*Contact:* Andrew Baker). In addition to its office in Guernsey, the firm is a founder member of TELFA (Trans-European Law Firms Association). TELFA is an association of independent commercial law firms which provides clients of each member firm with quick access to legal services in all the major jurisdictions of the European Union. Its members have offices Arnhem, Athens, Barcelona, Berlin, Brussels, Copenhagen, Dusseldorf, Edinburgh, Geneva, Glasgow, Halle, Lisbon, Luxembourg, Madrid, Milan, Nijmegen, Paris, Stockholm and Vienna. TELFA also has a central co-ordinating office in Brussels.

CONTACTS	
Banking	Philip Matthews, Peter Cull
Corporate/ commercial	Anthony Gubbins
Intellectual property	Jonathan Cornthwaite
Litigation	Suzanne Reeves
Lloyd's	Charles Hicks, Richard Hewitt
Pensions	Clive Weber
Private client	Nigel Goodeve-Docker
	Robert Dolman
Property	Michael Nicol

WEDLAKE SAINT

14 JOHN ST, LONDON, WC1N 2EB
DX: 407 Ch.Ln.

TEL: (0171) 405 9446
FAX: (0171) 242 9877

THE FIRM: Established for over 75 years, Wedlake Saint is a progressive firm of solicitors with a relatively young partnership and a well-earned reputation for providing practical legal advice for clients – both commercial and private – with authority, imagination and efficiency.

Wedlake Saint is a founder member of The Independent Law Group – an association of independent minded practices working together in an effort to enhance the range of specialist services members can offer clients on a nationwide basis.

PRINCIPAL AREAS OF WORK:

Property: (*Contact Partner:* Duncan Taylor). Extensive experience in both commercial and residential property. It handles all aspects of property development, town and country planning, housing associations, landlord and tenant law and compulsory purchases, as well as all aspects of offshore and international property work.

Litigation: (*Contact Partner:* Richard Price). Litigation is an expanding area of the firm's practice and includes general commercial disputes, personal injury claims, employers' liability, health and safety, building and engineering disputes, arbitration, contentious probate, family and child law and debt collection. The department also has particular experience in the law relating to education.

CONTACT PARTNER: Richard Price

Number of partners:	11
Assistant solicitors:	2
Other fee-earners:	7

WORKLOAD	
Litigation	25%
Transport	25%
Property	20%
Tax and probate	15%
Commercial	10%
Charities	5%

Transport: (*Contact Partner:* Barry Prior). Working in liaison with other specialist divisions within the firm, the transport law department provides substantial and wide ranging legal advice on all aspects of road transport including operators' licensing, road traffic prosecutions and accidents, employment legislation, commercial contracts, the formation, purchase and disposal of business as well as management buy-outs.

The firm is the only firm of solicitors to be a member of the Confederation of Passenger Transport Ltd (formerly Bus and Coach Council) and an associate member of the Freight Transport Association. The partner heading the department is a member of the Chartered Institute of Transport.

Commercial: (*Contact Partner:* Susan Woodman). The department handles all aspects of company law, flotations, mergers and acquisitions, management buy-outs, reconstructions and refinance, insolvency, pension schemes, commercial contracts, intellectual property rights and EC law.

It is also active in advising on the contentious and non-contentious aspects of employment law.

Tax and Probate: (*Contact Partner:* Brendan Hall). The department advises both private and corporate clients on tax planning, inheritance and estate planning, VAT and stamp duty, reliefs, allowances, claims and benefits and land transactions. The department also negotiates and deals with the Inland Revenue and conducts appeals before it. It handles trusts, wills and probate for its private clients.

NATURE OF CLIENTELE: Clients include public listed and USM quoted companies, substantial private companies, national charities, housing associations, property developers, trade associations, insurance companies, road haulage undertakings, educational institutions, trade unions and banks.

The firm publishes a range of brochures specifically designed to assist the business community as well as regular newsletters aimed at the employment and transport sectors and at private clients.

RECRUITMENT: The firm recruits two trainee solicitors every year. Candidates should apply by letter and CV to Recruitment Partner.

CONTACTS	
Agency	C. Ashmore
Arbitration	A.M. Usher
Charities	N.W. Saint
Commercial property	J. Woodhead
Commercial	S. Woodman
Employment	A.M. Usher
Health and safety	N. Tomlins
Litigation	R. Price/A. Musher
Personal injury	A.M. Usher
Residential property	D. Taylor
Road accident	A. Knott
Tax and probate	B. Hall
Transport	B.A. Prior

SOLICITORS
WEDLAKE SAINT

WEIGHTMAN RUTHERFORDS

RICHMOND HOUSE, 1 RUMFORD PLACE, LIVERPOOL, MERSEYSIDE, L3 9QW
DX: 14201

TEL: (0151) 227 2601
FAX: (0151) 227 3223

THE FIRM: One of the leading firms in the North West and the largest legal practice operating solely out of Liverpool, Weightman Rutherfords was formed by a merger in 1988 and can trace its origins back to 1827. A commercially-based firm, the practice has a broad range of skills and particular expertise in the fields of litigation, insurance, licensing and planning, employment, shipping and Admiralty, arbitration, property and construction. The firm prides itself on partner contact with clients.

PRINCIPAL AREAS OF WORK:

Litigation: (*Contact Partner:* I. Evans). The firm has earned a particularly strong reputation in this area; 52 fee earners handle a wide variety of contentious matters, including arbitration, insurance, professional indemnity, shipping, the cotton trade, engineering and construction disputes, banking cases, white collar fraud and heavyweight commercial litigation. The firm is Secretary to the Liverpool Shipowners' Association.

Licensing and Planning: (*Contact Partner:* M.D. Owen). Several partners have for many years concentrated on work for major breweries and leisure companies. *Work includes:* the acquisition of new retail outlets, planning applications, appeals and licensing applications.

Property: (*Contact Partner:* D. Morgan). The firm has many years experience of major commercial transactions, including development schemes, sales, acquisition and leasing, the property aspect of takeovers, mergers, acquisitions and reconstructions, leisure property, brewery loans, advice on landlord and tenant matters and work concerned with housing associations.

CONTACT PARTNERS: Mr A.V. Summers and Mr I.R. Evans

Number of partners:	28
Assistant solicitors:	46
Other fee-earners:	32

CONTACTS	
Commercial property	D. Morgan
Company and commercial	D. Hannon
Employment	J.M. Edge
Licensing	M.D. Owen
Litigation	I. Evans

Company/ Commercial: *(Contact Partner:* D.W. Hannon). The full range of corporate and commercial services is offered, including intellectual property work, sports law, transport, charitable trusts, franchising matters, international trade and advice on taxation problems.

Employment: *(Contact Partner:* J.M. Edge). All aspects of employment law are handled, including unfair dismissal, redundancy matters, sex and race discrimination cases and industrial disputes, including injunctions. The firm is a contributor to Kluwer's *Business Law Handbook* (Employment Section).

Private Client: *(Contact Partner:* A.D. Holt). *Work includes:* wills, trusts, probate, residential conveyancing, matrimonial and family problems, personal taxation advice and financial planning services.

NATURE OF CLIENTELE: The firm has clients throughout the UK and also globally; including major insurance companies, Lloyd's underwriters, the Shipping Industry, commodity merchants, breweries and leisure companies, property developers and private clients.

WESLEY GRYK 149 The Strand, London, WC2R 1JA **Tel:** (0171) 240 8485 **Fax:** (0171) 240 8486 **DX:** 51643 Covent Garden **Ptnrs:** 1 **Other Fee-earners:** 1. A niche immigration practice with a commitment to legal aid work. The firm has expertise of asylum, work permit applications and students' immigration.

WHATLEY, WESTON & FOX 15-16 The Tything, Worcester, Hereford & Worcs, WR1 1HD **Tel:** (01905) 203614 **Fax:** (01905) 22347 **DX:** 716264 **Ptnrs:** 7 **Asst Solrs:** 2 **Other Fee-earners:** 6. Known for its commercial work and has substantial insolvency experience. Business and commercial clients predominate but the firm also has a private clientele.

WORKLOAD			
Insolvency/comm lit	41%	Company & commercial	27%
Domestic property	16%	Matrimonial	12%
Probate	4%		

WHELDON HOULSBY & SCOTT Town Hall Chambers, 7 Beach Road, South Shields, Tyne & Wear, NE33 2QR **Tel:** (0191) 456 8721 **Fax:** (0191) 456 4125 **DX:** 60755 South Shields **Ptnrs:** 8 **Asst Solrs:** 7 **Other Fee-earners:** 10. Civil, criminal and family litigation, company, probate and trust, commercial property, housing associations and environment. Office in Newcastle upon Tyne.

WORKLOAD			
Commercial property	21%	Litigation	18%
Company	16%	Residential property	14%
Probate and trust	11%	Family	8%

WHISKERS

GATE HOUSE, THE HIGH, HARLOW, ESSEX, CM20 1LW
DX: 40502 Harlow

TEL: (01279) 441111
FAX: (01279) 444464

THE FIRM: Founded over 125 years ago, Whiskers is a progressive firm providing a wide range of legal services for private and business clients from its well-appointed offices in Harlow New Town [H], Epping [E] and Old Harlow [OH].

Stephen Thirsk, the Senior Partner, is the Secretary of the West Essex Law Society and Eugene Ahern is a Member of the Law Society Personal Injury and Child Care Panels. Stephen Thirsk and Derek King are Notaries.

PRINCIPAL AREAS OF WORK:
General Description:
Company and Commercial: John Roberts [H],
Litigation: Tim Bowles [H]
Child Care: Eugene Ahern [H]
Family and Matrimonial: Eugene Ahern [H], Tim Bowles [H], Kathryn Henry [E]
Wills, Trust and Probate: Derek King [E], Stephen Thirsk [H]
Licensing: Stephen Thirsk[H]
Conveyancing: Stephen Thirsk [H], Gerry Smith [E], Peter Cuffaro [OH]
Criminal: David Nichols [H]
Personal Injury: Eugene Ahern [H]
Housing Associations: John Roberts [H], Stephen Thirsk [H]

CONTACT PARTNER: Stephen Thirsk

Number of partners:	8
Assistant solicitors:	7
Other fee-earners:	1

CONTACTS	
Partnership secretary	Cindy Hulbert

OTHER AREAS OF WORK: The firm undertakes agency work at Epping and Harlow Magistrates Courts and at Harlow County Court (the Harlow office is in the same building as the Court).

OTHER OFFICES:

265 High Street, Epping, Essex.
Tel: (01992) 561111. *Fax:* (01992) 573642. *DX:* 40400 Epping.
Gothic House, Station Road, Old Harlow, CM17 0AP.
Tel: (01279) 641444. *Fax:* (01279) 411481. *DX:* 95852 Old Harlow.

WHITE & BOWKER

19 ST. PETER ST, WINCHESTER, HANTS, SO23 8BU
DX: 2506 Winchester

TEL: (01962) 844440
FAX: (01962) 842300

THE FIRM: White & Bowker was formed by the merger of two of the oldest firms of solicitors in Winchester and is a major force in the legal market in the south. The firm is well established in local community and business life. Three partners hold public appointments – Winchester Diocesan Registrar, Under Sheriff of Hampshire and HM Coroner Hampshire (Central). The practice is a member of Law South, a group of leading law firms in the South of England and has contacts in Europe through Groupe Monassier France, an organisation of commercial lawyers.

PRINCIPAL AREAS OF WORK:

Agricultural and Environmental Law: *(Contact Partner:* John Steel). *Work includes:* all aspects of agricultural law, mineral extraction, pollution control, planning, compulsory purchase and alternative land use. The firm is on the NFU and the Agricultural Mortgage Corporation panels of solicitors. John Steel holds an MA in Environmental Law.

Company/Commercial: *(Contact Partner:* Martin Tomsett). *Work includes:* company/partnership law with particular emphasis on business start-ups; management buy-outs, corporate finance, insolvency, franchising, employment matters, leasehold/freehold sale and purchase, site development, construction, licensing and leisure. The firm also specialises in all aspects of charity work.

Private Client: *(Contact Partner:* Gill Steel). *Work includes:* estate planning, wills, probate, tax, financial/ mortgage services, and trust administration and management.

Litigation: *(Contact Partner:* Niall Brook). *Work includes:* commercial litigation, property disputes, debt collection (computerised system), employment law (especially in relation to local authorities), personal injury and criminal law, and all aspects of family and matrimonial law.

Property: *(Contact Partner:* Peter White). *Work includes:* all forms of residential and commercial property transactions with particular expertise in housing trust and housing association work.

OTHER OFFICES: Southampton and Eastleigh.

FOREIGN LANGUAGES SPOKEN: French and German.

FOREIGN CONNECTIONS: Members of Groupe Monassier France.

CONTACT PARTNER: Mr A.F.M. Rhodes

Number of partners:	16
Assistant solicitors:	11
Other fee-earners:	15

WORKLOAD	
Litigation	36%
Commercial	22%
Private client (wills/ trusts/ probate)	21%
Agriculture and environment	11%
Residential property	10%

CONTACTS	
Agriculture and environment	John Steel
Commercial	Martin Tomsett
Litigation	Niall Brook
Private client	Gill Steel
Residential property	Jim Kennedy

WHITE & CASE 7-11 Moorgate, London, EC2R 6HH **Tel:** (0171) 726 6361 **Fax:** (0171) 726 8558 **Ptnrs:** 7 **Other Fee-earners:** 12. A global law firm, established in 1901. It handles corporate, capital markets and financial services transactions, litigation, arbitration and tax advice in the world's primary financial and commercial centres.

WORKLOAD			
Comp/comm/joint ventures	20%	Project finance	20%
Capital markets	20%	Corporate finance/M&A	20%
Telecommunications	10%	Construction	10%

WHITEHEAD MONCKTON 72 King St, Maidstone, Kent, ME14 1BL **Tel:** (01622) 690077 **Fax:** (01622) 690050 **DX:** 4807 **Ptnrs:** 14 **Asst Solrs:** 5 **Other Fee-earners:** 9. General practice with offices in Tenterden and West Malling. Best known for its company/ commercial work, its private client services and its litigation services.

WORKLOAD			
Lit (incl family)	30%	Company and commercial	25%
Private client	25%	Prop (incl commercial)	20%

WHITTLES Pearl Assurance House, 23 Princess Street, Manchester, M2 4ER
Tel: (0161) 228 2061 **Fax:** (0161) 236 1046 **Ptnrs:** 8 **Asst Solrs:** 15 **Other Fee-earners:** 31. Established in the 1920s, the firm is best known for personal injury litigation. Has another office in Leeds.

WORKLOAD			
Personal injury lit	90%	General private client	5%
Employment law	5%		

WIGGIN AND CO

THE QUADRANGLE, IMPERIAL SQUARE, CHELTENHAM, GLOS, GL50 1YX
DX: 7427

TEL: (01242) 224114
FAX: (01242) 224223

THE FIRM: Based in Cheltenham, with offices in Los Angeles and London, Wiggin and Co. has an international reputation for its specialist expertise in tax management for individuals. The firm has also expanded its resources to offer advice to general corporate clients and to those involved in the specialist fields of media and entertainment.

PRINCIPAL AREAS OF WORK:

Taxation: (*Contact:* Nic Stones or Michael Fullerlove). The firm offers specialist advice on UK and international tax, capital and income tax planning for individuals, including the establishment and restructuring of UK and overseas trusts, the appropriate structure for UK and overseas investment, international asset protection, and general tax advice to both public and private companies, their shareholders and executives.

Company/ Commercial: (*Contact:* Tim Osborne or Rod Marlow). The firm specialises in media and entertainment law, and advice on European Community legislation. Other services include public flotations, mergers and acquisitions, MBOs, corporate reorganisations and financing, intellectual property, insolvency and financial services compliance.

Commercial Property: (*Contact:* Paul Wilson). The firm undertakes development structuring, sale and leaseback funding, joint venture agreements, options, secured loan transactions, sale and purchase of agricultural land and private estates and time share in the UK and EC countries.

FOREIGN CONNECTIONS: The office in Los Angeles was opened to advise individuals and corporations on the West Coast of America wishing to do business in the UK and Europe, and to assist European clients with US investments and business activities. The firm has extensive experience in international matters and its wide range of international contacts is extended by its membership of the Wiggin Group of European Lawyers and Tax Advisers.

CONTACT PARTNER: Mr. J.N. Stones

Number of partners:	9
Assistant solicitors:	11
Other fee-earners:	5

WORKLOAD	
Private client	60%
Media and entertainment	35%
Property	5%

CONTACTS	
Commercial property	P.M. Wilson
Company and commercial	C.R.J. Marlow
EC legislation	C.R.J. Marlow
Immigration	M.W. Turner
International asset protection	M.R. Fullerlove
Media and entertainment	T.W. Osborne
Private client	J.N. Stones
Tax (corporate)	P.D. Hunston
UK and overseas investment	J.N. Stones

WIKBORG, REIN & CO

1 KNIGHTRIDER COURT, 2ND FLOOR, LONDON, EC4V 5JP

TEL: (0171) 236 4598
FAX: (0171) 236 4599

THE FIRM: Wikborg, Rein & Co is an international law firm founded in 1923. The two founding partners set the early course of the firm, establishing its reputation as a commercial firm and attracting clients from the world of shipping and other industries. Although one of the largest law firms in Norway, Wikborg, Rein & Co continues to operate on the basis of a close working relationship with each client. The firm is prepared, if required, to take on management responsibility for the detailed handling of transactions.

THE LONDON OFFICE: The London office is staffed by two Norwegian lawyers. In addition to providing liaison services for the firm's international clients on Norwegian business and Norwegian clients on international business, the office has particular expertise in the areas of finance and shipping.

CONTACT PARTNER:
Mr Lars Olav Askheim

LAWYERS:	
London:	2
Worldwide:	55

WORKLOAD	
Shipping	50%
Company/ commercial	30%
Oil/ offshore	20%

MAIN AREAS OF WORK:

Company & Corporate: *Work includes:* company formation, corporate acquisitions and disposals, demergers, finance, insolvency, joint ventures, liquidation, partnerships, registration services, share issues, voting rights.

Shipping: *Work includes:* agency, arrest, building contracts, broking, cargo claims, charters, collisions, finance, flag changes, insurance, management, mortgages, pollution, protection and indemnity claims, sales, salvage, terminals.

Oil and Gas: *Work includes:* construction contracts, drilling rigs, farm-ins, farm-outs, finance, acquisition of licence interests, offshore services, pipe-laying, pollution, R&D contracts, safety regulations, seismic surveys, supply vessels, tax, transportation and processing, unitisation.

Securities: *Work includes:* acquisitions, bonds, capital reorganisations, convertible issues, demergers, investor protection, mergers, private placings, public offers, registration services, Stock Exchange listings, trading disputes, underwriting agreements, venture capital.

Finance: *Work includes:* asset finance, debt rescheduling, guarantees, leases, loan agreements, mortgages, off-balance sheet instruments, security documentation.

OTHER OFFICES: Oslo, Bergen, Kobe.

WILDE & PARTNERS 10 John Street, London, WC1N 2EB **Tel:** (0171) 831 0800 **Fax:** (011) 430 0678 **DX:** 428 London **Ptnrs:** 6 **Asst Solrs:** 4 **Other Fee-earners:** 13. A general commercial practice particularly well-known for its factoring, leasing, debt collecting, insurance and insolvency related work.

WORKLOAD			
Commercial litigation	25%	Debt & fraud recovery	20%
Trade finance/banking	15%	Insurance	10%
Commercial property	10%	Insolvency	10%

WILDE SAPTE

1 FLEET PLACE, LONDON, EC4M 7WS	TEL: (0171) 246 7000
DX: 145	FAX: (0171) 246 7777

THE FIRM: Founded in 1785. The firm is a leading City and international practice representing UK and overseas clients from its London, Lloyd's, New York, Tokyo, Paris, Brussels and Hong Kong offices.

The partnership is progressive and its commitment to growth has resulted in the firm tripling in size over the last ten years. The reputation of the firm is built upon its wide financial and commercial experience and ability to give practical advice, as well as a full and comprehensive service to all its clients. The firm is particularly strong in banking, corporate finance, asset and project finance, property finance, insurance, aviation, shipping, insolvency and commercial litigation.

PRINCIPAL AREAS OF WORK:

Banking and Finance: (*Contact:* Adrian Miles). Covers all aspects of banking and finance including acquisition finance, leasing and project finance, aviation finance, rescheduling, workouts and insolvency, trade and transport finance and capital markets work.

Company and Commercial: (*Contact:* Helen Cleaveland). Covers a full range of corporate and commercial legal services for private and public companies including all aspects of corporate finance, mergers and acquisitions, competition law, venture capital, pension and employee share schemes and intellectual property.

Litigation: (*Contact:* Richard Caird). With 16 partners and over 50 assistants, this is one of the largest litigation practices in the City. Broadly, there are three working groups: banking and financial services, commercial litigation and insolvency and within these areas there are a number of specialisations including commercial fraud, construction, employment, intellectual property, shipping, property and environmental.

Insurance: (*Contact:* Philip Rocher). Acting for insurers and reinsurers, many of whom are household names in the UK and international markets, the insurance team's work is wide ranging and encompasses all classes of business. Inevitably, insurance work is strongly associated with dispute resolution, where the firm's lawyers deal with anything from straightforward liability claims to the most complex and substantial issues troubling today's market. With the help of specialist colleagues across the firm, they aim to meet all the industry's other legal needs.

CONTACT PARTNER: Steven Blakeley

UK:	
Number of partners:	71
Assistant solicitors:	157
Other fee-earners:	99
INTERNATIONAL:	
Number of Partners:	10
Assistant Solicitors:	15
Other fee-earners:	7

CONTACTS	
Acquisition finance	Justin Spendlove
Aviation	Colin Thaine
Company/ commercial	Helen Cleaveland
Construction	Derek Tadiello
Corporate lending	Richard Bethell-Jones
Corporate tax	Miles Walton
Employment	Guy Fifield
EU law/competition law	James Ashe-Taylor
Financial services	Richard Caird
Insolvency	Mark Andrews
Insurance	Philip Rocher
Intellectual property	John Hull
Leasing	Graham Smith
Litigation	Richard Caird
Pensions/ charities	Alan Jarvis

Insolvency: (*Contact:* Mark Andrews). Wilde Sapte provides a full range of insolvency related services, in acting for banks, trade creditors, companies and their directors, and insolvency practitioners from all the major accountancy firms. The firm has for many years held a pre-eminent position in this particular market where its extensive experience is well-known and universally acknowledged.

Property: (*Contact:* James Curtis). The firm's property department deals with all aspects of property work, specialising in property finance, property management work and tax-based property transactions.

The firm also has a number of specialist groups such as corporate tax whose function is to support the core practice areas. In addition, a series of cross-departmental groups have been set up, such as the Japanese Unit, the Spanish and Latin American Unit and the Pensions Group which are designed to meet the demands for particular expertise.

RECRUITMENT AND TRAINING: There are likely vacancies for 30 trainee solicitors in 1996.

The Director of Training organises an extensive programme of continuing education, including commercial skills. There is a trainee solicitors' induction course and skills training weekend. A full programme of continuing education is available in-house along with foreign language training.

Project finance	Mary Bonar
Property	James Curtis
Shipping	Robert Dibble
Structured finance & cap. mkts	John Walker

WILDE SAPTE

WILFORD McBAIN 1-3 Brixton Rd, London, SW9 6DE **Tel:** (0171) 582 6002 **Fax:** (0171) 793 0538 **DX:** 33256 Kennington **Ptnrs:** 3 **Asst Solrs:** 6 . Specialist firm dealing with all legal matters affecting children: adoption, wardship, child care, and abuse. Also general matrimonial work.

WORKLOAD			
Children (private law)	35%	Children (public law)	35%
Adoption	20%	Employment/pers injury	5%
Mental health	5%		

WILKIN CHAPMAN New Oxford House, Town Hall Square, Grimsby, Humbs, DN31 1HE **Tel:** (01472) 358234 **Fax:** (01472) 360198 **DX:** 13511 **Ptnrs:** 15 **Asst Solrs:** 11 **Other Fee-earners:** 29. Leading regional firm with strong commercial practice. Emphasis on agricultural and private client matters. Legal aid work undertaken.

WORKLOAD			
Commercial/ company	31%	Litigation	24%
Conveyancing	17%	Family	15%
Probate	13%		

WILKINSON MAUGHAN

SUN ALLIANCE HOUSE, 35 MOSLEY STREET, NEWCASTLE-UPON-TYNE, TYNE & WEAR, NE1 1XX DX: 61184	TEL: (0191) 261 1841 FAX: (0191) 261 8267

THE FIRM: With origins dating back to 1778, Wilkinson Maughan has become one of the leading firms in the North East. From prestigious premises in the heart of Newcastle, the firm offers a wide range of services to the commercial, professional and private client.

PRINCIPAL AREAS OF WORK:

Company/ Commercial: (*Contact Partner:* A.J. Davison). *Work includes:* company formations, management buy-outs, flotations, share issues, pension schemes, funding, franchising, EC law, competition law, computer contracts, employment matters and insolvency.

Litigation: (*Contact Partner:* M.T. Ord). *Work includes:* commercial, trading and construction disputes, professional negligence, personal injury, landlord and tenant, defamation, insurance, licensing, employment, family and matrimonial matters. Debt collection work is also undertaken.

Property: (*Contact Partner:* Claire Morgan). *Work includes:* commercial, industrial and agricultural property, landlord and tenant, development, planning and environmental law, mineral extraction and waste disposal sites and domestic conveyancing.

Tax, Probate and Trusts: (*Contact Partner:* John Luke). *Work includes:* wills, estate planning, charitable trusts, agriculture, financial services, and tax advice for both commercial and private clients.

OTHER OFFICES:

21 New Fetter Lane, London EC4A 1DL. *Tel:* (0171) 353 4100. *Fax:* (0171) 353 3739. *DX:* 375 London.

MANAGING PARTNER: Ronald Bradbeer

Number of partners:	24
Assistant solicitors:	30
Other fee-earners:	16

WORKLOAD	
Commercial property & commercial leases	31%
Commercial litigation	26%
Company/ commercial	26%
Private client	17%

CONTACTS	
Commercial property (freehold)	Claire Morgan
Commercial law	Michael Spriggs
Construction law	Lucilla Waugh
Debt collection	Lucy Winskell
Insolvency	David Hardman
Landlord and tenant	Roger Kellett
Tax and trusts	Helen Tavroges

WILKINSON, WOODWARD & LUDLAM

11 FOUNTAIN ST, HALIFAX, W. YORKS, HX1 1LU
DX: 16004 Halifax

TEL: (01422) 340711
FAX: (01422) 330417

THE FIRM: A modern, progressive practice, Wilkinson Woodward & Ludlam provides a comprehensive service to local and national clients alike. The emphasis is on a personal service led by a partner with the relevant specialised knowledge to advise both corporate clients and private individuals. The firm is a member of the Conquest network of solicitors' practices.

PRINCIPAL AREAS OF WORK:

Civil Litigation: *(Contact:* Jon Dyson). A large department deals with commercial litigation, including employment law and insolvency advice, while a separate group deals with personal injury and medical negligence cases, acting for both plaintiffs and defendant insurers.

Debt Recovery: *(Contact:* Richard Helliwell).

Company/ Commercial: *(Contact:* Ross Woodward). All aspects of advice including formation, acquisition and sale of private companies, franchise and distribution agreements, commercial property (including landlord and tenant matters), planning applications and licensing issues.

Private Client: A full range of services including domestic conveyancing *(Contact:* Andrew Crabtree), wills and financial services *(Contact:* Sarah Hodkinson) matrimonial and child care *(Contact:* Penny Manock), criminal *(Contact:* Laurence Walker).

CONTACT PARTNER: Ross Woodward

Number of partners:	8
Assistant solicitors:	3
Other fee-earners:	6

CONTACTS	
Civil litigation	Jon Dyson
Company and commercial	Ross Woodward
Criminal	Laurence Walker
Debt recovery	Richard Helliwell
Domestic conveyancing	Andrew Crabtree
Matrimonial and child care	Penny Manock
Wills and financial services	Sarah Hodkinson

WILKINSON WOODWARD & LUDLAM
s o l i c i t o r s

WILLCOX LANE CLUTTERBUCK (Inc. JAGGER SON & TILLEY)

55 CHARLOTTE STREET, BIRMINGHAM, W. MIDLANDS, B3 1PX
DX: 13011

TEL: (0121) 236 9441
FAX: (0121) 236 4733

THE FIRM: Willcox Lane Clutterbuck is a long-established firm in the city centre. It has a growing commercial practice, but still cherishes its traditional client base of private individuals and small to medium-sized businesses. It has recently been awarded a legal aid franchise.

PRINCIPAL AREAS OF WORK:

Company/Commercial: *2 Partners. Work includes:* company law, drafting of contracts, acquisitions and sales of businesses and companies of all types and sizes, business structuring, start-up advice to new businesses, and employment law.

Commercial and Agricultural Property and Construction: *3 Partners. Work includes:* the purchase, sale and financing of all types of freehold and leasehold properties for commercial users and investors, property development, employee relocation and planning law.

Litigation and Debt Collection: *3 Partners.* The firm handles a substantial volume of defendant personal injury, plaintiff personal injury and commercial litigation as well as matrimonial and general civil litigation. It has a computerised debt collection system for recovery of debts of all sizes.

Tax: *1 Partner.* The firm advises on tax planning and mitigation for individuals, trusts and companies.

Private Client: *2 Partners.* The firm is widely involved in the establishment, management and winding-up of trusts and charities. The firm also manages clients' financial affairs and investments as well as handling all aspects of wills and probate.

NATURE OF CLIENTELE: Clients include private individuals, public and private companies, charities and trusts.

CONTACT PARTNER: William Colacicchi

Number of partners:	9
Assistant solicitors:	3
Other fee-earners:	7

WORKLOAD	
Civil litigation	29%
Property	28%
Private client	23%
Commercial	13%
Criminal litigation	7%

CONTACTS	
Commercial	William Colacicchi
Commercial/ civil litigation	M. English
Criminal	J. Smitheman
Defendant personal injury	Trevor Ridgway
	M. Asokan
Matrimonial	J. Smitheman, Kate Ward
Private client	Carolyn Evans
Prop. / construct.	Susan Stott, Sean Dempsey

WILLIAM HATTON

TRINITY HOUSE, TRINITY ROAD, DUDLEY, W. MIDLANDS, DY1 1JB
DX: 12764 Dudley

TEL: (01384) 211211
FAX: (01384) 456165

THE FIRM: The practice was founded by William Hatton over 30 years ago, and in recent years has expanded rapidly to become one of the largest defendant personal injury practices in the Midlands. The firm offers competitive charging rates and a high degree of expertise with extensive knowledge of specific industrial diseases.

PRINCIPAL AREAS OF WORK:

Civil Litigation: *(Contact Partner:* A.T.R. Perry). The firm concentrates on civil litigation, primarily for insurance company clients, and with a well-established specialisation in personal injury claims arising from both road traffic and employers' liability. The practice has a long history of conducting disease litigation, with individuals specialising in claims involving particular industrial diseases, including deafness, asbestosis and R.S.I. Also specialises in medical negligence claims.

OTHER OFFICE: The firm has an additional office in Leicester. Both offices are situated to give easy access to the motorway network and hence enable the firm to cover a wide geographical area.

CONTACT PARTNER: Mr A.T.R. Perry

Number of partners:	6
Assistant solicitors:	2
Other fee-earners:	17

WORKLOAD	
Personal injury	90%
Commercial, conveyancing and probate	5%
Medical negligence	5%

WILLIAMS DAVIES MELTZER

LINTAS HOUSE, 15-19 NEW FETTER LANE, LONDON, EC4A 1AB
DX: 1026

TEL: (0171) 353 2500
FAX: (0171) 353 2552

THE FIRM: Williams Davies Meltzer is a specialist insurance and commercial litigation law firm. It is a team of lawyers with their own specialist areas of practice, covering the field of insurance litigation and contentious commercial work.

PRINCIPAL AREAS OF WORK:

Professional Indemnity: WDM acts for professionals in the field of construction (architects, engineers, surveyors etc), computing, accountants and lawyers, Lloyd's and non-Lloyd's brokers, financial intermediaries, advertising agencies, media and from many other areas.

Medical Malpractice: Work in this field includes cases of all kinds with novel issues in fields such as cosmetic surgery and radiotherapy. Instructions come from hospitals and clinics and various professional bodies, with members practising both inside and outside the NHS.

Accident and Injury Work: WDM undertakes employers', public and motor liability work for a variety of Lloyd's syndicates, composites and overseas insurers, from white collar claims to manufacturing, building, transport and power industries. Public sector work is also handled.

Products and Technical: Work includes defence cases in relation to a wide range of manufactured products and computer litigation.

Commercial & Contract Claims: Work includes: construction litigation, computer litigation, financial transactions, property disputes and plaintiff and defendant libel cases.

Employment: Work includes: wrongful dismissal and industrial tribunals, generally on behalf of employers.

NATURE OF CLIENTELE: The firm acts for Lloyd's underwriters, composite insurers and large European insurers, together with brokers and adjusters. In addition to clients from construction, manufacturing and the professions, WDM acts for American and Australasian clients and foreign law firms.

CONTACT PARTNER: Hugh V. Williams

Number of partners:	4
Assistant solicitors:	6
Other fee-earners:	4

WORKLOAD	
Professional indemnity	55%
Accident & injury	20%
Commercial and contract claims	10%
Products & technical	10%
Medical malpractice	5%

CONTACTS	
Accident & injury	Andrew Trott
Banking/ computer claims	Daniel Meltzer
Employers/ public liability	Jamie Colman
General liability	Hugh Williams
Medical negligence	Sian Davies
Products & technical	Andrew Trott
Professional indemnity	Hugh Williams
Reinsurance	Peter Court

WILLIAMSON & HORROCKS 10 Rood Lane, London, EC3M 8AP **Tel:** (0171) 623 4452 **Fax:** (0171) 626 3591 **Ptnrs:** 2 **Asst Solrs:** 3 . Known for commercial shipping law and Admiralty work.

WILLIAMSON & SODEN Stanton House, 54 Stratford Road, Shirley, Solihull, W. Midlands, B90 3LS **Tel:** (0121) 733 8000 **Fax:** (0121) 733 3322 **DX:** 20652 **Ptnrs:** 8 **Asst Solrs:** 6 **Other Fee-earners:** 9. Known for private client and company/ commercial work. Also handles litigation, conveyancing and probate. Other office in Birmingham City Centre.

WORKLOAD			
Criminal advocacy	40%	Company/comm/comm prop	%
Res conveyancing	13%	Civil litigation	13%
Family and matrimonial	12%	Personal injury	5%

WILLIAM STURGES & CO

12 CAXTON ST, LONDON, SW1H 0QY
DX: 2315 Victoria

TEL: (0171) 222 1391
FAX: (0171) 222 0361

THE FIRM: William Sturges & Co is a well established and expanding practice both in Central London and Ealing, which acts for commercial and private clients based in the UK and overseas and has a particular affinity with medium-sized companies and with estate and trust work. The firm also has a particular expertise in commercial property and development conveyancing. In every case the firm combines in-depth expertise with personal service to clients.

OTHER OFFICE: 3
9 The Mall, Ealing, London W5 3TF. *Tel:* (0181) 567 1481. *Fax:* (0181) 579 5352 *DX:* 5108 Ealing. (*Contact Partner:* Richard Rench).

CONTACT PARTNER: Ian Gavin-Brown	
Number of partners:	13
Assistant solicitors:	9
Other fee-earners:	15

WILLMETT & CO 27 Sheet St, Windsor, Berks, SL4 1BX **Tel:** (01753) 861381 **Fax:** (01753) 842172 **DX:** 3807 Windsor **Ptnrs:** 10 **Asst Solrs:** 9 **Other Fee-earners:** 6. A modern computerised practice known for conveyancing, probate, company and matrimonial. It has four offices within the Thames Valley area.

WORKLOAD			
Commercial conveyancing	30%	Domestic conveyancing	30%
Commercial litigation	20%	Matrimonial	10%
Probate	10%		

WILMER CUTLER & PICKERING 4 Carlton Gardens, London, SW1Y 5AA **Tel:** (0171) 839 4466 **Fax:** (0171) 873 8888 **Ptnrs:** 4 **Asst Solrs:** 8 **Other Fee-earners:** 4. An international firm, its London office is a multi-national partnership that advises on international commercial arbitration, ADR, litigation, aviation and transport, telecommunications, competition law and inward investment.

WORKLOAD			
Int arbitration	40%	Aviation	25%
Company commercial	15%		

WILSON BROWNE PO Box No. 8, Meadow Road, Kettering, Northants, NN16 8TN **Tel:** (01536) 410041 **Fax:** (01536) 410444 **DX:** 12802 **Ptnrs:** 17 **Asst Solrs:** 5 **Other Fee-earners:** 28. Broad commercial practice. Computerised conveyancing, trusts and debt collections also handled. Legal aid work is undertaken. Five other offices.

WILSON CHALMERS & HENDRY 33A Gordon Street, Glasgow, G1 3PH **Tel:** (0141) 248 7761 **Fax:** (0141) 248 3447 **DX:** 104 Glasgow **Ptnrs:** 6 **Asst Solrs:** 6 **Other Fee-earners:** 2. Deals primarily with defenders personal injury litigation, in which it is a leading practice. Private client and commercial property work is also undertaken.

WILSON & CO 697 High Road, London, N17 8AD **Tel:** (0181) 808 7535 **Fax:** (0181) 880 3393 **DX:** 52200 Tottenham 2 **Ptnrs:** 2 **Asst Solrs:** 12 **Other Fee-earners:** 8. Specialist immigration practice dealing with legally-aided refugee, asylum, and family union work, as well as business immigration.

WILSON, ELSER, MOSKOWITZ, EDELMAN & DICKER

141 FENCHURCH STREET, LONDON, EC3M 6BL

TEL: (0171) 623 6723
FAX: (0171) 626 9774

THE FIRM: The firm is one of the largest in the United States and has been serving clients for more than a quarter of a century. It has grown considerably during this period and now has offices in twelve major cities in the US, as well as in London and Tokyo.

Initially the practice was insurance-related, and the firm maintains a pre-eminent position with regard to all aspects of insurance law and the insurance industry. However it has broadened its services and expertise to meet the needs of clients in the following areas: corporate organisation, negotiation, rendering business advice for both domestic and international clients on acquisitions, mergers, regulatory matters, financing, real estate and leasing transactions, contract negotiations and drafting, employment law and tax advice. The firm maintains close relationships with insurance specialist law firms in Europe.

THE LONDON OFFICE: The London office concentrates on insurance and reinsurance work, including product liability, insurance broker errors and omissions and international arbitration. Mr Cherry is both a US lawyer and a solicitor.

LANGUAGES SPOKEN: German and French (London office).

OTHER OFFICES: New York, Baltimore, Chicago, Dallas, Los Angeles, Miami, Newark, Paris, Philadelphia, San Francisco, Washington DC, White Plains Tokyo.

CONTACT PARTNER: Thomas Cherry

LAWYERS:
London:	1
Worldwide:	395

WORKLOAD	
US defence litigation	50%
Insurance coverage disputes	30%
Arbitration	5%
Creditors' rights	5%
E & O brokers(US and UK)	5%
D & O	5%

WILSON NESBITT

77 HIGH STREET, BELFAST, BT18 9AQ

TEL: (01232) 428600
FAX: (01232) 428144

THE FIRM: Well-known for its private client work, Wilson Nesbitt has expanded its range of services to include company/ commercial, personal injury, and commercial property work. At the same time, the practice has maintained particular expertise in traditional areas – in relation to trusts, probate and taxation matters, the firm's qualified taxation expert is available to ensure that specific needs are accurately identified and protected.

PRINCIPAL AREAS OF WORK:

Private Client: *(Contact Partner:* Gilbert Nesbitt). The main areas of expertise are personal tax planning, portfolio management, trusts, probate, domestic conveyancing, and matrimonial work.

Company/ Commercial: *(Contact Partner:* Celia Worthington). Advice to individuals, companies and institutions on all aspects of corporate and commercial law, including computerised debt recovery.

Personal Injury: *(Contact Partners:* Ciaran Tully (Defence), Patrick Hunt (Plaintiff)). The firm undertakes both plaintiff and defence work, with particular strengths in motor-related defences.

Commercial Property: *(Contact Partner:* Gilbert Nesbitt). The firm acts for housing associations and other public and private sector commercial and residential property developers.

CONTACT PARTNER: Gilbert Nesbitt

Number of partners:	4
Assistant solicitors:	6
Other fee-earners:	4

WORKLOAD	
Litigation	33%
Conveyancing	28%
Wills, trusts, probate, tax	16%
Company/ commercial	15%
Criminal	4%
Matrimonial	4%

WILSONS Steynings House, Chapel Place, Fisherton St, Salisbury, Wilts, SP2 7RJ **Tel:** (01722) 412412 **Fax:** (01722) 411500 **DX:** 58003 **Ptnrs:** 16 **Asst Solrs:** 9 **Other Fee-earners:** 17. The firm is establishing a strong reputation for providing a sophisticated service from a country base dealing with tax planning and landed estates work.

WINCKWORTH & PEMBERTON (Inc. SHERWOOD & CO)

35 GREAT PETER STREET, WESTMINSTER, LONDON, SW1P 3LR
DX: 2312 Victoria

TEL: (0171) 593 5000
FAX: (0171) 593 5099

THE FIRM: Winckworth & Pemberton is a well established Westminster firm of solicitors which incorporates the leading parliamentary agents, Sherwood & Co. The firm offers a wide range of high-quality services to Government Departments and agencies, local authorities and police authorities. The firm has an established ecclesiastical and private client practice and acts for many institutional clients with a growing educational and charitable clientele.

PRINCIPAL AREAS OF WORK: The firm is run in seven departments in the Westminster office.

Parliamentary: (*Contact Partner:* Alison Gorlov). This department specialises in the promotion of and opposition to Private Bills in Parliament and similar legislation (Scottish Provisional Orders and Orders under the Harbours Act 1964 and the Transport and Works Act 1992) as well as charters and bye laws, and advises on all forms of primary and secondary legislation.

Housing and Local Government: (*Contact Partner:* Catherine Hand). Winckworth & Pemberton is one of the leaders in this field of work, acting for a large number of housing associations and local authorities.

Ecclesiastical and Education: (*Contact Partner:* Paul Morris). This department provides registries for several of the Church of England's dioceses and handles church property work. The senior ecclesiastical partner is the legal adviser to the Archbishop of Canterbury. The department also acts for schools, higher education colleges and educational charities.

Commercial Property: (*Contact Partner:* Robert Larard). This department does all kinds of commercial property work and town & country planning, notably for public utilities, institutions and clients in the licensed trade.

Litigation: (*Contact Partner:* Christopher Tipping). A wide variety of work is handled, including injunction actions, liquor licensing, personal injury claims, landlord & tenant disputes and matrimonial matters. Employment law and unfair dismissal is also practised here.

Commercial and Government Services: (*Contact Partner:* Nicholas Owston/ Peter Williams). The department handles work in the public and private sectors covering contentious and non-contentious commercial and construction law and includes employer liability, medical negligence, real and intellectual property and lotteries. Police law, administrative and constitutional law are practised on behalf of the firm's institutional clients.

Private Client: (*Contact Partner:* Hugh MacDougald). The firm acts for a number of landed estate owners and substantial trusts, and handles a significant amount of estate planning and probate work.

RECRUITMENT AND TRAINING: Qualified staff should apply in the first instance to the Partnership Secretary, Mr. T.F. Vesey.

The firm recruits three trainee solicitors each year – a 2:2 law or 2:1 non-law degree is usually required and applications should be made by handwritten letter (and CV) to Mr R.H.A. MacDougald.

OTHER OFFICES: Winckworth & Pemberton also has offices in Chelmsford and Oxford dealing with similar types of work.

SENIOR PARTNER: Robert Larard

Number of partners:	23
Assistant solicitors:	25
Other fee-earners:	25

WORKLOAD

Parliamentary	20%
Housing and local government	19%
Ecclesiastical and education	17%
Private client	15%
Commercial and government services	15%
Litigation	10%
Licensed property	4%

CONTACTS

Commercial/government service	Peter Williams
Ecclesiastical	Paul Morris
Education	Michael Thatcher
Family/proprietary company	Hugh MacDougald
Housing & local government	Catherine Hand
Litigation	Christopher Tipping
Parliamentary	Alison Gorlov

WINSTANLEY-BURGESS 378 City Rd, London, EC1V 2QA **Tel:** (0171) 278 7911 **Fax:** (0171) 833 2135 **DX:** 58253 Islington **Ptnrs:** 6 **Asst Solrs:** 6 **Other Fee-earners:** 5. Established 1975. Handles all areas of general practice including conveyancing, family law, crime, personal injuries and housing. Has strong legal aid base. Best-known for immigration law.

WORKLOAD

Immigration/nationality	40%	Crime	25%
Housing/conveyancing	15%	Other civil litigation	10%
Matrimonial	10%		

WINTER–TAYLORS Park House, London Rd, High Wycombe, Bucks, HP11 1BZ **Tel:** (01494) 450171 **Fax:** (01494) 441815 **DX:** 4403 **Ptnrs:** 19 **Asst Solrs:** 8 **Other Fee-earners:** 5. Founded 1885, now has five offices in Bucks. Sees itself as a community-oriented firm acting for local businesses and private clients.

WINWARD FEARON 35 Bow St, London, WC2E 7AU **Tel:** (0171) 836 9081 **Fax:** (0171) 836 8382 **DX:** 37959 **Ptnrs:** 14 **Asst Solrs:** 4 **Other Fee-earners:** 5. A rapidly expanding 12-partner practice, best known for insurance and construction law. Its varied client base ranges from public companies, national and international, to private clients.

WORKLOAD			
Construction	55%	Corporate	22%
Conveyancing	13%	Commercial	10%

WITHAM WELD

70 ST. GEORGE'S SQUARE, LONDON, SW1V 3RD
DX: 86164 Victoria 2

TEL: (0171) 821 8211
FAX: (0171) 630 6484

THE FIRM: Established for over 200 years, Witham Weld has a long-standing reputation in its work for every kind of client, including religious and civil institutions, charities and trusts, commercial and private clients. Today, the aim remains the same – to provide the highest quality legal services, founded on experience and expertise and supported by innovation and the use of modern working methods.

PRINCIPAL AREAS OF WORK: The firm provides advice and assistance in a wide range of areas including charity law, property, revenue and tax planning, wills and probates, company/ commercial, contracts, education, employment, computer, copyright, and all forms of litigation.

CONTACT PARTNER: Mrs Alexa Beale

Number of partners:	6
Assistant solicitors:	2
Other fee-earners:	3

WITHERS

12 GOUGH SQUARE, LONDON, EC4A 3DE
DX: 160

TEL: (0171) 936 1000
FAX: (0171) 936 2589

THE FIRM: A distinguished City firm, Withers combines an expanding, corporate practice with a long-established private client base. The departments cover private client, property, corporate, shipping and aviation, litigation and family work. The firm has a Paris office and legal connections worldwide.

PRINCIPAL AREAS OF WORK:

Agriculture: (*Contact:* Annabel Brenton). A comprehensive service to landowners and farmers including acquisition management and disposal of estates and farming businesses and agricultural land occupation; tenancies, share farm agreements and partnerships.

Charities: (*Contact:* Alison Paines). Advice to national, local and private charities on the appropriate forms of constitution, methods of charitable giving, appeals and fund raising, negotiation with the Charity Commission, contentious probate and related claims and commercial law concerning trading subsidiaries.

Commercial Litigation: (*Contact:* Margaret Robertson). *Work includes:* advice for a wide range of corporate clients in disputes concerning commercial contracts of all types; trade libel; intellectual property; Companies Act remedies; judicial review; banking; insurance and professional negligence and acting for professional and sporting bodies in disciplinary matters.

Conveyancing – Commercial: (*Contact:* Theresa Grant Peterkin). The commercial group advises buyers and sellers, lenders and borrowers, landlords and tenants of business premises – offices, shops and factories as well as property developers.

Conveyancing – Residential: (*Contact:* Henry Stuart). Advice is given on sales and purchase of all town and country properties. Private client services are enhanced by providing advice on purchases of property by individuals not resident in the UK.

Corporate: (*Contact:* Philip Durrance). Comprehensive advice for the business client, specialising in management buy-outs and buy-ins acting primarily for management teams and venture capitalists, mergers and acquisitions, corporate finance, taxation, financial services, banking work, regulatory issues and directors' responsibilities.

Employment: (*Contact:* Margaret Robertson). Contentious and non-contentious employment matters are handled by the Employment Group which regularly deals with agreements of remuneration arrangements for senior executives, wrongful and unfair dismissal; redundancy; discrimination; business transfers; ESOPS; injunctions to restrain competition and breach of confidence; trade union and labour relations.

CONTACT PARTNER: Margaret Robertson

UK:	
Number of partners:	31
Assistant solicitors:	27
Other fee-earners:	21
INTERNATIONAL:	
Number of Partners:	1

WORKLOAD	
Private client	44%
Property	15%
Litigation	13%
Corporate	12%
Family	11%
International	5%
	0%

CONTACTS	
Agriculture and estates	Annabel Brenton
Charities	Alison Paines
Commercial property	Theresa Grant-Peterkin
Company and commercial	Philip Durrance
Contentious probate	Dawn Goodman
Employment	Margaret Robertson
Environment	Henry Stuart
Family law	Diana Parker
Intellectual property	Stephen Digby

Environment: (*Contact:* Henry Stuart). The Environmental Group advises companies and individuals on all aspects of environmental law, compliance with UK and EC regulation and the environmental consequences of land ownership, management and exploitation.

Family: (*Contact:* Diana Parker). *Work includes:* pre-marital agreements, financial arrangements on divorce or separation, child abduction, residence and contact orders and other issues relating to children. Many cases embrace complex international dimensions; all entail careful consideration of financial issues and taxation consequences.

Intellectual Property: (*Contact:* Stephen Digby). *Work includes:* a specialist contentious and non-contentious service on all aspects of the creation, ownership, protection and use of IP assets; advising entertainment and leisure industries, publishing and television sectors, computer and information technology industries and industrial and pharmaceutical companies.

Local Government: (*Contact:* Tim Taylor). Work includes advice on local authority financial regulations, controlled companies, judicial review, contract matters, employment, litigation and CCT companies.

Private Client: (*Contact:* Murray Hallam). *Work includes:* tax and estate planning, asset structuring using companies, partnerships, trusts and wills, probate and the administration of estates and trusts, Court of Protection and heritage work, offshore trusts and international asset protection for high net worth individuals.

Shipping and Aviation: (*Contact:* Jonathan Eastwood). *Work includes:* contentious and non-contentious work including sophisticated tax-driven structures that often accompany the financing of ships. The firm has close associations in the major jurisdictions associated with such business.

Trust and Probate Litigation: (*Contact:* Dawn Goodman). The firm has an unusual depth of expertise in this area including: misapplication of assets, variation/ construction of trusts/ wills, trustees' removal/ appointment, Inheritance Act Applications and probate actions.

FOREIGN CONNECTIONS: The firm has a Paris office with a resident partner who is dually qualified as an English solicitor and French avocat (*Contact:* Jonathan Eastwood). In London, Spanish law is handled by Michael Soul through his associate firm, Michael Soul & Associates, who specialise in Anglo/ Spanish work. Strong connections exist with the United States. In addition, the firm has significant dealings with the Middle East, the Far East, North and West Africa, Canada and Australia.

LANGUAGES SPOKEN: French, Italian, German, Spanish, Russian and Dutch.

International	Jonathan Eastwood
Litigation	Margaret Robertson
Local Government	Tim Taylor
Management buy-outs	Tim Stocks
Private client	Murray Hallam
Residential property	Henry Stuart

WITHY KING & LEE

5 & 6 NORTHUMBERLAND BUILDINGS, QUEEN SQUARE, BATH, AVON, BA1 2JE
DX: 8014

TEL: (01225) 425731
FAX: (01225) 315562

THE FIRM: Withy King & Lee is one of the larger firms in the West Country and, while progressive, can trace its roots back to the mid 19th century. It is a member of LawNet the largest group of independent quality assured law firms in the UK. The firm handles both commercial and private client work.

PRINCIPAL AREAS OF WORK:

General Description: *Work includes:* Company formations, takeovers, amalgamations, partnerships, employment, intellectual property, commercial conveyancing, landlord and tenant, planning, general civil litigation and computerised Debt Collection, Medical negligence, Personal injury, Criminal, Family/ Matrimonial, Wills, Probate, Trusts, Residential conveyancing, Licensing, Financial services and Personal tax.

FOREIGN LANGUAGES: French and Italian.

RECRUITMENT AND TRAINING: *Contact:* M.C. Powell.

CONTACT PARTNER: Mr Mike Swift

Number of partners:	9
Assistant solicitors:	6
Other fee-earners:	15

WORKLOAD	
Commercial and general litigation	20%
Probate, trusts and wills	17%
Personal injury and medical negligence	17%
Company/ commercial	15%
Domestic conveyancing	12%
Matrimonial and child care	10%
Financial services/ tax	9%

WOLFERSTANS

DEPTFORD CHAMBERS, 60-64 NORTH HILL, PLYMOUTH, DEVON, PL4 8EP
DX: 8206

TEL: (01752) 663295
FAX: (01752) 672021

THE FIRM: Wolferstans, founded in 1812, is a general practice handling both commercial and private client work. All offices are computer linked. As a founder member of LawGroup U.K., the firm aims to provide an efficient and comprehensive service, whilst maintaining an emphasis on personal service and accessibility.

PRINCIPAL AREAS OF WORK:

Company/ Commercial: *Work includes:* company formations, acquisitions and sales, funding arrangements, management buy-outs, employment matters, licensing, commercial conveyancing and a wide range of commercial litigation.
Contact Partner: Nick Roper. *No. of partners:* 8.

Litigation: The firm has a specialist medical negligence unit (*Contact:* Simon Parford), and is on the panel of the National Association for Victims of Medical Accidents. There is a substantial personal injury department and the insurance department acts for all major insurers. Other work includes commercial litigation, criminal work and debt recovery.
The Bristol office managed by Andrew Gibson deals exclusively with personal injury litigation.
Contact Partner: R. Griggs. *No. of partners:* 11.

Matrimonial and Family: *Work includes:* separation and divorce, custody and access, adoption, child welfare, financial settlements and maintenance agreements.
Contact Partner: P.M. Thorneycroft (Matrimonial), J. Bennett (Children). *No. of partners:* 4.

Private Client: *Work includes:* wills, probate and trusts and residential conveyancing.
Contact Partner: John Chapman. *No. of partners:* 2.

OTHER AREAS OF WORK: The firm regularly appears on behalf of accused persons at courts martial and has extensive experience in inquests and inquiries.

LANGUAGES SPOKEN: French, Spanish, German.

OTHER OFFICES: Plymouth (3), Bristol.

CONTACT PARTNER: David J.L. Gabbitass

Number of partners:	21
Assistant solicitors:	18
Other fee-earners:	17

CONTACTS	
Children	Jeremy Bennett
Commercial	Nick Roper
Crime	David Teague
Insurance	Roy Griggs
Litigation	Bill Duncan
Matrimonial	Phil Thorneycroft
Personal injury	Chris Kallis
Private	John Chapman
Probate	Gill Hollinshead
Sport	David Gabbitass

WOLLASTONS

BRIERLY PLACE, NEW LONDON ROAD, CHELMSFORD, ESSEX, CM2 0AP
DX: 89703 Chelmsford 2

TEL: (01245) 211211
FAX: (01245) 354764

THE FIRM: A progressive firm providing a broad range of commercial legal services mainly for substantial private companies. The firm is particularly well known for its specialist expertise in company and commercial matters. Other specialist areas of law include employment, insolvency, commercial property, intellectual property, commercial litigation, education, business immigration, agriculture, banking, planning and environmental law, licensing and European law including distribution and agency agreements and cross-border litigation.

The firm is based in superb modern offices which are easily accessible from all parts of the South East. There are generous car parking facilities for visitors.

FOREIGN CONNECTIONS: The firm is an active member of IAG International, an association of independent professional firms represented throughout Europe and beyond.

CONTACT PARTNER: Richard Wollaston

Number of partners:	9
Assistant solicitors:	4
Other fee-earners:	8

WORKLOAD	
Property/ planning	33%
Company/ commercial incl employment	31%
Litigation	26%
Private client	10%

WOOD AWDRY WANSBROUGHS

NORTHGATE HOUSE, DEVIZES, WILTS, SN10 1JX DX: 42901	TEL: (01380) 723611 FAX: (01380) 728213
3 St. Mary St, Chippenham, Wilts SN15 3JL DX: 42901 Chippenham	Tel: (01249) 444422 Fax: (01249) 34204
5 Spa Road, Melksham, Wilts SN12 7PN DX:43900 Melksham	Tel: (01225) 703222 Fax: (01225) 709547

THE FIRM: Founded at the beginning of the 19th century the firm has been practising in Chippenham and Melksham since that time and for most of the 20th century in Devizes. The firm has built up a practice that is broadly based and combines specialised skills with a high level of personal service for private, business and agricultural clients.

PRINCIPAL AREAS OF WORK:

Private Client Services incl. Agricultural Law: (*Contact:* David Bousfield, Devizes. Hugo Richardson, Chippenham. Mrs Jackie Walton, Chippenham.

Company and Commercial: (*Contact:* Christopher Bromfield, Devizes).

Commercial Property: (*Contact:* Richard Drury, Devizes).

Residential Property: (*Contact:* Christopher Yates, Chippenham).

Litigation General: (*Contact:* Stuart McGregor Johnson, Devizes).

Litigation for Insurance Companies: (*Contact:* Robert Hams, Devizes).

Family Law: (*Contact:* George Burges, Chippenham).

Trusts probate and tax: (*Contact:* Mrs Jackie Walton, Chippenham).

RECRUITMENT AND TRAINING: The firm recruits professional staff of high calibre and offers opportunities for interesting work in agreeable surroundings. Enquiries to Richard Drury, Devizes. The firm recruits one or two trainee solicitors each year.

CONTACT PARTNER: Robin Boyd

Number of partners:	14
Assistant solicitors:	8
Other fee-earners:	8

WORKLOAD	
Civil/ criminal litigation	52%
Wills/ probate/ trusts	15%
Property	12%
Family/ matrimonial	6%
Agricultural	5%
Company/ commercial	4%
Employment	3%
Tax planning	3%

WOODCOCK & SONS West View, Princess Street, Haslingden, Rossendale, Lancs, BB4 6NW **Tel:** (01706) 213356 **Fax:** (01706) 211494 **DX:** 26252 Rawtenstall **Ptnrs:** 9 **Asst Solrs:** 6 **Other Fee-earners:** 10. Established in 1791, a provincial firm with an expanding general practice at Bury, Greater Manchester and Rossendale, Lancashire. Legal aid work undertaken.

WORKLOAD			
Conveyancing	36%	Civil litigation	24%
Family	19%	Criminal	7%
Probate	5%		

WOODFORD & ACKROYD

THE DIRECTOR GENERAL'S HOUSE, ROCKSTONE PLACE, SOUTHAMPTON, HANTS, SO15 2EP DX: 49678 Southampton 2	TEL: (01703) 321000 FAX: (01703) 321001

THE FIRM: Woodford & Ackroyd is a modern, progressive firm founded at the end of the Second World War, and is now one of Southampton's larger firms. It has always specialised in litigation and advocacy work, with nine of the eleven partners involved in a wide variety of contentious matters, although a considerable amount of non-contentious work is also handled. The firm holds a full Legal Aid Franchise. The firm is a member of Law Group UK.

PRINCIPAL AREAS OF WORK:

Litigation: (*Contact Partner:* Chris Hodgkinson). The firm has an established track record in personal injury litigation, medical and professional negligence claims. *Work also includes:* commercial, employment, construction and building disputes, family, matrimonial and child care matters, debt recovery and criminal work. Legal aid is available in appropriate cases.

Licensing: (*Contact Partner:* Michael Messent). Two partners specialise in this area of practice. General licensing work is undertaken with particular expertise in the area of betting, gaming and liquor licensing.

CONTACT PARTNER: Chris Hodgkinson

Number of partners:	11
Assistant solicitors:	1
Other fee-earners:	8

CONTACTS	
Commercial conveyancing	Michael Biddle
Debt collection	Phillip Broom
Domestic conveyancing	Gordon Denson
Employment	Philip Broom
Housing	Lisa Rochford
Immigration	Gordon Denson

OTHER AREAS OF WORK: A full range of commercial and private client work is handled, including family and children, immigration, employment and insolvency, commercial and residential conveyancing, estate development and planning, wills, probate, corporate and personal tax planning.·

CLIENTELE: Clients range from large public companies to individuals.

RECRUITMENT: The firm recruits one trainee solicitor a year. Applications to Gordon Denson.

Licensing (gaming/ betting)	Michael Messent
Licensing (liquor)	Jo Davies
Matrimonial/ family	Charles Ackroyd
Medical negligence	Chris Hodgkinson
Personal injury	Chris Hodgkinson
Tribunals/ civil litigation	Philip Broom
Wills, trusts and probate	Michael Biddle

WOODFORD-ROBINSON

4 CASTILIAN TERRACE, NORTHAMPTON, NORTHANTS, NN1 1LE
DX: 12424 Northampton 1

TEL: (01604) 24926/231444
FAX: (01604) 231457

THE FIRM: Established in 1908 by J.H. Woodford-Robinson, the practice is particularly noted for its work in criminal law, family and matrimonial, personal injury and mental health. The firm liaises with other professional businesses such as banks, building societies, estate agents and accountants. It also has close links with a number of barrister's chambers, both locally and in London. Legal aid is offered and 24 hour emergency legal work is available if required.

PRINCIPAL AREAS OF WORK: Criminal court cases and attendance at police stations; civil litigation including industrial accidents; insurance claims and all personal injury including medical negligence; (one member of The Law Society Personal Injury Panel) family disputes including custody, adoption and child care cases (two solicitors are members of The Law Society Children Panel); house conveyancing and related property matters; wills, probate and trusts; independent financial advice; company and commercial; licensing law and tribunal appearances, particularly mental health review and Social Security.

CONTACT PARTNER: Neil Foster

Number of partners:	5
Assistant solicitors:	1
Other fee-earners:	2

WORKLOAD	
Crime	50%
Family	15%
Conveyancing	10%
Personal injury and medical negligence	10%
Probate	5%

WOODROFFES

YORK HOUSE, 199 WESTMINSTER BRIDGE RD, LONDON, SE1 7UT
DX: 36502 Lambeth

TEL: (0171) 928 6855
FAX: (0171) 633 0459

THE FIRM: Founded by C.G. Woodroffe in 1877, it is a general practice with emphasis on individual attention and has arrangements with other firms to enable major matters to be handled. Office (with parking) overlooks Westminster Bridge and is close to Waterloo Station.

PRINCIPAL AREAS OF WORK: Known for problem solving in the company/ commercial field, European Court, charities, education and foreign work. Specialist department handling insurance claims for Lloyd's and insurance companies. Also transfer of works of art, conveyancing, arranging mortgages, wills, probate, litigation, tax, copyright, insolvency, landlord and tenant and most legal matters.

NATURE OF CLIENTELE: The firm acts for private clients in UK and abroad, public companies, banks and charities.

CONTACT PARTNER: Mr. P.M. Woodroffe

Number of partners:	2
Assistant solicitors:	4
Other fee-earners:	3

WOOLLCOMBE BEER WATTS

CHURCH HOUSE, QUEEN STREET, NEWTON ABBOT, DEVON, TQ12 2QP
DX: 59100 Newton Abbot

TEL: (01626) 331199
FAX: (01626) 61217

THE FIRM: Established in 1831, Woollcombe Beer Watts now has offices in six regional and local centres serving local businesses, private and legal aid clients.

PRINCIPAL AREAS OF WORK:

Litigation: *(Contact Partner: D.S. Reed; 18 Fee-earners). Work includes:* personal injury and accident compensation, specialist medical negligence work, consumer law, debt collection, terms of trading and all kinds of commercial and partnership disputes, and criminal matters, including police cases. A partner is a member of the referral panel of the Association of Victims of Medical Accidents and on the Law Society Medical Negligence Panel. Two partners are members of the Law Society Personal Injury Panel.

Property: *(Contact Partner: M.A. Setter; 12 Fee-earners). Work includes:* all aspects of commercial and residential conveyancing, planning and landlord and tenant law.

Company/ Commercial: *(Contact Partner: Robin Barrett; 4 Fee-earners).Work includes:* business acquisitions, mergers and formations, and the licensing of public houses and hotels.

Family: *(Contact Partner: Fiona Luscombe; 7 Fee-earners). Work includes:* family and matrimonial law, custody and care proceedings. Two partners are on the Law Society Children Panel and are members of the Solicitors Family Law Association.

Private Client: *(Contact Partner: Noel Rowlinson; 9 Fee-earners). Work includes:* wills, trusts, probate and tax advice.

OTHER OFFICES: Torquay, Totnes, Chagford, Bovey Tracey and Buckfastleigh.

CONTACT PARTNER: Mr D.S. Reed

Number of partners:	18
Assistant solicitors:	14
Other fee-earners:	23

WORKLOAD	
Litigation	32%
Wills, trust, probate, tax	21%
Property	20%
Family	17%
Company and commercial	8%
Others	2%

WRAGGE & CO

55 COLMORE ROW, BIRMINGHAM, W. MIDLANDS, B3 2AS
DX: 13036

TEL: (0121) 233 1000
FAX: (0121) 214 1099

THE FIRM: Wragge & Co, the largest single office law firm in Birmingham, provides its clients with cutting edge legal advice and commercial solutions. The emphasis is very much on understanding the client's business. The firm has a national and international reputation for excellence and is frequently referred to as the "City" law firm in Birmingham.

Based in the centre of Birmingham's professional community, Wragge & Co provides a comprehensive range of legal services. The client base includes over 80 listed companies and hundreds of private companies in a variety of industries as well as public authorities, banks, building societies and insurance companies.

Quality and client care are given top priority in Wragge & Co. In recognition of its commitment to quality, Wragge & Co is accredited with BS EN ISO 9001 - the first legal firm in Birmingham and the largest in the UK. Commitment to quality has meant commitment to efficiency, an approach that is appreciated by a growing client list.

Membership of the Norton Rose M5 group, a national association of seven law firms, provides a City of London presence, an international office network, a nationwide precedent bank and a training resource. Independently, Wragge & Co is known in many European and US cities through close links with high quality firms in those cities.

PRINCIPAL AREAS OF WORK:

Corporate Finance: *(Contact:* Ian Metcalfe). The corporate group advises on all aspects of a company's life from formation to flotation, through acquisitions, mergers, joint ventures and management buyouts. The group has also built an excellent reputation in the UK's business community for its high profile corporate finance deals.

SENIOR PARTNER: John Crabtree

Number of partners:	43
Assistant solicitors:	100
Other fee-earners:	47

WORKLOAD	
Corporate finance	35%
Commercial property	27%
Commercial litigation	23%
Banking and insolvency	10%
Pensions and trusts	5%

CONTACTS	
Asset finance	Julian Pallett
Banking and insolvency	Richard Haywood
Building societies	David Pettingale
Commercial litigation	Quentin Poole
Commercial property	Mark Dakeyne
Construction	Ashley Pigott
Corporate finance	Ian Metcalfe
Debt recovery	Quentin Poole

Property and Property Development: (*Contact:* Mark Dakeyne). This is a major group handling the acquisition, letting and sale of all types of property; funding; development and planning agreements; joint ventures; portfolio investment, property consortia and partnerships; project management agreements; building contracts; taxation; agricultural land and tenancies; commercial lease renewals and rent arbitrations and licensed properties.

Planning (*Contact:* Dan Hemming). Wragge & Co has a specialist unit handling planning applications, enquiries and appeals and advising on planning matters generally.

Intellectual Property: (*Contact:* Bill Jones). The intellectual property work includes advice on protection and licensing in the field of media, patents, trade mark designs, copyright and confidential information.

Commercial: (*Contact:* Gordon Harris). The commercial group comprises a number of specialist units dealing with all aspects of everyday trading in the UK and abroad. Areas of specialisation include franchising, computer contracts, finance agreements, media and entertainment and consumer credit.

Litigation: (*Contact:* Quentin Poole). Wragge & Co's litigation group offers a commercial and objective assessment of clients' problems whilst maintaining a realistic approach to settlement negotiations. It includes one of the largest employment law units in the country and is experienced in banking, insolvency, insurance and property litigation.

Competition and EU Law: (*Contact:* David Hamlett). Wragge & Co advises on all aspects of these disciplines. The competition work includes advice on sales distribution and agency networks; contracts with competitors and trade associations; making and handling complaints to the regulatory authority; merger control and anti trust compliance. As well as providing in-depth advice on EU law, the firm has a comprehensive Monitoring Service which covers policy initiatives and legal developments emanating from the EU.

Banking and Insolvency: (*Contact:* Richard Haywood). Wragge & Co has a reputation as a leading firm in commercial banking law. The banking and insolvency group caters for the needs of both lenders and borrowers. It has particular experience in syndicated loan agreements in addition to asset and project finance and securitisation. Within the group there are three licensed insolvency practitioners.

Building Societies: (*Contact:* David Pettingale). The firm's dedicated Building Societies Unit provides a comprehensive range of services which include commercial lending, debt recovery, treasury and computer contracts.

Pensions: (*Contact:* Gerald Hingley). One of the largest pensions groups outside London, Wragge & Co's pensions team acts for employers, pension fund trustees, actuaries, consultants, receivers and liquidators. The team advises on all legal aspects and documentation of occupational and other pension schemes and also advises corporate clients on the pension implications of the purchase or sale of the company business.

Inheritance and Estates: (*Contact:* Louise Woodhead). The firm provides independent advice to trusts, charities, executors and private individuals on their property, financial and tax affairs. Areas covered include: pensions, inheritance tax, wills, residential conveyancing, probate, private trusts, off-shore trusts and charities.

LANGUAGES SPOKEN: French, German, Italian, Spanish, Greek, Dutch, Mandarin, Cantonese & Japanese.

Employment	Andrew Manning Cox
Environmental	John Turner
EU law and competition	David Hamlett
Executive immigration	Nicola Mumford
Financial services	Peter Smith
Franchising	Gordon Harris
Inheritance estates	Louise Woodhead
Insurance	Mark Hick
Intellectual property & IT	Bill Jones
International	David Birch
National health service trusts	Susan Dearden
Pensions	Gerald Hingley
Property litigation	Suzanne Lloyd Holt
Tax	Kevin Poole
Town and country planning	Dan Hemming

WRIGHT HASSALL & CO 9 Clarendon Place, Leamington Spa, Warks, CV32 5QP **Tel:** (01926) 886688 **Fax:** (01926) 885588 **DX:** 11863 **Ptnrs:** 14 **Asst Solrs:** 7 **Other Fee-earners:** 19. Established 1846. A general practice known for litigation, property, trust and estate work, tax and investments, company/ commercial, corporate finance and agriculture.

WRIGHT, JOHNSTON & MACKENZIE

12 ST VINCENT PLACE, GLASGOW, G1 2EQ
DX: 129 Glasgow

TEL: (0141) 248 3434
FAX: (0141) 221 1226

CONTACT PARTNER: Campbell Black

Number of partners:	11
Assistant solicitors:	17
Other fee-earners:	13

WORKLOAD	
Private client	25%
Litigation	25%
Commercial property	25%
Corporate	25%

CONTACTS	
Commercial property	Colin Brass
Corporate	Alan Simpson
Litigation	Martin Stephen
Private client	Marjory Love

THE FIRM: A Glasgow practice dating back to 1869, Wright, Johnston & Mackenzie now also operate from a second principal office in Edinburgh. The firm advises a wide range of clients, from the individual to the most substantial business organisations. In 1992 the firm significantly broadened the range and depth of its services by forming the QLG national law group alongside 12 other firms throughout the UK. As a QLG member Wright, Johnston & Mackenzie has been pursuing an exhaustive quality programme which led to BS 5750 accreditation in 1994. Professional practitioners' skills are supported by the latest technology and by the QLG co-ordinated training and education policy for all lawyers and staff.

PRINCIPAL AREAS OF WORK:

Commercial Property: *(Contact Partner:* Colin Brass). A specialist service has always been provided by the firm to those involved in or dealing with commercial property, be they buyers, sellers, financiers, investors or developers. Originally acting for Scottish-based clients, the property sector's international dimension has led to the increased representation in Scotland of clients throughout the UK, Europe and beyond. The firm has maintained close and long-standing links with banks and leading financial institutions, offering expertise ranging from the straightforward purchase of commercial property to complex joint venture development projects.

Corporate Department: *(Contact Partner:* Alan Simpson). The department handles all aspects of the law arising from the complexity and regulation of corporate affairs. Particular expertise has been demonstrated in general corporate matters and in the fields of banking, finance, shipping and maritime law, intellectual property and environmental law. Although of medium-size, the practice has been involved in a high proportion of European Community matters, especially in relation to competition legislation. Moreover, the firm is in the process of establishing itself in the niche market of media and entertainment law.

Litigation Department: *(Contact Partner:* Martin Stephen). Representation in civil actions is the core of the department's activity, but clients are also represented before tribunals, boards, panels and other authorities. The firm has recently invested in a computerised debt collection system and also acts for banks and building societies in cases of repossession and personal insolvency.

Private Client: *(Contact Partner:* Marjory Love). The firm acts for individual clients in all financial and residential property matters. Over the years, particular experience and expertise has been developed in looking after clients' financial affairs. The department incorporates a dedicated financial services section which provides advice on all aspects of tax, inheritance and general financial planning. The firm also provides advice and assistance with conveyancing, finance and mortgages, and insurance. As member of the Glasgow and Edinburgh Solicitors Property Centres, a full service is provided for the sale of domestic property.

OTHER OFFICE: 4 North Charlotte Street, Edinburgh EH2 4HT. *Tel:* (0131) 225 4181. *Fax:* (0131) 225 1678.

FOREIGN LANGUAGES: French, German.

INTERNATIONAL CONNECTIONS AND ASSOCIATED OFFICES: As a member of QLG the firm has associated offices in London, Birmingham, Bristol, Crawley, Exeter, Leeds, Liverpool, Maidstone and Newcastle-upon-Tyne and Southampton. Also, the practice has established international links with European lawyers.

WRIGHT SON & PEPPER

9 GRAY'S INN SQUARE, LONDON, WC1R 5JF
DX: 35

TEL: (0171) 242 5473
FAX: (0171) 831 7454

THE FIRM: The firm has been established in Gray's Inn Square since 1800. In 1986 it amalgamated with Sole Sawbridge & Co., and in 1990 with Watkins Pulleyn. The object of the firm is to provide sound practical advice, quickly and efficiently, on a personal basis. The firm has invested in the latest information technology and office equipment and intends to keep abreast of developments in this area.

PRINCIPAL AREAS OF WORK:

General Description: Although historically a firm acting for private clients, it now concentrates on commercial work for the small-to-medium business, and specialist work such as that in the field of solicitors practice and partnership matters. Each solicitor is encouraged to have, in addition to a general knowledge of his field, a specialist knowledge of a particular area of law.

Company and Commercial: (*Contact:* Steve Alais). In addition to dealing with the normal range of commercial and company work, the firm has considerable experience in dealing with all forms of computer-related contracts and the setting up, funding and operation of private railways.

Commercial and Domestic Property: (*Contact:* Antony Wright). The emphasis is on offices, shop and factory/warehouse leases and developments, town planning and funding arrangements.

Professional Practice and Partnership Matters: (*Contact:* Nicholas Wright). The firm, in addition to its general and professional partnership work, advises solicitors with regard to the Solicitors Practice Rules and Solicitors Accounts Rules, partnership disputes, the break up of solicitors partnerships and advises solicitors who have financial difficulties. It also represents solicitors before the Solicitors Disciplinary Tribunal.

Family Law: (*Contact:* Paul Butner). All aspects of matrimonial, family, welfare and child care law are covered with special emphasis on ancillary relief in matrimonial proceedings.

Litigation: (*Contact:* Iain Miller or Derek Lavery). The firm handles general commercial and private litigation. High Court agency work is also undertaken.

Private Client and Tax: (*Contact:* Brian Wates). *Work includes:* probates, wills, settlements, trust formation and administration, powers of attorney, Court of Protection, investment advice, personal tax and estate planning.

OTHER AREAS OF WORK: The firm also handles intellectual property, building contract disputes, debt collection, employment, landlord and tenant, transport law, European Community law and consumer law.

NATURE OF CLIENTELE: The firm acts mainly for small to medium-sized businesses, professional and private clients.

FOREIGN CONNECTIONS: The firm has professional connections in Belgium and USA. French, German, Greek and Dutch are spoken.

CONTACT PARTNER: Nicholas Wright

Number of partners:	9
Assistant solicitors:	3
Other fee-earners:	6

WORKLOAD	
Solicitors' practice/partnership matters	21%
Property	16%
Matrimonial	16%
Litigation	16%
Company/commercial	16%
Trust and probate	15%

CONTACTS	
Company/commercial	S.M. Alais
Expert evidence (property)	A J Wright
Litigation	I Miller
Matrimonial	P L M Butner
Property	A J Wright
Sol. disciplinary proceedings	D T Morgan
Solicitors' practice/ p'ships	N J Wright
Trust & probate	B Wates

FIRMS OF ACCOUNTANTS

Accountants specialising in litigation support are listed in the accountants' A-Z, with details of the services they offer to solicitors, from forensic accounting to intellectual property or business valuations.

A.E. WYETH & CO

BRIDGE HOUSE, HIGH STREET, DARTFORD, KENT, DA1 1JR DX: 31904 Dartford *IBM Screenmail*	TEL: (01322) 297000 FAX: (01322) 297001
8 Stone Buildings, Lincoln's Inn, London WC2A 3TA. DX: 147 London Contact Partner: A.R.Tatton	Tel: (0171) 242 7588 Fax: (0171) 831 5674
43A High Street, Swanley, Kent BR8 8AD DX: 56500 Swanley	Tel: (01322) 663242 Fax: (01322) 668623

THE FIRM: A.E. Wyeth & Co. are a "City" firm, who have built an excellent reputation acting for a broad spectrum of clients, ranging from private individuals to large national organisations, insurance companies, Lloyds syndicates and multinational corporations, on a wide range of national and international legal matters. It operates highly efficient information and communications technology and provides a personal cost efficient legal service. The firm also undertakes legal aid work.

PRINCIPAL AREAS OF WORK:

Litigation: (*Contact:* Brian Williams, Maurice Nichols).
Personal injury, employers liability, motor claims, product liability, building and construction, commercial, professional and medical negligence, specialist "scheme" litigation department.

Private Client – non-contentious: (*Contact:* Peter Daniels).
Commercial and domestic conveyancing, wills and estate planning, probate, company formation, partnership agreements, charities.

Private Client – contentious: (*Contact:* Tom Challis).
Crime, family and matrimonial, debt collection, neighbour and boundary disputes, sale of goods.

AGENCY WORK: Both High Court (Central Office) and County Court (Dartford) undertaken.

JURISDICTIONS: The firm provides in-house legal advice from practitioners qualified in the following jurisdictions: USA (New York) and Scotland.

FOREIGN LANGUAGES SPOKEN: French.

CONTACT PARTNER: Mr Brian Williams	
Number of partners:	10
Assistant solicitors:	10
Other fee-earners:	22

CONTACTS	
Contentious private client	T. Challis
Litigation	B. Williams, M. Nichols
Non-contentious private client	P. Daniels

SOLICITORS

WYNNE BAXTER GODFREE 221 High Street, Lewes, E. Sussex, BN7 2AE **Tel:** (01273) 477071 **Fax:** (01273) 478515 **DX:** 3101 **Ptnrs:** 22 **Asst Solrs:** 8 **Other Fee-earners:** 14. A well-established East Sussex firm with five offices. Offers a comprehensive family and commercial service with a particular reputation for medical negligence, building society work, court and debt recovery work.

WORKLOAD			
Civil/criminal lit	25%	Prob/trusts/wills/tax	22%
Conveyancing	22%	Family	16%
Company and commercial	15%		

YAFFE JACKSON OSTRIN Princes Building, 81 Dale Street, Liverpool, Merseyside, L2 2HZ **Tel:** (0151) 236 5555 **Fax:** (0151) 236 2121 **DX:** 14205 **Ptnrs:** 10 **Asst Solrs:** 3 **Other Fee-earners:** 10. Has one of the largest criminal practices in Liverpool. Also handles personal injury, family, domestic and commercial conveyancing, probate, employment law and medical negligence.

YOUNG & PEARCE

58 TALBOT STREET, NOTTINGHAM, NOTTS, NG1 5GL DX: 10025	TEL: (0115) 959 8888 FAX: (0115) 947 5572

THE FIRM: Throughout its history the firm has specialised in all aspects of licensing law and all the partners have experience in this field. The firm is B.S.I. registered to BS5750. It has invested heavily in information technology. Over half the fee earners and all the support staff have terminals on the firm's computer network.

PRINCIPAL AREAS OF WORK:

Licensing: (*Contact Partners:* John Pearce, Tony Wilkinson). The firm is well known for its extensive licensing practice. There is expertise in liquor licensing, betting and gaming and other commercial and legal matters relating to the leisure industry generally. Clients range from large PLCs and other large concerns to small

CONTACT PARTNER: John Pearce	
Number of partners:	4
Assistant solicitors:	4
Other fee-earners:	3

businesses and include breweries, public houses, night clubs, restaurants, off-licences, casinos and bingo clubs, betting offices and amusement centres. A comprehensive service includes matters relating to purchase, loans and employment problems, appearances at courts, committees and tribunals and advice to clients on the running of their businesses. The firm has also built up experience and expertise in planning law and the law relating to food safety.

Property: (*Contact Partners:* John Pearce, John Gossage). The firm has a substantial practice in commercial property matters, both freehold and leasehold work, business takeovers, development work including building estates and most aspects of property and commercial law. A computer-based conveyancing support system has been used for estate development and domestic property work for many years.

OTHER AREAS OF WORK: The practice also undertakes litigation, family law and criminal work.

CONTACTS	
Crime	Tony Wilkinson
Licensing	John Pearce
Property	John Gossage

T.C. YOUNG & SON 30 George Square, Glasgow, G2 1LH **Tel:** (0141) 221 5562 **Fax:** (0141) 221 5024 **DX:** 78 Glasgow **Ptnrs:** 2 **Asst Solrs:** 1 **Other Fee-earners:** 2. A small firm with specialist experience of acting for charities and housing associations. General private client, trust and executry work is also undertaken.

WORKLOAD			
Housing associations	50%	General private client	20%
Charities	20%	Litigation	10%

ZAIWALLA & CO

33 CHANCERY LANE, LONDON, WC2A 1ZZ
DX: 0034 Ch.Ln.

TEL: (0171) 312 1000
FAX: (0171) 312 1100

THE FIRM: It is strong in international commercial litigation, shipping law, banking law, international arbitration, immigration, joint ventures and has a specialist Indian Law department. Commercial and domestic property conveyancing, probate and company/commercial matters are also handled. Associated firms are: Bombay and New York. International clientele, mainly from UK, South East Asia, Middle East and Greece. Languages spoken: Gujerati, Hindi, Marathi, German and Hebrew.

CONTACT PARTNER: Andrew J. Milne

Number of partners:	7
Assistant solicitors:	1
Other fee-earners:	1

ZERMANSKY & PARTNERS

10 BUTTS COURT, LEEDS, W. YORKS, LS1 5JS
DX: 12061

TEL: (0113) 245 9766
FAX: (0113) 246 7465

THE FIRM: The firm offers a comprehensive range of legal services and is committed to legal aid work. It is a member of Action for Victims of Medical Accidents, Lawyers for Enterprise, Union Law, Solicitors' Family Law Association, Leeds Chamber of Commerce and Industry and Leeds Law Society Childcare Panel. Family Mediation Association, Criminal Law Solicitors Association, Association of Lawyers for Children.

PRINCIPAL AREAS OF WORK:

Private Client: (a) *Fee-earners:* 7). *Work includes:* family and matrimonial law, welfare, wills, probate, trusts and tax.

(b) *Fee-earners:* 3). *Work includes:* criminal & child care.

Company and Commercial: (*Fee-earners:* 1). *Work includes:* all aspects of company/commercial work (with particular emphasis on small to medium sized businesses and new businesses), insolvency, employment matters, liquor and entertainment licensing and leisure and sport.

Property: (*Fee-earners:* 2). *Work includes:* commercial conveyancing, landlord and tenant and residential conveyancing.

Litigation: *Fee-earners:* 5). *Work includes:* commercial litigation, personal injury, medical negligence and other professional negligence, debt collection, consumer disputes, property litigation, landlord and tenant disputes, immigration, injunctions and criminal law.

FOREIGN LANGUAGES: Polish, Punjabi and Hindi.

CONTACT PARTNER: Mr Russell Graham

Number of partners:	8
Assistant solicitors:	3
Other fee-earners:	3

CONTACTS	
Company & commercial	David Honeybone
Litigation	Peter Wynne
Private client-general	Norman Taylor
Private client-crime/care	Alistair Babbington
Property	Russell Graham
Sports law	David Honeybone

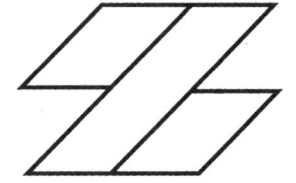

A–Z DIRECTORY OF ACCOUNTANTS
LITIGATION SUPPORT

ALEXANDERS

SELODUCT HOUSE, STATION ROAD, REDHILL, SURREY, RH1 1NF

TEL: (01737) 779500
FAX: (01737) 779548

CONTACT PARTNER:
Mr C.R.G. Tomaszewski

THE FIRM: For a number of years, Alexanders have been helping lawyers and their clients by providing forensic accounting, litigation support and expert witness services whenever financial issues are involved.

The firm has worked closely with insurance companies, lawyers, leading counsel and their clients, in such areas as the production of high quality reports, graphs and financial summaries of a clear, concise nature for presentation at court; litigation strategies; the examination and appraisal of documents through Discovery and assessing the quantum of claims or exposure.

Alexanders have a firm grasp of the laws of evidence and understand the necessity of providing reliable evidence. They also have first hand courtroom experience of both the Royal Courts of Justice and the Central Criminal Courts.

Computerised techniques employed by the firm ensure the accuracy of information supplied by Alexanders: databases are used for interrogation of financial information; statistical analysis checks patterns and trends and tests facts against expected values; graphics software provides simple visual interpretations of complex information.

THE PARTNERS: The Litigation Support Partners have all held senior positions within the top ten accountancy firms and have worked in public practice for a number of years. All partners are members of the British Academy of Experts and are qualified accountants with a wide range of business experience.

PRINCIPAL AREAS OF WORK: Alexanders have assisted in a wide variety of cases involving loss of earnings; professional negligence; negligence of Investment Managers; fraud; conspiracy to defraud; family and marital disputes; compliance with Investor Protection regulations; insurance claims; breach of contract claims; and offences under the Companies Acts.

ANTHONY BALLANTYNE & CO

5 LING COMMON ROAD, NORTH WOOTTON, KING'S LYNN, NORFOLK, PE30 3RE

TEL: (01553) 631535
FAX: (01553) 631535

CONTACT PARTNER:
Anthony Ballantyne MBAE

THE FIRM: This is a dedicated forensic accountancy practice founded in 1986.
SPECIALIST AREAS OF WORK:
PI Loss of Earnings/ Profits; Small Businesses allegations; Theft and Fraud.
OTHER AREAS OF WORK:
National, visiting practice. Quantum in all civil, and for the defence in criminal, litigation. Legal Aid welcome. Member of British Academy of Experts, and experienced in written and oral evidence from Tribunals to RCJ.

ARTHUR ANDERSEN

1 SURREY STREET, LONDON, WC2R 2PS
DX: 137 London Chancery Lane WC2

TEL: (0171) 438 3000
FAX: (0171) 831 1133

CONTACT PARTNER: David Ashton

Arthur Andersen has been providing litigation services to the UK legal profession since 1980. The litigation services practice, combines specialists in litigation with the resources of one of the world's largest accounting and business consulting firms. The litigation team in London consists of over 40 full-time partners, managers and staff.

LITIGATION SUPPORT PARTNERS:

David Ashton FCA, AI Arb, FBAE. Mr Ashton, who is a qualified mediator, has been responsible for expert reports produced and evidence adduced on over 80 cases of litigation and arbitration. He has given evidence in the High Court Chancery and Admiralty Divisions, and among others, to the Iran-US Arbitration Tribunal.

Richard Boulton ACA, MBAE. Mr Boulton specialises in damages assessment, company valuations, and regulatory disputes. He has led one of the world's largest fraud investigations. Mr Boulton has given evidence in the High Court, the Crown Court, and the Copyright Tribunal, and has acted as an independent expert appointed by the President of ICAEW.

Ray Hinton FCA. Mr Hinton is a member and the former Chairman of Arthur Andersen's Committee on Professional Standards in the UK, and is responsible for technical accounting issues and matters of alleged professional negligence. He is a member of the Accounting Standards Board.

Christopher Osborne ACA, MBAE. Mr Osborne specialises in the application of financial models and statistical techniques to commercial disputes. He heads the litigation support systems group which uses computer systems to assist with document management.

In addition, the litigation practice draws on the experience of specialist partners for their particular industry or technical expertise. This ensures that an appropriately balanced team is assembled to deal with each assignment.

PRINCIPAL AREAS OF WORK: Arthur Andersen can assist in a wide variety of financial disputes, either as a consulting expert or as an expert witness. **Service lines:** commercial contract claims, lost profits calculations, intellectual property disputes, post-acquisition disputes, fraud investigations, construction claims, insurance and professional negligence claims.

Arthur Andersen assists in all stages of the litigation process, from identifying, reviewing and analysing the key business issues, to trial preparation, and expert evidence.

LITIGATION CONTACTS:

Birmingham:	Contact: Richard Williams.	Tel: (0121) 626 4236.
Bristol:	Contact: Adam Mantzos.	Tel: (0117) 927 7436.
Cambridge:	Contact: Fred Hallsworth.	Tel: (01223) 353906.
Edinburgh:	Contact: Brian McGhee.	Tel: (0131) 469 6220.
Glasgow:	Contact: Eric Hagman.	Tel: (0141) 248 7941.
Leeds:	Contact: Mark Harman.	Tel: (0113) 241 6215.
Manchester:	Contact: Stuart Lees.	Tel: (0161) 200 0208.
Nottingham:	Contact: Richard Williams.	Tel: (0121) 626 4236.
Reading:	Contact: Bruce Gordon.	Tel: (01734) 563606.

BAKER TILLY

2 BLOOMSBURY STREET, LONDON, WC1B 3ST

TEL: (0171) 413 5100
FAX: (0171) 413 5101

THE FIRM: Baker Tilly is a national top twenty firm of Chartered Accountants with over 60 partners and 500 staff and is a member of BKR International with representatives in over 100 cities worldwide. Its partners have acted in over 300 litigation support cases, providing expert witness and forensic accounting services. They are not just experts in court - as practising accountants their evidence is based on practical and commercial experience. Cases include breach of contract (including computer installations and construction), other damages claims including loss of future profits, security for costs, share valuations including S459CA1985, medical negligence, personal injury and fatal accident claims, and acting for defendants in cases brought by the SFO which include George Walker, SEIL Trade Finance Ltd and as the DTI Inspector in the Barlow Clowes affair.

CONTACT PARTNERS: Chilton Taylor, Peter Dickerson, Ian Bond, Chris Hine

BINDER HAMLYN

20 OLD BAILEY, LONDON, EC4M 7BH

TEL: (0171) 489 9000
FAX: (0171) 489 6060

THE FIRM: Binder Hamlyn has been providing litigation support services for over 60 years. In addition to drawing on a core of specialists in litigation support and share and business valuations, the firm provides other expert witnesses who have given expert testimony in Court backed by day to day practical experience in the varied professional disciplines of one of the UK's leading firms of chartered accountants. Clients benefit from its unique position within the UK accounting profession. Binder Hamlyn is a separate, independently managed UK partnership within the Arthur Andersen worldwide organisation.

Each assignment is under the guidance of a core litigation specialist who, whether or not acting as the expert witness, ensures that there is effective liaison with instructing solicitors and that reports are appropriately structured, free of jargon and clear to the non-accountant. The service is co-ordinated from the Old Bailey office, although offices in key regional business centres can assist locally.

PRINCIPAL AREAS OF WORK: The firm handles quantum considerations in all kinds of commercial, professional negligence, computer systems, matrimonial and personal injury disputes, including structured settlements. The firm's experts provide opinions on liability in a variety of professional negligence disputes including matters concerning audit and other public reporting, corporate finance, taxation, VAT, trusts and personal financial planning. Binder Hamlyn also carries out Inland Revenue, VAT and fraud investigations as well as investigations for the DTI and other statutory and regulatory bodies.

NATURE OF CLIENTELE: Binder Hamlyn provides a full range of audit and accounting, tax advisory and consultancy services to our clients in four core markets: business, public sector, private clients and the voluntary sector. These include clients in construction, retail, insurance, shipping, chemicals, property, agriculture, the motor trade, advertising, transport, charities and engineering.

CONTACT LITIGATION SUPPORT SPECIALISTS IN OTHER UK OFFICES:
Leeds - Chris Roulston 0113 244 0204
Manchester - David Wilkinson 0161 228 6100
Newcastle - Peter Mickler/ Arthur Wappatt 0191 261 2481

CONTACT PARTNERS:
Richard Bolton, Mary Reilly
(direct dial 489 6209 or 6224 respectively, direct fax 6279)

BURNETT SWAYNE

CHARTER COURT, THIRD AVENUE, SOUTHAMPTON, HANTS, SO15 OAP

TEL: (01703) 702345
FAX: (01703) 702570

CONTACT PARTNER: Ken Ball

Number of Partners:	9
Total Staff:	95

Burnett Swayne, a substantial independent firm based in Southampton, has extensive experience of providing litigation support. Clear concise reporting, negotiating assistance and court attendance, including expert witness evidence, are all provided at provincial rates.

PRINCIPAL AREAS OF WORK:

Marital Breakdown:
– valuation of businesses
– valuation of shares in private companies
– assessment of income/ income requirement
– tax efficent arrangements

Partnership & Shareholder Disputes:
– investigations
– valuation of business
– cash flow forecasts, etc.
– tax efficient solutions

Personal Injury or Accident:
– assessment of loss of earnings, profit or capital growth
– computer modelling
– taxation implications

Consequential Loss:
– investigations
– assessment of loss by computer modelling
– taxation implications

Fraud & Negligence:
– investigations
– assessment of actual or consequential loss
– taxation implications

LITIGATION SUPPORT LED BY:

Ken Ball FCA ATII – 25 years in practice with tax bias. Experienced in partnership and shareholder disputes. Expert witness.

Geoffrey Porter FCA – Specialist in share valuations, damages claims and fraud investigation.

CAMPOS & STRATIS - Forensic Accountants

17 DEVONSHIRE SQUARE, LONDON, EC2M 4SQ

TEL: (0171) 247 4804
FAX: (0171) 247 4970

CONTACT PARTNERS:
Tony Levitt, Stephen Podgorney

THE FIRM: Campos & Stratis, founded in 1969, is a market leader specialising exclusively in forensic accounting and provides dedicated support to solicitors.

AREAS OF EXPERTISE: include expert witness; quantum review, including loss of profit/ business interruption; loss of earnings and pension benefits.

The firm works fast and efficiently, using the exact combination of human, computer and information resources demanded by each instruction. Every job is assigned a dedicated team led by a partner with the backing of an international organisation which they can call upon as and when it is needed.

Campos & Stratis aims to present a full, unbiased report of the real circumstances behind any action. The firm helps to create the context within which clients can take the most appropriate decision by offering:-
- **An enquiring and painstaking approach**
- **Client involvement at partner level**
- **Confidence in an adversarial environment**
- **Creativity**
- **Expert witness**
- **Imagination**
- **Realistic fees**
- **Sensitivity to cultural differences in companies and countries**
- **Specific investigative skills**
- **Tenacity**
- **Thorough knowledge of litigation procedures**

PRINCIPAL AREAS OF WORK:

Business interruption/ loss of profit	Professional malpractice
Product liability	Patent and copyright infringement
Fraud	Mergers and acquisitions
Personal injury/ fatal accident claims	Contract disputes
Business valuations	Construction

OPERATION: Once appointed by solicitors, Campos & Stratis investigates and checks the suppositions behind a claim. Highly experienced practitioners will know which documents should be available for discovery, both inside and outside any company. Campos & Stratis does only the work that is required on a claim and does not waste clients' time.

Instructing solicitors are provided with a professional report for use in litigation or negotiations, highlighting any errors or omissions in the claim and its strengths or weaknesses.

Claims can often be complicated, with side issues clouding the essence of a case. When this happens, it may be valuable for the instructing solicitors to direct the Campos & Stratis team to attend meetings with the other party's experts, on a Without Prejudice basis, to resolve specific areas of disagreement or confusion. The limits to these discussions will be set by the instructing solicitor. Such meetings can considerably reduce the time spent considering a claim, thus reducing overall costs.

Should a claim come to court, Campos & Stratis practitioners can clearly and succinctly explain evidence included in the accounting expert's report under examination-in-chief and cross-examination. They will also be available to attend the trial, to help Counsel formulate questions based on evidence given by any opposing accounting experts.

CHANTREY VELLACOTT

RUSSELL SQUARE HOUSE, 10-12 RUSSELL SQUARE, LONDON, WC1B 5LF

TEL: (0171) 436 3666
FAX: (0171) 436 8884

Dedicated litigation support team working with the firm's Legal Practices Group to serve the legal profession. Areas of expertise include business valuations, civil and criminal, fraud investigations, professional negligence, loss of profits claims, shareholder disputes and matrimonial proceedings.

CONTACT PARTNER: Ralph O'Beirne
Number of Partners: 43
Total Staff: 263

A.I. CHERRY

MOOR PARK HOUSE, 71 GARSTANG RD, PRESTON, LANCS, PR1 1LB
DX: 25405 Fulwood

TEL: (01772) 201015
FAX: (01772) 204739

CONTACT PARTNER:
Ian Cherry BA (Hons). FCA

Number of Partners:	2
Total Staff:	15

THE FIRM: A.I. Cherry specialises in forensic accounting. The firm acts for a large number of solicitors specialising in personal injury litigation, insurance companies and Lloyd's syndicates. It has also advised the Department of Transport, Ministry of Defence, the Treasury Solicitor, Lancashire Constabulary, several health authorities, and the Inland Revenue.

The firm is instructed mainly by defendants and insurers. It will accept instructions from plaintiffs and can bring a balanced and realistic approach to the quantification of special damages settlement of claims.

A high degree of partner involvement is a feature of the firm's work, and all professional staff are recruited from major firms of accountants.

LITIGATION SUPPORT PARTNER:
Mr Ian Cherry BA (Hons) FCA (1981), formerly responsible for forensic accounting department of a leading national practice. Advised defendants in first structured settlement approved in the UK. Extensive experience of appearing on radio and television, has had many articles published and has lectured on Forensic Accounting to fellow practitioners.

CLARK WHITEHILL

25 NEW STREET SQUARE, LONDON, EC4A 3LN

TEL: (0171) 353 1577
FAX: (0171) 583 1720

CONTACT PARTNER: Mark Ladd

Number of Partners:	78
Total Staff:	600

Clark Whitehill's specialist litigation support unit, in conjunction with appropriate industry or business specialists, handles procedures involved in the preparation and defence of claims. The unit maintains a training programme in order to keep abreast of current practice. This includes the use of barristers to improve court room techniques.

SERVICES PROVIDED:
Consequential loss of profits claims arising from fraud delays and faults for individuals, partnerships, companies and key executives. [**Mark Ladd (FCA, MBAE) – London.**]
Personal injury claims. Fatal accident claims. Medical negligence claims. Structured settlements. [**Humphrey Creed (FCA, MBAE) – Thames Valley.**
Professional negligence claims; particularly actions involving audit opinions, tax advice and profit forecasts. [**Mark Ladd (FCA, MBAE) – London; John Stalker (FCA, ATII) – High Wycombe.**]
Regulatory bodies: Expert reports on behalf of the Crown Prosecution Service, the DTI, Financial Services Act bodies. [**Howard Williams (FCA, MBAE) – London.**]

OTHER OFFICES WITH SPECIALISTS:
High Wycombe Tel: (01494) 462726.   Manchester Tel: (0161) 834 1654.
Reading Tel: (01734) 597222.

CLARK WHITEHILL
Chartered Accountants
A member of Horwath International

COOPERS & LYBRAND

PLUMTREE COURT, LONDON, EC4A 4HT
DX: 13164

TEL: (0171) 583 5000
FAX: (0171) 212 4863 or 212 6366

CONTACT PARTNERS:
Peter Benson, Rick Helsby, Chris Lemar,
Andrew Mainz or Tim Lawrence.

FORENSIC ACCOUNTING: Coopers & Lybrand is one of the largest firms of accountants and business advisers in the UK. Under the umbrella of Forensic Accounting, Coopers & Lybrand has a large team specialising in Litigation Support, Fraud Investigations and Tax Investigations.

LITIGATION SUPPORT: Coopers & Lybrand has worked on disputes with values ranging from a few thousand to over a hundred million pounds.

Each case is led by a partner who is closely involved. A thorough understanding of the litigation process is combined with specialist business knowledge drawn from the extensive resources available within the firm. Members of the firm are authors of *Litigation Support: The Coopers & Lybrand Guide to the Financial Assessment of Damages and Forensic Accountancy*, (Butterworths, 3rd Ed., 1995).

Principal Areas of Litigation Support Work are:

Loss of profits claims: an independent assessment of future profits.

Breach of contract and warranty: opinions on accounting issues and the value of items in dispute.

Professional negligence: advice and assessment of alleged negligence by other firms of accountants. Reports on quantum in cases involving negligence by members of other professions.

Construction disputes: assessment of quantum in claims arising from variations caused by delays or changing circumstances, quantum and assessment of claims provided.

Business interruption: assist insurers in achieving a fair settlement of insurance claims.

Divorce: a clear comprehensive statement of financial resources.

Intellectual property: help in valuing intellectual property rights and quantum of loss upon their infringement.

Personal injury: assessment of financial loss arising from personal injury.

Other Areas of work include: security for costs, re-insurance disputes, business valuations, wrongful dismissal and settlement negotiations. Specialists on business valuations work closely with the litigation support group.

NATIONAL FRAUD & INVESTIGATIONS GROUP: Coopers & Lybrand has a team of full-time investigation specialists, drawn from a variety of backgrounds, which is well placed to provide independent, professional and objective help and advice on all aspects of suspected fraud. Fraud investigation services include:
- Helping clients under investigation and their advisers.
- Negotiating with the authorities.

The international network of Coopers & Lybrand is used whenever necessary.

TAX INVESTIGATIONS: The firm assists on direct tax and VAT inquiries where there is a risk of penalties being imposed and, in exceptional cases criminal prosecution. Principal areas of direct tax investigations work are:
- Cases brought by the Inland Revenue's Special Compliance Office.
- PAYE Audit and Benefits Compliance.
- Audits conducted by the Revenue's Claims Branch.

On the indirect taxes side the focus is mainly on those cases where Customs/ VAT authorities in the UK and abroad are alleging fraud.

NATIONAL & INTERNATIONAL CONTACTS: Coopers & Lybrand has offices in 36 towns and cities in the United Kingdom. The firm is one of the world's leading professional services organisations. Through its member firms it deploys over 66,000 people, providing accounting and auditing, tax and consulting services on a globally integrated basis in 125 countries. Initial contact should either be with the firm's local office or one of the identified contact partners.

Contacts outside London:
Tony Parton (Birmingham - Tel:(0121) 200 4000).
Jeff Hunt (Manchester - Tel:(0161) 236 9191).
Nic Gower (Leeds - Tel:(0113) 231 4541).

DANIEL DJANOGLY & CO

ST ALPHAGE HOUSE, 2 FORE ST, LONDON, EC2Y 5DH

TEL: (0171) 256 7930
FAX: (0171) 638 2159

THE FIRM: A specialist practice dedicated to forensic accounting and litigation support, including negotiated settlements. The firm is mainly involved in the assessment of claims for loss of profits or loss of earnings. Principal areas of work include: business interruption, commercial disputes, personal injury and medical negligence. The firm is experienced in both plaintiff and defendant work. It regularly undertakes legal aid cases. It also serves the insurance industry and has particular experience in settling claims for loss of profits under business interruption insurance. **Law Society listed**.

CONTACT PARTNER: Daniel Djanogly

Number of Partners: 1

DOWNHAM TRAIN EPSTEIN

HOLLIS MOUNT, HOLLINS LANE, UNSWORTH, BURY, LANCS, BL9 8AT

TEL: (0161) 953 9510
FAX: (0161) 766 3685

Downham Train Epstein operates from a single site, north of Manchester and provides a comprehensive range of accountancy and related services. The firm's Forensic Accounting department has expanded rapidly in recent years and provides a broad range of services to the legal profession. Initial consultations will be provided free of charge and legally aided work is undertaken.

PRINCIPAL AREAS OF WORK: The firm acts for plaintiffs and defendants and is able to assist solicitors and their clients (insurance companies, commercial clients, local authorities or individuals) with the following:
- personal injury, medical negligence and fatal accident claims
- structured settlements
- consequential loss and business interruption claims
- commercial and contractual disputes
- matrimonial disputes
- Criminal Injuries Compensation Board claims
- fraud and financial irregularities
- business valuation disputes
- unfair/ wrongful dismissal claims
- negligence and professional indemnity claims
- expert advice and independent arbitration.

LITIGATION SUPPORT PARTNERS:

Doug Roberts BA, ACA – Heads up the Forensic Accounting department and specialises in medical negligence and personal injury work. He has lectured extensively on these subjects.

Nick Fail BA, ACA – Specialises in medical negligence and personal injury work, but is also regularly involved in consequential loss and commercial disputes.

CONTACT PARTNERS:
Doug Roberts, Nick Fail

Number of Partners: 10
Total Staff: 120

ERNST & YOUNG

BECKET HOUSE, 1 LAMBETH PALACE RD, LONDON, SE1 7EU
DX: 241

TEL: (0171) 928 2000
FAX: (0171) 928 1345

CONTACT PARTNER: Robert Hughes

ƎƖ ERNST & YOUNG

Ernst & Young's litigation support department comprises a core team of dedicated professionals with specialist training in report writing and the litigation process. On each assignment this team will be headed up by the partner within the firm whose practical experience and particular area of expertise is most relevant to the issues involved in the litigation or arbitration. In offering this service, Ernst & Young is able to draw upon its extensive resources to provide experts on all accounting-related matters from technical accounting issues to business valuations and covering all industry sectors. The firm has also shown itself to be firmly committed to training its partners in giving evidence in Court by staging "mock trials".

THE FIRM: Ernst & Young is a leading international firm of business and financial advisers, with offices throughout the country. Clients include organisations of all types and sizes, from blue-chip multinationals to governments, and from major financial institutions to private individuals.

LITIGATION SUPPORT PARTNERS: There are many partners within the firm who have acted as expert witnesses in litigation. In particular:

Robert Hughes FCA, Ernst & Young's National Head of Litigation Support, has acted as expert witness on a wide variety of litigation assignments involving acquisitions, anti-competitive practices and accountancy negligence. He also has considerable experience of giving evidence in Court.

Nigel Macdonald CA who served as President of the Institute of Chartered Accountants in Scotland in 1993/94 and is one of the firm's most experienced expert witnesses. His past assignments have included advising the United States Government and the Solicitor General of Jamaica and working with economists and other experts in international disputes.

John Allday FCA is a specialist in business and share valuations who has acted as expert witness for many leading industrial and financial companies in the United Kingdom and overseas, including giving evidence on several occasions at The International Court in the Hague. He has also carried out several determinations adjudicating as independent expert.

PRINCIPAL AREAS OF WORK: Assignments handled vary enormously and include the following: contractual disputes, claims following takeovers, audit negligence, computer-related disputes, construction and project abandonment claims, business valuation, fraud investigations, business interruption, monopoly enquiries, economic appraisals and share evaluation disputes.

An assignment team (combining technical skills, knowledge of the appropriate industry sector and litigation experience) is selected for each case. This team will include a project manager who acts as an 'intelligent layman' and ensures that all reports are intelligible to the non-specialist.

OTHER OFFICES: Ernst & Young has offices in most major towns and cities throughout the United Kingdom and each office has a designated partner with specific responsibility for Litigation Support as listed below:
Aberdeen (01224 640033) Alec Carstairs; *Belfast* (01232 246525) Graham Galbraith; *Birmingham* (0121 626 6262) Bob Ellison; *Bristol* (0117 929 0808) John Dornton; *Cambridge/ Peterborough* (01223 461200) Ian Maddison; *Cardiff* (01222 645444) Richard Coppock; *Dundee* (01382 313131) Graham Scott; *Edinburgh* (0131 226 6400) Richard Sweetman; *Exeter* (01392 433541) Jonathan Johns; *Glasgow* (0141 552 3456) Graeme Hogg; *Hull* (01482 325531) John Groves; *Inverness* (01463 237581) Peter Mearns; *Ipswich* (01473 217491) John Mullett; *Leeds* (0113 243 1221) David Buckley; *Leicester* (0116 254 9818) Michael Jones; *Liverpool* (0151 236 8214) David Weir; *Luton* (01582 400700) Simon Perry; *Manchester* (0161 953 9000) Richard Dyson; *Newcastle upon Tyne* (0191) 261 1063 Nigel Towers; *Norwich* (01603 660482) Philip Blanchflower; *Nottingham* (0115 958 8000) Graham Morgan; *Reading* (01734 500611) Clive Ward; *Sheffield* (0114 275 2929) John Kirkham; *Southampton* (01703 494100) Mike Stone; *Swindon* (01793 618822) Barbara Hadfield.

GRANT THORNTON

GRANT THORNTON HOUSE, MELTON STREET, EUSTON SQUARE,
LONDON, NW1 2EP   DX: 2100 Euston

TEL: (0171) 383 5100
FAX: (0171) 383 4715

CONTACT PARTNER: Philip Kabraji

Number of Partners:	211
Total Staff:	1758

THE FIRM: Grant Thornton is a leading national and international accounting and consultancy firm providing a comprehensive range of business advisory services to a wide variety of clients – from private individuals to major companies. The firm operates from over 45 offices in the UK and has an international network spanning some 80 countries.

A team of specialist forensic partners and staff offer extensive experience of commercial litigation, complex insurance claims, fraud and personal injury. Investigative financial, accounting and taxation services are provided to assist in the building of a case, obtaining settlement or the giving of expert evidence in Court.

Forensic services are available from most of the firm's UK offices. The main forensic centres however are in the London office (Partner in charge: Philip Kabraji) and the Leeds office (Partner in charge: Robin Hall).

PRINCIPAL AREAS OF EXPERTISE: The partners in the firm have experience in a wide number of business sectors, including construction, manufacturing, motor dealers, engineering, banking, financial, oil and gas, hotel and leisure, defence and professional services.

Partners with appropriate expertise and witness box experience are available to act in contractual and commercial disputes, consequential loss of profit claims, breach of warranty, business and share valuations, fraud, computer disputes, professional negligence claims, trade disputes (including advice on EC and US anti-dumping regulations), directors' disqualification hearings, personal injury, medical negligence and fatal accident claims, royalty disputes, matrimonial disputes and libel claims.

HAINES WATTS

STERLING HOUSE, 133 BARKEREND ROAD, BRADFORD, WEST YORKS, BD3 9AU

TEL: (01274) 393666
FAX: (01274) 307364

4-8 TABERNACLE STREET, LONDON, EC2A 4LU
DX 46642 (Barbican)

TEL: (0171) 628 1400
FAX: (0171) 628 1404

CONTACT PARTNERS:
Robert Barraclough FCA MBAE,
Donald Beskine ACA AHKSA MBAE

THE FIRM: Haines Watts is a top twenty UK accounting practice offering a comprehensive range of forensic and investigative accounting and litigation support services and have been instructed by more than one hundred firms of Solicitors and regulatory bodies. The service is led by Robert Barraclough, based in the North of England, and Donald Beskine in London. Robert is a Council Member of the Academy of Experts and has extensive forensic accounting experience in a wide variety of contentious situations. Donald has substantial experience in financial services and of the highly complex series of transactions that arise in cases of alleged fraud and other corporate impropriety. As well as being a UK Chartered Accountant he is also qualified in Hong Kong, and a member of the Academy of Experts. He had five years experience with IMRO and SIB where he led many complex regulatory investigations and disciplinary cases on matters including 'Maxwell' and related misconduct in regulated firms, including invesco MIM.

PRINCIPAL AREAS OF WORK: Haines Watts have experience in a wide range of areas and provide special reports and investigations for both plaintiff and defendant, as well as appearing as expert witness in Court and regulatory proceedings including:
- Business Interruption, Consequential Loss, and Breach of Warranty Claims;
- Fraud and white collar crime allegations
- Disputes over Pension Schemes and Management of Assets
- Personal Injury, Fatal Accident and Medical Negligence Claims

- Professional Negligence Claims
- Business Valuations
- Asset tracing and recovery
- Regulatory Disputes
- Financial Services
- Employment Claims
- Matrimonial Disputes

KIDSONS IMPEY

SPECTRUM HOUSE, 20-26 CURSITOR STREET, LONDON, EC4A 1HY	TEL: (0171) 405 2088
DX: 458 London	FAX: (0171) 334 4734
London and the South: Richard Freeman, Spectrum House, 20-26 Cursitor Street, London EC4A 1HY	Tel: (0171) 405 2088
The Midlands: Adrian Pym, Bank House, 8 Cherry Street, Birmingham B2 5AD	Tel: (0121) 631 2631
The North: Mark Blakemore, Devonshire House, 36 George Street, Manchester M1 4HA	Tel: (0161) 236 7733
Tim Sture, Barclays House, 41 Park Cross Street, Leeds LS1 2QH	Tel: (0113) 2422 868
East Anglia: Nigel Pratt, Friars Courtyard, 30 Princes Street, Ipswich, Suffolk IP1 1RJ	Tel: (01473) 216154
South West: John Kershaw, 3 Beaufort Buildings, Spa Road, Gloucester GL1 1XB	Tel: (01452) 527000

Kidsons Impey is a leading UK firm of Chartered Accountants and business advisors with offices throughout the country. The firm provides advice on all litigation support matters to companies, partnerships, sole traders, trustees, private individuals, regulatory bodies and Police Authorities and acts for both plaintiffs and defendants.

In selecting a team of forensic specialists for each assignment, Kidsons Impey draws upon the wealth of technical expertise, business and court experience within the firm. Through membership of HLB International the firm can enlist the skills of experts in over 240 offices in some 90 countries worldwide.

The firm provides expert witness reports, which are clear, concise and written in plain English, avoiding jargon and technical accounting terms as far as possible. The firm's service is highly responsive; it never loses sight of the fact that it forms only one part of a team of experts working on any case.

PRINCIPAL AREAS OF FORENSIC ACCOUNTING WORK:

Financial Inquiry Services: Fraud and corruption investigations; Establishing benefit of crime for the Criminal Courts; Evaluating loss to the victims of crime; Compensation claims for the Criminal Courts; Confiscation issues (DTOA and CJA); Acting as receivers for the Court in confiscation and litigation matters; Restraint order actions; Means enquiries conducted by Civil and Criminal Courts; Investigating money laundering; Tracing assets; Regulatory investigations conducted under the FSA; Companies Act and Charities Act.

Business Claims: Loss of profits; Commercial disputes; Civil fraud; Breach of contract; Computer related disputes; Fidelity: Intellectual property; Business interruption; Business valuations.

Personal Claims: Personal injury and fatal accident litigation; Matrimonial disputes; Compensation for loss of office; Libel.

OTHER FORENSIC ACCOUNTING MATTERS: Professional negligence; Insurance and reinsurance disputes; Arbitration and expert adjudication; Security for costs.

KPMG FORENSIC ACCOUNTING

8 SALISBURY SQUARE, LONDON, EC4Y 8BB
DX: 38050

TEL: (0171) 311 1000
FAX: (0171) 311 8880

PRINCIPAL SERVICES: KPMG's forensic accounting department has grown considerably in recent years and now has a team of more than 80 partners and professional staff throughout the UK.

EXPERT WITNESS: The firm provides specialist services in four broad areas:
- quantum of damages
- expert opinions on accounting, auditing and business matters
- valuations of businesses or assets in the context of disputes
- regulatory, statutory and disciplinary enquiries
- acting as experts, mediators or arbitrators to resolve disputes.

The provision of these services is enhanced by expert knowledge of various industry sectors including: banking, insurance, commodities, information technology, shipping, construction, leasing, retailing, healthcare and pharmaceutical, and intellectual property.

FRAUD INVESTIGATION: KPMG has developed particular expertise in handling investigations into fraud. Numerous assignments for government, police and public bodies bear witness to the firm's reputation in this area. One partner has published two keynote books on fraud prevention and detection. Another former partner is head of the Special Investigations Unit at the Bank of England.

THE FIRM: KPMG is one of the leading professional firms in the world and provides a comprehensive range of accountancy and consulting services. The firm has experience of working with organisations of all sizes: from governments to individuals, and from multinationals to privately-owned businesses. KPMG has over 72,000 personnel in 136 countries worldwide.

CONTACT PARTNER: John Ellison

OTHER FORENSIC ACCOUNTING CENTRES:

Birmingham:	Contact: Ian Starkey	Tel: (0121) 232 3000
Bristol:	Contact: Simon Pomeroy	Tel: (0117) 946400
Glasgow:	Contact: Robin Crawford	Tel: (0141) 226 5511
Leeds/Bradford:	Contact: Tim Taylor	Tel: (0113) 231 3000
Manchester:	Contact: Barry Drew	Tel: (0161) 838 4000
Nottingham:	Contact: Colin Morrell	Tel: (0115) 948 3444
Reading:	Contact: Alistair Hunter	Tel: (01734) 642000

LEIGH CARR

27 BLANDFORD STREET, LONDON, W1H 4EN

TEL: (0171) 935 7755
FAX: (0171) 935 9172

PRINCIPAL SERVICES: Personal injury and fatal accident claims • loss of profits and consequential loss • business and share valuations • professional negligence • matrimonial disputes • fraud and criminal cases • commercial disagreements • structured settlements. Legal aid work is undertaken.

THE FIRM: Leigh Carr, Chartered Accountants, is a medium-sized firm providing a comprehensive forensic accountancy service and is part of The Channel International Association with member firms world-wide.

CONTACT PARTNER: Laurence Sacker

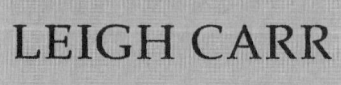

CHARTERED ACCOUNTANTS

LITTLEJOHN FRAZER

1 PARK PLACE, CANARY WHARF, LONDON, E14 4HJ
DX: 42660 Isle of Dogs

TEL: (0171) 987 5030
FAX: (0171) 987 9707

CONTACT PARTNER: Ian Hobbs

Number of Partners: 24
Total Staff: 195

Littlejohn Frazer's litigation support department was founded in 1986, chiefly to provide expert opinion on liability and quantum in cases of professional negligence involving other firms of accountants but the department's work now includes most areas of litigation support. The department is led by partners who co-ordinate the provision of services from other specialist departments within the firm, to ensure that appropriate technical expertise complements the firm's extensive experience of the litigation process which includes considerable trial experience.

The lead partner is a member of the British Academy of Experts and is the author of *The Role of the Expert Witness*, a guide for accountants published by the Institute of Chartered Accountants. The firm has broad experience of the insurance sector and in particular the Lloyd's market. Partners have experience of investigations for the DTI, and the firm has undertaken a number of assignments for the Serious Fraud Office. Legally aided work is undertaken, in both civil and criminal matters.

PRINCIPAL AREAS OF WORK:

CIVIL:
- accountants professional negligence
- financial consequences of:
  - personal injury
  - consequential loss, especially construction and fire-damage claims
  - divorce
  - insurance and re-insurance disputes
  - purchase and sales disputes

CRIMINAL:
- Serious fraud
- Companies Act offences

INVESTIGATIONS:
- computer consultancy
- breaches of Solicitors and RICS Accounts Rules
- for Self Regulatory Organisations (ICA, IBRC)
- DTI
- Serious Fraud Office
- Insurance (particularly Lloyd's)

LITIGATION SUPPORT PARTNERS:

I.C. Hobbs FCA: Member of British Academy of Experts. Specialises in accountants' negligence, quantification of loss, share valuations, tax as a non-specialist, serious fraud, personal injury. (Direct line:0171 369 4564)

A.H.F. Campbell FCA: Serious fraud, regulatory authority investigations, accountants' negligence, breach of financial warranties. (Direct line:0171 369 4565)

J.G. Ambler ACA: Computer consultancy, software contracts. (Direct line:0171 369 4589)

R.L. Green FCCA: Solicitors' Accounts Rules. (Direct line:0171 369 4587)

D.R.M. Frame FCA: Serious fraud. (Direct line:0171 369 4507)

M.T. Stenson ACA: Serious fraud, regulatory authority investigations. (Direct line:0171 369 4575)

PETER LOBBENBERG & CO

74 CHANCERY LANE, LONDON, WC2A 1AA
DX: 204 London/Chancery Lane

TEL: (0171) 430 9300
FAX: (0171) 430 9315

THE FIRM: A niche practice well-known for its expertise in litigation support (particularly matrimonial work, in which it is one of the market leaders) and share valuations, coupled with an efficient and caring tax/ financial advice service for private clients and trusts. As a member of Clark Whitehill Associates the firm has access to a wide range of facilities and specialisms.

LANGUAGES SPOKEN: German and French.

Mr Lobbenberg is a Fellow of the British Academy of Experts.

CONTACT PARTNER: Peter Lobbenberg

Number of Partners:	1
Total Staff:	2

MACNAIR MASON

ST CLARE HOUSE, 30-33 MINORIES, LONDON, EC3N 1DU

TEL: (0171) 481 3022
FAX: (0171) 488 4458

THE FIRM: Macnair Mason has practised in the heart of the City for almost 100 years. A dedicated forensic accounting team provides expert advice in support of the legal argument to produce cost effective resolution of disputes and litigation over the following key areas of dispute:

- loss of profits or earnings
- property and construction
- share and business valuations
- fidelity policies
- family and matrimonial
- intellectual property
- breach of contract and warranty
- insurance, banking and financial services
- computer system and installation
- professional negligence and liability claims
- personal injury and fatality claims
- fraud and other financial irregularities.

CONTACT PARTNERS: Stuart Markley, David Manning

Number of Partners: 11

MACNAIR MASON
CHARTERED ACCOUNTANTS

MOORES ROWLAND

CLIFFORD'S INN, FETTER LANE, LONDON, EC4A 1AS
DX: 283 London/ Chancery Lane

TEL: (0171) 831 2345
FAX: (0171) 831 6123

Moores Rowland has assisted lawyers in many cases, from complex share valuations and tax disputes to negligence claims and matrimonial disputes. The Litigation Support Service provides direct access to specialist partners, each one of whom can call upon a team of experienced professionals when further support is required.

CONTACT PARTNER: Nigel O'Neill

Number of Partners:	96
Total Staff:	560

Moores Rowland
Chartered Accountants

SERVICES:

Valuation of Shares and Businesses: Extensive valuation experience in cases ranging from family disputes and divorce cases to employees' share schemes problems and negotiations with tax authorities, and including intellectual property valuations.

Damages & Negligence Claims: Applies financial and accounting skills to prepare and support claims. Assists lawyers, insurance companies and other bodies in negotiations for settlements as well as providing expert witnesses.

Financial Services Act/ Regulatory Authorities Investigations: A considerable expertise has been established following the conduct of a number of such investigations on behalf of SRO's and others.

Fraud Investigations: The team has, to date, undertaken six major investigations for the DTI. It has worked with the Serious Fraud Office and the fraud squads of a number of police authorities. Experience of investigating financial records, computer systems and controls.

Matrimonial Disputes: Regularly helps spouses in financial settlement of divorce claims. Experience of investigating allegations of hidden assets and income.

Partnership Disputes: Helps to resolve taxation disputes, calculate equitable adjustments, prepare remuneration packages for partners leaving.

Employment Matters: Advises on financial and tax implications of termination packages; wide practical knowledge of manufacturing, public sector, retail and leisure, higher education and service industries.

Other Areas: Trust litigation; royalty disputes; patent, copyright and trademark infringement disputes; charter party disputes.

MOORE STEPHENS

ST PAUL'S HOUSE, WARWICK LANE, LONDON, EC4P 4BN

TEL: (0171) 334 9191
FAX: (0171) 248 3408

CONTACT PARTNER:
Civil – Julian Wilkinson,
Criminal – Gervase Hulbert

Number of Partners:	117
Total Staff:	660

Moore Stephens has many years experience of assisting the legal profession in litigation matters. The Litigation Support Team has worked on cases ranging from personal injury claims to fraud investigations for the Department of Trade and Industry. The firm's pre-eminence in marine accountancy means that it is often called upon to provide expert assistance in shipping and transport litigation.

LITIGATION SUPPORT PARTNERS: Mr Gervase Hulbert OBE FCA – Chairman of the International firm of Moore Stephens. Experienced in criminal investigations and forensic accounting covering the various types of fraud, misappropriation, misrepresentation, and other illegal or potentially illegal activities involving money. Has undertaken many international assignments. Awarded the OBE in 1993 for services to the accountancy profession.

Mr Paul Powell FCA – Member of the British Academy of Experts. Over ten years' experience as expert witness for Arbitration and High Court proceedings covering shipping and international transportation matters, consequential loss and professional negligence. Appointed by the DTI as an inspector in a major company investigation.

Mr Julian Wilkinson FCA – Chairman of the Moore Stephens' National Litigation Support Group. Many years' experience as expert witness for Arbitration and High Court proceedings with particular experience of shipping related matters including alleged scuttling claims and joint venture disputes. Also experienced in loss of profits claims.

Mr Andrew Nicholl FCA – Partner since 1985 and member of Moore Stephens technical committees both nationally and internationally. Has experience of interpretation of the application of accounting and auditing standards, including assessment of professional work by accountants. Has acted as expert accountant in a major case involving allegations of false accounting and various commercial matters. Has given evidence in Court.

The Litigation Support team assists in establishing facts, presenting opinions and conclusions, assessing the quantum of claims, and interpreting professional standards. A lead partner from the team co-ordinates the various specialists who may be required to give opinions in arbitrations, court actions and commercial disputes.

PRINCIPAL AREAS OF WORK:

Loss of Profits: Business interruption; product inadequacy; infringement of intellectual property rights; breach of contract or warranties; fraud, defalcation or misappropriation; personal injury or fatal accident.

Valuations: Businesses and business assets for settlement of commercial disputes; in separation or divorce cases.

Professional Negligence: Property and information technology matters; due diligence work in business acquisitions and disputes; taxation advice; insolvency; audit and accountancy.

International Trade Claims: Particularly shipping and transport matters.

OTHER OFFICES:

Bath:	(*Tel:* (01225) 424281)
Birmingham:	(*Tel:* (0121) 200 3077)
Dudley:	(*Tel:* (01384) 239996)
Edinburgh:	(*Tel:* (0131) 225 3820)
Enfield:	(*Tel:* (0181) 366 4331)
Glasgow:	(*Tel:* (0141) 332 8291)
Guildford:	(*Tel:* (01483) 38881)
Liverpool:	(*Tel:* (0151) 236 9044)
Salisbury:	(*Tel:* (01722) 335182)
Scarborough:	(*Tel:* (01723) 360361)
Shrewsbury:	(*Tel:* (01743) 235276)

NEVILLE RUSSELL

246 BISHOPSGATE, LONDON, EC2M 4PB

TEL: (0171) 377 1000
FAX: (0171) 377 8931

Neville Russell's national litigation support and forensic accounting team are regularly appointed by lawyers, commercial organisations, prosecuting authorities and regulators to investigate and advise on situations requiring independent and objective analysis and opinion from skilled and professional advisors.

The firm's technical expertise, familiarity with the litigation process, and wealth of experience in many financial and commercial sectors, combined with its ability to present financial information in an intelligible and imaginative way enables it to provide the legal profession with an extensive range of support services.

SPECIALISMS INCLUDE:
- Expert witness
- Contractual disputes
- Damage and loss quantification
- Fraud investigation
- Personal injury
- Arbitration

THE FIRM: As a leading national firm of Chartered Accountants, Neville Russell has 18 offices throughout the UK. The firm is a member of Nexia International, one of the best established worldwide networks of independent accounting firms.

CONTACT PARTNERS:: Peter Hyatt, Glyn Williams, Raymond Turner

Total Staff: 780

NEVILLE RUSSELL
Chartered Accountants

PANNELL KERR FORSTER

NEW GARDEN HOUSE, 78 HATTON GARDEN, LONDON, EC1N 8JA
DX: 479 Ch.Ln.

TEL: (0171) 831 7393
FAX: (0171) 405 6736

Pannell Kerr Forster's investigative accounting skills are regularly drawn upon by the legal profession. A highly skilled team acts for plaintiff and defendants, assisting solicitors or counsel in cases ranging in size from small disputes to highly complex actions. Multi-disciplinary teams of experts can be assembled from within the firm to handle the largest corporate actions. An impressive track record includes cases involving professional negligence, breach of contract, corporate disputes and insurance claims. The firm also assists in personal injury, fatal accident, fraud and divorce actions.

CONTACT PARTNER: William Moberly

PETERSON CONSULTING (UK)

29 WILSON ST, LONDON, EC2M 2SJ

TEL: (0171) 628 6666
FAX: (0171) 638 3203

International in scope, yet individual in approach, Peterson Consulting is unique in the range and depth of the expert services it provides. The firm specialises in providing independent expert analysis and opinion in relation to commercial disputes and litigation across many professional disciplines. With around 450 consultants in cities throughout the USA and in the UK, Peterson Consulting displays a strong commitment to provide superior financial and technical analysis. Teams of financial analysts, accountants, MBAs, claims professionals, architects, quantity surveyors, engineers and information systems professionals provide comprehensive fact-finding and expert economic analysis.

LITIGATION SUPPORT AND FORENSIC ACCOUNTING: *Services include:*
- contractual and tortious losses
- loss of profits
- business interruptions
- reinstatement claims
- business and share valuation

CONTACT PARTNER: Keith Pickavance

Total Staff: 450

- corporate finance
- intellectual property
- construction claims
- breach of warranties
- professional negligence
- fraud and financial irregularities
- matrimonial
- security for costs applications
- personal injury
- employment
- general financial investigations.

OTHER SERVICES: Peterson Consulting is also a leading provider of services in the fields of insurance/ reinsurance, insolvency, environment, information, construction and management consultancy.

TECHNOLOGY The firm is a leader in providing computerised litigation support technology. Capabilities include critical path analysis, database design and implementation, spreadsheet analysis and graphic representations.

PRICE WATERHOUSE

NO.1 LONDON BRIDGE, LONDON, SE1 9QL
DX: 38800 (London)

TEL: (0171) 939 3000
FAX: (0171) 939 5550

Price Waterhouse Forensic Services is a team of dedicated professionals and experts with considerable experience in litigation, arbitration and fraud investigation. The department is able to draw on the resources of the worldwide organisation with more than 450 offices in over 110 countries and is the focal point of the firm's European Forensic Services network.

CONTACT PARTNER: Mr David Bridger

| Number of Partners: | 480 |
| Total Staff: | 5250 |

REEVES & NEYLAN

CECIL SQUARE HOUSE, CECIL SQUARE, MARGATE, KENT, CT9 1BQ
DX: 30561 Margate

TEL: (01843) 227937
FAX: (01843) 226326

Reeves & Neylan's forensic accounting specialists offer a prompt, personal and highly professional service. The firm directs considerable resources to training and attending national seminars and conferences to ensure that it is constantly at the forefront of current developments. The focus is on providing the best, most cost-effective solutions to the problems faced by its clients.

CONTACT PARTNER: Alan Tinham

| Number of Partners: | 27 |
| Total Staff: | 200 |

LITIGATION SUPPORT & FORENSIC ACCOUNTING: *Services include:*

- personal injury, medical negligence and fatality claims
- business and share valuations
- divorce
- accountants' professional negligence
- fraud and financial irregularities
- commercial disputes
- security for costs.

OTHER SERVICES: Reeves & Neylan also provides specialist services to the legal profession in the following areas: estate planning, trusts and executorships; VAT consultancy; Solicitors' Accounts Rules audits; tax planning and consultancy; design and implementation of practice management information systems; practice finance arrangements; investigations.

SAGARS CHARTERED ACCOUNTANTS

ELIZABETH HOUSE, QUEEN STREET, LEEDS, WEST YORKS, LS1 2TW

TEL: (0113) 243 5402
FAX: (0113) 242 4326

Sagars Chartered Accountants, a leading independent firm based in Leeds, has extensive experience of providing litigation support. The firm acts for a large number of solicitors specialising in personal injury litigation, medical negligence, matrimonial disputes, loss of profits, claims and business valuations.

OTHER OFFICES: Kendal: Contact Geoff Sykes. Tel: (01539) 725032.

CONTACT PARTNER: Michael Turner

Number of Partners: 7
Total Staff: 80

SIM KAPILA

15 BERNERS STREET, LONDON, W1P 3DE

TEL: (0171) 636 7699
FAX: (0171) 636 7717

THE FIRM: Sim Kapila is a 'niche' practice which specialises in providing forensic accountancy services. The firm brings together several years' experience with major firms including the provision of expert evidence in court. It is committed to the development of forensic accountancy: aspects of this commitment include membership of the Academy of Experts, contributions to various legal journals and giving courses to solicitors.

SERVICES: Areas covered include disputes and claims involving personal injury and fatal accidents, loss of profits, business valuations, divorce cases, professional negligence, fraud and contractual disagreements.

The firm is happy to give an initial view without obligation on the financial and business aspects of any case.

CONTACT PARTNERS:
Rakesh Kapila or George Sim

Number of Partners: 2

SIMMONS COHEN FINE

27 JOHN STREET, LONDON, WC1N 2BL

TEL: (0171) 404 5891
FAX: (0171) 242 7640

Simmons Cohen Fine, with over 20 years experience in Forensic Accounting, are able to provide a comprehensive, commercial and pragmatic litigation support service to the legal profession.

The firm acts for both plaintiffs and defendants and deals with all types of litigation support work offering expert opinion and advice on claims relating to: commercial disputes, business and share valuations, personal accident and injury claims, matrimonial disputes, professional negligence, loss of profits.

CONTACT PARTNERS:
Anthony Simmonds, Thomas A. Lane

Number of Partners: 9

SINCLAIR SILVERMAN

ROMAN HOUSE, 296 GOLDERS GREEN ROAD, LONDON, NW11 9PT

TEL: (0181) 455 0011
FAX: (0181) 455 1199

THE FIRM: Sinclair Silverman has been actively involved in providing litigation support services to the legal profession since 1978. In order to ensure quality of evidence, the work is undertaken personally by the litigation support partner.

PRINCIPAL AREAS OF WORK: *Work includes:* acting as expert witness, investigations, valuations and other reports, particularly in respect of matrimonial proceedings; advising on commercial disputes, loss of profit claims, share and business valuations and partnership and shareholder disputes.

CONTACT PARTNER: David G Sinclair

Number of Partners: 2

LITIGATION SUPPORT PARTNER: David Sinclair, qualified in 1972 after receiving the Deloitte Plender Prize in Advanced Accounting; FCA 1979. Career spans experience in financial and business consultancy fields, property related activities, investment management, and development of special insurance products for niche markets. He was a founder member of a specialist panel of accountants assisting the City Fraud Squad and is a Licensed Insolvency Practitioner.

SMITH & WILLIAMSON

NO. 1 RIDING HOUSE ST, LONDON, W1A 3AS	TEL: (0171) 637 5377
DX: 53810 Oxford Circus N'th	FAX: (0171) 631 0741

LITIGATION SUPPORT SERVICE: Smith & Williamson has a dedicated litigation support team whose expertise covers the full range of forensic accounting, including assistance for regulatory bodies, civil litigation and investigations of fraud.

    The firm has experience in acting for either the plaintiff or the defendant and its objective is always to understand the wider implications of a case in order to provide a flexible and constructive approach to every assignment.

THE FIRM: Founded over 100 years ago, Smith & Williamson combines a firm of chartered accountants and an investment management house.

    Its full range of accountancy services covers accountancy, auditing, corporate finance, corporate recovery, corporate taxation, investigations, litigation support, management consulting and personal taxation.

CONTACTS: Peter J. Yeldon, Peter G. Mills, Iain J. Allan

Number of Partners:	77
Total Staff:	370

Smith & Williamson

OTHER OFFICES:
Guildford: *Contact* – Roger J. Haynes. *Tel:* (01483) 302200; *Fax:* (01483) 301232.
Salisbury: *Contact* – Allan F. Simmons. *Tel:* (01722) 411881; *Fax: (01722) 411438.*

TAX INVESTIGATION SERVICES

211 PICCADILLY, LONDON, W1V 9LD	TEL: (0171) 917 9941
	FAX: (0171) 439 0262

THE FIRM: Tax Investigation Services are an innovative niche firm, offering specialist advice to solicitors, Counsel and accountants on Customs & Excise investigations.

PRINCIPAL AREAS OF WORK:

Services include:
- advising on the VAT or Duty implications of a case.
- evaluation of schedules and calculations produced by Customs.
- providing expert witness evidence at trail.
- advice and assistance in negotiating compounded proceedings.

CONTACT PARTNER: Don Mavin

Number of Partners:	1

LITIGATION SUPPORT PARTNERS: Don Mavin AIIT, MBAE has spent several years in HM Customs & Excise, principally in the Investigation branch, dealing with all types of criminal offences involving Customs & Excise legislation with more recent experience as a VAT Specialist in one of the large accountancy firms. He is also a member of the Institute of Indirect Taxation and the British Academy of Experts.

OTHER OFFICES:
The firm has associated offices in Birmingham (0121) 356 2886 and Cardiff (01222) 761937.

TOUCHE ROSS & CO. FORENSIC SERVICES

STONECUTTER COURT, 1 STONECUTTER STREET, LONDON, EC4A 4TR
DX: 599

TEL: (0171) 936 3000
FAX: (0171) 936 2638

Touche Ross has a dedicated team of forensic specialists in offices throughout the country. The firm's forensic partners have significant experience as expert witnesses, both in the UK and in foreign courts. Where a case requires specific sector or industry expertise the firm is able to provide the appropriate expert, experienced in forensic matters.

The firm is accustomed to working to the requirements and timetable of the legal profession. The team includes computer specialists and experts in the presentation of complicated technical evidence in a legal format. The firm is able to provide appropriate support services to every stage of a dispute, both nationally and internationally. It is commercially minded and respects the demands of its clients, and we will always provide straight answers to solve problems.

There is an increasing incidence of international and cross border litigation. The firm has recent experience of conducting assignments overseas and regularly works with other Deloitte Touche Tohmatsu International offices around the world.

BUSINESS CLAIMS: The firm has considerable experience in general commercial disputes including claims for business interruption and loss of profits, product liability, breach of contract, fidelity and warranty and also valuations arising from disputes, arbitrations and reference to expert assessors. As one of the leading firms providing services to the public sector, Touche Ross has also assisted local authorities and government bodies in a wide range of such disputes.

PERSONAL CLAIMS: The firm has a significant reputation in personal injury, fatal accident medical negligence claims, and in the area of structured settlements. It also provides quantum reports in matrimonial disputes and libel actions.

PROFESSIONAL NEGLIGENCE: The firm provides expert opinion on negligence claims involving accountancy firms as well as quantum reports in claims against other professionals.

INSURANCE CLAIMS: The firm provides expert accountancy services to insurance companies, loss adjusters and commercial clients and has a significant record in acting for Lloyd's Syndicates involved in disputes. It is increasing its resources and expertise in the area in order to cut costs for insurance companies. It provides expert investigative and tracing services for insurers both in the UK and around the world.

FRAUD AND CRIMINAL WORK: Specialist services are provided in several offices. In London, the Commercial Investigations Group provides asset tracing services, fraud investigations and advice on controls to minimise the risk of fraud or money laundering. Touche Ross has recent experience of working for the Serious Fraud Office and for police authorities around the country.

COMPUTERISED LITIGATION SYSTEMS: The firm's involvement in several major liquidations has led it to develop a computerised database document management and retrieval system. It provides a document management service whenever a dispute is complicated and involves many documents.

CONTACT PARTNERS: Fergus Falk, Alan Bray, Mike Barford, Will Inglis

Number of Partners:	396
Total Staff:	6411

Touche Ross

FORENSIC ACCOUNTANCY CONTACTS IN THE UK:

Belfast:	Derek Irwin.	*Tel:* (01232) 322861.
Birmingham:	Richard Edwards.	*Tel:* (0121) 200 2211.
Bournemouth:	Mark Wallis.	*Tel:* (01202) 291655.
Bracknell:	Ken Chalk.	*Tel:* (01344) 54445.
Bristol:	Robert Taylor.	*Tel:* (0117) 921 1622.
Cambridge:	Robin Bligh.	*Tel:* (01223) 460222.
Cardiff:	Robert Taylor.	*Tel:* (01222) 481111.
Crawley:	Jack Cole.	*Tel:* (01293) 510112.
Dartford:	Ross Bull.	*Tel:* (01322) 277777.
Glasgow:	David Young.	*Tel:* (0141) 204 2800.
Jersey:	Peter Beamish.	*Tel:* (01534) 37770.
Leeds:	Brian Boothroyd.	*Tel:* (0113) 243 9021.
Leicester:	Dick Peters.	*Tel:* (0116) 2543598.
Liverpool:	Peter Uglow.	*Tel:* (0151) 236 0941.
London:	Fergus Falk.	*Tel:* (0171) 936 3000.
Manchester:	Peter Uglow.	*Tel:* (0161) 228 3456.
Milton Keynes:	Simon Radford.	*Tel:* (01908) 666665.
Newcastle-Upon-Tyne:	Minnow Powell.	*Tel:* (0191) 261 4111.
Nottingham:	Peter Hipperson.	*Tel:* (0115) 950 0511.
Southampton:	Harold Wilks.	*Tel:* (01703) 334124.

LARGEST FIRMS BY REGION

LONDON: THE 200 LARGEST FIRMS

The rankings in this table are determined by the number of solicitors working in this region and do not take into account solicitors overseas. They are based on partner and assistant solicitor figures only: all other fee-earners are excluded.

		Ptnrs	Asst Solrs	'95	'94	'93	'92			Ptnrs	Asst Solrs	'95	'94	'93	'92
1	Clifford Chance	170	545	715	654	678	701	51	Manches & Co	32	34	66	49	54	42
2	Linklaters & Paines	132	353	485	458	439	435	52	Nicholson Graham & Jones	34	32	66	66	55	48
3	Allen & Overy	111	302	413	368	378	334	53	Farrer & Co	36	29	65	69	69	74
4	Freshfields	109	289	398	351	359	396	54	Berrymans	20	43	63	54	52	52
5	Lovell White Durrant	118	269	387	362	370	348	55	Charles Russell	35	27	62	64	56	56
6	Slaughter and May	86	267	353	350	382	380	56	Mishcon De Reya	30	28	58	52	55	51
7	Simmons & Simmons	115	206	321	276	276	267	57	Withers	31	27	58	50	54	51
8	Herbert Smith	104	192	296	254	266	261	58	Lewis Silkin	25	32	57	47	40	32
9	Norton Rose	83	192	275	344	359	328	59	Speechly Bircham	33	23	56	60	49	54
10	Nabarro Nathanson	103	159	262	195	199	230	60	Wedlake Bell	31	25	56	53	46	49
11	Ashurst Morris Crisp	65	158	223	202	174	166	61	Kennedys	22	30	52	55	46	45
12	Wilde Sapte	61	142	203	195	168	178	62	Biddle & Co	28	22	50	44	38	38
13	Cameron Markby Hewitt	70	126	196	189	218	215	63	Forsyte Saunders Kerman	31	17	48	32	34	36
14	Denton Hall	73	107	180	225	239	222	64	Fladgate Fielder	28	15	43	36	33	38
15	McKenna & Co	63	103	166	215	207	214	65	Harbottle & Lewis	14	29	43	37	30	31
16	Stephenson Harwood	67	96	163	149	152	148	66	Winckworth & Pemberton	20	23	43	41	36	32
17	Frere Cholmeley Bischoff	59	97	156	164	-	-	67	Hammond Suddards	16	26	42	38	23	-
18	Taylor Joynson Garrett	64	85	149	134	130	152	68	Olswang	20	21	41	38	25	23
19	Rowe & Maw	62	86	148	148	127	136	69	Penningtons	23	18	41	65	69	65
20	Berwin Leighton	57	83	140	130	124	131	70	Pannone Pritchard Englefield	27	13	40	33	-	-
21	Barlow Lyde & Gilbert	58	79	137	125	125	135	71	The Simkins Partnership	22	18	40	35	34	34
22	Richards Butler	52	73	125	155	159	165	72	Baileys Shaw & Gillett	23	16	39	32	34	41
23	Clyde & Co	58	65	123	124	130	108	73	Bircham & Co	21	18	39	36	37	41
24	Theodore Goddard	46	76	122	122	140	150	74	Boodle Hatfield	20	19	39	52	41	34
25	Baker & McKenzie	48	73	121	113	113	106	75	Vizards	20	19	39	40	29	29
26	Watson Farley & Williams	29	92	121	94	84	84	76	Brecher & Co	25	13	38	37	36	42
27	S J Berwin & Co	51	67	118	116	103	114	77	Waltons & Morse	20	18	38	40	43	42
28	Lawrence Graham	55	59	114	110	105	115	78	Edward Lewis	13	24	37	35	27	-
29	Davies Arnold Cooper	40	73	113	113	104	84	79	Howard Kennedy	23	14	37	29	22	20
30	Eversheds	47	65	112	103	104	126	80	Le Brasseur J Tickle	22	15	37	28	-	-
31	Macfarlanes	48	62	110	109	105	104	81	Finers	26	10	36	36	38	43
32	D J Freeman	48	61	109	109	109	102	82	Jeffrey Green Russell	20	16	36	30	24	27
33	Travers Smith Braithwaite	39	68	107	104	94	87	83	Russell Jones & Walker	17	19	36	31	29	24
34	Masons	38	67	105	105	106	89	84	Constant & Constant	27	8	35	34	34	28
35	Reynolds Porter Chamberlain	36	65	101	83	80	78	85	Elborne Mitchell	13	22	35	36	32	32
36	Gouldens	32	64	96	83	77	75	86	Pinsent Curtis	15	20	35	21	17	15
37	Holman, Fenwick & Willan	44	47	91	85	81	86	87	Kingsley Napley	23	11	34	30	33	31
38	Dibb Lupton Broomhead	37	49	86	77	63	38	88	Russell–Cooke, Potter & Chapman	19	15	34	32	28	31
39	Titmuss Sainer Dechert	43	42	85	89	91	91	89	Amhurst Brown Colombotti	20	12	32	30	30	27
40	Ince & Co	43	41	84	86	86	76	90	Oswald Hickson Collier	14	18	32	20	22	23
41	Sinclair Roche & Temperley	36	48	84	83	76	72	91	Prince Evans	10	22	32	30	23	16
42	Beachcroft Stanleys	36	46	82	84	85	81	92	Lee & Pembertons	18	13	31	29	25	25
43	Alsop Wilkinson	35	45	80	78	79	75	93	T.V. Edwards	8	23	31	30	28	24
44	Field Fisher Waterhouse	46	33	79	77	80	82	94	Allison & Humphreys	14	16	30	28	27	25
45	Paisner & Co	37	40	77	75	67	59	95	Fishburn Boxer	13	17	30	27	22	22
46	Bird & Bird	30	43	73	72	69	62	96	Hempsons	16	14	30	29	33	33
47	Hill Taylor Dickinson	25	48	73	79	67	59	97	Middleton Potts	18	12	30	28	25	26
48	Trowers & Hamlins	32	41	73	69	63	59	98	Harris Rosenblatt & Kramer	16	13	29	24	21	20
49	Radcliffes Crossman Block	39	31	70	53	55	61	99	Rosling King	9	20	29	26	20	21
50	Bristows Cooke & Carpmael	24	42	66	51	49	50	100	Warner Cranston	14	15	29	28	25	24

		Ptnrs	Asst Solrs	Total No. of Solicitors			
				'95	'94	'93	'92
101	Beaumont and Son	14	14	28	25	25	25
102	Walker Martineau	12	16	28	28	31	37
103	Capsticks	12	15	27	18	18	18
104	Edwin Coe	19	8	27	25	21	23
105	Garrett & Co	12	15	27	-	-	-
106	Park Nelson Thompson Quarrell	17	10	27	21	-	-
107	Collyer–Bristow	16	10	26	24	22	22
108	Campbell Hooper	18	7	25	27	24	27
109	Davenport Lyons	12	13	25	17	22	23
110	Fisher Meredith	6	19	25	19	15	15
111	Fox Williams	11	14	25	22	19	22
112	Hobson Audley	11	14	25	25	25	25
113	Lee Bolton & Lee	14	11	25	20	17	18
114	Payne Hicks Beach	16	9	25	27	32	39
115	Wansbroughs Willey Hargrave	7	18	25	20	18	-
116	Druces & Attlee	16	8	24	24	25	20
117	E. Edwards Son & Noice	9	15	24	15	15	14
118	Edge & Ellison	8	16	24	21	18	21
119	Goodman Derrick	13	11	24	25	25	28
120	Hamlin Slowe	19	5	24	23	24	24
121	Marriott Harrison	18	6	24	23	16	16
122	Bentleys, Stokes & Lowless	11	12	23	23	23	17
123	Dawson & Co	17	6	23	26	26	32
124	Morgan Bruce	11	12	23	-	-	-
125	Peter Carter-Ruck & Partners	17	6	23	23	15	13
126	Rooks Rider	10	13	23	22	21	21
127	Rabin Leacock Lipman	15	7	22	22	20	20
128	Rakisons	11	11	22	20	20	17
129	Rees & Freres	14	8	22	-	-	-
130	William Sturges & Co	13	9	22	22	24	25
131	Coudert Brothers	6	15	21	23	18	5
132	Elliott & Company	11	10	21	21	19	-
133	Hextall, Erskine & Co	13	8	21	25	21	21
134	Hopkins & Wood	10	11	21	21	24	24
135	Julian Holy	12	9	21	15	11	9
136	Laytons	10	11	21	22	19	19
137	Stones Porter	12	9	21	18	15	16
138	Thomas Cooper & Stibbard	14	7	21	18	17	17
139	Bates, Wells & Braithwaite	11	9	20	18	17	13
140	Devonshires	16	4	20	19	14	11
141	Hodge Jones & Allen	9	11	20	20	20	19
142	Holmes Hardingham	10	10	20	18	20	18
143	Kingsford Stacey	12	8	20	20	21	20
144	Maxwell Batley	15	5	20	19	14	13
145	Memery Crystal	7	13	20	17	13	14
146	Sidley & Austin	6	14	20	-	-	-
147	Stringer Saul	15	5	20	16	16	14
148	Teacher Stern Selby	11	9	20	18	15	14
149	Gordon Dadds	13	6	19	18	18	18
150	Jarvis & Bannister	8	11	19	17	17	11
151	Lawrence Jones	12	7	19	19	19	19
152	McGrigor Donald	6	13	19	15	-	-
153	Osborne Clarke	10	9	19	16	15	14
154	Sharpe Pritchard	11	8	19	18	18	18
155	Sheridans	12	7	19	19	19	19
156	Tarlo Lyons	15	4	19	20	19	20
157	Alastair Thomson & Partners	10	8	18	15	15	13
158	Barnett Alexander Chart	9	9	18	-	-	-
159	Cartwright Cunningham Haselgrove & Co	12	6	18	22	21	21
160	Cumberland Ellis Peirs	15	3	18	18	19	19
161	Fox & Gibbons	11	7	18	31	35	35
162	Stephens Innocent	5	13	18	18	-	-
163	Stewarts	8	10	18	-	-	-
164	Winward Fearon	14	4	18	25	25	24
165	Anthony Gold, Lerman & Muirhead	6	11	17	15	15	14
166	Clintons	12	5	17	16	15	13
167	Freedman Church	12	5	17	-	-	-
168	Gregory, Rowcliffe & Milners	15	2	17	20	21	22
169	Lane & Partners	11	6	17	16	15	14
170	Rowley Ashworth	6	11	17	-	-	-
171	Seddons	11	6	17	19	12	17
172	Simmonds Church Smiles	15	2	17	15	15	16
173	Bindman & Partners	12	4	16	17	18	17
174	Church Adams Tatham & Co	10	6	16	14	13	-
175	Franks, Charlesly & Co	12	4	16	17	17	17
176	Glovers	11	5	16	16	15	17
177	Ingledew Brown Bennison & Garrett	10	6	16	16	16	17
178	Leigh Day & Co	7	9	16	-	-	-
179	Mackenzie Mills	8	8	16	18	16	15
180	Pothecary & Barratt	9	7	16	16	16	13
181	Royds Treadwell	10	6	16	16	13	16
182	Shaw and Croft	9	7	16	16	14	15
183	Beale and Company	9	6	15	15	13	13
184	Duthie Hart & Duthie	5	10	15	15	13	11
185	May, May & Merrimans	11	4	15	14	13	13
186	Pattinson and Brewer	9	6	15	-	-	-
187	Rayner, De Wolfe	9	6	15	-	-	-
188	Reid Minty	9	6	15	-	-	-
189	Stafford Young Jones	12	3	15	17	16	19
190	Underwood & Co	6	9	15	15	13	9
191	Bennett Taylor Tyrrell	11	3	14	16	17	19
192	Booth & Blackwell	10	4	14	16	16	17
193	Bower Cotton & Bower	10	4	14	14	15	14
194	Brown Cooper	8	6	14	-	-	-
195	Crockers	8	6	14	-	-	-
196	Debenham & Co	8	6	14	14	14	15
197	Evill & Coleman	7	7	14	-	-	-
198	Hunters	9	5	14	14	15	13
199	Jackson Parton	10	4	14	-	-	-
200	Kidd Rapinet	13	1	14	17	17	15

SOUTH EAST: THE 50 LARGEST FIRMS

The rankings in this table are determined by the number of solicitors working in this region. They are based on partner and assistant solicitor figures only: all other fee-earners are excluded.

		Ptnrs	Asst Solrs	Total No. of Solicitors			
				'95	'94	'93	'92
1	**Blake Lapthorn** *Fareham, Havant, Portsmouth, Southampton, Waterlooville*	28	48	**76**	73	64	66
2	**Shoosmiths & Harrison** *Northampton, Banbury, Reading, Southampton*	23	42	**65**	57	35	29
3	**Cole and Cole** *Oxford, Abingdon, Reading, Witney*	30	33	**63**	58	57	58
4	**Pictons (incorporating Smeathmans)** *St. Albans, Bedford, Hemel Hempstead, Luton, Milton Keynes, Stevenage, Watford*	30	25	**55**	57	50	44
5	**Thomson Snell & Passmore** *Tunbridge Wells, Cranbrook, Maidstone, Tonbridge*	37	12	**49**	48	50	50
6	**Thomas Eggar Verrall Bowles** *Chichester, Horsham, Worthing*	31	16	**47**	46	47	50
7	**Cripps Harries Hall** *Tunbridge Wells, Crowborough, Heathfield*	22	19	**41**	43	41	44
8	**Donne Mileham & Haddock** *Brighton, Crawley, East Grinstead, Lewes, Newhaven, Steyning, Worthing*	27	14	**41**	42	39	47
9	**Hart Brown & Co** *Guildford, Cobham, Cranleigh, Farnham, Godalming, Woking*	19	22	**41**	37	33	26
10	**Penningtons** *Basingstoke, Godalming, Newbury*	23	18	**41**	38	33	29
11	**Linnells** *Oxford, Bicester, Headington, Kidlington, Milton Keynes, Newport Pagnell, Wallingford*	20	18	**38**	38	41	39
12	**Clyde & Co** *Guildford*	17	20	**37**	33	38	46
13	**Iliffes Booth Bennett** *Uxbridge, Chesham, Hayes, Ingatestone, Slough*	20	15	**35**	33	-	-
14	**Coffin Mew & Clover** *Portsmouth, Cosham, Fareham, Gosport, Havant, Leigh Park, Southampton, Totton*	22	12	**34**	35	29	26
15	**Fennemores** *Milton Keynes, Luton*	12	21	**33**	33	26	28
16	**Kidd Rapinet** *Aylesbury, Basingstoke, Haslemere, High Wycombe, Maidenhead, Reading, Slough*	26	6	**32**	35	35	34
17	**Brachers** *Maidstone*	15	16	**31**	31	25	25
18	**Wynne Baxter Godfree** *Lewes, Brighton, Eastbourne, Lingfield, Seaford*	22	8	**30**	29	33	28
19	**Girlings** *Canterbury, Birchington, Broadstairs, Herne Bay, Margate, Ramsgate*	23	5	**28**	29	28	30
20	**Brain & Brain** *Reading, Basingstoke*	17	10	**27**	27	27	19
21	**Buss Murton** *Tunbridge Wells, Cranbrook, Hawkhurst, Staplehurst, Tenterden, Tonbridge*	18	9	**27**	24	24	20
22	**Clarks** *Reading*	11	16	**27**	26	27	30
23	**Pitmans** *Reading*	12	15	**27**	29	28	34
24	**White & Bowker** *Winchester, Eastleigh, Southampton*	16	11	**27**	25	23	24
25	**Winter–Taylors** *High Wycombe, Aylesbury, Hazlemere, Marlow, Princes Risborough*	19	8	**27**	27	24	31
26	**Glanvilles** *Portsmouth, Fareham, Havant, Newport, Waterlooville*	11	15	**26**	22	-	-
27	**Henmans** *Oxford, Woodstock*	12	14	**26**	24	22	25
28	**Charles Lucas & Marshall** *Newbury, Hungerford, Wantage*	19	6	**25**	25	25	28
29	**Barlows** *Guildford, Chertsey, Godalming*	11	13	**24**	23	22	19
30	**Hawkins Russell Jones** *Hitchin, Hatfield, Stevenage, Welwyn Garden City*	16	8	**24**	24	23	26
31	**Taylor Walton** *Luton, Harpenden, St Albans*	17	7	**24**	25	27	28
32	**Warner Goodman & Streat** *Fareham, Parkgate, Portchester, Portsmouth, Southampton, Waterlooville*	11	13	**24**	21	21	20
33	**Eric Robinson & Co** *Southampton, Eastleigh, Hythe*	12	11	**23**	-	-	-
34	**Hepherd Winstanley & Pugh** *Southampton*	14	9	**23**	22	22	20
35	**Paris Smith & Randall** *Southampton*	14	9	**23**	21	21	21
36	**Marshall & Galpin** *Oxford, Abingdon, Cowley, Summertown, Thame*	12	10	**22**	22	21	22
37	**Moore & Blatch** *Southampton, Lymington, Milford-on-Sea*	13	9	**22**	23	23	26
38	**Turberville Woodbridge** *Uxbridge, Hayes, Hillingdon*	11	11	**22**	23	24	17
39	**Darbys** *Oxford*	11	10	**21**	20	16	15
40	**Gepp & Sons** *Chelmsford, Colchester*	11	10	**21**	20	24	24
41	**Blandy & Blandy** *Reading*	11	9	**20**	20	20	19
42	**Boyes Turner & Burrows** *Reading, Staines*	11	9	**20**	-	-	-
43	**Burstows** *Crawley, Brighton, Horsham*	12	8	**20**	19	20	18
44	**Furley Page Fielding & Barton** *Canterbury, Whitstable*	15	5	**20**	20	18	19
45	**Matthew Arnold & Baldwin** *Watford*	14	6	**20**	20	20	19
46	**Sherwin Oliver** *Portsmouth, Fareham*	9	11	**20**	-	-	-
47	**Argles & Court** *Maidstone, Larkfield, Walderslade*	16	3	**19**	23	20	19
48	**B.P. Collins & Co** *Gerrards Cross, Beaconsfield, Chalfont St. Peter*	13	6	**19**	19	19	20
49	**Bower & Bailey** *Oxford, Banbury, Witney*	13	6	**19**	22	20	21
50	**Denton Hall** *London, Milton Keynes*	5	14	**19**	-	-	-

SOUTH WEST: THE 50 LARGEST FIRMS

The rankings in this table are determined by the number of solicitors working in this region . They are based on partner and assistant solicitor figures only: all other fee-earners are excluded.

		Ptnrs	Asst Solrs	Total No. of Solicitors			
				'95	'94	'93	'92
1	**Bond Pearce** *Plymouth, Exeter*	37	67	**104**	102	94	84
2	**Bevan Ashford** *Bristol, Crediton, Exeter, Plymouth, Taunton, Tiverton*	45	56	**101**	90	91	95
3	**Burges Salmon** *Bristol*	32	62	**94**	80	72	73
4	**Osborne Clarke** *Bristol*	28	48	**76**	76	74	89
5	**Clarke Willmott & Clarke** *Taunton, Bridgwater, Bristol, Chard, Crewkerne, Ruishton, Wellington, Yeovil*	39	20	**59**	85	85	84
6	**Lester Aldridge** *Bournemouth, Christchurch, Parkstone*	30	26	**56**	55	49	39
7	**Stephens & Scown** *Exeter, Liskeard, Lostwithiel, St. Austell, Truro*	26	29	**55**	51	45	38
8	**Wansbroughs Willey Hargrave** *Bristol*	17	38	**55**	57	58	55
9	**Veale Wasbrough** *Bristol*	24	30	**54**	53	49	59
10	**Foot & Bowden** *Plymouth*	25	15	**40**	34	31	32
11	**Lyons Davidson** *Bristol, Plymouth*	13	27	**40**	34	32	31
12	**Wolferstans** *Plymouth, Bristol, Plympton, Plymstock*	21	18	**39**	34	30	29
13	**Lawrence Tucketts** *Bristol*	14	23	**37**	34	34	33
14	**Cartwrights** *Bristol*	17	19	**36**	33	33	29
15	**Townsends** *Swindon*	21	12	**33**	34	29	23

#	Firm	Ptnrs	Asst Solrs	'95	'94	'93	'92
16	**Battens** — Yeovil, Bristol, Chard, Crewkerne, Dorchester, Shaftesbury, Sherborne, Weymouth	22	10	**32**	28	29	28
17	**Woollcombe Beer Watts** — Newton Abbot, Bovey Tracey, Buckfastleigh, Chagford, Torquay, Totnes	18	14	**32**	29	26	27
18	**Tozers** — Exeter, Dawlish, Newton Abbot, Paignton, Teignmouth, Torquay	18	11	**29**	22	20	20
19	**Thrings & Long** — Bath	12	16	**28**	22	21	10
20	**Davies and Partners** — Gloucester, Bristol	15	10	**25**	21	24	26
21	**Wilsons** — Salisbury	16	9	**25**	22	24	27
22	**Anstey Sargent & Probert** — Exeter, Plymouth	17	6	**23**	22	21	22
23	**Coles Miller** — Poole, Broadstone, Charminster, West Moors, Wimborne	13	10	**23**	19	17	14
24	**Porter Bartlett & Mayo** — Yeovil, Blandford Forum, Langport, Sherborne, Sturminster Newton	17	6	**23**	21	19	21
25	**Wood Awdry Wansbroughs** — Devizes, Melksham	14	8	**22**	18	20	21
26	**Burroughs Day** — Bristol, Portishead, Weston-super-Mare	12	9	**21**	21	22	22
27	**Ford Simey Daw Roberts** — Exeter, Exmouth, Sidmouth	16	5	**21**	20	23	21
28	**Trump and Partners** — Bristol	10	11	**21**	20	21	20
29	**Rickerby Jessop** — Cheltenham	15	5	**20**	20	25	25
30	**Steele Raymond** — Bournemouth, Wimborne	12	8	**20**	20	18	15
31	**Stones** — Exeter	12	7	**19**	22	23	23
32	**Trethowans** — Salisbury, Amesbury	10	9	**19**	20	23	16
33	**Wiggin and Co** — Cheltenham	9	10	**19**	18	18	21
34	**Bevirs** — Swindon, Calne, Wootton Bassett	12	6	**18**	17	21	18
35	**Bobbetts Mackan** — Bristol	5	13	**18**	18	14	13
36	**Charles Russell** — London, Cheltenham, Swindon	8	9	**17**	-	-	-
37	**Goughs** — Calne, Chippenham, Corsham, Devizes, Melksham	12	5	**17**	17	14	14
38	**J.W. Ward & Son** — Bristol, Axbridge, Bradley Stoke, Staple Hill, Weston-super-Mare, Worle	7	10	**17**	27	25	32
39	**Kirby Simcox** — Bristol, Bath, Thornbury	8	9	**17**	16	14	14
40	**Michelmores** — Exeter	10	7	**17**	17	15	14
41	**Bennett Metcalfe** — Bristol	9	7	**16**	15	-	-
42	**Crosse & Crosse** — Exeter	10	6	**16**	17	18	17
43	**Dodson Harding** — Taunton, Bridgwater, Wellington	11	5	**16**	15	16	16
44	**Laytons** — London, Bristol	8	8	**16**	-	-	-
45	**Middleton & Upsall** — Warminster, Bath, Frome, Trowbridge, Westbury	10	6	**16**	16	17	18
46	**Turners** — Bournemouth, Poole, Wimborne	13	3	**16**	14	14	13
47	**Bishop Longbotham & Bagnall** — Trowbridge, Bath, Bradford-on-Avon, Swindon	7	8	**15**	15	15	13
48	**Eastleys** — Paignton, Brixham	10	5	**15**	15	13	11
49	**John Hodge & Co** — Weston-super-Mare, Bristol, Clevedon, Wedmore, Yatton	9	6	**15**	15	13	12
50	**Nalder & Son** — Truro, Camborne, Falmouth, Newquay	8	7	**15**	-	-	-

WALES: THE 10 LARGEST FIRMS

The rankings in this table are determined by the number of solicitors working in this region. They are based on partner and assistant solicitor figures only: all other fee-earners are excluded.

#	Firm	Ptnrs	Asst Solrs	Total No. of Solicitors '95	'94	'93	'92
1	**Morgan Bruce** — Cardiff, Swansea	39	66	**105**	81	77	77
2	**Eversheds** — Cardiff, Bristol	37	58	**95**	71	59	51
3	**Hugh James Jones & Jenkins** — Cardiff, Bargoed, Blackwood, Merthyr Tydfil, Pontllottyn, Talbot Green, Treharris	36	31	**67**	67	64	62
4	**Edwards Geldard** — Cardiff, Monmouth	22	24	**46**	43	48	47
5	**Leo Abse & Cohen** — Cardiff	12	24	**36**	31	25	19
6	**Dolmans** — Cardiff	14	13	**27**	27	22	21
7	**Clement Jones** — Holywell, Bangor, Flint, Llandudno, Menai Bridge, Queensferry, Rhyl, Saltney, Wrexham	8	13	**21**	21	-	-
8	**Douglas Jones & Mercer** — Swansea, Ammanford, Gorseinon, Morriston, Mumbles	12	8	**20**	17	17	17
9	**Loosemores** — Cardiff, Canton, Grangetown, Roath	10	10	**20**	18	19	18
10	**Bevan Ashford** — Bristol, Cardiff	9	7	**16**	-	-	-

MIDLANDS: THE 50 LARGEST FIRMS

The rankings in this table are determined by the number of solicitors working in this region. They are based on partner and assistant solicitor figures only: all other fee-earners are excluded.

#	Firm	Ptnrs	Asst Solrs	Total No. of Solicitors '95	'94	'93	'92
1	**Eversheds** — Birmingham	57	116	**173**	153	157	160
2	**Edge & Ellison** — Birmingham, Leicester	59	90	**149**	132	121	118
3	**Wragge & Co** — Birmingham	43	100	**143**	134	123	119
4	**Pinsent Curtis** — Birmingham	43	64	**107**	93	92	96
5	**Shoosmiths & Harrison** — Northampton, Nottingham	39	39	**78**	78	64	29
6	**Browne Jacobson** — Nottingham	26	38	**64**	62	53	46
7	**Martineau Johnson** — Birmingham	24	39	**63**	56	53	55
8	**Freeth Cartwright Hunt Dickins** — Nottingham	31	31	**62**	62	-	-
9	**Dibb Lupton Broomhead** — Birmingham	19	28	**47**	41	-	-
10	**Shakespeares** — Birmingham	22	24	**46**	40	37	36
11	**Nelsons** — Nottingham	15	30	**45**	46	38	31
12	**Morton Fisher** — Worcester	19	20	**39**	39	37	30
13	**Herbert Wilkes** — Birmingham	12	25	**37**	29	19	21
14	**Toller Hales & Collcutt** — Northampton, Corby, Kettering, Wellingborough	15	19	**34**	31	27	27
15	**Higgs & Sons** — Brierley Hill	17	16	**33**	32	32	30
16	**Hatcher Rogerson** — Shrewsbury	19	12	**31**	20	20	19
17	**Lanyon Bowdler** — Shrewsbury	17	12	**29**	27	27	27
18	**Gateley Wareing** — Birmingham	11	17	**28**	26	23	17
19	**Harvey Ingram** — Leicester, Oadby	16	12	**28**	29	28	26
20	**Knight & Sons** — Newcastle-under-Lyme	15	13	**28**	28	28	24

		Ptnrs	Asst Solrs	'95	'94	'93	'92
21	**The Smith Partnership** *Derby, Swadlincote*	10	18	**28**	26	26	24
22	**Anthony Collins** *Birmingham*	8	19	**27**	27	25	25
23	**Hewitson Becke + Shaw** *Cambridge, Northampton*	12	15	**27**	27	28	26
24	**Roythorne & Co** *Spalding, Boston, Nottingham*	17	10	**27**	26	23	23
25	**Flint, Bishop & Barnett** *Derby, Ashbourne*	18	8	**26**	26	26	31
26	**Kent Jones and Done** *Stoke-on-Trent*	11	15	**26**	26	27	36
27	**Berryman & Co** *Nottingham*	13	12	**25**	19	19	17
28	**Haden Stretton Slater Miller** *Walsall*	20	5	**25**	25	25	25
29	**THM Tinsdills** *Stoke-on-Trent*	18	7	**25**	25	24	24
30	**Ironsides Ray & Vials** *Northampton, Leicester, Oakham*	15	9	**24**	24	24	27
31	**Robin Thompson & Partners** *Nottingham*	14	10	**24**	24	19	18
32	**Tyndallwoods** *Birmingham*	10	14	**24**	24	-	-
33	**Hawley & Rodgers** *Loughborough, Leicester, Nottingham*	12	11	**23**	25	22	17
34	**Foster Baxter Cooksey** *Wolverhampton*	14	8	**22**	23	23	21
35	**George Green & Co** *Warley*	10	12	**22**	20	18	18
36	**Grindeys** *Stoke-on-Trent*	10	12	**22**	18	17	17
37	**Rees Page** *Wolverhampton*	11	11	**22**	20	19	15
38	**Warren & Allen** *Nottingham, Bingham, Ilkeston*	11	11	**22**	23	19	16
39	**Wilson Browne** *Kettering, Corby, Higham Ferrers, Northampton, Rushden*	17	5	**22**	22	24	24
40	**Keely Smith & Jobson** *Lichfield*	10	11	**21**	21	18	18
41	**Manby & Steward** *Wolverhampton*	13	8	**21**	23	27	27
42	**Wright Hassall & Co** *Leamington Spa*	14	7	**21**	20	21	21
43	**Actons** *Nottingham*	10	10	**20**	20	17	16
44	**Brindley Twist Tafft & James** *Coventry*	11	9	**20**	20	20	21
45	**Elliot Mather Smith** *Chesterfield, Mansfield, Matlock*	15	5	**20**	18	18	17
46	**Howes Percival** *Northampton*	14	6	**20**	18	27	27
47	**Blakemores** *Coventry, Ashby-de-la-Zouch*	11	8	**19**	19	18	19
48	**Cartwright & Lewis** *Birmingham*	14	5	**19**	19	18	15
49	**Marron Dodds** *Leicester*	13	6	**19**	-	-	-
50	**Pickering & Butters** *Stafford*	12	7	**19**	20	21	21

EAST ANGLIA: THE 20 LARGEST FIRMS

The rankings in this table are determined by the number of solicitors working in this region and do not take into account solicitors overseas. They are based on partner and assistant solicitor figures only: all other fee-earners are excluded.

		Ptnrs	Asst Solrs	Total No. of Solicitors '95	'94	'93	'92
1	**Mills & Reeve** *Norwich, Cambridge*	48	72	**120**	114	109	98
2	**Eversheds** *Ipswich, Norwich*	48	34	**82**	76	80	76
3	**Hewitson Becke + Shaw** *Cambridge, Newmarket, Peterborough*	23	23	**46**	41	47	50
4	**Taylor Vinters** *Cambridge, Newmarket*	21	25	**46**	44	54	40
5	**Prettys** *Ipswich*	15	19	**34**	32	25	21
6	**Birketts** *Ipswich*	24	9	**33**	52	55	35
7	**Greenwoods** *Peterborough*	15	13	**28**	28	25	27
8	**Leathes Prior** *Norwich, North Walsham*	14	13	**27**	27	21	22
9	**Metcalfe Copeman & Pettefar** *Wisbech, King's Lynn, Peterborough, Thetford*	10	13	**23**	23	19	17
10	**Gotelee & Goldsmith** *Ipswich, Hadleigh*	14	6	**20**	21	18	18
11	**Hansell Stevenson** *Norwich*	13	7	**20**	20	16	13
12	**Leeds Day** *Sandy, Biggleswade, Huntingdon, St. Ives, St. Neots*	11	8	**19**	19	21	22
13	**Steele & Co** *Norwich, Cromer, Diss, Harleston, Thetford*	13	6	**19**	21	19	19
14	**Buckle Mellows** *Peterborough, Whittlesey*	11	7	**18**	-	-	-
15	**Ward Gethin** *King's Lynn, Hunstanton, Swaffham*	14	4	**18**	18	19	17
16	**Hunt & Coombs** *Peterborough*	7	10	**17**	-	-	-
17	**Bankes Ashton** *Bury St. Edmunds*	13	3	**16**	18	18	18
18	**Cozens–Hardy & Jewson** *Norwich*	10	6	**16**	18	18	17
19	**Dawbarns** *Wisbech, King's Lynn*	10	6	**16**	16	15	10
20	**Howes Percival** *Northampton, Ipswich, Norwich*	10	6	**16**	17	16	16

NORTH WEST: THE 50 LARGEST FIRMS

The rankings in this table are determined by the number of solicitors working in this region. They are based on partner and assistant solicitor figures only: all other fee-earners are excluded.

		Ptnrs	Asst Solrs	Total No. of Solicitors '95	'94	'93	'92
1	**Addleshaw Sons & Latham** *Manchester*	37	54	**91**	84	88	84
2	**Alsop Wilkinson** *Liverpool, Manchester*	34	46	**80**	76	78	75
3	**Lace Mawer** *Manchester, Liverpool*	40	37	**77**	76	69	63
4	**Weightman Rutherfords** *Liverpool*	28	46	**74**	64	57	49
5	**Davies Wallis Foyster** *Liverpool, Manchester*	37	34	**71**	67	68	60
6	**Hill Dickinson Davis Campbell** *Liverpool*	33	27	**60**	60	51	46
7	**Cobbett Leak Almond** *Manchester, Wilmslow*	31	27	**58**	55	52	49
8	**Halliwell Landau** *Manchester, Salford*	25	21	**46**	43	37	30
9	**Vaudreys** *Manchester*	12	34	**46**	34	33	25
10	**Pannone & Partners** *Manchester*	29	15	**44**	45	54	59
11	**Keogh Ritson** *Bolton*	15	26	**41**	35	35	25
12	**Rowlands** *Manchester, Droylsden, New Moston, Sale, Stockport, Urmston*	16	24	**40**	24	21	32
13	**Dibb Lupton Broomhead** *Manchester*	17	22	**39**	31	23	18
14	**James Chapman & Co** *Manchester*	19	20	**39**	28	26	23
15	**Brian Thompson & Partners** *Liverpool, Manchester*	21	17	**38**	38	35	-
16	**Elliott & Company** *Manchester*	13	25	**38**	26	26	-
17	**Eversheds** *Manchester*	20	18	**38**	46	51	42
18	**Forbes & Partners** *Blackburn, Accrington, Clitheroe, Preston*	14	24	**38**	32	25	25
19	**Davies Arnold Cooper** *Manchester*	10	26	**36**	36	30	20

		Ptnrs	Asst Solrs	'95	'94	'93	'92
20	**Slater Heelis** *Manchester, Sale*	18	18	**36**	40	37	37
21	**Brabner Holden Banks Wilson** *Liverpool, Preston*	16	19	**35**	35	36	35
22	**Hammond Suddards** *Manchester*	10	24	**34**	24	-	-
23	**Mace & Jones** *Liverpool, Huyton, Manchester*	15	19	**34**	29	29	28
24	**Walker Smith & Way** *Chester, Ellesmere Port*	19	15	**34**	29	29	28
25	**Aaron Freedmans** *Chester*	18	13	**31**	-	-	-
26	**Cuff Roberts** *Liverpool*	21	8	**29**	30	29	31
27	**Bullivant Jones & Company** *Liverpool*	7	20	**27**	20	20	16
28	**Russell & Russell** *Bolton, Bury, Chester, Manchester*	16	11	**27**	27	27	21
29	**Cartmell Shepherd** *Carlisle, Brampton, Carlisle (Rosehill), Penrith*	12	14	**26**	25	24	26
30	**Ingham Clegg & Crowther** *Preston, Blackpool, Cleveleys, Fleetwood, Knott End on Sea, Lancaster, Poulton-le-Fylde*	14	12	**26**	27	29	-
31	**J. Keith Park & Co** *St. Helens, Liverpool*	2	24	**26**	26	20	-
32	**Stephensons** *Leigh, Golborne, Hindley, St. Helens, Wigan*	15	11	**26**	26	21	13
33	**Jones Maidment Wilson** *Manchester, Altrincham*	10	14	**24**	19	19	22
34	**Canter Levin & Berg** *Liverpool, Kirkby, Skelmersdale, St. Helens*	11	12	**23**	-	-	-
35	**Wacks Caller** *Manchester*	14	9	**23**	-	-	-
36	**Burnetts** *Carlisle*	17	5	**22**	23	23	22
37	**Burton Copeland** *Manchester*	13	9	**22**	16	22	21
38	**Peter Rickson and Partners** *Preston, Manchester*	14	8	**22**	17	18	16
39	**Bell Lamb & Joynson** *Liverpool, Birkenhead, Chester, Runcorn, Wallasey*	16	5	**21**	18	17	16
40	**Birchall Blackburn** *Preston, Accrington, Bamber Bridge, Chorley, Manchester, Oswaldtwistle, Whalley*	13	8	**21**	20	18	20
41	**Fieldings Porter** *Bolton, Blackburn*	12	9	**21**	-	-	-
42	**Morecroft Urquhart** *Liverpool, Crosby, Moreton, Woolton*	14	7	**21**	20	18	14
43	**Bermans** *Liverpool, Manchester*	12	7	**19**	21	21	30
44	**Farleys** *Blackburn, Accrington*	9	10	**19**	19	19	19
45	**Linder Myers** *Manchester, Openshaw, Salford*	6	13	**19**	19	18	19
46	**Maxwell Entwistle & Byrne** *Liverpool, Ainsdale, Formby, Huyton, Kirkby, Maghull, West Kirby*	10	9	**19**	18	15	17
47	**Aaron & Partners** *Chester*	10	8	**18**	17	13	14
48	**Gorna & Co** *Manchester*	8	10	**18**	-	-	-
49	**Abson Hall** *Stockport, Macclesfield, Manchester*	11	6	**17**	18	18	18
50	**George Davies & Co** *Manchester, Wilmslow*	12	5	**17**	17	15	15

NORTH EAST: THE 50 LARGEST FIRMS

The rankings in this table are determined by the number of solicitors working in this region . They are based on partner and assistant solicitor figures only: all other fee-earners are excluded.

		Ptnrs	Asst Solrs	Total No. of Solicitors '95	'94	'93	'92
1	**Eversheds** *Newcastle-upon-Tyne, Leeds*	57	121	**178**	158	145	137
2	**Dibb Lupton Broomhead** *Bradford, Leeds, Sheffield*	66	101	**167**	163	141	135
3	**Booth & Co.** *Leeds*	41	91	**132**	132	133	111
4	**Hammond Suddards** *Leeds*	29	73	**102**	101	108	104
5	**Pinsent Curtis** *Leeds*	40	49	**89**	86	83	105
6	**Irwin Mitchell, inc. Kershaw Tucker** *Sheffield*	44	44	**88**	69	63	63
7	**Walker Morris** *Leeds*	26	50	**76**	76	66	63
8	**Dickinson Dees** *Newcastle upon Tyne*	35	32	**67**	60	56	53
9	**Wansbroughs Willey Hargrave** *Bristol*	18	36	**54**	38	34	27
10	**Wilkinson Maughan**	23	28	**51**	49	37	35
11	**Nabarro Nathanson** *Doncaster, Hull, Sheffield*	15	30	**45**	44	42	39
12	**Rollit Farrell & Bladon** *Hull*	31	14	**45**	44	41	42
13	**Andrew M. Jackson & Co** *Hull*	20	24	**44**	45	40	34
14	**Watson Burton** *Newcastle upon Tyne, Blyth, Cramlington, Forest Hall, Whitley Bay*	16	25	**41**	46	44	47
15	**Brian Thompson & Partners** *Newcastle-upon-Tyne*	23	16	**39**	39	39	-
16	**Gordons Wright & Wright** *Bradford*	20	16	**36**	31	33	32
17	**Jacksons** *Middlesbrough, Darlington, Stockton-on-Tees*	21	15	**36**	37	34	31
18	**Teeman Levine** *Leeds*	10	24	**34**	18	16	19
19	**Gosschalks** *Hull*	19	13	**32**	30	26	25
20	**Ward Hadaway** *Newcastle upon Tyne*	21	11	**32**	34	31	28
21	**Ford and Warren** *Leeds*	11	20	**31**	27	27	30
22	**Lupton Fawcett** *Leeds*	16	15	**31**	26	22	19
23	**Robert Muckle** *Newcastle-upon-Tyne*	11	20	**31**	26	20	25
24	**Hay & Kilner** *Newcastle-upon-Tyne, Gosforth, Jesmond, Wallsend*	16	13	**29**	27	26	26
25	**John Howell & Co** *Sheffield*	12	17	**29**	29	26	19
26	**Crutes** *Newcastle-upon-Tyne, Middlesbrough, Sunderland*	17	9	**26**	26	21	26
27	**Philip Hamer & Co** *Hull*	6	18	**24**	24	24	-
28	**Read Hind Stewart** *Leeds*	10	12	**22**	20	19	21
29	**Attey Bower & Jones** *Doncaster*	16	4	**20**	20	17	12
30	**Bury & Walkers** *Barnsley*	10	10	**20**	20	19	20
31	**Denison Till** *York*	15	5	**20**	17	20	23
32	**Ison Harrison & Co** *Leeds*	7	13	**20**	-	-	-
33	**Punch Robson** *Middlesbrough, Berwickhills, Stockton-on-Tees*	15	5	**20**	24	24	21
34	**Smith & Graham** *Hartlepool, Billingham, Durham, Hartlepool - Unity House, Peterlee*	13	7	**20**	17	18	17
35	**Tilly Bailey & Irvine** *Hartlepool, Barnard Castle*	13	7	**20**	20	17	14
36	**Askews** *Redcar, Guisborough, Middlesbrough*	12	7	**19**	17	18	15
37	**Stamp Jackson & Procter** *Hull*	11	8	**19**	18	18	17
38	**Taylor & Emmet** *Sheffield*	10	9	**19**	19	18	14
39	**Wake Smith** *Sheffield*	13	5	**18**	20	21	20
40	**Wilkin Chapman** *Grimsby*	11	7	**18**	18	17	25
41	**Garrett & Co** *London*	5	12	**17**	-	-	-
42	**Keeble Hawson** *Sheffield*	12	5	**17**	19	-	14
43	**Godlove Pearlman** *Leeds*	12	4	**16**	19	18	16
44	**Graysons** *Sheffield*	8	8	**16**	16	14	14
45	**Armitage Sykes Hall Norton** *Huddersfield*	8	7	**15**	-	-	-
46	**Ashton Morton Slack** *Sheffield*	10	5	**15**	15	12	15

		Ptnrs	Asst Solrs	'95	'94	'93	'92
47	**Brooke North and Goodwin** Leeds	10	5	**15**	17	21	21
48	**Harrowell Shaftoe** York	9	6	**15**	-	-	-
49	**Hartley & Worstenholme** Castleford	7	8	**15**	-	-	-
50	**Latimer Hinks** Darlington	7	8	**15**	-	-	-

SCOTLAND: THE 50 LARGEST FIRMS

The rankings in this table are determined by the number of solicitors working in this region. They are based on partner and assistant solicitor figures only: all other fee-earners are excluded.

		Ptnrs	Asst Solrs	Total No. of Solicitors '95	'94	'93	'92
1	**Dundas & Wilson CS** Edinburgh, Glasgow	32	67	**99**	99	-	-
2	**McGrigor Donald** Glasgow, Edinburgh	39	60	**99**	88	-	-
3	**Maclay Murray & Spens** Glasgow, Edinburgh	28	69	**97**	70	-	-
4	**Shepherd & Wedderburn WS** Edinburgh	27	42	**69**	68	-	-
5	**Brodies WS** Edinburgh	29	35	**64**	57	-	-
6	**Ross Harper & Murphy WS** Glasgow, Bellshill, East Kilbride, Glasgow Castlemilk, Glasgow Easterhouse, Glasgow Shawlands, Glasgow Maryhill, Hamilton, Rutherglen, Uddingston	24	39	**63**	52	-	-
7	**McClure Naismith Anderson & Gardiner** Glasgow, Edinburgh	18	44	**62**	65	-	-
8	**Biggart Baillie & Gifford** Glasgow, Edinburgh	23	35	**58**	59	-	-
9	**Ledingham Chalmers** Aberdeen, Edinburgh, Inverness	27	31	**58**	54	-	-
10	**Anderson Strathern WS** Edinburgh, Currie, Haddington	26	30	**56**	66	-	-
11	**W & J Burness WS** Edinburgh, Glasgow	27	26	**53**	54	-	-
12	**Paull & Williamsons** Aberdeen, Edinburgh	24	23	**47**	47	-	-
13	**MacRoberts** Glasgow, Edinburgh	20	23	**43**	44	-	-
14	**Thorntons WS** Dundee, Arbroath, Forfar, Perth	22	20	**42**	41	-	-
15	**Tods Murray WS** Edinburgh	24	18	**42**	42	-	-
16	**Bird Semple** Glasgow, Edinburgh	13	25	**38**	38	-	-
17	**Bishop and Robertson Chalmers** Glasgow, Edinburgh	19	19	**38**	38	-	-
18	**Dickson Minto WS** Edinburgh	12	24	**36**	34	-	-
19	**Morton Fraser Milligan WS** Edinburgh	19	17	**36**	36	-	-
20	**Drummond Miller WS** Edinburgh, Bathgate, Dalkeith, Glasgow, Kirkcaldy, Livingston, Musselburgh	21	13	**34**	35	-	-
21	**Peterkins** Aberdeen, Banchory, Glasgow, Inverurie	23	9	**32**	42	-	-
22	**Balfour & Manson** Edinburgh	18	13	**31**	39	-	-
23	**Blackadder Reid Johnston** Dundee, Broughty Ferry, Carnoustie, Kirriemuir, Monifieth	16	14	**30**	27	-	-
24	**Stronachs** Aberdeen, Inverurie, Westhill	18	12	**30**	27	-	-
25	**Aberdein Considine & Co** Aberdeen, Aboyne, Ballater, Banchory, Ellon, Inverurie, Peterhead	19	10	**29**	-	-	-
26	**Simpson & Marwick WS** Edinburgh, Aberdeen, Dundee, Glasgow	14	15	**29**	26	-	-
27	**Blair & Bryden** Greenock, Clydebank, Dumbarton, Dunoon, Port Glasgow	15	13	**28**	27	-	-
28	**Lindsays WS** Edinburgh	16	12	**28**	28	-	-
29	**Steedman Ramage WS** Edinburgh	12	16	**28**	23	-	-
30	**Wright, Johnston & Mackenzie** Glasgow, Edinburgh	11	17	**28**	27	-	-
31	**Alex Morison & Co WS** Edinburgh, Glasgow	17	10	**27**	26	-	-
32	**Fyfe Ireland** Edinburgh	9	18	**27**	27	-	-
33	**Archibald Campbell & Harley WS** Edinburgh	18	8	**26**	26	-	-
34	**Raeburn Christie & Co** Aberdeen, Banchory, Ellon, Stonehaven	12	14	**26**	29	-	-
35	**Bennett & Robertson** Edinburgh, Glasgow	16	8	**24**	24	-	-
36	**Dorman Jeffrey & Co** Glasgow, Edinburgh	14	9	**23**	23	-	-
37	**Henderson Boyd Jackson WS** Edinburgh, Glasgow	16	7	**23**	22	-	-
38	**Murray Beith & Murray WS** Edinburgh	11	11	**22**	22	-	-
39	**Russel & Aitken WS** Denny, Edinburgh, Falkirk	13	9	**22**	22	-	-
40	**Borland Montgomerie Keyden** Glasgow, Hamilton	13	8	**21**	21	-	-
41	**James & George Collie** Aberdeen	11	10	**21**	24	-	-
42	**MacArthur Stewart** Fort William, Comrie, Inverness, Lochgilphaed, Mallaig, Oban, Tobermory	13	8	**21**	20	-	-
43	**Miller Hendry** Perth, Alyth, Dundee	15	6	**21**	21	-	-
44	**Iain Smith & Company** Aberdeen, Stonehaven	10	10	**20**	19	-	-
45	**Gillespie Macandrew WS** Edinburgh	10	9	**19**	20	-	-
46	**Robin Thompson & Partners** Edinburgh, Glasgow	13	6	**19**	19	-	-
47	**Semple Fraser WS** Glasgow	7	12	**19**	19	-	-
48	**Harper Macleod** Glasgow	8	10	**18**	-	-	-
49	**Clark & Wallace** Aberdeen	11	6	**17**	-	-	-
50	**Ketchen & Stevens WS** Edinburgh, Galashiels, Glasgow	9	8	**17**	21	-	-

NORTHERN IRELAND: THE 10 LARGEST FIRMS

The rankings are based on the number of partners and assistant solicitors working in this region.

		Ptnrs	Asst Solrs	Total No. of Solicitors '95	'94	'93	'92
1	**Cleaver Fulton & Rankin** Belfast, Armagh, Bangor	9	14	**23**	22	-	-
2	**McKinty & Wright** Belfast	11	9	**20**	21	-	-
3	**C & H Jefferson** Belfast	7	10	**17**	15	-	-
4	**Carson & McDowell** Belfast	9	8	**17**	17	-	-
5	**L'Estrange & Brett** Belfast	7	9	**16**	14	-	-
6	**Elliott Duffy Garrett** Belfast	7	6	**13**	21	-	-
7	**P.A. Duffy & Co** Dungannon, Belfast, Cookstown, Magherafelt, Omagh	10	2	**12**	12	-	-
8	**Tughan & Co** Belfast	9	3	**12**	12	-	-
9	**Johns Elliot** Belfast	7	4	**11**	12	-	-
10	**O'Reilly Stewart** Belfast	4	7	**11**	-	-	-

OVERSEAS OFFICES

BRANCH OFFICE In dealing with a firm's branch office overseas a client can usually call on the services of both UK lawyers who have been transferred abroad and lawyers qualified in the foreign jurisdiction.

ASSOCIATED FIRM The term 'associated office' covers a variety of connections including membership of multi-national groupings, joint ventures and other reciprocal referral relationships. There are varying degrees of exclusivity and interdependence among these relationships. However, a typical arrangement, true of all these associations, is for associated firms to share offices and services, undertake joint marketing, exchange personnel and cross-refer clients on a non-exclusive basis. The associated firms are of generally similar size and character, and share expertise in the same – or at least complementary – disciplines.

Abu Dhabi
BRANCH OFFICE: Fox & Gibbons, Richards Butler, Simmons & Simmons, Trowers & Hamlins
ASSOCIATED FIRM: Berrymans

Algeria
ASSOCIATED FIRM: Mackrell Turner Garrett

Argentina
BRANCH OFFICE: Baker & McKenzie
ASSOCIATED FIRM: Mackrell Turner Garrett, Simmons & Simmons

Australia
BRANCH OFFICE: Blake Dawson Waldron *(Sydney, Melbourne, Brisbane, Perth, Canberra)*, Freehill Hollingdale & Page *(Sydney, Melbourne, Perth, Brisbane, Canberra)*, Mallesons Stephen Jaques *(Sydney, Melbourne, Perth, Canberra, Brisbane)*, Skadden, Arps, Slate, Meagher & Flom *(Sydney)*, Sullivan & Cromwell *(Melbourne)*, Baker & McKenzie *(Melbourne, Sydney)*, Coudert Brothers *(Sydney)*, Minter Ellison *(Brisbane, Sydney, Canberra, Melbourne, Adelaide, Perth)*
ASSOCIATED FIRM: Goodger Auden, Mackrell Turner Garrett *(Adelaide, Perth)*, McKenna & Co *(Sydney, Melbourne, Brisbane, Canberra)*

Austria
ASSOCIATED FIRM: Bates, Wells & Braithwaite, Blythe Liggins, Carrick Read Insolvency, Denton Hall, Goodger Auden, Hextall, Erskine & Co, Lane & Partners, Lawrence Tucketts, Mackrell Turner Garrett, Prettys, Stoneham Langton & Passmore, Veale Wasbrough

Bahrain
BRANCH OFFICE: Palmer Cowen, Norton Rose
ASSOCIATED FIRM: Addleshaw Sons & Latham, Bond Pearce, Booth & Co., Burges Salmon, Clifford Chance, M.B. Cuttle & Co, Freedman Church, Mills & Reeve, Veale Wasbrough

Barbados
ASSOCIATED FIRM: Glovers

Belgium
BRANCH OFFICE: Simpson Curtis, Turner Kenneth Brown, De Brauw Blackstone Westbroek, Dobson & Pinci, Dorsey & Whitney, A. & L. Goodbody, Hogan & Hartson, Jeantet & Associes, Lagerlöf & Leman, Mayer Brown & Platt, Oppenhoff & Radler, Skadden, Arps, Slate, Meagher & Flom, Thommessen Krefting Greve Lund, Uria & Menéndez, Allen & Overy, Alsop Wilkinson, Ashurst Morris Crisp, Baker & McKenzie, Beachcroft Stanleys, S J Berwin & Co, Berwin Leighton, Bircham & Co In Association with Dyson Bell Martin, Bird & Bird, Cameron Markby Hewitt, Clifford Chance, Coudert Brothers, Davies Arnold Cooper, Denton Hall, Dickinson Dees, Field Fisher Waterhouse, Freshfields, Gouldens, Hammond Suddards, Herbert Smith, Linklaters & Paines, Lovell White Durrant, Macfarlanes, Maclay Murray & Spens, Masons, McKenna & Co, Morton Fraser Milligan WS, Norton Rose, Osborne Clarke, Paisner & Co, Pinsent Curtis, Richards Butler, Rowe & Maw, Simmons & Simmons, Slaughter and May, Stephenson Harwood, Stibbe Simont Monahan Duhot, Taylor Joynson Garrett, Theodore Goddard, Titmuss Sainer Dechert, White & Case, Wilde Sapte, Wilmer Cutler & Pickering
ASSOCIATED FIRM: Bayer Rosin, Houseman Rohan & Benner, Silverman Livermore, Addleshaw Sons & Latham, Bates, Wells & Braithwaite, Berrymans, Biggart Baillie & Gifford, Bircham & Co In Association with Dyson Bell Martin, Bond Pearce, Booth & Co., Brecher & Co, Burges Salmon, Carrick Read Insolvency, Collyer–Bristow, Dutton Gregory & Williams, Elliott & Company, Eversheds, Foster Baxter Cooksey, Garrett & Co, Goodger Auden, Graham & Rosen, Gulbenkian Harris Andonian, Hextall, Erskine & Co, Irwin Mitchell, incorporating Kershaw Tucker, Lane & Partners, Lawrence Tucketts, Lea & Company, Mackrell Turner Garrett, Manby & Steward, McGrigor Donald, Mills & Reeve, Nicholson Graham & Jones, Paisner & Co, Peterkins, Philip Hamer & Co,

Prettys, Rakisons, Rollit Farrell & Bladon, Stoneham Langton & Passmore, Taylor Vinters, Tuckers, Veale Wasbrough, Wansbroughs Willey Hargrave, Wedlake Bell

Bermuda
ASSOCIATED FIRM: Mackrell Turner Garrett

Bolivia
ASSOCIATED FIRM: Simmons & Simmons

Brazil
BRANCH OFFICE: Baker & McKenzie, Beaumont and Son, Clyde & Co, Coudert Brothers
ASSOCIATED FIRM: Amhurst Brown Colombotti, Simmons & Simmons

Bulgaria
ASSOCIATED FIRM: Goodger Auden, Kenneth Elliott & Rowe, Veale Wasbrough

Canada
BRANCH OFFICE: Blake, Cassels & Graydon *(Toronto, Vancouver, Calgary)* Ottawa), Borden DuMoulin Howard Gervais *(Toronto, Vancouver, Calgary)*, Montreal), Skadden, Arps, Slate, Meagher & Flom *(Toronto)*, Stikeman Elliott *(Montreal, Toronto, Vancouver, Calgary, Ottawa)*, Tory Tory DesLauriers & Binnington *(Toronto)*, Baker & McKenzie *(Toronto)*
ASSOCIATED FIRM: Bermans *(Toronto)*, Cunningham, John & Co, Goodger Auden, Gross & Co. *(Montreal)*, Lane & Partners *(Toronto)*, Mackrell Turner Garrett *(Montreal, Toronto)*, Orchard *(Toronto)*

Cayman Islands
BRANCH OFFICE: Dawson & Co
ASSOCIATED FIRM: Masons

China
BRANCH OFFICE: Skadden, Arps, Slate, Meagher & Flom, Allen & Overy, Baker & McKenzie, Beiten Burkhardt Mittl & Wegener, Clifford Chance, Coudert Brothers, Denton Hall, Lovell White Durrant, Sinclair Roche & Temperley
ASSOCIATED FIRM: Ince & Co, Lovell White Durrant, Masons, Moorhead James, Nicholson Graham & Jones, Stephenson Harwood

Chile
BRANCH OFFICE: Baker & McKenzie
ASSOCIATED FIRM: Simmons & Simmons

Canary Islands
ASSOCIATED FIRM: Veale Wasbrough

Columbia
BRANCH OFFICE: Baker & McKenzie
ASSOCIATED FIRM: Simmons & Simmons

Costa Rica
ASSOCIATED FIRM: Simmons & Simmons

Cuba
ASSOCIATED FIRM: Rabin Leacock Lipman

Cyprus
ASSOCIATED FIRM: Biggart Baillie & Gifford, Elliott & Company, Goodger Auden, Paisner & Co, Reid Minty, Veale Wasbrough

Czech Republic
BRANCH OFFICE: De Brauw Blackstone Westbroek, Hogan & Hartson, Jeantet & Associes, Lagerlöf & Leman, Oppenhoff & Radler, Skadden, Arps, Slate, Meagher & Flom, Uria & Menéndez, Allen & Overy, Baker & McKenzie, Beiten Burkhardt Mittl & Wegener, De Bandt Van Hecke & Lagae, Debevoise & Plimpton, Lovell White Durrant, McKenna & Co, Norton Rose, Seddons, White & Case

ASSOCIATED FIRM: Turner Kenneth Brown, Bowcock Cuerden, Addleshaw Sons & Latham, Booth & Co., Burges Salmon, Clement Jones, Edwards Geldard, Macfarlanes, Mackrell Turner Garrett, Moorhead James, Rayner, De Wolfe, Stephens Innocent, Theodore Goddard, Veale Wasbrough

Denmark
BRANCH OFFICE: Berning Schluter Hald, Osborne Clarke, Reumert & Partners, Watson Farley & Williams

ASSOCIATED FIRM: Abbott King & Troen, Bates, Wells & Braithwaite, Biggart Baillie & Gifford, Denton Hall, Elliott & Company, Goodger Auden, Graham & Rosen, Gulbenkian Harris Andonian, Hedleys, Hewitson Becke + Shaw, Irwin Mitchell, incorporating Kershaw Tucker, Mackrell Turner Garrett, Peterkins, Simmons & Simmons, Stoneham Langton & Passmore, Veale Wasbrough, Wansbroughs Willey Hargrave

Dominican Republic
ASSOCIATED FIRM: Simmons & Simmons

Dubai
BRANCH OFFICE: Bryan Cave, Allen & Overy, Clifford Chance, Fox & Gibbons, Malkins, Nabarro Nathanson, Trowers & Hamlins

ASSOCIATED FIRM: Turner Kenneth Brown

Ecuador
ASSOCIATED FIRM: Simmons & Simmons

Egypt
BRANCH OFFICE: Hameed & Mallassi Advocates Ltd, Baker & McKenzie, Fox & Gibbons

ASSOCIATED FIRM: Masons, Veale Wasbrough

Eire
BRANCH OFFICE: A. & L. Goodbody, William Fry

ASSOCIATED FIRM: Amery–Parkes, Bates, Wells & Braithwaite, Biggart Baillie & Gifford, Bircham & Co In Association with Dyson Bell Martin, Elliott & Company, Eversheds, Goodger Auden, Gulbenkian Harris Andonian, Irwin Mitchell, incorporating Kershaw Tucker, Lawrence Tucketts, Mackrell Turner Garrett, Malcolm Lynch, Park Nelson Thompson Quarrell, Rootes & Alliott, Simmons & Simmons, Stephens Innocent, Stoneham Langton & Passmore, Veale Wasbrough, Wansbroughs Willey Hargrave

El Salvador
ASSOCIATED FIRM: Simmons & Simmons

Falkland Islands
BRANCH OFFICE: Ledingham Chalmers

ASSOCIATED FIRM: Andrew M. Jackson & Co

Finland
BRANCH OFFICE: White & Case

ASSOCIATED FIRM: Bates, Wells & Braithwaite, Garrett & Co, Goodger Auden, Lawrence Tucketts, Stoneham Langton & Passmore, Veale Wasbrough, Wansbroughs Willey Hargrave

France
BRANCH OFFICE: Fried, Frank, Harris, Shriver & Jacobson, Hogan & Hartson, Kevorkian Loughran & Co, Osler Renault, Skadden, Arps, Slate, Meagher & Flom, Stikeman Elliott, Sullivan & Cromwell, Allen & Overy, Ashurst Morris Crisp, Baker & McKenzie, Brecher & Co, Clifford Chance, Constant & Constant, Coudert Brothers, Debevoise & Plimpton, Frere Cholmeley Bischoff, Freshfields, Herbert Smith, Holman, Fenwick & Willan, Linklaters & Paines, Lovell White Durrant, Norton Rose, Osborne Clarke, Penningtons, Portner & Jaskel, Richards Butler, Rogers & Wells, Salans Hertzfeld & Heilbronn, Simmons & Simmons, Slaughter and May, Stibbe Simont Monahan Duhot, Watson Farley & Williams, White & Case, Wilde Sapte, Wilson, Elser, Moskowitz, Edelman & Dicker, Withers

ASSOCIATED FIRM: Andrew & Co, Triggs Turner, Bowcock Cuerden, Montgomerie & Co, Aaron & Partners, Addleshaw Sons & Latham, Alsop Wilkinson, Amery–Parkes, Barnett Alexander Chart, Bates, Wells & Braithwaite, Beachcroft Stanleys, Beaumont and Son, Berrymans, Biggart Baillie & Gifford, Bircham & Co In Association with Dyson Bell Martin, Bond Pearce, Boodle Hatfield, Booth & Co., Browne Jacobson, Burges Salmon, Carrick Read Insolvency, Clarks, Clement Jones, Clyde & Co, Collyer–Bristow, Cripps Harries Hall, Crosse & Crosse, Davies and Partners, Edmonds Bowen & Company, Edwards Geldard, Elliott & Company, Ellison & Co, Eversheds, Foster Baxter Cooksey, Freedman Church, Garrett & Co, Goldkorn Davies Mathias, Goodger Auden, Graham & Rosen, Gulbenkian Harris Andonian, Harris & Harris, Hedleys, Hewitson Becke + Shaw, Howes Percival, Hugh James Jones & Jenkins, Humphries Kirk, Irwin Mitchell, incorporating Kershaw Tucker, Kennedys, Kirk Jackson, Lane & Partners, Lawrence Tucketts, Mackrell Turner Garrett, McCormicks, Mills & Reeve, Moorhead James, Nabarro Nathanson, Nicholson Graham & Jones, Over Taylor Biggs, Paisner & Co, Park Nelson Thompson Quarrell, Payne Hicks Beach, Peter Carter-Ruck & Partners, Philip Hamer & Co, Prettys, Rabin Leacock Lipman, Radcliffes Crossman Block, Rodgers Horsley Whitemans, Rootes & Alliott, Russell–Cooke, Potter & Chapman, Shadbolt & Co, Shindler & Co, Slee Blackwell, Stephens Innocent, Stoneham Langton & Passmore, Taylor Vinters, Theodore Goddard, Tuckers, Veale Wasbrough, Vizards, Walker Charlesworth & Foster, Wansbroughs Willey Hargrave, Winward Fearon

Germany
BRANCH OFFICE: Bryan Cave (*Frankfurt am Main*), Hartwig (*Hamburg*), Ladas & Parry (*Munich*), Mayer Brown & Platt (*Berlin*), Skadden, Arps, Slate, Meagher & Flom (*Frankfurt*), Allen & Overy (*Frankfurt*), Baker & McKenzie (*Berlin, Frankfurt*), Beiten Burkhardt Mittl & Wegener (*Munich, Berlin, Frankfurt*), Clifford Chance (*Frankfurt*), Dabelstein & Passehl (*Hamburg*), Frere Cholmeley Bischoff (*Berlin*), Freshfields (*Frankfurt*), Linklaters & Paines (*Frankfurt*), Osborne Clarke (*Frankfurt*), Rogers & Wells (*Frankfurt*), Wilmer Cutler & Pickering (*Berlin*), Wilson, Elser, Moskowitz, Edelman & Dicker (*Cologne, Dusseldorf, Frankfurt*)

ASSOCIATED FIRM: Bayer Rosin, Palmer Cowen, Bates, Wells & Braithwaite (*Freiburg*), Berrymans (*Dusseldorf*), Biggart Baillie & Gifford, Boodle Hatfield, Brecher & Co (*Berlin, Frankfurt, Munich*), Carrick Read Insolvency (*Essen, Munich*), Charsley Harrison, Clarks (*Frankfurt*), Collyer–Bristow, Cripps Harries Hall (*Berlin, Munich, Frankfurt*), Crosse & Crosse (*Erlanger, Bavaria*), Curry CH. Hausmann Popeck, Denton Hall (*Dusseldorf, Frankfurt, Hamburg, Berlin, Chemnitz*), D J Freeman (*Berlin, Hamburg, Rostok*), Edwards Geldard, Elliott & Company (*Kiel*), Eversheds, Ford and Warren, Foster Baxter Cooksey (*Munich*), Garrett & Co (*Cologne, Dusseldorf, Erfurt, Frankfurt, Hamburg, Munich*), Goodger Auden, Graham & Rosen (*Kleve*), Gulbenkian Harris Andonian (*Guttersloh*), Hedleys, Hewitson Becke + Shaw (*Munich*), Hewitson Becke + Shaw (*Berlin*), Hugh James Jones & Jenkins (*Dusseldorf*), Humphries Kirk, Irwin Mitchell, incorporating Kershaw Tucker, Lane & Partners (*Dusseldorf, Hamburg*), Lawrence Tucketts, Macfarlanes, Mackrell Turner Garrett (*Duisburg, Hamburg, Munich*), Magrath & Co (*Munich*), Malcolm Lynch (*Cologne*), McCormicks (*Cologne*), McKenna & Co (*Stuttgart, Berlin, Frankfurt, Leipzig, Chemnitz*), Moorhead James (*Frankfurt*), Nicholson Graham & Jones (*Stuttgart, Berlin, Frankfurt, Dresden*), Over Taylor Biggs, Peter Carter-Ruck & Partners (*Munich*), Peterkins (*Bremen, Hamburg, Rostock*), Piper Smith & Basham, Powell Spencer & Partners, Prettys, Pye-Smiths (*Laarbruch, Paderborn*), Rodgers Horsley Whitemans (*Dortmund*), Rosling King (*Dusseldorf, Monchengladbach*), Simmons & Simmons, Stoneham Langton & Passmore, Taylor Joynson Garrett, Taylor Vinters (*Nuremberg, Dusseldorf, Dresden*), Veale Wasbrough (*Bonn, Berlin, Frankfurt*), Wansbroughs Willey Hargrave (*Hamburg, Rostock, Berlin*), Wiggin and Co (*Munich*), Winward Fearon (*Hamburg, Cologne, Dresden, Leipzig*)

Gibraltar
BRANCH OFFICE: Brooke North and Goodwin, Fox & Gibbons

ASSOCIATED FIRM: Howes Percival, Kirk Jackson, McCormicks, Veale Wasbrough

Greece
BRANCH OFFICE: Dobson & Pinci, Hill Taylor Dickinson, Holman, Fenwick & Willan, Ince & Co, Norton Rose, Watson Farley & Williams

ASSOCIATED FIRM: Addleshaw Sons & Latham, Bates, Wells & Braithwaite, Berrymans, Biggart Baillie & Gifford, Bond Pearce, Booth & Co., Burges Salmon, Elliott & Company, Goodger Auden, Gulbenkian Harris Andonian, Hughes Hooker, Irwin Mitchell, incorporating Kershaw Tucker, Lewis Moore, Mackrell Turner Garrett, Mills & Reeve, Paisner & Co, Stoneham Langton & Passmore, Veale Wasbrough

Guatemala
ASSOCIATED FIRM: Simmons & Simmons

Guernsey
BRANCH OFFICE: W & J Burness WS, Wedlake Bell

ASSOCIATED FIRM: Hylton-Potts, Mackrell Turner Garrett

Hong Kong
BRANCH OFFICE: Turner Kenneth Brown, Bryan Cave, Cravath, Swaine & Moore, Dorsey & Whitney, Mallesons Stephen Jaques, Milbank, Tweed, Hadley & McCloy, Osler Renault, Perkins Coie, Simpson Thacher & Bartlett, Skadden, Arps, Slate, Meagher & Flom, Stikeman Elliott, Sullivan & Cromwell, Tory Tory DesLauriers & Binnington, Allen & Overy, Alsop Wilkinson, Baker & McKenzie, Barlow Lyde & Gilbert, Beiten Burkhardt Mittl & Wegener, Clifford Chance, Clyde & Co, Coudert Brothers, Crump & Co., Debevoise & Plimpton, Denton Hall, Freshfields, Herbert Smith, Hill Taylor Dickinson, Holman, Fenwick & Willan, Ince & Co, Linklaters & Paines, Lovell White Durrant, Masons, McKenna & Co, Norton Rose, Richards Butler, Rogers & Wells, Simmons & Simmons, Sinclair Roche & Temperley, Slaughter and May, White & Case, Wilde Sapte

ASSOCIATED FIRM: Barr Ellison, Aaron & Partners, Addleshaw Sons & Latham, Bond Pearce, Booth & Co., Burges Salmon, M.B. Cuttle & Co, Davies and Partners, Davies Arnold Cooper, Eversheds, Evill & Coleman, Freedman Church, Gherson & Co, Gouldens, Howard Kennedy, Kennedys, Kidstons & Co, Mackrell Turner Garrett, Malkins, Mills & Reeve, Moorhead James, Penningtons, Peter Carter-Ruck & Partners, Stephenson Harwood, Taylor Joynson Garrett, Veale Wasbrough

Honduras
ASSOCIATED FIRM: Simmons & Simmons

Hungary
BRANCH OFFICE: Stikeman Elliott, Allen & Overy, Baker & McKenzie, Beiten Burkhardt Mittl & Wegener, Clifford Chance, Debevoise & Plimpton, McKenna & Co, Nabarro Nathanson, White & Case

ASSOCIATED FIRM: Edwards Geldard, Macfarlanes, Moorhead James, Piper

Smith & Basham, Rayner, De Wolfe, Theodore Goddard, Veale Wasbrough

Iceland
ASSOCIATED FIRM: Bates, Wells & Braithwaite

India
BRANCH OFFICE: Ashurst Morris Crisp, White & Case
ASSOCIATED FIRM: Palmer Cowen, Amhurst Brown Colombotti, Fox & Gibbons, Mackrell Turner Garrett, Veale Wasbrough, Zaiwalla & Co

Indonesia
BRANCH OFFICE: Freehill Hollingdale & Page, Coudert Brothers, White & Case
ASSOCIATED FIRM: Blake Dawson Waldron, Veale Wasbrough

Isle of Man
BRANCH OFFICE: Maitland & Co, Travers Smith Braithwaite
ASSOCIATED FIRM: Brooke North and Goodwin, Goodger Auden, Mackrell Turner Garrett

Iran
BRANCH OFFICE: Dr Anvari & Associates
ASSOCIATED FIRM: Pullig & Co

Israel
BRANCH OFFICE: Zellermayer, Pelossof & Schiffer

Italy
BRANCH OFFICE: Carnelutti, Dobson & Pinci, Amhurst Brown Colombotti, Baker & McKenzie, Frere Cholmeley Bischoff, Simmons & Simmons
ASSOCIATED FIRM: Bowcock Cuerden, Bates, Wells & Braithwaite, Biggart Baillie & Gifford, Bircham & Co In Association with Dyson Bell Martin, Carrick Read Insolvency, Clarks, Clement Jones, Clifford Chance, Collyer–Bristow, Edwards Geldard, Elliott & Company, Foster Baxter Cooksey, Frere Cholmeley Bischoff, Garrett & Co, Glovers, Goodger Auden, Graham & Rosen, Gulbenkian Harris Andonian, Hill Bailey Group, Howard Kennedy, Hugh James Jones & Jenkins, Irwin Mitchell, incorporating Kershaw Tucker, Lane & Partners, Lawrence Tucketts, Lee & Pembertons, Mackenzie Mills, Mackrell Turner Garrett, McCormicks, Moorhead James, Park Nelson Thompson Quarrell, Peter Carter-Ruck & Partners, Philip Hamer & Co, Prettys, Radcliffes Crossman Block, Stephens Innocent, Stoneham Langton & Passmore, Taylor Vinters, Veale Wasbrough, Vizards, Wansbroughs Willey Hargrave

Jamaica
ASSOCIATED FIRM: Stephens Innocent, Veale Wasbrough

Japan
BRANCH OFFICE: Milbank, Tweed, Hadley & McCloy, Simpson Thacher & Bartlett, Skadden, Arps, Slate, Meagher & Flom, Sullivan & Cromwell, Allen & Overy, Ashurst Morris Crisp, Baker & McKenzie, Clifford Chance, Coudert Brothers, Denton Hall, Freshfields, Linklaters & Paines, Lovell White Durrant, Macfarlanes, Sidley & Austin, Slaughter and May, White & Case, Wikborg Rein & Co, Wilde Sapte, Wilson, Elser, Moskowitz, Edelman & Dicker
ASSOCIATED FIRM: Berwin Leighton, Eversheds, Lane & Partners, Mackrell Turner Garrett, Simmons & Simmons, Veale Wasbrough

Jersey
BRANCH OFFICE: Eversheds, Gouldens
ASSOCIATED FIRM: M.B. Cuttle & Co, Goodger Auden, Mace & Jones, Mills & Reeve, Rakisons, Theodore Goddard, Veale Wasbrough

Jordan
BRANCH OFFICE: Hameed & Mallassi Advocates Ltd
ASSOCIATED FIRM: Veale Wasbrough

Kazakhstan
BRANCH OFFICE: Baker & McKenzie, Salans Hertzfeld & Heilbronn, White & Case

Kenya
ASSOCIATED FIRM: Veale Wasbrough

South Korea
ASSOCIATED FIRM: Eversheds, Lane & Partners, Mackrell Turner Garrett, Nicholson Graham & Jones, Veale Wasbrough

Kuwait
BRANCH OFFICE: Bryan Cave, Hameed & Mallassi Advocates Ltd
ASSOCIATED FIRM: Fox & Gibbons, Stephenson Harwood, Veale Wasbrough

Lebanon
ASSOCIATED FIRM: Fox & Gibbons, Goodger Auden, Kenneth Elliott & Rowe

Lithuania
ASSOCIATED FIRM: Paisner & Co

Luxembourg
BRANCH OFFICE: Maitland & Co
ASSOCIATED FIRM: Bates, Wells & Braithwaite, Biggart Baillie & Gifford, Collyer–Bristow, Elliott & Company, Garrett & Co, Gulbenkian Harris Andonian,

Irwin Mitchell, incorporating Kershaw Tucker, Lawrence Tucketts, Mackrell Turner Garrett, Prettys, Stoneham Langton & Passmore, Veale Wasbrough, Wansbroughs Willey Hargrave

Malaysia
ASSOCIATED FIRM: Goldkorn Davies Mathias, Mackrell Turner Garrett, Veale Wasbrough

Mexico
BRANCH OFFICE: Baker & McKenzie, White & Case
ASSOCIATED FIRM: Eversheds, Lane & Partners, Simmons & Simmons

Monaco
BRANCH OFFICE: Frere Cholmeley Bischoff

The Netherlands
BRANCH OFFICE: Baker & McKenzie, Clifford Chance, Stibbe Simont Monahan Duhot
ASSOCIATED FIRM: Lloyd Bragg, Bates, Wells & Braithwaite, Charsley Harrison, Collyer–Bristow, Compton Carr, Cripps Harries Hall, Denton Hall, Edwards Geldard, Eversheds, Garrett & Co, Goodger Auden, Graham & Oldham, Graham & Rosen, Gulbenkian Harris Andonian, Howes Percival, Irwin Mitchell, incorporating Kershaw Tucker, Lawrence Tucketts, Mackrell Turner Garrett, Peterkins, Philip Hamer & Co, Prettys, Simmons & Simmons, Stephens Innocent, Stoneham Langton & Passmore, Veale Wasbrough, Wansbroughs Willey Hargrave, Wiggin and Co

Nevis
ASSOCIATED FIRM: Goodger Auden

Norway
BRANCH OFFICE: Thommessen Krefting Greve Lund, Watson Farley & Williams
ASSOCIATED FIRM: Michael Bell & Co, Bates, Wells & Braithwaite, Biggart Baillie & Gifford, Elliott & Company, Garrett & Co, Lane & Partners, Mackrell Turner Garrett, Simmons & Simmons, Stoneham Langton & Passmore, Veale Wasbrough, Wansbroughs Willey Hargrave

New Zealand
ASSOCIATED FIRM: Mackrell Turner Garrett, Veale Wasbrough

Oman
BRANCH OFFICE: Fox & Gibbons, Trowers & Hamlins
ASSOCIATED FIRM: Penningtons, Veale Wasbrough

Pakistan
ASSOCIATED FIRM: Kennedys, Lane & Partners, Veale Wasbrough·

Panama
BRANCH OFFICE: Vallarino Vallarino & Rivera
ASSOCIATED FIRM: Biggart Baillie & Gifford, Elliott & Company, Mackrell Turner Garrett, Simmons & Simmons, Veale Wasbrough

Peru
ASSOCIATED FIRM: Simmons & Simmons

Paraguay
ASSOCIATED FIRM: Simmons & Simmons

The Phillipines
BRANCH OFFICE: Baker & McKenzie
ASSOCIATED FIRM: Eversheds, Mackrell Turner Garrett

Papua New Guinea
BRANCH OFFICE: Blake Dawson Waldron

Poland
BRANCH OFFICE: Hogan & Hartson, Jeantet & Associes, Allen & Overy, Amhurst Brown Colombotti, Baker & McKenzie, Clifford Chance, McKenna & Co, Nabarro Nathanson, Salans Hertzfeld & Heilbronn, White & Case
ASSOCIATED FIRM: Edwards Geldard, Goodger Auden, Macfarlanes, Middleton Potts, Prettys, Theodore Goddard, Veale Wasbrough

Portugal
BRANCH OFFICE: Simmons & Simmons
ASSOCIATED FIRM: Aaron & Partners, Bates, Wells & Braithwaite, Biggart Baillie & Gifford, Blythe Liggins, Edmonds Bowen & Company, Elliott & Company, Freedman Church, Garrett & Co, Goodger Auden, Gulbenkian Harris Andonian, Hedleys, Lawrence Tucketts, Mackrell Turner Garrett, McCormicks, Philip Hamer & Co, Stoneham Langton & Passmore, Veale Wasbrough

Puerto Rico
ASSOCIATED FIRM: Simmons & Simmons

Romania
BRANCH OFFICE: Sinclair Roche & Temperley, Taylor Joynson Garrett
ASSOCIATED FIRM: Berrymans

Russia
BRANCH OFFICE: Hogan & Hartson, Secretan Troyanov & Partners, Skadden,

Arps, Slate, Meagher & Flom, Allen & Overy, Baker & McKenzie, Beiten Burkhardt Mittl & Wegener, Clifford Chance, Coudert Brothers, Denton Hall, Freshfields, Gouldens, Linklaters & Paines, McKenna & Co, Norton Rose, Salans Hertzfeld & Heilbronn, Salans Hertzfeld & Heilbronn, Watson Farley & Williams, White & Case

ASSOCIATED FIRM: Addleshaw Sons & Latham, Bond Pearce, Booth & Co., Burges Salmon, Clyde & Co, Frere Cholmeley Bischoff, Mills & Reeve, Paisner & Co, Peter Carter-Ruck & Partners, Rabin Leacock Lipman, Stephens Innocent, Teeman Levine

South Africa

BRANCH OFFICE: Bowman Gilfillan Hayman Godfrey, Maitland & Co

ASSOCIATED FIRM: Garrett & Co, Green David Conway & Co, Mackrell Turner Garrett, Veale Wasbrough

Saudi Arabia

BRANCH OFFICE: Bryan Cave, Nader Law Offices, Baker & McKenzie, White & Case

ASSOCIATED FIRM: Clifford Chance, Fox & Gibbons, Goodger Auden, Veale Wasbrough

Singapore

BRANCH OFFICE: Freehill Hollingdale & Page, Mallesons Stephen Jaques, Milbank, Tweed, Hadley & McCloy, Osler Renault, Allen & Overy, Baker & McKenzie, Beaumont and Son, Clifford Chance, Clyde & Co, Coudert Brothers, Denton Hall, Freshfields, Herbert Smith, Holman, Fenwick & Willan, Ince & Co, Linklaters & Paines, Norton Rose, Sinclair Roche & Temperley, White & Case

ASSOCIATED FIRM: Addleshaw Sons & Latham, Berrymans, Bond Pearce, Booth & Co., Burges Salmon, Mackrell Turner Garrett, Mills & Reeve, Nicholson Graham & Jones, Trowers & Hamlins, Veale Wasbrough, Waterson Hicks

Slovakia

ASSOCIATED FIRM: Edwards Geldard

Spain

BRANCH OFFICE: Diaz-Bastien & Truan, Fernando Scornik Gerstein, Uria & Menéndez, Shook Hardy & Bacon, Allen & Overy, Amhurst Brown Colombotti, Baker & McKenzie, Clifford Chance, Davies Arnold Cooper, Freshfields, Osborne Clarke, Stephenson Harwood

ASSOCIATED FIRM: Ashton Bond Gigg, McKeag & Co, Bowcock Cuerden, Abbott King & Troen, Bates, Wells & Braithwaite, Berrymans, Biggart Baillie & Gifford, Boodle Hatfield, Carrick Read Insolvency, Clement Jones, Cripps Harries Hall, Edwards Geldard, Elliott & Company, Foster Baxter Cooksey, Garrett & Co, Goodger Auden, Graham & Rosen, Gross & Co., Gulbenkian Harris Andonian, Hughes Dowdall, Hugh James Jones & Jenkins, John Howell & Co, Kirk Jackson, Lawrence Tucketts, McCormicks, Nelson & Co, Ormerod Wilkinson Marshall, Peasegood Walker, Philip Hamer & Co, Prettys, Russell–Cooke, Potter & Chapman, Simmons & Simmons, Stephen Rimmer & Co, Stoneham Langton & Passmore, Taylor Vinters, Veale Wasbrough

Sudan

BRANCH OFFICE: Hameed & Mallassi Advocates Ltd

Sweden

BRANCH OFFICE: Advokatfirman Cederquist KB, Hamilton & Co Advokatbyrå HB, Baker & McKenzie, White & Case

ASSOCIATED FIRM: Michael Bell & Co, Bates, Wells & Braithwaite, Biggart Baillie & Gifford, Elliott & Company, Garrett & Co, Goodger Auden, Gulbenkian Harris Andonian, Lane & Partners, Lawrence Tucketts, Mackrell Turner Garrett, Osmond Gaunt & Rose, Stoneham Langton & Passmore, Veale Wasbrough, Wansbroughs Willey Hargrave

Switzerland

BRANCH OFFICE: Froriep Renggli & Partners, Maitland & Co, Secretan Troyanov & Partners, Shook Hardy & Bacon, Baker & McKenzie

ASSOCIATED FIRM: Bayer Rosin, Fremont & Co, Aaron & Partners, Bates, Wells & Braithwaite, Biggart Baillie & Gifford, Carrick Read Insolvency, Elliott & Company, Eversheds, Garrett & Co, Hylton-Potts, Lane & Partners, Mackrell Turner Garrett, Prettys, Rakisons, Sedgwick, Detert, Moran & Arnold, Simmons & Simmons, Stoneham Langton & Passmore, Veale Wasbrough, Waterson Hicks, Wedlake Bell

Taiwan

BRANCH OFFICE: Mallesons Stephen Jaques, Perkins Coie, Baker & McKenzie

ASSOCIATED FIRM: Eversheds, Nicholson Graham & Jones

Thailand

BRANCH OFFICE: Freehill Hollingdale & Page, Baker & McKenzie, Coudert Brothers, Freshfields, White & Case

Turkey

BRANCH OFFICE: White & Case

ASSOCIATED FIRM: Veale Wasbrough

United Arab Emirates

BRANCH OFFICE: Baileys Shaw & Gillett, Berrymans, Clyde & Co, Fox & Gibbons

ASSOCIATED FIRM: Frere Cholmeley Bischoff, Osmond Gaunt & Rose, Veale Wasbrough

Ukraine

BRANCH OFFICE: Baker & McKenzie, Salans Hertzfeld & Heilbronn

ASSOCIATED FIRM: Rabin Leacock Lipman

Uruguay

ASSOCIATED FIRM: Simmons & Simmons

USA

BRANCH OFFICE: Bracewell & Patterson (Houston, Dallas, Washington D.C., Austin), Bryan Cave (St. Louis, Missouri, Washington D.C., New York, Kansas City, Missouri, Overland Park, Kansas, Phoenix, Arizona, Los Angeles, California, Santa Monica, California), Carnelutti (New York), Cravath, Swaine & Moore (New York), De Brauw Blackstone Westbroek (New York), Dobson & Pinci (Atlanta, New York, San Diego, Miami), Dorsey & Whitney (Minneapolis, New York, Denver, Washington and others), Fried, Frank, Harris, Shriver & Jacobson (New York, Washington, Los Angeles), A. & L. Goodbody (New York), Hartwig, Jeantet & Associes (New York), Joel Z. Robinson (New York), Kevorkian Loughran & Co (New York), Ladas & Parry (New York, Chicago, Los Angeles), Lagerlöf & Leman (New York), Mallesons Stephen Jaques (New York), Mayer Brown & Platt (Chicago, Washington, New York, Houston, Los Angeles), Milbank, Tweed, Hadley & McCloy (New York, Los Angeles, Washington), Oppenhoff & Radler (New York), Osler Renault (New York), Singhania & Co (New York), Simpson Thacher & Bartlett (New York), Stikeman Elliott (New York, Washington), Uria & Menéndez (New York), Law Offices of C.S. Steinger (Des Moines, San Francisco), Allen & Overy (New York), Alsop Wilkinson (New York), Baker & McKenzie (Chicago, Dallas, Miami, New York, Palo Alto, San Diego, San Francisco, Washington DC), Beiten Burkhardt Mittl & Wegener (New York), Bermans (New York), Berwin Leighton (New York), Clifford Chance (New York), Collyer–Bristow (New York), Coudert Brothers (New York, Washington, San Francisco, San Jose, Los Angeles), De Bandt Van Hecke & Lagae (New York), Denton Hall (Los Angeles), Freshfields (New York), Lawrence Graham, Linklaters & Paines (New York), Lovell White Durrant (New York), Rogers & Wells (New York, Washington, Los Angeles), Salans Hertzfeld & Heilbronn (New York), Sidley & Austin (Chicago, Los Angeles, New York, Washington D.C.), Simmons & Simmons (New York), Slaughter and May (New York), Stibbe Simont Monahan Duhot (New York), Titmuss Sainer Dechert (New York, Philadelphia, Princeton, Washington, Boston, Harrisburg), Watson Farley & Williams (New York), White & Case (New York, Los Angeles, Miami, Washington), Wiggin and Co (Los Angeles), Wilde Sapte (New York), Wilmer Cutler & Pickering (Washington DC), Wilson, Elser, Moskowitz, Edelman & Dicker (13 offices)

ASSOCIATED FIRM: Bayer Rosin, Michael Bell & Co, Amhurst Brown Colombotti, Baileys Shaw & Gillett, Biggart Baillie & Gifford, Church Adams Tatham & Co (Washington DC, Virginia), Cunningham, John & Co, M.B. Cuttle & Co, Doberman Horsman (Cleveland, Ohio), Edge & Ellison (Pittsburgh), Elliott & Company (Chicago, Denver, New York), Eversheds, Fishburn Boxer, Fladgate Fielder, Goodger Auden, Gross & Co. (New York), Gulbenkian Harris Andonian (Los Angeles), Hewitson Becke + Shaw (San Diego), Howes Percival (Los Angeles), Hylton-Potts, Kennedys, Lane & Partners (New York, Washington, Los Angeles), Lawrence Graham, Lawrence Tucketts, Mackenzie Mills (New York), Mackrell Turner Garrett (Boston, Chicago, Florida, Los Angeles, New York, Wichita, San Francisco, Washington), Magrath & Co (New York), Max Bitel, Greene (Tampa, Orlando, Clearwater), Nabarro Nathanson (New York), Nicholson Graham & Jones, Oswald Hickson Collier, Paisner & Co (Boston, Miami, Washington DC, Chicago, Los Angeles, Newport Beach, New York), Peter Carter-Ruck & Partners (San Francisco), Piper Smith & Basham, Sedgwick, Detert, Moran & Arnold (San Francisco, New York, Chicago, Orange County, Los Angeles), Taylor Joynson Garrett, Taylor Vinters (New York, Washington), Theodore Goddard (New York), Trowers & Hamlins (Washington D.C., Austin, Houston, Dallas), Veale Wasbrough (Honolulu, Los Angeles, New York, Chicago), Zaiwalla & Co (New York)

Venezuela

BRANCH OFFICE: Baker & McKenzie, Clyde & Co

ASSOCIATED FIRM: Simmons & Simmons

Vietnam

BRANCH OFFICE: Freehill Hollingdale & Page, Baker & McKenzie, Clifford Chance, Coudert Brothers, Freshfields, Lovell White Durrant, Sinclair Roche & Temperley, White & Case

ASSOCIATED FIRM: Nicholson Graham & Jones

Yemen

ASSOCIATED FIRM: Fox & Gibbons

Zambia

ASSOCIATED FIRM: Veale Wasbrough

FOREIGN LAW FIRMS IN LONDON

Listed below are those firms which have given us information about the number of lawyers in their London office and main areas of law handled. The firms have been divided into the following five regions based on their country of origin:- Europe, Middle East & Africa, North America, South America and the Pacific Rim & Asia.

Country of Origin and Firm Name	Fee-Earners London	World	Main Areas of Practice

EUROPE

Belgium

De Bandt Van Hecke & Lagae *(0171) 600 3608*	1	135	Banking and finance, general corporate.

Denmark

Berning Schlüter Hald *(0171) 236 2023*	1	30	International transactions including banking and international arbitration and litigation.
Kromann & Münter *(0171) 404 4825*	2	90	Company/commercial, finance and banking.
Reumert & Partners *See entry in A - Z of Law Firms*	1	43	Banking and finance, shipping, company/commercial.

Eire

A. & L. Goodbody *(0171) 929 2425*	3	137	Mergers and acquisitions, corporate restructuring, banking and tax-based financing, corporate finance, share and loan issues, Stock Exchange flotations, joint ventures, competition law, financial services, ship and aircraft financing, corporate insolvency and examination, general corporate advice.
Matheson Ormsby Prentice *(0171) 404 0998*	3	70	Corporate (mergers and acquisitions, joint ventures, venture capital, MBO's); banking (security work); financial services (fund management, structured finance); general (including property, litigation, private client).
McCann FitzGerald *(0171) 379 0914*	9	124	Banking and finance, financial services, corporate/ commercial, aircraft finance.
William Fry *(0171) 430 2738*	3	67	Mergers and acquisitions, corporate finance, financial services, Stock Exchange matters.

Finland

Roschier-Holmberg & Waselius *(0171) 929 0966*	1	43	Banking and financial services, general corporate, mergers & acquisitions, litigation, insolvency, tax.

France

Jeantet & Associes *(0171) 600 3608*	2	100	Banking, mergers and acquisitions, securities regulations, insurance (exclusively French law).
Salans Hertzfeld & Heilbronn *(0171) 491 3735*	7	100	All aspects of foreign investments, trade and finance, including mergers and acquisitions, corporate finance and banking (particularly in France and Central and Eastern Europe and the states of the former Soviet Union).

Germany

Beiten Burkhardt Mittl & Wegener *(0171) 247 9191*	4	57	Corporate and commercial law, corporate tax planning, commercial litigation, probate, family law and estate planning.
Dabelstein & Passehl *(0171) 702 4661*	4	12	English shipping and commercial work; advice on German law.
Hartwig *(0171) 235 1504*	5	-	Insolvency, international notarial practice (real estate, companies and probate); commercial contracts.
Oppenhoff & Radler *(0171) 600 3609*	2	230	Corporate (mergers and acquisitions, restructuring, German subsidiaries); commercial (distribution, agency, licensing); banking/ finance, loan guarantee, factoring finance leasing agreements, security over German assets, investment funds.

Gibraltar

Marrache & Co *(0171) 581 2161*	3	18	General commercial litigation; international trade and commodities; the banking and insurance aspects of international trade; ship and aircraft finance work.

Italy

Carnelutti *(0171) 242 2268*	2	50	Banking, mergers and acquisitions, insurance, company/ commercial, litigation and aviation.
Chiomenti E. Associati Studio Legale *(0171) 495 6430*	3	60	Banking, corporate tax and general commercial.
Dobson & Pinci *(0171) 628 8163*	5	55	Corporate/commercial (mergers and acquisitions, joint ventures, taxation); banking, securities, property, telecommunications, entertainment, construction, oil and gas, food industries.
Studio Legale Bisconti *(0171) 489 9924*	1	15	Mergers and acquisitions, general corporate work.
Studio Legale Sutti *See entry in A - Z of Law Firms*	2	23	Commercial law (work includes commercial contracts, banking and financial, joint ventures, insolvency, international trade), intellectual property & competition, employment law & related matters.

The Netherlands

De Brauw Blackstone Westbroek *(0171) 600 1719*	5	250	Banking and securities law (bonds issues, loan agreements); derivatives, programmes (MTN/ CP/ debt insurance), share issues, Amsterdam Stock Exchange listings; intellectual property (patents, trademarks, tradenames); corporate (mergers and acquisitions, joint ventures).

Country of Origin and Firm Name	Fee-Earners London	World	Main Areas of Practice
Stibbe Simont Monahan Duhot *See entry in A - Z of Law Firms*	3	350	Banking, corporate finance, structured finance, project finance, leasing, capital markets, financial services, investment funds, mergers and acquisitions, joint ventures, taxation.

Norway

Bugge, Arentz-Hansen & Rasmussen (UK) ANS *See entry in A - Z of Law Firms*	2	50	Corporate and commercial (joint stock companies and other corporations); banking and finance (documentation, negotiations and agreements, project finance); financial regulations (establishment conditions and agency aspects); Stock Exchange/ securities law (Stock Exchange listing, flotations); mergers and acquisitions, corporate taxation, shipping and maritime law.
Thommessen Krefting Greve Lund *(0171) 404 4825*	2	70	Company (mergers and acquisitions); commercial (licensing, agency, distributorship); finance (financial instruments, banking, asset finance); inheritance, matrimonial.
Wikborg Rein & Co *See entry in A - Z of Law Firms*	2	55	Shipping (sale and purchase, chartering, financing and insurance); company law (acquisitions in Norway); securities law (Norwegian regulations); energy (petroleum law, offshore contracts).

Spain

Diaz-Bastien & Truan *(0171) 409 2018*	1	18	Company/commercial (mergers and acquisitions, distribution agreements); real estate (large developers); entertainment (TV productions, films).
Fernando Scornik Gerstein *(0171) 930 3593*	5	19	Private client, personal injury, company/commercial, litigation, probate and tax, property, immigration.
Hector Diaz & Co *(0171) 489 8119*	2	-	Private client.
Michael Soul & Associates *(0171) 353 3358*	3	12	Exclusively Spanish law practice: company and commercial, investment in Spain, personal and corporate tax, probate, residential, enforcements of judgments.
Uria & Menéndez *(0171) 600 3610*	2	85	Corporate (corporate finance, foreign investment in Spain); mergers and acquisitions (acquisition of Spanish companies by UK clients and vice versa and joint ventures); financial and securities (issues of securities, investment funds, securities markets); banking (syndicated loans, co-operation contracts); commercial (distribution, agency, free competition).

Sweden

Advokatfirman Cederquist KB *(0171) 489 1431*	3	25	General commercial law, intellectual property, competition law.
Grundberg Mocatta *(0171) 938 4966*	4	8	Company/commercial, tax, property, trusts and probate.
Hamilton & Co Advokatbyrå HB *(0171) 938 5408*	1	21	Insolvency (liquidation, reconstruction); general commercial, tax.
Lagerlöf & Leman *(0171) 606 1715*	4	125	Corporate and commercial, mergers & acquisitions, banking and finance, arbitration, East-West trade.

Switzerland

Froriep Renggli & Partners *(0171) 236 6000*	4	35	International commercial litigation/ arbitration, finance, banking, mergers & acquisitions, corporate crime.
Secretan Troyanov & Partners *(0171) 404 1199*	1	19	Swiss commercial law, banking, mergers and acquisitions, litigation, arbitration.

MIDDLE EAST & AFRICA

Egypt

Hameed & Mallassi Advocates Ltd *(0171) 258 0636*	3	-	Law of inheritance, commercial arbitration, Islamic sheria laws, patents, construction contracts, telecommunications laws, immigration and nationality.

Iran

Dr Anvari & Associates *(0171) 724 9073*	5	2	International trade contracts, banking and finance laws, investment laws, insurance and shipping laws, construction contracts and litigation, oil and gas contracts and laws.

Israel

Zellermayer, Pelossof & Schiffer *(0171) 629 1920*	5	11	Business and corporate finance.

South Africa

Bowman Gilfillan Hayman Godfrey *(0171) 430 0888*	2	85	Corporate finance, general commercial, tax planning, joint ventures, acquisitions, investments in South Africa.
Maitland & Co *(0171) 831 0369*	7	185	International corporate, trust & tax planning, mergers & acquisitions, shipping, commodities & trade law.
Mallinick Ress Richman & Closenberg *(0171) 930 8702*	4	350	Telecommunications, exchange control and investment, intellectual property, joint ventures in South Africa, immigration, private client services, arbitration, litigation.
Shepstone & Wylie (UK) *See entry in A - Z of Law Firms*	6	250	Shipping (South African maritime law); commodities (CIF, C&F and FOB contracts); banking (trade finance, asset and finance leasing); corporate finance (major inward and outward investments from South Africa, transnational tax business and investment planning); South African moratorium debt, general corporate and commercial.

Saudi Arabia

Nader Law Offices *(0171) 373 0975*	1	10	Litigation, construction, employment, arbitration, commercial.

Country of Origin and Firm Name	Fee-Earners London World	Main Areas of Practice

NORTH AMERICA

Canada

Blake, Cassels & Graydon *(0171) 374 2334*	2 350	Mergers and acquisitions, capital markets (debt and equity), banking, corporate/ commercial.
Borden DuMoulin Howard Gervais *(0171) 929 2099*	3 600	London office of Canadian barristers and solicitors (Internet: apage@borden.com) opened in 1993 practicing broad range of Canadian law, including general corporate/ commercial, acquisitions/ competition, international corporate law/ securities, banking, high technology, natural resources, international insolvency, international litigation and alternative dispute resolution.
Fasken Martineau *(0171) 929 2894*	2 375	Mergers and acquisitions, capital markets, insolvency, banking and project finance, litigation, general corporate and commercial.
McCarthy Tétrault *(0171) 583 5644*	2 523	Euromarkets (acting for issuers and lead managers in Canadian law Euro offerings); corporate finance (mergers and acquisitions, general corporate, acting for investors, purchasers, vendors and advisors in all aspects of Canadian project finance); international mining, oil and gas project work.
Osler Renault *(0171) 606 0777*	3 500	Securities (international offerings extended to Canada, particularly privatisations); capital markets (debt offerings in Europe by Canadian issuers); mergers and acquisitions (cross-border offerings involving Canadian companies, assets or shareholders); banking (bank finance transactions involving Canadian lenders or security on Canadian assets).
Stikeman Elliott *(0171) 378 0880*	9 325	Mergers and acquisitions, banking/ securities, capital markets, private capital/ taxation.
Tory Tory DesLauriers & Binnington *(0171) 831 8155*	2 260	Euromarkets, corporate finance, banking and aircraft finance, commercial transactions (acting for financial institutions, governments and multinational corporations).

USA

Bingham Englar Jones & Houston *(0171) 283 9541*	1 30	Insurance (representing insurers of financial institutions worldwide); commercial crime (investigating and resolving claims on behalf of insurers); reinsurance (advising both reinsureds and reinsurers on policy wordings and on settlement of disputes); banking (advising insurers and supervising counsel in contentious matters).
Bingham Dana & Gould *(0171) 799 2646*	1 -	International finance, tax planning and licences, joint ventures, cross-border acquisitions, equity investments, debt restructuring.
Bracewell & Patterson *(0171) 355 3330*	3 225	Energy and petrochemical industries.
Brobeck Hale & Dorr International *(0171) 638 6688*	8 700	Venture capital, corporate finance, mergers/ acquisitions and joint ventures, securities law, high technology, biotechnology.
Brown & Wood *(0171) 606 1888*	8 250	Corporate and securities, international tax, trusts and estates.
Bryan Cave *(0171) 896 1900*	8 431	Corporate & commercial, individual & corporate taxation, international litigation & arbitration, trusts & estates.
Cleary, Gottlieb, Steen & Hamilton *(0171) 614 2200*	21 475	International financial work including securities law and tax advice, structure of global offerings, synthetic securities issues, development and evaluation of new financial products.
Coudert Brothers *See entry in A - Z of Law Firms*	26 380	Corporate finance, mergers and acquisitions, joint ventures, euro-securities, international banking law, international tax and trust planning, telecommunications and media law, energy privatisations and infrastructure projects, arbitration and litigation).
Covington & Burling *(0171) 495 5655*	11 325	Intellectual property (computers, software, copyright); pharmaceuticals, food and drink (regulatory issues under EC and US laws); US regulatory issues (all forms of US business regulation); competition law (all issues of EC, UK and US competition policies).
Cravath, Swaine & Moore *(0171) 606 1421*	9 350	General US corporate, financial and securities law practice.
Crowell & Moring *(0171) 413 0011*	4 220	Antitrust, aviation, business crime, communications, construction, corporate finance, mergers & acquisitions, energy, environmental, government contracts, international employment, litigation, product liability & insurance.
Curtis, Mallet-Prevost, Colt & Mosle *See entry in A - Z of Law Firms*	4 200	Public international law, corporate transactions, litigation and arbitration, international taxation, trusts and estates.
Davis Polk & Wardwell *(0171) 418 1300*	20 405	Securities, banking, mergers and acquisitions, tax.
Debevoise & Plimpton *(0171) 329 0779*	9 324	Corporate, financial, international tax, telecommunications.
Diane Hinch *See entry in A - Z of Law Firms*	1 1	US immigration.
Dorsey & Whitney *(0171) 929 3334*	3 400	Corporate finance (asset securitisation, Eurobonds, other international securities offerings, capital market transactions).
Faegre & Benson *(0171) 623 6163*	3 300	Corporate and commercial.
Fried, Frank, Harris, Shriver & Jacobson *(0171) 972 9600*	5 434	Mergers and acquisitions, corporate finance, company and commercial.
Fulbright & Jaworski *(0171) 629 1207*	5 730	Middle East law and regulations, international arbitration, international project funding, corporate/ commercial, tax.
Law Offices of Gary M. Ferman *(0171) 499 5702*	1 1	US taxation, estate and trust administration and planning, US and UK immigration, US and UK corporate work.
Gibson Dunn & Crutcher *(0171) 925 0440*	9 700	Mergers, acquisitions and joint ventures (US companies, multinational companies, central and eastern Europe); commercial transactions (distribution, sales agency, licensing); banking and corporate finance (debt and equity finance, US securities, Islamic banking, secured transactions); international tax structuring.

Country of Origin and Firm Name	Fee-Earners London World	Main Areas of Practice
Gottesman Jones & Partners *See entry in A - Z of Law Firms*	4 4	Tax (including US and international tax planning); securities (including sale in Europe of securities of US issuers); joint ventures and investments in the US, venture capital, mergers and acquisitions, licence and distribution agreements.
Graham & James *(0171) 353 1840*	2 400	Corporate, banking, litigation.
Hancock Rothert & Bunshoft *(0171) 220 7567*	2 100	Insurance (Lloyd's & London market companies, direct insurance/ reinsurance litigation and advice); environmental pollution, asbestos, directors' and officers' liability, lawyers' errors and omissions, maritime, construction and recreational liability.
Haythe & Curley *(0171) 930 0061*	1 60	Oil and gas (exploration and development); private client (international trusts); project finance.
Hogan & Hartson *(0171) 638 9595*	3 500	European-based international corporate and commercial transactions, US-based corporate and securities matters, US regulatory counselling.
Holme Roberts & Owen LLC *(0171) 499 8776*	4 217	International finance, general corporate, intellectual property, information technology.
Joel Z. Robinson *(0171) 253 2404*	1 5	Corporate/commercial, immigration, taxation, property litigation.
Jones, Day, Reavis & Pogue *(0171) 493 9361*	9 1200	Corporate (UK and cross-border acquisitions and disposals, joint ventures, licensing, corporate finance, reorganisations, financings, US securities law); tax (US, UK and other cross-border tax issues, tax based new financial products).
Kevorkian Loughran & Co *(0171) 355 2051*	3 15	Tax planning, corporate, commercial, international business transactions, arbitration, intellectual property, general international practice.
Kilpatrick & Cody *(0171) 321 0477*	3 204	Company/commercial (establishment or acquisition of European businesses by US companies); securities (European offerings of securities by US issuers).
Kirkland & Ellis *(0171) 814 6682*	2 475	The firm engages in a wide range of US law practice areas including antitrust, arbitration and litigation, corporate finance, US government contracts, insurance litigation and counselling, intellectual property, mergers, acquisitions and leveraged buyouts, securities and venture capital.
Kroll & Tract *(0171) 621 1142*	3 100	Insurance and reinsurance.
Ladas & Parry *(0171) 242 5566*	2 65	Intellectual property (patents, trademarks, copyright); licensing. Clients include major corporations, particularly in the US.
Latham & Watkins *See entry in A - Z of Law Firms*	7 600	Corporate (corporate reconstructions, privatisations, communications and technology licensing); finance (bankruptcy, aircraft finance and project finance); general practice (real estate, environmental, employment, insurance, litigation, tax).
Le Boeuf Lamb Greene & Macrae *See entry in A - Z of Law Firms*	10 500	Civil litigation; US, UK and EC insurance regulation, corporate/ commercial, energy, project finance, insolvency and banking regulation.
Mayer Brown & Platt *(0171) 248 1465*	19 600	Finance, corporate, CIS.
Milbank, Tweed, Hadley & McCloy *(0171) 448 3000*	15 400	Project finance, aircraft leasing and finance, banking, environment, international capital markets, privatisation.
Morgan Lewis & Bockius *See entry in A - Z of Law Firms*	14 796	International and cross border financings, tax planning for corporations and individuals, international and cross-border business transactions.
O'Melveny & Myers *(0171) 256 8451*	5 554	Corporate finance, acquisition finance, capital markets, securitisation/ structured finance.
Pepper, Hamilton & Scheetz *See entry in A - Z of Law Firms*	4 300	Mergers and acquisitions, commercial/ corporate, immigration, litigation support.
Perkins Coie *(0171) 369 9966*	4 380	Mergers and acquisitions, project finance, aircraft finance, banking and capital markets.
Piper & Marbury *(0171) 638 3833*	2 -	Company law, general corporate work.
Rogers & Wells *See entry in A - Z of Law Firms*	12 500	Capital markets, securities, corporate, funds, banking, mergers and acquisitions, intellectual property, tax.
J. Scott Brown & Associates *(0181) 300 4475*	1 200	Eastern Europe and former Soviet Union (commercial and all other civil trade, privatisations); US litigation (general civil, white collar crime, US military courts martial); leisure and entertainment (film, television, hotels).
Sedgwick, Detert, Moran & Arnold *See entry in A - Z of Law Firms*	8 235	Litigation and counselling services (especially in relation to directors and officers, fidelity, commercial, environmental, products liability, insurance and reinsurance law); professional negligence, arbitration, employment law, construction and intellectual property law.
Shearman & Sterling *(0171) 920 9000*	20 530	Corporate finance, mergers and acquisitions, privatisations, private finance and banking, oil and gas.
Shook Hardy & Bacon *(0171) 821 5595*	6 401	Product liability and corporate finance.
Sidley & Austin *See entry in A - Z of Law Firms*	24 788	Banking and structured finance, asset securitisation, telecoms, IT, soft IP and media, taxation advice (on both domestic and international transactions), corporate finance and commercial matters, property and property finance.
Simpson Thacher & Bartlett *(0171) 246 8000*	12 400	Securities law (issuances of securities in the US, all matters involving the SEC); mergers and acquisitions (representation of acquirers, sellers and financial advisers); banking and project finance (representation of financial institutions).
Skadden, Arps, Slate, Meagher & Flom *(0171) 248 9929*	16 1100	Capital markets, banking, mergers and acquisitions, general corporate.
Squire Sanders & Dempsey *(0171) 830 0055*	1 400	Mergers and acquisitions, finance.
Law Offices of C.S. Steinger *(0171) 937 7733*	1 1	USA immigration (company and professional transfers, working visas).
Sullivan & Cromwell *(0171) 710 6500*	28 425	Capital market offerings with US participation, mergers and acquisitions, US litigation, US and European antitrust law.
B.C. Toms & Co *(0171) 638 7711*	2 10	Ukrainian legal issues, oil and gas, general commercial transactions, investment in the Ukraine.

Country of Origin and Firm Name	Fee-Earners London World	Main Areas of Practice
Vinson & Elkins *(0171) 491 7236*	4 400	International energy, project finance and development, general company and commercial.
White & Case *(0171) 726 6361*	17 565	Securities (private placements of debt and US public offerings); project finance, construction, telecommunications, Eastern Europe, general corporate, corporate finance and acquisitions, capital markets and securities, tax.
Whitman Breed Abbott & Morgan *(0171) 839 3226*	10 400	Pensions and probate.
Willkie Farr & Gallagher *(0171) 696 9060*	3 430	US flotations (all varieties of Stock Exchange listing); venture capital (negotiated acquisitions of stakes in start-up companies); corporate (venture/ LBO fund establishment, investment management arrangements).
Wilmer Cutler & Pickering *(0171) 839 4466*	14 400	International arbitration, aviation, company/commercial.
Wilson, Elser, Moskowitz, Edelman & Dicker *See entry in A - Z of Law Firms*	1 395	Reinsurance, insurance, coverage disputes, US defense litigation, directors and officers liability, creditors' rights, arbitration, insurance broker errors and omissions.
Winthrop, Stimson, Putnam & Roberts *(0171) 628 4931*	2 250	Banking, securities, acquisitions.

SOUTH AMERICA

Brazil

Noronha-Advogados *(0171) 581 5040*	5 100	Banking (mostly for international money centres dealing with Brazil); international corporate/ contracts (Brazilian or Portuguese investments in the UK and UK investments in jurisdictions where the firm is located); international tax planning.
Pinheiro Neto-Advogados *(0171) 606 8261*	1 100	General corporate, capital markets, international corporate finance, debt/ equity swaps, international contracts, tax, intellectual property, entertainment, privatisations, maritime law, EC law.

Jamaica

Myers Fletcher & Gordon *(0171) 610 4433*	3 50	Commerce, real estate, intellectual property.

Panama

Arias, Fabrega & Fabrega *(0171) 287 3277*	2 20	Maritime/admiralty, banking/ commercial, general corporate.
Arosemena Noriega & Contreras *(0171) 828 6313*	1 12	Corporate (banks, industrial and manufacturing concerns, real estate investments); shipping (shipowners, ship charters, companies operating ships in international trade).
Morgan & Morgan *(0171) 493 1978*	2 33	Offshore companies (formation and administration); shipping (registration and finance of ships); foreign investment (Latin America).
Patton Moreno & Asvat *(0171) 434 2024*	2 8	Shipping (registration of vessels, legal assistance in respect of financial documents); commercial (incorporation of companies, legal advice on Panamanian companies).
Quijano & Associates *(0171) 499 4654*	1 8	Corporate (incorporation of companies in Panama and other jurisdictions); maritime (vessel registration, mortgage registration).
Vallarino Vallarino & Rivera *(0171) 486 5324*	1 5	Shipping (Panamanian flagged vessels); commercial (Panamanian corporations: formation and related work); banking and tax.

PACIFIC RIM & ASIA

Australia

Allens Arthur Robinson *(0171) 248 6130*	3 750	General corporate, banking, capital markets, Australian and Asian investment.
Blake Dawson Waldron *(0171) 600 3030*	2 470	Mergers and acquisitions, Stock Exchange listings and rules, capital markets, banking and finance, joint ventures, foreign investments, general corporate advice, stamp duty and taxation, anti-trust law, general commercial law.
Corrs Chambers Westgarth *(0171) 929 4955*	2 365	Mergers and acquisitions, capital markets, competition law, banking and finance, general corporate/ commercial, taxation, intellectual property.
Freehill Hollingdale & Page *(0171) 283 9006*	4 495	Mergers and acquisitions, banking and finance, corporate, commercial, taxation.
Mallesons Stephen Jaques *(0171) 982 0982*	4 564	Finance/corporate (corporate reconstructions, international equity issues, takeovers, financings, insolvencies, privatisations, resources and project finance); intellectual property.
Minter Ellison *See entry in A - Z of Law Firms*	3 530	Company/commercial, financial services, banking, corporate finance, mergers and acquisitions, corporate tax, international work.

India

Singhania & Co *(0171) 828 3384*	4 50	Corporate/commercial, intellectual property, securities, project finance, litigation, arbitration.

SOLICITORS' CHARGES & REMUNERATION

URING the 1980s, solicitors' fees were usually charged by the hour, often with additional mark-ups for special or urgent services. Now, however, most commercial clients find it unacceptable to be billed on this basis. The market for legal services has become more competitive and there is considerable pressure on fees. The larger commercial clients have become sophisticated users of legal services and are expert at shopping around. To win new business, and to retain existing clients, firms have had

Tables A and B show the range of hourly rates that serve as a benchmark for firms of solicitors in London and the provinces in the four main areas of law. Charges have, on the whole, remained level during the past year for most areas of practice, and are likely to remain constant in the forseeable future due to continuing competitive pressure. Company commercial and property work has become price-sensitive – some firms suggesting that it is not always possible to charge for all the services they have provided. Litigation

TABLE A: PARTNER £/HOUR

	COMPANY/COMMERCIAL			COMMERCIAL LITIGATION			COMMERCIAL PROPERTY			PRIVATE CLIENT		
	LOW	AVG	HIGH	LOW	AVG	HIGH	LOW	AVG	HIGH	LOW	AVG	HIGH
LONDON	135	250	335	170	200	310	155	175	290	95	170	260
PROVINCES	65	115	220	70	110	220	65	100	180	60	95	170

TABLE B: ASSISTANT SOLICITOR £/HOUR

	COMPANY/COMMERCIAL			COMMERCIAL LITIGATION			COMMERCIAL PROPERTY			PRIVATE CLIENT		
	LOW	AVG	HIGH	LOW	AVG	HIGH	LOW	AVG	HIGH	LOW	AVG	HIGH
LONDON	90	140	215	80	125	225	75	115	200	70	90	135
PROVINCES	50	80	140	60	85	130	50	75	110	55	70	110

to bid low, even to the extent of charging uneconomic fees ('low-balling'). The present climate is rather more favourable, but beauty parades and fee negotiation seem to be here to stay.

Commercial clients now expect to discuss fees before any work takes place. With many firms offering their services at fixed or capped rates, the hourly rate often serves merely as a benchmark for negotiations. Fixed fees are commonplace for areas such as licensing, employment, residential conveyancing and commercial property, and will always be considered where the outcome is relatively predictable. Half the City firms' banking and syndicated loan transactions are done for fixed or capped fees. Charges are discounted where the client is prepared to commit to further business.

Specialisation still commands a premium where there is a technically excellent and well known practice group or individual. However, for the majority of firms, premium rates are more likely to reflect speed of service.

The latest trend in billing practices is 'accountability' – providing clients with detailed information about the cost of legal services. The former reticence of law firms to disclose their fees is disappearing. Using information technology, partners can itemise their bills, and ascertain the billing situation at any stage by the touch of a button.

rates increased slightly this year, though a downturn is expected when recession-led disputes thin out.

REMUNERATION
With the recovery in the economy gathering pace, last year's growth in new recruitment by larger firms has accelerated. This has been mirrored by continuing increases in salaries, particularly amongst two to four-year qualified solicitors, although the level of increases varies between regions.

Profit-related pay, which enables a firm to pay employees an extra £4,000 per annum free of income tax, is now firmly established in the larger firms, and many would expect to pay their assistants this maximum tax-free level.

LONDON
The most striking change in London has been the recovery in the core practice areas of commercial property and company/commercial – most strongly reflected in increased salaries for two- to four- year qualified solicitors, the group most in demand by employers. Amongst West End firms, the upturn has been less marked, and this is shown in a more modest increase in salaries.

US law firms continue to expand their presence in the London market. They are generally prepared to offer slightly higher salaries than the City firms.

SOUTH OF ENGLAND

The greatest demand for assistants has been in the one to three-year qualified range, with specialists in commercial property particularly sought after. Even so, salary rises in this region have not been spectacular.

The highest salaries in the South West are to be found in Bristol and in the South East in Oxford and Reading. In contrast, in such places as Maidstone and Tunbridge Wells, salary levels are lower.

MIDLANDS

As in other regions of the country, two to three-year qualified solicitors are most in demand. Some of the top salaries offered appear to be those designed to attract solicitors from outside the region, and there is usually a disparity between the levels offered to new recruits and those paid to existing employees. The highest salaries are to be found in the West midlands, especially among the large Birmingham firms.

THE NORTH

The highest levels of salaries are still to be found in the large commercial firms in Manchester and Leeds. These firms, some of which also have a presence in London, are prepared to offer substantially more than other firms in the region to attract the best calibre candidates. Salaries for specialist areas such as pensions and tax and property and commercial specialists have shown the greatest increase.

Newcastle has seen an increase in legal work and a corresponding rise in salaries. In Liverpool and Bradford remuneration is lower, making the disparity in salary levels in the North higher than in any other region in England.

THE TABLES

The salary ranges for Assistant Solicitors indicate the spectrum on which the great majority of salaries are found. Unlike the trainees figures, they do not cover salaries at the extreme top and bottom of the scale. Salary bands are likely to be adhered to more closely by the larger firms, smaller firms taking an an individual approach to their staff resulting in departures from the norm.

TRAINEES' REMUNERATION (£,000s)

	1st year	2nd year
LONDON: CITY	17.0 – 19.5	18.5 – 22.0
LONDON: WEST END	14.5 – 17.0	16.5 – 19.5
SOUTH EAST	11.0 – 12.5	11.5 – 14.5
SOUTH WEST	11.0 – 13.0	12.5 – 14.0
MIDLANDS	11.5 – 13.5	12.5 – 15.0
NORTH WEST	12.5 – 13.5	14 – 15.5
NORTH EAST	11.5 – 14.0	13 – 15.5
EAST ANGLIA	12.0 – 13.0	13 – 14.0

ASSISTANT SOLICITORS' REMUNERATION (£,000s)

Years Qualified	NQ	1 yr	2 yrs	3 yrs	4 yrs
LONDON: CITY	26 – 28.5	28 – 34	32 – 37	35 – 44	42 – 50
LONDON: WEST END	22 – 26.5	25 – 29	28 – 33	30 – 36	34 – 41
SOUTH EAST	18 – 22	20 – 23.5	22 – 26	23 – 28.5	25 – 32
SOUTH WEST	17 – 20	19 – 23	22 – 24	23 – 26	24 – 30
MIDLANDS	18.5 – 20.5	20 – 24	22 – 25	23 – 27	25 – 32
NORTH WEST	18 – 21	20 – 24	23 – 27	25 – 30	27 – 35
NORTH EAST	17.5 – 21.5	20 – 24	23 – 27	24 – 30	26 – 35
EAST ANGLIA	17.5 – 18.5	18 – 22	21 – 24	23 – 26	24 – 30

CHAMBERS & PARTNERS'

DIRECTORY OF THE LEGAL PROFESSION

THE BAR

CONTENTS *Barristers*

Specialist Lists and Profiles of Leading Barristers

Barristers' Charges

CHARGE rates at the Bar vary considerably. One clerk said that he had around 40 different barristers and around 40 different charge rates. Level of seniority, reputation and specialisation are the basic elements which determine an individual's charges. Clearly, a complex and difficult case in a highly specialised area in which only a few members of the Bar are competent will cost considerably more than a relatively routine case which can be handled by junior counsel. At present, most clerks do not charge for a barrister's time by the hour but on a value basis. For example, a short telephone conference concerning vital matters in a major M&A deal may be charged out at £500. Even where time-costing is used as a basis, an element of discretion by the clerk may still alter the total fee charged, depending on the full circumstances of the case.

Generally, all the clerks we spoke to stated that fees have remained at much the same level as last year's. The figures below represent broad ranges of the hourly rates one might expect to pay for relatively routine work in four main categories of work.

There is no practical alternative to using hourly charge rates to indicate the cost of using a barrister. As mentioned above, barristers clerks quote fees based on the nature of the work and the particular barrister instructed. However, behind these assorted charges there lies a common (if tacit) understanding of the appropriate rates per hour that can be commanded by barristers of the same seniority and experience. The table of hourly rates, therefore, is a useful guide provided it is appreciated that in practice barristers' clerks do not normally think in these terms.

Hourly Charge Rates				
SENIORITY	Commercial	Chancery	Common law	Criminal
QC	£200 – £350	£200 – £350	£175 – £250	£150 – £200
10 yrs call	£80 – £200	£100 – £200	£85 – £150	£75 – £110
Early years (3-4 yrs call)	£35 – £75	£50 – £100	£35 – £80	£50 – £60

Barristers' Remuneration

THE wide range of ability at the Bar and the reticence of most barristers to discuss their earnings makes it difficult to estimate reliable averages. The table below, therefore, provides only a general indication of earnings in two contrasting areas of law: criminal and commercial. The figures represent the annual income of barristers who are reasonably successful; those not fully employed will expect to earn less. The figures for commercial law show a broader spread than those for criminal law, due to the wide range of work available. It should be stressed that although some commercial lawyers earn salaries at the top of the range, the majority's earnings are towards the lower end. The earnings for a commercial pupillage include grants made available from chambers.

Annual earnings					
SENIORITY	Pupillage	1 –5 years	6 – 10 years	10 years +	Queen's Counsel
Criminal	£7,000 – £15,000	£20,000 – £35,000	£30,000 – £60,000	£40,000 – £100,000	£100,000 – £200,000+
Commercial	£10,000 – £20,000	£20,000 – £50,000	£50,000 – £175,000	£70,000 – £300,000	£200,000 – £500,000+

(The figure for Queen's Counsel in criminal chambers is for legal aid work. Privately funded work will pay more. Pupillage figures apply to the second six months, assuming the pupil is getting work. All figures are gross: the net figures of course will be lower. Being self-employed a barrister must pay clerks' fees and other expenses.)

INTERNATIONAL CONNECTIONS

A - Z set numbers are shown in square brackets. The section for the United States shows in italics the particular jurisdictions to which at least one member is admitted.

Anguilla
8 King's Bench Walk [114]

Antigua
11 King's Bench Walk [119]

Antilles
4 Breams Buildings [17], 2 Garden Court [67], 1 Gray's Inn Square [77], 5 King's Bench Walk [110], 8 King's Bench Walk [114], 1 Mitre Court Buildings [132]

Australia
Arbitration Chambers [1], Atkin Chambers [3], Counsels' Chambers [332], 2 Crown Office Row [35], Doughty Street Chambers [37], Enterprise Chambers [41], Enterprise Chambers [276], Enterprise Chambers [41], Enterprise Chambers [276], Essex Court Chambers [47], 4 Essex Court [45], 36 Essex Street [51], Falcon Chambers [54], 2 Field Court [56], 7 Fountain Court [232], Fountain Court [61], Francis Taylor Building [62], Godolphin Chambers [380], Gray's Inn Chambers [73], 1 Gray's Inn Square [77], 4-5 Gray's Inn Square [81], 10 King's Bench Walk [118], 1 Mitre Court Buildings [132], 11 New Square [148], 8 New Square [146], New Walk Chambers [290], 10 Old Square [156], Old Square Chambers [162], 10 Old Square [156], 2 Paper Buildings [167], 4 Pump Court [183], 6 Pump Court [186], Queen Elizabeth Building [189], 3 Raymond Buildings [192], 11 Stone Buildings [209], 3 Temple Gardens [218]

Bahamas
Erskine Chambers [42], 8 King's Bench Walk [114], 12 New Square [149], 10 Old Square [156], 3 Raymond Buildings [192], 3-4 South Square [199], 4 Stone Buildings [204]

Bangladesh
Forest House Chambers [60], 3 Paper Buildings [168]

Barbados
5 King's Bench Walk [110], 11 Old Square [158]

Belgium
Bracton Chambers [16], Brick Court Chambers [18], 4 Essex Court [45], 1 Essex Court [43], 20 Essex Street [50], 4-5 Gray's Inn Square [81], 12 Gray's Inn Square [86], 2 Harcourt Buildings [95], 2 Hare Court [99], 4 King's Bench Walk [109], 5 Paper Buildings [175], Four Raymond Buildings [193], Regency Chambers [251]

Bermuda
9 Bedford Row [10], Castle Chambers [269], Erskine Chambers [42], 1 Essex Court [43], Essex Court Chambers [47], 2 Garden Court [67], 3 Gray's Inn Square [80], 4-5 Gray's Inn Square [81], 3 Gray's Inn Square [80], 14 Gray's Inn Square [87], 11 King's Bench Walk [119], 11 New Square [148], 1 New Square [140], Old Square Chambers [248], 13 Old Square [160], Old Square Chambers [162], 3-4 South Square [199], 4 Stone Buildings [204]

Botswana
1 Crown Office Row [32], Doughty Street Chambers [37], 10 King's Bench Walk [117], 1 Middle Temple Lane [127]

British Virgin Islands
Holborn Chambers [0], 4 Stone Buildings [204]

Burma
2 Middle Temple Lane [129]

Canada
Eighteen Carlton Crescent [370], 1 Essex Court [44], 36 Essex Street [51], King Charles House [344], 3 Raymond Buildings [192]

Cayman Islands
Bracton Chambers [16], Erskine Chambers [42], Essex Court Chambers [47], 11 King's Bench Walk [119], 1 New Square [140], 3-4 South Square [199], 4 Stone Buildings [204]

Cyprus
9 Bedford Row [10], 4 Essex Court [45], 2 Paper Buildings [167]

Dominican Republic
1 Gray's Inn Square [77]

East Caribbean
11 King's Bench Walk [119], 12 New Square [149]

Eire
Arbitration Chambers [1], Arden Chambers [2], 33 Bedford Row [8], Doughty Street Chambers [37], 4 Essex Court [45], Essex Court Chambers [47], 4 Essex Court [45], Farrar's Building [55], 2 Field Court [56], 7 Fountain Court [232], 9 Gough Square [71], 3 Gray's Inn Place [75], 12 Gray's Inn Square [86], 2 Harcourt Buildings [93], Harcourt Chambers [348], 3 Hare Court [100], 12 King's Bench Walk [121], King Charles House [344], 8 King St [317], Lamb Building [123], Martin's Building [299], Newport Chambers [338], 8 New Square [146], 19 Old Buildings [151], Old Square Chambers [162], 5 Paper Buildings [174], 3 Paper Buildings [168], 5 Paper Buildings [174], 7 Queen Avenue [304], 3 Raymond Buildings [192], 11 South Square [200], 11 Stone Buildings [209], 11 Stone Chambers [253], Trinity Chambers [336]

Falkland Islands
13 Old Square [160]

Fiji
3 Raymond Buildings [192]

France
17 Bedford Row [6], Bracton Chambers [16], 2 Crown Office Row [34], 1 Dr Johnson's Buildings [38], 1 Essex Court [43], 4 Essex Court [45], 20 Essex Street [50], Francis Taylor Building [63], 4-5 Gray's Inn Square [81], 12 Gray's Inn Square [86], Littleton Chambers [126], New Walk Chambers [290]

Germany
3 Paper Buildings [170]

Ghana
1 Middle Temple Lane [128], 12 Old Square [159], 11 Old Square [158], 12 Old Square [159]

Gibraltar
2 Crown Office Row [35], Essex Court Chambers [47], Fountain Court [61], 9 Gough Square [71], 3 Gray's Inn Place [75], 3 Hare Court [100], Keating Chambers [103], 1 New Square [140], 3 Paper Buildings [168], Queen Elizabeth Building [189], 7 Stone Buildings [206]

Greece
4 Essex Court [45]

Guernsey
24 Old Buildings [154]

Hong Kong
Holborn Chambers [0], Atkin Chambers [3], 9 Bedford Row [10], 2 Crown Office Row [34], 1 Dr Johnson's Buildings [38], Erskine Chambers [42], 4 Essex Court [43], 4 Essex Court [45], Essex Court Chambers [47], 20 Essex Street [50], 36 Essex Street [51], Falcon Chambers [54], Farrar's Building [55], 3 Gray's Inn Place [75], 2-3 Gray's Inn Square [79], 12 Gray's Inn Square [86], 1 Hare Court [97], Iscoed Chambers [377], Keating Chambers [103], 2 King's Bench Walk [106], 11 King's Bench Walk [119], 5 King's Bench Walk [110], Littleton Chambers [126], 1 Mitre Court Buildings [132], 11 New Square [148], Three New Square [142], 1 New Square [140], Old Square Chambers [248], 9 Old Square [155], 13 Old Square [160], 2 Paper Buildings [167], 5 Paper Buildings [175], 5 Paper Buildings [174], 3 Paper Buildings [168], 5 Paper Buildings [174], 3 Raymond Buildings [192], 1 Serjeants' Inn [196], No. 1 Serjeants' Inn [195], 3-4 South Square [199], 4 Stone Buildings [204], 11 Stone Buildings [210], 199 Strand [211]

India
3 Dr Johnson's Buildings [40], 2 Middle Temple Lane [129], 1A Mitre Court Buildings [133], 8 New Square [146], 2 Paper Buildings [167]

Isle of Man
2 Gray's Inn Square Chambers [78], 22 Old Buildings [152], 13 Old Square [160]

Iran
International Law Chambers [102], Trinity Chambers [336]

Israel
Lamb Building [123], St. James's Chambers [325]

Italy
17 Bedford Row [6], Cloisters [29], 1 Dr Johnson's Buildings [38], 35 Essex Street [53], 1 Gray's Inn Square [77], 6 Gray's Inn Square [82], 24 Old Buildings [153]

Jamaica
Bracton Chambers [16], Gray's Inn Chambers [73], 3 Gray's Inn Square [80], 1 Gray's Inn Square [76], 8 King's Bench Walk [114]

Jersey
Reading Chambers [0], 9 Bedford Row [10], 1 Dr Johnson's Buildings [38], Old Square Chambers [248], 3 Paper Buildings [168]

Jordan
International Law Chambers [102]

Kenya
Essex Court Chambers [47], 10 King's Bench Walk [117]

Lesotho
17 Carlton Crescent [369], Doughty Street Chambers [37]

Libya
International Law Chambers [102]

Malaysia
Holborn Chambers [0], Reading Chambers [0], Atkin Chambers [3], 1 Dr Johnson's Buildings [38], Erskine Chambers [42], Essex Court Chambers [47], 2 Middle Temple Lane [130], 1 New Square [140], 10 Old Square [156], 13 Old Square [160], 3 Raymond Buildings [192]

Mauritius
1 Essex Court [43], 4 King's Bench Walk [109], 10 King's Bench Walk [117], 4 King's Bench Walk [109], Thomas More Chambers [220]

Namibia
1 Crown Office Row [32], Doughty Street Chambers [37]

Nepal
199 Strand [211]

New Zealand
9-12 Bell Yard [12], 1 Gray's Inn Square [77], 22 Old Buildings [152], 2 Paper Buildings [167], St. John's Chambers [249], 11 Stone Buildings [209]

Nigeria
Holborn Chambers [0], Prince Henry's Chambers [0], Francis Taylor Building [63], 10 King's Bench Walk [118], 12 Old Square [159], Pepy's Chambers [176], Pump Court Chambers [180]

Northern Ireland
Barnards Inn Chambers [4], Doughty Street Chambers [37], 4 Essex Court [45], Farrar's Building [55], 2 Garden Court [67], 3 Gray's Inn Place [75], 2 Hare Court [99], 5 King's Bench Walk [110], 8 New Square [146], 24 Old Buildings [154], 19 Old Buildings [151], Old Square Chambers [162], 13 Old Square [160], Old Square Chambers [162], Pump Court Chambers [180], 11 Stone Buildings [210]

Pakistan
Ealing Barristers Chambers [0], Forest House Chambers [60], 2 Middle Temple Lane [129], 8 New Square [146], 11 Old Square [158], Perivale Chambers [177]

Sierra Leone
1 Middle Temple Lane [128]

Singapore
Atkin Chambers [3], 4 Breams Buildings [17], 1 Dr Johnson's Buildings [38], Erskine Chambers [42], 5 Essex Court [46], 1 Essex Court [43], Essex Court Chambers [47], 20 Essex Street [50], 3 Gray's Inn Place [75], 4-5 Gray's Inn Square [81], 2-3 Gray's Inn Square [79], 11 King's Bench Walk [119], Lamb Chambers [124], Littleton Chambers [126], 11 New Square [148], 1 New Square [140], 13 Old Square [160], 3 Raymond Buildings [192], 3-4 South Square [199], Watford Chambers [381]

South Africa
1 Crown Office Row [32], Doughty Street Chambers [37], 1 Essex Court [43], Fountain Court [61], 4-5 Gray's Inn Square [81], Seven King's Bench Walk [113], Lamb Chambers [124], New Court Chambers [139], 19 Old Buildings [151], Old Square Chambers [162], 3-4 South Square [199], 11 Stone Buildings [210]

Spain
1 Essex Court [44], 4 Essex Court [45], 12 Gray's Inn Square [86], 24 Old Buildings [154]

Sri Lanka
2 Middle Temple Lane [129]

St. Helena
1 Crown Office Row [32]

St. Kitts and Nevis
1 Crown Office Row [32], 2 Harcourt Buildings [95]

St. Vincent
Essex Court Chambers [47]

Swaziland
Doughty Street Chambers [37]

Sweden
One Hare Court [98]

Switzerland
1 Essex Court [43], 24 Old Buildings [153]

Tanzania
2 Middle Temple Lane [130]

Trinidad & Tobago
1 Crown Office Row [32], 8 New Square [146]

Turkey
8 Gray's Inn Square [83], 2 Harcourt Buildings [95]

Turks & Caicos
33 Bedford Row [8]

USA
Reading Chambers [0] (District of Columbia), Arbitration Chambers [1] (California), Barnards Inn Chambers [4] (California), 33 Bedford Row [8] (New York) (California), 9 Bedford Row [10], 4 Breams Buildings [17] (New York) (Federal Court), Bridge St Chambers [309] (District of Columbia) (Illinois) (New York), Eighteen Carlton Crescent [370], 2 Crown Office Row [34], Doughty Street Chambers [37] (New York), Enterprise Chambers [41], Enterprise Chambers [276], Enterprise Chambers [41] (New York), Enterprise Chambers [276] (New York), 1 Essex Court [44], 1 Essex Court [43], 36 Essex Street [51], 2 Field Court [56] (New York), Fountain Court [61] (California), Godolphin Chambers [380], 3 Gray's Inn Place [75], 1 Gray's Inn Square [77], 4-5 Gray's Inn Square [81] (New York), 14 Gray's Inn Square [87] (Georgia), 1 Gray's Inn Square [77] (California), Hamilton House Chambers [88] (California), Hardwicke Building [96] (California), 2 Hare Court [99] (New York), 10 King's Bench Walk [118] (Massachusetts), 5 King's Bench Walk [110] (New York), 10 King's Bench Walk [118] (California), 8 King St [317] (New York), Lamb Chambers [124], Littleton Chambers [126] (New York), 1 Mitre Court Buildings [132], 2 Mitre Court Buildings [134] (California), 1 Mitre Court Buildings [132] (California), Mitre Court Chambers [136] (California) (Federal Court), New Court Chambers [139] (California), 11 New Square [148], 24 Old Buildings [153], 10 Old Square [156], Old Square Chambers [162] (New York), 10 Old Square [156] (Chicago), 1 Paper Buildings [163], 3 Paper Buildings [168], 1 Paper Buildings [163] (Texas), 3 Paper Buildings [168] (California) (Arizona), Queen Elizabeth Building [189] (California), 3 Raymond Buildings [192], 3-4 South Square [199] (Illinois) (Federal Court), St. Ive's Chambers [237] (Illinois) (Texas) (Federal Court), 11 Stone Buildings [210], 11 Stone Buildings [209], 11 Stone Buildings [210] (Iowa) (Pennsylvania) (New York), 11 Stone Buildings [209] (California)

West Indies
2 Crown Office Row [34], 1 Gray's Inn Square [77], 3 Gray's Inn Square [80]

Yemen
International Law Chambers [102]

Zimbabwe
Doughty Street Chambers [37], 1 Middle Temple Lane [127], 11 Old Square [158]

AGRICULTURE AND BLOODSTOCK

THIS area of law has been increasingly subject to European developments in recent years. In particular, Common Agricultural Policy reforms have led to changes in the arable, sheep and beef sectors. The new Agricultural Holdings Act will assist the creation of tenancies accommodating non-agricultural use of land.

LEADING SETS

FALCON CHAMBERS

The leading set in this field is **Falcon Chambers**. *Paul Morgan QC* and *Derek Wood QC* are highly respected specialists who deal with all aspects of this area including agricultural holdings and production control, acting for tenant

LEADING SILKS

Morgan, Paul *Falcon Chambers*	
Wood, Derek *Falcon Chambers*	
Gaunt, Jonathan *Falcon Chambers*	
Neuberger, David *Falcon Chambers*	

farmers and financial institutions. *Paul Morgan* has appeared in 'R v MAFF ex parte Cox', 'Creear v Fearon', 'Pennell v Payne', 'Welby v Casswell', 'Barclays Bank v Eustice' and 'John v George'. *Derek Wood* has a particular expertise in European aspects of this sector, and has edited 'Milk Quotas: Law and Practice' and 'The Handbook of

Milk Quota Compensation' together with *Joanne Moss*, an experienced junior in chambers who also specialises in agricultural work. In addition, *Joanne Moss* is also the editor of 'Muir Watt on Agricultural Holdings'.

LEADING JUNIORS

Moss, Joanne R. *Falcon Chambers*	
Rodger, Martin *Falcon Chambers*	
Brock, Jonathan *Falcon Chambers*	
Brudenell, Thomas *Queen Elizabeth Building*	
Cole, Edward *Falcon Chambers*	
Cranfield, Peter *3 Gray's Inn Place*	
Holgate, David *4 Breams Buildings*	
Hutton, Caroline *Enterprise Chambers*	

Also highly recommended were *David Neuberger QC* and *Jonathan Gaunt QC*. *Martin Rodger* is known for his work in agricultural tenancies. He appeared in the Court of Appeal in 'Pennel v Payne' in 1994, and is a member of the Agricultural Law Association. *Jonathan Brock* and *Edward Cole* are also highly regarded.

Caroline Hutton at **Enterprise Chambers** has been recommended, as has *Peter Cranfield* at **3 Gray's Inn Place**.

Specialists in bloodstock work, particularly relating to horses, include *Thomas Brudenell* at **Queen Elizabeth Building** and *David Holgate* at **4 Breams Buildings**.

LEADERS IN AGRICULTURE AND BLOODSTOCK

Brock, Jonathan
See under Property Litigation.

Brudenell, Thomas
See under Family Law.

Cole, Edward
Falcon Chambers (Jonathan Gaunt QC, David Neuberger QC), London (0171) 353 2484. Work includes agricultural holdings, Property Litigation, easements, boundaries, rights of way, restrictive covenants, etc.

Cranfield, Peter
See under Building Societies.

Gaunt QC, Jonathan
See under Property Litigation.

Holgate, David
See under Public and Administrative Law.

Hutton, Caroline
See under Property Litigation.

Morgan QC, Paul
See under Property Litigation.

Moss, Joanne R.
Falcon Chambers (Jonathan Gaunt QC, David Neuberger QC), London (0171) 353 2484. Called 1976. Member of the Agricultural Law Association. Editor of 'Milk

Quotas: Law and Practice' and 'Hill and Redman on Landlord & Tenant'.

Neuberger QC, David
See under Property Litigation.

Rodger, Martin
See under Property Litigation.

Wood QC, Derek
Falcon Chambers (Jonathan Gaunt QC, David Neuberger QC), London (0171) 353 2484. Called 1964, took silk 1978. Specialises in property law, including commercial Property Litigation, rent review, joint developments, construction disputes and professional negligence

ALTERNATIVE DISPUTE RESOLUTION

A S THE cost of litigation becomes ever more prohibitive, increasing numbers of parties, both companies and individuals, are turning towards alternative methods of resolving disputes. ADR is characterised by its flexibility: the parties are free to agree whatever procedural approach suits them. The most common form adopted is that of the 'mini-trial' in which a mediator appointed by the parties hears representations from both sides and encourages them to reach the most mutually advantageous compromise possible in the circumstances. Other advantages claimed for ADR include speed and privacy. It will prove effective, however, only in situations where all parties genuinely wish to compromise. Where positions are more entrenched, there still seems no viable alternative to traditional litigation.

Resolution, and a member of the Beldam Committee on ADR. *Roderick I'Anson Banks* at **48 Bedford Row** is a CEDR accredited mediator and offers expertise in particular in relation to partnership disputes. *Michael Burton QC* at **Littleton Chambers** has a strong reputation in this sector and has also been involved with CEDR. *Lawrence Kershen QC* at **Cloisters** is also a trained mediator. *John Tackaberry QC* at **Arbitration Chambers** has been involved in a number of disputes referred to CEDR.

At **Essex Court Chambers** *Martin Hunter* has represented parties in conciliations, mediations and other ADR procedures and has acted as conciliator and mediator. He is a member of the Institute of International Business Law and Practice Working Party on ADR. This set also has a number of associated members based outside this jurisdicition who are expert in ADR procedures, and are available to practise in England and Wales.

LEADING SILKS

Naughton, Philip	*3 Serjeants' Inn*	
Burton, Michael	*Littleton Chambers*	
Collins, Michael	*Essex Court Chambers*	
Kershen, Lawrence	*Cloisters*	
Ramsey, Vivian	*Keating Chambers*	
Tackaberry, John	*Arbitration Chambers*	

As this is a relatively new area of work, there are as yet no chambers which specialise in it. There are, however, a number of individual barristers with very good reputations for their expertise in this field.

Philip Naughton QC at **3 Serjeants' Inn,** a recognised specialist in this area, is a director of the Centre for Dispute

LEADING JUNIORS

Banks, Roderick I'Anson	*48 Bedford Row*	
Goodman, Andrew	*199 Strand*	
Hunter, Martin	*Essex Court Chambers*	

UP AND COMING

Brodie, Bruce	*39 Essex Street*	

Vivian Ramsey QC at **Keating Chambers** is well regarded in this area, as are *Andrew Goodman* at **199 Strand** and *Bruce Brodie* at **39 Essex Street.**

LEADERS IN ALTERNATIVE DISPUTE RESOLUTION

Banks, Roderick I'Anson
See under Partnership Law.

Brodie, Bruce
39 Essex Street (Colin Mackay QC), London (0171) 583 1111. Called 1993.

Burton QC, Michael
See under Commercial Law.

Collins QC, Michael
See under Arbitration.

Goodman, Andrew
See under Professional Negligence.

Hunter, Martin
See under Arbitration.

Kershen QC, Lawrence
Cloisters (David Turner-Samuels QC), London (0171) 583 0303. Called 1967, took silk 1992.

Naughton QC, Philip
See under Construction Law.

Ramsey QC, Vivian
See under Construction Law.

Tackaberry QC, John
See under Arbitration.

ARBITRATION

ARBITRATION provides a more informal method of dispute resolution than High Court litigation. Parties are able, if they wish, to ensure that the proceedings remain confidential. Most arbitrations deal with commercial matters such as shipping, insurance, construction, commodities, valuations and rent reviews, and international contracts stipulating that disputes be resolved under English Arbitration rules.

LEADING SETS

ESSEX COURT CHAMBERS

ATKIN CHAMBERS	1 ESSEX COURT
FOUNTAIN COURT	KEATING CHAMBERS
ARBITRATION CHAMBERS	BRICK COURT CHAMBERS
20 ESSEX STREET	

Essex Court Chambers are the leading set in this area. *V V Veeder QC* has an excellent reputation. He has sat as an arbitrator in all the major international centres including London, Paris and New York. As an advocate he has been instructed in a broad range of international commercial disputes, including maritime, commodity, chemical and petrochemical projects, engineering, construction, insurance and reinsurance, East-West trade and banking matters. He contributed to the drafting of the model law, and, since 1985, he has been co-editor of 'Arbitration International'.

Stewart Boyd QC is co-author of 'Mustill & Boyd on Commercial Arbitration'. *Gordon Pollock QC* and *Ian Hunter QC* are highly respected for their work in this field.

Among the juniors in chambers *Martin Hunter*, who is Sweet & Maxwell Professor of International Dispute Resolution at Nottingham Law School and a former litigation partner at Freshfields, has been involved in many international arbitrations under the auspices of the ICC, the LCIA, the AAA and the NAI. He is co-author of 'Law and Practice of International Commercial Arbitration'. *Graham Dunning* is also highly respected.

Atkin Chambers specialise in construction disputes. *Colin Reese QC* has a very good reputation, as do *John Blackburn QC* and *Anthony Butcher QC*. *Andrew White* has been recommended.

1 Essex Court are known for their work in this area. *Anthony Grabiner QC* has been recommended, as have *Steven Gee QC*, *Mark Barnes QC* and *Alan Redfern*, a former partner at Freshfields, who is co-author of 'Law and Practice of International Commercial Arbitration'. He has sat as an arbitrator in a series of major cases, including an appointment by HM Treasury and by the Government of Liberia in a World Bank arbitration in Washington. He has also acted as counsel in many international and domestic arbitrations, mostly concerned with the engineering and construction industry or with energy law. He regularly speaks on the subject at professional conferences.

Jeffrey Gruder has sat as an arbitrator in LMAA arbitrations and Lloyd's Arbitration Scheme hearings, and appeared as counsel in numerous ICC, LCIA and LMAA

LEADING SILKS

| Veeder, V.V. *Essex Court Chambers* |
| Blackburn, John *Atkin Chambers* |
| Boyd, Stewart *Essex Court Chambers* |
| Butcher, Anthony *Atkin Chambers* |
| Keating, Donald *Keating Chambers* |
| Ramsey, Vivian *Keating Chambers* |
| Reese, Colin *Atkin Chambers* |
| Rokison, Kenneth *20 Essex Street* |
| Tackaberry, John *Arbitration Chambers* |
| Uff, John *Keating Chambers* |
| Barnes, Mark *1 Essex Court* |
| Collins, Michael *Essex Court Chambers* |
| Cran, Mark *Brick Court Chambers* |
| Crowther, William *2 Temple Gardens* |
| Falconer, Charles *Fountain Court* |
| Fernyhough, Richard *Keating Chambers* |
| Gee, Steven *1 Essex Court* |
| Goldsmith, Peter *Fountain Court* |
| Grabiner, Anthony *1 Essex Court* |
| Gross, Peter *20 Essex Street* |
| Havers, Philip *1 Crown Office Row* |
| Howard, Michael N. *4 Essex Court* |
| Hunter, Ian *Essex Court Chambers* |
| Langley, Gordon *Fountain Court* |
| Mendelson, Maurice *2 Hare Court* |
| Moore-Bick, Martin *20 Essex Street* |
| Padfield, Nicholas *One Hare Court* |
| Pollock, Gordon *Essex Court Chambers* |
| Russell, Jeremy *4 Essex Court* |
| Scott, Peter *Fountain Court* |
| Smith, Andrew *Fountain Court* |
| Thomas, Christopher *Keating Chambers* |
| Wallace, Ian Duncan *Atkin Chambers* |

arbitrations. He has appeared in several arbitration related cases including 'Hayter v Nelson', 'Legumbres v Central Sul', 'The Montan', 'The Varena', 'The Luka Botic' and 'European Grain v Johnston'.

Fountain Court specialise in arbitrations connected with commercial law. *Peter Scott QC* has been involved in international arbitrations both as counsel and arbitrator. *Peter Goldsmith QC*, *Gordon Langley QC* and *Charles Falconer QC* have been recommended.

Keating Chambers are highly regarded for their work in construction disputes. *Vivian Ramsey QC* has been highly recommended. *Donald Keating QC*, *John Uff QC* and *Richard Fernyhough QC* are also well known in the field.

20 Essex St specialise in maritime work. *Kenneth Rokison QC*,

who is Chairman of the London Court of International Arbitration, *Peter Gross QC* and *Clifford Gill* have been recommended.

John Tackaberry QC at **Arbitration Chambers** is highly regarded for his work in this field. He has particular expertise in construction cases but has also appeared in arbitrations involving commodities and shipping disputes. He has served as Vice-President and Chairman of the Chartered Institute of Arbitrators.

At **Brick Court Chambers** *Mark Cran QC* has been recommended. Most members of chambers sit as arbitrators in commercial disputes.

LEADING JUNIORS

Hunter, Martin *Essex Court Chambers*

Redfern, Alan *1 Essex Court* | **White,** Andrew *Atkin Chambers*

Burr, Andrew *Atkin Chambers*	**Cooke,** John *4 Essex Court*	**Dunning,** Graham *Essex Court Chambers*
Gill, Clifford *20 Essex Street*	**Gruder,** Jeffrey *1 Essex Court*	**Hart,** David *1 Crown Office Row*
Shaw, Malcolm *Essex Court Chambers*		

UP AND COMING

Landau, Toby *Essex Court Chambers*

LEADERS IN ARBITRATION

Barnes QC, Mark
See under Banking.

Blackburn QC, John
See under Construction Law.

Boyd QC, Stewart
Essex Court Chambers (Gordon Pollock QC), London (0171) 813 8000. Called 1967, took silk 1981. All areas of commercial law. Sits on Lloyd's Legal Panel.

Burr, Andrew
Atkin Chambers (Anthony Butcher QC), London (0171) 404 0102.
Specialisation: Practises primarily in domestic and international construction disputes. Acts as advocate in litigation and arbitration and in an advisory capacity regarding ADR. Experienced in all aspects of construction law and professional negligence, particularly of architects, engineers and surveyors. General and articles editor *Construction Law Journal (Sweet and Maxwell)* general editor *Arbitration and Dispute Resolution Law Journal (Lloyds of London Press)* and editor *European Construction Contracts (Willey Chancery Law)*.
Prof. Membership: ACI Arb., ABA international associate, Swiss Arbitration Association, ORBA, COMBAR.
Career: Called November 1981. Joined chambers in 1983.
Personal: Educated at Barclay School, Stevenage and Trinity Hall, Cambridge. Lives in London.

Butcher QC, Anthony
See under Construction Law.

Collins QC, Michael
Essex Court Chambers (Pollock QC), London (0171) 813 8000. Called '71, silk '88.

Cooke, John
4 Essex Court (David Steel QC), London

(0171) 797 7970.
Specialisation: Specialist in commercial law and in international arbitration as both an advocate and an arbitrator. Particular emphasis on international and EC law, especially in the fields of competition, companies and intellectual property. Also undertakes general commercial litigation, insurance and banking work. Has acted as arbitrator in numerous domestic commercial arbitrations in the UK and Ireland, and in international arbitrations, including International Chamber of Commerce cases. Has appeared before the European Commission in European competition matters and before the European Court of Justice in commercial and inter-Member State litigation under EC Treaties. Has also appeared before the European Court and Commission of Human Rights.
Prof. Membership: Bencher of the Hon. Society of King's Inns. President, Council of the Bars of the European Community (CCBE) 1985-1987; Board Member, Chicago Bar Association/ UCD institutional Institute; International Law Association Committee on International Law in Municipal Courts; Irish National Committee of ICC Court of Arbitration; Chairman, Takeover Panel (Ireland).
Career: Called to the Bar of Ireland 1966. Called to the Bar of England and Wales 1971. Admitted to the Inner Bar (Ireland) (Senior Counsel) 1980. Called to the Bar of Northern Ireland 1984. Admitted to the Inner Bar of New South Wales (Queen's Counsel). Fellow of the Chartered Institute of Arbitrators.
Personal: Educated at Gonzaga College (Dublin), National University of Ireland (UCD)(BCL 1965, LL.B 1966), King's Inns (Dublin) and at Europe Institut Amsterdam. President of the Royal Zoological Society of Ireland 1987-1990. Director, Irish Centre for European Law, Trinity College, Dublin. Born 7th May 1944. Lives in Dublin.

Cran QC, Mark
See under Media and Entertainment.

Crowther QC, William
See under Personal Injury.

Dunning, Graham
See under Insurance and Reinsurance.

Falconer QC, Charles
See under Aviation.

Fernyhough QC, Richard
See under Construction Law.

Gee QC, Steven
See under Commercial Law.

Gill, Clifford
20 Essex Street (Kenneth Rokison QC), London (0171) 583 9294. Called 1989.

Goldsmith QC, Peter
See under Commercial Law.

Grabiner QC, Anthony
See under Commercial Law.

Gross QC, Peter
See under Aviation.

Gruder, Jeffrey
See under Insurance and Reinsurance.

Hart, David
See under Medical Negligence.

Havers QC, Philip
See under Environmental.

Howard QC, Michael N.
See under Shipping.

Hunter QC, Ian
See under Aviation.

Hunter, Martin
Essex Court Chambers (Gordon Pollock QC), London (0171) 813 8000. Called 1994. Specialist in all aspects of arbitration.

Keating QC, Donald

Keating Chambers (John Uff QC), London (0171) 240 6981.

Specialisation: From about 1960 to present construction law and allied subjects. As adviser and advocate has spent perhaps 50% of time in arbitrations, domestic and international. Appeared in seven leading cases in the House of Lords (including D & F Estates), many in Court of Appeal and High Court. Clients have included Governments, public bodies, international corporations and insurance companies. Arbitrator in many disputes, domestic and international (including hearings in Trinidad, Zambia, Singapore, Dominica) and conciliations in United Kingdom and Singapore. Recorder doing Official Referee work 1983-1987 and 1992 to present. Author of 'Keating on Building Contracts' (Editions 1 to 4, Consultant Editor, 5th Edition). Has also written numerous articles. Lecturer and tutor in construction law, University of London.

Prof. Membership: Fellow Chartered Institution of Arbitrators (1983); Society of Construction Arbitrators, European International Contractors List of Arbitrators, COMBAR.

Career: Called to the Bar 1950. Took silk 1972. Recorder.

Personal: British. Born 24th June 1924. Educated Kings College, London (BA). Lives in London. Bencher of Lincoln's Inn.

Landau, Toby

Essex Court Chambers (Gordon Pollock QC), London (0171) 813 8000. Called 1993.

Langley QC, Gordon

See under Commercial Law.

Mendelson QC, Maurice

2 Hare Court (C.W.G. Ross-Munro QC), London (0171) 583 1770. Called 1965, took silk 1992.

Moore-Bick QC, Martin

See under Shipping.

Padfield QC, Nicholas

See under Banking.

Pollock QC, Gordon

Essex Court Chambers (G. Pollock QC), London (0171) 813 8000. Called '68, silk 1979.

Ramsey QC, Vivian

See under Construction Law.

Reese QC, Colin

Atkin Chambers (Anthony Butcher QC), London (0171) 404 0102. Called 1973, took silk 1987. Specialist in arbitration and construction law.

Redfern, Alan

1 Essex Court (Anthony Grabiner QC), London (0171) 583 2000.

Specialisation: Main area of practice is as an arbitrator and adviser on international dispute resolution, including mediation and conciliation. Has over 30 years experience of complex international commercial arbitration cases. Before transferring to the Bar in May 1995, was the senior litigaton partner of the international law firm *Freshfields*. He is the co-author of a leading text book on "Law and Practice of International Commercial Arbitration" and has written extensively on arbitration issues in professional journals.

Prof. Membership: Fellow of Chartered Institute of Arbitrators, member of the ICC's International Commission on Arbitration and the Swiss Arbitration Association.

Career: Became a litigation partner in 1963, transferred to the Bar in 1995.

Rokison QC, Kenneth

20 Essex Street (K. Rokison QC), London (0171) 583 9294. Called 1961, took silk 1976.

Russell QC, Jeremy

See under Shipping.

Scott QC, Peter

See under Commercial Law.

Shaw, Malcolm

Essex Court Chambers (Gordon Pollock QC), London (0171) 813 8000. Called 1988.

Smith QC, Andrew

See under Commercial Law.

Tackaberry QC, John

Arbitration Chambers (John Tackaberry QC), London (0171) 267 2137.

Specialisation: Building and civil engineering litigation and arbitration, both in the UK and internationally. Increasingly involved in arbitration and was first QC to appear on List of Arbitrators of all three of the following organisations : Institute of Civil Engineers, Royal Institute of British Architects and the Chartered Institute of Arbitrators. Arbitrations are primarily in construction field but also include commodity and shipping disputes and arbitrations under French and Swiss law. Co-author of 'Construction Contract Dictionary', contributor to 'Liability of Contractors' (1986) and specialist editor for the 'Handbook of Arbitration Practice' (1987). Author of articles for specialist legal publications. Frequent contributor to conferences and courses run by, inter alia, the Chartered Institute of Arbitrators, National Federation of Building Trades Employers and Federation of Civil Engineering Contractors, as well as other conferences for individual companies and management organisations.

Prof. Membership: Fellow of Chartered Institute of Arbitrators (first Chairman), Society of Construction Arbitrators, Society of Construction Law (first President), European Society of Construction law (President 1985-87), American Arbitration Association, Supporting Member of London Maritime Arbitrators' Association.

Career: Called to the Bar 1967. Took silk 1982. Admitted to the Irish Bar 1987.

Appointed Recorder 1988. Admitted to practice at the Bar of California 1988. Admitted to practice at the New South Wales Bar 1989, and took silk 1990. Admitted to Panel of International Arbitrators, Indian Council of Arbitration 1991. Appointed member of Panel of Accredited Arbitrators, Singapore International Arbitration 1992. Elected UK Jurisdiction Council member of the Interpacific Bar Association (Tokyo) 1993.

Personal: Educated at Downside School, Somerset 1952-58; Trinity College, Dublin 1958-59 (Economics/French) and Downing College, Cambridge 1959-63 (BA Law 1963, MA 1969). Born 13th November 1939.

Thomas QC, Christopher

See under Construction Law.

Uff QC, John

See under Construction Law.

Veeder QC, V.V.

Essex Court Chambers (Gordon Pollock QC), London (0171) 813 8000. Called 1971, took silk 1986. Specialist in international trade, including international commercial arbitration. Born 14.12.1948.

Wallace QC, Ian Duncan

Atkin Chambers (Anthony Butcher QC), London (0171) 404 0102.

Specialisation: Construction contracts (and associated torts), professional liabilities of architects, surveyors and engineers, and arbitration in the construction field, both domestic and international. Author of a number of commentaries on the standard forms of contract, including the FIDIC 3rd and 4th and ICE 5th Editions and of "Construction Contracts: Principles and Policies" (1987) (Volume II envisaged 1995/1996). Editor of the 8th, 9th, 10th & 11th (1995) Editions of Hudson on Building & Civil Engineering Contracts. Contributor to the Law Quarterley Review, International Construction Law Review, Arbitration International, Australian Tort Law Review, Australian Construction Law Reporter, and Member of the Editorial Board and Contributor to Construction Law Journal. Visiting Professor King's College, London Centre of Construction Law and Management, and Visiting Scholar University of California at Berkeley. Particular interest and experience in drafting and policies of construction contracts. Draftsman of Singapore SIA (private sector) forms of building contract.

Career: Called to the Bar 1948. Queen's Counsel 1973. Joined E.J. Rimmer's Chambers in Lincoln's Inn (now at 1 Atkin Building, Gray's Inn) in 1951.

Personal: Educated at Loretto & Oriel College, Oxford. Lives in London.

White, Andrew

See under Construction Law.

AVIATION

A RELATIVELY small number of barristers specialise in this field. Of these, the majority offer expertise in relation to aircraft financing and leasing, as well as insurance and liability matters and the less complex aspects of regulation and route licensing. In addition, the more senior barristers also deal with the more substantial regulatory issues.

LEADING SETS	
5 BELL YARD	
4 ESSEX COURT	**ESSEX COURT CHAMBERS**
20 ESSEX STREET	**FOUNTAIN COURT**
FOUR RAYMOND BUILDINGS	

The leading set in this field is **5 Bell Yard** whose members act in many high-profile cases concerning cargo matters, insurance and leasing issues, and regulatory (Civil Aviation Authority and European) matters, as well as liability for personal injury under the Warsaw Convention. *Robert Webb QC* has an outstanding reputation as the leader in this field and is a Fellow of the Royal Aeronautical Society. He has appeared in most of the important aviation cases in recent years, dealing with all aspects of work including regulatory and mass disaster issues; in particular, test cases on the level

questions of the extent of the CAA's duty of care. Other well regarded juniors at this set include *Edward Bailey*.

Fountain Court, a commercial set, has several members who are leading figures in this area. A full range of work is covered including route licensing, accidents, carriage of goods, leasing and aircraft finance and all aspects of European law affecting the field. *Bruce Coles QC* was involved in the licensing of a new airline, Dragonair, in Hong Kong as well as disputes between Rolls Royce and airline operators involving engine performance. He lectures in aviation law to the Royal Aeronautical Society and Asian Institute of Management in Manila. *Anthony Boswood QC* is highly regarded, as are *Charles Falconer QC, Peter Scott QC, Timothy Walker QC* and *Trevor Philipson QC*. Among the juniors at the set those with very good reputations include the *Hon. Michael McClaren*, who appeared recently in 'Irish Aerospace (Belgium) NV v European Organisation for the Safety of Air Navigation', and *Simon Browne-Wilkinson*.

Better known as a European Law chambers, **Four Raymond Buildings** handles a limited amount of aviation work, dealing with its European and competition law aspects. *Richard Fowler QC* has acted recently in European Court Case 'IV/34.780 Virgin/BA', and in the UK Courts in

LEADING SILKS				
Crane, Michael *5 Bell Yard*		**Webb,** Robert *5 Bell Yard*		
Boswood, Anthony *Fountain Court*	**Coles,** Bruce *Fountain Court*		**Falconer,** Charles *Fountain Court*	
Fowler, Richard *Four Raymond Buildings*	**Glennie,** Angus *20 Essex Street*		**Gross,** Peter *20 Essex Street*	
Hunter, Ian *Essex Court Chambers*	**Lasok,** Paul *Four Raymond Buildings*		**Lever,** Jeremy *Four Raymond Buildings*	
Adkins, Richard *3-4 South Square*	**Milligan,** Iain *20 Essex Street*		**Philipson,** Trevor *Fountain Court*	
Scott, Peter *Fountain Court*	**Steel,** David W. *4 Essex Court*		**Walker,** Tim *Fountain Court*	

of damages recoverable in the latter. *Michael Crane QC* is also a leading figure, dealing with all types of case within the field including CAA regulatory and route licensing matters.

Among junior counsel the outstanding individuals at this chambers include *Andrew Lydiard* and *Philip Shepherd* who also deal with the full range of aviation work. *Paul Dean* and *Charlotte Jones* are highly regarded for their work on disaster matters including the M1 British Midland disaster. *Giles Kavanagh* has acted in 'Philcox v CAA' which has raised

'British Midland v S of S' (regarding BA/DanAir) and 'Air UK v BA'. *Jeremy Lever QC* is also highly regarded as is *Paul Lasok QC*.

Although primarily known as a commercial and shipping chambers, **4 Essex Court** also carry out aviation work. *David Steel QC* and *Paul Griffin* have appeared for Virgin Airlines. *Geoffrey Kinley* has acted for the Treasury in the Terminal 5 inquiry. *Charles Haddon-Cave* is involved in disaster litigation.

LEADING JUNIORS				
Lydiard, Andrew *5 Bell Yard*		**Shepherd,** Philip *5 Bell Yard*		
Bailey, Edward *5 Bell Yard*	**Browne-Wilkinson,** Simon *Fountain Court*		**Davies,** Huw *Essex Court Chambers*	
Dean, Paul *5 Bell Yard*	**Frank,** Ivor *4 King's Bench Walk*		**Green,** Nicholas *Brick Court Chambers*	
Griffin, Paul *4 Essex Court*	**Haddon-Cave,** Charles *4 Essex Court*		**Jones,** Charlotte *5 Bell Yard*	
Joseph, David *Essex Court Chambers*	**Kavanagh,** Giles *5 Bell Yard*		**Kinley,** Geoffrey *4 Essex Court*	
Lawson, Robert *5 Bell Yard*	**Males,** Stephen *20 Essex Street*		**McLaren,** Michael *Fountain Court*	
Owen, Tudor *9-12 Bell Yard*	**Reed,** Philip *5 Bell Yard*		**Saunders,** Nicholas *Queen Elizabeth Building*	
Taverner, Marcus *Keating Chambers*	**Wood,** Richard *20 Essex Street*			

Essex Court Chambers is primarily a commercial set but some members, notably *Ian Hunter QC* and *Huw Davies*, are highly thought of for their work in this area.

20 Essex Street also deals mainly with commercial matters although some tenants practise aviation law. *Angus Glennie QC*, *Peter Gross QC* and *Iain Milligan QC* are highly regarded in the field while, among the junior members of chambers, *Richard Wood* and *Stephen Males* enjoy good reputations.

Tudor Owen at **9/12 Bell Yard** and *Nicholas Green* at **Brick Court Chambers** are also known for their work in the field.

LEADERS IN AVIATION

Adkins QC, Richard
See under Insolvency.

Bailey, Edward
See under Professional Negligence.

Boswood QC, Anthony
See under Commercial Law.

Browne-Wilkinson, Simon
See under Banking.

Coles QC, Bruce
Fountain Court (Peter Scott QC), London (0171) 583 3335. Called 1963, took silk 1984. Practice encompasses contractual, commercial and tortious disputes, property rights, engineering and construction disputes, parliamentary work, aviation and employment law. Born 28.2.1937.

Crane QC, Michael
5 Bell Yard (Robert Webb QC), London (0171) 333 8811. Called 1975, took silk 1994. Practice covers general commercial litigation, including insurance, reinsurance and carriage by air. Born 1950.

Davies, Huw
Essex Court Chambers (Gordon Pollock QC), London (0171) 813 8000. Called 1985.

Dean, Paul
5 Bell Yard (Robert Webb QC), London (0171) 333 8811. Called 1982. Principal area of practice is aviation law. Born 18.5.1957.

Falconer QC, Charles
Fountain Court (Peter Scott QC), London (0171) 583 3335. Called 1974, took silk 1991.

Fowler QC, Richard
Four Raymond Buildings (Jeremy Lever QC), London (0171) 405 7211. Called 1969, took silk 1989. Principal area of practice is UK and EC competition law and trade regulation. Born 12.10.1946.

Frank, Ivor
4 King's Bench Walk (Peter Heppel), London (0171) 353 0478. Called 1979.

Glennie QC, Angus
20 Essex Street (Kenneth Rokison QC), London (0171) 583 9294. Called 1974, took silk 1991.

Green, Nicholas
See under Commercial Law.

Griffin, Paul
See under Banking.

Gross QC, Peter
20 Essex Street (Kenneth Rokison QC), London (0171) 583 9294. Called 1977, took silk 1992.

Haddon-Cave, Charles
4 Essex Court (David Steel QC), London (0171) 797 7970. Called 1978.

Hunter QC, Ian
Essex Court Chambers (Gordon Pollock QC), London (0171) 813 8000. Called 1967, took silk 1980.

Jones, Charlotte
5 Bell Yard (Robert Webb QC), London (0171) 333 8811. Called 1982. General commercial and civil practice includes aviation, banking and insurance, professional negligence and employment law.

Joseph, David
Essex Court Chambers (Gordon Pollock QC), London (0171) 813 8000. Called 1984.

Kavanagh, Giles
5 Bell Yard (Robert Webb QC), London (0171) 333 8811. Called 1984. Specialises in aviation, public law, local government and planning. Author of 'Coroners' Rules and Statutes' (Sweet & Maxwell 1985).

Kinley, Geoffrey
4 Essex Court (David Steel QC), London (0171) 797 7970. Called 1970.

Lasok QC, Paul
See under European Community Law.

Lawson, Robert
5 Bell Yard (Robert Webb QC), London (0171) 333 8811. Called 1989.

Lever QC, Jeremy
See under Public and Administrative Law.

Lydiard, Andrew
5 Bell Yard (Robert Webb QC), London (0171) 333 8811. Called 1980. Principal area of practice is commercial litigation with a particular emphasis on aviation. Born 25.8.1957.

Males, Stephen
20 Essex Street (Kenneth Rokison QC), London (0171) 583 9294. Called 1978.

McLaren, Michael
Fountain Court (Peter Scott QC), London (0171) 583 3335. Called 1981. Specialist in aviation, shipping, banking and professional negligence. Born 29.11.1958

Milligan QC, Iain
20 Essex Street (Kenneth Rokison QC), London (0171) 583 9294. Called 1973, took silk 1991.

Owen, Tudor
9-12 Bell Yard (Edmund Lawson QC), London (0171) 400 1800. Called 1974.

Philipson QC, Trevor
Fountain Court (Peter Scott QC), London (0171) 583 3335. Called 1972, took silk 1989.

Reed, Philip
5 Bell Yard (Robert Webb QC), London (0171) 333 8811. Called 1985.

Saunders, Nicholas
Queen Elizabeth Building (Geoffrey Brice QC), London (0171) 353 9153. Called 1989. Practice covers all aspects of aviation law. Born 20.7.1954.

Scott QC, Peter
See under Commercial Law.

Shepherd, Philip
5 Bell Yard (Robert Webb QC), London (0171) 333 8811. Called 1975. Specialises in commercial litigation, particularly aviation, aircraft finance and aviation insurance. Speaks French and Italian.

Steel QC, David W.
See under Shipping.

Taverner, Marcus
See under Construction Law.

Walker QC, Tim
See under Professional Negligence.

Webb QC, Robert
5 Bell Yard (Robert Webb QC), London (0171) 333 8811. Called 1971, took silk 1988. Principal areas of practice are aviation, insurance and reinsurance, commercial litigation and public and administrative law. Born 4.10.1948.

Wood, Richard
See under Banking.

BANKING

BANKING-related litigation continues to be a growth area covering the entire spectrum of banking law, including guarantees, charges, securities, swaps, letters of credit, performance bonds, negotiable instruments, loan agreements, banker/customer relationships and negligent security valuations. There has also been an increase in general advisory

LEADING SETS

BRICK COURT CHAMBERS	1 ESSEX COURT
FOUNTAIN COURT	3 GRAY'S INN PLACE
3-4 SOUTH SQUARE	

ERSKINE CHAMBERS	ESSEX COURT CHAMBERS

4 ESSEX COURT	20 ESSEX STREET
4-5 GRAY'S INN SQUARE	ONE HARE COURT
7 KING'S BENCH WALK	4 STONE BUILDINGS

work. Most barristers specialising in banking law belong to the Commercial Bar Association (COMBAR). **Brick Court Chambers**, **1 Essex Court**, **Fountain Court**, **3 Gray's Inn Place** and **3-4 South Square** have excellent reputations in this field.

As a leading commercial set, **Brick Court Chambers** has a number of leading banking law experts including *Jonathan Sumption QC* and *Mark Hapgood QC*. *Mark Howard* and *Richard Lord* are highly rated juniors.

1 Essex Court is a leading commercial set with a large group of experts in banking law. Chambers have been particularly involved in swaps litigation. *Anthony Grabiner QC*

Fountain Court is a commercial set with great depth of experience in banking. *Andrew Smith QC* has an excellent reputation and acted in 'Barclays Bank v Bank of England'. *Peter Scott QC*, who acted in 'Arab Monetary Fund v Hashim', and *Michael Brindle QC*, who acted in 'Shah v Bank of England' and 'Philipp Brothers v European Commission', are also highly respected. *David Railton* is a well-regarded junior.

3 Gray's Inn Place is a set with considerable banking law experience. *John Jarvis QC* is highly regarded having appeared in 'Tai Hing Cotton Limited v Liu Chong Bank Limited'. *Ewan McQuater* is a notable junior who has specialisation in all aspects of international and domestic banking law. He acted in 'Banque Bruxelles Lambert v Eagle Star', a landmark case in respect of negligent valuations of security. *William Blair QC* is very highly rated and he and *Ewan McQuater* are assistant editors of 'The Encyclopaedia of Banking Law'. *Neville Thomas QC*, *Richard Salter QC*, *Gregory Mitchell* and *Jonathan Nash* are also highly regarded.

3-4 South Square has many members who are experts in banking law. *Gabriel Moss QC* and *Richard Adkins QC* are highly regarded. *Richard Hacker*, *Robin Dicker*, *Mark Phillips* and *Robin Knowles* are very good juniors.

Robin Potts QC and *Richard Sykes QC* at **Erskine Chambers** have been very highly recommended. The chambers are particularly experienced in securities.

Essex Court Chambers is a commercial set which has members with expertise in banking law. *Gordon Pollock QC* has an excellent reputation for his work in this field.

LEADING SILKS

Sumption, Jonathan *Brick Court Chambers*		

Barnes, Mark *1 Essex Court*	**Blair**, William *3 Gray's Inn Place*	**Brindle**, Michael *Fountain Court*
Bueno, Antonio *5 Paper Buildings Incorporating European Law Chambers*	**Crystal**, Michael *3-4 South Square*	**Field**, Richard Alan *11 King's Bench Walk*
Glick, Ian *1 Essex Court*	**Gloster**, Elizabeth *1 Essex Court*	**Grabiner**, Anthony *1 Essex Court*
Lord Irvine of Lairg, *11 King's Bench Walk*	**Jarvis**, John *3 Gray's Inn Place*	**Moss**, Gabriel *3-4 South Square*
Pollock, Gordon *Essex Court Chambers*	**Potts**, Robin *Erskine Chambers*	**Salter**, Richard *3 Gray's Inn Place*
Scott, Peter *Fountain Court*	**Smith**, Andrew *Fountain Court*	**Strauss**, Nicholas *1 Essex Court*
Sykes, Richard *Erskine Chambers*		

Adkins, Richard *3-4 South Square*	**Bompas**, Anthony George *4 Stone Buildings*	**Flaux**, Julian *Seven King's Bench Walk*
Hapgood, Mark *Brick Court Chambers*	**Heslop**, Philip *4 Stone Buildings*	**Higham**, John *3-4 South Square*
Mowschenson, Terence *1 Essex Court*	**Rokison**, Kenneth *20 Essex Street*	**Southwell**, Richard *One Hare Court*
Thomas, R. Neville *3 Gray's Inn Place*	**Williamson**, Hazel *13 Old Square*	

is is well known and recently acted in 'Credit Suisse Fides Trust v Sergio Cuoghi'. *Ian Glick QC* is well regarded and acted in the 'Mount Banking Corporation' litigation. *Elizabeth Gloster QC* has an excellent reputation and has acted in many of the recent high profile cases such as the BCCI litigation.

Richard Millett is also well-regarded.

4 Essex Court and **20 Essex Street** are both leading commercial sets with several members with experience of banking matters. *Paul Griffin* and *Poonam Melwani* are recognised experts at **4 Essex Court** whilst *Kenneth Rokison QC*

LEADING JUNIORS

Browne-Wilkinson, Simon *Fountain Court*	**Davies,** Rhodri *1 Essex Court*	**de Garr Robinson,** Anthony *1 Essex Court*
Griffin, Paul *4 Essex Court*	**Gruder,** Jeffrey *1 Essex Court*	**Hollander,** Charles *Brick Court Chambers*
Jacobs, Nigel *4 Essex Court*	**Lewis,** Caroline *3 Gray's Inn Place*	**McQuater,** Ewan *3 Gray's Inn Place*
Melwani, Poonam *4 Essex Court*	**Mitchell,** Gregory *3 Gray's Inn Place*	**Nash,** Jonathan *3 Gray's Inn Place*
Onions, Jeffrey *1 Essex Court*	**Railton,** David *Fountain Court*	**Spencer-Lewis,** Neville *12 King's Bench Walk*
Arden, Peter *Enterprise Chambers*	**Chambers,** Dominic *One Hare Court*	**Chichester,** Julian *4-5 Gray's Inn Square*
Chivers, David *Erskine Chambers*	**Dicker,** Robin *3-4 South Square*	**Fenton,** Adam *Seven King's Bench Walk*
Hacker, Richard *3-4 South Square*	**Howard,** Mark *Brick Court Chambers*	**Jacobs,** Richard *Essex Court Chambers*
Knowles, Robin *3-4 South Square*	**Lord,** Richard *Brick Court Chambers*	**Lowenstein,** Paul *Littleton Chambers*
Malek, Ali *3 Gray's Inn Place*	**Malek,** Hodge M. *4-5 Gray's Inn Square*	**Millett,** Richard *Essex Court Chambers*
Phillips, Mark *3-4 South Square*	**Rabinowitz,** Laurence *1 Essex Court*	**Shekerdemian,** Marcia *11 Stone Buildings*
Thanki, Bankim *Fountain Court*	**Todd,** Michael *Erskine Chambers*	**Wood,** Richard *20 Essex Street*

UP AND COMING

Evans, James *3 Gray's Inn Place*	**Stonefrost,** Hilary *3-4 South Square*	**Wolfson,** David *3 Gray's Inn Place*

and *Richard Wood* are well known at **20 Essex Street**.

One Hare Court has strong experience in the international banking law field with *Richard Southwell QC* and *Dominic Chambers*. 7 **King's Bench Walk**, as a leading shipping and insurance set, also has expertise in banking with *Julian Flaux QC* and *Adam Fenton* being well regarded.

4-5 Gray's Inn Square has a number of members with banking expertise including *Hodge Malek*. **4 Stone Buildings** has a distinguished reputation with *Philip Heslop QC* and *George Bompas QC* in particular being highly regarded. *Neville Spencer-Lewis* specialises in Bank of England work at **12 King's Bench Walk**.

LEADERS IN BANKING

Adkins QC, Richard
See under Insolvency.

Arden, Peter
See under Insolvency.

Barnes QC, Mark
1 Essex Court (Anthony Grabiner QC), London (0171) 583 2000. Called 1974, took silk 1992.

Blair QC, William
3 Gray's Inn Place (R. Neville Thomas QC), London (0171) 831 8441. Called 1972, took silk 1994. Principal area of practice is banking and financial services law. Visiting Professor of Law at LSE, 1994.

Bompas QC, Anthony George
See under Company.

Brindle QC, Michael
Fountain Court (Peter Scott QC), London (0171) 583 3335.

Specialisation: Practice encompasses a variety of work in the commercial and corporate sphere as well as employment law. Emphasis is on banking and financial services, company law, professional negligence in financial and commercial matters, insurance and international trade. Experienced in City-related matters, including litigation arising out of audits, take-overs and rights issues. Practises in chancery as well as commercial and common law courts. Important cases include 'Caparo v. Dickman' [1989] (auditors' negligence); 'Micklefield v. SAC Technology' [1990] (employer share option scheme); 'Morgan Crucible v. Hill Samuel' [1990] (merchant banker's and auditor's negligence and take-over code); 'G & H Montage v. Irvani' [1990] (bills of exchange); 'Rome & Bathurst v. Punjab National Bank' [1990-92] (insurance); Re Bishopsgate Investment Management [1993] (constructive trust) ; 'Deposit Protection Board v. Dalia' [1993] (depositor compensation); 'Shah v Bank of England' [1994] (banking supervision) as 'Philipp Brothers v European Commission' [1994] (garnishee order). Author of journal articles.

Prof. Membership: Midland & Oxford Circuit.

Career: Called to the Bar in 1975 and joined *Fountain Court Chambers* in 1976. Took silk in 1992.

Personal: Educated at Westminster School 1965-69 and New College, Oxford (Double First in Classics and jurisprudence). Part-time lecturer in Jurisprudence at New College, Oxford 1976-82. Born 23rd June 1952. Lives in London.

Browne-Wilkinson, Simon
Fountain Court (Peter Scott QC), London (0171) 583 3335. Called 1981. Principal areas of practice are aviation, banking, insurance, professional negligence and fraud. Born in 1957.

Bueno QC, Antonio
5 Paper Buildings [Incorporating European Law Chambers] (Antonio Bueno QC), London (0171) 583 9275/4555. Called 1964, took silk 1989.

Chambers, Dominic
One Hare Court (Sir Patrick Neill QC, Richard Southwell QC), London (0171) 353 3171.

Specialisation: Principal area of practice is commercial law, including banking, conflicts, negotiable instruments, insurance & reinsurance, guarantees and indemnities. Also handles commercial fraud, partnership and professional negligence. Professional clients predominantly major City law firms.

Prof. Membership: COMBAR.

Career: Called to the Bar and joined *1 Hare Court* in 1987.

Personal: Educated at Harrow School 1976-81 and King's College, London 1983-86. Born 28th February 1963. Lives in London.

Chichester, Julian

4-5 Gray's Inn Square (Miss Elizabeth Appleby QC, The Hon. Michael Beloff QC), London (0171) 404 5252.

Specialisation: Principal area of practice is banking and commercial contract disputes. Other main areas of work are professional negligence (eg accountants in company acquisitions). Acted for major US Bank in Iranian assets freeze litigation. Clients include many large plcs.

Prof. Membership: Commercial Bar Association, Administrative Law Bar Association, International Bar Association, Professional Negligence Bar Association.

Chivers, David

See under Insolvency.

Crystal QC, Michael

See under Insolvency.

Davies, Rhodri

1 Essex Court (Anthony Grabiner QC), London (0171) 583 2000.

Specialisation: Principal area of practice is banking work acting for banks and large corporations, including swaps, letters of credit, negotiable instruments, mandates, facility letters, loan agreements and other financial disputes with or between banks. Acted in recent swaps litigation, representing various banks in 'Hazell v. London Borough of Hammersmith & Fulham' and in restitution claims in Kleinwort Benson v. Sandwell. Also handles general commercial work, encompassing contractual disputes, sale of goods, arbitration, insurance, reinsurance and professional negligence.

Prof. Membership: South Eastern Circuit, LCLCBA.

Career: Called to the Bar in 1979 and joined 1 Essex Court in 1980.

Personal: Educated at Winchester College 1970-74 and Downing College, Cambridge 1975-78. Leisure pursuits include running, walking and sailing. Born 29th January 1957. Lives in Harpenden, Herts.

de Garr Robinson, Anthony

1 Essex Court (Anthony Grabiner QC), London (0171) 583 2000. Called 1987. Specialises in banking, commercial law, company and insolvency. Born 4.7.1963

Dicker, Robin

See under Insolvency.

Evans, James

3 Gray's Inn Place (R. Neville Thomas QC), London (0171) 831 8441. Called 1991.

Fenton, Adam

Seven King's Bench Walk (Adrian Hamilton QC), London (0171) 583 0404. Called 1984.

Field QC, Richard Alan

See under Commercial Law.

Flaux QC, Julian

See under Insurance and Reinsurance.

Glick QC, Ian

1 Essex Court (Anthony Grabiner QC), London (0171) 583 2000.

Specialisation: Principal areas of practice are banking, commercial law, financial services, insurance, accountants' negligence and arbitration. Important cases include PCW litigation; Tin Council litigation; Crown Agent Enquiry; Woolwich BS v. CIR (restitution); Smith New Court v. Citibank (measure of damages in fraud); Gallagher v. Jones (application of accepted principles of commercial accountancy to computation of profits for tax purposes), Shah v. Bank of England (banking regulation); Deeny v. Gooda Walker (taxability of damages recovered in Lloyds' litigation) and R v. CIR ex p. Warburgs (judicial review of Revenue decisions). Conference speaker.

Prof. Membership: North Eastern Circuit, Commercial Bar Association

Career: Called to the Bar in 1970. At *Lamb Building* 1970-80. Joined 1 Essex Court in 1980. Junior Counsel to the Crown, Common Law 1985-87. Standing Counsel to the DTI in export credit cases 1985-87. Took Silk in 1987.

Personal: Educated at Bradford Grammar School and Balliol College, Oxford. Born 18th July 1948. Lives in London.

Gloster QC, Elizabeth

See under Insolvency.

Grabiner QC, Anthony

See under Commercial Law.

Griffin, Paul

4 Essex Court (David Steel QC), London (0171) 797 7970. Called 1979.

Gruder, Jeffrey

See under Insurance and Reinsurance.

Hacker, Richard

3-4 South Square (Michael Crystal QC), London (0171) 696 9900. Called 1977.

Hapgood QC, Mark

See under Commercial Law.

Heslop QC, Philip

See under Company.

Higham QC, John

See under Financial Services.

Hollander, Charles

Brick Court Chambers (Christopher Clarke QC), London (0171) 583 0777. Called 1978.

Howard, Mark

See under Insurance and Reinsurance.

Lord Irvine of Lairg QC,

See under Commercial Law.

Jacobs, Richard

See under Insurance and Reinsurance.

Jacobs, Nigel

4 Essex Court (David Steel QC), London (0171) 797 7970. Called 1983. Practice covers Shipping, Insurance, Admiralty and General Commercial work including banking. Born 31.5.1960.

Jarvis QC, John

3 Gray's Inn Place (R. Neville Thomas QC), London (0171) 831 8441. Called 1970, took silk 1989. Principal area of practice is banking law. Also commercial law, professional negligence and insurance. Born 20.11.1947.

Knowles, Robin

See under Insolvency.

Lewis, Caroline

See under Commercial Law.

Lord, Richard

Brick Court Chambers (Christopher Clarke QC), London (0171) 583 0777. Called 1981.

Lowenstein, Paul

See under Commercial Law.

Malek, Ali

See under Commercial Law.

Malek, Hodge M.

4-5 Gray's Inn Square (Miss Elizabeth Appleby QC, The Hon. Michael Beloff QC), London (0171) 404 5252.

Specialisation: Specialises in commercial Law, including accountancy, banking, company, financial services, fraud, insurance, securities, and shipping. Instructed in complex commercial litigation in the commercial court and in arbitrations, including Banque Financiere v. Westgate [1990] (banking and insurance fraud) Johnson Matthey v. Arthur Young (collapse of Johnson Matthey Bank), Ocean v. Bimeh Iran Insurance Company [1990] (reinsurance), Trafalgar Tours v. Henry (jurisdiction), Gucci v. Gucci [1991] (passing-off), Lombard Finance v. Brookplain [1991] (banking) and Westdeutsche Landesbank v. Islington [1994] (interest rate swaps). Instructed in fraud cases by Serious Fraud Office. Acted for SRO's in disciplinary proceedings. Joint Author of 'Discovery' (Sweet & Maxwell, 1992) Lectures on civil procedure.

Prof. Membership: COMBAR.

Personal: Educated at Bedford School 1968-77, University of the Sorbonne, 1978 and Keble College, Oxford 1978-82 (MA,BCL). Fellow of the Royal Numismatic Society (Council 1991-4).

McQuater, Ewan

3 Gray's Inn Place (R. Neville Thomas QC), London (0171) 831 8441.

Specialisation: Has specialised in international and domestic banking law since starting in practice. Range of banking work covers the entire spectrum, including guarantees, charges, securities, letters of credit, performance bonds, banker/customer relationship questions, negligent security valuations and Mareva Injunctions. Also has substantial practices in professional negligence (principally accountants, bankers, solicitors and valuers) and insolvency (all aspects, acting for liquidators, receivers, administrators, trustees in bankruptcy and other parties affected by insolvency). Acted in Libyan Arab Foreign Bank v. Bankers Trust [1989] and Libyan Arab Foreign Bank v. Manufacturers Hanover Trust [1989] concerning the US freeze on Libyan assets. Acted in the administration of the Parkfield Group (for the administrators) and the liquidation of Arrows Ltd (for the liquidators) both important insolvency decisions. Acted for the liquidators, both in England and the Cayman Islands, on the BCCI liquidation, and in the 'BBL' case (Banque Bruxelles Lambert v. Eagle Star), a landmark decision on negligent valuations of security and negligent bank lending. Also involved in the Maxwell litigation, (Bishopsgate Investment Management v. Mirror Group Newspapers). Assistant Editor of the 'Encyclopaedia of Banking Law' since 1987 and regular contributor to the *Journal of International Banking Law.*'

Prof. Membership: COMBAR.

Career: Called to the Bar 1985 and joined current Chambers 1986. Admitted to the Bar of the Cayman Islands.

Personal: Educated at Merchiston Castle School, Edinburgh (1975-80) and Cambridge University 1981-84 (MA Hons in Law, First Class). Leisure pursuits include rugby (Vice Captain, Belsize Park Rugby Club) and piano. Born 30th October 1962. Lives in London.

Melwani, Poonam

See under Commercial Law.

Millett, Richard

Essex Court Chambers (Gordon Pollock QC), London (0171) 813 8000.

Specialisation: Main areas of practice cover banking, insolvency, commercial litigation, reinsurance, company law, and media and entertainment. Major litigation includes the Maxwell, Polly Peck, Barings and BCCI cases. Co-author of 'The Law of Guarantees' (Longmans 1992) and regularly addresses conferences and seminars.

Prof. Membership: Commercial Bar Association.

Career: Called to the Bar 1985. Joined present chambers 1990.

Mitchell, Gregory

3 Gray's Inn Place (R. Neville Thomas QC), London (0171) 831 8441.

Specialisation: Principal area of practice is commercial law, specialising in banking law, corporate insolvency, financial services, company law, commercial fraud, intellectual property and solicitors' and accountants' negligence. Reported cases include Bank of Baroda v. Panessar. Produce Marketing Consortium (Nos 1 & 2), Femis Bank v. Lazar and TSB Private Bank International v. Chabra. Clients include foreign and domestic banks, building societies, insurance companies, corporations, and private individuals. Contributor of numerous articles to 'New Law Journal', 'Guardian Gazette' and 'Counsel'. Regularly addresses conferences.

Prof. Membership: COMBAR, London Common Law and Commercial Bar Association.

Career: Called to the Bar in 1979 and joined present chambers in 1981.

Personal: Educated at King's College, London (BA (Hons) 1977, Diploma in Law 1978, Ph.D 1981). Born 27th July 1954. Lives in London.

Moss QC, Gabriel

See under Insolvency.

Mowschenson QC, Terence

See under Insolvency.

Nash, Jonathan

3 Gray's Inn Place (R. Neville Thomas QC), London (0171) 831 8441.

Specialisation: Principal area of work is banking and commercial work, including domestic and international banking matters, security and sale of goods. Other main areas of work are corporate insolvency, arbitration and professional negligence (particularly of accountants, solicitors and surveyors). Acted in Al Saudi Bank v. Clarke Pixley (auditors negligence) and Deposit Protection Board v. Dahalia (obligations of deposit protection board).

Prof. Membership: COMBAR.

Career: Called to the Bar in 1986 and joined *3 Gray's Inn Place* in 1987.

Personal: BA (Oxon).

Onions, Jeffrey

1 Essex Court (Anthony Grabiner QC), London (0171) 583 2000. Called 1981.

Phillips, Mark

See under Insolvency.

Pollock QC, Gordon

See under Arbitration.

Potts QC, Robin

See under Company.

Rabinowitz, Laurence

See under Commercial Law.

Railton, David

Fountain Court (Peter Scott QC), London (0171) 583 3335. Called 1979.

Rokison QC, Kenneth

See under Arbitration.

Salter QC, Richard

3 Gray's Inn Place (R. Neville Thomas QC), London (0171) 831 8441.

Specialisation: Principal areas of practice are banking, commercial law, financial services, insolvency, professional negligence and building. Clients include most major UK and international banks. Contributor to 'Banks - Liability and Risk' (2nd ed 1995) and 'Banks and Remedies' (2nd ed 1992) for Lloyd's of London Press; and to Vol. 20 'Halsbury's Laws' (4th ed 1994 - Re-issue 'Guarantees'). Lecturer to the Chartered Institute of Arbitrators 1979-93. Lectured frequently on guarantees and other banking law topics.

Prof. Membership: London Common Law and Commercial Bar Association, COMBAR, Chartered Institute of Arbitrators.

Career: Called to the Bar 1975. Tenant at *3 Hare Court*, 1977-82, then joined current chambers. Bencher of the Inner Temple 1991. Member of the Council of Legal Education 1990. Chairman of the Board of Examiners, Bar Vocational Course, 1992-93. Took Silk in 1995.

Personal: Educated at Harrow County School for Boys 1963-70, Balliol College, Oxford 1970-73 and Inns of Court School of Law 1973-75. Chairman, Shoscombe Village Cricket Club.

Scott QC, Peter

See under Commercial Law.

Shekerdemian, Marcia

11 Stone Buildings (Michael Beckman QC), London (+44) 0171 831 6381. Called 1987. Specialist in corporate and individual insolvency. Born 16.11.1963.

Smith QC, Andrew

See under Commercial Law.

Southwell QC, Richard

One Hare Court (Sir Patrick Neill QC, Richard Southwell QC), London (0171) 353 3171.

Specialisation: Banking, insurance, major commercial litigation and arbitration, both domestic and international.

Prof. Membership: Chairman, Legal Services Committee, Bar Council 1990-91. Chairman, Professional Standards Committee, Bar Council 1988-90. Member of Executive of COMBAR.

Career: Judge of the Courts of Appeal of Jersey and Guernsey. Deputy President, Lloyd's Appeal Tribunal. Deputy Judge of the High Court.

Spencer-Lewis, Neville

12 King's Bench Walk (Ronald Walker QC), London (0171) 583 0811.

Specialisation: Principal area of specialisation is Banking Act work on behalf of the Bank of England in respect of illegal deposit-taking. Also deals with general civil work, including professional negligence, contract, misrepresentation (eg 'Royscot Trust v. Rogerson') etc.

Prof. Membership: London Common Law and Commercial Bar Association.

Career: Called to Bar 1970. Joined *12 Kings Bench Walk* in 1980.

Personal: Educated at Radley College and Pembroke College, Oxford. Lives in London.

Stonefrost, Hilary

3-4 South Square (Michael Crystal QC), London (0171) 696 9900. Called 1991.

Strauss QC, Nicholas

1 Essex Court (Anthony Grabiner QC), London (0171) 583 2000. Called 1965, took silk 1984.

Sumption QC, Jonathan

See under Commercial Law.

Sykes QC, Richard

See under Company.

Thanki, Bankim

Fountain Court (Peter Scott QC), London (0171) 583 3335.

Specialisation: Civil and commercial including general commercial, banking, aviation, professional negligence, administrative law, arbitration, carriage of goods, insurance and reinsurance, international trade, employment and disciplinary tribunals. Noteworthy cases include Deposit Protection Board v. Barclays Bank and Dalia (banking/ banking supervision), Bank of England- BCCI claims (tort/ banking supervision), Football Association v. Tottenham Hotspur (arbitration/contract/disciplinary), Gurtner v. Beaton (aviation/ agency), Southampton CC v. Academy Cleaning (local authority/ contract tenders), Re a firm of solicitors (solicitors/conflicts), British Coal v. Smith (employment/ equal pay), Kecskemeti v. Rubens Rabin (solicitors' negligence/ wills), BCCI v. Price Waterhouse (auditors' negligence), HIV haemophilia litigation, NRG v. Swiss Bank Corporation & others (reinsurance/professional negligence). Involved in civil and disciplinary aspects of Barlow Clowes and Polly Peck affairs. Lay clients include the Bank of England and major clearing and merchant banks as well as British Coal and The Football Association. Professional clients include most of the City law firms. Author of the forthcoming 'Carriage by Air' (Butterworths). Lectures on aviation law to international airlines.

Prof. Membership: Commercial Bar Association, Common Law & Commercial Bar Association.

Career: Called to the Bar 1988.

Personal: Educated at Balliol College, Oxford (MA, 1st Class Hons 1986). Harmsworth Scholar, Middle Temple 1988.

Thomas QC, R. Neville

See under Commercial Law.

Todd, Michael

See under Insolvency.

Williamson QC, Hazel

See under Property Litigation.

Wolfson, David

3 Gray's Inn Place (R. Neville Thomas QC), London (0171) 831 8441. Called 1992.

Wood, Richard

20 Essex Street (Kenneth Rokison QC), London (0171) 583 9294. Called 1975.

INDEXES TO PROFILES

Solicitors' Profiles The index to leading solicitors profiled in the Specialist Lists is located immediately after the section containing profiles of in-house lawyers. This index also includes heads of company legal departments.

Barristers' Profiles Profiles of leading barristers are indexed within the main *Barristers' Index* located at the end of the directory. Names of profiled barristers are set in bold type.

BUILDING SOCIETIES

A SET consistently recommended for building societies law is **11 Old Square Chambers**. Their expertise covers mergers and acquisitions, takeovers and conversions, standard

LEADING SETS

11 OLD SQUARE

documentation, constitution and powers and relations with members. Major cases handled include 'Halifax Building Society v. Edell (Building Society Ombudsman Scheme)' and 'Abbey National Building Society v. Building Societies Commision' (building society conversion).

Leading barristers include *Timothy Lloyd QC, Elizabeth Ovey* and *Malcolm Waters.*

LEADING SILKS

Lloyd, Timothy	*11 Old Square*

LEADING JUNIORS

Ovey, Elizabeth	*11 Old Square*
Waters, Malcolm	*11 Old Square*

Acton, Stephen	*11 Old Square*
Cranfield, Peter	*3 Gray's Inn Place*
Crawford, Grant	*11 Old Square*
Rowley, Keith	*11 Old Square*

UP AND COMING

Purkis, Kathryn	*11 Old Square*

LEADERS IN BUILDING SOCIETIES

Acton, Stephen
See under Chancery.

Cranfield, Peter
3 Gray's Inn Place (R. Neville Thomas QC), London (0171) 831 8441. Called 1982.

Crawford, Grant
11 Old Square (Timothy Lloyd QC), London (0171) 430 0341. Called 1974.

Lloyd QC, Timothy
See under Chancery.

Ovey, Elizabeth
11 Old Square (Timothy Lloyd QC), London (0171) 430 0341.

Specialisation: Principal specialist area of work is mortgage lending and building society law. Also handles general chancery work, including professional negligence. Joint editor of 'Wurtzburg and Mills - Building Society Law' and 'Current Law Commentary on Building Societies Act 1986'. Also lectures occasionally.

Prof. Membership: Chancery Bar Association.

Career: Called to the Bar 1978. Joined *11 Old Square* 1980.

Personal: Educated at Southampton Grammar School for Girls 1966-73 and St. Anne's College, Oxford 1974-77. Lives in London. Born 1st December 1954.

Purkis, Kathryn
11 Old Square (Timothy Lloyd QC), London (0171) 430 0341.

Specialisation: General chancery, principally real property, Property Litigation and realisation of securities. Has spoken at conferences addressing mortgage lenders on realisation of securities.

Prof. Membership: Chancery Bar Association, Young Women Lawyers.

Career: Called to the Bar 1991. Joined *11 Old Square* 1992.

Personal: Educated at Balliol College, Oxford BA (Hons) 1988-1990 and University of Cape Town, South Africa BA (Hons) 1984-87. Leisure interests include dining out and classic cars. Born 14th July 1966.

Rowley, Keith
See under Pensions.

Waters, Malcolm
11 Old Square (Timothy Lloyd QC), London (0171) 430 0341.

Specialisation: Principal areas of work are mortgage lending and building society law. Handles drafting of standard mortgage documentation, charities, professional negligence and general chancery work. Acted as junior counsel in Abbey National B.S. v. Building Societies Commission, Cheltenham & Gloucester B.S. v. Building Societies Commission and Halifax B.S. and Leeds P.B.S. v. Building Societies Commission. Acts for major building societies and other lending institutions. Joint editor of 'Wurtzburg & Mills - Building Society Law', and 'Current Law Commentary on the Building Societies Act 1986'. Member of working party involved in drafting Standard Conditions of Sale.

Prof. Membership: Chancery Bar Association, Professional Negligence Bar Association.

Career: Called to Bar 1977. Joined 11 Old Square 1978.

Personal: Educated at Whitgift School 1963-71 and St. Catherine's College Oxford 1972-76 (B.A. and B.C.L.). Lives in London.

CHANCERY

The term 'chancery' now covers a broad area of work: not only the traditional chancery areas but also the more commercial areas into which an increasing number of chancery chambers are moving. This expansion has been mirrored by the growing proportion of Chancery Division litigation being undertaken by some leading commercial sets. Many chancery practitioners now handle business disputes, financial services, company, insolvency and revenue law, in addition to the more traditional trusts and property law. Demand for chancery practitioners to handle international work has also increased. This section includes both the traditional chancery sets and the commercial chancery sets. Those who specialise in niche areas such as tax, landlord & tenant and other aspects of property-related work, pensions, intellectual property, insolvency and revenue are listed in the relevant specialist sections.

TRADITIONAL CHANCERY

LEADING SETS – LONDON - TRADITIONAL CHANCERY	
WILBERFORCE CHAMBERS	
5 STONE BUILDINGS	
3 NEW SQUARE	13 OLD SQUARE
8 STONE BUILDINGS	11 STONE BUILDINGS

Wilberforce Chambers is the leading chambers in the traditional chancery area. *Edward Nugee QC* acted in 'Hambro v Duke of Marlborough' and in 'Imperial Courage Mettoy v British Coal'. *Nicholas Warren QC* has an excellent reputation, and has appeared in 'Wilson v Law Debenture' and 'Drexel Burnham'. *Robert Ham QC* is well known for his expertise in trust and real property matters, and also appeared in 'Drexel Burnham' and in 'Simpson Curtis Pension Trustees v Reardon'. *David Lowe QC* was involved in 'Oldham DC v AG' and in 'Church Commissioners v British Railways Board'.

Brian Green has a very strong reputation as the leading junior for traditional chancery work. His reported cases include 'LRT v Hatt' and 'Nutting v Baldwin'. *Christopher Nugee* is highly respected in the traditional chancery areas, and acted in 'Harries v Church Commissioners' and in 'Target Life'.

HIGHLY REGARDED – LONDON - TRADITIONAL CHANCERY	
11 NEW SQUARE	12 NEW SQUARE
17 OLD BUILDINGS	10 OLD SQUARE
11 OLD SQUARE	7 STONE BUILDINGS

5 Stone Buildings is also highly regarded in this field. *Mark Herbert QC*, whose expertise includes trusts, tax and probate, and *Michael Hart QC* were particularly recommended. *Michael Hart QC*, who deals with trusts and property, appeared in 'Banco Exterior v Mann'. *Launcelot*

Henderson QC has a stong reputation in trusts, tax, and private client work and acted in 'Harries v Church Commissioners for England'.

Henry Harrod, a specialist in trusts and administration of estates, is a highly regarded junior. *Christopher Tidmarsh* has a wide ranging chancery practice principally dealing with trusts, wills, pensions, land and professional negligence. He is Standing Counsel to the Inland Revenue in chancery matters.

Another leading set in the traditional chancery field is **3 New Square**. *William Goodhart QC* has appeared in a number of recent high profile cases including 'Hambro v Duke of Marlborough' in which he acted for the trustees of the Blenheim Estate, and 'Re Beatty's Will Trusts'. *David Rowell* appeared as junior counsel in the former case. His busy practice is, however, mainly of an advisory nature with an emphasis on land law, trusts, wills and succession matters. *Bernard Weatherill* appeared as a junior in 'Re Beatty's Will Trusts' and in 'Winter v Boynton'.

8 Stone Buildings is a well-known chancery set. *Francis Barlow* and *Simon Taube* are highly regarded, particularly in relation to complex trust matters. *David Ainger* is also respected for his general chancery practice. *Christopher Cant* is a well-respected junior dealing with trusts and company matters at **11 Stone Buildings (Campion)**.

LEADING SILKS – LONDON - TRADITIONAL CHANCERY		
Nugee, Edward	*Wilberforce Chambers*	
Crampin, Peter	*11 New Square*	
Goodhart, William	*3 New Square*	
Ham, Robert	*Wilberforce Chambers*	
Hart, Michael	*5 Stone Buildings*	
Herbert, Mark	*5 Stone Buildings*	
Lowe, David	*Wilberforce Chambers*	
McCall, Christopher	*13 Old Square*	
Mowbray, John	*12 New Square*	
Warren, Nicholas	*Wilberforce Chambers*	
Henderson, Launcelot	*5 Stone Buildings*	
Martin, John	*Wilberforce Chambers*	
Price, Leolin	*10 Old Square*	
Proudman, Sonia	*11 New Square*	

At **13 Old Square (Christie)** *Christopher McCall QC* is pre-eminent in charities and property matters. *Leolin Price QC* is a well-known senior chancery silk at **10 Old Square**, handling trusts, land and partnership matters. He was recently involved in 'CIBC v Pitt'. *Shân Warnock-Smith's* principle areas of practice are trusts, estates and associated taxation.

Peter Crampin QC and *Sonia Proudman QC* are recommended at **11 New Square**. Members of chambers have been

LEADING JUNIORS – LONDON - TRADITIONAL CHANCERY

Green, Brian *Wilberforce Chambers*

Barlow, Francis *8 Stone Buildings*	**Harrod,** Henry *5 Stone Buildings*	**Jackson,** Dirik *11 New Square*
Nugee, Christopher *Wilberforce Chambers*	**Semken,** Christopher *1 New Square*	**Stewart Smith,** Rodney *1 New Square*
Taube, Simon *8 Stone Buildings*	**Taussig,** Anthony *Wilberforce Chambers*	**Topham,** Geoffrey J. *3 Stone Buildings*
Tucker, Lynton *12 New Square*	**Warnock-Smith,** Shan *10 Old Square*	**Weatherill,** Bernard *3 New Square*
Acton, Stephen *11 Old Square*	**Ainger,** David *8 Stone Buildings*	**Cant,** Christopher I. *11 Stone Buildings*
Chapman, Vivian R. *11 Stone Buildings*	**Child,** John *17 Old Buildings*	**Horne,** Roger *11 New Square*
Mason, Alexandra *17 Old Buildings*	**Powell-Jones,** Robert *13 Old Square*	**Rowell,** David *3 New Square*
Rowley, Keith *11 Old Square*	**Simmonds,** Andrew *5 Stone Buildings*	**Stanford,** David R. *3 Stone Buildings*
Tidmarsh, Christopher *5 Stone Buildings*	**Trace,** Anthony *13 Old Square*	

involved in recent cases such as 'Clark v Chief Land Registrar' and 'G S Fashions v B & Q Plc'. *Roger Horne* and *Dirik Jackson* are also highly regarded. At **12 New Square**, *John Mowbray QC* and *Lynton Tucker* are highly regarded in the trusts field.

17 Old Buildings deals with all aspects of modern chancery work with an emphasis on real property and trusts. *John Child*, a recognised trusts and tax expert, and *Alexandra Mason*, who is noted for her trusts and probate work, are highly respected. At **1 New Square** *Rodney Stewart-Smith* is noted for his property and trusts work, and *Christopher Semken* is highly regarded.

COMMERCIAL CHANCERY

In addition to their traditional practice, **13 Old Square (Christie)** also have distinguished members in the commercial chancery field. *David Oliver QC* is highly regarded. *John Nicholls*, *Robert Powell-Jones* and *Anthony Trace* and are well respected juniors.

LEADING SETS – LONDON COMMERCIAL CHANCERY

13 OLD SQUARE (Christie)	**4 STONE BUILDINGS**
ENTERPRISE CHAMBERS	**1 NEW SQUARE**
24 OLD BUILDINGS	**13 OLD SQUARE** (Sparrow)
9 OLD SQUARE	**3-4 SOUTH SQUARE**
3 STONE BUILDINGS	**7 STONE BUILDINGS**
11 STONE BUILDINGS	
5 NEW SQUARE	**11 OLD SQUARE**

4 Stone Buildings is a company/commercial set with general chancery practice. *Philip Heslop QC* and *George Bompas QC* are both well regarded particularly in the company, insolvency and financial services fields. *John Brisby* and *Jonathan Crow* are notable juniors practising in the same areas.

7 Stone Buildings is a chancery and commercial set where *Charles Aldous QC* is distinguished. He specialises in company/commercial matters and appeared in the recent cases of 'MGN Pension Trustees v Lehman Bros.' and 'G E Capital v Bankers Trust & Ors'. *Nigel Davis QC* and *David Unwin QC* are highly regarded for litigious chancery matters. *Guy Newey* is a respected junior. At **1 New Square**, *Eben Hamilton QC* is well known for his commercial chancery work. *James Munby QC* is also highly regarded.

3-4 South Square have a comprehensive chancery practice, particularly in the insolvency field, with *Michael Crystal QC* and *Gabriel Moss QC* being pre-eminent, as do **Enterprise Chambers**, a commercial chancery set.

LEADING SILKS– LONDON - COMMERCIAL CHANCERY

Aldous, Charles *7 Stone Buildings*	
Oliver, David *13 Old Square*	
Berry, Simon *9 Old Square*	
Crystal, Michael *3-4 South Square*	
Heslop, Philip *4 Stone Buildings*	
Hildyard, Robert *4 Stone Buildings*	
Mann, Anthony *Enterprise Chambers*	
Moss, Gabriel *3-4 South Square*	
Munby, James *1 New Square*	
Patten, Nicholas *9 Old Square*	
Purle, Charles *12 New Square*	
Sher, Jules *Wilberforce Chambers*	
Steinfeld, Alan *24 Old Buildings*	
Talbot, Patrick *13 Old Square*	
Vos, Geoffrey *3 Stone Buildings*	
Ashe, T. Michael *11 Stone Buildings*	
Bompas, Anthony George *4 Stone Buildings*	
Briggs, Michael *13 Old Square*	
Davis, Nigel *7 Stone Buildings*	
Etherton, Terence *Wilberforce Chambers*	
Hamilton, Eben W. *1 New Square*	
Kaye, Roger *24 Old Buildings*	
Lloyd, Timothy *11 Old Square*	
McDonnell, John B.W. *1 New Square*	
Newman, Catherine *13 Old Square*	
Steinfeld, Alan *24 Old Buildings*	
Unwin, David *7 Stone Buildings*	
Williamson, Hazel *13 Old Square*	

set with an emphasis on litigation. *Anthony Mann QC* has a broad commercial chancery practice with an emphasis on insolvency and banking and appeared in the recent case of 'Target Holdings v Redfern'. *Teresa Peacocke* is also well known and *Linden Ife* is a well respected junior in the commercial chancery field at **Enterprise Chambers**.

At **Thirteen Old Square (Sparrow)** *Patrick Talbot QC, Michael Briggs QC, Frank Hinks* and *John Whittaker* are well-regarded in this general chancery and commercial set. **11 Stone Buildings (Beckman QC)** is a general chancery set centred on company, insolvency and property. *Victor Joffe* is a recognised junior who has been involved in 'Freudiana' over the last twelve months. *Alan Steinfield QC* and *Roger Kaye QC*, both well known, are at **24 Old Buildings**. *Simon Berry QC* and *Nicholas Patten QC* at **9 Old**

Square are both highly rated. *Daniel Hochberg* and *John Dagnall* are well respected juniors. *Mark Cunningham* is a well regarded junior at **5 New Square**. **11 Old Square** is also a general commercial chancery set where *Timothy Lloyd QC* is a well-known chancery silk. **3 Stone Buildings** is a general commercial chancery set with a litigation bias. *Geoffrey Vos QC* is well regarded.

Jules Sher QC at **Wilberforce Chambers** is very highly regarded, and acted in 'City of London BS v Flegg' and in 'Credit Suisse v The Council of the Borough of Allerdale'. *Terry Etherton QC* at the same chambers is highly thought of and appeared in 'McDonald v Horn' and in 'Tate Access Floors v Boswell'.

At **5 Stone Buildings**, *Alastair Norris* is well-known for his professional negligence work.

OUTSIDE LONDON

28 North John St, Liverpool, is a well established set of chancery chambers. *William George, Nicholas Orr* and *Ian Johnson* are highly regarded with general chancery practices including land and professional negligence expertise. Also in Liverpool, **7 Queen Avenue** is a set devoted exclusively to chancery and related commercial work with *Nicholas Riddle* and *John McCarroll* being well respected. **St James' Chambers** in Manchester is a chancery and common law set with *Anthony Elleray QC* being a highly regarded silk.

Members of the chambers acted in the recent cases of 'Griffiths and Anor v Yorkshire Bank plc' and 'Alsop Wilkinson v Neary and Ors'. **9 St John St** in Manchester also has members recognised for their expertise in chancery, namely

Ian Leeming QC and *Michael Johnson*. In Birmingham, **7 Fountain Court** has members who are experts in complex chancery matters, such as *John Randall QC*. In Bristol, **Guildhall Chambers** is a well regarded set with *John Boggis QC* handling traditional chancery matters.

LEADERS IN CHANCERY

Acton, Stephen
11 Old Square (Timothy Lloyd QC),
London (0171) 430 0341.

Specialisation: Specialises in general Chancery work with a particular emphasis on 'commercial Chancery' and company law. Practice includes company and insolvency work; partnership; land law and securities (especially institutional lending); conveyancing disputes; equitable remedies and trusts; probate and estates; landlord and tenant (particularly commercial leases); contractual disputes and commercial Chancery litigation generally; professional negligence in the above fields. Recent reported cases include Parker-Tweedale v. Dunbar Bank (No.1 mortgagee's duty of care) and (No.2 mortgagee's right to costs); Norwich & Peterborough BS v. Steed (No.1 leave to appeal out of time) and (No.2 rectification of land registry). Re Dennis (severance of joint tenancy by act of bankruptcy). Articles include 'Creditors and Administration Orders' in Palmer's *In Company* (March 1993).

Prof. Membership: Chancery Bar Association; Professional Negligence Bar Association.

Career: Called to the Bar 1977, Joined present Chambers 1978. Lectured in company and partnership law at Holborn Law Tutors 1977-1979 and wrote the HLT Company Law Handbook.

Personal: Educated at Ilford County High School for Boys 1964-1971 and at Trinity College, Cambridge 1972-1976 (double first; starred 1st in Law Part II). Leisure pursuits include golf, tennis, skiing, theatre, cinema and supporting Tottenham Hotspur. Born 27th April 1953. Lives in London.

Ainger, David
8 Stone Buildings (Michael Mark, Francis Barlow), London (0171) 242 5002.

Specialisation: Principal area of specialisation is chancery; he is a general chancery practitioner with both an advisory and litigation practice. In addition to work in real property, professional negligence, fraud, partnership, trusts (including breach of trust), pensions, probate, banking and insurance, he has experience of public inquiries, local government, water, waterways and highways, ecclesiastical law, commons and similar matters. He has conducted litigation in Hong Kong and the Isle of Man and advised on Chancery matters in other jurisdictions.

Career: Appointed one of the Conveyancing Counsel of the Supreme Court in November 1991.

Aldous QC, Charles
7 Stone Buildings (Charles Aldous), London (0171) 404 5055.

Specialisation: Specialises in chancery company law, professional negligence

(accountancy), and general commercial litigation. Recent notable cases include 'Macmillan v. Lehman Bros. & Others' (action for recovery of Berlitz shares), 'Mirror Group Newspaper Pension Trustees v. Lehman Bros'. (1994) (action to recover Maxwell Pension fund assets), 'GE Capital v. Bankers Trust & Others' (1994) (action for damages against auditors, accountants etc. in relation to management buy-out of Magnet), 'Grand Metropolitan v. The William Hill Group).

Career: Called 1967, took silk 1985.

Personal: Educated at Harrow, and UCL London. Lives in Suffolk and London.

Allen QC, J.H.
39 Park Square (T.M.A. Bubb), Leeds (0113) 2456633.

Ashe QC, T. Michael
11 Stone Buildings (D.J.M. Campion), London (0171) 404 5055. Called 1971, took silk 1994. Main areas of practice are company law, financial services, securities regulation and commercal fraud. Born 10.3.1949.

Barlow, Francis
8 Stone Buildings (Michael Mark, Francis Barlow), London (0171) 242 5002.

Specialisation: The full range of Chancery practice, both contentious and non-contentious, with particular emphasis on wills, trusts and charities (and associated tax law), probate and administration, property law and professional negligence. A joint editor of 'Williams on Wills' and a correspondent of 'Private Client Business'.

Career: Called to the Bar 1965.

Behrens, John
10 Park Square (A.N. Campbell QC), Leeds (0113) 2455438.

Berry QC, Simon
See under Property Litigation.

Boggis QC, John
Guildhall Chambers (John Royce QC), Bristol (0117) 9273366. Called 1972, took silk 1993.

Bompas QC, Anthony George
See under Company.

Briggs QC, Michael
See under Company.

Brisby, John
See under Financial Services.

Cant, Christopher I.
11 Stone Buildings (D.J.M. Campion), London (0171) 404 5055. Called 1973.

Chapman, Vivian R.
11 Stone Buildings (D.J.M. Campion), London (0171) 404 5055. Called 1970. Principal area of practice is general chancery work, in particular property litigation. Born 3.1.1947.

Child, John
17 Old Buildings (Geoffrey Jaques), London (0171) 405 9653. Called 1966.

Corbett, James
7 Fountain Court (Rex Tedd QC), Birmingham (0121) 236 8531. Called 1975.

Crampin QC, Peter
11 New Square (Peter Crampin QC, Miles Shillingford), London (0171) 831 0081. Called 1976, took silk 1993.

Crow, Jonathan
See under Company.

Crystal QC, Michael
See under Insolvency.

Cunningham, Mark
5 New Square (James Sunnucks), London (0171) 404 0404. Called 1980.

Dagnall, John
9 Old Square (Robert Reid QC), London (0171) 405 4682. Called 1983.

Davies, Stephen
Guildhall Chambers (John Royce QC), Bristol (0117) 9273366. Called 1983.

Elleray QC, Anthony
St. James's Chambers (R.A. Sterling), Manchester (0161) 834 7000. Called 1977, took silk 1993.

Etherton QC, Terence
See under Property Litigation.

George, William
20 North John St (Mr. William George), Liverpool (0151) 236 6757. Called 1968.

Goodhart QC, William
3 New Square (Sir William Goodhart QC), London (0171) 405 5577 (5 lines).

Specialisation: Principal area of practice is Chancery work, encompassing pension funds, trusts and estates, property, consumer credit and personal taxation. Other main area of work is company law and insolvency. Recent cases include Forward Trust v. Whymark [1990] (consumer credit), Davies v. Richards & Wallington Industries [1990] (pensions) and Hambro v. Duke of Marlborough [1994] (trusts). Co-author of 'Specific Performance' (the leading modern authority on this subject), and sections of Halsbury's Laws on specific performance and corporations.

Prof. Membership: Chancery Bar Association, International Commission of Jurists, Institute for Fiscal Studies.

Career: Called to the Bar 1957. In practice at the Chancery Bar since 1960. Took Silk 1979. Member Bar Council Professional Standards Committee 1986-89. Member of Law Commission Standing Committee on Conveyancing 1987-89. Knighted for political and public services 1989.

Personal: Educated at Eton College 1946-51, Trinity College, Cambridge 1953-57 (BA, MA) and Harvard Law School 1957-58 (LL.M). Chairman, Court of Discipline of Cambridge University since 1993. Born 18th January 1933.

Green, Brian
See under Pensions.

Ham QC, Robert
Wilberforce Chambers (Edward Nugee QC), London (0171) 306 0102. Called 1973, took silk 1994.

Hamilton QC, Eben W.
See under Company.

Harrison, Christopher
See under Financial Services.

Harrod, Henry
5 Stone Buildings (Henry Harrod), London (0171) 242 6201.

Specialisation: Specialises in all areas of Chancery work.

Prof. Membership: Chancery Bar Association.

Career: Called to the Bar 1963. Tenant at 46 Grainger Street, Newcastle-upon-Tyne 1964-1968 before joining 4 Paper Buildings in 1968. Member of present chambers since 1969 and head since 1990. Conveyancing Counsel of the Court 1991. Bencher of Lincoln's Inn 1991. Appointed Recorder 1993.

Personal: Educated at the Dragon School, Oxford 1945-1952, Eton College 1952-1957 and at Christ Church, Oxford 1958-1961. Born 6th January 1939. Lives in London.

Hart QC, Michael
5 Stone Buildings (Henry Harrod), London (0171) 242 6201.

Specialisation: General Chancery litigation and advice, with particular emphasis on trusts, property, pensions and professional negligence. Recent reported cases: pensions - Stannard v. Fisons, British Coal v. B.C. Staff Scheme, Taylor v. Lucas Pensions Trust (1994) PLR 8; on insurance: Lonsdale & Thompson Ltd v. Black Arrow; on banking: Imperial Life v. Efficient Distributors, Banco Exterior v. Mann; on housing: Hughes v. Borough of Greenwich; on tracing: Barlow Clowes v. Vaughan; on contract: Nutting v. Baldwin; and on revenue law: IRC v. McGuckian.

Career: Called 1970, took silk 1987

Henderson QC, Launcelot
5 Stone Buildings (Henry Harrod), London (0171) 242 6201. Called 1977, took silk 1995.

Herbert QC, Mark
5 Stone Buildings (Henry Harrod), London (0171) 242 6201.

Specialisation: Principal area of practice is general chancery work, including trusts, capital taxation, taxation of trusts, probate, family provision, charities and off-shore trusts. Also handles pensions work, particularly advice and litigation on occupational pensions for trustees, employers and members. Important cases include Re Rank's Settlement Trust [1979]; Re Billson's Settlement Trusts [1984]; Mettoy Pension Trustees v. Evans [1990]; Re Christy Hunt Pension Fund [1991]; Fitzwilliam v. IRC [1993]. Co-Editor of 'Whiteman and Wheatcroft on Capital Gains Tax' and 'Whiteman on Capital Gains Tax'. Other publications include 'The Drafting and Variation of Wills'.

Prof. Membership: Chancery Bar Association; Revenue Bar Association; Association of Pension Lawyers.

Career: Called to the Bar 1974. Tenant at 17 Old Buildings 1975-1977 before joining Queen Elizabeth Building in 1977. At present chambers since 1991. Took Silk 1995.

Personal: Educated at Lancing College 1962-1966 and King's College, London 1967-1970. Born 12th November 1948. Lives in London

Hinks, Frank
See under Partnership Law.

Hochberg, Daniel
9 Old Square (Robert Reid QC), London (0171) 405 4682. Called 1982.

Horne, Roger
11 New Square (Peter Crampin QC, Miles Shillingford), London (0171) 831 0081.

Jackson, Dirik
11 New Square (Peter Crampin QC, Miles Shillingford), London (0171) 831 0081. Called 1969.

Jarman, Milwyn
9 Park Place (Philip Rees), Cardiff (01222) 382731.

Joffe, Victor
11 Stone Buildings (Michael Beckman QC), London (+44) 0171 831 6381. Called 1975. Main areas of practice are company law and corporate insolvency.

Johnson, Ian
20 North John St (Mr. William George), Liverpool (0151) 236 6757. Called 1982.

Johnson, Michael
9 St. John Street (John Hand QC), Manchester (0161) 955 9000. Called 1972.

Jones, Geraint
9 Park Place (Philip Rees), Cardiff (01222) 382731.

Kaye QC, Roger
24 Old Buildings (C.A. Brodie QC), London (0171) 404 0946. Called 1970, took silk 1989.

Leeming QC, Ian
9 St. John Street (John Hand QC), Manchester (0161) 955 9000. Called 1970, took silk 1988.

Lloyd QC, Timothy
11 Old Square (Timothy Lloyd QC), London (0171) 430 0341. Called 1970, took silk 1986. Specialist Chancery practitioner. Undertakes a variety of work in the areas of land law, corporate law and trusts. Born 30.11.1946.

Lowe QC, David
Wilberforce Chambers (Edward Nugee QC), London (0171) 306 0102. Called 1965, took silk 1984.

Mann QC, Anthony
Enterprise Chambers (Benjamin Levy), London (0171) 405 9471.

Specialisation: Broad commercial chancery practice with an emphasis on insolvency and banking law. Recent reported cases include Re MC Bacon [1990] (insolvency, transactions at undervalue); Re David Meek Plant Ltd [1993] (proceedings for recovery of leased equipment); National Westminster Bank v Skelton [1993] (cross-claims in mortgage possession actions) Smith New Court v Citibank [1994] (damages for fraud); Kleinwort Benson v South Tyneside [1993] and South Tyneside v Svenska [1994] (local authority swaps; ultra vires transactions; interest; Re Secure & Provide Plc [1992] (public interest winding up petitions); Nestlé v National Westminster Bank [1993] (principles for assessing losses arising from breach of trust) and Target Holdings v Redfern [1995] (solicitor negligence and breach of trust).

Martin QC, John
Wilberforce Chambers (Edward Nugee QC), London (0171) 306 0102. Called 1972, took silk 1991.

Mason, Alexandra
17 Old Buildings (Geoffrey Jaques), London (0171) 405 9653. Called 1981.

McCall QC, Christopher
See under Pensions.

McCarroll, John J.
7 Queen Avenue (Nicholas Riddle), Liverpool (0151) 236 8240. Called 1988.

McDonnell QC, John B.W.
See under Company.

Moss QC, Gabriel
See under Insolvency.

Mowbray QC, John
12 New Square (John Mowbray QC), London (0171) 405 3808. Called 1953, took silk 1974.

Munby QC, James
See under Commercial Law.

Newey, Guy
See under Company.

Newman QC, Catherine
13 Old Square (Mr. E.W.H. Christie), London (0171) 404 4800.

Specialisation: Principal area of work encompasses business and commercial chancery work, including corporate insolvency, business agreements and breach of contract, loans and security, and professional negligence. Other main area of work is land law and equity. Acted (for the London Borough of Hammersmith and Fulham) at all stages of the Swaps litigation: capacity, restitution and successive claims.

Prof. Membership: Chancery Bar Association.

Career: Called to the Bar 1979 and joined present chambers in 1980. Appointed Deputy Registrar in Bankruptcy 1991. Took silk in 1995.

Personal: Educated at Convent of the Sacred Heart High School 1965-72 and University College, London. (LL.B 1st Class Hons.) 1979). Harmsworth Scholar of the Middle Temple 1979-80. Born 7th February 1954. Lives in London.

Nicholls, John
See under Insolvency.

Norris, Alastair
5 Stone Buildings (Henry Harrod), London (0171) 242 6201.

Specialisation: Chancery and business related litigation; professional negligence.

Prof. Membership: Chancery Bar Association, Professional Negligence Bar.

Career: Called to the Bar 1973. Joined Chambers in 1974. F.C.I. Arb. Concentrates on Chancery and business related litigation, with particular specialisation in professional negligence (solicitors, barristers, accountants and surveyors). Instructed by most of the major London and provincial panel firms. Acts as arbitrator. Also practises from Exeter.

Personal: Educated at Pates Grammar School, Cheltenham and St. John's College, Cambridge. Born 17th December 1950.

Nugee QC, Edward
Wilberforce Chambers (Edward Nugee QC), London (0171) 306 0102.

Specialisation: Mainstream Chancery practice, with emphasis on trusts, occupational pension schemes, revenue law, landlord and tenant and property law generally. Has appeared in a substantial number of landlord and tenant, revenue and other appeals in the House of Lords, and in many of the leading cases on pension schemes.

Career: Called 1955, Inner Temple (Bencher 1976, Treasurer 1996); Q.C. 1977.

Personal: Educated Radley College; Worcester College, Oxford (Eldon Law Scholar). T.D. 1964.

Nugee, Christopher
Wilberforce Chambers (Edward Nugee QC), London (0171) 306 0102. Called 1983.

Oliver QC, David
See under Insolvency.

Orr, Nicholas
20 North John St (Mr. William George), Liverpool (0151) 236 6757. Called 1970.

Patten QC, Nicholas
See under Commercial Law.

Peacocke, Teresa R.
See under Commercial Law.

Powell-Jones, Robert
13 Old Square (Mr. E.W.H. Christie), London (0171) 404 4800. Called 1978.

Price QC, Leolin
10 Old Square (Leolin Price QC), London (0171) 405 0758.

Specialisation: Principal areas of practice are chancery and commercial work, trusts, land, charities and partnership. Other main areas are taxation, constitutional and administrative law. Important cases include R v. HM Treasury ex p. Smedley [1985]; Craven v. White [1989]; Brady v. Brady [1989]; Thomas v. University of Bradford [1987]; National Westminster Bank v. Morgan [1985]; Lloyd's Bank v. Rossel [1990]; CIBC v. Pitt [1994]; Baden v. Societe Generale [1993] and Harvela v. Royal Trust [1986]. Lectures to various bodies on legal, trust and tax matters.

Prof. Membership: Chancery Bar Association, Chartered Institute of Arbitrators. Bencher of the Middle Temple since 1970. New South Wales Bar Association.

Career: Called to the Bar in 1949 and joined chambers at 10 Old Square in 1952. Took Silk in 1968. Called to the Bahamas Bar (QC 1969) and the Bar of New South Wales (QC 1987) (chambers at Selborne Chambers, 174 Phillip Street, Sydney, NSW. Tel: 612 233 51888 Fax: 612 233 1137). Treasurer of Middle Temple, 1990. Called to the British Virgin

Islands Bar 1994.

Personal: Educated at the Judd School, Tonbridge and Keble College, Oxford (MA). Chairman, Institute of Child Health since 1976; Governor and Trustee of Great Ormond Street Hospital for Sick Children since 1972; Chancellor of the Diocese of Swansea & Brecon since 1982. Interests include politics. Born 11th May 1924. Lives in Hampstead and Llanbedr, near Crickhowell, Powys.

Proudman QC, Sonia
11 New Square (Peter Crampin QC, Miles Shillingford), London (0171) 831 0081.

Specialisation: Practice covers general chancery and commercial work, with particular specialisation in trusts, charities and bankers' securities.

Prof. Membership: Chancery Bar Association, Charity Law Association.

Career: Called to the Bar in 1972. Joined chambers at 11 New Square in 1974. Took Silk in 1994.

Personal: Educated at St. Paul's Girls' School 1960-67 and Lady Margaret Hall, Oxford 1968-71 (BA 1st Class Hons in Jurisprudence). Governor of Redcliffe School since 1989. Lincoln's Inn Hall Representative since 1990. Interests include cinema (1930-1950), theatre, literature, fashion, food and gossip. Member of Hurlingham and CWIL clubs. Born 30th July 1949. Lives in London.

Purle QC, Charles
See under Company.

Randall QC, John
7 Fountain Court (Rex Tedd QC), Birmingham (0121) 236 8531. Called 1978, took silk 1995.

Riddle, Nicholas F.
7 Queen Avenue (Nicholas Riddle), Liverpool (0151) 236 8240. Called 1970.

Rowell, David
3 New Square (Sir William Goodhart QC), London (0171) 405 5577 (5 lines). Called 1972. Principal areas of practice are banking, commercial law, financial services and insolvency. Born 2.10.1951.

Rowley, Keith
See under Pensions.

Semken, Christopher
1 New Square (Eben Hamilton QC), London (0171) 405 0884. Called 1977.

Sher QC, Jules
Wilberforce Chambers (Edward Nugee QC), London (0171) 306 0102. Called 1968, took silk 1981.

Simmonds, Andrew
See under Professional Negligence.

Stanford, David R.
3 Stone Buildings (D. R. Stanford), London (0171) 242 4937. Called 1951.

Steinfeld QC, Alan
24 Old Buildings (C.A. Brodie QC), London (0171) 404 0946. Called 1968, took silk 1987.

Sterling, Robert
St. James's Chambers (R.A. Sterling), Manchester (0161) 834 7000.

Stewart Smith, Rodney
1 New Square (Eben Hamilton QC), London (0171) 405 0884. Called 1964.

Stockill, David
5 Fountain Court (Anthony Barker QC), Birmingham (0121) 606 0500.

Talbot QC, Patrick
See under Insolvency.

Taube, Simon
8 Stone Buildings (Michael Mark, Francis Barlow), London (0171) 242 5002. Called 1980.

Taussig, Anthony
Wilberforce Chambers (Edward Nugee QC), London (0171) 306 0102.
Specialisation: Equity and trusts, land/conveyancing, revenue, pensions, financial services, charities, housing associations.
Career: Called to the Bar 1966. Conveyancing Counsel of the Court since 1991. Publication: 'Housing associations and their committees'. A guide to the legal framework. 1992.
Personal: Educated at Winchester College and Magdalen College, Oxford.

Tidmarsh, Christopher
5 Stone Buildings (Henry Harrod), London (0171) 242 6201.

Specialisation: Chancery practitioner, with a particular emphasis on trusts, pension schemes, property litigation and professional negligence. Important cases include British Coal v. British Coal Staff Superannuation Scheme Trustees [1994]; Stannard v. Fisons [1991]; Taylor v. Lucas Pension Trust Ltd [1994], (all pensions). Hughes v. Greenwich LBC (1994), (right to buy); Imperial Life Assurance Company of Canada v. Efficient Distributors [1992], (Bahamian mortgage legislation), and re a Debtor (415 of 1993)[1994](bankruptcy).
Prof. Membership: Chancery Bar Association.
Career: Called to the Bar 1985. Joined present chambers 1986.
Personal: Educated at Merton College, Oxford (BA) 1980-83. Born 11th December 1961. Lives in London.

Topham, Geoffrey J.
See under Pensions.

Trace, Anthony
See under Property Litigation.

Tucker, Lynton
12 New Square (John Mowbray QC), London (0171) 405 3808. Called 1971.

Unwin QC, David
7 Stone Buildings (Charles Aldous QC), London (0171) 405 3886. Called 1971, took silk 1995.

Walford, Richard
11 Old Square (Timothy Lloyd QC), London (0171) 430 0341. Called 1984.

Warnock-Smith, Shan
10 Old Square (Leolin Price QC), London (0171) 405 0758.
Specialisation: Principal area of practice encompasses trusts, estates and associated taxation. Handles both advisory and contentious work in connection with on and off-shore trusts and estates, variations of trust, rectification of settlements and wills and probate actions. Other main areas of work are commercial property advice and litigation. Recent cases include Midland Bank v. Wyatt (first case on 'sham' trusts in the UK) and Weatherhill v. Pearce (execution of wills). Also involved in Olympia and York subsidiaries property litigation. Clients include lay and professional trustees and executors in the UK and abroad, accountants, private client and commercial property departments. Regular lecturer at professional conferences. Contributor of articles to various legal periodicals.
Prof. Membership: Society of Trust and Estate Practitioners, Charity Law Association, Chancery Bar Association, Elected Member of Bar Council from 1994.
Career: Called to the Bar 1971. Full time lecturer in law (City Guildhall University) 1970-78 and part time 1978-81. Joined present chambers in 1979.
Personal: Educated at Westlake High School, Auckland, New Zealand 1961-63, Portsmouth High School 1963-67 and King's College, London 1967-70 (LL.B) and 1970-72 (LL.M): Trustee of National Newpin (a charity involved in preventing child abuse). Leisure pursuits include interior decoration, aerobics, opera, gardening and novels. Lives in London. Two children.

Warren QC, Nicholas
See under Pensions.

Weatherill, Bernard
See under Company.

Whittaker, John
See under Partnership Law.

Williamson QC, Hazel
See under Property Litigation.

Wood, Graeme
Assize Court Chambers (Graeme Wood), Bristol (0117) 9264587. Called 1968.

CHARITIES

W HILE there are no sets associated as a whole with this very specialised area, a number of individual barristers enjoy excellent reputations for their expertise within it. *Francesca Quint* at **11 Old Square** undertakes advisory

LEADING SILKS– LONDON

Picarda, Hubert	*10 Old Square*	
McCall, Christopher	*13 Old Square*	
Nugee, Edward	*Wilberforce Chambers*	
Proudman, Sonia	*11 New Square*	
Venables, Robert	*24 Old Buildings*	

work on setting up charities, amending constitutions, negotiating with the Charities Commission, arrangements with other charities and trading companies, and resolving disputes. She has appeared in 'Gunning v Buckfast Abbey Trustees' and 'Re MJK Kay Decd'. *Hubert Picarda QC* at **10 Old Square** is also very well known in this field. He is the author of 'Picarda – Law and Practice Relating to Charities'. *Christopher McCall QC* at **13 Old Square** has acted for the Treasury Solicitor in charity matters, and prior to taking silk he was Junior Counsel to the Attorney General in this area 1981-87. He is a member of the Charity Law Association and has written many articles on the subject. Of the juniors in this

set *William Christie* is highly regarded in this sector.

Other respected figures in this area of law include *Sonia Proudman QC* and *Thomas Dumont* at **11 New Square** who are both members of the Charity Law Association. *Edward Nugee QC* at **Wilberforce Chambers** enjoys a strong

LEADING JUNIORS– LONDON

Quint, Francesca	*11 Old Square*	
Christie, William	*13 Old Square*	
Dumont, Thomas	*11 New Square*	
Jaques, Geoffrey	*17 Old Buildings*	

reputation, as does *Geoffrey Jaques* at **17 Old Buildings**. *Robert Venables QC* **24 Old Buildings** is highly regarded.

REGIONS

Outside London *John Fryer-Spedding* of **Trinity Chambers** in Newcastle has been recommended for his work in this field.

LEADING JUNIORS– REGIONS

Fryer-Spedding, J.H.	*Trinity Chambers*

LEADERS IN CHARITIES

Christie, William
13 Old Square (Mr. E.W.H. Christie), London (0171) 404 4800.

Specialisation: All aspects of water and the water industry, rights of navigation, fishing rights, foreshore, rivers and canals. Charities, settling charitable objects, application and misapplication of charitable funds. Restraint of trade and competition law particularly sole trading agreements and petroleum distribution.

Prof. Membership: Chancery Bar Association, Bar European Group.

Career: Called to the Bar 1952, Head of Chambers at 13 Old Square.

Dumont, Thomas
11 New Square (Peter Crampin QC, Miles Shillingford), London (0171) 831 0081. Called 1979.

Fryer-Spedding, J.H.
Trinity Chambers (J.T. Milford QC), Newcastle upon Tyne (0191) 232 1927. Called 1970.

Jaques, Geoffrey
17 Old Buildings (Geoffrey Jaques), London (0171) 405 9653. Called 1963.

McCall QC, Christopher
See under Pensions.

Nugee QC, Edward
See under Chancery.

Picarda QC, Hubert
10 Old Square (Leolin Price QC), London (0171) 405 0758. Called 1962, took silk 1992.

Proudman QC, Sonia
See under Chancery.

Quint, Francesca
11 Old Square (James Thrower), London (0171) 242 5022. Also Castle Chambers, Exeter (01392) 420 345.

Specialisation: Principal area of practice is chancery work, with a focus on charities. Work includes advisory work on setting up charities, amending constitutions, negotiating with Charity Commission, schemes, arrangements with other charities or trading companies and dispute resolution. Other main areas of practice are trusts, land, probate and capital taxation, particularly deeds of variation, Inheritance Act applications, advice and litigation relating to land or trusts. Recent cases include Gunning v. Buckfast Abbey Trustees (dispute between parents and charity school); Re WHVS Higby Will Trust (contest between Oxford College and next of

kin as beneficiary of substantial bequest); Re MJK Kay Deceased (partition of estate) and Henrietta Barnett School Governors v. Hampstead Garden Suburb Institute (dispute between voluntary school and landlord charity). Clients include educational establishments and charities and city livery companies. Publications include 'Running a Charity' (Jordans, 1994) and 'Charities: The Law & Practice' (Longmans, 1994, co-author). Convenor, Charities Group of CEDR (Centre for Dispute Resolution).

Prof. Membership: Chancery Bar Association, Charity Law Association, Education Law Association, Society of Trust and Estate Practitioners (branch Committee Member).

Career: Called to the Bar 1970. Law Reporter, All England Law Reports, 1970-71. Charity Commission Legal Assistant 1972-74, Assistant Commissioner 1974-84 and Deputy Commissioner 1984-89. Joined present Chambers 1990.

Personal: Educated at St. Paul's Girls' School 1958-65 and Kings College, London 1966-69 (LLB, AKC). Trustee/adviser to various charities and kindred institutions. Born 1.10.1947. Lives in London and Exeter.

Venables QC, Robert
24 Old Buildings (M.E.P. Jump), London (0171) 242 2744. Called 1973, took silk 1990.

CIVIL LIBERTIES

NOT ALL barristers acting in cases raising civil liberties issues are 'civil liberties' lawyers, and the lists below only include those who regularly represent the individual against the state. The term itself covers at least four different areas: housing law, discrimination, freedom of speech and expression, and actions against the police. It can be extended to include many further aspects of criminal defence work, immigration law and employment law, but specialists in these areas have been listed (with appropriate emphases) in the relevant sections.

LEADING SETS – LONDON	
DOUGHTY STREET CHAMBERS	
CLOISTERS	14 TOOKS COURT
2 GARDEN COURT	MITRE HOUSE CHAMBERS

Doughty Street Chambers emerges as the pre-eminent set, containing practitioners with expertise across the entire range of civil liberties work. Leading silks particularly recommended are *Geoffrey Robertson QC* and newly appointed silks *Andrew Nicol QC* and *Edward Fitzgerald QC*. Both *Geoffrey Robertson QC* and *Andrew Nichol QC* have particular expertise in freedom of expression matters, whilst *Edward Fitzgerald QC* is a leading authority in the rights of prisoners and psychiatric patients. He has represented prisoners and mental patients both in the English Courts and in Strasbourg, and has written articles on psychological defences, rights of prisoners and mental patients. From an array of talented juniors, *Ben Emmerson*, who has appeared in numerous leading public law cases recently, is particularly well regarded. His work includes representing applicants before the European Court and Commission of Human Rights, civil actions against the police, and prisoners rights. He is also editor of 'European Human Rights Review'. *Phillippa Kaufman* has been described as chambers 'rising star', and her practice includes prisoners' rights, housing, immigration, mental health and social security law. She was Chair of the Free Representation Unit (FRU) 1992-1993.

HIGHLY REGARDED – LONDON	
2 HARE COURT	6 KING'S BENCH WALK
1 PUMP COURT	

Close on the heels of **Doughty Street Chambers**, comes **14 Tooks Court** and **Cloisters**.

At **14 Tooks Court,** members are highly experienced in all aspects of civil liberties, with particular strength in the fields of public order, racial discrimination and civil actions against the police. Leading silks at the set are *Michael Mansfield QC* and *Alper Ali Riza QC*, who undertakes civil liberties, immigration nationality and refugee law, and European Union and Human Rights law. Prominent cases that *Alper Ali*

Riza QC has handled include 'R v Home Secretary ex parte Budgaway' (refugee law-House of Lords) and 'R v Naillie' (House of Lords-criminal law, refugee and immigration law). He also acted in 'R v Home Secretary ex parte Cheblok' (National Security-the Gulf War detainee cases). At the junior end of chambers, *Tanoo Mylvaganam* has been recommended.

Cloisters is a long established civil liberties set, which despite its large volume of general public, commercial and criminal law, still retains a number of committed and highly-talented civil liberties practitioners. *Stephen Solley QC* has an excellent reputation for handling criminal cases with civil liberties aspects. Also recommended to us is newly appointed silk *Robin Allen QC*. He has particular expertise in discrimination work, has been involved in various high profile cases including 'Hampson v Department for Education and Science' (discrimination and the state).

Other leading sets in this field are **Mitre House Chambers** and **2 Garden Court**.

LEADING SILKS– LONDON	
Beloff, Michael *4-5 Gray's Inn Square*	
Lord Lester, *2 Hare Court*	
Mansfield, Michael *14 Tooks Court*	
Pannick, David *2 Hare Court*	
Riza, Alper Ali *14 Tooks Court*	
Robertson, Geoffrey *Doughty Street Chambers*	
Allen, Robin *Cloisters*	
Blake, Nicholas *2 Garden Court*	
Fitzgerald, Edward *Doughty Street Chambers*	
Hendy, John *Old Square Chambers*	
Kadri, Sibghat *6 King's Bench Walk*	
Nicol, Andrew *Doughty Street Chambers*	
Scrivener, Anthony *2-3 Gray's Inn Square*	
Solley, Stephen *Cloisters*	

Mitre House Chambers has a strong commitment to civil liberties work. Both *Francis Gilbert* and *Mark Guthrie* are known for their criminal defence work with an emphasis on civil liberties. *Francis Gilbert* has particular expertise in cases with a political origin and has been involved in poll tax and South Africa House cases. Also recommended is *Victoria Teggin* who is known for her work in relation to prisoners' rights.

2 Garden Court is well known for immigration and criminal defence work, and is developing a strong reputation in the housing field. *Nicholas Blake QC's* practice includes immigration, housing, miscarriages of justice, actions against the police and discrimination. *David Watkinson, Jan Luba* and *Stephen Cottle* are all highly regarded in the field of housing law. *David Watkinson* covers all aspects and has handled lead cases including 'Puhlhofer v LB Hillingdon' and 'R v Bexley BC ex parte B'. He is co-author of 'Squatting Trespass and Civil Liberties' as well as a contributor to various articles. *Jan Luba* also writes regularly for the legal press on the subject and is particularly interested in administrative law aspects of public housing provision and homelessness.

Other highly regarded members are *Henry Blaxland*, *Terry*

particularly well known for his civil liberties work. At the junior end *Sylvester Carrott* and *Linda Pearce* are well regarded for their housing work, whilst *Andrew Gumbiti-Zimuto* has been recommended to us for his race discrimination expertise.

1 Pump Court has an excellent reputation in the fields of housing, and civil actions against the police. Leading practi-

LEADING JUNIORS– LONDON

Clayton, Richard *New Court Chambers*	**Clover,** Anthony *New Court Chambers*	**Gilbert,** Francis *Mitre House Chambers*
Lang, Beverley *2 Hare Court*	**Latham,** Robert *1 Pump Court*	
Beale, Judith *2 Hare Court*	**Blaxland,** Henry *2 Garden Court*	**Carrott,** Sylvester *6 King's Bench Walk*
Cottle, Stephen *2 Garden Court*	**Duffy,** Peter *Essex Court Chambers*	**Emmerson,** Ben *Doughty Street Chambers*
Forster, Sarah *14 Gray's Inn Square*	**Gill,** Tess *Old Square Chambers*	**Goulding,** Paul *2 Hare Court*
Gumbiti-Zimuto, Andrew *6 King's Bench Walk*	**Guthrie,** Mark J. *Mitre House Chambers*	**Higham,** Paul *1 Pump Court*
Luba, Jan *2 Garden Court*	**McKeon,** Caroline *1 Pump Court*	**Munyard,** Terry *2 Garden Court*
Mylvaganam, Tanoo *14 Tooks Court*	**Owen,** Tim *2 Garden Court*	**Pearce,** Linda *6 King's Bench Walk*
Rose, Dinah *2 Hare Court*	**Treverton-Jones,** Gregory *Farrar's Building*	**Watkinson,** David *2 Garden Court*

UP AND COMING

Kaufman, Phillippa *Doughty Street Chambers*	**Teggin,** Victoria *Mitre House Chambers*

Munyard and *Tim Owen*. *Henry Blaxland* is well known for public order work with a wide experience of political demonstration cases, and *Terry Munyard's* workload includes civil actions against the police and advice on issues concerning HIV and AIDS. He has also written articles, contributed to various publications and broadcast on national TV and radio on the rights of lesbians and gay men, the Local Government Act 1988 and prisoners' rights and inquests. *Tim Owen's* main areas of practice include public law, civil actions against the police and prisoner private law actions.

Also highly regarded in this field are **2 Hare Court, 6 King's Bench Walk** and **1 Pump Court**.

Whilst **2 Hare Court** is well known for appearances on behalf of the state, several members regularly appear on behalf of the individual. Leading silks at the set are *Lord Lester QC* and *David Pannick QC*. At the junior end *Judith Beale* (known for discrimination, nationality and immigration matters), *Beverley Lang* (acted in 'Thomas v NUM'; right of striking miners to picket), *Paul Goulding* (known for employment and discrimination matters) and *Dinah Rose* are particularly well regarded.

6 King's Bench Walk is well known for its work in the discrimination field, and also has a team of practitioners with expertise in housing law. Head of Chambers *Sibghat Kadri QC* is

tioners at the set are *Robert Latham*, *Paul Higham* and *Caroline McKeon*.

Notable individuals in other chambers that deserve particular mention are *Michael Beloff QC* (**4-5 Gray's Inn Square**), *Richard Clayton* (**New Court Chambers**) who has an excellent reputation for handling actions against the police and handled much of the litigation against the West Midlands Serious Crime Squad, *Anthony Clover* (**New Court Chambers**) who has considerable experience of appearing in civil actions against the police, and has represented numerous prisoners in actions against the Home Office, *Peter Duffy* (**Essex Court Chambers**) who is former Chair of Amnesty International, *Sarah Forster* (**14 Gray's Inn Square**) who handles civil liberties and educational aspects of childcare work and also has 15 years Mental Health Review Tribunal experience, *Tess Gill* (**Old Square Chambers**) who is an expert in race and sex discrimination and *Gregory Treverton-Jones* (**Farrar's Building**) who recently wrote a book on prisoners' rights.

OUTSIDE LONDON

LEADING JUNIORS– REGIONS

Darlow, Paul *St. John's Chambers, Bristol*

LEADERS IN CIVIL LIBERTIES

Allen QC, Robin
See under Employment.

Beale, Judith
See under Employment.

Beloff QC, Michael
See under Public and Administrative Law.

Blake QC, Nicholas
See under Immigration.

Blaxland, Henry
2 Garden Court (I. Macdonald QC, O. Davies), London (0171) 353 1633. Called 1978.

Carrott, Sylvester
6 King's Bench Walk (Sibghat Kadri QC), London (0171) 353 4931. Called 1980.

Clayton, Richard
New Court Chambers (George Carman QC), London (0171) 583 6166.

Specialisation: Principal areas of practice are public law and civil liberties, encompassing judicial review (including education, professional disciplinary matters and homelessness cases) and civil actions against the police. Also handles employment and discrimination law. Acted in R v. Chief Constable of South Wales ex p Merrick [1994] 1 WLR 663 (the right to legal advice); R v. Chief Constable of West Midlands Police ex p Wiley [1995] 1 AC 274 (public interest immunity); R v. Home Secretary ex p Hickey No 2 [1995] 1 WLR 734 (Home Office secrecy in 'miscarriages of justice' cases); R v. Home Secretary ex p Goswell, 'The Times' 29th December 1994 (police complaints procedure); Hellewell v. Chief Constable of Derbyshire [1995] 1 WLR 804 (breach of confidence); R v. Northern & Yorkshire Regional Health Authority ex p Trivedi [1995] 1 WLR 961 (the disciplinary procedure for General Practitioners) inter alia. Clients include numerous victims of West Midlands Serious Crime Squad. Author of 'Practice and Procedure at Industrial Tribunals' (LAAG, 1986), 'Suing the Police' (Longmans, 1989), 'Civil Actions Against the Police' (Sweet & Maxwell, 2nd Ed. 1992) and 'A Practical Guide to Judicial Review' (Longmans, 1993). Contributor to legal periodicals, radio and television broadcasts. Regular lecturer, including Law Society Further Education Programme.

Prof. Membership: Administrative Law Bar Association, Employment Law Practitioners' Association, Police Actions Lawyers' Group, Liberty, Society of Labour Lawyers, Legal Action Group (Committee since 1985).

Career: Called to the Bar 1977. South Islington Law Centre 1980-82. With *Osler, Hoskin & Harcourt*, Toronto 1982-83. Joined

New Court Chambers 1988.

Personal: Educated New College, Oxford. Member of Labour Party since 1973. Candidate, Wandsworth Borough Council 1982 and Parliamentary Candidate 1992 against Attorney General, Sir Nicholas Lyell QC MP. Leisure pursuits include reading, cinema, theatre and travel. Born 25th May 1954. Lives in London.

Clover, Anthony
New Court Chambers (George Carman QC), London (0171) 583 6166.

Specialisation: Professional negligence (medical; solicitors; etc). Contract and commercial. Civil liberties: Junior counsel for members of the Maguire family at Sir John May's Inquiry concerning the Guilford and Woolwich Bombings, and in Court of Appeal [1992] 1 QB 936. Represented the Headteacher of Highbury Grove Comprehensive School at the Disciplinary Inquiry into running of the school (1993). Considerable experience of appearing (for plaintiffs and defendants) in civil actions against the police; has represented prisoners in actions against the Home Office. Criminal law: defence; and prosecuting, instructed by Customs and Excise.

Prof. Membership: Professional Negligence Bar Association.

Career: Called (Middle Temple) 1971. (Astbury Scholarship). Recorder: 1995.

Personal: Educated at Stowe; and Exeter College, Oxford (Exhibitioner).

Cottle, Stephen
2 Garden Court (I. Macdonald QC, O. Davies), London (0171) 353 1633. Called 1984.

Darlow, Paul
St. John's Chambers (Roderick Denyer QC), Bristol (0117) 9213456. Called 1973.

Duffy, Peter
See under Public and Administrative Law.

Emmerson, Ben
Doughty Street Chambers (Geoffrey Robertson QC), London (0171) 404 1313.

Specialisation: Civil liberties and international human rights law, including representation of applicants before the European Court and Commission of Human Rights; civil actions against police and public law, particularly prisoners' rights. Also criminal law, especially political offences and cases involving police malpractice; Commonwealth capital appeals, extradition, deportation and international enforcement of asset confiscation. Editor of *European Human Rights Review* (Sweet & Maxwell). Litigation consultant to INTERIGHTS (International Centre for Legal Protection of Human Rights); Council of Europe Repre-

sentative on Human Rights Courses in Central and Eastern Europe.

Career: Called to the Bar 1986.

Personal: Bristol University 1982-85. Born 30th August 1963.

Fitzgerald QC, Edward
See under Public and Administrative Law.

Forster, Sarah
14 Gray's Inn Square (Joanna Dodson QC, Glenn Brasse), London (0171) 242 0858. Called 1976. Principal area of practice is family law. Majority of work is child care, with special emphasis on medical, mental and ethical aspects. Born 28.8.1953.

Gilbert, Francis
Mitre House Chambers (Francis P. Gilbert), London (0171) 583 8233. Called 1980. Principal area of practice is crime, including public order, public nuisance, sexual offences and fraud. Born in 1950.

Gill, Tess
See under Employment.

Goulding, Paul
See under Employment.

Gumbiti-Zimuto, Andrew
6 King's Bench Walk (Sibghat Kadri QC), London (0171) 353 4931. Called 1983.

Guthrie, Mark J.
Mitre House Chambers (Francis P. Gilbert), London (0171) 583 8233.

Specialisation: Principal area of practice is criminal defence work. Particular expertise in drugs offences, serious violent offences, public order cases, cases involving exercise of police powers and cases with a civil liberties element. Also handles civil actions against police.

Prof. Membership: Criminal Bar Association, Haldane Society of Socialist Lawyers.

Career: Called to the Bar 1984. Joined Mitre House Chambers 1988.

Personal: Educated at Manchester University 1980-83 (LL.B Hons).

Hendy QC, John
See under Employment.

Higham, Paul
1 Pump Court (Robert Latham), London (0171) 583 2012. Called 1982.

Kadri QC, Sibghat
6 King's Bench Walk (Sibghat Kadri QC), London (0171) 353 4931. Called 1969, took silk 1989.

Kaufman, Phillippa
Doughty Street Chambers (Geoffrey Robertson QC), London (0171) 404 1313. Called 1991. Civil practitioner specialising in employment, prisoners' rights, administrative law, landlord and tenant, housing and personal injury. Born 1966.

Lang, Beverley
See under Public and Administrative Law.

Latham, Robert
1 Pump Court (Robert Latham), London (0171) 583 2012. Called 1976.

Lester QC, Lord
See under Public and Administrative Law.

Luba, Jan
2 Garden Court (I. Macdonald QC, O. Davies), London (0171) 353 1633. Called 1980.

Mansfield QC, Michael
See under Criminal Law (General).

McKeon, Caroline
1 Pump Court (Robert Latham), London (0171) 583 2012. Called 1983.

Munyard, Terry
2 Garden Court (I. Macdonald QC, O. Davies), London (0171) 353 1633. Called 1972.

Mylvaganam, Tanoo
14 Tooks Court (Michael Mansfield QC), London (0171) 405 8828. Called 1983.

Nicol QC, Andrew
See under Immigration.

Owen, Tim
2 Garden Court (I. Macdonald QC, O. Davies), London (0171) 353 1633.

Specialisation: Main areas of practice are public law (especially prison, police and inquest law), civil actions against the police and prisoners' private law actions (assault, negligence and misfeance). Other areas include criminal law with experience in terrorist cases and cases involving prison law element, public order and appellate work. Privy Council (pro bono) and ECHR work. Co-author of 'Prison Law: Text & Materials', OUP 1993.

Prof. Membership: Haldane Society, ALBA, INQUEST Lawyers' Group.

Career: Called 1983.

Personal: Educated at Atlantic College and London School of Economics. Lives in London.

Pannick QC, David
See under Public and Administrative Law.

Pearce, Linda
6 King's Bench Walk (Sibghat Kadri QC), London (0171) 353 4931. Called 1982.

Riza QC, Alper Ali
14 Tooks Court (Michael Mansfield QC), London (0171) 405 8828. Called 1973, took silk 1991. Principal area of practice covers civil liberties, immigration, nationality and refugee law. Born 16.3.1948.

Robertson QC, Geoffrey
See under Public and Administrative Law.

Rose, Dinah
See under Employment.

Scrivener QC, Anthony
See under Public and Administrative Law.

Solley QC, Stephen
See under Crime: Fraud.

Teggin, Victoria
Mitre House Chambers (Francis P. Gilbert), London (0171) 583 8233. Called 1990. Specialises in civil liberties and criminal defence work, particularly in public order cases. Born 11.10.1957.

Treverton-Jones, Gregory
Farrar's Building (Lord Williams of Mostyn QC), London (0171) 583 9241. Called 1977. General common law practice including civil liberties, judicial review, employment and personal injury. Born 23.11.1954.

Watkinson, David
2 Garden Court (I. Macdonald QC, O. Davies), London (0171) 353 1633. Called 1972. Specialises in Housing Law. Born 6.10.1947.

COMMERCIAL LAW

BY virtue of the breadth and depth of experience available at these chambers, the three top-ranking sets are widely considered to be **1 Essex Court, Fountain Court** and **Brick Court Chambers** .

Following the death of *Sam Stamler QC* **1 Essex Court** are now headed by *Anthony Grabiner QC,* one of the star performers at the commercial Bar. Chambers also have several other top ranking silks and juniors who regularly appear in high profile cases. *Elizabeth Gloster QC* acted in the local authority/interest rate swaps litigation and more recently for the liquidators of Barlow Clowes. *Peter Leaver QC* was involved in the Mirror Pension Fund litigation and the Tin Council saga, as was *Ian Glick QC.*

Of the numerous experienced juniors in this set *Jeffrey Gruder* is a specialist in international trade finance and letters of credit. *Rhodri Davies,* well known for his work in the banking field, was also involved in the swaps litigation mentioned above. *Jeffrey Onions, Kenneth Maclean* and *John McCaughran* are all highly regarded. *Laurence Rabinowitz* is editor of 'Weinberg & Blank on Takeovers and Mergers.'

Fountain Court is a large and long established set led by *Peter Scott QC,* also considered to be a star practitioner. His practice covers a broad spread of commercial work, particularly banking, and much of his work and that of the chambers as a whole, is international in character. *Michael Brindle QC* is very experienced in City-related litigation arising out of audits, take-overs and rights issues. He acted in the leading case of 'Caparo v Dickman' (accountant's negligence). *Anthony Boswood QC* is well known for his Lloyd's work and

the chambers have several other leading silks with excellent reputations in this field.

There is also strength in depth amongst the juniors, including *Bankim Thanki* who acted for the Football Association in the Spurs/FA Cup litigation and lectures and writes on aviation law. *Stephen Moriarty,* known for his insurance

LEADING SILKS – LONDON

Grabiner, Anthony *1 Essex Court*	**Pollock,** Gordon *Essex Court Chambers*	**Scott,** Peter *Fountain Court*
Sumption, Jonathan *Brick Court Chambers*		
Aikens, Richard *Brick Court Chambers*	**Barnes,** Mark *1 Essex Court*	**Boswood,** Anthony *Fountain Court*
Bratza, Nicolas *One Hare Court*	**Brindle,** Michael *Fountain Court*	**Burnton,** Stanley *1 Essex Court*
Burton, Michael *Littleton Chambers*	**Carr,** Christopher *1 Essex Court*	**Clarke,** Christopher *Brick Court Chambers*
Falconer, Charles *Fountain Court*	**Gloster,** Elizabeth *1 Essex Court*	**Goldsmith,** Peter *Fountain Court*
Hamilton, Adrian *Seven King's Bench Walk*	**Hapgood,** Mark *Brick Court Chambers*	**Hirst,** Jonathan *Brick Court Chambers*
Howard, Michael N. *4 Essex Court*	**Irvine of Lairg,** Lord *11 King's Bench Walk*	**Jarvis,** John *3 Gray's Inn Place*
Johnson, David *20 Essex Street*	**Kentridge,** Sydney *Brick Court Chambers*	**Langley,** Gordon *Fountain Court*
Leaver, Peter *1 Essex Court*	**Lever,** Jeremy *Four Raymond Buildings*	**Littman,** Mark *12 Gray's Inn Square*
Rokison, Kenneth *20 Essex Street*	**Southwell,** Richard *One Hare Court*	**Steel,** David W. *4 Essex Court*
Thomas, R. Neville *3 Gray's Inn Place*		
Brice, Geoffrey *Queen Elizabeth Building*	**Cooke,** Jeremy *Seven King's Bench Walk*	**Cran,** Mark *Brick Court Chambers*
Dohmann, Barbara *2 Hare Court*	**Eder,** Bernard *Essex Court Chambers*	**Field,** Richard Alan *11 King's Bench Walk*
Flint, Charles *2 Hare Court*	**Gee,** Steven *1 Essex Court*	**Geering,** Ian *3 Gray's Inn Place*
Glasgow, Edwin *39 Essex Street*	**Glick,** Ian *1 Essex Court*	**Goode,** Roy *2 Hare Court*
Hunt, David *2 Hare Court*	**Kealey,** Gavin *Seven King's Bench Walk*	**MacGregor,** Alastair R. *1 Essex Court*
Mayes, Ian *Littleton Chambers*	**Merriman,** Nicholas *3 Gray's Inn Place*	**Moger,** Christopher *4 Pump Court*
Ross-Munro, Colin *2 Hare Court*	**Salter,** Richard *3 Gray's Inn Place*	**Seymour,** Richard *Four Raymond Buildings*
Smith, Andrew *Fountain Court*	**Stadlen,** Nicholas *Fountain Court*	**Storey,** Jeremy *4 Pump Court*
Strachan, Mark *1 Crown Office Row*	**Strauss,** Nicholas *1 Essex Court*	**Teare,** Nigel *4 Essex Court*
Temple, Anthony *4 Pump Court*	**Tomlinson,** Stephen *Seven King's Bench Walk*	**Tugendhat,** Michael *5-6 Raymond Buildings*
Walker, Tim *Fountain Court*		

experience, is the Editor of the Insurance section of 'Chitty on Contracts' (26th & 27th editions).

Brick Court Chambers specialise in commercial cases with particular emphasis on shipping, insurance, banking, administrative law and EC law. As would be expected there are several heavyweight silks and juniors in this set including *Jonathan Sumption QC* who can fairly be considered a specialist in most areas of commercial law, and the illustrious *Sydney Kentridge QC*.

regarded for their experience in the shipping and trade arbitration side of commodities work, especially *Kenneth Rokison QC, David Johnson QC, Nicholas Hamblen, Timothy Young, Christopher Hancock* and *David Owen* who is also Assistant Editor of 'MacGillivray on Insurance Law'.

3 Gray's Inn Place is an established commercial set. *Neville Thomas QC*'s practice encompasses all aspects of commercial contracts, acting for banks, shipping, trading and property companies, and commodity traders. *John*

LEADING JUNIORS – LONDON

Beazley, Thomas *2 Hare Court*	Birch, Elizabeth *20 Essex Street*	Butcher, Christopher *Seven King's Bench Walk*
Davies, Rhodri *1 Essex Court*	Doctor, Brian *Fountain Court*	Dowley, Dominic *One Hare Court*
Freedman, S. Clive *3 Gray's Inn Place*	Grainger, Ian *1 Essex Court*	Gruder, Jeffrey *1 Essex Court*
Hamblen, Nicholas *20 Essex Street*	Hancock, Christopher *20 Essex Street*	Jacobs, Richard *Essex Court Chambers*
Leggatt, George *Brick Court Chambers*	Loebl, Daphne *Fountain Court*	Malek, Ali *3 Gray's Inn Place*
Otton-Goulder, Catharine *Brick Court Chambers*	Owen, David *20 Essex Street*	Persey, Lionel *Queen Elizabeth Building*
Phillips, Stephen *3 Gray's Inn Place*	Rabinowitz, Laurence *1 Essex Court*	Richards, Stephen *Four Raymond Buildings*
Selvaratnam, Vasanti *Queen Elizabeth Building*	Smouha, Joe *Essex Court Chambers*	Thanki, Bankim *Fountain Court*
Young, Timothy *20 Essex Street*		

Algazy, Jacques *Cloisters*	Bate, Stephen *Four Raymond Buildings*	Berry, Steven *Essex Court Chambers*
Browne-Wilkinson, Simon *Fountain Court*	Chambers, Dominic *One Hare Court*	de Lacy, Richard *3 Gray's Inn Place*
Dyer, Allen *4 Pump Court*	Eadie, James *One Hare Court*	Garland, David *Brick Court Chambers*
Graham, Charles *1 Essex Court*	Green, Alison *Queen Elizabeth Building*	Hochhauser, Andrew *Essex Court Chambers*
Kay, Jervis *Queen Elizabeth Building*	Lewis, Caroline *3 Gray's Inn Place*	Lockey, John *Essex Court Chambers*
Lord, Richard *Brick Court Chambers*	Lowenstein, Paul *Littleton Chambers*	MacLean, Kenneth *1 Essex Court*
McCaughran, John *1 Essex Court*	Melwani, Poonam *4 Essex Court*	Moriarty, Stephen *Fountain Court*
Onions, Jeffrey *1 Essex Court*	Orr, Craig *Fountain Court*	Peacocke, Teresa R. *Enterprise Chambers*
Railton, David *Fountain Court*	Reffin, Clare *1 Essex Court*	Robertson, Patricia *Fountain Court*
Rowland, John *4 Pump Court*	Thom, James *Queen Elizabeth Building*	Tozzi, Nigel *4 Pump Court*
Whiteley, Miranda *Queen Elizabeth Building*	Wynter, Colin *Devereux Chambers*	

UP AND COMING

Cavender, David *1 Essex Court*	Hage, Joseph *1 Essex Court*

Essex Court Chambers are another set with members who can advise across the whole spectrum of international, commercial and European law. The main areas of work include international trade and transport, banking and financial services, commercial agreements, commodity transactions and insurance/re-insurance. The leading practitioners are *Gordon Pollock QC*, who is certainly amongst the top half dozen silks at the commercial Bar, and *Bernard Eder QC*.

The juniors include *Richard Jacobs, Joe Smouha, Andrew Hochhauser, Steven Berry,* and *John Lockey*.

20 Essex Street have members who can advise on a wide range of domestic and international commercial matters. *Kenneth Rokison QC*, head of chambers, has an outstanding reputation in the commercial field. Of the juniors, *Elizabeth Birch* has a broad commercial practice and acts both as a mediator and an arbitrator (on the panel of Lloyd's Arbitration Scheme) and is Secretary of the Commercial Bar Association (COMBAR). The chambers are particularly well

Jarvis QC also has a very wide practice in banking and commercial law generally, appearing in a number of high profile cases including the 'Tai Hang Cotton Mill' case in the Privy Council. He is the author of numerous published works, International Editor of the 'Journal of Banking and Finance Law' and represented Ian Maxwell before the House of Commons Select Committee inquiring into the Maxwell pension fund scandal. The set has a number of highly regarded juniors including *Ali Malek, Stephen Phillips, Richard de Lacy,* and *Clive Freedman*.

4 Essex Court specialise in a wide spectrum of commercial law but with a particular bias towards maritime law, international trade, insurance and EC law. *David Steel QC* is involved in commercial and shipping arbitrations both as counsel and arbitrator, and is a founding member of the City Disputes Panel. *Michael Howard QC* also specialises in commercial disputes, particularly those in connection with international trade, shipping or insurance.

7 Kings Bench Walk have a number of silks with a wide range of experience. *Jeremy Cooke QC* has acted in the Feltrim Names litigation. *Gavin Kealey QC* specialises in banking, insurance and commercial contracts of all kinds, and *Stephen Tomlinson QC* has extensive commercial arbitration experience and has been appointed by the London Court of International Arbitration and the ICC.

1 Hare Court is a relatively small but long established set specialising in all aspects of commercial work, both domestic and international, particularly banking, insurance and re-insurance. *Richard Southwell QC* specialises in banking, insurance and international arbitration and is currently Deputy President of the Lloyd's Appeal Tribunal. *Nicolas Bratza QC* is well known for his many appearances on behalf of the UK

Government at the European Court of Human Rights in Strasbourg and is a UK member of the European Commission of Human Rights. *Dominic Dowley*, *James Eadie* and *Dominic Chambers* are all highly regarded juniors.

2 Hare Court's main reputation is for work in the fields of commercial, employment and public law. *Colin Ross-Munro QC* has a wealth of experience in all these fields and has appeared in numerous high profile cases over the years including the recent long running saga of 'Arab Monetary Fund v Hashim'. There are several other vastly experienced commercial silks in this set including *David Hunt QC* who acted in the epic 'Derby v Weldon' litigation, *Barbara Dohmann QC*, and the distinguished academic *Professor Roy Goode QC*. Of the juniors *Thomas Beazley* is very experienced.

OUTSIDE LONDON

LEADING SILKS – REGIONS

Leveson, Brian Henry	*Byrom Chambers, Manchester*	
Mitting, J.	*4 Fountain Court, Birmingham*	
Randall, John	*7 Fountain Court, Birmingham*	
Wingate-Saul, Giles	*Byrom Chambers, Manchester*	

At the provincial Bar it is probably fair to say that there are currently only a handful of practitioners who could be regarded as commercial law specialists: most of the heavyweight work dealt with by regional firms of solicitors is still sent to the London Bar. However, those who have established a good reputation for work in this field include *John Randall QC, David Lock* and *James Corbett* all at **7 Fountain Court, Birmingham** and also in Birmingham, *John Mitting QC* (**4 Fountain Court**).

In Manchester, *Giles Wingate-Saul QC* and *Brian Leveson QC* (**Byrom Chambers**) have strong reputations for their commercial practices. *Stephen Davies* (**Guildhall Chambers, Bristol**) is also well-known for his commercial work.

LEADING JUNIORS – REGIONS

Bartley Jones, Edward	*Exchange Chambers, Liverpool*
Browne, Louis	*Peel House, Liverpool*
Cogley, Stephen	*Hollins Chambers, Manchester*
Corbett, James	*7 Fountain Court, Birmingham*
Davies, Stephen	*Guildhall Chambers, Bristol*
Edis, Andrew	*14 Castle St, Liverpool*
Lock, David	*7 Fountain Court, Birmingham*
Myerson, Simon	*Park Court Chambers, Leeds*
Sander, A.T.	*Oriel Chambers, Liverpool*

LEADERS IN COMMERCIAL LAW

Aikens QC, Richard
Brick Court Chambers (Christopher Clarke QC), London (0171) 583 0777. Called 1973, took silk 1986.

Algazy, Jacques
Cloisters (David Turner-Samuels QC), London (0171) 583 0303. Called 1980. Has a growing reputation as a general commercial practitioner with specialist expertise in European law and public/administrative law.

Barnes QC, Mark
See under Banking.

Bartley Jones, Edward
Exchange Chambers (William Waldron QC), Liverpool (0151) 236 7747.

Bate, Stephen
See under Media and Entertainment.

Beazley, Thomas
See under Financial Services.

Berry, Steven
See under Insurance and Reinsurance.

Birch, Elizabeth
20 Essex Street (Kenneth Rokison QC), London (0171) 583 9294.

Specialisation: Handles a broad range of commercial law matters including shipping, sale of goods, commodities, international trade, oil and gas, carriage by land, sea and air, banking and financial services, insurance and reinsurance, all types of contractual disputes and all related work such as agency,

arbitration, bailment, conflict of laws and disciplinary proceedings. Practises mainly in the Commercial and Admiralty Courts. Clients include UK based and international companies, international trading houses, shipping, shipbuilding and chartering interests, insurance companies and individuals. Also sits as arbitrator (appointed to the panel of the Lloyd's Arbitration Scheme) and as mediator in commercial/contractual disputes.

Prof. Membership: Fellow of the Chartered Institute of Arbitrators (FCIarb), Supporting member of the London Maritime Arbitrators Association (LMAA), The Academy of Experts - Accredited Mediator (QDR), Secretary of The Commercial Bar Association (COMBAR).

Career: Called to the Bar in 1978 and joined *20 Essex Street* in 1980.

Personal: Leisure interests include family. Lives in London.

Boswood QC, Anthony
Fountain Court (Peter Scott QC), London (0171) 583 3335. Called 1970, took silk 1986.

Bratza QC, Nicolas
One Hare Court (Sir Patrick Neill QC, Richard Southwell QC), London (0171) 353 3171.

Brice QC, Geoffrey
See under Shipping.

Brindle QC, Michael
See under Banking.

Browne, Louis
Peel House (David M. Harris QC), Liverpool (0151) 236 0718.

Browne-Wilkinson, Simon
See under Aviation.

Burnton QC, Stanley
1 Essex Court (Anthony Grabiner QC), London (0171) 583 2000. Called 1965, took silk 1982. Specialises in commercial litigation, including banking, company acquisitions, auditors' and accountants' negligence and arbitration.

Burton QC, Michael
Littleton Chambers (Michael Burton QC), London (0171) 797 8600.
Specialisation: Wide range of practice in general commercial litigation in the Commercial, Q.B. and Chancery Divisions and arbitration. Has had reported cases in the fields of employment and trade unions, intellectual property, defamation and entertainment, Mareva injunctions, European and public law, Convention and P.I.L., insurance, banking and insolvency, professional negligence, letters of request, extradition and elections.
Prof. Membership: COMBAR; London Common Law and Commercial Bar Association; Bar Council (Legal Services Committee); ORBA.
Career: Called Grays Inn 1970. Joined 2 Crown Office Row (now Littleton Chambers) 1971, Head of Chambers 1991; Recorder, Deputy High Court Judge. Bencher of Grays Inn.
Personal: Educated at Eton College and Balliol College, Oxford. Lives in London with 4 daughters.

Butcher, Christopher
Seven King's Bench Walk (Adrian Hamilton QC), London (0171) 583 0404. Called 1986.

Carr QC, Christopher
1 Essex Court (Anthony Grabiner QC), London (0171) 583 2000. Called 1968, took silk 1983.

Cavender, David
1 Essex Court (Anthony Grabiner QC), London (0171) 583 2000. Called 1993.

Chambers, Dominic
See under Banking.

Clarke QC, Christopher
Brick Court Chambers (Christopher Clarke QC), London (0171) 583 0777. Called 1969, took silk 1984.

Cogley, Stephen
Hollins Chambers (Howard Baisden), Manchester (0161) 835 3451. Called 1984.

Cooke QC, Jeremy
Seven King's Bench Walk (Adrian Hamilton QC), London (0171) 583 0404. Called 1976, took silk 1990. Specialises in all aspects of commercial law. Born 28.9.1949.

Corbett, James
See under Chancery.

Cran QC, Mark
See under Media and Entertainment.

Davies, Rhodri
See under Banking.

Davies, Stephen
See under Chancery.

de Lacy, Richard
See under Financial Services.

Doctor, Brian
Fountain Court (Peter Scott QC), London (0171) 583 3335. Called 1991.

Dohmann QC, Barbara
See under Insurance and Reinsurance.

Dowley, Dominic
One Hare Court (Sir Patrick Neill QC, Richard Southwell QC), London (0171) 353 3171. Called 1983. Insurance/reinsurance and banking specialist. Born 25.3.1958.

Dyer, Allen
See under Professional Negligence.

Eadie, James
See under Banking.

Eder QC, Bernard
Essex Court Chambers (Gordon Pollock QC), London (0171) 813 8000. Called 1975, took silk 1990.

Edis, Andrew
See under Public and Administrative Law.

Falconer QC, Charles
See under Aviation.

Field QC, Richard Alan
11 King's Bench Walk (Lord Irvine of Lairg QC), London (0171) 583 0610.
Specialisation: Principal area of practice is Commercial Law. Has appeared in a wide range of matters in this area including insurance, banking and E.C Competition law. Other areas of practice include professional negligence, especially auditors' negligence, and public law.
Prof. Membership: ALBA; COMBAR; London Common Law and Commercial Bar Asociation.
Career: 1967-1977 taught in the law faculties of the Universities of British Columbia; Honk Kong; and McGill; called to the Bar 1977; appointed Queen's Counsel 1987; Assistant Recorder 1995.
Personal: Educated: Bristol University (LLB) and London University (LLM).

Flint QC, Charles
2 Hare Court (C.W.G. Ross-Munro QC), London (0171) 583 1770.
Specialisation: Commercial law specialist. Practice covers substantial corporate litigation in all divisions of the High Court, and financial services litigation, including disciplinary tribunals. Has a particular interest in commercial fraud. Practice also covers judicial review in a commercial context, including judicial review of Inland Revenue decisions. Interesting cases include R v. Inland Revenue ex p. Matrix Securities [1994] 1 WLR 334 (judicial review/tax). Also acted for the plaintiff in Arab Monetary Fund v. Hashim [1991] 2 AC 114.
Prof. Membership: Fellow of the Chartered Institute of Arbitrators, London Common Law and Commercial Bar Association, Administrative Law Bar Association.
Career: Called to the Bar 1975, joining present chambers in the same year. Appointed Junior Counsel to the Crown (Common Law) 1991-1995 and took Silk 1995.
Personal: Educated at Cambridge University (MA).

Freedman, S. Clive
3 Gray's Inn Place (R. Neville Thomas QC), London (0171) 831 8441.
Specialisation: General commercial litigation, in particular cases involving technical issues, large quantities of documents and/or computer support.
Career: Called to the Bar in 1975.
Personal: Educated at Harrow School and Trinity College, Cambridge.

Garland, David
Brick Court Chambers (Christopher Clarke QC), London (0171) 583 0777. Called 1986.

Gee QC, Steven
1 Essex Court (Anthony Grabiner QC), London (0171) 583 2000.

Specialisation: Commercial law and litigation, insurance/reinsurance, contracts, banking, arbitration, shipping, aviation, computer law.
Author: 'Mareva Injunctions and Anton Piller relief' (3rd ed: 1995).

Prof. Membership: COMBAR.

Career: QC (1993); formerly standing junior Counsel to DTI (ECGD). Foreign Jurisdictions: Antigua.

Geering QC, Ian
3 Gray's Inn Place (R. Neville Thomas QC), London (0171) 831 8441.

Specialisation: Commercial law, specialising in civil claims based on international and domestic commercial fraud and claims for restitution. Banking, insurance and professional negligence.

Prof. Membership: COMBAR, London Common Law and Commercial Association.

Career: Queen's Counsel 1991. Recorder 1995.

Glasgow QC, Edwin
See under Insurance and Reinsurance.

Glick QC, Ian
See under Banking.

Gloster QC, Elizabeth
See under Insolvency.

Goldsmith QC, Peter
Fountain Court (Peter Scott QC), London (0171) 583 3335. Called 1972, took silk 1987.

Goode QC, Roy
2 Hare Court (C.W.G. Ross-Munro QC), London (0171) 583 1770. Called 1988, took silk 1990. Specialist in commercial law and consumer credit. Professor of English Law, University of Oxford. Born 6.4.1933.

Grabiner QC, Anthony
1 Essex Court (Anthony Grabiner QC), London (0171) 583 2000. Called 1968, took silk 1981.

Graham, Charles
1 Essex Court (Anthony Grabiner QC), London (0171) 583 2000.

Specialisation: Principal area of practice is general commercial law including a wide range of commercial litigation. Particular emphasis on disputes arising out of takeovers and the role of merchant banks and accountants in relation thereto, auditors' negligence, franchising agreements, bank guarantees and facilities etc. and performance bonds. Also handles insurance related matters and work in connection with private international law.

Prof. Membership: South Eastern Circuit, Commercial Bar Association.

Career: Called to the Bar in 1986 and joined *1 Essex Court* in 1987.

Personal: Educated at Wellington College 1974-79 and University College, Oxford 1980-84 MA Classics (First Class Honours). Born 1st April 1961. Lives in London.

Grainger, Ian
1 Essex Court (Anthony Grabiner QC), London (0171) 583 2000. Called 1978.

Green, Alison
See under Insurance and Reinsurance.

Gruder, Jeffrey
See under Insurance and Reinsurance.

Hage, Joseph
See under Company.

Hamblen, Nicholas
20 Essex Street (Kenneth Rokison QC), London (0171) 583 9294. Called 1981. Practice covers shipping, insurance and re-insurance, commodities, conflict of laws and arbitrations. Born 23.9.1957.

Hamilton QC, Adrian
Seven King's Bench Walk (Adrian Hamilton QC), London (0171) 583 0404. Called 1949, took silk 1973. Specialises in commercial and arbitration work.

Hancock, Christopher
20 Essex Street (Kenneth Rokison QC), London (0171) 583 9294. Called 1983.

Hapgood QC, Mark
Brick Court Chambers (Christopher Clarke QC), London (0171) 583 0777. Called 1979, took silk 1994.

Hirst QC, Jonathan
Brick Court Chambers (Christopher Clarke QC), London (0171) 583 0777. Called 1975, took silk 1990.

Hochhauser, Andrew
See under Company.

Howard QC, Michael N.
See under Shipping.

Hunt QC, David
2 Hare Court (C.W.G. Ross-Munro QC), London (0171) 583 1770.

Specialisation: Specialist in all aspects of commercial law, with a particular emphasis on arbitration, civil fraud, shipping (dry work), shipbuilding and ship repairing. Practice also covers general contract and tort, and private international law. Interesting recent cases include Standard Bank v. Bank of Tokyo 1995 (banking), Pertamina v. Thahir [1992-94] Singapore (bribery); Dubai Bank Ltd. v. Galadari [1989-92] (fraud); Derby & Co. Ltd. v. Weldon [1990-91] (fraud); Publications include articles for the *Solicitors' Journal*.

Prof. Membership: COMBAR

Career: Called to the Bar 1969. Took Silk

1987. Appointed Recorder of the Crown Court 1991. Vice-Chairman of Gray's Inn Continuing Education Committee.

Personal: Educated at Charterhouse School 1960-65 and Trinity College, Cambridge 1965-68. Working knowledge of French. Leisure pursuits include sailing, golf and skiing. Born 22nd June 1947. Lives in Tunbridge Wells.

Lord Irvine of Lairg QC, Lord
11 King's Bench Walk (Lord Irvine of Lairg QC), London (0171) 583 0610.

Specialisation: Principal area of practice is Commercial Law: general contractual disputes; insurance, re-insurance, futures, financial services and banking. Has appeared in numerous actions for major banks and companies both in this country and overseas (Hong Kong, Singapore and Cayman Islands). Other areas of practice include public law, employment law and defamation.

Prof. Membership: ALBA; COMBAR and London Common Law and Commercial Bar Association.

Personal: Educated: Inverness Royal Academy: Hutchesons' Boys' Grammar School; Glasgow University (MA, LLB); Cambridge University, (BA (1st Class Hons. with Distinction); LLB (1st Class Hons.)). University Prize in Jurisprudence.

Career: University lecturer, London School of Economics 1965-68; Called to the Bar 1967; Appointed Queen's Counsel 1978; Head of Chambers at *11 King's Bench Walk* since foundation in 1981; Bencher of the Inner Temple 1985; Recorder 1985-88; Elevated to the peerage 1987; Shadow Lord Chancellor, House of Lords 1992 to date.

Jacobs, Richard
See under Insurance and Reinsurance.

Jarvis QC, John
See under Banking.

Johnson QC, David
20 Essex Street (Kenneth Rokison QC), London (0171) 583 9294. Called 1967, took silk 1978.

Kay, Jervis
Queen Elizabeth Building (Geoffrey Brice QC), London (0171) 353 9153.

Kealey QC, Gavin
Seven King's Bench Walk (Adrian Hamilton QC), London (0171) 583 0404. Called 1977, took silk 1994. Specialises in all aspects of commercial law.

Kentridge QC, Sydney
Brick Court Chambers (Christopher Clarke QC), London (0171) 583 0777. Called 1977, took silk 1984. Has a wide ranging practice including general commercial law, insurance and reinsurance, media and entertainment and defamation.

Langley QC, Gordon
Fountain Court (Peter Scott QC), London (0171) 583 3335. Called 1966, took silk 1983.

Leaver QC, Peter
1 Essex Court (Anthony Grabiner QC), London (0171) 583 2000.

Specialisation: Main areas of practice are commercial law, insurance, banking and financial services. Involved in Tin Council and Mirror Pension Fund litigation and the Ford Europe case in the ECJ. Contributor to 'Pre-Trial and Pre-Hearing Procedures Worldwide' (Graham & Trotman and IBA, 1990).

Prof. Membership: COMBAR, IBA, Bar European Group, Midland & Oxford Circuit, London Common Law & Commercial Bar Association, Society of Commonwealth Lawyers.

Career: Called to the Bar in 1967. At 4 Paper Buildings 1968-72, and joined current chambers in 1973. Took silk in 1987. Member of General Council of the Bar 1987-90 (Chairman of the Bar Committee, 1989). Appointed Recorder and Director of IMRO in 1994. Bencher of Lincoln's Inn 1995.

Personal: Educated at Aldenham School and Trinity College, Dublin. Leisure pursuits include being a football referee, sport, wine, opera and theatre. Born 28th November 1944.

Leggatt, George
Brick Court Chambers (Christopher Clarke QC), London (0171) 583 0777. Called 1983.

Lever QC, Jeremy
See under Public and Administrative Law.

Leveson QC, Brian Henry
Byrom Chambers (B.A. Hytner QC), Manchester (0161) 834 5238.

Lewis, Caroline
3 Gray's Inn Place (R. Neville Thomas QC), London (0171) 831 8441.

Specialisation: Commercial litigation; in particular, claims based on international and domestic commercial fraud, banking, financial services and insolvency.

Prof. Membership: COMBAR, London Common Law and Commercial Bar Association.

Career: Called to the Bar 1988.

Littman QC, Mark
12 Gray's Inn Square (Mark Littman QC), London (0171) 404 4866. Called 1947, took silk 1961. Specialist in all aspects of domestic and international commercial arbitration. Born 4.9.1920.

Lock, David
7 Fountain Court (Rex Tedd QC), Birmingham (0121) 236 8531.

Lockey, John
Essex Court Chambers (Gordon Pollock QC), London (0171) 813 8000. Called 1987. Specialist in commercial law. Born 8.4.1963.

Loebl, Daphne
Fountain Court (Peter Scott QC), London (0171) 583 3335. Called 1985. Principal area of practice is commercial law. Also covers professional negligence, employment and computer-related disputes. Born in 1962.

Lord, Richard
See under Banking.

Lowenstein, Paul
Littleton Chambers (Michael Burton QC), London (0171) 797 8600.

Specialisation: Principal area of practice is commercial and business law, covering all aspects of commercial litigation, in particular private international law, multinational litigation, restraint of trade and employment covenants and commercial property disputes. Other main areas of practice are banking and bank security documentation, including building society security documentation, mortgages and professional negligence (especially of solicitors, surveyors and valuers). Recent notable cases include The Evia Luck [1992]; J.A. Mont v. Mills [1993]; Hanover Insurance Brokers v. Shapiro [1994]; Re: Shoe Lace Ltd (in liquidation) [1994] and Nicholls v. Kinsey [1994]. Lectures regularly on specific areas of civil procedure and private international law.

Prof. Membership: COMBAR.

Career: Called to the Bar 1988 and joined current chambers 1989 (when located at 2 Crown Office Row).

Personal: Educated at Westminster School 1977-81, Manchester University 1983-86 (LL.B Hons) and Cambridge University 1986-87 (LL.M). Leisure pursuits include sailing and skiing. Born 31st December 1963. Lives in London.

MacGregor QC, Alastair R.
1 Essex Court (Anthony Grabiner QC), London (0171) 583 2000.

Specialisation: Practice covers a wide range of commercial litigation, including, in particular, disputes relating to takeovers, share sales agreements, newspaper and other distributorships, the oil industry, partnerships and joint ventures, banking transactions and securities, conflict of laws and negligence on the part of auditors and merchant bankers. Recent important cases include De Bry v.Fitzgerald [1990];I AII E.R. 560; Aiglon Ltd v. Gau Shan Co Ltd. [1993], I Lloyd's Ref 164; Habib Bank v. Jaffer; Gamlestaden Plc v. Casa de Suecia SA [1994] I Lloyd's 433; Hallett v. B.B.B.C; Bailey v. News International; Re British & Commonwealth Holdings Plc.

Prof. Membership: South Eastern Circuit, COMBAR.

MacLean, Kenneth
1 Essex Court (Anthony Grabiner QC), London (0171) 583 2000.

Specialisation: Principally commercial law.

Prof. Membership: COMBAR. New York State Bar.

Career: Called to the Bar and joined 1 Essex Court in 1985.

Personal: Educated at Cambridge University (1980) and Harvard Law School (1982). Born 9th February 1959.

Malek, Ali
3 Gray's Inn Place (R. Neville Thomas QC), London (0171) 831 8441. Called 1980. Specialises in all aspects of commercial law, particularly banking and international trade. Born 1956.

Mayes QC, Ian
Littleton Chambers (Michael Burton QC), London (0171) 797 8600.

Specialisation: Commercial litigation and arbitration.

Prof. Membership: COMBAR, Revenue Bar Association.

Career: Called to the Bar 1974. DTI Investigation into London Capital Group Ltd; Treasury Counsel to Inland Revenue 1983-1993; Silk 1993; Chairman of Disciplinary Committee, Lloyd's of London. Languages: French, German.

McCaughran, John
1 Essex Court (Anthony Grabiner QC), London (0171) 583 2000.

Specialisation: Principal area of practice is commercial litigation.

Prof. Membership: Commercial Bar Association

Career: Called to the Bar in 1982.

Personal: Educated at Methodist College, Belfast 1969-76 and Trinity Hall, Cambridge 1977-80. Born 24th April 1958. Lives in London.

Melwani, Poonam
4 Essex Court (David Steel QC), London (0171) 797 7970.

Specialisation: Specialises in all aspects of commercial law, international trade and shipping. Practice also covers professional negligence.

Prof. Membership: COMBAR

Career: Called to the Bar 1988. Joined present chambers 1990.

Personal: Educated at Wycombe Abbey 1980-1985 and Sidney Sussex College,

Cambridge 1985-1988. Leisure pursuits include theatre and restaurants. Born 20th May 1967. Lives in London.

Merriman QC, Nicholas
See under Financial Services.

Mitting QC, J.
4 Fountain Court (Richard Wakerley QC), Birmingham (0121) 236 3476.

Moger QC, Christopher
4 Pump Court (Bruce Mauleverer QC), London (0171) 353 2656.

Specialisation: General commercial and common law, especially insurance, construction matters; professional negligence, and regulatory and disciplinary proceedings.

Prof. Membership: ORBA; LCLBA; COMBAR; PNBA; Barristers' Overseas Advocacy Committee.

Career: Called 1972: joined 4 Pump Court 1973: Assistant Recorder 1990: Silk 1992: Recorder 1993.

Personal: Educated Sherborne School 1963-68 and Bristol University 1969-71 (LL.B Hons). Born 28th July 1949.

Moriarty, Stephen
See under Insurance and Reinsurance.

Myerson, Simon
Park Court Chambers (Gilbert Gray QC, Brian Walsh QC), Leeds (0113) 2433277.

Onions, Jeffrey
1 Essex Court (Anthony Grabiner QC), London (0171) 583 2000. Called 1981.

Orr, Craig
Fountain Court (Peter Scott QC), London (0171) 583 3335.

Specialisation: Practice covers all areas of commercial law, including, in particular Lloyd's Names litigation, City related litigation (especially merchant banking-related matters), accountants' negligence actions, commercial fraud (civil actions), banking and insurance litigation. Important cases include British & Commonwealth v. Quadrex and Samuel Montagu litigation, Caparo v. Dickman [1990]; Eagle Trust v. Cowan de Groot [1992]; and Society of Lloyd's v Mason and Clementson.

Prof. Membership: COMBAR.

Career: Called to the Bar in 1986 and joined *Fountain Court* in 1988.

Personal: Educated at Cambridge University 1981-84 (MA) and Oxford University (BCL, Vinerian Scholar). Born 8th January 1962.

Otton-Goulder, Catharine
Brick Court Chambers (Christopher Clarke QC), London (0171) 583 0777. Called 1983.

Owen, David
20 Essex Street (Kenneth Rokison QC), London (0171) 583 9294. Called 1983. Practice includes commercial law, arbitration, insurance and reinsurance, sale of goods and professional negligence. Born 21.1.1958.

Peacocke, Teresa R.
Enterprise Chambers (Benjamin Levy), London (0171) 405 9471.

Specialisation: Principal area of practice is litigation in all areas of commercial/chancery law, particularly professional negligence, partnership law, property, landlord and tenant, company law, insolvency and bankruptcy, and banking. Professional negligence cases include White v. Jones (solicitors' negligence, House of Lords) and Roberts v. J. Hampson & Co. Other areas of professional negligence handled include accountants, tax consultants, barristers, architects, engineers and surveyors.

Prof. Membership: Professional Negligence Bar Association, Anglo-American Real Property Institute, Agricultural Law Association, Association of Women Barristers, American Women Lawyers in London Group.

Career: Called to the Bar 1982: tenant at 7 New Square 1982-89, then joined Enterprise Chambers.

Personal: Educated at University of Michigan (Analytical Philosophy and Logic BA 1977, MA 1979). Lives in London.

Persey, Lionel
Queen Elizabeth Building (Geoffrey Brice QC), London (0171) 353 9153.

Specialisation: Principal area of practice is in all aspects of maritime law and general commercial law. Has considerable experience of charterparty and bill of lading disputes, salvage, collision, insurance (marine and non-marine), oil industry litigation, shipbuilding disputes, product liability, arbitration law and Admiralty practice. Recent leading cases include *The Maciej Rataj* (ECJ) and *Skinner v. Department of Transport* (whether Coastguard owes a duty of care). Clients include leading professional practices, the major P&I Clubs, and Government departments. Has sat as a commercial arbitrator.

Prof. Membership: COMBAR, London Common Law and Commercial Bar Association, London Maritime Arbitrators Association.

Career: Called to the Bar 1981. Joined Queen Elizabeth Building in 1984. Member of the Gibraltar Bar. Member of Supplementary Panel of Treasury Counsel 1991.

Phillips, Stephen
3 Gray's Inn Place (R. Neville Thomas QC), London (0171) 831 8441.

Specialisation: Principal area of practice is commercial and business law. Work includes general contractual disputes, banking and finance, company law and insolvency,

international and domestic trade, commercial fraud, professional negligence and gaming contracts. Clients include banks and other financial institutions, insurance companies and funds and casinos. Contributor to 'The Encyclopaedia of Banking Law.'

Prof. Membership: Wales and Chester Circuit, COMBAR, London Common Law and Commercial Bar Association.

Career: Called to the Bar 1984 and joined present chambers 1985.

Personal: Educated at King's School, Chester 1973-80 and University College, Oxford 1980-83. Born 10th October 1961.

Pollock QC, Gordon
Essex Court Chambers (Gordon Pollock QC), London (0171) 813 8000. Called 1968, took silk 1979.

Rabinowitz, Laurence
1 Essex Court (Anthony Grabiner QC), London (0171) 583 2000. Called 1987. Main areas of practice are commercial law, financial services, oil and gas disputes, and professional negligence. Born 3.5.1960.

Railton, David
See under Banking.

Randall QC, John
See under Chancery.

Reffin, Clare
1 Essex Court (Anthony Grabiner QC), London (0171) 583 2000.

Specialisation: Commercial law, general but including banking, civil claims arising out of commercial frauds, professional negligence. Extensive experience in ex parte and other interlocutory applications. Cases include The Salvation Army Trustee Company v Ford & others ("letter of credit" fraud); Maxwell-related litigation; Omar v Omar (reported case on "Bankers Trust" discovery).

Career: Called to the Bar in 1981. Solicitor of The Supreme Court of The Gambia 1982.

Personal: Born in 1959, graduate of King's College Cambridge.

Richards, Stephen
See under Public and Administrative Law.

Robertson, Patricia
Fountain Court (Peter Scott QC), London (0171) 583 3335. Called 1988. Principal area of practice is banking and commercial law. Also handles employment, some EC law, insurance and professional negligence. Born 1.8.1964

Rokison QC, Kenneth
See under Arbitration.

Ross-Munro QC, Colin
2 Hare Court (C.W.G. Ross-Munro QC), London (0171) 583 1770. Called 1951, took silk 1972. Principal area of practice is

commercial law. Born 2.10.1951.

Rowland, John
See under Insurance and Reinsurance.

Salter QC, Richard
See under Banking.

Sander, A.T.
Oriel Chambers (Andrew T. Sander), Liverpool (0151) 236 7191. Called 1970.

Scott QC, Peter
Fountain Court (Peter Scott QC), London (0171) 583 3335.

Specialisation: Commerical Law. Practice covers a broad spread of commercial and civil work. Particular specialities include banking, financial services, professional negligence, insurance, City regulatory and public administration matters. Much of his work is international in character and European Community Law is an integral part of it. Important cases include Hazell v. Hammersmith & Fulham Borough Council (HL) [1991] (swaps/ local authorities/banking); National Westminster Bank v. Morgan (HL) [1985] (banking/undue influence); Bank Leumi v. British National Insurance Co Ltd [1988] (insurance); Devis v. Atkins (HL)(employment); Arab Monetary Fund v. Hashim (banking, commercial fraud) [1994] and Defrenne v. Sabena (ECJ) (European Law and employment). Has acted both for and against the Bank of England and many other banks including all the London Clearing Banks and a variety of foreign banks, merchant banks and other financial institutions both in the UK and abroad. Has appeared in the courts of Hong Kong and Bermuda, as well as the European Court of Justice and the European Court of Human Rights. Involved in international arbitrations both as Counsel and Arbitrator.

Prof. Membership: COMBAR, Midland & Oxford Circuit, London Common Law & Commercial Bar Association (Chairman 1983-85).

Career: Called to the Bar and joined *Fountain Court Chambers* in 1960. Took silk in 1978. Chairman of the Bar Council 1987. Member of Interception of Communications Tribunal. Bencher of the Middle Temple.

Personal: Educated at Monroe High School, Rochester, New York and Balliol College, Oxford. Born 19th April 1935. Lives in London.

Selvaratnam, Vasanti
Queen Elizabeth Building (Geoffrey Brice QC), London (0171) 353 9153. Called 1983. Principal areas of practice are shipping and general commercial law.

Seymour QC, Richard
Four Raymond Buildings (Jeremy Lever QC), London (0171) 405 7211. Called 1972, took silk 1991. Specialist in commercial law.

Smith QC, Andrew
Fountain Court (Peter Scott QC), London (0171) 583 3335.

Specialisation: Principal area of work is commercial law, especially insurance, reinsurance, banking and dry shipping law. Also handles professional negligence work relating to accountants, solicitors, brokers, surveyors and doctors, employment, computer and parliamentary work. Acts for major banks, insurance companies, syndicates and professional firms. Sits as an arbitrator.

Prof. Membership: London Common Law and Commercial Bar Association (Secretary 1983-1991), South Eastern Circuit.

Career: Called to the Bar 1974. Joined *Fountain Court* 1975. County Court Rules Committee 1979-1983 and Queen's Bench Procedural Committee 1986-1990. Took silk in 1990. Vice-Chairman of Bar Standards Review Body 1994. Assistant Recorder 1991. Assistant Parliamentary Boundary Commissioner 1993.

Personal: Educated at Wyggeston Grammar School for Boys. Graduated from Wadham College, Oxford with BA Literae Humaniores and BA Jurisprudence (First Class). Astbury Scholar at Middle Temple 1974. Born 31st December 1947.

Smouha, Joe
Essex Court Chambers (Gordon Pollock QC), London (0171) 813 8000. Called 1986.

Southwell QC, Richard
See under Banking.

Stadlen QC, Nicholas
Fountain Court (Peter Scott QC), London (0171) 583 3335. Called 1976, took silk 1991.

Steel QC, David W.
See under Shipping.

Storey QC, Jeremy
4 Pump Court (Bruce Mauleverer QC), London (0171) 353 2656.

Specialisation: Practice encompasses commercial work (particularly insurance, reinsurance and banking), personal injury, building and construction and general common law. Has acted in Lloyd's arbitrations, reinsurance run-off disputes, letter of credit frauds, Brussels Convention disputes, and computer software litigation. Also handles professional negligence for both plaintiffs and defendants particularly against accountants, solicitors, surveyors, brokers, engineers and architects. Clients include major domestic and international banks and insurers, Lloyd's syndicates and tariff companies. Member of drafting sub-committee of London Common Law and Commercial Bar Association, re amendments to RSC; sole author of Association's paper to Law Commission on proposed abolition of hearsay rule in civil proceedings. Conducted advocacy

courses in Kuala Lumpur, Trinidad, Hong Kong and Mauritius.

Prof. Membership: COMBAR, London Common Law and Commercial Bar Association (Committee), Official Referees' Bar Association, Barristers Overseas Advocacy Committee (Chairman).

Career: Called to the Bar 1974 and joined 4 Pump Court in 1976 Appointed Assistant Recorder (Western Circuit) 1990. Took Silk 1994. Appointed Recorder (Western Circuit) 1995.

Personal: Educated at Uppingham School 1966-70 and Downing College, Cambridge (Scholar, BA Law 1st Class, MA). Leisure pursuits include cricket, travel and theatre. Born 21st October 1952.

Strachan QC, Mark
1 Crown Office Row (Mark Strachan QC), London (0171) 583 9292.

Specialisation: Principal area of practice is commercial and common law work, including contract, sale of goods, commercial fraud, professional negligence and judicial review. Does a broad range of appellate work in the Privy Council involving commercial, common law and criminal cases, and specialises in the written constitutions of the Commonwealth. Undertakes arbitration work and is available to sit as an Arbitrator. Undertakes susbtantial personal injury and medical negligence actions. Frequently undertakes cases with a French element, where his fluent French assists.

Prof. Membership: COMBAR

Career: Called to the Bar 1969. Silk 1987. Sits as a Deputy High Court Judge of the High Court in the Queen's Bench Division.

Strauss QC, Nicholas
See under Banking.

Sumption QC, Jonathan
Brick Court Chambers (Christopher Clarke QC), London (0171) 583 0777. Called 1975, took silk 1986. Specialises in all aspects of commercial law. Born 9.12.1948.

Teare QC, Nigel
4 Essex Court (David Steel QC), London (0171) 797 7970. Called 1974, took silk 1991.

Temple QC, Anthony
See under Professional Negligence.

Thanki, Bankim
See under Banking.

Thom, James
Queen Elizabeth Building (Geoffrey Brice QC), London (0171) 353 9153.

Specialisation: Principal area of practice is commercial law, with an emphasis on commercial contracts, banking and commercial lending. Other main area of work is commercial landlord and tenant including dilapidations, service charge disputes, rent reviews and lease renewals, and general commercial property work. Also deals with professional negligence cases, frequently concerning commercial property transactions, against solicitors, surveyors, valuers, architects, accountants, engineers and others. Clients include building societies (commercial lending departments), banks, professional indemnity insurers and property companies. Joint author of 'Handbook of Dilapidations' (Sweet & Maxwell, 1992). Regular speaker at conferences and seminars on the law of landlord and tenant.

Prof. Membership: Professional Negligence Bar Association, COMBAR.

Career: Called to the Bar 1974. Tenant at *3 Paper Buildings* 1974-83, then joined *2 Serjeants' Inn* (later *218 Strand*) which merged to become present chambers in 1992.

Personal: Educated at Felsted School 1965-68 and Corpus Christi College, Oxford 1969-73 (BA 1972, BCL 1973). Born 19th October 1951. Lives in Hampstead, London.

Thomas QC, R. Neville

3 Gray's Inn Place (R. Neville Thomas QC), London (0171) 831 8441.

Specialisation: Principal area of practice encompasses all aspects of commercial contracts, especially for banks, shipping companies, trading companies, commodity dealers and property companies.

Prof. Membership: Commercial Bar Association, London Common Law Bar Association.

Career: Called to the Bar and joined present chambers 1962. Took Silk 1975. Recorder 1975-81. Master of the Bench, Inner Temple 1985.

Personal: Educated at Oxford University (MA 1960, BCL 1961). Born 31st March 1936. Lives in London.

Tomlinson QC, Stephen

See under Insurance and Reinsurance.

Tozzi, Nigel

See under Media and Entertainment.

Tugendhat QC, Michael

5-6 Raymond Buildings (Patrick Milmo QC), London (0171) 242 2902. Called 1969, took silk 1986. Practice encompasses commercial law, media and entertainment and insurance law. Born 21.10.1944.

Walker QC, Tim

See under Professional Negligence.

Whiteley, Miranda

Queen Elizabeth Building (Geoffrey Brice QC), London (0171) 353 9153. Called 1985. Principal areas of practice are commercial law and shipping.

Wingate-Saul QC, Giles

Byrom Chambers (B.A. Hytner QC), Manchester (0161) 834 5238. Called 1967, took silk 1983.

Wynter, Colin

Devereux Chambers (Peter Weitzman QC), London (0171) 353 7534. Called 1984. Specialist in commercial law, including insurance and reinsurance, employment and construction. Born 11.9.1960.

Young, Timothy

20 Essex Street (Kenneth Rokison QC), London (0171) 583 9294. Called 1977. Main area of practice is commercial law and international trade. Born 1.12.1953.

INDEXES TO PROFILES

Solicitors' Profiles The index to leading solicitors profiled in the Specialist Lists is located immediately after the section containing profiles of in-house lawyers. This index also includes heads of company legal departments.

Barristers' Profiles Profiles of leading barristers are indexed within the main *Barristers' Index* located at the end of the directory. Names of profiled barristers are set in bold type.

COMPANY

M OST chancery and commercial sets practise some element of company law from advising on the structuring, management and administration of companies, takeovers, acquisitions and mergers, financing, reorganisations

and restructuring of companies, schemes of arrangement and reduction of capital, to EU and international aspects of company law. **Erskine Chambers**, an impressive set distinguished by its depth of experience and knowledge, are preeminent in this field. Other leading commercial chambers with expertise in this field are **4 Stone Buildings, 1 New Square, 13 Old Square**, and **3-4 South Square**.

Erskine Chambers are the leading company chambers specialising in company law and related matters. In addition to the complex technical and advisory matters handled, a substantial amount of the work in chambers is of a litigious nature. Many of the members are held in high esteem. In particular, *Richard Sykes QC*, Consultant Editor of 'Gore-Browne on Companies', and *Robin Potts QC* are highly distinguished. *David Richards QC* and *Sir Thomas Stockdale* are also well regarded and both contribute to 'Buckley on the Companies Acts'. Other members who must be mentioned are *Leslie Kosmin QC, David Mabb, Martin Moore, Catherine Roberts* and *Michael Todd* who is Junior Counsel to the Crown in Chancery.

also acted in the BCCI, Polly Peck and Bishopsgate litigations. *George Bompas QC* has acted in many of the major company matters in recent years, such as the Guinness affair, Blue Arrow, Brent Walker and BCCI.

Jonathan Crow and *Malcolm Davis-White* are both Junior Counsel to the Crown in Chancery. *John Brisby* and *Peter Griffiths* are also well-regarded. Many members contribute to the company sections in 'Atkins Court Forms', 'Butterworths Company Law Precedents' and the 'Encyclopaedia of Forms & Precedents' and other publications.

1 New Square has a strong company practice with *John McDonnell QC* having an excellent reputation. *Robin Hollington* is also highly regarded. **13 Old Square (Christie)** also undertake company work. *Michael Lyndon-Stanford QC* and *David Oliver QC* are well recognised. *Matthew Collings* is a notable junior.

At **7 Stone Buildings**, *Charles Aldous QC, Nigel Davis QC, Guy Newey, Christopher Parker* and *Michael Green* have excellent reputations as does *Alan Boyle QC* at **13 Old Square (Sparrow)**.

All members of **3-4 South Square** have company law expertise. Those worthy of particular mention are *Michael Crystal QC, Simon Mortimore QC* and *Richard Adkins QC*. Notable juniors include *Richard Hacker, Robin Dicker* and *Lexa Hilliard*.

1 Essex Court is a commercial set also advising on company matters. *Elizabeth Gloster QC* is well-regarded. Her recent caseload has included acting in 'Heron Group

LEADING SILKS

Potts, Robin *Erskine Chambers*	Sykes, Richard *Erskine Chambers*	
Aldous, Charles *7 Stone Buildings*	Bompas, Anthony George *4 Stone Buildings*	Boyle, Alan *13 Old Square*
Davis, Nigel *7 Stone Buildings*	Gloster, Elizabeth *1 Essex Court*	Goodhart, William *3 New Square*
Hamilton, Eben W. *1 New Square*	Heslop, Philip *4 Stone Buildings*	Hildyard, Robert *4 Stone Buildings*
Kosmin, Leslie *Erskine Chambers*	Purle, Charles *12 New Square*	Richards, David *Erskine Chambers*
Stubbs, W.F. *Erskine Chambers*		
Adkins, Richard *3-4 South Square*	Briggs, Michael *13 Old Square*	Crystal, Michael *3-4 South Square*
Curry, Peter *4 Stone Buildings*	Lyndon-Stanford, Michael *13 Old Square*	Mann, Anthony *Enterprise Chambers*
McDonnell, John B.W. *1 New Square*	Mortimore, Simon *3-4 South Square*	Newman, Catherine *13 Old Square*
Oliver, David *13 Old Square*		

4 Stone Buildings have an excellent reputation with a number of distinguished individuals, including *Philip Heslop QC* and *Robert Hildyard QC* who acted in 'Stena NV v Sea Containers Limited'. *Philip Heslop QC*

reconstruction', 'Barlow Clowes International', 'BCCI' and 'Stena NV v Sea Containers Limited'. **Enterprise Chambers** also have members dealing in company law such as *Anthony Mann QC* and *Geoffrey Zelin* who have been recommended.

LEADING JUNIORS

Mabb, David *Erskine Chambers*	**Stockdale,** Thomas *Erskine Chambers*	

Brisby, John *4 Stone Buildings*	**Chivers,** David *Erskine Chambers*	**Collings,** Matthew *13 Old Square*
Crow, Jonathan *4 Stone Buildings*	**Davis-White,** Malcolm *4 Stone Buildings*	**Gillis,** Richard *1 Essex Court*
Girolami, Paul *13 Old Square*	**Green,** Michael A. *7 Stone Buildings*	**Hollington,** Robin *1 New Square*
Joffe, Victor *11 Stone Buildings*	**Moore,** Martin *Erskine Chambers*	**Newey,** Guy *7 Stone Buildings*
Parker, Christopher *7 Stone Buildings*	**Roberts,** Catherine *Erskine Chambers*	**Snowden,** Richard *Erskine Chambers*
Stokes, Mary *Erskine Chambers*	**Todd,** Michael *Erskine Chambers*	

Arden, Peter *Enterprise Chambers*	**de Garr Robinson,** Anthony *1 Essex Court*	**Dicker,** Robin *3-4 South Square*
Gillyon, Philip *Erskine Chambers*	**Giret,** Jane *11 Stone Buildings*	**Griffiths,** Peter *4 Stone Buildings*
Hacker, Richard *3-4 South Square*	**Harman,** Sarah *4 Stone Buildings*	**Hilliard,** Lexa *3-4 South Square*
Hochhauser, Andrew *Essex Court Chambers*	**Hoser,** Philip *1 New Square*	**Marten,** Hedley *3 New Square*
Nicholson, Rosalind *4 Stone Buildings*	**Ritchie,** Richard *24 Old Buildings*	**Smith,** Stephen *12 New Square*
Stewart, Lindsey *7 Stone Buildings*	**Weatherill,** Bernard *3 New Square*	**Zelin,** Geoffrey *Enterprise Chambers*

UP AND COMING

Hage, Joseph *1 Essex Court*	**Thompson,** Andrew *Erskine Chambers*

LEADERS IN COMPANY

Adkins QC, Richard
See under Insolvency.

Aldous QC, Charles
See under Chancery.

Arden, Peter
See under Insolvency.

Bompas QC, Anthony George
4 Stone Buildings (Peter Curry QC),
London (0171) 242 5524.
Specialisation: Principal area of practice is
company law (all aspects, including minority
shareholders proceedings and insolvency)
and financial services. Other main area of
practice is professional negligence work. Has
been instructed in many of the major, widely
publicised, company matters in recent years,
including the Guinness affair, the Blue Arrow, the Barlow Clowes, and the Brent
Walker and BCCI affairs. Author of 'Investigations by the DTI' in Tolley's 'Company
Law' (3rd Ed.). Other main area of practice is
professional negligence work.
Prof. Membership: Chancery Bar Association, Insolvency Lawyers' Association.
Career: Called to the Bar 1975 and joined
present chambers in 1976. Junior Counsel to
the DTI 1989-94. Took Silk in 1994.
Personal: Educated at Merchant Taylors'
School, Northwood 1964-69 and Oriel College, Oxford 1970-74. Born 6th November
1951.

Boyle QC, Alan
13 Old Square (Charles Sparrow QC),
London (0171) 242 6105. Called 1972, took
silk 1991.

Briggs QC, Michael
13 Old Square (Charles Sparrow QC),
London (0171) 242 6105. Called 1978, took
silk 1994.

Brisby, John
See under Financial Services.

Chivers, David
See under Insolvency.

Collings, Matthew
13 Old Square (Mr. E.W.H. Christie),
London (0171) 404 4800. Called 1985. Principal area of practice is company, insolvency
and financial services. Born 13.8.1961.

Crow, Jonathan
4 Stone Buildings (Peter Curry QC),
London (0171) 242 5524.
Specialisation: Principal area of practice is
company law, encompassing all aspects of
company and related litigation. Other main
areas of work are insolvency, financial services, and media and entertainment including
litigation relating to corporate insolvency,
SRO Disciplinary Tribunals, and management and distribution agreements. Acted in
Guinness, Barlow Clowes and Polly Peck litigation. Clients include listed and private
companies, directors and shareholders,
banks and financial institutions, film and music managers and performers, and

government departments. Lectures at City
solicitors' firms and Official Receivers in-
house training courses.
Prof. Membership: Chancery Bar Association, Insolvency Lawyers Association.
Career: Called to the Bar 1981 and joined
present chambers in 1983. Appointed Junior
Counsel to the Crown in Chancery, 1994.
Personal: Educated at St Paul's School 1971-
75. Oxford University 1976-79 and City
University 1979-80. Member of the Athenaeum and The Royal Geographical Society.
Born 25th June 1958. Lives in London.

Crystal QC, Michael
See under Insolvency.

Curry QC, Peter
4 Stone Buildings (Peter Curry QC),
London (0171) 242 5524. Called 1953, took
silk 1973.

Davis QC, Nigel
7 Stone Buildings (Charles Aldous QC),
London (0171) 405 3886.
Specialisation: Principal area of practice is
chancery, with emphasis on company, insolvency, banking and property litigation and
also general commercial litigation. Has acted
for banks and institutions (both UK and overseas) and for a range of licensed insolvency
practitioners and professional practices. Has
appeared in a number of reported cases, on
subjects extending to company meetings;
constructive trusts; insurance; worldwide
mareva injunctions; insolvency; and real
property. Acted as counsel to the inquiry of
the Board of Banking Supervision into the

collapse of Barings Bank. Other areas of practice include professional negligence (solicitors), both for plaintiff and defendant; partnership; and media and entertainment.

Personal: Education: Charterhouse; University College, Oxford (MA). Residence: Richmond.

Davis-White, Malcolm
See under Financial Services.

de Garr Robinson, Anthony
See under Banking.

Dicker, Robin
See under Insolvency.

Gillis, Richard
1 Essex Court (Anthony Grabiner QC), London (0171) 583 2000.

Specialisation: Specialises in company/commercial disputes, insolvency, banking and professional negligence. Other principal areas of practice include, commercial fraud, contract (including share and business sale agreement, restaint of trade, sale of goods and retention of title) disciplinary proceedings, directors' disqualification, insurance, partnership.

Prof. Membership: Chancery and Commercial Bar and Insolvency Lawyers Association.

Career: Called to the Bar in 1982.

Personal: Educated at Balliol College, Oxford (MA, BCL). Born 25th November 1958.

Gillyon, Philip
Erskine Chambers (Richard Sykes QC), London (0171) 242 5532. Called 1988.

Giret, Jane
See under Insolvency.

Girolami, Paul
13 Old Square (Mr. E.W.H. Christie), London (0171) 404 4800. Called 1983. Principal area of practice is chancery work, particularly involving company and insolvency litigation. Born 5.12.1959.

Gloster QC, Elizabeth
See under Insolvency.

Goodhart QC, William
See under Chancery.

Green, Michael A.
See under Insolvency.

Griffiths, Peter
4 Stone Buildings (Peter Curry QC), London (0171) 242 5524.

Specialisation: Principal area of practice is company law, focusing on insolvency and minority shareholder disputes. Other main areas of work include partnership, civil fraud, bankruptcy and professional negligence. Contributor to 'Atkins Court Forms' Vol 10 (Companies Winding Up) 1988 and 'Encyclo-

paedia of Forms and Precedents' 5th Ed Vol 11 (Companies).

Prof. Membership: Chancery Bar Association, Insolvency Lawyers' Association.

Career: Called to the Bar in 1977 and joined present chambers in 1978.

Personal: Educated at Repton 1966-71 and St. Catharine's College, Cambridge, 1972-75.

Hacker, Richard
See under Banking.

Hage, Joseph
1 Essex Court (Anthony Grabiner QC), London (0171) 583 2000. Called 1991.

Hamilton QC, Eben W.
1 New Square (Eben Hamilton QC), London (0171) 405 0884. Called 1962, took silk 1981.

Harman, Sarah
4 Stone Buildings (Peter Curry QC), London (0171) 242 5524. Called 1987.

Heslop QC, Philip
4 Stone Buildings (Peter Curry QC), London (0171) 242 5524.

Specialisation: Principal area of practice encompasses company and financial services law, corporate insolvency and banking.

Prof. Membership: Chancery Bar Association, Insolvency Lawyers' Association.

Career: Called to the Bar 1970 and joined present chambers in 1972. Joint Junior Counsel (Chancery) DTI 1980-85. Took Silk in 1985. Deputy Chairman, IMRO Membership Tribunal since 1988. Joint DTI Inspector, Consolidated Goldfields Plc 1988. Bencher Lincoln's Inn, 1993. Called to the Hong Kong, Bermuda and Gibraltar Bars for specific cases.

Personal: Educated at Haileybury 1961-66 and Christ's College, Cambridge 1967-71 (B.A. Hons 1970, LL.M 1971). President, Cambridge Union Society 1971. Born 24 April 1948.

Hildyard QC, Robert
4 Stone Buildings (Peter Curry QC), London (0171) 242 5524.

Specialisation: Principally, company law, corporate insolvency, financial services and company/commercial litigation. Specialist in insurance company transfer schemes. Other work areas include insurance/reinsurance litigation. Recent court cases include Macmillan v. BIT (Maxwell litigation/conflicts of laws), NRG Victory (insurance company transfer scheme), LDDC v. Regalian (restitution), Kurz v. Stella Musical (choice of jurisdiction clause) and Charter Re ('pay to be paid' reinsurance clause). Contributor: Butterworth's Enclyclopaedia of Forms and Precedents (company volume); Tolley's Company Law.

Prof. Membership: Chancery Bar Associa-

'tion, Insolvency Lawyers' Association.

Career: Called to the Bar in 1977, Junior Counsel to the Crown (Chancery) 1992-94, appointed Queen's Counsel 1994.

Personal: Educated at Eton College; Christ Church Oxford. Languages: Spanish.

Hilliard, Lexa
3-4 South Square (Michael Crystal QC), London (0171) 696 9900.

Hochhauser, Andrew
Essex Court Chambers (Gordon Pollock QC), London (0171) 813 8000. Called 1977.

Hollington, Robin
1 New Square (Eben Hamilton QC), London (0171) 405 0884.

Specialisation: Principal areas of work are Company Law and Insolvency. Author of 'Minority Shareholders' Rights' (Sweet & Maxwell, 2nd Ed. 1994).

Prof. Membership: Chancery Bar Association.

Career: Called to the Bar 1979 and joined 1 New Square 1981.

Personal: Educated at Oxford University 1974-77 (MA) and University of Pennsylvania 1977-78 (LL.M). Born 30th June 1955.

Hoser, Philip
See under Insolvency.

Joffe, Victor
11 Stone Buildings (Michael Beckman QC), London (+44) 0171 831 6381. Called 1975. Main areas of practice are company law and corporate insolvency.

Kosmin QC, Leslie
Erskine Chambers (Richard Sykes QC), London (0171) 242 5532. Called 1976, took silk 1994. Principal areas of practice are company law and corporate insolvency. Born 12.8.1952.

Lyndon-Stanford QC, Michael
13 Old Square (Mr. E.W.H. Christie), London (0171) 404 4800. Called 1962, took silk 1979.

Mabb, David
Erskine Chambers (Richard Sykes QC), London (0171) 242 5532. Called 1979.

Mann QC, Anthony
See under Chancery.

Marten, Hedley
3 New Square (Sir William Goodhart QC), London (0171) 405 5577 (5 lines).

Specialisation: Specialist in a broad area of commercial Chancery work including company law, contract, insolvency, landlord & tenant, and trusts. Practice also covers cases under the Company Directors Disqualification Act 1986. Important cases include

Cowan v Department of Health [1991] (landlord & tenant, trusts); Vestey v. Clifton-Brown [1991] (Variation of Trusts Act 1958); Re Packaging Direct Ltd [1993] (Director's Disqualification).

McDonnell QC, John B.W.

1 New Square (Eben Hamilton QC), London (0171) 405 0884. Called 1968, took silk 1984.

Moore, Martin

Erskine Chambers (Richard Sykes QC), London (0171) 242 5532. Called 1982.

Mortimore QC, Simon

See under Financial Services.

Newey, Guy

7 Stone Buildings (Charles Aldous QC), London (0171) 405 3886.

Specialisation: General Chancery practice includes charities, company, financial services, insolvency, property and solicitors' negligence.

Career: Called to the Bar 1982. Joined present Chambers 1983. One of the Junior Counsel to the Crown (Chancery). Junior Counsel to the Charity Commissioners.

Personal: Educated at Tonbridge School and Queens' College, Cambridge (BA 1st class, LL.M 1st class, MA). Bar Exams 1st class, 1982. Born 21st January 1959. Lives in Sevenoaks, Kent.

Newman QC, Catherine

See under Chancery.

Nicholson, Rosalind

4 Stone Buildings (Peter Curry QC), London (0171) 242 5524. Called 1987.

Oliver QC, David

See under Insolvency.

Parker, Christopher

7 Stone Buildings (Charles Aldous QC), London (0171) 405 3886. Called 1984. Main areas of practice are company and insolvency law. Also undertakes general Chancery work. Born 13.10.1958.

Potts QC, Robin

Erskine Chambers (Richard Sykes QC), London (0171) 242 5532.

Specialisation: Specialist in all aspects of company law including insolvency. Experience extends to practice in overseas courts such as Bermuda, Hong Kong, Bahamas,

Cayman Islands and Gibraltar. Interesting cases include the Paramount Case [1995] Court of Appeal and House of Lords (acting for the successful airline pilots); Macmillan IZNC v. BIT [1994] (arising out of the Maxwell affair). Also represented British Land Plc in litigation brought by Stanhope Properties. Has fought several section 459 petitions including two major trials in the past year.

Prof. Membership: Commercial Bar Association; Insolvency Lawyers Association.

Career: Called to the Bar 1968. Joined present chambers 1969. Took silk 1982.

Personal: Educated at Wolstanton Grammar School, Newcastle-under-Lyme, and at Magdalen College, Oxford (BA and BCL) 1963-1967. Bigelow Fellow, University of Chicago Law School 1967-1968. Leisure pursuits include history, gardening, travel and wine. Born 2nd July 1944. Lives in London.

Purle QC, Charles

12 New Square (John Mowbray QC), London (0171) 405 3808. Called 1970, took silk 1989.

Richards QC, David

Erskine Chambers (Richard Sykes QC), London (0171) 242 5532. Called 1974, took silk 1992.

Ritchie, Richard

24 Old Buildings (C.A. Brodie QC), London (0171) 404 0946. Called 1978.

Roberts, Catherine

Erskine Chambers (Richard Sykes QC), London (0171) 242 5532. Called 1986.

Smith, Stephen

12 New Square (John Mowbray QC), London (0171) 405 3808. Called 1983.

Snowden, Richard

See under Financial Services.

Stewart, Lindsey

7 Stone Buildings (Charles Aldous QC), London (0171) 405 3886. Called 1983. Main areas of practice are Chancery and commercial litigation. Born 24.4.1961.

Stockdale, Thomas

Erskine Chambers (Richard Sykes QC), London (0171) 242 5532. Called 1966.

Stokes, Mary

Erskine Chambers (Richard Sykes QC), London (0171) 242 5532. Called 1989.

Stubbs QC, W.F.

Erskine Chambers (Richard Sykes QC), London (0171) 242 5532. Called 1957, took silk 1978.

Sykes QC, Richard

Erskine Chambers (Richard Sykes QC), London (0171) 242 5532. Called 1958, took silk 1981. Specialist in all aspects of company law including takeovers, mergers and acquisitions, financing, reorganisation and restructuring, accounting and auditing requirements, and corporate insolvency. Born 28.5.1934.

Thompson, Andrew

Erskine Chambers (Richard Sykes QC), London (0171) 242 5532. Called 1991.

Todd, Michael

See under Insolvency.

Weatherill, Bernard

3 New Square (Sir William Goodhart QC), London (0171) 405 5577 (5 lines).

Specialisation: Principal area of practice is company and insolvency law and practice, covering directors' duties, liquidations and receiverships, minority shareholders' actions, unfair prejudice and just and equitable petitions, company meetings and organisation. Other areas of work are property and general Chancery work, particularly guarantees and securities, mortgage law, landlord and tenant matters and (not least) professional negligence. Clients include building societies and lending institutions, property companies, liquidators and administrative receivers.

Prof. Membership: Chancery Bar Association, Professional Negligence Bar Association.

Career: Called to the Bar 1974 and joined 3 New Square in 1976. Elected member of the Bar Council 1989-92 and 1993-95. Chairman of the Bar Services Committee 1992.

Personal: Educated at Malvern College 1964-69, Principia College, Illinois, USA 1970 and Kent University 1970-73. Leisure pursuits include wine, lawn tennis and real tennis. Born 20th May 1951. Lives in Putney.

Zelin, Geoffrey

Enterprise Chambers (Benjamin Levy), London (0171) 405 9471. Called 1984.

COMPUTER LAW

COMPUTER law is an expanding area of practice combining intellectual property law (predominantly the protection of software copyrights) with contractual matters arising out of agreements to supply and maintain computer systems.

Specialists tend therefore to come from the leading intellectual property and commercial chambers. **8 New Square**, the pre-eminent intellectual property set, and **11 South Square** emerge as the leading specialist chambers in this field. At **8 New Square** members of chambers undertake a broad spectrum of information technology and telecommunication work and also have experience of European and competition law (which is of increasing importance).

Following the loss of *Hugh Laddie QC* to the Bench, chambers' leading silks are *John Baldwin QC*, *David Kitchin QC* and *Peter Prescott QC*. *Martin Howe* is chambers' outstanding junior counsel, while *Richard Meade* has been described as a rising star.

At **11 South Square** *Henry Carr* (recommended by all practitioners canvassed) and *Michael Silverleaf* enjoy national reputations in the field. *Nicholas Pumfrey QC* is also held in high regard.

Other highly recommended intellectual property sets are **Three New Square** and **19 Old Buildings**.

Three New Square (formerly **6 Pump Court**) boasts eminent practitioners in *Simon Thorley QC*, *Guy Burkill* and *Andrew Waugh*. *Colin Birss* is chambers' rising star. *Alastair Wilson QC* (who heads chambers) and *Graham Shipley* are **19 Old Buildings**' most highly recommended practitioners. *Rory Sullivan* was also recommended and described as chambers' most promising 'younger practitioner'.

Atkin Chambers, a leading construction set, contains several members with experience of computer contract disputes. Of these *Andrew White* and *David Streatfeild-James* are particularly recommended.

Individual practitioners to feature prominently in our research include *Nicholas Davidson QC* of **4 Paper Buildings** and *Selwyn Bloch* of **Littleton Chambers**.

We are aware of only one barrister to practise almost exclusively in the field of telecoms: *Sa'id Mosteshar* of **Hamilton House Chambers**. He is the Chairman of the Satellite IBA Communications Sub-Committee, past Chairman of the Outer Space Committee and is experienced in the regulatory and transactional aspects of communications law, ranging from computer networking and broadcasting to telecommunications and outer space law.

OUTSIDE LONDON

LEADERS IN COMPUTER LAW

Baldwin QC, John
See under Intellectual Property.

Birss, Colin
Three New Square (David E.M. Young QC), London (0171) 405 1111.

Bloch, Selwyn
See under Employment.

Brindle QC, Michael
See under Banking.

Burkill, Guy
Three New Square (David E.M. Young QC), London (0171) 405 1111. Called 1981.

Carr, Henry
See under Intellectual Property.

Cunningham, Graham
Francis Taylor Building (N.P. Valios QC), London (0171) 353 7768.
Specialisation: All aspects of computers and information technology, and telecommunications, technology transfer, all types of commercial trading relationships, intellectual property law and competition law. Former legal director and management team member with computer company, Wang, and legal adviser on technology transfer agreements with ITT Corporation. Accredited mediator with CEDR for alternative dispute resolution. Clients are mostly large computer and telecommunications companies.
Career: Called 1976. Joined *Francis Taylor Building* in 1994.
Personal: Educated at Cranleigh School and Brunel University.

Davidson QC, Nicholas
4 Paper Buildings (Harvey McGregor QC), London (0171) 353 3366.
Specialisation: Solicitors' and financial negligence. Other main areas of work cover general commercial cases, including computer litigation.
Prof. Membership: Professional Negligence Bar Association (Hon. Treasurer), Bar European Group, COMBAR, Society for Computer and Law.
Career: Called 1974; joined present Chambers 1975. Silk 1993.
Personal: Educated at Winchester 1964-69 (Scholar) and Trinity College Cambridge (Exhibitioner in Economics) 1969-72.

Drysdale Wilson, Alexander
See under Intellectual Property.

Freedman, S. Clive
See under Commercial Law.

Gee QC, Steven
See under Commercial Law.

Heywood, Michael E.
Bridge St Chambers (Peter Keenan), Manchester (0161) 834 8468.

Howe, Martin
See under Intellectual Property.

Kitchin QC, David
See under Intellectual Property.

Lever QC, Jeremy
See under Public and Administrative Law.

Meade, Richard
See under Intellectual Property.

Mosteshar, Sa'id
Hamilton House Chambers (Sa'id Mosteshar), London (0171) 402 2010. Fax: (0171) 402 3231.
Specialisation: Principal practice in all regulatory and tansactional aspects of communications law, ranging from telecommunications to computer networking and broadcasting; leading practitioner in outer space law covering transactions, regulations and public international law of outer space, with considerable experience in matters such as rights to orbital positions and frequencies ('Telenor v. British Sky Broadcasting Group Plc', 'National Transcommunications Limited', 'Nordiska Satellitaktiebolaget' and 'Swedish Space Corporation'). Other main areas of practice cover intellectual property rights and licensing, including those arising in multimedia projects and the use of the Internet.
Prof. Membership: FCA; IBA Chairman of Satellite Communications Sub-Committee, Past Chairman Outer Space Committee; ABA Past Chairman European Communication Committee; FCBA; IISL.
Career: Called to the English Bar 1975, California Bar 1980. Author of EC Regulation of Telecommuications; Satellite Communications; Research and Inventions in Outer Space; Co-author Satellite and Cable Television; and many other books and articles. Visiting Fellow and Professor at UCL and UCSD.
Education: Southampton, LSE and Oxford.

Prescott QC, Peter
See under Intellectual Property.

Pumfrey QC, Nicholas
See under Intellectual Property.

Shipley, Graham
19 Old Buildings (Alastair Wilson QC), London (0171) 405 2001.
Specialisation: Principal area of practice encompasses intellectual property and technology work, including electronic and computer cases and EC aspects. Regular seminar speaker, and has appeared on radio

and television ('Science Now') broadcasts.
Prof. Membership: Patent Bar Association, Chancery Bar Association.
Career: Called to the Bar 1973 and joined present chambers in 1975, when located at *3 Pump Court*.
Personal: Educated at King's School, Chester 1959-66, Trinity College, Cambridge 1966-71 (B.A. Mathematics 1969, Diploma in Computer Science, Distinction 1970) and Inns of Court School of Law 1971-73. Former Director of 'Trinity 69 Foundation' charity. Leisure pursuits include electronics, house restoring, woodwork, Japanese cookery and motor cycle riding. Born 10th January 1948. Lives in Saffron Walden.

Silverleaf, Michael
See under Intellectual Property.

Smith QC, Andrew
See under Commercial Law.

Streatfeild-James, David
See under Construction Law.

Sullivan, Rory
19 Old Buildings (Alastair Wilson QC), London (0171) 405 2001.

Susman, Peter
New Court Chambers (George Carman QC), London (0171) 583 6166.
Specialisation: Principal areas of practice are litigation arising from commercial contracts (with particular experience of disputes arising from the supply of computer systems) and professional negligence cases.
Prof. Membership: London Common Law Bar Association.
Career: Called to the Bar 1966. Associate with *Messrs Debevoise & Plimpton, Attorneys,* New York City, USA 1970-72. Joined current chambers 1967. Appointed Recorder 1993.
Personal: Educated Dulwich College 1953-61, Lincoln College, Oxford 1961-64 (Oldfield Scholar and BA 1964, MA 1969) and University of Chicago Law School, 1964-65 (British Commonwealth Fellow and Fulbright Scholar, JD 1965). Leisure pursuits include clarinet, squash, windsurfing and skiing. Born 20th February 1943.

Thorley QC, Simon
Three New Square (David E.M. Young QC), London (0171) 405 1111. Called 1972, took silk 1989.

Waugh, Andrew
Three New Square (David E.M. Young QC), London (0171) 405 1111. Called 1982.

White, Andrew

See under Construction Law.

Wilson QC, Alastair

19 Old Buildings (Alastair Wilson QC), London (0171) 405 2001.

Specialisation: Principal area of practice is intellectual property and technology cases, including EC aspects. Other areas of work include lotteries and setting aside Anton Piller orders. Cases of importance include, inter alia, Chelsea Man v. Chelsea Girl, Intergraph v. SSI, PLG (Netlon) v. Ardon and Chiron v. Murex. Clients include British Railways Board, Ford Motor Company, Associated Newspapers, Irish Dairy Board and Netlon. Has presented numerous seminars on intellectual property and computer law. Recently made a video on trade mark law for Legal Network Television.

Prof. Membership: Society for Computers and Law, Patent Bar Association, Committee Member of Chancery Bar Association.

Career: Called to the Bar 1968 and joined current chambers when located at 3 Pump Court in 1970. Took Silk in 1987. Appointed Assistant Recorder in 1993.

Personal: Educated at Wellington College and Pembroke College. Leisure pursuits include gardening, building and shooting. Born 26th May 1946. Lives in Norwich.

CONSTRUCTION LAW

WHILE many of the general commercial chambers have expertise in building and civil engineering disputes, the increasing complexity of construction law as a discipline in its own right, with its own system of courts and tribunals has created a specialist bar.

Keating Chambers emerge as the leading set with 29 specialists handling building contract litigation and arbitration (including ICC and FIDIC) work for contractors, property developers and owners, the NHBC, government departments and local authorities. Members are also experienced in mechanical engineering, insurance and professional negligence cases for architects, engineers, surveyors and their insurers.

LEADING SETS	
ATKIN CHAMBERS	**KEATING CHAMBERS**
1 PAPER BUILDINGS	**4 PUMP COURT**
2 CROWN OFFICE ROW	**39 ESSEX STREET**
3 SERJEANTS' INN	**2 TEMPLE GARDENS**

Richard Fernyhough QC and *Vivian Ramsey QC* have been highly recommended. Chambers also have eminent silks in *John Uff QC* (head of chambers and visiting professor at King's College, London), *John Marrin QC*, *Christopher Thomas QC*, *Stephen Furst QC* and *Timothy Elliott QC*. *Robert Gaitskill QC* is a former electrical engineer. He has a particular specialisation in power stations and electrical and mechanical engineering matters.

At the junior end of chambers, *Marcus Taverner* and *Paul Darling* have been recommended very highly as have *Philip Boulding*, *Rosemary Jackson*, *Peter Coulson*, *Finola O'Farrell* and *Adrian Williamson*. Other experienced practitioners include *Ian Pennicott*, *Alexander Nissen*, *Michael Bowsher*, *Nerys Jefford* and *Louise Randall*.

The other leading set is **Atkin Chambers** with 28 barristers practising almost exclusively in construction law. Chambers cover the whole spectrum of building and engineering activity including contracts for industrial process plants, for the building of aircraft, ships, oil/gas exploration rigs and professional negligence claims. Recent cases have included 'Coppee Lavalin NV v. Ken Ren Chemicals and Fertilisers Ltd' and 'GMTC Tool and Equipment Ltd v. Warwick Marine'. *John Blackburn QC*, *Colin Reese QC*, *Robert Akenhead QC* and *Nicholas Dennys QC* are chambers' leading silks, while *Nicholas Baatz*, *Andrew White*, *Martin Bowdery*, *Stephen Dennison* and *William Godwin* are held in high regard. *Stephanie Barwise* has been described as a rising star. Other highly recommended sets include **1 Paper Buildings** and **4 Pump Court**.

1 Paper Buildings, whilst a common law set, has several practitioners who have specialised in construction law. *John Slater QC*, and *Andrew Bartlett QC* are well respected. *Bruce Mauleverer QC* and *David Blunt QC* of **4 Pump Court** both undertake construction work as part of their common law practice. Other recommended chambers include **2 Crown Office Row** (*Rupert Jackson QC* is particularly highly regarded), **39 Essex Street**, **3 Serjeants' Inn** and **2 Temple Gardens** (where *Patrick Twigg QC* was highly recommended).

LEADING SILKS

Blackburn, John *Atkin Chambers*	**Fernyhough,** Richard *Keating Chambers*	**Ramsey,** Vivian *Keating Chambers*

Akenhead, Robert *Atkin Chambers*	**Bartlett,** Andrew *1 Paper Buildings*	**Blunt,** David *4 Pump Court*
Butcher, Anthony *Atkin Chambers*	**Dennys,** Nicholas *Atkin Chambers*	**Elliott,** Timothy *Keating Chambers*
Furst, Stephen *Keating Chambers*	**Gaitskell,** Robert *Keating Chambers*	**Gray,** Richard *39 Essex Street*
Jackson, Rupert *2 Crown Office Row*	**Keating,** Donald *Keating Chambers*	**Marrin,** John *Keating Chambers*
Mauleverer, P. Bruce *4 Pump Court*	**Reese,** Colin *Atkin Chambers*	**Slater,** John *1 Paper Buildings*
Thomas, Christopher *Keating Chambers*	**Twigg,** Patrick *2 Temple Gardens*	**Uff,** John *Keating Chambers*

Collins, Martin *Keating Chambers*	**Fenwick,** Justin *2 Crown Office Row*	**Friedman,** David *4 Pump Court*
Knight, Brian *Atkin Chambers*	**Naughton,** Philip *3 Serjeants' Inn*	**Seymour,** Richard *Four Raymond Buildings*
Speaight, Anthony *12 King's Bench Walk*	**Tackaberry,** John *Arbitration Chambers*	**ter Haar,** Roger *2 Crown Office Row*
Vallance, Philip *1 Crown Office Row*	**Walker,** Ronald *12 King's Bench Walk*	**Wilmot-Smith,** Richard *39 Essex Street*

LEADING JUNIORS

Baatz, Nicholas *Atkin Chambers*	**Boulding,** Philip *Keating Chambers*	**Bowdery,** Martin *Atkin Chambers*
Bowsher, Michael *Keating Chambers*	**Coulson,** Peter *Keating Chambers*	**Darling,** Paul *Keating Chambers*
Dennison, Stephen *Atkin Chambers*	**Godwin,** William *Atkin Chambers*	**Jackson,** Rosemary *Keating Chambers*
Jefford, Nerys *Keating Chambers*	**Nissen,** Alexander *Keating Chambers*	**O'Farrell,** Finola *Keating Chambers*
Pennicott, Ian *Keating Chambers*	**Randall,** Louise *Keating Chambers*	**Steynor,** Alan *Keating Chambers*
Streatfeild-James, David *Atkin Chambers*	**Taverner,** Marcus *Keating Chambers*	**White,** Andrew *Atkin Chambers*
Williamson, Adrian *Keating Chambers*		

Acton Davis, Jonathan *4 Pump Court*	**Barwise,** Stephanie *Atkin Chambers*	**Burr,** Andrew *Atkin Chambers*
Coles, Steven *1 Paper Buildings*	**Davies,** Jane *1 Paper Buildings*	**Dumaresq,** Delia *Atkin Chambers*
Fraser, Peter *Atkin Chambers*	**Freedman,** S. Clive *3 Gray's Inn Place*	**Goddard,** Andrew *Atkin Chambers*
Jones, Nigel *Hardwicke Building*	**Manzoni,** Charles *39 Essex Street*	**McDonald,** John *2 Temple Gardens*
Nicholson, Jeremy *4 Pump Court*	**O'Rourke,** Mary *3 Serjeants' Inn*	**Planterose,** Rowan *12 Gray's Inn Square*
Powles, John *1 Paper Buildings*	**Raeside,** Mark *Atkin Chambers*	**Royce,** Darryl *Atkin Chambers*
Stewart, Roger *2 Crown Office Row*	**Stimpson,** Michael *12 King's Bench Walk*	**Thomas,** David *2 Temple Gardens*
Ticciati, Oliver *4 Pump Court*	**Wright,** Ian *3 Serjeants' Inn*	

UP AND COMING

Hargreaves, Simon *Keating Chambers*

LEADERS IN CONSTRUCTION LAW

Acton Davis, Jonathan

4 Pump Court (Bruce Mauleverer QC), London (0171) 353 2656.

Specialisation: Practice covers construction law work and professional negligence, also general common law matters. Clients include most large construction companies, insurers and other commercial bodies.

Prof. Membership: Official Referees' Bar Association, Professional Negligence Bar Association, COMBAR, London Common Law Bar Association.

Career: Called to the Bar 1977 and joined 4 Pump Court 1978, Member of Bar Council 1993 to date, Bencher of Inner Temple.

Personal: Born 15th January 1953. Educated at Harrow School and P.C.L. LLB (Lond.) Leisure pursuits include cricket and South Western France. Lives in London.

Akenhead QC, Robert

Atkin Chambers (Anthony Butcher QC), London (0171) 404 0102. Called 1972, took silk 1989. Principal area of practice is construction and civil engineering-related work. Born 15.9.1949.

Baatz, Nicholas

Atkin Chambers (Anthony Butcher QC), London (0171) 404 0102. Called 1978. Principal area of practice is construction and civil engineering-related work.

Bartlett QC, Andrew

1 Paper Buildings (Robert Nelson QC), London (0171) 583 7355. Called 1974, took silk 1993.

Barwise, Stephanie

Atkin Chambers (Anthony Butcher QC), London (0171) 404 0102.

Specialisation: General commercial including all aspects of the law relating to the construction and civil engineering industry both in litigation and arbitration. Practice also involves professional negligence in general and in particular of architects, engineers and surveyors. A further area of specialisation is rights appurtenant to land and property: party wall disputes, easements including interference with rights of support, e.g. acted in Midland Bank plc v. Bardgrove Property Services 60 BLR 1 (Court of Appeal 1992).

Prof. Membership: Secretary of Official Referees' Bar Association. London Common Law and Commercial Bar Association.

Career: Called to the Bar 1988. Joined *1 Atkin Building* in 1989.

Personal: Educated at Bolton School and Cambridge University (Downing College). Fluent in French and German.

Blackburn QC, John

Atkin Chambers (Anthony Butcher QC), London (0171) 404 0102. Called 1969, took silk 1984. Principal area of practice is construction and civil engineering-related work. Born 13.11.1945.

Blunt QC, David

4 Pump Court (Bruce Mauleverer QC), London (0171) 353 2656.

Specialisation: Principal area of practice is in the Official Referees Court, dealing with construction, professional indemnity and computer software cases. Other areas of work include banking, employment, intellectual property and competition law, insurance and reinsurance, commercial landlord and tenant, gaming and licensing, judicial review and private and public international law. Involved in Anglesey Marine Terminal Bill and North Wales Hydro Electricity Bill. Important cases include Northern Regional Health Authority v. Derek Crouch Construction Co Ltd and another [1984] (JCT Contract, courts/ arbitrators powers); Science Research Council v Nasse, BL Cars Ltd (Formerly Leyland Cars) v. Vyas [1980] (discovery; confidentiality); Hughes v. DHSS, Coy v. DHS [1985] (employment, civil service, retiring age) and Salvage Association v. Sema Group plc (software). Has run advocacy courses for British Council in Malaysia, Mauritius and in Sri Lanka.

Prof. Membership: Official Referees' Bar Association, Employment Law Bar Association.

Career: Called to the Bar 1967 and joined 4 Pump Court in 1968. Appointed Recorder 1991. Took Silk 1992. Deputy Official Referee 1993.

Personal: Educated at Farnham Grammar School 1954-61, Trinity Hall Cambrige 1963-66. Bar Finals: Colombos Prize for Public International Law, Harmsworth Scholar, Churchill Pupillage Award; was legal adviser and scriptwriter to TV programme 'Crown Court' in 1970's. Parliamentary candidate for Liberal Party in 1978, 1979 and 1983. Leisure pursuits include reading, writing, walking, cycling and old cars. Born 25th October 1944.

Boulding, Philip

Keating Chambers (John Uff QC), London (0171) 240 6981.

Specialisation: All aspects of construction and engineering contracts, including the position and liability of professionals (Architects, Engineers, etc.) in relation thereto (both contentious and non-contentious). Has considerable experience in his field, both in the UK and abroad (especially the Far East). Clients have included major domestic and international developers and contractors, well known professionals and Governments. Has acted as Arbitrator in construction disputes and continues to accept appointments. Professional Membership: COMBAR, ORBA (Committee Member).

Career: Called to the Bar 1979. Joined the Chambers of Donald Keating Q.C. in 1980.

Personal: Educated at Downing College, Cambridge University (Scholar). 1st Class Honours Degree. Post-graduate LL.B. Degree.

Bowdery, Martin

Atkin Chambers (Anthony Butcher QC), London (0171) 404 0102. Called 1980.

Bowsher, Michael

Keating Chambers (John Uff QC), London (0171) 240 6981. Called 1985.

Burr, Andrew

See under Arbitration.

Butcher QC, Anthony

Atkin Chambers (Anthony Butcher QC), London (0171) 404 0102. Called 1957, took silk 1977. Principal area of practice is construction and civil engineering-related work. Born 6.4.1934.

Coles, Steven

1 Paper Buildings (Robert Nelson QC), London (0171) 583 7355. Called 1983.

Collins QC, Martin

Keating Chambers (John Uff QC), London (0171) 240 6981. Called 1952, took silk 1972.

Coulson, Peter

Keating Chambers (John Uff QC), London (0171) 240 6981. Called 1982.

Darling, Paul

Keating Chambers (John Uff QC), London (0171) 240 6981. Called 1983.

Davies, Jane

1 Paper Buildings (Robert Nelson QC), London (0171) 583 7355. Called 1981.

Dennison, Stephen

Atkin Chambers (Anthony Butcher QC), London (0171) 404 0102. Called 1986. Principal area of practice is construction and civil engineering-related work.

Dennys QC, Nicholas

Atkin Chambers (Anthony Butcher QC), London (0171) 404 0102. Called 1975, took silk 1991. Principal area of practice is construction and civil engineering-related work.

Dumaresq, Delia

Atkin Chambers (Anthony Butcher QC), London (0171) 404 0102. Called 1984. Principal area of practice is construction and civil engineering-related work. Member of Australian Bar. Born 25.7.1947.

Elliott QC, Timothy

Keating Chambers (John Uff QC), London (0171) 240 6981.

Specialisation: Construction Law and related professional negligence. Clients have included major construction companies and developers, specialist sub-contractors, insurers, architects, engineers and surveyors etc. Also sits as an Arbitrator.

Prof. Membership: COMBAR, ORBA.

Career: Called to the Bar 1975. Joined *Keating* in 1976. Q.C. in 1992.

Personal: Educated at Marlborough College and Trinity College, Oxford. Lives in London.

Fenwick QC, Justin

2 Crown Office Row (Rupert Jackson QC), London (0171) 797 8000. Called 1980, took silk 1993.

Fernyhough QC, Richard

Keating Chambers (John Uff QC), London (0171) 240 6981. Called 1970, took silk 1986.

Fraser, Peter

Atkin Chambers (Anthony Butcher QC), London (0171) 404 0102. Called 1989.

Freedman, S. Clive

See under Commercial Law.

Friedman QC, David

4 Pump Court (Bruce Mauleverer QC), London (0171) 353 2656.

Specialisation: Principal area of practice covers all stages and all aspects of construction and engineering litigation and arbitration, both domestic and international. Experience of drafting standard form contracts. Also deals with professional negligence, particularly in relation to claims relating to professionals in the construction field. Has chaired seminars on design and build contracts.

Prof. Membership: Official Referees' Bar Association (Vice-Chairman and representative of ORBA on the General Council of the Bar).

Career: Called to the Bar 1968. Tenant at 3 Paper Buildings 1970-92. Took Silk and appointed Assistant Recorder 1990. Joined *4 Pump Court* 1992.

Personal: Educated at Tiffin Boys' School, Kingston-upon-Thames and Lincoln College, Oxford 1963-67 (MA, BCL). Born 1st June 1944.

Furst QC, Stephen
Keating Chambers (John Uff QC),
London (0171) 240 6981. Called 1975, took
silk 1991.

Gaitskell QC, Robert
Keating Chambers (John Uff QC),
London (0171) 240 6981. Called 1978, took
silk 1994.

Goddard, Andrew
Atkin Chambers (Anthony Butcher QC),
London (0171) 404 0102. Called 1985.

Godwin, William
Atkin Chambers (Anthony Butcher QC),
London (0171) 404 0102. Called 1986.

Gray QC, Richard
39 Essex Street (Colin Mackay QC),
London (0171) 583 1111. Called 1970, took
silk 1993.

Hargreaves, Simon
Keating Chambers (John Uff QC),
London (0171) 240 6981. Called 1991.

Jackson, Rosemary
Keating Chambers (John Uff QC),
London (0171) 240 6981. Called 1981.

Jackson QC, Rupert
2 Crown Office Row (Rupert Jackson
QC), London (0171) 797 8000. Called
1972, took silk 1987. Practice covers professional negligence and construction law. Born
7.3.1948.

Jefford, Nerys
Keating Chambers (John Uff QC),
London (0171) 240 6981. Called 1986.

Jones, Nigel
Hardwicke Building (Walter Aylen QC),
London (0171) 242 2523. Called 1976.

Keating QC, Donald
See under Arbitration.

Knight QC, Brian
Atkin Chambers (Anthony Butcher QC),
London (0171) 404 0102. Called 1964, took
silk 1981. Principal area of practice is con-
struction and civil engineering-related work.
Born 5.5.1941.

Manzoni, Charles
39 Essex Street (Colin Mackay QC),
London (0171) 583 1111. Called 1988.

Marrin QC, John
Keating Chambers (John Uff QC),
London (0171) 240 6981. Called 1974, took
silk 1990.

Mauleverer QC, P. Bruce
4 Pump Court (Bruce Mauleverer QC),
London (0171) 353 2656. Called 1969, took
silk 1985. Principal area of practice covers

construction and professional negligence.
Born 22.11.1946.

McDonald, John
2 Temple Gardens (Patrick Phillips QC),
London (0171) 583 6041. Called 1981. Construction law practice includes delay/loss
and expense claims, defects claims, Official
Referee's cases and arbitrations.

Naughton QC, Philip
3 Serjeants' Inn (Adrian Whitfield QC),
London (0171) 353 5537 Mbl (0385) 736844.

Specialisation: Specialist in construction
and engineering law, including domestic and
international contract disputes, often of a
highly technical nature, within the steel,
chemical and other large industries. Commercial and manufacturing contracts.
Professional negligence, particularly in relation to surveyors, architects and lawyers.
Long experience in all aspects employment
Law. Also medical law. A recognised expert
in the field of Alternative Dispute Resolution.
Director of Centre for Dispute Resolution
and accredited mediator.

Prof. Membership: Centre for Dispute Reso-
lution (Director); Bar Mutual Indemnity
Fund (Director); London Common Law and
Commercial Bar Association (Committee
Member). ORBA, ELBA, COMBAR, IBA.

Career: Held various positions in the chemical and chemical engineering industry
1964-71. Called to the Bar 1970. Joined present chambers 1973. Took Silk 1988.

Personal: Educated at Nottingham University (LL.B) 1961-64.

Nicholson, Jeremy
4 Pump Court (Bruce Mauleverer QC),
London (0171) 353 2656.

Specialisation: Principal areas of practice
are construction and professional negligence
work, covering all aspects of litigation, arbitration and advisory matters. Has acted in
international arbitrations concerning maritime construction in the Gulf. Also deals with
general commercial and contract law. Clients
include insurers, contractors, building owners, engineers, architects, surveyors and
solicitors. Speaker at various seminars for solicitors.

Prof. Membership: Official Referees' Bar As-
sociation, Professional Negligence Bar
Association, COMBAR, London Common
Law and Commercial Bar Association.

Career: Called to the Bar 1977 and joined 4
Pump Court 1978.

Personal: Educated at Rugby School 1968-
73, Trinity Hall, Cambridge 1973-76 (MA)
and College of Law 1976-77 (Harmsworth
Scholar). Born 21st March 1955.

Nissen, Alexander
Keating Chambers (John Uff QC),
London (0171) 240 6981. Called 1985.

O'Farrell, Finola
Keating Chambers (John Uff QC),
London (0171) 240 6981. Called 1983.

O'Rourke, Mary
See under Medical Negligence.

Pennicott, Ian
Keating Chambers (John Uff QC),
London (0171) 240 6981. Called 1982.

Planterose, Rowan
12 Gray's Inn Square (Mark Littman
QC), London (0171) 404 4866.

Specialisation: Principal areas of practice
are building and engineering and general
commercial litigation. Other areas include
more general professional negligence and
practice and procedural matters in litigation
and arbitration. Engineering related work
has ranged widely and included train building and computer and telephone technology.

Prof. Membership: ORBA (Committee
Member); COMBAR; Chartered Institute of
Arbitrators (Council Member).

Career: Called to the Bar in 1978.

Personal: Educated at Eastbourne College
and Downing College, Cambridge University. Lives in London and Gloucestershire.

Powles, John
1 Paper Buildings (Robert Nelson QC),
London (0171) 583 7355. Called 1975.

Raeside, Mark
Atkin Chambers (Anthony Butcher QC),
London (0171) 404 0102. Called 1982.

Ramsey QC, Vivian
Keating Chambers (John Uff QC),
London (0171) 240 6981. Called 1979, took
silk 1992. Specialises in construction law.
Member of the Institute of Civil Engineers.

Randall, Louise
Keating Chambers (John Uff QC),
London (0171) 240 6981. Called 1988.

Reese QC, Colin
See under Arbitration.

Royce, Darryl
Atkin Chambers (Anthony Butcher QC),
London (0171) 404 0102. Called 1976. Principal areas of practice are banking,
commercial law, financial services and insolvency. Born 2.10.1951.

Seymour QC, Richard
See under Commercial Law.

Slater QC, John
1 Paper Buildings (Robert Nelson QC),
London (0171) 583 7355. Called 1969, took
silk 1987.

Speaight QC, Anthony
12 King's Bench Walk (Ronald Walker

QC), London (0171) 583 0811. Called 1973, took silk 1995. Principal areas of practice are construction, professional negligence and other contractual, tort and property-related work.

Stewart, Roger
See under Professional Negligence.

Steynor, Alan
Keating Chambers (John Uff QC), London (0171) 240 6981. Called 1975.

Stimpson, Michael
12 King's Bench Walk (Ronald Walker QC), London (0171) 583 0811. Called 1969.

Streatfeild-James, David
Atkin Chambers (Anthony Butcher QC), London (0171) 404 0102. Called 1986. Principal area of practice is construction and civil engineering-related work.

Tackaberry QC, John
See under Arbitration.

Taverner, Marcus
Keating Chambers (John Uff QC), London (0171) 240 6981. Called 1981.

ter Haar QC, Roger
See under Professional Negligence.

Thomas, David
2 Temple Gardens (Patrick Phillips QC), London (0171) 583 6041. Called 1982.

Thomas QC, Christopher
Keating Chambers (John Uff QC), London (0171) 240 6981.

Specialisation: Construction and engineering. Litigation, arbitration and ADR involving major projects, including power, transport, chemical and oil/offshore installations, UK and overseas. Allied work includes bonds and guarantees, professional negligence, environment, insurance and appointments as Arbitrator. Overseas practice in ICC and international arbitrations, both as advocate and Arbitrator. Knowledge of French and comparative (civil) law.

Prof. Membership: Lincoln's Inn, called 1973. Fellow of Chartered Institute of Arbitrators. Int'l Bar Assoc. Combar.

Career: QC, 1989. Admitted to the Bar of Gibraltar, 1990. Assistant Recorder.

Personal: Born 1950. University of Kent,(First Class Hons). Diplome de Droit Comparé, 1972. PhD, King's College, London, thesis on comparative law (English/French), 1994.

Ticciati, Oliver
4 Pump Court (Bruce Mauleverer QC), London (0171) 353 2656.

Specialisation: Principal area of practice is professional negligence particularly relating to solicitors, surveyors and engineers. Also personal injury work. Clients mainly insurance companies.

Prof. Membership: Official Referees Bar Association, COMBAR, Personal Injuries Bar Association.

Career: Mathematics Master, Radley College 1972-6. Called to the Bar 1979 and joined 4 Pump Court in 1980.

Personal: Educated at Magdalen School, Oxford 1960-67, Sidney Sussex College 1968-71 (Mathematics) and St. John's College, Oxford 1971-72 (Post Graduate Certificate of Education). Leisure pursuits include music (cello), squash and Italian.

Twigg QC, Patrick
2 Temple Gardens (Patrick Phillips QC), London (0171) 583 6041. Called 1967, took silk 1985.

Uff QC, John
Keating Chambers (John Uff QC), London (0171) 240 6981. Called 1970, took silk 1983.

Vallance QC, Philip
See under Environmental.

Walker QC, Ronald
See under Personal Injury.

White, Andrew
Atkin Chambers (Anthony Butcher QC), London (0171) 404 0102. Called 1980. Principal area of practice is construction and civil engineering-related work.

Williamson, Adrian
Keating Chambers (John Uff QC), London (0171) 240 6981. Called 1983.

Wilmot-Smith QC, Richard
39 Essex Street (Colin Mackay QC), London (0171) 583 1111. Called 1978, took silk 1994.

Wright, Ian
3 Serjeants' Inn (Adrian Whitfield QC), London (0171) 353 5537 Mbl (0385) 736844.

Specialisation: Practice covers construction and engineering law. Principal areas of work include standard form and ad hoc building and engineering contracts; defects in design and workmanship; contractual performance, loss and expense claims; foundation failures; professional negligence of architects, engineers and surveyors, litigation (particularly Official Referees' Business); arbitration and negotiated settlements. Instructed on projects involving concrete, steel, masonry and timber structures and components, curtain walling, pressure vessels, marine works, dredging, mechanical and electrical services, precision metal alloy castings, temporary works, railway buildings, traditional and piled foundations, tree root nuisance, open cast mining (several claims in excess of £4 million); and nuclear waste processing plant (£7 million claim by contractor). Clients include private and local authority employers, public bodies, property developers, contractors, sub-contractors, house owners, insurance companies, valuers and construction professionals.

Prof. Membership: Institution of Civil Engineers, Institution of Structural Engineers, Official Referees' Bar Association (Committee Member).

Career: Consulting Civil and Structural Engineer before being called to the Bar. Wide experience of building and engineering projects with consultants and contactors in UK and overseas, including 7 years in private practice as consulting engineer. Called to the Bar 1989 and joined 3 Serjeants' Inn in 1991.

Personal: Educated at Methodist College, Belfast 1960-66; University of Manchester 1966-69 (BSC Hons, Engineering), Imperial College, University of London 1974-75 (MSc, Concrete Structures): 1987-88, Diploma in Law and CLE/ Inns of Court School of Law 1988-89. Leisure pursuits include architecture, furniture design, design and technology of aircraft and Formula 1 racing cars, wine and cooking, and tennis. Born 18 August 1947. Lives in London.

CONSUMER LAW

CONSUMER law covers food and safety labelling, prices, trades descriptions, weights and measures, environmental protection, pollution, consumer safety and consumer credit law.

LEADING SETS

GOUGH SQUARE CHAMBERS

The leading chambers in this area are **Gough Square Chambers**, where all members specialise in this field, acting for major retailers and food producers as well as banks and finance houses. Particularly highly regarded are *Claire Andrews*, who has acted for the London Borough of Bexley, *Frederick Philpott*, who has appeared on behalf of Asda and Dixons and is the co-author of a well known text book on Sale of Goods litigation, *William Hibbert* and *Peter Sayer*. Members of chambers have appeared in a number of important cases in this field recently including 'R v Warwickshire County Council ex parte Johnson', ' Greater Manchester Justices ex parte ALDI', 'Lynch v Royal Bank of Scotland' and 'First National Bank v Syed'.

HIGHLY REGARDED

ARDEN CHAMBERS	ESSEX COURT CHAMBERS
2-3 GRAY'S INN SQUARE	FOUR RAYMOND BUILDINGS
5-6 RAYMOND BUILDINGS	3 RAYMOND BUILDINGS
3 TEMPLE GARDENS	

Other chambers do not specialise in the field to the same extent. However, there are a number of individual barristers who are very highly regarded for their consumer work. At **4 Raymond Buildings** *A G Guest QC*, Professor of English Law at London University, is highly regarded for his consumer credit work. *Karl Scholz* at **3 Temple Gardens** has an excellent reputation for his trading standards expertise. He acts for several local authorities including Sussex County Council.

LEADING SILKS

Cordara, Roderick	*Essex Court Chambers*
Guest, Anthony	*Four Raymond Buildings*
Scrivener, Anthony	*2-3 Gray's Inn Square*

At **2/3 Gray's Inn Square** which is a general common law chambers *Anthony Scrivener QC, Richard Rundell, Geoffrey Stephenson* and *Ian Albutt* are well thought of in this sector. *Richard Spearman* at **5/6 Raymond Buildings** is co-author of a well known text book on Sale of Goods litigation. *Roderick Cordara QC* at **Essex Court Chambers** deals with food and safety work and is a member of the Food Law Group. *Kevin De Haan* at **3 Raymond Buildings** has a good reputation in this area, as does *Christopher Balogh* at **Arden Chambers**.

LEADING JUNIORS

Andrews, Claire	*Gough Square Chambers*
Hibbert, William	*Gough Square Chambers*
Philpott, Frederick	*Gough Square Chambers*
Sayer, Peter	*Gough Square Chambers*
Scholz, Karl	*3 Temple Gardens*
Spearman, Richard	*5-6 Raymond Buildings*
Albutt, Ian	*2-3 Gray's Inn Square*
Balogh, Christopher	*Arden Chambers*
De Haan, Kevin	*3 Raymond Buildings*
Rundell, Richard	*2-3 Gray's Inn Square*
Stephenson, Geoffrey	*2-3 Gray's Inn Square*

LEADERS IN CONSUMER LAW

Albutt, Ian
2-3 Gray's Inn Square (Anthony Scrivener QC), London (0171) 242 4986. Called 1981.

Andrews, Claire
Gough Square Chambers (Frederick Philpott), London (0171) 353 0924.
Specialisation: Consumer law - experienced in civil litigation prosecuting and defending regulatory offences, and advising on interpretation of statutes. Cases include: R v. Warwickshire CC [1993] AC 583 (misleading prices); LB Bexley v. Gardner Merchant [1991] COD (improvement notices). Clients have included food and other wholesalers and retailers and enforcement authorities. Other main areas of practice include landlord and tenant, employment and commercial fraud.
Prof. Membership: Food Law Group, ALBA, EBA, London Common Law and Commercial Bar Association.

Balogh, Christopher
Arden Chambers (Andrew Arden QC), London (0171) 353 3132. Called 1984.

Cordara QC, Roderick
Essex Court Chambers (Gordon Pollock QC), London (0171) 813 8000. Called 1975, took silk 1994.

De Haan, Kevin
See under Licensing.

Guest QC, Anthony
Four Raymond Buildings (Jeremy Lever QC), London (0171) 405 7211. Called 1956, took silk 1987. Principal area of practice is commercial and consumer law.

Hibbert, William
Gough Square Chambers (Frederick Philpott), London (0171) 353 0924.
Specialisation: Defending regulatory prosecutions, advising on credit and loan agreements and acting in civil litigation. Clients include finance houses, product

manufacturers, food producers and multiple retailers. Other main areas of practice include corporate, commercial, insolvency and fraud matters.

Prof. Membership: London Common and Commercial Bar Association.

Career: Called to the Bar 1979.

Personal: Charterhouse and Worcester College, Oxford. Lives in London.

Philpott, Frederick
Gough Square Chambers (Frederick Philpott), London (0171) 353 0924.

Specialisation: Consumer Law - Consumer credit (drafting of regulated credit and hire agreements, advising on consumer credit advertising, licensing, acting in civil litigation, e.g. extortionate credit bargains - Ketley v. Scott [1951] '1 CR 241 and in criminal prosecutions - Carrington Carr v. Leicester [1993] Crim LR 938), Food Safety (criminal

proceedings), misleading prices - R v. Warwickshire CC [1993] AC 583, Trades Descriptions, Weights and Measures, Fair Trading Act. Clients include Banks, Finance Houses, Food Producers, Supermarkets.

Prof. Membership: Food Law Group.

Career: Called 1974.

Rundell, Richard
2-3 Gray's Inn Square (Anthony Scrivener QC), London (0171) 242 4986. Called 1971.

Sayer, Peter
Gough Square Chambers (Frederick Philpott), London (0171) 353 0924.

Specialisation: Consumer Law - Consumer Credit, Credit and Charge Cards, Trades Descriptions and Fair Trading. Also Financial Services Act work and Fraud (Criminal and Civil). Clients include Banks, Finance

Houses, Card Issuers and Retailers. Has written 'Credit Cards and the Law' (Fourmat) and articles in Legal Journals.

Career: Called to the Bar 1975. Formerly in-house Counsel to Access, the joint Credit Card Company Ltd and American Express Europe Ltd.

Scholz, Karl
3 Temple Gardens (John Coffey), London (0171) 353 3102. Called 1973.

Scrivener QC, Anthony
See under Public and Administrative Law.

Spearman, Richard
5-6 Raymond Buildings (Patrick Milmo QC), London (0171) 242 2902. Called 1977.

CRIME: FRAUD

THE RECENT economic recession uncovered a large number of commercial frauds, and the subsequent criminal proceedings provided an unprecedented volume of work for lawyers.

LEADING SETS

3 HARE COURT	5 KING'S BENCH WALK
QUEEN ELIZABETH BUILDING	3 RAYMOND BUILDINGS
36 ESSEX STREET	1 HARE COURT
6 KING'S BENCH WALK	5 PAPER BUILDINGS
LITTLETON CHAMBERS	1 MIDDLE TEMPLE LANE

The pre-eminent chambers are **Hollis Whiteman Chambers (Queen Elizabeth Building), 3 Hare Court, 3 Raymond Buildings** and **5 King's Bench Walk**.

has been involved in numerous prominent cases. Other leading silks at the set with excellent reputations are *Alan Suckling QC*, prosecuting in the Maxwell trial, and previously in Barlow Clowes, *Vivian Robinson QC*, *Graham Boal QC* and *David Evans QC* who has appeared in several large fraud cases, including the Blue Arrow Trial and the Guinness case (on behalf of a merchant bank).

The set also has many able juniors in this field: *David Calvert-Smith* (Senior Treasury Counsel), *Thomas Kark*, *Peter Kyte*, *Neill Stewart* and *Peter Finnigan* (who was involved in the Brinks Mat case), are all well regarded. Chambers also boast four Junior Treasury Counsel (*William Boyce*, *Richard Horwell*, *J. Kelsey–Fry* and *Mark Ellison*), all of whom have excellent reputations.

Fraud has become an important part of **3 Hare Court's** practice, covering corporate, financial services, insolvency,

LEADING SILKS

Bevan, Julian *Queen Elizabeth Building*	Jones, Alun *3 Raymond Buildings*	Lawson, Edmund *9-12 Bell Yard*
Amlot, Roy *6 King's Bench Walk*	Arlidge, Anthony *5 King's Bench Walk*	Carman, George *New Court Chambers*
Clegg, William *3 Hare Court*	Gloster, Elizabeth *1 Essex Court*	Hill, Michael *36 Essex Street*
Kalisher, Michael *1 Hare Court*	Lawson, Michael *36 Essex Street*	Lissack, Richard *2 King's Bench Walk*
Mathew, John *5 Paper Buildings*	Moses, Alan *4-5 Gray's Inn Square*	Purnell, Nicholas *36 Essex Street*
Scrivener, Anthony *2-3 Gray's Inn Square*	Suckling, Alan B. *Queen Elizabeth Building*	
Batten, Stephen *3 Raymond Buildings*	Caplan, Jonathan *5 Paper Buildings*	Evans, David H. *Queen Elizabeth Building*
Godfrey, Howard *3 Hare Court*	Goldberg, Jonathan *3 Temple Gardens*	Hacking, Anthony *1 King's Bench Walk*
Harman, Robert *2 Harcourt Buildings*	Nicholls, Clive *3 Raymond Buildings*	Robinson, Vivian *Queen Elizabeth Building*
Rook, Peter *5 King's Bench Walk*	Shaw, Antony *4 Brick Court*	Thwaites, Ronald *10 King's Bench Walk*
Trollope, Andrew *1 Middle Temple Lane*	Whitehouse, David *3 Raymond Buildings*	

Hollis Whiteman Chambers have a very strong commercial fraud team, defending and prosecuting in many high profile cases. The chambers also provide assistance to the major enforcement, supervisory and regulatory agencies

revenue and VAT work. Several practitioners at the set have been recommended to us for their expertise. Leading silks are *Howard Godfrey QC* and *William Clegg QC* (who has defended in many high profile cases of alleged fraud).

HIGHLY REGARDED SILKS

Austin-Smith, Michael *36 Essex Street*	Birnbaum, Michael *1 Hare Court*	Croxford, Ian *2-3 Gray's Inn Square*
Lawson-Rogers, Stuart *36 Essex Street*	Nicholls, Colin *3 Raymond Buildings*	Penry-Davey, David *2-3 Gray's Inn Square*
Roberts, Jeremy *9 Gough Square*	Rogers, John *9 Gough Square*	Singh, Kuldip *5 Paper Buildings*
Temple, Victor *6 King's Bench Walk*		
Day, Douglas *Farrar's Building*	Rawley, Alan D. *35 Essex Street*	Rhodes, Robert *Littleton Chambers*
Boal, Graham *Queen Elizabeth Building*	Cocks, David *5 King's Bench Walk*	Solley, Stephen *Cloisters*
Walker, Raymond *1 Harcourt Buildings*		

including the Serious Fraud Office, the Inspectorate of the Department of Trade and Industry and H.M. Customs and Excise. Of the many leading silks at the set, *Julian Bevan QC* has been particularly recommended for his expertise, and

From an array of leading juniors, *Nigel Ingram* (who is Standing Counsel on circuit to the DTI), *Margaret Barnes*, *Brian Altman*, *Keith Mitchell* and *James Sturman* have been particularly recommended to us.

3 Raymond Buildings has wide experience in commercial fraud cases, including complex commercial cases in the Far East. Several members of chambers are on the panel of DTI inspectors. *Alun Jones QC*, veteran of Blue Arrow and other major trials, heads the legal team for Kevin Maxwell in the current trial. *Clare Montgomery*, a leading junior in the set, is also part of the Kevin Maxwell team and has been

including those concerning banking, insurance, letters of credit and guarantees, corruption and money laundering.

Leading criminal set **1 Hare Court**, has a well regarded commercial fraud practice from which *Michael Kalisher QC* and *Michael Birnbaum QC* have been recommended. **6 King's Bench Walk** is another established criminal set that has been highly recommended for commercial fraud. *Roy*

LEADING JUNIORS– LONDON

Montgomery, Clare *3 Raymond Buildings*		
Altman, Brian *3 Hare Court*	**Bromley-Martin,** Michael *3 Raymond Buildings*	**Calvert-Smith,** David *Queen Elizabeth Building*
Cameron, Alexander *3 Raymond Buildings*	**Chawla,** Mukul *9-12 Bell Yard*	**Ellison,** Mark *Queen Elizabeth Building*
Hackett, Philip *Cloisters*	**Horwell,** Richard E. *Queen Elizabeth Building*	**Ingram,** Nigel *3 Hare Court*
Kark, Thomas V.W. *Queen Elizabeth Building*	**Kelsey-Fry,** J. *Queen Elizabeth Building*	**Lucas,** Noel *1 Middle Temple Lane*
Miskin, Charles *36 Essex Street*	**Peters,** Nigel *5 King's Bench Walk*	**Stafford-Michael,** Simon *4 King's Bench Walk*
Stewart, Neill A. *Queen Elizabeth Building*	**Sturman,** James *3 Hare Court*	**Wood,** Michael *36 Essex Street*
Boyce, William H. *Queen Elizabeth Building*	**Doyle,** Peter *9-12 Bell Yard*	**Mehigan,** Simon *5 Paper Buildings*
Mitchell, Keith *3 Hare Court*	**Richardson,** P. James *36 Essex Street*	

described as a 'QC in waiting'. She was also counsel in the Guinness and Brent Walker trials, and in the 'Morgan Grenfell' case which involved insider dealing. Other notable practitioners at the set are *Clive Nicholls QC*, *Colin Nicholls QC*, *Stephen Batten QC*, *David Whitehouse QC* and well regarded juniors include *Michael Bromley-Martin*, *Tania Bromley-Martin* and *Alexander Cameron*.

5 King's Bench Walk has a number of members with

Amlot QC, *Victor Temple QC* and *David Perry* are all well regarded. *Roy Amlot QC* defended the Barlow Clowes, Blue Arrow, Brent Walker and Polly Peck fraud cases.

5 Paper Buildings is a very experienced set, handling both criminal and civil aspects of commercial fraud. Members of chambers have appeared in the Guinness, Blue Arrow and Nissan trials. Leading silks at the set are *John Mathew QC* (head of chambers), *Jonathan Caplan QC* and *Kuldip Singh*

HIGHLY REGARDED JUNIORS

Barnes, Margaret *3 Hare Court*	**Bowes,** Michael *36 Essex Street*	**Bromley-Martin,** Tania *3 Raymond Buildings*
Perry, David *6 King's Bench Walk*		
Finnigan, Peter Anthony *Queen Elizabeth Building*		
Gardiner, Nicholas *1 Middle Temple Lane*	**King,** Philip *1 Middle Temple Lane*	**Kyte,** Peter E. *Queen Elizabeth Building*

excellent reputations for commercial frauds, Inland Revenue and Customs and Excise offences. Silks particularly recommended at the set are *Anthony Arlidge QC* and *Peter Rook QC*, counsel for Robert Bunn in the Maxwell trial. Able juniors at the set include *Nigel Peters* who is Standing Counsel to H.M. Customs and Excise.

Other recommended chambers are **36 Essex Street, 1 Hare Court, 6 King's Bench Walk** and **5 Paper Buildings**.

36 Essex Street handle both the criminal and civil aspects of commercial fraud. Leading silks at the set requiring particular mention are *Michael Hill QC*, who is counsel to Larry Trachtenberg in the current Maxwell trial, *Nicholas Purnell QC*, *Michael Lawson QC*, *Stuart Lawson-Rogers QC* and *Michael Austin-Smith QC*.

Juniors at the set highly commended for their commercial fraud practices are *James Richardson* (junior to *Michael Hill* in Maxwell), *Michael Bowes*, *Michael Wood* and *Charles Miskin*. *Charles Miskin* handles fraud and regulatory cases

QC. *Simon Mehigan* is a well regarded junior.

Littleton Chambers (formerly **2 Crown Office Row**) also has several barristers with strong commercial fraud practices. *Robert Rhodes QC* has been particularly recommended for his expertise.

Other notable silks with established reputations are *Edmund Lawson QC* (**9-12 Bell Yard**) who is acting for Ian Maxwell. *George Carman QC* (**New Court Chambers**), *Elizabeth Gloster QC* (**1 Essex Court**), *Alan Moses QC* (**4-5 Gray's Inn Square**), *Anthony Scrivener* QC (**2-3 Gray's Inn Square**) and *Richard Lissack QC* (**2 King's Bench Walk**) who is part of the prosecution team in the Maxwell trial.

Other leading juniors who have been particularly recommended to us are *Mukul Chawla* (**9-12 Bell Yard**), *Noel Lucas* (**1 Middle Temple Lane**), *Peter Doyle* (**9-12 Bell Yard**) who is currently representing Ian Maxwell and *Philip Hackett* (**Cloisters**) who represents Robert Bunn in the Maxwell trial.

Altman, Brian
3 Hare Court (Michael Lewis QC), London (0171) 353 7561. Called 1981.

Amlot QC, Roy
6 King's Bench Walk (Michael Worsley QC), London (0171) 583 0410.

Specialisation: Principal area of practice is criminal law with an emphasis on high profile, serious crime cases and commercial fraud. Defence work includes Barlow Clowes, Blue Arrow, Brent Walker and Polly Peck (for the Liquidator). Prosecution work includes the Brighton bombing, Guildford Four (on appeal) and Clive Ponting cases. Editor, 'Phipson on Evidence' (11th Edition).

Prof. Membership: Criminal Bar Association.

Career: Called to the Bar 1963 and became a tenant of 6 King's Bench Walk in 1964. Treasury Counsel 1977-89. Took Silk 1989.

Personal: Educated at Dulwich College 1953-60. School Governor, Dulwich College. Leisure pursuits include skiing, music, squash, and windsurfing. Born 22nd September 1942. Lives in London.

Arlidge QC, Anthony
5 King's Bench Walk (David Cocks QC), London (0171) 797 7600. Called 1962, took silk 1981.

Austin-Smith QC, Michael
36 Essex Street (Michael Hill QC), London (0171) 413 0353. Called 1969, took silk 1990.

Barnes, Margaret
3 Hare Court (Michael Lewis QC), London (0171) 353 7561.

Specialisation: Principal area of practice is criminal law, particularly fraud cases, including mortgage and VAT fraud and fraud on the Legal Aid Fund. Major cases include R v. Linskill, R v. Reece (solicitors' fraud), R v. Harding and others (VAT fraud), R v. Trevelyan (corruption by Ministry of Defence official) and R v. Griffiths (child abduction).

Prof. Membership: Criminal Bar Association.

Career: Former solicitor. Articles with Ingham Clegg & Crowther, Blackpool 1968-71 and assistant solicitor 1971-73. Solicitor with Davis Hanson 1975-76. Called to the Bar and joined current chambers 1976.

Personal: Educated at Haslingden Grammar School, Rossendale, Lancashire 1955-63 and University of Sheffield 1963-67 (B. Jur). Leisure pursuits include a house in France, walking and theatre. Born 24th October 1944. Lives in London.

Batten QC, Stephen
3 Raymond Buildings (Clive Nicholls QC), London (0171) 831 3833. Called 1968, took silk 1989.

Bevan QC, Julian
Queen Elizabeth Building (Hollis Whiteman Chambers), London (0171) 583 5766. Called 1962, took silk 1991.

Birnbaum QC, Michael
1 Hare Court (Michael Kalisher QC), London (0171) 353 5324. Called 1969, took silk 1992.

Boal QC, Graham
Queen Elizabeth Building (Hollis Whiteman Chambers), London (0171) 583 5766. Called 1966, took silk 1993. Specialist in criminal law, particularly fraud.

Bowes, Michael
36 Essex Street (Michael Hill QC), London (0171) 413 0353.

Specialisation: Main area of practice is criminal law, specialising in commercial fraud. Has also prosecuted and defended across the range of serious crime. Other areas of practice are financial regulatory work and police disciplinary proceedings.

Prof. Membership: Criminal Bar Association, South Eastern Circuit.

Career: Called to the Bar in 1980 and joined 36 Essex Street in 1981.

Personal: Educated at St George's College, Weybridge (1969-75), Manchester University (LL.B) 1976-79. Born on 22nd December 1956.

Boyce, William H.
Queen Elizabeth Building (Hollis Whiteman Chambers), London (0171) 583 5766.

Bromley-Martin, Tania
3 Raymond Buildings (Clive Nicholls QC), London (0171) 831 3833.

Bromley-Martin, Michael
3 Raymond Buildings (Clive Nicholls QC), London (0171) 831 3833. Called 1979. Principal areas of practice are commercial fraud and licensing. Born 27.4.1955.

Calvert-Smith, David
Queen Elizabeth Building (Hollis Whiteman Chambers), London (0171) 583 5766. Called 1969.

Cameron, Alexander
3 Raymond Buildings (Clive Nicholls QC), London (0171) 831 3833. Called 1986. Has substantial experience in commercial fraud cases. Born 27.8.1963.

Caplan QC, Jonathan
5 Paper Buildings (John Mathew QC), London (0171) 583 6117. Called 1973, took silk 1991.

Carman QC, George
See under Defamation.

Chawla, Mukul
9-12 Bell Yard (Edmund Lawson QC), London (0171) 400 1800. Called 1983.

Clegg QC, William
3 Hare Court (Michael Lewis QC), London (0171) 353 7561.

Specialisation: Specialist in defending in cases of alleged fraud. Cases include R. v. De Vandiere (VAT fraud); R. v. Alder (international bank fraud); R. v. Vanderval (letter of credit fraud); R. v. Hales (solicitors' legal aid fraud); R. v. Morley (fraudulent trading); R. v. Smith (100m bank fraud) and R. v. Smithson (100m company fraud). Cases of a more general nature include R. v. Stagg (Wimbledon Common murder), R. v. Varathadasan (Tamil Tigers) and R. v. McMahon (UDA terrorists). Has also been instructed in a lengthy public enquiry by the Medical Protection Society and a number of cases in the Court of Appeal Criminal Division and Divisional Court. Was a member of the standing committee of Justice on fraud trials and prepared submissions to the Fraud Trials Committee chaired by Roskill (HMSO 1986).

Prof. Membership: Criminal Bar Association, South Eastern Circuit (Committee member).

Career: Called to the Bar 1972 and joined present chambers in 1973. Took silk 1991. Appointed Recorder 1992.

Personal: Educated at Bristol University (LL.B). Leisure pursuits include squash, cricket and wine. Born 5th September 1949.

Cocks QC, David
5 King's Bench Walk (David Cocks QC), London (0171) 797 7600. Called 1961, took silk 1982.

Croxford QC, Ian
2-3 Gray's Inn Square (Anthony Scrivener QC), London (0171) 242 4986. Called 1976, took silk 1993.

Day QC, Douglas
Farrar's Building (Lord Williams of Mostyn QC), London (0171) 583 9241.

Specialisation: Specialist criminal practice, with a particular emphasis on commercial fraud. Acts for both prosecution and defence. Practice also covers personal injury and professional negligence. Important cases include R v. Kelland (the Britannia Park trial), the longest jury trial in English legal history. Defence counsel R v. Harris and R v. Kitchin. Has undertaken several Serious Fraud Office prosecutions.

Prof. Membership: Criminal Bar Association; Commercial and Common Law Bar Association; Society for Computers and Law; Professional Conduct Committee of the Bar Council 1989-92.

Career: Called to the Bar 1967. Joined present chambers 1980, after twelve years at 2 Pump Court (J Thomas QC MP). Appointed Recorder of the Crown Court 1987. Took silk 1989. Assistant Parliamentary Boundary Commissioner 1992. Deputy High Court Judge 1994.

Personal: Educated at Bec School 1955-62, and at Selwyn College, Cambridge 1963-66. Highly computer literate with a keen interest on the use of computers in court.

Doyle, Peter
9-12 Bell Yard (Edmund Lawson QC), London (0171) 400 1800. Called 1975. Practises general common law and criminal law including fraud cases.
Born 29.12.1951.

Ellison, Mark
Queen Elizabeth Building (Hollis Whiteman Chambers), London (0171) 583 5766.

Specialisation: Criminal practice specialising in commercial fraud and Treasury Counsel work. Interesting cases include both the Guinness trial and appeal.

Career: Called 1979. Appointed Junior Treasury Counsel to the Crown at the Central Criminal Court 1994.

Personal: Educated at Pocklington School, Skinners School and the University of Wales.

Evans QC, David H.
Queen Elizabeth Building (Hollis Whiteman Chambers), London (0171) 583 5766.

Specialisation: Crime, in particular criminal fraud. Has appeared in several large fraud cases R v. Grobb and Posgate, the Blue Arrow trial (appeared for the Co. UBS/ Phillips and Drew) was briefed in the Guinness Case for a merchant bank. Since taking silk has continued to be briefed in large criminal fraud cases both for the S.F.O and the Fraud Investigation Group (CPS) and the defence.

Prof. Membership: Criminal Bar Association

Career: Called to the Bar 1972. Q.C. 1991.

Personal: Educated at the University of London (BSc Econ. M.Sc) and the University of Oxford (B.A. Oxon).

Finnigan, Peter Anthony
Queen Elizabeth Building (Hollis Whiteman Chambers), London (0171) 583 5766. Called 1978. Practice covers commercial fraud and Revenue offences.

Gardiner, Nicholas
1 Middle Temple Lane (Colin Dines, Andrew Trollope QC), London (0171) 583 0659 (12 lines). Called 1967.

Gloster QC, Elizabeth
See under Insolvency.

Godfrey QC, Howard
3 Hare Court (Michael Lewis QC), London (0171) 353 7561.

Goldberg QC, Jonathan
3 Temple Gardens (Jonathan Goldberg QC), London (0171) 583 1155. Called 1971, took silk 1989.

Hackett, Philip
Cloisters (David Turner-Samuels QC), London (0171) 583 0303.

Specialisation: Practice is principally in the area of fraud and corporate insolvency, both civil and criminal. In particular representation of directors, officers and corporations in connection with potential criminal proceedings. Speciality in advising auditors, accountants, company directors, insolvency practitioners, partners and trustees. All issues connected with Serious Fraud Office, DTI investigations including advising institutions and witnesses on obligations to comply with requests and notices from the Serious Fraud Office. Has experience of broad range of commercial work including banking, insurance and reinsurance. Also advises on related issues such as international judicial assistance and money laundering provisions, major fraud cases include Maxwell, Baqi (BCCI), Gokal (BCCI), Savings Investment Bank, Isle of Man, and Re Arrows. Also specialises in issues from regulatory prosecutions concerning health and safety, trades descriptions and environmental pollution including advising corporations, directors and partners on liability. Principal cases include: Herald of Free Enterprise, R v. Kenchington Little Plc and R v. Flint and Neil.

Prof. Membership: International Bar Association, Institute of Arbitrators, Criminal Bar Association, International Institute of Insolvency Practitioners (INSOL).

Career: Member of the Race Relations Committee of the Bar Council and implementation Sub-Committee of the Race Relations/Sex Relations Committee of the Bar Council.

Hacking QC, Anthony
1 King's Bench Walk (Mr J.B.S. Townend QC), London (0171) 583 6266. Called 1965, took silk 1983.

Harman QC, Robert
See under Criminal Law (General).

Hill QC, Michael
36 Essex Street (Michael Hill QC), London (0171) 413 0353. Called 1958, took silk 1979. Principal area of practice is criminal law, particularly commercial fraud. Born 22.5.1935

Horwell, Richard E.
Queen Elizabeth Building (Hollis Whiteman Chambers), London (0171) 583 5766.

Ingram, Nigel
3 Hare Court (Michael Lewis QC), London (0171) 353 7561. Called 1972.

Jones QC, Alun
3 Raymond Buildings (Clive Nicholls QC), London (0171) 831 3833.

Specialisation: Principal areas of practice are commercial crime and extradition. Acts in cases of serious and complex fraud, both trials and advisory work, primarily for the defence. Undertakes extradition and advisory work for foreign governments and fugitives. Appears frequently on appeal or review in criminal cases and associated matters such as coroners' cases. Notable cases include the Alexander Howden reinsurance trials (appearing for Kenneth Grob in the first SFO trial, 1989-90); the Blue Arrow Trial 1990-91 (defending Stephen Clark); the defence of Andrew Kent in an alleged fraud against The Securities Association (1993) and the Maxwell Criminal Trial (defending Kevin Maxwell, 1995). Involved in eight full House of Lords appeals in extradition cases, acting in six of them for foreign governments. Author of 'Jones on Extradition' (Sweet & Maxwell, 1995).

Prof. Membership: Bar Council, Criminal Bar Association.

Career: Called to the Bar in 1972 and joined current chambers in 1973. Took silk 1989. Appointed Recorder 1992.

Personal: Educated at Oldershaw Grammar School, Wallasey 1960-67 and Bristol University 1967-70. Leisure pursuits include bridge, cricket, gardening and writing (currently working on book concerning the law of conspiracy). Born 19th March 1949. Lives in Greenwich, London.

Kalisher QC, Michael
1 Hare Court (Michael Kalisher QC), London (0171) 353 5324. Called 1970, took silk 1984.

Kark, Thomas V.W.
Queen Elizabeth Building (Hollis Whiteman Chambers), London (0171) 583 5766.

Kelsey-Fry, J.
Queen Elizabeth Building (Hollis Whiteman Chambers), London (0171) 583 5766. Called 1978.

King, Philip
1 Middle Temple Lane (Colin Dines, Andrew Trollope QC), London (0171) 583 0659 (12 lines). Called 1974.

Kyte, Peter E.
Queen Elizabeth Building (Hollis Whiteman Chambers), London (0171) 583 5766.

Lawson QC, Edmund
9-12 Bell Yard (Edmund Lawson QC), London (0171) 400 1800.

Specialisation: Specialist in commercial crime and accounting/auditing negligence. Acts mainly for defendants in large fraud cases as well as advising government departments in relation to insider dealing and regulatory affairs. Has considerable experience in advising on accounting and auditing matters. Practice also covers general crime, particularly the defence of police officers, and judicial review, with a specialisation in abuse of process applications. Interesting cases include 'Blue Arrow' (defended UBS Phillips & Drew); 'Maxwell' (defence of Ian Maxwell); the 'Pan-El' case, acting for *Coopers & Lybrand* in Singapore. Also defended police officers in the prosecutions following the 'Guildford Four' and 'Birmingham Six' cases.

Prof. Membership: Criminal Bar Association.

Career: Called to the Bar 1971. Pupil then tenant at *13 King's Bench Walk* 1971-1976. Joined present chambers 1976. Took silk 1988. Head of chambers since 1989.

Personal: Educated at the City of Norwich School and at Trinity Hall, Cambridge 1967-1970. Leisure pursuits include music and rugby. Born 17th April 1948. Lives in London.

Lawson QC, Michael
36 Essex Street (Michael Hill QC), London (0171) 413 0353. Called 1969, took silk 1991. Specialises in criminal law including general criminal and commercial fraud work. Born 3.2.1946.

Lawson-Rogers QC, Stuart
36 Essex Street (Michael Hill QC), London (0171) 413 0353. Called 1969, took silk 1994. Handles all areas of criminal law, particularly fraud and Customs & Excise cases. Born 23.3.1946.

Lissack QC, Richard
2 King's Bench Walk (Anthony Donne QC), London (0171) 353 1746.

Lucas, Noel
1 Middle Temple Lane (Colin Dines, Andrew Trollope QC), London (0171) 583 0659 (12 lines). Called 1979.

Mathew QC, John
5 Paper Buildings (John Mathew QC), London (0171) 583 6117. Called 1949, took silk 1977.

Mehigan, Simon
5 Paper Buildings (John Mathew QC), London (0171) 583 6117. Called 1980.

Miskin, Charles
36 Essex Street (Michael Hill QC), London (0171) 413 0353.

Specialisation: Fraud and regulatory cases including those concerning banking, insurance, letters of credit and guarantees, trade, corruption, money laundering, advance fees, loan churning and public revenue. Other

main areas of practice include general crime, disciplinary cases and civil cases involving both fraud and police law.

Prof. Membership: Criminal Bar Association.

Career: Called to the Bar 1975 (Gray's). Joined what is now *36 Essex Street* in 1977. Assistant Recorder of the Crown Court, 1992. Standing Counsel to the Inland Revenue (Crime), 1993.

Personal: Educated at Charterhouse School and Worcester College, Oxford. Lives in London.

Mitchell, Keith
3 Hare Court (Michael Lewis QC), London (0171) 353 7561. Called 1981.

Montgomery, Clare
3 Raymond Buildings (Clive Nicholls QC), London (0171) 831 3833.

Specialisation: Criminal law, particularly commercial fraud and extradition. Counsel in Guinness, Brent Walker, Maxwell and Morgan Grenfell insider dealing ring trials. Counsel in leading extradition cases; Osman and Hagan v. Croft. Also administrative law, immigration and prison law. Practitioner editor 'Archbold Criminal Pleading, Evidence and Practice'.

Career: Called to the Bar 1980. 1992 Supplementary Panel (Common Law).

Moses QC, Alan
See under Public and Administrative Law.

Nicholls QC, Colin
See under Criminal Law (General).

Nicholls QC, Clive
3 Raymond Buildings (Clive Nicholls QC), London (0171) 831 3833. Called 1957, took silk 1982.

Penry-Davey QC, David
2-3 Gray's Inn Square (Anthony Scrivener QC), London (0171) 242 4986. Called 1965, took silk 1988.

Perry, David
6 King's Bench Walk (Michael Worsley QC), London (0171) 583 0410. Called 1980. Principal area of practice is criminal law, especially commercial fraud. Born 7.9.1956.

Peters, Nigel
5 King's Bench Walk (David Cocks QC), London (0171) 797 7600.

Specialisation: Main areas of practice are criminal law and judicial review. Criminal law: specialising in drug trafficking, serious fraud, revenue offences and allied financial investigations. Other main areas of practice include obscene publications, licensing and public entertainment law. Judicial review: specialising in disputes in connection with the criminal process, licensing and public entertainment law. This often involves aspects

of international and European law.

Career: Called to the Bar 1976. Standing Counsel to HM Customs and Excise, Assistant Recorder.

Purnell QC, Nicholas
36 Essex Street (Michael Hill QC), London (0171) 413 0353.

Specialisation: Principal area of practice is criminal law, particularly commercial fraud. Work includes financial regulatory and professional disciplinary tribunals. Member of the Lord Chancellor's Advisory Committee on Legal Education and Conduct since 1991. Member of the Criminal Committee Judicial Studies Board since 1991.

Prof. Membership: South Eastern Circuit.

Career: Called to the Bar and joined *36 Essex Street* in 1968. Prosecuting Counsel, Inland Revenue 1977-79. Treasury Counsel 1979-85. Took Silk in 1985. Recorder since 1986. Bencher of the Middle Temple since 1990.

Personal: Educated at the Oratory School 1958-62 and King's College, Cambridge 1963-66(MA). Governor of the Oratory School. Born 29th January 1944.

Rawley QC, Alan D.
35 Essex Street (Alan Rawley QC), London (0171) 353 6381. Called 1958, took silk 1977.

Rhodes QC, Robert
Littleton Chambers (Michael Burton QC), London (0171) 797 8600. Called 1968, took silk 1989. Specialises in complex white-collar fraud and other high profile cases. Born 2.8.1945.

Richardson, P. James
36 Essex Street (Michael Hill QC), London (0171) 413 0353. Called 1975. Specialist area of practice is criminal law. Editor of *Archbold, Criminal Pleading, Evidence and Practice* (1982-).

Roberts QC, Jeremy
9 Gough Square (Michael Brent QC), London (0171) 353 5371. Called 1965, took silk 1982. Principal area of practice is criminal work, with an emphasis on fraud cases. Born 26.4.1941.

Robinson QC, Vivian
See under Criminal Law (General).

Rogers QC, John
9 Gough Square (Michael Brent QC), London (0171) 353 5371. Called 1963, took silk 1979.

Rook QC, Peter
5 King's Bench Walk (David Cocks QC), London (0171) 797 7600. Called 1973, took silk 1991.

Scrivener QC, Anthony
See under Public and Administrative Law.

Shaw QC, Antony
See under Family Law.

Singh QC, Kuldip
5 Paper Buildings (John Mathew QC), London (0171) 583 6117.
Specialisation: A principal area of practice is all aspects of commercial fraud, both criminal and civil, as well as compliance, regulatory and disciplinary proceedings, tribunals and inquiries, DTI Inquiries, financial services, insider dealing, money laundering etc. His work includes protecting the interests of clients who are not parties to but are concerned with or interested in such litigation, and also advising them on matters such as disclosure obligations, witness summonses, and on attempts by others to obtain material from such clients. Will not identify specific clients, but has appeared on behalf of or advised individuals, corporations (including multi-nationals), major clearing banks and merchant banks, accountants (including several of the Big Six), liquidators, administrators, regulatory bodies, witnesses, victims of fraud etc, in most of the leading fraud cases of the past decade. Is instructed by a large number of the major firms of solicitors in the City of London, London and elsewhere. Other main areas of practice include the civil and criminal liability of corporations, directors, banks, accountants etc; professional negligence of accountants; commercial litigation; defamation; media law; contempt; environmental law; trade descriptions; food and drugs.
Prof. Membership: International Bar Association, London Common Law and Commercial Bar Association, Criminal Bar Association.
Career: Called 1975. Queen's Counsel 1993.

Co-opted member of the Bar Council. Vice Chairman of the Bar's Law Reform Committee, and member of the Bar's Professional Conduct Committee.
Personal: Born 30 August 1954. Brought up and educated in London, where he lives.

Solley QC, Stephen
Cloisters (David Turner-Samuels QC), London (0171) 583 0303.
Specialisation: Encompasses criminal commercial fraud and general crime especially cases with civil liberties aspects. Major cases include R v. BAQI (1994). (BCCI defence), the Herald of Free Enterprise prosecution (defending Captain Lewry); R v. Charles and another (Red Dwarf); Re Isle of Man Savings and Investment Bank Fraud, the Bestwood fraud and Barlow Clowes case, R v. Mitchell. Also acted for Howard Marks in major drug smuggling case. Appeared on television programmes concerning fraud and insider dealing. Author of 'Money laundering' article for The Times, 1994. Lectured at the Lamplugh Trust Conference, Warwick University, 1994.
Prof. Membership: Criminal Bar Association, International Bar Association.
Career: Inspector of Insider Dealing (DTI) 1987-90. Appointed Recorder 1988. Took Silk 1989.
Personal: Member of Board of Directors of Hackney Empire Theatre. Born 5th November 1946. Lives in London.

Stafford-Michael, Simon
4 King's Bench Walk (Peter Heppel), London (0171) 353 0478. Called 1982.

Stewart, Neill A.
Queen Elizabeth Building (Hollis Whiteman Chambers), London (0171) 583 5766. Called 1973.

Sturman, James
3 Hare Court (Michael Lewis QC), London (0171) 353 7561. Called 1982.

Suckling QC, Alan B.
Queen Elizabeth Building (Hollis Whiteman Chambers), London (0171) 583 5766. Called 1963, took silk 1983.

Temple QC, Victor
6 King's Bench Walk (Michael Worsley QC), London (0171) 583 0410. Called 1971, took silk 1993. Principal area of practice is crime (particularly fraud) and extradition. Born 23.2.1941.

Thwaites QC, Ronald
10 King's Bench Walk (Ronald Thwaites QC), London (0171) 353 2501. Called 1970, took silk 1987. Principal areas of practice are general criminal law and commercial fraud. Born 21.1.1946.

Trollope QC, Andrew
1 Middle Temple Lane (Colin Dines, Andrew Trollope QC), London (0171) 583 0659 (12 lines). Called 1971, took silk 1991.

Walker QC, Raymond
1 Harcourt Buildings (Raymond Walker QC), London (0171) 353 0375/3655. Called 1966, took silk 1988.

Whitehouse QC, David
See under Criminal Law (General).

Wood, Michael
36 Essex Street (Michael Hill QC), London (0171) 413 0353. Called 1976. Specialises in criminal work with an emphasis on commercial fraud. Born 22.10.1953.

INDEXES TO PROFILES

Solicitors' Profiles The index to leading solicitors profiled in the Specialist Lists starts on page 495. This index also includes heads of company legal departments.

Barristers' Profiles Profiles of leading barristers are indexed within the main *Barristers' Index* located at the end of the directory. Names of profiled barristers are set in bold type.

CRIMINAL LAW (GENERAL)

VIRTUALLY all chambers which do not practise exclusively in chancery or commercial law handle some criminal work, from minor motoring offences and petty theft to burglary and murder. Additionally, several London sets practise in crime on the circuits, such as **9 Bedford Row** on the Midland and Oxford Circuit and **Pump Court Chambers** on the Western Circuit. The list of leading chambers below, has been divided into three groups – those best known for prosecution work, those with a bias towards defence and those receiving equal recommendations for handling both. (Most chambers, however, undertake a certain amount of both prosecution and defence work).

PROSECUTION

Of the chambers highly recommended for prosecution expertise, **1 Hare Court, 5 King's Bench Walk** and **6 King's Bench Walk** emerge as the pre-eminent sets.

LEADING SETS – LONDON - PROSECUTION	
1 HARE COURT	5 KING'S BENCH WALK
6 KING'S BENCH WALK	
2 HARCOURT BUILDINGS	5 PAPER BUILDINGS

1 Hare Court, one of London's largest criminal sets, contains many talented silks and juniors at all levels of call. Silks that deserve particular mention are *Michael Kalisher QC* (head of chambers) and *Michael Birnbaum QC*. Also highly recommended are *Martin Heslop QC* and *Stephen Kramer QC*, who both took silk this year.

HIGHLY REGARDED – LONDON - PROSECUTION
4 BRICK COURT

From the numerous notable juniors at the set, *Jonathan Laidlaw* (recently appointed Junior Treasury Counsel) and *David Waters* (Senior Treasury Counsel) have been particularly recommended, whilst *Nicholas Coleman, Jeremy Benson, Kenneth Millett, Andrew Lloyd-Eley* and *Sallie Bennett-Jenkins* are all well regarded.

5 King's Bench Walk is a strong criminal set covering all aspects. It is especially known for handling drugs and problems arising from the Drug Trafficking Offences Act, and all types of sexual offences and pornography (including those against children). Leading silks at the set include *Linda Stern QC* and *Peter Carter QC*. The set also contains several able juniors of which *Stephen Harvey* and *Nigel Peters* have been particularly recommended. Also highly regarded are *David Green, John Ryder* and *John Black*.

The third set in the leading prosecution trio is **6 King's Bench Walk,** although they also undertake a certain amount of defence work. The set has been involved in various recent high profile cases including Brent Walker, the Brighton bombing and Guildford Four (on appeal). *Ann Curnow QC,* who also has a sizable defence practice, has an excellent reputation. Other silks that deserve a mention are *Victor Temple*

QC, Roy Amlot QC (editor 'Phipson on Evidence'), *Bruce Houlder QC, Dorian Lovell-Pank QC* and *David Spens QC* (who took silk earlier this year). Chambers also have a number of strong juniors of which *Nigel Sweeney* (Senior Treasury Counsel), *Nicholas Hilliard* (Junior Treasury Counsel), *Mark Dennis* (Junior Treasury Counsel) and *Anthony Leonard* have been particularly recommended.

5 Paper Buildings and **2 Harcourt Buildings** also enjoy excellent reputations for criminal prosecution work. Although they have a strong bias towards commercial fraud, **5 Paper Buildings** still enjoy an excellent reputation for general criminal work and contain outstanding counsel at all levels of call. Leading silks at the set include head of chambers *John Mathew QC, Michael Corkery QC* and *Timothy Cassel QC*. Juniors at the set, *Edward Jenkins* and *Miranda Moore*, are also well regarded.

2 Harcourt Buildings continues to maintain a strong reputation for criminal work leaning towards prosecution. Head of chambers, *Robert Harman QC*, has been recommended for his expertise. Other leading silks at the set include *Nigel Mylne QC, Nicholas Atkinson QC, Michael Sayers QC* and *Peter Cooper QC*. Juniors at the set that have been recommended to us are *John Bevan* (Senior Treasury Counsel) and *Nicholas Loraine-Smith* (Junior Treasury Counsel).

4 Brick Court, where head of chambers *Anne Rafferty QC* is Chairman of the Criminal Bar Association, has been recommended as a set whose reputation is steadily increasing. The set undertakes all aspects of criminal law across the whole range of courts, including police disciplinary hearings and courts martial cases.

DEFENCE

Of the chambers with a bias towards criminal defence, **3 Hare Court** and **3 Gray's Inn Square** have emerged as the clear leading sets.

LEADING SETS – LONDON - DEFENCE	
3 GRAY'S INN SQUARE	3 HARE COURT
DOUGHTY STREET CHAMBERS	
14 TOOKS COURT	

3 Hare Court is a strong specialist criminal set handling the full range of criminal work, with particular experience in defence. Members practise principally in London, East Anglia and South East, but also undertake work elsewhere in

HIGHLY REGARDED – LONDON - DEFENCE	
1 MIDDLE TEMPLE LANE	3 TEMPLE GARDENS
2 GARDEN COURT	

England and Wales, as well as abroad. Leading silks to note are *William Clegg QC* and *Howard Godfrey QC*. *William Clegg QC*, in particular, has a superb reputation, and has defended in many high profile cases including 'R v Stagg' (Wimbledon Common murder) and 'R v McMahon' (UDA terrorists).

The set also contains numerous talented juniors of which *Charles Conway, Andrew Munday, John Caudle, Nigel Lithman, Brian Altman, James Sturman* and *Richard Matthews* have been particularly recommended to us.

3 Gray's Inn Square, a set of experienced criminal practitioners, has a strong reputation for defence work. Chambers handle all categories of serious criminal cases including murder, terrorism, fraud, robbery, sexual and drugs cases. Head of chambers, *Rock Tansey QC*, has an excellent reputation amongst his peers, and has been involved in many notable cases including the attempted murder of the Israeli Ambassador, the Tottenham and Lewisham riot cases and many high profile terrorist cases. (He also handles cases involving human rights and civil liberties). Other silks recommended at the set are *John Perry QC*, who also practises in Bermuda, and *Nadine Radford QC* (who took silk earlier this year).

The chambers also have several talented juniors including *George Carter-Stephenson* and *Steven Kay* (Secretary of the Criminal Bar Association), *Ronald Jaffa*, *Rudi Fortson*, who is known for drugs work and is author of 'Law on the Misuse of Drugs', *Jeremy Dein* and *Diana Ellis*.

Also highly recommended are **Doughty Street Chambers**. Although a common law set, chambers have several highly regarded silks and juniors specialising in criminal defence work. Members handle all aspects of criminal law, but have particular experience of cases involving civil liberties, and have been involved in several high profile cases, including Sara Thornton, the Guildford Four and the Bridgewater Three.

Leading silks at the set who should be mentioned are head of chambers *Geoffrey Robertson QC*, *Christopher Sallon QC*, *Peter Thornton QC* (who is a contributing editor to 'Archbold'), and *Helena Kennedy QC*, who enjoys a high profile for her criminal practice. As well as acting in many prominent cases of the last decade, *Helena Kennedy QC* has been a frequent broadcaster and journalist on law and women's rights, and author of numerous texts including 'Eve was Framed' (1992).

14 Tooks Court, also a civil liberties orientated set, enjoys a strong reputation for high profile criminal defence work. Head of chambers, *Michael Mansfield QC*, has an excellent reputation and conducted the successful Birmingham Six appeal. Other notable members of chambers include *Adrian Fulford QC* and juniors *Stephen Kamlish* and *John Reilly*.

Other recommended sets with a bias towards defence are **1 Middle Temple Lane**, **3 Temple Gardens** and **2 Garden Court**. **1 Middle Temple Lane**, a set established 17 years ago, has continued to flourish in size and range of work undertaken. Particularly recommended at the set are *Andrew Trollope QC*, *Nicholas Gardiner*, *Michael Borrelli* and *Noel Lucas*.

Specialist criminal set, **3 Temple Gardens**, undertakes 75% defence work and head of chambers, *Jonathan Goldberg QC*, has been recommended. Also well regarded at the set is junior *David Nathan*.

2 Garden Court is a common law set with a strong reputation for criminal defence, and well regarded for handling cases raising 'civil liberty' issues. Notable practitioners at the set are *Ian Macdonald QC*, *Owen Davies*, *Icah Peart* and *Courtenay Griffiths*, who was junior counsel in the 'Blacklock murder trial' and has acted in other prominent cases such as Risley Remand Centre Riot trial.

PROSECUTION & DEFENCE

LEADING SETS – LONDON - BOTH	
1 CROWN OFFICE ROW	36 ESSEX STREET
QUEEN ELIZABETH BUILDING	3 RAYMOND BUILDINGS
9 BEDFORD ROW	

HIGHLY REGARDED SETS – LONDON - BOTH
PUMP COURT CHAMBERS

LEADING SILKS– LONDON - PROSECUTION AND DEFENCE		
Clegg, William *3 Hare Court*	**Jones,** Alun *3 Raymond Buildings*	**Mansfield,** Michael *14 Tooks Court*
Amlot, Roy *6 King's Bench Walk*	**Boney,** Guy *Pump Court Chambers*	**Curnow,** Ann *6 King's Bench Walk*
Elfer, David *1 Paper Buildings*	**Ferguson,** Richard *1 Crown Office Row*	**Fulford,** Adrian *14 Tooks Court*
Goldring, John B. *9 Bedford Row*	**Langdale,** Timothy *Queen Elizabeth Building*	**Mathew,** John *5 Paper Buildings*
Nicholls, Clive *3 Raymond Buildings*	**Nutting,** John *3 Raymond Buildings*	**Penry-Davey,** David *2-3 Gray's Inn Square*
Robertson, Geoffrey *Doughty Street Chambers*	**Robinson,** Vivian *Queen Elizabeth Building*	**Tansey,** Rock *3 Gray's Inn Square*
Thwaites, Ronald *10 King's Bench Walk*	**Trollope,** Andrew *1 Middle Temple Lane*	
Batten, Stephen *3 Raymond Buildings*	**Birnbaum,** Michael *1 Hare Court*	**Blunt,** Oliver *Furnival Chambers*
Coonan, Kieran *6 Pump Court*	**Corkery,** Michael *5 Paper Buildings*	**Coward,** J. Stephen *9 Bedford Row*
Feinberg, Peter *1 Crown Office Row*	**Glass,** Anthony T. *Queen Elizabeth Building*	**Godfrey,** Howard *3 Hare Court*
Goldberg, Jonathan *3 Temple Gardens*	**Gray,** Gilbert *3 Raymond Buildings*	**Harman,** Robert *2 Harcourt Buildings*
Jeffreys, David A. *Queen Elizabeth Building*	**Kalisher,** Michael *1 Hare Court*	**Kennedy,** Helena *Doughty Street Chambers*
Macdonald, Ian *2 Garden Court*	**Nicholls,** Colin *3 Raymond Buildings*	**Seabrook,** Robert *1 Crown Office Row*
Shaw, Antony *4 Brick Court*	**Solley,** Stephen *Cloisters*	**Temple,** Victor *6 King's Bench Walk*
Whitehouse, David *3 Raymond Buildings*		

HIGHLY REGARDED SILKS - LONDON - PROSECUTION AND DEFENCE

Barnes, Timothy 9 Bedford Row	**Carter**, Peter 5 King's Bench Walk	**Farrer**, David J. 9 Bedford Row
Grindrod, Helen Globe House	**Heslop**, Martin 1 Hare Court	**Hill**, Michael 36 Essex Street
Houlder, Bruce 6 King's Bench Walk	**Leslie**, Stephen 1 Crown Office Row	**Lovell-Pank**, Dorian 6 King's Bench Walk
O'Conner, Patrick 1 Crown Office Row	**Pascoe**, Nigel Pump Court Chambers	**Rafferty**, Anne J. 4 Brick Court
Roberts, Jeremy 9 Gough Square	**Sallon**, Christopher Doughty Street Chambers	**Spokes**, John Pump Court Chambers
Stern, Linda 5 King's Bench Walk	**Thornton**, Peter Doughty Street Chambers	
Atkinson, Nicholas 2 Harcourt Buildings	**Austin-Smith**, Michael 36 Essex Street	**Cassel**, Timothy 5 Paper Buildings
Cooper, Peter 2 Harcourt Buildings	**Grey**, Robin D. Queen Elizabeth Building	**Lawson**, Edmund 9-12 Bell Yard
Mylne, Nigel 2 Harcourt Buildings	**Nice**, Geoffrey Farrar's Building	**Raggatt**, Timothy 1 King's Bench Walk
Bate, David Queen Elizabeth Building	**de Silva**, Desmond 2 Paper Buildings	**Edwards**, Susan 36 Essex Street
Gale, Michael 6 Pump Court	**Hallett**, Heather 6 Pump Court	**Khayat**, Georges M 10 King's Bench Walk
Korner, Joanna 6 King's Bench Walk	**Kramer**, Stephen 1 Hare Court	**Lawson**, Michael 36 Essex Street
Perry, John 3 Gray's Inn Square	**Radford**, Nadine 3 Gray's Inn Square	**Sayers**, Michael 2 Harcourt Buildings
Spens, David 6 King's Bench Walk		

Of chambers that have been equally recommended for defence and prosecution work, **Hollis Whiteman Chambers** (Queen Elizabeth Building), **1 Crown Office Row**, **36 Essex Street** and **3 Raymond Buildings** emerge as the leading sets.

Premier set, **Hollis Whiteman Chambers**, handles all aspects of criminal work, with members often involved in high profile cases. Although based in London, particularly at the Central Criminal Court, members of chambers practise throughout England and Wales and internationally. The large set of 51 tenants contains many talented silks and

Juniors that deserve a special mention are *David Calvert-Smith* who is Senior Treasury Counsel, *William Boyce*, *Richard Horwell*, *John Kelsey-Fry*, and *Mark Ellison*, who are all Junior Treasury Counsel, and *Ian Winter*.

1 Crown Office Row is an extremely strong set containing excellent practitioners at all levels of call. Head of chambers, *Richard Ferguson QC* (former Chair of the Criminal Bar Association) has been particularly recommended to us. Other well regarded silks at the set are *Peter Feinberg QC*, *Stephen Leslie QC* and *Patrick O'Conner QC*.

From the many talented juniors, *Sasha Wass* (who is

LEADING JUNIORS- LONDON - PROSECUTION AND DEFENCE

Calvert-Smith, David Queen Elizabeth Building		
Altman, Brian 3 Hare Court	**Bevan**, John 2 Harcourt Buildings	**Conway**, Charles 3 Hare Court
Dennis, Mark 6 King's Bench Walk	**Garlick**, Paul Pump Court Chambers	**Harvey**, Stephen 5 King's Bench Walk
Hilliard, Nicholas 6 King's Bench Walk	**Jaffa**, Ronald 3 Gray's Inn Square	**Jenkins**, Edward 5 Paper Buildings
Laidlaw, Jonathan 1 Hare Court	**Leonard**, Anthony 6 King's Bench Walk	**Lithman**, Nigel 3 Hare Court
Loraine-Smith, Nicholas 2 Harcourt Buildings	**Martin-Sperry**, David 1 Crown Office Row	**Mitchell**, Andrew Furnival Chambers
Munday, Andrew 3 Hare Court	**Peters**, Nigel 5 King's Bench Walk	**Pownall**, Orlando 1 Crown Office Row
Sturman, James 3 Hare Court	**Sweeney**, Nigel 6 King's Bench Walk	**Wass**, Sasha 1 Crown Office Row
Waters, David 1 Hare Court		
Borrelli, Michael 1 Middle Temple Lane	**Boyce**, William H. Queen Elizabeth Building	**Burke**, Trevor 1 Crown Office Row
Carter-Stephenson, George 3 Gray's Inn Square	**Coffey**, John 3 Temple Gardens	**Coleman**, Nicholas 1 Hare Court
Ellison, Mark Queen Elizabeth Building	**Gardiner**, Nicholas 1 Middle Temple Lane	**Green**, David 5 King's Bench Walk
Griffiths, Courtenay 2 Garden Court	**Hackett**, Philip Cloisters	**Horwell**, Richard E. Queen Elizabeth Building
Janner, Daniel 36 Essex Street	**Kamlish**, Stephen 14 Tooks Court	**Kelsey-Fry**, J. Queen Elizabeth Building
Lucas, Noel 1 Middle Temple Lane	**Nathan**, David 3 Temple Gardens	**Richardson**, P. James 36 Essex Street
Ryder, John 5 King's Bench Walk	**Whittam**, Richard Furnival Chambers	**Wolkind**, Michael 10 King's Bench Walk

juniors. Particularly recommended are *Vivian Robinson QC*, *Timothy Langdale QC*, *David Jeffreys QC*, *Anthony Glass QC* (who was involved in the Guildford Police cases) and *David Bate QC*.

currently defending Rosemary West), *Orlando Pownall* (Senior Treasury Counsel), *David Martin-Sperry* and *Trevor Burke* are highly respected.

36 Essex Street is a major criminal set with a good mixture of prosecution and defence work. The set has a large number of able practitioners and a strong reputation at both silk and junior level. Leading silks at the set are *Michael Hill QC* (head of chambers), *Michael Lawson QC*, *Susan Edwards QC* and *Michael Austin-Smith QC*.

From a number of notable juniors, *Daniel Janner*, *Bernard Phelvin* and *James Richardson*, who has been editor of 'Archbold' since 1982, have been particularly recommended.

Leading criminal set **3 Raymond Buildings** has vast experience in the full range of criminal work, both prosecution and defence. Chambers have been involved in many high profile cases including the Herald of Free Enterprise and various IRA cases. The set contains numerous leading silks, including *Clive Nicholls QC* (head of chambers), *Colin Nicholls QC*, *Alun Jones QC*, *Gilbert Gray QC*, *Stephen Batten QC*, *David Whitehouse QC* and *John Nutting QC* who took silk earlier this year.

Also highly regarded for both defendant and prosecution work are **9 Bedford Row** and **Pump Court Chambers**, both of which have members who practise on the circuits. **9 Bedford Row** (formerly **2 Crown Office Row**) has a strong emphasis on the Midland and Oxford circuit and is often involved in high profile cases. Well known silks at the set are *Stephen Coward QC*, who acted for the defence in the 'Rachel McLean murder' case and defended the bosun in the 'Herald of Free Enterprise' case, *David Farrer QC*, *Timothy Barnes QC* and *John Goldring QC*.

Pump Court Chambers, a common law set, undertake a large amount of criminal work on the Western Circuit. Head of chambers, *Guy Boney QC*, recently prosecuted in the highly publicised case of the gang who set light to more than £1 million in a failed raid on a Securicor van. Other recommended members of chambers are *John Spokes QC*, *Nigel Pascoe QC* and *Paul Garlick*.

Notable individuals in other chambers include: *Stephen Solley QC*, who acted in 'R v Charles' (Red Dwarf) and *Philip Hackett* (**Cloisters**), *Ronald Thwaites QC* and *Michael Wolkind* (**10 King's Bench Walk**), *Anthony Shaw QC*

(**4 Brick Court**), *Oliver Blunt QC*, *Andrew Mitchell* and *Richard Whittam* (**Furnival Chambers**), *Kieran Coonan QC* for medical related crime (**6 Pump Court**), *David Elfer QC* (**1 Paper Buildings**), *David Penry-Davey QC* (**2-3 Gray's Inn Square**) and *Robert Seabrook QC* (**1 Crown Office Row**) who is a member of the Criminal Justice Consultative Council (Home Office).

HIGHLY REGARDED JUNIORS– LONDON · BOTH	
Benson, Jeremy	*1 Hare Court*
Black, John	*5 King's Bench Walk*
Davies, Owen	*2 Garden Court*
Dein, Jeremy	*3 Gray's Inn Square*
Fortson, Rudi	*3 Gray's Inn Square*
Frank, Ivor	*4 King's Bench Walk*
Moore, Miranda	*5 Paper Buildings*
Peart, Icah	*2 Garden Court*
Phelvin, Bernard	*36 Essex Street*
Caudle, John	*3 Hare Court*
Ellis, Diana	*3 Gray's Inn Square*
Kay, Steven	*3 Gray's Inn Square*
Lloyd-Eley, Andrew	*1 Hare Court*
Millett, Kenneth	*1 Hare Court*
Owen, Tudor	*9-12 Bell Yard*
Upward, Patrick Charles	*9 Gough Square*
Winter, Ian	*Queen Elizabeth Building*
Bennett-Jenkins, Sallie	*1 Hare Court*
Bryant-Heron, Mark	*9-12 Bell Yard*
Feder, Ami	*Lamb Building*
Matthews, Richard	*3 Hare Court*
Reilly, John	*14 Tooks Court*
Smith, Zoë	*Hardwicke Building*
Vine, James	*Hardwicke Building*
Weekes, Anesta	*Cloisters*

OUTSIDE LONDON

In Bristol, the leading criminal set is **Albion Chambers** led by *Charles Barton QC* and the recently appointed silk *James Tabor QC*. They are ably backed up by *Neil Ford*, *Martin Picton*, *Julian Lambert*, and *Patrick Burrowes*.

Birmingham's most highly ranked set is **1 Fountain Court** where *David Crigman QC* and *Anthony Hughes QC* lead a very experienced team which includes *Melbourne Inman* and *Richard Griffith-Jones*. From the other Birmingham sets, experienced silks and juniors include *Stephen Linehan QC* (**5 Fountain Court**) and *Richard Wakerley QC* and *John Saunders QC* (**4 Fountain Court**). *Rex Tedd QC*, and *Christopher Hotten QC* are well known criminal practitioners at **7 Fountain Court**.

No.1 High Pavement in Nottingham is a specialist criminal set containing several highly experienced practitioners, including *Peter Joyce QC*.

Liverpool has a large number of busy criminal practitioners. The leading criminal set is **25-27 Castle Street** where *Stephen Riordan QC* is highly regarded. **Martin's Building** is a general common law and commercial set with a growing reputation for its criminal practice.

In Manchester, **Lincoln House Chambers** has a leading position within the flourishing criminal Bar. Among its highly regarded members are *David Sumner* and *James Gregory*. Other leading sets include **18 St Johns Street** (*Rodney Klevan QC* and *Peter Birkett QC*), and **28 St John Street** (*Anthony Gee QC* and *Clement Goldstone QC*).

Leeds has two leading criminal sets: **Park Court Chambers**, which has a strong team of experienced criminal practitioners with a large number of silks and juniors highly experienced in this field; and **St Pauls Chambers**, a general common law set which specialises in crime.

HIGHLY REGARDED SILKS– REGIONS

Barker, Anthony *5 Fountain Court, B'ham*	**Barton,** Charles *Albion Chambers, Bristol*	**Birkett,** Peter *18 St. John Street, Manch*
Carus, Roderick *9 St. John Street, Manch.*	**Crigman,** David *1 Fountain Court, B'ham*	**Davies,** Leighton *9 Park Place, Cardiff*
Farley, Roger *40 King St, Manch.*	**Garside,** Charles *9 St. John Street, Manch.*	**Gee,** Anthony *28 St. John St, Manch*
Goldstone, L. Clement *28 St. John St, Manch.*	**Henriques,** Richard *Deans Court Chambers, Man.*	**Hotten,** Christopher *7 Fountain Court, B'ham*
Hughes, Anthony *1 Fountain Court, B'ham*	**Joyce,** Peter *No.1 High Pavement, Nott.*	**Klevan,** Rodney C. *18 St. John Street, Manch*
Linehan, Stephen *5 Fountain Court, B'ham*	**Morris,** Antony *Peel Court Chambers, Manch.*	**Palmer,** Anthony *3 Fountain Court, B'ham*
Poole, David *Deans Court Chambers, Manch.*	**Riordan,** Stephen *25-27 Castle Street, Liverpool*	**Saunders,** J. *4 Fountain Court, B'ham*
Smith, Roger *No.6 Fountain Court, B'ham*	**Smith,** Robert *Park Court Chambers, Leeds*	**Steer,** David *The Corn Exchange, Liverpool*
Tabor, James *Albion Chambers, Bristol*	**Tedd,** Rex *7 Fountain Court, B'ham*	**Thomas,** Roger *9 Park Place, Cardiff*
Treacy, Colman *3 Fountain Court, B'ham*	**Turner,** David *Exchange Chambers, Liverpool*	**Wakerley,** R.M. *4 Fountain Court, B'ham*

HIGHLY REGARDED JUNIORS– REGIONS

Andrews, Philip B. *Young Street Chambers. Manch*	**Atherton,** Robert K. *Peel House, Liverpool*	**Aubrey,** David *The Corn Exchange, Liverpool*
Aylmer-Evans, T. *Assize Court Chambers, Bristol*	**Brennand,** T.W. *Manchester House Chambers, Man.*	**Burbidge,** James *7 Fountain Court, B'ham*
Burrowes, Patrick *Albion Chambers, Bristol*	**Carr,** Peter *St. Ive's Chambers, B'ham*	**Cattan,** Philip D. *28 St. John St, Manch.*
Davies, Trefor *Iscoed Chambers, Swansea*	**Everard,** William *King Charles House, Nott.*	**Ford,** Neil *Albion Chambers, Bristol*
Goode, Rowena *28 St. John St, Manch.*	**Gozem,** Guy *Lincoln House Chambers, Manch.*	**Gregory,** James *Lincoln House Chambers, Manch.*
Griffith-Jones, Richard *1 Fountain Court, B'ham*	**Harvey,** Colin T. *St. Paul's Chambers, Leeds*	**Haynes,** Peter *7 Fountain Court, B'ham*
Herman, Raymond C. *Peel House, Liverpool*	**Inglis,** Richard *King Charles House, Nott.*	**Inman,** Melbourne *1 Fountain Court, B'ham*
Jackson, Keith *King Charles House, Nott.*	**Jackson,** John *40 King St, Manch.*	**Jacobs,** Peter *9 Park Place, Cardiff*
Lambert, Julian *Albion Chambers*	**Long,** A.P. *Peel Court Chambers, Manch.*	**Macur,** Julia *St. Ive's Chambers, B'ham*
Marks, R.L. *Peel Court Chambers, Manch.*	**McCreath,** Alistair *No.6 Fountain Court, B'ham*	**Nuttall,** Andrew *Lincoln House Chambers, Manch.*
Pickup, James *Lincoln House Chambers, Manch.*	**Picton,** Martin *Albion Chambers, Bristol*	**Qureshi,** Shamim *Assize Court Chambers, Bristol*
Riordan, Kevin *Iscoed Chambers, Swansea*	**Rouch,** Peter C. *Iscoed Chambers, Swansea*	**Smith,** Shaun *No.1 High Pavement, Nott.*
Sumner, David *Lincoln House Chambers, Manch.*	**Taylor,** Gregg *9 Park Place, Cardiff*	**Wait,** John *1 Fountain Court, B'ham*
Williams, Christopher M. *32 Park Place, Cardiff*	**Wright,** Peter *Lincoln House Chambers, Manch.*	

LEADERS IN CRIMINAL LAW (GENERAL)

Altman, Brian
3 Hare Court (Michael Lewis QC),
London (0171) 353 7561. Called 1981.

Amlot QC, Roy
See under Crime: Fraud.

Andrews, Philip B.
Young Street Chambers (Christopher
Limb),   Manchester (0161) 833 0489.

Atherton, Robert K.
Peel House (David M. Harris QC),
Liverpool (0151) 236 0718.

Atkinson QC, Nicholas
2 Harcourt Buildings (Robert Harman
QC),   London (0171) 353 2112. Called
1971, took silk 1991.

Aubrey, David J.M.
32 Park Place (Christopher Williams),
Cardiff (01222) 397364.

Aubrey, David
The Corn Exchange (David Steer QC,
I. Goldrein),   Liverpool (0151) 227
1081/5009. Called 1974.

Austin-Smith QC, Michael
36 Essex Street (Michael Hill QC),
London (0171) 413 0353. Called 1969, took
silk 1990.

Aylmer-Evans, Timothy
Assize Court Chambers (Graeme Wood),
Bristol (0117) 9264587.

Barker QC, Anthony
5 Fountain Court (Anthony Barker QC),
Birmingham (0121) 606 0500. Called 1966,
took silk 1985.

Barnes QC, Timothy
9 Bedford Row (Stephen Coward QC),
London (0171) 242 3555. Called 1968, took
silk 1986.

Barton QC, Charles
Albion Chambers (J.C.T. Barton QC),
Bristol (0117) 9272144. Called 1969, took
silk 1989.

Bate QC, David
Queen Elizabeth Building (Hollis
Whiteman Chambers),   London (0171)
583 5766.

Batten QC, Stephen
3 Raymond Buildings (Clive Nicholls
QC),   London (0171) 831 3833. Called
1968, took silk 1989.

Bennett-Jenkins, Sallie
1 Hare Court (Michael Kalisher QC),
London (0171) 353 5324. Called 1984.

Benson, Jeremy
1 Hare Court (Michael Kalisher QC),
London (0171) 353 5324.

Bevan, John
2 Harcourt Buildings (Robert Harman QC), London (0171) 353 2112. Called 1970.

Birkett QC, Peter
18 St. John Street (Rodney C. Klevan QC), Manchester (0161) 834 9843.

Birnbaum QC, Michael
1 Hare Court (Michael Kalisher QC), London (0171) 353 5324. Called 1969, took silk 1992.

Black, John
5 King's Bench Walk (David Cocks QC), London (0171) 797 7600. Called 1975.

Blunt QC, Oliver
Furnival Chambers (Andrew Mitchell), London (0171) 583 0434. Called 1974, took silk 1994. Criminal law specialist. Born 8.3.1951.

Boney QC, Guy
Pump Court Chambers (Guy Boney QC), London (0171) 353 0711. Called 1968, took silk 1990.

Borrelli, Michael
1 Middle Temple Lane (Colin Dines, Andrew Trollope QC), London (0171) 583 0659 (12 lines). Called 1977.

Boyce, William H.
Queen Elizabeth Building (Hollis Whiteman Chambers), London (0171) 583 5766.

Brennand, T.W.
Manchester House Chambers (J.D.S. Wishart), Manchester (0161) 834 7007.

Bryant-Heron, Mark
9-12 Bell Yard (Edmund Lawson QC), London (0171) 400 1800.

Burbidge, James
7 Fountain Court (Rex Tedd QC), Birmingham (0121) 236 8531. Called 1979.

Burke, Trevor
1 Crown Office Row (Richard Ferguson QC), London (0171) 797 7111. Called 1981.

Burrowes, Patrick
Albion Chambers (J.C.T. Barton QC), Bristol (0117) 9272144.

Calvert-Smith, David
Queen Elizabeth Building (Hollis Whiteman Chambers), London (0171) 583 5766. Called 1969.

Carr, Peter
St. Ive's Chambers (Mr. Edward Coke), Birmingham (0121) 236 0863/0929.

Carter QC, Peter
5 King's Bench Walk (David Cocks QC), London (0171) 797 7600. Called 1974, took silk 1995. Principal area of practice is criminal law, primarily fraud cases, but also across the whole range of offences. Born 8.8.1952.

Carter-Stephenson, George
3 Gray's Inn Square (Rock Tansey QC), London (0171) 831 2311. Called 1975.

Carus QC, Roderick
9 St. John Street (John Hand QC), Manchester (0161) 955 9000. Called 1971, took silk 1990.

Cassel QC, Timothy
5 Paper Buildings (John Mathew QC), London (0171) 583 6117. Called 1965, took silk 1988. Principal areas of practice are criminal law and licensing law. Born 30.4.1942.

Cattan, Philip D.
28 St. John St (Charles Bloom QC), Manchester (0161) 834 8418.

Caudle, John
3 Hare Court (Michael Lewis QC), London (0171) 353 7561. Called 1976.

Clegg QC, William
See under Crime: Fraud.

Coffey, John
3 Temple Gardens (John Coffey), London (0171) 353 3102. Called 1970.

Coleman, Nicholas
1 Hare Court (Michael Kalisher QC), London (0171) 353 5324. Called 1970.

Conway, Charles
3 Hare Court (Michael Lewis QC), London (0171) 353 7561. Called 1969.

Coonan QC, Kieran
6 Pump Court (Kieran Coonan QC), London (0171) 583 6013. Called 1971, took silk 1990. Principal areas of practice are medical and health law and personal injury. Other main area is criminal law. Born 29.10.1946.

Cooper QC, Peter
2 Harcourt Buildings (Robert Harman QC), London (0171) 353 2112. Called 1974, took silk 1993.

Corkery QC, Michael
5 Paper Buildings (John Mathew QC), London (0171) 583 6117. Called 1949, took silk 1981. Practice covers general criminal law and commercial fraud. Born 20.5.1926.

Coward QC, J. Stephen
9 Bedford Row (Stephen Coward QC), London (0171) 242 3555.
Specialisation: Practice encompasses all

aspects of serious criminal law from murder to fraud. Acted for defence in the Rachel McLean murder case and defended the bosun in the Herald of Free Enterprise case. Clients include SFO, CPS (HQ and CPS areas on Midland and Oxford Circuit).
Prof. Membership: Criminal Bar Association.
Career: Lecturer, Bramshill Police College, 1962. Called to the Bar 1964 and joined current chambers in 1965. Appointed Recorder 1980. Took silk 1984. Currently head of chambers.
Personal: Educated at King James Grammar School, Almondbury and University College, London (LL.B). Leisure pursuits include gardening, wine and singing. Born 15th November 1937. Lives in Northampton.

Crigman QC, David
1 Fountain Court (Anthony Hughes QC), Birmingham (0121) 236 5721. Called 1969, took silk 1989.

Curnow QC, Ann
6 King's Bench Walk (Michael Worsley QC), London (0171) 583 0410. Called 1957, took silk 1985.

Davies, Owen
2 Garden Court (I. Macdonald QC, O. Davies), London (0171) 353 1633. Called 1973.

Davies, Trefor
Iscoed Chambers (Wyn Richards), Swansea (01792) 652988/9.

Davies QC, Leighton
9 Park Place (Philip Rees), Cardiff (01222) 382731.

Dein, Jeremy
3 Gray's Inn Square (Rock Tansey QC), London (0171) 831 2311.

Dennis, Mark
6 King's Bench Walk (Michael Worsley QC), London (0171) 583 0410.

de Silva QC, Desmond
2 Paper Buildings (Desmond de Silva QC), London (0171) 936 2611. Called 1964, took silk 1984.

Edwards QC, Susan
36 Essex Street (Michael Hill QC), London (0171) 413 0353.

Elfer QC, David
1 Paper Buildings (Roger Titheridge QC), London (0171) 353 3728. Called 1964, took silk 1981.

Ellis, Diana
3 Gray's Inn Square (Rock Tansey QC), London (0171) 831 2311. Called 1978. Practice encompasses all aspects of criminal law.

Ellison, Mark

Queen Elizabeth Building (Hollis Whiteman Chambers), London (0171) 583 5766.

Specialisation: Criminal practice specialising in commercial fraud and Treasury Counsel work. Interesting cases include both the Guinness trial and appeal.

Career: Called 1979. Appointed Junior Treasury Counsel to the Crown at the Central Criminal Court 1994.

Personal: Educated at Pocklington School, Skinners School and the University of Wales.

Everard, William

King Charles House (Richard Inglis), Nottingham (0115) 9418851. Called 1973.

Farley QC, Roger

40 King St (John Hoggett QC), Manchester (0161) 832 9082.

Farrer QC, David J.

9 Bedford Row (Stephen Coward QC), London (0171) 242 3555. Called 1967, took silk 1986.

Feder, Ami

Lamb Building (Kenneth Wheeler), London (0171) 797 7788.

Specialisation: Principal area of practice is fraud work in both the criminal and civil fields and general commercial and international work. Clients have included company directors, bankers, accountants and solicitors/lawyers from England and Israel. Also practices at 9 Malchei, Israel Square, Tel-Aviv 64163.
Tel: 03-5243381.

Prof. Membership: Criminal Bar Association; Common Law and Commercial Bar Association; European Bar Asociation.

Career: Called to the Bar 1965; Member of the Israel Bar.

Personal: Educated in Israel (Hebrew University of Jerusalem, the branch in Tel Aviv) and in England (London LSE).

Feinberg QC, Peter

1 Crown Office Row (Richard Ferguson QC), London (0171) 797 7111.

Ferguson QC, Richard

1 Crown Office Row (Richard Ferguson QC), London (0171) 797 7111. Called 1956, took silk 1973.

Ford, Neil

Albion Chambers (J.C.T. Barton QC), Bristol (0117) 9272144.

Fortson, Rudi

3 Gray's Inn Square (Rock Tansey QC), London (0171) 831 2311. Called 1976. Extensive criminal law experience, particularly relating to drugs, money-laundering and fraud. Born 2.3.1952.

Frank, Ivor

4 King's Bench Walk (Peter Heppel), London (0171) 353 0478. Called 1979.

Fulford QC, Adrian

14 Tooks Court (Michael Mansfield QC), London (0171) 405 8828. Called 1978, took silk 1994. Principal area of work is criminal law, administrative law and judicial review, personal injury and civil liberties. Born 8.1.1953.

Gale QC, Michael

6 Pump Court (Michael Gale QC), London (0171) 797 8400.

Specialisation: Criminal law with particular emphasis on commercial fraud and insider dealing, also general common law and licensing. Extensive defence practice. Prosecutes for Director of Public Prosecutions and Crown Prosecution Service, Department of Trade and Industry and H.M. Customs and Excise.

Career: Called to the Bar 1957. Harmsworth Scholar, Middle Temple. Recorder of the Crown Court since 1977. Queen's Counsel 1979. Master of the Bench of the Middle Temple. Member of the General Council of the Bar (1987-1994). Legal Assessor to the General Medical Council.

Personal: Educated Grocers' School and King's College, Cambridge (Exhibitioner). MA. Cantab. 1956-1958 National Service with Royal Fusiliers and Joint Services School for linguists. Member of the MCC and United Oxford and Cambridge University Club.

Gardiner, Nicholas

1 Middle Temple Lane (Colin Dines, Andrew Trollope QC), London (0171) 583 0659 (12 lines). Called 1967.

Garlick, Paul

Pump Court Chambers (Guy Boney QC), London (0171) 353 0711. Called 1974.

Garside QC, Charles

9 St. John Street (John Hand QC), Manchester (0161) 955 9000. Called 1971, took silk 1993.

Gee QC, Anthony

28 St. John St (Charles Bloom QC), Manchester (0161) 834 8418.

Glass QC, Anthony T.

Queen Elizabeth Building (Hollis Whiteman Chambers), London (0171) 583 5766.

Specialisation: Practice encompasses all aspects of criminal law, with a specialisation in commercial fraud, V.A.T. fraud and drugs importations since taking silk. Also regularly acts in robbery, rape and murder cases. Recently involved in Barlow Clowes, BCCI and Guildford police cases.

Prof. Membership: Criminal Bar Association, South Eastern Circuit.

Career: Called to the Bar 1965 and joined current chambers in 1982. Appointed Recorder 1985. Took silk 1986.

Personal: Educated at Royal Masonic Schools 1948-58 and Lincoln College, Oxford 1960-63. Born 6th June 1940. Lives in London.

Godfrey QC, Howard

3 Hare Court (Michael Lewis QC), London (0171) 353 7561.

Goldberg QC, Jonathan

3 Temple Gardens (Jonathan Goldberg QC), London (0171) 583 1155. Called 1971, took silk 1989.

Goldring QC, John B.

9 Bedford Row (Stephen Coward QC), London (0171) 242 3555.

Specialisation: Practice encompasses serious crime work, fraud (both civil and criminal) and medical cases. Prosecuted in the Beverley Allitt murder. Represented one of the Consultants before the General Medical Council in the case concerning alleged payment for organ (kidney) transplants. Has been involved in a number of cases involving alleged tax fraud: in particular, Carmel College, Charlton and others (offshore tax fraud involving professional Defendants). Aveling Barford pension case. Clients include CPS, (Headquarters and provincial), SFO, Solicitor to Inland Revenue and numbers of independent solicitors.

Prof. Membership: Criminal Bar Association, International Bar Association, National Institute of Trial Advocacy, United States (part of the faculty on occasion).

Career: Called to the Bar 1969 and joined current chambers. Took Silk and appointed Recorder 1987. Deputy Senior Judge, Sovereign Base Area, Cyprus 1991.

Personal: Educated at Wyggeston Grammar School and Exeter University. Leisure pursuits include gardening and skiing. Born 9th November 1944. Lives in London and Rutland.

Goldstone QC, L. Clement

28 St. John St (Charles Bloom QC), Manchester (0161) 834 8418.

Goode, Rowena

28 St. John St (Charles Bloom QC), Manchester (0161) 834 8418.

Gozem, Guy

Lincoln House Chambers (Mukhtar Hussain QC), Manchester (0161) 832 5701.

Gray QC, Gilbert

3 Raymond Buildings (Clive Nicholls QC), London (0171) 831 3833. Called 1953, took silk 1971.

Green, David
5 King's Bench Walk (David Cocks QC), London (0171) 797 7600. Called 1979. Principal area of practice is serious crime cases, and breach of pollution control legislation. Born 8.7.1954.

Gregory, James
Lincoln House Chambers (Mukhtar Hussain QC), Manchester (0161) 832 5701.

Grey QC, Robin D.
Queen Elizabeth Building (Hollis Whiteman Chambers), London (0171) 583 5766.
Specialisation: Criminal law. Defends and prosecutes in all areas of criminal law, with a particular emphasis on large-scale fraud in recent years. Has also defended in over thirty high-profile murder cases during the course of his career. Successfully defended in the Richardson Gang case of 1970s, in the "Nasty Tales" case at the time of the Oz trial, in the "King Squealer" robberies in the late 1970s, and in the Brinks Matt case in the early 1990s. Fraud trials include a successful defence in the Eagle Trust case (1993). In the past three years has defended solicitors, accountants and bank managers in relation to white collar offences. Has considerable experience lecturing on professional conduct, jury trials and criminal procedure. Has also written articles for the Centre for Policy Studies and the Criminal Bar Association newsletter. Practice also includes civil matters arising out of criminal cases.
Prof. Membership: Bar Council, Society of Forensic Medicine, Criminal Bar Association, International Bar Association, Eastern Europe Forum and the Council of Russian and UK Cooperation.
Career: Called to the Bar 1957 and worked as Crown Counsel in Aden 1959-63, before joining present chambers in 1963. Took Silk in 1979 and was appointed Recorder in the same year. Chairman of the Police Appeals Tribunal 1988. Adviser to the Foreign Office in Russian Federation jury trials in 1993.

Griffith-Jones, Richard
1 Fountain Court (Anthony Hughes QC), Birmingham (0121) 236 5721. Called 1974.

Griffiths, Courtenay
2 Garden Court (I. Macdonald QC, O. Davies), London (0171) 353 1633. Called 1980. Practice covers all aspects of criminal law and actions against the police.

Grindrod QC, Helen
Globe House (Helen Grindrod), London (0171) 240 7277.

Hackett, Philip
See under Crime: Fraud.

Hallett QC, Heather
6 Pump Court (Michael Gale QC),

London (0171) 797 8400.
Specialisation: Criminal law specialist. Deals with all serious criminal offences.
Prof. Membership: South Eastern Circuit, Criminal Bar Association, Family Law Bar Association.
Career: Called to the Bar and joined 6 Pump Court in 1972. Took Silk and was appointed Recorder in 1989. Director of Public Affairs for the Bar Council 1992-94. Leader of South Eastern Circuit from 1995.
Personal: Educated at Oxford University (MA). Leisure interests include family, theatre and music. Born 16th December 1949. Lives in London.

Harman QC, Robert
2 Harcourt Buildings (Robert Harman QC), London (0171) 353 2112. Called 1954, took silk 1974.

Harvey, Colin T.
St. Paul's Chambers (Nigel Sangster), Leeds (0113) 2455866.

Harvey, Stephen
5 King's Bench Walk (David Cocks QC), London (0171) 797 7600.

Haynes, Peter
7 Fountain Court (Rex Tedd QC), Birmingham (0121) 236 8531. Called 1983.

Henriques QC, Richard
Deans Court Chambers (H. K. Goddard QC), Manchester (0161) 834 4097.

Herman, Raymond C.
Peel House (David M. Harris QC), Liverpool (0151) 236 0718.

Heslop QC, Martin
1 Hare Court (Michael Kalisher QC), London (0171) 353 5324. Called 1972, took silk 1995.

Hill QC, Michael
36 Essex Street (Michael Hill QC), London (0171) 413 0353. Called 1958, took silk 1979. Principal area of practice is criminal law, particularly commercial fraud. Born 22.5.1935

Hilliard, Nicholas
6 King's Bench Walk (Michael Worsley QC), London (0171) 583 0410.

Horwell, Richard E.
Queen Elizabeth Building (Hollis Whiteman Chambers), London (0171) 583 5766.

Hotten QC, Christopher
7 Fountain Court (Rex Tedd QC), Birmingham (0121) 236 8531. Called 1972, took silk 1994.

Houlder QC, Bruce
6 King's Bench Walk (Michael Worsley QC), London (0171) 583 0410.

Hughes QC, Anthony
1 Fountain Court (Anthony Hughes QC), Birmingham (0121) 236 5721. Called 1970, took silk 1990.

Inglis, Richard
King Charles House (Richard Inglis), Nottingham (0115) 9418851.

Inman, Melbourne
1 Fountain Court (Anthony Hughes QC), Birmingham (0121) 236 5721. Called 1979.

Jackson, Keith
King Charles House (Richard Inglis), Nottingham (0115) 9418851.

Jackson, John
40 King St (John Hoggett QC), Manchester (0161) 832 9082.

Jacobs, Peter
9 Park Place (Philip Rees), Cardiff (01222) 382731.

Jaffa, Ronald
3 Gray's Inn Square (Rock Tansey QC), London (0171) 831 2311. Called 1974.

Janner, Daniel
See under Employment.

Jeffreys QC, David A.
Queen Elizabeth Building (Hollis Whiteman Chambers), London (0171) 583 5766. Called 1958, took silk 1981. Practice covers all aspects of general and commercial criminal law.

Jenkins, Edward
5 Paper Buildings (John Mathew QC), London (0171) 583 6117. Called 1977.

Jones QC, Alun
See under Crime: Fraud.

Joyce QC, Peter
No.1 High Pavement (John B. Milmo QC), Nottingham (0115) 9418218. Called 1968, took silk 1991.

Kalisher QC, Michael
1 Hare Court (Michael Kalisher QC), London (0171) 353 5324. Called 1970, took silk 1984.

Kamlish, Stephen
14 Tooks Court (Michael Mansfield QC), London (0171) 405 8828. Called 1979. Principal area of practice is criminal defence work. Also handles extradition cases and actions against the police. Born 1.11.1955.

Kay, Steven
3 Gray's Inn Square (Rock Tansey QC), London (0171) 831 2311. Called 1977. Principal area of work is criminal law, particularly fraud and drug traffiking. Born 4.8.1954.

Kelsey-Fry, J.
See under Crime: Fraud.

Kennedy QC, Helena
Doughty Street Chambers (Geoffrey Robertson QC), London (0171) 404 1313.
Specialisation: Principal area of practice is criminal law, undertaking leading work of all kinds. Also handles judicial review, public inquiries and sex discrimination work. Has acted in many of the prominent cases of the last decade including the Guildford Four Appeal and the Brighton Bombing Trial. Led Inquiry into health environmental and safety aspects of the Atomic Weapons Establishment at Aldermaston for Reading Borough Council - findings reported in 'Secrecy versus Safety'. Chancellor of Oxford Brookes University and commissioner on the National commssioner on Education. Frequent broadcaster and journalist on law and women's rights. Created the BBC TV series 'Blind Justice', and presented, inter alia, Raw Deal on Medical Negligence (1989), the Trial of Lady Chatterley's Lover (1990) and Time Gentlemen, Please for BBC Scotland (TV Programme award winner, 1994 Industrial Journalism awards). Author of 'Eve Was Framed' (1992), 'Balancing Acts' (1989) and 'Child Sexual Abuse Within the Family' (1985). Frequent conference speaker and lecturer. Visiting lecturer for Diploma in Forensic Psychology and adviser to the Mannheim Institute on Criminology, LSE. Chair of Commission for Inquiry into violence in Penal Institutions for Children.
Prof. Membership: Howard League (Council Member), Charter 88 (Chair), Standing Committee for Youth Justice (Chair), British Council Law Advisory Committee.
Career: Called to the Bar 1972. Tenant at 2 Garden Court 1974-84 and 14 Tooks Court 1984-88. Took silk 1991.
Personal: Educated at Holyrood School, Glasgow. Honorary Doctor of Laws Strathclyde University (1992), Teesside University (1993), Keele University (1994), Lancaster University (1994) and Leeds Metropolitan University (1995). Received Women's Network award (for work on women and justice) 1992 and UK Woman of Europe award 1995. On Board of Hampstead Theatre, a Fellow of the Royal Society of Arts and Chair of London International Festival of Theatre. Born 12th May 1950. Lives in London.

Khayat QC, Georges M
10 King's Bench Walk (Ronald Thwaites QC), London (0171) 353 2501. Called 1967, took silk 1992.

Klevan QC, Rodney C.
18 St. John Street (Rodney C. Klevan QC), Manchester (0161) 834 9843.

Korner QC, Joanna
6 King's Bench Walk (Michael Worsley QC), London (0171) 583 0410.
Specialisation: Practice focuses on all aspects of general criminal law. Lectures to Victim Support Groups.
Prof. Membership: Criminal Bar Association, South-Eastern Circuit.
Career: Called to the Bar 1974 and became a tenant of current chambers in 1975. Appointed Recorder 1995. Took Silk 1993. Member Crown Court Rules Committee 1994 and Co-opted Member, General Council of the Bar 1994.

Kramer QC, Stephen
1 Hare Court (Michael Kalisher QC), London (0171) 353 5324.
Specialisation: Criminal law specialist.
Prof. Membership: Criminal Bar Association.
Career: Called to the Bar in 1970. Joined *1 Hare Court*, Temple in 1988 from *10 King's Bench Walk*. Assistant Recorder 1987-91. Recorder since 1991. Standing Counsel (Crime) to Customs & Excise 1989-1995. Appointed QC 1995.
Personal: Educated at Keble College, Oxford and the University of Nancy (France). Born 12th September 1947.

Laidlaw, Jonathan
1 Hare Court (Michael Kalisher QC), London (0171) 353 5324.

Lambert, Julian
Albion Chambers (J.C.T. Barton QC), Bristol (0117) 9272144.

Langdale QC, Timothy
Queen Elizabeth Building (Hollis Whiteman Chambers), London (0171) 583 5766.

Lawson QC, Edmund
See under Crime: Fraud.

Lawson QC, Michael
36 Essex Street (Michael Hill QC), London (0171) 413 0353. Called 1969, took silk 1991. Specialises in criminal law including general criminal and commercial fraud work. Born 3.2.1946.

Leonard, Anthony
6 King's Bench Walk (Michael Worsley QC), London (0171) 583 0410. Called 1978. Principal area of practice is crime, especially fraud. Born 21.4.1956.

Leslie QC, Stephen
1 Crown Office Row (Richard Ferguson QC), London (0171) 797 7111.

Linehan QC, Stephen
5 Fountain Court (Anthony Barker QC), Birmingham (0121) 606 0500. Called 1970, took silk 1993.

Lithman, Nigel
3 Hare Court (Michael Lewis QC), London (0171) 353 7561. Called 1976.

Lloyd-Eley, Andrew
1 Hare Court (Michael Kalisher QC), London (0171) 353 5324. Called 1979.

Long, A.P.
Peel Court Chambers (Michael Shorrock QC), Manchester (0161) 832 3791.

Loraine-Smith, Nicholas
2 Harcourt Buildings (Robert Harman QC), London (0171) 353 2112. Called 1977.

Lovell-Pank QC, Dorian
6 King's Bench Walk (Michael Worsley QC), London (0171) 583 0410.

Lucas, Noel
1 Middle Temple Lane (Colin Dines, Andrew Trollope QC), London (0171) 583 0659 (12 lines). Called 1979.

Macdonald QC, Ian
See under Immigration.

Macur, Julia
St. Ive's Chambers (Mr. Edward Coke), Birmingham (0121) 236 0863/0929. Called 1979.

Mansfield QC, Michael
14 Tooks Court (Michael Mansfield QC), London (0171) 405 8828. Called 1967, took silk 1989.

Marks, R.L.
Peel Court Chambers (Michael Shorrock QC), Manchester (0161) 832 3791.

Martin-Sperry, David
1 Crown Office Row (Richard Ferguson QC), London (0171) 797 7111. Called 1971. Principal area of practice is criminal defence work ranging from City fraud and money laundering to murder and drug offences. Born 21.6.1946.

Mathew QC, John
5 Paper Buildings (John Mathew QC), London (0171) 583 6117. Called 1949, took silk 1977.

Matthews, Richard
3 Hare Court (Michael Lewis QC), London (0171) 353 7561.

McCreath, Alistair
No.6 Fountain Court (Roger Smith QC),
Birmingham (0121) 233 3282. Called 1972.

Millett, Kenneth
1 Hare Court (Michael Kalisher QC),
London (0171) 353 5324.

Mitchell, Andrew
Furnival Chambers (Andrew Mitchell),
London (0171) 583 0434. Called 1976.

Moore, Miranda
5 Paper Buildings (John Mathew QC),
London (0171) 583 6117. Called 1983.

Morris QC, Antony
Peel Court Chambers (Michael
Shorrock QC), Manchester (0161) 832
3791.

Moss QC, Christopher
5 Essex Court (Jeremy Gompertz QC),
London (0171) 583 2825.

Munday, Andrew
3 Hare Court (Michael Lewis QC),
London (0171) 353 7561. Called 1973.

Mylne QC, Nigel
2 Harcourt Buildings (Robert Harman
QC), London (0171) 353 2112. Called
1963, took silk 1984.

Nathan, David
3 Temple Gardens (Jonathan Goldberg
QC), London (0171) 583 1155. Called
1972.

Nice QC, Geoffrey
Farrar's Building (Lord Williams of
Mostyn QC), London (0171) 583 9241.
Specialisation: Principal areas of practice
are crime and general common law. Other ar-
eas are personal injury, medical and
professional negligence, commercial and ad-
ministrative law.
Prof. Membership: South Eastern Circuit.
Career: Called to the Bar (Inner Temple) and
joined *Farrars Building* in 1971. Appointed
Recorder of the Crown Court in 1987. Took
Silk in 1990.

Nicholls QC, Clive
3 Raymond Buildings (Clive Nicholls
QC), London (0171) 831 3833. Called
1957, took silk 1982.

Nicholls QC, Colin
3 Raymond Buildings (Clive Nicholls
QC), London (0171) 831 3833. Called
1957, took silk 1981.

Nuttall, Andrew
Lincoln House Chambers (Mukhtar
Hussain QC), Manchester (0161) 832
5701.

Nutting QC, John
3 Raymond Buildings (Clive Nicholls
QC), London (0171) 831 3833. Called
1968, took silk 1995. Specialist criminal
prosecutor. First Senior Treasury Counsel
since 1993. Born 28.8.1942.

O'Conner QC, Patrick
1 Crown Office Row (Richard Ferguson
QC), London (0171) 797 7111. Called
1970, took silk 1993.

Owen, Tudor
See under Aviation.

Palmer QC, Anthony
3 Fountain Court (Colman Treacy QC),
Birmingham (0121) 236 5854. Called 1962,
took silk 1979.

Pascoe QC, Nigel
Pump Court Chambers (Guy Boney
QC), London (0171) 353 0711.
Specialisation: Serious crime, including
fraud. Also defamation and Courts Martial
work.
Prof. Membership: Leader of the Western
Circuit.
Career: Called in 1966, joining 3 Pump
Court. Recorder: 1979. Silk: 1988.
Personal: Presents 'The Trial of Penn &
Mead'.

Peart, Icah
2 Garden Court (I. Macdonald QC, O.
Davies), London (0171) 353 1633. Called
1978.

Penry-Davey QC, David
2-3 Gray's Inn Square (Anthony
Scrivener QC), London (0171) 242 4986.
Called 1965, took silk 1988.

Perry QC, John
3 Gray's Inn Square (Rock Tansey QC),
London (0171) 831 2311. Called 1975, took
silk 1989. Principal area of practice is criminal law.

Peters, Nigel
5 King's Bench Walk (David Cocks QC),
London (0171) 797 7600.
Specialisation: Main areas of practice are
criminal law and judicial review. Criminal
law: specialising in drug trafficking, serious
fraud, revenue offences and allied financial
investigations. Other main areas of practice
include obscene publications, licensing and
public entertainment law. Judicial review:
specialising in disputes in connection with
the criminal process, licensing and public entertainment law. This often involves aspects
of international and European law.
Career: Called to the Bar 1976. Standing
Counsel to HM Customs and Excise, Assistant Recorder.

Phelvin, Bernard
36 Essex Street (Michael Hill QC),
London (0171) 413 0353. Called 1971.

Pickup, James
Lincoln House Chambers (Mukhtar
Hussain QC), Manchester (0161) 832
5701.

Picton, Martin
Albion Chambers (J.C.T. Barton QC),
Bristol (0117) 9272144.

Pownall, Orlando
1 Crown Office Row (Richard Ferguson
QC), London (0171) 797 7111. Called
1975.

Qureshi, Shamim
Assize Court Chambers (Graeme Wood),
Bristol (0117) 9264587.

Radford QC, Nadine
3 Gray's Inn Square (Rock Tansey QC),
London (0171) 831 2311. Called 1974, took
silk 1995.

Rafferty QC, Anne J.
4 Brick Court (Anne Rafferty QC),
London (0171) 583 8455.

Raggatt QC, Timothy
1 King's Bench Walk (James Hunt QC),
London (0171) 353 8436. Called 1972, took
silk 1993.

Reilly, John
14 Tooks Court (Michael Mansfield QC),
London (0171) 405 8828. Called 1972.

Richardson, P. James
36 Essex Street (Michael Hill QC), London (0171) 413 0353. Called 1975. Specialist
area of practice is criminal law. Editor of
*Archbold, Criminal Pleading, Evidence and
Practice* (1982-).

Riordan QC, Stephen
25-27 Castle Street (Stephen Riordan
QC), Liverpool (0151) 236 5072. Called
1972, took silk 1992.

Riordan, Kevin
Iscoed Chambers (Wyn Richards),
Swansea (01792) 652988/9.

Roberts QC, Jeremy
9 Gough Square (Michael Brent QC),
London (0171) 353 5371. Called 1965, took
silk 1982. Principal area of practice is criminal work, with an emphasis on fraud cases.
Born 26.4.1941.

Robertson QC, Geoffrey
See under Public and Administrative Law.

Robinson QC, Vivian
Queen Elizabeth Building (Hollis
Whiteman Chambers), London (0171)
583 5766. Called 1967, took silk 1986.

Rouch, Peter Christopher
Iscoed Chambers (Wyn Richards),
Swansea (01792) 652988/9.

Ryder, John
5 King's Bench Walk (David Cocks QC),
London (0171) 797 7600. Called 1980.
Criminal defence in all serious crime, including commercial fraud; disciplinary tribunals.

Sallon QC, Christopher
Doughty Street Chambers (Geoffrey
Robertson QC), London (0171) 404 1313.
Called 1973, took silk 1994. Principal area of
practice is crimial defence. Born 2.10.1951.

Saunders QC, J.
4 Fountain Court (Richard Wakerley
QC), Birmingham (0121) 236 3476. Called
1972, took silk 1991.

Sayers QC, Michael
2 Harcourt Buildings (Robert Harman
QC), London (0171) 353 2112. Called
1970, took silk 1988.

Seabrook QC, Robert
1 Crown Office Row (Robert Seabrook
QC), London (0171) 797 7500. Called
1964, took silk 1983. Principal area of practice is professional (including medical)
negligence. Also serious crime and commercial fraud. Born 6.10.1941.

Shaw QC, Antony
See under Family Law.

Smith, Zoë
Hardwicke Building (Walter Aylen QC),
London (0171) 242 2523. Called 1970.

Smith QC, Roger
No.6 Fountain Court (Roger Smith QC),
Birmingham (0121) 233 3282. Called 1972,
took silk 1992.

Smith QC, Robert
Park Court Chambers (Gilbert Gray
QC, Brian Walsh QC), Leeds (0113)
2433277.

Smith, Shaun
No.1 High Pavement (John B. Milmo
QC), Nottingham (0115) 9418218.

Solley QC, Stephen
See under Crime: Fraud.

Spens QC, David
6 King's Bench Walk (Michael Worsley
QC), London (0171) 583 0410. Called
1973, took silk 1995.

Spokes QC, John
Pump Court Chambers (Guy Boney
QC), London (0171) 353 0711. Called
1955, took silk 1973.

Steer QC, David
The Corn Exchange (David Steer QC, I.
Goldrein), Liverpool (0151) 227
1081/5009. Called 1974, took silk 1993.

Stern QC, Linda
5 King's Bench Walk (David Cocks QC),
London (0171) 797 7600. Called 1971, took
silk 1991.

Sturman, James
3 Hare Court (Michael Lewis QC),
London (0171) 353 7561. Called 1982.

Sumner, David
Lincoln House Chambers (Mukhtar
Hussain QC), Manchester (0161) 832
5701.

Sweeney, Nigel
6 King's Bench Walk (Michael Worsley
QC), London (0171) 583 0410. Called
1976.

Tabor QC, James
Albion Chambers (J.C.T. Barton QC),
Bristol (0117) 9272144.

Tansey QC, Rock
3 Gray's Inn Square (Rock Tansey QC),
London (0171) 831 2311.
Specialisation: Specialist criminal silk involved in major cases including spying,
industrial espionage, terrorism, murder, riots,
drug trafficking, money laundering, fraud
and armed robbery. Also handles cases involving human rights and civil liberties.
Notable cases include the attempted murder
of the Israeli Ambassador; the Tottenham and
Lewisham riot cases; blackmail of Heinz Plc
by a police officer; the New Cross fire inquest; attempted murder of a barrister and
many terrorist cases. Represented the Directorate of Human Rights of the Council of
Europe at a conference in May 1994 in St Petersburg, Russia, the theme of which was
'Human Rights and the Rule of Law in the
Criminal Justice System of an Emerging Democracy'. Since 1990 has organised
Criminal Bar Association's Annual Lectures.
Recently organised two major conferences
on forensic science (June 1994) and the
Criminal Justice and Public Order Act
(March 1995).
Prof. Membership: Bar Council, Criminal
Bar Association (committee member).
Career: Called to the Bar 1966. Tenant at the
chambers of Eric Myers QC, 3 Hare Court
1967-74, and at the chambers of John Platts
Mills QC, Cloisters, Pump Court 1974-86.
Joined present chambers in 1986, before becoming its head in 1988. Took Silk 1990.
Appointed Recorder 1995.
Personal: Educated at Bristol University
(LL.B and Diploma in Social Studies).
School governor and ex-local councillor. Interests include politics, theatre, opera,
football, tennis and golf. Lives in London

Taylor, Gregg
9 Park Place (Philip Rees), Cardiff
(01222) 382731.

Tedd QC, Rex
7 Fountain Court (Rex Tedd QC),
Birmingham (0121) 236 8531. Called 1970,
took silk 1993.

Temple QC, Victor
6 King's Bench Walk (Michael Worsley
QC), London (0171) 583 0410. Called
1971, took silk 1993. Principal area of practice is crime (particularly fraud) and
extradition.
Born 23.2.1941.

Thomas QC, Roger
9 Park Place (Philip Rees), Cardiff
(01222) 382731.

Thornton QC, Peter
Doughty Street Chambers (Geoffrey
Robertson QC), London (0171) 404 1313.
Specialisation: Principal area of practice is
criminal defence work including commercial fraud; appellate work, notably Privy
Council appeals (Caribbean, Mauritius,
Hong Kong) often in capital cases; and all
forms of serious crime including murder, terrorism, Official Secrets Act, corruption and
drugs cases. Other main area of work is civil
rights cases including actions against the police or government, suspects' and prisoners'
rights and the rights of prisoners of war, of
children, complainants and solicitors' representatives in police stations. Recent reported
cases include Walker v. R [1994] (Privy
Council jurisdiction: appeal against death
sentence); R v Basford and Lawless (witness
too ill to continue); R v. Aroyewumi [1994]
(sentencing in Class A drugs cases); Freemantle v. R [1994] (the proviso in
identification cases) and Re W [1994] (rights
of children). Author of 'Public Order Law'
(Blackstone Press 1987) and 'Decade of Decline:Civil Liberties in the Thatcher Years'
(Liberty 1989). Editor of the Penguin Civil
Liberty Guide (1989) and currently contributing editor to Archbold. Regular
broadcaster on legal and civil liberty topics.
Teaches advocacy and criminal evidence to
solicitors and barristers. Has lectured and
chaired seminars, on trial by jury, PACE, police powers, the CPS, evidence, white collar
crime, emergency powers, miscarriages of
justice, and the right of silence.
Prof. Membership: Midland and Oxford Circuit, Criminal Bar Association,
Administrative Law Bar Association, Chairman of the Civil Liberties Trust.
Career: Called to the Bar 1969. Tenant at *1
King's Bench Walk* 1971-78 and at *1 Dr.
Johnson's Buildings* 1978-90. Founder member of *Doughty Street Chambers* in 1990 and
currently deputy head of chambers. Took
Silk 1992. Appointed Assistant Recorder
1994.

Thwaites QC, Ronald
10 King's Bench Walk (Ronald Thwaites QC), London (0171) 353 2501. Called 1970, took silk 1987. Principal areas of practice are general criminal law and commercial fraud. Born 21.1.1946.

Treacy QC, Colman
3 Fountain Court (Colman Treacy QC), Birmingham (0121) 236 5854. Called 1971, took silk 1990.

Trollope QC, Andrew
1 Middle Temple Lane (Colin Dines, Andrew Trollope QC), London (0171) 583 0659 (12 lines). Called 1971, took silk 1991.

Turner QC, David
Exchange Chambers (William Waldron QC), Liverpool (0151) 236 7747. Called 1971, took silk 1991.

Upward, Patrick Charles
9 Gough Square (Michael Brent QC), London (0171) 353 5371. Called 1972.

Vine, James
Hardwicke Building (Walter Aylen QC), London (0171) 242 2523. Called 1977.

Wait, John
1 Fountain Court (Anthony Hughes QC), Birmingham (0121) 236 5721. Called 1972.

Wakerley QC, R.M.
4 Fountain Court (Richard Wakerley QC), Birmingham (0121) 236 3476. Called 1965, took silk 1982.

Wass, Sasha
1 Crown Office Row (Richard Ferguson QC), London (0171) 797 7111. Called 1981.

Waters, David
1 Hare Court (Michael Kalisher QC), London (0171) 353 5324. Called 1973.

Weekes, Anesta
Cloisters (David Turner-Samuels QC), London (0171) 583 0303. Called 1981.

Whitehouse QC, David
3 Raymond Buildings (Clive Nicholls QC), London (0171) 831 3833. Called 1969, took silk 1990. Principal area of practice is advocacy, especially criminal, disciplinary, regulatory and licensing work.

Whittam, Richard
Furnival Chambers (Andrew Mitchell), London (0171) 583 0434.

Williams, Christopher M.
32 Park Place (Christopher Williams), Cardiff (01222) 397364. Called 1972.

Winter, Ian
Queen Elizabeth Building (Hollis Whiteman Chambers), London (0171) 583 5766.

Specialisation: Specialist in criminal law with a particular emphasis on fraud and white collar crime. Acted for the defence in the Lady Aberdour and Swindon Town FC frauds. Practice also covers police powers and civil liberties law. Even split between prosecution and defence work.

Prof. Membership: Bar Council Legal Services Committee.

Career: Called to the Bar in 1988. Joined present chambers in 1990.

Prof. Membership: Educated at Bristol University 1984-87. Leisure pursuits include international rally driving and playing the saxophone and piano. Born 25th March 1966. Lives in Chelsea.

Wolkind, Michael
10 King's Bench Walk (Ronald Thwaites QC), London (0171) 353 2501. Called 1976.

Wright, Peter
Lincoln House Chambers (Mukhtar Hussain QC), Manchester (0161) 832 5701.

DEFAMATION

MAINTAINING their positions as the leading defamation sets, **1 Brick Court** and **5-6 Raymond Buildings** maintain their position as the leading defamation sets, covering the whole range of defamation work including commercial and trade libel and technical pleading and drafting.

(most notably, in the Frank Warren/Terry Marsh libel action), *Adrienne Page* and *Heather Rogers* (who emerges as the highest ranked junior defamation specialist in London). *Sophia Roper* is chambers' rising star.

LEADING SETS

1 BRICK COURT	5-6 RAYMOND BUILDINGS

In terms of the number of practitioners recommended, **1 Brick Court** has a slight edge over **5-6 Raymond Buildings** with *Andrew Caldecott QC* emerging as the most highly recommended silk in London. *Tom Shields QC* and *David Eady QC* (formerly a member of Neill LJ's Committee on Defamation Law and Practice) are the sets' other outstanding practitioners, whilst *Richard Hartley QC*, *Richard Rampton QC* and *Geoffrey Shaw QC* are also held in high regard. At the junior end, *Manuel Barca*, *Patrick Moloney*, *Victoria Sharpe* and *Stephen Suttle* enjoy excellent reputations in the field. *Jane Phillips*, *Benjamin Hinchcliff* and *Rupert Elliott* have been described as rising stars.

HIGHLY REGARDED

DOUGHTY STREET CHAMBERS

Charles Gray QC and *Desmond Browne QC* are **5-6 Raymond Buildings**' leading lights, both having represented national newspapers, television stations and numerous individuals from the worlds of politics and entertainment. *Charles Gray QC* represented Upjohn in a four month case ('Upjohn Co v BBC & ors') relating to the drug Halcion; *Desmond Browne QC* has acted in 'Oyston v Times Newspapers', 'Cooper v Roger Cook & Central TV', 'Connery v News Group' and 'Koo Stark v Mirror Group Newspapers'. *James Price QC* who recently took silk is also highly regarded. Highly recommended juniors include *Mark Warby*

LEADING SILKS

Caldecott, Andrew	*1 Brick Court*
Carman, George	*New Court Chambers*
Lord Williams of Mostyn,	*Farrar's Building*

Beloff, Michael	*4-5 Gray's Inn Square*
Browne, Desmond	*5-6 Raymond Buildings*
Eady, David	*1 Brick Court*
Gray, Charles	*5-6 Raymond Buildings*
Shields, Thomas	*1 Brick Court*

Hartley, Richard	*1 Brick Court*
Kentridge, Sydney	*Brick Court Chambers*
Milmo, Patrick	*5-6 Raymond Buildings*
Nathan, Stephen	*2 Hare Court*
Nicol, Andrew	*Doughty Street Chambers*
Price, James	*5-6 Raymond Buildings*
Rampton, Richard	*1 Brick Court*
Robertson, Geoffrey	*Doughty Street Chambers*
Shaw, Geoffrey	*1 Brick Court*

Doughty Street Chambers contains a small, but growing number of defamation practitioners, most notably *Geoffrey Robertson QC*, *Andrew Nicol* QC and *Michael Grieve*.

Other individual practitioners who are frequently instructed for their formidable advocacy skills include *George Carman QC* of **New Court Chambers**, *Michael Beloff QC* of **4-5 Gray's Inn Square** and *Lord Williams of Mostyn QC* at **Farrar's Building.**

LEADING JUNIORS

Barca, Manuel *1 Brick Court*	Moloney, Patrick *1 Brick Court*	Rogers, Heather *5-6 Raymond Buildings*
Sharp, Victoria *1 Brick Court*		
Crystal, Jonathan *Cloisters*	Elliott, Rupert *1 Brick Court*	Grieve, Michael *Doughty Street Chambers*
Lewis, Adam *2 Hare Court*	Maidment, Kieran *Doughty Street Chambers*	Page, Adrienne *5-6 Raymond Buildings*
Phillips, Jane *1 Brick Court*	Suttle, Stephen *1 Brick Court*	Warby, Mark *5-6 Raymond Buildings*

UP AND COMING

Hinchliff, Benjamin *1 Brick Court*	Marzec, Alexandra *5-6 Raymond Buildings*	Roper, Sophia *5-6 Raymond Buildings*

Barca, Manuel
1 Brick Court (Richard Hartley QC),
London (0171) 353 8845. Called 1986.

Beloff QC, Michael
See under Public and Administrative Law.

Browne QC, Desmond
5-6 Raymond Buildings (Patrick Milmo
QC), London (0171) 242 2902.

Specialisation: Defamation and media law.
Recent reported libel cases include Ex p
Coventry Newspapers, CA [1993]; Derbyshire CC v. Times Newspapers HL [1993];
Telnikoff v. Matusevitch HL [1992]; Keays v.
Murdoch Magazines CA [1991]; Acted
throughout the Spycatcher litigation in London and Strasbourg, and (as a junior) for
Private Eye, including the Goldsmith litigation. Other main area of practice is
environmental law. Acted for successful defendants in Graham v. Rechem (a 15-month
toxic nuisance action).

Prof. Membership: Western Circuit.

Career: Called to the Bar 1969. Legal correspondent for 'British Medical Journal'
1970-79. Took silk 1990. Appointed Recorder 1994.

Personal: Educated at Eton and New College, Oxford (Scholar) 1965-68. Born 5th
April 1947. Leisure pursuits include Aus-
traliana, Venice, and the Sussex Downs.

Caldecott QC, Andrew
1 Brick Court (Richard Hartley QC),
London (0171) 353 8845.

Specialisation: Defamation, confidence,
contempt of court and media related law generally.

Career: Called to the Bar 1975.

Personal: Educated Eton College and New
College, Oxford. Lives in London.

Carman QC, George
New Court Chambers (George Carman
QC), London (0171) 583 6166.

Specialisation: Has appeared in major trials
in defamation, contract and commercial and
copyright cases as well as certain areas of the
criminal law in recent years. Appeared in trials in Malaysia, Hong Kong, Singapore and
Bermuda and advisory work in the United
States.

Career: Called to the Bar 1953. QC 1971.
Bencher *Lincoln's Inn* 1978.

Personal: Educated at Balliol College, Oxford; 1st Class Honours Law.

Crystal, Jonathan
Cloisters (David Turner-Samuels QC),
London (0171) 583 0303.

Specialisation: Specialist in defamation law.
Acts for both plaintiffs and publishers. Practice also covers business law and sports law.

Of the many trials conducted some well-
known examples include, Richard
Branson/Virgin Atlantic v. British Airways
(the 'dirty-tricks' libel action); Sarfraz
Nawaz v. Alan Lamb (the cricket ball tampering libel); Smith v. Houston (which resulted
in the largest damages award for a slander action); Wheeler v. Leicester City Council
(freedom of speech involving a rugby club);
Jason Donovan v. The Face (libel brought by
the well-known entertainer); Chohan v. Oxford University Press (libel of Sixth leader in
book, 1p damages). Also has wide experience
in drafting contracts and rules, such as the
first rules for the Premier League and standard IT contracts for local authorities.

Prof. Membership: COMBAR; British Association for Sport and Law.

Career: Called to the Bar 1972. Tenant at 2
Harcourt Buildings 1973-1992. Joined pre-
sent Chambers 1992. Legal reader,
Associated Newspapers until 1985.

Personal: Educated at Leeds Grammar
School and at Queen Mary College, University of London 1968-1971. Director,
Tottenham Hotspur FC 1991-1993. Leisure
pursuits include sport and travel. Born 20th
December 1949. Married with young children. Lives in London.

Eady QC, David
1 Brick Court (Richard Hartley QC),
London (0171) 353 8845.

Specialisation: Principal area of practice encompasses media law, including defamation
and contempt. Co-author of 'The Law of
Contempt' (Sweet and Maxwell). Member of
the Calcutt Committee on Privacy (1989-90)
and of Neill L.J.'s Committee on Defamation
Law and Practice 1990-91.

Prof. Membership: South Eastern Circuit,
COMBAR.

Career: Called to the Bar 1966 and joined
current chambers 1967. Took silk 1983. Appointed Recorder 1986. Bencher (Middle
Temple) 1991.

Personal: Educated at Trinity College, Cambridge 1961-65 (MA, LL.B). Born 24th
March 1943.

Elliott, Rupert
1 Brick Court (Richard Hartley QC),
London (0171) 353 8845. Called 1988.

Gray QC, Charles
5-6 Raymond Buildings (Patrick Milmo
QC), London (0171) 242 2902. Called
1966, took silk 1984. Principal area of practice is media and defamation law including
copyright, restraint of trade and confidence.
Born 6.7.1942.

Grieve, Michael
Doughty Street Chambers (Geoffrey
Robertson QC), London (0171) 404 1313.
Called 1975.

Hartley QC, Richard
1 Brick Court (Richard Hartley QC),
London (0171) 353 8845. Called 1956, took
silk 1976.

Hinchliff, Benjamin
1 Brick Court (Richard Hartley QC),
London (0171) 353 8845. Called 1992.

Kentridge QC, Sydney
See under Commercial Law.

Lewis, Adam
2 Hare Court (C.W.G. Ross-Munro QC),
London (0171) 583 1770.

Specialisation: Domestic and European
Community aspects of commercial, competition and public law. Defamation and media
law (libel reader for *The Observer*).

Career: Call 1985. Professional experience
with *Wilmer Cutler & Pickering* in Washington D.C. and London and *McCutcheon Doyle
Brown & Enersen* in San Francisco between
1985-87, and in the Cabinet of Sir Leon Brittan, European Commisioner responsible for
competition and financial institutions, in
Brussels in 1991-1992.

Personal: Fluent in French and a working
knowledge of German.

Maidment, Kieran
Doughty Street Chambers (Geoffrey
Robertson QC), London (0171) 404 1313.

Specialisation: Specialist in criminal law.
Civil practice covers defamation, including
libel advice to various diverse publications
and actions against the police.

Career: Called to the Bar 1989.

Personal: Education: LL.B (LSE), MA
(KCL). Born 1963.

Marzec, Alexandra
5-6 Raymond Buildings (Patrick Milmo
QC), London (0171) 242 2902. Called 1990.

Milmo QC, Patrick
5-6 Raymond Buildings (Patrick Milmo
QC), London (0171) 242 2902.

Moloney, Patrick
1 Brick Court (Richard Hartley QC),
London (0171) 353 8845. Called 1976. Principal area of practice is defamation and
media law. Born 2.7.1953.

Nathan QC, Stephen
2 Hare Court (C.W.G. Ross-Munro QC),
London (0171) 583 1770.

Specialisation: Principal area of practice is
defamation (both for plaintiffs and defendants) and general commercial law covering
contract and negligence claims. Former libel
reader for *The Observer*. Other main areas of
practice are financial services, construction
law and gaming and lotteries.

Prof. Membership: COMBAR, London Common Law and Commercial Bar Association (Committee Member), Bar European Group.

Career: Called to the Bar 1969 and joined current chambers 1970. Appointed Assistant Recorder 1989. Took Silk 1993.

Personal: Educated at Cranleigh School, Surrey and New College, Oxford (MA).

Nicol QC, Andrew
See under Immigration.

Page, Adrienne
5-6 Raymond Buildings (Patrick Milmo QC), London (0171) 242 2902. Called 1974.

Phillips, Jane
1 Brick Court (Richard Hartley QC), London (0171) 353 8845. Called 1989.

Price QC, James
5-6 Raymond Buildings (Patrick Milmo QC), London (0171) 242 2902. Called 1974, took silk 1995.

Rampton QC, Richard
1 Brick Court (Richard Hartley QC), London (0171) 353 8845. Called 1965, took silk 1987.

Robertson QC, Geoffrey
See under Public and Administrative Law.

Rogers, Heather
5-6 Raymond Buildings (Patrick Milmo QC), London (0171) 242 2902. Called 1983.

Roper, Sophia
5-6 Raymond Buildings (Patrick Milmo QC), London (0171) 242 2902. Called 1990.

Sharp, Victoria
1 Brick Court (Richard Hartley QC), London (0171) 353 8845. Called 1979.

Shaw QC, Geoffrey
1 Brick Court (Richard Hartley QC), London (0171) 353 8845.

Shields QC, Thomas
1 Brick Court (Richard Hartley QC), London (0171) 353 8845. Called 1973, took silk 1993.

Specialisation: Defamation, confidence, contempt of court and media related law generally.

Career: Called to the Bar 1973.

Suttle, Stephen
1 Brick Court (Richard Hartley QC), London (0171) 353 8845. Called 1980.

Warby, Mark
5-6 Raymond Buildings (Patrick Milmo QC), London (0171) 242 2902.

Specialisation: Principal area of practice is defamation work covering libel, slander and malicious falsehood. Also handles breach of confidence, literary and artistic copyright, passing off, and sale and supply of goods and serices cases. Acted in Brent Walker v. Time Out [1991] (libel) and Frank Warren v. Terry Marsh [1992] (libel). Newspaper Night Lawyer 1981-86. Legal Correspondent 'Small Business Outlook' 1984-85.

Prof. Membership: Gray's Inn.

Career: Called to the Bar 1981 and joined current chambers 1983.

Personal: Educated at Bristol Grammar School 1969-76 and St. John's College, Oxford 1977-80 (MA). Born 10th October 1958. Lives in Camberwell, London.

Williams of Mostyn QC, Lord
Farrar's Building (Lord Williams of Mostyn QC), London (0171) 583 9241. Called 1965, took silk 1978. Specialist in defamation and media law. Born 5.2.1941.

INDEXES TO PROFILES

Solicitors' Profiles The index to leading solicitors profiled in the Specialist Lists starts on page 495. This index also includes heads of company legal departments.

Barristers' Profiles Profiles of leading barristers are indexed within the main *Barristers' Index* located at the end of the directory. Names of profiled barristers are set in bold type.

ECCLESIASTICAL LAW

Q UESTIONS of 'faculty jurisdiction', ie applications for the grant of a faculty allowing alterations to be made

2 HARCOURT BUILDINGS

to ecclesiastical buildings, and disciplinary issues regarding the clergy, are heard in the Consistory Courts. Issues relating to ritual and theology are dealt with by the Court of Ecclesiastical Causes Reserved.

LEADING SILKS

Cameron, Sheila *2 Harcourt Buildings*	
Boydell, Peter *2 Harcourt Buildings*	
Clark, Christopher *Pump Court Chambers*	
George, Charles *2 Harcourt Buildings*	
Gray, Robert *2 Mitre Court Buildings*	

The leading chambers are **2 Harcourt Buildings** whose tenants include the highly respected specialists *Sheila Cameron QC* who is the Vicar General of the Province of Canterbury and Chancellor of the Diocese of London and Chelmsford, and *Peter Boydell QC* who is Chancellor of the Diocese of Truro, Oxford and Worcester. *Charles George QC* has advised and represented petitioners seeking faculties under the

ecclesiastical jurisdiction of the Church of England, while among the juniors in chambers *Philip Petchey* is highly regarded for his work in the field.

Nigel Seed at **3 Paper Buildings**, who is Chancellor of the Diocese of Leicester, has been highly recommended. At **Pump Court Chambers** *Christopher Clark QC* is Chancellor of the Diocese of Winchester while *Mark Hill* is the Vice-Chancellor, and is the author of 'Hill on Ecclesiastical law'. *Timothy Briden* at **1 Temple Gardens** is highly regarded. He is a member of the Ecclesiastical Law Society, and editor of 'Macmorran's Handbook for Churchwardens and Parochial Church Councillors' and 'Moore's Introduction to English Canon Law'. *Michael Douglas* at **4 Pump Court** is well known. *Robert Gray QC* at **2 Mitre Court Buildings** is Chancellor of the Diocese of Southwark and *June Rodgers* at **2 Harcourt Buildings** is Chancellor of the Diocese of Gloucester.

LEADING JUNIORS

Seed, Nigel *3 Paper Buildings*	
Briden, Timothy J. *1 Temple Gardens*	
Douglas, Michael *4 Pump Court*	
Hill, Mark *Pump Court Chambers*	
Petchey, Philip *2 Harcourt Buildings*	
Rodgers, June *2 Harcourt Buildings*	
Wakefield, Robert *17 Old Buildings*	

LEADERS IN ECCLESIASTICAL LAW

Boydell QC, Peter
2 Harcourt Buildings (Peter Boydell QC), London (0171) 353 8415. Called 1948, took silk 1965.

Briden, Timothy J.
1 Temple Gardens (Hugh Carlisle QC), London (0171) 583 1315.
Specialisation: Principal area of practice is ecclesiastical law. Editor, 'Macmorran's Handbook for Churchwardens and Parochial Church Councillors' and 'Moore's Introduction to English Canon Law'. Also handles personal injury cases.
Prof. Membership: Inner Temple, Ecclesiastical Law Society.
Career: Called to the Bar 1976 and joined *1 Temple Gardens* 1977. Appointed Chancellor of the Diocese of Bath and Wells 1993.
Personal: Educated at Ipswich School 1958-70 and Downing College Cambridge (BA

1974; LL.B 1975; MA 1978). Born 29th October 1951. Lives in South London.

Cameron QC, Sheila
See under Parliamentary.

Clark QC, Christopher
Pump Court Chambers (Guy Boney QC), London (0171) 353 0711. Called 1969, took silk 1989.

Douglas, Michael
4 Pump Court (Bruce Mauleverer QC), London (0171) 353 2656. Called 1974.

George QC, Charles
See under Parliamentary.

Gray QC, Robert
2 Mitre Court Buildings (Michael FitzGerald QC), London (0171) 583 1380. Called 1969, took silk 1983.

Hill, Mark
Pump Court Chambers (Guy Boney QC), London (0171) 353 0711. Called 1987. Principal area of practice is ecclesiastical law. Other main areas are personal injury and professional negligence. Born 7.8.1965.

Petchey, Philip
See under Parliamentary.

Rodgers, June
2 Harcourt Buildings (Patrick Eccles), London (0171) 353 6961. Called 1971.

Seed, Nigel
3 Paper Buildings (Michael Parroy QC), London (0171) 583 8055. Called 1978.

Wakefield, Robert
See under Property Litigation.

EMPLOYMENT

A S THE public become more aware of their employment rights the demand for barristers in this field increases. Employment law covers a wide spectrum ranging from issues of discrimination, equal opportunities, transfer of

undertakings, trade union disputes and health and safety at work, to more traditional areas like redundancy and unfair dismissal. It is an area which is increasingly influenced by European law, particularly the Convention on Human Rights, with many employment cases going to the European Commission or to the European Court of Justice in Strasbourg.

The leading set in this field is **11 King's Bench Walk** which has no fewer than seven silks specialising in this area, including *Patrick Elias QC* and *Eldred Tabachnik QC*, widely regarded as the two current leading practitioners in employment law. *Elizabeth Slade QC* is Chairman of the Employment Law Bar Association and was the original author of 'Tolley's Employment Law Handbook'. *Alan Wilkie QC* has a wealth of experience, is on the Editorial

Old Square Chambers is a set traditionally associated with trade union and employee representation. *John Hendy QC*, *John Hand QC* and *Jeremy Mc Mullen QC* are all highly recommended, and *Lord Wedderburn QC* and *Prof. Bob Hepple* are well known academics. Of the juniors mention should be made of *Thomas Linden* and of *Tess Gill* who specialises in sex and race discrimination claims and has published work on equality law.

2 Hare Court is primarily a commercial/public law set but several members have an excellent reputation in employment law. *Lord Lester QC* and *David Pannick QC* are well known for appearing in high profile cases. *David Pannick QC* has particular experience of taking cases to the European Court of Justice in Luxembourg both for and against the U.K. including Dekker on the rights of pregnant workers, Enderby on indirect sex discrimination and Neath and Ardel on pension benefits and equality. He recently acted in the Ministry of Defence pregnant servicewomen litigation.

Paul Goulding, *Monica Carrs-Frisk*, and *Gerard Clarke* are very well regarded juniors. *Dinah Rose* has recently been involved in both the MoD litigation and the 'school dinner-ladies' Equal Pay Act case in the House of Lords. *Beverley Lang* is a part time Industrial Tribunal Chairman and acted for Alison Halford in her well publicised sex discrimination action against the Merseyside Police.

Littleton Chambers (formerly 2 Crown Office Row) also have several high profile practitioners led by *Michael Burton QC*. Amongst the juniors *John Bowers* is very experienced in all aspects of employment law. He acted in the marathon case of 'Payne v Port of London Authority' (198 days) and in the recent litigation surrounding the dismissal

Board of 'Tolley's Journal of Employment Law' and is a regular conference speaker.

Christopher Jeans is probably the outstanding junior but other members are also highly regarded including *John Cavanagh*, *Timothy Pitt-Payne*, *Adrian Lynch*, and *Jonathan Swift*. *Peter Wallington* is the Editor of 'Butterworths Employment Law Handbook'. *Sean Jones*, *Paul Nicholls* and *Peter Oldham* are seen as up and coming juniors.

of homosexuals in the armed forces. He is the author of several published works on the subject, including 'Bowers on Employment Law'. *Andrew Clarke* is recommended for his expertise, as is *Antony Sendall* who was involved in the 'Terry Venables v Alan Sugar/Spurs' High Court Action. *Selwyn Bloch* is the co-author of 'Employment Covenants and Confidential Information'.

LEADING JUNIORS– LONDON

Jeans, Christopher James Marwood   *11 King's Bench Walk*

Bean, David *Devereux Chambers*	**Bowers,** John *Littleton Chambers*	**Carss-Frisk,** Monica *2 Hare Court*
Cavanagh, John Patrick *11 King's Bench Walk*	**Clarke,** Andrew *Littleton Chambers*	**Gill,** Tess *Old Square Chambers*
Goulding, Paul *2 Hare Court*	**Hillier,** Andrew *5 Bell Yard*	**Hogarth,** Andrew *12 King's Bench Walk*
Linden, Thomas *Old Square Chambers*	**Pitt-Payne,** Timothy Sheridan *11 King's Bench Walk*	**Rose,** Dinah *2 Hare Court*
Thompson, Andrew *Francis Taylor Building*	**Wallington,** Peter *11 King's Bench Walk*	

Bear, Charles *11 King's Bench Walk*	**Beggs,** John *3 Serjeants' Inn*	**Bloch,** Selwyn *Littleton Chambers*
Bothroyd, Shirley *Littleton Chambers*	**Carr,** Bruce *Devereux Chambers*	**Clark,** Peter *Devereux Chambers*
Clarke, Gerard *2 Hare Court*	**Cottle,** Anthony *3 Serjeants' Inn*	**Downing,** Ruth *Devereux Chambers*
Duggan, Michael *Littleton Chambers*	**Eady,** Jennifer *Old Square Chambers*	**Gay,** Vivienne *Cloisters*
Greening, Richard *Devereux Chambers*	**Griffith-Jones,** David *Devereux Chambers*	**Hochhauser,** Andrew *Essex Court Chambers*
Kerr, Tim *4-5 Gray's Inn Square*	**Lang,** Beverley *2 Hare Court*	**Lemon,** Roy *Devereux Chambers*
Lynch, Adrian C. E. *11 King's Bench Walk*	**McNeill,** Jane *Farrar's Building*	**Meade,** Philip *Old Square Chambers*
Mehigan, Simon *5 Paper Buildings*	**Millar,** Gavin *Doughty Street Chambers*	**Neaman,** Sam *4 Paper Buildings*
O'Rourke, Mary *3 Serjeants' Inn*	**Pearl,** David A. *4 King's Bench Walk*	**Rose,** Paul *Old Square Chambers*
Sendall, Antony *Littleton Chambers*	**Simler,** Ingrid *Devereux Chambers*	**Sutton,** Mark *Queen Elizabeth Building*
Swift, Jonathan Mark *11 King's Bench Walk*	**Westgate,** Martin *Doughty Street Chambers*	

UP AND COMING

Jones, Seán *11 King's Bench Walk*	**Kibling,** Thomas *Cloisters*	**Nicholls,** Paul *11 King's Bench Walk*
Oldham, Peter *11 King's Bench Walk*		

Devereux Chambers has numerous experienced junior-swith *David Bean* and *David Griffith-Jones* being particularly highly regarded.

Cloisters is also traditionally associated with employee representation. *Laura Cox QC* acted recently in the MoD pregnancy dismissal cases and in the Webb pregnancy discrimination case before the European Court of Justice. *Brian Langstaff QC* appeared in the recent landmark 'school dinner-ladies' case ('Ratcliffe v North Yorkshire County Council'). *Vivienne Gay* is well known for her expertise in discrimination and equal opportunities work.

Other notable practitioners include *Michael Beloff QC, Cherie Booth QC, W. Robert Griffiths QC* (**4-5 Gray's Inn Square**), *Michael Brindle QC, Charles Falconer QC, Nicholas Underhill QC* (**Fountain Court**) and *Christopher Carr QC* (**1 Essex Court**).

OUTSIDE LONDON

In Manchester, **9 St John Street** is a very strong set in this area. *John Hand QC* has an excellent reputation in the field. *Paul Gilroy* and *Jonathan Parkin* are highly regarded juniors.

LEADING SILKS– REGIONS

Hand, John *9 St. John Street, Manchester*

Paul Cape at **New Court Chambers** in Newcastle has been recommended to us. In Birmingham, *Kevin O'Donovan* (**5 Fountain Court**) is highly regarded. *Philip Marshall* at **Iscoed Chambers** in Swansea is well-known in this field.

LEADING JUNIORS– REGIONS

Benson, John *14 Castle St, Liverpool*
Cotter, Barry *Old Square Chambers, Bristol*
Gilroy, Paul *9 St. John Street, Manchester*
Horlock, Timothy *9 St. John Street, Manchester*
Jones, Jennifer *5 Fountain Court, Birmingham*
Marshall, Philip Derek *Iscoed Chambers, Swansea*
O'Donovan, Kevin *5 Fountain Court, Birmingham*
Parkin, Jonathan *9 St. John Street, Manchester*
Stobart, John *King Charles House, Nottingham*

UP AND COMING

Cape, Paul *New Court Chambers, Newcastle*

LEADERS IN EMPLOYMENT

Allen QC, Robin
Cloisters (David Turner-Samuels QC), London (0171) 583 0303. Called 1974, took silk 1995. Specialises in discrimination, employment and public law. Born 18.2.1951.

Bean, David
Devereux Chambers (Peter Weitzman QC), London (0171) 353 7534. Called 1976. Principal area of practice is employment and trade union law. Born 25.3.1954.

Bear, Charles
11 King's Bench Walk (Lord Irvine of Lairg QC), London (0171) 583 0610. Called 1986. Main areas of practice are employment and commercial law. Also covers judicial review and public law. Born 26.4.1963.

Beggs, John
3 Serjeants' Inn (Adrian Whitfield QC), London (0171) 353 5537 Mbl (0385) 736844.
Specialisation: Principal areas of practice are medical negligence, employment, civil actions involving the police and solicitors' negligence. Junior in Salih v. Enfield HA and junior in the first successful military PTSD claim against the MOD arising out of the Falklands War. In employment field has substantial experience of industrial disputes, unfair dismissal and particularly race discrimination claims. In police actions has considerable jury trial experience. In Rastin v. British Steel & others.
Prof. Membership: PNBA.
Career: Called to the Bar 1989. Joined *3 Serjeant's Inn* in 1989.
Personal: Educated at Chislehurst and Sidcup Grammar School, and Brunel University.

Beloff QC, Michael
See under Public and Administrative Law.

Benson, John
14 Castle St (Adrian Smith), Liverpool (0151) 236 4421. Called 1978.

Bloch, Selwyn
Littleton Chambers (Michael Burton QC), London (0171) 797 8600. Called 1982. Practice covers business law and employment matters.

Bothroyd, Shirley
Littleton Chambers (Michael Burton QC), London (0171) 797 8600. Called 1982. Principal areas of practice are commercial law and interlocutory and injunctive relief.

Bowers, John
Littleton Chambers (Michael Burton QC), London (0171) 797 8600. Called 1979. Principal area of practice is employ-

ment law (individual and collective) and discrimination. Born 2.1.1956.

Brindle QC, Michael
See under Banking.

Burke QC, Jeffrey
Devereux Chambers (Peter Weitzman QC), London (0171) 353 7534. Called 1964, took silk 1984. Principal areas of practice are Personal Injuries, Professional Negligence and Employment law. Born 15.12.1941.

Burton QC, Michael
See under Commercial Law.

Booth QC, Cherie
See under Public and Administrative Law.

Cape, Paul
New Court Chambers (David Robson QC), Newcastle upon Tyne (0191) 232 1980.

Carr QC, Christopher
See under Commercial Law.

Carr, Bruce
Devereux Chambers (Peter Weitzman QC), London (0171) 353 7534. Called 1986. Specialist in employment law including wrongful and unfair dismissal, trade disputes and large scale redundancy. Regularly appears before the Employment Appeals Tribunal. Born 21.6.1960.

Carss-Frisk, Monica
2 Hare Court (C.W.G. Ross-Munro QC), London (0171) 583 1770.
Specialisation: Employment law, with a particular emphasis on discrimination in both domestic and EU law, and judicial review, including the European Convention on Human Rights (in the commercial context). Also handles general commercial contract disputes and commercial fraud. Acted in R. v. Secretary of State for Employment, ex p. Equal Opportunities Commission (1992-94, case reached House of Lords concerning failure of Secretary of State to amend the Employment Protection (Consolidation) Act 1978 to comply with EU law).
Prof. Membership: Employment Lawyers Association, Administrative Law Bar Association, COMBAR.
Career: Called to the Bar 1985 and joined current chambers in 1986.
Personal: Educated at London University (LL.B, 1983) and Oxford University (BCL, 1984). Fluent in Finnish and Swedish. Member of Board of Interrights.

Cavanagh, John Patrick
11 King's Bench Walk (Lord Irvine of Lairg QC), London (0171) 583 0610. Called 1985. Main areas of practice are em-

ployment law, local government and public law. Born 17.6.1960.

Clark, Peter
Devereux Chambers (Peter Weitzman QC), London (0171) 353 7534. Called 1970.

Clarke, Andrew
Littleton Chambers (Michael Burton QC), London (0171) 797 8600.
Specialisation: Experienced employment lawyer, having appeared in this area before all relevant courts and tribunals. Particular specialism in disputes relating to restrictive covenants and confidential information. Also handles commercial and company law matters, both relating to employment (including directors' duties) and generally. Acted for PLA in docks dispute, in relation to industrial action and the two year Industrial Tribunal. Appeared in numerous important cases on individual employment rights and restrictive covenants. Clients include major UK companies, solicitors' firms and senior employees. Author of several articles on employment law and evidence.
Prof. Membership: Employment Law Bar Association; COMBAR (Committee Member).
Career: Called to the Bar 1980 and joined *Littleton Chambers* in 1981.
Personal: Educated at Crewe County Grammar School, King's College London 1974-77 (LL.B) and Lincoln College, Oxford 1977-79 (BCL). Leisure pursuits include playing and watching cricket and football, and collecting modern prints and porcelain. Lives in Cheshunt. Born 23rd August 1956.

Clarke, Gerard
2 Hare Court (C.W.G. Ross-Munro QC), London (0171) 583 1770.
Specialisation: General commercial law, with a heavy emphasis on employment work, including unfair dismissal, redundancy and anti-discrimination law, injunctive proceedings concerning confidential information, restrictive covenants and employee competition. Commercial work ranges from warranty claims on sales of businesses to commercial fraud, sale of goods and finance leasing. Also practises in administrative law, defamation and media law. Recent interesting cases include Spring v. Guardian Assurance PLC [1994] 3 WLR 354.
Prof. Membership: Employment Lawyers' Association, Employment Law Bar Association, Administrative Law Bar Association.
Career: Called to the Bar 1986. Legal Assistant to Comptroller and City Solicitor, Corporation of London, advising on employment law, 1986. Voluntary work for the Free Representation Unit and several Citizens Advice Bureaux and other advice centres since 1985. Occasional Spokesman for the

National Council for Civil Liberties from 1989-90. Joined present chambers 1987.

Personal: Born 1962. Educated at University of Oxford (MA).

Cotter, Barry

Old Square Chambers (Hon. John Melville Williams QC), Bristol (0117) 9277111. Called 1985.

Cottle, Anthony

3 Serjeants' Inn (Adrian Whitfield QC), London (0171)353 5537 Mbl(0385)736844.

Specialisation: Principal area of practice: employment, acting for senior directors, particularly group finance directors, senior management, major companies public and private. Clients have included major public and private companies and leading professional practices. Other main areas of practice: company law, insurance and reinsurance, general commercial litigation, professional negligence (accountants and solicitors) and general chancery work. Cases include: Lansing Linde Ltd v. Kerr; Hounslow v. Pilling; Balbosa v. Ayoub Ali; Camden v. Bromley Park Garden Estates Ltd.

Prof. Membership: London Common Law and Commercial Bar Association.

Career: Called 1978.

Personal: Educated London University; employment experience in the oil industry; lives in London; enjoys literature, music and sport.

Cox QC, Laura

Cloisters (David Turner-Samuels QC), London (0171) 583 0303.

Specialisation: Practice is divided evenly between employment law and medical negligence. Employment work includes sex and race discrimination and equal pay, and is predominantly Industrial Tribunal, Employment Appeal Tribunal and beyond advisory work and representation, with some judicial review. Medical negligence work includes claims of the utmost severity, such as cerebral palsy. Recent cases include: Webb v. EMO Air Cargo (UK) Ltd (European Court of Justice and HL - pregnancy discrimination); Pickstone v. Freemans (I.T. and EAT - equal pay); Tredget v. Bexley H.A. (nervous shock in medical negligence), part-timers' pensions cases, MoD pregnancy dismissals, R v. MoD ex parte Smith and Others (armed forces homosexuals) and Ferreira v. American Embassy Employees' Association (CA Order 17 CCR automatic strike-out). Clients include trade unions and individual members, applicants and respondents in employment and discrimination cases and plaintiffs in medical negligence cases. Regular conference and seminar speaker on both fields of practice.

Prof. Membership: Employment Law Bar Association (Committee). Professional Negligence Bar Association. Association of Personal Injury Lawyers, Administrative Law Bar Association, Personal Injuries Bar Association, Association of Women Barristers, Legal Action Group, American Trial Lawyers' Association.

Career: Appointed Recorder 1995. Vice-Chairman of Bar Council Sex Discrimination Committee 1995.

Personal: Educated at Wolverhampton High School for Girls 1963-70 and Queen Mary College, London University 1970-73 (LL.B) and 1973-75 (LL.M). Leisure pursuits (work and three children permitting) include music, cooking, theatre, cinema, swimming, watching football and reading. Born 1951.

Downing, Ruth

Devereux Chambers (Peter Weitzman QC), London (0171) 353 7534. Called 1978. Specialist in employment law including sex and race discrimination, unfair dismissal and equal pay. Practice also covers personal injury and medical negligence. Born 19.9.1954.

Duggan, Michael

Littleton Chambers (Michael Burton QC), London (0171) 797 8600. Called 1984.

Eady, Jennifer

Old Square Chambers (Hon. John Melville Williams QC), London (0171) 831 0801. Called 1989.

Elias QC, Patrick

11 King's Bench Walk (Lord Irvine of Lairg QC), London (0171) 583 0610.

Specialisation: Principal area of practice is Employment Law. Has appeared for individuals, trade unions, multi-national businesses, local authorities and employers' federations in a wide range of matters in this area. Other areas of practice include public law on behalf of and against local authorities and statutory bodies.

Prof. Membership: ALBA; COMBAR and London Common Law and Commercial Bar Association.

Career: University lecturer, Cambridge University 1972-1985. Called to the Bar 1973; Appointed Queen's Counsel 1991; Deputy High Court Judge 1994; Bencher of the Inner Temple 1995.

Personal: Educated: Cardiff High School; Exeter University, Cambridge University.

Falconer QC, Charles

See under Aviation.

Gay, Vivienne

Cloisters (David Turner-Samuels QC), London (0171) 583 0303. Called 1974. Specialises in personal injury acting mainly for plaintiffs. Born 23.12.1951.

Gill, Tess

Old Square Chambers (Hon. John Melville Williams QC), London (0171) 831 0801.

Specialisation: Principal areas of practice are employment and industrial law, health and safety and environment. She specialises in particular in sex and race discrimination, equal pay and European law including public law aspects. Cases include Stewart v. Cleveland Guest (Engineering) Ltd [1994] IRLR 440 (sexual harassment), Roscoe v. Hargreaves [1991] ICR (pension claim under Article 119); Hewcastle Catering Ltd v. Ahmed [1991] IRLR 473,CA (illegal employment contracts); London Borough of Newham v. Nalgo [1992] IRLR (labour injunctions) and Reay and Hope v. BFNL (claim on behalf of children of nuclear power workers who contracted leukaemia).

Prof. Membership: European Commission's legal network of experts on equality directives. Management Committee member of Public Law Project, and Environmental Law Foundation.

Career: Prior to transferring to the Bar in 1989, was solicitor since 1967, with trade union and private practice experience. Appointed as part-time industrial tribunal chairman in 1995, has published work on equality law and health and safety.

Gilroy, Paul

9 St. John Street (John Hand QC), Manchester (0161) 955 9000. Called 1985.

Goudie QC, James

11 King's Bench Walk (Lord Irvine of Lairg QC), London (0171) 583 0610.

Specialisation: Specialises in all aspects of employment law, with particular emphasis on TUPE, Restrictive Covenants and European Law relating to employment matters. Other main areas of practice include: Public Law (Capital Finance) and Commercial (Contractual disputes, insurance).

Career: Solicitor 1966 to 1970. Called to the Bar Inner Temple 1970. Bencher, Recorder, Chairman Law Reform Committee, General Council of the Bar, Chairman Administrative Law Bar Association, Chairman Society of Labour Lawyers.

Personal: Educated at Deans Close School, Cheltenham and L.S.E. (LL.B Hons). F.C.I. Arb.

Goulding, Paul

2 Hare Court (C.W.G. Ross-Munro QC), London (0171) 583 1770.

Specialisation: Specialist in all aspects of employment law, (including restraint of trade, transfer of undertakings, discrimination) judicial review and financial services.

Prof. Membership: Employment Lawyers' Association, Administrative Law Bar Association, London Common Law & Commercial Bar Association.

Career: St Edmund Hall, Oxford. Call 1984.

Greening, Richard

Devereux Chambers (Peter Weitzman QC), London (0171) 353 7534. Called 1975. Employment law specialist. Born 27.8.1953

Griffith-Jones, David

Devereux Chambers (Peter Weitzman QC), London (0171) 353 7534.

Specialisation: Specialist in all aspects of employment law including wrongful and unfair dismissals, pensions, racial and sex discrimination, equal pay, TUPE Regulations, trade disputes, restraint of trade and injunctions. Practice also covers general common and commercial law including business disputes, professional negligence and Lloyd's Tribunals. Also lectures on trade disputes and other employment law issues.

Prof. Membership: COMBAR; London Common Law and Commercial Bar Association. Employment Lawyers' Association; Employment Law Bar Association; Industrial Law Society.

Career: Called to the Bar 1975. FCIArb 1991. Assistant Recorder 1992.

Personal: Educated at Marlborough College 1966-1971 and at Bristol University (LL.B) 1971-74. Born 7th March 1953.

Griffiths QC, W. Robert

See under Public and Administrative Law.

Hand QC, John

9 St. John Street (John Hand QC), Manchester (0161) 955 9000.

Specialisation: Is experienced in most areas of common law litigation (including appearing at and conducting inquiries), concentrates on employment law, personal injury litigation and environmental law and is familiar with EC law principles. His employment law practise involves both individual employment law and industrial disputes. Recent areas of interest have been the scope of picketing (Middlebrook Mushrooms v. TGWU), transfer of undertakings (Wren v. Eastbourne DC) and collective redundancy (Green v. British Aerospace). Has appeared in a number of important discrimination cases, including Jenkins v. Kingsgate Clothing and the Alison Halford case.

Prof. Membership: Employment Law Association, Employment Law Bar Association, Personal Injury Bar Association, Association of Personal Injury Lawyers, Professional Negligence Bar Association, Bar European Group.

Career: Called 1972 (Gray's Inn); Queen's Counsel (1988); Recorder 1991.

Hendy QC, John

Old Square Chambers (Hon. John Melville Williams QC), London (0171) 831 0801.

Specialisation: Primarily trade union and industrial relations cases. Has appeared in most of the leading cases over the last 15 years. Also deals with employment law more generally. Extensive practice also in P.I and medical negligence. Standing counsel to NUM, NUJ and POA; co-author of: 'Redgrave's Health and Safety', 'Munkman's Employer's Liability' and 'Personal Injry Practice'.

Prof. Membership: ILS, ELA, ELBA, APIL, PIBA, ATLA, CLBA, ABA, SE. Circuit, W. Circuit, Chair Institute of Employment Rights 1989-.

Career: Called 1972 Gray's; Director Newham Rights Centre 1973-76; practice 1977-; silk 1987.

Personal: LLB London (external); LLM (Queens, Belfast).

Hillier, Andrew

5 Bell Yard (Robert Webb QC), London (0171) 333 8811. Called 1972. Principal area of work is employment law, although he has a general common law practice. Also deals with professional negligence and mental health work. Born 4.5.1949.

Hochhauser, Andrew

See under Company.

Hogarth, Andrew

12 King's Bench Walk (Ronald Walker QC), London (0171) 583 0811.

Specialisation: All aspects of employment and trade union law. Has had particular experience of Transfer of Undertakings cases, sex discrimination claims, especially those arising from a failure to give equal pension rights to part time employees, and employment disputes connected with insolvent companies and their receivers.

Career: MA (Cantab). Called to the Bar 1974. Joined *12 King's Bench Walk* in 1975.

Horlock, Timothy

9 St. John Street (John Hand QC), Manchester (0161) 955 9000. Called 1981.

Irvine of Lairg QC, Lord

See under Commercial Law.

Jeans, Christopher James Marwood

11 King's Bench Walk (Lord Irvine of Lairg QC), London (0171) 583 0610. Called 1980. Specialises in employment law. Born 24.1.1956.

Jones, Seán

11 King's Bench Walk (Lord Irvine of Lairg QC), London (0171) 583 0610.

Specialisation: Principal area of practice is employment law, including discrimination. Acts for both applicants and respondents. Has been instructed by individuals, unions, multi-national businesses, small firms, local authorities and employer's federations. Has lectured/ tutored at Nottingham University, Worcester College, Oxford and King's College, London and given seminars, including addressing the Employment Lawyers' Association.

Prof. Membership: ELBA, COMBAR.

Career: Called to the Bar and joined present chambers in 1991.

Personal: Educated at Colchester Royal Grammar School 1977-84 and Worcester College, Oxford 1985-89 (BA Hons in Jurisprudence, BCL). Born 9th July 1966. Lives in London.

Jones, Jennifer

5 Fountain Court (Anthony Barker QC), Birmingham (0121) 606 0500.

Kerr, Tim

4-5 Gray's Inn Square (Miss Elizabeth Appleby QC, The Hon. Michael Beloff QC), London (0171) 404 5252. Called 1983. Principal areas of practice are administrative law, employment and general commercial law. Born 15.2.1958.

Kibling, Thomas

Cloisters (David Turner-Samuels QC), London (0171) 583 0303.

Specialisation: Specialises in employment law with a paticular emphasis upon discrimination, trades union law and individual employment rights. Publications include 'The Employment Law Handbook' (LAG).

Career: Called to the Bar 1990. Joined present chambers 1991. Has ten years experience working in law centres.

Personal: Born 19th August 1957.

Lang, Beverley

See under Public and Administrative Law.

Langstaff QC, Brian

See under Personal Injury.

Lemon, Roy

Devereux Chambers (Peter Weitzman QC), London (0171) 353 7534. Called 1970. Principal areas of practice are employment, business law and injunctions. Born 31.3.1946.

Lester QC, Lord

See under Public and Administrative Law.

Linden, Thomas

Old Square Chambers (Hon. John Melville Williams QC), London (0171) 831 0801.

Specialisation: Specialist employment lawyer with balanced employer/employee practice, perhaps best known for work on the Transfer of Undertakings Regulations and the other areas which have a European dimension in a number of the leading cases in this field. Other main areas of practice are restraint of trade and general commercial work. Regular speaker and writer on specialist areas.

Prof. Membership: Employment Lawyers' Association (member of the management committee) Industrial Law Society and Employment Law Bar Association.

Career: 1984-1988, BA and BCL at Oxford. Called 1989 at Gray's Inn. Taken on at Old Square Chambers 1990.

Lynch, Adrian Charles Edmund

11 King's Bench Walk (Lord Irvine of

Lairg QC), London (0171) 583 0610. Called 1983. Principal areas of practice are employment, commercial and public law.

Marshall, Philip Derek
Iscoed Chambers (Wyn Richards), Swansea (01792) 652988/9.

McMullen QC, Jeremy
Old Square Chambers (Hon. John Melville Williams QC), London (0171) 831 0801.

Specialisation: Employment, personal injury. Includes discrimination, contracts, restrictive covenants, industrial action, directorships, dismissal, injunctions, inquiries eg Clapham Junction, Westminster Auditor. Part-time Industrial Tribunal Chairman.

Prof. Membership: Former Chair ILS and ELBA; ACAS independent expert.

Career: Called 1971, worked in New York and for GMB before practising in 1984. Silk 1994.

Personal: Educated at Oxford and LSE.

McNeill, Jane
Farrar's Building (Lord Williams of Mostyn QC), London (0171) 583 9241. Called 1982. Principal areas of practice are employment, personal injury and professional negligence. Born 18.3.1957.

Meade, Philip
Old Square Chambers (Hon. John Melville Williams QC), London (0171) 831 0801. 1, Verulam Buildings, Gray's Inn, London. Tel: (0171) 831 0801 and 47 Corn Street, Bristol. BS1 1HT. Tel: (0117) 9277111.

Specialisation: Environmental law, personal injury law including product liability, employment and discrimination law, as well as general common law. Has particular knowledge of the application of European law to the above areas. Acts for both plaintiffs/applicants and defendants/respondants, and is familiar with multi-plaintiff actions. Regularly lectures and writes on European Law. Consultant to the European Commission on Health and Safety.

Prof. Membership: Association of Personal Injury Lawyers, Employment Law Bar Association, Environmental Law Foundation, and Bar European Group.

Career: Called to the Bar 1989; member Western Circuit, and practises from chambers' annexe in Bristol.

Personal: Visiting fellow and occasional lecturer, Durham University; LLM, European University Institute, Florence.

Mehigan, Simon
5 Paper Buildings (John Mathew QC), London (0171) 583 6117. Called 1980.

Millar, Gavin
Doughty Street Chambers (Geoffrey Robertson QC), London (0171) 404 1313.

Specialisation: Specialises in employment and public law. Frequently appears in the Industrial and Employment Appeals Tribunal in trade union and discrimination cases and, in addition, handles all types of high court employment litigation, including collective labour law. Undertakes a considerable amount of judicial review work in both employment and public law, often acting for public sector workers and unions. Also has a specialist practice in local government and election law. Other areas of specialisation include defamation and media law (including reading a number of national dailies for libel), medical and professional negligence, and personal injury work.

Personal: Member of Westminster City Council from 1985 to 1994 and served on its Social Services, Policy and Resources, Contacts, Education and Housing Committees. Born 1956.

Naughton QC, Philip
See under Construction Law.

Neaman, Sam
4 Paper Buildings (Lionel Swift QC), London (0171) 583 0816.

Specialisation: Principal area of practice is employment law including unfair dismissal, sex and race discrimination and redundancy, primarily in the banking, insurance, finance and computer industries. Other main areas of work are banking, securities and consumer credit, specialising in cheque and credit card law, in particular under S.75 of The Consumer Credit Act. Has conducted a wide range of general litigation in all courts and tribunals. Reported cases include First Sport Ltd v. Barclays Bank Plc and Winchester Cigarette Co Ltd v. Payne (No's 1 and 2) at the Court of Appeal. Clients include major banks, insurance companies and computer companies.

Career: Called to the Bar 1988 and joined present chambers in the same year.

Personal: Educated at Oxford University 1983-86 (BA Hons) and City University 1986-1987 (Dip.Law). Leisure pursuits include boxing (member Angel ABC since 1986 and active boxer since 1980), and playing drums in jazz and rhythm and blues bands. Born 28th April 1964. Lives in London.

Nicholls, Paul
11 King's Bench Walk (Lord Irvine of Lairg QC), London (0171) 583 0610.

Specialisation: Specialises in all aspects of employment law, including unfair dismissal, discrimination, collective disputes and European law relating to employment matters. Restrictive covenants, confidential information and interlocutory injunctions. Also handles general commercial work, including sale of goods, insurance and contract disputes.

Prof. Membership: Industial Law Society; Employment Bar Association.

Personal: Educated at Sheffield University (LLB 1st class) 1986-1989 and at Oxford University (BCL 1st Class, Vinerian Scholar) 1989-1990. Sometime lecturer at King's College, London. Born 27th November 1967. Lives in Battersea, London.

Career: Called to the Bar 1992. Joined present Chambers 1993.

O'Donovan, Kevin
5 Fountain Court (Anthony Barker QC), Birmingham (0121) 606 0500. Called 1978.

Oldham, Peter
11 King's Bench Walk (Lord Irvine of Lairg QC), London (0171) 583 0610.

O'Rourke, Mary
See under Medical Negligence.

Pannick QC, David
See under Public and Administrative Law.

Pardoe QC, Alan
Devereux Chambers (Peter Weitzman QC), London (0171) 353 7534. Called 1971, took silk 1988. Principal areas of practice are commercial law, employment and insurance and reinsurance. Born 16.8.1943.

Parkin, Jonathan
9 St. John Street (John Hand QC), Manchester (0161) 955 9000. Called 1978.

Pearl, David A.
4 King's Bench Walk (Nicholas Jarman QC), London (0171) 353 3581.

Specialisation: Specialises in employment law and professional negligence. Practice also covers personal injury work.

Prof. Membership: Employment Law Bar Association.

Career: Called to the Bar 1977. Joined present chambers 1986. Part-time Industrial Tribunal Chairman since September 1994.

Personal: Educated at Ilford County High School 1965-1972 and Pembroke College, Cambridge 1972-1975. Born 19th March 1954.

Pitt-Payne, Timothy Sheridan
11 King's Bench Walk (Lord Irvine of Lairg QC), London (0171) 583 0610. Called 1989. Main areas of practice are employment and commercial law. Born 18.11.1964.

Rose, Paul
Old Square Chambers (Hon. John Melville Williams QC), London (0171) 831 0801. Called 1981.

Rose, Dinah
2 Hare Court (C.W.G. Ross-Munro QC), London (0171) 583 1770. Called 1989. Specialises in discrimination, employment law, public law and human rights. Recent cases include actions brought by pregnant servicewomen against MOD.

Sendall, Antony

Littleton Chambers (Michael Burton QC), London (0171) 797 8600.

Specialisation: Principal areas of practice are: Employment; all areas including: wrongful and unfair dismissal, transfer of undertakings, discrimination, equal pay, restraint of trade and trade union law. Professional indemnity; primarily solicitors' and surveyors' negligence, but includes some accountants' negligence. Commercial work: all forms of contractual and other commercial disputes, including interlocutory injunctions.

Prof. Membership: Employment Law Bar Association, Employment Lawyers' Association, Industrial Law Society, Professional Negligence Bar Association and London Commercial & Common Law Bar Association. Chambers member of COMBAR.

Career: Called to the Bar 1984. Joined 2 Crown Office Row in 1985. Chambers moved to new address in February 1995.

Personal: Educated at Royal Grammar School, High Wycombe, 1972-79 and Scholar of Robinson College, Cambridge (1980-83) (First Class Honours Degree in Law). Born 1st July 1961. Lives in Beaconsfield, Bucks.
E-mail Addresses: 100256.1417@compuserve.com or private LINK mailbox.

Serota QC, Daniel

Littleton Chambers (Michael Burton QC), London (0171) 797 8600.

Simler, Ingrid

Devereux Chambers (Peter Weitzman QC), London (0171) 353 7534.

Specialisation: Principal area of practice is employment, encompassing all areas of individual and collective employment law, including discrimination, restraint of trade and business transfers. Also handles general commercial work, professional negligence and personal injury work. Contributor to 'Tolleys' Employment Law'.

Prof. Membership: Employment Law Bar Association: Industrial Law Society; Commercial Law Bar Association.

Career: Called to the Bar 1988 and joined current chambers 1988.

Personal: Educated at Cambridge University 1982-85 (MA) and University of Amsterdam 1985-86 (Diploma in European law). Born 17th September 1963.

Slade QC, Elizabeth Ann

11 King's Bench Walk (Lord Irvine of Lairg QC), London (0171) 583 0610.

Specialisation: Specialises in all aspects of employment law with particular emphasis on European aspects of Employment Law; Transfer of Undertakings; Sex and Race Discrimination; Equal Pay; Employment aspects of pensions. Leading cases include: Foster & Others v. British Gas; Reed Executive plc v.

Somers; Shepherd v. Jerrom.

Prof. Membership: Employment Law Bar Association; member of ALBA; Bar European Group; Chambers membership of COMBAR; London Common Law & Commercial Bar Association.

Career: Called to the Bar in 1972; original author 'Tolley's Employment Handbook'; 1990 Bencher of the Inner Temple; 1992 Appointed QC; 1994 Master of the Staff, Inner Temple; Chair of Employment Law Bar Association 1995-96.

Personal: Education: Lady Margaret Hall, Oxford. Exhibitioner.

Stobart, John

King Charles House (Richard Inglis), Nottingham (0115) 9418851.

Supperstone QC, Michael Alan

11 King's Bench Walk (Lord Irvine of Lairg QC), London (0171) 583 0610.

Specialisation: Specialises in all aspects of employment law. Other main areas of practice include public and administrative law.

Prof. Membership: Employment Law Bar Association, Vice Chairman of Administrative Law Bar Association; Commercial Bar Association; London Common Law & Commercial Bar Association.

Career: Called to the Bar in 1973. Appointed Queen's Counsel 1992. Assistant Recorder.

Personal: Educated at St. Paul's School and Lincoln College, Oxford (MA; BCL).

Sutton, Mark

Queen Elizabeth Building (Geoffrey Brice QC), London (0171) 353 9153.

Specialisation: Principal area of practice is employment law, covering all aspects of contentious employment work including unfair and wrongful dismissals, restraint of trade and confidentiality. Handles a broad range of tribunal work including redundancy, race and sex discrimination and transfer of undertakings. Also instructed in professional negligence cases. Clients include insurance companies, banks, plcs, local authorities, health authorities and NHS Trusts.

Career: Called to the Bar 1982.

Personal: BA Hons, Dip Law. Born 25th June 1958.

Swift, Jonathan Mark

11 King's Bench Walk (Lord Irvine of Lairg QC), London (0171) 583 0610.

Tabachnik QC, Eldred

11 King's Bench Walk (Lord Irvine of Lairg QC), London (0171) 583 0610.

Specialisation: Principal area of practice is employment law. Has appeared in numerous matters for individuals, trade unions, multinational businesses, local authorities and employer's federations in the areas of unfair dismissal, wrongful dismissal, discrimina-

tion, collective disputes, restraint of trade, European law relating to employment.

Prof. Membership: ALBA; COMBAR: London Common Law and Commercial Bar Association.

Career: Called to the Bar 1970; Appointed Queen's Counsel 1982.

Personal: Educated at University of Cape Town and London University (LLM).

Thompson, Andrew

Francis Taylor Building (Alan Tyrrell QC), London (0171) 797 7250. Called 1969. Principal area of practice is employment law. Also covers education and EC law. Born 28.11.1945.

Underhill QC, Nicholas

Fountain Court (Peter Scott QC), London (0171) 583 3335. Called 1976, took silk 1992. Specialist in commercial, employment and public law. Born 12.5.1952.

Wallington, Peter

11 King's Bench Walk (Lord Irvine of Lairg QC), London (0171) 583 0610. Called 1987. Principal areas of practice are employment law and public law. Born 25.3.1947.

Wedderburn QC, Lord

Old Square Chambers (Hon. John Melville Williams QC), London (0171) 831 0801. Called 1953, took silk 1990.

Westgate, Martin

Doughty Street Chambers (Geoffrey Robertson QC), London (0171) 404 1313. Called 1985. Specialist in public law with a particular emphasis on cases involving homelessness, landlord and tenant, employment law and discrimination.

Wilkie QC, Alan Fraser

11 King's Bench Walk (Lord Irvine of Lairg QC), London (0171) 583 0610.

Specialisation: Specialises in all aspects of employment law. Other main areas of practice include public, especially local government, law and commercial law.

Prof. Membership: Administrative Bar Association; Commercial Bar Association; Education Law; London Common Law & Commercial Bar Association.

Career: Called to the Bar 1974. Appointed Queen's Counsel 1992. Recorder.

Personal: Educated at Balliol College, Oxford. B.A., BCL. Warner Exhibitioner. Lecturer at Exeter College, Oxford and at Southampton University.

Williams QC, John Melville

Old Square Chambers (Hon. John Melville Williams QC), London (0171) 831 0801. Called 1955, took silk 1977.

ENVIRONMENTAL

BARRISTERS are handling increasing amounts of environmental work within the context of other subjects such as planning and European law. As a result, a number of London chambers have developed a specialism in the field, with members experienced in all aspects of environmental law.

LEADING SETS	
4 BREAMS BUILDINGS	3 GRAY'S INN PLACE
4-5 GRAY'S INN SQUARE	1 SERJEANTS' INN
1 CROWN OFFICE ROW	2 HARCOURT BUILDINGS
2 MITRE COURT BUILDINGS	

4 Breams Buildings, **4-5 Gray's Inn Square** and **1 Serjeant's Inn** emerge as the leading sets with **1 Crown Office Row** and **3 Gray's Inn Place** also highly recommended.

Following the loss of *Robert Carnwath QC* to the Bench, **4 Breams Buildings** leading silks are *Christopher Lockhart-Mummery QC* and *Michael Barnes QC*. At the junior end of chambers, *David Holgate, Christopher Katkowski* and *David Elvin* are held in high regard.

4-5 Gray's Inn Square boasts London's most consistently recommended environmental specialist: *Jeremy Sullivan QC*. Chambers also has eminent practitioners in *Duncan Ouseley QC* and *John Steel QC*.

Lionel Read QC, head of **1 Serjeant's Inn** , is one of London's highest ranking environmental specialists and former Chairman of the Local Government, Planning and Environmental Bar Association. Chambers comprises 23 members including *Rhodri Price Lewis* (author of 'Waste Management Journal of Planning and Environmental Law 1993'), *John Pugh-Smith, Roy Martin* and *William Upton*.

At **3 Gray's Inn Place** *James Cameron* specialises in international environmental agreements; the relationship between international trade and environmental law; 'toxic tort'

litigation and has also represented Greenpeace. *Philippe Sands* and *Maurice Sheridan* are also active in the field.

Philip Vallance QC is **1 Crown Office Row's** leading light although chambers also has highly-regarded practitioners in *Philip Havers QC, Nigel Pitt, Margaret Bowron, Paul Rees, David Hart* and *William Edis*.

Other sets which have developed expertise in environmental matters as an adjunct to their planning practices include **2 Harcourt Buildings** and **2 Mitre Court Buildings**.

LEADING SILKS	
Fitzgerald, Michael	*2 Mitre Court Buildings*
Read, Lionel	*1 Serjeants' Inn*
Sullivan, Jeremy	*4-5 Gray's Inn Square*
Barnes, Michael	*4 Breams Buildings*
Lockhart-Mummery, Christopher	*4 Breams Buildings*
Ouseley, Duncan	*4-5 Gray's Inn Square*
Steel, John	*4-5 Gray's Inn Square*
Vallance, Philip	*1 Crown Office Row*
Drabble, Richard	*4 Breams Buildings*
Havers, Philip	*1 Crown Office Row*
Hicks, William	*1 Serjeants' Inn*
Horton, Matthew	*2 Mitre Court Buildings*
Moriarty, Gerald	*2 Mitre Court Buildings*
Ryan, Gerard	*2 Harcourt Buildings*
Vandermeer, Roy	*2 Harcourt Buildings*
Widdicombe, David	*2 Mitre Court Buildings*
Williams, John Melville	*Old Square Chambers*

At **2 Harcourt Buildings**, *Roy Vandermeer QC, Gerard Ryan QC* (instructed in the Hinkley Point inquiry and Chairman of the Loscoe gas explosion inquiry) and *Robert*

LEADING JUNIORS		
Cameron, James *3 Gray's Inn Place*		
Bates, John H. *2 Paper Buildings*	**Bowron,** Margaret *1 Crown Office Row*	**Edis,** William *1 Crown Office Row*
Holgate, David *4 Breams Buildings*	**Katkowski,** Christopher *4 Breams Buildings*	**Lewis,** Rhodri Price *1 Serjeants' Inn*
Martin, Roy *1 Serjeants' Inn*	**Pitt,** Nigel *1 Crown Office Row*	**Pugh,** Charles *Old Square Chambers*
Pugh-Smith, John *1 Serjeants' Inn*	**Rees,** Paul *1 Crown Office Row*	**Sands,** Philippe *3 Gray's Inn Place*
Sheridan, Maurice *3 Gray's Inn Place*	**Upton,** William *1 Serjeants' Inn*	
Allardice, Miranda *Pump Court Chambers*	**Birtles,** William *Old Square Chambers*	**Comyn,** Timothy *2 Harcourt Buildings*
Elvin, David *4 Breams Buildings*	**Gill,** Tess *Old Square Chambers*	**Green,** Nicholas *Brick Court Chambers*
Hart, David *1 Crown Office Row*	**Harvey,** John Gilbert *4 King's Bench Walk*	**Howell Williams,** Craig *2 Harcourt Buildings*
King, Neil *2 Mitre Court Buildings*	**Lindblom,** Keith *2 Harcourt Buildings*	**McCracken,** Robert *2 Harcourt Buildings*
McRory, Richard *Brick Court Chambers*	**Meade,** Philip *Old Square Chambers*	**Mynors,** Charles *2 Harcourt Buildings*
Ornsby, Suzanne *2 Harcourt Buildings*	**West,** Lawrence *2 Harcourt Buildings*	

UP AND COMING
Jones, Gregory *2 Harcourt Buildings*

McCracken (author of 'Liability of Funding Institutions for Contaminated Land') are well-regarded in the field.

2 Mitre Court Buildings predominantly handle domestic environmental matters including waste disposal and pollution control, whilst **Brick Court Chambers** handle environmental issues in the context of European cases.

At **Old Square Chambers**, *Charles Pugh* (founder-member of the Environmental Law Foundation) has developed an environmental specialism from the representation of plaintiffs in multi-party personal injury actions.

At **2 Paper Buildings**, *John Bates* (former Chairman of the UK Environmental Law Association) practises exclusively in environmental law including water and waste, land use cases, criminal prosecutions and judicial review.

LEADERS IN ENVIRONMENTAL

Allardice, Miranda
Pump Court Chambers (Guy Boney QC), London (0171) 353 0711. Called 1982. Specialist on the Inheritance (Provision For Family and Dependants) Act 1975. Practice also covers environmental law. Born 5.3.1959.

Barnes QC, Michael
See under Planning and Local Government.

Bates, John H.
2 Paper Buildings (Desmond de Silva QC), London (0171) 936 2611. Called 1973.

Birtles, William
Old Square Chambers (Hon. John Melville Williams QC), London (0171) 831 0801.
Specialisation: Principal areas of practice are environmental, planning and local government law. Has had considerable experience in both civil and criminal aspects of pollution claims including land contamination (arising from oil, toxic waste and industrial waste disposal), water (e.g. Barry Docks, Cardiff), air (particularly industrial smells and noise). Major inquiries include the Sizewell B Nuclear Power Station Inquiry (1984-1986), the second Part I Environmental Protection Act Inquiry (Cumbria 1994), the Westminster Council District Audit Inquiry (1994-1995) and various internal inquiries for local authorities.
Prof. Membership: Planning and Local Government Bar Association; Administrative Law Bar Association; Council Member United Kingdom Environmental Law Association; Environmental Law Foundation.
Career: Academic lawyer 1968-1974. Called to the Bar 1970. Joined Old Square Chambers 1986. Recorder 1993. Publications etc: Co-author of 'Planning and Environmental Law' (Longman 1994 with Richard Stein); co-author of 'Local Government Finance Law' (Sweet & Maxwell 1997 with Anna Forge). Numerous articles and chapters in books. Frequent speaker at legal conferences.

Bowron, Margaret
1 Crown Office Row (Robert Seabrook QC), London (0171) 797 7500. Called 1978.

Cameron, James
3 Gray's Inn Place (R. Neville Thomas QC), London (0171) 831 8441. Called 1987. Principal area of practice encompasses international, EC and UK environmental law. Born 28.10.1961.

Comyn, Timothy
2 Harcourt Buildings (Peter Boydell QC), London (0171) 353 8415. Called 1980.

Drabble QC, Richard
See under Public and Administrative Law.

Edis, William
1 Crown Office Row (Robert Seabrook QC), London (0171) 797 7500. Called 1985.

Elvin, David
See under Landlord and Tenant.

Fitzgerald QC, Michael
2 Mitre Court Buildings (Michael FitzGerald QC), London (0171) 583 1380. Called 1961, took silk 1980. Principal areas of practice are parliamentary, planning and local government law. Born 9.6.1936.

Gill, Tess
See under Employment.

Green, Nicholas
See under Commercial Law.

Hart, David
See under Medical Negligence.

Harvey, John Gilbert
4 King's Bench Walk (Nicholas Jarman QC), London (0171) 353 3581.
Specialisation: Specialist fields are planning and environmental law, professional negligence and arbitration. Has held part-time teaching appointments at University level, acted as an external examiner in law, and addressed numerous seminars on medical negligence and related matters, contract and employment law. Is currently editing and writing part of a book in the professional negligence field.
Prof. Membership: Midland & Oxford Circuit, Local Government Planning &

Environmental Bar Association, Professional Negligence Bar Association, International Bar Association, Criminal Bar Association, Family Law Bar Association.
Career: Called to the Bar in 1973. Joined present chambers in 1982 (previously practised in Birmingham). Assistant Recorder since 1992.
Personal: Educated at Repton and Birmingham University (LL.B Hons 1972, FCIArb 1993). Interests outside the law are music (Chairman of the Lichfield Festival Association) and the other performing arts, skiing, golf and occasionally watching cricket. Born 6th February 1951. Lives in Sutton Coldfield.

Havers QC, Philip
1 Crown Office Row (Robert Seabrook QC), London (0171) 797 7500. Called 1974, took silk 1995. Principal areas of practice are public and administrative law, medical negligence and environmental group litigation. Born 16.6.1950.

Hicks QC, William
See under Public and Administrative Law.

Holgate, David
See under Public and Administrative Law.

Horton QC, Matthew
2 Mitre Court Buildings (Michael FitzGerald QC), London (0171) 583 1380. Called 1969, took silk 1989.

Howell Williams, Craig
2 Harcourt Buildings (Peter Boydell QC), London (0171) 353 8415.
Specialisation: Town and country planning, environment and parliamentary law. Member of the Supplementary Panel of Junior Treasury Counsel (Planning).
Prof. Membership: Local Government Planning and Environmental Bar Association (Secretary), Parliamentary Bar Mess.

Jones, Gregory
2 Harcourt Buildings (Peter Boydell QC), London (0171) 353 8415. Called 1991. Principal areas of practice are planning, environmental, local government and administrative law. Born 4.1.1968.

Katkowski, Christopher
See under Planning and Local Government.

King, Neil
See under Planning and Local Government.

Lewis, Rhodri Price
1 Serjeants' Inn (Lionel Read QC), London (0171) 583 1355.

Specialisation: Principal area of practice is town and country planning and environmental law including judicial review, public inquiries and statutory appeals to the High Court. Clients include development and waste disposal companies, waste regulation authorities and county and district councils. Author of article on 'Waste Management' in *Journal of Planning and Environmental Law 1993*.

Prof. Membership: Local Government Planning and Environmental Bar Association, Midland and Oxford Circuit.

Career: Called to the Bar 1975. Appointed Assistant Recorder 1994. Member of Treasury Solicitor's Supplementary Panel (Planning).

Personal: M.A. Oxon 1970-73, Dip.Crim (Cantab) 1973-74. Born 7th June 1952.

Lindblom, Keith
See under Planning and Local Government.

Lockhart-Mummery QC, Christopher
See under Planning and Local Government.

Martin, Roy
1 Serjeants' Inn (Lionel Read QC), London (0171) 583 1355. Called 1990.

McCracken, Robert
2 Harcourt Buildings (Peter Boydell QC), London (0171) 353 8415. Called 1973. Principal area of practice is environmental law, especially land use and planning. Born 15.3.1950.

McRory, Richard
Brick Court Chambers (Christopher Clarke QC), London (0171) 583 0777. Called 1974.

Meade, Philip
See under Employment.

Moriarty QC, Gerald
2 Mitre Court Buildings (Michael FitzGerald QC), London (0171) 583 1380. Called 1951, took silk 1974.

Mynors, Charles
2 Harcourt Buildings (Peter Boydell QC), London (0171) 353 8415. Called 1988.

Ornsby, Suzanne
2 Harcourt Buildings (Peter Boydell QC), London (0171) 353 8415. Called 1986.

Ouseley QC, Duncan
See under Public and Administrative Law.

Pitt, Nigel
1 Crown Office Row (Robert Seabrook QC), London (0171) 797 7500. Called 1976.

Pugh, Charles
See under Health & Safety Law.

Pugh-Smith, John
1 Serjeants' Inn (Lionel Read QC), London (0171) 583 1355.

Specialisation: Planning, Local Government, Environmental and Parliamentary matters. Involved in numerous public inquiries for both private and public sectors with recent emphases on discount food shopping, contaminated land and waste issues.

Prof. Membership: Local Government, Planning and Environmental Bar Association (Committee Member), United Kingdom Environmental Law Association, Environmental Law Foundation.

Career: Called to the Bar 1977. Joined *Serjeants' Inn* 1984. Publications include "Neighbours and the Law" (1st & 2nd Editions: 1988 & 1993) and regular contributions to the *Journal of Planning and Environmental Law*. Joint Editorial Adviser for *Property, Planning and Compensation Reports*.

Personal: Born 1954. Lives, mainly, in Norfolk.

Read QC, Lionel
1 Serjeants' Inn (Lionel Read QC), London (0171) 583 1355. Called 1954, took silk 1973.

Rees, Paul
1 Crown Office Row (Robert Seabrook QC), London (0171) 797 7500. Called 1980.

Ryan QC, Gerard
See under Planning and Local Government.

Sands, Philippe
3 Gray's Inn Place (R. Neville Thomas QC), London (0171) 831 8441. Called 1985.

Sheridan, Maurice
3 Gray's Inn Place (R. Neville Thomas QC), London (0171) 831 8441. Called 1984.

Steel QC, John
See under Planning and Local Government.

Sullivan QC, Jeremy
See under Planning and Local Government.

Upton, William
1 Serjeants' Inn (Lionel Read QC), London (0171) 583 1355.

Specialisation: Main area of practice is town and country planning and environmental law. Clients include local authorities, developers and local amenity groups. Assistant author 'Neighbours & the Law' (Sweet & Maxwell, 2nd edn, 1994). Editor for 'Current Law Monthly Digest' and reporter for P.& C.R. Experienced lecturer.

Prof. Membership: Local Government Planning & Environmental Bar Association, UK Environmental Law Association, Environmental Law Foundation.

Career: Called to the Bar in 1990.

Personal: Educated at Trinity College, Cambridge 1985-89 (MA & LL.M). Member of Management Committee, Planning Aid for London. Fellow of the Royal Society of Arts. Born 1965.

Vallance QC, Philip
1 Crown Office Row (Robert Seabrook QC), London (0171) 797 7500. Called 1968, took silk 1989. Principal area of practice is professional negligence and related aspects with regard to environmental and construction law. Born 20.12.1943.

Vandermeer QC, Roy
2 Harcourt Buildings (Peter Boydell QC), London (0171) 353 8415. Called 1955, took silk 1978.

West, Lawrence
2 Harcourt Buildings (Roger Henderson QC), London (0171) 583 9020.

Specialisation: Principal areas are general public and commercial law, environmental law, and insurance law, including personal injury and medical negligence. Clients acted for include British Telecom, British Rail, Shell, Legal & General, Eagle Star and Provincial.

Prof. Membership: BEG, LCCBA, LGBA.

Career: Called to the Bar in 1973 in Ontario, and in 1979 in England. Practised with *McCarthy Tetrault* until 1979. Joined *2 Harcourt Buildings* in October 1980.

Personal: Educated at De La Salle 'Oaklands' Toronto 1959-64, University of Toronto 1964-70 (B.A. and LLB) and London School of Economics 1970-71 (LLM). Lives in Little London near Tadley, Hants. Born 6th July 1946.

Widdicombe QC, David
See under Parliamentary.

Williams QC, John Melville
See under Employment.

EUROPEAN COMMUNITY LAW

A S EUROPEAN law continues to impinge on English law, barristers are becoming correspondingly more expert in it. Areas most affected include environmental law, intellectual property, employment, financial services, insurance, revenue and competition law. The decisions of the European Court of Justice are binding on national courts. In addition, human rights issues are heard by the European Court of Human Rights in Strasbourg, which is a separate institution from the European Union.

LEADING SETS

FOUR RAYMOND BUILDINGS

BRICK COURT CHAMBERS

The leading set in this area is **4 Raymond Buildings** which handles all aspects of EU law with particular emphasis on competition issues. All members practise in the field and the majority contribute to 'Bellamy and Child on Common Market Law of Competition'. *Jeremy Lever QC* has an outstanding reputation for both general European and competition work, and has appeared in numerous reported cases.

Richard Fowler QC has considerable expertise in competition law, and has appeared in European 'Cases IV/33.709/33.932' relating to sugar, 'Cases IV/33.126/33.322' relating to cement, 'Case IV/34.780' concerning Virgin and BA and 'Cases T-2/93, T-3/93' in which the parties were Air France and Commission (Dan Air/TAT).

Kenneth Parker QC is well known for competition work. *Paul Lasok QC* specialises in the EU aspects of agriculture, competition, VAT and trade law. He is the author of 'The European Court of Justice: Practice and Procedure' and numerous articles on European Community Law, in particular competition law, published in 'European Competition Law Review' and other periodicals.

Nicholas Paines practises in EU-related aspects of agriculture, employment, free movement of goods, public procurement, sex discrimination, social security and VAT. He has appeared in a number of cases in the European Court including 'Coloroll' and related cases on pensions, the Sunday Trading cases, the Phil Collins copyright case, 'Corbeau' and 'REIFF', a case relating to competition issues.

Jonathan Turner is also highly regarded, especially for competition work. *Rhodri Thompson* practises in this area; his cases include 'Case C-360/92'regarding the Net Book Agreement, 'Case T-83/91', 'Tetra Pak II', and 'Case C-327/93', 'Red Hot Dutch'. *Christopher Vadja* is also highly regarded.

Brick Court Chambers are a leading commercial set.

Members of chambers handle all aspects of EU law. *David Vaughan QC* has been very highly recommended, and has written extensively on EU matters. *Nicholas Forwood QC* who is based in Brussels, along with *Mark Clough* and several other members, has been highly recommended, as has *Gerald Barling QC*. *Derrick Wyatt QC* is also known for his practice in this field.

Among juniors in chambers *Nicholas Green* has been very highly recommended for his competition work, and for his particular expertise in intellectual property-related matters.

At **1 Essex Court** *Thomas Sharpe QC*, who has been highly recommended, has appeared in a wide range of Article 85, 86 and 92 cases and general EU law cases in the European Court of Justice and the High Court including 'Telecom Corporation of New Zealand v Clear Communications'. He has contributed to the European Community Law section of 'Halsbury's Laws', and to the 'European Law Review'.

LEADING SILKS

Lever, Jeremy *Four Raymond Buildings*	
Vaughan, David *Brick Court Chambers*	
Barling, Gerald *Brick Court Chambers*	
Forrester, Ian *2 Hare Court*	
Forwood, Nicholas *Brick Court Chambers*	
Fowler, Richard *Four Raymond Buildings*	
Isaacs, Stuart *4-5 Gray's Inn Square*	
Lasok, Paul *Four Raymond Buildings*	
Layton, Alexander *2 Temple Gardens*	
Parker, Kenneth *Four Raymond Buildings*	
Plender, Richard Owen *20 Essex Street*	
Sharpe, Thomas *1 Essex Court*	
Toulmin, John *3 Gray's Inn Place*	
Tyrrell, Alan *Francis Taylor Building*	
Wyatt, Derrick *Brick Court Chambers*	

Stephen Morris at **20 Essex Street** undertakes work concerning Articles 85 and 86, restrictive trade practices, the free movement of goods and agriculture within the EU and intellectual property licensing. He has contributed to 'Bellamy and Child on Common Market Law of Competition'.

Dr Philippa Watson at **Essex Court Chambers** has been recommended for her work in this sector. *Peter Duffy* appeared in the ECJ cases concerning 'van Schijndel and van Veen', and 'Brasserie du Pecheur/ Factortame (No. 3)'.

Green, Nicholas *Brick Court Chambers*

Anderson, David *Brick Court Chambers*	**Brealey,** Mark *Brick Court Chambers*	**Clough,** Mark *Brick Court Chambers*
Duffy, Peter *Essex Court Chambers*	**Hewson,** Barbara *Four Raymond Buildings*	**Lewis,** Adam *2 Hare Court*
Morris, Stephen *20 Essex Street*	**Paines,** Nicholas *Four Raymond Buildings*	**Sutton,** Alastair *2 Hare Court*
Thompson, Rhodri *Four Raymond Buildings*	**Trepte,** Peter *4 Essex Court*	**Turner,** Jonathan *Four Raymond Buildings*
Vajda, Christopher *Four Raymond Buildings*	**Watson,** Philippa *Essex Court Chambers*	
Belgrave, Susan *Arden Chambers*	**Mercer,** Hugh *Essex Court Chambers*	

Hoskins, Mark *Brick Court Chambers*	**Kelly,** Marie *3 Paper Buildings*

LEADERS IN EUROPEAN COMMUNITY LAW

Anderson, David
Brick Court Chambers (Christopher Clarke QC), London (0171) 583 0777. Called 1985.

Barling QC, Gerald
Brick Court Chambers (Christopher Clarke QC), London (0171) 583 0777. Called 1972, took silk 1991.

Belgrave, Susan
Arden Chambers (Andrew Arden QC), London (0171) 353 3132.

Specialisation: Principal area of practice is local government law including competitive tendering, EC public procurement rules, housing, environment and landlord and tenant matters. Other main area of work is employment including discrimination cases and transfer of undertakings. Author of several articles for legal periodicals, particularly on EC law topics and author of forthcoming book 'Nuisance and Harrassment' (Lemos Publications). Conducts seminars for Council of Legal Education on EC Law and for Institute of Housing and local authorities on aspects of housing law.

Prof. Membership: Administrative Law Bar Association, Bar European Group, Director of ACA Lawyers Group, Housing Law Practitioners Association.

Career: Called to the Bar 1989. Associate with *Stanbrook and Hooper* Brussels 1990-1992. Joined current chambers in 1993.

Personal: Educated at Heriot-Watt (BA, Hons 1981), London School of Economics (MSc (Econ) 1986), University of the West Indies, Barbados (LL.B Hons, 1988) and Université Libre de Bruxelles (Licence Spéciale en Droit Européen, 1992). Fluent in French and Spanish.

Brealey, Mark
Brick Court Chambers (Christopher

Clarke QC), London (0171) 583 0777. Called 1984.

Clough, Mark
Brick Court Chambers (Christopher Clarke QC), London (0171) 583 0777. Called 1978.

Duffy, Peter
See under Public and Administrative Law.

Forrester QC, Ian
2 Hare Court (C.W.G. Ross-Munro QC), London (0171) 583 1770.

Specialisation: European Community Law. Has practised from Brussels since 1972. Work includes competition, patent licences, distribution and joint ventures, discriminatory pricing, representing plaintiff and defendant before European Courts and arbitral tribunals. Also advises on trade, customs and dumping, EFTA, GATT, and EC measures on, inter alia, fisheries, steel, pharmaceuticals, semiconductors, automotive parts, professional practices, agriculture, sugar, dangerous substances and glass containers. Has contested national measures in violation of EC Treaty and constitutional conflicts. Clients include international companies, trade associations and governments. Appeared before the European Court of Justice in, inter alia, DCL v. Commission and Bulloch, Bethell v. Commission, Control Data v. Commission (I and II), Du Pont v. Customs & Excise, Government of Gibraltar v. Commission, Canon v. Council, Liberal Democrats v. European Parliament and BBC et al v. Commission (the Magill case). Addresses numerous conferences and seminars in Europe, the USA and Japan on EC trade, competition, legal and political topics. Author and co-author of numerous articles on EC competition and trade topics and of translations of the German Civil Code, Commercial Code and Introductory Law.

Prof. Membership: Faculty of Advocates, New York Bar, European Trade Law Association (Chairman).

Career: Called to the Bar 1972. Took Silk 1988 and joined current chambers 1989.

Personal: Educated at Kelvinside Academy, Glasgow 1946-62 and University of Glasgow 1962-67 (MA History and Literature 1965, LL.B, 1967). Visiting Professor, Glasgow University. Leisure pursuits include travel. Born 13th January 1945. Lives in Brussels.

Forwood QC, Nicholas
Brick Court Chambers (Christopher Clarke QC), London (0171) 583 0777. Called 1970, took silk 1987.

Fowler QC, Richard
See under Aviation.

Green, Nicholas
See under Commercial Law.

Hewson, Barbara
Four Raymond Buildings (Jeremy Lever QC), London (0171) 405 7211.

Specialisation: Specialist in Chancery and commercial litigation, particularly EC competition law. Practice also covers judicial review. Regularly addresses conferences and seminars.

Prof. Membership: Chancery Bar Association; Bar European Group; COMBAR.

Career: Called to the Bar 1985. Tenant at 11 New Square, Lincoln's Inn 1987-1991. Joined present chambers 1991. Called to the Bar of Ireland 1991. Contributor, JUSTICE Report on Protection of the Small Investor 1992. Member, JUSTICE Working Party on Public Interest Interventions 1994. Co-opted, Council of JUSTICE 1994. Elected representative, Bar Council of England & Wales 1992-4. Member, Bar Council's Sex

Discrimination Committee 1992-. Chairwoman, Association of Women Barristers, 1995-6.

Personal: Educated at St. Leonards/Mayfield School 1972-1979 and at Trinity Hall, Cambridge 1979-1982. Born 2nd June 1961. Lives in London.

Hoskins, Mark
Brick Court Chambers (Christopher Clarke QC), London (0171) 583 0777.

Specialisation: Principal area of practice is European Union law. Other main area of work is commercial law, particularly banking and conflict of laws. Co-author of 'Remedies in EC Law' (Longman, 1994).

Career: Called 1991. Référendaire to Judge David Edward, European Court of Justice Luxembourg, 1994-95.

Isaacs QC, Stuart
See under Shipping.

Kelly, Marie
3 Paper Buildings (Michael Parroy QC), London (0171) 583 8055. Called 1992.

Lasok QC, Paul
Four Raymond Buildings (Jeremy Lever QC), London (0171) 405 7211.

Specialisation: Specialist in all aspects of European Community law. Practises in both London and Brussels. Main areas of work include agriculture, competition, trade law (anti-dumping) and VAT. Publications include 'The European Court of Justice: Practice and Procedure' (Butterworths 2nd edition 1994), 'Lasok and Bridge's Law and Institutions of the European Union' (with D. Lasok QC) (Butterworths 1994), as well as numerous articles on EC and competition law in the 'European Competition Law Review' and other periodicals. Contributed (with J Lever QC) the chapter on merger legislation in the European Community in 'Weinberg & Blank on Take-Overs and Mergers' (Sweet & Maxwell). Consultant editor (with D. Vaughan QC) of 'Butterworths European Court Practice' (1993). Contributed sections on EC law to 'Halsbury's Laws of England', 4th edition, '1991 Law of the European Communities' (Butterworths). Also contributed to 'Stair Memorial Encyclopaedia of the Laws of Scotland' (Butterworths). Frequent speaker on EC law at conferences and seminars.

Prof. Membership: Bar European Group.

Career: Called to the Bar 1977. At the Commission of the European Communities 1979. Legal secretary (law clerk) to Advocate-General J.P Warner and Advocate-General Sir Gordon Slynn, Court of Justice of the European Communities 1980-84. Private practice in Brussels, specialising in European Community law 1985-87.

Personal: Educated at Jesus College, Cambridge 1972-75 (MA) and at Exeter University 1975-77 (LL.M). PhD Exeter

University 1986. Born 16th July 1953. Lives in London.

Layton QC, Alexander
2 Temple Gardens (Patrick Phillips QC), London (0171) 583 6041.

Specialisation: Within a wide-ranging commercial and common law practice, specialises in cross-border litigation, particularly in connection with other European countries and the USA. Other principal fields of practice include insurance, reinsurance and professional negligence. Has acted in litigation arising from the collapse of the BCCI and Maxwell empires and of London United Investments, and in many cases involving the Brussels Convention (such as Re Harrods (Buenos Aires) Ltd, Tesam v. Schuh Mode, New Hampshire v. Strabag Bau, etc.). Co-author 'European Civil Practice' (1989), a leading practitioner's work on European civil litigation.

Prof. Membership: COMBAR, British-German Jurists' Association (Chairman 1988-1993), London Common Law and Commercial Bar Association, Bar European Group.

Career: Called 1976; QC 1995.

Lever QC, Jeremy
See under Public and Administrative Law.

Lewis, Adam
See under Defamation.

Mercer, Hugh
Essex Court Chambers (Gordon Pollock QC), London (0171) 813 8000. Called 1985. Called 1985. Specialist in commercial and European Community law, with a particular emphasis on cross-frontier litigation. Born 4.12.1962.

Morris, Stephen
20 Essex Street (Kenneth Rokison QC), London (0171) 583 9294. Called 1981. Specialist in EC and UK competition law and EC trade law. Born 18.5.1957.

Paines, Nicholas
Four Raymond Buildings (Jeremy Lever QC), London (0171) 405 7211.

Specialisation: EC law and administrative law. Areas of EC practice include agriculture, employment, free movement of goods, pensions, public procurement, sex discrimination, social security and VAT. Also handles UK and EC competition law and general commercial litigation. Has appeared in several cases in the European Court. Contributor to Bellamy and Child, 'Common Market Law of Competition'; Halsbury's Laws of England; and Vaughan: 'Law of the European Communities'.

Prof. Membership: Bar Council, Bar European Group (Vice-Chairman), Administrative Law Bar Association, UK Association for European Law.

Career: Called to the Bar 1978. Supplementary Panel of Junior Counsel to the Crown (Common Law) 1993.

Personal: Educated at Oxford University 1973-76 (MA, Jurisprudence) and Brussels University 1977-78 (Licence Speciale en Droit Europeen).

Parker QC, Kenneth
Four Raymond Buildings (Jeremy Lever QC), London (0171) 405 7211. Called 1975, took silk 1992.

Plender QC, Richard Owen
20 Essex Street (Kenneth Rokison QC), London (0171) 583 9294.

Specialisation: Specialist in European Community law, public international law and administrative law. Also experienced in extradition and immigration. Important cases include, in the European Court of Justice: British Steel v. Commission (1995); British Airways v. Commission (1995). Francovitch & Bonifaci v. Italy (1991); France & Germany v. Council (1991); Johnson v. Chief Constable of RUC (1986); R v. Pieck (1980); in the House of Lords and Court of Appeal: Kuwait Airways v. Iraq Airways and Iraq (1995) HL: R v. Manchester Crown Court (1993) HL; Re International Tin Council (1988) CA; R v. Home Secretary ex parte Sivakumaran (1988) HL; Burgoin SA v. MAFF (1985) CA; Holder v. R (1978) PC; Kakis v. Cyprus (1978) HL. Publications include 'International Migration Law' (2nd Ed. 1988); 'Fundamental Rights' (1973); 'Cases and Materials on the Law of European Communities' with J Usher (3rd Ed. 1993); 'Introduccion al Derecho Comunitario Europeo' with J. Peres Santos (1984); 'Basic Documents on International Migration Law' (1988); 'Legal History and Comparative Law: Essays in honour of Albert Kirafy' (1990); 'The European Contracts Convention: The Rome Convention on Choice of Law for Contracts' (1991). Also contributes to 'Halsbury's Laws of England', 'Encyclopedia of Public International Law' and 'Vaughan Law of the European Communities Service' and various journals.

Personal: Bar European Group; COMBAR; Immigration Law Practitioners Association; South Eastern Circuit.

Career: Called to the Bar 1974. Joined present chambers 1984. Took Silk 1989. Consultant, United Nations Law and Population Programme, 1972-74. Lecturer 1974-85, Reader 1985-87, Director, Centre of European Law, 1987-88, King's College, London. Legal Adviser, United Nations High Commissioner for Refugees, 1974-77. Leverhulme Fellow, Yale Law School, 1980. *Référendiare*, Court of Justice of the European Communities, 1980-83. Honorary Senior Member, Robinson College, Cambridge since 1983. British Academy Fellow, Soviet Academy of Sciences, 1985. Director of studies 1989, Director of Research 1990, Hague Academy of International Law. Honorary Visiting Professor, City University since 1990. *Professeur associé*, Université de droit, d'économie et des sciences sociles de Paris 1990. Legal Adviser to the States of Jersey and Guernsey since 1989.

Personal: Educated at Dulwich College 1954-64, and Queens College, Cambridge (BA 1967, LL.B 1968, LL.D 1993). Sheffield University PhD 1971. Illinois LL.M 1971, JSD 1972. Fluent in French and a working knowledge of Spanish. Born 9th October 1945.

Sharpe QC, Thomas

1 Essex Court (Anthony Grabiner QC), London (0171) 583 2000. Called 1976, took silk 1994. Principal areas of practice are UK and EU competition law, utility regulation, public law.

Sutton, Alastair

2 Hare Court (C.W.G. Ross-Munro QC), London (0171) 583 1770.

Specialisation: Specialist in all aspect of European Community law and international trade law. Current practice can be divided into advisory work and litigation. Undertakes advisory work for governments, companies and trade associations on all areas of EC Law and on external relations with other countries, in particular Japan, Central and Eastern Europe, the EFTA states and North America. Also advises on the internal market, trade policy, competition and state aids, intellectual property, telecommunications, financial services, audiovisual policy, environmental protection and social policy. Also covers advisory work on international trade law within GATT/WTO. Contentious work includes representing clients in the European Court of Justice. Acted for the applicants in the following cases: Liberal Democrats v. European Parliament (action for failure to act); Ferchimex S.A. v. Commission (antidumping); and Titan Cement v. Commission (state aids). Also acted for the applicants in the EFTA Court in Scottish Salmon Growers Association v. EFTA (state aids). Publications include 'Trends in the Regulation of International Trade in Textiles', 'Yearbook of World Affairs', 1977; 'Relations between the European Community and Japan in 1982 & 1983', 'Oxford Yearbook of European Law', 1983; 'Financial Services and Competition Policy' Butterworth's Competition Law, 1991; Butterworth's European Law Service, 1992 (co-editor); 'EC Insurance Law', Butterworth, 1992; Commentary on EC legal developments in 1992 in Butterworth's Annual European Review, 1993; and 'European Union and the Rule of Law in Maastricht and Beyond' (The Federal Trust, 1994).

Career: Called to the Bar 1972. Lecturer in EC and Public International Law, University College, London 1967-73. Commission of the European Communities 1973-89. EC ne-

gotiator for textiles agreements 1973-77. First Secretary, Commission Delegation in Japan 1979-84. Principal administrator for international trade policy in the Directorate-General for External Relations, 1984-85. Member of Cabinet of Lord Cockfield, Vice-President of the European Commission, 1985-88. Head of Division for Insurance, EC Commission, 1989. Since 1990, partner in the firm *Forrester, Norall & Sutton*, Brussels, and a barrister at current chambers. Visiting Fellow, Centre for European Legal Studies, Faculty of Law, University of Cambridge, 1993-94. Visiting Fellow (Parsons Fellowship), Faculty of Law, University of Sydney, Australia.

Personal: Educated at Aberdeen University (LL.B) 1963-66, and at Univesity College, London (LL.M & Diploma in International and Comparative Air and Space Law) 1966-67. Languages include French, Spanish and Japanese. Leisure pursuits include golf, squash and rugby. Born 5th January 1945. Lives in Brussels.

Thompson, Rhodri

Four Raymond Buildings (Jeremy Lever QC), London (0171) 405 7211.

Specialisation: European Community law including administrative law and competition. Spent two years in Brussels, acting in several major EC law competition cases. Cases include Publishers Association v. Commission (Net Book Agreement, appeal to ECJ); Tetra Pak International S.A. v. Commission (Tetra Pak II); R v. Secretary of State for Foreign and Commonwealth Affairs, ex parte Rees-Mogg (Maastricht challenge); R v. Secretary of State for National Heritage ex parte Continental Television (Red Hot Dutch case). Contributor to 'Bellamy & Child, Common Market Law of Competition', (4th Edn 1993); 'Weinberg & Blank on Takeovers and Mergers' and author of 'The Single Market for Pharmaceuticals' (Butterworths, 1994). Regular speaker at conferences/in house seminars on EC law.

Toulmin QC, John

3 Gray's Inn Place (R. Neville Thomas QC), London (0171) 831 8441. Called 1965, took silk 1980. Principal area of practice is commercial and EC law and arbitration. Also handles medical law and Administrative law cases. Born 14.2.1941.

Trepte, Peter

4 Essex Court (David Steel QC), London (0171) 797 7970. Called 1987. Practice covers European and International procurement, competition law and energy and utilities.

Turner, Jonathan

Four Raymond Buildings (Jeremy Lever

QC), London (0171) 405 7211. Called 1988.

Tyrrell QC, Alan

Francis Taylor Building (Alan Tyrrell QC), London (0171) 797 7250. Fax (0171) 797 7299. Also at 205 Bd. St. Germain, 75007 Paris (1) 45449192. Fax (1) 42221507.

Specialisation: General common law practitioner, with a particular emphasis on European Community law. Practice also covers employment law and crime. Important cases include Wells v. United Kingdom (European Court of Human Rights 1994-95); ITP Ltd v. Commission (ECJ 1991) (Magill - abuse of intellectual property right); Black v. Yates (1991) (civil judgements and jurisdiction/ Brussels convention); British Leyland v. Armstrong Patents (1987) (copyright/EC law). Publications include 'The Legal Profession in the New Europe' (Basil Blackwell, 1993).

Prof. Membership: Bar European Group (Chairman 1986-88); Western Circuit; London Common Law and Commercial Bar Association; Chartered Institute of Arbitrators; London Court of International Arbitration; British Academy of Experts; International Practice Committee of the Bar Council (Chairman 1988).

Career: Called to the Bar 1956. Joined present chambers 1960. Appointed Recorder 1972. Took Silk 1976. Bencher of Grays Inn 1986. Lord Chancellor's Visitor, 1990; Deputy High Court Judge, Queens Bench Division 1990. F.C.I. (Arb) 1993.

Personal: Educated at London School of Economics (LL.B) 1954. Director (non-exec) Medical Protection Society. Director (non-exec) Papworth Hospital NHS Trust. Member of the European Parliament 1979-84. Fluent in French. Born 27th June 1933.

Vajda, Christopher

Four Raymond Buildings (Jeremy Lever QC), London (0171) 405 7211. Called 1979. Practice covers EC and competition law, judicial review and computer law.

Vaughan QC, David

See under Commercial Law.

Watson, Philippa

Essex Court Chambers (Gordon Pollock QC), London (0171) 813 8000. Called 1988.

Wyatt QC, Derrick

Brick Court Chambers (Christopher Clarke QC), London (0171) 583 0777. Called 1972, took silk 1993.

FAMILY LAW

A S WELL as a handful of highly-specialised matrimonial chambers, there are many barristers working in general common law sets who have considerable experience in the field. All the sets of chambers listed below are well known for their family work, but **Queen Elizabeth Building, 1 Mitre Court Buildings,** closely followed by **1 King's Bench Walk** and **29 Bedford Row Chambers,** have particularly strong reputations.

1 Mitre Court Buildings is an established set, with all members practising exclusively in the field of family law. The standard reference work on the subject, 'Rayden and Jackson on Divorce and Family matters' is co-edited by two members at chambers. The set handled the recent high profile case 'B v B', concerning pension rights for wives. Silks at the set who deserve particular mention are *Bruce Blair QC, Mark Everall QC* (recommended for handling cases with an international aspect), *Michael Horowitz QC, Judith Hughes QC* and *Jeremy Posnansky QC* (who has a special interest in cases with medical aspects). Among the many excellent juniors at the set, *Nicholas Mostyn*, author of 'Child's Pay: The Complete Guide to the Child Support Act 1991', has been particularly recommended. Other leading juniors at the set are *Nigel Dyer, Martin Pointer* and *Philip Moor.*

Queen Elizabeth Building, is a leading family law set, and *Florence Baron QC* who recently took silk, has been particularly recommended for her expertise. Other leading family silks at the set are head of chambers *Ian Karsten QC, David Bodey QC* and *Paul Coleridge QC,* who has particular expertise in handling heavy financial disputes between wealthy spouses (frequently international) and child disputes involving both private and public law. Leading juniors at chambers are *Andrew Moylan, Timothy Amos* and *Thomas Brudenell.*

The expanding chambers at **29 Bedford Row** has a fast growing reputation and *Timothy Scott QC*, who has been particularly recommended, has recently taken silk. Out of a number of highly regarded juniors, *Nicholas Francis* emerges as the leading light. His workload includes acting for media personalities and handling family cases where banks and mortgagees have intervened. He also has

considerable experience in the field of wasted costs, acting in the lead case 'C v C' (wasted costs) along with fellow member *Howard Shaw*. Also highly regarded are *Lucy Stone* (who has represented a number of well known individuals from the world of entertainment), *Charles Atkins, Philip Cayford, Neil Sanders,* and *Clare Renton* who is a qualified family mediator. Chambers have been involved in many other reported family cases during the last 12 months including 'M v M' (child abduction) and 'Whiston v W' (bigamy).

1 King's Bench Walk is one of the top sets in the field and *Barry Singleton QC* has an excellent reputation for, and vast experience in, childcare and complex financial matters. Other leading silks at the set who have been particularly recommended are *Richard Anelay QC, Camden Pratt QC* and *Judith Parker QC*, who is particularly known for handling cases with medico-legal issues and cases with international aspects, including inter-country adoption and child

abduction. *James Turner*, a leading junior at the set, deserves particular mention for his expertise in handling financial matters and international abduction work. He has appeared in financial cases in the Grand Court of the Cayman Islands. Other well-regarded juniors include *Deborah Eaton* and *Andrew McFarlane.*

LEADING JUNIORS– LONDON

Mostyn, Nicholas   *1 Mitre Court Buildings*

Amos, Timothy *Queen Elizabeth Building*	**Cohen,** Jonathan *4 Paper Buildings*	**Dyer,** Nigel *1 Mitre Court Buildings*
Francis, Nicholas *29 Bedford Row Chambers*	**Hildyard,** Marianna *4 Brick Court*	**Meston,** Lord *Queen Elizabeth Building*
Moor, Philip *1 Mitre Court Buildings*	**Moylan,** Andrew *Queen Elizabeth Building*	**Pointer,** Martin *1 Mitre Court Buildings*
Setright, Henry *1 Gray's Inn Square*	**Stone,** Lucy *29 Bedford Row Chambers*	**Turner,** James *1 King's Bench Walk*

Atkins, Charles *29 Bedford Row Chambers*	**Balcombe,** David *1 Crown Office Row*	**Brasse,** Gillian *14 Gray's Inn Square*
Brudenell, Thomas *Queen Elizabeth Building*	**Budden,** Caroline *22 Old Buildings*	**Cayford,** Philip *29 Bedford Row Chambers*
Davidson, Katharine *1 Mitre Court Buildings*	**Duckworth,** Peter *29 Bedford Row Chambers*	**Eaton,** Deborah *1 King's Bench Walk*
Higson Smith, Gillian *Gray's Inn Chambers*	**Horrocks,** Peter *22 Old Buildings*	**Howard,** Charles *New Court Chambers*
Jackson, Peter *4 Paper Buildings*	**Johnstone,** Mark *Pump Court Chambers*	**McFarlane,** Andrew *1 King's Bench Walk*
Renton, Clare *29 Bedford Row Chambers*	**Rowe,** Judith *22 Old Buildings*	**Sanders,** Neil *29 Bedford Row Chambers*
Shaw, Howard *29 Bedford Row Chambers*	**Sternberg,** Michael *4 Paper Buildings*	**Willbourne,** Caroline *One Garden Court*
Wingert, Rachel *Gray's Inn Chambers*		

Of the other sets highly regarded for family work, **1 Garden Court**, a specialist family set, has an establishedreputation and *Alison Ball QC* has recently taken silk there. **4 Paper Buildings**, a strong matrimonial chambers, is known for handling a considerable amount of Official Solicitor work. *Jonathan Cohen* at the set has been particularly recommended for his expertise. **4 Brick Court** *(David Medhurst)* has particular experience in child care work as do **14**

Gray's Inn Square. 4 Brick Court *(Anthony Shaw QC)* also contains several well-regarded family law practitioners.

Notable individuals in other chambers that deserve particular mention are *James Munby QC* **(1 New Square)** and *Henry Setright* **(1 Gray's Inn Square)**, who have both received frequent recommendations for their expertise in handling child related matters.

OUTSIDE LONDON

The majority of chambers outside London offer expertise in this area as part of their general common law practice. Those individuals detailed below have been recommended for their work in all aspects of this field, ranging from child care matters to high value ancillary relief claims.

HIGHLY REGARDED SILKS - REGIONS

Bloom, Charles   *28 St. John St*
Evans, Mark   *St. John's Chambers*
Harris, David M.   *Peel House*
Hindley, Estella   *5 Fountain Court*
Kushner, Lindsey   *28 St. John St*

HIGHLY REGARDED JUNIORS - REGIONS

Bridge, Rowena *King Charles House*	**Brown,** Stephanie *5 Fountain Court*	**Clark,** B.J. *Ropewalk Chambers*
Dinan-Hayward, Deborah *Assize Court Chambers*	**Ferguson,** Christopher *Assize Court Chambers*	**George,** Gareth *9 Park Place*
Harris, David J. *32 Park Place*	**Henke,** Ruth *Iscoed Chambers*	**Hodgson,** Margaret *St. Ive's Chambers*
Irving, Gillian *9 St. John Street*	**Isaacs,** Paul *9 Woodhouse Square*	**Kennedy,** Michael J. *Peel House*
Macur, Julia *St. Ive's Chambers*	**Morgan,** Lynne *32 Park Place*	**Owen,** Gail A. *Peel House*
Parry, Isabel *9 Park Place*	**Riley,** Christine *9 St. John Street*	**Roddy,** Maureen B. *Peel House*
Shelton, Gordon E. *Broadway House*	**Somerville,** Bryce *No.6 Fountain Court*	**Thomas,** Sybil *3 Fountain Court*
Wildblood, Stephen *Albion Chambers*	**Wills-Goldingham,** Claire *Albion Chambers*	**Wood,** Martin J. *Broadway House*

Amos, Timothy
Queen Elizabeth Building (Ian Karsten QC), London (0171) 797 7837. Called 1987.

Anelay QC, Richard
1 King's Bench Walk (Mr J.B.S. Townend QC), London (0171) 583 6266. Called 1970, took silk 1993.

Atkins, Charles
29 Bedford Row Chambers (Evan Stone QC), London (0171) 831 2626. Called 1975.

Balcombe, David
1 Crown Office Row (Robert Seabrook QC), London (0171) 797 7500. Called 1980.

Ball QC, Alison
One Garden Court (Miss Eleanor F. Platt QC, Miss Alison Ball QC), London (0171) 797 7900. Called 1972, took silk 1995.

Baron QC, Florence
Queen Elizabeth Building (Ian Karsten QC), London (0171) 797 7837. Called 1976, took silk 1995. Principal area of practice is family law.

Blair QC, Bruce
1 Mitre Court Buildings (P.E.J. Focke QC), London (0171) 797 7070. Called 1969, took silk 1989.

Bloom QC, Charles
28 St. John St (Charles Bloom QC), Manchester (0161) 834 8418. Called 1963, took silk 1987.

Bodey QC, David
Queen Elizabeth Building (Ian Karsten QC), London (0171) 797 7837. Called 1970, took silk 1991.

Brasse, Gillian
14 Gray's Inn Square (Joanna Dodson QC, Glenn Brasse), London (0171) 242 0858. Called 1977. Practice encompasses all areas of family law. Born 19.6.1953.

Bridge, Rowena
King Charles House (Richard Inglis), Nottingham (0115) 9418851.

Brown, Stephanie
5 Fountain Court (Anthony Barker QC), Birmingham (0121) 606 0500. Called 1982.

Brudenell, Thomas
Queen Elizabeth Building (Ian Karsten QC), London (0171) 797 7837. Called 1977. Specialises in family law and equine litigation.

Budden, Caroline
22 Old Buildings (John Samuels QC), London (0171) 831 0222.

Specialisation: Principal area of practice is family law work including public and private law aspects of the Children Act, adoption, wardship, child abduction, matrimonial finance and solicitors' negligence relating to family law matters.

Prof. Membership: Family Law Bar Association, Professional Negligence Bar Association.

Career: Called to the Bar 1977; founder member *22 Old Buildings* in 1987.

Personal: Educated at Alfred Colfox School, Bridport, Dorset, and Bristol University (LL.B 1976). Born 30 July 1954. Lives in London.

Cayford, Philip
29 Bedford Row Chambers (Evan Stone QC), London (0171) 831 2626.

Specialisation: Family practice, heavily biased towards ancillary relief and matters with a commercial bias including company and entertainment law contracts. Also handles a wide range of common law, commercial, entertainment, and other family law matters. Reported Court of Appeal decisions on Hague Convention and jurisdiction issues, on a derivative shareholder action arising from breakdown of family owned company, and on setting aside consent orders. Other reported decisions on children cases, professional negligence actions, inquests, etc. Clients included MP's, Peers, well-known business men and entertainers, barristers, surgeons etc.

Prof.l Membership: Middle Temple.

Career: Called to the Bar 1975; joined 29 Bedford Row 1978.

Personal: Educated at Marlborough College 1965-70 and University of Wales (Cardiff) 1971-74. Producer/Director of several natural history/conservation documentaries for BBC and National Geographic. Author of booklets and articles on conservation and travel. Photographs appear in National Geographic, Sunday Times. Leisure pursuits include flying and cricket. Born on 28th July 1952. Lives in London.

Clark, B.J.
Ropewalk Chambers (Richard Maxwell QC), Nottingham (0115) 9472581/2/3/4.

Cohen, Jonathan
4 Paper Buildings (Lionel Swift QC), London (0171) 583 0816.

Specialisation: Principal area of practice encompasses all areas of family law, in particular matrimonial finance, professional negligence arising out of finance cases, and childcare.

Prof. Membership: Family Law Bar Association, Common Law Bar Association, Criminal Law Association.

Career: Called to the Bar 1974 and joined present chambers in 1975. Appointed Assistant Recorder 1993.

Personal: School Governor. Member of Area Committee Legal Aid Board. Born 1951.

Coleridge QC, Paul
Queen Elizabeth Building (Ian Karsten QC), London (0171) 797 7837. Called 1970, took silk 1993. Principal areas of practice are family law and personal injury.

Davidson, Katharine
1 Mitre Court Buildings (P.E.J. Focke QC), London (0171) 797 7070. Called 1987.

Dinan-Hayward, Deborah
Assize Court Chambers (Graeme Wood), Bristol (0117) 9264587.

Dodson QC, Joanna
14 Gray's Inn Square (Joanna Dodson QC, Glenn Brasse), London (0171) 242 0858.

Specialisation: Practice encompasses all aspects of family law.

Prof. Membership: Family Law Bar Association.

Career: Called to the Bar 1971. Joined *14 Gray's Inn Square* in 1991 and took silk in 1993.

Personal: Educated at James Allen's Girls School 1956-63 and Newnham College, Cambridge (BA 1967, MA 1971). Born 5th September 1945. Lives in London.

Duckworth, Peter
29 Bedford Row Chambers (Evan Stone QC), London (0171) 831 2626. Called 1971.

Dyer, Nigel
1 Mitre Court Buildings (P.E.J. Focke QC), London (0171) 797 7070. Called 1982.

Eaton, Deborah
1 King's Bench Walk (Mr J.B.S. Townend QC), London (0171) 583 6266. Called 1985.

Evans QC, Mark
St. John's Chambers (Roderick Denyer QC), Bristol (0117) 9213456. Called 1971, took silk 1995.

Everall QC, Mark
1 Mitre Court Buildings (P.E.J. Focke QC), London (0171) 797 7070.

Specialisation: Work includes matrimonial finance, public and private law children cases, adoption, and cases with an international aspect. Editor, Rayden & Jackson on Divorce & Family Matters.

Prof. Membership: Family Law Bar Association; Bar European Group; International Academy of Matrimonial Lawyers: Administrative Law Bar Association.

Career: Took silk in 1994.

Ferguson, Christopher
Assize Court Chambers (Graeme Wood), Bristol (0117) 9264587.

Francis, Nicholas
29 Bedford Row Chambers (Evan Stone QC), London (0171) 831 2626.

Specialisation: Principal area of practice is matrimonial ancillary relief work, including property disputes and cases where banks or other mortgagees have intervened. Other main areas of practice are wasted costs and solicitors' negligence; also handles children cases: residence, contact, education and abduction. Other areas include professional negligence and franchising law. Cases include Re P (A Minor) [1992] (Education); Re D (minors) [1993] (conciliation - disclosure of information); and C. v. C [1994] (wasted costs order). Articles includes 'Mediation: where do you draw the line?' and several articles on ancillary relief for *Family Law*. Regular lecturer on costs and discovery; and contributor to Legal Network TV.

Pro. Membership: Family Law Bar Association (commitee member). Bar Council Professional Conduct Committee, Legal Aid and Fees Committee.

Career: Called to the Bar in 1981 and joined *29 Bedford Row* in 1982. Elected to the Bar Council in November 1994.

Personal: Educated at Radley College 1971-76 and Doening College, Cambridge 1977-80 (BA Law 1980, MA 1984). Leisure pursuits include racing dinghies. Born 22nd April 1958. Lives in London.

George, Gareth
9 Park Place (Philip Rees), Cardiff (01222) 382731.

Harris QC, David M.
Peel House (David M. Harris QC), Liverpool (0151) 236 0718.

Harris, David J.
32 Park Place (Christopher Williams), Cardiff (01222) 397364.

Henke, Ruth
Iscoed Chambers (Wyn Richards), Swansea (01792) 652988/9.

Higson Smith, Gillian
Gray's Inn Chambers (Brian Jubb), London (0171) 404 1111.

Specialisation: Principal area of practice is child care law. Has wide experience in representing local authorities and children/guardians ad Litem in public law proceedings

in adoption; residence and contact disputes and private wardship, at all levels of the Family Court.

Prof. Membership: Member of the Family Law Bar Association.

Career: Called to the Bar: November 1973.

Hildyard, Marianna
4 Brick Court (David Medhurst), London (0171) 797 8910. Called 1977.

Hindley QC, Estella
5 Fountain Court (Anthony Barker QC), Birmingham (0121) 606 0500. Called 1971, took silk 1992.

Hodgson, Margaret
St. Ive's Chambers (Mr. Edward Coke), Birmingham (0121) 236 0863/0929. Called 1975.

Horowitz QC, Michael
1 Mitre Court Buildings (P.E.J. Focke QC), London (0171) 797 7070. Called 1968, took silk 1990. Called 1968, took silk 1990. Specialises in family law, including ancillary relief, childcare and child abduction. Born 18.10.1943.

Horrocks, Peter
22 Old Buildings (John Samuels QC), London (0171) 831 0222.

Specialisation: Principal area of practice is child law, both public and private, including disputes as to residence and contact, care proceedings, adoption and abduction. Other areas of work include probate, boundaries and easements, personal injuries and crime.

Prof. Membership: Family Law Bar Association.

Career: Called to the Bar in 1977; founder member of present chambers in 1987.

Personal: Educated at Winchester 1968-72, Trinity Hall, Cambridge 1973-76 and College of Law 1976-77. Leisure pursuits include real tennis, cricket and opera. Born 31st January 1955. Lives in London.

Howard, Charles
New Court Chambers (George Carman QC), London (0171) 583 6166.

Specialisation: Family Law. Not only conventional areas but also related matters including Inheritance Act and Probate disputes, constructive trust issues, family-oriented judicial review and solicitor's negligence in relation to family work. Also handles a considerable amount of personal injury litigation, medical negligence cases, judicial review and actions against the police. Has represented a former Permanent Secretary in Crown Agent's Inquiry, acted in the inquiry into the death of Tyra Henry and represented the 4 Turks who sold their kidneys for onward transmission to private patients in this country.

Career: Called to the Bar in 1975. In full-time practice since 1976.

Personal: Educated at Sherborne School, Dorset 1964-68, St. John's College, Cambridge 1969-72 and St. Anthony's College, Oxford 1972-73. Leisure interests include cricket, tennis, the theatre, cinema, walking and travel. Born 7th March 1951. Lives in London.

Hughes QC, Judith
1 Mitre Court Buildings (P.E.J. Focke QC), London (0171) 797 7070. Called 1974, took silk 1994.

Irving, Gillian
9 St. John Street (John Hand QC), Manchester (0161) 955 9000.

Isaacs, Paul
9 Woodhouse Square (John Morris Collins), Leeds (0113) 2451986.

Jackson, Peter
4 Paper Buildings (Lionel Swift QC), London (0171) 583 0816. Called 1978. Practice encompasses all aspects of family law. Born 9.12.1955.

Johnstone, Mark
Pump Court Chambers (Guy Boney QC), London (0171) 353 0711.

Specialisation: Financial provision on divorce. Practice also covers family provision under the Inheritance Act 1975, child care and residence proceedings. Important cases include Lloyds Bank v. Egremont & Egremont [1990]; Re N [1992]; and Hampshire County Council v. S [1993]. Wrote three chapters in 'Brown on Divorce'.

Prof. Membership: Family Law Bar Association

Career: Called to the Bar 1984.

Karsten QC, Ian
Queen Elizabeth Building (Ian Karsten QC), London (0171) 797 7837.

Specialisation: Principal areas of practice are Family Law and Medical Negligence. Specially interested in cases with a foreign or international element. Has appeared in numerous leading cases. Undertakes work in most fields of Common Law.

Career: Called 1967; commenced practice 1969; Silk 1990; Recorder 1994. Formerly Lecturer in Law, LSE (Contract, Tort, Private International Law).

Kennedy, Michael J.
Peel House (David M. Harris QC), Liverpool (0151) 236 0718.

Kushner QC, Lindsey
28 St. John St (Charles Bloom QC), Manchester (0161) 834 8418. Called 1974, took silk 1992.

Levy QC, Allan

17 Bedford Row (Allan Levy QC), London (0171) 831 7314.

Specialisation: Principal areas of practice: child law and medical law. Has appeared in numerous leading cases in these fields, such as Re F (1990) (House of Lords, consent to medical treatment); Re M (1994) (House of Lords, Children Act s31) and many Court of Appeal cases; represented Department of Health in Cleveland Inquiry; frequently acted as amicus curiae. Author of ' Wardship Proceedings'; 'Custody and Access'; 'Adoption of Children'; 'Focus on Child Abuse'; 'Refocus on Child Abuse' and numerous articles. Chairman, Staffordshire CC 'Pindown' Inquiry 1990-91. Frequent broadcaster on TV and radio and has lectured at universities and professional seminars.

Prof. Membership: Fellow, Royal Society of Medicine, Honorary Legal Advisor National Children's Bureau; Council of Justice; Fellow, International Association of Matrimonial lawyers since 1992. elected Member Bar Council since 1994.

Career: Called to the Bar in 1969. Took silk in 1989. Appointed Recorder 1993. Bencher, Inner Temple.

Personal: Educated at Bury Grammar School 1953-61 and Hull University 1961-64. Leisure pursuits include travel. Born 17th August 1942. Lives in London.

Macur, Julia

St. Ive's Chambers (Mr. Edward Coke), Birmingham (0121) 236 0863/0929. Called 1979.

McFarlane, Andrew

1 King's Bench Walk (Mr J.B.S. Townend QC), London (0171) 583 6266.

Specialisation: Principal area of practice is family law. Handles all aspects and has particular expertise in the law relating to children (both public and private law), international child abduction and adoption. Co-author with David Hershman of 'Children: Law & Practice' (Family Law 1991) and contributor to 'Family Court Practice' (Family Law 1995). Regular lecturer at nationally organised conferences and seminars.

Prof. Membership: Family Law Bar Association, Association of Lawyers for Children, British Agencies for Adoption and Fostering.

Career: Called to the Bar in 1977. At Priory Chambers, Birmingham 1978-93 and remains a door tenant there. Joined 1 King's Bench Walk in 1993. Appointed Assistant Recorder in 1994.

Personal: Educated at Shrewsbury School 1968-72 and Durham University 1972-76. Currently studying at the University of Wales (LLM (Canon Law) course 1994-96). Leisure interests include theatre, conjuring, walking and his children. Born 20th June 1954. Lives in Malvern.

Meston, Lord

Queen Elizabeth Building (Ian Karsten QC), London (0171) 797 7837. Called 1973. Principal areas of practice are family, general common law and employment.

Moor, Philip

1 Mitre Court Buildings (P.E.J. Focke QC), London (0171) 797 7070.

Specialisation: Family law, with particular emphasis on the financial aspects of marital breakdown. Regular lecturer and contributor (with Nicholas Mostyn as co-author) to 'Family Law' magazine.

Prof. Membership: Family Law Bar Association (Committee Member since 1987 and current Head of Education & Training).

Career: Called to the Bar in 1982 and joined *1 Mitre Court Buildings* in 1983. Member of General Council of the Bar 1987-89. Council of Legal Education 1988-91 (Board of Examiners 1989-92). Phillips Committee on Financing Pupillage (1989).

Personal: Educated at Canford School 1972-77 and Pembroke College, Oxford 1978-81. Leisure pursuits include cricket, football and rugby union. Lives in Bromley.

Morgan, Lynne

32 Park Place (Christopher Williams), Cardiff (01222) 397364.

Mostyn, Nicholas

1 Mitre Court Buildings (P.E.J. Focke QC), London (0171) 797 7070. Called 1980.

Moylan, Andrew

Queen Elizabeth Building (Ian Karsten QC), London (0171) 797 7837. Called 1978.

Munby QC, James

See under Commercial Law.

Murdoch QC, Gordon

4 Paper Buildings (Lionel Swift QC), London (0171) 583 0816. Called 1970, took silk 1995. Principal area of practice is family law work. Also handles general civil litigation. Born 7.6.1947.

Owen, Gail A.

Peel House (David M. Harris QC),

Liverpool (0151) 236 0718.

Parker QC, Judith

1 King's Bench Walk (Mr J.B.S. Townend QC), London (0171) 583 6266.

Specialisation: All aspects of family law, including medico-legal issues, child care and adoption, divorce and matrimonial finance, international aspects of family law (including intercountry adoption and child abduction), and specialist appellate advocacy.

Prof. Membership: Family Law Bar Association.

Career: Called to the Bar in 1973 and was

appointed a Q.C. in 1991.

Parry, Isabel

9 Park Place (Philip Rees), Cardiff (01222) 382731.

Pauffley QC, Anna

4 Paper Buildings (Lionel Swift QC), London (0171) 583 0816. Called 1979, took silk 1995.

Platt QC, Eleanor F.

One Garden Court (Miss Eleanor F. Platt QC, Miss Alison Ball QC), London (0171) 797 7900. Called 1960, took silk 1982.

Pointer, Martin

1 Mitre Court Buildings (P.E.J. Focke QC), London (0171) 797 7070. Called 1976. Handles all types of family law, but principally financial relief claims. Born 17.7.1953.

Posnansky QC, Jeremy

1 Mitre Court Buildings (P.E.J. Focke QC), London (0171) 797 7070.

Specialisation: Family law. Since taking silk in 1994 (first application), has continued to cover all aspects of family law, including ancillary relief and children. Handled at least 6 reported cases in 1994. Special interest in cases with medical aspects. Has addressed seminars for the F.L.B.A.

Prof. Membership: Family Law Bar Association; Medico-Legal Society. Admitted to the Bar of Antigua.

Career: Called to the Bar in 1972. Joined present chambers in 1991, having previously been at *22 Old Buildings*, Lincoln's Inn. Appointed Assistant Recorder in 1993. Took silk in 1994.

Personal: Educated at St. Paul's School 1964-69. Leisure pursuits include scuba diving and travelling with his family. Born 8th March 1951. Lives in London.

Pratt QC, Camden

1 King's Bench Walk (Mr J.B.S. Townend QC), London (0171) 583 6266. Called 1970, took silk 1992. Principal areas of practice are family (especially international child abduction) and environmental law (especially pollution). Born 14.12.1947.

Renton, Clare

29 Bedford Row Chambers (Evan Stone QC), London (0171) 831 2626.

Specialisation: Principal area of practice is family law including law as it affects cohabitees; confidentiality and publicity in family law. Other areas of practice include personal injury both for plaintiffs and defendants and general common law work.

Prof. Membership: Family Law Bar Association; Statute Law Society; Family Mediation Association.

Career: Called to the Bar 1972. Joined chambers at *20 Bedford Row* in 1980.

Riley, Christine
9 St. John Street (John Hand QC),
Manchester (0161) 955 9000.

Roddy, Maureen B.
Peel House (David M. Harris QC), Liverpool (0151) 236 0718.

Rowe, Judith
22 Old Buildings (John Samuels QC),
London (0171) 831 0222.
Specialisation: Principal area of practice is
family law, particularly public law child care
cases, education law and judicial review. Clients include numerous local authorities and
guardians.
Prof. Membership: Family Law Bar Association.
Career: Called to the Bar 1979. Joined current chambers 1988.
Personal: Educated at Rednock School,
Gloucestershire 1968-74 and University College, London 1975-78. Leisure pursuits
include theatre, travel, watersports and gardening. Born 7th August 1957. Lives in
London.

Sanders, Neil
29 Bedford Row Chambers (Evan Stone
QC), London (0171) 831 2626. Called
1975. Principal area of practice is matrimonial finance and children, including child
abduction cases. Born 17.4.1953.

Scotland QC, Patricia
1 Gray's Inn Square (Patricia Scotland
QC), London (0171) 405 3000. Called
1977, took silk 1991.

Scott QC, Timothy
29 Bedford Row Chambers (Evan Stone
QC), London (0171) 831 2626. Called
1975, took silk 1995. Principal area of practice is family law, often with an international
element. Born 19.7.1949.

Setright, Henry
1 Gray's Inn Square (Patricia Scotland
QC), London (0171) 405 3000. Called
1979.

Shaw, Howard
29 Bedford Row Chambers (Evan Stone
QC), London (0171) 831 2626. Called
1973. Principal area of practice is family law.
Also medical negligence.

Shaw QC, Antony
4 Brick Court (Mr. Antony Shaw QC),
London (0171) 797 7766. Called 1975, took
silk 1994.

Shelton, Gordon E.
Broadway House (Sydney Levine),
Bradford (01274) 722560.

Singleton QC, Barry
1 King's Bench Walk (Mr J.B.S.
Townend QC), London (0171) 583 6266.
Called 1968, took silk 1989.

Hayward Smith QC, Rodger
1 King's Bench Walk (Mr J.B.S.
Townend QC), London (0171) 583 6266.
Specialisation: Specialises in family law and
criminal law. Editor of 'Jackson's Matrimonial Finance and Taxation' (5th and 6th edns)
and *Practitioners' Child Law Bulletin*.
Prof. Membership: South Eastern Circuit,
Family Law Bar Association, Criminal Bar
Association.
Career: Called to the Bar in 1967 and joined
1 King's Bench Walk in 1968. Appointed Recorder in 1986. Took Silk 1988. Deputy High
Court Judge, Family Division since 1991.
Personal: Educated at Brentwood School
and St. Edmund Hall, Oxford.

Somerville, Bryce
No.6 Fountain Court (Roger Smith QC),
Birmingham (0121) 233 3282. Called 1980.

Sternberg, Michael
4 Paper Buildings (Lionel Swift QC),
London (0171) 583 0816.
Specialisation: All aspects of family and
family-related law including matrimonial, finance, Children Act applications,
international abduction, wardship, disputes
between unmarried persons, Inheritance Act
claims, Applications to remove children from
jurisdiction, and child law with specific reference to sexual/satanic abuse and contested
adoptions. Matrimonial finance work includes investigation of overseas trusts and
companies and all aspects of membership of
Lloyd's in divorce settlements. Recent cases
include Re F (A minor: Paternity Test) (a
leading authority on blood tests in disputed
paternity cases) ancillary relief cases where
assets were substantial, and cases of uxoricide (murder of one parent by another).
Clients have included entertainers, publishers, politicians, industrialists, and the Official
Solicitor to the Supreme Court.
Prof. Membership: Family Law Bar Association. Assistant Secretary Family Law Bar
Association 1986-1988.
Career: Called to the Bar 1975 and joined 3
Dr. Johnson's Buildings. Moved to present
chambers in 1994.
Personal: Educated at Carmel College, Wallingford 1962-70, Queen's College,
Cambridge 1970-74. (MA, LL.M). Governor
of North London Collegiate School, Trustee
of Sternberg Charitable Settlement. Freeman
of the City of London and Member of the
Worshipful Company of Horners. Member of
Reform Club and City Livery Club. Born
12th September 1951.

Stone, Lucy
29 Bedford Row Chambers (Evan Stone
QC), London (0171) 831 2626. Called
1983.

Thomas, Sybil
3 Fountain Court (Colman Treacy QC),
Birmingham (0121) 236 5854.

Turner, James
1 King's Bench Walk (Mr J.B.S.
Townend QC), London (0171) 583 6266.
Specialisation: Principal areas of practice
encompass all areas of criminal law, family
law and administrative law. Criminal work
includes both prosecution and defence and
regular instructions to represent medical
practitioners in connection with both criminal and disciplinary matters. Considerable
knowledge and experience of technical and
procedural points of law. Co-Editor of
'Archbold: Criminal Pleading, Evidence and
Practice'. Within family law, has particular
expertise in financial matters and international child abduction work and has appeared
in finance cases in the Grand Court of the
Cayman Islands. Speaker at criminal and
family law conferences. Administrative law
practice includes work for the Treasury Solicitor.
Prof. Membership: Called to the Bar and
joined current Chambers, 1976. Member of
Criminal Bar Association and Family Law
Bar Association.
Personal: Educated at Robertsbridge Secondary Modern School, Bexhill Grammar
School and the University of Hull (LLB
(Hons) 1975). Born 23rd November 1952.
Lives in London.

Wildblood, Stephen
Albion Chambers (J.C.T. Barton QC),
Bristol (0117) 9272144. Called 1981.

Willbourne, Caroline
One Garden Court (Miss Eleanor F.
Platt QC, Miss Alison Ball QC), London (0171) 797 7900. Called 1970.

Wills-Goldingham, Claire
Albion Chambers (J.C.T. Barton QC),
Bristol (0117) 9272144.

Wingert, Rachel
Gray's Inn Chambers (Brian Jubb),
London (0171) 404 1111.
Specialisation: Principal area of practice is
family law including public and private law
children cases, ancillary relief and property
disputes between unmarried couples. Author
of "Capital Provision for Children of Unmarried Parents" in *Family Law*.
Prof. Membership: Family Law Bar Association.
Career: Called to the Bar 1980 and joined
chambers in Lincoln's Inn. Moved to present
chambers in 1990.
Personal: Educated at London University
(LL.B 1979, LL.M 1986). Lives in London.

Wood, Martin J.
Broadway House (Sydney Levine),
Bradford (01274) 722560.

FINANCIAL SERVICES

THE Financial Services Act 1986 and related legislation provides protection to investors by regulating those who sell financial services to the public. Protection is provided through the SIB and self regulatory organisations such as the SFA, IMRO, and PIA. Counsel advise on the Financial

LEADING SETS

BRICK COURT CHAMBERS	ERSKINE CHAMBERS
3 GRAY'S INN PLACE	3-4 SOUTH SQUARE
1 ESSEX COURT	2 HARE COURT
4 STONE BUILDINGS	

Services Act and the complex regulations made pursuant to it and also advise the regulatory bodies on the conduct of their own activities. Advice is commonly given on the interpretation and accurate operation of the rules and the assorted methods of protection and enforcement available to investors under the Act. Compliance procedures and advice is the bulk of the work undertaken.

Erskine Chambers, Brick Court Chambers, 3 Gray's Inn Place and **3-4 South Square** are the leading sets in the

and have been particularly recommended for their contentious financial services work.

William Blair QC, Nicholas Merriman QC, Richard Salter QC, Richard de Lacy, Caroline Lewis and *Gregory Mitchell* are all well regarded at **3 Gray's Inn Place**. A number of the members at the insolvency specialist set at **3-4 South Square** have expertise in financial services. In particular, *Michael Crystal QC, Simon Mortimore QC, John Higham QC* and juniors, such as *Robin Knowles* and *Mark Phillips*.

4 Stone Buildings have an extremely impressive group of specialists with members acting on behalf of a number of the regulatory bodies. *Philip Heslop QC* and *George Bompas QC* have excellent reputations. *Philip Heslop QC* has been Deputy Chairman of IMRO Membership Tribunal since 1988. Other notable members of the set are *Robert Hildyard QC, John Brisby, Jonathan Crow* and *Malcolm Davis-White*.

1 Essex Court also have a number of experts in this field, such as *Elizabeth Gloster QC* and *Ian Glick QC*. *Jeffrey Gruder* has also advised the regulatory bodies.

Other chambers have individuals whose practices encompass financial services. *Barbara Dohmann QC, David*

LEADING SILKS

Sykes, Richard *Erskine Chambers*

Blair, William *3 Gray's Inn Place*	**Bompas,** Anthony George *4 Stone Buildings*	**Crystal,** Michael *3-4 South Square*
Gloster, Elizabeth *1 Essex Court*	**Heilbron,** Hilary *Brick Court Chambers*	**Henderson,** Roger *2 Harcourt Buildings*
Heslop, Philip *4 Stone Buildings*	**Higham,** John *3-4 South Square*	**Mawrey,** Richard *2 Harcourt Buildings*
Merriman, Nicholas *3 Gray's Inn Place*	**Mortimore,** Simon *3-4 South Square*	**Potts,** Robin *Erskine Chambers*
Powell, John L. *2 Crown Office Row*	**Salter,** Richard *3 Gray's Inn Place*	**Sumption,** Jonathan *Brick Court Chambers*
Chambers, Nicholas *Brick Court Chambers*	**Dohmann,** Barbara *2 Hare Court*	**Donaldson,** David *2 Hare Court*
Etherton, Terence *Wilberforce Chambers*	**Glick,** Ian *1 Essex Court*	**Hildyard,** Robert *4 Stone Buildings*
Mowschenson, Terence *1 Essex Court*	**Oliver,** David *13 Old Square*	

financial services law field.

Richard Sykes QC is highly respected for his financial services expertise, particularly for his advisory work, at **Erskine Chambers**, as are *Robin Potts QC* and *Richard Snowden*.

Jonathan Sumption QC, Nicholas Chambers QC and *Hilary Heilbron QC* are well known at **Brick Court Chambers**

Donaldson QC and *Thomas Beazley* at **2 Hare Court** have acted for and against regulatory bodies. *Roger Henderson QC, Richard Mawrey QC* and *Daniel Worsley* at **2 Harcourt Buildings** also have considerable expertise. *John L Powell QC* and *Eva Lomnicka* are well known as the authors of 'Encyclopaedia of Financial Services' at **2 Crown Office Row**.

LEADING JUNIORS

Brisby, John *4 Stone Buildings*	**Crow,** Jonathan *4 Stone Buildings*	**de Lacy,** Richard *3 Gray's Inn Place*
Gruder, Jeffrey *1 Essex Court*	**Lewis,** Caroline *3 Gray's Inn Place*	**Lomnicka,** Eva *2 Crown Office Row*
Snowden, Richard *Erskine Chambers*	**Worsley,** Daniel *2 Harcourt Buildings*	
Beazley, Thomas *2 Hare Court*	**Davis-White,** Malcolm *4 Stone Buildings*	**Hamilton,** Peter *4 Pump Court*
Harrison, Christopher *4 Stone Buildings*	**Knowles,** Robin *3-4 South Square*	**Mitchell,** Gregory *3 Gray's Inn Place*
Phillips, Mark *3-4 South Square*	**Rabinowitz,** Laurence *1 Essex Court*	

Beazley, Thomas

2 Hare Court (C.W.G. Ross-Munro QC),
London (0171) 583 1770.

Specialisation: Practice encompasses commercial law (including insurance and reinsurance), private international law and financial services. Commercial work includes acting for and against Lloyd's syndicates, acting in claims relating to takeovers and general international commercial and banking disputes. Recently conducted a substantial run-off insurance arbitration for a major insurance company. Financial services work includes acting for and against regulatory bodies (SFA, IMRO and SIB) for clients under DTI investigations. Has acted for and against a number of foreign states in commercial litigation. Joint author of the Report of the Bar Council and the Law Society to the Law Commission on Choice of Law in Tort and Delict.

Prof. Membership: COMBAR.

Career: Called to the Bar 1979 and since 1980 practised as a commercial barrister. Recently appointed an Arbitrator by the London Court of International Arbitration.

Personal: Working knowledge of Dutch, French and German.

Blair QC, William

See under Banking.

Bompas QC, Anthony George

See under Company.

Brisby, John

4 Stone Buildings (Peter Curry QC),
London (0171) 242 5524.

Specialisation: Practice encompasses litigation and advice in the fields of company, financial services and insolvency law. Contributor to 'Butterworths Company Law Precedents'.

Prof. Membership: Chancery Bar Association.

Career: Called to the Bar in 1978 and became a tenant at *4 Stone Buildings* 1980.

Personal: Educated at Westminster School 1969-73 and Scholar of Christchurch, Oxford 1974-77. Born 8th May 1956. Lives in London.

Chambers QC, Nicholas

Brick Court Chambers (Christopher Clarke QC), London (0171) 583 0777. Called 1966, took silk 1985.

Crow, Jonathan

See under Company.

Crystal QC, Michael

See under Insolvency.

Davis-White, Malcolm

4 Stone Buildings (Peter Curry QC),
London (0171) 242 5524.

Specialisation: Principal area of practice encompasses company, insolvency and financial services law. Contributor to 'Atkin' Vol. 9 (Companies), and Vol. 10 (Companies winding up).

Prof. Membership:

Career: Called to the Bar in 1984 and joined present chambers in 1985. Appointed Junior Counsel to the Crown (Chancery) in 1994.

Personal: Educated at St Edmund's College, Old Hall Green, Ware 1969-78 and Hertford College, Oxford 1979-83. Born 18th September 1960. Lives in Sidlesham, Chichester.

de Lacy, Richard

3 Gray's Inn Place (R. Neville Thomas QC), London (0171) 831 8441.

Specialisation: Principal area of practice is commercial law, particularly banking, finance, financial services, accountants', solicitors' and barristers' professional indemnity. Also deals with insolvency, company law and arbitration. Acts for clearing banks, major accountancy firms and leading insolvency practitioners. Specialist editor 'Bullen & Leake & Jacob: Precedents of Pleading' (13th Edn).

Prof. Membership: Fellow of The Chartered Institute of Arbitrators, COMBAR, Chancery Bar Association, Panel of Arbitrators, FIMBRA.

Career: Called to the Bar 1976. Harmsworth Scholar, Middle Temple.

Personal: Educated at Hymers College, Hull (1965-71) and Clare College, Cambridge 1972-75 (MA 1979). Born 4th December 1954.

Dohmann QC, Barbara

See under Insurance and Reinsurance.

Donaldson QC, David

See under Commercial Law.

Etherton QC, Terence

See under Property Litigation.

Glick QC, Ian

See under Banking.

Gloster QC, Elizabeth

See under Insolvency.

Gruder, Jeffrey

See under Insurance and Reinsurance.

Hamilton, Peter

4 Pump Court (Bruce Mauleverer QC),
London (0171) 353 2656.

Specialisation: Principal area of practice is financial services work, covering all aspects of life assurance, including selling practices, administration of policies, claims, agency, regulatory and disciplinary aspects relating to insurance companies; also interpretation and application of the Insurance Companies Act 1982 and regulations. Author of 'Life Assurance Law and Practice' (1995 FT, Law and Tax).

Prof. Membership: Life Assurance Legal Society, Professional Negligence Bar Association, Bar Association for Commerce, Finance and Industry.

Career: Called to the Bar 1968. Tenant at 2 Dr. Johnson's Buildings, 1968-77. Company Secretary and head of legal department, Allied Dunbar Assurance plc (formerly Hambro Life Assurance) 1977-1991. Member, Lautro Disciplinary Panel, 1990-95. Joined present chambers 1991.

Personal: Educated at Rhodes University (South Africa) 1960-62, (BA) and Cambridge University 1963-65 (MA). Trustee, International Childcare Trust. Leisure pursuits include riding, birdwatching, woodwork, theatre and music. Born 20th April 1941.

Harrison, Christopher

4 Stone Buildings (Peter Curry QC),
London (0171) 242 5524. Called 1988.

Heilbron QC, Hilary

Brick Court Chambers (Christopher Clarke QC), London (0171) 583 0777. Called 1971, took silk 1987.

Henderson QC, Roger

2 Harcourt Buildings (Roger Henderson QC), London (0171) 583 9020.

Specialisation: Specialises in common law and public law. Work covers professional negligence, contract, personal injuries, judicial review, local government, parliamentary and finance, especially local government finance and public transport. Cases handled include R. Sec of State for Environment ex.p. Brent, and re Westminster City Council. Counsel for British Rail in Clapham Inquiry, counsel to Kings Cross Enquiry. Has acted for British Rail, Railtrack, British Telecom and London Regional Transport, Stock Exchange and many local authorities.

Prof. Membership: Bencher of Inner Temple 1985. Member of St Kitts & Nevis Bar.

Career: Called to the bar in 1964. Joined *2 Harcourt Buildings* in 1966. Took silk in 1980. Recorder from 1983, Deputy High Court Judge from 1987. Chairman of Civil Service Arbitration Tribunal 1994.

Personal: Educated at Radley College 1956-61. First Class Honours in Law at St. Catharine's College Cambridge. Positions held include Chairman Council of Governors of London Hospital Medical College, former president of British Academy of Forensic Sciences. Leisure pursuits include fly fishing, gardening, shooting and travel. Born 21st April 1943.

Heslop QC, Philip
See under Company.

Higham QC, John
3-4 South Square (Michael Crystal QC),
London (0171) 696 9900.
Specialisation: Called 1976, silk 1992.
Broad commercial practice with particular interests in financial services, banking and
professional negligence, as well as insolvency. Lectures extensively and has written a
number of books and articles; joint editor of
'The Law and Practice of Corporate Administrations' published in October 1994.
Prof. Membership: Member of Chancery Bar
Association and Executive Member of COM-BAR.

Hildyard QC, Robert
See under Company.

Knowles, Robin
See under Insolvency.

Lewis, Caroline
See under Commercial Law.

Lomnicka, Eva
2 Crown Office Row (Rupert Jackson
QC), London (0171) 797 8000.
Specialisation: Advisory work in consumer
credit, securities regulation and financial
services, reflecting publications: (1) 'Encyclopedia of Consumer Credit Law';
(2) 'Lomnicka and Powell, Encyclopedia of
Financial Services Law; (3) 'Palmer's Company Law' (Parts 5 & 11); (4) 'Ellinger and
Lomnicka, Modern Banking Law'.
Career: Professor of Law, King's College
London. Called to the Bar 1974.
Personal: Born 17 May 1951; 1969-73 Girton College, Cambridge (MA, LLB;
Chancellor's Medal). Married with 3 children.

Mawrey QC, Richard
2 Harcourt Buildings (Roger Henderson
QC), London (0171) 583 9020.
Specialisation: Main areas of practise are
commercial law and local authority work.
Commercial work includes contracts, leasing, finance and credit law, financial services,
computer law and commercial drafting. Local authority work covers contracts, public
procurement, public liability, finance, employment and all aspects of passenger
transport. Advising on local taxation, land development, housing, community services
and computer problems. Author of 'Computers and the Law'. Specialist Editor:
Butterworths 'County Court Precedents and
Pleadings' and 'Bullen & Leake & Jacob's
Precedents of Pleadings'.
Prof. Membership: London Common Law
and Commercial Bar Association, Local Government Planning and Environmental Bar
Association.
Career: Called to the Bar 1964 and joined
present chambers 1965. Appointed Assistant
Recorder 1981. Took Silk 1986. Appointed
Recorder 1986 and Deputy High Court Judge
1994.
Personal: Scholar of Rossall School and Exhibitioner of Magdalen College, Oxford (BA
Jurisprudence 1963, First Class Honours, and
Eldon Scholar of Oxford University 1964,
MA 1967.) Born 20th August 1942. Lives in
London.

Merriman QC, Nicholas
3 Gray's Inn Place (R. Neville Thomas
QC), London (0171) 831 8441. Called
1969, took silk 1988.

Mitchell, Gregory
See under Banking.

Mortimore QC, Simon
3-4 South Square (Michael Crystal QC),
London (0171) 696 9900. Called 1972, took
silk 1991.

Mowschenson QC, Terence
See under Insolvency.

Oliver QC, David
See under Insolvency.

Phillips, Mark
See under Insolvency.

Potts QC, Robin
See under Company.

Powell QC, John L.
See under Professional Negligence.

Rabinowitz, Laurence
See under Commercial Law.

Salter QC, Richard
See under Banking.

Snowden, Richard
Erskine Chambers (Richard Sykes QC),
London (0171) 242 5532. Called 1986. Principal areas of practice are company law,
corporate insolvency and financial services.
Born 22.3.1962

Sumption QC, Jonathan
See under Commercial Law.

Sykes QC, Richard
See under Company.

Worsley, Daniel
2 Harcourt Buildings (Roger Henderson
QC), London (0171) 583 9020.
Specialisation: Finance House and Consumer Credit Law, advisory and litigation
work, fraud and disciplinary proceedings.
All other contract and common law work.
Substantial past criminal practice. Editor of
pleadings section of Goode on Consumer
Credit.
Career: Called 1971. Legal Assessor to NCC
(Nurses' disciplinary body) since 1983. Recorder 1993.

FIRMS OF ACCOUNTANTS

Accountants specialising in litigation support are listed in the accountants' A-Z, with details
of the services they offer to solicitors, from forensic accounting to intellectual property or
business valuations.

IMMIGRATION

THE ASYLUM and Immigration Appeals Act 1993 removed the right of appeal by visitors, students and their dependants against refusal of leave to enter the UK As a consequence of this, applications for judicial review have increased, bringing more work to those chambers with expertise in public/immigration law. In addition to general principles of public law, a knowledge of EU law governing freedom of movement is of growing importance to specialists in this field.

LEADING SETS

2 GARDEN COURT

The leading set is, unquestionably, **2 Garden Court**. The work of these chambers covers the entire field of immigration and nationality law, from refugee and political asylum cases to work permit schemes and executive immigration. *Ian Macdonald QC* is President of the I.L.P.A. (Immigration Law Practitioners' Association) and both he and *Nicholas Blake QC* are very experienced and highly recommended. *Laurie Fransman* (co-founder of I.L.P.A.) is the Bar's leading authority on nationality law and the author of the standard authoritative textbook on the subject 'Fransman's British Nationality Law'. Amongst the other juniors *Richard Scannell* is very highly regarded, as are *Owen Davies, Inderpal Rahal*, and *Frances Webber*.

HIGHLY REGARDED

DOUGHTY STREET CHAMBERS	39 ESSEX STREET
2 HARE COURT	6 KING'S BENCH WALK
14 TOOKS COURT	

Of the other sets with specialists in this area, **14 Tooks Court** is a chambers with a reputation for a strong commitment to civil liberties. It has a number of individuals with immigration law experience. *Alper Riza QC* edits Butterworth's 'Immigration Law Service' and has appeared in a number of House of Lords cases in recent years. *Martin Soorjoo* is also highly regarded and is a member of the ILPA and a frequent contributor to the media on immigration and nationality law issues.

Doughty Street Chambers is another set with a strong liberal tradition of defending citizen's rights. *Andrew Nicol QC* is well regarded and is the author of a number of published works in this field including 'Subjects, Citizens, Aliens and Others'. Of the juniors *Aswini Weereratne* is also recommended.

2 Hare Court is a leading public law chambers with extensive experience in this field. There are several members with particular expertise in immigration including *David Pannick QC* (one of the many areas in which he has an excellent reputation), *Judith Beale* and *Mark Shaw* who has contributed to Halsbury on 'Immigration and Nationality'.

39 Essex Street have several members with experience of immigration matters partly due to the chambers' long association with the Treasury Panel. *Nigel Pleming QC, Robert Jay* and *Alison Foster* are all experienced in this type of work.

6 Kings Bench Walk is a multi-racial set which has, since its inception 20 years ago, been involved in all aspects of immigration law and related areas of judicial review. *Sibghat Kadri QC* has a strong reputation, as do juniors *Manjit Gill, Harjit Grewal* and *Stephanie Harrison*.

LEADING SILKS

Macdonald, Ian *2 Garden Court*	
Beloff, Michael *4-5 Gray's Inn Square*	
Blake, Nicholas *2 Garden Court*	
Kadri, Sibghat *6 King's Bench Walk*	
Nicol, Andrew *Doughty Street Chambers*	
Pannick, David *2 Hare Court*	
Pleming, Nigel *39 Essex Street*	
Riza, Alper Ali *14 Tooks Court*	

Notable practitioners include *Michael Beloff QC* (**4-5 Gray's Inn Square**); *Declan O'Dempsey* (**4 Brick Court**) who is co-editor with *Michael Supperstone QC* (**11 Kings Bench Walk**) of 'Immigration: The Law and Practice'. *Michael Shrimpton*, (**Francis Taylor Building**) specialises in immigration and EC law and has been Chairman of the Immigration Appeal Tribunal since 1992.

LEADING JUNIORS

Fransman, Laurie *2 Garden Court*	
Beale, Judith *2 Hare Court*	
Davies, Owen *2 Garden Court*	
Foster, Alison *39 Essex Street*	
Gill, Manjit *6 King's Bench Walk*	
Grewal, Harjit *6 King's Bench Walk*	
Jay, Robert *39 Essex Street*	
O'Dempsey, Declan *4 Brick Court*	
Rahal, Inderpal Kaur *2 Garden Court*	
Scannell, Richard *2 Garden Court*	
Shaw, Mark *2 Hare Court*	
Shrimpton, Michael *Francis Taylor Building*	
Webber, Frances *2 Garden Court*	
Weereratne, Aswini *Doughty Street Chambers*	

UP AND COMING

Finch, Nadine *1 Pump Court*	
Harrison, Stephanie *6 King's Bench Walk*	
Soorjoo, Martin *14 Tooks Court*	

OUTSIDE LONDON

James Gillespie, **Enfield Chambers** and *Mukhtar Hussain QC*, **Lincoln House Chambers**, Manchester, are also recommended specialists.

LEADERS IN IMMIGRATION

Beale, Judith
See under Employment.

Beloff QC, Michael
See under Public and Administrative Law.

Blake QC, Nicholas
2 Garden Court (I. Macdonald QC, O. Davies), London (0171) 353 1633.

Specialisation: Practice involves public law and human rights case generally with particular emphasis on immigration, nationality and asylum. Recent cases in the area of immigration and asylum include Surinder Singh (ECJ), Vilvarajah (ECtHR), Chahal (CA), Mehari (QBD), Chung (CA), Re T (CA), Naillie (HL), Savchenkov (CA). Co author of the leading textbook on immigration law. Cases in the field of human rights, the environment and miscarriages of justice include Rees (ECtHR), Macdonalds v. Dhatt (CA), Judith Ward (CA), R v. HMIP (the Greenpeace challenge to THORP) QBD, Guerra v. Republic of Trinidad (PC).

Prof. Membership: ALBA, ILPA (Chair 1993-1996), JUSTICE.

Career: Called to the Bar (Middle Temple) 1974, joined present chambers 1975; QC (1994). Principal publications include, 'New Nationality Law' (Butterworths) (1983); Macdonald 'Immigration Law and Practice in the UK' (3rd and 4th editions).

Personal: Educated at Cranleigh School, Surrey; Magdalene College, Cambridge. Married with 3 children. Lives in London.

Davies, Owen
See under Criminal Law (General).

Finch, Nadine
1 Pump Court (Robert Latham), London (0171) 583 2012. Called 1991.

Foster, Alison
See under Construction Law.

Fransman, Laurie
2 Garden Court (I. Macdonald QC, O. Davies), London (0171) 353 1633. Called 1979. Principal area of practice is immigration and nationality work, particularly corporate. Born 4.7.1956.

Gill, Manjit
6 King's Bench Walk (Sibghat Kadri QC), London (0171) 353 4931.

Specialisation: Main area of practice is public law with a particular emphasis on immigration, education, housing/local government, welfare benefits and human rights generally. Also heavily involved in discrimination and employment law and landlord and tenant and other common law fields. Numerous reported immigration cases.

Career: Called 1982. Has worked for UK Immigrants Advisory Service. He is on the A-G's Supplementary Panel of Junior Counsel to the Crown (Common Law) and is regularly instructed by the CRE.

Prof. Membership: Member of Immigration Law Practitioners Association, Administrative Law Bar Association, Education Law Association, Discrimination Law Association.

Personal: He has spoken at national and international conferences and convened training sessions on international human rights, immigration and racial harassment linked areas of the law. Languages: Punjabi/Urdu.

Gillespie, James
Enfield Chambers (Peter C.C. Gibbs), Enfield (0181) 364 5627.

Specialisation: Offers specialist advice and representatation in all aspects of immigration and nationality law, including asylum. Considerable experience of conducting cases before immigration Adjudicators and the Immigration Appeal Tribunal, judicial review and appeals to the Court of Appeal. Acts for a wide range of immigration clients, including prominent Middle East dissidents. Conducts training courses in immigration law for solicitors. Managing Editor of "Tolley's Immigration and Nationality Law and Practice".

Prof. Membership: Founder member of the Immigration Law Practitioners Association and member of executive committee 1985-1992.

Career: Before being called to the Bar in 1991 worked for the Joint Council for the Welfare of Immigrants representing clients in the Immigration Appeal Tribunal.

Grewal, Harjit
6 King's Bench Walk (Sibghat Kadri QC), London (0171) 353 4931. Called 1980.

Harrison, Stephanie
6 King's Bench Walk (Sibghat Kadri QC), London (0171) 353 4931. Called 1991.

Hussain QC, Mukhtar
Lincoln House Chambers (Mukhtar Hussain QC), Manchester (0161) 832 5701. Called 1971, took silk 1992.

Jay, Robert
39 Essex Street (Colin Mackay QC), London (0171) 583 1111. Called 1981.

Kadri QC, Sibghat
6 King's Bench Walk (Sibghat Kadri QC), London (0171) 353 4931. Called 1969, took silk 1989.

Macdonald QC, Ian
2 Garden Court (I. Macdonald QC, O. Davies), London (0171) 353 1633. Called 1963, took silk 1988.

Nicol QC, Andrew
Doughty Street Chambers (Geoffrey Robertson QC), London (0171) 404 1313. Called 1978, took silk 1995.

O'Dempsey, Declan
4 Brick Court (Mr. Antony Shaw QC), London (0171) 797 7766.

Specialisation: Principal areas of practice are immigration and employment law. Has considerable experience in discrimination, immigration, asylum and human rights cases. Particular areas of specialism include judicial review, administrative and employment tribunals and employment law relating to trade unions and senior employees. With Michael Supperstone QC he is the author of 'Immigration: The Law and Practice' (3rd) edition (Longman), and writes two of the Unfair Dismissal chapters in 'Tolley's Employment Law'. Other main areas of practice include professional negligence (including solicitors and medical), personal injury and contract law. E-Mail address odempsey @ compulink.co.uk; has WLRs and ICRs on CD Rom providing an instant search facility and is on the LINK.

Prof. Membership: Immigration Law Practitioners Association. Employment Law Bar Association, London Common Law and Commercial Bar Association, and the Administrative Law Bar Association and the Immigration Law Practitioners' Association.

Career: Called to the Bar in 1987, full-time Employment Law caseworker for the Free Representation Unit 1987-88.

Pannick QC, David
See under Public and Administrative Law.

Pleming QC, Nigel
39 Essex Street (Colin Mackay QC), London (0171) 583 1111. Called 1971, took silk '92.

Rahal, Inderpal Kaur
2 Garden Court (I. Macdonald QC, O. Davies), London (0171) 353 1633. Called 1985. Specialist in immigration law, representing clients at all levels and in all areas.

Riza QC, Alper Ali
See under Civil Liberties.

Scannell, Richard
2 Garden Court (I. Macdonald QC, O. Davies), London (0171) 353 1633. Called 1986.

Shaw, Mark
See under Public and Administrative Law.

Shrimpton, Michael
Francis Taylor Building (Alan Tyrrell QC), London (0171) 797 7250. Called 1983. Specialist in constitutional and administrative law, with a particular emphasis on its immigration and EC aspects. Born 9.3.1957.

Soorjoo, Martin
14 Tooks Court (Michael Mansfield QC), London (0171) 405 8828. Called 1990. Practice includes judicial review.

Webber, Frances
2 Garden Court (I. Macdonald QC, O.Davies), London (0171) 353 1633. Called '78.

Weereratne, Aswini
Doughty Street Chambers (Geoffrey Robertson QC), London (0171) 404 1313. Called 1986.

INSOLVENCY

SIXTY per cent of work undertaken by **3-4 South Square** is insolvency work and as a result the set continues to maintain its formidable reputation as the leader in insolvency. *Michael Crystal QC*, who is a member of the Insolvency Rules Committee, and *Gabriel Moss QC* have distinguished reputations, the latter being well known for administration matters. Both have acted in the BCCI and Maxwell litigations.

Most members of the set have been highly recommended, including *Simon Mortimore QC*, *Richard Adkins QC*, *Robin Knowles*, *Mark Phillips*, *William Trower* and *Robin Dicker*. *Christopher Brougham QC* and *John Briggs* are also highly rated for personal insolvency. Various insolvency related publications are written and edited within chambers such as

Polly Peck litigations, the recent case of 'Tottenham Hotspur v Edennote Limited' and in 'Bishopsgate Investment Management Limited v Maxwell & Anor'. *George Bompas QC* has also been instructed in the BCCI, Blue Arrow and Barlow Clowes litigation. *Jonathan Crow* acted as a junior in the Guinness, Barlow Clowes and Polly Peck cases.

Erskine Chambers has a strong corporate insolvency practice. *Robin Potts QC* is highly respected in contentious matters. He acted for the pilots in the 'Paramount Airways' case. Members of chambers have also acted in the BCCI, Polly Peck and Maxwell litigations. *Leslie Kosmin QC* is highly regarded as are juniors, *Michael Todd* and *David Chivers*. *Eben Hamilton QC* and *Robin Hollington* at **1 New Square** are well known in the insolvency field.

Enterprise Chambers is a well regarded set with some strong insolvency experts. *Anthony Mann QC* is particularly known for administration work such as in 'Barclays Bank v Sibec Developments'. *Peter Arden* has acted in many of the recent large scale insolvency cases including Leyland DAF and Ferranti, as have others in the set.

At **24 Old Buildings** both personal and corporate insolvency are handled. *Roger Kaye QC* is highly recommended.

11 Stone Buildings has an increasingly well recognised expertise in insolvency. *Victor Joffe* who recently joined the set has an excellent reputation in corporate insolvency for

'Muir Hunter on Insolvency' and 'Butterworths Insolvency Law Handbook'.

Members of **13 Old Square (E.W.H. Christie)** practise both personal and corporate insolvency law. *David Oliver QC* and *Richard McCombe QC* are highly recommended. *Richard McCombe* was recently involved in the BCCI litigation. *Matthew Collings* is a well regarded junior who has acted for companies in the Maxwell group as well as in the BCCI and Polly Peck litigations.

Another leading set of chambers handling insolvency work is **4 Stone Buildings** with *Philip Heslop QC* being highly recommended, having appeared in the BCCI and

both litigious and advisory work. Other well regarded juniors are *Jane Giret* and *Raquel Agnello*.

3 Gray's Inn Place is also involved in the insolvency field as a result of its considerable banking expertise. *Nigel Davis QC* at **7 Stone Buildings** and *Michael Briggs QC* at **13 Old Square (Sparrow QC)** are also highly regarded.

Elizabeth Gloster QC (**1 Essex Court**) has acted in recent high profile cases, such as Barlow Clowes, BCCI and the Paramount related litigation, and appeared in 'Canary Wharf v WPP' and 'Law Debenture Trust Corp. v Ural Caspian Oil Corp'. From the same set, *Terence Mowschenson QC* and *Anthony de Garr Robinson* have also been recommended.

LEADING JUNIORS - LONDON

Arden, Peter *Enterprise Chambers*	**Briggs,** John *3-4 South Square*	**Brisby,** John *4 Stone Buildings*
Chivers, David *Erskine Chambers*	**Collings,** Matthew *13 Old Square*	**Crow,** Jonathan *4 Stone Buildings*
Davis-White, Malcolm *4 Stone Buildings*	**Dicker,** Robin *3-4 South Square*	**Giret,** Jane *11 Stone Buildings*
Griffiths, Peter *4 Stone Buildings*	**Hacker,** Richard *3-4 South Square*	**Hoser,** Philip *1 New Square*
Joffe, Victor *11 Stone Buildings*	**King,** Michael *24 Old Buildings*	**Knowles,** Robin *3-4 South Square*
Marks, David *3-4 South Square*	**McQuater,** Ewan *3 Gray's Inn Place*	**Nicholls,** John *13 Old Square*
Pascoe, Martin *3-4 South Square*	**Phillips,** Mark *3-4 South Square*	**Prevezer,** Susan *3-4 South Square*
Ritchie, Richard *24 Old Buildings*	**Sheldon,** Richard *3-4 South Square*	**Snowden,** Richard *Erskine Chambers*
Stockdale, Thomas *Erskine Chambers*	**Todd,** Michael *Erskine Chambers*	**Trower,** William *3-4 South Square*
Agnello, Raquel *11 Stone Buildings*	**Arnold,** Mark *3-4 South Square*	**Atherton,** Stephen *3-4 South Square*
Corbett, Sandra *1 New Square*	**de Garr Robinson,** Anthony *1 Essex Court*	**de Lacy,** Richard *3 Gray's Inn Place*
Girolami, Paul *13 Old Square*	**Green,** Michael A. *7 Stone Buildings*	**Hilliard,** Lexa *3-4 South Square*
Hollington, Robin *1 New Square*	**Ife,** Linden *Enterprise Chambers*	**Miles,** Robert *4 Stone Buildings*
Millett, Richard *Essex Court Chambers*	**Mitchell,** Gregory *3 Gray's Inn Place*	**Newey,** Guy *7 Stone Buildings*
Pirie, Fernanda *13 Old Square*	**Zacaroli,** Antony *3-4 South Square*	

UP AND COMING

Goodison, Adam *3-4 South Square*	**Rollason,** Michael *1 Essex Court*

OUTSIDE LONDON

While most specialist practitioners in this sector are based in London, a number of barristers outside the capital have been recommended to us. They are detailed here.

LEADING SILKS - REGIONS

Smith, Peter *40 King St, Manchester*

LEADING JUNIORS - REGIONS

Chaisty, Paul *40 King St, Manchester*
Davies, Stephen *Guildhall Chambers. Bristol*
Dunn, Katherine *40 King St, Manchester*
Jarman, Milwyn *9 Park Place, Cardiff*
Jones, Geraint *9 Park Place, Cardiff*
Stockill, David *5 Fountain Court, Birmingham*
Wood, Graeme *Assize Court Chambers, Bristol*

LEADERS IN INSOLVENCY

Adkins QC, Richard
3-4 South Square (Michael Crystal QC), London (0171) 696 9900. Called 1982, took silk 1995.

Agnello, Raquel
11 Stone Buildings (Michael Beckman QC), London (+44) 0171 831 6381. Called 1986. Specialist in company law, insolvency law and general commercial law. 29.3.1963.

Arden, Peter
Enterprise Chambers (Benjamin Levy), London (0171) 405 9471.
Specialisation: Principal areas of practice are business and financial law, particularly banking, bank and other securities, insolvency (corporate and individual) and related areas.

Arnold, Mark
3-4 South Square (Michael Crystal QC), London (0171) 696 9900. Called 1988.

Atherton, Stephen
3-4 South Square (Michael Crystal QC), London (0171) 696 9900.

Bannister QC, Edward Alexander
1 New Square (Eben Hamilton QC), London (0171) 405 0884. Called 1973, took silk 1991.

Bompas QC, Anthony George
See under Company.

Briggs QC, Michael
See under Company.

Briggs, John
3-4 South Square (Michael Crystal QC), London (0171) 696 9900.

Brisby, John
See under Financial Services.

Brougham QC, Christopher
3-4 South Square (Michael Crystal QC), London (0171) 696 9900.

Chaisty, Paul
40 King St (John Hoggett QC), Manchester (0161) 832 9082. Called 1982.

Chivers, David
Erskine Chambers (Richard Sykes QC), London (0171) 242 5532. Called 1983. Principal area of practice is company law including corporate insolvency. Born 17/1/1960.

Collings, Matthew
See under Company.

Corbett, Sandra
1 New Square (Eben Hamilton QC),
London (0171) 405 0884.

Crow, Jonathan
See under Company.

Crystal QC, Michael
3-4 South Square (Michael Crystal QC),
London (0171) 696 9900.
Specialisation: Commercial and financial
law.
Career: Called to the Bar, Middle Temple,
1970; Queen's Counsel 1984; Bencher Middle
Temple 1993; Senior Visiting Fellow
Centre for Commercial Law Studies, University of London since 1987; DTI Inspector
1988-89, 1992; Member Insolvency Rules
Committee since 1993.

Davies, Stephen
See under Chancery.

Davis QC, Nigel
See under Company.

Davis-White, Malcolm
See under Financial Services.

de Garr Robinson, Anthony
See under Banking.

de Lacy, Richard
See under Financial Services.

Dicker, Robin
3-4 South Square (Michael Crystal QC),
London (0171) 696 9900. Called 1986.

Dunn, Katherine
40 King St (John Hoggett QC),   Manchester (0161) 832 9082.

Giret, Jane
11 Stone Buildings (Michael Beckman
QC),   London (+44) 0171 831 6381. Called
1981. Principal area of practice is company
law and insolvency.

Girolami, Paul
See under Company.

Gloster QC, Elizabeth
1 Essex Court (Anthony Grabiner QC),
London (0171) 583 2000.
Specialisation: Principal areas of expertise
are company law, banking, insurance and insolvency. Also covers commercial fraud,
financial services and professional negligence. Recent major cases include acting for
the banks in the local authority/interest rate
swaps litigation - Hazell v. Hammersmith &
Fulham Borough Council (1992) (House of
Lords); prosecuting in the criminal trials arising out of the Guinness bid for Distillers
(1990) and (1991); litigating in Bermuda in
connection with Stena's contested bid for Sea
Containers (1989); representing the liquidators of Barlow Clowes in litigation against

various directors and third party professionals (1992-1995); acting for
banks/administrators of Olympia & York, Canary Wharf; acting for the Society of Lloyd's
in a case involving the question of priority between the Society and various Names as to
who benefitted from certain Stop Loss Policies (1993); representing the
recently-appointed trustees of Maxwell Pension Funds in relation to the Maxwell
collapse (1992-1995); acting for the D.T.I in
the case of Sher v. The Policy Holders Protection Board (1993). Called to the Bars of
Bermuda, Gibraltar and the Isle of Man for
specific cases. Working knowledge of
French.
Prof. Membership: Chancery Bar Association, COMBAR, Insolvency Lawyers'
Association.
Career: Called to the Bar in 1971. Member of
the panel of junior counsel representing the
DTI in company matters 1982-89. Took Silk
in 1989. Bencher of the Inner Temple and
Deputy High Court Judge of the Chancery Division in 1992, Judge of the Court of Appeal
of Jersey & Guernsey (part-time) in 1994 and
Recorder 1995.
Personal: Educated at Roedean School 1962-
67 and Girton College, Cambridge 1967-70.
Born 5th June 1949.

Goodison, Adam
3-4 South Square (Michael Crystal QC),
London (0171) 696 9900.

Green, Michael A.
7 Stone Buildings (Charles Aldous QC),
London (0171) 405 3886.
Specialisation: Principal areas of work are
company and insolvency law. Also handles
large scale commercial actions, having been
involved for 3 years in Maxwell litigation
(acting for Lehman Brothers), and now involved in the Lloyds litigation (acting on
behalf of auditors). Recent cases include
Derby v. Weldon and Macmillan Inc. v.
Bishopsgate Investment Trust Plc.
Career: Called to the bar in 1987. Joined 7
Stone Buildings in 1988.
Personal: Educated at University College
School 1971-82, and Jesus College Cambridge 1983-86. Leisure pursuits include
skiing, squash and tennis. Born 23rd October
1964.

Griffiths, Peter
See under Company.

Hacker, Richard
3-4 South Square (Michael Crystal QC),
London (0171) 696 9900. Called 1977.

Hamilton QC, Eben W.
See under Company.

Heslop QC, Philip
See under Company.

Higham QC, John
See under Financial Services.

Hilliard, Lexa
3-4 South Square (Michael Crystal QC),
London (0171) 696 9900.

Hollington, Robin
See under Company.

Hoser, Philip
1 New Square (Eben Hamilton QC),
London (0171) 405 0884. Called 1982.

Ife, Linden
Enterprise Chambers (Benjamin Levy),
London (0171) 405 9471.
Specialisation: Principal area of practice is
commercial chancery, including banking and
securities, insolvency, financial services,
commercial agreements and civil fraud.
Regularly receives instructions from major
clearing banks and other financial institutions, and from insolvency practitioners.
Financial services work includes appearing
at disciplinary tribunals appointed by Lautro
and other regulatory bodies. Notable recent
cases include Gaskell (William) Group Ltd v.
Highley [1993] (fixed and floating charges),
Lipe Ltd v. Leyland Daf Ltd [1993] (receivers' undertakings) and In re a Debtor (no. 340
of 1992) [1993] (execution and statutory demands).

Jarman, Milwyn
See under Chancery.

Joffe, Victor
11 Stone Buildings (Michael Beckman
QC),   London (+44) 0171 831 6381. Called
1975. Main areas of practice are company
law and corporate insolvency.

Jones, Geraint
See under Chancery.

Kaye QC, Roger
See under Chancery.

King, Michael
24 Old Buildings (C.A. Brodie QC),
London (0171) 404 0946.

Knowles, Robin
3-4 South Square (Michael Crystal QC),
London (0171) 696 9900. Called 1982.

Kosmin QC, Leslie
See under Company.

Mann QC, Anthony
See under Chancery.

Marks, David
3-4 South Square (Michael Crystal QC),
London (0171) 696 9900. Called 1974.

McCombe QC, Richard
13 Old Square (Mr. E.W.H. Christie), London (0171) 404 4800. Called 1975, took silk 1989.

McQuater, Ewan
3 Gray's Inn Place (R. Neville Thomas QC), London (0171) 831 8441.

Specialisation: Has specialised in international and domestic banking law since starting in practice. Range of banking work covers the entire spectrum, including guarantees, charges, securities, letters of credit, performance bonds, banker/customer relationship questions, negligent security valuations and Mareva Injunctions. Also has substantial practices in professional negligence (principally accountants, bankers, solicitors and valuers) and insolvency (all aspects, acting for liquidators, receivers, administrators, trustees in bankruptcy and other parties affected by insolvency). Acted in Libyan Arab Foreign Bank v. Bankers Trust [1989] and Libyan Arab Foreign Bank v. Manufacturers Hanover Trust [1989] concerning the US freeze on Libyan assets. Acted in the administration of the Parkfield Group (for the administrators) and the liquidation of Arrows Ltd (for the liquidators) both important insolvency decisions. Acted for the liquidators, both in England and the Cayman Islands, on the BCCI liquidation, and in the "BBL" case (Banque Bruxelles Lambert v. Eagle Star), a landmark decision on negligent valuations of security and negligent bank lending. Also involved in the Maxwell litigation, (Bishopsgate Investment Management v. Mirror Group Newspapers). Assistant Editor of the 'Encyclopaedia of Banking Law' since 1987 and regular contributor to the *Journal of International Banking Law.*'

Prof. Membership: COMBAR.

Career: Called to the Bar 1985 and joined current Chambers 1986. Admitted to the Bar of the Cayman Islands.

Personal: Educated at Merchiston Castle School, Edinburgh (1975-80) and Cambridge University 1981-84 (MA Hons in Law, First Class). Leisure pursuits include rugby (Vice Captain, Belsize Park Rugby Club) and piano. Born 30th October 1962. Lives in London.

Miles, Robert
4 Stone Buildings (Peter Curry QC), London (0171) 242 5524.

Millett, Richard
See under Banking.

Mitchell, Gregory
See under Banking.

Mortimore QC, Simon
See under Financial Services.

Moss QC, Gabriel
3-4 South Square (Michael Crystal QC), London (0171) 696 9900. Called 1974, took silk 1989.

Mowschenson QC, Terence
1 Essex Court (Anthony Grabiner QC), London (0171) 583 2000.

Specialisation: Principal areas of practice: company/commercial matters including matters involving the law relating to banking (including bills of exchange, letters of credit, syndicated loan agreements), breach of trust, conflict of laws, contract (including conditions of sale, share and business sale agreements, licensing and franchising, restraint of trade, retention of title, and sale of goods), companies (including shareholder disputes, shareholder agreements, technical aspects of company law, takeovers, Stock Exchange regulations, broking and dealing), equitable remedies, financial services (including matters relating to the various self regulatory organisations), insolvency, insurance, partnership, and professional negligence. Reported cases including Derby v Weldon, Sharneyford Supplies v Edge, Elliss v BP Oil Northern Ireland Refinery Ltd, Re Westock Realisations Ltd, Dept of Environment v Bates, Investment and Pensions Services v Gray, Acatos v Watson and Crimpfil Ltd v Barclays Bank plc.

Prof. Membership: Chancery and Commercial Bar and Insolvency Lawyers Associations.

Career: Called to the bar in 1977. Queen's Counsel 1995.

Personal: Educated at Eagle School and Peterhouse. London University (LLb(Hons)) and Oxford BCL (Hons). FCIArb 1989.

Newey, Guy
See under Company.

Newman QC, Catherine
See under Chancery.

Nicholls, John
13 Old Square (Mr. E.W.H. Christie), London (0171) 404 4800. Called 1986.

Oliver QC, David
13 Old Square (Mr. E.W.H. Christie), London (0171) 404 4800. Called 1972, took silk 1986.

Pascoe, Martin
3-4 South Square (Michael Crystal QC), London (0171) 696 9900. Called 1977.

Phillips, Mark
3-4 South Square (Michael Crystal QC), London (0171) 696 9900. Called 1984.

Pirie, Fernanda
13 Old Square (Mr. E.W.H. Christie), London (0171) 404 4800.

Potts QC, Robin
See under Company.

Prevezer, Susan
3-4 South Square (Michael Crystal QC), London (0171) 696 9900. Called 1983.

Ritchie, Richard
24 Old Buildings (C.A. Brodie QC), London (0171) 404 0946. Called 1978.

Rollason, Michael
1 Essex Court (Anthony Grabiner QC), London (0171) 583 2000.

Salter QC, Richard
See under Banking.

Sheldon, Richard
3-4 South Square (Michael Crystal QC), London (0171) 696 9900.

Smith QC, Peter
40 King St (John Hoggett QC), Manchester (0161) 832 9082.

Snowden, Richard
See under Financial Services.

Steinfeld QC, Alan
See under Chancery.

Stockdale, Thomas
See under Company.

Stockill, David
See under Chancery.

Stubbs QC, W.F.
See under Company.

Sykes QC, Richard
See under Company.

Thomas QC, R. Neville
See under Commercial Law.

Todd, Michael
Erskine Chambers (Richard Sykes QC), London (0171) 242 5532. Called 1977. Principal area of practice is company law including corporate insolvency and banking securities. Born 16.2.1953.

Trower, William
3-4 South Square (Michael Crystal QC), London (0171) 696 9900.

Vos QC, Geoffrey C.
See under Insurance and Reinsurance.

Wood, Graeme
See under Chancery.

Zacaroli, Antony
3-4 South Square (Michael Crystal QC), London (0171) 696 9900. Called 1987.

INSURANCE AND REINSURANCE

Insurers frequently seek to avoid meeting claims on the basis either of misrepresentation or non-disclosure of the risk by the assured, or of mistakes as to the amount of the premium charged against the risk insured. Disputes of a similar nature also arise between insurers and their reinsurers. In addition, recent years have seen a number of large scale actions in the Commercial Court concerning the well publicised problems in the Lloyd's market.

LEADING SETS

ESSEX COURT CHAMBERS	7 KING'S BENCH WALK
BRICK COURT CHAMBERS	
20 ESSEX STREET	FOUNTAIN COURT

Essex Court Chambers are extremely highly regarded. *John Thomas QC* has an excellent reputation in both reinsurance and general insurance work. *V V Veeder QC* is also very well known. He has a wide-ranging international practice which includes insurance and reinsurance work. *Bernard Eder QC* has enjoyed a high profile in the Lloyd's litigation, acting for the members' agents and managing agents in 'Gooda Walker' and the managing agents in 'Feltrim'. Also highly thought of are *Gordon Pollock QC*, *Ian Hunter QC*, *Stewart Boyd QC* and *Roderick Cordara QC*. Among the juniors in chambers *Richard Jacobs* has been highly recommended, as have *Steven Berry*, who appeared as junior counsel in 'Pan Atlantic v Pine Top', *John Lockey*, and *Simon Bryan* who appeared as junior counsel in 'Brown and Sword Daniels v KMR Services'.

At **Seven King's Bench Walk** *Julian Flaux QC* has an excellent reputation in this area. *Adrian Hamilton QC's* highly regarded practice covers both marine and non-marine

insurance. *Jeremy Cooke QC* appeared in the Lloyd's litigation on behalf of the 'Feltrim' names group. *Gavin Kealey QC* acted in 'Suncorp Insurance v Milano' which raised issues of reinsurance law. *Jonathan Gaisman QC* is a recently-appointed silk who specialises in reinsurance work and arbitration. Highly recommended juniors in this set include *Christopher Butcher* and *Dominic Kendrick* who acted in 'Bates v Barrow' and 'Marcan v Polish Steamship'.

Brick Court Chambers are a leading set in this field. *Jonathan Sumption QC* is highly respected for his expertise in general insurance, reinsurance and Lloyd's work. *Christopher Clarke QC*, *Sydney Kentridge QC*, *Jonathan Hirst QC*, *Richard Aikens QC* and *Mark Hapgood QC* also enjoy excellent reputations. Among the juniors in chambers *Stephen Ruttle* and *Mark Howard* are highly regarded.

HIGHLY REGARDED – LONDON

5 BELL YARD	1 ESSEX COURT
3 GRAY'S INN PLACE	4-5 GRAY'S INN SQUARE
4 PUMP COURT	

Fountain Court is a well known commercial set with a strong insurance practice. *Anthony Boswood QC* has acted in Lloyd's matters. *Stephen Moriarty* is a highly regarded junior in this set, as is *Raymond Cox* who has acted for insurers and reinsurers in 'Standard Chartered Bank v Standard Chartered Bank Insurance Company Limited', 'Re ERAS EIL' and 'DR Insurance Co v Seguros America Banamex'.

Kenneth Rokison QC at **20 Essex Street** has a very good reputation for his general insurance work. He has appeared in 'Re PCW Syndicates', a Lloyd's case with far-reaching implications for the reinsurance market.

LEADING SILKS

Aikens, Richard *Brick Court Chambers*	**Beloff,** Michael *4-5 Gray's Inn Square*	**Boswood,** Anthony *Fountain Court*
Boyd, Stewart *Essex Court Chambers*	**Clarke,** Christopher *Brick Court Chambers*	**Cooke,** Jeremy *Seven King's Bench Walk*
Crane, Michael *5 Bell Yard*	**Eder,** Bernard *Essex Court Chambers*	**Flaux,** Julian *Seven King's Bench Walk*
Hamilton, Adrian *Seven King's Bench Walk*	**Hunter,** Ian *Essex Court Chambers*	**Kentridge,** Sydney *Brick Court Chambers*
Pollock, Gordon *Essex Court Chambers*	**Rokison,** Kenneth *20 Essex Street*	**Sumption,** Jonathan *Brick Court Chambers*
Thomas, John *Essex Court Chambers*	**Toulson,** Roger *2 Crown Office Row*	**Veeder,** V.V. *Essex Court Chambers*
Webb, Robert *5 Bell Yard*		

Collins, Michael *Essex Court Chambers*	**Cordara,** Roderick *Essex Court Chambers*	**Cran,** Mark *Brick Court Chambers*
Dehn, Conrad *Fountain Court*	**Dohmann,** Barbara *2 Hare Court*	**Donaldson,** David *2 Hare Court*
Edelman, Colin *Devereux Chambers*	**Edwards-Stuart,** Antony *2 Crown Office Row*	**Field,** Richard Alan *11 King's Bench Walk*
Gaisman, Jonathan *Seven King's Bench Walk*	**Gee,** Steven *1 Essex Court*	**Gross,** Peter *20 Essex Street*
Hapgood, Mark *Brick Court Chambers*	**Hirst,** Jonathan *Brick Court Chambers*	**Irvine of Lairg,** Lord *11 King's Bench Walk*
Kealey, Gavin *Seven King's Bench Walk*	**Langley,** Gordon *Fountain Court*	**Mowschenson,** Terence *1 Essex Court*
Saloman, Timothy *Seven King's Bench Walk*	**Simon,** Peregrine *Brick Court Chambers*	**Smith,** Andrew *Fountain Court*
Temple, Anthony *4 Pump Court*	**Tomlinson,** Stephen *Seven King's Bench Walk*	**Vos,** Geoffrey C. *3 Stone Buildings*
Walker, Tim *Fountain Court*		

LEADING JUNIORS- LONDON

Beazley, Thomas *2 Hare Court*	**Berry,** Steven *Essex Court Chambers*	**Butcher,** Christopher *Seven King's Bench Walk*
Cox, Raymond *Fountain Court*	**Dunning,** Graham *Essex Court Chambers*	**Howard,** Mark *Brick Court Chambers*
Jacobs, Richard *Essex Court Chambers*	**Kendrick,** Dominic *Seven King's Bench Walk*	**Lord,** David W. *3 Stone Buildings*
Moriarty, Stephen *Fountain Court*	**Philipps,** Guy *Fountain Court*	**Phillips,** Rory *3 Gray's Inn Place*
Rowland, John *4 Pump Court*	**Ruttle,** Stephen *Brick Court Chambers*	**Weitzman,** Tom *3 Gray's Inn Place*
Bryan, Simon *Essex Court Chambers*	**Edwards,** David *Seven King's Bench Walk*	**Egan,** Marion *1 Paper Buildings*
Fenton, Adam *Seven King's Bench Walk*	**Foxton,** David *Essex Court Chambers*	**Graham,** Charles *1 Essex Court*
Green, Alison *Queen Elizabeth Building*	**Gruder,** Jeffrey *1 Essex Court*	**Hofmeyr,** Stephen *Seven King's Bench Walk*
Howe, Timothy *Fountain Court*	**Leggatt,** George *Brick Court Chambers*	**Lockey,** John *Essex Court Chambers*
Lyon, Victor *Essex Court Chambers*	**May,** Juliet *3 Gray's Inn Place*	**Nash,** Jonathan *3 Gray's Inn Place*
Owen, David *20 Essex Street*	**Palmer,** Howard *2 Temple Gardens*	**Railton,** David *Fountain Court*
Schaff, Alistair *Seven King's Bench Walk*	**Slade,** Richard *Brick Court Chambers*	**Spearman,** Richard *5-6 Raymond Buildings*
Templeman, Mark *Essex Court Chambers*	**Tozzi,** Nigel *4 Pump Court*	**Turner,** Janet *3 Gray's Inn Place*
Warby, Mark *5-6 Raymond Buildings*		

Geoffrey Voss QC at **3 Stone Bulidings** has appeared for the Lloyd's names group in 'Gooda Walker'.

Michael Beloff QC at **4/5 Gray's Inn Square** acted in 'Pan Atlantic v Pinetop', the recent case on material non-disclosure of risk.

At **5 Bell Yard** *Michael Crane QC* acted in one of the first of the recent Lloyd's cases, 'Brown and Sword-Daniels v

KMR Services'. *Robert Webb QC* is also well regarded.

Roger Toulson QC at **2 Crown Office Row** is well known for his work in this field.

At **4 Pump Court** *John Rowland* has been recommended.

Those barristers specialising in marine and aviation insurance may be found listed in the relevant sections.

LEADERS IN INSURANCE AND REINSURANCE

Aikens QC, Richard
See under Commercial Law.

Beazley, Thomas
See under Financial Services.

Beloff QC, Michael
See under Public and Administrative Law.

Berry, Steven
Essex Court Chambers (Gordon Pollock QC), London (0171) 813 8000. Called 1984.

Boswood QC, Anthony
See under Commercial Law.

Boyd QC, Stewart
See under Arbitration.

Bryan, Simon
Essex Court Chambers (Gordon Pollock QC), London (0171) 813 8000.
Specialisation: Specialist in insurance and reinsurance, shipping, commercial law and arbitration. Has experience acting for Lloyd's syndicates, members and managing agents. Practice also covers professional negligence.
Prof. Membership: Commercial Bar Association

Personal: Called to the Bar 1988.
Career: Educated at Arnold School 1977-1984 and at Magdalene College, Cambridge 1984-87. Born 23rd November 1965.

Butcher, Christopher
Seven King's Bench Walk (Adrian Hamilton QC), London (0171) 583 0404. Called 1986.

Clarke QC, Christopher
See under Commercial Law.

Collins QC, Michael
See under Arbitration.

Cooke QC, Jeremy
See under Commercial Law.

Cordara QC, Roderick
Essex Court Chambers (Gordon Pollock QC), London (0171) 813 8000. Called 1975, took silk 1994.

Cox, Raymond
See under Professional Negligence.

Cran QC, Mark
See under Media and Entertainment.

Crane QC, Michael
5 Bell Yard (Robert Webb QC), London (0171) 333 8811. Called 1975, took silk 1994. Practice covers general commercial litigation, including insurance, reinsurance and carriage by air. Born 1950.

Dehn QC, Conrad
See under Commercial Law.

Dohmann QC, Barbara
2 Hare Court (C.W.G. Ross-Munro QC), London (0171) 583 1770.
Specialisation: Insurance and Reinsurance; Financial Services; Banking; Private International Law; Commercial Fraud (civil); Commercial Arbitration; Disciplinary Tribunals; Regulatory Tribunals.
Prof. Membership: Committee of COM-BAR; London Common Law and Commercial Bar Association.
Career: Called to the Bar in 1971; Queen's Counsel 1987; Recorder 1990.
Personal: Educated in German and American schools, Universities of Erlangen, Mainz and Paris. Languages: German, French, Spanish.

Donaldson QC, David
See under Commercial Law.

Dunning, Graham

Essex Court Chambers (Gordon Pollock QC), London (0171) 813 8000. Called 1982. Specialist in all aspects of international and commercial law, particularly banking and finance, commodities and trade, insurance and reinsurance, professional negligence, shipping and transport. Born 13.3.1958

Edelman QC, Colin

Devereux Chambers (Peter Weitzman QC), London (0171) 353 7534.

Specialisation: Principal areas of practice are commercial law, insurance and reinsurance and professional negligence. Recent insurance/ reinsurance related cases in which he has appeared include Hayter v. Nelson [1990] (reinsurance/ arbitration), Youell v. Bland Welch (The 'Superhulls Cover' case) [1992] (reinsurance/ reinsurance brokers' negligence), Iron Trades v. Imperio [1991] (reinsurance), Summers v. Congreve Horner & Co and Independent Insurance Co [1992] (surveyors' professional indemnity insurance) and Eagle Star v. Provincial Insurance [1993] (contribution between insurers). Has been involved in a number of the Lloyd's Names actions (eg. Outhwaite, Warrilow, Merrett and Wellington). Has written articles for 'International Insurance Law Review' and the 'British Insurance Law Association Journal'. Regular speaker/chairman at Euro-Forum conferences on insurance and reinsurance topics.

Prof. Membership: Commercial Bar Association, member of Middle Temple and Midlands & Oxford Circuit.

Career: Called to the Bar in 1977 and has been a tenant at *Devereux Chambers* since 1979. Appointed Assistant Recorder in 1993. Took Silk in 1995.

Personal: Educated at Haberdashers' Aske's School, Elstree 1961-72 and Clare College, Cambridge 1973-76. Leisure pursuits include skiing, walking, badminton. Born 2nd March 1954. Lives in London.

Eder QC, Bernard

Essex Court Chambers (Gordon Pollock QC), London (0171) 813 8000. Called 1975, took silk 1990.

Edwards, David

Seven King's Bench Walk (Adrian Hamilton QC), London (0171) 583 0404.

Edwards-Stuart QC, Antony

2 Crown Office Row (Raymond Kidwell QC), London (0171) 797 8100.

Specialisation: Principal area of practice is insurance, reinsurance and general commercial litigation and advice. Considerable experience of major insurance and reinsurance disputes, both marine and non-marine, together with highly complicated technical commercial cases including radioactive contamination (Merlins v. BNFL, a leading test case), microbiology and chemistry (AKZO v.

Cyprus, contaminated paint) and electron beam welding (Burnley Engineering v. Cambridge Vacuum Engineering). Other main areas of practice involve professional negligence work particularly concerning architects and engineers, but also insurance brokers, Lloyd's agents, solicitors, accountants and surveyors, both for plaintiffs and defendants. Also involved in several major construction cases and arbitrations. Clients have included major insurance companies, BNFL, leading professional practices and large construction firms.

Prof. Membership: COMBAR, London Common Law and Commercial Bar Association.

Career: Called to the Bar 1976 and joined *2 Crown Office Row* in 1977. Took Silk in 1991 and appointed Assistant Recorder in the same year.

Personal: Education:Sherborne School, Dorset 1960-64, RMA Sandhurst 1965-66, St. Catharine's College, Cambridge 1969-72. Married with 4 children. Leisure pursuits include restoring property in France, theatre, fishing and shooting. Born 2nd November 1946. Lives in London.

Egan, Marion

1 Paper Buildings (Robert Nelson QC), London (0171) 583 7355.

Fenton, Adam

See under Banking.

Field QC, Richard Alan

See under Commercial Law.

Flaux QC, Julian

Seven King's Bench Walk (Adrian Hamilton QC), London (0171) 583 0404. Called 1978, took silk 1994.

Foxton, David

Essex Court Chambers (Gordon Pollock QC), London (0171) 813 8000. Called 1989. Specialist in all aspects of commercial law including insurance, computer supply cases, professional negligence and shipping. Born 14.10.1965.

Gaisman QC, Jonathan

Seven King's Bench Walk (Adrian Hamilton QC), London (0171) 583 0404. Called 1979, took silk 1995.

Gee QC, Steven

See under Commercial Law.

Graham, Charles

See under Commercial Law.

Green, Alison

Queen Elizabeth Building (Geoffrey Brice QC), London (0171) 353 9153.

Specialisation: Principal area of practice is insurance and reinsurance law, acting for insurance and reinsurance companies, insurance brokers, Lloyd's syndicates and in-

sureds. Also handles financial services law (particularly mortgage/insurance related cases), professional negligence and general commercial work, including EC law. Major cases include Home Insurance Co v. Adas and others, Adas and others v. Overseas Union, Barber v. Lloyd's Underwriters, Denby v. The Hellenic Mediterranean Lines, Impac v. Dorler, Re S, Lysander v. Suchak, PMMI v. Unigard Insurance Co and Union America Insurance Co v. Halvanon. Editorial Adviser on 'Insurance Contract Law' (2 vols) by Merkin & McGee (Kluwer & Co). European Community law editor of 'Current Law'. Author of articles on insurance, environmental and EC law. Former law lecturer and tutor and has addressed various legal conferences and seminars.

Prof. Membership: British Insurance Law Association (Chairman since 1994), Bar European Group, Professional Negligence Bar Association, COMBAR, IBA, British Institute of International and Comparative Law, Council of the Bar (Law Reform Committee member).

Career: Called to the Bar 1974.

Personal: Educated at Bromley High School; University College, London (LL.M 1973); and University of Louvain (studying Belgian and EC law). Leisure pursuits include tennis, ballet and music.

Gross QC, Peter

See under Aviation.

Gruder, Jeffrey

1 Essex Court (Anthony Grabiner QC), London (0171) 583 2000.

Specialisation: Principal areas of practice are insurance and reinsurance and banking. Has wide experience in both marine and non-marine reinsurance cases, acting for both insurers and assureds. Has also been involved in the current Lloyd's litigation. Other areas of practice are shipping and transport work, financial services and commodity disputes. Particular specialism in international trade finance and letters of credit. Usually advises banks. Recently involved in Standard Bank v. Bank of Tokyo (Waller J. 1995). Other important cases have included Sheldon v. Outhwaite [1995]; Indian Grace [1993]; Euro-diam v. Bathurst [1990]; "Miss Jay Jay" [1987] and "Nai Genova" [1984]. Appears frequently in arbitrations. Clients include major banks, insurance companies and corporations. Supervisor at Cambridge University 1977-79. Previously lecturer at Central London Polytechnic on International Trade (1977-81).

Prof. Membership: COMBAR.

Career: Called to the Bar in 1977. At *4 Essex Court* (now *Essex Court Chambers*) 1978-93. Joined current chambers in 1993.

Personal: Educated at City of London School 1966-72 and Trinity Hall, Cambridge 1973-76. Born 18th September 1954. Interests include tennis, theatre, cinema and reading. Lives in Radlett.

Hamilton QC, Adrian
See under Commercial Law.

Hapgood QC, Mark
See under Commercial Law.

Hirst QC, Jonathan
See under Commercial Law.

Hofmeyr, Stephen
Seven King's Bench Walk (Adrian Hamilton QC), London (0171) 583 0404. Called 1982. Practice covers insurance and reinsurance (marine and non-marine), international trade and shipping, banking and professional negligence. Born 10th February 1956.

Howard, Mark
Brick Court Chambers (Christopher Clarke QC), London (0171) 583 0777. Called 1980.

Howe, Timothy
Fountain Court (Peter Scott QC), London (0171) 583 3335.

Hunter QC, Ian
Essex Court Chambers (Gordon Pollock QC), London (0171) 813 8000. Called 1967, took silk 1980.

Irvine of Lairg QC, Lord
See under Commercial Law.

Jacobs, Richard
Essex Court Chambers (Gordon Pollock QC), London (0171) 813 8000. Called 1979.

Kealey QC, Gavin
See under Commercial Law.

Kendrick, Dominic
Seven King's Bench Walk (Adrian Hamilton QC), London (0171) 583 0404. Called 1981. Specialist in all aspects of commercial law. Born 23.5.1955

Kentridge QC, Sydney
See under Commercial Law.

Langley QC, Gordon
See under Commercial Law.

Leggatt, George
See under Commercial Law.

Lockey, John
See under Commercial Law.

Lord, David W.
3 Stone Buildings (D. R. Stanford), London (0171) 242 4937.
Specialisation: Principal area of practice is chancery and commercial law. Work includes media and entertainment, insurance and reinsurance, company law, insolvency and bankruptcy. Acted in Deeny and Others v.

Gooda Walker Ltd and Others on behalf of the Gooda Walker Action Group (Lloyd's Names).
Prof. Membership: Middle Temple, Lincoln's Inn, Chancery Bar Association.
Career: Called to the Bar in 1987 and became a tenant at *3 Stone Buildings* in 1988.
Personal: Educated at King's School Rochester 1971-81 and Bristol University 1982-86 (LL.B Hons). Leisure pursuits include most sports, especially skiing, tennis and hockey. Born 28th September 1964. Lives in London.

Lyon, Victor
Essex Court Chambers (Gordon Pollock QC), London (0171) 813 8000. Called 1980.

May, Juliet
3 Gray's Inn Place (R. Neville Thomas QC), London (0171) 831 8441. Called 1988.

Moriarty, Stephen
Fountain Court (Peter Scott QC), London (0171) 583 3335.
Specialisation: Practice encompasses common law and general commercial work, including insurance and reinsurance, professional negligence and banking. Major cases include Re State of Norway's Application [1990]; Caparo Industries v. Dickman [1990]; Lord Napier and Ettrick v. R. F. Kershaw Ltd [1993]; Henderson v. Merrett Syndicates Ltd [1994] and Feltrim Underwriting v. Arbuthnott [1994]. Editor, Insurance Section, 'Chitty on Contracts' (26th and 27th Editions).
Prof. Membership: Society of Public Teachers of Law, London Common Law and Commercial Bar Association, COMBAR.
Career: Fellow and Tutor in Law, Exeter College, Oxford 1979-86. Called to the Bar 1986 and joined current chambers in the same year.
Personal: Educated at Brasenose College, Oxford, 1974-78 (BA 1977, BCL 1978 and Vinerian Scholar). Born 14th April 1955.

Mowschenson QC, Terence
See under Insolvency.

Nash, Jonathan
See under Banking.

Owen, David
See under Commercial Law.

Palmer, Howard
2 Temple Gardens (Patrick Phillips QC), London (0171) 583 6041. Called 1977. Principal area of practice is disputes concerning the interpretation and enforcement of contracts of insurance and reinsurance.

Philipps, Guy
Fountain Court (Peter Scott QC), London (0171) 583 3335. Called 1986. Principal areas of practice are insurance and reinsur-

ance (including Lloyd's disputes), banking and international trade. Born 25.7.1961.

Phillips, Rory
3 Gray's Inn Place (R. Neville Thomas QC), London (0171) 831 8441.
Specialisation: Principal area of practice is insurance and reinsurance, acting for and against private companies, Lloyd's syndicates and brokers. Currently acting for managing and members' agents and their insurers in the Lloyd's Names litigation. Also deals with professional negligence matters, acting for and against insurance/reinsurance brokers, solicitors, accountants, architects and engineers.
Prof. Membership: COMBAR.
Career: Called to the Bar 1984.
Personal: Educated at Eton College and King's College, Cambridge. Born 1961.

Pollock QC, Gordon
See under Arbitration.

Railton, David
See under Banking.

Rokison QC, Kenneth
See under Arbitration.

Rowland, John
4 Pump Court (Bruce Mauleverer QC), London (0171) 353 2656.
Specialisation: Principal area of practice is insurance disputes, predominantly reinsurance, but also direct insurance. Closely involved in Lloyd's names litigation representing Members Agents, Managing Agents and Lloyd's Auditors. Also involved in a number of major ICC Arbitrations, inter alia, for Total Oil Company in relation to worldwide uranium sales and for Sogex Construction Group concerning a desalination plant in Saudi Arabia. Also carries out casino licensing work and provides commercial law advice to overseas lawyers, particularly in Switzerland and the USA. Clients include Lloyd's syndicates, insurers and reinsurers, insurance brokers and intermediaries, financial institutions and general corporate clients.
Prof. Membership: COMBAR.
Career: Called to the Bar in 1979 and joined 4 Pump Court in 1980.
Personal: Educated at Aquinas College, Perth, Western Australia; University of Western Australia (B.Econs, Hons) and King's College, University of London LL.B (Hons). Born 17th January 1952. Lives in London.

Ruttle, Stephen
See under Professional Negligence.

Saloman QC, Timothy
Seven King's Bench Walk (Adrian Hamilton QC), London (0171) 583 0404.

Schaff, Alistair
Seven King's Bench Walk (Adrian Hamilton QC),   London (0171) 583 0404. Called 1983.

Simon QC, Peregrine
Brick Court Chambers (Christopher Clarke QC),   London (0171) 583 0777. Called 1973, took silk 1991.

Slade, Richard
Brick Court Chambers (Christopher Clarke QC),   London (0171) 583 0777.

Smith QC, Andrew
See under Commercial Law.

Spearman, Richard
5 Raymond Buildings (Patrick Milmo QC),   London (0171) 242 2902. Called 1977.

Sumption QC, Jonathan
See under Commercial Law.

Temple QC, Anthony
See under Professional Negligence.

Templeman, Mark
Essex Court Chambers (Gordon Pollock QC),   London (0171) 813 8000. Called 1981.

Thomas QC, John
Essex Court Chambers (Gordon Pollock

QC),   London (0171) 813 8000. Called 1969, took silk 1984.

Tomlinson QC, Stephen
Seven King's Bench Walk (Adrian Hamilton QC),   London (0171) 583 0404. Called 1974, took silk 1988. Specialises in commercial work, especially insurance and reinsurance, sale of goods, shipping and international trade. Born 29.3.52.

Toulson QC, Roger
2 Crown Office Row (Rupert Jackson QC),   London (0171) 797 8000. Called 1969, took silk 1986.

Tozzi, Nigel
See under Media and Entertainment.

Turner, Janet
3 Gray's Inn Place (R. Neville Thomas QC),   London (0171) 831 8441. Called 1979.

Veeder QC, V.V.
Essex Court Chambers (Gordon Pollock QC),   London (0171) 813 8000. Called 1971, took silk 1986. Specialist in international trade, including international commercial arbitration. Born 14.12.1948.

Vos QC, Geoffrey C.
3 Stone Buildings (D. R. Stanford), London (0171) 242 4937.

Specialisation: Principal area of practice is

chancery and commercial litigation, insurance and reinsurance and financial services. Acted in Deeny v. Gooda Walker, Cox v. Bankside, MGN Pension Trustees Limited v. Invesco, Scher v. Policyholder Protection Board, R v. Independent Television Commission ex p. TSW and Re M.C. Bacon Limited amongst others.

Prof. Membership: Secretary of Chancery Bar Association, Inner Temple, Lincoln's Inn.

Career: Called to the Bar 1977 and joined current chambers in 1979. Took Silk in 1993.

Personal: Educated at University College School, and Gonville and Caius College, Cambridge.

Walker QC, Tim
See under Professional Negligence.

Warby, Mark
See under Defamation.

Webb QC, Robert
See under Aviation.

Weitzman, Tom
3 Gray's Inn Place (R. Neville Thomas QC),   London (0171) 831 8441. Called 1984.

INTELLECTUAL PROPERTY

A S ONE of the more specialised areas of practice at the Bar, intellectual property is the mainstay of only a handful of chambers. The three leading specialist sets dominate the list, with other notable experts found in more general practice sets.

LEADING SETS	
8 NEW SQUARE	
THREE NEW SQUARE	11 SOUTH SQUARE
1 ESSEX COURT	19 OLD BUILDINGS

The largest specialist set, **8 New Square**, continues to be pre-eminent. It produced the last two judges in the Patents Court, Sir Robin Jacob and Sir Hugh Laddie and handles work across the full range of the IP spectrum, from patents and trademarks to media, entertainment and franchising. It is especially noted for technical scientific cases such as genetic engineering, pharmaceuticals and electronics. Most of the barristers have a science background.

HIGHLY REGARDED	
NEW COURT	5 NEW SQUARE

David Kitchin QC, recommended as the leading IP barrister has an all-round IP practice but is particularly known for his expertise in patents. Notable cases include 'Chiron v Organon', one of the major patent biotechnology cases, and 'Compaq v Dell', which was concerned with the comparative use of a trade mark in advertising.

Other highly recommended silks are *John Baldwin, Michael Fysh* and *Peter Prescott. John Baldwin QC* is known for his copyright work, having acted in 'BBC Enterprises v Hi-Tech Xtravision', concerning international copyright infringement and 'LA Gear v Hi-Tec Sports'. *Michael Fysh QC*, head of chambers, is a member of seven Bars around the world including New South Wales, Pakistan and Trinidad. He also practises in Singapore, where permanent call is not possible. Notable cases in which he has been involved include 'CBS Songs v Amstrad Consumer Electronics' in the House of Lords (which declined to ban the sale of twin cassette machines as facilitating copyright infringement) and, more recently, 'Optical Coating Laboratory Inc v Pilkington PE Ltd' in the Court of Appeal.

Peter Prescott QC has been involved in numerous cases of general importance beyond intellectual property including 'Universal Thermosensors v Hibben', which led to new guidelines for the granting and exercise of Anton Piller orders. He is particularly recommended, though, for his expertise in patent litigation and was involved in the two recent major cases, 'Chiron v Organon' and 'Biogen v Medeva'.

Also highly regarded is *Mark Platts-Mills QC* who has recently been made a silk. With a wide IP practice, ranging from patents and trade marks to passing off, he was involved

in 'Hutchison Telecommunications v Hook', which concerned copyright and secondary infringement in the 'Rabbit' logo, and 'Universal Thermosensors v Hibben'.

The set also includes some highly recommended juniors. *James Mellor* has an all-round practice but is particularly recommended for his trademark and copyright work. He was involved in 'Boots v Superdrug', a passing off case concerning the get-up of sun protection products, and 'Mattel v Hasbro' which involved the design of the heads of Sindy and Barbie dolls. *Daniel Alexander*, only called in 1988, has already established a reputation for his patent work, having been junior in 'Chiron' and also 'Greenpeace v Plant Genetic Systems' which concerned the patent of a plant variety.

Other highly regarded juniors are *Fiona Clark, Martin Howe* and *Alexander Drysdale Wilson. Fiona Clark* has a mainly soft IP practice, handling trade mark and copyright work. *Martin Howe* is regarded for his expertise in patents, particularly biotechnology. *Alexander Drysdale Wilson* is known for trade mark infringment and passing off work.

The set also includes two barristers under five years call who are highly recommended as up-and -coming juniors. *Richard Meade* is noted for his work in 'Chiron' as second junior to *Robin Jacob* and *David Kitchin. Michael Tappin* is also strongly tipped by his peers for a bright future.

11 South Square and **3 New Square** complete the triumvirate of leading IP sets.

11 South Square handle all forms of IP work from patents and trade marks to entertainment and media law and performer's rights. Members of chambers also appear in the European Court of Justice. Again, many of the barristers have technical backgrounds. *Christopher Floyd QC*, the Head of Chambers, and also a member of the Irish Bar, is regarded as one of the leading IP silks in the country. He is especially recommended for his work in major patent actions. He was involved in the recent 'Gerber Garment Technology v Lectra Systems', important for its decision in the measure of damages for patent infringment, and 'Merrell-Dow v Norton' which is due to reach the House of Lords. *Nicholas Pumfrey QC*, the other silk in the set, is also highly regarded with a reputation among many of his colleagues as the best trade mark advocate at the Bar.

Henry Carr is recommended as one of the two leading IP juniors. Despite not having a science background, he is said to have an extraordinary ability to master complicated patent cases. He is also noted for his copyright work and acted in 'R v Registered Designs Appeal Tribunal ex parte Ford Motor Company', a designs case which involved the 'must match' provisions of the Copyright Act. *Michael Silverleaf* and *Richard Arnold* are also highly recommended. *Michael Silverleaf* handles a broad range of cases but is especially noted as Junior Counsel to the Treasury for Patents and for his expertise in computer cases. He was involved in the 'Holly Hobbie Trade Mark' which dealt a prohibition on trade mark trafficking. *Richard Arnold* is renowned for his involvement in complex patent actions. He acted in 'Molnlycke v Proctor and Gamble', dubbed the 'Nappy Wars', which concerned the obviousness of the surface of disposable nappies. He is also known for his trade mark work and has handled some of the important cases such as 'Chanel v L'Arome', which concerned the comparative advertising of perfume. *Henry Whittle* is highly regarded, particularly on electronics cases.

LEADING SILKS

Kitchin, David	*8 New Square*	
Floyd, Christopher	*11 South Square*	
Hobbs, Geoffrey	*1 Essex Court*	
Prescott, Peter	*8 New Square*	
Thorley, Simon	*Three New Square*	
Watson, Antony	*Three New Square*	
Baldwin, John	*8 New Square*	
Englehart, Robert	*2 Hare Court*	
Fysh, Michael	*8 New Square*	
Garnett, Kevin	*5 New Square*	
Morcom, Christopher	*1 Essex Court*	
Platts-Mills, Mark	*8 New Square*	
Pumfrey, Nicholas	*11 South Square*	
Rayner James, Jonathan	*5 New Square*	
Wilson, Alastair	*19 Old Buildings*	
Young, David	*Three New Square*	

3 New Square, previously at 6 Pump Court, offer the full range of IP service. Additionally, members will handle related aspects of EC law and also general commercial litigation with a technical aspect. Among the silks, *Antony Watson QC* and *Simon Thorley QC* are highly recommended. *Antony Watson QC* is currently Deputy Chairman of the Copyright Tribunal but it is for his patent work that he is most renowned, having been involved in major patent actions such as 'Chiron v Organon'. He won the Pilkington arbitration which had lasted several years. *Simon Thorley QC* has taken the place of Hugh Laddie as Chairman of the Patent Bar Association and is particularly recommended for cases concerning chemical and biochemical patents. He has also carved out a niche specialism in food and drink passing off actions, appearing before the House of Lords in 'Erven Warnink v Townend and Sons', which concerned the passing off of advocaat. *David Young QC*, a deputy judge, is also highly regarded for patents work. He was involved in 'American Cyanamid v Ethicon' in which the House of Lords laid down the 'balance of convenience' test for granting interlocutory injunctions.

The set also contains a number of notable juniors. *Andrew Waugh* is rated as the country's leading IP junior, jointly with *Henry Carr*. He has been involved in a range of major cases including 'Biogen v Medeva', which concerned the patentability of hepatitis genes, and 'Hyperion Records v Warner Music' regarding copyright infringement by sampling. *Guy Burkill* has an oustanding reputation for information technology and electronics, compounded by his involvement in

'Pavel v Sony', a dispute regarding the invention of the 'Walkman'. Also highly regarded is *Denise McFarland* who handles both patents and 'soft' IP matters such as copyright but is better known for her expertise in the latter. *Colin Birss* is rated as one of the top up- and -coming IP barristers at the Bar, having already acted in major cases such as 'Merrell-Dow v Norton', a patent action due to reach the House of Lords.

19 Old Buildings is another specialist IP set, also handling the additional areas of pharmaceutical registration, pollution and lotteries and gaming. *Alastair Wilson QC*, the head of chambers, is recommended as one of the leading IP silks and has handled a number of major cases. These include 'PLG Research v Ardon', a dispute on the issue of novelty in the Patents Act; 'British Leyland v Armstrong', which concerned the indirect infringment of copyright, and 'Lock v Beswick', the setting aside of an Anton Piller Order. He has also been recommended as one of the best silks for computer cases.

LEADING JUNIORS

Carr, Henry	*11 South Square*	
Waugh, Andrew	*Three New Square*	
Alexander, Daniel	*8 New Square*	
Arnold, Richard	*11 South Square*	
Burkill, Guy	*Three New Square*	
Mellor, James	*8 New Square*	
Mill, Ian	*2 Hare Court*	
Silverleaf, Michael	*11 South Square*	
Ashton, Arthur	*1 Essex Court*	
Bloch, Michael	*1 Essex Court*	
Bragge, Nicolas	*New Court*	
Clark, Fiona	*8 New Square*	
Dickens, Paul	*5 New Square*	
Drysdale Wilson, Alexander	*8 New Square*	
Howe, Martin	*8 New Square*	
McFarland, Denise	*Three New Square*	
Vitoria, Mary	*8 New Square*	
Whittle, C.D. (Henry)	*11 South Square*	
Wyand, Roger	*1 Essex Court*	

UP AND COMING

Birss, Colin	*Three New Square*	
Himsworth, Emma	*1 Essex Court*	
Meade, Richard	*8 New Square*	
Tappin, Michael	*8 New Square*	

The chambers of *Christopher Morcom QC* at **1 Essex Court**, a substantial common law and commercial set, are also well-regarded for intellectual property owing to a specialist group of practitioners. *Christopher Morcom* is a highly recommended silk with a reputation as one of the leading experts in trade marks. He represented Coca Cola in its unsuccessful attempt to register the distinctive bottle as a trade mark under the old Trade Marks Act, and acted in 'Imperial Group v Philip Morris' which involved the illegality of 'ghost' trade marks. *Roger Wyand* is a highly recommended junior with a broadly based practice.

New Court are also a recommended set. Specialising in the full range of intellectual property matters, they also handle work involving technical contracts, defamation and competition work. *Nicolas Bragge* is particularly recommended as a specialist. He acted in the 'Elderflower Champagne' passing off case, 'Taittinger v Allbev which went to the Court of Appeal.

5 New Square handles traditional chancery work but has also has a reputation for intellectual property, in particular entertainment law and other copyright work. *Jonathan Rayner-James QC* and *Kevin Garnett QC* are highly regarded silks and *Paul Dickens*, a junior, is noted for his entertainment practice.

Geoffrey Hobbs QC, of Anthony Grabiner's chambers at **1 Essex Court**, is highly recommended as one of the leading intellectual property silks, particularly noted for trade mark and copyright litigation. He acted in 'Reckitt and Colman v Borden', the House of Lords case concerning the passing off of the Jif lemon, and also acted in the Court of Appeal case, 'Colgate-Palmolive v Markwell', which concerned parallel imports and trade mark infringement. The set also includes *Emma Himsworth* who has been recommended as a up-and-coming junior.

2 Hare Court, a set with an outstanding reputation in other areas of law, contains two highly regarded individuals in the field on copyright. *Robert Englehart QC*, a Deputy High Court judge, and *Ian Mill*, are both highly regarded for their expertise in entertainment law, acting in many of the major decided and ongoing entertainment cases.

LEADERS IN INTELLECTUAL PROPERTY

Alexander, Daniel
8 New Square (Michael Fysh QC SC), London (0171) 405 4321.

Specialisation: Specialises principally in intellectual property, competition, EC and scientific commercial law. Also environmental and administrative law. Practice includes advocacy, drafting and advisory work in a wide variety of cases, many with EC and international aspects. Sample contested cases include Apple Corps v. Apple Computer (trade marks - contract - Article 85/EC - foreign competition law), Chiron v. Organon (genetic engineeering patent - Patents Act, section 44 - conflict of laws), Greenpeace v. Plant Genetic Systems (genetic engineering - plant varieties and environmental law - European Patent Office), ICI v. Montedison (chemical patent), Great Lakes v. Texaco (commercial contracts), Portman v. MAFF (judicial review, EC Law). Joint editor of 'Clark & Lindsell on Torts' and the 'Encyclopedia of UK and European Patent Law'. Joint author (with Mr Justice Jacob) of 'Guidebook to Intellectual Property Law'. Author of various articles on legal and scientific topics and a regular lecturer and speaker at seminars. Speaks fluent German and good French.

Prof. Membership: Bar European Group, Chancery Bar Association, Environmental Law Foundation, Patent Bar Association.

Career: Called to the Bar and admitted to the New York Bar in 1988. Joined current chambers in 1989.

Personal: Educated at University College, Oxford (BA, Physics and Philosophy, 1985), Central London Polytechnic (Dip.Law 1986) and Harvard Law School (LLM, 1987). Born 4th October 1963.

Arnold, Richard
11 South Square (Christopher Floyd QC), London (0171) 405 1222. Called 1985.

Ashton, Arthur
1 Essex Court (Christopher Morcom QC), London (0171) 936 3030.

Specialisation: Principal area of practice is trade marks and copyright. Other main areas of practice include Industrial Designs, Patents, Trade Secrets and Passing Off. Practice covers advice and the conduct of litigation. Clients have included major corporations from Europe, the United States and Japan.

Career: Called to the Bar; England and Wales 1988; South Africa 1975; Botswana 1978.

Prof. Membership: Educated at Rhodes University and University of Louvain. Lives in London.

Baldwin QC, John
8 New Square (Michael Fysh QC SC), London (0171) 405 4321.

Specialisation: Specialises in all aspects of intellectual property law, including patents, trade marks, copyrights, confidential information, computer law, entertainment law, passing off, trade libel, EC law, data protection, restrictive covenants and restraint of trade. Co-editor of 'Patent Law of Europe and the United Kingdom' (Butterworths). Has contributed numerous articles to scientific journals. Recent reported cases include Hoechst UK Ltd v. Chemiculture Ltd (1993) FSR 270 (confidential information, information obtained under statutory power); BBC Enterprises v. Hi-Tech (1991) 2 AC 327 (satellite television decoders); CHC Software Care Ltd v. Hopkins & Wood (1993) FRS (malicious falsehood, discovery).

Career: Called to the Bar 1977 (Gray's Inn). Took Silk 1991.

Personal: Educated at Nelson Grammar School 1958-1965, Leeds University (BSc 1st Class Hons Agricultural Chemistry) 1965-1968 and St Johns College, Oxford (PhD) 1968-1972. Oxford University Research Fellow (computer modelling)

1972-1975. British Council Fellowship for research in Holland 1975. Soil Science Society of Great Britain Prize 1975. Born 15th August 1947.

Birss, Colin
Three New Square (David E.M. Young QC), London 0171 405 1111. Called 1990.

Bloch, Michael
1 Essex Court (Anthony Grabiner QC), London (0171) 583 2000.

Specialisation: Principal areas of practice are general commercial and intellectual property, arbitration and defamation. Professional clients include many City law firms.

Prof. Membership: Chancery Bar Association, Commercial Bar Association

Career: Called to the Bar in 1979. At 1 Brick Court 1979-87. Joined *1 Essex Court* in 1987.

Personal: Educated at Bedales School and the universities of Cambridge (MA) and East Anglia (M Phil). Trustee of Childline and Governor of Bedales School. Born 18th October 1951. Lives in London.

Bragge, Nicolas
New Court (John Fitzgerald), London (0171) 797 8999. Called 1972. Principal areas of practice are copyright, media, computers and trademarks. Born in 1948.

Burkill, Guy
Three New Square (David E.M. Young QC), London 0171 405 1111. Called 1981.

Carr, Henry
11 South Square (Christopher Floyd QC), London (0171) 405 1222.

Specialisation: Principal areas of practice are patents, copyrights, designs and trade marks. Leading cases include R.v.Registrar of Designs ex parte Ford Motor Company

(House of Lords) R.v.Licensing Authority ex parte Smith Kline & French (House of Lords) and Scotia.v.Norgine (European Court). Also has a substantial practice in computer contracts (including negligence claims); and judicial review relating to the grant of product licences. In addition, has appeared in numerous cases in the Data Protection Tribunal on behalf of the Registrar.

Career: Called to the Bar 1982. Joined *11 South Square* in 1983.

Personal: Educated at Hertford College, Oxford and the University of British Columbia. Lives in London.

Clark, Fiona
8 New Square (Michael Fysh QC SC), London (0171) 405 4321.

Specialisation: Specialises in all aspects of intellectual property law including related contractual and EC matters, breach of confidence and trade libel. Has a particular interest in copyright, designs (both registered and unregistered) and trade marks. Also has extensive experience of product branding and in media and entertainment law. Practice embraces a wide range of cases with a high technical content covering areas such as mechanical and construction engineering, computer software, electronics, architectural design and textiles. Publications include 'Encyclopedia of United Kingdom and European Patent Law' (co-author). Reported cases: Johnstone Safety v. Peter Cook, Southco v. Dzus Fasteners, Consorzio del Prosciutto di Parma v. Marks and Spencer, Dalgetty v. Food Brokers, McDonald v. Graham. Guest lecturer at the 1993 International Conference of the Institute of Trade Mark Agents.

Prof. Membership: Patent Bar Association; Chancery Bar Association.

Career: Called to the Bar 1982. Occasional case reporter the Fleet Street Reports and Reports of Patent Cases.

Personal: Educated at Trinity College, Cambridge. Competent in French and German.

Dickens, Paul
5 New Square (James Sunnucks), London (0171) 404 0404.

Specialisation: Principal areas are copyright and design rights, moral rights, performers' rights, trade marks, passing off, confidential information, media and entertainment law and computer law. Particular interest in musical copyright infringement, information technology, multimedia and Internet. Clients include leading companies and artistes in the entertainment field and national newspapers. Joint Consulting Editor for Intellectual Property matters, Butterworths' Encyclopaedia of Forms and Precedents. Facilities for electronic transfer of pleadings, opinions [etc] worldwide, computer to computer, in many WP formats.

Prof. Membership: Patent Bar Association, Chancery Bar Association.

Career: M.A. (Cantab), A.R.C.O., former Organ Scholar (Cantab). Called in 1978. Joined *5 New Square* in 1980.

Personal: Recitalist/accompanist at local concerts, school governor, skiing, tennis. Married with 4 children.

Drysdale Wilson, Alexander
8 New Square (Michael Fysh QC SC), London (0171) 405 4321.

Specialisation: Specialist in all aspects of intellectual property law including patents, copyright, registered and unregistered designs, trade marks, passing off and confidential information. Practice also covers the enforcement of intellectual property rights in the fields of entertainment, media (including newspapers), advertising and telecommunications. Other specialist areas include computer law (both the protection of rights in hardware and software and complaints concerning allegedly faulty hardware and software); the Data Protection Act 1984 and its implications; common law restraint of trade (particularly in its application to sporting issues); and commercial cases with a significant scientifc or technical content.

Career: Called to the Bar 1981.

Personal: Educated at Salesian College, Farnborough and at The Royal Military College of Science, Shrivenham (BSc Engineering, 1st class). Born 1958.

Englehart QC, Robert
See under Commercial Law.

Floyd QC, Christopher
11 South Square (Christopher Floyd QC), London (0171) 405 1222. Called 1975, took silk 1992.

Fysh QC, Michael
8 New Square (Michael Fysh QC SC), London (0171) 405 4321.

Specialisation: Specialist in all aspects of intellectual property and European Community law. Experienced in litigation and advisory work both in the English courts and in overseas jurisdictions. Publications include 'Russell-Clarke on Registered Designs' 5th edition (Sweet & Maxwell 1974); 'The Industrial property Citator' (European Law Centre 1982 and supplements); 'Spycatcher Cases' (Sweet & Maxwell 1989); 'Breach of Confidence' (with F. Gurry) 2nd edition (Oxford University Press, in preparation). Also editor of 'Reports of Patent Cases' (The Patent Office) and 'Fleet Street Reports' (London, Sweet & Maxwell) 1974-1995.

Prof. Membership: Member, Bar Council of England and Wales; Chairman, Central and East European Sub-Committee; Vice-Chairman, Central Asia and Transcaucasian Law Association.

Career: Called to the Bar 1965. Took silk 1989. Head of chambers since 1993. Calls to overseas Bars: Northern Ireland 1974 (QC

1990), Ireland 1975 (Senior Counsel 1994), New South Wales 1975, Bombay and Supreme Court of India 1982, Pakistan 1987, Trinidad and Tobago 1990 (Senior Counsel 1990). Has also practised at the Malaysian and Singapore Bars and before the European Patent Office, Munich. Lecturer, WIPO, Geneva.

Personal: Educated at Downside School, Grenoble University, France 1958-1959 and at Oxford University (BA natural sciences) 1959-1962, MA 1969. Languages include French and a working knowledge of Russian. Born USA, 1940.

Garnett QC, Kevin
See under Media and Entertainment.

Himsworth, Emma
1 Essex Court (Anthony Grabiner QC), London (0171) 583 2000. Called 1993.

Hobbs QC, Geoffrey
1 Essex Court (Anthony Grabiner QC), London (0171) 583 2000. Called 1977, took silk 1991.

Howe, Martin
8 New Square (Michael Fysh QC SC), London (0171) 405 4321.

Specialisation: Specialist in all aspects of intellectual property, including patents, trade marks and copyrights. Also specialises in European Community law mainly but not exclusively relating to intellectual property. Practice emphasises 'heavy' technology cases, particularly those involving computers, and commercial cases with a heavy technical content. Regularly appears before the European Patent Office in Munich. Publications include 'Halsbury's Laws on Trade Marks, Trade Names and Designs' 1984 and 1995 editions (joint editor with Mr Justice Jacob); and 'Europe and the Constitution after Maastricht' (Nelson & Pollard, Oxford 1993). Important recent cases include Pioneer v. Warner [1995] (patents: direct product of process); Biogen v. Medeva (1994)(CA: patents; genetic engineering); Ibcos v. Barclays [1994] (copyright: computer programmes).

Career: Called to the Bar 1978.

Personal: Educated at Winchester College 1968-72 and at Trinity Hall, Cambridge BA 1973-1977, MA 1979. Baker Prize for Engineering 1974. Tripos Part I (Engineering) 1975, 1st class. Tripos Part II (Law) 1977, class 2:1. Everard ver Heyden Prize (for advocacy) 1978.

Kitchin QC, David
8 New Square (Michael Fysh QC SC), London (0171) 405 4321.

Specialisation: All areas of intellectual property including patents, trade marks, passing off, copyright, designs, malicious falsehood, confidential information, media and entertainment law, computer law and EC and other competition law with an intellectual property element. Also handles some technical commercial work. Publications include 'The Trade Marks Act 1994' (Sweet & Maxwell) co-author; 'Kerly's Law of Trade Marks and Trade Names' (Sweet & Maxwell) co-editor; 'Patent Law of Europe and the United Kingdom' (Butterworths) co-editor.

Prof. Membership: Chancery Bar Association, Patents Bar Association.

Career: Called to the Bar 1977 and joined chambers 1979. Took Silk 1994. Chairman, Code of Practice Committee, National Office of Animal Health (1995).

Personal: Educated at Oundle School 1968-72 and Fitzwilliam College, Cambridge 1973-76. Born 30th April 1955.

McFarland, Denise
Three New Square (David E.M. Young QC), London 0171 405 1111. Called 1987.

Meade, Richard
8 New Square (Michael Fysh QC SC), London (0171) 405 4321.

Specialisation: Specialises in all aspects of intellectual property. Has experience of biotechnology patent litigation (including Chiron v Organon, acting for the plaintiffs), electronics patent litigation, computer copyright and contractual litigation, European competition law, especially 'Euro defences' and questions of jurisdiction under the Brussels Convention, in addition to broad experience of intellectual property generally. Publications include Atkins' Court Forms section on Trade Marks and Trade Names (editor); Supreme Court Practice (Trade Marks and Patents) (assistant editor); Kerly's Law of Trade Marks (co-author, in preparation). Also contributes reports and commentaries to Masons Computer Law Reports.

Prof. Membership: Lincoln's Inn.

Career: With Andersen Consulting (information technology management consultancy) 1988-90. First in year on Bar Vocational Course (1990-91) and winner of Scarman Scholarship, Ede & Ravenscroft and Wilfred Parker Prizes. Called to the Bar in 1991.

Personal: Educated at William Ellis School, Gospel Oak, North London 1978-84 and University College, Oxford 1985-88 (BA). Born 14th November 1966.

Mellor, James
8 New Square (Michael Fysh QC SC), London (0171) 405 4321.

Specialisation: Has a wide-ranging intellectual property practice in patents (electronics/chemical/mechanical devices/biotech), copyright and designs (engineering drawings/databases/computer software/literary works/Sony walkie-talkies), trade marks and passing off ('Neighbours'/Levi's/Rolex/Walt Disney) and confidential information (chemical formulae/business information). Important cases handled include Wellcome v.

Genentech (1987 - genetic engineering patent)(noting brief), Essex Electric v. IPC (UK) (1990 - trade marks and passing off - ex-distributor - threats to customers), Fyffes v. Chiquita (1991 - trade marks - Articles 85/86 EEC), Rediffusion v. Link-Miles (1992 - flight simulator patent), Levi's V BTC (1993 - international counterfeiting of Levi's 501 jeans) and Boots v. Superdrug (1993 - get-up of sun protection products). Work experience in a variety of engineering disciplines in the UK, France, Germany, Somalia, the Congo and Iraq. Co-editor of 'Kerly on Trade Marks', Co-contributor to the EEC Intellectual Property Notes for the ICLQ and editor of 'Computers - Atkin's Court Forms'.

Prof. Membership: Patent Bar Association, Chancery Bar Association.

Career: Called to the Bar in 1986 and joined current chambers in 1987.

Personal: Educated at Rugby School and King's College, Cambridge (MA, Eng). Leisure activities include windsurfing, skiing, cycling, running, sailing, reading and music. Born 16th May 1961.

Mill, Ian
See under Media and Entertainment.

Morcom QC, Christopher
1 Essex Court (Christopher Morcom QC), London (0171) 936 3030. Called 1963, took silk 1991. Specialist in intellectual property law, with a particular emphasis on trademarks. Born 4.2.1939.

Platts-Mills QC, Mark
8 New Square (Michael Fysh QC SC), London (0171) 405 4321.

Specialisation: Specialist in all aspects of intellectual property, including patents, trade marks, passing off, registered designs, copyright and design right.
Also handles commercial work with a technical content. Recent interesting cases include Hutchison Telecommunications v. Hook [1994] (copyright, secondary infringement - "Rabbit" logo); Apple Corps v. Cooper [1993] (copyright - Sergeant Pepper's Lonely Hearts Club band" photographs); Universal Thermosensors v. Hibben [1992] (Breach of confidence, Anton Piller practice - design of thermo sensors, competition by ex-employees).

Career: Called to the Bar 1974. Joined present chambers 1975. Took silk 1995.

Personal: Educated at Bryanston School 1963-1969 and at Balliol College, Oxford (BA Engineering Science and Economics) 1969-1972. Born 17th January 1951.

Prescott QC, Peter
8 New Square (Michael Fysh QC SC), London (0171) 405 4321.

Specialisation: Specialist in all aspects of intellectual property law. Has been involved in numerous reported cases, recent examples of which include: Aztech Systems Pte v. Crea-

tive Technology Ltd; Bayer v. Norton; Imperial Chemical Industries v. Montedison; National Research Development Corp v. The Wellcome Foundation; Consorzio del Prosciutto di Parma v. Marks & Spencer. Publications include 'Modern Law of Copyright' Butterworths 1980 1994 and 'Data Processing and the Law' (chapter in) Sweet & Maxwell 1984. Notes in Law Quarterly Review: 'Finding out who to sue' (1973) 89 LQR 482 and 'American Cyanamid v. Ethicon' (1975) 91 LQR 168. Contributions to European Intellectual Property Review include 'Towards a small claims patent court' 10 EIPR 246; 'Trade marks invisible at point of sale: some corking cases' 12 EIPR 241; 'Was AutoCad wrongly decided?' (1992) 6 EIPR 191.

Prof. Membership: Patent Bar Association; Chancery Bar Association.

Career: Called to the Bar 1970. Took Silk 1990.

Personal: Educated at St George's College (Argentina), Dulwich College, University College London (BSc Physics) and Queen Mary College London (MSc Nuclear Engineering). Fluent in Spanish. Leisure pursuits include flying, music, reading and, formerly, programming in assembler language. Born 23rd January 1943.

Pumfrey QC, Nicholas
11 South Square (Christopher Floyd QC), London (0171) 405 1222. Called 1975, took silk 1990.

Rayner James QC, Jonathan
5 New Square (James Sunnucks), London (0171) 404 0404.

Specialisation: Principal areas of practice are media and entertainment law and intellectual property law, in particular contract, licensing, confidence, copyright, design rights, performers' rights, trade marks and passing off. Advisory and litigation. Specialisation in EC aspects.
Co-editor of 'Copinger and Skone James' on copyright since 1980. Joint Consulting Editor for 'The Encyclopaedia of Forms and Precedents' (Entertainment). Member of Editorial Board of 'Entertainment Law Review'.

Career: Commenced practice in 1975, having been called to the Bar in 1971. Appointed Silk in 1988. Member of the Chancery Bar Association, Patent Bar Association and of Centrebar. Assistant Recorder since 1994.

Personal: Born 26th July 1950. Educated at King's College School, Wimbledon 1961-68, Christ's College, Cambridge 1968-72 (M.A.; LL.B.) and Brussels University 1972-73 (Lic. spec. Droit Europeen). Lives in London.

Silverleaf, Michael
11 South Square (Christopher Floyd QC), London (0171) 405 1222.

Specialisation: Intellectual property, computer law, entertainment and media, disputes with high technical content and related EC and domestic competition law.

Prof. Membership: Patent Bar Association, Chancery Bar Association.

Career: Member of *Gray's Inn*. Called 1980. Junior Counsel to the Treasury in Patent Matters since 1991.

Personal: Publications: 'Passing off Law and Practice' (Butterworths), 'Butterworths Patent Litigation' (contributor), 'Computer Law' (Blackstone) (contributor). Attended King's College School, Wimbledon, Imperial College (BSc, Physics).

Tappin, Michael

8 New Square (Michael Fysh QC SC), London (0171) 405 4321.

Specialisation: Specialises in all aspects of intellectual property law, but with a particular interest in chemical and biotechnological patent work and also in matters relating to pharmaceutical licensing. Co-editor of 'Encyclopaedia of United Kingdom and European Patent Law'.

Prof. Membership: Patent Bar Association.

Career: Called to the Bar and joined current chambers in 1991.

Personal: Educated at Cheltenham Grammar School 1975-82, St. John's College, Oxford 1982-87. Merton College, Oxford

(1987-89) BA 1st Class Hons in Chemistry, D.Phil in Biochemistry. Born 11th November 1964.

Thorley QC, Simon

Three New Square (David E.M. Young QC), London 0171 405 1111. Called 1972, took silk 1989.

Vitoria, Mary

8 New Square (Michael Fysh QC SC), London (0171) 405 4321.

Specialisation: Specialises in intellectual property law and media law, covering patents, copyright, trade marks, passing off, performers' rights, design rights, confidential information and contracts relating to the above. Co-author of 'Modern Law of Copyright and Designs'; Editor of *Fleet Street Reports* and *Reports of Patent Cases*; Chief Editor of 'Encyclopedia of UK and European Patent Law'; Author of section on patents in 'Halsbury's Laws' (Vol 35); and Editor of *European Intellectual Property Review*.

Prof. Membership: Chancery Bar Association, Patent Bar Association.

Career: Called to the Bar in 1975. Lecturer in Law at Queen Mary College, London University 1975-78. Joined 8 New Square in 1978.

Personal: Educated at London University

(BSc and PhD in Chemistry, LL.B). Leisure interests include opera, travel and bird watching.

Watson QC, Antony

Three New Square (David E.M. Young QC), London 0171 405 1111. Called 1968, took silk 1986.

Waugh, Andrew

Three New Square (David E.M. Young QC), London 0171 405 1111. Called 1982.

Whittle, C.D. (Henry)

11 South Square (Christopher Floyd QC), London (0171) 405 1222. Called 1975.

Wilson QC, Alastair

See under Computer Law.

Wyand, Roger

1 Essex Court (Christopher Morcom QC), London (0171) 936 3030. Called 1973.

Young QC, David

Three New Square (David E.M. Young QC), London 0171 405 1111. Called 1966, took silk 1980.

EDITORIAL POLICY

In this edition, the lists of specialist firms include profiles of individual practitioners - solicitors and barristers - who have been recommended most frequently to our researchers. Editorial policy is to identify leading practitioners on merit: it is not possible to buy a place in our biographical lists. Inclusion of a profile in this directory is based solely on expertise and reputation.

Enormous effort has been invested by our ten-strong research team (mainly solicitors and barristers) in canvassing recommendations and identifying leaders. We are confident in the overall accuracy of the results. However, mistakes and misjudgements are inevitable, and if readers have any suggestions regarding our listings we should be very pleased to hear from them.

LICENSING

LICENSING work has traditionally been the preserve of the criminal bar. Many common law sets of chambers also handle this work, but no set is exclusively devoted to it. This is partly due to the large proportion of licensing work which is dealt with entirely by solicitors.

Highly respected QCs and juniors include *Richard Beckett QC, Gilbert Gray QC, Kevin De Haan, Andrew Muir, James Rankin* (all of whom are from **3, Raymond Buildings**) and *Susanna FitzGerald* (**1 Essex Court**).

LEADING SETS – LONDON

3 RAYMOND BUILDINGS

3 Raymond Buildings has a formidable national reputation and several members practise exclusively in licensing law with particular specialisms in betting, gaming, lotteries, liquor and public entertainment. Preparation and advice relating to applications and objections is given at all levels from local committees to the Divisional Court. Some of their clients include Rank Organisation, Ladbrokes and Weatherspoon Organisation.

LEADING SILKS– LONDON

Beckett, Richard	*3 Raymond Buildings*	
Gray, Gilbert	*3 Raymond Buildings*	

LEADING JUNIORS– LONDON

De Haan, Kevin	*3 Raymond Buildings*	
FitzGerald, Susanna	*1 Essex Court*	
Muir, Andrew	*3 Raymond Buildings*	
Rankin, James	*3 Raymond Buildings*	
Bromley-Martin, Michael	*3 Raymond Buildings*	
Forster, Jane Tracy	*13 King's Bench Walk*	
Monkcom, Stephen	*Francis Taylor Building*	

OUTSIDE LONDON

In Manchester, *John Hugill QC* is a well-known licensing specialist.

LEADING SILKS– REGIONS

Hugill, J.	*Peel Court Chambers, Manchester*	
Farmer, Michael	*Sedan House, Chester*	
Goldstone, L. Clement	*28 St. John St, Manchester*	
Saunders, J.	*4 Fountain Court, Birmingham*	

LEADING JUNIORS– REGIONS

Wadsley, Peter	*St. John's Chambers, Bristol*	
Gosling, J.	*4 Fountain Court, Birmingham*	
Grundy, Clare	*28 St. John St, Manchester*	
Humphry, Richard	*28 St. John St, Manchester*	

UP AND COMING

Walsh, M.	*Peel Court Chambers, Manchester*	

LEADERS IN LICENSING

Beckett QC, Richard
3 Raymond Buildings (Clive Nicholls QC), London (0171) 831 3833.
Specialisation: Licensing. Work includes preparation and advice relating to applications and objections in all licensing matters, such as liquor, gaming, betting and amusement centres, representing parties at all levels from local committees to Divisional Court. Advises on lotteries and other related activities. Clients include the Rank Organisation, Ladbrokes and the J.D. Weatherspoon Organisation.
Career: Called to the Bar 1965 and joined present chambers 1967. Took silk 1987.

Bromley-Martin, Michael
See under Crime: Fraud.

De Haan, Kevin
3 Raymond Buildings (Clive Nicholls

QC), London (0171) 831 3833. Called 1976. Specialises in all areas of environmental law, consumer protection and licensing, including criminal aspects.

Farmer QC, Michael
Sedan House (Derek R. Halbert), Chester (01244) 348282.

FitzGerald, Susanna
1 Essex Court (Anthony Grabiner QC), London (0171) 583 2000.
Specialisation: Specialises in liquor, gaming, betting and public entertainment licensing and lotteries law. Has represented or advised major leisure and gaming operators, retail liquor companies and breweries. Professional clients include major licensing solicitors, City and West End firms, and the CPS. Author of articles published in 'Licensing Review' and 'The Solicitors' Journal'.

Contributor to 'Gambling and Public Policy' (1991). Has drafted submissions to the government on changes in licensing law and has been asked to draft submissions on amendments to the Gaming Act 1968 for Business in Sport and Leisure. Has lectured at conferences and spoken at seminars in the UK and abroad. Has also appeared on radio.
Prof. Membership: CLCBA, South Eastern Circuit, Commercial Women in Law, Society for the Study of Gambling (Committee Member). Director of Business in Sport & Leisure. Mediator accredited by CEDR.
Career: Called to the Bar in 1973 and joined present chambers in 1975.

Forster, Jane Tracy
13 King's Bench Walk (Graeme Williams QC), London (0171) 353 7204. Called 1975.

Goldstone QC, L. Clement
28 St. John St (Charles Bloom QC),
Manchester (0161) 834 8418.

Gosling, J.
4 Fountain Court (Richard Wakerley
QC), Birmingham (0121) 236 3476.

Gray QC, Gilbert
3 Raymond Buildings (Clive Nicholls
QC), London (0171) 831 3833. Called
1953, took silk 1971.

Grundy, Clare
28 St. John St (Charles Bloom QC),
Manchester (0161) 834 8418.

Hugill QC, J.
Peel Court Chambers (Michael
Shorrock QC), Manchester (0161) 832
3791. Called 1954, took silk 1976.

Humphry, Richard
28 St. John St (Charles Bloom QC),
Manchester (0161) 834 8418.

Monkcom, Stephen
Francis Taylor Building (Alan Tyrrell
QC), London (0171) 797 7250.
Specialisation: General common law practice, with a particular emphasis on licensing law. Practice also covers betting, gaming and lotteries. Publications include 'Smith & Monkcom: The Law of Betting, Gaming and Lotteries' (Butterworths 1987)'.
Career: Called 1974. Joined present chambers 1976.
Personal: Born 9th June 1949.

Muir, Andrew
3 Raymond Buildings (Clive Nicholls
QC), London (0171) 831 3833. Called
1975. Principal area of practice is licensing.
Born 25.12.1951.

Rankin, James
3 Raymond Buildings (Clive Nicholls
QC), London (0171) 831 3833.
Specialisation: All aspects of licensing law including liquor, public entertainment, betting and gaming and bingo licenses. Has had

considerable experience in applying and opposing. Was briefed by the respondent in the Court of Appeal case of SITKI. Also specialises in Judicial Review, and appears regularly in the Divisional Court. Advises in lottery work.
Career: Called to the Bar 1983. Joined *3 Raymond Buildings* (Formerly *Queen Elizabeth Building*) in 1984.
Personal: Educated at Eton and Buckingham University.

Saunders QC, J.
4 Fountain Court (Richard Wakerley
QC), Birmingham (0121) 236 3476. Called
1972, took silk 1991.

Wadsley, Peter
St. John's Chambers (Roderick Denyer
QC), Bristol (0117) 9213456.

Walsh, M.
Peel Court Chambers (Michael
Shorrock QC), Manchester (0161) 832
3791.

FIRMS OF ACCOUNTANTS

Accountants specialising in litigation support
are listed in the accountants' A-Z, with details
of the services they offer to solicitors, from
forensic accounting to intellectual property or
business valuations.

MEDIA AND ENTERTAINMENT

MANY disputes in the media and entertainment field are ordinary business disputes and tend to be handled by commercial sets, although they often straddle other issues such as copyright, competition law, freedom of speech and defamation. Barristers specialising in these areas may be found elsewhere in the directory.

LEADING SETS

2 HARE COURT	
BRICK COURT CHAMBERS	ESSEX COURT CHAMBERS
5 NEW SQUARE	
DOUGHTY STREET CHAMBERS	3 GRAY'S INN PLACE
8 NEW SQUARE	5-6 RAYMOND BUILDINGS
11 SOUTH SQUARE	11 STONE BUILDINGS

2 Hare Court emerges as the leading set with outstanding practitioners in *Robert Englehart QC* (commercial) and *Ian Mill* who was instructed in the George Michael litigation and is particularly known for music copyright work. Members of chambers have experience of both the commercial and copyright sides of entertainment law.

Other highly regarded commercial sets include **Brick Court Chambers** and **Essex Court Chambers**.

Mark Cran QC and *Sydney Kentridge QC* are **Brick Court's** leading lights, *Mark Cran QC* having particular experience of the music business.

Essex Court Chambers gains its reputation in the field from its head of chambers: *Gordon Pollock QC*, although the set also has well-respected practitioners at the junior end.

Doughty Street Chambers, **3 Gray's Inn Place** and **11 Stone Buildings** are also experienced in the field. **Doughty Street's** most highly recommended practitioners are *Geoffrey Robertson QC* and *Andrew Nicol QC* (who took silk in 1995) whilst at **3 Gray's Inn Place** *Andrew Sutcliffe*, who handles both contractual and intellectual property issues, is well respected. Members of chambers at **11 Stone Buildings** have experience of the commercial side of entertainment law. *Murray Rosen QC* also undertakes copyright work.

5 New Square emerges as the leading set undertaking copyright work for media and entertainment clients. *Jonathan Rayner James QC* and *Kevin Garnett QC* are both highly experienced in the field.

Other chambers renowned for their intellectual property work include **8 New Square** and **11 South Square**. **8 New Square** boasts *Peter Prescott QC* and *David Kitchin QC* ('News Group Newspapers v Independent Television Publications', 'Rank Films v Video Information Centre') as its eminent silks. *Michael Silverleaf* at **11 South Square** is well respected in the field.

5-6 Raymond Buildings in addition to handling libel cases for media clients, also undertakes a substantial amount of commercial work. *Charles Gray QC* has been highly recommended.

LEADING SILKS

Englehart, Robert *2 Hare Court*
Cran, Mark *Brick Court Chambers*
Garnett, Kevin *5 New Square*
Gray, Charles *5-6 Raymond Buildings*
Kentridge, Sydney *Brick Court Chambers*
Kitchin, David *8 New Square*
Pollock, Gordon *Essex Court Chambers*
Rayner James, Jonathan *5 New Square*
Robertson, Geoffrey *Doughty Street Chambers*
Baldwin, John *8 New Square*
Browne, Desmond *5-6 Raymond Buildings*
Burton, Michael *Littleton Chambers*
Nicol, Andrew *Doughty Street Chambers*
Prescott, Peter *8 New Square*
Rosen, Murray *11 Stone Buildings*
Vos, Geoffrey C. *3 Stone Buildings*

Individual practitioners to feature prominently in our research include *Stephen Bate* at **4 Raymond Buildings**, *Edward Faulks* at **1 Serjeant's Inn**, *David Lord* at **3 Stone Buildings**, and *Nigel Tozzi* at **4 Pump Court**.

LEADING JUNIORS

Mill, Ian *2 Hare Court*		
Bate, Stephen *Four Raymond Buildings*	Faulks, Edward *No. 1 Serjeants' Inn*	Lord, David W. *3 Stone Buildings*
Silverleaf, Michael *11 South Square*	Sutcliffe, Andrew *3 Gray's Inn Place*	Tozzi, Nigel *4 Pump Court*
Bryan, Simon *Essex Court Chambers*	Crow, Jonathan *4 Stone Buildings*	Dickens, Paul *5 New Square*
Michaels, Amanda *5 New Square*	Millett, Richard *Essex Court Chambers*	Price, Richard *Littleton Chambers*
Waksman, David *3 Gray's Inn Place*		

UP AND COMING

Saini, Pushpinder *2 Hare Court*

Baldwin QC, John
See under Intellectual Property.

Bate, Stephen
Four Raymond Buildings (Jeremy Lever QC), London (0171) 405 7211. Called 1981. Born 26.6.1958. Main areas of practice: television, film, video, New Media and telecommunications.

Browne QC, Desmond
See under Defamation.

Bryan, Simon
See under Insurance and Reinsurance.

Burton QC, Michael
See under Commercial Law.

Cran QC, Mark
Brick Court Chambers (Christopher Clarke QC), London (0171) 583 0777. Called 1973, took silk 1988.

Crow, Jonathan
See under Company.

Dickens, Paul
See under Intellectual Property.

Englehart QC, Robert
See under Commercial Law.

Faulks, Edward
See under Professional Negligence.

Garnett QC, Kevin
5 New Square (James Sunnucks), London (0171) 404 0404.

Specialisation: Practises extensively in the field of media and entertainment with a particular leaning to music industry and publishing work. Also practises widely in the Intellectual Property field with an emphasis on copyright. Is Senior Editor of Copinger and Skone James on Copyright. Other main area of practice is general Chancery litigation.

Gray QC, Charles
See under Defamation.

Kentridge QC, Sydney
See under Commercial Law.

Kitchin QC, David
See under Intellectual Property.

Lord, David W.
See under Insurance and Reinsurance.

Michaels, Amanda
5 New Square (James Sunnucks), London (0171) 404 0404.

Specialisation: Intellectual property, with an emphasis on copyright, trade marks and passing off. Entertainment law, including music industry, advertising and television disputes. General Chancery and commercial litigation. Call: 1981.

Personal: BA in law from Durham, MA in Advanced European Studies from College of Europe, Bruges. Fluent French. Author of 'A Practical Guide to Trade Marks' ESC/Sweet & Maxwell.

Mill, Ian
2 Hare Court (C.W.G. Ross-Munro QC), London (0171) 583 1770.

Specialisation: Principal area of practice is commercial law, with specialist knowledge and experience in the music and other media industries including intellectual property aspects. Major cases include Panayiotou v. Sony Music (the George Michael case) and Silvertone v. Mountfield (the Stone Roses case). Addressed Euroforum conference on copyright in the music industry, December 1994.

Prof. Membership: Middle Temple.

Career: Called to the Bar 1981 and joined current chambers 1982.

Personal: Educated at Epsom College 1971-75 and Trinity Hall, Cambridge 1976-80 (MA in Classics and Law). Leisure pursuits include food and wine, travel, theatre and opera. Born 9th April 1958. Lives in London.

Millett, Richard
See under Banking.

Nicol QC, Andrew
See under Immigration.

Pollock QC, Gordon
See under Arbitration.

Prescott QC, Peter
See under Intellectual Property.

Price, Richard
Littleton Chambers (Michael Burton QC), London (0171) 797 8600.

Specialisation: Principal areas of entertainment and media law experience include film, video and music rights and financing disputes, copyright infringement and piracy, the 'fair dealing' provisions of copyright law (BBC v. British Sky Broadcasting Ltd. 1991), Anton Piller and Mareva injunctions, and corporate/partnership disputes within the entertainment industry. Clients have included major film and music production and distribution companies and broadcasters, and leading artists, directors and producers. Also specialises in election and administrative law, and professional negligence work.

Prof. Membership: COMBAR, London Common Law and Commercial Bar Association.

Career: Called to the Bar in 1969. Joined present Chambers in 1987, having previously been a member of Chambers of the late Lewis Hawser Q.C.

Personal: Educated at King Edward VII School, Sheffield, and King's College London.

Rayner James QC, Jonathan
See under Intellectual Property.

Robertson QC, Geoffrey
See under Public and Administrative Law.

Rosen QC, Murray
11 Stone Buildings (Michael Beckman QC), London (+44) 0171 831 6381. Called 1976, took silk 1993. Main areas of practice are media, entertainment and sports law, banking, fraud, insolvency and professional negligence. Born 26.8.1953.

Saini, Pushpinder
2 Hare Court (C.W.G. Ross-Munro QC), London (0171) 583 1770.

Specialisation: Commercial law (including copyright and entertainment law) public law (including human rights) and employment law. Cases include Panayiotou v. Sony (George Michael), A&M Records v. VCI Ltd, ZYX Music v. King, Wailer v. Island Records, R v. Radio Authority ex p. Guardian Media Group and Airdale Health Authority v. Bland. Called to the Bar 1991. Co-author of forthcoming Halsbury's Laws Volume on European Convention on Human Rights.

Prof. Membership: Justice, ELA, ALBA.

Personal: Languages: Urdu, Punjabi, Hindi, French.

Silverleaf, Michael
See under Intellectual Property.

Sutcliffe, Andrew
3 Gray's Inn Place (R. Neville Thomas QC), London (0171) 831 8441. Fax: 831 8479.

Specialisation: Commercial and chancery litigation; in particular media and entertainment law (appeared in leading cases Elton John v Dick James and Zang Tumb Tuum v Holly Johnson), intellectual property, banking and professional negligence. Also sale of goods and general contract cases. Clients have included artistes, major record and publishing companies, clearing and merchant banks.

Prof. Membership: COMBAR, London Common Law and Commercial Bar Association, Chancery Bar Association.

Career: Called to the Bar 1983. Joined *3 Gray's Inn Place* 1984.

Personal: Educated at Winchester College and Worcester College Oxford.

Tozzi, Nigel

4 Pump Court (Bruce Mauleverer QC), London (0171) 353 2656.

Specialisation: General commercial and common law practice covering all areas, including contract disputes, professional negligence, insurance, employment, agency, construction, professional disciplinary hearings and gaming.

Prof. Membership: COMBAR, Professional Negligence Bar Association.

Career: Called to the Bar and joined present chambers 1980.

Personal: Educated at Exeter University (LL.B Hons first class) 1976-79. Leisure pursuits include hockey, theatre and cinema. Born 31st August 1957.

Vos QC, Geoffrey C.

See under Insurance and Reinsurance.

Waksman, David

3 Gray's Inn Place (R. Neville Thomas QC), London (0171) 831 8441.

Specialisation: Entertainment law. Has had considerable experience of contentious and advisory work in this field, concerning both contractual and intellectual property aspects. Other main areas of practice are banking, financial services and general commercial litigation. Clients include major record and publishing companies, artistes, clearing and international banks and other financial institutions. Has lectured extensively on commercial law topics.

Prof. Membership: Commercial Bar Association.

Career: Called to the Bar 1982.

Personal: Educated at Manchester and Oxford Universities. Leisure pursuits include sailing, walking, and playing guitar. Lives in London and the Lake District.

MEDICAL NEGLIGENCE

MEDICAL negligence is a growing area and most chambers with a personal injury practice will handle a certain amount of it. However, they would not be considered specialists for inclusion in this section.

The pre-eminent chambers is **3 Serjeants' Inn** with five silks and a large number of excellent juniors practising in the area. The chambers act for plaintiffs and defendants in medical and dental negligence, and are one of the few chambers with expertise in disciplinary work and professional ethics. Tenants have appeared in many of the major cases in the field, including 'De Martell v Sutton HA' (1993) and 'Salih v Enfield HA' (1991).

Silks with outstanding reputations include *John Grace QC, Adrian Whitfield QC* and *Robert Francis QC* (the latter two are also well known for handling work in the expanding area of medical ethics). *Adrian Whitfield QC* and *Robert Francis QC* appeared in the high profile case 'Re F' (Mental Patient Sterilisation) (1990) HL and both regularly lecture and write on various aspects of medical law and practice. *Nicola Davies QC*, also a well regarded silk, regularly lectures on medico-legal issues and has been leading counsel in a number of prominent cases, as well as regularly appearing for defendants at tribunal hearings.

Among junior counsel the outstanding individuals are *Huw Lloyd, Adrian Hopkins, Christopher Johnston, James Watson, Angus Moon* and *Mary O'Rouke*.

The other leading sets in the area are **1 Crown Office Row**, **6 Pump Court** and **1 Paper Buildings**.

1 Crown Office Row has an excellent reputation, with all members having substantial experience in the field. *James Badenoch QC, Robert Owen QC, Stephen Miller QC* and *Terence Coghlan QC* deserve a particular mention as leading silks. Recently appointed silk, *Philip Havers QC* has also been recommended for his expertise.

Chambers undertake all aspects of medical work, appearing for both plaintiffs and defendants in major medical negligence actions, and also have expertise in disciplinary and professional ethics matters. The set has been involved in many reported cases including 'Wilsher v Essex Health Authority', representing the Health Authorites involved in the Myodil Litigation and the Benzodiazepine Group litigation.

Out of the many excellent juniors, *David Hart, Margaret Bowron* and *Sally Smith* are especially well known.

6 Pump Court handles a large amount of high profile plaintiff and defendant medical negligence, and also undertakes disciplinary work. *Kieran Coonan QC* is especially well-known and has been involved in the HIV Haemophiliac litigation and 'W v Egdell' (CA), a case concerning medical breach of confidence. Well regarded juniors at the set include *Siobhan Goodrich, David Morris, Andrew Hockton* and *Dr. Simon Taylor*.

1 Paper Buildings is a common law set with a strong medical negligence practice. Leading silks in the field are *Robert Nelson QC* and *Michael Spencer QC*. Also highly regarded is *Dr. Michael Powers QC*, who took silk recently. Among the juniors recommended for expertise is *Richard Hone*.

Other outstanding silks in the field include *Daniel Brennan QC* (**39 Essex Street**) and *Laura Cox QC* (**Cloisters**) who deals with claims of the utmost severity such as cerebral palsy, and acted in 'Tredget v Bexley HA' (nervous shock in medical negligence).

Also highly recommended is newly appointed silk *Simeon Maskrey QC* (**9, Bedford Row**) who undertakes work for plaintiffs and defendants in medical negligence and disciplinary matters. He handled Gardner v Lincs. Health Authority, one of the earliest wrongful birth cases. *Jean Ritchie QC* (**4 Paper Buildings**) and *Michael Brent QC* (**9 Gough Square**) are also well known in the field.

LEADING JUNIORS– LONDON

Bowron, Margaret *1 Crown Office Row*	**Goodrich,** Siobhan *6 Pump Court*	**Hart,** David *1 Crown Office Row*
Hockton, Andrew *6 Pump Court*	**Hone,** Richard *1 Paper Buildings*	**Hopkins,** Adrian *3 Serjeants' Inn*
Irwin, Stephen *Doughty Street Chambers*	**Lewis,** Charles *Old Square Chambers*	**Lloyd,** Huw *3 Serjeants' Inn*
Moon, Angus *3 Serjeants' Inn*	**Morris,** David *6 Pump Court*	**O'Rourke,** Mary *3 Serjeants' Inn*
Pratt, Duncan *New Court Chambers*	**Smith,** Sally *1 Crown Office Row*	**Taylor,** Simon *6 Pump Court*
Watson, James *3 Serjeants' Inn*		
Buchan, Andrew *Cloisters*	**Goodwin,** Deirdre *13 King's Bench Walk*	**Hillier,** Andrew *5 Bell Yard*
Lehain, Philip *199 Strand*	**May,** Kieran *199 Strand*	**Ough,** Richard *4 Paper Buildings*
Reddihough, John Hargreaves *9 Gough Square*	**Seys Llewellyn,** Anthony *Farrar's Building*	**Shaw,** Howard *29 Bedford Row Chambers*
Welchman, Charles *New Court Chambers*		

UP AND COMING

Johnston, Christopher *3 Serjeants' Inn*

Highly regarded juniors that have been particularly recommended are *Charles Lewis* (**Old Square Chambers**), *Stephen Irwin* (**Doughty Street Chambers**), *Howard Shaw* (**29 Bedford Row**) and *Duncan Pratt* (**New Court Chambers**).

OUTSIDE LONDON

This area of work is closely related to personal injury, and a number of specialists in that field also practise in this one. However, the barristers listed below have been particularly recommended as offering expertise in medical negligence matters outside London.

LEADING PRACTITIONERS – OUTSIDE LONDON ()

Goldrein, Ian *The Corn Exchange (Liverpool)*
Donovan, Scott *Derby Sq Chs (Liverpool)*
Shorrock, Michael *Peel Ct Chs (Manchester)*

LEADERS IN MEDICAL NEGLIGENCE

Badenoch QC, James

1 Crown Office Row (Robert Seabrook QC), London (0171) 797 7500.

Specialisation: Principal area of practice is medical negligence and medically-related work. Also handles personal injury matters. Major cases include Wilsher v. Essex Area Health Authority (House of Lords); the Wendy Savage enquiry; and Dobbie v. Medway Health Authority (Court of Appeal). Contributor to 'Medical Negligence' (Powers and Harris, Butterworths 1990 and 2nd Edn. 1994).

Prof. Membership: Professional Negligence Bar Association, London Common Law Bar Association.

Career: Called to the Bar in 1967 and joined current chambers in 1968. Appointed Recorder 1987. Took silk 1989. Deputy High Court Judge 1994.

Personal: Educated at Dragon School, Oxford; Rugby School 1959-63 and Magdalen College, Oxford (MA) 1964-67. Born 24th July 1945. Lives in London.

Bowron, Margaret

See under Environmental.

Brennan QC, Daniel

39 Essex Street (Colin Mackay QC), London (0171) 583 1111. Called 1967, took silk 1985.

Brent QC, Michael Leon

9 Gough Square (Michael Brent QC), London (0171) 353 5371. Called 1961, took silk 1983. Principal area of practice is plaintiff personal injury and medical negligence cases. Born 8.6.1936.

Buchan, Andrew

Cloisters (David Turner-Samuels QC), London (0171) 583 0303.

Specialisation: Serious personal injury and medical negligence. Also professional negligence work in these fields. Has a special interest in mental health law. Recent reported cases include Littrell v. United States of America (liability of USA for negligent medical treatment on a US Air-force base); Biles v. North East Thames Regional Health Authority (damages for negligent sterilisa-

tion); Walker v. Northumberland County Council (first successful stress induced breakdown caused by work case). Publications include 'Personal Injury Practice and Procedure, the guide to litigation in the county court and the High Court' (1994) co-author.

Prof. Membership: PIBA, PNBA, APIL, AVMA, Inquest, ILSoc.

Career: Called to the Bar 1981.

Personal: Born 6th December 1956.

Coghlan QC, Terence

1 Crown Office Row (Robert Seabrook QC), London (0171) 797 7500.

Specialisation: Covers all aspects of medical work including medical negligence. Has appeared for both plaintiffs and defendants in numerous medical negligence actions and arbitrations as well as regularly appearing in the GMC, GDC and other disciplinary bodies. Does advisory work for health authorities on medico-legal problems. Also handles coroners work, professional negligence of accountants, surveyors and architects, personal injury, insurance, disaster litigation and general common law work.

Represented all the health authorities involved in the "Myodil" litigation. Clients have included the Medical Defence Union, Medical Protection Society, MDDUS, the Welsh Office and leading medical negligence solicitors. Has lectured at various seminars on personal injury and medical negligence matters and also appeared on television.

Prof. Membership: Professional Negligence Bar Association, London Common Law Bar Association.

Career: Called to the Bar in 1968. Appointed Recorder of the Crown Court in 1989. Took Silk in 1993.

Personal: Education: New College, Oxford (BA, MA).

Coonan QC, Kieran
6 Pump Court (Kieran Coonan QC), London (0171) 583 6013. Called 1971, took silk 1990. Principal areas of practice are medical and health law and personal injury. Other main area is criminal law. Born 29.10.1946.

Cox QC, Laura
See under Employment.

Davies QC, Nicola
3 Serjeants' Inn (Adrian Whitfield QC), London (0171)353 5537 Mbl(0385)736844.

Specialisation: Practice covers all aspects of medical law, including medically related crime. Cases as Junior Counsel include Sidaway v. Board of Governors of the Bethlem and Maudsley Hospital [1985], Cleveland Child Abuse Inquiry [1987] and GMC hearing involving sale of human kidney to Turkish nationals. Acted as Leading Counsel in R v. North West Thames Regional Health Authority and Riverside Health Authority and the Secretary of State for Health, ex parte Rhys Daniels [1993] (judicial review of decision to close the bone marrow unit of the Westminster Children's Hospital); the public inquiry into the death of Georgina Robinson [1994]; Secretary of State for the Home Office v. Derek Robb [1994] (rights of prisoner to refuse food and duty of treating doctor to observe such wishes); and Chairman of Committee of Inquiry into death of Jonathan Newby [1995]. Author of 'Medico-legal issues in Endoscopy' (in 'Quality control in Endoscopy') and 'Legal Aspects of Day Care Surgery' (in 'Day-care Anasthesia and Sedation'). Lectures on medico legal issues.

Career: Called to the Bar in 1976. Member of the Supplementary Treasury Panel (common law) 1988-92. QC 1992. Assistant Recorder 1995.

Personal: Educated at Bridgend Girls Grammar 1964-71 and Birmingham University 1971-74. Non-Executive Director of the Bethlem and Maudsley NHS Trust.

De Wilde QC, Robin
199 Strand (R.M. Stewart QC), London (0171) 379 9779. Called 1971, took silk 1993.

Francis QC, Robert
3 Serjeants' Inn (Adrian Whitfield QC), London (0171)353 5537 Mbl(0385)736844.

Specialisation: Principal area of practice is medical law, including medical negligence actions for plaintiffs and defendants, ethical cases concerning treatment of patients (particularly termination of treatment), and disciplinary proceedings (General Dental Council, General Dental Council etc.). Leading cases include: Re F (Mental Patient: Sterilization), Airedale NHS Trust v. Bland, Roy v. Kensington etc FPC, B v. Croydon HA. Other areas of practice include administrative law, employment, crime.

Prof. Membership: Professional Negligence Bar Association, LCLCBA, CBA.

Career: Called to the Bar 1973; Queen's Counsel 1992.

Personal: Uppingham School, Exeter University. Born 4th April 1950.

Goodrich, Siobhan
6 Pump Court (Kieran Coonan QC), London (0171) 583 6013. Called 1980.

Goodwin, Deirdre
13 King's Bench Walk (Graeme Williams QC), London (0171) 353 7204. and 32 Beaumont Street, Oxford (01965) 311 066.

Specialisation: Principal area of practice is medical negligence and catastrophic injury claims including birth trauma, neurological insult, brain damage resulting from head injuries, paraplegia and tetraplegia, industrial accidents and occupational diseases. Acted as Junior counsel for the plaintiff in Bolitho v. City and Hackney Health Authority [1993]. Lectures to health professionals on medicolegal matters including risk management e.g. May 1993 on informed consent to international symposium on nuclear medicine (Holland); and to Hospitals and G.P. practices on consent and risk management. On Euroforum Special Damages Panel, March 1994.

Prof. Membership: Association of Personal Injury Lawyers, Bar Professional Negligence Association, Birth Trauma Litigation Group, American Trial Lawyers Association.

Career: Called to the Bar 1974.

Personal: Educated at Sandown Grammar School 1962-69 and University College, London 1969-72. Founder and musical director of Millenium Music which gives concerts for charity. Member of G.P. Patients' Participation Group. Leisure pursuits include music (solo and accompanist piano, organ, choral singing and conducting), medieval history, theatre, family life and hill walking. Born 14th April 1951. Lives in Monks Risborough, Buckinghamshire.

Grace QC, John
3 Serjeants' Inn (Adrian Whitfield QC), London (0171)353 5537 Mbl(0385)736844. Called 1973, took silk 1994.

Hart, David
1 Crown Office Row (Robert Seabrook QC), London (0171) 797 7500. Called 1982. Practice covers construction law, environmental matters and professional negligence.

Havers QC, Philip
See under Environmental.

Hillier, Andrew
See under Employment.

Hockton, Andrew
6 Pump Court (Kieran Coonan QC), London (0171) 583 6013. Called 1984. Specialist in medical negligence. Practice covers inquests, pharmaceutical and product liability, disciplinary work and professional negligence. Born 19.9.1957.

Hone, Richard
1 Paper Buildings (Robert Nelson QC), London (0171) 583 7355. Called 1970.

Hopkins, Adrian
3 Serjeants' Inn (Adrian Whitfield QC), London (0171)353 5537 Mbl(0385)736844.

Specialisation: Deals with all aspects of medical law, including medical negligence, professional ethics and discipline. Recent cases include Re F (A mental patient - sterilisation); Re C (refusal of medical treatment) and Re G and Re S (PVS cases). Also handles matters relating to coroners courts.

Prof. Membership: Western Circuit, Professional Negligence Bar Association.

Career: Called to the Bar and joined 3 Serjeants' Inn in 1984.

Personal: Educated at Warwick School and St. Peter's College, Oxford. Leisure interests include gardening, swimming and travel. Born 16th May 1961. Lives in London.

Irwin, Stephen
Doughty Street Chambers (Geoffrey Robertson QC), London (0171) 404 1313. Called 1976. Principal area of practice is medical negligence work. Born 5.2.1953.

Johnston, Christopher
3 Serjeants' Inn (Adrian Whitfield QC), London (0171)353 5537 Mbl(0385)736844.

Specialisation: Principal areas of practice are medical and dental negligence, medical ethics and employment. Considerable experience acting for both plaintiff and defendant in all aspects of medico-legal work, including high value claims (brain damage, blindness, serious physical injury). Experience in medical ethics work (B v. Croydon Health Authority, [1995] 1 All E R 683, CA: force feeding of mental patient. Also persistent vegetative state case). Acting for defendant in first dental negligence class action. Professional disciplinary work (General Dental Council). Other main area of practice is employment: industrial tribunal claims including unfair dismissal and race and sex discrimination (particualrly in health context). Also experienced in solicitor's negligence. Co-author of Bar Council's submission and response to Office of Fair Trading's Report on "Extortionate Credit Bargains".

Prof. Membership: Professional Negligence Bar Association.

Career: Called to the Bar in 1990. Joined *Serjeants' Inn* in 1991.

Personal: School: Ballymena Academy. University: Trinity Hall, Cambridge (Law, 1st class). Interests: cinema and history.

Lehain, Philip

See under Personal Injury.

Lewis, Charles

Old Square Chambers (Hon. John Melville Williams QC), London (0171) 831 0801.

Specialisation: Medical negligence on behalf of patients. Also personal injuries. Wrote the first textbook on the medical negligence action. Now in its third edition: "Medical Negligence, a Practitioner's Guide" (published by Tolleys). Has lectured extensively and published numerous articles.

Prof. Membership: Bar Professional Negligence Association; Bar Personal Injuries Group; Association of Personal Injury Lawyers.

Career: Called to the Bar 1963. Joined *Old Square Chambers* 1991.

Personal: Educated at Charterhouse and Oriel College, Oxford. Interests include opera, singing, cycling and the English countryside.

Lloyd, Huw

3 Serjeants' Inn (Adrian Whitfield QC), London (0171) 353 5537 Mbl(0385)736344. Called 1975. Specialises in medical law and medical negligence.

Maskrey QC, Simeon

9 Bedford Row (Stephen Coward QC), London (0171) 242 3555. Called 1977, took silk 1995. Principal area of practice is medical negligence work. Born 17.5.1955.

May, Kieran

See under Personal Injury.

Miller QC, Stephen

See under Professional Negligence.

Moon, Angus

3 Serjeants' Inn (Adrian Whitfield QC), London (0171) 353 5537 Mbl(0385)736344.

Specialisation: Specialist in medical negligence and construction law. Practice also covers employment law. Important cases include Walford v. Miles (1992); ReC(medical treatment) (1989); Khan v. Ainslie (1993); Bowers v. Harrow Health Authority (1995).

Career: Called to the Bar 1986. Joined present chambers 1987.

Personal: Educated at King's College, Taunton and Christ's College, Cambridge (MA, Law). Born 17th September 1962.

Morris, David

6 Pump Court (Kieran Coonan QC), London (0171) 583 6013.

Specialisation: Specialises in medical law, including medical negligence, medical disciplinary work, inquests and criminal cases with medical disputes. Practice also covers personal injury and general crime.

Prof. Membership: Professional Negligence Bar Association.

Career: Called to the Bar 1976. Joined present chambers 1977.

Personal: Educated at Bristol University (LL.B) 1971-1974. Leisure pursuits include theatre and sport. Born 4th September 1953. Lives in London.

Nelson QC, Robert

See under Professional Negligence.

O'Rourke, Mary

3 Serjeants' Inn (Adrian Whitfield QC), London (0171) 353 5537 Mbl(0385)736344.

Specialisation: Medical law (and medically related matters such as Dental, Pharmaceutical and Nursing) - all aspects including negligence/malpractice, professional misconduct and disciplinary matters, judicial review involving medical, pharmaceutical, dental and nursing Regulations and legislation, Coroner's Inquests and medical and related employment issues. Considerable High Court trial experience in medical negligence field on behalf of Health Authorities and Defence Organisations. Other areas of practice include Employment Law (all aspects including Industrial Tribunal and EAT work, High Court wrongful dismissal claims and restrictive covenant cases, and advisory work on contracts and disciplinary codes): and Construction law (including cases in the Official Referee's Court and acting in construction and civil engineering arbitrations for Employers, Main Contractors and subcontractors in all types of claims including all major standard form contracts).

Prof. Membership: Professional Negligence Bar Association (PNBA); Employment Law Bar Association; Official Referee's Bar Association (ORBA); Bar European Group (BEG).

Career: Called to the Bar November 1981. Pupillage undertaken in present Chambers Sept. 1982 - Sept. 1983 and in practice in same Chambers since.

Personal: Educated at King's College, London (LL.B). Living in London.

Ough, Richard

4 Paper Buildings (Harvey McGregor QC), London (0171) 353 3366.

Specialisation: Principal area of practice

encompasses medical law and medical negligence, acting on behalf of both plaintiffs and defendants. Reported cases include Fletcher v. Sheffield Health Authority and Re E (a minor), both at the Court of Appeal. Author of 'The Mareva Injunction and Anton Piller Order' (Butterworths, 2nd Ed. 1993).

Prof. Membership: Honourable Society of the Inner Temple, General Medical Council (Principal List), Fellow of the Chartered Institute of Arbitrators.

Career: Called to the Bar 1985. Part-time SSAT Chairman and Assistant Deputy Coroner, St. Albans Watford, District.

Owen QC, Robert

1 Crown Office Row (Robert Seabrook QC), London (0171) 797 7500.

Specialisation: Profesional negligence, medical negligence, product liability, multi-party actions, disaster litigation, commercial fraud.

Prof. Membership: London Common Law and Commercial Bar Association, Chairman, Professional Negligence Bar Association.

Career: Called 1968, QC 1988, Recorder 1987, DTI Inspector 1990, Deputy High Court Judge 1994.

Powers QC, Michael

1 Paper Buildings (Robert Nelson QC), London (0171) 583 7355.

Specialisation: Medical negligence (plaintiff and defendant). Co-editor of the leading textbook 'Medical Negligence' (Butterworths 1990, 1994). Pharmaceutical law and all areas of common law touching upon medical and scientific matters. Group litigation for plaintiffs and defendants. Clients include *Mckenna & Co, Linklaters & Paines, Ashurst Morris Crisp, Wedlake Bell, Irwin Mitchell, Hart Brown, Russell Jones & Walker* and many other leading firms.

Prof. Membership: Professional Negligence Bar Association; London Common Law and Commercial Bar Association; Fellow Royal Society of Medical, British Medical Association, Association of Anaesthetists, Medico-Legal Society.

Career: Medical Practice (1972-1980): Obstetrics, Medicine, Anaesthesia, ITU and GP. Called to the Bar (Lincoln's Inn) 1979; QC 1995. President of the South of England Coroners' Society (1987/88). Founder member of Society of Doctors in Law. Chapters in many books; writes and lectures widely.

Personal: Enthusiasm for advocacy and training of trial skills. Recreations: technology, sailing, walking, music and photography.

Pratt, Duncan

New Court Chambers (George Carman QC), London (0171) 583 6166.

Specialisation: Principally practises in medical negligence and substantial personal injury claims. Considerable experience of claims involving birth and brain injuries of the utmost severity. Lectures to local Law Societies and to other organisations on topics related to medical negligence, pleadings and interlocutory proceedings. Other areas of practice solicitors' negligence, product liability, employment and related contractual claims. Professional clients include both specialised medical negligence departments and general litigation departments.

Prof. Membership: Professional Negligence Bar Association, AVMA, Employment Law Bar Association.

Career: Called to the Bar 1971. Joined chambers 1972.

Personal: Educated RGS Newcastle and University College, Oxford. Lives in London. Leisure pursuits include choral singing, local amenity societies, theatre, concert and opera.

Reddihough, John Hargreaves

9 Gough Square (Michael Brent QC), London (0171) 353 5371.

Specialisation: Principal areas of practice are personal injury, medical and professional negligence. Over 20 years' experience of all aspects of such work including cases involving injuries of utmost severity resulting from accident or medical negligence, fatal accidents claims and industrial disease. Acted in cases involving severe brain damage, paraplegia, loss of limbs etc. Also handles matters of general commercial law (sale and carriage of goods, insurance and reinsurance, contract and tort) and criminal advocacy. Clients include trade unions, insurance companies, health authorities and NHS Trusts.

Prof. Membership: Midland and Oxford Circuit.

Career: Called to the Bar 1969 and joined current chambers in 1972. Standing Counsel, H.M. Customs & Excise 1989. Appointed Recorder 1994.

Personal: Educated at Manchester Grammar School 1959-65 and Birmingham University 1965-68 (LL.B Hons). Leisure pursuits include skiing, gardening, running, music and reading. Born 6th December 1947.

Ritchie QC, Jean

4 Paper Buildings (Harvey McGregor QC), London (0171) 353 3366.

Specialisation: All aspects of medical negligence and medical work, also personal injury work. Acts for plaintiffs and health Trusts and authorities. Cases include Re F [1990], De Martell v. Merton and Sutton Health Authority [1993] and [1995] and Ritchie v. Chichester Health Authority [1994].

Contributor to 'Safe Practice in Obstetrics and Gynaecology' (Ed. Clements) 1994. Conducted workshop at AVMA Conference.

Prof. Membership: Professional Negligence Bar Association.

Career: Called to the Bar 1970. Silk 1992. Recorder 1993. Member of Supreme Court Rules Committee from 1993. Chairman of Inquiry into care of Christopher Clunis 1993-94.

Personal: Kings College London (LL.B) and McGill University, Montreal (LL.M).

Seys Llewellyn, Anthony

See under Personal Injury.

Shaw, Howard

See under Family Law.

Smith, Sally

1 Crown Office Row (Robert Seabrook QC), London (0171) 797 7500. Called 1977.

Spencer QC, Michael

1 Paper Buildings (Robert Nelson QC), London (0171) 583 7355. Called 1970, took silk 1989.

Stewart QC, Robin

See under Professional Negligence.

Taylor, Simon

6 Pump Court (Kieran Coonan QC), London (0171) 583 6013.

Specialisation: Specialises in medical law, including medical negligence, medical disciplinary work, health service administrative law, inquests and criminal cases involving medical disputes. Spokesman for the Professional Negligence Bar Association on medical negligence.

Prof. Membership: Professional Negligence Bar Association (Executive Committee); British Academy of Forensic Sciences; Society of Doctors In Law; British Medical Association.

Career: Qualified doctor. Called to the Bar 1984. Joined present chambers 1989.

Personal: Educated at Cambridge (BA Hons) 1983. MB BChir 1987. Born 4th June 1962. Lives in London.

Watson, James

3 Serjeants' Inn (Adrian Whitfield QC), London (0171) 353 5537 Mbl (0385) 736844.

Specialisation: Principally litigation relating to the medical profession and other

professionals particularly in the construction industry. Also personal injury, employment and general commercial work.

Prof. Membership: Professional Negligence Bar Association, CEDR Accredited Mediator.

Personal: MA (Cantab). Called to the Bar 1979.

Welchman, Charles

New Court Chambers (George Carman QC), London (0171) 583 6166.

Specialisation: Handles a wide range of medical negligence and personal injury litigation, including a sizeable proportion of birth injury claims involving injuries of the utmost severity. Major cases include Gascoine v. Sheridan [1994 5 MED LR 437]. Lectures to Legal Action Group/AVMA and other organisations on medical negligence and related topics.

Prof. Membership: Professional Negligence Bar Association, AVMA.

Career: Called to the Bar 1966. Joined current chambers in 1991. Appointed Recorder 1994.

Personal: Educated at West Buckland School, Exeter Technical College and University College London. Leisure pursuits include theatre, opera, jazz, cricket (spectator) and inland waterways (navigator). Born 1943. Lives in Clapham, London.

Whitfield QC, Adrian

3 Serjeants' Inn (Adrian Whitfield QC), London (0171) 353 5537 Mbl (0385) 736844.

Specialisation: Principal area of practice is medical negligence and other medical law, including treatment decisions. Cases include Sidaway, Hotson, in Re F (Sterilisation) and de Martell. Has extensive G.M.C and other tribunal experience. Acts for plaintiffs and defendants. Visiting Research Fellow at Centre of Medical Law and Ethics, King's College, London. Writes and lectures regularly on medico-legal subjects.

Prof. Membership: London Common Law and Commercial Bar Association, Professional Negligence Bar Association, Medico-Legal Society.

Career: Call 1964: Recorder 1981: Queen's Counsel 1983: Chairman of NHS Tribunal 1993.

Personal: Educated Ampleforth College and Magdalen College Oxford: Demy (Open Scholar). Lives in London.

PARLIAMENTARY

PARLIAMENTARY law involves advising on private and hybrid bills and orders, and representing their promoters and opponents. Counsel also provide advice on the implications of proposed legislation for industry, commerce and the various professions.

Parliamentary law tends to be the preserve of the Planning Bar and therefore **4-5 Gray's Inn Square. 2 Harcourt Buildings, 2 Mitre Court Buildings** and **1 Serjeants' Inn** are the leading sets. Most planning and environmental sets will have their parliamentary practitioners. Specialists in this field belong to the Parliamentary Bar Mess and the Planning and Environment Bar Association.

At **4-5 Gray's Inn Square**, several members are experienced parliamentary law practitioners. *Jeremy Sullivan QC, Elizabeth Appleby QC* and *Gregory Stone QC* are notable silks. *Nicholas Huskinson* and *Thomas Hill* are respected juniors.

At **2 Harcourt Buildings**, there are a number of highly regarded members in this field, namely *Peter Boydell QC,*

respected. *Richard Glover* is a highly regarded junior.

1 Serjeants' Inn has a number of parliamentary specialists. *Lionel Read QC, David Woolley QC, Patrick Clarkson QC* and *Christopher Whybrow QC* are particularly noted. All these silks promote and oppose private and hybrid bills, and advise on other parliamentary procedures and development proposals. Members have promoted the Dartford-Thurrock Crossing Bill and the British Rail (Liverpool Street Station) Bill. *John Pugh-Smith* is a well known junior.

There are a number of individuals at other chambers who have considerable expertise in the parliamentary field. *Nigel Macleod QC, Christopher Lockhart-Mummery QC* and *John Howell QC* are well known silks at **4 Breams Buildings**. *Nigel Macleod QC* has appeared in major public inquiries and parliamentary bill proceedings concerning major development inquiries. *Christopher Katkowski* and *Nathalie Lieven* are highly regarded juniors.

Conrad Dehn QC, Bruce Coles QC and *Andrew Smith QC* are well known parliamentary practitioners at **Fountain Court**. *Murray Shanks* and *Daphne Loebl* are well regarded juniors. *George Laurence QC* is highly distinguished at **12 New Square** and has promoted and opposed bills before both Houses of Parliament on numerous occasions. He successfully opposed the Crossrail Bill in 1994. *Charles Sparrow QC* at **13 Old Square** has a prestigious reputation in the

Sheila Cameron QC, Gerald Ryan QC, Robin Purchas QC and *Charles George QC.* Members of this set have been involved in the promoting or opposing of many bills such as the King's Cross Railways Bill and the Crossrail Bill. *Andrew Tait* and *Craig Howell Williams* are highly regarded juniors.

Most members of **2 Mitre Court Buildings** specialise in this field. *Michael Fitzgerald QC* has acted for the government promoting the Channel Tunnel Bill and for many promoters and opponents of private bills. *Susan Hamilton QC, William Glover QC, Gerald Moriarty QC, Anthony Andersen QC* and *George Bartlett QC* are also highly

Parliamentary field. *Nicholas Asprey* at these chambers has been recommended as a well known junior.

A number of counsel from the leading chambers are involved in the Channel Tunnel Rail Link Bill, currently before Parliament. *Jeremy Sullivan QC* and *Nicholas Huskinson* at **4-5 Gray's Inn Square** and *Robin Purchas QC* and *Philip Petchey* at **2 Harcourt Buildings** are promoting the Bill. *Charles George QC* of **2 Harcourt Buildings,** *Michael Fitzgerald QC* at **2 Mitre Court Buildings,** *Malcolm Spence QC* at **2-3 Gray's Inn Square,** *Gregory Stone QC* at **4-5 Gray's Inn Square** and *Lionel Read QC* at **1 Serjeants' Inn** are appearing on behalf of the petitioners.

LEADING JUNIORS

Asprey, Nicholas *13 Old Square*	**Hargreaves,** Sara Jane *12 New Square*	**Hill,** Thomas *4-5 Gray's Inn Square*
Huskinson, Nicholas *4-5 Gray's Inn Square*	**Lindblom,** Keith *2 Harcourt Buildings*	**Petchey,** Philip *2 Harcourt Buildings*
Tait, Andrew *2 Harcourt Buildings*		
Farrow, Kenneth *13 Old Square*	**Glover,** Richard *2 Mitre Court Buildings*	**Howell Williams,** Craig *2 Harcourt Buildings*
Katkowski, Christopher *4 Breams Buildings*	**Lieven,** Nathalie *4 Breams Buildings*	**Loebl,** Daphne *Fountain Court*
Newcombe, Andrew *2 Harcourt Buildings*	**Pugh-Smith,** John *1 Serjeants' Inn*	**Shanks,** Murray *Fountain Court*
Thomas, Megan *1 Serjeants' Inn*		

LEADERS IN PARLIAMENTARY

Anderson QC, Anthony
See under Planning and Local Government.

Appleby QC, Elizabeth
See under Public and Administrative Law.

Asprey, Nicholas
13 Old Square (Charles Sparrow QC), London (0171) 242 6105. Called 1969.

Bartlett QC, George
2 Mitre Court Buildings (Michael FitzGerald QC), London (0171) 583 1380. Called 1966, took silk 1986.

Boydell QC, Peter
See under Ecclesiastical Law.

Cameron QC, Sheila
2 Harcourt Buildings (Peter Boydell QC), London (0171) 353 8415. Called 1957, took silk 1983.

Clarkson QC, Patrick
1 Serjeants' Inn (Lionel Read QC), London (0171) 583 1355. Called 1972, took silk 1991. Practice covers planning, local government, parliamentary and environmental law.

Coles QC, Bruce
See under Aviation.

Dehn QC, Conrad
Fountain Court (Peter Scott QC), London (0171) 583 3335. Called 1952, took silk 1968. Principal area of practice is commercial law, including insurance and reinsurance and professional negligence. Also covers parliamentary and administrative law. Born 24.11.1926.

Farrow, Kenneth
13 Old Square (Charles Sparrow QC), London (0171) 242 6105. Called 1966.

Fitzgerald QC, Michael
See under Environmental.

George QC, Charles
2 Harcourt Buildings (Peter Boydell QC), London (0171) 353 8415. Called

1974, took silk 1992. Practice encompasses planning, administrative law, parliamentary law and ecclesiastical matters. Born 8.6.1945.

Glover QC, William
2 Mitre Court Buildings (Michael FitzGerald QC), London (0171) 583 1380. Called 1950, took silk 1969.

Glover, Richard
2 Mitre Court Buildings (Michael FitzGerald QC), London (0171) 583 1380. Called 1984.

Hamilton QC, Susan
2 Mitre Court Buildings (Michael FitzGerald QC), London (0171) 583 1380.

Specialisation: Practice encompasses local government, planning, highway, environmental and parliamentary law. Work includes large planning inquiries (eg Gatwick Airport North Terminal and Stansted Airport) with a speciality in open cast coal mining. Parliamentary work includes private and hybrid Bills such as Broads Bill, Port of Immingham (new harbour area), Crossrail - Green Park Bill, Channel Rail Link, Cardiff Bay Barrage Bill and Dartford River Crossing Bill. Also invoved in Highway inquiries. Acted in Bolton v. Secretary of State, recently heard in the House of Lords. Author of 'Modern Law of Highways' (1981) and Halsbury's Laws Vol. 21 'Highways' and Vol. 39 'Rating'.

Prof. Membership: Parliamentary Bar Mess, Planning and Environment Law Association.

Career: Called to the Bar and joined current chambers 1975. Took Silk and appointed Assistant Recorder 1993.

Personal: Educated at Hove Grammar School for Girls 1957-63. Married 1977, to D.E.P Kelly, two sons. Leisure pursuits include sailing, gardening, cooking, tapestry, reading and travelling.

Henderson QC, Roger
See under Financial Services.

Hicks QC, William
See under Public and Administrative Law.

Hargreaves, Sara Jane
12 New Square (John Mowbray QC), London (0171) 405 3808. Called 1979.

Hill, Thomas
See under Planning and Local Government.

Howell QC, John
See under Public and Administrative Law.

Howell Williams, Craig
See under Environmental.

Huskinson, Nicholas
4-5 Gray's Inn Square (Miss Elizabeth Appleby QC, The Hon. Michael Beloff QC), London (0171) 404 5252. Called 1971. Principal areas of practice are local government, planning, administrative, and parliamentary law and landlord and tenant matters.

Katkowski, Christopher
See under Planning and Local Government.

Laurence QC, George
12 New Square (John Mowbray QC), London (0171) 405 3808.

Specialisation: Practice encompasses property litigation (including landlord and tenant, planning and judicial review), parliamentary and countryside law (rights of way, commons). Has appeared frequently as counsel before opposed Bill Committees in both Houses of Parliament. Appeared in Fairfold Props Ltd v. Exmouth Dock Co [1990] (mandatory injunction to compel withdrawal of Parliamentary Bill). Acted in numerous reported cases on rights of way, including Celsteel v. Alton House [1986]; R v. Secretary of State for Environment ex parte Stewart [1987] (evidence of public highway - wrongful exclusion - statutory ouster) and R v. Secretary of State Ex parte Bagshaw [1994] (test for inclusion of new public path on definitive map).

Prof. Membership: Chancery Bar Association, Administrative Law Bar Association, Planning and Environment Bar Association, Parliamentary Bar Association.

Career: Called to the Bar 1972. Joined 9 *Old Square* 1973; current chambers January 1991. Took Silk April 1991. Appointed Assistant Recorder 1993.

Personal: Educated at University of Cape Town 1966-68 (BA) and University College, Oxford 1969-71 (MA). Rhodes Scholar. Leisure pursuits include sport and theatre. Born 15th January 1947. Lives in London.

Lieven, Nathalie
4 Breams Buildings (Christopher Lockhart-Mummery QC), London (0171) 430 1221.

Lindblom, Keith
See under Planning and Local Government.

Lockhart-Mummery QC, Christopher
See under Planning and Local Government.

Loebl, Daphne
See under Commercial Law.

Macleod QC, Nigel
4 Breams Buildings (Christopher Lockhart-Mummery QC), London (0171) 430 1221.

Specialisation: Planning, local government, environmental, parliamentary, public, and administrative law. Has appeared in many major public inquiries, including highways, shopping, nuclear, airports, housing, and waste development proposal inquiries, as well as in Parliamentary Bill proceedings concerning major development projects. Clients have included Government Departments, local authorities, and major organisations and companies.

Prof. Membership: Vice Chairman Local Government Planning and Environmental Bar Association; member of Administrative Law Bar Association and the Parliamentary Bar Mess.

Career: Called to Bar 1961; QC 1979; Recorder 1981; Deputy High Court Judge sitting on Planning Cases, since 1992; Bencher Gray's Inn 1993.

Personal: M.A., B.C.L., Christ Church Oxford. Lives in London and Derbyshire.

Moriarty QC, Gerald
See under Public and Administrative Law.

Newcombe, Andrew
2 Harcourt Buildings (Peter Boydell QC), London (0171) 353 8415.

Specialisation: Principal areas of practice are parliamentary and planning work. Also deals with all areas associated with planning, including compulsory purchase, local government, environmental and general public law.

Prof. Membership: Local Government, Planning & Environmental Bar Association.

Career: Called to the Bar in 1987 and joined *2 Harcourt Buildings* in 1989.

Personal: Educated at Kingston Grammar School 1964-71 and Durham University 1971-74. Born 6th February 1953.

Petchey, Philip
2 Harcourt Buildings (Peter Boydell QC), London (0171) 353 8415. Called 1976.

Pugh-Smith, John
See under Environmental.

Purchas QC, Robin
2 Harcourt Buildings (Peter Boydell QC), London (0171) 353 8415.

Specialisation: Principal areas of practice are parliamentary, planning and government work, compulsory purchase, compensation, public and administrative and environmental law.

Prof. Membership: Parliamentary Bar Mess; Planning and Environment Bar Association: South Eastern Circuit.

Career: Called to the Bar in 1968 and joined *2 Harcourt Buildings* in 1969. Took silk in 1987. Appointed Recorder in 1989.

Personal: Educated at Marlborough College and Trinity College, Cambridge (Senior Exhibitioner). Born 12th June 1946.

Read QC, Lionel
See under Environmental.

Ryan QC, Gerard
See under Planning and Local Government.

Shanks, Murray
Fountain Court (Peter Scott QC), London (0171) 583 3335. Called 1984. Main areas of practice are banking, insurance, employment, insolvency, partnerships, parliamentary work and professional negligence. Born 19.6.1960.

Smith QC, Andrew
See under Commercial Law.

Sparrow QC, Charles
13 Old Square (Charles Sparrow QC), London (0171) 242 6105. Called 1950, took silk 1966.

Spence QC, Malcolm
See under Planning and Local Government.

Stone QC, Gregory
4-5 Gray's Inn Square (Miss Elizabeth Appleby QC, The Hon. Michael Beloff QC), London (0171) 404 5252.

Specialisation: Specialises in planning and parliamentary law. Practice also covers local government, highways, administrative law and environmental law. Important work includes the Channel Tunnel Rail Link Bill; Terminal 5, Heathrow; Belvedere Waste to Energy plant; M25 MSA Inquiry; M40 MSA Inquiry; British Rail (No3) Bill; Toxic Waste Incinerator Inquiries.

Prof. Membership: Planning and Environment Bar Association; Parliamentary Bar Association.

Career: Called to the Bar 1976. Joined present chambers 1991. Took Silk 1994. Standing Counsel to Department of Trade and Industry for South Eastern Circuit (1989-1990).

Personal: Educated at L'Universite de Rennes, France 1965, The Queen's College, Oxford 1966-1969, and Manchester University 1970-1972. Born 12th December 1946. Lives in London.

Sullivan QC, Jeremy
See under Planning and Local Government.

Tait, Andrew
2 Harcourt Buildings (Peter Boydell QC), London (0171) 353 8415.

Specialisation: Main areas of practice are parliamentary, planning, environmental, administrative and local government work.

Prof. Membership: Parliamentary Bar; Planning & Environment Bar Association.

Career: Called to the Bar in 1981 and joined *2 Harcourt Buildings* in 1982.

Personal: Educated at Hertford College, Oxford. Born 18th May 1957.

Thomas, Megan
1 Serjeants' Inn (Lionel Read QC), London (0171) 583 1355. Called 1987. Specialist in town and country planning and environmental law. Born 30.7.1964

Whybrow QC, Christopher
1 Serjeants' Inn (Lionel Read QC), London (0171) 583 1355. Called 1965, took silk 1992. Principal areas of practice cover parliamentary, planning and local government and environmental law. Born 7.8.1942.

Widdicombe QC, David
2 Mitre Court Buildings (Michael FitzGerald QC), London (0171) 583 1380. Called 1950, took silk 1965.

Woolley QC, David
1 Serjeants' Inn (Lionel Read QC), London (0171) 583 1355. Called 1962, took silk 1980. Principal area of practice is local government and parliamentary law. Born 9.6.1939.

PARTNERSHIP LAW

MOST chancery chambers have some experience in this field of practice. However only a handful of them have a strong specialism in partnership law which includes the drafting of new agreements, revision of existing agreements, division of assets upon dissolution and representation in partnership disputes.

Other recommended chambers include **1, New Square** (Eben Hamilton QC), **13 Old Square** (Mr.E.W.H.Christie) and **13 Old Square** (Charles Sparrow QC). The latter's expertise relates primarily to medical partnerships.

LEADING SETS

48 BEDFORD ROW

1 NEW SQUARE	**13 OLD SQUARE (CHRISTIE)**
13 OLD SQUARE (SPARROW)	

Among these, **48, Bedford Row** have a formidable reputation. Specialising exclusively in this area, they handle all aspects of partnership law from representation in partnership disputes, arbitrations and mediations to drafting and reviewing agreements. Clients include solicitors, accountants, doctors, surveyors and financial and commercial institutions. *Roderick I'Anson Banks*, editor of 'Lindley & Banks on Partnership' is widely acknowledged as the leading barrister for partnership matters.

LEADING SILKS

Briggs, Michael   *13 Old Square*

Burton, Michael   *Littleton Chambers*

Cherryman, John   *4 Breams Buildings*

Davis, Nigel   *7 Stone Buildings*

Elias, Patrick   *11 King's Bench Walk*

Lerego, Michael   *Fountain Court*

LEADING JUNIORS

Banks, Roderick I'Anson   *48 Bedford Row*

Behar, Richard   *1 Essex Court*

Bonney, Charles J.   *48 Bedford Row*

Hinks, Frank   *13 Old Square (Sparrow)*

Levy, Benjamin   *Enterprise Chambers*

Whittaker, John   *13 Old Square, (Sparrow)*

LEADERS IN PARTNERSHIP LAW

Banks, Roderick I'Anson
48 Bedford Row (Roderick I'Anson Banks),   London (0171) 430 2005.
Specialisation: Exclusively partnership law. Has specialised in this area since 1977. Handles all aspects of partnership law from the drafting and review of agreements to advice and representation in partnership disputes, arbitrations and mediations. Acts for solicitors, doctors, accountants, and other professional firms both large and small, as well as various financial and commercial institutions. Editor of 'Lindley & Banks on Partnership', Author and Editor of 'The Encyclopedia of Professional Partnerships'. Contributor of articles to 'Legal Business', 'Solicitors' Journal' and 'The Lawyer'. Has conducted seminars for NIS Group, National Law Tutors, Jordans and various solicitors' firms and has appeared in two videos for Legal Network TV.
Prof. Membership: Lincoln's Inn.
Career: Called to the Bar 1974 and joined *3 Stone Buildings,* (Chambers of D.R. Stanford). Set up *48 Bedford Row Chambers* in 1991 with Charles Bonney, as the only chambers specialising exclusively in partnership law. CEDR Accredited Mediator, 1993.
Personal: Educated at Westminister School 1965-69 and University College London 1970-73. Leisure pursuits include reading, films, collecting autographs and art deco. Born 5 December 1951. Lives in Beare Green, Surrey.

Behar, Richard
1 Essex Court (Anthony Grabiner QC), London (0171) 583 2000.

Bonney, Charles J.
48 Bedford Row (Roderick I'Anson Banks),   London (0171) 430 2005.
Specialisation: Specialises exclusively in partnership law relating to professional, commercial and limited partnerships and joint ventures. Work covers the full range of legal services from drafting new agreements and reviewing existing agreements to advice and representation in partnership disputes, arbitrations and mediations. Clients include solicitors, doctors, accountants, surveyors, financial and commercial institutions and a wide range of professional clients. Author of 'Solicitors' Partnerships: The Law in Practice' (Longman, 1992).
Prof. Membership: Lincoln's Inn.
Career: Called to the Bar 1969. Tenant of *3 Stone Buildings* (Chambers of D.R. Stanford) 1974-1991. Joined Roderick I'Anson Banks in 1991 to establish the chambers at *48 Bedford Row*.
Personal: Educated at St. Paul's School 1959-64 and Pembroke College Oxford 1965-1968. Leisure pursuits include the topography of Rome, opera and food and wine. Born 19th February 1946. Lives in Enfield, Middlesex.

Briggs QC, Michael
See under Company.

Burton QC, Michael
See under Commercial Law.

Cherryman QC, John
4 Breams Buildings (Christopher Lockhart-Mummery QC),   London (0171) 430 1221. Called 1955, took silk 1982.

Davis QC, Nigel
See under Company.

Elias QC, Patrick
See under Employment.

Hinks, Frank
13 Old Square (Charles Sparrow QC), London (0171) 242 6105. Called 1973.

Lerego QC, Michael
Fountain Court (Peter Scott QC),   London (0171) 583 3335. Called 1972, took silk 1995. Main areas of practice are banking, professional negligence, insurance and partnership. Born 6.5.1949

Levy, Benjamin
Enterprise Chambers (Benjamin Levy), London (0171) 405 9471. Called 1956. Specialist in landlord and tenant and general chancery work including partnership. Born 2.1.1934.

Whittaker, John
13 Old Square (Charles Sparrow QC), London (0171) 242 6105. Called 1969.

PENSIONS

T HE PENSIONS Bar, concentrated in London, has developed rapidly over the last ten years, since Millett J's landmark decision in the 'Courage' case opened the floodgates of pensions litigation before the Courts. In recent years, the 'Maxwell' case and other less dramatic or well publicised similar cases, have heightened awareness of the vulnerability of pension funds, and given rise to a greater readiness to take legal steps to protect them. In addition, pensions law and practice has been affected by mergers, insolvencies, tax changes, European employment law and cross-border fund-holding rules.

LEADING SETS

WILBERFORCE CHAMBERS

35 ESSEX STREET

Pensions work is allied to the traditional work of the Chancery Bar, in particular to trusts law, and the chancery chambers listed below have strong practitioners in the field. Wilberforce Chambers has emerged as the leading pensions chambers. 35 Essex Street also has an excellent reputation in the field at both silk and junior level. Also well-regarded are 5 Stone Buildings and 7 Stone Buildings.

HIGHLY REGARDED

5 STONE BUILDINGS	7 STONE BUILDINGS
3 STONE BUILDINGS	

At **Wilberforce Chambers** *Nicholas Warren QC* has been particularly recommended for his expertise. Other leading silks at the set are *Edward Nugee QC, Robert Ham QC, Jules Sher QC* and *Terence Etherton QC. Brian Green* at the chambers emerges as the leading junior and *Christopher Nugee* and *Charles Turnbull* also have excellent reputations for their pensions practice.

35 Essex Street has a small team of barristers specialising in the field, and *Nigel Inglis-Jones QC* and *John Stephens* both have vast experience ensuring their high reputation for pensions expertise at the Bar. *Richard Hitchcock*, a junior at chambers, has also been highly recommended.

LEADING SILKS

Warren, Nicholas	*Wilberforce Chambers*
Ham, Robert	*Wilberforce Chambers*
Nugee, Edward	*Wilberforce Chambers*
Etherton, Terence	*Wilberforce Chambers*
Hart, Michael	*5 Stone Buildings*
Inglis-Jones, Nigel J.	*35 Essex Street*
Sher, Jules	*Wilberforce Chambers*

James Clifford at **7 Stone Buildings,** who is also regarded as one of the leading pensions juniors, merits a particular mention. **5 Stone Buildings** has a strong pensions practice and *Michael Hart QC* has been recommended as a leading silk. Also well known for pensions expertise are *Geoffrey Topham* and *Sarah Asplin* at **3 Stone Buildings.**

LEADING JUNIORS

Green, Brian	*Wilberforce Chambers*
Clifford, James	*7 Stone Buildings*
Stephens, John L.	*35 Essex Street*
Asplin, Sarah J.	*3 Stone Buildings*
Hitchcock, Richard G.	*35 Essex Street*
Nugee, Christopher	*Wilberforce Chambers*
Topham, Geoffrey J.	*3 Stone Buildings*
Turnbull, Charles	*Wilberforce Chambers*

LEADERS IN PENSIONS

Asplin, Sarah J.

3 Stone Buildings (D. R. Stanford), London (0171) 242 4937.

Specialisation: Principal area of practice encompasses pensions litigation, advice and drafting. Acts for beneficiaries, principal employers and trustees in relation to questions of construction, winding up, merger and general administration and also recovery of assets misappropriated in breach of trust, particularly in the aftermath of the Maxwell affair. Also deals with general chancery matters including trusts, probate and partnership advice and litigation. Junior Counsel in Imperial Group Pensions Trust Ltd v. Imperial Tobacco Ltd; British Coal Corporation v. British Coal Staff Superannuation Scheme Ltd; Kelly v. British Coal Corporation and Others and claims made by Maxwell Communication Works Pension Scheme. Clients include individuals, trustee companies and corporations.

Prof. Membership: Chancery Bar Association, Revenue Bar Association, Association of Pension Lawyers.

Career: Called to the Bar 1984 and joined 3 Stone Buildings 1985.

Personal: Educated at Southampton College for Girls 1976-8; Fitzwilliam College, Cambridge 1979-82 (MA Law); St Edmund Hall, Oxford 1982-83 (BCL) and College of Legal Education 1983-4. Member of local parish church. Leisure pursuits include listening to music. Born 16th September 1959.

Clifford, James

7 Stone Buildings (Charles Aldous QC), London (0171) 405 3886.

Specialisation: Specialises in pensions. Also handles general chancery (especially trusts) and general civil litigation. Recent cases handled include Mettoy Pension Trustees Limited v. Evans, Coloroll Pension Trustees Limited v. Russell, Thrells Ltd v. Lomas and Nestle v. Nat. West Bank. Contibutor to *British Pension Lawyer*.

Prof. Membership: Association of Pension Lawyers, Chancery Bar Association.

Career: Called to the bar in 1984.

Personal: Educated at Oxford University (BA).

Etherton QC, Terence
See under Property Litigation.

Green, Brian
Wilberforce Chambers (Edward Nugee QC), London (0171) 306 0102.
Specialisation: Pensions and Private Client (as well as having wide-ranging experience of broader chancery and revenue work).
Prof. Membership: APL, Revenue Bar Association.
Career: Called to the Bar 1980. Member of Revenue Law Committee of the Law Society since 1994. (1978-85 tenured lectureship in-Law at L.S.E).
Personal: Educated at Ilford County High School and St Edmund Hall Oxford (BA, BCL: double first).

Ham QC, Robert
See under Chancery.

Hart QC, Michael
See under Chancery.

Hitchcock, Richard G.
35 Essex Street (Alan Rawley QC), London (0171) 353 6381. Called 1989.

Inglis-Jones QC, Nigel J.
35 Essex Street (Alan Rawley QC), London (0171) 353 6381.
Specialisation: Has 35 years' experience as an occupational pensions schemes specialist. Also deals with other trusts, contract, tort and criminal fraud. Major cases handled include Re Imperial Foods Pension Scheme; Re Courage Group's Pension Schemes [1987]; Mettoy Pension Trustee v. Evans [1990]; Davis v. Richards & Wallington Industries Ltd [1990]; LRT Pension Fund Trustee Co Ltd v. Hatt & others [1993]; British Coal Corporation v. British Coal Staff Superannuation Scheme [1994] and Re:Prudential Assurance Pension Scheme. Author of 'The Law of Occupational Pension Schemes' (Sweet & Maxwell). Has spoken at and chaired many

conferences and seminars.
Prof. Membership: Chancery Bar Association, Association of Pensions Lawyers, Western Circuit. Bencher of the Inner Temple since 1982.
Career: National Service with the Grenadier Guards (subaltern) 1953-55. Called to the Bar in 1959 and joined chambers at *35 Essex Street* in 1960. Took Silk in 1982. Recorder 1978-93. Deputy Social Security Commissioner since 1993.
Personal: Educated at Eton College 1948-53 and Trinity College, Oxford 1955-58. Leisure pursuits include fishing, collecting English drinking glass and English miniature glass, gardening and travelling. A member of the congregation of St.Paul's church, Onslow Square. Born 7th May 1935. Lives in London.

Nugee QC, Edward
See under Chancery.

Nugee, Christopher
See under Chancery.

Sher QC, Jules
See under Chancery.

Stephens, John L.
35 Essex Street (Alan Rawley QC), London (0171) 353 6381.
Specialisation: Principal area of practice is pensions, covering all aspects of UK occupational pension schemes. Also deals with offshore trusts and claims to ownership of antiquities (i.e claims by nations, museums, temples, etc to ownership of ancient works of art). Frequently addresses both commercial and legal conferences.
Prof. Membership: Association of Pensions Lawyers, Chancery Bar Association.
Career: Called to the Bar in 1975. Joined present chambers in 1977.
Personal: Educated at Oxford University (BA, 1974). Born 30th March 1953. Leisure pursuits include travel. Lives in London.

Topham, Geoffrey J.
3 Stone Buildings (D. R. Stanford), London (0171) 242 4937.
Specialisation: Main field of practice is occupational pension schemes, acting for members, pensioners, trustees and employers (cases include Imperial Tobacco, Courage, Brooks v. Brooks). Other main areas are trusts and estates, and capital taxes.
Prof. Membership: Chancery Bar Association, Association of Pensions Lawyers, Associate of Pensions Management Institute, Revenue Bar Association.
Career: Called June, 1964. Member of Lincoln's Inn. Joined *3 Stone Buildings* in 1965.
Personal: Educated at Haileybury and Trinity Hall, Cambridge.

Turnbull, Charles
Wilberforce Chambers (Edward Nugee QC), London (0171) 306 0102. Called 1975.

Warren QC, Nicholas
Wilberforce Chambers (Edward Nugee QC), London (0171) 306 0102.
Specialisation: Main areas of practice are in the fields of pensions and private client business, both advisory and litigation. Has appeared in many of the leading pensions cases including Imperial Foods, Courage, Thrells, LRT, Coloroll and Chloride. Also has wide experience of revenue litigation having formerly been standing junior counsel to the Inland Revenue in Chancery matters.
Prof. Membership: Association of Pensions Lawyers (Main Committee member); Chancery Bar Association (Committee member); Revenue Bar Association.
Career: BA(Oxon) 1970; Called to the Bar in 1972; QC 1993.

INDEXES TO PROFILES

Solicitors' Profiles The index to leading solicitors profiled in the Specialist Lists starts on page 495. This index also includes heads of company legal departments.

Barristers' Profiles Profiles of leading barristers are indexed within the main *Barristers' Index* located at the end of the directory. Names of profiled barristers are set in bold type.

PERSONAL INJURY

WHILE many members of the common law bar handle a substantial amount of personal injury, there are few sets that can be regarded as specialist chambers. There are, however, a large number of highly respected practitioners in the field. A small number of practitioners have also been

LEADING SETS – LONDON	
39 ESSEX STREET	12 KING'S BENCH WALK
OLD SQUARE CHAMBERS	
2 CROWN OFFICE ROW	FARRAR'S BUILDING
2 TEMPLE GARDENS	
9 BEDFORD ROW	DEVEREUX CHAMBERS
9 GOUGH SQUARE	199 STRAND

recommended to us for their expertise in health and safety work, and these individuals are included in the lists below. Medical negligence, a smaller specialist area within personal injury, is discussed in a separate section of this directory.

39 Essex Street is well known for its strong personal injury practice. *Daniel Brennan QC* has been particularly recommended for his expertise and has considerable experience of multi-party actions, having been instructed in leading pharmaceutical cases. He is the current Chair of the Personal Injury Bar Association. Other well regarded practitioners in this field include *Michael Tillett* (who has extensive experience of claims involving asbestosis), *Charles Brown, Neil Block, Geoffrey Brown, Christian Du Cann* and rising star *Sean Wilken*.

health and safety work, and *John Hendy QC. John Hendy QC* is an appointed advisor to the European Commision on UK Health and Safety law and is co-author of 'Redgrave on Health & Safety' with *Michael Ford* (**Doughty Street Chambers**).

At the junior end, *Charles Pugh, Nigel Cooksley, Matthias Kelly* (who has particular expertise in radioactive pollution) and *Toby Kempster* (particularly industrial-related personal injury claims) are all well regarded. *Charles Pugh* has a strong reputation in the growth area of personal injury claims resulting from environmental factors. His prominent cases include 'Rockley v Coalite' and 'Graham v Re-chem' (alleged injury to livestock and contamination of land arising from toxic waste incineration). *Matthias Kelly* and *Philip Meade* act as advisors to the European Commission on UK Health and Safety law.

HIGHLY REGARDED – LONDON	
29 BEDFORD ROW CHAMBERS	35 ESSEX STREET
2 HARCOURT BUILDINGS	1 PAPER BUILDINGS
1 TEMPLE GARDENS	
1 PLOWDEN BUILDINGS	

12 King's Bench Walk is well known for its strong personal injury practice with a mix of insurance company and trade union work. Head of chambers *Ronald Walker QC* has an excellent reputation and talented juniors at the set include *Allan Gore* who has particular experience in transport mass accidents and disasters, and industrial diseases (particularly asbestosis), and *Frank Burton* (co-author of 'Personal Injury Limitation Law').

LEADING SILKS– LONDON		
Brennan, Daniel *39 Essex Street*		
Ashworth, Piers *2 Harcourt Buildings*	**Baker,** Nigel R.J. *9 Bedford Row*	**Cherry,** John M. *1 Temple Gardens*
Crowther, William *2 Temple Gardens*	**Henderson,** Roger *2 Harcourt Buildings*	**Hendy,** John *Old Square Chambers*
Livesey, Bernard *2 Crown Office Row*	**MacDuff,** Alistair *Devereux Chambers*	**Pugh,** Vernon *2-3 Gray's Inn Square*
Pulman, George F. *1 Temple Gardens*	**Spencer,** Michael *1 Paper Buildings*	**Ullstein,** Augustus *29 Bedford Row Chambers*
Walker, Ronald *12 King's Bench Walk*	**Williams,** John Melville *Old Square Chambers*	
Brent, Michael Leon *9 Gough Square*	**Burke,** Jeffrey *Devereux Chambers*	**Collender,** Andrew *2 Temple Gardens*
Langstaff, Brian *Cloisters*	**Marshall-Andrews,** R.G. *4 Paper Buildings*	**McMullen,** Jeremy *Old Square Chambers*
O'Brien, Dermod *2 Temple Gardens*	**Pitchford,** Christopher *Farrar's Building*	**Purchas,** Christopher *2 Crown Office Row*
Ritchie, Jean *4 Paper Buildings*	**Stewart,** Robin *199 Strand*	**Strachan,** Mark *1 Crown Office Row*
Walker, Raymond *1 Harcourt Buildings*	**Wilkinson,** Nigel V.M. *2 Crown Office Row*	**Williams,** John Leighton *Farrar's Building*

Old Square Chambers is a well known set, traditionally associated with plaintiff and trade union work. The set has particular expertise in disaster litigation with members instructed in cases including the King's Cross and Clapham rail disasters. Leading silks at the set are *John Melville Williams QC* (former President of the Association of Personal Injury Lawyers), who also has an established reputation for

2 Temple Gardens have an excellent reputation. Leading silks include *William Crowther QC, Dermod O'Brien QC* and *Andrew Collender QC*, and at the junior end, *Benjamin Browne* has been particularly recommended.

Farrar's Building is a common law set handling a large amount of personal injury work. *John Leighton Williams QC* and *Christopher Pitchford QC* are well known silks at the set, and at the junior end *Edward Southwell* (who has particular expertise in industrial disease and injury including deafness, lung disorders and RSI), *Alan Jeffreys, Anthony Seys Llewellyn, Tom McDermott* and *Simon Browne* are all highly regarded.

leading expert on WRVLD, and *Nicolas Hillier* (who is known for industrial deafness work) have been particularly recommended. Also well regarded are *John Reddihough* and *Duncan Macleod*.

9 Bedford Row is another common law set with extensive

LEADING JUNIORS– LONDON

Brown, Charles *39 Essex Street*	**Browne,** Benjamin *2 Temple Gardens*	**Burton,** Frank *12 King's Bench Walk*
Craven, Richard *1 Plowden Buildings*	**Du Cann,** Christian *39 Essex Street*	**Foster,** Catherine *1 Plowden Buildings*
Gore, Allan Peter *12 King's Bench Walk*	**Holmes,** Jonathan *1 Plowden Buildings*	**King,** Simon P. *9 Bedford Row*
Lowe, William *1 Plowden Buildings*	**McIntyre,** Bruce *1 Plowden Buildings*	**Trotter,** David *1 Plowden Buildings*
Wheatley, Simon *9 Bedford Row*	**Worthington,** Stephen *12 King's Bench Walk*	

Ashford-Thom, Ian *1 Temple Gardens*	**Block,** Neil *39 Essex Street*	**Brown,** Geoffrey B. *39 Essex Street*
Browne, Simon *Farrar's Building*	**Carling,** Christopher *Old Square Chambers*	**Coley,** William L. *35 Essex Street*
Cooksley, Nigel *Old Square Chambers*	**Eastman,** Roger *2 Harcourt Buildings*	**Foy,** John Leonard *9 Gough Square*
Glancy, Robert *Devereux Chambers*	**Goddard,** Christopher *Devereux Chambers*	**Hillier,** Nicolas Peter *9 Gough Square*
Jeffreys, Alan *Farrar's Building*	**Kelly,** Matthias *Old Square Chambers*	**Kempster,** Toby *Old Square Chambers*
Killalea, Stephen *Devereux Chambers*	**Lehain,** Philip *199 Strand*	**Macleod,** Duncan *9 Gough Square*
Matthews, Dennis *5 Bell Yard*	**May,** Kieran *199 Strand*	**McDermott,** Tom *Farrar's Building*
Moat, Frank *Pump Court Chambers*	**Pendlebury,** Jeremy *9 Bedford Row*	**Pugh,** Charles *Old Square Chambers*
Reddihough, John Hargreaves *9 Gough Square*	**Saunt,** Thomas *2 Crown Office Row*	**Seys Llewellyn,** Anthony *Farrar's Building*
Snowden, Steven *2 Crown Office Row*	**Southwell,** Edward *Farrar's Building*	**Tillett,** Michael *39 Essex Street*
Westcott, David G. *35 Essex Street*		

UP AND COMING

Scott, Ian *Old Square Chambers*	**Wilken,** Sean *39 Essex Street*	

2 Crown Row is well known for its personal injury practice. Members also have considerable experience in disaster litigation, having been instructed in both the King's Cross and Clapham rail disasters. Notable silks at the set are *Christopher Purchas QC* and *Nigel Wilkinson QC*.

Several members at **Devereux Chambers** specialise in personal injury, health and safety and industrial related personal injury claims, including asbestos, work related upper limb disorders (WRULD), deafness and silicosis in welders' fumes cases. Highly regarded silks are *Jeffrey Burke QC* and *Alistair MacDuff QC* (well known for industrial related personal injury). Able juniors at chambers include *Robert Glancy, Christopher Goddard* and *Stephen Killalea. Christopher Goddard* is a co-author of 'Health and Safety - The New Legal Framework' (Butterworths 1993).

199 Strand is a well established chambers handling personal injury work at all levels. Head of chambers *Robin Stewart QC* is highly thought of and able juniors who have been recommended for their expertise are *Philip Lehain* (who has particular emphasis on sports injuries), and *Kieran May* (especially asbestos-related diseases, industrial deafness and serious accident work).

Common law set, **9 Gough Square** undertake a large amount of personal injury work. *Michael Brent QC* is a well known personal injury silk and specialises in structured settlements. At the junior end of chambers, *John Foy*, who is a

personal injury expertise and leading silk *Nigel Baker QC* is particularly well regarded. Chambers has gained junior *Jeremy Pendlebury* (formerly at **1 Harcourt Buildings**), who handles industrial accidents, fatal accidents and industrial disease claims. *Simon King* is another notable junior in this field at the set.

At **29 Bedford Row**, *Augustus Ullstein QC*, whose personal injury practice has included appointment by the Federal District Court in Ohio, USA, to the Foreign Fracture Panel in the Shiley Heart Valve litigation, is particularly well regarded.

1 Temple Gardens handle a large volume of personal injury work. *John Cherry QC* (who has appeared in leading structured settlement cases) and *George Pulman QC* (known for nuclear-related cases), have been particularly recommended. *Ian Ashford-Thom* is a well regarded junior and *Tim Briden* has been recommended for his health and safety expertise.

2 Harcourt Buildings is a general common law set with personal injury expertise. *Roger Henderson QC* and *Piers Ashworth QC* have excellent reputations as leading silks in the field. At the junior end of chambers, *Roger Eastman* is held in high regard.

35 Essex Street is a set with personal injury expertise, acting for plaintiffs and insurers. *William Coley* and *David Westcott* (who handles head and spinal injuries), are well known in this field.

At **1 Paper Buildings** , *Michael Spencer QC* has an excellent reputation for personal injury and also health and safety work. *Jonathan Waite* at chambers has also been recommended for his health and safety expertise.

1 Plowden Buildings has been frequently recommended for its expertise in this field. From an array of talented juniors, *Bruce McIntyre, William Lowe, David Trotter, Richard Craven, Jonathan Holmes* and *Catherine Foster* have been highly recommended to us.

Notable silks in other chambers include *Bernard Livesey QC* (**2 Crown Office Row**), *Vernon Pugh QC* (**2-3 Gray's Inn Square**), *Jean Ritchie QC* and *Robert Marshall-Andrews QC* (**4 Paper Buildings**), *Raymond Walker QC* (Head of chambers, **1 Harcourt Buildings**) and *Brian Langstaff QC* (**Cloisters**) whose prominent cases include 'Walker v Northumberland C.C'. He is the author of 'The Health & Safety at Work' section in vol.20 of Halsbury's Laws (4th Edition).

Notable juniors in other chambers include *Dennis Matthews* and *Andrew Lydiard*, particularly for health and safety work (**5 Bell Yard**) and *Frank Moat* (**Pump Court Chambers**).

OUTSIDE LONDON

Most common law sets undertake this type of work as part of their general practice. All the names listed in the table have been recommended us.

Peter Andrews QC and *Mark Anderson* at **3 Fountain Court** in Birmingham have established a strong reputation for their personal injury work, as have *Nicholas Worsley QC*, *Gareth Evans QC*, *Paul Bleasdale* and *Ralph Lewis* at **5 Fountain Court**.

In Manchester, *Raymond Machell QC* at **Deans Court Chambers** is well-known for his expertise in this field. At **9 St John Street** *Nicholas Hinchcliffe* and *Timothy Horlock* have been recommended.

Ian Murphy QC (**9 Park Place, Cardiff**) is held in high regard for this area of work. *Charles Rees QC* at **30 Park Place** is also well-regarded. *Neil Bidder* at **30 Park Place** has also been recommended as has John Venmore at **30 Park Place**.

LEADING SILKS– REGIONS
Andrews, Peter *3 Fountain Court, Birmingham*
Evans, Gareth *5 Fountain Court, Birmingham*
Griffiths, Peter *30 Park Place, Cardiff*
Machell, Raymond Donatus *Deans Court Chambers, Manchester*
Murphy, Ian *9 Park Place, Cardiff*
Rees, John Charles *33 Park Place, Cardiff*
Stockdale, David Andrew *Deans Court Chambers, Manchester*
Williams, Wyn Lewis *33 Park Place, Cardiff*
Worsley, Nicholas *5 Fountain Court, Birmingham*

In Swansea, *Christopher Vosper* at **Angel Chambers** has a strong reputation in this field.

LEADING JUNIORS– REGIONS		
Anderson, Mark *3 Fountain Court, B'ham*	**Bidder,** Neil *33 Park Place, Cardiff*	**Bleasdale,** Paul *5 Fountain Court, B'ham*
Fewtrell, N.A. *5 John Dalton St, Manch.*	**Gregory,** Philip *No.6 Fountain Court, B'ham*	**Griffiths,** Lawrence *Iscoed Chambers, Swansea*
Hatton, David *Park Court Chambers, Leeds*	**Hinchliffe,** Nicholas *9 St. John Street, Manch.*	**Holdsworth,** Robert *5 Fountain Court, B'ham*
Horlock, Timothy *9 St. John Street, Manch.*	**Hunjan,** Satinder *5 Fountain Court, B'ham*	**Inglis,** Richard *King Charles House, Notts.*
Isherwood, John *Assize Court Chambers, Bristol*	**Jackson,** Simon *Park Court Chambers, Leeds*	**Jones,** Nicholas David *33 Park Place, Cardiff*
Keehan, Michael *St. Ive's Chambers, B'ham*	**Lewis,** Ralph *5 Fountain Court, B'ham*	**Marshall,** Philip D. *Iscoed Chambers, Swansea*
Rees, Philip *9 Park Place, Cardiff*	**Roach,** Michael *Albion Chambers, Bristol*	**Thomas,** K.S. *5 John Dalton St, Manch.*
Venmore, John *30 Park Place, Cardiff*	**Vosper,** Christopher *Angel Chambers, Swansea*	**Walters,** Jonathan *33 Park Place, Cardiff*
Williams, Lloyd *30 Park Place, Cardiff*	**Williams,** Karl *9 Park Place, Cardiff*	**Wood,** William *5 Fountain Court, B'ham*

HEALTH AND SAFETY

The following have been recommended to us for their expertise in Health and Safety. Profiles for the individual barristers may appear in the Personal Injury section as well as Health and Safety.

LEADING SILKS– LONDON
Hendy, John *Old Square Chambers*
Spencer, Michael *I Paper Buildings*
Williams, John Melville *Old Square Chambers*

LEADING JUNIORS– LONDON
Briden, Timothy J. *1 Temple Gardens*
Goddard, Christopher *Devereux Chambers*
Lydiard, Andrew *5 Bell Yard*
Meade, Philip *Old Square Chambers*
Pugh, Charles *Old Square Chambers*
Waite, Jonathan *I Paper Buildings*

UP AND COMING
Ford, Michael. *Doughty Street Chambers*

Anderson, Mark
3 Fountain Court (Colman Treacy QC),
Birmingham (0121) 236 5854.

Andrews QC, Peter
3 Fountain Court (Colman Treacy QC),
Birmingham (0121) 236 5854. Called 1970,
took silk 1991.

Ashford-Thom, Ian
1 Temple Gardens (Hugh Carlisle QC),
London (0171) 583 1315.

Specialisation: Practice covers common law
and public law work, primarily personal injuries and disaster litigation, including
inquests, professional negligence, judicial review and employment law.

Prof. Membership: Common Law and Commercial Bar Association, Administrative Law
Bar Association.

Career: Called to the Bar 1977 and joined
current chambers in 1979.

Personal: Educated at Exeter University
1972-6 (LL.B). Bracton Law Prize. Born
13th October 1953. Lives in London.

Ashworth QC, Piers
See under Environmental.

Baker QC, Nigel R.J.
9 Bedford Row (Stephen Coward QC),
London (0171) 242 3555.

Specialisation: Principal area of practice is
personal injury with an emphasis on maximum severity claims, sports injuries and
medical negligence cases. Also involved in
serious crime cases, both prosecuting and defending. Clients include leading insurance
companies. Addresses medico-legal societies
in personal injury and medical negligence
seminars. Chairman Fulbourn Hospital Enquiry.

Prof. Membership: Common Law Bar Asso-
ciation. Founder Member, Hertfordshire
Medico-legal Society. Personal Injury Bar
Association.

Career: Called to the Bar 1969 and joined
present chambers 1973 (when located at 2
Crown Office Row). Appointed Recorder
1985. Took Silk 1988. Sits as Deputy High
Court Judge, 1995. Member of Bar Council
1985.

Personal: Educated at Norwich School,
Southampton University 1961-64 (BA Law
1st Class) and Queen's College, Cambridge
1964-66 (LLM). Leisure pursuits include
football, fell-walking, gardening and music.
Born 21st December 1942. Lives in Letchworth.

Bidder, Neil
33 Park Place (Wyn Williams QC),
Cardiff (01222) 233313.

Bleasdale, Paul
5 Fountain Court (Anthony Barker QC),
Birmingham (0121) 606 0500. Called 1978.

Block, Neil
39 Essex Street (Colin Mackay QC),
London (0171) 583 1111. Called 1980.

Brennan QC, Daniel
39 Essex Street (Colin Mackay QC),
London (0171) 583 1111. Called 1967, took
silk 1985.

Brent QC, Michael Leon
9 Gough Square (Michael Brent QC),
London (0171) 353 5371. Called 1961, took
silk 1983. Principal area of practice is plaintiff personal injury and medical negligence
cases. Born 8.6.1936.

Brown, Geoffrey B.
39 Essex Street (Colin Mackay QC),
London (0171) 583 1111. Called 1981.

Brown, Charles
39 Essex Street (Colin Mackay QC),
London (0171) 583 1111. Called 1976.

Browne, Benjamin
2 Temple Gardens (Patrick Phillips QC),
London (0171) 583 6041. Called 1976. Practice covers personal injury and professional
indemnity and insurance work. Has handled
a large number of tetraplegic, paraplegic and
brain damage cases.

Browne, Simon
Farrar's Building (Lord Williams of
Mostyn QC), London (0171) 583 9241.

Specialisation: Practice covers general
common law with particular specialisation in
personal injury and medical negligence.

Prof. Membership: South Eastern Circuit.

Career: Called to the Bar in 1982.

Personal: Born 5th November 1959.

Burke QC, Jeffrey
Devereux Chambers (Peter Weitzman
QC), London (0171) 353 7534. Called
1964, took silk 1984. Principal areas of practice are Personal Injuries, Professional
Negligence and Employment law. Born
15.12.1941.

Burton, Frank
12 King's Bench Walk (Ronald Walker
QC), London (0171) 583 0811.

Specialisation: Principal area of practice is
personal injury work with an emphasis on industrial diseases and medical negligence.
Co-author of 'Medical Negligence Case
Law' and 'Personal Injury Limitation Law',
both published by Butterworths.

Prof. Membership: Personal Injury Bar Association, Member of Executive.

Career: University lecturer 1974-83. Called
to the Bar and joined present chambers 1982.

Personal: B.A. Hons 1st Class and PhD.
Born 19th June 1950. Lives in London.

Carling, Christopher
Old Square Chambers (Hon. John
Melville Williams QC), London (0171)
831 0801. Called 1969.

Cherry QC, John M.
1 Temple Gardens (Hugh Carlisle QC),
London (0171) 583 1315. Called 1961, took
silk 1988.

Coley, William L.
35 Essex Street (Alan Rawley QC),
London (0171) 353 6381.

Specialisation: Principal area of practice is
personal injury, both plaintiff and defendant
work but principally defendant. Also handles
professional negligence.

Prof. Membership: Western Circuit, London
Common Law & Commercial Bar Association.

Career: Called to the Bar in 1980 and joined
35 Essex Street in 1981.

Personal: Educated at Radley College 1971-
75 and Downing College, Cambridge
1976-79. Born 20th September 1957.

Collender QC, Andrew
2 Temple Gardens (Patrick Phillips QC),
London (0171) 583 6041. Called 1969, took
silk 1991. Wide experience of substantial personal injury actions with specialisations in
occupational claims, especially repetitive
strain injuries.

Cooksley, Nigel
Old Square Chambers (Hon. John Melville
Williams QC), London (0171) 831 0801.

Specialisation: Principal area of practice for
many years has been personal injury litigation and has a widespread practice
throughout the country, particularly in the
North East. Other areas of practice include
professional negligence and contract.

Prof. Membership: Personal Injury Bar Association, Association of Personal Injury
Lawyers, London Common Law and Commercial Bar Association.

Career: Called to the Bar in 1975.

Personal: Educated at Felsted School and
Cambridge University. Lives in North Hertfordshire. Outside interests include sport.

Craven, Richard
1 Plowden Buildings (Bruce McIntyre,
William Lowe), London (0171) 583 0808.

Crowther QC, William
2 Temple Gardens (Patrick Phillips QC),
London (0171) 583 6041. Called 1963, took
silk 1980.

Du Cann, Christian
39 Essex Street (Colin Mackay QC),
London (0171) 583 1111. Called 1982.

Eastman, Roger
2 Harcourt Buildings (Roger Henderson
QC), London (0171) 583 9020.
Specialisation: Predominantly common law
practice with a particular emphasis on personal injury matters, health and safety (civil
and criminal prosecution and defence work)
and professional negligence (especially
medical negligence). Also deals with the law
relating to markets.
Prof. Membership: Criminal Bar Association, COMBAR, Professional Negligence
Bar Association, Official Referees' Bar Association, Personal Injury Bar Association.
Career: Called to the Bar 1978 and joined
current chambers in 1981.
Personal: Educated at Maidstone Grammar
School 1964-72; St. John's College, Durham
1972-75; and Council of Legal Education
1976-78. Regular tutor, Council of Legal
Education. Lectures and undertakes Legal
Network Television video work. Leisure pursuits include music, art, sport and food and
wine. Born 23rd May 1953. Lives in London.

Evans QC, Gareth
5 Fountain Court (Anthony Barker QC),
Birmingham (0121) 606 0500. Called 1973,
took silk 1994.

Fewtrell, N.A.
5 John Dalton St (M.J.H. Lamberty),
Manchester (0161) 834 6875.

Foster, Catherine
1 Plowden Buildings (Bruce McIntyre,
William Lowe), London (0171) 583 0808.

Foy, John Leonard
9 Gough Square (Michael Brent QC),
London (0171) 353 5371.
Specialisation: Practice encompasses plaintiff and defendant personal injury and
medical negligence work, with a particular
emphasis on occupational disease. Appeared
in Mountenay v. Bernard Matthews [1994],
Mughal v. Reuters Ltd [1993]; Hunt v.
Douglas Roofing [1990] and Arnold v.
CEGB [1988], inter alia. Clients include all
major trade unions. Frequently chairs and ad-
dresses conferences and seminars, and has
appeared on BBC TV and radio.
Prof. Membership: Association of Personal
Injury Lawyers.
Career: Called to the Bar and joined 9 Gough
Square in 1969.
Personal: LL.B (Hons) Birmingham Univer-
sity, 1967. Leisure pursuits include sports.
Born 1st June 1946. Lives in Suffolk.

Glancy, Robert
Devereux Chambers (Peter Weitzman
QC), London (0171) 353 7534.

Specialisation: Principal areas of practice
are personal injury and medical negligence
cases, professional negligence generally (architects, engineers, surveyors and solicitors),
construction law and employment law. Considerable experience of industrial disease
cases such as repetitive strain injury, asbestos
related conditions and welder's fume cases.
Appeared in case of D.F. Estates v. Church
Commisioners for England on economic loss
in tort and whether builder is liable for subcontractor.
Prof. Membership: Personal Injury Bar Association.
Career: Called to the Bar 1972. Assistant Recorder 1993.
Personal: Educated at Manchester Grammer
School and St. John's College, Cambridge.
Lives in London.

Goddard, Christopher
Devereux Chambers (Peter Weitzman
QC), London (0171) 353 7534. Called
1973. Principal area of practice is workplace
personal injury litigation. Born 4.9.1950.

Gore, Allan Peter
12 King's Bench Walk (Ronald Walker
QC), London (0171) 583 0811.
Specialisation: Principal area of practice
covers personal injury work. Special interest
and experience in transport mass accidents
and disasters, and in industrial disease cases,
particularly concerning asbestos. Other main
area of practice is professional negligence,
encompassing a whole range of medical, dental and legal cases both contentious and
non-contentious. Contributing author to 'Butterworths County Court Precedents and
Pleadings: Division Q on Personal Injury';
and to forthcoming edition of 'Cordery on Solicitors: Division J on Negligence'. Regular
conference and seminar speaker.
Prof. Membership: Executive of Association
of Personal Injury Lawyers and Personal
Injury Bar Association. Professional
Negligence Bar Association.
Career: Called to the Bar 1977. Joined cur-
rent chambers in 1991.
Personal: Educated at Purley Grammar
School, Croydon 1962-69, and Trinity Hall,
Cambridge 1970-74. Born 25th August 1951.
Lives in London.

Gregory, Philip
No.6 Fountain Court (Roger Smith QC),
Birmingham (0121) 233 3282.

Griffiths QC, Peter
30 Park Place (Philip Richards),
Cardiff (01222) 398421.

Griffiths, Lawrence
Iscoed Chambers (Wyn Richards),
Swansea (01792) 652988/9.

Hatton, David
Park Court Chambers (Gilbert Gray QC,

Brian Walsh QC), Leeds (0113) 2433277.

Henderson QC, Roger
See under Financial Services.

Hendy QC, John
See under Employment.

Hillier, Nicolas Peter
9 Gough Square (Michael Brent QC),
London (0171) 353 5371. Called 1982.

Hinchliffe, Nicholas
9 St. John Street (John Hand QC),
Manchester (0161) 955 9000. Called 1980.

Holdsworth, Robert
5 Fountain Court (Anthony Barker QC),
Birmingham (0121) 606 0500.

Holmes, Jonathan
1 Plowden Buildings (Bruce McIntyre,
William Lowe), London (0171) 583 0808.

Horlock, Timothy
9 St. John Street (John Hand QC),
Manchester (0161) 955 9000. Called 1981.

Hunjan, Satinder
5 Fountain Court (Anthony Barker QC),
Birmingham (0121) 606 0500.

Inglis, Richard
King Charles House (Richard Inglis),
Nottingham (0115) 9418851.

Isherwood, John
Assize Court Chambers (Graeme Wood),
Bristol (0117) 9264587.

Jackson, Simon
Park Court Chambers (Gilbert Gray
QC, Brian Walsh QC), Leeds (0113)
2433277.

Jeffreys, Alan
Farrar's Building (Lord Williams of
Mostyn QC), London (0171) 583 9241.
Specialisation: Principal area of practice is
personal injury litigation, both plaintiff and
defendant. Work includes motor, employer's
and public liability claims. Other main area
of practice is medical and solicitor's negli-
gence and general insurance work.
Career: Called to the Bar in 1970 (Gray's
Inn) and joined *Farrar's Building* in 1971.
Recorder since 1993.
Personal: Born 27th September 1947. Edu-
cated at Llandaff Cathedral School (to 1961),
Ellesmere College 1961-66 and King's College, London 1966-69. Lives in London.

Jones, Nicholas David
33 Park Place (Wyn Williams QC),
Cardiff (01222) 233313.

Keehan, Michael
See under Family Law.

Kelly, Matthias
Old Square Chambers (Hon. John Melville Williams QC), London (0171) 831 0801. London Tel: (0171) 831 0801

Specialisation: Personal injuries. Has dealt with all types of PI for both Plaintiff and Defendants. Particular specialisation in catastrophic injuries including brain injuries. Experienced in complicated litigation including radioactive pollution: (Merlin v. BNFL (1990) 3 WLR 383). Other cases: H v. MOD (1991) 2 QB 103, Rastin v. British Steel (1994) 1 WLR 732.

Prof. Membership: Environmental Law Foundation; Secretary, Personal Injury Bar Association.

Career: Called to the bar 1979. Member Irish Bar (Belfast and Dublin). Member New York State Bar and US Federal Bar. Consultant to the European Commission on UK Health and Safety Law.

Kempster, Toby
Old Square Chambers (Hon. John Melville Williams QC), London (0171) 831 0801.

Specialisation: Concentrates primarily on employment law and personal injury law. His employment practice covers both individual and collective rights, dealing with contractual and statutory remedies. His personal injury practice is mainly work or industry related, but he has been involved in multi-plaintiff product liability, disease and 'disaster' cases.

Prof. Membership: APIL, ILS and ELA.

Career: Member of chambers since 1982.

Killalea, Stephen
Devereux Chambers (Peter Weitzman QC), London (0171) 353 7534. Called 1981. Principal areas of practice are personal injuries and employment law. Born 25.1.1959.

King, Simon P.
9 Bedford Row (Stephen Coward QC), London (0171) 242 3555. Called 1987. Established personal injury practice; increasing amount of professional negligence work. Born 22.12.1963.

Langstaff QC, Brian
Cloisters (David Turner-Samuels QC), London (0171) 583 0303.

Specialisation: Principal area of practice is personal injury, collective employment and Trade Union cases. Has been instructed in most major industrial disputes (eg ambulancemen's strike, coal strike, Wapping) since the early 1980s and many important collective employment and Trade Union cases, although majority of practice has been in cases of serious personal injury (usually caused at work). Other area of practice is medical negligence, including actions against drug producers. Important cases include Page v. Hull University (employment),

Walker v. Northumberland C.C. (personal injury: stress at work), Reay & Hope v BNFL (The 'Sellafield' case), Peach v. Metropolitan Police (Fatal assault by police/discovery issues), Ratcliffe v. North Yorkshire C.C. (Equal Pay), News International v. SOGAT (picketing: the 'Wapping' dispute) and Clarke & Others v. NUM (Miners' strike). Major lay clients include most Trade Unions and their members as well as legally aided victims of accidents (both factory and medical). Professional clients include Trade Union solicitors (in private practice and in-house), law centres and medical and environmental practices. Author of 'The Health & Safety at Work' section in Vol. 20 of Halsbury's Laws (4th edn) and of various articles in journals. Former senior lecturer in law. Conference speaker on equal pay and employment issues.

Prof. Membership: LCLCBA; ELBA; ALBA; APIL; Industrial Law Society; PIBA (Committee Member).

Career: Called to the Bar in 1971. Lecturer in law 1971-75. Joined present Chambers in 1977. Appointed Assistant Recorder in 1991, Recorder 1995. Took Silk in 1994.

Personal: Educated at George Heriot's School, Edinburgh 1953-66 and St. Catharine's College, Cambridge 1967-70. Chairman of Governors of local primary school. Enjoys sport, theatre and TV, politics, mowing the lawn, his family and travel. Born 30th April 1948. Lives in Suffolk.

Lehain, Philip
199 Strand (R.M. Stewart QC), London (0171) 379 9779.

Specialisation: Specialist in the areas of medical negligence and personal injury, with a particular emphasis on sports injuries. Practice also covers Professional Negligence and Misconduct, Employment, Construction and General Commercial.

Prof. Membership: Professional Negligence Bar Association, Actions for Victims of Medical Accidents, COMBAR.

Career: Called to the Bar 1978. Joined present chambers 1990.

Personal: Educated at Queen Mary College, London (LL.B). Working knowledge of French. Leisure pursuits include rugby, cricket, skiing, music and cinema. Born 1st September 1955. Lives in London.

Lewis, Ralph
5 Fountain Court (Anthony Barker QC), Birmingham (0121) 606 0500.

Livesey QC, Bernard
2 Crown Office Row (Rupert Jackson QC), London (0171) 797 8000.

Specialisation: Principal specialisation is litigation in the following fields: general common law, personal injuries, professional negligence (architects, doctors, engineers, solicitors, surveyors and valuers) and insurance. Leading cases include Spring v.

Guardian Assurance (negligent references); Ancell v. Chief Constable of Bedfordshire (liability of police).

Prof. Membership: COMBAR, Bar European Group; Personal Injuries Bar Association.

Career: Called to the Bar 1969. Appointed Recorder 1987. Silk in 1990.

Personal: Educated at Peterhouse, Cambridge (MA, LLB).

Lowe, William
1 Plowden Buildings (Bruce McIntyre, William Lowe), London (0171) 583 0808.

MacDuff QC, Alistair
Devereux Chambers (Peter Weitzman QC), London (0171) 353 7534.

Specialisation: Principal area of practice encompasses personal injuries, industrial diseases, and medical negligence with many years' experience acting for both plaintiffs and defendants. Work includes large amounts of asbestosis, R.S.I and deafness litigation. Also handles some crime and building work. Has considerable lecturing and seminar experience.

Prof. Membership: Appointed Recorder of the Crown Court, 1987.

Career: Called to the Bar 1969. Took Silk 1993.

Personal: Educated at Ecclesfield Grammar School 1955-62. London School of Economics 1962-65 (LL.B) and Sheffield University 1965-67 (LL.M). Born 26th May 1945. Lives in London.

Machell QC, Raymond Donatus
Deans Court Chambers (H. K. Goddard QC), Manchester (0161) 834 4097.

Macleod, Duncan
See under Medical Negligence.

Marshall, Philip Derek
Iscoed Chambers (Wyn Richards), Swansea (01792) 652988/9.

Marshall-Andrews QC, R.G.
4 Paper Buildings (Harvey McGregor QC), London (0171) 353 3366.

Matthews, Dennis
See under Medical Negligence.

May, Kieran
199 Strand (R.M. Stewart QC), London (0171) 379 9779.

Specialisation: Principal area of practice is personal injury work, particularly asbestos-related diseases, industrial deafness and serious accident work. Also handles professional negligence matters, particularly in the medical and legal fields.

Prof. Membership: Professional Negligence Bar Association.

Career: Called to the Bar 1971 and joined 199 Strand in 1972.

Personal: Educated at Oxford University (BA).

McDermott, Tom
Farrar's Building (Lord Williams of Mostyn QC), London (0171) 583 9241.

Specialisation: Practice covers general common law matters with an emphasis on personal injury. Also handles professional and medical negligence and employment.

Prof. Membership: South Eastern Circuit.

Career: Called to the Bar and joined *Farrar's Building* in 1980.

Personal: Educated at University College, London (LL.B, 1978) and Queen's College, Cambridge (Institute of Criminology) (M.Phil, 1979). Called to the Irish Bar, King's Inns, Dublin in 1991. Born 11th September 1955. Lives in Hertfordshire.

McIntyre, Bruce
1 Plowden Buildings (Bruce McIntyre, William Lowe), London (0171) 583 0808.

McMullen QC, Jeremy
See under Employment.

Moat, Frank
Pump Court Chambers (Guy Boney QC), London (0171) 353 0711. Called 1970. Personal injury specialist, with a particular emphasis on industrial accidents and diseases. Also covers professional negligence and family law.

Murphy QC, Ian
9 Park Place (Philip Rees), Cardiff (01222) 382731.

O'Brien QC, Dermod
2 Temple Gardens (Patrick Phillips QC), London (0171) 583 6041. Called 1962, took silk 1983.

Pendlebury, Jeremy
9 Bedford Row (Stephen Coward QC), London (0171) 242 3555.

Specialisation: Specialises in the areas of professional negligence, personal injury and contract law. Within the field of professional negligence, practice concentrates mainly on medical negligence, solicitor's negligence and surveyor's negligence. Personal injury work includes industrial accident, fatal accident and industrial disease claims. Contract work covers general contract and consumer claims. Recent reported cases include Singh v. Duport Harper Foundries Ltd (1994) 2 All ER 889; Hoskins v. Wiggins Teape (1994) PIQR P337.

Prof. Membership: Inner Temple.

Career: Called to the Bar 1980. *1 Harcourt Buildings*, Temple 1982-1994. Joined present Chambers 1994.

Personal: Educated at Eastbourne College 1970-1975, Kent University 1976-1979 and the Inns of Court Law School 1979-1980. Born 23rd September 1957.

Pitchford QC, Christopher
Farrar's Building (Lord Williams of Mostyn QC), London (0171) 583 9241. Called 1969, took silk 1987. General common law practitioner, with a particular emphasis on personal injury and crime. Born 28.3.1947.

Pugh, Charles
See under Health & Safety Law.

Pugh QC, Vernon
2-3 Gray's Inn Square (Anthony Scrivener QC), London (0171) 242 4986.

Pulman QC, George F.
1 Temple Gardens (Hugh Carlisle QC), London (0171) 583 1315. Called 1971, took silk 1989.

Purchas QC, Christopher
2 Crown Office Row (Raymond Kidwell QC), London (0171) 797 8100. Called 1966, took silk 1990. Principal areas of practice are personal injury, construction and professional negligence. Born 20.6.1943.

Reddihough, John Hargreaves
See under Medical Negligence.

Rees QC, John Charles
33 Park Place (Wyn Williams QC), Cardiff (01222) 233313.

Rees, Philip
9 Park Place (Philip Rees), Cardiff (01222) 382731.

Ritchie QC, Jean
See under Medical Negligence.

Roach, Michael
Albion Chambers (J.C.T. Barton QC), Bristol (0117) 9272144. Called 1975.

Saunt, Thomas
2 Crown Office Row (Raymond Kidwell QC), London (0171) 797 8100. Called 1974.

Seys Llewellyn, Anthony
Farrar's Building (Lord Williams of Mostyn QC), London (0171) 583 9241.

Specialisation: General common law practice, including personal injury, medical negligence, and contract and insurance. Also building and Official Referee's business.

Career: Called 1972. Joined chambers 1974. Appointed Recorder 1990.

Personal: King's School, Chester 1957-67; Jesus College, Oxford 1967-71 (MA and BCL). Fluent in French; working knowledge of German. Assistant Boundary Commissioner. Leisure pursuits include music, sport and art. Born 24th April 1949. Lives in Buckinghamshire.

Snowden, Steven
2 Crown Office Row (Raymond Kidwell QC), London (0171) 797 8100.

Southwell, Edward
Farrar's Building (Lord Williams of Mostyn QC), London (0171) 583 9241.

Specialisation: Wide ranging personal injury practice, both plaintiff and defendant, with emphasis in recent years on industrial disease/injury (including deafness, lung disorders, RSI etc). Also handles medical and solicitors' negligence. Lay clients have included the Ford Motor Company, British Rail, the M.O.D. and ICI. Professional clients include *A.E.Wyeth & Co* and *Beachcroft Stanley*.

Prof. Membership: London Common Law Bar Association, South Eastern Circuit.

Career: Called to the Bar in 1970 and joined *Farrar's Building* in 1971. Recorder since 1987.

Personal: Educated at Charterhouse School 1959-64. Assistant Boundary Commissioner. Chairman of NHS Trust Disciplinary Inquiry Panels.

Spencer QC, Michael
1 Paper Buildings (Robert Nelson QC), London (0171) 583 7355. Called 1970, took silk 1989.

Stewart QC, Robin
See under Professional Negligence.

Stockdale QC, David Andrew
Deans Court Chambers (H. K. Goddard QC), Manchester (0161) 834 4097.

Strachan QC, Mark
See under Commercial Law.

Thomas, K.S.
5 John Dalton St (M.J.H. Lamberty), Manchester (0161) 834 6875.

Tillett, Michael
39 Essex Street (Colin Mackay QC), London (0171) 583 1111. Called 1965.

Trotter, David
1 Plowden Buildings (Bruce McIntyre, William Lowe), London (0171) 583 0808.

Ullstein QC, Augustus
See under Professional Negligence.

Venmore, John
30 Park Place (Philip Richards), Cardiff (01222) 398421.

Vosper, Christopher
Angel Chambers (T. Glanville Jones), Swansea (01792) 464623.

Walker QC, Ronald
12 King's Bench Walk (Ronald Walker QC), London (0171) 583 0811. Called 1962, took silk 1983.

Walker QC, Raymond
1 Harcourt Buildings (Raymond Walker QC), London (0171) 353 0375/3655. Called 1966, took silk 1988.

Walters, Jonathan
33 Park Place (Wyn Williams QC), Cardiff (01222) 233313.

Westcott, David G.
35 Essex Street (Alan Rawley QC), London (0171) 353 6381.

Specialisation: Principal area of practice is cases of severe personal injury, especially head and spinal (including sporting) injuries. Other main areas of practice are professional negligence (of lawyers, doctors and surveyors), contract and sale of goods. Important cases include Van Oppen v. Harpur Trust (schoolboy breaking neck playing rugby) and Linden Gardens v. Lenesta Sludge (HL) (principles of recovery of damages - contract assigned).

Prof. Membership: Western Circuit, London Common Law & Commercial Bar Association.

Career: Called to the Bar in 1982 and joined *35 Essex Street* in 1983.

Personal: Educated at Cranleigh School 1965-75 and Brasenose College, Oxford

1976-79, 80-81 (BA, BCL). Born 14th May 1957. Lives in London.

Wheatley, Simon
9 Bedford Row (Stephen Coward QC), London (0171) 242 3555.

Wilken, Sean
39 Essex Street (Colin Mackay QC), London (0171) 583 1111. Called 1991.

Wilkinson QC, Nigel V.M.
2 Crown Office Row (Raymond Kidwell QC), London (0171) 797 8100. Called 1973, took silk 1990.

Williams QC, John Melville
See under Employment.

Williams QC, John Leighton
Farrar's Building (Lord Williams of Mostyn QC), London (0171) 583 9241.

Specialisation: General common law, with emphasis on personal injuries and medical negligence work.

Career: Called to the Bar 1964. Appointed Recorder 1985. Took silk 1986. Member of the Criminal Injuries Compensation Board since 1987. Master of the Bench, *Grays Inn* 1994.

Williams, Lloyd
30 Park Place (Philip Richards), Cardiff (01222) 398421.

Williams QC, Wyn Lewis
33 Park Place (Wyn Williams QC), Cardiff (01222) 233313.

Williams, Karl
9 Park Place (Philip Rees), Cardiff (01222) 382731.

Wood, William
5 Fountain Court (Anthony Barker QC), Birmingham (0121) 606 0500. Called 1970.

Worsley QC, Nicholas
5 Fountain Court (Anthony Barker QC), Birmingham (0121) 606 0500. Called 1966, took silk 1993.

Worthington, Stephen
12 King's Bench Walk (Ronald Walker QC), London (0171) 583 0811. Called 1976.

LEADERS IN HEALTH & SAFETY LAW

LONDON

Briden, Timothy J.
1 Temple Gardens (Hugh Carlisle QC), London (0171) 583 1315.

Specialisation: Principal area of practice is ecclesiastical law. Editor, 'Macmorran's Handbook for Churchwardens and Parochial Church Councillors' and 'Moore's Introduction to English Canon Law'. Also handles personal injury cases.

Prof. Membership: Inner Temple, Ecclesiastical Law Society.

Career: Called to the Bar 1976 and joined 1 Temple Gardens 1977. Appointed Chancellor of the Diocese of Bath and Wells 1993.

Personal: Educated at Ipswich School 1958-70 and Downing College Cambridge (BA 1974; LL.B 1975; MA 1978). Born 29th October 1951. Lives in South London.

Ford, Michael
Doughty Street Chambers (Geoffrey Robertson QC), London (0171) 404 1313. Called 1992.

Goddard, Christopher
Devereux Chambers (Peter Weitzman QC), London (0171) 353 7534. Called

1973. Principal area of practice is workplace personal injury litigation. Born 4.9.1950.

Lydiard, Andrew
5 Bell Yard (Robert Webb QC), London (0171) 333 8811. Called 1980. Principal area of practice is commercial litigation with a particular emphasis on aviation. Born 25.8.1957.

Meade, Philip
See under Employment.

Pugh, Charles
Old Square Chambers (Hon. John Melville Williams QC), London (0171) 831 0801.

Specialisation: Principal areas of practice are accident claims (road traffic, rail, aviation, workplace, particularly toxic exposure) and pollution/nuisance claims. Has had considerable experience with major accidents, i.e. Kings Cross, Clapham Junction, Manchester Airport, Kegworth; with pollution claims involving personal injury (Camelford water) and alleged injury to livestock and contamination of land arising from toxic waste incineration (Rockley v. Coalite; Graham v. Re-chem). Nuisance litigation includes water (e.g. fishfarms) noise, dust, and the leading cases of Hunter v. Canary

Wharf Limited.

Prof. Membership: Personal Injury Bar Association; Environmental Law Foundation.

Career: Called to the Bar 1975. Joined *Old Square Chambers* in 1989.

Personal: Co-author of Toxic Torts (Cameron May, 2nd ed. 1995, with Martyn Day). Member of the editorial board of the Journal of Personal Injury Litigation. Course tutor in the Summer School on Environmental Law organised by the Foundation for International Law & Developement (FIELD). Invited speaker at numerous conferences including the American Trial Lawyers Association Annual Convention.

Spencer QC, Michael
1 Paper Buildings (Robert Nelson QC), London (0171) 583 7355. Called 1970, took silk 1989.

Waite, Jonathan
1 Paper Buildings (Robert Nelson QC), London (0171) 583 7355. Called 1978.

Williams QC, John Melville
Old Square Chambers (Hon. John Melville Williams QC), London (0171) 831 0801. Called 1955, took silk 1977.

PLANNING AND LOCAL GOVERNMENT

ALTHOUGH many solicitors now represent their clients at local planning inquiries, High Court work and complex inquiries largely remain the province of the barrister. A number of chambers in London have developed a

specialism in this area, undertaking a broad spectrum of planning law including environmental, compulsory purchase, public infrastructure projects and local government work.

Nigel Macleod QC and *Richard Drabble QC* who acted in cases involving Liverpool and Manchester airports. At the junior end of chambers, *Christopher Katkowski* (London's most highly recommended junior planning specialist), and *John Male* are held in high regard. *David Smith* is also currently working on the Heathrow Terminal 5 case. *Nathalie Lieven* is chambers' rising star.

Jeremy Sullivan QC (the most consistently recommended silk in our research) is **4-5 Gray's Inn Square**'s outstanding practitioner, although chambers also has eminent practitioners in *David Mole QC* (who represents major developers, government departments and local authorities), *John Steel QC* (instructed in the Stansted and Filton airport, M3, M25 and M42 inquiries) and *Duncan Ouseley QC* (former Chairman of Hampshire Structure Plan EIP). Chambers' leading

LEADING SILKS– LONDON

Sullivan, Jeremy *4-5 Gray's Inn Square*		
Barnes, Michael *4 Breams Buildings*	**Fitzgerald,** Michael *2 Mitre Court Buildings*	**Howell,** John *4 Breams Buildings*
Lockhart-Mummery, Christopher *4 Breams Bldgs*	**Mole,** David *4-5 Gray's Inn Square*	**Ouseley,** Duncan *4-5 Gray's Inn Square*
Read, Lionel *1 Serjeants' Inn*	**Spence,** Malcolm *2-3 Gray's Inn Square*	**Steel,** John *4-5 Gray's Inn Square*
Vandermeer, Roy *2 Harcourt Buildings*		
Anderson, Anthony *2 Mitre Court Buildings*	**Arden,** Andrew *Arden Chambers*	**Ash,** Brian *4-5 Gray's Inn Square*
Bartlett, George *2 Mitre Court Buildings*	**Boydell,** Peter *2 Harcourt Buildings*	**Dinkin,** Anthony *2-3 Gray's Inn Square*
Drabble, Richard *4 Breams Buildings*	**Eyre,** Graham *2-3 Gray's Inn Square*	**George,** Charles *2 Harcourt Buildings*
Hicks, William *1 Serjeants' Inn*	**Hockman,** Stephen *6 Pump Court*	**Macleod,** Nigel *4 Breams Buildings*
Mawrey, Richard *2 Harcourt Buildings*	**Moriarty,** Gerald *2 Mitre Court Buildings*	**Newberry,** Clive *4-5 Gray's Inn Square*
Phillips, Richard *2 Harcourt Buildings*	**Porten,** Anthony *2-3 Gray's Inn Square*	**Pugh,** Vernon *2-3 Gray's Inn Square*
Purchas, Robin *2 Harcourt Buildings*	**Roots,** Guy *2 Mitre Court Buildings*	**Ryan,** Gerard *2 Harcourt Buildings*
Silsoe, Lord *2 Mitre Court Buildings*	**Taylor,** John *2 Mitre Court Buildings*	**Widdicombe,** David *2 Mitre Court Buildings*

Of these, **4 Breams Buildings** and **4-5 Gray's Inn Square** emerge as the leading sets.

4 Breams Buildings has a strong complement of silks which includes *Christopher Lockhart-Mummery QC* who is involved in work on Heathrow Terminal 5, *Michael Barnes QC* who was the Inspector on Hinkley Point and

juniors include *Timothy Corner* and *Peter Village* ('Costco' case, 'Hinkley Point C' and M40 inquiries).

2 Mitre Court is London's next highest ranking planning set with members of chambers having appeared in Sizewell B, Hinkley Point and Stansted, Gatwick and Heathrow airport inquiries.

LEADING JUNIORS– LONDON

Katkowski, Christopher *4 Breams Buildings*		
Alesbury, Alun *2 Mitre Court Buildings*	**King,** Neil *2 Mitre Court Buildings*	**Lindblom,** Keith *2 Harcourt Buildings*
Male, John *4 Breams Buildings*	**Nardecchia,** Nicholas *2-3 Gray's Inn Square*	**Pugh-Smith,** John *1 Serjeants' Inn*
Cameron, Neil *1 Serjeants' Inn*	**Caws,** Eian *4 Breams Buildings*	**Corner,** Timothy *4-5 Gray's Inn Square*
Fookes, Robert *2 Mitre Court Buildings*	**Harrison,** Peter *6 Pump Court*	**Holgate,** David *4 Breams Buildings*
Lieven, Nathalie *4 Breams Buildings*	**Lowe,** Mark *2-3 Gray's Inn Square*	**Smith,** David *4 Breams Buildings*
Stephenson, Geoffrey *2-3 Gray's Inn Square*	**Straker,** Timothy *2-3 Gray's Inn Square*	**Village,** Peter M. *4-5 Gray's Inn Square*

UP AND COMING

White, Sasha *1 Serjeants' Inn*		

Michael Fitzgerald QC (who promoted the Channel Tunnel Bill on behalf of the Government) is chambers' leading silk. Well respected juniors include *Neil King* and *Alun Alesbury* (who acted as an inspector on the Windermere inquiry). Also highly regarded is **1 Serjeants' Inn** where *Lionel*

Read QC, *William Hicks QC* and *John Pugh-Smith* are experienced in the field and *Sasha White* is a rising star.

Other sets with planning expertise include **2-3 Gray's Inn Square** and **2 Harcourt Buildings** where *Roy Vandermeer QC* who acts for Tesco and *Keith Lindblom* are held in high regard.

OUTSIDE LONDON

In Birmingham, *Martin Kingston QC* and *Harry Wolton QC* of **5 Fountain Court** undertake a broad range of planning work.

Manchester's planning expertise may be found at **40 King Street** where *Andrew Gilbart QC, John Hoggett QC, Stephen Sauvain QC, Frances Patterson* and *David Manley* have been recommended.

LEADING SILKS- REGIONS

Gilbart, Andrew *40 King St, (Manchester)*

Hoggett, John *40 King St, (Manchester)*

Kingston, Martin *5 Fountain Court, (Birmingham)*

Sauvain, Stephen *40 King St, (Manchester)*

Williams, Wyn Lewis *33 Park Place, (Cardiff)*

Wolton, Harry *5 Fountain Court, (Birmingham)*

LEADING JUNIORS- REGIONS

Jarman, Milwyn *9 Park Place, (Cardiff)*

Jones, Geraint *9 Park Place, (Cardiff)*

Jones, Timothy *7 Fountain Court, (Birmingham)*

Manley, David *40 King St, (Manchester)*

Patterson, Frances *40 King St, (Manchester)*

Richards, Wyn *Iscoed Chambers (Cardiff)*

UP AND COMING

Goatley, Peter *5 Fountain Court, (Birmingham)*

LEADERS IN PLANNING AND LOCAL GOVERNMENT

Alesbury, Alun
See under Public and Administrative Law.

Anderson QC, Anthony
2 Mitre Court Buildings (Michael FitzGerald QC), London (0171) 583 1380.

Specialisation: Practice encompasses planning, rating, compulsory purchase, parliamentary and local government law. Involved in Stansted Airport Inquiry, Manchester Regional Shopping Inquiry, Exeter Sub-Regional Shopping Inquiry and Crawley Business Parks Inquiry amongst others. Joint Editor 'Ryde on Rating' (12th and 13th Editions).

Prof. Membership: Planning and Environment Bar Association.

Career: Called to the Bar 1964 and joined current chambers 1965. Took Silk 1982. Appointed Recorder 1995.

Personal: Educated at Harrow School and Magdalen College, Oxford. Born 12th September 1938. Lives in London.

Arden QC, Andrew
See under Public and Administrative Law.

Ash QC, Brian
4-5 Gray's Inn Square (Miss Elizabeth Appleby QC, The Hon. Michael Beloff QC), London (0171) 404 5252. Called 1975, took silk 1990. Principal area of practice is planning and local government. Also

judicial review. Born 31.1.1941.

Barnes QC, Michael
4 Breams Buildings (Christopher Lockhart-Mummery QC), London (0171) 430 1221. Called 1965, took silk 1981.

Bartlett QC, George
See under Parliamentary.

Boydell QC, Peter
See under Ecclesiastical Law.

Cameron, Neil
1 Serjeants' Inn (Lionel Read QC), London (0171) 583 1355.

Caws, Eian
4 Breams Buildings (Christopher Lockhart-Mummery QC), London (0171) 430 1221.

Corner, Timothy
4-5 Gray's Inn Square (Miss Elizabeth Appleby QC, The Hon. Michael Beloff QC), London (0171) 404 5252.

Specialisation: Major part of practice is in the fields of town and country planning, local government and public law. Planning work includes appeals throughout the country within the retail sector, housing, offices, listed buildings, waste disposal and minerals. Also undertakes planning appeals in the High

Court. Interesting recent cases include R v. Thurrock Borough Council ex parte Tesco Stores [1994] JPL 328 (judicial review of permission for warehouse club; appeared for Tesco); R v. City of Wakefield MDC and British Coal Corporation [1994] JPL 341 (judicial review of permission for opencast mining; bias by local planning authority; appeared for British Coal). Examples of recent public inquiries include, in the retail sector, the successful appeal for B&Q's 100,000 sq ft depot store in Merton in 1993. Also acted for British Coal Corporation at Brynhenllys, South Wales, in its successful appeal for opencasting of coal on a 400 acre site, and for AMEC and the London Institute in the call-in inquiry (Autumn 1994) into their proposals for a leisure centre for Southwark and accommodation for 1200 students at Elephant and Castle.

Prof. Membership: Planning & Environment Bar Association (Committee member and co-ordinator of the continuing education programme).

Career: Called to the Bar 1981. Tenant in the Chambers of Sir Frank Layfield QC 1982-1993. Joined present chambers in 1993.

Personal: Educated at Bolton School 1966-1976 and Magdalen College, Oxford (BA Jurisprudence and BCL) 1976-1980. Languages include French and some Italian. Leisure pursuits include opera singing, walking, gardens and comparative philology. Born 25th July 1958. Lives in London.

Dinkin QC, Anthony
2-3 Gray's Inn Square (Anthony Scrivener QC), London (0171) 242 4986. Called 1968, took silk 1991.

Drabble QC, Richard
See under Public and Administrative Law.

Eyre QC, Graham
2-3 Gray's Inn Square (Anthony Scrivener QC), London (0171) 242 4986. Called 1954, took silk 1970.

Fitzgerald QC, Michael
See under Environmental.

Fookes, Robert
2 Mitre Court Buildings (Michael FitzGerald QC), London (0171) 583 1380. Called 1975.

George QC, Charles
See under Parliamentary.

Gilbart QC, Andrew
40 King St (John Hoggett QC), Manchester (0161) 832 9082.

Goatley, Peter
5 Fountain Court (Anthony Barker QC), Birmingham (0121) 606 0500.

Harrison, Peter
6 Pump Court (Michael Gale QC), London (0171) 797 8400.
Specialisation: Most aspects of local government law. In particular planning and environmental matters, prosecutions, hackney carriage and private hire law.
Prof. Membership: Planning and Environment Bar Association, Criminal Bar Association, South Eastern Circuit.
Career: Called to the Bar 1987.
Personal: Educated at Durham University 1983-86. Born 14th February 1965. Lives in Islington, London.

Hicks QC, William
See under Public and Administrative Law.

Hockman QC, Stephen
6 Pump Court (Michael Gale QC), London (0171) 797 8400.
Specialisation: Principal area of practice is local government, planning and administrative law.
Prof. Membership: Planning and Environment Bar Association, Administrative Law Bar Association.
Career: Called to the Bar in 1970 and joined 6 Pump Court in 1971. Appointed Recorder 1987. Took Silk 1990.
Personal: Educated at Eltham College, London (1955-65) and Jesus College, Cambridge (1966-69). Born 4th January 1947. Lives in London.

Hoggett QC, John
40 King St (John Hoggett QC), Manchester (0161) 832 9082.

Holgate, David
See under Public and Administrative Law.

Howell QC, John
See under Public and Administrative Law.

Jarman, Milwyn
See under Chancery.

Jones, Timothy
7 Fountain Court Chambers, Birmingham). London (0171) 353 3132.
Specialisation: Principal area of practice is planning work, representing local authorities and developers in local plan inquiries, development control appeals and High Court applications. Other main area of practice is judicial review representing local authorities and applicants in judicial reviews relating to planning, housing, caravan sites, rating and disabled persons. Important litigation handled includes Buckley v. United Kingdom [1994] (complaint to European Human Rights Commission by Romany of effect of planning and criminal law on her traditional lifestyle); Wychavon D.C. v. SoS for the Environment [1994] (local authority did not have standing to bring proceedings for non-implementation of a European Community Directive); R v. SoS for the Environment ex p. T.Smith [1988] (declaration that county council in breach of its duty in relation to caravan sites) and Wyre Forest D.C. v. SoS for the Environment & Allens [1990] (planning permission should be interpreted in accordance with extended definition in statute rather than normal English usage).
Prof. Membership: Planning & Environment Bar Association, Administrative Law Bar Association, Midland & Oxford Circuit.
Career: Called to the Bar in 1975. Practises from both 7 Fountain Court, Birmingham and Arden Chambers, London.
Personal: Educated at Christ's Hospital, Jesus College Cambridge and the London School of Economics. Called to the Bar of Ireland in 1990. Born 1951.

Jones, Geraint
See under Chancery.

Katkowski, Christopher
4 Breams Buildings (Christopher Lockhart-Mummery QC), London (0171) 430 1221. Called 1982.

King, Neil
2 Mitre Court Buildings (Michael FitzGerald QC), London (0171) 583 1380.
Specialisation: Practice encompasses town and country planning, compulsory purchase and compensation, rating, local government, environmental and public and administrative law. Joint Editor, 'Ryde on Rating and the Council Tax'.

Prof. Membership: Planning and Environment Bar Assocation.
Career: Called to the Bar 1980 and joined current chambers 1982.
Personal: Educated at Harrow School 1970-74 and New College, Oxford 1975-78. Married with 4 children. Leisure pursuits include music, golf and real tennis. Born 14th November 1956. Lives in Whitchurch-on-Thames.

Kingston QC, Martin
See under Public and Administrative Law.

Lieven, Nathalie
See under Parliamentary.

Lindblom, Keith
2 Harcourt Buildings (Peter Boydell QC), London (0171) 353 8415.
Specialisation: Planning, Local Government, Parliamentary, Compulsory Purchase and Compensation Law. Work for both private and public sector clients.
Prof. Membership: Planning and Environment Bar Association; Parliamentary Bar Mess.
Career: Called to the Bar 1980. Joined 2 Harcourt Buildings (Peter Boydell QC) in 1981.

Lockhart-Mummery QC, Christopher
4 Breams Buildings (Christopher Lockhart-Mummery QC), London (0171) 430 1221. Called 1971, took silk 1986.

Lowe, Mark
2-3 Gray's Inn Square (Anthony Scrivener QC), London (0171) 242 4986. Called 1972.

Macleod QC, Nigel
See under Parliamentary.

Male, John
4 Breams Buildings (Christopher Lockhart-Mummery QC), London (0171) 430 1221. Called 1976.

Manley, David
40 King St (John Hoggett QC), Manchester (0161) 832 9082.

Mawrey QC, Richard
See under Financial Services.

Mole QC, David
4-5 Gray's Inn Square (Miss Elizabeth Appleby QC, The Hon. Michael Beloff QC), London (0171) 404 5252. Called 1970, took silk 1990. Principal area of practice is local government and administrative law and judicial review. 1.4.1943.

Moriarty QC, Gerald
See under Public and Administrative Law.

Nardecchia, Nicholas
2-3 Gray's Inn Square (Anthony Scrivener QC), London (0171) 242 4986. Called 1974.

Newberry QC, Clive

4-5 Gray's Inn Square (Miss Elizabeth Appleby QC, The Hon. Michael Beloff QC), London (0171) 404 5252. Called 1978, took silk 1993.

Ouseley QC, Duncan

See under Public and Administrative Law.

Patterson, Frances

40 King St (John Hoggett QC), Manchester (0161) 832 9082.

Phillips QC, Richard

2 Harcourt Buildings (Peter Boydell QC), London (0171) 353 8415.

Specialisation: Principal areas of practice are planning and local government work. Also handles licensing cases.

Prof. Membership: Planning & Environment Bar Association. Member of S. Eastern Circuit.

Career: Called to the Bar 1970 and joined 2 *Harcourt Buildings* in 1971. Assistant Parliamentary Boundary Commissioner. Took silk in 1990.

Personal: Educated at Kings School, Ely and Sidney Sussex College, Cambridge 1966-69. Born 8th August 1947.

Porten QC, Anthony

2-3 Gray's Inn Square (Anthony Scrivener QC), London (0171) 242 4986. Called 1969, took silk 1988.

Pugh QC, Vernon

2-3 Gray's Inn Square (Anthony Scrivener QC), London (0171) 242 4986.

Pugh-Smith, John

See under Environmental.

Purchas QC, Robin

See under Parliamentary.

Read QC, Lionel

See under Environmental.

Richards, Wyn

Iscoed Chambers (Wyn Richards), Swansea (01792) 652988/9.

Roots QC, Guy

2 Mitre Court Buildings (Michael FitzGerald QC), London (0171) 583 1380.

Specialisation: Main areas of practice are planning and local government and public and administrative law. Experienced in town and country plannning, environmental law, compulsory purchase and compensation, rating and other areas of local government, parliamentary and administrative law. Has been involved in many leading planning, environmental, compulsory purchase and rating cases acting for a wide cross section of clients in the public and private sectors, city and provincial solicitors and direct access professional clients. Has spoken at and

chaired numerous conferences and seminars. General Editor of 'Ryde on Rating and the Council Tax'.

Prof. Membership: Local Government and Planning Bar Association, Administrative Law Bar Association.

Career: Called to the Bar in 1969. Joined 2 *Mitre Court Buildings* in 1972. Took Silk in 1989. Appointed Assistant Recorder in 1992.

Personal: Educated at Winchester College and Brasenose College, Oxford (MA in Jurisprudence).

Ryan QC, Gerard

2 Harcourt Buildings (Peter Boydell QC), London (0171) 353 8415. Called 1955, took silk 1981.

Sauvain QC, Stephen

40 King St (John Hoggett QC), Manchester (0161) 832 9082.

Silsoe QC, Lord

2 Mitre Court Buildings (Michael FitzGerald QC), London (0171) 583 1380. Called 1955, took silk 1972. Principal area of practice is planning and environmental law. Born 2.5.1930.

Smith, David

See under Landlord and Tenant.

Spence QC, Malcolm

2-3 Gray's Inn Square (Anthony Scrivener QC), London (0171) 242 4986.

Specialisation: Specialises in planning and parliamentary work. Many years experience of attending planning inquiries and appearing before the Lands Tribunal in compensation for compulsory purchase cases. Also many appearances in the High Court and Court of Appeal in planning and compensation cases. Parliamentary work includes appearances before Select Committee in relation to the Channel Tunnel Bill and the Channel Tunnel Rail Link Bill.

Prof. Membership: Chairman of Planning and Environment Bar Association.

Career: Called to the Bar (Gray's Inn) in 1958. Took Silk in 1979. Recorder of the Crown Court.

Steel QC, John

4-5 Gray's Inn Square (Miss Elizabeth Appleby QC, The Hon. Michael Beloff QC), London (0171) 404 5252.

Specialisation: Town and country planning, administrative law and local government law. Practice covers public inquiries, judicial review and high court litigation.

Prof. Membership: Planning and Environment Bar Association; Administrative Law Bar Association.

Career: Called to the Bar 1978. Joined present chambers 1978. Silk 1993.

Personal: Educated: Harrow School 1967-1972 and Durham University (BSc Hons chemistry) 1973-1976. Chairman, Kandahar

Ski Club. Director, The Busoga Trust (water relief in Africa). Leisure pursuits include flying (helicopter and fixed wing), skiing and walking. Born 4th June 1954. Lives near Chipping Norton, Oxon.

Stephenson, Geoffrey

2-3 Gray's Inn Square (Anthony Scrivener QC), London (0171) 242 4986. Called 1971.

Straker, Timothy

See under Public and Administrative Law.

Sullivan QC, Jeremy

4-5 Gray's Inn Square (Miss Elizabeth Appleby QC, The Hon. Michael Beloff QC), London (0171) 404 5252. Called 1968, took silk 1982. Principal area of practice is planning and local government, public and parliamentary law. Born 17.9.1945.

Taylor QC, John

2 Mitre Court Buildings (Michael FitzGerald QC), London (0171) 583 1380. Called 1958, took silk 1983. Practice encompasses planning, environmental and local government law. Born 22.4.1931.

Vandermeer QC, Roy

2 Harcourt Buildings (Peter Boydell QC), London (0171) 353 8415. Called 1955, took silk 1978.

Village, Peter M.

4-5 Gray's Inn Square (Miss Elizabeth Appleby QC, The Hon. Michael Beloff QC), London (0171) 404 5252.

Specialisation: Specialist in all aspects of planning and local government, particularly public inquiries and challenges in the High Court (both statutory and judicial review) including challenges to local plans; Compulsory Purchase and Lands Tribunal.

Prof. Membership: Local Government and Planning Bar Association.

Career: Called to the Bar 1983. Joined present chambers 1985.

Personal: Educated at Repton 1974-79 and at Leeds University (LL.B Hons) 1979-82. Leisure pursuits include shooting, fly fishing and cooking. Born 3rd February 1961 in Yorkshire. Lives in London and Derbyshire. Married with 3 children.

White, Sasha

1 Serjeant's Inn (Lionel Read QC). London (0171) 583 1355.

Widdicombe QC, David

See under Parliamentary.

Williams QC, Wyn Lewis

33 Park Place (Wyn Williams QC), Cardiff (01222) 233313.

Wolton QC, Harry

5 Fountain Court (Anthony Barker QC), Birmingham (0121) 606 0500.

PROFESSIONAL NEGLIGENCE

NEGLIGENCE claims arise from the work of many different professions, and as such they are often dealt with by barristers who specialise in the particular work in question. Nonetheless, there are chambers which undertake a large amount of professional negligence work, and these are detailed below.

LEADING SETS

2 CROWN OFFICE ROW	2 CROWN OFFICE ROW
BRICK COURT CHAMBERS	KEATING CHAMBERS
7 KING'S BENCH WALK	4 PUMP COURT
2 TEMPLE GARDENS	

2 Crown Office Row (Jackson) is the leading set in this area. Members of chambers handle a broad range of claims for plaintiffs and defendants. *Rupert Jackson QC* has been very highly recommended for his expertise. He is co-author of 'Jackson and Powell on Professional Negligence' with *John Powell QC*, whose practice covers a broad range of work relating in particular to accountants and auditors, barristers and solicitors, insurance brokers and financial intermediaries, surveyors and valuers, and engineers and architects. *Roger Toulson QC* has an excellent reputation for his expertise in this field. *Christopher Gibson QC* has also been recommended. *Iain Hughes* acts in cases involving solicitors, surveyors and valuers, barristers and accountants. His clients include major professional insurers, building societies and centralised lenders. *Roger Stewart* is highly regarded and undertakes mainly defendant work in relation to claims against architects, engineers, solicitors, surveyors,

accountants and insurance brokers.

Members of chambers have appeared in 'Swingcastle v Gibson', 'Watts v Morrow,' 'HIT Finance v Lewis & Tucker,' the BBL litigation both at first instance and in the Court of Appeal, 'Wood v The Law Society', and 'Verderame v The Commercial Union'. Several members are contributors to 'Jackson and Powell on Professional Negligence.'

At **2 Crown Office Row (Kidwell)** *Michael Harvey QC*, who also appeared in 'BBL v Eagle Star', is a prominent specialist, as is *Roger ter Haar QC*. *Antony Edwards-Stuart QC* undertakes work involving insurance brokers, Lloyd's agents, solicitors, accountants and surveyors. Among the juniors in chambers *Richard Lynagh* is well known for his expertise in this sector, as is *Anna Guggenheim*. *Guy Anthony* undertakes all aspects of work in this area, in relation especially to solicitors, but also to surveyors and accountants.

Seven King's Bench Walk is essentially a commercial set, which includes a number of barristers with considerable expertise in this area, particularly in insurance-related claims. *Julian Flaux QC, Jeremy Cooke QC, Adrian Hamilton QC, Jonathan Gaisman QC* and *Christopher Butcher* have all been recommended.

Keating Chambers is a set specialising in construction law, and members of chambers offer considerable expertise in connection with claims in this area. *Richard Fernyhough QC, Christopher Thomas QC, Timothy Elliott QC* and *Vivian Ramsey QC* are highly regarded. *Peter Coulson, Marcus Taverner* and *Philip Boulding* are among the respected juniors in chambers.

Brick Court Chambers is a well known commercial set,

LEADING SILKS

Cooke, Jeremy *Seven King's Bench Walk*	**Crowther,** William *2 Temple Gardens*	**Flaux,** Julian *Seven King's Bench Walk*
Gibson, Christopher *2 Crown Office Row*	**Gloster,** Elizabeth *1 Essex Court*	**Harvey,** Michael *2 Crown Office Row*
Jackson, Rupert *2 Crown Office Row*	**Powell,** John L. *2 Crown Office Row*	**Slater,** John *1 Paper Buildings*
Temple, Anthony *4 Pump Court*	**ter Haar,** Roger *2 Crown Office Row*	**Toulson,** Roger *2 Crown Office Row*
Aikens, Richard *Brick Court Chambers*	**Aylen,** Walter *Hardwicke Building*	**Bartlett,** Andrew *1 Paper Buildings*
Brown, Simon *1 Paper Buildings*	**Burke,** Jeffrey *Devereux Chambers*	**Crampin,** Peter *11 New Square*
Davidson, Edward *4 Stone Buildings*	**Davies,** Richard *39 Essex Street*	**Desch,** Stephen *2 Crown Office Row*
Edelman, Colin *Devereux Chambers*	**Edwards-Stuart,** Antony *2 Crown Office Row*	**Elliott,** Timothy *Keating Chambers*
Elliott, Nicholas *3 Gray's Inn Place*	**Fernyhough,** Richard *Keating Chambers*	**Foskett,** David *1 Crown Office Row*
Gaisman, Jonathan *Seven King's Bench Walk*	**Glasgow,** Edwin *39 Essex Street*	**Goldsmith,** Peter *Fountain Court*
Hamilton, Adrian *Seven King's Bench Walk*	**Hapgood,** Mark *Brick Court Chambers*	**Jarvis,** John *3 Gray's Inn Place*
Kealey, Gavin *Seven King's Bench Walk*	**Langley,** Gordon *Fountain Court*	**Livesey,** Bernard *2 Crown Office Row*
Mackay, Colin *39 Essex Street*	**Miller,** Stephen *1 Crown Office Row*	**Mowschenson,** Terence *1 Essex Court*
Nelson, Robert *1 Paper Buildings*	**Philipson,** Trevor *Fountain Court*	**Phillips,** Patrick *2 Temple Gardens*
Playford, Jonathan *2 Harcourt Buildings*	**Ramsey,** Vivian *Keating Chambers*	**Seabrook,** Robert *1 Crown Office Row*
Stewart, Robin *199 Strand*	**Sumption,** Jonathan *Brick Court Chambers*	**Thomas,** Christopher *Keating Chambers*
Ullstein, Augustus *29 Bedford Row Chambers*	**Vallance,** Philip *1 Crown Office Row*	**Walker,** Tim *Fountain Court*
Weitzman, Peter *Devereux Chambers*		

LEADING JUNIORS

Boswell, Lindsay *4 Pump Court*	**Butcher,** Christopher *Seven King's Bench Walk*	**Coulson,** Peter *Keating Chambers*
Hughes, Iain *2 Crown Office Row*	**Stewart,** Roger *2 Crown Office Row*	

Anthony, Guy *2 Crown Office Row*	**Asif,** Jalil *2 Crown Office Row*	**Bailey,** Edward *5 Bell Yard*
Boulding, Philip *Keating Chambers*	**Browne,** Benjamin *2 Temple Gardens*	**Carr,** Sue *2 Crown Office Row*
Cox, Raymond *Fountain Court*	**Cross,** James *4 Pump Court*	**Dyer,** Allen *4 Pump Court*
Faulks, Edward *No. 1 Serjeants' Inn*	**Gillis,** Richard *1 Essex Court*	**Goodman,** Andrew *199 Strand*
Guggenheim, Anna *2 Crown Office Row*	**Hodge,** David *9 Old Square*	**Holdsworth,** James *2 Crown Office Row*
Holwill, Derek *4 Paper Buildings*	**Hooper,** Toby *12 King's Bench Walk*	**Hutton,** Caroline *Enterprise Chambers*
Iwi, Quintin *2 Harcourt Buildings*	**Jones,** Nigel *Hardwicke Building*	**Leggatt,** George *Brick Court Chambers*
Lynagh, Richard *2 Crown Office Row*	**Malek,** Ali *3 Gray's Inn Place*	**Munro,** Kenneth *5 Bell Yard*
Norris, Alastair *5 Stone Buildings*	**Phillips,** Rory *3 Gray's Inn Place*	**Pittaway,** David *No. 1 Serjeants' Inn*
Pooles, Michael *4 Paper Buildings*	**Popplewell,** Andrew *Brick Court Chambers*	**Railton,** David *Fountain Court*
Ross, John *No. 1 Serjeants' Inn*	**Ruttle,** Stephen *Brick Court Chambers*	**Ryan,** A. *Verulam Chambers*
Simmonds, Andrew *5 Stone Buildings*	**Stuart-Smith,** Jeremy *2 Temple Gardens*	**Sutcliffe,** Andrew *3 Gray's Inn Place*
Taverner, Marcus *Keating Chambers*	**Thanki,** Bankim *Fountain Court*	**Treasure,** Francis *199 Strand*
Turner, Janet *3 Gray's Inn Place*	**Vandyck,** William *1 Paper Buildings*	**Waite,** Jonathan *1 Paper Buildings*

specialising in the banking and insurance fields. *Jonathan Sumption QC* is well regarded, as are *Richard Aikens QC* and *Mark Hapgood QC*. Among the juniors in this set, *Andrew Popplewell, George Leggatt,* and *Stephen Ruttle* are respected for their work in this area.

At **4 Pump Court** *Anthony Temple QC* has a good reputation, as do *Allen Dyer* and *James Cross*. *William Crowther QC* and *Patrick Phillips QC* at **2 Temple Gardens** have strong reputations, as do *Benjamin Browne* and *Jeremy Stuart-Smith* at the same chambers.

At **39 Essex Street** *Colin Mackay QC, Edwin Glasgow QC* and *Richard Davies QC* have been recommended. *John Slater QC, Robert Nelson QC, Andrew Bartlett QC, Simon Brown QC, William Vandyck* and *Jonathan Waite* at **1 Paper Buildings (Robert Nelson)** are well regarded.

LEADERS IN PROFESSIONAL NEGLIGENCE

Aikens QC, Richard
See under Commercial Law.

Anthony, Guy
2 Crown Office Row (Raymond Kidwell QC), London (0171) 797 8100. Called 1972. Principal area of practice covers professional negligence and personal injury work. Born 5.3.1950.

Asif, Jalil
2 Crown Office Row (Rupert Jackson QC), London (0171) 797 8000.
Specialisation: Principal area of practice encompasses all aspects of professional negligence cases especially of solicitors, surveyors and doctors. Other main areas of work are personal injury and contract construction claims. Was one of generic Counsel in the HIV Haemophiliacs claims. Acts for the Solicitors Indemnity Fund, major building societies and insurers of chartered surveyors. Assistant Editor: 'Jackson & Powell on Professional Negligence'. Elected Member of Bar Council since 1993.
Prof. Membership: Professional Negligence Bar Association, London Common Law and Commercial Bar Association, COMBAR.
Career: Called to the Bar 1988. Became a tenant at *2 Crown Office Row* in 1989.
Personal: Educated at Twyford High School, Acton 1977-83, and St. Paul's School, then Peterhouse, Cambridge. Leisure pursuits include cinema, music, reading and cycling. Born 25th March 1965.

Aylen QC, Walter
Hardwicke Building (Walter Aylen QC), London (0171) 242 2523.

Bailey, Edward
5 Bell Yard (Robert Webb QC), London (0171) 333 8811. Called 1970. Area of practice covers professional negligence, aviation, insurance and insolvency.

Bartlett QC, Andrew
See under Construction Law.

Boswell, Lindsay
4 Pump Court (Bruce Mauleverer QC), London (0171) 353 2656.

Boulding, Philip
See under Construction Law.

Brown QC, Simon
1 Paper Buildings (Robert Nelson QC), London (0171) 583 7355. Called 1976, took silk 1995. Principal area of practice is professional negligence (valuers, accountants, surveyors, architects, engineers and solicitors). Born 23.8.1952.

Browne, Benjamin
See under Personal Injury.

Burke QC, Jeffrey
Devereux Chambers (Peter Weitzman QC), London (0171) 353 7534. Called 1964, took silk 1984. Principal areas of practice are Personal Injuries, Professional Negligence and Employment law. Born 15.12.1941.

Butcher, Christopher
Seven King's Bench Walk (Adrian Hamilton QC), London (0171) 583 0404. Called 1986.

Carr, Sue
2 Crown Office Row (Rupert Jackson QC), London (0171) 797 8000.
Specialisation: Principal area of practice is professional negligence: solicitors, medical, surveyors, barristers, accountants, architects, and engineers. Also handles general contract and insurance work, employment and personal injury. Important cases include Broadley v Guy Clapham [1993], Hopkins & MacKenzie [1994] (both concerning limitation); Interdesco S.A v Nullifire Ltd [1992] (registration of foreign judgment) and Morley v Heritage Plc [1993] (employment). Fluent in French and German.
Prof. Membership: Professional Negligence Bar Association, Commercial and Common Law Bar Association.
Career: Called to the Bar 1987 and joined 2 Crown Office Row in 1988.
Personal: Born 1st September 1964. Educated at Wycombe Abbey School 1976-82 and Trinity College, Cambridge 1983-86 (MA). Leisure pursuits include sports, music and acting.

Cooke QC, Jeremy
See under Commercial Law.

Coulson, Peter
See under Construction Law.

Cox, Raymond
Fountain Court (Peter Scott QC), London (0171) 583 3335. Called 1982. Main areas of practice are banking, commercial law, insurance and reinsurance and professional negligence. Born 6.5.1959

Crampin QC, Peter
See under Chancery.

Cross, James
4 Pump Court (Bruce Mauleverer QC), London (0171) 353 2656. Called 1985.

Crowther QC, William
See under Personal Injury.

Davidson QC, Edward
4 Stone Buildings (Peter Curry QC), London (0171) 242 5524.
Specialisation: Principal area of practice is professional negligence, particularly of solicitors, barristers and accountants. Other main area of practice covers property and commercial matters including trusts. Lloyd's related work. Company litigation and petrol solus ties. Acted in, inter alia, Banco Ambrosiano litigation and Eagle Star v. Provincial Insurance (Privy Council).
Prof. Membership: Chancery Bar Association, Professional Negligence Bar Association.
Career: Called to the Bar 1966 and joined current Chambers 1968. Took Silk 1994.
Personal: Educated at The King's School, Canterbury and Gonville & Caius College,

Cambridge (M.A.,LLB). Born 1943.

Davies QC, Richard
39 Essex Street (Colin Mackay QC), London (0171) 583 1111. Called 1973, took silk 1994.

Desch QC, Stephen
2 Crown Office Row (Raymond Kidwell QC), London (0171) 797 8100. Called 1962, took silk 1980. Called 1962, took silk 1980. Practice covers insurance, professional negligence, construction law, commercial law and general common law. Born 17.11.1939.

Dyer, Allen
4 Pump Court (Bruce Mauleverer QC), London (0171) 353 2656.
Specialisation: Principal areas of practice are commercial law, construction and professional negligence.
Prof. Membership: COMBAR, London Common Law and Commercial Bar Association, Official Referees' Bar Association, Professional Negligence Bar Association.
Career: Called to the Bar in 1976 and joined 4 Pump Court in 1977.
Personal: Educated at Eton College 1965-70 and Bristol University 1971-74. Born 22nd March 1952.

Edelman QC, Colin
See under Insurance and Reinsurance.

Edwards-Stuart QC, Antony
See under Insurance and Reinsurance.

Elliott QC, Timothy
See under Construction Law.

Elliott QC, Nicholas
See under Banking.

Faulks, Edward
No. 1 Serjeants' Inn (Crawford Lindsay QC), London (0171) 353 9901.
Specialisation: Principal area of practice is professional negligence, particularly medical, veterinary, local authorities and solicitors. Also handles general common law work including personal injury and media-related work. Appeared in Lonrho v. Fayed [1993] M .v Newham London Borough [1994] T. v. Surrey County Council [1994], and litigation arising out of radiotherapy and HIV haemophilia cases. Clients include hospitals, local authorities, police authorities, insurance companies and individual plaintiffs. Media clients include publishers, literary agents and advertising agencies. Author of articles on medical and veterinary negligence and has addressed these topics and local authority negligence at conferences and seminars.
Prof. Membership: Fellow of Chartered Institute of Arbitrators, Common Law & Commercial Bar Association, Professional

Negligence Bar Association.
Career: Called to the Bar 1973 and became a member of present Chambers in 1974.
Personal: Educated at Wellington College, 1963-68 and Jesus College, Oxford 1969-72. Former literary agent. Leisure pursuits include cricket. Born 19th August 1950. Lives in London.

Fernyhough QC, Richard
See under Construction Law.

Flaux QC, Julian
See under Insurance and Reinsurance.

Foskett QC, David
1 Crown Office Row (Robert Seabrook QC), London (0171) 797 7500.
Specialisation: All fields of common law advocacy including medical and other professional negligence, personal injury, contract and general domestic commercial work. He also has experience in civil and criminal fraud cases, administrative law and judicial review, family law and employment law. He is currently retained in connection with matters arising from the Kegworth Air Disaster. He is the author of 'The Law and Practice of Compromise' (Sweet & Maxwell), the 4th edition of which is due to be published in late 1995.
Prof. Membership: Fellow of the Chartered Institute of Chartered Arbitrators. London Common Law and Commercial Bar Association, Administrative Law Bar Association and Family Law Bar Association.
Career: Called to the Bar 1972. Queen's Counsel 1991. Assistant Recorder 1992-1995. Recorder 1995-.
Personal: Educated at Warwick School and Kings College, London. Lives in London and Dorset.

Gaisman QC, Jonathan
Seven King's Bench Walk (Adrian Hamilton QC), London (0171) 583 0404. Called 1979, took silk 1995.

Gibson QC, Christopher
2 Crown Office Row (Rupert Jackson QC), London (0171) 797 8000. Called 1976, took silk 1995.

Gillis, Richard
See under Company.

Glasgow QC, Edwin
See under Insurance and Reinsurance.

Gloster QC, Elizabeth
See under Insolvency.

Goldsmith QC, Peter
See under Commercial Law.

Goodman, Andrew
199 Strand (R.M. Stewart QC), London (0171) 379 9779.

Specialisation: Practice encompasses professional negligence (primarily of solicitors and surveyors) property and landlord and tenant law (specialising in forfeiture) and business-format franchising and distribution licencing. Also deals with general commercial law and some administrative law. Acted in Di Palma v. Victoria Square Property Co [1986], Papistel v. Phillips [1988]; United Dominions Trust v. Stillpoint Trustees [1993]; Mcleish v. Amoo-Gottfried & Co [1993] and North Yorkshire Trading Standards Dept v. Willams [1994]. Accredited CEDR mediator. Publications include 'The Court Guide' (1995, 10th Ed) and the RCJ guide.

Prof. Membership: Professional Negligence Bar Association (Secretary); Executive Committee, London Common Law and Commercial Bar Association, ACI Arb.

Career: Called to the Bar 1978. Joined *199 Strand* in 1990.

Personal: Educated at Southampton University (LL.B). Author of books on Victorian theatre, London and the performing arts. Born 4th June 1956. Lives in Loughton, Essex.

Guggenheim, Anna
2 Crown Office Row (Raymond Kidwell QC), London (0171) 797 8100.

Specialisation: Specialises in common law, commercial law and Official Referee's business.

Prof. Membership: London Common Law & Commercial Bar Association; COMBAR; Official Referees Bar Association.

Career: Called to the Bar 1982, joining *2 Crown Office Row* in the same year.

Personal: Educated at Somerville College, Oxford (BA Jurisprudence) 1978-1981. Born 2nd September 1959. Lives in London.

Hamilton QC, Adrian
See under Commercial Law.

Hapgood QC, Mark
See under Commercial Law.

Harvey QC, Michael
2 Crown Office Row (Raymond Kidwell QC), London (0171) 797 8100. Called 1966, took silk 1982.

Hodge, David
9 Old Square (Robert Reid QC), London (0171) 405 4682. Called 1979.

Holdsworth, James
2 Crown Office Row (Raymond Kidwell QC), London (0171) 797 8100. Called 1977. Practice covers professional negligence, insurance, personal injury, administrative law, building disputes and general common law.

Holwill, Derek
4 Paper Buildings (Harvey McGregor QC), London (0171) 353 3366.

Specialisation: Principal area of practice is professional negligence including medical negligence cases. Acts primarily for defendant insurance companies, Solicitors Indemnity Fund and Health Authorities, but also some work for plaintiffs. Also handles commercial litigation and general common law work, including personal injury cases. Reported cases include Landall v. Dennis Faulkner and Alsop.

Prof. Membership: Professional Negligence Bar Association

Career: Called to the Bar 1982 and joined present chambers 1983.

Personal: Leisure pursuits include Lindy Hop, scuba diving and travel. Born on 25th September 1959. Lives in London.

Hooper, Toby
12 King's Bench Walk (Ronald Walker QC), London (0171) 583 0811.

Specialisation: Principal area of practice consists of claims relating to professional negligence, material damage, building contracts, personal injury, employment contracts and insurance contracts. Author of articles for legal periodicals on a variety of topics concerning substantive law, evidence, procedure and practice and has lectured and directed professional training programmes on these topics and on advocacy.

Prof. Membership: London Common Law and Commercial Bar Association, Professional Negligence Bar Association, Official Referees Bar Association, Employment Law Bar Association, Employment Lawyers Association.

Career: Called to the Bar 1973 and joined current chambers 1974.

Personal: Educated at Downside School 1964-69 and Durham University 1969-72. Leisure pursuits include walking, music (especially choral singing) and reading. Born 14th December 1950. Lives in London.

Hughes, Iain
2 Crown Office Row (Rupert Jackson QC), London (0171) 797 8000.

Specialisation: Principal area of practice is professional negligence. Work covers all aspects of professional negligence and, in particular, actions involving solicitors, surveyors and valuers, architects, barristers, accountants and doctors. Also handles personal injury and general common law. Clients include major professional insurers and indemnifiers, building societies and centralised lenders. Editor: Jackson and Powell on Professional Negligence; 3rd Edn and supplements. Has addressed conferences and seminars on professional negligence and related subjects.

Prof. Membership: Professional Negligence Bar Association.

Career: Called to the Bar 1974 and joined current chambers in 1977.

Personal: Educated at Bristol University 1969-73. Born 7th December 1950.

Hutton, Caroline
See under Property Litigation.

Iwi, Quintin
2 Harcourt Buildings (Roger Henderson QC), London (0171) 583 9020. Called 1956.

Jackson QC, Rupert
See under Construction Law.

Jarvis QC, John
See under Banking.

Jones, Nigel
Hardwicke Building (Walter Aylen QC), London (0171) 242 2523. Called 1976.

Kealey QC, Gavin
See under Commercial Law.

Langley QC, Gordon
See under Commercial Law.

Leggatt, George
See under Commercial Law.

Livesey QC, Bernard
See under Personal Injury.

Lynagh, Richard
2 Crown Office Row (Raymond Kidwell QC), London (0171) 797 8100. Called 1975. Specialist in professional negligence and insurance law. Also handles general common law and personal injury work. Born 14.11.1952.

Mackay QC, Colin
39 Essex Street (Colin Mackay QC), London (0171) 583 1111. Called 1967, took silk 1989.

Malek, Ali
See under Commercial Law.

Miller QC, Stephen
1 Crown Office Row (Robert Seabrook QC), London (0171) 797 7500.

Specialisation: Professional Negligence, particularly medical negligence and medically related disciplinary and Inquiry work. Interesting cases include: Wilsher v. Essex Health Authority; Gold v. Haringey Health Authority; Aboul Hosn v. The Trustees of the Italian Hospital; AB v. Wyeth and others (Benzodiazepine litigation); Johnstone v. Campden & Islington Heath Authority; Al-Kandari v. J R Brown & Co; Talbot v. Berkshire County Council; Zeebrugge Ferry Inquiry and criminal proceedings. Publications include a chapter in 'Medical Negligence' (contributor) Powers & Harris (Butterworths 1994 2nd Edition). Regular speaker at conferences and seminars on the subject of medical negligence and damages.

Prof. Membership: Professional Negligence Bar Association; London Common Law & Commercial Bar Association; Personal Injury Bar Association.

Career: Called to the Bar 1971; Silk 1990. Appointed Recorder of the Crown Court 1993.

Personal: Educated at Oxford University (BA).

Mowschenson QC, Terence

See under Insolvency.

Munro, Kenneth

5 Bell Yard (Robert Webb QC), London (0171) 333 8811. Called 1973. Practice includes the acquisition, development and disposal of land, building and construction, landlord and tenant and professional negligence.

Nelson QC, Robert

1 Paper Buildings (Robert Nelson QC), London (0171) 583 7355. Called 1965, took silk 1985.

Norris, Alastair

See under Chancery.

Philipson QC, Trevor

See under Aviation.

Phillips QC, Patrick

2 Temple Gardens (Patrick Phillips QC), London (0171) 583 6041. Called 1964, took silk 1980.

Phillips, Rory

See under Insurance and Reinsurance.

Pittaway, David

No. 1 Serjeants' Inn (Crawford Lindsay QC), London (0171) 353 9901.

Specialisation: Professional negligence work for plaintiffs and defendants, including medical cases, solicitors, accountants, insurance brokers and financial advisers. Has been instructed in cases involving misdiagnosis of cancer, obstetrics and gynaecology, paediatrics (including renal failure), negligent treatment of a mental patient, negligent conduct by solicitors of medical negligence and personal injury litigation, and negligent advice by accountants on the sale of companies, including a major football club. Other main area of practice is general commercial and contract work, including carriage of goods and employment (including director's disqualification, wrongful dismissal and restrictive covenants). Lay clients include NHS trusts, major insurance companies and plaintiff companies and individuals. Contributor to 'Atkins Court Forms' (Negligence and Professional Negligence/Carriers). Lecturer on medical negligence and personal injury at seminars for solicitors and lay/professional clients.

Prof. Membership: Professional Negligence Bar Association, London Common Law Bar Association, Midland & Oxford Circuit.

Career: Called to the Bar in 1977 and joined *No.1 Serjeants' Inn* in 1979.

Personal: Educated at Uppingham School

1968-72 and Sidney Sussex College, Cambridge 1973-77. Born 29th June 1955. Lives in London.

Playford QC, Jonathan

2 Harcourt Buildings (Roger Henderson QC), London (0171) 583 9020. Called 1962, took silk 1982.

Pooles, Michael

4 Paper Buildings (Harvey McGregor QC), London (0171) 353 3366.

Specialisation: Principal area of practice is professional negligence, particularly concerning solicitors. Also acts for and against members of the Bar, accountants, surveyors, architects, engineers and doctors. Other main areas of practice are personal injury and general insurance matters, on behalf of a large number of insurance companies.

Prof. Membership: Professional Negligence Bar Association, COMBAR.

Career: Called to the Bar 1978 and joined present chambers in 1980.

Personal: Educated at Perse School, Cambridge, 1967-74 and University of London 1974-7. Born 14th December 1955. Lives in Cambridge.

Popplewell, Andrew

See under Insurance and Reinsurance.

Powell QC, John L.

2 Crown Office Row (Rupert Jackson QC), London (0171) 797 8000.

Specialisation: Professional negligence, financial services and securities regulation (UK, EC and international), insurance and construction law. Practice reflects his main publications: (1) 'Jackson & Powell on Professional Negligence' and (2) 'Lomnicka and Powell, Encyclopedia of Financial Services Law' (Sweet & Maxwell). Other main areas of practice include arbitration, commercial contracts, collective investment schemes, privatisation contracts and regulation generally.

Prof. Membership: COMBAR, Bar European Group, PNBA, Society of Construction Law (President 1991-93).

Career: Called to the Bar in 1974. Took silk in 1990. Attorney of the Turks and Caicos Islands.

Personal: Educated at Christ College, Brecon, Amman Valley Grammar School and Trinity Hall, Cambridge 1969-73 (MA, LLB). Welsh speaker. Born 14th September 1950. Lives in London and Trap, Dyfed. Married with 3 children.

Railton, David

See under Banking.

Ramsey QC, Vivian

See under Construction Law.

Ross, John

No. 1 Serjeants' Inn (Crawford Lindsay QC), London (0171) 353 9901.

Specialisation: Principal area of practice is professional negligence work, particularly relating to surveyors, architects, engineers, insurance brokers and solicitors. Other main area of work includes general commercial/contract work including carriage of goods, arbitrations, letter rogatory and private international law; and asbestos-related work. Clients include most of the major insurance companies, underwriters, finance houses and asbestos industry companies. Addresses seminars for solicitors and other professional clients or surveyors negligence.

Prof. Membership: Official Referees' Bar Association, Professional Negligence Bar Association, Common Law and Commercial Bar Association.

Career: Called to the Bar and joined No.1 Serjeants Inn 1971. Appointed Recorder 1994.

Personal: Educated at University College, London LL.B 1968, LL.M.

Ruttle, Stephen

Brick Court Chambers (Christopher Clarke QC), London (0171) 583 0777. Called 1976.

Ryan, A.

Verulam Chambers (Michael Edwards QC), London (0171) 242 7646.

Specialisation: Principal area of practice is professional negligence (doctors, dentists, accountants, solicitors, surveyors) both for plaintiffs and defendants. Has had considerable experience in the Official Referees' Court in building disputes and surveyors negligence cases. Clients include major professional indemnity insurance companies.

Prof. Membership: London Common Law and Commercial Bar Association.

Career: Called to the Bar 1972.

Personal: Educated at Stirling High School, Edinburgh University and Keele University.

Seabrook QC, Robert

1 Crown Office Row (Robert Seabrook QC), London (0171) 797 7500. Called 1964, took silk 1983. Principal area of practice is professional (including medical) negligence. Also serious crime and commercial fraud. Born 6.10.1941.

Simmonds, Andrew

5 Stone Buildings (Henry Harrod), London (0171) 242 6201.

Specialisation: Specialises in disputes relating to occupational and personal pension schemes. Experience covers both 'internal' disputes involving trustees, employers and members (e.g as to rule amendments, use of surplus, bulk transfers and cash equivalents) as well as prosecuting and defending claims for professional negligence in a pensions context (e.g against solicitors and auditors). Lay clients include trustees, including independent trustees appointed under S.119 PSA

1993, employers, individual and representative members, insolvency practitioners, solicitors, auditors, member's dependents, bankers, fund managers and pensions consultants. Has acted as arbitrator in a pensions dispute.

Career: Called 1980.

Slater QC, John
See under Construction Law.

Stewart QC, Robin
199 Strand (R.M. Stewart QC), London (0171) 379 9779.

Specialisation: Principal area of practice is professional and medical negligence and personal injury as well as many structured settlements. Other areas are medical related crime and some contract and other common law work. Cases of note include Jobling v. Associated Dairies Ltd [1982], Housecroft v.Burnett [1986], Fitzgerald v.Lane & Patel [1989] and Woodrup v. Nichol [1993]. Clients include Evill & Coleman, Field Fisher Waterhouse, Irwin Mitchell and Le Brasseur J. Tickle.

Prof. Membership: Professional Negligence Bar Association (Chairman 1991-93), North Eastern Circuit. Member of Professional Conduct Committee of Bar Council 1991-93.

Career: Called to the Bar in 1963. At 6 Pump Court 1963-65 and in industry 1965-70. In chambers in Newcastle-upon-Tyne (46 Grainger Street) 1970-88. Appointed Recorder and took silk in 1978. Joined *199 Strand* in 1978. Bencher, Middle Temple, since 1988.

Personal: Educated at Winchester College 1951-57 and New College, Oxford 1958-61. Tynedale District Councillor 1972-76. Parliamentary candidate, Newcastle-upon-Tyne West, 1974. Leisure interests include Scottish family history, silver, pictures and France. Born 5th August 1938. Lives in Sevenoaks.

Stewart, Roger
2 Crown Office Row (Rupert Jackson QC), London (0171) 797 8000. Called 1986. Principal areas of practice are professional negligence and construction work. Born 17.8.1963.

Stuart-Smith, Jeremy
2 Temple Gardens (Patrick Phillips QC), London (0171) 583 6041. Called 1978.

Sumption QC, Jonathan
See under Commercial Law.

Sutcliffe, Andrew
See under Media and Entertainment.

Taverner, Marcus
See under Construction Law.

Temple QC, Anthony
4 Pump Court (Bruce Mauleverer QC), London (0171) 353 2656. Called 1968, took silk 1986. General commercial and common law practice, specialising in insurance and reinsurance, fraud, professional negligence. Born 21.9.1945.

ter Haar QC, Roger
2 Crown Office Row (Raymond Kidwell QC), London (0171) 797 8100. Called 1974, took silk 1992. Practice encompasses professional negligence, construction law and insurance and reinsurance work. Born 14.6.1952.

Thanki, Bankim
See under Banking.

Thomas QC, Christopher
See under Construction Law.

Toulson QC, Roger
2 Crown Office Row (Rupert Jackson QC), London (0171) 797 8000. Called 1969, took silk 1986.

Treasure, Francis
See under Personal Injury.

Turner, Janet
3 Gray's Inn Place (R. Neville Thomas QC), London (0171) 831 8441. Called 1979.

Ullstein QC, Augustus
29 Bedford Row Chambers (Evan Stone QC), London (0171) 831 2626.

Specialisation: Principal area of practice is professional negligence for all professions, both for Plaintiffs and Defendants. Has had considerable experience of multi-party litigation including Opren (Nash v. Ely Lilly) and Myodil (Chrzanowska v. Glaxo Laboratories Limited). Other main areas of practice are personal injuries, which has included appointment by the Federal District Court in Ohio, USA to the Foreign Fracture Panel in the Shiley Heart Valve litigation. Also practises substantially in the Family Division.

Prof. Membership: ORBA, FLBA, A.T.L.A. (US) Member Gibraltar Bar.

Career: Called to the Bar 1970. QC 1992. Joined *29 Bedford Row* 1991.

Personal: Educated at Bradfield College and LSE. Lives in London.

Vallance QC, Philip
See under Environmental.

Vandyck, William
1 Paper Buildings (Robert Nelson QC), London (0171) 583 7355.

Waite, Jonathan
1 Paper Buildings (Robert Nelson QC), London (0171) 583 7355. Called 1978.

Walker QC, Tim
Fountain Court (Peter Scott QC), London (0171) 583 3335. Called 1968, took silk 1985. Specialist in arbitration, aviation, banking, insurance and reinsurance, general common law and professional negligence.

Weitzman QC, Peter
Devereux Chambers (Peter Weitzman QC), London (0171) 353 7534. Called 1952, took silk 1973. Principal areas of practice are personal injury and professional (particularly medical) negligence. Born 20.6.1926.

PROPERTY LITIGATION

WHILE many members of the chancery and common law Bars handle a substantial amount of contentious property work, relatively few sets can be regarded as specialising in this area of law.

FALCON CHAMBERS	
4 BREAMS BUILDINGS	9 OLD SQUARE
ENTERPRISE CHAMBERS	13 OLD SQUARE
WILBERFORCE CHAMBERS	

Falcon Chambers emerges as the leading set, with members practising almost exclusively in landlord and tenant and property law. *Jonathan Gaunt QC* (who regularly contributes to the landlord and tenant volume of 'Halsbury's Laws' and lectures on the subject) is chambers' leading light, although the set also has outstanding silks in *Paul Morgan QC, David Neuberger QC, Kirk Reynolds QC* and *Kim Lewison QC. Kirk Reynolds QC* has a particular expertise in rent reviews and is the author of 'The Handbook of Rent Review'. *Kim Lewison QC* has written a number of books on business leases.

At the junior end, *Martin Rodger* (editor of 'Woodfall on Landlord and Tenant'), *Nicholas Dowding, Jonathan Brock* and *Barry Denyer-Green* are particularly highly regarded, while *Stephen Jourdan* is chambers' rising star.

Ranking a close second in our research comes **4 Breams Buildings**, a well-known planning set with a substantial landlord and tenant practice. *Michael Barnes QC* and *Joseph Harper QC* are highly recommended practitioners with *John Furber QC, John Male, David Elvin, Jonathan Karas* and *Nicholas Taggart* also well thought of. Members of chambers are editors of or contributors to 'Hill and Redman's Law of Landlord and Tenant' and 'Halsbury's Laws – Landlord and Tenant'.

Of the chancery sets, **Enterprise Chambers, 9 Old Square, 13 Old Square** and **Wilberforce Chambers** are highly regarded.

Simon Berry QC is **9 Old Square's** outstanding practitioner. Other experienced counsel include *Robert Reid QC, Michael Driscoll QC, Judith Jackson QC, David Hodge* and *John McGhee. Michael Driscoll* acted in 'Esculas Property'. *Timothy Harry* is one of the editors of 'Hill and Redmans Law of Landlord and Tenant'.

Barnes, Michael	*4 Breams Buildings*	
Berry, Simon	*9 Old Square*	
Etherton, Terence	*Wilberforce Chambers*	
Gaunt, Jonathan	*Falcon Chambers*	
Lewison, Kim	*Falcon Chambers*	
Morgan, Paul	*Falcon Chambers*	
Neuberger, David	*Falcon Chambers*	
Reid, Robert	*9 Old Square*	
Reynolds, Kirk	*Falcon Chambers*	
Williamson, Hazel	*13 Old Square*	
Arden, Andrew	*Arden Chambers*	
Briggs, Michael	*13 Old Square*	
Driscoll, Michael	*9 Old Square*	
Furber, John	*4 Breams Buildings*	
Ham, Robert	*Wilberforce Chambers*	
Harper, Joseph	*4 Breams Buildings*	
Jackson, Judith	*9 Old Square*	
Laurence, George	*12 New Square*	
Nugee, Edward	*Wilberforce Chambers*	
Steinfeld, Alan	*24 Old Buildings*	
Wood, Derek	*Falcon Chambers*	

Enterprise Chambers boasts a number of practitioners with experience in the field including *Benjamin Levy* (who has appeared in some 50 reported cases), *David Halpern, Caroline Hutton* ('Saunders v. Edwards', 'Aspen Properties

Arkush, Jonathan *11 Stone Buildings*	**Brock,** Jonathan *Falcon Chambers*	**Denyer-Green,** Barry *Falcon Chambers*
Dowding, Nicholas *Falcon Chambers*	**Elvin,** David *4 Breams Buildings*	**Halpern,** David *Enterprise Chambers*
Hutton, Caroline *Enterprise Chambers*	**Ife,** Linden *Enterprise Chambers*	**Karas,** Jonathan *4 Breams Buildings*
Levy, Benjamin *Enterprise Chambers*	**Male,** John *4 Breams Buildings*	**Rodger,** Martin *Falcon Chambers*
Barker, James *Enterprise Chambers*	**Bowles,** Timothy *Barnards Inn Chambers*	**Fancourt,** Timothy *Falcon Chambers*
Harry, Timothy *9 Old Square*	**Hodge,** David *9 Old Square*	**Huskinson,** Nicholas *4-5 Gray's Inn Square*
Jourdan, Stephen *Falcon Chambers*	**McAllister,** Ann *Enterprise Chambers*	**McGhee,** John *9 Old Square*
Nugee, Christopher *Wilberforce Chambers*	**Pymont,** Christopher *13 Old Square*	**Radevsky,** Anthony *5 Bell Yard*
Seitler, Jonathan *New Court Chambers*	**Taussig,** Anthony *Wilberforce Chambers*	**Thom,** James *Queen Elizabeth Building*
Trace, Anthony *13 Old Square*	**Wakefield,** Robert *17 Old Buildings*	

Taggart, Nicholas *4 Breams Buildings*

v. Ratcliffe', 'Ponderosa v. Pengap'), and *Linden Ife* and *Ann McAllister*.

At **13 Old Square**, *Hazel Williamson QC* is one of London's most consistently recommended practitioners, *Christopher Pymont* is also held in high regard.

Terence Etherton QC, Robert Ham QC and *Edward Nugee*

QC at **Wilberforce Chambers** are all leading practitioners. At the junior end of chambers *Christopher Nugee* is well respected.

Other prominent practitioners include *Alan Steinfeld QC* at **24 Old Buildings**, *Andrew Arden QC* at **Arden Chambers** and *Jonathan Arkush* at **11 Stone Buildings**.

LEADERS IN PROPERTY LITIGATION

Arden QC, Andrew
See under Public and Administrative Law.

Arkush, Jonathan
11 Stone Buildings (Michael Beckman QC),   London (+44) 0171 831 6381. Called 1977. Specialises in chancery work and commercial litigation.

Barker, James
Enterprise Chambers (Benjamin Levy), London (0171) 405 9471.

Barnes QC, Michael
See under Planning and Local Government.

Berry QC, Simon
9 Old Square (Robert Reid QC),   London (0171) 405 4682. Called 1977, took silk 1990.

Bowles, Timothy
Barnards Inn Chambers (Timothy Bowles),   London (0171) 242 8508.

Briggs QC, Michael
See under Company.

Brock, Jonathan
Falcon Chambers (Jonathan Gaunt QC, David Neuberger QC),   London (0171) 353 2484. Called 1977. Practice includes agricultural holdings, land law, landlord and tenant and charities. Editor of 'Woodfall on Landlord & Tenant'.

Denyer-Green, Barry
Falcon Chambers (Jonathan Gaunt QC, David Neuberger QC),   London (0171) 353 2484.

Dowding, Nicholas
Falcon Chambers (Jonathan Gaunt QC, David Neuberger QC),   London (0171) 353 2484. Called 1979.

Driscoll QC, Michael
9 Old Square (Robert Reid QC),   London (0171) 405 4682. Called 1970, took silk 1992.

Elvin, David
4 Breams Buildings (Christopher Lockhart-Mummery QC),   London (0171) 430 1221. Called 1983.

Etherton QC, Terence
Wilberforce Chambers (Edward Nugee QC),   London (0171) 306 0102. Called 1974, took silk 1990.

Fancourt, Timothy
Falcon Chambers (Jonathan Gaunt QC, David Neuberger QC),   London (0171) 353 2484.

Specialisation: Principal area of practice is real property related chancery work (litigation oriented). This includes commercial property matters, landlord and tenant, surveyors' and solicitors' professional negligence, conveyancing, building contracts, mortgages, easements and restrictive covenants, equity and trusts and commercial contracts. Other main area is bankruptcy and insolvency. Author of 'Megarry: The Rent Acts' (11th edition), cumulative supplements 1989, 1991 and 1993.

Prof. Membership: Lincoln's Inn, Chancery Bar Association, Commercial Bar Association.

Career: Called to the Bar in 1987 and joined *Falcon Chambers* in 1989.

Personal: Educated at Whitgift School 1974-82 and Gonville & Caius College, Cambridge 1983-86. Born 30th August 1964.

Furber QC, John
See under Chancery.

Gaunt QC, Jonathan
Falcon Chambers (Jonathan Gaunt QC, David Neuberger QC),   London (0171) 353 2484.

Specialisation: With David Neuberger QC is the joint Head of *Falcon Chambers*, the members of which specialise in landlord and tenant property law. Called to the Bar in 1972 and took silk in 1991. One of the Editors of the landlord and tenant volume of Halsbury's Laws', having recently re-written the sections on repairing covenants, rent and rent review. Is also in the process of preparing a new edition of *Gale on Easements*.

Halpern, David
Enterprise Chambers (Benjamin Levy), London (0171) 405 9471. Called 1978. Principal area of practice is commercial chancery, dealing primarily with property, landlord & tenant, and professional negligence. Born 23.5.1956.

Ham QC, Robert
See under Chancery.

Harper QC, Joseph
4 Breams Buildings (Christopher Lockhart-Mummery QC),   London (0171) 430 1221. Called 1970, took silk 1992.

Harry, Timothy
See under Chancery.

Hodge, David
9 Old Square (Robert Reid QC),   London (0171) 405 4682. Called 1979.

Huskinson, Nicholas
See under Parliamentary.

Hutton, Caroline
Enterprise Chambers (Benjamin Levy), London (0171) 405 9471.

Specialisation: Practice covers all aspects of real property law, principally landlord and tenant (commercial, agricultural and residential) and including conveyancing, boundaries, easements, equitable rights and trusts of land, mortgages and professional negligence, insolvency and fraud matters related to property. Major cases include Saunders v. Edwards; Culworth Estates v. Licensed Victuallers'; Aspen Properties v. Ratcliffe and Ponderosa v. Pengap. Clients include property companies, retailers and banks. Contributed to commercial conferences on landlord and tenant.

Prof. Membership: Justice, Association of Women Barristers.

Career: Called to the Bar 1979 and joined *Enterprise Chambers* 1981. Chairman Disciplinary and Appeals Tribunal for licensed conveyancing 1988-93.

Personal: Educated at Clare College, Cambridge 1975-78. Leisure pursuits include embroidery, reading, walking, theatre and art history. Born 25th March 1956. Lives in London.

Ife, Linden
See under Insolvency.

Jackson QC, Judith
9 Old Square (Robert Reid QC),   London (0171) 405 4682. Called 1975, took silk 1994.

Jourdan, Stephen
Falcon Chambers (Jonathan Gaunt QC, David Neuberger QC), London (0171) 353 2484. Called 1989.

Karas, Jonathan
4 Breams Buildings (Christopher Lockhart-Mummery QC), London (0171) 430 1221. Called 1986.

Laurence QC, George
See under Parliamentary.

Levy, Benjamin
Enterprise Chambers (Benjamin Levy), London (0171) 405 9471. Called 1956. Specialist in landlord and tenant and general chancery work including partnership. Born 2.1.1934.

Lewison QC, Kim
Falcon Chambers (Jonathan Gaunt QC, David Neuberger QC), London (0171) 353 2484.

Specialisation: Specialises in Chancery and real property law. Practice covers landlord and tenant, rent review, interpretation of contracts, agricultural holdings, conveyancing, easements, restrictive covenants, compulsory acquisitions, suretyship and professional negligence in connection with real property. Publications include 'Woodfall on Landlord and Tenant' (General Editor since 1990); 'The Interpretation of Contracts' (1989); 'Lease or Licence' (1985); 'Development Land Tax' (1976); 'Drafting Business Leases' (all four editions, latest 1993). Consultant Editor of *Property & Compensation Reports* since 1990. Recent reported cases include Colchester BC v. Smith (1992) Ch 421 (adverse possession); London & Leeds Estates v. Paribas (1993) (rent review); Connaught Restaurants v. Indoor Leisure (1993) (set off). In 1988 appointed by the Department of the Environment as a member of the Study Team investigating professional negligence and insurance against professional liability.

Prof. Membership: COMBAR; London Common Law & Commercial Bar Association; Chancery Bar Association.

Career: Called to the Bar in 1975 (Cassell and Hardwick Scholarships, Lincoln's Inn). Member of *Falcon Chambers* since 1976. Took Silk 1991. Appointed Assistant Recorder in 1993.

Personal: Educated at St. Paul's School 1965-70 and Downing College, Cambridge (1st Class Hons in both English Tripos) 1970-73. Fluent French speaker. Council Member of the Liberal Jewish Synagogue. Leisure activities include visiting France. Born 1st May 1952. Lives in London.

Male, John
4 Breams Buildings (Christopher Lockhart-Mummery QC), London (0171) 430 1221. Called 1976.

McAllister, Ann
Enterprise Chambers (Benjamin Levy), London (0171) 405 9471.

Career: Read law and languages at Newnham College, Cambridge. After graduating in 1975 went to LSE and gained an LL.M in law. Taught law for three years at the University of London (School of Oriental and African Studies). Called to the Bar in 1982. Principal area of practice is landlord and tenant and property law, although practice also includes all aspects of general chancery law (mortgages, partnerships, guarantees, insolvency) and, increasingly, professional negligence work. An editor of "Current Law" since 1985.

McGhee, John
9 Old Square (Robert Reid QC), London (0171) 405 4682. Called 1984.

Morgan QC, Paul
Falcon Chambers (Jonathan Gaunt QC, David Neuberger QC), London (0171) 353 2484. Called 1975, took silk 1992. Main area of practice is real property, particularly landlord and tenant matters. Born 17.8.1952.

Neuberger QC, David
Falcon Chambers (Jonathan Gaunt QC, David Neuberger QC), London (0171) 353 2484.

Specialisation: Is one of the leading barristers specialising in property law. Has been in practice for some twenty years, eight of them as a QC. Joint head of *Falcon Chambers* which is possibly the leading set of Chambers specialising almost exclusively in property law. Frequently appears in Court and in arbitrations and advises in relation to all aspects of litigation. Practice also involves much general advisory work, in conference and in writing. For the past five years, has sat from time to time as a Deputy High Court Judge.

Nugee QC, Edward
See under Chancery.

Nugee, Christopher
See under Chancery.

Pymont, Christopher
13 Old Square (Mr. E.W.H. Christie), London (0171) 404 4800.

Specialisation: Practice encompasses company law, landlord and tenant matters, chancery work and insolvency.

Prof. Membership: Chancery Bar Association.

Career: Called to the Bar 1979 and joined *13 Old Square* in 1980.

Personal: Educated at Marlborough College and Christchurch, Oxford (MA). Born 16th March 1956.

Radevsky, Anthony
5 Bell Yard (Robert Webb QC), London (0171) 333 8811.

Specialisation: Landlord and tenant law

relating to commercial and residential property, leasehold enfranchisement, rent review, dilapidations and service charges. Also handles mortgages, specific performance of contracts for the sale of land, restrictive covenants and professional negligence claims against solicitors and surveyors both for plaintiffs and the Solicitors' Indemnity Fund. Author of 'Service of Documents' (Longman, 2nd Edn, 1989); 'Drafting Pleadings' (Tolley, 2nd Edn 1995).

Prof. Membership: Chancery Bar Association.

Career: Called to the Bar 1978 and joined *1 Temple Gardens*. Joined current chambers in 1993.

Personal: Educated at Alleyn's School, Dulwich 1966-73 and Southampton University 1974-77 (LL.B, Hons). Born 22nd August 1955.

Reid QC, Robert
See under Sports Law.

Reynolds QC, Kirk
Falcon Chambers (Jonathan Gaunt QC, David Neuberger QC), London (0171) 353 2484.

Specialisation: Called to the Bar 1974. Queen's Counsel 1993. Full time practice as landlord and tenant specialist at *Falcon Chambers* since 1975. Co-author 'The Handbook of Rent Review', 'The Renewal of Business Tenancies' and 'Dilapidations: the Modern Law and Practice'. Member of Editorial Boards 'New Property Cases' and 'Rent Review and Lease Renewal Quarterly'. Blundell Memorial Lecturer 1982, 1987 and 1993. Advisor to Royal Institution of Chartered Surveyors on arbitration practice and Course Tutor on official R.I.C.S. training courses for arbitrators.

Prof. Membership: Member of R.I.C.S. Committee producing and revising official Guidance Notes for Arbitrators and Independent Experts. Appointed on a number of occasions by President of R.I.C.S. and President of Law Society as arbitrator, and by arbitrators as Legal Assessor.

Rodger, Martin
Falcon Chambers (Jonathan Gaunt QC, David Neuberger QC), London (0171) 353 2484. Called 1986. Principal area of practice is commercial and agricultural property, including landlord and tenant matters. Born 11.2.1962.

Seitler, Jonathan
New Court Chambers (George Carman QC), London (0171) 583 6166.

Specialisation: All aspects of property litigation. This includes the following: Landlord and Tenant, Bank Securitisation and Negligence Claims against Solicitors and Valuers. Acts for both landlords and tenants, banks and their customers and, in professional negligence actions, Plaintiffs and insurers. Reported cases include SDF v. Barnes (a leading test case on Time Orders). Co-author of 'Property Finance Negligence: Claims Against Solicitors and Valuers' to be published by FT Law & Tax (Longman) in early 1996. Lectures widely both for lecture companies and in-house. Topics include, 'Tenant Default', 'Property Misdescriptions', 'Residential Letting', 'Inquisitorial Pleadings', 'Enforcement of Judgments' and 'How to Strengthen your Client's Position Before Trial'.

Prof. Membership: Professional Negligence Bar Association.

Career: Called to the Bar 1985.

Personal: Educated at Pembroke College, Oxford. Lives in London.

Steinfeld QC, Alan
See under Chancery.

Taggart, Nicholas
4 Breams Buildings (Christopher

Lockhart-Mummery QC), London (0171) 430 1221.

Taussig, Anthony
See under Chancery.

Thom, James
See under Commercial Law.

Trace, Anthony
13 Old Square (Mr. E.W.H. Christie), London (0171) 404 4800. Called 1981. Principal area of practice covers insolvency, chancery and commercial work.

Wakefield, Robert
17 Old Buildings (Geoffrey Jaques), London (0171) 405 9653.

Specialisation: Practice encompasses property (enforcement and protection of easements, restrictive covenants and property rights), sale of land, solicitors' and

surveyors' professional negligence; commercial tenancies; mortgages; inheritance; probate; chancery work; and ecclesiastical law (faculty jurisdiction and church property).

Prof. Membership: Chancery Bar Association.

Career: Called to the Bar 1969 and joined present chambers 1983. Appointed Recorder 1993.

Personal: Educated at Birmingham University 1964-67 and Brasenose College, Oxford 1967-69. Lives in London.

Williamson QC, Hazel
13 Old Square (Mr. E.W.H. Christie), London (0171) 404 4800. Called 1972, took silk 1988.

Wood QC, Derek
See under Agriculture and Bloodstock.

INDEXES TO PROFILES

Solicitors' Profiles The index to leading solicitors profiled in the Specialist Lists is located immediately after the section containing profiles of in-house lawyers. This index also includes heads of company legal departments.

Barristers' Profiles Profiles of leading barristers are indexed within the main *Barristers' Index* located at the end of the directory. Names of profiled barristers are set in bold type.

PUBLIC AND ADMINISTRATIVE LAW

THIS area of law is mainly concerned with actions against public bodies brought in the High Court through the medium of judicial review. Direct instructions from the legal departments of local authorities and other public bodies form a significant part of the practice of a number of chambers. With the privatisation of public services, judicial review will be increasingly applied to the decisions of newly established bodies such as hospital trusts and schools which have opted out of local authority control.

LEADING SETS – LONDON

4-5 GRAY'S INN SQUARE

| 4 BREAMS BUILDINGS | 2-3 GRAY'S INN SQUARE |
| 2 HARE COURT | 11 KING'S BENCH WALK |

4/5 Gray's Inn Square is a leading set in this field. *Michael Beloff QC* is the most prominent figure and, as one of the most highly respected advocates at the Bar, has acted for a number of government departments, several foreign governments including those of Iraq, Guyana and Trinidad, and over fifty local authorities. He has appeared in many reported cases of major importance including 'Home Office v Barnes', 'R v MAAF ex parte Greenpeace Limited', 'O'Reilly v Mackman', 'R v Department of Employment ex parte EOC', 'E v Dorset County Council' and 'R v MMC ex parte NHBC'.

QC was one of the Treasury Counsel as a junior and has been much in demand since taking silk. He appeared in the House of Lords in 'Bolton MBC and others v Secretary of State' and the 'Manchester Ship Canal Co Ltd and Tesco Stores v Secretary of State for the Environment' and others, and has recently been instructed by the Hong Kong Government.

Alan Moses QC was standing counsel to the Inland Revenue as a junior, and is well known as a particularly strong advocate in judicial review proceedings. *Cherie Booth QC* acted in 'E v Dorset County Council', 'R v Universities Funding Council ex parte The Institute of Dental Surgery' and 'Kingsbury v Northampton County Council'.

Among the juniors in chambers *Rabinder Singh* is highly regarded for his work in this field, and acts for local authorities, central government departments, public interest groups and individuals such as students and immigrants. He appeared in 'R v Home Secretary ex parte Bentley'. *Clive Lewis* acted in 'R v Secretary of State for the Home Department ex parte Adams', 'R v Hackney LBC ex parte G'. and 'R v Secretary of State for the Environment ex parte RSPB'. *Richard McManus* is Junior Counsel to the Crown and has advised the Department of Trade and Industry in connection with an action relating to export licences. He has appeared in 'R v Wolverhampton ex parte Mould', and 'R v Cleveland County Council ex parte Cleveland Care Homes Association'. *Tim Corner* acted in 'R v Thurrock BC ex parte Tesco Stores' and 'R v City of Wakefield MDC and British Coal

LEADING SILKS– LONDON

Beloff, Michael *4-5 Gray's Inn Square*		
Appleby, Elizabeth *4-5 Gray's Inn Square*	**Arden,** Andrew *Arden Chambers*	**Baxendale,** Presiley *2 Hare Court*
Caws, Genevra *4-5 Gray's Inn Square*	**Elias,** Patrick *11 King's Bench Walk*	**Goudie,** James *11 King's Bench Walk*
Hicks, William *1 Serjeants' Inn*	**Howell,** John *4 Breams Buildings*	**Lord Irvine of Lairg,** *11 King's Bench Walk*
Lord Lester, *2 Hare Court*	**Moses,** Alan *4-5 Gray's Inn Square*	**Neill,** Patrick *One Hare Court*
Ouseley, Duncan *4-5 Gray's Inn Square*	**Pannick,** David *2 Hare Court*	**Read,** Lionel *1 Serjeants' Inn*
Robertson, Geoffrey *Doughty Street Chambers*	**Scrivener,** Anthony *2-3 Gray's Inn Square*	**Sullivan,** Jeremy *4-5 Gray's Inn Square*
Supperstone, Michael Alan *11 King's Bench Walk*	**Wade,** William *4-5 Gray's Inn Square*	
Allen, Robin *Cloisters*	**Blake,** Nicholas *2 Garden Court*	**Booth,** Cherie *4-5 Gray's Inn Square*
Drabble, Richard *4 Breams Buildings*	**Fitzgerald,** Edward *Doughty Street Chambers*	**Gordon,** Richard *39 Essex Street*
Griffiths, W. Robert *4-5 Gray's Inn Square*	**Kentridge,** Sydney *Brick Court Chambers*	**Newman,** Alan *Cloisters*
Pleming, Nigel *39 Essex Street*	**Porten,** Anthony *2-3 Gray's Inn Square*	**Roots,** Guy *2 Mitre Court Buildings*
Samuels, John *22 Old Buildings*	**Steel,** John *4-5 Gray's Inn Square*	**Strauss,** Nicholas *1 Essex Court*
Tabachnik, Eldred *11 King's Bench Walk*	**Wilkie,** Alan Fraser *11 King's Bench Walk*	

Jeremy Sullivan QC, recently appointed Attorney General to the Prince of Wales, has also been very highly recommended and has appeared in numerous cases including 'Matson v Corporation of London'. His clients include Union Railways and the Department of Transport. *Genevra Caws QC* and *Elizabeth Appleby QC* have both been highly recommended for their work in this field. *Duncan Ouseley*

Corporation'. *Professor Sir William Wade QC*, author of 'Wade on Administrative Law', is well known for his advisory work.

2 Hare Court are also very highly regarded in this area. *David Pannick QC* has acted in judicial review proceedings for the Lord Chancellor (defending challenges to legal aid provisions by the Law Society), Red Hot Television, Lord

Rees-Mogg (challenging the Maastricht Treaty), the Home Secretary (concerning the treatment of mandatory life prisoners), and the Secretary of State for Health (concerning the closing of the Accident and Emergency Ward at St Bartholomew's hospital). He is the author of 'Judicial Review of the Death Penalty'.

Presily Baxendale QC appeared in the Scott Inquiry into exports of defence equipment to Iraq, 'Nottinghamshire CC v Sec.of State for Environment' and 'Avon v Sec. of State for Education'. *Lord Lester of Herne Hill QC* is well known in this area. He acted in 'R v Barnet LBC', 'R v Sec. of State for Social Services ex parte Wellcome Foundation' and 'AG v Guardian Newspapers'.

Among the juniors in chambers, *Michael Fordham* has a good reputation in this field. He is the author of the 'Judicial Review Handbook', and is a lecturer in administrative law at Hertford College, Oxford. *Mark Shaw* deals with all areas of public law including judicial review, immigration, nationality, monopolies and mergers commission work, regulatory organisations, social security, health and social services. He has appeared in 'R v London Boroughs Transport Committee ex parte Freight Transport Association Ltd', 'R v Monopolies and Mergers Commission ex parte South Yorkshire Transport' and 'R v Sec. of State for Transport ex parte Richmond LBC'.

At **2/3 Gray's Inn Place** *Anthony Scrivener QC* has an excellent reputation. He has acted in the recent dispute between former members of Westminster City Council and the District Auditor over the sale of council properties. *Anthony Porten QC* is also well known for his work in this field, as are *Timothy Straker* and *Geoffrey Stephenson*.

James Goudie QC at **11 King's Bench Walk** has an excellent reputation, as does *Michael Supperstone QC*. They are joint authors of 'Supperstone and Goudie on Judicial Review'. In addition, *Michael Supperstone* is the author of the Administrative Law title of 'Halsbury's Laws of England', and sits on the editorial committee of 'Public Law'. *Patrick Elias QC* and *Lord Irvine of Lairg QC* also have very good reputations in this area.

4 Breams Buildings is a well regarded set in this field. *John Howell QC* has a very good reputation, and *Richard Drabble QC* is also known for his work in public law. Among the juniors in chambers *David Holgate*, who is Junior Counsel to the Inland Revenue (Rating and Valuation) has been recommended.

OUTSIDE LONDON

5 Fountain Court, in Birmingham, are well thought of in this area. *Martin Kingston QC*, *Ian Dove* and *Paul Bleasdale* have good reputations. At **14 Castle Street,** in Liverpool, *Andrew Edis* is well regarded.

LEADERS IN PUBLIC AND ADMINISTRATIVE LAW

Alesbury, Alun
2 Mitre Court Buildings (Michael FitzGerald QC), London (0171) 583 1380.

Specialisation: Practice encompasses town and country planning, public and administrative law, parliamentary and local government work (including highways, compulsory purchase and rating). Involved in Windscale Inquiry, Vale of Belvoir Inquiry, Stansted/Heathrow Terminal 5 Inquiry (all as advocate) and Windermere Inquiry (as Inspector). Clients include developers, landowners, local and other public authorities and the Government.

Prof. Membership: Planning and Environment Bar Association (Founder Member 1986 and Hon. Sec. 1986-88), Parliamentary Bar Mess.

Career: Called to the Bar 1974 and joined current chambers 1975.

Personal: Educated at Cambridge University 1967-70 (MA). Leisure pursuits include walking, travel and sailing. Born 14th May 1949. Lives in West Marden, West Sussex.

Allen QC, Robin
See under Employment.

Appleby QC, Elizabeth
4-5 Gray's Inn Square (Miss Elizabeth Appleby QC, The Hon. Michael Beloff QC), London (0171) 404 5252. Called 1965, took silk 1979.

Arden QC, Andrew
Arden Chambers (Andrew Arden QC), London (0171) 353 3132.

Specialisation: Principal areas of practice are housing law, local government and landlord and tenant matters. Also compulsory competitive tendering. Clients include numerous local authorities and public bodies, private landlords, tenants and homeless people. General Editor 'Encyclopaedia of Housing Law' since 1978 and of Housing Law Reports since 1981. Involved in several local government inquiries and reviews. Author and co-author of numerous textbooks on housing law, landlord and tenant and local government law.

Prof. Membership: Administrative Law Bar Association; Planning and Environment Bar Association.

Career: Called to the Bar 1974. Director, Small Heath Community Law Centre 1976-78. Silk 1991. Founded Arden Chambers in 1993.

Personal: Educated at University College London 1969-72 (LLB). Writes novels and thrillers. Born 20th April 1948. Lives in London.

Ayers, Guy
Octagon House Chambers (Paul H. Downes), Norwich (01603) 623186. Called 1979.

Barlow, Craig
29 Bedford Row Chambers (Evan Stone QC), London (0171) 831 2626. Called 1992.

Baxendale QC, Presiley
2 Hare Court (C.W.G. Ross-Munro QC), London (0171) 583 1770.

Specialisation: Principal area of practice is public and administrative law. Also deals with local government, education, employment and general commercial law matters. Counsel to the Inquiry into Exports of Defence Equipment and Dual Use of Goods to Iraq. Other important cases include *Nottinghamshire CC v. SOS for the Environment* [1986], *Avon v. SOS for Education (1) and (2)*, charge capping litigation and anti-competitive tendering litigation for the Secretary of State.

Prof. Membership: London Common Law and Commercial Bar Association, Administrative Law Bar Association.

Career: Called to the Bar and joined *2 Hare Court* in 1974. Appointed Junior Counsel to Crown (Common Law). Took silk in 1992.

Personal: Educated at Oxford University (MA). Governor of the LSE. Vice-Chairman of Executive Committee of Justice.

Beloff QC, Michael
4-5 Gray's Inn Square (Miss Elizabeth Appleby QC, The Hon. Michael Beloff QC), London (0171) 404 5252.

Specialisation: Extremely wide ranging practice encompasses litigation and arbitration, covering a large number of areas including public law and judicial review, commercial matters, EU law, employment law, libel, sports law, insurance, immigration, civil liberties and shipping. Has appeared in more than 250 reported cases in House of Lords, Privy Council, European Court of Justice, European Court of Human Rights and courts in Hong Kong, Singapore, Kuala Lumpur, Kuching, Bermuda, Gibraltar and Belfast. Has appeared in 3 major public inquiries: Crown Agents 1980-82; Brixton Disorders 1981 (Scarman Inquiry) and Sentosa Collision (Singapore, 1983). Chaired inquiry into academic plagiarism for University of Oxford 1987. Women's Legal Defence Award 1991. Clients have included governments, local authorities, unions, national newspapers, terrestrial television channels, banks, insurance companies, major ports, corporations, universities, statutory bodies pressure groups, sporting organisations, and leading individuals and personalities from all fields of achievement including the Aga Khan, L. Ron Hubbard, Robert Maxwell, The Chief Rabbi, Frank Bruno, George Best, Sebastian Coe, and Stefan Edberg. Author of numerous articles for legal periodicals. Books include Butterworths 'The Sex Discrimination Act 1976'. Regularly addresses

conferences, including Sweet and Maxwell Conference on Judicial Review (Chairman 1990-91 and 1993-94), Singapore Law Academy (1992), Hong Kong Bar Association (1994), FCO-arranged 'Human Rights in the UK' (for Mayor of Moscow (1991) and ALBA 'Judicial Review 2001 - a Prophetic Odyssey' (1994). Consultant Editor, *Environmental Judicial Review Bulletin* and *Commercial Judicial Review Bulletin*.

Prof. Membership: COMBAR, Administrative Law Bar Association (First Chairman, now Emeritus Chairman and Vice-President), Planning and Environment Bar Association, Environmental Law Foundation (Advisory Council).

Career: Called to the Bar 1967. Legal Correspondent for *New Society* 1971-79 and *Observer* 1979-81. Took silk 1981. Appointed Recorder of the Crown Court 1984. Master of the Bench, Grays Inn 1988. Deputy High Court Judge (QBD) 1989. Nominated to sit in Divisional Court of QBD 1992. Joint Head of Chambers since 1993. Judge of the Court of Appeal of Guernsey and Jersey 1995. President-Elect Trinity College, Oxford 1996.

Personal: Born 18th April 1942. Educated at Dragon School, Oxford 1950-54, Eton College 1954-60 (King's Scholar and Captain of School 1960) and Magdalen College, Oxford 1960-65 (BA History Class 1, 1963: Jurisprudence BA 1965, MA 1967). Moved motion which procured admission of women to full membership of the Oxford Union 1964. Lecturer in law, Trinity College, Oxford 1965-66. Completed 5 marathons, including London marathon (twice). Honorary member of International Athletics Club. Member of Gridiron (Oxford), Vincents (Oxford) and Reform Club (on Political Committee). Lives in London and Oxford.

Blake QC, Nicholas
See under Immigration.

Bleasdale, Paul
5 Fountain Court (Anthony Barker QC), Birmingham (0121) 606 0500. Called 1978.

Booth QC, Cherie
4-5 Gray's Inn Square (Miss Elizabeth Appleby QC, The Hon. Michael Beloff QC), London (0171) 404 5252.

Specialisation: Specialist in public and administrative law. Also specialises in all aspects of employment law, including collective action, trade union rights and sex and race discrimination. Interesting public law cases include R v. University Funding Council ex parte The Institute of Dental Surgery [1994], and Kingsbury v. Northants County Council [1993], E v. Dorset County Council and Christmas v. Hampshire County Council [1995], in the education field; R v. Yorkshire Regional Health Authority ex parte Suri [1994], and R v. Joint Committee on Higher

Education ex parte Goldstein [1993], in the medical field. Notable employment law cases include Department of Transport v. Gallacher [1994], Fitzpatrick v. British Railways Board (1992) concerning trade union rights and Meade-Hill v. British Council (1995) sex discrimination. Occasional lecturer on employment and administrative law matters.

Prof. Membership: Employment Law Bar Association, Administrative Law Bar Association, COMBAR, Industrial Law Society.

Career: Called to the Bar 1976. Tenant at New Court Chambers 1977-91, before joining present chambers in 1991. Former Chair of Bar Information Technology Committee. Current Vice Chair (IT) of Bar Services and Information Technology Committee. Took Silk in 1995.

Personal: Educated at Seafield Grammar School 1965-72, and at the London School of Economics (LL.B) 1972-75. Former Parliamentary candidate for Thanet North in 1983. School governor, governor of LSE. Leisure pursuits include keep fit, theatre, reading and her children. Born 23rd September 1954. Lives in Islington.

Bowen, Nicholas
29 Bedford Row Chambers (Evan Stone QC), London (0171) 831 2626. Called 1984.

Bradley, Anthony
Cloisters (David Turner-Samuels QC), London (0171) 583 0303.

Specialisation: Administrative and constitutional law, representing applicants for judicial review and public authorities, and advising on constitutional issues. Important cases include M v. Home Office [1994] and R v. Devon County Council ex p. Baker [1995]. Publications include 'Wade & Bradley, Constitutional and Administrative Law' (11th ed. 1993 - with K.D. Ewing). Consultant on administrative law to the Commonwealth Secretariat.

Prof. Membership: Administrative Law Bar Association, Education Law Association.

Career: Formerly a solicitor (1960-89). Fellow of Trinity Hall, Cambridge 1960-68. Professor of Constitutional Law, University of Edinburgh 1968-89. Called to the Bar in 1989.

Personal: Educated at Emmanuel College, Cambridge 1954-58. Hon LLD, Staffordshire University (1993).

Brown, Paul
4-5 Gray's Inn Square (Miss Elizabeth Appleby QC, The Hon. Michael Beloff QC), London (0171) 404 5252.

Caws QC, Genevra
4-5 Gray's Inn Square (Miss Elizabeth Appleby QC, The Hon. Michael Beloff QC), London (0171) 404 5252. Called 1970, took silk 1991.

Corner, Timothy
See under Planning and Local Government.

De Mello, Rambert
6 King's Bench Walk (Sibghat Kadri QC), London (0171) 353 4931. Called 1983.

Dove, Ian
5 Fountain Court (Anthony Barker QC), Birmingham (0121) 606 0500. Called 1986.

Drabble QC, Richard
4 Breams Buildings (Christopher Lockhart-Mummery QC), London (0171) 430 1221. Called 1975, took silk 1995.

Edis, Andrew
14 Castle St (Adrian Smith), Liverpool (0151) 236 4421. Called 1980.

Elias QC, Patrick
See under Employment.

Fitzgerald QC, Edward
Doughty Street Chambers (Geoffrey Robertson QC), London (0171) 404 1313. Called 1978, took silk 1995. Specialises in public law, criminal law and mental health and European human rights law. Born 1953.

Fordham, Michael
2 Hare Court (C.W.G. Ross-Munro QC), London (0171) 583 1770.

Specialisation: Specialist in public and administrative law, with a particular interest in judicial review. Practice also covers environmental law and sports law. Author of 'Judicial Review Handbook' and 'Judicial Review Update'. Lectures in administrative law at Hertford College, Oxford. Called to the Bar 1990.

Personal: Educated at Spalding Grammar School, Hertford College, Oxford (BA & BCL), and University of Virginia (LL.M). Oxford Hockey Blue (1986). Awarded Karmel, Mould and Prince of Wales Scholarships at Gray's Inn.

Gallivan, Terence
6 King's Bench Walk (Sibghat Kadri QC), London (0171) 353 4931.

Giffin, Nigel
11 King's Bench Walk (Lord Irvine of Lairg QC), London (0171) 583 0610.

Specialisation: Specialises principally in most aspects of public and administrative law including education, local authority powers, local government finance, housing, elections, competitive tendering and commercial judicial review. Also undertakes advisory work in all these fields.
Practice also covers employment law, especially public sector work, and general commercial law. Employment work includes transfer of undertakings, dismissals, dis-

crimination and restrictive covenants. Commercial work includes general contract, professional negligence and CMR (carriage by road). Important cases include Hazell v. Hammersmith & Fulham LBC (House of Lords; local authority interest rate swaps); Palmer v. A.B.P. (House of Lords; personal contracts and union membership); R v. A.B.P. ex parte Plymouth CC (judicial review of animal exports); R v. Institute of Chartered Accountants ex parte Brindle (Court of Appeal; stay of disciplinary proceedings pending litigation); R v. Warwickshire CC ex parte Collymore (discretionary awards, judicial review). Contributor to the Administrative Law title of 'Halsbury's Laws of England'; co-author of several editions of 'Tolley's Employment Handbook'.

Prof. Membership: Administrative Law Bar Association; Education Law Association; Planning and Environment Bar Association.

Career: Called to the Bar 1986. Joined present chambers 1987.

Personal: Educated at Worcester College, Oxford (BA Hons 1st class) 1982-1985. Born 1963.

Gordon QC, Richard
39 Essex Street (Colin Mackay QC), London (0171) 583 1111. Called 1972, took silk 1994. Public and administrative law specialist practising in all areas of judicial review. Born 26.11.1948.

Goudie QC, James
See under Employment.

Griffiths QC, W. Robert
4-5 Gray's Inn Square (Miss Elizabeth Appleby QC, The Hon. Michael Beloff QC), London (0171) 404 5252.

Specialisation: Has an inter-disciplinary practice with an emphasis on public law. Main areas of practice are public and employment law, planning and commercial matters. Acted in numerous appellate cases for Government Departments as Junior Counsel to the Crown, inter alia Delaney v. Staples and Mclaren v. The Home Office (civil service contracts). Junior Counsel for the Home Office in the Strangeways Inquiry. Extensive commercial and planning practice as a leader.

Prof. Membership: Administrative Law Bar Association, COMBAR, Planning and Environment Bar Association.

Career: Called to the Bar 1974. Junior Counsel to the Crown (common law) 1989-93. Took Silk 1993.

Personal: Educated at Haverfordwest Grammar School and St Edmund Hall, Oxford. Leisure pursuits include reading, collecting modern first editions, and cricket. Born 24th September 1948.

Hamlin, Patrick
22 Old Buildings (John Samuels QC), London (0171) 831 0222.

Specialisation: Principal area of practice is

local government law, particularly in the fields of public health/environmental protection matters, licensing, planning and listed buildings and judicial review. Cases include Orchard Leigh Properties (fixtures and fittings in listed buildings), The Time Life Building and Eaves v. Mendip B.C. (Glastonbury Festival licensing). Also handles professional negligence and general commercial work. Wide range of local authority clients.

Prof. Membership: Administrative Law Bar Association.

Career: Called to the Bar 1970. Appointed Recorder 1994.

Personal: Educated at Birkenhead School and Inns of Court School of Law (McCaskie Scholarship). Assistant Parliamentary Boundary Commissioner. Leisure pursuits include skiing, listed buildings and English furniture. Born 4th August 1947. Lives in London.

Herberg, Javan
2 Hare Court (C.W.G. Ross-Munro QC), London (0171) 583 1770. Called 1992.

Hicks QC, William
1 Serjeants' Inn (Lionel Read QC), London (0171) 583 1355. Called 1975, took silk 1995. Principal areas of practice are local government law and parliamentary law. Born 11.6.1951.

Hobson, John
4-5 Gray's Inn Square (Miss Elizabeth Appleby QC, The Hon. Michael Beloff QC), London (0171) 404 5252.

Holgate, David
4 Breams Buildings (Christopher Lockhart-Mummery QC), London (0171) 430 1221. Called 1978.

Holt, John
East Anglian Chambers (John Holt), Norwich (01603) 617351. Called 1970.

Howell QC, John
4 Breams Buildings (Christopher Lockhart-Mummery QC), London (0171) 430 1221. Called 1979, took silk 1993.

Huskinson, Nicholas
See under Parliamentary.

Irvine of Lairg QC,
See under Commercial Law.

Jay, Robert
See under Immigration.

Katkowski, Christopher
See under Planning and Local Government.

Kentridge QC, Sydney
See under Commercial Law.

Kingston QC, Martin
5 Fountain Court (Anthony Barker QC), Birmingham (0121) 606 0500. Called 1972, took silk 1992.

Lang, Beverley
2 Hare Court (C.W.G. Ross-Munro QC), London (0171) 583 1770.

Specialisation: Public law, civil liberties, employment and discrimination law. Interesting cases include DPP v. Hutchinson (Greenham Common Byelaws held unlawful by the House of Lords.); Lloyd v. McMahon (surcharged Liverpool Labour Councillors); Thomas v. NUM (right of striking miners to picket); Halford v. Sharples (acted for Assistant Chief Constable Alison Halford in her sex discrimination claim against Merseyside Police); Christmas v. Hampshire County Council (duty of care owed by teachers to children with special education needs). Publications include articles for the *Modern Law Review*, *Industrial Law Journal* and *Legal Action*.

Career: Called to the Bar 1978. Appointed part-time chairman of Industrial Tribunal 1995. Former lecturer in law at the University of East Anglia.

Personal: Born 13th October 1955.

Lord Lester QC,
2 Hare Court (C.W.G. Ross-Munro QC), London (0171) 583 1770. Called 1963, took silk 1975. Specialist in public and administrative law, employment law, civil liberties, media, commercial and EC law. Born 3.7.1936.

Lewis, Clive
4-5 Gray's Inn Square (Miss Elizabeth Appleby QC, The Hon. Michael Beloff QC), London (0171) 404 5252. Called 1987. Principal areas of practice are public law, EC law, education and local government. Born 13.6.1960.

Lieven, Nathalie
See under Parliamentary.

Macpherson, Mary
2 Mitre Court Buildings (Michael FitzGerald QC), London (0171) 583 1380.

Specialisation: Practice encompasses public and administrative law, planning, local government, education, highways, rating and council tax. Involved in Public Inquiries concerning planning, roads and Unitary Development Plans and at the High Court in planning and judicial review cases. Parliamentary law work includes Jubilee Line Extension (Southwark LBC) 1991 and Crossrail (Residents' Association of Mayfair) 1994. Acted for Secretary of State for the Environment in the High Court. Promoted Unitary Development Plans for Solihull MBC, Ealing LBC and Hillingdon LBC.

Editor of 'Ryde on Rating', 'Butterworths Forms and Precedents (Rating and Council Tax)' and 'Atkins Court Forms' (Rating, Council Tax, Environmental Law).

Prof. Membership: Planning and Environment Bar Association (Committee Member).

Career: Former journalist specialising in education and town and country planning. Worked on *Scottish Daily Express*, *Yorkshire Post*, *N.U.T. Journal*, *Times Educational Supplement* and *London Evening Standard*. Investigator, Local Government Ombudsman 1978-82. Called to the Bar 1982 and joined current chambers 1987.

Personal: Educated at St Mary's School, Gerrards Cross 1949-53; Ancaster House School, Bexhill 1953-60; University of Grenoble, France (Diplome d'Etudes Francaises) 1960-61; and University of Edinburgh (MA) (Hons) 1966. Attended City University 1982-83 (Diploma in Law) and CLE Bar Finals 1983-84. Leisure pursuits include riding, skiing, theatre and cinema. Born 2nd August 1942. Lives in London.

McCarthy, Roger
22 Old Buildings (John Samuels QC), London (0171) 831 0222.

Specialisation: Principal area of practice is public law, with main emphasis on local authority, health authority/ trust functions, tribunals and enquiries. Other main area of practice encompasses all aspects of work under the Children Act. Clients include private individuals, commercial bodies, local authorities, health authorities and health trusts.

Prof. Membership: Administrative Law Bar Association, Family Law Bar Association.

Career: Called to the Bar 1975; founder member *22 Old Buildings* in 1987.

Personal: Educated at Wimbledon College 1961-69 and Kingston Polytechnic 1971-74. Born 4th July 1951. Lives in London.

McManus, Richard
4-5 Gray's Inn Square (Miss Elizabeth Appleby QC, The Hon. Michael Beloff QC), London (0171) 404 5252. Called 1982. Principal area of practice is public law and judicial review. Also handles general commercial work. Born 15.9.58.

Millar, Gavin
See under Employment.

Morrow, Graham
See under Commercial Law.

Moses QC, Alan
4-5 Gray's Inn Square (Miss Elizabeth Appleby QC, The Hon. Michael Beloff QC), London (0171) 404 5252. Called 1968, took silk 1990.

Neill QC, Patrick
One Hare Court (Sir Patrick Neill QC, Richard Southwell QC), London (0171) 353 3171. Called 1951, took silk 1966.

Newman QC, Alan
Cloisters (David Turner-Samuels QC), London (0171) 583 0303.

Specialisation: Main areas of practice are commercial law, general international law (including EC law), constitutional and administrative law, defamation. Recent interesting commercial cases include Brinks Limited v. Trustee in Bankruptcy of Noye & others (1995) (an extensive commercial action involving tracing the proceeds of the Brink's Mat robbery). References before the European Court of Justice include Reading BC v. Payless DIY Limited (1993) 1 CMLR 426 (legality of Sunday trading legislation), and Overseas Union Insurance Limited v. New Hampshire Company (1992) QB 434 (Reinsurance. Article 21 of the Brussels Convention). Recent constitutional and administrative cases include R v. Horseferry Magistrates' Court ex parte Bennet (1994) 1 AC 42 (House of Lords. Circumvention of proper extradition procedure into UK. Abuse of process jurisdiction). Defamation cases include Derbyshire County Council v. Times Newspapers Limited (1992) QB 770 (Court of Appeal. Impact of European Convention on Human Rights on defamation law. Right of local authority to sue in libel).

Prof. Membership: Administrative Law Bar Association; Bar European Group; International Bar Association.

Career: Called to the Bar 1968. Attorney-at-law, State Bar of California, USA 1976. Took Silk 1989. Appointed Recorder 1991.

Personal: Educated at City of London School and Trinity Hall, Cambridge MA(Law 1st Class Hons) and LL.B(International law). Foundation Scholar (Trinity Hall) and Astbury Law Scholar (Middle Temple). Fluent in French with a working knowledge of Spanish. Leisure pursuits include Scuba diving, cinema, theatre, food and wine. Born 30th April 1946.

Ouseley QC, Duncan
4-5 Gray's Inn Square (Miss Elizabeth Appleby QC, The Hon. Michael Beloff QC), London (0171) 404 5252. Called 1973, took silk 1992.

Paines, Nicholas
See under European Community Law.

Pannick QC, David
2 Hare Court (C.W.G. Ross-Munro QC), London (0171) 583 1770. Called 1979, took silk 1992. Specialist in administrative and public law, civil liberties, employment law, EC law, immigration, discrimination and media law. Fellow of All Souls College, Oxford. Columnist for *The Times* and member of the editorial board of *Public Law*.

Pleming QC, Nigel
See under Immigration.

Porten QC, Anthony
See under Planning and Local Government.

Pugh, Charles
See under Health & Safety Law.

Qureshi, Khawar M.
One Hare Court (Sir Patrick Neill QC, Richard Southwell QC), London (0171) 353 3171. Called 1990.

Read QC, Lionel
See under Environmental.

Richards, Stephen
Four Raymond Buildings (Jeremy Lever QC), London (0171) 405 7211. Called 1975.

Robertson QC, Geoffrey
Doughty Street Chambers (Geoffrey Robertson QC), London (0171) 404 1313. Called 1973, took silk 1988.

Roots QC, Guy
See under Planning and Local Government.

Rose, Dinah
See under Employment.

Roth, Peter M.
Four Raymond Buildings (Jeremy Lever QC), London (0171) 405 7211. Fax: (0171) 405 2084. LDE: 257.

Specialisation: Public law (e.g. R v. Chief Constable of Sussex ex p. International Trader's Ferry); EC law and UK competition law (e.g. Associated Dairies v. Baines); Commercial litigation and ADR; Professional negligence (e.g. Hemmens v. Wilson Browne).

Career: Publications: Contributing Editor, 'Bellamy & Child's Common Market Law of Competition' (4th ed.); General Editor (5th ed.).

Personal: MA (Oxon), LL.M. Called to the Bar, 1976. Harmsworth Scholar, Middle Temple. Visiting Associate Professor, Univ. of Pennsylvania Law School, 1987.

Samuels QC, John
22 Old Buildings (John Samuels QC), London (0171) 831 0222.

Specialisation: Principal area of practice is public and administrative law. Has extensive experience in Crown Office work in a wide variety of cases, many in the House of Lords. Involved in Sunday Trading litigation of all levels, 1982-94, leading to change in law with Sunday Trading Act 1994. Acted in Ronan Point case (collapsed tower block) and in Calveley v. Chief Constable of Liverpool [1989] (availability of judicial review and consequential damages claim); Smoker v. LFCDA [1991] (deductibility of pension benefits) and Mendip BC v. B&Q (cross undertakings in damages). Clients include London Fire Brigade and many County Councils, Metropolitan authorities, London Boroughs and district councils. Other main area of practice is medico-legal work including catastrophic personal injury claims, plaintiff medical negligence claims and other professional negligence cases with medical components. Also handles child care cases. Recent cases include Re W (A minor) [1993] (medical treatment for anorexic) and Re J (a minor) [1990] (child abduction). Author of Action Pack (Counsel's Guide to Chambers Administration), and contributor to 'Halsbury's Laws of England' (Pleading). Speaker at various legal conferences.

Prof. Membership: South Eastern Circuit, Administrative Law Bar Association, Professional Negligence Bar Association, Family Law Bar Association.

Career: Called to the Bar 1964. Took Silk 1981. Appointed Deputy High Court Judge (1983) and Recorder (1985). Founder of current chambers in 1987 (and its Head). Bencher, Lincoln's Inn since 1990.

Personal: Educated at Charterhouse (1954-59), and Queens' College, Cambridge (1960-63). Trustee, Richmond Parish Lands Charity. Leisure pursuits include travel, Cornwall and the acquisition, conservation and restoration of antiques. Born 15th August 1940. Lives in Richmond, Surrey.

Scrivener QC, Anthony
2-3 Gray's Inn Square (Anthony Scrivener QC), London (0171) 242 4986. Called 1958, took silk 1975.

Shaw, Mark
2 Hare Court (C.W.G. Ross-Munro QC), London (0171) 583 1770.

Specialisation: Principal area of practice is administrative/public law, with an emphasis on judicial review, immigration and nationality, monopolies and mergers commission, regulatory/disciplinary organisations, prisons, social security, health and social services. Also handles local government, human rights and EC law. Involved in numerous reported cases in the High Court and above: see especially the Immigration Appeal Reports. Publications include 'Halsbury's Laws of England' (4th Edn) volume on Immigration and Nationality, and 'The Primary Purpose Rule: A Rule With No Purpose' (co-author, Justice, 1993).

Prof. Membership: Administrative Law Bar Association (Committee Member), Immigration Law Practitioners Association, Justice.

Career: Member of Borough Solicitor's Department, Bournemouth Borough Council 1985-86. Stagiaire at the European Parliament (Human Rights Unit) 1986. Called to the Bar 1987 and joined current chambers in 1988. Member of Crown's Supplementary Panel of Counsel (Common Law) 1992.

Personal: Educated at Durham University (BA) and Cambridge University (LL.M). Born 6th June 1962.

Singh, Rabinder
4-5 Gray's Inn Square (Miss Elizabeth Appleby QC, The Hon. Michael Beloff

QC), London (0171) 404 5252. Called 1989. Principal areas of practice are public law, employment law and human rights. Born 6.3.1964.

Steel QC, John
See under Planning and Local Government.

Stephenson, Geoffrey
See under Planning and Local Government.

Straker, Timothy
2-3 Gray's Inn Square (Anthony Scrivener QC), London (0171) 242 4986.

Specialisation: Principal area of practice is local government, public law and town and country planning work. Has acted in many leading public law cases concerning, inter alia, housing and housing benefits, Sunday trading, caravan sites and 'new age travellers' free speech, professional advertising, discrimination, professional conduct and Privy Council Appeals. Represented the returning officer in the first challenge to a European election result. Acts for many local authorities and regulatory bodies.

Prof. Membership: Attorney-General's Supplementary Panel of Treasury Counsel (dealing with planning cases), Administrative Law Bar Association, Planning and Environment Bar Association, Crown Office Users' Committee.

Career: Called to the Bar 1977. Joined *2/3 Gray's Inn Square* 1978.

Personal: Educated at Malvern College and Downing College, Cambridge (1st Class Hons). Senior Harris Scholar, Downing College Prize for Law, Holt Scholar of Gray's Inn, awarded Lord Justice Holker Senior Award. Born 25th May 1955.

Strauss QC, Nicholas
See under Banking.

Sullivan QC, Jeremy
See under Planning and Local Government.

Supperstone QC, Michael Alan
See under Employment.

Tabachnik QC, Eldred
See under Employment.

Thorold, Oliver
Doughty Street Chambers (Geoffrey Robertson QC), London (0171) 404 1313. Called 1971. Specialist in medical negligence and mental health law. Born 1945.

Wade QC, William
4-5 Gray's Inn Square (Miss Elizabeth Appleby QC, The Hon. Michael Beloff QC), London (0171) 404 5252. Called 1946, took silk 1968.

Wilkie QC, Alan Fraser
See under Employment.

Wolfe, David
4-5 Gray's Inn Square (Miss Elizabeth Appleby QC, The Hon. Michael Beloff QC), London (0171) 404 5252.

REVENUE

MANY general chancery sets include barristers able to advise on tax elements of trusts and other chancery work. These sets can be found in the chancery section.

Solicitors have increased the amount of advice they provide in this field. However, as a result of the introduction of Direct Professional Access, the role of counsel has not greatly diminished. Accountants, among others, instruct barristers direct without dealing first with a solicitor.

The leading set in this area is **Gray's Inn Chambers**. Members of chambers appear before Commissioners and VAT tribunals, in the Supreme Court, the House of Lords, the Privy Council, and the European Court of Justice. However, the bulk of their work is advisory, assisting taxpayers in disputes with the Inland Revenue or Customs, and advising clients on arranging their business and personal tax affairs. *Andrew Park QC* is the leading figure in this area. He specialises in particular in contentious work, usually representing the taxpayer, although he does appear from time to time for the Inland Revenue. *David Goldberg QC* has been highly recommended for both contentious and non-contentious work in this sector. He is also co-author of 'The Law of Partnership Taxation'.

Michael Flesch QC also has an excellent reputation across the whole range of this field. In recent years, he has worked chiefly on large corporate transactions. He is Chairman of the Revenue Bar Association, and was a part-time lecturer in Revenue Law at University College London for almost twenty years. *David Goy QC* is highly regarded for his broad

practice in this area and has particular expertise in relation to the tax aspects of real property transactions. He acted in 'Lubbock Pine v Customs' (VAT on surrenders of tenancies); 'Lasmo (TNS) Ltd v IRC' (oil taxation); and 'IRC v Willoughby' (regarding taxation under s. 739 ICTA). He and *John Walters* are joint authors of 'VAT on Property' and consultant editor of 'Butterworths Tax Planning'.

Among the juniors in chambers *Felicity Cullen* has been recommended. She deals primarily with commercial tax, but is also able to offer an expertise in relation to personal taxation. She is a member of the BTR Case Note Panel and of the Law Society's Revenue Law Subcommittee on Income Tax.

Pump Court Tax Chambers enjoy an excellent reputation as a specialist set in this sector. *Andrew Thornhill QC* has been very highly recommended for his work in this area. *David Milne QC* is also highly regarded and has a particular expertise in the contentious aspects of tax law. *Stephen*

Allcock QC is highly thought of. Among the juniors in chambers *Kevin Prosser* has been very highly recommended. *Giles Goodfellow* and *Janek Mathews* are also well known.

At **11 New Square** *John Gardiner QC* has been highly recommended. He appeared in 'Pattison v Marine Midland', 'International Commercial Bank v Willingate' and the two 'Woolwich' cases. *Peter Trevett QC* is well known for his expertise in this sector. *Jonathan Peacock* is a well known junior who advises on all aspects of UK tax law, including VAT, Customs and Excise duties and EU levies administered by HM Customs and Excise. He also appeared in the Woolwich Building Society litigation, and is a regular contributor to 'The Tax Journal'.

At **3 Temple Gardens** *Richard Bramwell QC, Alun James* and *Michael Sherry* have been recommended. *Barry McCutcheon* and *Patrick Soares* at **8 Gray's Inn Square** are well regarded.

At **24 Old Buildings** *Rex Bretton QC* has a very good reputation in this field. *Robert Venables QC* and *Stephen Brandon* are also recommended.

Graham Aaronson QC at **1 Essex Court** has been very highly recommended for his work in commercial taxation, having particular expertise in structured finance, reorganisations, insurance companies, oil taxation, capital allowances and transfer pricing. He appeared in 'Ellis v BP Oil' and 'BMI (No.3) v Mellvish'.

LEADERS IN REVENUE

Aaronson QC, Graham
1 Essex Court (Anthony Grabiner QC), London (0171) 583 2000.

Specialisation: Principal area of practice is commercial taxation, covering all aspects, in particular structured finance, corporate reorganisations, insurance taxation, oil taxation, capital allowances and transfer pricing. Acted in Scorer v. Olin Energy Systems, Elliss v. BP Oil and BMI (NO. 3) v. Melluish. Clients include major companies, city solicitors and the 'Big 6' accountancy firms.

Prof. Membership: Revenue Bar Association, Institute of Fiscal Studies (Member of Executive Committee). Chairman, Tax Law Review Committee since 1994. Bencher of Middle Temple since 1992.

Career: Called to the Bar 1966 and joined 4 Pump Court 1968-73. Managing Director of Worldwide Plastics Development Ltd 1973-77. Tenant at Queen Elizabeth Building 1978-1991. Took Silk 1982. Joined current Chambers in 1991. Director Bridgend Group Plc 1973-92. Advisor on tax reform to Israel Treasury 1986-89.

Personal: Educated at City of London School and Trinity Hall, Cambridge 1963-66 (Waraker Law Scholar). Founder, Standford Grange Rehabilitation Centre for Offenders. Born 31st December 1944. Lives in Stanmore, Middlesex.

Allcock QC, Stephen J.A.
Pump Court Tax Chambers (Andrew Thornhill QC), London (0171) 414 8080. Called 1975, took silk 1993. Principal area of practice is Revenue law.

Barlow, Francis
See under Chancery.

Bramwell QC, Richard
3 Temple Gardens (David Braham QC), London (0171) 353 7884.

Specialisation: Principal areas of practice are corporate and personal tax planning and tax disputes. Author of 'Taxation of Companies and Company Reconstructions' (6th

Edition, 1994).

Career: Called to the Bar 1967 and joined current chambers in 1969. Took silk in 1989.

Brandon, Stephen
24 Old Buildings (M.E.P. Jump), London (0171) 242 2744.

Brennan, Timothy
Devereux Chambers (Peter Weitzman QC), London (0171) 353 7534. Called 1981. Called 1981. Practises principally public and Revenue law, employment, discrimination and professional negligence. Born 1958.

Bretten QC, Rex
24 Old Buildings (M.E.P. Jump), London (0171) 242 2744. Called 1965, took silk 1980.

Cullen, Felicity
Gray's Inn Chambers (Milton Grundy), London (0171) 242 2642.

Flesch QC, Michael
Gray's Inn Chambers (Milton Grundy), London (0171) 242 2642.

Specialisation: Advises on all aspects of revenue law, and appears before the Commissioners, High Court, Court of Appeal, House of Lords and Privy Council in revenue cases. Regular lecturer on tax-related topics.

Prof. Membership: Revenue Bar Association, Bar Council.

Career: Called to the Bar 1963. Teaching Fellow, University of Chicago 1963-64. Part-time lecturer in Revenue law, University College London 1964-82. Joined present chambers 1965. Took Silk 1983.

Personal: Educated at Gordonstoun School 1953-58 and University College, London 1959-62 (LL.B Class 1, Hons). Governor of Gordonstoun School since 1976. Leisure pursuits include all forms of sport. Keen Arsenal and Middlesex supporter, member of MCC, Twickenham and Wimbledon debenture holder. Born 11th March 1940. Lives in London.

Gardiner QC, John
11 New Square (John Gardiner QC), London (0171) 242 4017.

Specialisation: Revenue law. Involved in the two Woolwich cases, Pattison v. Marine Midland, Ensign Tankers (Leasing) v. Stokes and International Commercial Bank v. Willingale.

Prof. Membership: Revenue Bar Association.

Career: Called to the Bar 1968 and joined *11 New Square* in 1970. Took Silk 1982.

Personal: Educated at Bancroft's School, Woodford 1957-63 and Fitzwilliam College, Cambridge 1964-68 (LL.M, M.A.) Born 28th February 1946. Lives in London.

Goldberg QC, David
Gray's Inn Chambers (Milton Grundy), London (0171) 242 2642.

Specialisation: Practice concentrates on revenue law and commercial litigation with a tax or financial aspect. Clients include solicitors, accountants and corporations. Co-author of ' Introduction to Company Law' (1971, 3rd Edn 1987) and ' The Law of Partnership Taxation' (1976, 2nd Edn 1979). Author of various articles and notes for legal periodicals, mainly concerning tax and company law.

Prof. Membership: Revenue Bar Association, Chancery Bar Association.

Career: Called to the Bar and joined current chambers in 1971. Took Silk 1987.

Personal: Educated at Plymouth college and London School of Economics 1966-70 (LL.B, LL.M). Chairman of Trustees of the Skills Workshop for Anatomical Techniques. Leisure pursuits include reading, writing letters and thinking. Born 12th August 1947. Lives in London.

Goodfellow, Giles W.J.
Pump Court Tax Chambers (Andrew Thornhill QC), London (0171) 414 8080.

Goy QC, David

Gray's Inn Chambers (Milton Grundy),
London (0171) 242 2642.

Specialisation: Specialist in all aspects of
revenue law. Has particular expertise in the
tax aspects of real property transactions, and
in all types of tax litigation. Important cases
include Lubbock Fine v. H.M. Customs &
Excise [1994] (VAT on the surrender of tenancies); LASMO (TNS) Ltd v. IRC [1994] (oil
taxation); IRC v Willoughby [1995] (taxation
under s.739 ICTA). Publications include
'VAT on Property' (co-author) (Sweet &
Maxwell 2nd Edition 1993), and Butterworths Tax Planning (consultant editor).
Regular speaker on the subject of revenue
law.

Prof. Membership: Revenue Bar Association.

Career: Called to the Bar 1973. Joined present chambers 1974. Took Silk 1991.

Personal: Educated at Haberdashers' Askes
School and King's College, London. Born
11th May 1949. Lives in Guildford.

Grundy, Milton

Gray's Inn Chambers (Milton Grundy),
London (0171) 242 2642.

Specialisation: Principal area of practice is
international tax planning with particular ref-
erence to inward investment into and outward
investment from the United Kingdom.
Author of 'Tax Havens: Offshore Business
Centre' (Sweet & Maxwell 6th Ed, 1993) and
co-author of 'Asset Protection Trusts' (Key
Haven Publications, 2nd Ed 1993). Editor of
'The Offshore Financial Centre Report
(Campden Publishing, 4th Ed 1995).

Prof. Membership: President International
Tax Planning Association, Institute of Taxation.

Career: Called to the Bar 1954. Began
Gray's Inn Chambers in 1965.

Personal: Educated at Sedbergh School
1940-44 and Caius College, Cambridge
1948-51. Chairman, Warwick Arts Trust.
Chairman, International Management Trust.
Author of 'Venice an Anthology Guide' and
co-author of 'Mediterranean Vernacular'.
Born 13th June 1926. Lives in London.

Herbert QC, Mark

5 Stone Buildings (Henry Harrod), London (0171) 242 6201.

Specialisation: Principal area of practice is
general chancery work, including trusts, capital taxation, taxation of trusts, probate, family
provision, charities and off-shore trusts. Also
handles pensions work, particularly advice
and litigation on occupational pensions for
trustees, employers and members. Important
cases include Re Rank's Settlement Trust
[1979]; Re Billson's Settlement Trusts
[1984]; Mettoy Pension Trustees v. Evans
[1990]; Re Christy Hunt Pension Fund
[1991]; Fitzwilliam v. IRC [1993]. Co-Editor
of 'Whiteman and Wheatcroft on Capital
Gains Tax' and 'Whiteman on Capital Gains
Tax'. Other publications include 'The Drafting

and Variation of Wills'.

Prof. Membership: Chancery Bar Association; Revenue Bar Association; Association
of Pension Lawyers.

Career: Called to the Bar 1974. Tenant at 17
Old Buildings 1975-1977 before joining
Queen Elizabeth Building in 1977. At present
chambers since 1991.
Took Silk 1995.

Personal: Educated at Lancing College
1962-1966 and King's College, London
1967-1970. Born 12th November 1948.
Lives in London

Hitchmough, Andrew

**Pump Court Tax Chambers (Andrew
Thornhill QC),** London (0171) 414 8080.

James, Alun

3 Temple Gardens (David Braham QC),
London (0171) 353 7884.

Specialisation: Principal area of practice
covers tax and VAT. Business tax includes
corporate work; advice for owner-managed
businesses and employee-related issues, especially share and incentive schemes and
employee benefit trusts. Also handles personal tax matters for private clients.
Co-author of 'Taxation of Companies and
Company Reconstructions' (Sweet & Maxwell, 6th Ed 1994).

Prof. Membership: Revenue Bar Association.

Career: Called to the Bar 1986 and joined 3
Temple Gardens 1988.

Personal: Scholar of St. John's College, Ox-
ford (BA, Hons 1st Class, Jurisprudence,
BCL). Born 15th January 1964. Lives in
Coventry.

Kessler, James

24 Old Buildings (M.E.P. Jump), London (0171) 242 2744.

Specialisation: Revenue law, more particularly CGT, IHT, and what is loosely described
as 'private client' work; offshore trusts; also
taxation of charities.
Has a particular fondness for trust drafting
(having written the leading textbook on the
subject).

Career: Called to the bar 1984.

Mathews, Janek

**Pump Court Tax Chambers (Andrew
Thornhill QC),** London (0171) 414 8080.

McCutcheon, Barry

8 Gray's Inn Square (Patrick C. Soares),
London (0171) 242 3529. Called 1975. Spe-
cialist in all aspects of revenue law. Author of
'McCutcheon on Inheritance Tax'.

Meadway, Susannah

**8 Stone Buildings (Michael Mark,
Francis Barlow),** London (0171) 242
5002.

Milne QC, David C.

**Pump Court Tax Chambers (Andrew

Thornhill QC),** London (0171) 414 8080.
Called 1970, took silk 1987. Specialist in
revenue law. Born 22.9.1945.

Park QC, Andrew

Gray's Inn Chambers (Milton Grundy),
London (0171) 242 2642. Called 1964, took
silk 1978.

Peacock, Jonathan

11 New Square (John Gardiner QC),
London (0171) 242 4017.

Specialisation: Revenue law. Work encompasses advice on all aspects of UK tax,
including VAT, Customs and Excise duties
and EC levies administered by HM Customs
and Excise; tax litigation in all tribunals (including tax-related aspects of commercial
disputes, judicial review and professional
negligence). Involved in the Woolwich Building Society litigation resulting in the
recovery of over £100 million from the Inland Revenue.

Prof. Membership: Revenue Bar Association, Chancery Bar Association.

Career: Called to the Bar 1987; joined current chambers 1988.

Personal: Educated at King's School, Macclesfield 1975-79, Nunthorpe Grammar
School, York 1979-82 and Corpus Christi
College, Oxford 1983-86 (1st Class Degree
in Jurisprudence). Born 21st April 1964.

Prosser, Kevin J.

**Pump Court Tax Chambers (Andrew
Thornhill QC),** London (0171) 414 8080.

Specialisation: Principal area of practice is
Revenue law, including litigation. Co-author
of Potter and Prosser, 'Tax Appeals' (Sweet
& Maxwell).

Career: Called to the Bar 1982 and joined
present chambers in 1983.

Personal: Was once expelled from Tanzania
for spying.

Sherry, Michael

3 Temple Gardens (David Braham QC),
London (0171) 353 7884.

Specialisation: Revenue law, covering all aspects of direct and indirect taxation for
commercial and substantial private clients.
Co-author 'Whiteman on Income Tax'
(Sweet & Maxwell, 3rd Edn 1988) and
author of 'Tax Planning for Family Company
Shareholders' (Key Haven 1993).

Prof. Membership: Institute of Chartered Accountants, Institute of Taxation, Institute of
Indirect Taxation, Gray's Inn.

Career: Called to the Bar in 1978. With Ernst
& Young 1978-83, then joined 3 Temple Gardens in 1984.

Personal: Scholar of Lincoln College, Oxford 1974-77. Inns of Court School of Law
1977-78. Leisure pursuits include bridge and
croquet. Born 8th May 1956. Lives in
Sissinghurst.

Soares, Patrick C.

8 Gray's Inn Square (Patrick C. Soares), London (0171) 242 3529.

Specialisation: Specialist in all aspects of revenue law, including structuring land transactions for the optimum tax position, value added tax and stamp duty on land transactions, taxation of overseas trusts and international estate and trust planning. Also conducts tax appeals at all levels. Publications include 'Vat Planning for Property Transactions', 'Land and Tax Planning', 'Trusts and Tax Planning', 'Taxation of Non-Resident Trusts', 'Taxation of Land Development', 'Offshore Investment in UK Property' and 'Tax Strategy for Conveyancing Transactions'. Tax editor of the 'Property Law Bulletin' and co-editor of 'Trusts for Europe'.

Prof. Membership: Fellow of the Institute of Taxation.

Career: Called to the Bar 1983. Previously a tax partner in a leading firm of London solicitors, having been admitted a solicitor in 1972.

Personal: Educated at University College, London (MA Taxation).

Stockton, Fay

See under Insolvency.

Thornhill QC, Andrew R.

Pump Court Tax Chambers (Andrew Thornhill QC),   London (0171) 414 8080. Called 1969, took silk 1985. Revenue law specialist. Born 4.8.1943.

Tidmarsh, Christopher

See under Chancery.

Trevett QC, Peter

11 New Square (John Gardiner QC), London (0171) 242 4017. Called 1971, took silk 1992.

Venables QC, Robert

See under Charities.

Walters, John

Gray's Inn Chambers (Milton Grundy), London (0171) 242 2642.

Whiteman QC, Peter

Queen Elizabeth Building (Hollis Whiteman Chambers),   London (0171) 583 5766. Called 1967, took silk 1977.

EDITORIAL POLICY

In this edition, the lists of specialists include profiles of individual practitioners - solicitors and barristers - who have been recommended most frequently to our researchers. Editorial policy is to identify leading practitioners on merit: it is not possible to buy a place in our biographical lists. Inclusion of a profile in this directory is based solely on expertise and reputation.

Enormous effort has been invested by our ten-strong research team (mainly solicitors and barristers) in canvassing recommendations and identifying leaders. We are confident in the overall accuracy of the results. However, mistakes and misjudgements are inevitable, and if readers have any suggestions regarding our listings we should be very pleased to hear from them.

SHIPPING

TRADITIONALLY, work in this field has been carried out by a small group of specialist chambers. This work falls into two categories: 'wet' (collisions and salvage) and 'dry' (sales, charterparties and bills of lading, and trade finance). The majority of these sets undertake all aspects of shipping law. However, some chambers offer a particular strength in 'wet' matters. All of the sets mentioned below have an excellent reputation in this area.

Brick Court Chambers are a well known commercial set with a strong shipping practice. *Richard Aikens QC* enjoys an excellent reputation, as does *Christopher Clarke QC*. *Richard Lord* is a well regarded junior practising in this field.

Essex Court Chambers are a leading commercial maritime set with a large dry shipping practice. *Stewart Boyd QC* is a leading figure in this field. He is co-editor of 'Scrutton on Charterparties and Bills of Lading'. He has appeared in countless cases and arbitrations, both in the English courts and overseas, including 'Bijela', 'The Houda', 'Padre Island' and 'Goodluck'. He regularly lectures and publishes on the subject.

considerable expertise in marine insurance and arbitration. He has recently been involved in arbitrations concerning charterparties, bills of lading, joint ventures and shipbuilding disputes, and liability for pollution clean-up costs.

Well known juniors in this set include *Graham Dunning, Steven Berry* and *Joe Smouha*.

4 Essex Court are a leading commercial set with a strong practice in this area. *David Steel QC* is a leading figure in the field. He has been involved as an advocate or arbitrator in numerous disputes concerning shipbuilding, sale, charterparties, conference lines, collision, salvage, insurance and reinsurance. He is the Wreck Commissioner for England and Wales, a member of the Steering Committee on the new English Arbitration Act, and co-editor of 'Temperley on the Merchant Shipping Acts' and 'Kennedy on Salvage'.

Michael Howard QC acts for shipowners, charterers, insurers, P&I Clubs and salvage companies. He contributed the chapter on frustration of contract and shipping law to 'Frustration and Force Majeure', and is also a member of the Lloyd's Panel of Salvage Arbitrators. *Belinda Bucknall QC* specialises in admiralty work, and especially in drafting marine insurance policies. She also carries out some dry work.

Charles Macdonald QC also specialises in admiralty work. *Jeremy Russell QC* acted in 'The Winson', 'The Marion' and 'The Pulkovo v The Oden'. He has addressed a number of conferences in London and Singapore on shipping matters. *Nigel Teare QC* is also a

LEADING SILKS– LONDON

Steel, David W. *4 Essex Court*

Aikens, Richard *Brick Court Chambers*	**Boyd,** Stewart *Essex Court Chambers*	**Brice,** Geoffrey *Queen Elizabeth Building*
Bucknall, Belinda *4 Essex Court*	**Eder,** Bernard *Essex Court Chambers*	**Flaux,** Julian *Seven King's Bench Walk*
Gross, Peter *20 Essex Street*	**Howard,** Michael N. *4 Essex Court*	**Hunter,** Ian *Essex Court Chambers*
Macdonald, Charles *4 Essex Court*	**Pollock,** Gordon *Essex Court Chambers*	**Rokison,** Kenneth *20 Essex Street*
Siberry, Richard *Essex Court Chambers*	**Stone,** Richard *Queen Elizabeth Building*	**Sumption,** Jonathan *Brick Court Chambers*
Teare, Nigel *4 Essex Court*		

Clarke, Christopher *Brick Court Chambers*	**Collins,** Michael *Essex Court Chambers*	**Cooke,** Jeremy *Seven King's Bench Walk*
Gaisman, Jonathan *Seven King's Bench Walk*	**Gee,** Steven *1 Essex Court*	**Gilman,** Jonathan *Essex Court Chambers*
Hamilton, Adrian *Seven King's Bench Walk*	**Havelock-Allan,** Mark *20 Essex Street*	**Hirst,** Jonathan *Brick Court Chambers*
Johnson, David *20 Essex Street*	**Legh-Jones,** Nicholas *20 Essex Street*	**Milligan,** Iain *20 Essex Street*
Moore-Bick, Martin *20 Essex Street*	**Reeder,** John *Queen Elizabeth Building*	**Russell,** Jeremy *4 Essex Court*
Simon, Peregrine *Brick Court Chambers*	**Thomas,** John *Essex Court Chambers*	**Tomlinson,** Stephen *Seven King's Bench Walk*
Willmer, John *Seven King's Bench Walk*		

Jonathan Gilman QC is the author of 'Arnould on Marine Insurance'. *Gordon Pollock QC* acted in the 'Ikarian Reefer' and 'Glacier Bay'. *Bernard Eder QC* also acted in 'Bijela', as well as 'Texaco Melbourne'. *Richard Siberry QC* deals in all aspects of dry shipping work, and has appeared in cases such as 'The Pina', 'The Varna' and 'The Lefthero'. He also sits as a maritime arbitrator. *Michael Collins QC* has

highly regarded silk in this area.

Simon Rainey and *Luke Parsons* are well respected juniors, as are *Timothy Brenton* (who has appeared in 'The Devotion v The Golden Polydinamos', 'The Coral' and 'The Yamatogawa' and is on the editorial board of 'International Maritime Law'), and *Simon Kverndal* (who is a supporting member of the London Maritime Arbitrators' Association).

20 Essex Street are a leading dry shipping chambers although members carry out some 'wet' work. *Kenneth Rokison QC* is a highly regarded specialist who has been involved in many leading cases and sits as an arbitrator. *Peter Gross QC* acted in 'Glacier Bay'. *Iain Milligan QC* also sits as an arbitrator in maritme matters, as does *Mark Havelock-Allan QC*. *David Johnson QC* is well known for his work in the field.

Among the juniors in chambers *Timothy Young* is co-editor of 'Voyage Charters', and *Nicholas Hamblen* is also well thought of in this area.

Queen Elizabeth Building are very well known as a leading admiralty chambers and enjoy a growing commercial salvage and collision practice. *Richard Stone QC, John Reeder QC* and *Geoffrey Brice QC* are all members of the Lloyd's Panel of Salvage Arbitrators, hearing salvage disputes. The latter is Visiting Professor of Maritime Law at Tulane University in New Orleans. He has, together with *Richard Stone QC*, been involved in the 'Nagasaki Spirit' case concerning the International Salvage Convention of 1989. *Richard Stone* has also appeared in the 'San Nicholas' Collision with the 'Fraternity L' action'.

Lionel Persey, Nigel Meeson and *Jervis Kay* are highly regarded junior barristers in this field. *Nigel Meeson* is a visiting lecturer at University College, London, and has appeared in the dry shipping case 'Partenreederei M/S Heidberg v Grosvenor Grain and Feed Co. Ltd'.

At **Seven King's Bench Walk** *Julian Flaux QC* is a leading silk dealing with all aspects of the field. *John Willmer QC* practises mainly on the admiralty side. *Stephen Tomlinson QC* is a supporting member of the London Maritime Arbitrators' Association, and has appeared in 'Ventouris v Mountain', 'The Italia Express', 'Nereide SPA v Bulk Oil', 'The Laura Prima' and 'Continental Illinois v Alliance Assurance', 'The Captain Panagos DP'. *Jeremy Cooke QC* (also a member of the LMAA) appeared in 'The Marel'. *Adrian Hamilton QC* is well regarded.

Well known juniors in this set include *Alistair Schaff* who advises on marine insurance and international sale of goods contracts. He acted in 'The Maceij Racaj' and 'The Kyriaki'. *Robert Bright*'s lay clients include P&I Clubs, Lloyd's members' agents and insurance companies. *Dominic Kendrick* is also a well regarded junior. He recently appeared in 'Anna H' and 'Nogar Marin'.

LEADING JUNIORS– LONDON

Dunning, Graham *Essex Court Chambers*	**Meeson,** Nigel *Queen Elizabeth Building*	**Parsons,** Luke *4 Essex Court*
Persey, Lionel *Queen Elizabeth Building*	**Rainey,** Simon *4 Essex Court*	**Schaff,** Alistair *Seven King's Bench Walk*
Young, Timothy *20 Essex Street*		
Baker, Andrew *20 Essex Street*	**Berry,** Steven *Essex Court Chambers*	**Blackburn,** Elizabeth *Queen Elizabeth Building*
Brenton, Timothy *4 Essex Court*	**Bright,** Robert *Seven King's Bench Walk*	**Butcher,** Christopher *Seven King's Bench Walk*
Foxton, David *Essex Court Chambers*	**Goldstone,** David *Queen Elizabeth Building*	**Gruder,** Jeffrey *1 Essex Court*
Hamblen, Nicholas *20 Essex Street*	**Jacobs,** Richard *Essex Court Chambers*	**Kay,** Jervis *Queen Elizabeth Building*
Kendrick, Dominic *Seven King's Bench Walk*	**Kverndal,** Simon *4 Essex Court*	**Lord,** Richard *Brick Court Chambers*
Matthews, Duncan *20 Essex Street*	**Melwani,** Poonam *4 Essex Court*	**Priday,** Charles *Seven King's Bench Walk*
Smouha, Joe *Essex Court Chambers*	**Sussex,** Charles *4 Essex Court*	**Whiteley,** Miranda *Queen Elizabeth Building*

LEADERS IN SHIPPING

Aikens QC, Richard
See under Commercial Law.

Baker, Andrew
20 Essex Street (Kenneth Rokison QC), London (0171) 583 9294. Called 1988.

Berry, Steven
See under Insurance and Reinsurance.

Blackburn, Elizabeth
Queen Elizabeth Building (Geoffrey Brice QC), London (0171) 353 9153.

Specialisation: Principal areas of practice are shipping, Admiralty, marine insurance, international trade and commercial law. Deals with all aspects of carriage of goods, salvage, collision, towage, marine pollution, marine insurance and personal injury arising out of marine accidents. Specialist in conflicts of law and jurisdictional issues. Also deals with arbitration as one of the few members of the commercial bar to be appointed a commercial arbitrator whilst still a junior counsel. Also handles principal/surety guarantee disputes. Major cases include 'The Goring' [1988] (House of Lords - leading salvage case); 'The Abidin Daver' (one of the most important jurisdictional decisions of the 1980s); and towage cases involving very large structures such as floating dry docks. Experienced in disputes concerning engineering and metallurgical expert issues. Clients include P&I Clubs, international salvors, shipowners and charterers and shipping solicitors.

Prof. Membership: London Maritime Arbitrators Association (supporting member), COMBAR, British Maritime Law Association, U.K. Environmental Law Association.

Career: Called to the Bar 1978 and joined current chambers 1980. Examiner of the High Court 1987-90.

Personal: Educated at City of London School for Girls and Manchester University (BA Hons, 1976). Leisure pursuits include gardening, antiques, painting and family life. Born 5th October 1954. Lives in West Sussex.

Boyd QC, Stewart
Essex Court Chambers (Gordon Pollock QC), London (0171) 813 8000. Called 1967, took silk 1981. Specialises in all areas of commercial law, particularly arbitration, banking and shipping. Sits on Lloyd's Legal Panel.

Brenton, Timothy
4 Essex Court (David Steel QC), London (0171) 797 7970.
Specialisation: Principal areas of practice are shipping (including Admiralty), international trade, commercial contracts, insurance (marine and non-marine), reinsurance, sale and carriage of goods (international and domestic) and commercial fraud. On editorial board of 'International Maritime Law' (Sweet and Maxwell). Standing Counsel to the Treasury Solicitor in Admiralty matters.
Prof. Membership: COMBAR, supporting member of London Maritime Arbitration Association.
Career: Royal Navy 1975-79. Lecturer in law at King's College, London 1979-80. Called to the Bar 1981 and joined 4 Essex Court.
Personal: Educated at King's School, Rochester to 1975; Bristol University 1976-79 (LLB) and Bar School 1980-81. Born 4th November 1957.

Brice QC, Geoffrey
Queen Elizabeth Building (Geoffrey Brice QC), London (0171) 353 9153.
Specialisation: Principal areas of practice are admiralty and commercial law (including arbitration). Author of 'Maritime Law of Salvage' (2nd ed. 1993) and numerous articles in periodicals in the UK, USA and Europe.
Career: Called to the Bar and joined present chambers in 1960. Lloyd's Salvage Arbitrator 1978, Wreck Commissioner 1978. Took Silk 1979. Appointed Recorder 1980 and Bencher of Middle Temple 1986. Visiting Professor of Maritime Law, Tulane University, USA since 1989.
Personal: Educated at University College, London (LL.B 1959). Born 21st April 1938. Lives in London.

Bright, Robert
Seven King's Bench Walk (Adrian Hamilton QC), London (0171) 583 0404. Called 1987. Principal area of practice covers shipping, insurance and reinsurance work. Born 22.8.1964.

Bucknall QC, Belinda
4 Essex Court (David Steel QC), London (0171) 797 7970. Called 1974, took silk 1988.

Butcher, Christopher
Seven King's Bench Walk (Adrian Hamilton QC), London (0171) 583 0404. Called 1986.

Clarke QC, Christopher
See under Commercial Law.

Collins QC, Michael
See under Arbitration.

Cooke QC, Jeremy
See under Commercial Law.

Dunning, Graham
See under Insurance and Reinsurance.

Eder QC, Bernard
Essex Court Chambers (Gordon Pollock QC), London (0171) 813 8000. Called 1975, took silk 1990.

Flaux QC, Julian
See under Insurance and Reinsurance.

Foxton, David
See under Insurance and Reinsurance.

Gaisman QC, Jonathan
Seven King's Bench Walk (Adrian Hamilton QC), London (0171) 583 0404. Called 1979, took silk 1995.

Gee QC, Steven
See under Commercial Law.

Gilman QC, Jonathan
Essex Court Chambers (Gordon Pollock QC), London (0171) 813 8000. Called 1965, took silk 1990.

Goldstone, David
Queen Elizabeth Building (Geoffrey Brice QC), London (0171) 353 9153. Called 1986.

Gross QC, Peter
See under Aviation.

Gruder, Jeffrey
See under Insurance and Reinsurance.

Hamblen, Nicholas
20 Essex Street (Kenneth Rokison QC), London (0171) 583 9294. Called 1981. Practice covers shipping, insurance and re-insurance, commodities, conflict of laws and arbitrations. Born 23.9.1957.

Hamilton QC, Adrian
See under Commercial Law.

Havelock-Allan QC, Mark
20 Essex Street (Kenneth Rokison QC), London (0171) 583 9294. Called 1974, took silk 1993.

Hirst QC, Jonathan
See under Commercial Law.

Howard QC, Michael N.
4 Essex Court (David Steel QC), London (0171) 797 7970.
Specialisation: Principal areas of practice are international commercial and shipping law, including insurance, international trade and sale of goods. Extensive experience of arbitrations both as counsel and as arbitrator in many international arbitrations connected with international trade, shipping or insurance. Acts for shipowners, charterers, insurers, P&I Clubs and salvage companies.
Prof. Membership: COMBAR, London Common Law and Commercial Bar Association.
Career: Called to the Bar 1971. Tenant at Queen Elizabeth Building 1972-89. Took Silk 1986. Member of the Panel of Salvage Arbitrators appointed by the Committee of Lloyd's since 1989. Joined Essex Court in 1990. Appointed Recorder 1993.
Personal: Educated at Clifton College, 1960-64 and Magdalen College, Oxford 1965-70 (MA BCL). Leisure pursuits include books, music and sport. Born 10th June 1947. Lives in London.
Other: Joint editor, 'Phipson on Evidence' (ed McKendrick, 2nd Edn 1995) and author of articles in legal periodicals. Visiting Professor of Law, Essex University 1987-92, Visiting Lecturer in Shipping Law, London University 1994-.

Hunter QC, Ian
See under Aviation.

Jacobs, Richard
See under Insurance and Reinsurance.

Johnson QC, David
20 Essex Street (Kenneth Rokison QC), London (0171) 583 9294. Called 1967, took silk 1978.

Kay, Jervis
Queen Elizabeth Building (Geoffrey Brice QC), London (0171) 353 9153.

Kendrick, Dominic
See under Insurance and Reinsurance.

Kverndal, Simon
4 Essex Court (David Steel QC), London (0171) 797 7970. Called 1982. Principal areas of practice are maritime and general commercial law. Born 22.4.1958.

Legh-Jones QC, Nicholas
20 Essex Street (Kenneth Rokison QC), London (0171) 583 9294. Called 1968, took silk 1987.

Lord, Richard
See under Banking.

Macdonald QC, Charles
4 Essex Court (David Steel QC), London (0171) 797 7970. Called 1972, took silk 1992.

Matthews, Duncan
See under Commercial Law.

Meeson, Nigel
Queen Elizabeth Building (Geoffrey Brice QC), London (0171) 353 9153. Called 1982.

Melwani, Poonam
See under Commercial Law.

Milligan QC, Iain
See under Aviation.

Moore-Bick QC, Martin
20 Essex Street (Kenneth Rokison QC),
London (0171) 583 9294.

Specialisation: Shipping (including shipbuilding contracts, charterparty disputes and
all aspects of carriage of goods by sea), international sale of goods, insurance and
reinsurance (marine and non-marine), and arbitration law. Practice also includes banking
and financial transactions, oil and gas industry contracts and professional negligence
(brokers). Since 1986 has acted as arbitrator
in a variety of international commercial arbitrations, including arbitrations under the
rules of The London Court of International
Arbitration and the I.C.C.

Career: Called to the Bar November 1969.
Joined present chambers (then at *3 Essex
Court, Temple*) January 1971. Queen's Coun-
sel 1986. Recorder 1990. Approved to sit as
Deputy High Court Judge 1994. Bencher, In-
ner Temple 1992.

Prof. Membership: COMBAR; South Eastern Circuit.

Personal: Educated at The Skinners' School,
Tunbridge Wells and Christ's College, Cambridge.

Parsons, Luke
4 Essex Court (David Steel QC),
London (0171) 797 7970. Called 1985.

Persey, Lionel
See under Commercial Law.

Pollock QC, Gordon
See under Arbitration.

Priday, Charles
Seven King's Bench Walk (Adrian
Hamilton QC), London (0171) 583 0404.

Specialisation: Principal areas of practice
are shipping, banking, insurance and general
commercial work, acting for shipowners,
charterers, oil traders, other commodity traders, banks, insurance companies and brokers.
Reported cases include The "Deichland"
[1990] (jurisdiction); The "Maciej Rataj"
[1991] (jurisdiction - has been to the European Court of Justice); The "Kyzicos" [1989]
(charterparty - laytime); The "Ulyanovsk"
[1990] and the "European Enterprise" [1989]
(construction of Hague-Visby rules).

Prof. Membership: London Maritime
Arbitration Association.

Career: Called to the Bar and joined Seven
King's Bench Walk in 1982.

Rainey, Simon
4 Essex Court (David Steel QC),
London (0171) 797 7970. Called 1982.

Reeder QC, John
Queen Elizabeth Building (Geoffrey
Brice QC), London (0171) 353 9153.
Called 1971, took silk 1989.

Rokison QC, Kenneth
See under Arbitration.

Russell QC, Jeremy
4 Essex Court (David Steel QC),
London (0171) 797 7970.

Specialisation: Specialist in shipping law
and international trade. Practice covers shipping, Admiralty, insurance (marine and
non-marine), sale and carriage of goods (domestic and international). Also handles
commercial arbitrations both as advocate and
occasionally as arbitrator. Has addressed a
number of conferences in London and Singapore on shipping matters.

Prof. Membership: COMBAR; London
Common Law and Commercial Bar Associa-
tion; London Maritime Arbitrators
Association (supporting member).

Career: Called to the Bar 1975. Joined
present chambers 1977. Took silk 1994.

Schaff, Alistair
Seven King's Bench Walk (Adrian
Hamilton QC), London (0171) 583 0404.
Called 1983.

Siberry QC, Richard
Essex Court Chambers (Gordon Pollock
QC), London (0171) 813 8000. Called
1974, took silk 1989.

Simon QC, Peregrine
Brick Court Chambers (Christopher
Clarke QC), London (0171) 583 0777.
Called 1973, took silk 1991.

Smouha, Joe
See under Commercial Law.

Steel QC, David W.
4 Essex Court (David Steel QC), London (0171) 797 7970. Called 1966, took silk
1981. Specialises in commercial law with
particular emphasis on maritime and insurance law. Born 7.5.43.

Stone QC, Richard
Queen Elizabeth Building (Geoffrey
Brice QC), London (0171) 353 9153.
Called 1951, took silk 1968.

Sumption QC, Jonathan
See under Commercial Law.

Sussex, Charles
4 Essex Court (David Steel QC),
London (0171) 797 7970.

Specialisation: Practice encompasses shipping, insurance, banking and international
trade. Includes advisory work and advocacy
both in the commercial court and arbitration,
and on appeal. Other main area of work is
Hong Kong Law, appearing in the Hong
Kong Supreme Court, Privy Council and
Hong Kong arbitrations.

Prof. Membership: Western Circuit; COM-
BAR; Hong Kong Bar Association.

Career: Admitted as a solicitor 1976 and in
practice 1976-82. Called to the Bar 1982.
Called to the Hong Kong Bar 1983, and in
full-time practice at the Bar of Hong Kong
1983-89. Called to the New South Wales Bar
1989. Joined 4 Essex Court 1989.

Personal: Educated at St. Peter's School,
Southborne 1962-1969, King's College,
London 1970-73 (LL.B 1973) and College of
Law, Lancaster Gate 1974. Born 9th July
1951. Lives in Binley, Hampshire.

Teare QC, Nigel
4 Essex Court (David Steel QC),
London (0171) 797 7970. Called 1974, took
silk 1991.

Thomas QC, John
Essex Court Chambers (Gordon Pollock
QC), London (0171) 813 8000. Called
1969, took silk 1984.

Tomlinson QC, Stephen
See under Insurance and Reinsurance.

Whiteley, Miranda
Queen Elizabeth Building (Geoffrey
Brice QC), London (0171) 353 9153.
Called 1985. Principal areas of practice are
commercial law and shipping.

Willmer QC, John
Seven King's Bench Walk (Adrian
Hamilton QC), London (0171) 583 0404.
Called 1955, took silk 1967.

Young, Timothy
20 Essex Street (Kenneth Rokison QC),
London (0171) 583 9294. Called 1977. Main
area of practice is commercial law and international trade. Born 1.12.1953.

SPORTS LAW

THERE ARE no chambers specialising in sports law, which covers diverse areas such as disciplinary proceedings, personal injury, sponsorship and taxation issues. Solicitors therefore tend to instruct barristers who specialise in the area of law in which a particular problem has arisen.

LEADING SILKS– LONDON

Beloff, Michael *4-5 Gray's Inn Square*

Bramwell, Richard *3 Temple Gardens*

Burton, Michael *Littleton Chambers*

Flint, Charles *2 Hare Court*

Pannick, David *2 Hare Court*

Reid, Robert *9 Old Square*

Baker, Nigel R.J. *9 Bedford Row*

Stewart, Nicholas *4 New Square*

Talbot, Patrick *13 Old Square*

A number of barristers, however, have recognised expertise in the field, most notably *Edward Grayson* of **9-12 Bell Yard** who is probably the only lawyer who can be regarded as a sports specialist. In addition to conducting high-profile cases such as 'Elliott v. Saunders' and 'Liverpool Football Club', he is the author of the two leading texts in the area: 'Sport and the Law' and 'Medicine, Sport and the Law' and has advised numerous regulatory bodies including the International Athletic Federation, the Sports Council and the Central Council for Physical Recreation.

Also highly regarded is *Michael Beloff QC* of **4-5 Gray's Inn Square** (an honourary member of the International Athletics Club) who has represented the Rugby Football Union, Commonwealth Games Federation, IAAF, the British Olympic Athletics Team (Barcelona), a number of football clubs and a wealth of sporting personalities.

LEADING JUNIORS– LONDON

Grayson, Edward *9-12 Bell Yard*

Fordham, Michael *2 Hare Court*

Singh, Gurdial *Goldsmith Chambers*

Other silks to feature prominently in our research include *Richard Bramwell QC* of **3 Temple Gardens**, *Michael Burton QC* of **Littleton Chambers**, *David Pannick QC* and *Charles Flint QC* of **2 Hare Court** and *Robert Reid QC* of **9 Old Square**.

Highly recommended junior counsel include *Gurdial Singh* of **Goldsmith Chambers** and *Michael Fordham* of **2 Hare Court**.

OUTSIDE LONDON

Outside London *Antony Berrisford* of **Ropewalk Chambers** in Nottingham has been recommended.

LEADING JUNIORS– REGIONS

Berrisford, A. *Ropewalk Chambers (Nottingham)*

LEADERS IN SPORTS LAW

Baker QC, Nigel R.J.
See under Personal Injury.

Beloff QC, Michael
See under Public and Administrative Law.

Berrisford, A.
Ropewalk Chambers (Richard Maxwell QC), Nottingham (0115) 9472581/2/3/4.

Bramwell QC, Richard
See under Revenue.

Burton QC, Michael
See under Commercial Law.

Flint QC, Charles
See under Commercial Law.

Fordham, Michael
See under Public and Administrative Law.

Grayson, Edward
9-12 Bell Yard (Edmund Lawson QC), London (0171) 400 1800.

Specialisation: Practice encompasses all areas of sports related law including administration, contracts, charities, crime, personal injuries, real and personal property, taxation and VAT. Major cases include Aldershot Football Club v. Banks (restraint of trade); Alder v. Moore (football/insurance); Currie v. Barton & Rippon (tennis/natural justice); Mark Johnson: Criminal Injuries Compensation Board (rugby injury); R v. Chapman (football/assault); Serville v. Constance (boxing/passing off); Swindon Town v. Football League (natural justice); Worthing Rugby Football Club Trustees v. IRC (land taxation); Mark Johnson: Criminal Injuries Compensation Board (rugby injury); Elliott v. Saunders and Liverpool Football Club (personal injury terminating playing career); O'Neill v. Fashanu and Wimbledon Football Club (personal injuries terminating playing careers); Morell v. Owen (disabledathletics/personalinjury).Rayner v.CenterParcsLtd(diving/swimming: tetraplegics.Saxton and Davies (Barcelona Olympic Games drugs dispute). Clients include sports-related individuals, clubs, and governing bodies in London provinces and overseas. Author of 'Sport and the Law' (Butterworths); Co-author 'Medicine, Sport and the Law' (Blackwell Scientific Publications); 'Sponsorship Law' (Sweet and Maxwell). Contributor to 'Law Society's Gazette', 'New Law Journal', 'Legal Executive', 'The Times', and the 'Daily and Sunday Telegraph'. Addressed conferences, inter alia, of the International Athletic Federation (Monaco), South African Sports Medicine Congress (Cape Town), Sports Council and Central Council of Physical Recreation; and has appeared on television and radio.

Prof. Membership: Association of Personal Injury Lawyers, Criminal Bar Association. Founder President British Association for Sport and Law.

Career: Called to the Bar 1948. Joined current chambers in 1972.

Personal: Educated at Taunton's School, Southampton and Exeter College, Oxford. Fellow of the Royal Society of Medicine. Leisure pursuits include work.

Pannick QC, David

See under Public and Administrative Law.

Reid QC, Robert

9 Old Square (Robert Reid QC), London (0171) 405 4682. Called 1965, took silk 1980.

Singh, Gurdial

Goldsmith Chambers (Peter Morrish), London (0171) 353 6802. Called 1989.

Stewart QC, Nicholas

4 New Square (Nicholas Stewart QC), London (0171) 404 3800. Fax: (0171) 404 3900

Specialisation: Most areas of civil litigation, with particular emphasis on Chancery and commercial matters. Work includes company and partnership matters, contractual disputes, housing, trusts, pensions, insolvency, probate and estate matters, financial frauds and professional negligence by lawyers, accountants and surveyors. Also handles negligence and nuisance actions, disputes involving sporting bodies and judicial review. Now undertakes white-collar and environmental criminal cases. Has appeared before the House of Lords, Privy Council and the Court of Appeal in reported cases on numerous occasions. Recent interesting cases include Law v. Cunningham John [1994] (solicitors' negligence; standard of care; reliance on clients' instructions; causation); Newport AFC v. Football Association of Wales [1995] (restaint of trade; jurisdiction to grant interlocutory injunction). Has published a number of articles on legal and professional matters for both the specialist and general press. Regularly addresses conferences and seminars in England and abroad. Has made a number of TV and radio appearances acting as a spokesman for the Bar and recently as Chairman of the Bar Human Rights Committee. Media experience also includes co-writing and narrating two recent series of dramatised cases 'No Further Questions' for BBC Radio 4.

Prof. Membership: UK Vice-President and Director of Publications, Union Internationale des Avocats; Chairman, Bar Human Rights Committee of England and Wales.

Career: Called to the Bar 1971. Tenant at 9 Old Square, Lincoln's Inn (now Enterprise Chambers) 1972-1991. Moved to 15 Old Square in 1991 (leader of Business & Property Law Group and member of the Environmental Law Group). Set up own chambers at 4 New Square in February 1994. Took silk 1987. Since 1991 has sat as a Deputy High Court Judge in the Chancery Division.

Personal: Educated at Oxford University (BA PPE) 1965-1968. Certified Diploma in Accounting and Finance, Charted Institute of Certified Accountants 1976. Has good knowledge of French and Spanish. Leisure pursuits include walking and Spain. Born 16th April 1947. Lives in London.

Prof. Membership:

Talbot QC, Patrick

See under Insolvency.

THE BAR OUTSIDE LONDON

THE SOUTH EASTERN CIRCUIT

Brighton, Cambridge, Canterbury, Chelmsford, Chichester, Colchester, Ipswich, Norwich, Eastbourne, Enfield, Harrow-on-the-Hill, Guildford, Lewes, Maidstone, Reading, Redhill & St. Albans.

Brighton

Sussex Chambers is a general common law set handling criminal law, general civil litigation, matrimonial, property and planning law. The head of chambers, Paul Ashwell, specialises in property and commercial litigation. Nicholas Hall and Stuart Lambert handle criminal and matrimonial work.

At *Crown Office Row Chambers* Christopher Smyth and Anthony Niblett are known for their general common law practice including professional negligence, building, criminal and personal injury work.

Cambridge

Fenners Chambers has developed areas of specialisation particularly in criminal and family law. Simon Tattersall, Lindsay Davies and Susan Epsley are all well-known for their family law work. Jane Bridge has co-authored three books on family law including a new guide to the 1989 Children Act. Caroline Pointon and Gareth Hawkesworth have strong reputations in criminal law. Caroline Pointon specialises in fraud and acts as Standing Counsel to the Inland Revenue.

Regency Chambers under Raymond Croxon QC handles general common law matters with individual specialists in commercial, environmental law, planning and tax. The chambers also have a branch in Peterborough of equal status.

Canterbury

Becket Chambers undertake a wide range of common law matters including crime, family law and personal injury. Roy Warne's set, *Stour Chambers*, handles common law and chancery.

Chelmsford

Tindal Chambers is an established common law set which undertakes chancery, commercial, planning, personal injury, family and criminal law. The head of chambers, Anthony Nicholson, handles mostly chancery and commercial law. Bruce Silvester undertakes a large amount of civil and commercial litigation work. Caroline Beasley-Murray is well-regarded for matrimonial law.

Chichester

Chichester Chambers, under Michael Beckman QC, have eleven barristers permanently based in Chichester led by Charles Taylor, an authority on the Mobile Homes Act and a commercial fraud specialist. Lucinda Davies and Wendy Rowlinson are highly regarded for their matrimonial and family law work, and appear regularly for local authorities in care proceedings. Adam Smith and Mary Loosemore are also recognised in this field. Clifford Darton and Gavin Argent handle general civil work.

Colchester, Ipswich & Norwich

The largest chambers in East Anglia are the *East Anglian Chambers* of John Holt in Colchester, *East Anglian Chambers* in Ipswich and *East Anglian Chambers* in Norwich. They all handle general common law work and have a well-established team of family law practitioners. This team includes Anthony Kefford, Timothy McLoughlin, Celia Miller, Roderick Newton and Peter Wain. Highly regarded for personal injury work are John Holt and Andrew Marsden. Andre de Moller has a high reputation for criminal law.

At *Octagon House Chambers* in Norwich, Paul Downes and Michael Clare are recognised for their criminal law work. Philip Curl and Timothy Townshend are well-known for their matrimonial work, and both handle child care cases.

Eastbourne

Eastbourne has two sets of chambers. *King's Chambers* and *Eastbourne Chambers* handling a wide range of common law.

Enfield, Harrow-on-the-Hill

Enfield Chambers is a common law set whose work includes criminal, family and personal injury matters. *Harrow on the Hill Chambers* handles common law work and property-oriented chancery matters.

Guildford

Jeffrey Widdup's set, *Guildford Chambers*, maintains a breadth of common law expertise and many of its members specialise. Jeffrey Widdup has a strong personal interest in planning, and Suzan Matthews QC has built up a reputation locally in family law, particularly wardship cases. Janet Haywood, a practitioner in family law, recently joined this set.

Lewes

The *Westgate Chambers* offer a diverse range of expertise including patent law and police and civil liberties work. Clare Jakens and Timothy Sisley have been recommended for family law.

Maidstone

Maidstone Chambers is a general common law set. *6-8 Mill Street* is an annex of *6 Pump Court* (Michael Gale QC).

Reading

At the *Chambers of Neville Digby*, Neville Digby specialises in company law and insolvency (including the company laws of Hong Kong, Singapore, Malaysia and Malawi.) Clifford Joseph, who also practises from *3 Verulam Buildings, Gray's Inn,* has expertise in planning and local government law. Manjeet Mendhir is able to advise in Malaysian and Singapore law.

Redhill

Redhill Chambers is a general common law set, with several members also practising criminal and family law. The set is also based at 11 Bolt Court.

St. Albans

St Albans Chambers, Stuart Stevens' set, also at 3 King's Bench Walk, undertake general common law work including crime, civil, matrimonial and landlord and tenant.

THE WESTERN CIRCUIT

Bournemouth, Bristol, Exeter, Plymouth, Portsmouth, Southampton, Taunton, Truro & Winchester.

Bournemouth

Lorne Park Chambers, an annexe of *3 Paper Buildings,* is a set of chambers covering all areas of law. Michael Parroy QC, David Bartlett and Michael Norman undertake chancery work.

Bristol

Bristol acquired its own mercantile court in July 1993, presided over by His Honour Judge Raymond Jack QC. It therefore continues to provide a first class commercial service to solicitors and local businesses.

The three main commercial sets are *Guildhall Chambers*, *St. John's Chambers* and *Old Square Chambers*, an annexe of John Melville Williams QC's set in Lincoln's Inn. From *Guildhall Chambers* John Boggis QC, George Newsom, Stephen Davies and Martha Maher have excellent reputations for their chancery work, as do Roger Kaye QC and Leslie Blohm from *St. John's Chambers*. Nigel Hamilton QC and Richard Stead, of *St. John's Chambers*, have been highly recommended for commercial law, with Richard Stead receiving particular praise for his work in construction law and personal injury.

On the family law side, Stephen Wildblood, Paul Barclay and Michael Roach of *Albion Chambers* are highly

regarded. Mark Evans QC and Christopher Sharp of *St. John's Chambers* are the principal counsel for financial aspects of family law. They are also well-known for their personal injury work. Finally, Sheelagh Corfield of *Guildhall Chambers*, proficient in most areas of family law, specialises in child work.

Albion Chambers is one of the leading criminal sets, with a large number of able advocates covering all aspects of criminal law. Charles Barton QC and Neil Ford are particularly well-respected in this area.

All Saints Chambers and *Assize Court Chambers* are proficient in handling a wide range of common law matters.

Notable Practitioners - Bristol

ALBION CHAMBERS (J.C.T. Barton QC)

CIVIL: Michael W. Roach (1975) *Personal injury*;

FAMILY: Sally Porter (1970); Paul Barclay (1972); Michael W. Roach (1975); Stephen Wildblood (1980);

CRIME: Charles Barton QC (1969, 1989); John Tabor (1974); Neil M. Ford (1976); Gavin Chalmers (1978); Julian Lambert (1983); Michael Mather-Lees (1981); Martin T. Picton (1981); Patrick C.H. Burrowes (1988).

ALL SAINTS CHAMBERS (Simon Quadrat)

CRIME: David Lane QC (1968, 1991); Simon Quadrat (1969); Christopher Taylor (1982); Nigel Pascoe QC (1966, 1988) (Door Tenant), Libel.

ASSIZE COURT CHAMBERS (Graeme Wood)

CIVIL: Graeme Wood (1968) *Chancery*; John Tackaberry QC (1967, 1982); *International Commercial Arbitration (Door Tenant)*; John Isherwood (1978); *Personal Injury*;

CRIME: Shamim Qureshi (1982); Philip Warren (1988) previously a solicitor.

GUILDHALL CHAMBERS (John Royce QC)

CIVIL: John Royce QC (1970, 1987) *Commercial, Personal Injury*; Adrian Palmer QC (1972, 1992) *Commercial, Personal Injury*; John Boggis QC (1972, 1993) *Chancery*; Adam Chippindall (1975) *Civil*; Ian Glen (1973) *Judicial Review, Licensing*;Ralph Wynne-Griffiths (1981)*Construction*; Stephen Davies (1983) *Chancery, Insolvency*;John Virgo (1983) *Landlord and Tenant*; Martha Maher (1987) *Chancery*; George Newsom (1973) *Chancery*; Peter Barrie (1976) Personal Injury; Ian Pringle (1979) *Personal Injury*; Robert Thomas (1991) *Employment*;

FAMILY: Christopher Gosland (1966); Sheelagh Corfield (1975) *General, Child Abduction*;Adam Chippindall (1975); Brian Watson (1978); Catriona Duthie (1981);

CRIME: John Royce QC (1970, 1987) *Fraud*; Adrian Palmer QC (1972, 1992) *Fraud*; Ian Pringle (1979); Richard Smith (1986); Peter Blair (1983).

OLD SQUARE CHAMBERS (Hon. John Melville Williams QC)

CIVIL: Christopher Carling (1969) Personal Injury; Barry Cotter (1985) *Employment*; Jennifer Lemkey (1987) *Commercial*; Tess Gill (1990) *Employment*.

ST. JOHN'S CHAMBERS (Roderick Denyer QC)

CIVIL: Nigel Hamilton QC (1965, 1981) *Commercial, Personal Injury*; Roger Kaye QC (1970, 1989) *Chancery, Commercial*; Roderick Denyer QC (1970, 1990) *Employment, Personal Injury*; Mark Evans QC (1971) *Personal Injury*; Paul Darlow (1973) *Personal Injury*; Christopher Sharp (1975) *Personal Injury*; Richard

Stead (1979) *Commercial, Construction, Personal Injury*; Leslie Blohm (1982) *Chancery*; John Blackmore (1983) *Chancery*; Julian Ironside (1985) *Commercial*;

FAMILY: Mark Evans QC (1971, 1975); Nicholas Marston (1975); Christopher Sharp (1975) *Financial*; Richard Bromilow (1977); Ralph Dixon (1980); Susan Jacklin (1980); Glyn Edwards (1987); Louise O'Neill (1989);

CRIME: Roderick Denyer QC (1970, 1990); Alun Jenkins (1972); Ian Bullock (1975); Mark Horton (1976); Michael Longman (1978); Robert Duval (1979); Ian Dixey (1984); Simon Morgan (1988). Susan Evans (1989).

Exeter

At *Walnut House* Francis Gilbert QC, head of chambers, Paul Dunkels QC and Geoffrey Mercer are highly thought of for their civil and criminal law expertise. Martin Edmunds is highly respected in the field of landlord and tenant. Corinne Searle, John Neligan and Shane Lyon handle family law matters with Corinne Searle specialising in child work. Sarah Munro is highly regarded for her criminal practice.

At *33 Southernhay East* members specialise in civil work, with a strong emphasis on family proceedings. Hugh Lewis, George Meredith and David Tyzack are well-known for their family law expertise. David Tyzack is Chairman of the Devon and Cornwall Family Law Bar Association.

At *Barnfield Chambers* David Steele specialises in criminal law, and Mark Horton handles all aspects of family law. Martin Meeke specialises in consumer law, and is also recognised for his family and criminal work. Mark Whitehall has an established common law practice.

At *Castle Chambers* the head of chambers, Christina Gorna, is highly respected for her family law work.

Plymouth

King's Bench Chambers are a large common law set and an annexe of *2 King's Bench Walk*. Anthony Donne QC of this set is well-known for criminal and personal injury work. Llewellyn Sellick handles a large amount of criminal defence work. Heather Burwin and Miranda Robertshaw are known for family law work.

Devon Chambers undertake general common law work. Peter Telford is a specialist in all aspects of local authority work, particularly community charge actions. Robert Linford is highly regarded for his admiralty, medical negligence and mental health work.

Portsmouth

The *Portsmouth Barristers' Chambers*, under Andrew Parsons, undertake all common law work. The head of chambers handles mostly civil and chancery cases. At *Guildhall Chambers Portsmouth*, Edo de Vries specialises in tax law.

Southampton

College Chambers of Southampton and Portsmouth were formed in 1989 by a group of established practitioners from the annexes of two London chambers. They offer a wide range of services including licensing, employment and landlord and tenant and have several matrimonial and child care specialists including Robin Belben, Jonathan Swift and Douglas Taylor. Barrington Myers is well-known for his planning expertise.

Members of the chambers at *17 Carlton Crescent*, under Jeremy Gibbons QC handles all areas of crime, including corporate crime and fraud. A wide range of civil litigation is covered, including local government work, matrimonial and Children Act work. The set has wide experience in trading standards and regulatory crime work, with Nick Haggan and Malcolm Gibney highly regarded in these areas of law. Margaret Pine-Coffin is well respected for child care work.

The set at *Eighteen Carlton Crescent*, under Andrew Massey, undertakes a wide range of work, including a substantial amount of matrimonial cases. Alastair Haig-Haddon has a good reputation in this area, as does Martin Blount. Philip Goddard is known for his criminal law work.

Taunton

South Western Chambers handles a broad range of common law matters. The head of chambers, Brian Lett, is highly regarded for prosecuting and defending serious and complex criminal cases.

Truro

Godolphin Chambers is a general common law set under Barry Van Den Berg handling both civil and criminal work including planning, agricultural, family, professional negligence and local government work.

Winchester

Pump Court Chambers, an annexe of Guy Boney QC's set at *3 Pump Court, Temple*, were the first set to establish themselves in Winchester. The set handles a wide range of cases including licensing, professional negligence and child care work. Paul Garlick is Standing Counsel for HM Customs and Excise. John Aspinall QC, Geoffrey Still and Frank Abbott all handle a large number of heavy criminal cases.

Also in Winchester are the chambers at *4 St. Peter Street*, under Michael Parroy QC. The set undertakes a variety of work including crime, medical negligence, building and commercial work, chancery, matrimonial and planning.

THE MIDLANDS & OXFORD CIRCUIT

Birmingham, Leicester, Northampton, Oxford, Nottingham & Solihull.

Birmingham

Birmingham has a heavy concentration of civil and commercial work and in October 1993 acquired a Mercantile Court. The judge of the court, His Honour Judge Malcolm Lee QC who previously practised from 4 Fountain Court, was a well-known civil, commercial and licensing practitioner. A local commercial Bar Association was established in December 1991; its chairman is John Mitting QC.

5 Fountain Court is one of the largest sets of chambers in the United Kingdom with a range of expertise including personal injury, planning, general civil and commercial, family and criminal law. Its highly recommended team of civil practitioners includes Kevin O'Donovan in employment law, Stephen Linehan QC in licensing and criminal and Harry Wolton QC and Martin Kingston QC in planning. Estella Hindley QC has a fine reputation for her family law work, and Anthony Barker QC is highly regarded for his criminal practice.

Other chambers with specialist civil expertise include: *4 Fountain Court*, where John Mitting QC is well-known for his commercial and professional negligence work, and *7 Fountain Court* where Rex Tedd QC, James Corbett, John Randall and David Lock are widely respected for their expertise in the chancery and commercial field. These chambers have great expertise in director's disqualification cases also.

Priory Chambers is well regarded in the commercial field, with such notable practitioners as Patrick McCahill. It is the largest family law set in Birmingham and has several experienced practitioners in this field including Patricia Deeley and David Hershman.

3 Fountain Court also has well-known family practitioners, such as Donald Hamilton who is particularly strong on the financial aspects of family law. Mark Anderson is a well-known commercial practitioner.

David Hershman of *Priory Chambers* is the co-author of *Children Law and Practice*, a leading work on child law.

Notable Practitioners - Birmingham

1 FOUNTAIN COURT (Anthony Hughes QC)
FAMILY: Robin Rowland (1977);

CRIME: David Crigman QC (1969, 1989); Anthony Hughes QC (1970, 1990) *Fraud*; Richard Griffith-Jones (1974); John Wait (1972); Melbourne Inman (1979).

3 FOUNTAIN COURT (Donald Hamilton)
CIVIL: Peter Andrews QC (1970, 1991) *Medical Negligence*; Colman Treacy QC (1971, 1990) *General Civil*; Patrick Darby (1978) *Employment*; Mark Anderson (1985) *Commercial*;

FAMILY: Donald Hamilton (1969) *Financial*; Sybil Thomas (1976) *Children*;

CRIME: Colman Treacy QC (1971, 1990) *Fraud*; Anthony Palmer QC (1962, 1979).

4 FOUNTAIN COURT (Richard Wakerley QC)
CIVIL: John Mittling QC (1970, 1987) *Commercial*;

CRIME: Richard Wakerly QC (1965, 1982) *Fraud*; John Saunders QC (1972, 1991).

5 FOUNTAIN COURT (Harry Wolton QC)
CIVIL: Harry Wolton QC (1969, 1982) *Planning*; Martin Kingston QC (1972, 1992) *Planning*; David Stembridge QC (1955, 1990) *Civil*; Aubrey Craig (1987) *Commercial* (previously a lawyer in the United States); Stephen Oliver-Jones (1970) *Personal Injury, Medical Negligence*; Nicholas Worsley QC (1966, 1993) *Personal Injury, Medical Negligence*; Stephen Linehan QC (1970, 1993) *Licensing*; William Wood (1970) *Personal Injury*; Mark Eades (1974), *Licensing;* Satinder Hunjan (1984) *Licensing;* Jennifer Jones *(1991) Employment*; Gareth Evans (1973) *Personal Injury*;

Jeremy Cahill (1975) *Personal Injury;* Kevin O'Donovan (1978) *Employment*; Ralph Lewis (1978) *Personal Injury;* Paul Bleasdale (1978) *Personal Injury*; Robert Holdsworth (1979) *Peronal Injury*; David Stockill (1985) *Chancery*.

FAMILY: Estella Hindley QC (1971, 1992); Anne Smallwood (1977); Stephanie Brown (1982) *Children*; Lorna Meyer (1986);

CRIME: Anthony Barker QC (1966, 1985) *Fraud*; Stephen Linehan QC (1970, 1993); Michael Elsom (1972).

NO.6 FOUNTAIN COURT (Roger Smith)
CIVIL: Philip Gregory (1975) *General civil, personal injury*; Bryce Somerville (1980) *Licensing*; Avtar Khangure (1985) *Commercial, Insolvency*;

FAMILY: Bryce Somerville (1980);

CRIME: Roger Smith QC (1972, 1992); Alistair McCreath (1972).

7 FOUNTAIN COURT (Rex Tedd QC)
CIVIL: Rex Tedd QC (1970, 1993) *Commercial*; James Corbett (1975) *Chancery, Commercial, Directors Disqualification;*; John Randall (1978) *Chancery, Commercial*; William Davis (1975) *Personal Injury*; David Lock (1985) *Chancery, Commercial*; Timothy Jones (1975) *Planning;*

FAMILY: Guy Spollon (1976);

CRIME: Rex Tedd QC (1970, 1993); Christopher Hotten QC (1972, 1994); William Davis (1975); James Burbridge (1979); Peter Haynes (1983).

PRIORY CHAMBERS (Patricia Deeley)
CIVIL: Stephen Campbell (1982) *General Civil*; Patrick McCahill (1975) *General Commercial*; Lorna Findley (1987) *Judicial Review, Housing*;

FAMILY: Patricia Deeley (1970) *Finance*; Ronald Newbold (1965); David Hershman (1981) *Children*;

CRIME: Michael Garrett (1967); Graham Cliff (1973); William Pusey (1977).

ST. IVE'S CHAMBERS (Edward Coke)
FAMILY: Margaret Hodgson (1975) *Children*; Julia Macur (1979) *Children*;Peter Anthony (1981); Michael Keehan (1982); Rehna Azim (1984) *Children*; Jayne Mullen (1989);

CRIME: Peter Carr (1976); Julia Macur (1979).

Leicester
The three main sets of chambers in Leicester handle most areas of law. Donald Harmer, a qualified architect, of *New Walk Chambers* is well-known for his arbitration work, and Rebecca Fitton-Brown has a good reputation in family law. Paul Atkinson is highly regarded for civil litigation work. Timothy Clark of *2 New St* is considered an expert in the matrimonial field. Alexandra Scott is also known for her family work and Robert Brown is an expert in criminal law. Graham Buchanan and William Bach of *65-67 King St* are recognised in the field of criminal law. The fourth set of chambers, *21 Portland Rd*, is that of John Whitmore, with particular expertise in civil liberties and equal opportunities.

Northampton and Oxford
There are two sets in Northampton. The members of *22 Albion Place* undertake a variety of work including family,

criminal and civil litigation and now have an annex in Coventry known as Counsel's Chambers. *1 King's Bench Walk* is an annexe of *1 King's Bench Walk* in London.

At *Harcourt Chambers*, in Oxford, Thomas Corrie and Jonathan Baker are known for all aspects of family law, with Thomas Corrie being noted for matrimonial finance and Jonathan Baker for children work. At *1 Alfred Street*, an annexe of *3 Paper Buildings*, the head of chambers is Michael Parroy QC. Leo Curran is well-respected for his family law work. *King's Bench Chambers*, an annexe of *13 Kings Bench Walk*, undertake the whole range of common law matters including contract, personal injury, landlord and tenant, family and criminal law.

Nottingham

Of the four Nottingham sets, *No.1 High Pavement* is the only specialist criminal set, with 34 criminal specialists and 4 licensing specialists. Peter Joyce QC and John Milmo QC lead the field in heavy crime, with Peter Joyce QC known for his expertise in sex cases and John Milmo QC in fraud. Other senior criminal practitioners include Stuart Rafferty, Gregory Dickinson, Shaun Smith and Balraj Bhatia. Also known for their criminal work are Jonathan Teare, John Warren, Peter Walmsley and Godfrey Napthine. Promising juniors include Maureen Baker, Christopher Geeson and Andrew Easteal.

St. Mary's Chambers also has some highly regarded criminal and family practitioners. Both R. Calder Jose and Dudley Bennett are known for their criminal advocacy. Mark Rogers, Jeremy Lea, Stuart Farquhar, Nigel Page, Christopher Butler and Deborah Eaton are recognised for their family law work. Maureen Casey and Beryl Gilead are particularly noted for children work.

Highly regarded at *King Charles House* are Richard Inglis for his personal injury work, Amanda Cranny, Rowena Bridge, Vivien Buchanan, Richard Toombs and Patrick Gallaher for family law, and James Howlett for his expertise in Town and Country planning. William Everard, Keith Jackson and Martin Elwick are known for their criminal practice and John Stobart has employment law experience.

At *Ropewalk Chambers*, Richard Maxwell QC, William Woodward QC and Antony Goldstaub QC are highly regarded for their personal injury work and their professional negligence expertise. Ian McLaren QC, Graham Machin and Steven Beresford undertake a large amount of civil work including insurance and Town & Country planning. Heather Swindells and Alison Hampton are known for their landlord and tenant work, with Heather Swindells QC also recognised for her family work, especially in the fields of adoption, child custody and wardship. Robert Owen and Richard Swain handle a large amount of personal injury work. Anthony Berrisford has some sports law experience.

Solihull, Stoke-on-Trent and Wolverhampton

Berkeley Chambers under Anthony Smith QC in Solihull is a set specialising in planning and building work. In Stoke-on-Trent, *Regent Chambers* handles general civil matters including matrimonial cases, industrial tribunal work and also some crime. Peter Crichton-Gold is Head of Chambers. *Clock Chambers* in Wolverhampton is a recently established set dealing with the full range of civil and criminal matters.

THE WALES & CHESTER CIRCUIT

Cardiff, Chester, Newport & Swansea.

Cardiff

Almost half the barristers on the circuit practise from the four sets of chambers in *Park Place, Cardiff*.

The largest of the Cardiff sets, *9 Park Place*, has five recorders, and one assistant recorders among its tenants. A general common law set, it is strong in personal injury and crime. Ian Murphy QC, is held in particularly high esteem for personal injury as are Roger Thomas QC and Leighton Davies QC for crime. Gareth George and Isobel Parry are well-known for their family law practice. Geraint Jones and Milwyn Jarman undertake a large amount of chancery and professional negligence work.

At *30 Park Place* Andrew Green specialises in commercial law and is the Chairman of the Commercial Bar Association in Cardiff. William Gaskell is often instructed in licensing and general civil work. The chambers has a well-established team of family law practitioners which includes James Tillyard, Jane Crowley, Mark Furness and Helen Mifflin. Peter Griffiths QC is highly regarded in respect of criminal matters – particularly those involving fraud. Other members offer particular expertise in judicial review, social security, trade union and employment matters. Five of the senior members are recorders. John Venmore practises mainly in personal injury. Huw Davies is well known for his criminal practice.

At Christopher Williams's chambers at *32 Park Place* David Harris and Lynne Morgan are known for their work in the family law field, and David Aubrey and Christopher Williams have established fine reputations for their criminal work. J. Meirion Davies has a substantial personal injury practice. The chambers as a whole are a common law set with emphasis on crime, family law and some planning.

The chambers of Wyn Williams at *33 Park Place* are a broadly-based common law set with some emphasis on crime and personal injury. Several tenants have specialist expertise, including Wyn Williams QC, who also has a substantial reputation for planning work, and Neil Bidder who is recognised for his personal injury work. Keith Bush, a qualified engineer, is highly regarded for his construction and contract work.

Notable Practitioners - Cardiff

9 PARK PLACE (Philip Rees)

CIVIL: Karl Williams (1982) *Personal Injury*, Nicholas Cooke (1977) *Personal Injury*; Geraint James (1976) *Chancery, Professional Negligence*; Milwyn Jarman (1980) *Chancery, Professional Negligence*;

FAMILY: Gareth George (1977); Isobel Parry (1979);

CRIME: Roger Thomas QC (1969, 1994); Leighton Davies QC (1975, 1994); Peter Jacobs (1973); Gregory Taylor (1974); Ian Pritchard-Witts (1976); Marian Lewis (1987).

30 PARK PLACE (Philip Richards)

CIVIL: Andrew Green (1974) *Commercial*; William Gaskell (1970) *Licensing, General Civil*; John Venmore (1971) *Personal Injury*,

Huw Davies *Crime*; Peter Griffiths QC (1970,1995) *Personal Injury*; Lloyd Williams (1981) *Personal Injury*;

FAMILY: Mark Furness (1970); Jane Crowley (1976); James Tillyard (1978); Helen Miflin (1982);

CRIME: Peter Griffiths QC (1970, 1995) *Fraud, VAT evasion*; Patrick Curran QC (1972) *Fraud.*

32 PARK PLACE (Christopher Williams)

CIVIL: J. Merrion Davies (1975) *Personal Injury*;

FAMILY: David Harris (1979); Lynne Morgan (1984);

CRIME: Christopher Williams (1972); David Aubrey (1976); Wayne Price (1992); David Webster (1993) *formerly a solicitor.*

33 PARK PLACE (Wyn Williams QC)

CIVIL: Keith Bush (1977) *Construction, Contract*; Wyn Williams QC (1974, 1992) *Personal injury, Planning*; John Charles QC (1972, 1991)

CIVIL: Nicholas David Jones (1987) *Personal Injury, Personal Injury*; John Walters (1984) *Personal Injury*;

CRIME: Charles Cook (1966); Gerald Price QC (1969, 1992); N. Gareth Jones (1970); Colin Davies (1973); Jennet Treharne (1975).

Chester

The largest chambers in Chester are those of Philip Hughes at *40 King St*. The set undertakes a wide range of work, including chancery, industrial tribunals, crime, family and civil litigation. Catherine O'Leary is highly regarded in the family law field as are Roger Dutton and Gordon Cole, for crime.

At *White Friars Chambers*, has a substantial criminal base and also handles family and general common law, Kevin Burnett has a large local planning practice and is also recommended for family law, as is Sarah Leigh.

Sedan House is a common law and criminal chambers, with Geoffrey Little and Michael Chambers recommended for their common law practices.

Newport

Newport has a general common law set, *Newport Chambers*.

Swansea

The largest of the three Swansea sets is *Iscoed Chambers*. The head of chambers, Wyn Richards is frequently retained by local authorities in planning matters. Several members of chambers, Peter Rouch, Trefor Davies, Kevin Riordan and Philip Marshall, are known for their criminal work. Philip Marshall is highly regarded for his employment practice.

Angel Chambers, under T. Glanville Jones, are a general set with a strong matrimonial reputation. Christopher Vosper has a strong reputation for matrimonial law, as well as for personal injury and general litigation. Christopher McKay specialises in family law.

Gower Chambers are a set undertaking a broad cross-section of work, including matrimonial, civil and criminal. The head of chambers, Bryan Thomas, is highly regarded for his

civil and criminal work, particularly in serious crime. Davina Gammon is known for her matrimonial expertise.

Notable Practitioners - Swansea

ANGEL CHAMBERS (T. Glanville Jones)

CIVIL: Christopher Vosper (1977) *Personal Injury*;

FAMILY: Christopher McKay (1976); Christopher Vosper (1977).

GOWER CHAMBERS (Bryan Thomas)

CIVIL: Bryan Thomas (1978) *General*;

FAMILY: Davina Gammon (1979);

CRIME: Bryan Thomas (1978) *Crime.*

ISCOED CHAMBERS:

CIVIL: Philip Marshall (1975) *Employment, Personal Injury*; Lawrence Griffiths (1957) *Personal Injury*; D. Wyn Richards (1968) *Planning & Local Government*;

FAMILY: Ruth Henke (1987) *Child Law*;

CRIME: Trefor Davies (1972) *Crime*; Kevin Riordan (1972) *Crime*; Peter Rouch (1972) *Crime.*

THE NORTHERN CIRCUIT

Liverpool, Manchester & Preston.

Liverpool

Several sets in Liverpool, such as *14 Castle St* and *Martin's Building*, offer a range of civil and commercial expertise which rivals that of the London Bar.

At *14 Castle St* Adrian Lyon and Robert Warnock are highly respected for their civil work, as is John Benson for his employment law work. Andrew Edis is respected for his commercial practice. Graham Morris and Andrew Moran from *Martin's Building* are known for their experience in the commercial field, and Robert Fordham QC of the same chambers is well regarded for family law.

The two specialist chancery sets are *20 North John St* and *7 Queen Avenue*. William George, Nicholas Orr and Ian Johnson from *20 North John St* are all highly regarded for their chancery work. *7 Queen Avenue* group of well-known chancery practitioners includes Nicholas Riddle and Colin Green.

At *Exchange Chambers* Bill Braithwaite QC is recognised for his expertise in personal injury litigation and Michael Wood is one of 5 commercial specialists in chambers. Henry Globe QC is known for his criminal work. Edward Bartley-Jones is well known for his chancery work. At the *The Corn Exchange* Ian Goldrein and Margaret de Haas are known for their personal injury work, they are co-editors of 'Butterworths' Personal Injury Litigation'. Richard Isaacson is Standing Counsel for the Customs and Excise.

The main set with a substantial family law practice is *Peel House* (David Harris QC) which has a well-established team including Maureen Roddy, Ross Duggan and Gail Owen.

Other highly regarded practitioners are Andrew Sander (for his leasing expertise) at *Oriel Chambers* and Nigel Gilmour QC (for personal injury) at *Peel House* (Nigel Gilmour QC).

Notable Practitioners - Liverpool

14 CASTLE ST (Adrian Smith)

CIVIL: Robert Warnock (1977) *Civil*; Eric Goldrein (1961) *Judicial Review*; Adrian Lyon (1975) *Civil, Employment*; John Benson (1978) *Licensing,Employment*;

FAMILY: Robert Warnock (1977); Jacqueline Wall (1986); Adrian Lyon (1975); Michael Sellars (1980);

CRIME: Adrian Smith (1973); David Geey (1970); Andrew Edis (1980).

25-27 CASTLE STREET (Stephen Riordan QC)

FAMILY: Wendy-Jane Lloyd (1983);

CRIME: Stephen Riordan QC (1972, 1992); Gerard Wright QC (1954, 1973); Brian Lewis (1973); Pamela Badley (1974); Michael Henshell (1975); Brendan Carville (1980); Peter Davies (1986); Simon Driver (1991).

CHAVASSE COURT CHAMBERS (Andrew Mattison)

FAMILY: Graham Pickavance (1973) *Children*; Theresa Pepper (1973); Elizabeth Cliffs (1975); John McDermott (1976);

CRIME: Michael Bagley (1984); Andrew Mattison (1963); John McDermott (1976).

DERBY SQUARE CHAMBERS (John Phipps)

CIVIL: Graham Morrow (1974) *Commercial;* Scott Donovan (1974) *Medical Negligence and Pharmaceutical Product Liability* Thomas Ryan (1979) *Licensing; Employment*; John Phipps (1970) *Medical Negligence*; Simon Newton (1981) *Personal Injury* .

EXCHANGE CHAMBERS (William Waldron QC)

CIVIL: Bill Braithwaite QC (1970, 1992) *Personal Injury;* Michael Wood (1989) *Commercial*; Richard Isaacson (1972).

FAMILY: Judith Fordham (1991 – formerly a solicitor); Karen Gregory (1985):

CRIME: David Turner QC (1971, 1991); Henry Globe QC (1972, 1994).

MARTIN'S BUILDING (R.A. Fordham QC)

CIVIL: Graham Morris (1975) *Commercial*; Andrew Moran (1976) *Commercial*; Robert Fordham QC (1976, 1993) *Personal Injury*; David Geey (1970) *Civil, Personal Injury*;

FAMILY: Robert Fordham QC (1976, 1993) *Ancillary Relief*; Mark Chatterton (1983); Deirdre McGuire (1987);

CRIME: David Boulton (1970); Stuart Baker (1974); Michael Davies (1979) *Judicial Review, Crime;* Andrew Menary (1982); Stephen Knapp (1986).

20 NORTH JOHN ST (William George)

CIVIL: William George (1968) *Chancery and commercial*; Nicholas Orr (1970) *Chancery and commercial*; Ian Johnson (1982) *Chancery and commercial.*

ORIEL CHAMBERS (Bryan S. Joynes)

CIVIL: Andrew Sander (1970) *Commercial, Leasing, Health & Safety*; Norman Wright (1974) *Personal Injury*; William Rankin (1972) *Personal Injury*; Peter Cowan (1980) *Personal Injury, Medical Negligence, Health & Safety*; Peter Goodbody (1986) *Commercial*; Alan Sellers (1991) *Commercial*, previously a solicitor;

FAMILY: William Rankin (1972) *Financial*; Anthony Edwards (1972).

PEEL HOUSE (David Harris QC)

CIVIL: David Harris QC (1969, 1989) *Commercial, Medical Negligence*; Graham Wood (1979) *Civil*; Simon Holder (1989) *Civil;*

FAMILY: David Harris QC (1969, 1989); Maureen Roddy (1977);Ross Duggan (1978); Gail Owen (1980); Michael Kennedy

(1985);

CRIME: Michael E. Wolff (1964); Robert Atherton (1970); Raymond Herman (1972); David Williams (1990); John Gibson (1993);

COMMERCIAL: Louis Browne (1988).

PEEL HOUSE (Nigel Gilmour QC)

CIVIL: Nigel Gilmour QC (1970, 1990) *Personal Injury*; Christopher Alldis (1970) *Personal Injury*; Charles Feeny (1977) *Personal Injury*; Peter Gregory (1982) *Personal Injury*; Mark Beheney (1986) *Personal Injury*;

FAMILY: Martyn Bennet (1969) *Financial.*

7 QUEEN AVENUE (Nicholas Riddle)

CIVIL: Nicholas F. Riddle (1970) *Chancery*; Edward B. Jones (1975) *Chancery*; Colin R. Green (1982) *Chancery*; John McCarroll (1988) *Chancery.*

THE CORN EXCHANGE (David Steer QC & I. Goldrein)

CIVIL: Ian Goldrein (1975) *Commercial, Personal Injury (including Medical Negligence)*; Margaret de Haas (1977) *Personal Injury (including Medical Negligence)* ; Kevin Grice (1977) *Civil*;

FAMILY: Margaret de Haas (1977) *Financial*; Andrew Loveridge (1983); Janet Reaney (1987);

CRIME: David Steer QC (1974, 1993); David Aubrey (1974); Richard Pratt (1980).

Manchester

The Manchester bar provides an excellent commercial service to solicitors through three specialised courts: the Mercantile Court, the Chancery Court (used in particular for company law disputes and insolvency) and the Official Referees Court which deals with building disputes and other complex cases.

40 King St group of experienced planning practitioners includes John Hoggett QC, Andrew Gilbart QC, Stephen Sauvain and Francis Patterson. The set also provides able counsel in the area of general commercial law, most notably Peter Smith QC, Philip Raynor and Paul Chaisty.

Peel Court Chambers has a number of well-known licensing specialists, including John Hugill QC and Michael Shorrock QC, who is also a leading criminal practitioner.

9 St. John Street and *Deans Court Chambers* offer a wide range of commercial and civil expertise. At *9 St. John Street* John Hand QC and Nicholas Hinchcliffe have excellent reputations for employment law, as does Michael Johnson for his chancery work. Gillian Irving is well regarded for her family practice. At *Deans Court Chambers* Raymond Machell QC is known for his expertise in personal injury law, and Michael Black is highly regarded in the field of construction law. Alan Booth is well thought of for family work.

Byrom Chambers and *St. James's Chambers* also contain counsel experienced in the civil law field. At *Byrom Chambers* Giles Wingate-Saul QC, Brian Leveson QC and Geoffrey Frank Tattersall QC all have good reputations for their commercial practices. At *St. James's Chambers* Robert Sterling, Anthony Elleray QC and Mark Cawson are all known for their chancery and commercial work.

One of the leading family law sets is that of Charles Bloom QC at *28 St. John St.* Its team of well-respected practitioners includes Charles Bloom QC, Lindsay Kushner QC, Bernard Wallwork, Sarah Singleton and Charles Eastwood.

At *Lincoln House Chambers* Mukhtar Hussain QC is well regarded for his work in immigration law. David Sumner has a strong reputation in general crime and commercial fraud.

At *Young Street Chambers* Lesley Newton is respected for her family work. Ernst Ryder at *8 King Street* is well known in the same field.

Notable Practitioners - Manchester

BRIDGE ST CHAMBERS (Peter Keenan)
CIVIL: John Lambert (1977) *Computer, Intellectual Property*; Michael Heywood (1975) *Commercial*.

BYROM CHAMBERS (B.A. Hytner QC)
CIVIL: Ben Hytner QC (1952, 1970) *Personal Injury*; Giles Wingate Wingate-Saul QC (1967, 1983) *Chancery, Commercial*; David Clarke QC (1965, 1979) *Personal Injury*; Brian Leveson QC (1970, 1986) *Commercial*; Geoffrey Frank Tattersall QC (1970, 1992) *Commercial, Personal Injury*; Timothy King QC (1973, 1991) *Personal Injury*; Caroline Swift QC (1977, 1993) *Personal Injury* ; Andrew Moran QC (1976, 1994) *Commercial*; Michael Black QC (1978, 1995) *Commercial, Construction*.

CRIME: Brian Leveson QC (1970, 1986); John Price QC (1961, 1980).

DEANS COURT CHAMBERS (H.K. Goddard QC)
CIVIL: Raymond Machell QC (1973, 1988) *Personal Injury; Professional Negligence*; Stephen Grime QC (1970, 1987) *Commercial, Personal Injury, Construction*; John R. Gregory (1972) *Chancery*; Mark Turner (1981) *Personal Injury, Commercial*;Craig Sephton (1981) *Commercial, Personal Injury*; Patrick Field (1981) *Personal Injury*; David Stockdale QC (1975, 1995) *Personal Injury*; Philip Butler (1979) *Personal Injury; Professional Negligence*; Timothy Smith (1982) *Commercial*.

FAMILY: Diane Eaglestone (1971); Alan Booth (1978); Karen Brody (1986);

CRIME: David Poole QC (1968; 1984); Richard Henriques QC (1967, 1986); Kevin Talbot (1970).

5 JOHN DALTON ST (J.C.W. Bailey)
CIVIL: Nicholas Fewtrell (1977) *Commercial*; Timothy R. Ryder (1977) *Personal Injury*; Paul Holmes (1979) *Employment*; Keith Thomas (1969) *Personal Injury*.

HOLLINS CHAMBERS (Howard Baisden)
CIVIL: David Berkley (1979) *Commercial*; Stephen Coyley (1984) *Commercial*.

8 KING ST (Brendan Hegarty QC)
CIVIL: Thomas Brendan Hegarty QC (1970, 1992) *Chancery, Commercial*; Keith Armitage (1970) *Medical Negligence*; Tim Mort (1972) *Employment, Professional Negligence*; David Eccles (1976) *Personal Injury*; Jeffrey Terry (1977) *Commercial, Insolvency*; Gerard McDermott (1978) *Employment, Personal Injury*; Digby Jess (1978) *Professional Negligence, Commercial*; Philip Holmes (1980) *Commercial, Personal Injury*; Peter Main (1981) *Personal Injury*; Stephen Davies (1985) *Commercial, Banking*; Michael Smith (1989) *Personal Injury*;

FAMILY: Ernest Ryder (1981) *Children*; Elisabeth Rylands (1973); Kim Foudy (1982).

40 KING ST (John Hoggett QC)
CIVIL: Peter Smith QC (1975, 1992) *Chancery, Commercial*; Andrew Gilbart QC (1972, 1991) *Planning*; John Hoggett QC (1969, 1986) *Planning*; Stephen Sauvain (1977) *Planning*; Frances Patterson (1977) *Planning*; Philip Raynor (1973) *Commercial*; Paul Chaisty (1982) *Insolvency, Commercial*; Nicholas Braslavsky (1983) *Personal Injury*; Mark Halliwell (1985) *Chancery*; Simon Hilton (1987) *Commercial*; Fiona Ashworth (1988) *Personal Injury*.

FAMILY   : Philip Raynor (1973) *Finance*; Sonia Gal (1983); Fiona Ashworth (1988).

CRIME   : Roger Farley QC (1974, 1993); John Jackson (1970).

38 KING ST WEST (Paul Chambers)
CIVIL: John McNeill (1974) *Personal Injury*; Peter Harrison (1983) *Personal Injury*.

58 KING ST. (Beverly Lunt)
FAMILY: Beverly Lunt (1977).

LINCOLN HOUSE CHAMBERS (Mukhtar Hussain QC)
CIVIL: Mukhtar Hussain QC (1971, 1992) *Immigration*; David Allan (1974) *Personal Injury*;

CRIME: David Sumner (1963) *Commercial Fraud*; James Gregory (1970); Mukhtar Hussain QC (1971, 1992); Guy Gozem (1972); James Pickup (1976); Peter Wright (1981); Andrew Nuttall (1978).

MANCHESTER HOUSE CHAMBERS (J.D.S. Wishart)
CRIME: John Wishart (1974); Wayne Jackson (1984); Timothy Brennand (1987); Brendan Kelly (1988).

OLD COLONY HOUSE (Susan Klonin) :
CIVIL: F.M.Khan (1988) *Immigration*.

CRIME: Susan Klonin (1970).

PEEL COURT CHAMBERS (Michael Shorrock QC)
CIVIL: Michael Shorrock QC (1966, 1988) *Licensing, Medical Negligence, Personal Injury*; John Hugill QC (1954, 1976) *Licensing*; Christopher Melton (1982) *Medical Negligence, Personal Injury*;

FAMILY: Fiorella Brereton (1979);

CRIME: Michael Shorrock QC (1966, 1988); Anthony Morris QC (1970, 1991); Richard Marks (1975); Andrew Long (1981).

ST. JAMES'S CHAMBERS (R.A. Sterling)
CIVIL: Robert Sterling (1970) *Chancery*; Anthony Elleray QC (1977, 1993) *Chancery*; Peter Cawson (1982) *Chancery*;

CRIME: Arthur Stuttard (1967); Barrie Searle (1975).

FAMILY: Barrie Searle (1975).

9 ST. JOHN STREET (John Hand QC)
CIVIL: Michael Johnson (1971) *Chancery*; Charles Garside QC (1972, 1993) *Employment*; John Hand QC (1977, 1988) *Employment*; Ian Leeming QC (1970, 1988) *Chancery*; Jonathan Parkin (1978) *Employment*; Nicholas Hinchcliffe (1980) *Employment, Personal Injury*; Timothy Horlock (1981) *Employment, Personal Injury*; Nigel Grundy (1983) *Personal Injury*; Paul Gilroy (1985) *Personal Injury*; Ian Little (1989) *Personal Injury*; Christopher Kennedy (1989); *Personal Injury*;

FAMILY: Leslie Portnoy (1961); Christine Riley (1974); Gillian Irving (1984);

CRIME: Roderick Carus QC (1971, 1990); Charles Garside QC (1972, 1993); Nicholas Clarke (1981); Michael Murray (1979); Michael Leeming (1983).

18 ST. JOHN STREET (Rodney C. Klevan QC)
CIVIL: Mark Laprell (1979) *Commercial, Personal Injury*; Alastair Forrest (1972); *Personal Injury*; David Heaton (1983) *Personal Injury, Commercial*.

FAMILY: Andrew Blake (1971) *Financial*; Alastair Forrest (1972) *Financial*;

CRIME: Rodney Klevan QC (1966, 1984); Jonathan Foster QC (1970, 1989); Peter Birkett QC (1972, 1989); Jonathan Geake (1969); Martin Steiger (1969); William Morris (1970); Raymond Wigglesworth (1974).

28 ST. JOHN ST (Charles Bloom QC)

CIVIL: Anthony Rumbelow QC (1967, 1990) *Planning*; Michael Redfern QC (1970, 1993) *Personal Injury*; Stephen Stewart (1975) *Civil, Personal Injury*; Charles Chruszcz QC (1973, 1992) *Civil*; Clive Freedman (1978) *Commercial* (Door Tenant); Philip Grundy (1980) *Personal Injury*; James Rowley (1987) *Personal Injury*.

FAMILY: Charles Bloom QC (1963, 1987); Lindsay Kushner QC (1974, 1992); Martin Allweis (1970); Bernard Wallwork (1976); Sarah Singleton (1983); Charles Eastwood (1988);

CRIME: Anthony Rumbelow QC (1967, 1990); Anthony Gee QC (1972, 1990); Clement Goldstone QC (1971, 1993); Philip Cattan (1970); Paul Taylor (1985); Rowena Goode (1974).

YOUNG STREET CHAMBERS (Christopher Limb)

FAMILY: Lesley Newton (1977).

CRIME: Philip Andrews (1977).

Preston

Preston has four sets of chambers. *15 Winckley Square*, has 25 tenants, among whom, Stephen Dodds, Barbara Watson and Jane Cross, are well-known for their wardship and family cases; David Kenny for his civil litigation work, particularly personal injury and insurance litigation; Peter Anderson for his personal injury work; and Roger Baldwin for his criminal practice. *New Bailey Chambers* is an expanding common law set which handles chancery, personal injury, family and crime. The remaining two sets are annexes: *Deans Court Chambers* is an annexe of a set of the same name in Manchester. The other, *4 Camden Place*, is an annexe of *5 John Dalton St*. Keith Thomas of this set handles a large amount of criminal work.

THE NORTH EASTERN CIRCUIT

Bradford, Hull, Leeds, Middlesborough, Newcatle upon Tyne, Sheffield & York.

Bradford

Broadway House, the only set of chambers in Bradford, undertakes general common law work. Among the tenants, Martin Wood is considered to be a leading specialist in family law, with David Kelly and Gordon Shelton also well regarded in this field, and David Mitchell, Roger Thomas and Jonathan Rose are known for their criminal law work.

Hull

The one set of chambers in Hull, *Wilberforce Chambers*, is a general common law set, which specialises in family law, civil litigation and crime. Paul Miller is known for his general civil practice, Bernard Gateshill for his personal injury

work, Jane Hands and John Godfrey for family law, and Paul Genney and Tony Stevenson for criminal law.

Leeds

The Leeds Bar is handling an increasing amount of civil and commercial work and is therefore keen to acquire its own Mercantile Court.

It has maintained its reputation for insolvency, with Hugo Groves (*Enterprise Chambers*), James Allen QC (*39 Park Square*), John Behrens (*10 Park Square*) and David Rose (*6 Park Square*) highly regarded in this field.

Park Court Chambers is the largest of the 12 sets in Leeds with a strong contingent of well-established criminal silks and juniors including James Stewart QC, Robert Smith QC, Simon Bourne-Arton QC and Simon Jackson. *St. Paul's Chambers* also have several experienced criminal practitioners handling serious fraud and large criminal cases.

Family practitioners remain relatively well spread throughout the 12 sets. Jane Shipley and Eleanor Hamilton of *6 Park Square*, are highly regarded, as is Sally Cahill of *39 Park Square*. Elizabeth O'Hare of *Pearl Chambers* and Paul Issacs of *9 Woodhouse Square* are also recognised in this field.

Notable Practitioners - Leeds

ENTERPRISE CHAMBERS (Benjamin Levy)

CIVIL: Hugo Groves (1980) *Chancery, Commercial, Insolvency*; Charles Morgan (1978) *Commercial*.

PARK COURT CHAMBERS (Gilbert Gray QC & Brian Walsh QC)

CIVIL: Robert Smith QC (1971, 1986) *Civil*; David Hatton (1976) *Personal Injury*; Simon Jackson (1982) *Personal Injury*; Alistair McDonald (1983) *Civil*; Michael Taylor (1980) *Personal Injury*;

CRIME: Gilbert Gray QC (1953, 1971); James Chadwin QC (1958, 1978); James Stewart QC (1966, 1982); Michael Harrison QC (1969, 1989); Malcolm Swift QC (1970, 1990); Robert Smith QC (1971, 1986); Simon Bourne-Arton QC (1975, 1994); Tom Bayliss (1977); Simon Jackson (1982); Simon Myerson (1986).

6 PARK SQUARE (Shaun M. Spencer QC)

CIVIL: David Rose (1977) *Insolvency*; James Goss (1975) *Personal Injury*;

FAMILY: Jane Shipley (1974); Eleanor Hamilton (1979) *Children*;

CRIME: Stephen W. Williamson QC (1964, 1981); Simon Lawler QC (1971, 1993); Tim Stead (1979); Eleanor Hamilton (1979).

10 PARK SQUARE (A.N. Campbell QC)

CIVIL: John Behrens (1972) *Chancery, Insolvency, Personal Injury*; John Munkman (1948) *Personal Injury*; Andrew Dallas (1978) *Commercial, Company, Personal Injury*;

CRIME: Andrew Campbell QC (1972, 1994); Julian Goose (1984)

FAMILY: Julian Goose (1984).

25 PARK SQUARE (J.H. Muir)

CIVIL: Charles Ekins (1980) *Commercial*;

CRIME: John Muir (1969) *Fraud*; Stephen Gullick (1971); Geoffrey Marson (1975);

FAMILY: Marilyn Fricker (1969); Peter Hunt (1974); Steven Garth (1983).

32 PARK SQUARE (J.W. Mellor)

FAMILY: Jill Black QC (1976,1994); Louise Hallam (1984);

CRIME: Peter Collier QC (1970, 1992).

37 PARK SQUARE (John Sleightholme)

CIVIL: Paul Kirtley (1982) *Personal Injury*;

FAMILY: Stephen Glover (1978); Rodney Ferm (1972); Amanda Ginsburg (1985);

CRIME: Stephen Glover (1978).

39 PARK SQUARE (T.M.A. Bubb)

CIVIL: James Allen QC (1973, 1995) *Chancery, Insolvency*;

CRIME: Timothy Bubb (1970);

FAMILY: Sally Cahill (1978).

PEARL CHAMBERS (Martin Bethel QC)

CIVIL: Martin Bethel QC (1965, 1983) *Personal Injury*; Stuart Brown QC (1974, 1991) *Personal Injury*; Howard Elgot (1974) *Personal Injury*; George Sigsworth (1977) *Personal Injury*; David Zucker (1986) *Personal Injury*; Christopher Saul (1987) *Personal Injury*;

FAMILY: Angela Finnerty (1976); Elizabeth O'Hare (1980); Lindy Armitage (1985).

ST. PAUL'S CHAMBERS (Nigel Sangster)

CRIME: David Wilby (1974); Peter Benson (1975); Colin Harvey (1975); Ian Dobkin (1971); Nigel Sangster (1976); Jeremy Barnett (1980); Guy Keal(1982); Andrew Lees (1984); Howard Crowson (1987); Andrew Stubbs (1988); Christopher Batty (1989).

9 WOODHOUSE SQUARE (John Morris Collins)

CIVIL: Benjamin Nolan QC (1971, 1992) *Personal Injury, Medical Negligence*; Raphael Cohen (1981) *Insolvency*;

CRIME: Gerald Lumley (1972); Simon Jack (1974);

FAMILY: Paul Isaacs (1974); Raphael Cohen (1981); Helen Hendry (1983) *Children*; Roger Bickerdike (1986).

Middlesborough

There are 3 sets of chambers in Middlesborough. *Fountain Chambers* under Peter J.B. Armstrong is a broadly-based set specialising in all areas of the law. At *Cleveland Chambers* several members specialise in family, criminal and employment law. *Counsels' Chambers* under Stuart Lightwing handle a wide variety of work including landlord & tenant, commercial law, administrative law, professional negligence and personal injury matters.

Newcastle upon Tyne

There are four sets of chambers in Newcastle, all of which undertake a wide range of work.

At *Trinity Chambers*, John Milford QC and Toby Hedworth are well-known for their criminal expertise. Rachel Hudson has an excellent reputation as a family lawyer. Ian Atherton is recognised for his construction expertise and Simon Wood is well-known for his personal injury work. The set has strong chancery and commercial groups with approximately ten members of chambers specialising in these fields.

At *New Court Chambers* David Robson QC and Glenn Gatland are well regarded for their criminal work. Jeremy Freedman is known for personal injury litigation, and Paul Cape is highly regarded for his expertise in employment law.

From *Broad Chare Chambers*, Christopher Walton handles employment law, Sally Bradley, handling many wardship cases, is highly regarded for her family law work, Paul Batty and Eric Elliott have strong reputations in criminal law, and John Mitchell handles a large amount of medical negligence work.

Two barristers noted for non-contentious work, particularly in land law and trusts, are C.J.F Vane of *Trinity Chambers* and Ian Dawson at *67 Westgate Rd*.

Members of the London set of chambers, *No.1 Plowden Buildings*, undertake a large amount of work on the North Eastern Circuit. William Lowe, David Trotter and Jonathan Holmes all handle personal injury work. Michael Heywood and Catherine Foster are recognised for general commercial law. David Trotter and Peter Morton handle employment law. Jane Probyn is known for family law and in particular child care work.

Sheffield and York

Sheffield has three sets of chambers all of which cover the whole range of general common law. At *12 Paradise Square* Annabelle Walker and Graham Robinson have strong reputations in matrimonial law, Peter Heppel QC has an excellent reputation for his general civil practice, and Roger Keen QC, Michael Murphy QC and Jeremy Baker are well-known for their criminal law practice. James Baird and Peter Kelson of *Bank House Chambers* also handle criminal law work, as does Ian Storey of *Figtree Lane Chambers*.

The one set of chambers in York, *York Chambers*, also undertakes the whole range of general common law. Simon Hawkesworth QC is highly regarded for his medical negligence work. Michael Taylor and Michael Bowerman are recommended for criminal and personal injury law. Martin Lindsay handles a large amount of general civil work.

CHAMBERS & PARTNERS'

DIRECTORY OF THE LEGAL PROFESSION

Barristers' A–Z

A–Z DIRECTORY OF THE BAR – LONDON

1
et No.

ARBITRATION CHAMBERS (John Tackaberry QC)

22 WILLES ROAD, LONDON, NW5 3DS
DX: 46454 Kentish Town

TEL: (0171) 267 2137
FAX: (0171) 482 1018

MEMBERS:
John Tackaberry QC (1967)(QC-1982), Derrick Morris (1983).

THE CHAMBERS: John Tackaberry is a specialist practitioner whose principal area of expertise is international and domestic construction disputes: and in related areas. Acts as advocate both in litigation and arbitration and also as arbitrator with particular experience in ICC arbitrations.

He is a Registered Arbitrator and admitted to various panels of Arbitrators in this country. He is also a Fellow of the Chartered Institute of Arbitrators and the Faculty of Building. He is admitted to practise at the Bars of California and the Irish Republic and as a QC in New South Wales. Ex-chairman of C.I.Arb, ex-president of Society of Construction Law & European Society of Construction Law. Member of and/or on the arbitration panels of the Chartered Institute of Arbitrators (Past Chairman), European Society of Construction Law (Past President), Faculty of Building (Fellow), UK Society of Construction Law (Past President), Inst. of Civil Engineers, Royal Inst. of British Architects, Los Angeles Center for Commercial Arbitration, American Arbitration Association; Association of Arbitrators in South Africa, Indian Council of Arbitration and Singapore International Arbitration Council.

Prior to being called to the Bar, Derrick Morris had a comprehensive career in the building and civil engineering industries. Since his call to the Bar he has had substantial experience as an advocate in building and civil engineering particularly in the field of arbitrations. A great deal of Mr Morris's experience has been gained in arbitration work in South East Asia and the Far East as well as in England and Wales.

Mr Morris has written and contributed articles and papers to a number of journals and conferences – particularly on legal matters in the construction and engineering field in South East Asia and the Far East.

Additional areas of practice include planning and local government, professional negligence and international law.

ASSOCIATE MEMBERS: Declan O'Mahoney, Brendan Kilty, Ben Beaumont and Karen Gough.

HEAD OF CHAMBERS:
John Tackaberry QC

SEN. CLERK:
Pearl O'Brien

TENANTS: 2

2
et No.

ARDEN CHAMBERS (Andrew Arden QC) Arden Chambers, 59 Fleet Street, London, EC4Y 1JU **Tel:** (0171) 353 3132 **Fax:** (0171) 353 2774 **DX:** 29 (Ch.Ln.) **Sen. Clerk:** Andrea Tracy **Tenants:** 16 A specialist set, particularly for housing, landlord and tenant, local government and related fields (English and European).

3
et No.

ATKIN CHAMBERS (Anthony Butcher QC)

1 ATKIN BUILDING, GRAY'S INN, LONDON, WC1R 5AT
DX: 1033

TEL: (0171) 404 0102
FAX: (0171) 405 7456

MEMBERS:
Anthony Butcher QC (1957)(QC-1977), Ian Duncan Wallace QC (1948)(QC-1973), Desmond Wright QC (1950)(QC-1974), Brian Knight QC (1964)(QC-1981), John Blackburn QC (1969)(QC-1984), Colin Reese QC (1973)(QC-1987), Robert Akenhead QC (1972)(QC-1989), Nicholas Dennys QC (1975)(QC-1991), Donald Valentine (1956), Darryl Royce (1976), Nicholas Baatz (1978), Andrew White (1980), Martin Bowdery (1980), Andrew Burr (1981),

HEAD OF CHAMBERS:
Anthony Butcher QC

SEN. CLERK:
Stuart Goldsmith, David Barnes

TENANTS: 28

Mark Raeside (1982), Delia Dumaresq (1984), Stephen Dennison (1986),
Andrew Goddard (1985), David Streatfeild-James (1986), William Godwin (1986),
Stephanie Barwise (1988), Simon Lofthouse (1988), Robert Clay (1989),
Peter Fraser (1989), Dominique Rawley (1991), Chantal-Aimee Doerries (1992),
Steven Walker (1993), Fiona Parkin (1993).

THE CHAMBERS: A set which has for over forty years specialised in all aspects of the law relating to construction and civil engineering. Formerly at 22 Old Buildings in Lincoln's Inn, chambers moved in 1987 to their present more spacious accommodation at 1 Atkin Building.

WORK UNDERTAKEN:

Main Areas of Work: The work of chambers covers the whole spectrum of construction activity: building contracts; civil engineering contracts; contracts for industrial process plants; contracts for the building of aircraft, ships, oil/gas exploration rigs and production platforms. Chambers work also embraces the law of torts in so far as it relates to construction and property disputes including professional negligence and rights relating to real property. Members advise upon, and act for, parties involved in both domestic and international projects. The majority of disputes arising in relation to international contracts are resolved by arbitration. In the domestic context, either litigation or arbitration may be appropriate and all members of chambers are able to act in either forum.

Additional Areas: Members of chambers also deal with computer law, insurance and reinsurance, planning, compensation and aspects of Government regulation which affect construction projects.

Direct Professional Access matters are accepted.

CHAMBERS FACILITIES: Chambers are equipped with up-to-date computers and office technology. The software is Wordperfect version 5.1. On request, 3.5 inch disks can be supplied, either in Wordperfect or ASCII. Documents may be exchanged via LIX (LON 075).

A brochure is available on request.

4
Set No.

BARNARDS INN CHAMBERS (Timothy Bowles)

HALTON HOUSE, 20/23 HOLBORN, LONDON, EC1N 2JD
DX: 336 Ch.Ln.

TEL: (0171) 242 8508
FAX: (0171) 404 3139

THE CHAMBERS: Barnards Inn Chambers was established in 1993 by a small group of experienced barristers with specialist practices in different fields. It operates as a professionally managed legal practice, offering the traditional services of the bar in a modern working environment with a flexible approach to meet the requirements of contemporary solicitors and their clients.

Each member of chambers has a particular area of expertise, and does not invite instructions outside that area. Overall, the chambers provide specialist advice and representation in a wide and complementary range of disciplines. The Director of Chambers and the Administrator assist instructing professionals in their choice of counsel and will give a candid assessment of a member's suitability and availability for a particular case.

Chambers is also an accredited Law Society external course provider with an in-house and open seminar programme. Chambers' brochure is available on request.

HEAD OF CHAMBERS:
Timothy Bowles

DIRECTOR OF CHAMBERS:
Andrea Kennedy

CHAMBERS ADMINISTRATOR:
Andrew Flanagan

TENANTS: 11

MEMBERS:

Timothy Bowles (1973), Piers Reed (1974), John Bryant (1976),
Simon Blackford (1979), Charles Bott (1979), Mark Love (1979),
Alan Saggerson (1981), Timothy C. Dutton (1985), Craig Moore (1989),
Fiona McCreath (1991), Scott Sullivan (1991).

WORK UNDERTAKEN: The major areas of practice covered by members of chambers include: banking, company/ commercial, consumer law, civil rights, criminal law, employment matters, environmental law (and the law relating to animals), family and matrimonial law, judicial review and local government law, insolvency, landlord and tenant, mortgages and guarantees, personal injury and professional negligence, travel and tourism, pollution, trading standards and fraud, trade descriptions and health and safety matters.

BARRISTERS COMMON LAW CHAMBERS (M. Rahman)
108 Brick Lane, London, E1 6RL **Tel:** (0171) 375 3012 **Fax:** (0171) 375 3068 **Sen.
Clerk:** Anjna Jossie **Tenants:** 2 Handle immigration, housing, family and general
common law set.

17 BEDFORD ROW (Allan Levy QC) 17 Bedford Row, London,
WC1R 4EB **Tel:** (0171) 831 7314 **Fax:** (0171) 831 0061 **DX:** 370 **Sen. Clerk:** Ian
Boardman **Tenants:** 20 General common law practice but with rapidly expanding
chancery and commercial expertise.

29 BEDFORD ROW CHAMBERS (Evan Stone QC)

29 BEDFORD ROW CHAMBERS, LONDON, WC1R 4HE

DX: 1044

TEL: (0171) 831 2626

FAX: (0171) 831 0626

MEMBERS:
Evan Stone QC (1954)(QC-1979), Lord Archer QC (1952)(QC-1971),
Augustus Ullstein QC (1970)(QC-1992), Timothy Scott QC (1975)(QC-1995),
John Zieger (1962), Peter Duckworth (1971), Peter Ralls (1972),
The Hon. Clare Renton (1972), Howard Shaw (1973), John Tonna (1974),
Mark Warwick (1974), Neil Sanders (1975), Philip Cayford (1975),
Charles Atkins (1975), Geoffrey Ames (1976), Simon Gill (1977),
Stephen Boyd (1977), Simon Edwards (1978), Michael Keane (1979),
Jonathan Ferris (1979), Deborah Bangay (1981), Ann Hussey (1981),
Nicholas Francis (1981), John Wilson (1981), Paul Storey (1982),
Lucy Stone (1983), Timothy Walker (1983), Nicholas Bowen (1984),
David Holland (1986), Stephen Reynolds (1987), Rupert Butler (1988),
Nicholas Chapman (1990), Robert Peel (1990), Nicola Gray (1990),
Jonathan Southgate (1992), Stuart Hornett (1992), Craig Barlow (1992),
Victoria Domenge (1993), Brenton Molyneux (1994), Duncan Kynoch (1994).

Door Tenant:
Professor Robert Upex.

HEAD OF CHAMBERS:
Evan Stone QC

CLERKS:
Robert Segal

TENANTS: 40

THE CHAMBERS: Bedford Row Chambers is a progressive and growing set committed
to providing its clients with an effective and efficient legal service. It works out of
one of the Bar's largest and most contemporary offices, having just added a further
50% to its office space by taking over its neighbouring premises. Bedford Row
Chambers resides in two Grade II listed buildings, completely modernised and wired
for the latest technology and with room to expand.

WORK UNDERTAKEN:
General Description: The work of the chambers is primarily in commercial, property,
family, personal injury and general common law and extends to a wide range of
litigation, advisory and drafting work.
Chancery: Breach of trust, Court of Protection, partnership, trusts, wills and probate.
Commercial: Arbitration, building and construction, commercial, companies, con-
sumer credit, contract, economic torts, guarantees, licensing, misrepresentation,
and sale of goods.
Common Law: Injunctions, employment, libel and slander, nuisance and property-related torts, personal injuries, tort, professional negligence.
Family: Family law and family provision.
Intellectual Property: Confidential information, intellectual property, copyright and
passing off, trade marks and trade names.
Insolvency: Bankruptcy, insolvency, liquidations and administrations and receivership.
Property: Conveyancing, housing, land law, landlord and tenant, mortgages and
securities, planning, rent reviews.

33 BEDFORD ROW (David Barnard) 33 Bedford Row, London, WC1R 4JH **Tel:** (0171) 242 6476 **Fax:** (0171) 831 6065 **DX:** 75 **Sen. Clerk:** Neville Ackerley **Tenants:** 28 General common law set. Specialists in the following areas: landlord and tenant and property work, criminal law, personal injury, family and matrimonial.

48 BEDFORD ROW (Roderick I'Anson Banks)

48 BEDFORD ROW, LONDON, WC1R 4LR
DX: 284 LDE

TEL: (0171) 430 2005
FAX: (0171) 831 4885

MEMBERS:
Roderick I'Anson Banks (1974) LLB London, Charles J. Bonney (1969) MA (Oxon).

THE CHAMBERS: A set of chambers specialising exclusively in partnership law which provides solicitors and other professional and trading partnerships with a full range of legal services, from the drafting of new agreements and the review of existing agreements to advice and representation in partnership disputes, arbitrations and mediations.

We aim, where possible, to assist clients with the process of resolving disputes without recourse to litigation and provide constant support from the embryonic stages of a developing dispute right through to the conclusion of any litigation or until a negotiated settlement is reached.

Partnership Healthcheck (leaflet available) has been specifically developed to assist solicitors' firms in preparing and updating their agreements. Direct Professional Access work is undertaken.

PUBLICATIONS: Roderick I'Anson Banks is the editor of *Lindley & Banks on Partnership*, the recently revised edition of the authoritative guide to partnership law, and the author and editor of the *Encyclopedia of Professional Partnerships*. Charles Bonney is the author of *Solicitors Partnerships – the Law in Practice* and is contributor to the revised 4th ed. of Halsbury's Laws of England.

HEAD OF CHAMBERS:
Roderick I'Anson Banks

PRACTICE MANAGER:
Mrs Kim Pangratis

TENANTS: 2

9 BEDFORD ROW (Stephen Coward QC)

9 BEDFORD ROW, LONDON, WC1R 4AZ
DX: 347 (Ch.Ln.)

TEL: (0171) 242 3555
FAX: (0171) 242 2511

THE CHAMBERS: The chambers of Stephen Coward QC at 9 Bedford Row are a long-established set of chambers, whose members have a wide experience of advocacy and advisory work in a number of specialised fields. Instructions are accepted from lawyers and professional clients in the United Kingdom and from abroad.

WORK UNDERTAKEN:

Civil Litigation: Chambers advise upon and present cases in the following areas:- building and construction work, commercial contracts, computer and information technology law, employment and labour law, insurance and reinsurance law, inheritance and family provision, landlord and tenant, partnership disputes, compensation for personal injury and death, product liability and consumer law, professional negligence and malpractice. Chambers belong to the Alternative Dispute Register.

Criminal Law: Chambers undertake all types of serious criminal work both for the prosecution and defence, and within chambers there are specialists in commercial and international fraud, revenue and tax, food and drugs, health and safety, trade descriptions and road traffic.

Tribunals: Members of chambers appear and advise in Criminal Injuries Compensation Board cases, disciplinary tribunals of professional and other bodies, European law in the domestic context, industrial tribunals and the Employment Appeal Tribunal, judicial review and Divisional Court work, licensing, public inquiries and Sunday trading.

HEAD OF CHAMBERS:
Stephen Coward QC

SEN. CLERK:
Christopher A. Owen

TENANTS: 44

9
BEDFORD
ROW

For any further information concerning individual members of chambers and areas of practice, as well as the current level of fees and charging rates, please contact the Senior Clerk, Mr. Christopher Owen.

FOREIGN CONNECTIONS AND LANGUAGES SPOKEN: Instructions are welcomed from overseas lawyers directly. Several members of chambers speak one or more foreign languages fluently; and several members have taught and lectured on legal matters in the United States. There are practising door tenants in Bermuda, Hong Kong and Jersey.

11
Set No.

5 BELL YARD (Robert Webb QC)

5 BELL YARD, LONDON, WC2A 2JR   TEL: (0171) 333 8811
DX: 400   FAX: (0171) 333 8831

MEMBERS:
Robert Webb QC (1971)(QC-1988), Robin Mathew QC (1974)(QC-1992), Michael Crane QC (1975)(QC-1994), Edward Bailey (1970), Andrew Hillier (1972), Dennis Matthews (1973), Kenneth Munro (1973), Gordon Bennett (1974), Philip Shepherd (1975), Angus Macpherson (1977), Michael Soole (1977), Anthony Radevsky (1978), Andrew Lydiard (1980), Paul Dean (1982), Charlotte Jones (1982), Michael Sullivan (1983), Giles Kavanagh (1984), David Fisher (1985), Philip Reed (1985), Matthew Reeve (1987), Stephen Schaw-Miller (1988), Raymond Ng (1987), Robert Lawson (1989), Akhil Shah (1990), Hannah Brown (1992), William Hansen (1992), John Russell (1993).

DOOR TENANTS:
Philip Goodenday (1946), Richard Gardiner (1969), Kamala Das (1975), Richard Selwyn Sharpe (1985), Ralph Wynne-Griffiths (1981).

WORK UNDERTAKEN: Members of 5 Bell Yard practise in most areas of civil and commercial law. In particular, expertise is offered by individual members in one or more of the following:

Aviation Law: Liability – passenger and cargo; leasing; regulatory – C.A.A. and European; insurance.

Commercial Law: Banking; carriage of goods; commercial contracts; company and insolvency; insurance and reinsurance; tax.

Civil Law: Building and engineering; landlord and tenant; personal injury; professional and medical negligence; product and environmental liability; mass disasters.

Public and Employment Law: Judicial review; mental health; National Health service; pharmaceutical; coroners; town & country planning; individual and collective employment; trade union; disciplinary tribunals; public inquiries.

HEAD OF CHAMBERS:
Robert Webb QC

SEN. CLERK:
Kevin Moore

TENANTS: 27

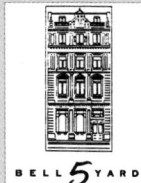

BELL 5 YARD

12
Set No.

9-12 BELL YARD (Edmund Lawson QC)

9-12 BELL YARD, LONDON, WC2   TEL: (0171) 400 1800
DX: 390   FAX: (0171) 404 1405

THE CHAMBERS: An established common law set. The chambers originally had a strong 'criminal' bias, but in the last decade, Chambers have, whilst retaining a number of criminal law specialists, extended further into general common law areas, with the result that a wide spectrum of expertise is offered. Members are actively engaged in assisting various professional organisations in the continued development of the Bar's work.

MEMBERS:
Edmund Lawson QC (1971)(QC-1988) MA (Cantab),
D. Anthony Evans QC (1965)(QC-1983) BA (Cantab),
Alex Carlile QC (1970)(QC-1984), Jeremy Carter-Manning QC (1975)(QC-1993),
Herbert Kerrigan QC (1970)(QC-1992), Edward Grayson (1948) MA (Oxon),
Peter Caton (1963) MA (Oxon), Richard Cherrill (1967), Martin Field (1966),

HEAD OF CHAMBERS:
Edmund Lawson QC

SEN. CLERK:
Thomas Dixon, Gary Reed

TENANTS: 42

Sonia Woodley (1968), Martin Binning (1969), Ross Fitzpatrick (1972),
Alison Barker (1973) LLB, Harmsworth Law Scholar 1973,
John Greaves (1973) LLB (Lond), Anthony Heaton-Armstrong (1973),
Tudor Owen (1974) LLB (Lond), Alexander Cranbrook (1975) BA,
Peter Doyle (1975) LLB, Stephen John (1975), John Harwood-Stevenson (1975),
Timothy Spencer (1976), Philip Katz (1976), Peter Moss (1976),
Keith Hadrill (1977), Michael Orsulik (1978), Diane Chan (1979),
John Alban Williams (1979), John McGuinness (1980), Michael Egan (1981),
Mukul Chawla (1983), Christine Laing (1984), Philippa McAtasney (1985),
Tracey Elliott (1986), Mark Bryant-Heron (1986), Rosina Cottage (1988),
William Hughes (1989), Adrian Chaplin (1990), Alexandra Healy (1992),
Mark Seymour (1992), Richard Jory (1993), Suzanne Reeve (1993),
Warwick Tatford (1993).

WORK UNDERTAKEN:

Civil: Professional negligence (particularly accountancy/ auditing), commercial contract, building and arbitration, banking, company and general chancery, tort (including personal injury), planning, local government, family, and landlord and tenant.

Criminal: Defence and prosecution work undertaken. Many members specialise in fraud work.

Additional areas: Judicial review, police work (discipline, advisory and union work), licensing, aviation and sports-related problems.

CLIENTELE: Lay clients include the solicitors and accountancy professions, City institutions, the Police Federation and its members, local government organisations, retailers, brewing and allied organisations, and a varied private clientele.

LANGUAGES SPOKEN: French, German, Spanish, Russian, Hindi and Urdu.

RECRUITMENT & TRAINING: Tenancy applications to Edmund Lawson QC. On average, there are four pupils in chambers at any one time. Applications to Mark Bryant-Heron by mid-October, with detailed CV and references. Awards are currently under review. A good degree is essential.

13
Set No.

BELL YARD CHAMBERS Bell Yard Chambers, 116-118 Chancery Lane, London, WC2A 1PP **Tel:** (0171) 306 9292 **Fax:** (0171) 404 5143 **DX:** 0075 **Sen. Clerk:** Mrs Karen McGilvery **Tenants:** 22 A specialist criminal set of chambers established in 1989 which has expanded from 12 to 25 members.

14
Set No.

10 BOLT COURT (Stuart Cakebread)

10 BOLT COURT, LONDON, EC4A 3DB	TEL: (0171) 583 0510
DX: 496	FAX: (0171) 583 7770

THE CHAMBERS: A general common law set, which has continued to expand steadily since its establishment in 1983 and its move to its present location in 1987. Members accept instructions from the approved professions under the Direct Professional Access scheme.

MEMBERS:
Stuart Cakebread (1978), Janet Boston (1976), Alun Jenkins (1981), Nergis Anne Mathew (1981), Dean Powell (1982), William Holland (1982), Timothy Banks (1983), Neil Petersen (1983), Gabrielle Posner (1984), Charles Briefel (1984), Jonathan Whitfield (1985), Francis Moraes (1985), Jonathan Steinert (1986), Carlo Talacchi (1986), Jonathan Dunne (1986), Stuart Whitehouse (1987), Andrea Minichiello (1988), Christopher Maynard (1988), Clare Roberts (1988), Douglas Livingstone (1989), Janet Feather (1990), Christopher Rice (1991), Juliette Levy (1992), Caroline Whysall (1993), Robin Powell (1993).

WORK UNDERTAKEN: General chancery work, child law, consumer credit, criminal law, family law, housing, insolvency, judicial review, landlord and tenant, licensing, medical negligence, personal injury, planning and local government, professional negligence, and property and land law.

HEAD OF CHAMBERS:
Stuart Cakebread

SEN. CLERK:
Joanne Thomas

TENANTS: 25

15
Set No.

11 BOLT COURT **(Richard Mandel)** 11 Bolt Court, London, EC4A 3DQ **Tel:** (0171) 353 2300 **Fax:** (0171) 353 1878 **DX:** 0022 **Sen. Clerk:** John Bowker **Tenants:** 22 A general common law set, with several members also practising in criminal and family law. Planning and local authority work also important.

16
Set No.

BRACTON CHAMBERS **(Ian McCulloch)** Bracton Chambers, Hamilton House, 1 Temple Avenue, London, EC4Y 0HA **Tel:** (0171) 353 2557/4212 **Fax:** (0171) 353 3325 **DX:** 416 LDE **Sen. Clerk:** David Roberts **Tenants:** 5 A general common law set, handling a wide range of criminal, civil and matrimonial matters.

17
Set No.

4 BREAMS BUILDINGS (Christopher Lockhart-Mummery QC)

| 4 BREAMS BUILDINGS, LONDON, EC4A 1AQ | TEL: (0171) 430 1221 |
| DX: 1042 | FAX: (0171) 430 1677 |

THE CHAMBERS: A specialist planning and property set, which moved from 2 Paper Buildings to spacious, self-contained, air conditioned modern chambers, just off Chancery Lane. The accommodation has six floors, of which one is for administration and one dedicated to conference facilities.

HEAD OF CHAMBERS:
Christopher Lockhart-Mummery QC

SEN. CLERK:
Stephen Graham

JUN. CLERK Jay Fullilove

TENANTS: 35

MEMBERS:
Christopher Lockhart-Mummery QC (1971)(QC-1986),
Rt. Hon. Lord Rippon QC (1948)(QC-1964)*, Nigel Macleod QC (1961)(QC-1979),
Michael Barnes QC (1965)(QC-1981), John Cherryman QC (1955)(QC-1982) LLB,
Rt. Hon. Michael Howard QC (1964)(QC-1982), David Hands QC (1965)(QC-1988),
Kingsland QC (1972)(QC-1988), Joseph Harper QC (1970)(QC-1992),
John Howell QC (1979)(QC-1993), John Furber QC (1973)(QC-1995),
Richard Drabble QC (1975)(QC-1995), Richard Moshi (1955),
Colin Sydenham (1963) MA (Cantab), Stephen Bickford-Smith (1972),
Eian Caws (1974), Robert Bailey-King (1975), Anne Seifert (1975),
Peter Sutherland (1975), Christopher Lewsley (1976), John Male (1976),
David Holgate (1978), Rt. Hon Viscount Dilhorne (1979), David Smith (1980),
Anne Williams (1980), Christopher Katkowski (1982), Alice Robinson (1983),
David Elvin (1983), Jonathan Karas (1986), Timothy Mould (1987),
Nathalie Lieven (1989), John Litton (1989), Nicholas Taggart (1991),
Karen McHugh (1992), David Forsdick (1993).
* Rt. Hon. Michael Howard QC is presently the Member of Parliament for Folkestone and Home Secretary; Peter Sutherland is the former Director General of the General Agreement on Tariffs and Trade (GATT).

Members of chambers belong to both the Local Government, Planning and Environmental Bar Association, of which Nigel Macleod is Vice-Chairman and Anne Williams is Treasurer, and the Administrative Law Bar Association. The Rt. Hon. Lord Rippon QC and Stephen Bickford-Smith sit as arbitrators and the Rt. Hon. Viscount Dilhorne sits as a chairman of Value Added Tax tribunals. Christopher Katowski is a member of the Panel of Junior Counsel to the Crown, Common Law, and four other members of chambers are on the Supplementary Panel. David Holgate is Junior Counsel to the Inland Revenue on Rating and Valuation matters. In addition, five members of chambers are recorders.

Publications: *Works include: Hill's Law of Town and Country Planning (4th Edition); Town Planning Law Handbook and Casebook; Atkin's Court Forms – Town and Country Planning (editor); Hill and Redman's Law of Landlord and Tenant (several members are editors); Halsbury's Laws – Landlord and Tenant (contributory editors); Halsbury's Laws – Town & Country Planning (edited entirely within chambers); Encyclopaedia of Rating and Local Taxation (editor); Atkin's Court Forms – Rating and Community Charge and Journal of Planning Law (members of the Editorial Boards); Corfield and Carnwath's Compulsory Acquisition and Compensation; Halsbury's Laws – European Communities (contributory editors); Emden's Building Contracts and Practice (editor).*

WORK UNDERTAKEN:

Main Areas of Work: Administrative law; construction; environment; housing; judicial review; landlord and tenant; local government; parliamentary; planning and property.

Additional Areas: Agriculture; arbitration; European Community Law, international law, energy, consumer credit, financial services, revenue and tax law and welfare.

CLIENTELE: Developers, property companies, local authorities and government regulatory bodies. Members accept Direct Professional Access from the approved professions.

FOREIGN CONNECTIONS: Michael Barnes QC is a member of the Singapore Bar; Joseph Harper QC is a member of the Antigua Bar; and Peter Sutherland is an Attorney of the New York Bar and an Attorney and Counsellor of the Supreme Court of the USA.

ASSOCIATED CHAMBERS: 40 King Street, Manchester.

RECRUITMENT & TRAINING: Tenancy and pupillage applications should be addressed to Mr. David Elvin may be sent at any time. Six pupils are taken annually and awards totalling £30,000 are offered. Mini-pupillages are available – please apply to the clerk for further details.

18
Set No.

BRICK COURT CHAMBERS (Christopher Clarke QC) 15-19 Devereux Court, London, WC2R 3JJ **Tel:** (0171) 583 0777 **Fax:** (0171) 583 9401 **DX:** 302 **Sen. Clerk:** D. Neave **Tenants:** 41 The chambers specialise in commercial cases with particular emphasis on shipping, insurance, banking, administrative law, defamation and entertainment, and EC law.

19
Set No.

1 BRICK COURT (Richard Hartley QC)

1 BRICK COURT, TEMPLE, LONDON, EC4Y 9BY
DX: 468

TEL: (0171) 353 8845
FAX: (0171) 583 9144

HEAD OF CHAMBERS:
Richard Hartley QC

SEN. CLERK:
John Woodcock

TENANTS: 19

THE CHAMBERS: These chambers have specialised in the law of libel and slander for over 75 years. The work of chambers now also covers all aspects of media and information law, including contempt of court, breach of confidence, and broadcasting law; some general common law and commercial work and judicial review is undertaken.

MEMBERS:

Richard Hartley QC (1956)(QC-1976), Richard Rampton QC (1965)(QC-1987), David Eady QC (1966)(QC-1983), Geoffrey Shaw QC (1968)(QC-1991), Thomas Shields QC (1973)(QC-1993), Harry Boggis-Rolfe (1969), Andrew Caldecott QC (1975)(QC-1994), Edward Garnier QC (1976)(QC-1995), Patrick Moloney (1976), Stephen Suttle (1980), Victoria Sharp (1979), Harvey Starte (1985), Manuel Barca (1986), Timothy Atkinson (1988), Rupert Elliott (1988), Jane Phillips (1989), Caroline Addy (1991), Benjamin Hinchliff (1992), Giles Crown (1993).

Members of chambers are experienced in the pre-publication review of newspapers, books, radio and television programmes and have written or contributed to most of the leading works on defamation and contempt of court including Gatley on *Libel and Slander*, Duncan and Neill on *Defamation*, Carter-Ruck on *Libel and Slander*, Arlidge and Eady on *Contempt of Court*, *Halsbury's Laws of England*, *Bullen & Leake & Jacob's Precedents of Pleading* and *Atkin's Forms and Precedents*. Members of chambers frequently receive instructions from Commonwealth and foreign jurisdictions and frequently conduct cases in such jurisdictions.

20
Set No.

4 BRICK COURT (David Medhurst)

4 BRICK COURT, TEMPLE, LONDON, EC4Y 9AD
DX: 491

TEL: (0171) 797 8910
FAX: (0171) 797 8929

THE CHAMBERS: A progressive and expanding set who are able to provide a comprehensive service to solicitors.

MEMBERS:
Mr Edward Lyons QC (1952)(QC-1974), David Medhurst (1969),
Mervyn Burton (1973), Mira Chatterjee (1973), Nicholas Easterman (1975),
David Burgess (1975), Robert Colover (1975), Graham Clark (1976),
Andrew Turton (1977), Marianna Hildyard (1977), Janet Mitchell (1978),
Michael Haynes (1979), Fiona Rowling (1980), Graham Blower (1980),
Jane Hill (1980), Richard St Clair-Gainer (1983), Susan Quinn (1983),
Marc Roberts (1984), Peter Lynch (1985), Simon Molyneux (1986),
Matthew Farmer (1987), Michael Mylonas-Widdall (1988), Tobias Long (1988),
Beverly Cripps (1988), Colin Ishmael (1989), Alexa Rea (1990),
Abigail Sheppard (1990), Annabel Wentworth (1990), Peter Binder (1990),
Nicholas Dugdale (1992), Michael Simon (1992), Edward Knapp (1992),
Gwynneth Knowles (1993).
David Medhurst is the author of *A Brief and Practical Guide to EC Law*.

HEAD OF CHAMBERS:
David Medhurst

SEN. CLERK:
Michael Corrigan

TENANTS: 33

WORK UNDERTAKEN: The chambers are broadly divided into teams specialising in three main areas:
Criminal: for prosecution and defence, from motoring offences to murder and fraud. Edward Lyons QC specialises in mortgage and long-firm frauds.
Family and Matrimonial: particularly child care for solicitors and local authorities.
UK Commercial: all related aspects, such as company law, business tenancies, partnership law, sale of goods actions, employment law. Members practising in the commercial field are able to identify the European Community law applications.
In addition, members have specific areas of expertise in their individual practices, handling local government and administrative law, immigration, construction, housing, landlord and tenant, licensing, personal injury and police cases.

CLIENTELE: Individuals, local authorities and building societies. Members of chambers accept Direct Professional Access from the approved professions.

FOREIGN LANGUAGES: French, Italian, Spanish, Hindu, Russian, Greek.

RECRUITMENT & TRAINING: Tenancy applications should be sent to Robert Colover marked 'Tenancy'. Applications for pupillage should be sent to Jane Hill or Abigail Sheppard. At any one time, chambers have two first six months pupils, and two second six months pupils. Chambers' awards are in accordance with Bar Council recommendations. Mini-pupillages are available.

21
et No.

4 BRICK COURT (Anne Rafferty QC)

4 BRICK COURT, TEMPLE, LONDON, EC4Y 9AD
DX: 453

TEL: (0171) 583 8455
FAX: (0171) 353 1699

THE CHAMBERS: A long established set of chambers dealing mainly with criminal work. Chambers undertake both prosecution and defence cases in all criminal courts.

MEMBERS:
Anne J. Rafferty QC (1973)(QC-1990)*, H. Michael Self QC (1951)(QC-1973)*,
Mary W. Colton (1955)*, Patricia May (1965)+, Richard Germain (1968),
Jane Lockyer (1970), Andrew Bright (1973), Shane Sheridan (1973),
Jane Mirwitch (1974), Owen J. Williams (1974), Peter Testar (1974),
Derek Zeitlin (1974), Antony B. Pitts (1975), Nicholas Jones (1975)+,
Anthony C. Berry QC (1976)(QC-1994), Robert Fortune (1976) LLB Hons (Lond),
Richard J. Carey-Hughes (1977), Elizabeth Marsh (1979), Jonathan Markson (1980),
Matthew A. Kennedy (1981), Justin Rouse (1982), Michael N. Speak (1983),
James Henderson (1984), Abbas Lakha (1984), Ignatius L. Hughes (1986),

HEAD OF CHAMBERS:
Anne Rafferty QC

SEN. CLERK:
Michael Eves

TENANTS: 32

David Whittaker (1986), John Cammegh (1987), Martin Polaine (1988),
Louise D'Arcy (1988), Simon Stirling (1989), Roger Smart (1989),
Iain Wicks (1990).
* *Recorder*
\+ *Assistant Recorder*

WORK UNDERTAKEN: All aspects of criminal law in courts ranging from the Magistrates' Court through to the Crown Court, the Court of Appeal Criminal Division, the House of Lords and the Privy Council. Chambers also undertake licensing work, police disciplinary hearings and court martial cases and some matrimonial cases.

RECRUITMENT & TRAINING: There is a pupillage committee – application with detailed CV and references to Patricia May. There are, on average, 4-10 pupils in chambers at any one time, with both 6 and 12 month pupillages available.

22
Set No.

4 BRICK COURT (Antony Shaw QC)

4 BRICK COURT, TEMPLE, LONDON, EC4Y 9AD
DX: 404 (Ch.Ln.)

TEL: (0171) 797 7766
FAX: (0171) 797 7700

THE CHAMBERS: Chambers undertake a wide range of work which falls into three main fields: civil, crime and family.

MEMBERS:
Mr Antony Shaw QC (1975)(QC-1994), Miss Angelica Mitchell (1972),
Edgar Prais (1990), Mr Adrian Taylor (1977), Miss Jane Drew (1976),
Miss Catherine Nicholes (1977), Mr Aditya Kumar Sen (1977),
Anthony Wadling (1977), Miss Vera Mayer (1978), Mrs Anne Spratling (1980),
Melanie Lewis (1980), Mr Martin Seaward (1978), Mrs Meena Gill (1982),
Mr Andrew Cohen (1982), Mrs Martha Cover (1979), Charles Burton (1983),
Mr Nicholas O'Brien (1985), Mr David Boyd (1977),
Miss Constance Briscoe (1983), Mr John Lyons (1986), Miss Anne Gibberd (1985),
Mr Mark Mullins (1988), Michael Magarian (1988), Declan O'Dempsey (1987),
Mr Peter Rowlands (1990), Mr Michael Conning (1990), Mr Piers Mostyn (1989),
Miss Frances Orchover (1989), Miss Fenella Morris (1990),
Mr Michael Baker (1990), Mr Andrew Short (1990), Miss Anthea Parker (1990),
Miss Julia Krish (1992), Miss Jillian Brown (1991), Michael Horton (1993),
Helen Curtis (1992).

WORK UNDERTAKEN:
Civil: Housing, landlord and tenant, personal injury, employment (including discrimination and trade union law), professional negligence (including medical negligence), judicial review, inquests, mental health, chancery, contract and consumer protection.
Crime: Including serious fraud and drugs.
Family: Including divorce, matrimonial finance, public and private Children Act proceedings, child abduction, domestic violence, adoption, wardship, inheritance and cohabitees.
LANGUAGES: French, Italian, Spanish, Bengali, Punjabi, Hindi, Hebrew and Slovak.

HEAD OF CHAMBERS:
Mr. Antony Shaw QC

CHAMBERS MANAGER:
Anne Bates

SENIOR CLERK:
Paul Sampson

1ST JUNIOR CLERK: Brendan O'Rourke
2ND JUNIOR CLERK: George Mo

OFFICE JUNIOR: Paul Rudd

TENANTS: 35

23
Set No.

BRIDEWELL CHAMBERS (Colin Challenger)

BRIDEWELL CHAMBERS, 2 BRIDEWELL PLACE, LONDON, EC4V 6AP
DX: 383

TEL: (0171) 797 8800
FAX: (0171) 797 8801

MEMBERS:
Colin Challenger (1970), Jo Boothby (1972), Gordon Pringle (1973),
Juliet Oliver (1974), Neville Willard (1976), Ernest James (1977),
Adrienne Knight (1981), Vincent Williams (1985), Ian Lawrie (1985),
David Josse (1985), Dafydd Enoch (1985), Adam Clemens (1985),
Simon Walsh (1987), Lauren Soertsz (1987), Patricia Roberts (1987),
Sally Atherton (1987), Jo Farquharson (1988), Cressida Burnet (1989),

HEAD OF CHAMBERS:
Colin Challenger

SEN. CLERK:
Norman Brooks

TENANTS: 25

Mark Graffius (1990), Paul Michell (1991), Carolyn Rothwell (1991),
Alan Walmsley (1991), Brian Cummins (1992),
Andrew Slaughter (1993), Lloyd Sefton-Smith (1993).

WORK UNDERTAKEN: All aspects of business and commercial law, professional negligence and Official Referee work. Crime.

Civil practices encompass personal injury work, police cases, judicial review, licensing, road traffic, matrimonial, children, employment, housing and landlord and tenant.

A significant proportion of chambers' work is undertaken on behalf of insurers.

Specialist criminal practitioners deal with all aspects of crime including commercial fraud.

LANGUAGES SPOKEN: French and German.

RECRUITMENT & TRAINING: Pupillage and tenancy applications may be sent at any time, to Ian Lawrie (with CV).

24
et No.
BRITTON STREET CHAMBERS (Marvin Gederon) First Floor, 20 Britton Street, London, EC1M 5NQ **Tel:** (0171) 608 3765 **Fax:** (0171) 608 3746 **DX:** 53329 Clerkenwell EC1 **Sen. Clerk:** Martyn Ellis **Tenants:** 15 Criminal and civil work including defence, Crown prosecution and immigration appeals.

25
et No.
BYROM CHAMBERS (B.A. Hytner QC) 61 Fleet Street, London, EC4Y 1JV **Tel:** (0171) 353 4363 **Fax:** (0171) 583 1491 **DX:** 341 **Sen. Clerk:** Peter Collison **Tenants:** 24 General common law set handling a wide range of matters including contracts, sale of goods, commercial intellectual property, employment law, crime, family, landlord and tenant and judicial review. Also in Manchester.

26
et No.
CHAMBERS OF MARTIN BURR (Martin Burr) Eldon Chambers, 30-32 Fleet Street, London, EC4Y 1AA **Tel:** (0171) 353 4636 **Fax:** (0171) 353 4637 **DX:** 463 (Ch.Ln.) **Sen. Clerk:** Colin Middleton **Tenants:** 21 The areas of law covered include: chancery (especially trusts, wills etc.), charities, common law, company, crime, ecclesiastical, employment, family and child welfare, landlord and tenant, personal injury, planning and local government, and revenue.

27
et No.
CHANCERY CHAMBERS (Lawrence St. Ville) 70-72 Chancery Lane, London, WC2A 3XD **Tel:** (0171) 405 6879 **Fax:** (0171) 430 0502 **Sen. Clerk:** D.P.A. Barnes **Tenants:** 23 Broadly-based common law chambers with the majority of the work being in the criminal sector. Also specialise in immigration, family law and housing.

28
et No.
74 CHANCERY LANE (M.R. Ameen) 74 Chancery Lane, Lincoln's Inn, London, WC2A 1AA **Tel:** (0171) 405 1833 **Fax:** (0171) 405 0291 **DX:** 62 London **Sen. Clerk:** Ms Sheila Twum-Barima **Tenants:** 10 A general common law set, with a criminal practice, also handling family and licensing work and specialising in immigration.

29
et No.
CLOISTERS (Miss C.V. Bevington) Cloisters, 1 Pump Court, Temple, London, EC4Y 7AA **Tel:** (0171) 583 5123 **Fax:** (0171) 353 3383 **DX:** 0018 **Sen. Clerk:** Mr Paul Bloomfield **Tenants:** 20 The chambers have a general practice with a wide range of work.

30
Set No.

CLOISTERS (David Turner-Samuels QC)

CLOISTERS, 1 PUMP COURT, TEMPLE, LONDON, EC4Y 7AA
DX: 452

TEL: (0171) 583 0303
FAX: (0171) 583 2254

HEAD OF CHAMBERS:
David Turner-Samuels QC

SEN. CLERK:
Michael Martin

TENANTS: 39

THE CHAMBERS: Cloisters is a progressive and expanding set of chambers fully equipped to meet the wide and growing demands of modern practice.

Chambers was founded in 1954 by D.N. Pritt QC, one of the most distinguished silks of his day. Pritt was a passionate champion of civil liberties within the rule of law both in the United Kingdom and around the world. Society and the law have changed dramatically since Pritt's day, but his views on law and justice are as relevant now as they have ever been.

Today, Cloisters remains committed to developing the service it provides to meet its clients' changing needs. Chambers provides a broad range of expertise while maintaining its specialist reputation in specific areas. Expansion of recent years into areas such as commercial work and media law has not reduced traditional commitments to civil liberties and the rights of the individual.

As well as recently providing more comfortable and spacious conference facilities, chambers has adopted new technology to support and enhance its administration to enable it to provide the best possible service to clients.

Cloisters welcomes direct access instructions from overseas lawyers and from those professions both in the United Kingdom and abroad who are entitled under the Bar Rules to use this facility.

MEMBERS:
David Turner-Samuels QC (1939)(QC-1972),
John Platts-Mills QC (1932)(QC-1964) MA, Anna Worrall QC (1959)(QC-1989) LLB, Alan Newman QC (1968)(QC-1989) MA, LLB (Cantab),
Elizabeth Lawson QC (1969)(QC-1989) LLB, Stephen Solley QC (1969)(QC-1989) LLB, Lawrence Kershen QC (1967)(QC-1992),
Philip Sapsford QC (1974)(QC-1992), Brian Langstaff QC (1971)(QC-1994) BA (Cantab), Laura Cox QC (1975)(QC-1994) LLB (Hons), LLM,
Arthur Davidson QC (1953)(QC-1976), Robin Allen QC (1974)(QC-1995) BA (Oxon), Roderick Price (1971) LLB, Stuart Montrose (1972) LLB,
Jonathan Crystal (1972), Vivienne Gay (1974) LLB, LLM, Peter Guest (1975) BA (Hons), Thomas Culver (1976) BA, JD, LLB (Cantab), DipCrim (Cantab),
Philip Hackett (1978), Philip Engelman (1979) LLB (Hons),
Jacques Algazy (1980) LLB. DES Eur, Anesta Weekes (1981) BA (Hons), Edward Quist-Arcton (1981) BA (Oxon), Gareth Rees (1981), Andrew Buchan (1981), Michael Turner (1984), Antony White (1983) BA (Cantab) (Law), Timothy Horgan (1982) BA (Hons), Jerome Lynch (1983) BA (Hons),
Pauline Hendy (1985) BA (Hons), Anthony Bradley (1989) BA, MA, LLM (Cantab), Patricia Hitchcock (1988) BA (Oxon), Paul Epstein (1988) BA (Oxon),
Paul Spencer (1988), Thomas Kibling (1990), Jason Galbraith-Marten (1991), Christopher Quinn (1992), Matthew Ryder (1992), Rufus D'Cruz (1993).

ASSOCIATE MEMBERS:
Peter Pimm, David Thomas, John Whitmore, Amir Majid.

WORK UNDERTAKEN: Members of chambers have continued to be involved in the development of important areas of the law. There is considerable overlap between the categories of work listed, and the cases set out below are examples of recent cases of interest in which members of chambers have been instructed:

Administrative/ Public/ Local Government Law: Members have appeared in a wide variety of cases in this important and developing field including the "charge-capping" cases, local and national government publicity cases (from GLC awareness campaign to poll tax leaflets), housing (**ex parte Puhlhofer**), education (**ex parte Gunning, McGoldrick v. Brent, R. v. Derbyshire CC ex parte Times Supplement, R.V. Cleveland and Secretary of State ex parte CRE**), universities (**Thomas v. Bradford University ex parte Vijayatunga, ex parte Page**), planning (**Rose Theatre Trust**), local authority conventions (**ex parte Lovelace**) and legal aid (**R. v. The Lord Chancellor ex parte The Law Society**).

Civil Liberties: Cloisters undertakes a wide variety of civil liberties work and in particular discrimination (sex and race), prisoners' rights and immigration and in support of minority or neglected groups. Cases of interest include discrimination in the workplace (**Price v. Civil Service Commission),** racial discrimination in the police (**PC Singh v. Chief Constable of Nottinghamshire,** and the army (**R. v. Defence Council ex parte Anderson and ex parte Malcolm and Khan v. General Medical Council),** racial discrimination in Bar Finals (**Ershad v. The Council of Legal Education and the Bar Council),** oppressive acts by public and private bodies (**R. v. Barnet, ex parte Johnson),** secrecy surrounding acts of state (**ex parte Hosenball),** prisoners (**Payne, Leach, Hague and Alexander),** immigrants (**Azam, Clark** and **Van Duyn v. The Home Office),** mental health (**Pickering v. The Liverpool Daily Post, ex parte Mulchay),** travellers (**Mills v. Cooper)** and children (**Tyra Henry ex parte O), ex parte Bennett** (abuse of process), and **UNCL v. Johnstone,** (privilege against self-incrimination), **(R. v. The MoD ex parte Graeme Grady and others),** (1995), (ban on homosexuals).

Commercial/ Company Law: General company, commercial work and associated matters such as domestic and international commercial agreements, Brussels Convention work, banking and financial services, insurance, reinsurance, partnership, building contract, property, arbitration and insolvency. Members have been involved in recent litigation arising out of BCCI, Maxwell, Arrows and Polly Peck.

Criminal: Members continue to be involved in a full range of traditional criminal work as well as in developing areas such as confiscation of assets, money laundering, interception of telecommunications, issues of principle as in **R. v. Brown & Others (House of Lords)** and substantial commercial fraud prosecuted by the SFO (BCCI, Arrows, Maxwell, Bestwood).

General Common Law: Including landlord and tenant, professional negligence, family and planning law.

Industrial and Employment Law: This is an area to which great importance has always been attached in these chambers. Members of Cloisters undertake the full range of work from trade union law, other aspects of individual and collective employment law and health and safety to equal pay, discrimination and harassment at work. Members undertake tribunal and appellate work ranging from small claims to the House of Lords. Members have been involved in recent cases central to the development of the law in relation to equal pay (**Cox v. Lloyds, Ratcliffe v. North Yorks CC** (1995) (House of Lords) (Equal Pay in competitive tendering), **Lucas v. West Sussex CC),** unfair dismissal (**Polkey v. A.E. Dayton Services),** Wages Act (**Delaney v. Staples),** direct discrimination (**Clark and Powell v. Ely Kynoch, Hampson), Walker v. N.Tyneside Borough Metropolitan Council** (1994) (stress at work) and harassment (**Brace).** The involvement of members of Chambers with trade union law extends from the watermark cases of the post war era (**Barnard)** through cases such as **Leary v. NUVB** and **Stephenson v. URTU** to more recent trades disputes such as Wapping, the miners' strike and the dispute involving the ambulance workers and the Manchester railway guards. Advice has been given to trade unions in connection with major amalgamations; recent cases include **Commissioner for Metropolitan Police v. Locker** (PII in discrimination cases).

Media Law: Chambers has developed rapidly in its expertise in media law, including defamation and intellectual property, and recent cases of interest include **Branson v. British Airways, Jason Donovan v. The Face, Bookbinder v. Tebbitt, Board of Control for Cricket in Pakistan v. Sunday Telegraph and Others, Wheeler v Leicester City Council, Red Hot Television** and **Sawrij v. Lynx.**

Personal Injury and Medical Negligence: Experienced practitioners are available at all levels of seniority, acting principally on behalf of plaintiffs. Members have developed considerable expertise in disaster litigation, having been involved in the Hillsborough, Zeebrugge and Purley cases, and class actions such as the Myodil and Fluoracite litigation and Sellafield Leukaemia case.

International/ EC/ Commonwealth: Cloisters can offer advice in all aspects of EC work. There are members who are fluent in a variety of languages and who are associated with European and other overseas law firms as well as having experience of working in other EC countries and at the EC Commission, and appearing before the European Court at Luxembourg, the Court of Human Rights at Strasbourg and the Human Rights Committee of the United Nations at Geneva. Recent European cases include **ex parte Gallagher** (Prevention of Terrorism Act) and **Webb v. EMO Air Cargo** (pregnancy discrimination) and **R. v. Secretary of State for**

Environment ex parte Friends of the Earth. A number of members are admitted to overseas jurisdictions, including US State and Federal Bars and work for US law firms and other foreign attorneys, both through English solicitors and by direct access. Members have wide experience in Commonwealth law including constitutional law and in Privy Council work of all types and have appeared in many leading cases including recently **Pratt and Morgan v. AG of Jamaica** and **Attorney General of Hong Kong v. Reid** and **Guerra v. A.G of Trinidad (1995).** Cloisters values its long tradition in this area and its many connections with Commonwealth and overseas jurisdictions, including United States of America: **Clarence Lackey v. State of Texas** (Supreme Court of the United States) (1995), **Nicholas Ingram v. Zant** (Supreme Court of the United States) (1995).

For more information about the work undertaken by members of Cloisters or for a copy of our brochure please contact the Senior Clerk, Michael Martin.

31
Set No.
CROWN OFFICE ROW (Richard Ferguson QC) 1 Crown Office Row, Temple, London, EC4Y 7HH **Tel:** (0171) 797 7111 **Fax:** (0171) 353 3923 **DX:** 226 **Sen. Clerk:** Patrick Duane **Tenants:** 40 General common law set handling both civil and criminal work with the emphasis on criminal.

32
Set No.
1 CROWN OFFICE ROW (Mark Strachan QC)

1 CROWN OFFICE ROW (3RD FLOOR), TEMPLE, LONDON, EC4Y 7HH
DX: 212

TEL: (0171) 583 9292
FAX: (0171) 353 9292

THE CHAMBERS: The chambers are a long-established set, having been founded by Sir Frank Soskice in 1945, upon his appointment as Solicitor-General. A comprehensive service is offered in all areas of law, with the exception of the well-recognised specialist fields, such as revenue. It has always had a strong connection with the work of the Privy Council. The chambers accept Direct Professional Access.

HEAD OF CHAMBERS:
Mark Strachan QC

SEN. CLERK:
James Donovan

TENANTS: 21

MEMBERS:
Mark Strachan QC (1969)(QC-1987), Sir J.G. Le Quesne QC (1947)(QC-1962), J.D. Guthrie QC (1975)(QC-1993), J. Gray (1962), M. Irvine (1964), I. McLeod (1969), T. Walker (1973), S. Neville-Clarke (1973), W. Hewitson (1975), A. Young (1977), P. Janusz (1979), P. Knox (1983), J. Dingemans (1987), M. Lazarus (1987), P. Dean (1987), J. O'Neill (1987), H. Stevens (1990), Aedeen Boadita-Cormican (1990), Paul Marshall (1991), Aidan Casey (1992), Farzana Aslam (1993).

WORK UNDERTAKEN:
General Description: Commercial and common law, although individual practices differ significantly.

MAIN AREAS OF WORK:
General Commercial: Both domestic and international, (including I.C.C. and other arbitrations), banking, negotiable instruments, agency, insurance, sale and carriage of goods, building and engineering disputes, employment and industrial relations and professional negligence.

Appellate Work: In the Privy Council from overseas, covering most fields of law and in particular commercial and general common law work, cases dealing with the written constitutions of Commonwealth countries and criminal law.

Common Law: Most forms of non-specialist civil litigation including personal injury, medical negligence and landlord and tenant work.

FOREIGN LANGUAGES: French, Italian, Spanish, Dutch, German, Irish.

OFFICE EQUIPMENT: The chambers use WordPerfect software: – 3.5" discs will be provided.

RECRUITMENT & TRAINING: The chambers seek to have three pupils at any time, and offer both two, twelve month funded and one funded six month and one second six months unfunded pupillage. These arrangements are flexible however, and outstand-

ing candidates are never turned away. The funded pupils can receive awards of up to £12,000. Offers of pupillage are made only to candidates who are considered to have the potential to be tenants of these chambers. Applicants should not be deterred by the large number of relatively junior tenants, which is the consequence of current expansion, and not a bar to further growth.

1 CROWN OFFICE ROW (Robert Seabrook QC)

1 CROWN OFFICE ROW (GROUND FLOOR), TEMPLE, LONDON, EC4Y 7HH
DX: 1020

TEL: (0171) 797 7500
FAX: (0171) 797 7550

THE CHAMBERS: A long-established set of chambers which aims to offer a comprehensive service of advisory work and advocacy and whose members have a wide experience in a number of specialist fields principally professional negligence, domestic commercial contract, administrative and construction law. Chambers accept Direct Professional Access. A number of tenants (*) practise mainly from an annexe at Blenheim House, 120 Church Street, Brighton BN1 1WH Tel: (01273) 625625 which is available for local conferences.

HEAD OF CHAMBERS:
Robert Seabrook QC

SEN. CLERK:
Alan Smith

TENANTS: 36

MEMBERS:
Robert Seabrook QC (1964)(QC-1983), Robert Owen QC (1968)(QC-1988),
Duncan Matheson QC (1965)(QC-1989), Philip Vallance QC (1968)(QC-1989),
James Badenoch QC (1967)(QC-1989), Stephen Miller QC (1971)(QC-1990),
David Foskett QC (1972)(QC-1991), Terence Coghlan QC (1968)(QC-1993),
Guy Mansfield QC (1972)(QC-1994), Philip Havers QC (1974)(QC-1995),
Christopher Smyth (1972), Gregory Chambers (1973), Anthony Niblett (1976),
Nigel Pitt (1976), Sally Smith (1977), Margaret Bowron (1978), Paul Rees (1980),
David Balcombe (1980), James King-Smith (1980), David Hart (1982),
Martin Forde (1984), William Edis (1985), Janet Waddicor (1985),
John Gimlette (1986), David L. Evans (1988), Amanda Grant (1988),
Paul Rogers (1989), Angus McCullough (1990), Lucy Freeman (1990),
Keeley Bishop (1990), John Whitting (1991), Emma Fallon (1991),
Martin Downs (1990), Jeremy Cave (1992), Richard Booth (1993),
Philippa Whipple (1994).

WORK UNDERTAKEN: Professional negligence in particular medical and solicitors' negligence, domestic commercial contract, adminstrative law and judicial review, construction law, planning, personal injury, representation at public inquiries and before professional disciplinary tribunals, human rights and European Community law, matrimonial and family law, landlord and tenant and employment. Criminal work is undertaken, in particular fraud and other serious crime. Individual members specialise in different fields which are set out in detail in a brochure which is available upon request.

CHAMBERS FACILITIES: Two large conference rooms are available but members of chambers are willing, in appropriate cases, to travel to clients/ solicitors for conferences.

Chambers use WordPerfect 6.0 software.

RECRUITMENT & TRAINING: There are on average three pupils preferably for 12 months. Generous awards for at least two pupils are available for the first six months of at least 7,000 with a guaranteed level of earnings of at least 7,000 in the second six months. Normally a first or upper second degree is required. Applications for 1995 are closed. This Chambers is a member of the Common Law Chambers Pupillage Application Scheme (COMPAS) whereby a single application is made to all participating chambers, who will select and interview from the pool of applicants pursuant to commonly agreed rules. For details of the scheme and an application form, write to Martin Spencer, COMPAS Secretary, 4 Paper Buildings, Temple, London WC4Y 7EX.

2 CROWN OFFICE ROW (Rupert Jackson QC)

2 CROWN OFFICE ROW, SECOND FLOOR, TEMPLE, LONDON, EC4Y 7HJ
DX: 1041

TEL: (0171) 797 8000
FAX: (0171) 797 8001

HEAD OF CHAMBERS:
Rupert Jackson QC

SEN. CLERK:
Hugh Riley

TENANTS: 33

THE CHAMBERS: Commercial and general common law. The chambers have additional premises at 1 Crane Court, *Fax:* (0171) 797 8023.

MEMBERS:
Rupert Jackson QC (1972)(QC-1987), Roger Toulson QC (1969)(QC-1986),
John L. Powell QC (1974)(QC-1990), Bernard Livesey QC (1969)(QC-1990),
Justin Fenwick QC (1980)(QC-1993), Michael Brooke QC (1968)(QC-1994),
Christopher Critchlow (1973), Iain Hughes (1974), Eva Lomnicka (1974),
Christopher Gibson QC (1976)(QC-1995), Simon Russen (1976),
Charles Douthwaite (1977), Glen Tyrell (1977), Gavin Hamilton (1979),
Andrew Stafford (1980), Barbara Kaplan (1980), Simon Monty (1982),
Martin Fodder (1983), Mark Cannon (1985), Ian Holtum (1985), Paul Parker (1986),
Roger Stewart (1986), Sue Carr (1987), Hugh Evans (1987), Jalil Asif (1988),
Fiona Sinclair (1989), Nicholas Brown (1989), Andrew Nicol (1991),
Ben Hubble (1992), Charles Phipps (1992), Paul Sutherland (1992),
Graeme McPherson (1993), Aisha Bijlani (1993).

Publications: Rupert Jackson QC and John L. Powell QC are the general editors of *Professional Negligence* and six further members of chambers are contributing editors to individual chapters of the third edition, published by Sweet & Maxwell in the Common Law Library series. John L. Powell QC and Eva Lomnicka are co-authors of the Sweet and Maxwell *Encyclopaedia of Financial Services*, and are contributing editors to Palmer's *Company Law*. Eva Lomnicka is co-editor of the Sweet and Maxwell *Encyclopaedia of Consumer Credit* and is a Reader in Law at King's College, London. Members of chambers contribute to a variety of professional journals.

WORK UNDERTAKEN:
Main Areas of Work: Advocacy, advice and drafting in the main fields of commercial and common law, for UK and overseas clients. Certain members accept direct professional access from the approved professions.

Major areas of practice are professional negligence, building and engineering, commercial litigation and arbitration, insurance and reinsurance law and employment.

Chambers have members who are specialists in financial services and securities regulation (in the UK, EC and international), in banking and consumer credit, landlord and tenant, environment and planning, judicial review and personal injury work.

In the field of professional negligence there are members with expertise in the work of doctors, solicitors and barristers, architects and engineers, surveyors and valuers, estate agents and auctioneers, accountants, insurance brokers and other financial intermediaries.

The chambers have considerable experience in multi-party litigation in medical, product liability, disaster and fraud recovery actions, and injunctive and other pre-emptive relief procedures.

FOREIGN CONNECTIONS: Michael Brooke QC is also a practising avocat at the Paris Bar. Barbara Kaplan is a member of the Hong Kong Bar and also practises from Des Voeux Chambers, Hong Kong.

LANGUAGES SPOKEN: There are members of chambers fluent in the major European languages.

2 CROWN OFFICE ROW (Raymond Kidwell QC)

2 CROWN OFFICE ROW, TEMPLE, LONDON, EC4Y 7HJ
DX: 344 London LIX: LON 144

TEL: (0171) 797 8100
FAX: (0171) 797 8101

THE CHAMBERS: Founded over 50 years ago, chambers now have 35 members including 12 QCs. Individuals or teams of counsel are available to undertake a wide variety of litigation, arbitration and advisory work, both within the UK and internationally.

MEMBERS:
Raymond Kidwell QC (1951)(QC-1968), Sir Michael Ogden QC (1950)(QC-1968), Patrick Bennett QC (1949)(QC-1969), John Archer QC (1950)(QC-1975), Graeme Hamilton QC (1959)(QC-1978), Stephen Desch QC (1962)(QC-1980), John Crowley QC (1962)(QC-1982), Michael Harvey QC (1966)(QC-1982), Christopher Purchas QC (1966)(QC-1990), Nigel V.M. Wilkinson QC (1973)(QC-1990), Antony Edwards-Stuart QC (1976)(QC-1991), Roger ter Haar QC (1974)(QC-1992), Jonathan Woods (1965), Guy Anthony (1972), David Tucker (1973), Thomas Saunt (1974), George Gadney (1974), Richard Lynagh (1975), Michael Kent (1975), James Holdsworth (1977), Andrew Phillips (1978), John Greenbourne (1978), Anna Guggenheim (1982), Deborah Taylor (1983), Ian Swan (1985), Jane DeCamp (1987), Steven Snowden (1989), Susan Hodgson (1989), Jason Evans-Tovey (1990), Rohan Pershad (1991), Simon Howarth (1991), Andrew Rigney (1992), Leigh-Ann Mulcahy (1993), Clive Weston (1993), Patrick Blakesley (1993).

MAIN AREAS OF WORK: General commercial litigation and arbitration (including ICC arbitrations) involving contractual disputes of all kinds; general common law, including claims in negligence, nuisance and other torts; insurance and reinsurance contract disputes; professional negligence, including that of architects, engineers, surveyors, lawyers, accountants and doctors; construction and engineering disputes, both in the Official Referee's court and in domestic and international arbitrations; product liability claims of all types, including large-scale coordinated actions; and personal injury claims, including disaster litigation and cases of severe and permanent disablement.

OTHER AREAS OF EXPERTISE: Administrative law and judicial review; environmental law; European law; planning inquiries and appeals; employment law; and commercial fraud, both civil and criminal.

LANGUAGES: French, German, Italian.

HEAD OF CHAMBERS:
Raymond Kidwell QC

CLERK:
David Newcomb

TENANTS: 35

DEVEREUX CHAMBERS (Peter Weitzman QC)

DEVEREUX CHAMBERS, DEVEREUX COURT, LONDON, WC2R 3JJ
DX: 349 (Ch.Ln.) LIX: LON 119

TEL: (0171) 353 7534
FAX: (0171) 353 1724

THE CHAMBERS: Devereux Chambers offers a comprehensive inter-disciplinary service to all its clients. Its hallmarks are team work coupled with a friendly but commercial approach. It can draw on the expertise of specialist counsel at all levels of seniority to offer advice and to resolve a wide range of disputes efficiently and cost-effectively. Chambers also places great emphasis on advocacy and Members of Chambers regularly appear before courts and tribunals at all levels.

MEMBERS:
Peter Weitzman QC (1952)(QC-1973), Leslie Joseph QC (1952)(QC-1978), Diana Cotton QC (1964)(QC-1983), Jeffrey Burke QC (1964)(QC-1984), Alan Pardoe QC (1971)(QC-1988), Alistair MacDuff QC (1969)(QC-1993), Colin Edelman QC (1977)(QC-1995), Rudolf Russell (1950), Peter Clark (1970), Roy Lemon (1970), Robert Glancy (1972), Peter Wulwik (1972), Ian Smith (1972), Gerald Rabie (1973), Christopher Goddard (1973), Ian Lee (1973), Elizabeth Andrew (1974), Richard Greening (1975), David Griffith-Jones (1975), David Bean (1976), Ruth Downing (1978), Nicholas Bard (1979), Timothy Brennan (1981), Stephen Killalea (1981), Colin Wynter (1984),

HEAD OF CHAMBERS:
Peter Weitzman QC

SEN. CLERK:
Elton Maryon

PRACTICE MANAGERS:
Rochelle Haring, Clifford Holland

TENANTS: 37

Bruce Carr (1986), Ingrid Simler (1987), Joanna Heal (1988),
Philip Thornton (1988), James Tayler (1989), Nicholas Randall (1990),
Keith Bryant (1991), Richard Harrison (1991), Natasha Joffe (1992),
Andrew Burns (1993), Peter Edwards (1992), Dijen Basu (1994).

The senior members of chambers are Deputy High Court Judges and Recorders/Assistant Recorders. Chambers also has two members of the Criminal Injuries Compensation Board, two legal members of the Mental Health Independent Review Tribunal, a member of the London Maritime Arbitration Association, a Chairman of Various Inquiries, a Professor of Law, an ACAS Industrial Arbitrator, a Chairman of the Social Security Appeals Tribunal, an additional Junior Counsel to the Inland Revenue, a member of the Supplementary Panel of Treasury Counsel (Common Law), a member of the Bar Council, two members of the Professional Conduct Committee of the Bar Council and two Fellows of the Chartered Institute of Arbitrators. Chambers also includes founder members and a current Secretary of the Employment Law Bar Association and members of the Commercial Bar Association, the Administrative Law Bar Association and the London Common Law and Commercial Law Bar Association.

PUBLICATIONS: Members of Chambers have written or contributed to: *Harvey on Industrial Relations and Employment Law*, Tolley's *Employment Law, Smith and Wood on Industrial Law*, Halsbury's *Laws* and Longman's *Litigation Practice*. Professor Ian Smith, Christopher Goddard and Nicholas Randall are co-authors of *Health and Safety - The New Legal Framework*, (Butterworth, 1993). David Bean is the author of *Injunctions* (Longmans 6th ed., 1994) and co-author of *Enforcement of Injunctions and Undertakings*, (Jordans, 1991). Members of Chambers also contribute to various professional publications and periodicals.

WORK UNDERTAKEN: The major areas of practice are civil and commercial law, especially; Administrative and Local Government law, Commercial Law, Construction Litigation, Emergency procedures and pre-emptive remedies, Employment law (including litigation at all levels concerning wrongful and unfair dismissal, redundancy, transfers of undertakings and the Acquired Rights Directive, restrictive covenants, protection of confidential information, pensions. professional disciplinary tribunals, strikes and other trade disputes and trade union law), Insurance and Reinsurance, Medical Negligence, Personal Injury Litigation (including the effect of the Health and Safety Directives), Professional Negligence (including litigation concerning surveyors, architects, accountants, solicitors, insurance and reinsurance underwriters and brokers, merchant bankers, and investment managers), Race and Sex discrimination and Equal Pay (including the Equal Treatment Directives). In these categories Devereux Chambers can and does provide specialist teams of counsel at all levels of seniority to conduct large scale litigation. In addition, individual members of Devereux Chambers offer expertise in the following areas: Crime, Defamation, Entertainment law, Environmental law, Industrial Diseases, Landlord and Tenant (including Rent Assessment Committee work), Mortgage and Guarantee litigation (including secured lending under the Consumer Credit Act), Property Litigation, Revenue Litigation, Telecommunications law. Members of chambers also offer expertise in European law and have experience of practice in the European Court of Justice.

RECRUITMENT & TRAINING: Devereux Chambers prides itself on the calibre of its pupils to ensure that the high standards of Chambers are maintained. Generous pupillage awards are available to those with high ability and strong inter-personal skills. Tenancy and pupillage applications to David Griffith -Jones.

OTHER MATTERS:
- Devereux Chambers aims to offer competitive rates which the Senior Clerk will be happy to discuss. Estimates of fees will be given on request.
- Instructions by Professional Direct Access are accepted by agreement.
- Chambers is fully computerised to ensure maximum efficiency.
- Members of Chambers are available to give lectures and present seminars in their specialist fields.
- A programme of seminars to be run in Chambers is planned for 1996.
- Conferences and consultations may be conducted outside chambers (including out of London) upon request.
- A brochure is available on request and the Senior Clerk and Practice Managers will be happy to give more detailed information about members of chambers and areas of expertise.

37
et No.

DOUGHTY STREET CHAMBERS (Geoffrey Robertson QC)

DOUGHTY STREET CHAMBERS, 11 DOUGHTY STREET, LONDON, WC1N 2PG
DX: 223 (Ch.Ln.)

TEL: (0171) 404 1313
FAX: (0171) 404 2283

THE CHAMBERS: All members of these chambers are committed to its liberal tradition of defending freedom and citizens' rights irrespective of the popularity of the cause or client, and to positive support of the legal aid system. The chambers are fully computerised, helping to ensure day-to-day efficiency. Chambers' brochure is available upon request.

MEMBERS:

Geoffrey Robertson QC (1973)(QC-1988), Sir Louis Blom-Cooper QC (1952)(QC-1970), Richard Maxwell QC (1968)(QC-1988), Helena Kennedy QC (1972)(QC-1991), Peter Thornton QC (1969)(QC-1992), Christopher Sallon QC (1973)(QC-1994), Jonah Walker-Smith (1963), Oliver Thorold (1971), Frank Panford (1972), David Farrington (1973), Edward Rees (1973), Richard Allfrey (1974), Michael Grieve (1975), James Wood (1975), Stephen Irwin (1976), Nicholas Paul (1980), Gavin Millar (1981), Kate Markus (1981), Isabella Forshall (1982), Penelope Barrett (1982), Paul Bogan (1983), Tim Owen (1983), David Bentley (1984), Heather Williams (1985), Martin Westgate (1985), Ben Emmerson (1986), Aswini Weereratne (1986), Jill Evans (1986), Anthony Metzer (1987), Keir Starmer (1987), Sally Hatfield (1989), Robin Oppenheim (1988), Michelle Strange (1989), Kieran Maidment (1989), Paul Taylor (1989), Hugh Barton (1989), Sadakat Kadri (1989), Andrew Hall (1991), Phillippa Kaufman (1991), Quincy Whitaker (1991), Michael Ford (1992), Ian Wise (1992).

ASSOCIATE TENANTS:

Justice Ismail Mahommed SC (1956, South African Bar, 1984 English Bar) (SC-1974), Guy Ollivry QC (1957, QC-1987), Fenton Ramsahoye SC (1953, SC-1971), Adrian Hardiman SC (1974 Ireland, 1988 England and Wales SC-1989), Prof. Kevin Boyle (1971 N.Ireland Bar, 1992 English Bar), Christine Booker (1977), Julian Fulbrook (1977), Geraldine Van Bueren (1980), Dr Jill Peay (1991), Jonathan Cooper (1992).

Members of chambers are the authors of leading textbooks in their specialisations, lecture to universities and polytechnics and advise on radio, television and film productions. They are involved with numerous associations including the Administrative Law Bar Association, Liberty, the Haldane Society, the Howard League for Penal Reform, the Society of Labour Lawyers, the Criminal Bar Association and the Immigration Law Practitioners' Association.

WORK UNDERTAKEN:

Actions against the Police: *Work includes:* civil actions against the police in cases of assault, false imprisonment, malicious prosecution, negligence and misfeasance. Chambers act for clients in all parts of the country and have experience of most regional and city police forces.

Contract and Equity: Contract experience ranges from commercial litigation and corporate actions to disputes affecting sole traders and partnerships. In conjunction with chambers' involvement with media law, several members have developed a speciality in entertainment law. In the field of equitable remedies, members regularly develop and present arguments concerning estoppels, constructive and resulting trusts. This has particular application in the fields of housing and real property and in protecting the rights of co-owners and occupiers.

Criminal: All areas of the criminal law are handled and at all levels, including specialisations such as commercial fraud, drugs, public order, official secrets and contempt of court. Members are experienced in related subjects such as extradition, judicial review and Privy Council proceedings (including capital appeals from the Commonwealth). Chambers' experience of cases involving civil liberties extends to this field and members have been involved in several recent notorious miscarriages of justice cases, including the Guildford Four, the Birmingham Six, the Tottenham Three, Sarah Thornton, Amelia Rossiter, Kiranjit Ahluwalia, and the Bridgewater Three.

HEAD OF CHAMBERS: Geoffrey Robertson QC	
PRACTICE MANAGER: Christine Kings	
SEN. CLERK: Michelle Simpson	
TENANTS: 44	

Discrimination: Acting most frequently on the grounds of race and sex, members also advise on issues of religion, disability, sexuality, age and positive action. A number of members act in cases backed by the CRE and the EOC including equal pay claims.

Employment: Cases encompass litigation in statutory tribunals and the High Court, across a wide range of matters from unfair dismissal and redundancy to discrimination, representing individuals and trade unions. (Several members have successfully taken actions on behalf of employees to the European Commission of Human Rights).

European, International and Commonwealth Law: Members frequently appear in International and European Courts and several Senior Counsel are practising members of Commonwealth Bars. Advice in relation to public and private international law, constitutional law and human rights is provided to international corporations, political parties and for publications in other jurisdictions. Several members have participated in the Council of Europe programmes to advise the new governments in Eastern Europe.

Housing and Landlord and Tenant Law: Experienced practitioners are involved in complex litigation at appellate level and in relation to homelessness and Children Act cases in the Divisional Court. County Court work is handled including possession actions, eviction cases, disrepair claims, applications concerning service charges and other aspects of housing management.

Immigration: Several members specialise in all aspects of immigration and nationality law, especially those involving refugees and/ or European law.

Inquests: Chambers are able to offer advice and representation on all aspects of law in relation to inquests. Members' expertise derives from regular appearances in Coroners' Courts and is enhanced by overlapping špecialisms in chambers of medical negligence, personal injury, mental health, prisoners' rights, civil actions against the police and public law.

Media Law and Defamation: Members have extensive experience in dealing with contempt of court, reporting restrictions, breach of copyright and confidence, malicious falsehood, official secrecy, obscenity, blasphemy and related matters, including the protection of journalistic sources. In the field of defamation a number of members are regularly engaged to advise national newspapers, book publishers and television productions. Advice is also given on the 1990 Broadcasting Act and on drafting of media laws in developing countries.

Medical Negligence and Personal Injury: Chambers contains an array of experienced practitioners at all levels of seniority, available for County Court, High Court and Criminal Injuries Compensation cases, and representation at inquests, inquiries and tribunals. Work is frequently handled on a team basis and class action experience includes the Opren, Myodil, HIV and Benzodiazepine cases.

Mental Health: Members have been involved with numerous cases of judicial review of decisions affecting patients and public authorities, and have wide experience of mental health review tribunals, hospitals and social services inquiries, inquests and the Court of Protection.

Prisoners' Rights: *Work includes:* developing prisoners' rights to judicial review in areas such as parole, disciplinary hearings and censorship, and representing prisoners in civil actions.

Professional Negligence: *Work includes:* cases involving lawyers, surveyors and accountants. As well as traditional civil litigation they have appeared in connection with disciplinary proceedings and wasted cost orders.

Public and Administrative Law: Chambers undertake almost every type of judicial review handling many local government, education, housing, homelessness and mental health cases, as well as appeals from criminal and civil courts and other tribunals and inquiries. Matters handled involve immigration, election, media and prisoners' rights, public sector workers and policies of government ministries. There is a specific expertise in relation to education and childrens' rights in such areas as special needs, admission appeals and pupil exclusions.

LANGUAGES SPOKEN: French, German, Italian, Greek, Spanish, Czech, Hebrew.

RECRUITMENT & TRAINING: Chambers offer grants of £3,000 for first or second six month pupillages. Two mini-pupillage courses per year.

1 Dr JOHNSON'S BUILDINGS (Martin Thomas QC)

1 DR JOHNSON'S BUILDINGS, TEMPLE, LONDON, EC4Y 7AX
DX: 297

TEL: (0171) 353 9328
FAX: (0171) 353 4410

THE CHAMBERS: 1 Dr Johnson's Buildings are a broadly-based common law set. In addition to their practices in this jurisdiction the senior silks have substantial experience in Hong Kong, Singapore and South Africa. Juniors have complementary practices. There are associated chambers in Chester (Sedan House) and Lewes (Westgate Chambers).

HEAD OF CHAMBERS:
Martin Thomas QC

SEN. CLERK:
John Francis

TENANTS: 19

MEMBERS:
Lord Hooson QC (1949)(QC-1960), John Mortimer QC (1948)(QC-1966),
Martin Thomas QC (1967)(QC-1979), Colin Hart-Leverton QC (1957)(QC-1979),
Donald Von Landauer (1953), Peter Digney (1968), Robert Britton (1973),
John Sabido (1976), James Dean (1977), Jennifer Oldland (1978),
Clifford Mailer (1987), Alexander Granville (1978), Nicholas Hamblin (1981),
Dingle Clark (1981), Sylvester McIlwain (1985), Gordon Wignall (1987),
Camille Habboo (1987), Graham Brodie (1989), Hilary Pollock (1993).

WORK UNDERTAKEN: Administrative law, arbitration, substantial criminal cases (including serious fraud), courts martial, and police cases, extradition, foreign laws, immigration, judicial review, licensing, matrimonial, mental health, personal injury and professional negligence. Chambers accept direct access from the approved professions.

FOREIGN CONNECTIONS AND LANGUAGES SPOKEN: One member (Donald Von Landauer) practises solely in Paris and St. Helier, Channel Islands; door tenants have connections in Hong Kong, Ireland and Rome.

2 DR JOHNSON'S BUILDINGS (Fergus Mitchell)

2 DR JOHNSON'S BUILDINGS, TEMPLE, LONDON, EC4Y 7BA
DX: 429 or 460 Ch.Ln

TEL: (0171) 353 4716/8778
FAX: (0171) 334 0242

THE CHAMBERS: 2 Dr Johnson's Buildings is a busy criminal and common law set of chambers offering practitioners in a variety of fields at all levels of seniority.

HEAD OF CHAMBERS:
Fergus Mitchell

CLERKS:
Alan Conner, Kevin Crawley, Chris Blake, Danny Bartlett, Ashley Baum

TENANTS: 43

MEMBERS:
Fergus Mitchell (1971)[+], Alan Bayliss (1966)[+], Dennis Gould (1969),
Anthony Fogg (1970), Graham J. Davies (1971), Thomas Clunie (1973),
David Batcup (1974), Richard Bruce (1968), David Wurtzel (1974),
Robert Sherman (1977), Ian Wheatley (1977), Grant Armstrong (1978),
Susan Williams (1978), Stephen Mejzner (1978), Nicholas Rhodes (1981),
Brian Stork (1981), David Barnes (1981), Mark Tomassi (1981), Pamela Oon (1982),
Thomas Buxton (1983), Tyrone Belger (1984), Bernard Tetlow (1984),
Carolyn Marsh (1985), Gordon Ross (1986), David Taylor (1986),
Graham B. Davies (1986), Jonathon Rose (1986), John Buck (1987),
Paul Hopkins (1989), Anna Hamilton-Shield (1989), Neil Hawes (1989),
Frances Hastings (1990), Alan Fraser (1990), Michael Lavers (1990),
David Williams (1990), Clare Wade (1990), Paul Phillips (1991),
Claire Robinson (1991), Mary Teresa Deignan (1991), Jennifer Edwards (1992),
Charles Hale (1992), Robert Benzynie (1992), Julia Flanagan (1993).
[+] *Sit as Recorders.*

WORK UNDERTAKEN:
Criminal Law: Criminal practitioners accept instructions in both prosecution and defence work. A number of members of chambers have been involved in substantial fraud and drugs cases as well as cases involving serious sexual offences.
Civil Litigation: In particular chambers provide civil practitioners who specialise in the areas of personal injury, landlord and tenant and other property work, general commercial and contractual litigation, actions against the police and employment law.

Family Law: Chambers can offer practitioners who are experienced in all aspects of family law, including divorce, ancillary relief, Children Act work and domestic violence cases.

LANGUAGES: French and Welsh.

40
Set No. **3 Dr JOHNSON'S BUILDINGS (J.A. Hodgson)** 3 Dr Johnson's Buildings, (Grnd Floor North), Temple, London, EC4Y 7BA **Tel:** (0171) 353 4854 **Fax:** (0171) 583 8784 **DX:** 1009 **Sen. Clerk:** John E. Hubbard **Tenants:** 19 A general common law set of chambers with a long-established specialisation in family cases.

41
Set No. # ENTERPRISE CHAMBERS (Benjamin Levy)

9 OLD SQUARE, LINCOLN'S INN, LONDON, WC2A 3SR
DX: 301

TEL: (0171) 405 9471
FAX: (0171) 242 1447

Enterprise Chambers are a London commercial chancery set with a fully equipped branch in Leeds. Members organise and speak at conferences and appear as advocates at arbitrations and other tribunals. All members accept direct professional access work.

MEMBERS:
Benjamin Levy (1956), Anthony Mann QC (1974)(QC-1992),
Timothy Jennings (1962), Anthony Templeman QC (1974)(QC Australia-1987),
David Halpern (1978), Charles Morgan (1978), Caroline Hutton (1979),
Michael James (1976), Teresa R. Peacocke (1982), Linden Ife (1982),
Ann McAllister (1982), Peter Arden (1983), Geoffrey Zelin (1984),
Leslie Michaelson (1985), Jacqueline Baker (1985), James Barker (1984),
Hugo Groves (1980), Nicholas Carlisle (1988), Laura Garcia-Miller (1989),
Zia Bhaloo (1990), James Pickering (1991), Hugh Jory (1992),
Bridget Williamson (1993).

MAIN AREAS OF WORK UNDERTAKEN:
Banking, securities and insolvency
Building, construction and engineering
Company, contract and partnership
Equitable remedies (including Anton Piller and Mareva orders)
Intellectual property
Insurance
Judicial review
Landlord and tenant, and housing
Professional negligence (except medical negligence)
Property
Trusts, pensions and probate

ADDITIONAL SPECIALISATIONS: include financial services, pension schemes, copyright, water law, shipping disputes, cross border litigation, employment, public utilities and transport law.

LANGUAGES: French, Italian, Portuguese, Spanish.

For further information and details of charging rates, please see the chambers brochure.

HEAD OF CHAMBERS:
Benjamin Levy

CLERKS:
Barry Clayton, Justine Hickman,
Tony Armstrong

TENANTS: 23

ERSKINE CHAMBERS (Richard Sykes QC)

ERSKINE CHAMBERS, 30 LINCOLN'S INN FIELDS, LONDON, WC2A 3PF
DX: 308

TEL: (0171) 242 5532
FAX: (0171) 831 0125

MEMBERS:
Richard Sykes QC (1958)(QC-1981) MA (Cantab), R.A.K. Wright QC (1949)(QC-1973) MA (Oxon), W.F. Stubbs QC (1957)(QC-1978) MA, LLB (Cantab),
Oliver Weaver QC (1965)(QC-1985) MA, LLM, Sir Thomas Stockdale (1966) MA (Oxon), Robin Potts QC (1968)(QC-1982) BA, BCL (Oxon),
David Richards QC (1974)(QC-1992) MA (Cantab), John Cone (1975) LLB,
Leslie Kosmin QC (1976)(QC-1994) MA, LLM (Harvard),
Michael Todd (1977) BA, David Mabb (1979) MA (Cantab),
Martin Moore (1982) BA (Oxon), David Chivers (1983) BA (Cantab),
Miss Ceri Bryant (1984) MA, LLM (Cantab), Richard Snowden (1986) MA (Cantab), LLM (Harvard), Miss Catherine Roberts (1986) MA, LLM (Cantab),
Philip Gillyon (1988) BA (Cantab), Mary Stokes (1989), Andrew Thompson (1991),
Dan Prentice (1982) LLB (Belfast) JD (Chicago), MA (Oxon),
Nigel Dougherty (1993) BA, LLM.

HEAD OF CHAMBERS:
Richard Sykes QC

SEN. CLERK:
Mike Hannibal

TENANTS: 21

WORK UNDERTAKEN: Company law: companies, partnerships and other forms of business organisation (their formation, conduct, financing, reorganisation, acquisition, amalgamation, disposal and dissolution and their accounting requirements); corporate insolvency and administration orders; financial services; share transactions, minority rights, directors' duties, internal disputes; corporate fraud; EC and international aspects. Advice, drafting and litigation.

RECRUITMENT & TRAINING: The maximum period for any pupillage is 6 months. Awards are given to suitable candidates, and the level of awards is under constant review. Students considering pupillage are encouraged to apply for a mini-pupillage (for which financial assistance is available). All applications to be addressed to Andrew Thompson, with those to commence in the year beginning 1st October 1997 to be received by September 1996.

1 ESSEX COURT (Anthony Grabiner QC)

1 ESSEX COURT, TEMPLE, LONDON, EC4Y 9AR
DX: 430 (Ch.Ln.)

TEL: (0171) 583 2000
FAX: (0171) 583 0118

THE CHAMBERS: The chambers of Anthony Grabiner QC at 1 Essex Court were founded in 1966; at that time there were 4 members. There are now 50 members of chambers, of whom 15 are Queen's Counsel.

CLERKS:
Robert Ralphs (Home 0181 449 8472), Mary Grey (Home 0181 542 7364)
Paul Shrubsall (Home 01474 872 590), Alastair Davidson (Home 0181 646 2115)

HEAD OF CHAMBERS:
Anthony Grabiner QC

CLERKS:
Robert Ralphs

TENANTS: 46

MEMBERS:
Anthony Grabiner QC (1968)(QC-1981), Stanley Burnton QC (1965)(QC-1982),
Graham Aaronson QC (1966)(QC-1982), Christopher Carr QC (1968)(QC-1983),
Nicholas Strauss QC (1965)(QC-1984), Roydon Thomas QC (1960)(QC-1985),
Peter Leaver QC (1967)(QC-1987), Ian Glick QC (1970)(QC-1987),
Miss Elizabeth Gloster QC (1971)(QC-1989), Geoffrey Hobbs QC (1977)(QC-1991),
Mark Barnes QC (1974)(QC-1992), Steven Gee QC (1975)(QC-1993),
Alastair R. MacGregor QC (1974)(QC-1994), Thomas Sharpe QC (1976)(QC-1994),
Terence Mowschenson QC (1977)(QC-1995), Richard Behar (1965),
Richard Hayward (1969), Miss Susanna FitzGerald (1973), Michael Malone (1975),
Miss Fay Stockton (1976), Jeffrey Gruder (1977), Ian Grainger (1978),
Thomas Ivory (1978), Rhodri Davies (1979), Michael Bloch (1979),
Stephen Auld (1979), Alan Griffiths (1981), Jeffrey Onions (1981),
Clare Reffin (1981), John McCaughran (1982), Richard Gillis (1982),
Andrew Lenon (1982), Kenneth MacLean (1985), Charles Graham (1986),
Anthony de Garr Robinson (1987), Laurence Rabinowitz (1987),

Neil Kitchener (1991), Joseph Hage (1991), Alain Choo Choy (1991), Andrew Feldman (1991), Michael Rollason (1992), David Cavender (1993), Daniel Toledano (1993), Zoë O'Sullivan (1993), Emma Himsworth (1993), Alan Redfern (1995), Jacob Grierson (1993), Lisa Cooke (1994), Edmund Nourse (1994), Graeme Halkerston (1994).

WORK UNDERTAKEN: The range of work done is very wide and embraces almost every aspect of domestic and international commerce and finance. That work includes (but is by no means limited to) Arbitrations; Agency: distribution, licence and franchise agreements; Banking: bills of exchange, mortgages and pledges, forfaiting, guarantees, loan agreements, letters of credit, performance bonds and swaps; Building: shipbuilding contracts and construction disputes; Commodities: futures and options; Company and Insolvency: administrators and receivers, and minority actions; Company Acquisitions: breach of warranty, share and business sale agreements, management buyouts, shareholders' agreements, and takeovers and mergers; Competition: monopolies and mergers commission, Office of Fair Trading, EC Commission, restrictive practices, restraint of trade and economic torts; Contractual disputes; Conflict of laws; Employment: breach of confidence, employment contracts, health and safety at work, restraint of trade, trade unions, transfer of undertakings, unfair and wrongful dismissal; European Community law; Financial Services: cases before SROs and Lloyd's disciplinary tribunals, Stock Exchange practice and insider trading; Insurance and Reinsurance; Intellectual Property: breach of confidence, copyright, passing off, patents, service marks and trade marks; Interlocutory Applications; Landlord and Tenant (commercial); Licensing: betting and gaming, entertainment, liquor and lotteries; Matrimonial Finance; Oil Industry law; Partnership; Personal injuries; Professional negligence; accountants, auctioneers, financial advisers, solicitors, surveyors and valuers; Public and Administrative Law: judicial review and local government; Public International Law: state and diplomatic immunity; Public Utility Regulation: electricity, gas, telecommunications, transport and water; Sale and Supply of Goods (domestic and international): conditions of sale, consumer credit and protection, leasing, product liability and retention of title; Securities: bonds and shares; Shipping: bills of landing, charterparties and carriage of goods; Tax; Trusts; Wills and Probate.

RECRUITMENT & TRAINING: Chambers offer 5 x 12 month pupillages each year. Chambers operate an award scheme whereby pupils are guaranteed an income of £24,000, of which part may, at the discretion of chambers, be advanced during a prospective pupil's year at the Inns of Court School of Law. Applicants for pupillage should (save in exceptional circumstances) have at least an upper second class degree. They should send full CVs to: Ian Glick QC, marked 'pupillage'. Although there is no deadline and later applications will be entertained, applicants are advised to apply during their first year at university, if reading law, or their first year studying law, if they have degrees in other subjects.

44
Set No. # 1 ESSEX COURT (Christopher Morcom QC)

1 ESSEX COURT, TEMPLE, LONDON, EC4Y 9AR
DX: 371

TEL: (0171) 936 3030
FAX: (0171) 583 1606

THE CHAMBERS: A substantial common law and commercial set, incorporating a specialist group of intellectual property practitioners.

MEMBERS:
Christopher Morcom QC (1963)(QC-1991), Amedee Turner QC (1954)(QC-1976), Sir Ivan Lawrence QC (1962)(QC-1981), Patrick Mullen (1967), David Micklethwait (1970), Roger Wyand (1973), Roger Bull (1974), Malcolm Chapple (1975), Arthur Ashton (1988), Peter Farmery (1979), Mark Lyne (1981), Norman Joss (1982), Prof. John N. Adams (1984), Grace Ong (1985), Philip Goddard (1985), Barry Coulter (1985), Paul Diamond (1985), Guy Tritton (1987), Peter John (1989), Jessica Jones (1991), Julian Benson (1991), Rachel Lawrence (1992), Elizabeth Barrett (1992), Michael Edenborough (1992), Nicholas Grundy (1993).

HEAD OF CHAMBERS:
Christopher Morcom QC

SEN. CLERK:
Geoffrey C.B. Maw

TENANTS: 25

DOOR TENANTS:
Graeme Mew (Solicitor Toronto Canada) 1982; David Kay (Solicitor Chicago) (1979). Donal F.O'Kelly (1973), Philip Zornosa (1983)(Madrid).

WORK UNDERTAKEN: Arbitration, agency & franchising, contractual disputes including sale of goods and services, commercial law, company law, insolvency, financial services, banking and consumer credit, criminal law, employment, family law, housing, intellectual property (including patents, trademarks and passing off, copyright and designs, confidential information, information technology and applicable EC law) landlord and tenant, local government, partnership law, personal injuries, professional negligence, mortgage law.

4 ESSEX COURT

4 ESSEX COURT, TEMPLE, LONDON, EC4Y 9AJ

TEL: (0171) 797 7970
FAX: (0171) 353 0998

THE CHAMBERS: Members of Chambers at 4 Essex Court (formerly situated at 2 Essex Court) are available to give specialist advice (including direct advice to foreign lawyers and members of certain other professional bodies) and to undertake advocacy work in their respective fields. They conduct all types of commercial litigation in London and abroad, together with arbitrations and marine, aviation and other inquiries. A European Law Group has been established within chambers.

Information on the specialist fields of practice of particular members can be obtained from chambers' staff.

HEAD OF CHAMBERS:
David Steel QC

SEN. CLERK:
Gordon Armstrong

TENANTS: 33

MEMBERS:
David W. Steel QC (1966)(QC-1981), Michael N. Howard QC (1971)(QC-1986), Belinda Bucknall QC (1974)(QC-1988), Nigel Teare QC (1974)(QC-1991), Charles Macdonald QC (1972)(QC-1992), Jeremy Russell QC (1975)(QC-1994), John Cooke (1966) (SC-1980), John de Cotta (1955), John Ferry (1956), George Economou (1965), Simon Gault (1970), Geoffrey Kinley (1970), Giles Caldin (1974), Charles Sussex (1982), Charles Haddon-Cave (1978), Paul Griffin (1979), Timothy Brenton (1981), Michael Nolan (1981), Marion Smith (1981), Simon Rainey (1982), Simon Kverndal (1982), Nigel Jacobs (1983), Luke Parsons (1985), Simon Croall (1986), Peter Trepte (1987), Nigel Cooper (1987), Poonam Melwani (1989), Catherine Burgin (1990), James M. Turner (1990), Robert Thomas (1992), Nevil Phillips (1992), Rose Heybrook (1993), Thomas Macey-Dare (1994).

European Law Group:
John Cooke SC (Dublin), John de Cotta (Malaga), John Ferry (Brussels), George Economou (Greece), Simon Rainey (London), Peter Trepte (Brussels), Nigel Cooper (London), James M. Turner (London), Robert Thomas (London).

Door Tenants:
Michael Thomas CMG QC (1955)(QC-1973), Ronny Tong QC (1974)(QC-1990), Robert Ribeiro QC (1978)(QC-1990), Prof. Nicholas Gaskell(1976), Michel Koenig (1953), Prof. Francis D. Rose (1983), George Cumming (1987).

WORK UNDERTAKEN:
General Description: Members of chambers specialise in a wide spectrum of commercial law, with a particular emphasis on maritime law, international trade, insurance and EC law.

Main Areas of Work: *Commercial Law, Shipping and International Trade:* including banking, carriage of goods by sea, land and air, marine and non-marine casualties, marine and general insurance and reinsurance, salvage, collision and oil-pollution, domestic and international sale of goods; ship and civil construction and financing. *Business Law and Financial Services:* including insurance and reinsurance, banking, securities and commodities trading, company law and insolvency. *EC Law:* including competition law, intellectual property, public procurement, mergers and acquisitions and the business law aspects of 1992 and the Single European Market.

Entertainment and Media Law.
Employment Law.
Judicial Review: in related areas.

FOREIGN CONNECTIONS: There are members of the French, Irish, Northern Irish, Spanish, Greek, Cyprus, New South Wales and Hong Kong Bars in chambers. There is a close association with Temple Chambers in Hong Kong.

46
Set No.

5 ESSEX COURT (Jeremy Gompertz QC)

5 ESSEX COURT, TEMPLE, LONDON, EC4Y 9AH
DX: 1048

TEL: (0171) 583 2825
FAX: (0171) 583 1723

THE CHAMBERS: General common law chambers which were established over 40 years ago.

MEMBERS:
Jeremy Gompertz QC (1962)(QC-1988), Mervyn Roberts (1963), Christopher Moss QC (1972)(QC-1994), Marie Catterson (1972), Nicholas Ainley (1973), John Bassett (1975), Nicholas Wilcox (1977), Simon Freeland (1978), Peter Spink (1979), Gerard Pounder (1980), Sandra Stanfield (1984), Fiona Barton (1986), Andrew Waters (1987), Simon Davenport (1987), Max Hill (1987), Stephanie Farrimond (1987), Anne Studd (1988), Georgina Kent (1989), Giles Powell (1990), Evelyn Pollock (1991), Jason Beer (1992), Samantha Leek (1993).
Several members of chambers are recorders and assistant recorders.

HEAD OF CHAMBERS:
Jeremy Gompertz QC

SEN. CLERK:
Michael Dean

TENANTS: 21

WORK UNDERTAKEN: Chambers are an established common law set. The principal areas of practice are professional negligence, personal injuries (including group litigation), civil jury actions for false imprisonment and malicious prosecution (mainly for defendants), judicial review, general commercial common law (including sale of goods, restraint of trade, confidentiality, consumer credit and employment), family (especially matrimonial finance) and all aspects of criminal law (including serious fraud) both for prosecution and defence. Members of chambers also have expertise in probate, company and partnership, landlord and tenant, EC law, licensing, police law and public interest immunity in civil and criminal litigation.

LANGUAGES SPOKEN: French, German and Mandarin.

RECRUITMENT & TRAINING: Tenancy and pupillage applications should be sent to Mr J. Bassett; pupillage applications for 1996 to be submitted by the 1st September 1995. Up to two pupillage awards are offered, of £6,000 each, for twelve months commencing in October. Up to three non-funded first six months' pupillages are also available.

47
Set No.

ESSEX COURT CHAMBERS (Gordon Pollock QC)

(formerly Four Essex Court)
24 LINCOLN'S INN FIELDS, LONDON, WC2A 3ED
DX: 320 LIX: LON 167

TEL: (0171) 813 8000
FAX: (0171) 813 8080

For round the clock information and assistance telephone (0171) 813 8000 (international +44 71 813 8000)

THE CHAMBERS: Barristers at Essex Court Chambers advise across the whole spectrum of international, commercial, and European law and act as advocates in all categories of litigation and commercial arbitration worldwide.

MEMBERS:
Gordon Pollock QC (1968)(QC-1979), Ian Hunter QC (1967)(QC-1980), Stewart Boyd QC (1967)(QC-1981), John Thomas QC (1969)(QC-1984), V.V. Veeder QC (1971)(QC-1986), Michael Collins QC (1971)(QC-1988), Richard Siberry QC (1974)(QC-1989), Jonathan Gilman QC (1965)(QC-1990), Bernard Eder QC (1975)(QC-1990), Roderick Cordara QC (1975)(QC-1994),

HEAD OF CHAMBERS:
Gordon Pollock QC

SEN. CLERK:
David Grief

TENANTS: 47

Anthony Dicks (1961), Anthony Bessemer-Clark (1968), Jack Beatson (1972),
Simon Crookenden (1975), Andrew Hochhauser (1977),
Christopher Greenwood (1978), Richard Jacobs (1979), David Mildon (1980),
Victor Lyon (1980), Mark Smith (1981), Geraldine Andrews (1981),
Graham Dunning (1982), Mark Templeman (1981), Steven Berry (1984),
David Joseph (1984), Richard Millett (1985), Huw Davies (1985),
Joe Smouha (1986), Martin Griffiths (1986), Karen Troy-Davies (1981),
John Lockey (1987), Peter Duffy (1978), Hugh Mercer (1985), Simon Bryan (1988),
David Foxton (1989), Dr Philippa Watson (1988), Prof. Malcolm Shaw (1988),
Sara Cockerill (1990), John Snider (1982), Vernon Flynn (1991), Brian Dye (1991),
Nigel Eaton (1991), Claire Blanchard (19 0), Perdita Cargill-Thompson (1993),
Vaughan Lowe (1993), Toby Landau (1993), Paul Stanley (1993),
Martin Hunter (1994), Philippa Hopkins (1994), Paul McGrath (1994),
James Collins (1995), James O'Reilly (1983).
The Rt. Hon. Sir Michael Kerr, a former Lord Justice of Appeal, R.A. MacCrindle
QC of Counsel, Shearman & Sterling, Paris, Jean-Yves de Cara Professeur Agrégé
des facultés de Droit.

ASSOCIATED MEMBERS: Essex Court Chambers has a number of overseas and university associates, all of whom can be contacted through the Administration: the Hon Andrew Rogers QC, former Chief Judge of the Commercial Division, Supreme Court, New South Wales; Gavin Griffith QC, Solicitor General of Australia; Martin Daly SC, Senior Counsel, Trinidad and Tobago, Garry Downes QC (Australia), President U.I.A. 1994/95; Basil Markesinis, Professor of European Law, in the University of Oxford, Professor of Anglo-America Law, University of Leiden; Professor Karl-Heinz Böcksteigel, Chair of International Business law and Director of International Aerospace Law, Cologne University; Robert Stevens, Master, Pembroke College, Oxford, and practising with Covington and Burling, London; Murray Smith, practising with Campney & Murphy, Vancouver; Neil Kaplan QC, former High Court Judge in Hong Kong; Judge Howard M. Holtzmann, former Judge, Iran - United States Claims Tribunal in the Hague; Rajsoomer Lahlah, former Chief Justice of Mauritius.

PUBLICATIONS: A number of works on international and commercial law have been written or edited by members. These include: *Arnould on Marine Insurance* (co-editor: Jonathon Gilman QC). *Mustill & Boyd on Commercial Arbitration* (co-author: Stewart Boyd QC), *Scrutton on Charterparties* (co-editor: Stewart Boyd QC), *Chitty on Contracts* (co-editor: Jack Beatson), *International Law* (Professor Malcolm Shaw), *The Law of Guarantees* (Geraldine Andrews and Richard Millett), *International Commercial Arbitration* (co-author: Martin Hunter), *The Law of the Sea* (co-author: Vaughan Lowe); *Commercial Debt in Europe, Recovery & Remedies* (Hugh Mercer).

WORK UNDERTAKEN: At Essex Court Chambers the fields of work are Administrative Law and Judicial Review, Arbitration, Aviation, Banking and Financial Services, Chinese Law, Commercial Agreements, Commodity Transactions, Competition Law, Computer Law, Construction and Engineering, Corporate Affairs, Employment Law, Entertainment Law, European Law, French Law, Human Rights, Immigration Law, Industrial Relations, Insolvency, Insurance and Reinsurance, Intellectual Property, International Commercial Fraud, International Trade and Transport, Irish Law, Maritime Law, Oil and Gas, Professional Negligence, Public International Law, Tribunals and Inquiries and VAT Law.

PROFESSIONAL AFFILIATIONS AND ACTIVITIES: Some senior members of Chambers sit as Deputy Judges of the High Court or as Recorders and have acted as Inspectors to the DTI in Inquiries under the Companies Acts and as Chairmen on various Appeal and Disciplinary Committees, including those of Lloyds and other City institutions. One barrister is a member of the Supplementary Treasurer Panel, Common Law.

FOREIGN CONNECTIONS: Members also act as advocates in the Courts and Tribunals of Europe, and in courts and international arbitrations in many overseas jurisdictions to include: European Commission, Court of First Instance, European Court of Justice, Commission and European Court of Human Rights, in the Courts of Australia, Belfast, Dublin, Hong Kong, Singapore, Malaysia, Bermuda, Gibraltar, St Vincent, Brunei, Kenya and the Cayman Islands.

LANGUAGES SPOKEN: French, German, Spanish, Italian, Chinese.

48
Set No.

ESSEX HOUSE CHAMBERS (Yosefaly Serugo-Lugo) Essex House, 375 High Street, Stratford, London, E15 4QZ **Tel:** (0181) 536 1077 **Fax:** (0181) 555 7135 **Sen. Clerk:** Badru Male **Tenants:** 10 Chambers undertakes work on immigration, judicial review, civil, landlord and tenant, medical negligence, crime, international law, personal injury, child care/family, European law.

49
Set No.

46 ESSEX STREET (Geoffrey Hawker) 46 Essex Street, London, WC2R 3GH **Tel:** (0171) 583 8899 **Fax:** (0171) 483 8800 **DX:** 1014 **Sen. Clerk:** Stephen English **Tenants:** 23 Work includes arbitration, tax and chancery, construction, criminal law, family, landlord and tenant, personal injury, planning, professional negligence.

50
Set No.

20 ESSEX STREET (Kenneth Rokison QC)

20 ESSEX STREET, LONDON, WC2R 3AL
DX: 0009 (Ch.Ln.)

TEL: (0171) 583 9294
FAX: (0171) 583 1341

MEMBERS:
Kenneth Rokison QC (1961)(QC-1976), Francis Vallat QC (1935)(QC-1961), Elihu Lauterpacht QC (1950)(QC-1970), David Johnson QC (1967)(QC-1978), Murray Pickering QC (1963)(QC-1985), Martin Moore-Bick QC (1969)(QC-1986), Nicholas Legh-Jones QC (1968)(QC-1987), Richard Owen Plender QC (1974)(QC-1989), Iain Milligan QC (1973)(QC-1991), Angus Glennie QC (1974)(QC-1991), Peter Gross QC (1977)(QC-1992), Mark Havelock-Allan QC (1974)(QC-1993), Julian Cooke (1965), Christopher Russell (1973), Richard Wood (1975), Timothy Young (1977), Patricia Phelan (1977), Stephen Males (1978), Elizabeth Birch (1978), Edmund Broadbent (1980), Nicholas Hamblen (1981), Stephen Morris (1981), David Owen (1983), Christopher Hancock (1983), Duncan Matthews (1986), Geraldine Clark (1988), Andrew Baker (1988), Clifford Gill (1989), Daniel Bethlehem (1988), Charles Mackenzie (1990), Michael Coburn (1990), Lawrence Akka (1991), Clare Ambrose (1992), Karen Maxwell (1992), Graham Charkham (1993), Guy Morpuss (1991).

HEAD OF CHAMBERS:
Kenneth Rokison QC

SEN. CLERK:
Neil Palmer

TENANTS: 36

WORK UNDERTAKEN: Barristers at 20 Essex Street advise on a wide range of domestic and international commercial law and finance, and appear as counsel in litigation and commercial arbitration worldwide; work includes (but is not limited to):

Commercial: Admiralty, agency, arbitration, aviation, bailment, banking and financial services; carriage by land, sea and air, commodities and futures, company law and partnership, conflicts of laws, construction; disciplinary proceedings, entertainment law, insurance and reinsurance; international sales and commodity trading; oil and gas; professional negligence; sale of goods; shipping; all types of domestic and international commercial agreements.

European Community: Two members practise in both London and Brussels specialising in the substantive law of the European Community including harmonisation, competition law and trade regulations, free movement of goods, persons and services, agriculture, intellectual property and environmental law and policy. All members advise on such areas as the Brussels Convention and the Rome Convention.

International: Members of chambers engaged in this field appear before the International Court of Justice and other international tribunals.

Senior members act as arbitrators in both domestic and international arbitrations.
Languages Spoken: Arabic, French, German, Italian and Spanish.

FOREIGN CONNECTIONS: Two members also practise in Brussels. Subject to admission to local bars, instructions are accepted to appear in the courts of Hong Kong, Singapore, Malaysia and other foreign jurisdictions.

ADMINISTRATION: *Office Hours:* 8.30 a.m. – 6.45 p.m. weekdays.
Out of Office Hours: Neil Palmer: (0181) 660 2633 Mobile (0831) 505863
Brian Lee: (0181) 642 5865.

36 ESSEX STREET (Michael Hill QC)

36 ESSEX STREET, LONDON, WC2 3AS
DX: 148 (LDE)

TEL: (0171) 413 0353
FAX: (0171) 413 0374

THE CHAMBERS: A long-established criminal set which has branched out into other areas. Apart from mainstream crime, there is an increasing emphasis on commercial fraud, financial services regulatory work and judicial review. Other principal areas of work include disciplinary tribunals, licensing, and inquests. Members are involved actively with the Inns of Court, the Bar Council, the Criminal Bar Association, the Council of Legal Education, various South Eastern Circuit Committees, Justice and the International Society for the Reform of Criminal Law.

HEAD OF CHAMBERS:
Michael Hill QC

CHAMBERS MANAGERS:
David Burt/Andrea Blick

PRACTICE MANAGERS:
Nicholas Hopgood/Christopher Doe

TENANTS: 36

MEMBERS:
  Michael Hill QC (1958)(QC-1979)*, Nicholas Purnell QC (1968)(QC-1985)*,
  Michael Austin-Smith QC (1969)(QC-1990)*, Michael Lawson QC (1969)(QC-1991)*,
  Susan Edwards QC (1972)(QC-1993)*, Stuart Lawson-Rogers QC (1969)(QC-1994)*,
  Bernard Phelvin (1971)*, The Hon. Charles Byers (1973)*, Charles Miskin (1975),
  P. James Richardson (1975), Michael Wood (1976), Brendan Finucane (1976),
  Justin Wigoder (1977), Simon Davis (1978), Philip Shorrock (1978),
  Roderick James (1979), Michael Bowes (1980), Daniel Janner (1980),
  Graham Cooke (1983), Joanna Glynn (1983), Jane Calnan (1984),
  Rupert Pardoe (1984), Andrew Carnes (1984), Alan Kent (1986),
  Johannah Cutts (1986), Wayne Cranston-Morris (1986), Simon Waley (1988),
  Heather Norton (1988), Alison Jones (1988), William Carter (1989),
  Alison Blood (1990), Nicholas Papadopulos (1990), Isobel Ascherson (1991),
  Simon Medland (1991), Mark Fenhalls (1992), Andrew Hurst (1992).
  Door Tenant: Ian Goldsworthy QC*
  * *Recorders.*

WORK UNDERTAKEN:
Criminal: Members conduct cases for the defence and prosecution at all levels. Chambers has considerable experience in the preparation and conduct of large cases and is able to provide teams to deal with all problems which may arise in connection with actual or potential criminal proceedings, be they national or international.
Civil: Members are involved in areas of common law, mostly (but not exclusively) where they form part of multi-disciplinary case teams or when the matters are crime related.

ADDITIONAL AREAS OF WORK: Members frequently advise on matters which may relate to criminal, regulatory or disciplinary proceedings, such as DTI investigations, insolvency proceedings and other investigations. Individuals specialise in civil actions brought against the police, public and administrative law, employment law, extradition, personal injury, planning, matrimonial, inquiries and defamation.

PUBLICATIONS: James Richardson is the editor of *Archbold*.

RECRUITMENT & TRAINING:
Tenancy Applications: To Michael Wood.
Pupillage: Chambers offers two twelve-month pupillages (funded) and three first six-month pupillages (unfunded). Sponsored pupils are accepted additionally. Full details are published in the Bar Council's *Chambers' Pupillages and Awards Handbook*. Applications addressed to David Burt, Chambers Manager.
Mini-pupillages: A limited number are available. Applications to Mark Fenhalls.

TRAINING: Members of chambers devise, conduct and attend professional and continuing education programmes and seminars. In addition, chambers has an internal continuing education programme for members and pupils. Seminars (including advocacy training) are run for chambers pupils, together with those from Fountain Court and 39 Essex Street.

39 ESSEX STREET (Colin Mackay QC)

39 ESSEX STREET, LONDON, WC2R 3AT
DX: 298

TEL: (0171) 583 1111
FAX: (0171) 353 3978

THE CHAMBERS: 39 Essex Street is an established but modern and expanding set of chambers, which previously practised from 2 Garden Court in the Temple. Chambers' work consists of most areas of civil law. They provide a complete advocacy service for the High Court, County Court and arbitration proceedings, including all the associated advisory and pleading work.

MEMBERS:
Colin Mackay QC (1967)(QC-1989), Simon Goldblatt QC (1953)(QC-1972), Daniel Brennan QC (1967)(QC-1985), Edwin Glasgow QC (1969)(QC-1987), Nigel Pleming QC (1971)(QC-1992), Richard Gray QC (1970)(QC-1993), Richard Davies QC (1973)(QC-1994), Richard Wilmot-Smith QC (1978)(QC-1994), Michael Tillett (1965), Alan Cooper (1969), Claire Miskin (1970), Richard Gordon QC (1972)(QC-1994), David Melville (1975), Roderick Noble (1977), Colin McCaul (1978), Charles Brown (1976), Neil Block (1980), Geoffrey B. Brown (1981), Robert Jay (1981), Christian Du Cann (1982), Charles Cory-Wright (1984), Alison Foster (1984), Jonathan Bellamy (1986), Stuart Catchpole (1987), Charles Manzoni (1988), Steven Kovats (1989), Eleanor Grey (1990), Bernard Doherty (1990), Vincent Nelson (1980), Jennifer Richards (1991), Sean Wilken (1991), Bruce Brodie (1993), Alan Maclean (1993), Matthew Seligman (1994), Tim Ward (1994), Colin Brownlie McCaul (1978) LLB.

WORK UNDERTAKEN: The principal areas of chambers' work are contract, commercial and insurance law, public law, construction and property law, accident litigation, employment, professional negligence and malpractice. There are members of chambers who also undertake family and criminal work.

Chambers offer expertise in European Community law. Members act in other common law jurisdictions such as Hong Kong and Singapore.

Over the last ten years the set has developed a particular strength in public and administrative law: amongst their number are juniors on the treasury panel.

CLIENTELE: Chambers act for a wide range of clients, from multinational corporations and major insurance companies to trade unions; from national and local government to the individual citizen, whether privately paying or legally aided.

Instructions are accepted direct from professional clients within or outside England and Wales as permitted by Bar regulations.

RECRUITMENT & TRAINING: 39 Essex Street offer: up to 4 pupillages for 12 months with scholarship awards of £17,500.

Chambers would hope to take on as a tenant at least one pupil. There are opportunities for all pupils to undertake paid work on their own account in the second 6 months of pupillage. The decision as to offers of pupillage depends in particular upon: academic record (a first or upper second class degree is usually required), performance at interview, performance in any mini-pupillage and references.

HEAD OF CHAMBERS:
Colin Mackay QC

SEN. CLERK:
Nigel Connor

TENANTS: 35

35 ESSEX STREET (Alan Rawley QC)

35 ESSEX STREET, TEMPLE, LONDON, WC2R 3AR
DX: 351 London

TEL: (0171) 353 6381
FAX: (0171) 583 1786

THE CHAMBERS: The chambers, comprising 25 full-time practising barristers and one academic members of the Bar, are organised as a number of specialist groups, providing advice and representation in a variety of fields.

Outside office hours, and during week-ends and public holidays, contact can always be arranged – in the first instance – through the duty clerk on (01860) 292695 or in an emergency on the Clerk's Nightline (01483) 720252.

Among the practical facilities provided by chambers are large dedicated conference rooms with television and video facilities.

HEAD OF CHAMBERS:
Alan Rawley QC

SEN. CLERK:
Mr. Derek Jenkins

TENANTS: 26

MEMBERS:

Alan D. Rawley QC (1958)(QC-1977) MA (Oxon),
Sir David C. Calcutt QC (1955)(QC-1972) MA, LLB, MuSB (Cantab),
Nigel J. Inglis-Jones QC (1959)(QC-1982) BA (Oxon),
Dominik Lasok QC (1954)(QC-1982) LLM, PhD, Dr Juris, LLD,
Christopher Wilson-Smith QC (1965)(QC-1986), Philip C. Mott QC (1970)(QC-1991) MA (Oxon), Linda E. Sullivan QC (1973)(QC-1994) BA (Hons),
Richard E.R.S. Rains (1963) LLB, Hywel I. Jenkins (1974) LLB (Hons),
John L. Stephens (1975) BA (Oxon), Richard M. Mawhinney (1977) BA (Oxon),
William L. Coley (1980) MA (Cantab), Robin S. Tolson (1980) BA (Cantab),
Stephen Climie (1982) BA (Lincoln), David G. Westcott (1982) BA (Oxon), BCL,
Christopher M. Kemp (1984) BA (Oxon), Dip Law, Harry Trusted (1985) MA
(Cantab), Andrew J.M. Spink (1985) BA (Cantab), Alison McCormick (1988) BA
(Oxon), Susan C. Freeborn (1989) BA (Cantab), Richard G. Hitchcock (1989) BA
(Oxon), Jonathan E.S. Hand (1990) BA(Oxon), Thomas R.G. Leeper (1993) BA
(Hons), Nathan W. Tavares (1992) BSE (Hons), Grace Malden (1993) (Cantab),
Matthew J. Phillips (1993) (Oxon).

CATEGORIES OF WORK:

Building and Engineering
Commercial Fraud
European & International Law
Contract
Family Law
Intellectual Property
Local Government Law
Medical Negligence
Occupational Pension Schemes & Trusts
Personal Injury
Property Law
Professional Negligence

FOREIGN CONNECTIONS: Dominik Lasok QC can advise on Polish law and chambers have an Italian affiliate practising in Milan, Avv. Mauto Rubino-Sammartano.

LANGUAGES SPOKEN: French, German, Italian, and Polish.

FALCON CHAMBERS (Jonathan Gaunt QC & David Neuberger QC)

54
: No.

FALCON COURT, LONDON, EC4Y 1AA
DX: 408

TEL: (0171) 353 2484
FAX: (0171) 353 1261

THE CHAMBERS: A long-established set specialising in the litigation of law of real property. Members act for clients ranging from large City firms to sole practitioners; from financial institutions and major property companies to legally-aided individuals; for landlords and tenants, and vendors and purchasers; and they offer the same degree of commitment irrespective of the client's identity, size or financial power. Chambers have strong links with the Royal Institution of Chartered Surveyors and with the Chartered Institute of Arbitrators.

HEAD OF CHAMBERS:
Jonathan Gaunt QC, David Neuberger QC

SEN. CLERK:
Mark Clewley

TENANTS: 25

MEMBERS:

Derek Wood QC (1964)(QC-1978) MA, BCL, David Neuberger QC (1974)(QC-1987) MA, Jonathan Gaunt QC (1972)(QC-1991) BA, Kim Lewison QC (1975)(QC-1991) MA, Paul Morgan QC (1975)(QC-1992) MA, Kirk Reynolds QC (1974)(QC-1993) MA, Edwin Prince (1955),
Paul de la Piquerie (1966) LLB, Jonathan Brock (1977) MA,
Joanne R. Moss (1976) MA, Nicholas Dowding (1979) MA,
Erica Foggin (1980) MA, Edward Cole (1980) MA, Wayne Clark (1982) LLB, BCL,
Guy Fetherstonhaugh (1983) BSc, Martin Rodger (1986) BA,
Timothy Fancourt (1987) MA, Barry Denyer-Green (1972) LLM, PhD,
Stephen Jourdan (1989) MA, Gary Cowen (1990) LLB, Jonathan Small (1990) BA,

Janet Bignell (1992) MA, BCL, Martin Dray (1992) LLB M.Jur.,
Caroline Shea (1994) MA, Anthony Tanney (1994) BA (Durham) M.Jur.
Five members of chambers are Recorders, one of whom sits as a Deputy Judge of the
High Court, Chancery Division.
All members of chambers are members of The Chancery Bar Association, The Commercial Bar Association, and the London Common Law and Commercial Bar Association.

WORK UNDERTAKEN: All aspects of property law, including landlord and tenant work, housing, conveyancing, commercial property, mortgages, agricultural holdings and production controls, rent review and valuation disputes, professional negligence, town planning and compulsory purchase, and building and engineering disputes. Members undertake chancery and common law work related to these fields of practice, particularly insolvency law. Members of chambers are often willing to accept appointments as arbitrators or legal assessors. Direct Professional Access is welcomed in appropriate cases by all members.

PUBLICATIONS: Members of chambers have written or edited a large number of publications, including *Megarry on the Rent Acts* (11th ed.); *Woodfall on Landlord and Tenant; Milk Quotas: Law and Practice; The Handbook of Milk Quota Compensation; The Handbook of Rent Review; Renewal of Business Tenancies: Law and Practice; Drafting Business Leases; The Interpretation of Contracts; Dilapidations: The Modern Law and Practice; Leasehold Enfranchisement; Muir Watt on Agricultural Holdings; Butterworths County Court Precedents and Pleadings; Hill and Redman on Landlord and Tenant; Compulsory Purchase and Compensation;* and *Development and Planning Law.* Chambers' members have contributed to the Landlord and Tenant section of *Halsbury's Laws* (4th ed.) and to the Housing section of *Atkin's Court Forms*; and one is the editor of the *Estates Gazette Law Reports.*

LANGUAGES: French, German and Italian.

FOREIGN CONNECTIONS: One member is qualified to practise in Victoria, Australia; a door tenant practises in Hong Kong.

---

55 FARRAR'S BUILDING (Lord Williams of Mostyn QC)
Set No.

FARRAR'S BUILDING, TEMPLE, LONDON, EC4Y 7BD
DX: 406

TEL: (0171) 583 9241
FAX: (0171) 583 0090

THE CHAMBERS: A long-established common law set undertaking a wide range of London civil work as well as retaining strong links with the South Eastern and Wales and Chester Circuits. Specialist expertise in particular areas (such as general commercial, personal injury, landlord and tenant, building work, employment and crime) exists at all levels of seniority, thus ensuring excellent back-up facilities. Chambers' administration is fully computerised. Three silks are members of the Criminal Injuries Compensation Board, and the Head of Chambers is the former Chairman of the Bar and was Chairman of the Professional Conduct Committee of the Bar Council. Other members serve on the Bar Council and specialist Bar Association committees.

HEAD OF CHAMBERS:
Lord Williams of Mostyn QC

SEN. CLERK/PRACTICE MANAGER:
Alan Kilbey

CH'S. MANAGER: Janet Eades

TENANTS: 30

MEMBERS:
Lord Lord Williams of Mostyn QC (1965)(QC-1978)*,
Michael Lewer QC (1958)(QC-1983)*, Gerard Elias QC (1968)(QC-1984)*,
John Leighton Williams QC (1964)(QC-1986)*,
Christopher Pitchford QC (1969)(QC-1987)*, Douglas Day QC (1967)(QC-1989)*,
Peter Birts QC (1968)(QC-1990)*, Geoffrey Nice QC (1971)(QC-1990)*,
Patrick Harrington QC (1973)(QC-1993)*, Edward Southwell (1970)*,
Alan Jeffreys (1970)*, Anthony Webb (1970)*, Richard Nussey (1971),
Anthony Seys Llewellyn (1972)*, William Norris (1974), Stephen Rubin (1977),
Gregory Treverton-Jones (1977), Stephen Jones (1978), Tim Dutton (1979),
Tom McDermott (1980), Jane McNeill (1982), Simon Browne (1982),
Tracy Ayling (1983), Daniel Matovu (1985), Jonathan Watt-Pringle (1987),
Andrew Peebles (1987), David Wicks (1989), James Todd (1990),
Helen Hobhouse (1990), Lucy Moorman (1992).
* Recorder

WORK UNDERTAKEN:
Main Areas: Professional negligence, medical negligence, personal injury, employment and industrial relations, commercial, landlord and tenant and property law, insurance, building, defamation, betting and licensing.
Additional Areas: Judicial review, civil rights of prisoners, trespass, rights of way and countryside law, planning and agricultural work (including milk quotas).
Criminal Law: Heavy crime, especially fraud. Prosecution and defence work of all kinds and on all circuits.
FOREIGN CONNECTIONS: Lord Williams QC has been called to the Bar of Hong Kong, the Bar of Northern Ireland and the Bar of Ireland and Thomas McDermott is a member of the Bar of Ireland.

56
t No.

2 FIELD COURT (Norman Palmer)

2 FIELD COURT, GRAY'S INN, LONDON, WC1
DX: 457

TEL: (0171) 405 6114
FAX: (0171) 831 6112

THE CHAMBERS: A commercial and general common law set with members practising in a wide variety of fields.
MEMBERS:
Prof. Norman E. Palmer (1973) MA BCL (Oxon),
Nicholas Bridges-Adams (1958) MA (Oxon), Dip. Ed, FCIArb,
Prof Michael Furmston (1960) (Oxon) LLM, Jeffrey Littman (1974) MA (Cantab),
Kay Jones (1974) BA, William Bowring (1974) BA, Philip Walter (1975) MA (Cantab), Ashley Underwood (1976) LLB, Hilton Harrop-Griffiths (1978) BA,
Jane Bennington (1981) BA, Franklin Evans (1981) BA, Lucy Theis (1982) LLB,
Bryan McGuire (1983) LLB, MPhil (Cantab), Timothy Carlisle (1984),
Belinda Schwehr (1985), James Presland (1985) BA,
Neville Stevenson-Watt (1985) MA (Cantab), LLB, Joshua Swirsky (1987) BA,
Katrina Armstrong-Myers (1988) LLB, Kelvin Rutledge (1989) LLB, LLM,
Eleri Vodden Lewis (1989) LLB, Joanna Youll (1989),
Rowena Champion (1990) (Eng), Richard Deighton (1990), Ian Fox (1990),
Lisa Giovannetti (1990), Miss Susan George (1990), Paul Finch (1990),
Rex Howling (1991), Michael Nicholson (1993).
Publications: *Claims to Possession of Land* (Philip Walter and J. Harris); contributions to *New Law Journal* and American Bar Association publications (Kay Jones); articles on family law (Neville Stevenson-Watt); *Bailment* (Norman Palmer). *Emden* (Joint ed. Norman Palmer) *Interests in Goods* (Joint ed. Norman Palmer), *Law of Contract* of which Michael Furmston is one of three editors.
MAIN AREAS OF WORK: General common law including claims in negligence, nuisance and other torts; contractual disputes and professional negligence; all aspects of family law including matrimonial finance and child care litigation; real property disputes, housing and landlord and tenant; administrative and local government; insolvency, company; employment, licensing.
FOREIGN CONNECTIONS: Kay Jones is an associate member of the American Bar Association.
LANGUAGES SPOKEN: French, Italian, German, Russian and Welsh.
RECRUITMENT & TRAINING: Tenancy and pupillage applications should be sent to Joanna Youll. Two awards a year are offered to pupils who intend to practise after completion of twelve months pupillage in chambers. Applications must be received by 1st October for pupillages starting in October of the following year.

HEAD OF CHAMBERS:
Norman Palmer
SEN. CLERK:
Michael Clark
TENANTS: 30

TWO FIELD COURT

7
No.

3 FIELD COURT (Raana Sheikh) 3 Field Court, Gray's Inn, London, WC1R 5EP **Tel:** (0171) 831 5344 **Fax:** (0171) 242 7799 **Sen. Clerk:** Miss S. Doyle **Tenants:** 13 Small established set practising general common law with an emphasis on crime (defence and prosecution). Also matrimonial, licensing, personal injury, commercial and property, including landlord and tenant.

58
Set No.
FIELD COURT CHAMBERS (Melanie Spencer) Field Court Chambers, Grays Inn, London, WC2A 5EP **Tel:** (0171) 404 7474 **Fax:** (0171) 404 7475 **DX:** 136 (Ch.Ln.) **Sen. Clerk:** Paul Mellor **Tenants:** 9 A civil set emphasising company and commercial although individuals' specialisations include professional negligence, family and personal injury.

59
Set No.
54 FLEET STREET (R.P. Gibbons) 54 Fleet Street, London, EC4Y 1JV **Tel:** (0171) 583 3354 **Fax:** (0171) 353 2142 **DX:** 324 **Sen. Clerk:** Adrian G. Attwell **Tenants:** 14 Predominantly criminal practice. Also undertakes civil litigation including matrimonial, probate and immigration law. Also landlord and tenant, housing, tax-capital and income, personal injury, insolvency, banking, chancery (general).

60
Set No.
FOREST HOUSE CHAMBERS (David Singer) Forest House, 8 Gainsborough Road, London, E11 1HT **Tel:** (0181) 558 2126 **Fax:** (0181) 556 6125 **Sen. Clerk:** David Singer **Tenants:** 4 General common law set handling criminal, immigration and family law matters.

61
Set No.
FOUNTAIN COURT (Peter Scott QC)

FOUNTAIN COURT, TEMPLE, LONDON, EC4Y 9DH
DX: 5

TEL: (0171) 583 3335
FAX: (0171) 353 0329/1794

THE CHAMBERS: A large and long-established set of chambers, practising primarily in the commercial field but with a wide range of other specialities. Much of the work is international in character. The size of chambers enables them to supply teams of counsel at all levels of seniority, to deal with large-scale litigation. Chambers' administration has kept pace with recent developments in organisation and technology.

MEMBERS:
Conrad Dehn QC (1952)(QC-1968), The Hon. Christopher Bathurst QC (1959)(QC-1978), Peter Scott QC (1960)(QC-1978), Bruce Coles QC (1963)(QC-1984), Gordon Langley QC (1966)(QC-1983), Charles Gibson (1966), Tim Walker QC (1968)(QC-1985), Anthony Boswood QC (1970)(QC-1986), Peter Goldsmith QC (1972)(QC-1987), Trevor Philipson QC (1972)(QC-1989), Michael Lerego QC (1972)(QC-1995), Andrew Smith QC (1974)(QC-1990), Charles Falconer QC (1974)(QC-1991), Michael Brindle QC (1975)(QC-1992), Nicholas Underhill QC (1976)(QC-1992), Nicholas Stadlen QC (1976)(QC-1991), Timothy Wormington (1977), David Railton (1979), Brian Doctor (1991), Gillian Keene (1980), The Hon. Michael McLaren (1981), Simon Browne-Wilkinson (1981), Philip Brook Smith (1982), Raymond Cox (1982), Thomas Keith (1984), Murray Shanks (1984), Daphne Loebl (1985), Guy Philipps (1986), Stephen Moriarty (1986), Craig Orr (1986), Timothy Howe (1987), Bankim Thanki (1988), Patricia Robertson (1988), Jeffrey Chapman (1989), Brian Napier (1990), Derrick Dale (1990), Marcus Smith (1991), Paul Gott (1991), Veronique Buehrlen (1991), Andrew Mitchell (1992), Richard N. Handyside (1993), John C. Taylor (1993), Richard J.L. Coleman (1994), James S. Butters (1994), Adam R. Tolley (1994).
Practising part-time:
Peter Carter QC (1947, QC-1990), (Emeritus Fellow and Tutor in Law, Wadham College, Oxford).
Richard Hooley (1984), (Fellow and Tutor in Law, Fitzwilliam College, Cambridge).
Andrew Burrows (1985), Professor of English Law, University College, London; Law Commissioner for England and Wales.

HEAD OF CHAMBERS:
Peter Scott QC

EXECUTIVE MANAGER (SEN. CLERK):
Barry Down

FIRST JUNIOR CLERK: Mark Watson

CHAMBERS ADMINISTRATOR:
Maureen Hobart

TENANTS: 45

WORK UNDERTAKEN: The mainstream of chambers' work is in commercial and business law, including in particular:

- arbitration
- sale of goods
- international trade
- banking and financial services
- shipping
- aviation (including air transport licensing)
- 'City' regulatory work (including Lloyd's disciplinary tribunals)
- professional negligence
- insurance and reinsurance
- takeovers and mergers
- oil and gas contract

EC law is an aspect of much of this work.

OTHER SPECIALITIES INCLUDE:

- administrative law and judicial review
- building disputes
- employment law (including industrial disputes and sex discrimination and equal pay)
- media and entertainment law
- medical and pharmaceutical law (including medical negligence)
- parliamentary bills
- personal injury (including disaster litigation)

62
Set No.

FRANCIS TAYLOR BUILDING (Phillip Matthews)

FRANCIS TAYLOR BUILDING, TEMPLE, LONDON, EC4Y 7BY
DX: 211

TEL: (0171) 353 9942
FAX: (0171) 353 9924

THE CHAMBERS: A long-established set combining strong civil and criminal teams. As well as London and the South East, Chambers receives and undertakes work throughout England and Wales.

MEMBERS:
Phillip Matthews (1974), Stephen Williamson QC (1964)(QC-1981),
Gavin Merrylees (1964), Dennis Naish (1966), Philip Conrath (1972),
Jamie De Burgos (1973), Frank Gillibrand (1974), Kate Mallison (1975),
D.A. Pears (1975), Paul Staddon (1976), Ian Wade (1977), Mark Dencer (1978),
Simon Michael (1978), Kerstin Boyd (1979), Alasdair Smith (1981),
Henrietta Manners (1981), Sebastian Reid (1982), Stella Reynolds (1983),
Jane Carpenter (1984), Jacqueline Matthews-Stroud (1984), Philip Dixon (1986),
Karoline Sutton (1986), Nathalie Guimard (1987), Clare Huggett (1987),
Michael Buckpitt (1988), Gerald Wilson (1989), Philip Rainey (1990),
Gilbert Chirimuuta (1990), Nicholas Barraclough (1990), Stephen Heath (1992),
Howard Jones (1992), Catriona Maclaren (1993), Andrew Butler (1993).

HEAD OF CHAMBERS:
Phillip Matthews
SEN. CLERK:
Gerald Miller
CLERKS:
Kathryn Thornton, Ian Hogg, Ryan Bartlett
OFFICE ADMINISTRATOR: Sandra Gidaree
TENANTS: 33

WORK UNDERTAKEN: Francis Taylor Building has chosen to build a strong team dealing with all areas of civil and criminal work, so as to provide most solicitors with a "one-stop" service. That service is provided within the framework of specialist teams whose principal fields are landlord and tenant, property and commercial, professional (especially medical) negligence, personal injuries, criminal law, family, employment, wills, probate and licensing. A chambers brochure is available on request.

SECOND FLOOR
FRANCIS
TAYLOR
BUILDING
barristers chambers

63
Set No.

FRANCIS TAYLOR BUILDING (Alan Tyrrell QC)

FRANCIS TAYLOR BUILDING (3RD FLOOR), TEMPLE, LONDON, EC4Y 7BY
DX: 46 London Chancery Lane

TEL: (0171) 797 7250
FAX: (0171) 797 7299

HEAD OF CHAMBERS:
Alan Tyrrell QC

SEN. CLERK:
Kenneth Oliver

TENANTS: 23

THE CHAMBERS: Founded in the Temple at the turn of the last century, this is a common law set whose members have considerable experience of practice in both traditional and emergent fields. Chambers has amongst its membership specialists in commercial arbitration, European Community, employment, education, computer, licensing and gaming law. Chambers continues to maintain and strengthen its working relations with overseas lawyers, particularly those from within the Community, and is able to call upon the assistance of established overseas practitioners when necessary. Chambers aim to provide a friendly, fast and efficient service and will, if requested, provide written work on disc or by modem.

PUBLICATIONS: Alan Tyrrell QC is Joint Editor of *The Legal Profession in the New Europe – A Handbook for Practitioners*, (Blackwell 1992). Andrew Thompson is Joint Editor of *Harvey on Industrial Relations and Employment Law,* (Butterworths), and also a contributor to Halsbury's Laws, *Trade and Labour*. Stephen Monkcom is co-author of Smith and Monkcom *The Law of Betting, Gaming and Lotteries*, (Butterworths 1987), and also a contributor to the *Encyclopedia of Forms and Precedents* vol 17, *Gaming, Betting and Lotteries*.

MEMBERS:
Alan Tyrrell QC (1956)(QC-1976) FCI Arb,
Lord Thomas of Gwydir QC (1947)(QC-1965), John Hall QC (1948)(QC-1967) FCI Arb, Edward Raw (1963), Christopher Mitchell-Heggs (1966),
Andrew Thompson (1969), Timothy Shuttleworth (1971), David Guy (1972) FCI Arb, Stephen Monkcom (1974), Basil Yoxall (1975) FCI Arb,
Michael Shrimpton (1983), Mark Kelly (1985), Mark Loveday (1986),
Brian Riley (1986), Christopher Bamford (1987), Sheila Phil-Ebosie (1988),
Becket Bedford (1989), Purvaise Punwar (1989), Giles Bark-Jones (1990),
Tom Skinner (1992), Jacqui Gilliatt (1992), Ann Bevitt (1992).

PRINCIPAL AREAS OF WORK: Commercial Arbitration, contract, consumer credit, computers, crime, employment, education, family and matrimonial, housing, licensing, media and defamation, all aspects of property related law, planning, Private International, professional negligence, personal injury and road traffic.

Members have been advising on European Community Law and appearing before the Commission and Court of Justice at Luxembourg, and the Commission and Court of Human Rights at Strasbourg, for more than 15 years. In this period strong links have been developed with the Community's institutions. In addition to the established Community fields Chambers has a particular specialisation in public procurement and employment. Practitioners of varying call are available to advise and tenants will give lectures on aspects of Community Law by request.

FOREIGN CONNECTIONS: Christopher Mitchell-Heggs has his own offices in Paris and is a member of the Paris Bar. Sheila Phil-Eboise is also a member of the Nigerian Bar. Chambers is a member of Eurolink and InterAct Europe EEIG.

64
Set No.

FRANCIS TAYLOR BUILDING (N.P. Valios QC)

FRANCIS TAYLOR BUILDING, TEMPLE, LONDON, EC4Y 7BY
DX: 441

TEL: (0171) 353 7768
FAX: (0171) 353 0659

HEAD OF CHAMBERS:
N.P. Valios QC

JOINT SEN. CLERKS:
Janet Clark, David Green

TENANTS: 30

THE CHAMBERS: Chambers covers all areas of common law, with specialisations principally in personal injury, family and crime, mainly on the South Eastern Circuit, although several members also belong to the Midland and Oxford and the Western Circuits and work is undertaken throughout the UK.

MEMBERS:
Nicholas P. Valios QC (1964)(QC-1991), David Barker QC (1954)(QC-1976),
Nicholas P. Riddell (1964), Peter R. Lewis (1964), John M. Cartwright (1964),
John Rylance (1968), James W. Mason (1969), Graham Lodge (1971) LLB,

Edward G. Lewis (1972), Timothy J. Grice (1975) MA (Oxon),
Mark Piercy (1976) BA (Oxon), Graham Cunningham (1976),
Wendy Parker (1978) MA, David Mayall (1979), Simon E.P. Cheves (1980) BA
(Dunhelm), Janet Bazley (1980), Richard H.F. Jones (1984) LLB (Wales),
James T.N. Scobie (1984) BA, Dip. Law, Alastair J. McFarlane (1985) LLB (Hons),
Joseph Giret (1985), Tonia Clark (1986), Christine Scott (1986),
Garfield Braithwaite (1987) LLB (Hons), Sarah Morgan (1988),
Nicholas Deal (1989), Sarah Roberts (1991), Shira Ancliffe (1991),
Isabelle Watson (1991), Simon Taylor (1993).

WORK UNDERTAKEN: Chambers provides teams of practitioners in the following areas: (i) personal injury; (ii) professional negligence; (iii) family work, including matrimonial finance and childcare litigation; (iv) criminal law, prosecuting and defending, including serious fraud work, Courts Martial, road traffic and haulage law; (v) insolvency; (vi) Official Referees business, building and civil engineering law; (vii) contract, including sale of goods; (viii) landlord and tenant; (ix) employment; (x) intellecutal property, including computer and information law; (xi) licensing.

65
Set No.

FURNIVAL CHAMBERS (Andrew Mitchell) 32 Furnival Street, London, EC4A 1JQ **Tel:** (0171) 583 0434 **Fax:** (0171) 353 3987 **DX:** 72 **Sen. Clerk:** John Gutteridge **Tenants:** 38 A set of specialist criminal practitioners with additional expertise in confiscation, commercial fraud, and all other aspects of criminal law.

66
Set No.

ONE GARDEN COURT (Miss Eleanor F. Platt QC & Miss Alison Ball QC)

ONE GARDEN COURT, TEMPLE, LONDON, EC4Y 9BJ
DX: 1034 (Ch.Ln.)

TEL: (0171) 797 7900
FAX: (0171) 797 7929

THE CHAMBERS: Formed as a specialist family set in January 1989, by a group of well-established family law practitioners. The set has expanded rapidly, with recruitment at all levels of seniority and its members have particular experience in family law.

MEMBERS:
Eleanor F. Platt QC (1960)(QC-1982), Alison Ball QC (1972)(QC-1995),
Ellen B. Solomons (1964), Caroline Willbourne (1970), John Mitchell (1972),
Peter Nathan (1973), Jennifer Beckhough (1973), Suzanne H. Shenton (1973),
Elizabeth Szwed (1974), Sheron Bedell-Pearce (1978), Martin O'Dwyer (1978),
Ann Marie Wicherek (1978), Kay Halkyard (1980), Veronica Lachkovic (1982),
Susannah Walker (1985), Paul Rippon (1985), Caroline Rylance (1983),
Gary Crawley (1988), Caroline Lester (1988), Gillian Cleave (1988),
Alan Inglis (1989), Catherine Jenkins (1990), Ariff Rozhan (1990),
Ian Robbins (1991), Kathryn Edwards (1991), Nora O'Flaherty (1991),
Joanna Geddes (1992), Andrew Norton (1992).

HEAD OF CHAMBERS:
Miss Eleanor F. Platt QC, Miss Alison Ball QC

SEN. CLERK:
Peter Hoskins

SECOND CLERK: Howard Rayner
FEES CLERK: Anitra Jones

TENANTS: 28

WORK UNDERTAKEN: One Garden Court is a specialist family law set of chambers offering a comprehensive service to solicitors, local authorities, child care professionals and their clients. Members practise at all levels in the law relating to marriage, divorce, the Children Act 1989, wardship, cohabitation, inheritance, child abduction, criminal child abuse and all other aspects of family law. All are members of the Family Law Bar Association. Direct Professional Access work, including from guardians ad litem, may be accepted by individual members of chambers if considered appropriate. Mediation is available from those members who are FMA trained and qualified.
Additional Areas: Personal injuries and medical negligence (Ellen B. Solomons).

ASSOCIATED CHAMBERS: Miss Bedell-Pearce practises from Denton, North Yorks, LS29 0HE, *Tel:* 01943 817230.

RECRUITMENT & TRAINING: Tenancy and pupillage applications to Miss Ann Marie Wicherek with detailed CV and references.

Family Law Chambers

67
Set No.

2 GARDEN COURT (I. Macdonald QC & O. Davies) 2 Garden Court, Temple, London, EC4Y 9BL **Tel:** (0171) 353 1633 **Fax:** (0171) 353 4621 **DX:** 34 (Ch.Ln.) **Sen. Clerk:** Colin Cook **Tenants:** 47 A general common law set specialising in crime, family and matrimonial law, housing, immigration, private international law, administrative law and judicial review.

68
Set No.

GLOBE HOUSE (Helen Grindrod QC) 4 Temple Place, London, WC2R 3HP **Tel:** (0171) 240 7277 **Fax:** (0171) 240 7977 **DX:** 425 (Ch.Ln.) **Sen. Clerk:** Mark Auger **Tenants:** 9 A set of specialist criminal practitioners with expertise in all aspects of criminal law.

69
Set No.

GOLDSMITH BUILDING (John Griffith Williams QC)

GOLDSMITH BUILDING, TEMPLE, LONDON, EC4Y 7BL
DX: 435

TEL: (0171) 353 7881
FAX: (0171) 353 5319

HEAD OF CHAMBERS:
John Griffith Williams QC

SEN. CLERK:
Edith A. Robertson

TENANTS: 22

THE CHAMBERS: A long-established set of chambers, whose members have wide experience in conducting all aspects of common law litigation. Members practise mainly in London and the South East; however, chambers also have strong connections with the Northern and Wales and Chester Circuits: having Queen's Counsel who practise on circuit.

MEMBERS:
John Griffith Williams QC (1968)(QC-1985), Michael Maguire QC (1949)(QC-1967), Eric Somerset Jones QC (1952)(QC-1978),
Christopher Llewellyn-Jones QC (1965)(QC-1990), Robin Hay (1964),
Harry Martineau (1966), Martin Hall-Smith (1972),
Christopher Morris-Coole (1974), John Gallagher (1974), Charles Calvert (1975),
Robert Leonard (1976), Patrick Routley (1979), Christopher Wilson (1980),
Michael Curtis (1982), Andrew Ritchie (1985), Debora Price (1987),
Mark Maitland-Jones (1986), Kate Purkiss (1988), Gordon Dawes (1989),
David Burles (1984), Nicholas Brooke (1991), Louise Eyeington (1993).

WORK UNDERTAKEN:
Main Areas of Work:
Negligence: personal injuries; professional negligence; industrial accidents and diseases.
Commercial Law: commercial contracts; company law; insurance; partnerships; restraint of trade; insolvency; agency; guarantees and securities.
Building Law: construction contracts and Official Referees' business.
Property: contract and conveyance; mortgages; boundaries, trespass and adverse possession; easements and covenants; nuisance.
Landlord and Tenant: business, residential and agricultural leases; Rent and Housing Acts and Landlord and Tenant Acts.
Family Law: divorce; custody, care, wardship and adoption of children; foreign and international aspects of divorce and child law; matrimonial finance; proceedings under Inheritance Acts and wills.
Additional Areas: Consumer law, including sale and supply of goods and services; consumer credit; environmental; banking; employment law; defamation; general chancery work; intellectual property; criminal law; licensing; planning and local government law; judicial review; tribunals; mental health work; maritime and aviation law and Scots law. Members of chambers accept Direct Professional Access work.

CHAMBERS FACILITIES: Most barristers have their own computer equipment and operate on Wordperfect software.

70
Set No.

GOLDSMITH CHAMBERS (Peter Morrish) Goldsmith Building, Temple, London, EC4Y 7BL **Tel:** (0171) 353 6802 **Fax:** (0171) 583 5255 **DX:** 376 **Sen. Clerk:** Mrs Celia Monksfield **Tenants:** 31   A common law set of chambers with an emphasis on criminal and family work.

71
Set No.

9 GOUGH SQUARE (Michael Brent QC)

9 GOUGH SQUARE, LONDON, EC4A 3DE
DX: 439

TEL: (0171) 353 5371
FAX: (0171) 353 1344

THE CHAMBERS: A well-established common law set which in January 1994 moved from 2 Dr Johnson's Buildings to new premises in the elegant surroundings of Gough Square which have been refurbished in order to provide comprehensive modern facilities (including spacious conference rooms and wheelchair access) within a traditional environment.

HEAD OF CHAMBERS:
Michael Brent QC

PRACTICE DIRECTOR:
Joanna Poulton

TENANTS: 36

MEMBERS:
Michael Leon Brent QC (1961)(QC-1983), John Gorman QC (1953)(QC-1974), Beryl Philis Cooper QC (1960)(QC-1977), John Rogers QC (1963)(QC-1979), Jeremy Roberts QC (1965)(QC-1982), John Michael Lee (1960), Martin Edward von Simson (1964), John Leonard Foy (1969), John Hargreaves Reddihough (1969), Andrew Bruce Baillie (1970), Christopher John Gray (1970), Richard Merz (1972), Kenneth George Aylett (1972), Patrick Charles Upward (1972), David Cliff Gerrey (1975), Michael John Joyce (1976), Trevor Glyn Davies (1978), Frederick Ferguson (1978), Grahame Linley Aldous (1979), Duncan Macleod (1980), Nicolas Peter Hillier (1982), Roger Hiorns (1983), Simon Carr (1984), Gaurang Naik (1985), Jacob Levy (1986), Jonathan C. Loades (1986), Alexander Verdan (1987), Edwin Buckett (1988), Andrew Wheeler (1988), Stephen Glynn (1990), Jane Sinclair (1990), Clare Padley (1991), John Tughan (1991), Jeremy Crowther (1991), Aileen Downey (1991), Laura Begley (1993).

WORK UNDERTAKEN: Chambers is a mixed-speciality set, providing a comprehensive service in Civil, Criminal and Family Law.

Civil Litigation: Specialist areas include Personal Injury (including Disaster Litigation, Marine Accident & Industrial Disease), Professional Negligence (including Medical Negligence and Structured Settlements), Landlord & Tenant, Property, Contract & Tort, Judicial Review, Employment Law, Civil Jury Actions.

Criminal Law: Commercial Fraud is a particular specialisation. Chambers offers expertise in all areas of criminal work at all levels, for both the prosecution and the defence, and has a strong presence on the Midland and Oxford Circuit.

Family Law: All areas of family law and child care (both private and public law). Members appear regularly before all levels of court and have considerable experience acting for both lay clients and local authorities.

Members of Chambers accept Direct Professional Access work.

72
Set No.

GOUGH SQUARE CHAMBERS (F. Philpott)

6-7 GOUGH SQUARE CHAMBERS, LONDON, EC4A 3DE
DX: 476

TEL: (0171) 353 0924
FAX: (0171) 353 2221

THE CHAMBERS: A general common law/ commercial and chancery set, with a bias toward consumer law. There is a chambers brochure available upon request.

HEAD OF CHAMBERS:
Frederick Philpott

SEN. CLERK:
Mr Bob Weekes

TENANTS: 12

MEMBERS:
Frederick Philpott (1974), Claire Andrews (1979), William Hibbert (1979), Peter Sayer (1975), Barry Stancombe (1983), Jonathan Goulding (1984), Anthony Bell (1985), Stephen Neville (1986), Julia Smith (1988), Julian Gun Cuninghame (1989), Cyrus Katrak (1991), Anthony Vines (1993).

WORK UNDERTAKEN:
General Description: Common law, commercial and chancery work.
Main Areas of Work: Consumer credit, sale of goods, land, landlord and tenant, company, employment, food and safety law, insolvency, partnership, personal injuries, professional negligence, building, and crime.
PUPILLAGE: Pupillage applications to Anthony Vines. First or upper second class degree preferred. Awards are available.

GRAY'S INN CHAMBERS (Milton Grundy)

GRAY'S INN CHAMBERS, GRAY'S INN, LONDON, WC1R 5JA
DX: 352

TEL: (0171) 242 2642
FAX: (0171) 405 4078

THE CHAMBERS: An established and flourishing set of chambers of specialist tax practitioners, offering advocacy and advisory services on all aspects of taxation and at all levels of seniority.

MEMBERS:
Milton Grundy (1954), Andrew Park QC (1964)(QC-1978),
Michael Flesch QC (1963)(QC-1983), David Goldberg QC (1971)(QC-1987),
David Goy QC (1973)(QC-1991), John Walters (1977), Felicity Cullen (1985),
Philip Baker (1979), Hugh McKay (1990).

Appointments and Memberships: All members of chambers belong to the Revenue Bar Association of which Michael Flesch QC is Chairman. Milton Grundy is President of the International Tax Planning Association; he is the draftsman of the Trusts of the Cayman Islands and (with Philip Baker) of the IBC Act and the Trusts Act of Belize. John Walters is a chartered accountant and an Associate of the Institute of Taxation. Philip Baker and Hugh McKay are visiting lecturers at London University.

Publications: Members have written, contributed to or edited the following: *The World of International Tax Planning; Tax Havens: An Introduction to Company Law; The Law of Partnership Taxation; A Practical Guide to Capital Transfer Tax; Tax and Investment; British Tax Encyclopaedia; Whiteman on Income Tax; Property and VAT; Butterworths Tax Planning; British Tax Review; Asset Protection Trusts; Double Taxation Conventions and International Tax Law; Value Added Tax Encyclopedia* and various articles on international tax developments.

AREAS OF PRACTICE: The chambers deal with all aspects of United Kingdom revenue law, each member having developed particular areas of interest, including corporate tax planning; international business and offshore trusts; property transactions; acquisitions, mergers and takeovers, trusts and inheritance tax. Members appear in tax cases before Commissioners and VAT tribunals, in the Supreme Court, the House of Lords, the Privy Council, the Court of Justice of the European Communities, and the Courts of certain colonies and Commonwealth jurisdictions. They give advice assisting taxpayers who are in dispute with the Inland Revenue or Customs, and advise clients on the planning of their business and personal affairs to minimise the impact of taxation.

Chambers act for companies, charities and private clients. Direct Professional Access is accepted from the appropriate professional bodies.

FOREIGN CONNECTIONS: Members of chambers advise clients in Hong Kong, Singapore and Australia, New Zealand, the USA and Mauritius. The chambers also advise the revenue departments of Commonwealth countries and ex-colonies on the interpretation of their statutes.

LANGUAGES SPOKEN: French, Chinese (Mandarin and some Cantonese), some Arabic, Hebrew, German and Italian.

OFFICE EQUIPMENT: The chambers are fully computerised, with IBM compatible wordprocessing equipment WP5.1 and computerised accounts. Documents can be transferred via direct computer links and via Link and the Internet.

HEAD OF CHAMBERS:
Milton Grundy
SENIOR CLERK:
John Regan
TENANTS: 9

GRAY'S INN CHAMBERS (Brian Jubb)

GRAY'S INN CHAMBERS, GRAY'S INN, LONDON, WC1R 5JA
DX: 0074 (Ch.Ln.)

TEL: (0171) 404 1111
FAX: (0171) 430 1522

HEAD OF CHAMBERS:
Brian Jubb

SEN. CLERK:
Gordon Breadmore

TENANTS: 28

MEMBERS:
Brian Jubb (1971), Charles Fletcher-Cooke (1936), Caroline Rodger (1968),
Richard Clough (1971), Gillian Higson Smith (1973), Rozanna Malcolm (1974),
David Houston (1976), Janette Haywood (1977), Diane Redgrave (1977),
Cherry Harding (1978), Rachel Wingert (1980), Gillian Marks (1981),
Heather MacGregor (1982), Geoffrey Mott (1982), Melanie Nazareth (1984),
Timothy Compton (1984), Melanie Den Brinker (1984), Robert Dashwood (1984),
Noah Weiniger (1984), Jeremy Rosenblatt (1985), Alistair Perkins (1986),
Nigel Cox (1986), Gemma Taylor (1987), Ian Lewis (1989), Joanna Clarke (1993),
Nicholas Stonor (1993), Justin Gray (1993).

DOOR TENANTS:
Doreen Hinchliffe (1953), George Warr (1975),
Lindsey Oliver (1977), Marilyn Freeman (1986).

AREAS OF PRACTICE Chambers specialise in all aspects of Family Law including adoption (UK and foreign), international child abduction, Children Act proceedings (public and private), divorce, matrimonial finance and inheritance. Chambers is also well established in the fields of Administrative Law and Immigration. Chancery, Commercial and General Common Law work is also undertaken, including Landlord and Tenant, Housing, Personal Injury, Professional and Medical Negligence, Building, Licensing, Tribunals and Crime.

PUBLICATIONS: Several members of Chambers have written books and regularly contribute academic papers within their areas of practice.

3 GRAY'S INN PLACE (R. Neville Thomas QC)

3 GRAY'S INN PLACE, GRAY'S INN, LONDON, WC1R 5EA
DX: LDE 331

TEL: (0171) 831 8441
FAX: (0171) 831 8479

HEAD OF CHAMBERS:
R. Neville Thomas QC

SENIOR PRACTICE MANAGER:
Roger Merry-Price

TENANTS: 44

THE CHAMBERS: 3 Gray's Inn Place is an established commercial set of chambers in Gray's Inn. Chambers accept direct access work from other professions and regularly accept instructions from overseas lawyers.

MEMBERS:
R. Neville Thomas QC (1962)(QC-1975), John Toulmin QC (1965)(QC-1980),
Nicholas Merriman QC (1969)(QC-1988), John Jarvis QC (1970)(QC-1989),
Christopher Symons QC (1972)(QC-1989), Ian Geering QC (1974)(QC-1991),
William Blair QC (1972)(QC-1994), Nicholas Elliott QC (1972)(QC-1995),
Richard Salter QC (1975)(QC-1995), S. Clive Freedman (1975),
Richard de Lacy (1976), Gregory Mitchell (1979), Janet Turner (1979),
Ali Malek (1980), Michael Kay (1981), Andrew Onslow (1982),
David Waksman (1982), Peter Cranfield (1982), Andrew Sutcliffe (1983),
Stephen Phillips (1984), Rory Phillips (1984), Tom Weitzman (1984),
Ewan McQuater (1985), Anne Wakefield (1968), Philippe Sands (1985),
Jonathan Nash (1986), James Cameron (1987), Ross Cranston (1976),
Caroline Lewis (1988), Juliet May (1988), Maurice Sheridan (1984),
Start Angharad (1988), Adrian Beltrami (1989), Amanda Green (1990),
Annie Hockaday (1990), John Odgers (1990), Jonathan Mark Phillips (1991),
James Evans (1991), David Wolfson (1992), Jonathan Harold Marks (1992),
David Quest (1993), Richard Edwards (1993), Jonathan Davies-Jones (1994),
David Pope (1995).

Door Tenants:
Derek Wheatley QC, Aarif Barma (HK), Michael Blair, James Crawford,
Alaric Dalziel, Louise Edwards, Baroness Elles, Mark Freedland, Paul Heim,
Arjan Sakhrani QC (HK), Ronny Wong QC (HK), Volker Heinz, Alan Boyle.

WORK UNDERTAKEN: Chambers cover the whole range of commercial, contractual and civil common law work, particularly: *Banking and Financial Services:* for major banks and financial institutions, and those who use their services. The work includes disputes concerning bank securities, cheques, bills of exchange, letters of credit and transactions involving banks and financial institutions, securities regulation and investor protection. All aspects of *Company Law* and *Insolvency. International and Domestic Commercial Fraud. Insurance and Reinsurance* for major national and international insurance companies and their insureds, for Lloyd's Syndicates and for brokers and intermediaries both in and out of court/ arbitration. *Environmental Law:* the work covers domestic English law, European Community law and International law. The Environmental Law Group within chambers covers a broad range of commercial and public interest activities. *EC/ International* including competition law, financial services and environmental law. *Entertainment* for performers, managers, film, record and recording companies. *International Trade/ Dry Shipping* including carriage of goods, charterparties and bills of lading.

Other Areas of Work: *Work includes: Professional Negligence,* in particular accountants/ auditors, surveyors/ valuers, architects, engineers, solicitors, brokers and the medical profession; *Construction; Sale of Goods, Intellectual Property,* particularly passing off, copyright and design rights, *Product Liability, Administrative Law* and *Judicial Review.* Employment, including restraint of trade, pensions and transfers of undertakings; pensions law (including EC aspects); general property litigation, including landlord and tenent; agricultural law (including EC aspects); partnership.

RECRUITMENT: Chambers offer substantial awards for pupils, and can offer accommodation in a flat in chambers. Applications should be made by 31st July in the year preceding the pupillage year.

FOREIGN CONNECTIONS: Work is regularly undertaken in Hong Kong, Singapore and in other countries with British connections. Chambers do work for US, EC and other foreign law firms. In addition, there are members of the Irish, Northern Ireland and Gibraltar Bar in Chambers. French, Italian, German, Portuguese, Spanish, Welsh and Russian are spoken by various members of Chambers.

3
Gray's Inn Place

76 Set No. **1 GRAY'S INN SQUARE (Jocelyn Gibbs & Carl Teper)** 1 Gray's Inn Square, Gray's Inn, London, WC1R 5AA **Tel:** (0171) 405 8946/8 **Fax:** (0171) 405 1617 **DX:** 1013 **Sen. Clerks:** John Salter, Phil Boye-Anawomah, Kathryn Waller **Tenants:** 42 The chambers are a common law set, with individual barristers specialising in a variety of areas.

77 Set No. **1 GRAY'S INN SQUARE (Patricia Scotland QC)** 1 Gray's Inn Square, Gray's Inn, London, WC1R 5AG **Tel:** (0171) 405 3000 **Fax:** (0171) 405 9942 **DX:** 238 **Clerks:** Steven Ashton, Mark Venables **Tenants:** 25 Commercial, international law, arbitration, serious crime, general civil, family, children, international child abduction, public law and judicial review.

2 GRAY'S INN SQUARE CHAMBERS

2 GRAY'S INN SQUARE, GRAY'S INN, LONDON, WC1R 5AA
DX: 43 LDE

TEL: (0171) 242 0328
FAX: (0171) 405 3082

HEAD OF CHAMBERS:
Acting - Giles Eyre

PRACTICE MANAGER:
Paul Simpson

SENIOR CLERK: Bill Harris

TENANTS: 30

THE CHAMBERS: The chambers seek to provide a responsive, courteous and efficient service in all areas of common law practice. Through the use of modern administrative systems, a management committee and a spirit of teamwork, chambers are able to meet the varied requirements of solicitors. Specialisation is achieved through the establishment of practice groups, which enables members to pool their specialist knowledge and expertise and to offer a full and professional service to clients.

MEMBERS:
Peter Leighton (1966), Keith Knight (1969), Barrie Lawrence Nathan (1969) LLB, Giles Eyre (1974), John Robson (1974) LLB (Hons)(Lond),
Edward Cross (1975) LLB, Richard Robinson (1977), Peter Fortune (1978) MA, BA (Hons), Christopher McConnell (1979), David Hughes (1980), Milan Dulovic (1982), Jane Rayson (1982) LLB (Hons), Roderick Jones (1983) BA (Hons),
Jacqueline Marks (1984), Anthony Moore (1984) BA (Hons), John Church (1984), Nerida Harford-Bell (1984), Fawzia King (1985) BA (Hons),
Surinder Bhakar (1986) LLB (Hons)(Lond) LLM (Cantab), Sorrel Dixon (1987), Susan Baldock (1988), Adrian Roberts (1988), Mark Whalan (1988) BA (Hons), Terence Woods (1989), Joanne Brown (1990), Andrea Rivers (1990),
James Arney (1992), Pattie Walsh (1992), Rebecca Priestley (1989),
Henry Drayton (1993).

Publications: Peter Fortune is a contributor to Blackstone's *Criminal Practice (Road Traffic and Evidence).* Jane Rayson is co-author of *How to make Applications in the Family Proceedings Court.*

WORK UNDERTAKEN:

Family: Matters covered encompass child law including public and private Children Act proceedings, adoption, wardship and child abduction, matrimonial and related proceedings (including property and financial disputes and disputes between co-habitees).

Criminal: Members practise in all areas of crime, receiving instructions on behalf of the prosecution and defence. The set has considerable experience of the criminal aspects of trade descriptions, food safety, pollution cases and of civil actions against the police.

Personal Injury: Members act for individuals, trade unions and insurance company clients, as both plaintiff and defendant, in claims arising from accidents at work, medical negligence, road traffic accidents, occupiers' liability and defective products.

Contract/ Commercial: Areas of law covered include contract and tort, professional negligence, sale of goods, agency, bills of exchange, banking, building and engineering contracts, consumer credit, insurance, guarantee and suretyship.

Employment: Chambers undertakes advisory and advocacy work in Industrial Tribunals, the E.A.T., the High Court and internal disciplinary hearings. Specific areas of expertise are unfair dismissal, redundancy, discrimination and the provision of advice to employers prior to the dismissal of employees and directors.

Property: Chambers offers representation and advice on all property matters including public and private sector housing, business tenancies and all aspects of landlord and tenant law, trusts, claims to possession of land, easement and mortgage disputes, conveyancing, and disputes involving joint owners and cohabitees.

LANGUAGES: French, Serbo-Croat, Malay and Punjabi.

WRITTEN WORK: Paperwork can be provided on disc or by electronic mail, as well as on paper or tape. WordPerfect 5.1 is the principal system used but other DOS and MAC formats are available.

CHARGES: Comprehensive details of chambers' fee structures are available from the clerk.

RECRUITMENT AND TRAINING: Pupillage applications to Joanne Brown with CV and stamped addressed envelope. Mini-pupillages and student visits are available. Sponsored pupils are accepted.

79 2-3 GRAY'S INN SQUARE (Anthony Scrivener QC)
Set No.

2-3 GRAY'S INN SQUARE, GRAY'S INN, LONDON, WC1R 5JH
DX: 316 (Ch.Ln.)

TEL: (0171) 242 4986
FAX: (0171) 405 1166

THE CHAMBERS: A long-established set, now based in Gray's Inn. Its roots are in the common law but over the last 40 years it has also developed a local government and commercial practice. Former members of chambers include Sir Edward Marshall Hall KC, Lord Birkett, Lord Chief Justice Widgery and Lord Bridge of Harwich.

MEMBERS:
Anthony Scrivener QC (1958)(QC-1975), Sir Graham Eyre QC (1954)(QC-1970),
Malcolm Spence QC (1958)(QC-1979), Patrick Ground QC (1960)(QC-1981),
Christopher Cochrane QC (1965)(QC-1988), David Penry-Davey QC (1965)(QC-1988),
John Haines (1967), Anthony Dinkin QC (1968)(QC-1991),
Anthony Porten QC (1969)(QC-1988), Vernon Pugh QC (1969)(QC-1986),
Ian Croxford QC (1976)(QC-1993), Richard Rundell (1971), Mark Lowe (1972),
Geoffrey Stephenson (1971), David Lamming (1972),
Adrian Trevelyan Thomas (1974), Nicholas Nardecchia (1974),
Timothy Straker (1977), Tobias Davey (1977), Graham Stoker (1977),
Ian Albutt (1981), Mary Cook (1982), Morag Ellis (1984), James Findlay (1984),
Katie Astaniotis (1985), Michael Bedford (1985), Philip Kolvin (1985),
Thomas Lowe (1985), Simon Bird (1987), Joanna Smith (1990), Robin Green (1992),
Harriet Murray (1992), Peter Miller (1993), Ian Ponter (1993), Philip Coppel (1994).

WORK UNDERTAKEN:
General Description: Local government, administrative law, planning, commercial, common law and crime.
Main Areas of Work: A wide variety of expertise is available. All areas of local government and common law are covered. There is particular emphasis on public law, planning and commercial work (including landlord and tenant, insurance, banking and arbitration both in the UK and abroad). The terms on which direct access work will be accepted can be obtained from the Senior Clerk. There is a wide experience of personal injury and professional negligence claims. A number of silks and juniors specialise in criminal law. Several members of chambers have practised in the Far East including Hong Kong and Singapore.
FOREIGN LANGUAGES: French, Italian, Greek and German.
RECRUITMENT & TRAINING: Pupils are received each year; pupillage funds are available.

HEAD OF CHAMBERS:
Anthony Scrivener QC
SEN. CLERK:
Martin Hart
FIRST JUNIOR CLERK:
Christopher Broom
TENANTS: 35

80 3 GRAY'S INN SQUARE (Rock Tansey QC)
Set No.

3 GRAY'S INN SQUARE, GRAY'S INN, LONDON, WC1R 5AH
DX: 1043 (Ch.Ln.)

TEL: (0171) 831 2311
FAX: (0171) 404 4939

THE CHAMBERS: A specialist criminal law set of chambers, established in 1975, which primarily undertakes criminal defence work. Some members have additional expertise in civil litigation. Chambers' administration is fully computerised.

MEMBERS:
Rock Tansey QC (1966)(QC-1990), John Perry QC (1975)(QC-1989),
William Taylor (1990) (Scot), David Hooper (1971), Nadine Radford QC (1974)(QC-1995),
Colin Allan (1971), Ronald Jaffa (1974), Brendan Keany (1974),
Jonathan Mitchell (1974), George Carter-Stephenson (1975), Philip Statman (1975),
Michael Gledhill (1976), Donald Campbell (1976), Rudi Fortson (1976),
Steven Kay (1977), Chester Beyts (1978), Diana Ellis (1978),
Roger Offenbach (1978), Robert Anthony (1979), Paul Mendelle (1981),
Daniel Flahive (1982), Jeremy Dein (1982), Simon Pentol (1982), Bill Maley (1982),
Ian Jobling (1982), Leroy Redhead (1982), Kaly Kaul (1983),
Karen Hammond (1985), Gary Summers (1985), James Mulholland (1986),
David Young (1986), Colin Wells (1987), Alison Levitt (1988), Peter Moffatt (1985),
Sarah Harris (1989), Helen Valley (1990), Arlette Piercy (1990),
Emma Akuwudike (1992).

HEAD OF CHAMBERS:
Rock Tansey QC
SEN. CLERK:
Graham Islin
TENANTS: 37

WORK UNDERTAKEN: Chambers offer practitioners experienced in all categories of serious criminal cases including murder, terrorism, fraud, robbery, sexual and drug cases. Other areas of work undertaken are personal injury, contract, employment, landlord and tenant and licensing cases.

FOREIGN CONNECTIONS AND LANGUAGES SPOKEN: Mr. John Perry QC also practises in Bermuda and is a member of the West Indian Bar. Mr. William Taylor QC (Scot) also practises in Scotland. French, German and Italian are spoken.

PUBLICATIONS AND OTHER ACTIVITIES: Rudi Fortson; *Law on the Misuse of Drugs* and co-author of *Archbold*.
Donald Campbell; *Marine Fraud*.
Gary Summers; Designer of Marshall, the Computer Software Programme for Criminal Trial Lawyers (especially those dealing with fraud and other multi-document cases). Steven Kay is the Secretary of the Criminal Bar Association and writes on matters of legal interest in various legal journals.
Some members of chambers also lecture solicitors in criminal procedure and advocacy including P.A.C.E. 1984.

RECRUITMENT & TRAINING: Up to eight second and third six month pupillages each year. Applications to the Pupillage Secretary.

4-5 GRAY'S INN SQUARE

4-5 GRAY'S INN SQUARE, GRAY'S INN, LONDON, WC1R 5AY
DX: 1029

TEL: (0171) 404 5252
FAX: (0171) 242 7803

THE CHAMBERS: A large commercial set which favours an interdisciplinary approach, particularly where public and commercial law meet.

HEAD OF CHAMBERS:
Miss Elizabeth Appleby QC,
The Hon. Michael Beloff QC

SEN. CLERK:
Leslie Page

TENANTS: 45

MEMBERS:
Elizabeth Appleby QC (1965)(QC-1979), Michael Beloff QC (1967)(QC-1981), Professor Sir William Wade QC (1946)(QC-1968), Jeremy Sullivan QC (1968)(QC-1982), Gary Flather QC (1962)(QC-1984), Sir Gordon Borrie QC (1952)(QC-1986), Robin Barratt QC (1970)(QC-1989), Alan Moses QC (1968)(QC-1990), David Mole QC (1970)(QC-1990), Brian Ash QC (1975)(QC-1990), Genevra Caws QC (1970)(QC-1991), Stuart Isaacs QC (1975)(QC-1991), Duncan Ouseley QC (1973)(QC-1992), W. Robert Griffiths QC (1974)(QC-1993), John Steel QC (1978)(QC-1993), Clive Newberry QC (1978)(QC-1993), Gregory Stone QC (1976)(QC-1994), Cherie Booth QC (1976)(QC-1995), Sam Aaron (1986), Michael Burrell (1965), Robin Campbell (1969), Nicholas Huskinson (1971), Julian Chichester (1977), John Hobson (1980), Timothy Corner (1981), Richard McManus (1982), Peter M. Village (1983), Hodge M. Malek (1983), Tim Kerr (1983), Peter Havey (1984), Jane Oldham (1985), Paul Stinchcombe (1985), Kishore Sharma (1986), Richard Humphreys (1986), Clive Lewis (1987), James Ramsden (1987), Thomas Hill (1988), Rabinder Singh (1989), Sarah Moore (1990), Helen Mountfield (1991), Paul Brown (1991), Andrew Tabachnik (1991), David Wolfe (1992), Murray Hunt (1992), Andrew Fraser-Urquhart (1993).
The Heads of Chambers are recorders and Deputy High Court Judges. Several members are also recorders. Chambers also have two officers of the Local Government and Planning Bar Association and had the first two Chairmen of the Administrative Law Bar Association. One member is a former Junior Counsel to the Inland Revenue, two are Junior Counsel to the Crown on Common Law. One practitioner is an international arbitrator.

Publications: Members of chambers have written or contributed to: *The Sex Discrimination Act; Halsbury's Laws 4th Ed., Vol.45; Judicial Review, Butterworths* (contributing editor); *Public Law; Current Legal Problems; Irish Jurist;* revised notes to sections of *The Town and Country Planning Act 1971, (Encyclopaedia of Planning); Lumley's Public Health,* (joint editor); *Woodfall's Landlord and Tenant,* (assistant editor); *EC Banking Law; Banking and the Competition Law of the EC,* (consultant editor); *EC Case Citator; Paget's Law of Banking; Journal of International Banking Law; Crown Office Digest,* (co-editors). Clive Lewis is author of *Judicial Remedies in Public Law.*

FORMER MEMBERS:
The Right Honourable Lord Justice Schiemann; The Honourable Mr Justice Keene;
The Honourable Mr Justice Collins; Richard Yorke QC (1956)(QC-1971);
Sir Douglas Frank QC, former President of the Lands Tribunal; His Honour Judge
Bernard Marder QC, President of the Lands Tribunal; Victor Wellings QC, former
President of the Lands Tribunal; Norman Wise.

DOOR TENANTS:
Professor G.H. Treitel QC; Professor E.P. Ellinger; Sir John Freeland QC (1952, QC-
1987); Marc Dassesse (Brussels Bar); Professor Sir D.G.T. Williams; Patrick Patelin
(Juriste d'Entreprise, Paris); Edmond McGovern (also in Brussels); Narinder Hargun
(Bermuda); Dr. Ami Barau; Lady Fox, QC.

WORK UNDERTAKEN:
General Description: The chambers cover a wide range of specialist areas, in particular
administrative and planning law, commercial law and EC.

MAIN AREAS OF WORK:
Public Law/ Town and Country Planning Law: *Work includes:* local government, town
and country planning, highways, rating, environmental, markets, constitutional,
parliamentary, civil liberties, public health, welfare and social security, licensing,
education, immigration, extradition, nationality, elections, air, public inquiries and
all areas of judicial review.

Commercial Law: *Work includes:* banking, financial services, accounting, negotiable
instruments, insurance and reinsurance, shipping, sale of goods, company and
insolvency, partnership, building and engineering disputes, commercial fraud,
domestic, international and ICC arbitrations.

General Common Law (Civil): *Work includes:* landlord and tenant, libel, confidentiality and contempt, professional negligence, road traffic (operators' licensing),
domestic associations.

Employment Law: *Work includes:* industrial relations, trade unions, sex and racial
discrimination.

ADDITIONAL AREAS OF WORK: European Community/ Convention law and competition and restrictive practices.

FOREIGN CONNECTIONS: Members of chambers have appeared at the Privy Council,
the European Court of Justice and of Human Rights, international arbitration tribunals
and other courts worldwide, including Hong Kong, the Far East, Bermuda and
Anguilla. One member is a former Judge of the Court of Appeal in Swaziland and a
current Judge of the Court of Appeal in Lesotho.

OTHER MATTERS: The chambers have been the first set to appoint an academic panel
as a research and advisory facility. Its members are Dr. P. Craig (Administrative),
Professor M. Grant (Local government and planning), P. Davies (Employment),
Professor J. Usher (EC), Professor E. Barendt (Media, human rights, welfare).

6 GRAY'S INN SQUARE (Michael Boardman)

82
Set No.

6 GRAY'S INN SQUARE, GRAY'S INN, LONDON, WC1R 5AZ
DX: 224

TEL: (0171) 242 1052
FAX: (0171) 405 4934

THE CHAMBERS: Chambers deals with every aspect of criminal advocacy and advice
in all courts and on circuits throughout the country. In addition, individual tenants
deal in depth with matrimonial and child work as well as specialisations in Immigration, Housing and Personal Injury. The traditional clerks combine over 45 years of
experience with a modern approach and will be happy to advise on individual
expertise.

HEAD OF CHAMBERS:
Michael Boardman

SEN. CLERK:
Russell Kinsley

TENANTS: 27

MEMBERS:
Michael Boardman (1979), David Owen Thomas QC (1952)(QC-1972),
James Chadwin QC (1958)(QC-1978), Malcolm Swift QC (1970)(QC-1988),
Ram Yajnik (1965), Mario Addezio (1971), Ashley Gordon (1973),
Alan Landsbury (1975), Stuart Trimmer (1977), George Heimler (1978),

Louis Kopieczek (1983), Ann Evans (1983), Philip Misner (1984), Wayne Cleaver (1986), Nicholas Lobbenberg (1987), Sean Minihan (1988), Maureen O'Connor (1988), Grant Van Stone (1988), Jane Bickerstaff (1989), Judy Khan (1989), James Beck (1989), Win Hunter (1990), Helen Smith (1990), Sean Sidhu-Brar (1991), William England (1991), Ann Marie McKay (1992), Mark McAulay (1993).

LANGUAGES: French, German, Spanish, Italian, Hindi, Punjabi, Urdu and Mandarin Chinese.

---

8 GRAY'S INN SQUARE (Patrick C. Soares)

83
et No.

8 GRAY'S INN SQUARE (Patrick C. Soares) 8 Gray's Inn Square, Gray's Inn, London, WC1R 5AZ **Tel:** (0171) 242 3529 **Fax:** (0171) 404 0395 **DX:** 411 (Ch.Ln.) **Sen. Clerk:** Marie Burke **Tenants:** 7 All categories of revenue law including stamp duty, international estate planning, property, trusts, ESOPs. Also town planning, local government, judicial review.

10-11 GRAY'S INN SQUARE (Alan Masters)

84
t No.

10-11 GRAY'S INN SQUARE, GRAY'S INN, LONDON, WC1R 5JD
DX: 484

TEL: (0171) 405 2576
FAX: (0171) 831 2430

THE CHAMBERS: A mixed set encompassing criminal and civil law, with the emphasis on criminal work. Most members handle both, with individual specialisations; however, four members practise exclusively in criminal law, four solely in civil matters. The administration of Chambers is carried out by a management company, through a board of directors.

MEMBERS:
Hugh Sheppard (1976), Bhasker Ghorpade (1973), Jean McCreath (1978), Alan Masters (1979), Charles Judge (1981), Anthony Rimmer (1983), John Donnelly (1983), Ruth Johnson (1984), Thomas Bailey (1984), Michael Forward (1984), Carolyn Marsh (1985), Marion Smullen (1985), Pamela Brain (1985), Marc Willers (1987), Ciaran Magill (1988).

WORK UNDERTAKEN:

Criminal: Both prosecution and defence work, ranging from driving offences to fraud and murder.

Civil: Landlord and tenant and planning work in particular. The Chambers undertake family law, dealing with matrimonial and domestic violence, wardship and care cases and financial settlements within marriage.

ADDITIONAL AREAS OF WORK: A wide range of civil matters including administrative law, chancery, civil rights, commercial, company, contract, construction, crofting law, consumer and consumer credit law, courts martial, employment, housing, immigration, bankruptcy and insolvency, intellectual property, judicial review, licensing, local government, mental health, personal injury, nuisance, land law, police cases, probate, product liability, professional negligence, property, shipping and sale of goods. General injunctive work is also handled.

CLIENTELE: The chambers act for individuals, companies and businesses. Direct Professional Access is accepted from approved professional bodies.

RECRUITMENT & TRAINING: Tenancy and pupillage applications should be sent to the Head of Chambers, Mr Alan Masters. two forst six months' and three second six months' pupillages are available. Pupils are offered 3000 for their first six months; good opportunities for fee earning in second six months.

HEAD OF CHAMBERS:
Alan Masters

SEN. CLERK:
Matthew Jones

TENANTS: 17

85
Set No.

10 GRAY'S INN SQUARE (Philip Meredith) 10 Gray's Inn Square, Gray's Inn, London, WC1R 5JL **Tel:** (0171) 242 1044 **Fax:** (0171) 831 3082 **DX:** 466 (Ch.Ln.) **Sen. Clerk:** David Skinner **Tenants:** 20 Broadly-based set covering criminal work, matrimonial and general civil litigation including property work.

86
Set No.

12 GRAY'S INN SQUARE (Mark Littman QC)

12 GRAY'S INN SQUARE, LONDON, WC1R 5JP
DX: 0055 (Ch.Ln.)

TEL: (0171) 404 4866
FAX: (0171) 404 4812

HEAD OF CHAMBERS:
Mark Littman QC

SEN. CLERK:
Barry Packman

JUNIOR CLERK Lee Cutler

TENANTS: 16

THE CHAMBERS: The Chambers were founded by Mark Littman, QC, in 1980. They offer specialist advocacy, advice, drafting and arbitration services to solicitors and to those with direct access to the Bar. They are one of the specialist commercial sets of chambers which belongs to the Commercial Bar Association.

MEMBERS:
Mark Littman QC (1947)(QC-1961), Brian McClure (1976),
Rowan Planterose (1978), Andrzej Kolodziej (1978), Shane Dougall (1980),
Thomas Jefferies (1981), Conor Quigley (1985), Monique Allan (1986),
Séan Naidoo (1990), Martin Gibson (1990), Marc Rowlands (1990),
Rupert Higgins (1991), Niamh McCarthy (1991), Tony Dymond (1993),
Philip Lewis (1958), John Finnis (1970).
Mark Littman QC, is a UK member of the International Council of Commercial Arbitration. In addition, Mark Littman QC, Rowan Planterose and Andrzej Kolodziej are Fellows, and Brian McClure is an Associate of the Chartered Institute of Arbitrators. Members of chambers are happy to accept instructions or lecture in any language in which they are fluent.

WORK UNDERTAKEN:
Commercial: *Work includes:* banking, shipping, insurance, negotiable instruments, sale of goods, commodities, competition, international trade and financial services.
European Community: *Work includes:* agriculture, competition, environmental law, financial services, internal market law, jurisdiction and foreign judgments, public procurement, state aids and taxation.
Commercial Property: *Work includes:* contracts and conveyancing, drafting, easements, landlord and tenant, rating, rent reviews and restrictive covenants.
Chancery: *Work includes:* company, insolvency, partnerships, passing off, suretyship and wills and intestacy.
Planning and Environmental Law: *Work includes:* compulsory purchase, enforcement, planning and pollution.
Construction Law: *Work includes:* building and engineering.
Additional Areas: Commercial conciliation and arbitration (ICC and LMAA), administrative law, computers, consumer credit, defamation, electronics, employment law, judicial review and professional negligence.
CLIENTELE: Public and private companies, institutions and individuals.
FOREIGN LANGUAGES: Afrikaans, Dutch, French, German, Italian, Polish, Russian and Spanish.
Owing to excellent facilities, members of Chambers are pleased to offer a rapid and efficient service to their clients.

14 GRAY'S INN SQUARE(Joanna Dodson QC and Glenn Brasse)

14 GRAY'S INN SQUARE, GRAY'S INN, LONDON, WC1R 5JP
DX: 399 (Ch.Ln.)

TEL: (0171) 242 0858
FAX: (0171) 242 5434

HEAD OF CHAMBERS:
Joanna Dodson QC, Glenn Brasse

SEN. CLERK:
Stephen Lavell

TENANTS: 28

THE CHAMBERS: A family and civil set with particular expertise in children's cases and financial matters, with a strong general common law side.

MEMBERS:
Joanna Dodson QC (1971)(QC-1993), Glenn Brasse (1972),
Charles Bloom QC (1963)(QC-1987), Miss Louise S. Godfrey QC (1972)(QC-1991),
Lindsey Kushner QC (1974)(QC-1992), Patricia Dangor (1970),
Norman Patterson (1971), Joanna Hall (1973), Mhairi McNab (1974),
Barbara Slomnicka (1976), David Turner (1976), Sarah Forster (1976),
Gillian Brasse (1977), Brenda Morris (1978), Kate Hudson (1981),
Caroline Reid (1982), Peter Herbert (1982), Karen McLaughlin (1982),
Monica Ford (1984), Mark Emanuel (1985), Pamela Warner (1985),
Stephen Lyon (1987), Michelle Corbett (1987) LLB (Hons), Samantha King (1990),
David Bedingfield (1991), David Vavrecka (1992), Jenny Kent (1994),
Jane De Zonie (1994).
Members of chambers belong to the Family Law Bar Association.

WORK UNDERTAKEN:
Main Areas of Work: Family and matrimonial, including wardship, adoption, care, children and ancillary relief; personal injury, including running-down accidents; employment and labour law; landlord and tenant and housing; licensing work; building and construction and contract cases.

Additional Areas of Work: Civil liberties, crime, company, discrimination, ecclesiastical, judicial review, police cases, product liability, professional negligence, sale of goods and welfare.

CLIENTELE: Individuals, companies, local authorities, guardians ad litem, the Official Solicitor.

FOREIGN CONNECTIONS: Patricia Dangor is a member of the Bermuda Bar and David Bedingfield is a member of the Georgia Bar.

ASSOCIATED CHAMBERS: Charles Bloom QC is a head of chambers in Manchester.

RECRUITMENT & TRAINING: Tenancy applications should be sent to Joanna Dodson QC; pupillage applications to Jane De Zonie. Two first six and two second six months pupils are taken each year. Awards of £3,000 are offered for the first six months of pupillage and minimum earnings are guaranteed at that level for the second six. Mini-pupillages are available.

HAMILTON HOUSE CHAMBERS (Sa'id Mosteshar) Hamilton House, Temple, London, EC4Y 0HA **Tel:** (0171) 402 2010 **Fax:** (0171) 402 3231 **Sen. Clerk: Tenants:** 1 Specialist practitioner with expertise in communications and broadcasting law, information technology law and space law.

1 HARCOURT BUILDINGS (Simon Buckhaven) 1 Harcourt Buildings, Temple, London, EC4Y 9DA **Tel:** (0171) 353 9421 **Fax:** (0171) 353 4170 **DX:** 417 **Sen. Clerk:** William Lavell **Tenants:** 21 General common law set. Also practise in chancery, commercial, company law, crime, and fraud.

90 Set No.

1 HARCOURT BUILDINGS (Ellis Meyer)

1 HARCOURT BUILDINGS, TEMPLE, LONDON, EC4Y 9DA
DX: 1057

TEL: (0171) 797 7979
FAX: (0171) 797 7980

MEMBERS:
Ellis Meyer (1938), Peter Rowland (1947), Nigel Ley (1969),
Randolph Fields (1980), Richard Briden (1982), Orlando Gibbons (1982),
Romasa Butt (1985), Geoffrey White (1985), Raymond Harries (1988),
Ian Lamacraft (1989), Linda Wagner (1990), June Raybaud (1991),
John Lumsdon (1991).

WORK UNDERTAKEN: Arbitration, chancery work, company law, commercial, contract, insurance, revenue, succession and VAT, medical negligence, personal injury. Individual specialisations in crime, landlord and tenant and family.

HEAD OF CHAMBERS:
Ellis Meyer

SEN. CLERK:
Justine Briars

TENANTS: 14

91 Set No.

1 HARCOURT BUILDINGS (Raymond Walker QC) 1 Harcourt Buildings, Temple, London, EC4Y 9DA **Tel:** (0171) 353 0375/3655 **Fax:** (0171) 583 5816 **DX:** 1051 **Sen. Clerk:** John Collins **Tenants:** 18 A long-established set specialising in commercial law, landlord and tenant, local government, professional negligence and personal injury.

92 Set No.

2 HARCOURT BUILDINGS (Peter Boydell QC)

2 HARCOURT BUILDINGS, TEMPLE, LONDON, EC4Y 9DB
DX: 402 LDE

TEL: (0171) 353 8415
FAX: (0171) 353 7622

THE CHAMBERS: A set with a parliamentary, planning and local government practice which has been built up over more than half a century.

MEMBERS:
Peter Boydell QC (1948)(QC-1965), Roy Vandermeer QC (1955)(QC-1978),
Gerard Ryan QC (1955)(QC-1981), Sheila Cameron QC (1957)(QC-1983),
Robin Purchas QC (1968)(QC-1987), Richard Phillips QC (1970)(QC-1990),
Charles George QC (1974)(QC-1992), Christopher Beaumont (1950),
Robert McCracken (1973), Philip Petchey (1976), Jonathan Milner (1977),
Andrew Kelly (1978), Timothy Comyn (1980), Keith Lindblom (1980),
Andrew Tait (1981), Craig Howell Williams (1983), Suzanne Ornsby (1986),
Meyric Lewis (1986), Andrew Newcombe (1987), Charles Mynors (1988),
Gregory Jones (1991), Douglas Edwards (1992).

WORK UNDERTAKEN:
Main Areas of Work: Parliamentary, planning, environmental, local government, rating and administrative law. All members of chambers practise principally within these areas of work.

Additional Areas: Ecclesiastical law, common land, restrictive covenants and easements.

RECRUITMENT & TRAINING: Pupillage: up to six pupils are taken, generally in their second six months. Awards are offered to some candidates. Applications to the Pupillage Committee.

HEAD OF CHAMBERS:
Peter Boydell QC

SEN. CLERK:
Allen Collier

FIRST JUNIOR CLERK:
Paul Munday

TENANTS: 22

93 Set No.

2 HARCOURT BUILDINGS (Patrick Eccles QC) 2 Harcourt Buildings, Temple, London, EC4Y 9DB **Tel:** (0171) 353 6961 **Fax:** (0171) 353 6968 **DX:** 373 **Sen. Clerk:** Brian Wheeler **Tenants:** 21 Members of chambers are principally engaged in family and civil litigation. Additional premises at Harcourt Chambers, Churchill House, St. Aldates Courtyard, 38 St. Aldates, Oxford OX1 1BA.

2 HARCOURT BUILDINGS (Robert Harman QC)

2 HARCOURT BUILDINGS, TEMPLE, LONDON, EC4Y 9DB
DX: 489

TEL: (0171) 353 2112
FAX: (0171) 353 8339

THE CHAMBERS: A substantial and long established set with 6 QCs and a Senior Treasury and Junior Treasury Counsel which concentrates exclusively on criminal work.

MEMBERS:

Robert Harman QC (1954)(QC-1974) BA (Oxon), Petre Crowder QC (1948)(QC-1964), Patrick Whelon (1954), Nigel Mylne QC (1963)(QC-1984), Michael Sayers QC (1970)(QC-1988) MA (Cantab), John Bevan (1970) MA (Cantab), Nicholas Atkinson QC (1971)(QC-1991), John Williams (1973) LLB, Stephen Smyth (1974), Peter Cooper QC (1974)(QC-1993), Stephen Clayton (1973), Nicholas Loraine-Smith (1977) BA (Oxon), Mark Gadsden (1980) BA (Oxon), Robin Leach (1979) MA (St Andrews), Aftab Jafferjee (1980) BA (Dunelm), Richard Onslow (1982), Timothy Probert-Wood (1983), Rhyddian Willis (1984), Ian Darling (1985) LLB (Lond), Patrick Gibbs (1986) BA (Oxon), Lucia Whittle-Martin (1985), Jonathan Rees (1987), Marina Churchill (1989), Stewart Hamblin (1990), Peter Clement (1988), Toby Fitzgerald (1993), Peter Coombe (1994).

WORK UNDERTAKEN: Members of Chambers cover all criminal work for both prosecution and defence, practising on the South Eastern and Western Circuits. In addition to handling cases from murder to shoplifting, members specialise in commercial, revenue and VAT frauds, drugs cases, extradition, defences under the Food and Drugs Act, Courts Martial and ecclesiastical jurisdiction.

CLIENTELE: Both individuals and public and private companies.

PUPILLAGE: Applicants for pupillage to Mr. Ian Darling. Applications can be sent at any time. Chambers have four to five pupils completing six and twelve month pupillages at any one time. Mini-pupillages are available.

HEAD OF CHAMBERS:
Robert Harman QC

SEN. CLERK:
Michael Watts

TENANTS: 27

---

2 HARCOURT BUILDINGS (Roger Henderson QC)

2 HARCOURT BUILDINGS (GROUND FLOOR), TEMPLE, LONDON, EC4Y 9DB
DX: 1039

TEL: (0171) 583 9020
FAX: (0171) 583 2686

THE CHAMBERS: The chambers have a general practice with a very wide spread of work. Members of chambers have their own specialities and the chambers aim to provide a choice of specialist in any area of work undertaken.

MEMBERS:

Roger Henderson QC (1964)(QC-1980) *, Piers Ashworth QC (1956)(QC-1973) *, Jonathan Playford QC (1962)(QC-1982) *, Richard Mawrey QC (1964)(QC-1986) *, Quintin Iwi (1956), Adrian Brunner QC (1968)(QC-1994) *, Adrian Cooper (1970) *, Daniel Worsley (1971) *, Bernard O'Sullivan (1971), Stephen Powles QC (1972)(QC-1995) *, Gavin Gore-Andrews (1972), Andrew Jordan (1974), Jonathan Harvey (1974), Kenneth Hamer (1975) *, Andrew Prynne QC (1975)(QC-1995), Lawrence West (1979), Roger Eastman (1978), Sara Staite (1979), Barbara Cameron (1979), James Palmer (1983), Charles Gibson (1984), George Alliott (1981), Conrad Griffiths (1986), Benjamin Battcock (1987), Marina Wheeler (1987), Wendy Outhwaite (1990), Averil Harrison (1990), Patrick Green (1990), Charles Bourne (1991), Prashant Popat (1992), Oliver Campbell (1992), Isabella Zornoza (1993), Malcolm Sheehan (1993).
* *Recorder/Assistant Recorder.*

WORK UNDERTAKEN: Contract and business law; insurance; employment law; personal injury; professional negligence; building and construction; consumer law; public law; local government; land and environmental law; family and inheritance; crime (especially fraud).

HEAD OF CHAMBERS:
Roger Henderson QC

SEN. CLERK:
John White

TENANTS: 33

STANBROOK AND HENDERSON: Members of chambers also practise at the above address in association with English barristers of the firm of Stanbrook & Hooper, 2 Rue de Taciturne, B-1040 Brussels, under the name **Stanbrook and Henderson. Stanbrook and Henderson** practises in all areas of European Community Law and is able to offer a full combined service in both English and EC Law. Additional contact numbers are: *Tel:* (0171) 353 0101. *Fax:* (0171) 404 5258.

HARDWICKE BUILDING (Walter Aylen QC)

HARDWICKE BUILDING, LINCOLN'S INN, LONDON, WC2A 3SB
DX: 393 LIX. 107 London

TEL: (0171) 242 2523
FAX: (0171) 831 6968

THE CHAMBERS: A set of chambers providing a comprehensive and experienced service in all aspects of the law.

Increasingly, sets are practising within limited areas of the law, yet few legal problems – especially those giving rise to litigation – fit so easily into narrow confines.

Divided into specialist departments, Hardwicke Building enables solicitors and others with direct access to the Bar to instruct one set of chambers in the knowledge that the necessary expertise will be available to them under one roof.

Hardwicke Building itself comprises some of the most modern accommodation at the Bar and its vision of the future is supported by excellent administrative facilities and the latest technology.

HEAD OF CHAMBERS:
Walter Aylen QC

CHIEF EXECUTIVE:
Anthony L. Wells BSc (Econ) FCA

CLERKS: Kevin Mitchell Greg Piner
Jason Housden Denise Braithwaite

TENANTS: 64

MEMBERS:
Walter Aylen QC (1962)(QC-1983), Philip Raynor QC (1973)(QC-1994),
Romie Tager QC (1970)(QC-1995), David Radford (1969), Zoë Smith (1970),
Robert Willer (1970), Michael Hopmeier (1974), Kenneth Craig (1975),
Philip Kremen (1975), David Cattle (1975), Nigel Jones (1976),
Stephen Lennard (1976), Stephen Warner (1976), John Landaw (1976),
Graham Hulme (1977), James Vine (1977), Steven Weddle (1977),
Michael Oliver (1977), Philip Wakeham (1978), Penny Wilson (1979),
Nicholas Baker (1980), Rory Field (1980), David Matthias (1980),
Indira Ramsahoye (1980), David Aaronberg (1981), Anne Bradwell (1981),
Hugh Jackson (1981), Alan Smith (1981), Neil Mendoza (1982),
William Bojczuk (1983), Ian Brook (1983), Debbie Taylor (1984),
John Greenan (1984), Nicholas Hopkins (1984), Lindsey MacDonald (1985),
Karl King (1985), Justin Webster (1985), Montague Palfrey (1985),
Michelle Stevens-Hoare (1986), Tom Nicholson Pratt (1986), Francis Lloyd (1987),
Judith Spooner (1987), Finola Moore (1988), Paul Reed (1988), Peter Kirby (1989),
Ann Mulligan (1989), Steven Woolf (1989), Chris Murgatroyd (1989),
Alexis Campbell (1990), Rachel Baker (1990), Sara Benbow (1990),
Eithne Ryan (1990), Kyriakos Argyropoulos (1991), Kevin McCartney (1991),
Ingrid Newman (1992), David Preston (1993), Emily Formby (1993),
Julia Jarzabkowski (1993), Roshi Amiraftabi (1993), Sabuhi Chaudhry (1993),
Philip Raynor QC (1973)(QC-1994), Roshi Amiraftabi (1993),
Chaudhry Sabuhi (1993), Brian St. Louis (1994).

WORK UNDERTAKEN: Arbitration, administration, banking, building and construction, chancery, children, commercial, company, contract, conveyancing, criminal, defamation, employment, European law, financial services, fraud, insolvency, insurance, intellectual property, international law, judicial review, landlord and tenant, licensing, matrimonial and family, partnership, personal injury & medical negligence, planning, probate, professional negligence, property, public law and public utilities.

97
Set No.

1 HARE COURT (Michael Kalisher QC)

1 HARE COURT, TEMPLE, LONDON, EC4Y 7BE
DX: 444 (Ch.Ln.)

TEL: (0171) 353 5324
FAX: (0171) 353 0667

MEMBERS:
Michael Kalisher QC (1970)(QC-1984), John Lloyd-Eley QC (1951)(QC-1970),
Sir Allan Green QC (1959)(QC-1987), Paul Worsley QC (1970)(QC-1990),
Michael Birnbaum QC (1969)(QC-1992), Raymond Sturgess (1961),
Brian Warner (1969), Nicholas Coleman (1970), Stephen Kramer QC (1970)(QC-1995),
Miss Jacqueline Samuel (1971), Martin Heslop QC (1972)(QC-1995),
John Jones (1972), Charles Salmon (1972), David Waters (1973),
Miss Louise Kamill (1974), Paul Dodgson (1975), Paul Clark (1975),
Andrew Radcliffe (1975), Martin Hicks (1977), Jeremy Benson (1978),
Andrew Lloyd-Eley (1979), Andrew Colman (1980), David Howker (1982),
Jonathan Laidlaw (1982), Miss Sally Howes (1983), James Dawson (1984),
 Miss Sallie Bennett-Jenkins (1984), Michael Holland (1984),
Miss Shani Barnes (1986), Kenneth Millett (1988), Michael Logsdon (1988),
John Hardy (1988), Iain Morley (1988), Brendan Kelly (1988),
Miss Parmjit-Kaur Cheema (1989), Christopher Hehir (1990),
Miss Alex Lewis (1990), Craig Ferguson (1992), Miss Ruth McEwen (1992),
Kate Bex (1992), Nina Grahame (1993).

THE CHAMBERS: Chambers has long been established as a set specialising in criminal law and ancillary matters. Members prosecute and defend at all levels and act for many firms of solicitors, both large and small, throughout England and Wales and in Hong Kong. **Specialisations** include commercial fraud and corruption cases, financial services work, trade descriptions, and extradition.

HEAD OF CHAMBERS:
Michael Kalisher QC

SEN. CLERK:
Deryk Butler

FIRST JUNIOR CLERK: Ian Fitzgerald

CHAMBERS ADMINISTRATOR:
Stephen Wall

TENANTS: 41

98
Set No.

ONE HARE COURT (Sir Patrick Neill QC & Richard Southwell QC)

1 HARE COURT, TEMPLE, LONDON, EC4Y 7BE
DX: 0065 (Ch.Ln.) LIX: LON 353

TEL: (0171) 353 3171
FAX: (0171) 583 9127

THE CHAMBERS: A long-established set of chambers specialising in commercial, international, and related fields of litigation, arbitration and legal advice. The chambers are members of the Commercial Bar Association (COMBAR).

MEMBERS:
Sir Patrick Neill QC (1951)(QC-1966), Richard Southwell QC (1959)(QC-1977),
Howard Page QC (1967)(QC-1987), Nicolas Bratza QC (1969)(QC-1988) *,
Nicholas Padfield QC (1972)(QC-1991), Professor William Ballantyne (1977),
Paul Smith (1978), Dominic Dowley (1983), James Eadie (1984),
Dominic Chambers (1987), Andrew J. Moran (1989), Nicholas Lavender (1989),
Khawar M. Qureshi (1990), Mary-Emma Smith (1991), Alison Padfield (1992),
Anouschka Zagorski (1993).
* *Member of the European Commission of Human Rights.*

DOOR TENANTS:
Professor Ingrid De Lupis Frankopan (1977).

FORMER MEMBERS: Sir Henry Fisher, President of Wolfson College, Oxford 1975-85, Arbitrator; Lord Slynn of Hadley, Lord of Appeal in Ordinary (former Judge of the Court of Justice of the European Communities); Sir Roger Parker, former Lord Justice of Appeal, Arbitrator; Sir Mark Waller, a Justice of the High Court; H.H. Judge Raymond Jack QC, Circuit Mercantile Judge of the Bristol Mercantile Court.

WORK UNDERTAKEN:
General Description: All aspects of commercial practice, with an emphasis on international work.

MAIN AREAS OF WORK: Arbitration; commercial contracts; banking; international trade; insurance and reinsurance; construction and engineering; commercial fraud;

HEAD OF CHAMBERS:
Sir Patrick Neill QC, Richard Southwell QC

SENIOR CLERKS:
Barry C. Ellis, Paul Ballard

TENANTS: 17

negotiable instruments; documentary credits; commercial aspects of company and insolvency law; partnerships; Privy Council appeals; professional negligence; constitutional and administrative law; financial markets and services; public international law; conflict of laws.

ADDITIONAL AREAS: Scandinavian and environmental law (Professor De Lupis Frankopan); and Arab laws (Professor Ballantyne).

CLIENTELE: Brochure available on request. Chambers operate the Direct Professional Access scheme.

FOREIGN CONNECTIONS: A high proportion of work originates overseas. Subject to admission to local bars, instructions are accepted to appear in the courts of Hong Kong, Singapore, Malaysia and other foreign jurisdictions. The chambers are members of the London Court of International Arbitration.

2 HARE COURT (C.W.G. Ross-Munro QC)

2 HARE COURT, TEMPLE, LONDON, EC4Y 7BH
DX: 281

TEL: (0171) 583 1770
FAX: (0171) 583 9269

THE CHAMBERS: The chambers' main reputation is for its work in the fields of commercial, employment and public law; however, the specialisations of individual members within these categories are diverse. The chambers are fully computerized – running IBM compatible equipment, using Word Perfect 5.1 software – and aim to offer an efficient and cost-effective service.

HEAD OF CHAMBERS:
C.W.G. Ross-Munro QC

PRACTICE MANAGER:
Julia Hornor

SEN. CLERK Martin Smith

TENANTS: 46

MEMBERS:

Colin Ross-Munro QC (1951)(QC-1972), Stanley Brodie QC (1954)(QC-1975),
Lord Lester QC (1963)(QC-1975), Sir Ian Sinclair QC (1952)(QC-1979),
Ian Brownlie QC (1958)(QC-1979), David Donaldson QC (1968)(QC-1984),
Robert Englehart QC (1969)(QC-1986), David Hunt QC (1969)(QC-1987),
Barbara Dohmann QC (1971)(QC-1987), Andrew Pugh QC (1961)(QC-1988),
Ian Forrester QC (1972)(QC-1988), Roy Goode QC (1988)(QC-1990),
Maurice Mendelson QC (1965)(QC-1992), Jonathan Harvie QC (1973)(QC-1992),
Presiley Baxendale QC (1974)(QC-1992), David Pannick QC (1979)(QC-1992),
Jeffrey Jowell QC (1965)(QC-1993), Stephen Nathan QC (1969)(QC-1993),
Charles Flint QC (1975)(QC-1995), Gerald Levy (1964), Dawn Oliver (1965),
Alastair Sutton (1972), Hugo Page (1977), Judith Beale (1978),
Beverley Lang (1978), Thomas Beazley (1979), Ian Mill (1981),
Paul Goulding (1984), Anthony Peto (1985), Monica Carss-Frisk (1985),
Gerard Clarke (1986), Adam Lewis (1985), Robert Anderson (1986),
Mark Shaw (1987), Andrew Green (1988), Robert Howe (1988),
Adrian Briggs (1989), Dinah Rose (1989), Michael Fordham (1990),
Pushpinder Saini (1991), Thomas Croxford (1992), Javan Herberg (1992),
Joanna Pollard (1993), Andrew Hunter (1993), Gemma White (1994),
Jane Collier (1994).

Associate Members:

Judge David Edward CMG QC,
The Rt. Hon. Sir Leon Brittan Kt PC QC, Anthony Steen MP,
Professor Ian Kennedy, Dan Joel, Robin Morse, Maurice Fitzmaurice.
Members of chambers are recorders, arbitrators of the ICC and London Court of International Arbitration, members of the Institute of International Law, the ICSID Panel of Arbitrators and Conciliators and the INTELSAT Panel of Experts. Chambers have the Panel Chairman of Appeals under the Consumer Credit Act, who also sits on the DTI Advisory Committee on Arbitration, and a former legal adviser to the Foreign and Commonwealth Office.

Publications: Works include: *Principles of Public International Law; Commercial Law; Legal Problems of Credit and Security; Hire Purchase Law and Practice; Principles of Corporate Insolvency Law; Consumer Credit Legislation; Constitutional and Administrative Law; de Smith Woolf & Jowell Judicial Review of Administrative Action* (1995); *Vienna Convention on the Law of Treaties; Interna-*

tional Law Commission; Halsbury on Aliens, Arbitration and the European Convention on Human Rights.

WORK UNDERTAKEN:

Commercial: *Work includes:* international trade, banking, insurance, carriage of goods, conflict of laws, corporate fraud, financial services, regulatory tribunals, defamation, media and entertainment and intellectual property.

Public: *Work includes:* judicial review both for and against public bodies arising from decisions in areas such as freedom of expression, equality of treatment, immigration, education, social security, housing, planning and local government. The combined expertise of members in commercial and public law proves particularly valuable in City regulation and financial services cases. Chambers also specialises extensively in employment law.

Additional Areas: International and European law.

FOREIGN CONNECTIONS: The chambers have close links with a network of lawyers across Europe, and members have a wide-ranging experience of advocacy before English, European and Commonwealth courts and tribunals. Members of chambers appear before the European Court of Justice and the European Court of Human Rights, with two senior members practising in European Community law from Brussels.

LANGUAGES SPOKEN: French, German, Italian, Spanish, Finnish, Swedish, Urdu, Hindi, Punjabi, Japanese.

RECRUITMENT & TRAINING: Applications for pupillage should be sent with a detailed CV and stamped addressed envelope to the Pupillage Committee. A first or upper second class degree is usually required, although not necessarily in law. Up to three pupillage awards of up to £20,000 are available. All pupils receive at least Bar Council recommended minimum funding. Mini-pupillages for a week in June or July of the preceding year are strongly encouraged for potential pupils of the chambers.

100 3 HARE COURT (Michael Lewis QC)
Set No.

3 HARE COURT, TEMPLE, LONDON, EC4Y 7BJ
DX: 17

TEL: (0171) 353 7561
FAX: (0171) 353 7741

THE CHAMBERS: A specialist criminal set, comprising four QCs, 30 juniors and six clerks.

MEMBERS:
Michael Lewis QC (1956)(QC-1975)*, John Morris QC (1954)(QC-1973)*,
Howard Godfrey QC (1970)(QC-1991)*, William Clegg QC (1972)(QC-1991)*,
Robert Flach (1950), Charles Conway (1969), Deborah Champion (1970),
Nigel Ingram (1972)+, Andrew Munday (1973), Mark Halsey (1974),
Robert Neill (1975), Andrew Williams (1975), Margaret Barnes (1976),
John Caudle (1976), Nigel Lithman (1976), Anthony Abell (1977),
John Dodd (1979), Michael Levy (1979), John Livingston (1980),
Maura McGowan (1980), Brian Altman (1981), Peter Lodder (1981),
Keith Mitchell (1981), James Sturman (1982), Jane McIvor (1983),
Gelaga King (1985), Mark Milliken-Smith (1986),
Christopher Campbell-Clyne (1988), Richard Matthews (1989),
Thomas Derbyshire (1989), James Ageros (1990), Christine Agnew (1992),
Michael Epstein (1992), John Hurlock (1993).

HEAD OF CHAMBERS:
Michael Lewis QC

SEN. CLERK:
John Grimmer

TENANTS: 34

MAIN AREAS OF WORK: Chambers handle the full range of criminal work, private and publicly funded, for both prosecution and defence. Members practise principally in London, East Anglia and the South-East, but they also work elsewhere in England and Wales as well as abroad. Fraud remains an important part of chambers' practice, covering corporate, financial services, insolvency, revenue and VAT work. Tenants also undertake judicial review, licensing and tribunal work.

Recorder + Standing Counsel to the Department of Trade & Industry

ADDITIONAL AREAS OF WORK: Immigration.

LANGUAGES: Dutch, French, German, Hebrew and Welsh, Italian, Serbo-Croat and Krio (Sierra Leone).

101 **HOLBORN CHAMBERS (Stuart Stevens)** 6 Gate Street, Lin-
Set No. coln's Inn Fields, London, WC2A 3HP **Tel:** (0171) 242 6060 **Fax:** (0171) 242 2777
DX: 159 **Sen. Clerk:** Matthew Jones **Tenants:** 27 Varied practice including work
in the areas of crime, civil, matrimonial, landlord and tenant, industrial and land
tribunals and chancery.

102 INTERNATIONAL LAW CHAMBERS (Sami D. El-Falahi)
Set No.

ILC HOUSE, 77-79 CHEPSTOW ROAD, BAYSWATER, LONDON, W2 5QR

TEL: (0171) 221 5684
FAX: (0171) 221 5685

Brussels Office: ILC House, 91-93 Avenue Emile Max, Bruxelles 1040, Belgium

Tel: +32 (2) 732 5663/735 23 91
Fax: +32 (2) 734 96 37
Telex: 20334 MAGNEX B

THE CHAMBERS: Founding members of Professionals Network International, this set
provides expertise in English, EC, International laws and commercial laws of certain
Arab countries.

MEMBERS:
Sami D. El-Falahi (1972), Andreas O'Shea (1993).

WORK UNDERTAKEN: With an office in Brussels and connections in Amman, Jordan;
Baghdad, Iraq; Cairo, Egypt, United States and the Yemen, Chambers are able to offer
advice not only in English and EC law but also in international and especially Arab
world laws, including International Arbitration and Settlement of Disputes, Drafting
of Commercial Agreements, Company Laws, Conflict of Laws, Construction Agreements, EC law, Human rights, Negligence and Personal Injury, Shipping and Marine
Settlement. Advocacy is also undertaken in all English as well as European Community Courts.

LANGUAGES: Arabic.

HEAD OF CHAMBERS:
Sami D. El-Falahi

SEN. CLERK:
Mrs Christine Lanscombe

TENANTS: 2

103 KEATING CHAMBERS (John Uff QC)
Set No.

10 ESSEX STREET, OUTER TEMPLE, LONDON, WC2R 3AA
DX: 1045

TEL: (0171) 240 6981
FAX: (0171) 240 7722

THE CHAMBERS: A set specialising in all aspects of construction and civil engineering
law that has expanded substantially over the past decade. In 1984 chambers moved
from 11 King's Bench Walk to more spacious premises at 10 Essex Street.
Chambers operate with a large, experienced team of administrative staff, headed
by the Senior Clerk and supported by his assistant and the chambers' Administrator.
The set is equipped with up-to-date computers and office technology and provides an
efficient and friendly service. Donald Keating QC is the original author of the standard
text book *Building Contracts* which is now written by a former member of chambers,
Mr Justice May, with assistance from members of chambers. John Uff QC is the author
of a number of books and articles on construction and engineering disputes. He is also
the visiting professor and director of The Centre for Construction Law at King's
College, London. Martin Collins QC is a Judge of the Courts of Appeal of Jersey and
Guernsey. This chambers has substantial involvement in international arbitrations
both as juniors and as silks.

MEMBERS:
Donald Keating QC (1950)(QC-1972), Martin Collins QC (1952)(QC-1972),
John Uff QC (1970)(QC-1983), Richard Fernyhough QC (1970)(QC-1986),
Christopher Thomas QC (1973)(QC-1989), John Marrin QC (1974)(QC-1990),
Stephen Furst QC (1975)(QC-1991), Timothy Elliott QC (1975)(QC-1992),
Vivian Ramsey QC (1979)(QC-1992), Alan Steynor (1975),
Robert Gaitskell QC (1978)(QC-1994), Philip Boulding (1979),
Rosemary Jackson (1981), Marcus Taverner (1981), Peter Coulson (1982),

HEAD OF CHAMBERS:
John Uff QC

SEN. CLERK:
Barry Bridgman

TENANTS: 29

Ian Pennicott (1982), Paul Darling (1983), Finola O'Farrell (1983),
Adrian Williamson (1983), Michael Bowsher (1985), Alexander Nissen (1985),
Nerys Jefford (1986), Louise Randall (1988), Robert Evans (1989),
Sarah Hannaford (1989), Simon Hargreaves (1991), Richard Harding (1992),
Jane Lemon (1993), Piers Stansfield (1993).

WORK UNDERTAKEN:

General Description: All aspects of construction and civil engineering law, landlord and tenant and other property-related work.

Main Areas of Work: Building and engineering contracts, in the U.K and abroad, litigation and arbitration (including ICC and FIDIC arbitration), development contracts, contractual claims under construction contracts, claims in respect of defective buildings, professional negligence in building and construction matters. Local authority work (including building control work). European community law in particular public procurement.

Appointments as Arbitrator: Senior members of chambers act as arbitrators and legal assessors, through the ICC, internationally and in the UK, ranging from very substantial construction and commercial matters to the smaller arbitrations.

Additional Areas of Work: Mechanical and chemical engineering cases – most types of commercial and insurance contracts – general professional negligence – performance bonds and warranties – Mareva and other types of injunctions.
Some members also practise in information technology law, aviation law, landlord and tenant, planning and other property-related matters.

NATURE OF CLIENTELE: Building contractors; property developers and owners; specialist contractors; government departments and agencies; local authorities; architects; engineers; quantity surveyors; surveyors; insurance companies and professional indemnity insurers.

FOREIGN CONNECTIONS: Many members of chambers act and advise in litigation or arbitration abroad, in particular in Hong Kong, Singapore, the Middle East and in Paris (the headquarters of the ICC).

RECRUITMENT: Both six and twelve month pupillages are offered. Chambers' policy is that pupils accepted on the pupillage scheme are guaranteed to receive at least £15,000 over a twelve month period.

04
t No.

1 KING'S BENCH WALK (James Hunt QC)

1 KING'S BENCH WALK, TEMPLE, LONDON, EC4Y 7DB
DX: 360

TEL: (0171) 353 8436
FAX: (0171) 353 2647

THE CHAMBERS: The set was established in the late ninteenth century, and has a diverse common law practice in London and on the Midland and Oxford Circuit. A steady expansion in members has led to an increasingly specialist service within the general common law field. Chambers have recently acquired premises in Northampton, at 24 Albion Place, to provide conference and other facilities for their East Midland practitioners. These are fully computerised.

HEAD OF CHAMBERS:
James Hunt QC

PRACTICE MANAGER:
Peter Bennett

TENANTS: 39

MEMBERS:

J. Hunt QC (1968)(QC-1987), B.R. Escott-Cox QC (1954)(QC-1974),
M.R. Bowley QC (1962)(QC-1981), M. Pert QC (1970)(QC-1992),
Timothy Raggatt QC (1972)(QC-1993), F.M. Oldham QC (1977)(QC-1994),
M. Stokes QC (1971)(QC-1994), R.A. Benson QC (1974)(QC-1995),
A. Urquhart (1963), S. Waine (1969), C. Metcalf (1972), D. Lee (1973),
M. Fowler (1974), A.G. Mainds (1977), C.W. Lewis (1977), A. Neaves (1977),
H. Morrison (1977), D. Farrell (1978), C. Gargan (1978), M. Beddoe (1979),
M. Kushner (1980), C.J. Donnellan (1981), R. Wilson (1981), Lynn Tayton (1981),
C. Plunkett (1983), W. Harbage (1983), S. Bull (1984), J. Ecob (1985),
R. Underwood (1986), A. Malik (1987), G. Aspden (1988), A. Johnson (1990),
M. Lowe (1991), J. Gibson (1991), S. Alford (1992), S. Gaunt (1992),
R Dean (1993), D Lloyd-Jones (1993), Martin Beddoe (1979).

Several members of Chambers are recorders or assistant recorders, and two are deputy High Court Judges. Philip Cox QC is the President of Mental Health Review Tribunals. Some members belong to the Criminal Bar Association and the Family Law Bar Association. All are members of the Midland and Oxford Circuit.

WORK UNDERTAKEN:

Main Areas of Work: Personal injury litigation with specialists in paraplegia and brain damage; professional and medical negligence; commercial and company law; consumer law and consumer credit; family law, including matrimonial finance, property and childcare; landlord and tenant; crime, including commercial fraud; contract, including sale of goods; and planning.

Additional Areas: Administrative law, agriculture, arbitration, aviation, banking, Chancery including probate, computer law, construction, boundary disputes, courts martial, defamation, discrimination, EEC, employment, environment, housing, immigration, insolvency, Islamic law, judicial review, licensing, animal and equestrian cases, local government, mental health, pharmaceuticals, police cases, product liability, property and sports law.

CLIENTELE: Mostly individuals; some companies.

FOREIGN LANGUAGES: French, Spanish, Urdu, Punjabi.

OFFICE EQUIPMENT: Chambers use IBM compatible word processing equipment and Meridian barristers sofware on a Unix/LAN/WAN network.

RECRUITMENT & TRAINING: Chambers offer twelve months' pupillages, reviewable by both parties after the first six, and divided into two sets of six. The Midland and Oxford Circuit covers a wide area, and pupils should be prepared for extensive travel and higher travelling expenses than those of a London-based practice. Pupillage awards of £10,000 for the first six months are available, with a guaranteed income of £6000 for the second six months. Mini-pupillages are available. Chambers have an excellent record of recruitment from pupils. Tenancy and pupillage applications to Francis Oldham.

105
Set No.

1 KING'S BENCH WALK (James Townend QC)

1 KING'S BENCH WALK, TEMPLE, LONDON, EC4Y 7DB
DX: L.D.E. Delivery only

TEL: (0171) 583 6266
FAX: (0171) 583 2068

THE CHAMBERS: These chambers are a large, long established set, specialising in family and criminal law, with strength at all levels of seniority. Teams of counsel are provided for more protracted, complex and important cases. The work of chambers is principally in London and on the South Eastern Circuit, but work is also undertaken throughout the country.

HEAD OF CHAMBERS:
Mr J.B.S. Townend QC

SEN. CLERK:
Mr. David Dear

TENANTS: 41

MEMBERS:

James Townend QC (1962)(QC-1978) MA (Oxon),
Anthony Hacking QC (1965)(QC-1983) MA (Oxon),
Rodger Hayward Smith QC (1967)(QC-1988) MA (Oxon),
Barry Singleton QC (1968)(QC-1989) MA (Cantab), Judith Parker QC (1973)(QC-1991) BA (Oxon), Camden Pratt QC (1970)(QC-1992) MA (Oxon),
Pamela Scriven QC (1970)(QC-1992) LLB (London),
Richard Anelay QC (1970)(QC-1993) BA (Bristol), Roderic Wood QC (1974)(QC-1993) BA (Oxon), Clive Newton (1968) MA (Oxon), BCL (Oxon),
Michael Warren (1971) MA (Oxon), Andrew McDowall (1972) MA (Oxon), BCL (Lond), John Reddish (1973) MA (Oxon), Charles Kemp (1973) LLB (Lond),
Gordon Jackson QC (1979)(QC-1989) LLB (St. Andrews),
Stephen Bellamy (1974) MA (Cantab), John Tanzer (1975) BA,
James Turner (1976) LLB (Hull), David Rennie (1976) BA,
Andrew McFarlane (1977), Suzanne Coates (1978) LLB (Lond), SRN,
Caroline Lister (1980), Anthony Kirk (1981) LLB (Lond), AKC,
Susan R Maidment (1968) LLB, LLM (LSE), LLD (Keele),
Julian Woodbridge (1981), Christopher Pocock (1984) BA (Oxon),

Lewis Marks (1984) BA (Oxon), Stephen Shay (1984) BA (Oxon),
Deborah Eaton (1985), Sarah O'Connor (1986) LLB, Deiniol Cellan-
Jones (1988) BA (Oxon), Philip Marshall (1989) LLB, Elizabeth Selman (1989) LLB
(Lond), Richard Barton (1990), Caroline Gibson (1990), Joanna Grice (1991),
Rebecca James (1992), James Roberts (1993), Richard Harrison (1993),
Ian Cook (1994), Shona Mulholland (1994).

WORK UNDERTAKEN:

Main Areas of Work: The chambers specialise in all aspects of family law, including
matrimonial finance and child care litigation, and in criminal law, both prosecution
and defence, including serious fraud work.

Other Areas of Work: The chambers have varied common law expertise. *Work includes:* personal injury, professional and medical negligence, contracts (including
sale of goods), planning, landlord and tenant, judicial review, insolvency, employment and industrial disputes, tribunals, inquiries and Official Referees' business,
police cases and human rights cases in the UK and at the European Court.

MEMBERSHIPS: Institute of Chartered Arbitrators, British Institute of International &
Comparative Law, Family Law Bar Association and International Academy of
Matrimonial Lawyers.

PUBLICATIONS: R. Hayward Smith QC & Clive Newton are editors of the forthcoming
Jackson & Davies *Matrimonial Finance & Taxation.* James Turner and Stephen Shay
are editors of Archbold: *Criminal Pleading Evidence & Practice.* Andrew Mcfarlane
is co-author of Hershman and Mcfarlane: *Children Law and Practice.*

06 2 KING'S BENCH WALK (Lord Campbell of Alloway QC)

2 King's Bench Walk, Temple, London, EC4Y 7DE **Tel:** (0171) 353 9276
Fax: (0171) 353 9949 **DX:** 477 **Sen. Clerk:** Kate Dennison **Tenants:** 31 Covers
broad cross-section of work. Apart from general common law and criminal practice
they also work in areas as diverse as EC law, education appeals, and vaccine damage
cases.

07 2 KING'S BENCH WALK (Anthony Donne QC)

2 King's Bench Walk, Temple, London, EC4Y 7DE **Tel:** (0171) 353 1746 **Fax:** (0171) 583
2051 **DX:** 1032 **Sen. Clerk:** Mr. R.L.D. Plager **Tenants:** 50 The chambers have an
annexe in Plymouth, Devon.

08 4 KING'S BENCH WALK (Peter Heppel QC)

4 KING'S BENCH WALK, TEMPLE, LONDON, EC4Y 7DL
DX: 422

TEL: (0171) 353 0478
FAX: (0171) 583 3549

Door Tenants: Diana Allen, Peter Davis, Phillip Henry, Walter Rudeloff, Nobukata
Naritomi.

THE CHAMBERS: Common law set specialising in commercial fraud, financial services, serious criminal fraud and insurance and reinsurance.

MEMBERS:

Peter Heppel QC (1970)(QC-1992), John Toogood (1957), Kenneth Cameron (1969),

Anthony Dalgleish (1971), Greville Davis (1976), Clive Anderson (1976),
Bruce Stuart (1977), Ivor Frank (1979), Mark Paltenghi (1979),
Chris Van Hagen (1980), Andrew Gordon-Saker (1981), Justin Shale (1982),
Simon Stafford-Michael (1982), David Harounoff (1984), Martin Hurst (1985),
Anika Khan (1988), David Stern (1989), Laura Cobbs (1989),
Graham Huston (1991), Sarah Ainsworth (1991), Samuel Jarman (1989),
Anne Crossfield (1993), Nigel Hood (1993), Emma Edhem (1993).

HEAD OF CHAMBERS:
Peter Heppel

SEN. CLERK:
Ian Lee

TENANTS: 24

109
Set No.

4 KING'S BENCH WALK (Nicholas Jarman QC)

4 KING'S BENCH WALK, TEMPLE, LONDON, EC4Y 7DL
DX: 1050

TEL: (0171) 353 3581
FAX: (0171) 583 2257

MEMBERS:
Nicholas Jarman QC (1965)(QC-1985), Basil Hillman (1968),
Robert Spencer Bernard (1969), John Gilbert Harvey (1973), Moira Pooley (1973),
John Denniss (1974), David A. Pearl (1977), Barnaby Evans (1978),
Denise Sloam (1979), Jonathan Cowen (1983), John Riley (1983),
Reginald Arkhurst (1984), Peter Nightingale (1986) *, Benjamin Gumpert (1987),
Andrew Granville Stafford (1987), Rhodri Williams (1987) +,
Adrienne Morgan (1988), Satvinder Juss (1989), Claire Jacobs (1989),
John Metcalf (1990), Kevin Higgins (1990), Paul Wakerley (1990),
Cressida Murphy (1991), Michael Skelley (1991), Kim Preston (1991),
Giles Curtis-Raleigh (1992), Sara Rudman (1992), Hefin Rees (1992),
Fania Stoney (1993), Brendan Davis (1994).
+*Currently practising abroad *Formerly a solicitor*

HEAD OF CHAMBERS:
Nicholas Jarman QC

CLERKS:
Lee Cook, Philip Burnell, Mrs Marion Capon,
Miss Jayne Barnes

TENANTS: 30

SUMMARY OF EXPERTISE: These Chambers were formed in 1972 by a group of experienced practitioners, mainly members of the Midland and Oxford Circuit, with expertise in most common law fields. In recent years, the policy of chambers has been to encourage development of groups of specialists in a wide variety of such fields. There are several members of chambers with specialist expertise in each of the fields listed below. In addition, these chambers accept instructions in all other forms of common law work. Chambers are pleased to be able to offer expert advice upon EC law applicable to any of these areas of specialist or general practice.

SPECIALIST AREAS: Specialist areas (Contact either the Senior Clerk or the group co-ordinator, named after each speciality for further details): (1) Construction, including arbitration (John Harvey); (2) Criminal Law (Robert Spencer Bernard); (3) Employment (David A. Pearl); (4) E.C. (Rhodri Williams); (5) Family (Denise Sloam); (6) Immigration (Cressida Murphy); (7) Personal Injury (John Denniss); (8) Planning and Local Government, including environmental and mineral (Moira Pooley); (9) Professional Negligence, in all forms, including medical (John Harvey); (10) Property Law, including landlord and tenant (Cressida Murphy).

CIRCUIT PRACTITIONERS: Most members of chambers are members of the Midland and Oxford Circuit. Instructions are accepted from any location and on a Direct Professional Access basis, where appropriate.

FOREIGN LANGUAGES AND CONNECTIONS: Chambers has connections with Brussels and Mauritius. Members of Chambers include speakers of French, German, Italian and Welsh.

110
Set No.

5 KING'S BENCH WALK (David Cocks QC)

5 KING'S BENCH WALK, TEMPLE, LONDON, EC4Y 7DN
DX: 478 (Ch.Ln.)

TEL: (0171) 797 7600
FAX: (0171) 797 7648/9

THE CHAMBERS: A general common law set with 10 QCs, which specialises in criminal law and serious crimes in particular. Members practise in London and on the South East Circuit.

MEMBERS:
David Cocks QC (1961)(QC-1982), Sir Derek Spencer QC (1961)(QC-1980),
Anthony Arlidge QC (1962)(QC-1981), James Stewart QC (1966)(QC-1982),
Henry Green QC (1962)(QC-1988), David Lederman QC (1966)(QC-1990),
Linda Stern QC (1971)(QC-1991), Peter Rook QC (1973)(QC-1991),
Richard Sutton QC (1969)(QC-1993), Christopher Ball QC (1972)(QC-1993),
Peter Carter QC (1974)(QC-1995), David Radcliffe (1966),
Austen Issard-Davies (1969), Rosamund Horwood-Smart (1974), John Black (1975),
Nigel Peters (1976), Nicholas Fooks (1978), David Green (1979),

HEAD OF CHAMBERS:
David Cocks QC

SEN. CLERK:
Kenneth Darvill

FIRST JUNIOR: Mark Bennett

TENANTS: 44

Stephen Harvey (1979), Patricia Lynch (1979), David Etherington (1979),
Jonathan Fisher (1980), John Ryder (1980), Linda Dobbs (1981), Ian Leist (1981),
Alexander Milne (1981), Richard Kovalevsky (1983), Janine Sheff (1983),
Rupert Overbury (1984), Mark Lucraft (1984), Angela Morris (1984),
Brendan Morris (1985), David Marshall (1985), Robert Boyle (1985),
Jane Bewsey (1986), Shane Collery (1988), David Williams (1988) GRSC, Dip LL,
John Anderson (1989), Sara Lawson (1990), Allison Clare (1992),
Paul Hardy (1992), Tom Forster (1993), Barnaby Jameson (1993).
Chambers have standing counsel to the Inland Revenue and HM Customs and Excise,
DTI Inspectors, recorders and assistant recorders.

Publications: Arlidge and Parry on *Fraud;* Arlidge and Eady on *Contempt; Journal
of International Banking Law* (UK Correspondent); Dobbs and Lucraft, *Road
Traffic Law and Practice* (Sweet & Maxwell 1994); Rook and Ward, *Sexual
Offences* (Waterlows 1990); Carter and Harrison *Offences of Violence* (Waterlows
1991); Fisher and Merrills *Pharmacy Law and Practices* (Blackwells 1995).

WORK UNDERTAKEN:

Main Areas of Work: *Criminal:* commercial fraud, inland revenue and customs and
excise offences, drugs and problems arising from the Drug Trafficking Offences
Act, extradition, child abuse, obscene publications, road traffic, licensing, and
offences involving forensic experts.

Common Law: family, judicial review, contract, tort, personal injury, medical
negligence, professional negligence and disciplinary and domestic tribunal work.

Other areas of work carried out by certain members: immigration, privy council,
administrative, lotteries, local government, libel, media, European, commercial,
landlord and tenant, public law, peerage, child care, civil liberties, Soviet law,
product liability, health and safety at work and aviation.

CLIENTELE: Individuals, public and private companies, HM Customs and Excise,
local authorities, Serious Fraud Office and CPS government departments. Chambers
operate the Direct Professional Access scheme.

FOREIGN CONNECTIONS: Nigel Peters is a member of the Northern Ireland Bar and
Barbados Bar. David Marshall is a member of the Hong Kong Bar & New York Bar.

LANGUAGES SPOKEN: French, Italian, Russian and Spanish.

RECRUITMENT & TRAINING: Applications for tenancy should be sent to David Cocks
QC; pupillage applications to Shane Collery. Chambers have up to seven pupils at
any one time, four of whom are guaranteed £10,000 for the year. Mini-pupillages are
available.

---

11 No. 6 KING'S BENCH WALK (Sibghat Kadri QC)

6 KING'S BENCH WALK, TEMPLE, LONDON, EC4Y 7DR
DX: 471 (Ch.Ln.)

TEL: (0171) 353 4931
FAX: (0171) 353 1726

THE CHAMBERS: A multi-racial set established 23 years ago and committed to defending the rights and liberties of the individual. The set is fully computerised. Members
accept Direct Professional Access from the approved professions.

HEAD OF CHAMBERS:
Sibghat Kadri QC

SEN. CLERK:
Gary Jeffery

TENANTS: 30

MEMBERS:
Sibghat Kadri QC (1969)(QC-1989), Tariq Rafiq (1961), William Geldart (1975) BA
(Open), James Bowen (1979), Harjit Grewal (1980) BA (Hons)(Cantab),
Sylvester Carrott (1980), Terence Gallivan (1981) BA (Dunelm), LLB (Cantab),
Linda Pearce (1982) LLB, Manjit Gill (1982),
Andrew Gumbiti-Zimuto (1983) BA(Hons) Law, Rambert De Mello (1983),
Shaun Wallace (1984), Michael Cogan (1986), Robin Howat (1986) BA(Hons)
(Dunelm), Helen Clarke (1988) BA (Oxon), Emily Driver (1988),
Martin Taylor (1988), Alev Giz (1988), Peter Clark (1988), Lorna Tagliavini (1989),
Manjit Singh Panesar (1989), Colm Davis-Lyons (1990), Rona Neathey (1991),
Malek Wan Daud (1991), Stephanie Harrison (1991), Stephen Knafler (1993),
Maryam Najand (1994).

MAIN AREAS OF WORK:

Criminal Law: All aspects of crime, including public order cases, complex frauds and Customs & Excise offences. Members act only for the defence, save in a small number of private prosecutions.

Property, Housing and Landlord and Tenant: Including all aspects of residential property work, judicial review of local authority housing decisions, and advisory work for local government housing departments.

Discrimination Law: Several members are specialists in the field of race and sex discrimination, and regularly advise and act for individuals, local authorities and the Commission for Racial Equality.

Immigration Law: Since its inception, chambers have been involved in all aspects of immigration law and related areas of judicial review.

Individual members are also experts in education law, Muslim family law, and law relating to the Indian subcontinent.

ADDITIONAL AREAS OF WORK: Administrative law and judicial review, agricultural law, general chancery work (including associations and charities), civil actions against the police, commercial law, employment law, environmental law, family law (including matrimonial law, wardship and childcare), personal injury, planning and local government, and welfare law.

PUBLICATIONS: Harjit Grewal is the author of *The Handbook on Race Discrimination* and *The Handbook on Sex Discrimination*. Linda Pearce has written *The Mobile Home Handbook* and is a contributor to Vol. 27 of *Halsbury's Laws* (Landlord and Tenant). Sylvester Carrott is the co-author of *Quiet Enjoyment*.

LANGUAGES: French, German, Italian, Punjabi, Urdu, Turkish.

112
Set No.

6 KING'S BENCH WALK (Michael Worsley QC)

6 KING'S BENCH WALK, TEMPLE, LONDON, EC4Y 7DR
DX: 26 (Ch.Ln.)

TEL: (0171) 583 0410
FAX: (0171) 353 8791

THE CHAMBERS: A specialist criminal set with ten QCs and one Senior and two Junior Treasury Counsel. Chambers have particular experience in advocacy in the higher courts. Members also handle civil work with individual specialisations.

HEAD OF CHAMBERS:
Michael Worsley QC

SEN. CLERK:
Mr. David Garstang

TENANTS: 34

MEMBERS:

Michael Worsley QC (1955)(QC-1985), Ann Curnow QC (1957)(QC-1985), Roy Amlot QC (1963)(QC-1989), Baroness Ann Mallalieu QC (1970)(QC-1988), James Curtis QC (1970)(QC-1993), Victor Temple QC (1971)(QC-1993), Dorian Lovell-Pank QC (1971)(QC-1993), Joanna Korner QC (1974)(QC-1993), Bruce Houlder QC (1969)(QC-1994), David Spens QC (1973)(QC-1995), David Fisher (1973), Howard Vagg (1974), Jonathan Turner (1974), Wendy Joseph (1975), Nigel Sweeney (1976), Mark Dennis (1977), Anthony Leonard (1978), Philippa Jessel (1978), Marks Moore (1979), David Perry (1980), Nicholas Hilliard (1981), Andrew Brierley (1984), Martyn Bowyer (1984), Simon Denison (1984), Emma Broadbent (1986), Irena Ray-Crosby (1990), Dean Armstrong (1985), Peter Grieves-Smith (1989), Timothy Cray (1989), Andrew Oldland (1990), Simon Laws (1991), Duncan Penny (1992), Jason Dunn-Shaw (1992), Annabel Darlow (1993).

Eight members of chambers are recorders and one is a D.T.I. Inspector. Additionally, members belong to the Criminal Bar Association and the Bar Senate. Mr. Dennis is an editor on *Archbold*.

WORK UNDERTAKEN:

Main Areas of Work: *Criminal:* For both prosecution and defence mainly in London and the South Eastern Circuit specialising in commercial crime, fraud, VAT cases and regulatory work.

Civil: Libel, police law, false imprisonment/ malicious prosecutions, some commercial, defamation and professional tribunals.

Other specialities: Members appear before coroners' courts, inquiries, disciplinary and industrial tribunals; also work is undertaken involving trade descriptions, extradition, licensing matters and human rights.

FOREIGN LANGUAGES: French, German, Italian and Spanish.

RECRUITMENT & TRAINING: Applications for tenancy should be sent to the Head of Chambers; those for pupillage to Emma Broadbent. There are eight pupils in chambers at any one time. Awards and mini-pupillages are available.

---

13 No. 7 KING'S BENCH WALK (Adrian Hamilton QC)

7 KING'S BENCH WALK, TEMPLE, LONDON, EC4Y 7DS
DX: 239 (Ch.Ln.) LIX: LON 081

TEL: (0171) 583 0404
FAX: (0171) 583 0950
Telex: 887491 KB LAW G

MEMBERS:
Adrian Hamilton QC (1949)(QC-1973), John Willmer QC (1955)(QC-1967), Stephen Tomlinson QC (1974)(QC-1988)*, Jeremy Cooke QC (1976)(QC-1990)+, Timothy Saloman QC (1975)(QC-1993), Prof. Francis Reynolds QC (1960)(QC-1993), Gavin Kealey QC (1977)(QC-1994), Julian Flaux QC (1978)(QC-1994), Jonathan Gaisman QC (1979)(QC-1995), Alastair Stewart-Richardson (1952), Dominic Kendrick (1981), Charles Priday (1982), Alistair Schaff (1983), Adam Fenton (1984), Julia Dias (1982), Stephen Hofmeyr (1982), Christopher Butcher (1986), Stephen Kenny (1987), Richard Southern (1987), Robert Bright (1987), Gavin Geary (1989), David Bailey (1989), David Edwards (1989), David Allen (1989), Simon Picken (1989), Andrew Wales (1992), Siobán Healy (1993), Stephen Phillips (1993), Rebecca Sabben-Clare (1993), Jawdat Khurshid (1994), Richard Waller (1994).
* *Recorder*
+ *Assistant Recorder*

HEAD OF CHAMBERS:
Adrian Hamilton QC

CLERKS::
Linda Stinton, Bernie Hyatt, Greg Leyden

TENANTS: 31

WORK UNDERTAKEN: Established in 1883, this set of chambers has had a successful and prestigious history. Predominantly a commercial set, with much of its work being international in character, 7 King's Bench Walk has 31 members including eight practising QCs.

Principal fields of practice include commercial agreements, international trade and transport, insurance/ reinsurance, and shipping and Admiralty, many members being also Supporting Members of the London Maritime Arbitrators' Association. Other areas of specialisation include professional negligence, banking and financial services, oil and gas, and commodity transactions.

Although chambers' work is primarily that of advocacy, it offers great expertise in advisory work and arbitration.

LANGUAGES: Dutch, Flemish, French, German, Italian and Russian.

---

14 No. 8 KING'S BENCH WALK (L.G. Woodley QC) 8 King's Bench Walk, Temple, London, EC4Y 7DU **Tel:** (0171) 797 8888 **Fax:** (0171) 797 8850 **DX:** 195 **Sen. Clerk:** Paul McCusker **Tenants:** 42 General common law set undertaking both criminal and civil work.

15 No. 9 KING'S BENCH WALK (Ali Mohammed Azhar) 9 King's Bench Walk, Temple, London, EC4Y 7DX **Tel:** (0171) 353 9564 **Fax:** (0171) 353 7943 **Sen. Clerk:** John Lee **Tenants:** 16 Has practitioners in criminal, civil, family, immigration and industrial law. A mixed set with Asian, African and English barristers, two of whom are experts in Islamic and Hindu law.

116
Set No.

9 KING'S BENCH WALK (F. Ashe Lincoln QC)

9 KING'S BENCH WALK, TEMPLE, LONDON, EC4Y 7DX
DX: 472

TEL: (0171) 353 7202
FAX: (0171) 583 2030

MEMBERS:
F. Ashe Lincoln (1929), Surendra Popat (1969), Peter Gribble (1972),
Michael Hartman (1975), Peter Marsh (1975), Keith Stones (1975),
Alice Deschampsneufs (1976), Peter Lozynski (1977), Michael Greenslade (1982),
Amir Sultan (1983), Isabel Delamere (1985), Karen Neville (1986),
Miles Trigg (1987), Susan Brown (1989), Zacharias Miah (1990),
Bosmath Sheffi (1991), Peter St. John Howe (1992), Harry Potter (1993),
Obi Ouska (1993), Dominic Buckwell (1993), Paul Parlou (1993),
Elaine Sneller (1994).

HEAD OF CHAMBERS:
F. Ashe Lincoln QC

SEN. CLERK:
Gary Morgan

JUNIOR CLERKS:
Gary Nichols/ Simon Duggan

TENANTS: 22

117
Set No.

10 KING'S BENCH WALK (Jan Paulusz)

10 KING'S BENCH WALK, TEMPLE, LONDON, EC4Y 7EB
DX: 24

TEL: (0171) 353 7742
FAX: (0171) 583 0579

THE CHAMBERS: General common law chambers undertaking a wide range of work
with members specialising in criminal law (both prosecution and defence), matrimonial, company/ commercial and chancery law, personal injury and landlord and tenant.

MEMBERS:
Jan Paulusz (1957), Richard Brock (1957), Colin Hart (1966), Doris Urquhart (1967),
Philip Harris (1968), Claudius Algar (1972), Susan Tapping (1975),
Carlton Christensen (1977), Angus Robertson (1978), Reid Pearce (1979),
Bernadette Miscampbell (1980), William Lanigan (1980),
Elizabeth Goodchild (1981), Mark Eldridge (1982), Stephen Crouch (1982),
Jane Davies (1983), Peter Gray (1984), Alison Thompson (1986),
Andrew Evans (1984), Andrew Judge (1986), Alison Robins (1987),
Fiona Greenwood (1986), Michael Arnheim (1988), Sally Dent (1989),
David Devoy Williams (1989), Siân Spier (1989), Keith Hotten (1990),
Simon Cheetham (1991), Charlotte Carter (1992).

Door Tenants: Charles Vaudin (1971), Mustafa Habib (1980).

MEMBERSHIPS: One member of chambers is a member of the British Academy of
Forensic Sciences and an expert in firearms and ballistics.

WORK UNDERTAKEN:

Main Areas of Work: A wide range of criminal work from the most serious cases –
murder, sexual offences, robbery and burglary, commercial and VAT fraud – to
motoring offences. All aspects of divorce, ancillary relief, custody and childcare,
including wardship, domestic violence and child abduction procedures, company,
commercial and chancery matters, personal injury and landlord and tenant.

Additional Areas of Work: Arbitration, banking, carriage of goods, consumer credit,
construction, defamation, employment, discrimination, housing, immigration, insolvency, inheritance, pharmaceuticals, probate, property, trusts, wills, professional negligence, welfare law, licensing and courts martial.

LANGUAGES SPOKEN: French, Greek, Spanish, German, Dutch, Sinhalese,
Cantonese.

RECRUITMENT & TRAINING: Applications for pupillage should be sent to the Secretary
of the Pupillage Committee. Mini-pubillages are also available. Tenancy applications
to the Tenancy Committee.

HEAD OF CHAMBERS:
Jan Paulusz

SEN. CLERK:
Paul Harding

TENANTS: 29

118
Set No.

10 KING'S BENCH WALK (Ronald Thwaites QC) 10 King's Bench Walk, Temple, London, EC4Y 7EB **Tel:** (0171) 353 2501 **Fax:** (0171) 353 0658 **DX:** 294 (Ch.Ln.) **Sen. Clerk:** Mr C. Drury **Tenants:** 35 Specialise mainly in criminal law (defence and prosecution) although members also practise general common law, civil actions and some chancery work.

119
Set No.

11 KING'S BENCH WALK (Lord Irvine of Lairg QC)

11 KING'S BENCH WALK, TEMPLE, LONDON, EC4Y 7EQ
DX: 368 (Ch.Ln.)

TEL: (0171) 583 0610
FAX: (0171) 583 9123/ 3690

WORK UNDERTAKEN: The 25 members of these chambers (eight of whom are Queen's Counsel) provide specialist legal advice and advocacy services covering the following three principal areas:

Commercial Law/ International Trade: Arbitration (domestic and international); insurance and reinsurance; banking (especially letters of credit, guarantees and performance bonds); carriage of goods; international and domestic sales of goods; Stock Exchange, commodities and futures transactions; financial services; mergers and acquisitions; corporate and insolvency law; professional negligence (particularly accountants' negligence); music and film agreements; intellectual property.

Public and Administrative Law: Local authorities, especially their powers and financing; judicial review of central and local government and other public bodies, including financial services institutions; competitive tendering and public authority contracts; education; sex and race discrimination; elections; civil liberties; immigration; EC public law; housing and housing associations; environmental law.

Employment Law: Company directors; share options; incentive bonuses and pension rights; wrongful and unfair dismissal; the protection of confidential information; restrictive covenants; transfers of undertakings; sex and race discrimination and equal pay; strikes and other trade disputes; trade union membership; EC employment law.

PUBLICATIONS: Members of chambers have written or contributed to *Halsbury's Laws (Administrative Law Title); Goudie & Supperstone on Judicial Review; Harvey on Industrial Relations and Employment Law; Butterworths Employment Law Handbook; Tolley's Employment Handbook; Immigration Law and Practice.*
Office hours: 8.00am to 7.00pm Monday to Friday.
Out of office hours: *Tel:* (01831) 304714.
Full brochure available upon request.

HEAD OF CHAMBERS:
Lord Irvine of Lairg QC

SEN. CLERK:
Philip Monham

TENANTS: 25

120
Set No.

11 KING'S BENCH WALK (F.J. Muller QC) 11 King's Bench Walk, Temple, London, EC4Y 7EQ **Tel:** (0171) 353 3337 **Fax:** (0171) 583 2190 **Sen. Clerk:** Mr. A.T. Blaney **Tenants:** 19 General common law and criminal chambers with specialisations in family law, chancery work, employment, landlord and tenant, contract, commercial, planning and medical negligence.

12 KING'S BENCH WALK (Ronald J. Walker QC)

12 KING'S BENCH WALK, TEMPLE, LONDON, EC4Y 7EL
DX: 1037 (Ch.Ln.)

TEL: (0171) 583 0811
FAX: (0171) 583 7228

HEAD OF CHAMBERS:
Ronald Walker QC

CLERKS:
Mr Ronald Munday and Mr Tony Day

TENANTS: 40

THE CHAMBERS: The chambers were formed by the amalgamation of two established civil chambers, in order to provide expertise in depth, within a modern professional structure. A specialist Construction Unit forms part of the chambers, comprising a group of barristers with established expertise in building and engineering work: in several cases they have specialised in construction work throughout their careers.

WORK UNDERTAKEN:

Commercial: including banking, credit transactions and accountants' negligence.

Construction: including all standard form building and engineering contracts; and architects', engineers' and surveyors' negligence.

Employment: and race relations and equal opportunity cases.

Insurance and Reinsurance: drafting and constructing policies, material damage claims, solicitors' negligence and other professional indemnity work.

Personal Injury and Medical Negligence: including industrial disease claims and disaster inquiries.

Property Law: in particular, landlord and tenant.

Public Law: including judicial review, local government and environmental law.

PUBLICATIONS: Members of chambers have written, edited or contributed to various publications, including: *Walker & Walker: The English Legal System; Bullen & Leake & Jacob's Precedents of Pleadings; Master and Servant* in *Halsbury's Laws of England,* 3rd Edition; *Master and Servant,* (in *Atkins Encylopaedia of Court Forms – 2nd Edition); Law of Defective Premises; Architects Journal Legal Handbook; Construction Disputes: Liability and the Expert Witness; Odgers: Pleading and Practice; Consumer Credit Law and Practice; Medical Negligence: Case Law; Architect's Legal Handbook; Butterworths Personal Injury Litigation Service; Commercial Litigation: Pre-emptive Remedies; Personal Injury Litigation Law.*

RECRUITMENT & TRAINING: Chambers is a member of the Common Law Chambers Pupillage Application Scheme (COMPAS): a single application is made to all participating chambers, who select from the pool of applicants according to commonly agreed rules. For details and application form contact: Martin Spencer, COMPAS, 4 Paper Buildings, Temple, London EC4Y 7EX. Pupils offered a funded first 6-months pupillage are likely to be invited to stay for a second 6 month. Second 6-months pupils are offered a guaranteed income of £7,500.

CLIENTELE: The chambers' Construction Unit receives an increasing volume of Direct Professional Access instructions from construction professionals such as chartered surveyors, engineers and architects.

—12—
KINGS
BENCH
WALK

13 KING'S BENCH WALK (Graeme Williams QC) 13 King's Bench Walk, Temple, London, EC4Y 7EN **Tel:** (0171) 353 7204 **Fax:** (0171) 583 0252 **DX:** 359 **Sen. Clerk:** Stephen Buckingham **Tenants:** 35 Contract, commercial, personal injury, landlord and tenant, building, licensing, employment, professional negligence, planning, family and criminal law.

LAMB BUILDING (Kenneth Wheeler) Lamb Building, Temple, London, EC4Y 7AS **Tel:** (0171) 797 7788 **Fax:** (0171) 353 0535 **DX:** 1038 (Ch.Ln.) **Sen. Clerk:** Martin Secrett **Tenants:** 29 The chambers have an emphasis on commercial matters, with some general chancery work undertaken. The set is also known for its criminal and family law work.

124
Set No.

LAMB CHAMBERS (Jonathan Cole)

LAMB BUILDING, TEMPLE, LONDON, EC4Y 7AS
DX: 418

TEL: (0171) 797 8300
FAX: (0171) 797 8308

THE CHAMBERS: Lamb Chambers provides a complete advisory and representation service utilising the expertise and facilities of three specialist groups structured as pyramids to ensure a range of seniority and experience.

Jonathan Cole (1964), Michael Burke-Gaffney QC (1959)(QC-1977),
Julian Priest QC (1954)(QC-1974), Ian Leeming QC (1970)(QC-1988),
Christopher Gardner QC (1968)(QC-1994), J.A.L. Sterling (1953),
John Leslie (1969), Donald Anderson (1969), Anthony McNeile (1970),
David Ellis (1970), Mark West (1973), David di Mambro (1973),
Jeremy Carey (1974), Anthony Connerty (1974), Stephen Shaw (1975),
Martin Farber (1976), Simon Brilliant (1976), Robert Thoresby (1978),
Colin Mendoza (1983), Paul M. Emerson (1984), Kim Franklin (1984),
Thomas Graham (1985), Patrick Rolfe (1987), Simon Wood (1987),
Claire Thompson (1989), Gerard van Tonder (1990), James Stuart (1990),
Karen Walden-Smith (1990), Katherine Gough (1990), Elizabeth F. Haggerty (1994),
Rhiannon Jones (1993), Simon Bell (1994).

HEAD OF CHAMBERS:
Jonathan Cole

SEN. CLERK:
Mr John Kelly

TENANTS: 32

WORK UNDERTAKEN:

Business Law: The group specialises in all business related litigation including the law and practice of banking, commercial contracts, companies, consumer credit, corporate and personal insolvency, partnership, sale and carriage of goods together with applications for urgent interlocutory relief in these areas.

Personal Injury & Professional Negligence: The group specialises in all forms of tortious litigation including personal injury, fatal accidents, associated professional negligence especially medical and solicitors' negligence, consumer protection, product liability, structured and infant settlements and insurance.

Property Planning and Construction: The group's work covers virtually all issues concerning land, ranging from planning to contract development, construction, landlord and tenant together with associated torts including professional negligence of architects, engineers, surveyors and solicitors.

125
Set No.

LION COURT (Steven Jacobs)

CHANCERY HOUSE, 53-64 CHANCERY LANE, LONDON, WC2A 1SJ
DX: 98 (Ch.Ln.)

TEL: (0171) 404 6565
FAX: (0171) 404 6659

THE CHAMBERS: Lion Court is a common law set offering a wide range of experience and expertise. Chambers have developed flexible working practices and a fresh modern approach to administration incorporating the use of fully up-to-date technology.

WORK UNDERTAKEN: Crime, general common law, probate, commercial law, insolvency, insurance, banking, employment, personal injury, criminal injuries, matirmonial, family, childcare, licensing, local authority, planning, landlord and tenant, immigration, media and judicial review.

LANGUAGES SPOKEN: French, German, Spanish and Italian.

MEMBERS:

Steven Jacobs (1974), Neil Taylor QC (1949)(QC-1975), Laraine Kaye (1971),
David Wolchover (1971), Shini Cooksley (1975), Georgina Nicholas (1983),
Steve Hosking (1988), Paul Brinkworth (1990), Allison Fordham (1990),
Wendy Datta (1989), John Honey (1990), Stephen Bailey (1991),
Gudrun Fama (1991), Louise McCullough (1991), Helene Pines Richman (1992),
Paul Kattel (1993).

HEAD OF CHAMBERS:
Steven Jacobs

PRACTICE MANAGER:
Kim Brown

ADMINISTRATION CLERK:
Brian Newton

TENANTS: 17

126
Set No.

LITTLETON CHAMBERS (Michael Burton QC)

3 KING'S BENCH WALK NORTH, TEMPLE, LONDON, EC4Y 7HR
DX: 1047

TEL: (0171) 797 8600
FAX: (0171) 797 8699

MEMBERS:
Michael Burton QC (1970)(QC-1984), Michel Kallipetis QC (1968)(QC-1989), Robert Rhodes QC (1968)(QC-1989), Daniel Serota QC (1969)(QC-1989), Ian Mayes QC (1974)(QC-1993), Richard Price (1969), Colin Manning (1970), Richard Perkoff (1971), Philip Bartle (1976), Mark Lomas (1977), Timothy Higginson (1977), Clive Freedman (1977), John Bowers (1979), Andrew Clarke (1980), Caroline Harry Thomas (1981), John Davies (1981), Shirley Bothroyd (1982), Selwyn Bloch (1982), Antony Sendall (1984), Ian Gatt (1985), Michael Duggan (1984), Paul Lowenstein (1988), Raoul Downey (1988), Martyn Barklem (1989), Charles Samek (1989), Jeffrey Bacon (1989), Jeremy Lewis (1992), Naomi Ellenbogen (1992).

DOOR TENANTS:
Donald Harris (1958), Mohamed Syed (1989), Prof. Niel MacCormick.

WORK UNDERTAKEN:
General Description: A set practising in all areas of civil and commercial law with a wide spread of work including all aspects of business and employment law, intellectual property and commercial fraud.

Main Areas of Work: The specialities of individual members of chambers include: employment law (19 barristers), banking (10 barristers), intellectual property (14 barristers), commercial crime and tax fraud (7 barristers), professional negligence, defamation, entertainment law (7 barristers), matrimonial finance and children, and consumer credit law.

Additional Areas: Administrative law, agriculture, arbitration, carriage of goods, chancery, charities, civil liberties, competition law, computer law, construction, corporate finance, discrimination, education, EC, environment, family, financial services, foreign laws, franchising, housing, immigration, insolvency, insurance, international trade, judicial review, landlord and tenant, licensing, local government, mental health, parliamentary, pensions, personal injury, pharmaceuticals, planning, private international law, probate, product liability, property, revenue law, sale of goods, shipping, sports law, telecommunications, transport, trusts, welfare and wills.

LANGUAGES SPOKEN: French, German, Italian and Cantonese.

RECRUITMENT & TRAINING: Members of chambers fund up to 8 pupils per 6 months. Applications marked 'Pupillage Application' should be sent to David Douglas, Chief Executive.

HEAD OF CHAMBERS:
Michael Burton QC

CHIEF EXECUTIVE:
David Douglas

CLERKS: Deborah Anderson, Alistair Coyne
FEES CLERK Tony Shaddock

A/C'S RECEIVABLE MANAGER:
Nita Johnston

TENANTS: 28

127
Set No.

1 MIDDLE TEMPLE LANE (Colin Dines & Andrew Trollope QC)

1 MIDDLE TEMPLE LANE, TEMPLE, LONDON, EC4Y 9AA
DX: 464

TEL: (0171) 583 0659 (12 lines)
FAX: (0171) 353 0652

THE CHAMBERS: Chambers were established in December 1976 by Mr. Ronald Grey QC, and since then have flourished, growing both in size and in the quality and range of work undertaken. Members practise mainly in London, the South East and the Home Counties, but have accepted cases all over the country. Outside office hours, the senior clerk can be contacted on (0181) 527 3259.

MEMBERS:
Colin Dines (1970), Andrew Trollope QC (1971)(QC-1991), Roger Backhouse QC (1971)(QC-1984), Francis Wybrants (1961), David Ashby (1963), Nicholas Gardiner (1967), Graham Arran (1969), Tony Docking (1969), Godfree Browne (1971), Jonathan Davies (1971), Brian Argyle (1972), Andrew Campbell (1972), Sam Katkhuda (1974), Gopal Hooper (1973), Philip King (1974), Brian Reece (1974),

HEAD OF CHAMBERS:
Colin Dines, Andrew Trollope QC

SEN. CLERK:
Michael Strong

TENANTS: 36

John Plumstead (1975), Michael Borrelli (1977), Ian Copeman (1977),
Bernard Eaton (1978), Noel Lucas (1979), Christopher Amor (1984),
Emma Gluckstein (1985), Simon Mayo (1985), Mark Rainsford (1985),
Andrew Marshall (1986), Richard Butcher (1985), Barbara Strachan (1986),
James Lachkovic (1987), Harry Bowyer (1989), Avirup Chaudhuri (1990),
Anthony Korda (1988), Rachel Bright (1991), Richard Beynon (1990),
Philomena Murphy (1992), Natasha Wong (1993).
Most members belong to the Criminal Bar Association, and several serve on various
committees connected with criminal law. In addition, two members are on the Immi-
gration Panel for the Home Office. Five members are recorders and two are assistant
recorders. Sam Katkhuda is the author of a book on drafting indictments.

WORK UNDERTAKEN:

Main Areas of Work: *Criminal:* For both prosecution and defence, with an increasing
amount of serious white-collar crime. Members have recently acted in major VAT,
company and mortgage fraud cases. The whole range of crime is also handled from
murder, drugs and sexual offences to motoring offences and juvenile crime.

Additional Areas of Work: Courts martial; employment law; immigration, for applicants and the government; licensing; extradition and medical negligence.

FOREIGN CONNECTIONS: Godfree Browne is a member of the Zimbabwe and Botswana Bars and an advocate in the High Court of Zimbabwe.

LANGUAGES SPOKEN: Arabic, French and German.

RECRUITMENT & TRAINING: Tenancy applications to Colin Dines/ Noel Lucas; pupillage applications to Barbara Strachan. Chambers usually have between seven and ten
pupils and applications are welcome at any time. Pupillage awards and mini-pupillages are available at chambers' discretion.

128
Set No.

1 MIDDLE TEMPLE LANE (Wilfred Forster-Jones) 1 Middle
Temple Lane, Temple, London, EC4Y 9AA **Tel:** (0171) 353 0853 **Fax:** (0171) 583
2823 **DX:** 0008 **Sen. Clerk:** Charles Aboah **Tenants:** 7 General common law set
handling crime, discrimination, employment, fraud, housing, immigration, judicial
review, police cases, landlord and tenant and family.

129
Set No.

2 MIDDLE TEMPLE LANE (Satya Dhama) 2 Middle Temple
Lane, Temple, London, EC4Y 9AA **Tel:** (0171) 583 4540 **Fax:** (0171) 583 9178
Sen. Clerk: Barry Leach **Tenants:** 10 General common law set with specialist
practitioners in French, EC, Mohammedan and Hindu law. Also undertake criminal
cases (mainly defence) and family law matters.

130
Set No.

2 MIDDLE TEMPLE LANE (Harjit Singh) 2 Middle Temple
Lane, Temple, London, EC4Y 9AA **Tel:** (0171) 353 1356 **Fax:** (0171) 583 4928
DX: 0072 **Sen. Clerk:** Michael J. McCormack **Tenants:** 8 Common law set with
emphasis on crime, immigration, matrimonial, employment, industrial tribunals, civil
litigation, chancery and landlord and tenant.

131
et No.

4 MIDDLE TEMPLE LANE (Mr.N.A. Mittelholzer) 4 Middle
Temple Lane, Temple, London, EC4Y 9AA **Tel:** (0171) 353 8815 **Fax:** (0171) 353
8815 **DX:** 207 (Ch.Ln.) **Sen. Clerk:** **Tenants:** 2 A small set of chambers with an
established common law practice in the fields of criminal and family law, landlord
and tenant, courts martial and personal injuries.

1 MITRE COURT BUILDINGS (P.E.J. Focke QC)

1 MITRE COURT BUILDINGS, TEMPLE, LONDON, EC4Y 7BS
DX: Delivery Only

TEL: (0171) 797 7070
FAX: (0171) 797 7435

HEAD OF CHAMBERS:
P.E.J. Focke QC

SEN. CLERK:
Mr. R. Beams

TENANTS: 29

THE CHAMBERS: An established set specialising in family and matrimonial law. Joseph Jackson, who became Head of Chambers in 1969, was the editor of what is now the standard reference work on the subject, *Rayden and Jackson on Divorce and Family Matters.* Chambers still have two members who co-edit the book. Nicholas Mostyn is the author of *Child's Pay: The Complete Guide to the Child Support Act 1991.* The first female Lord Justice, Lord Justice Butler-Sloss, was a tenant, and other former members of chambers have received judicial appointments to the Family Division.

MEMBERS:
Paul Focke QC (1964)(QC-1982), Mary Hogg QC (1968)(QC-1989),
Bruce Blair QC (1969)(QC-1989), Michael Horowitz QC (1968)(QC-1990),
John Elvidge (1968), Richard Bond (1970), Jeremy Posnansky QC (1971)(QC-1994),
Judith Hughes QC (1974)(QC-1994), Mark Everall QC (1975)(QC-1994),
Martin Pointer (1976), Robin Spon-Smith (1976), Valentine LeGrice (1977),
Heather Pope (1977), Nicholas Mostyn (1980), Nicholas Carden (1981),
Catriona Murfitt (1981), Nigel Dyer (1982), Philip Moor (1982),
Charles Todd (1983), Christopher Wood (1986), Nicholas Cusworth (1986),
Katharine Davidson (1987), Richard Todd (1988), Rachel Platts (1989),
Gavin Smith (1981), Timothy Bishop (1991), Elisabeth Todd (1990),
Geoffrey Kingscote (1993), Louise Potter (1993), David Langwallner (1993).
Paul Focke QC is a director of the Bar Mutual Indemnity Fund. All members of
chambers belong to the Family Law Bar Association.

WORK UNDERTAKEN: All aspects of family and matrimonial law, including: divorce; ancillary relief and separation agreements; domicile; childwork encompassing custody, wardship, access and paternity cases and work under the Inheritance (Provision for Family and Dependants) Act.

CLIENTELE: Individuals and local authorities.

FOREIGN CONNECTIONS: Hong Kong, Australia (New South Wales), New Zealand and U.S.A. Jeremy Posnansky QC is admitted to the Bar of Antigua.

LANGUAGES SPOKEN: French and German.

1A MITRE COURT BUILDINGS (Mrs. K. Purie-Harwell)
1A Mitre Court Buildings, Temple, London, EC4Y 7BS **Tel:** (0171) 353 6365 **Fax:**
Sen. Clerk: Tenants: 4 General common law practice with a specialisation in crime.

2 MITRE COURT BUILDINGS (Michael FitzGerald QC)

2 MITRE COURT BUILDINGS, TEMPLE, LONDON, EC4Y 7BX
DX: 0032 Chancery Lane

TEL: (0171) 583 1380
FAX: (0171) 353 7772

HEAD OF CHAMBERS:
Michael FitzGerald QC

SEN. CLERK:
Robert Woods

TENANTS: 26

THE CHAMBERS: A long-established and well known set currently comprising 26 members of whom 12 are Q.Cs. All members specialise in Planning and Local Government.

MEMBERS:
Michael Fitzgerald QC (1961)(QC-1980), William Glover QC (1950)(QC-1969),
David Widdicombe QC (1950)(QC-1965), Lord Lord Silsoe QC (1955)(QC-1972),
Gerald Moriarty QC (1951)(QC-1974), Anthony Anderson QC (1964)(QC-1982),
John Taylor QC (1958)(QC-1983), George Bartlett QC (1966)(QC-1986),
Robert Gray QC (1969)(QC-1983), Matthew Horton QC (1969)(QC-1989),
Guy Roots QC (1969)(QC-1989), Susan Hamilton QC (1975)(QC-1993),
Charles Fay (1955), John Grove (1963), Alun Alesbury (1974),

Robert Fookes (1975), Nicholas Burton (1979), Neil King (1980),
Michael Humphries (1982), Richard Glover (1984), Mary Macpherson (1984),
Sebastian Head (1987), Michael Druce (1988), Murziline Parchment (1989),
Reuben Taylor (1990), Professor Victor Moore (1992).

WORK UNDERTAKEN: The main specialist area practised by all members comprise Planning and Local Government which includes town and country planning, environmental law, compulsory purchase and compensation, rating and council tax, utilities and infrastructure, local government, public and administrative, Parliamentary bills and Transport and Works Act. All members appear at public inquiries, the Lands Tribunal and the Courts

CLIENTELE: A wide range including companies, corporations, public and private utilities, local authorities, government departments and foreign governments, individuals and residents associations. Instructions are accepted under the Direct Access Scheme.

FOREIGN CONNECTIONS: Members have appeared or advised in relation to a number of jurisdictions including Hong Kong, Jersey and Bermuda.

RECRUITMENT & TRAINING: Applications for tenancy should be addressed to Michael FitzGerald QC. Applications for pupillage should be addressed to Sebastian Head. Chambers have two to three pupils at any one time and substantial awards are available for pupils; details will be provided on application. Mini-pupillage are also available.

135
Set No.

2 MITRE COURT BUILDINGS (Michael Pearson)

2 MITRE COURT BUILDINGS, (FIRST FLOOR), TEMPLE, LONDON, EC4Y 7BX
DX: 0023 London Chancery Lane

TEL: (0171) 353 1353
FAX: (0171) 353 8188

HEAD OF CHAMBERS:
Michael Pearson

SEN. CLERK:
John Markham

TENANTS: 16

THE CHAMBERS: The set is long-established and aims to offer an efficient, friendly and comprehensive service. All members practise from London on the South Eastern but several also have strong connections on both the Western and the Midland and Oxford circuits.

MEMBERS:
Michael Pearson (1952) BCL, MA (Oxon), Florence O'Donoghue (1959),
Peter Hunt (1964) MA (Cantab), FLBA, Michael Harris (1970) MA (Oxon),
John Parker (1975) BSc (Lond), Valerie Weaver (1979), Barry Forward (1981),
Andrew Dickens (1983), Roger Gray (1984), James Holmes-Milner (1989),
Delyth Evans (1991), Alison Throp (1992) BA Hons, Sarah Clover (1993) LLM BA Hons,
Adrian Maxwell (1993) BA Hons (Oxon).

DOOR TENANT:
David Wade (1959), David Langwallner (1993).

WORK UNDERTAKEN: Most members of Chambers practise in one or more of the following areas:- crime, family, landlord and tenant/ property, general common law and chancery.

In addition, some members undertake work in specific fields of practice e.g. administrative law, building, conveyancing, child abduction, defamation, ecclesiastical law, employment, licensing, personal injury, planning, professional negligence and wardship.

136 MITRE COURT CHAMBERS (John Burton)

Set No.

MITRE COURT CHAMBERS, TEMPLE, LONDON, EC4Y 7BP
DX: 449 Ch.Ln.

TEL: (0171) 353 9394
FAX: (0171) 353 1488

HEAD OF CHAMBERS:
John Burton

CLERKS:
Robert Ruegg & William Ingleton

TENANTS: 24

THE CHAMBERS: Established in 1983, chambers aims to provide efficient and business-like service to both lay and professional clients. Expertise is available in a wide range of areas. Chambers is fully computerised using WordPerfect software (other software may be available on request). Chambers offers guaranteed turnaround times for paperwork. Conferences can be arranged at short notice either in chambers, solicitors' offices or elsewhere. All fees are negotiable with the clerks. Members of chambers practise mainly in the South East, but are keen to expand an existing nationwide service. Chambers currently receives significant work from the Midlands, Merseyside and the North East. All members of chambers undertake Direct Professional Access from architects, civil engineers, surveyors, accountants and loss adjusters. Brochures available on request.

MEMBERS:
John M. Burton (1979), Peter Shier (1952), Bob Grewal (1960),
James Cartwright (1968), Graeme Ford (1972), Brian Wrobel (1973),
Gillian Frost (1979), Peter J. Hofford (1979), Julian Nutter (1979),
Bartholomew V. O'Toole (1980), Alexander Laban (1980), Roger Turner (1982),
Leslie Wise (1985), Pieter Briegel (1986), Anthony K. Montgomery (1987),
Ian C. Bridge (1988), Neil Mercer (1988), Diana Bretherick (1989),
Andrew Forsyth (1989), Christopher Blake (1990), Julia Goring (1991),
Carl Hackman (1990), Philip Brown (1991), Mukhtiar S. Otwal (1991).

AREAS OF WORK:

Criminal: A large percentage of chambers work is defending and prosecuting in the Crown Courts. There are specialists in sexual offences, serious fraud, car crime, drugs, and violent crime of all types. Instructions are received from the DSS and various local authorities in matters such as planning enforcement, trade descriptions and food safety. We are a preferred set for the Crown Prosecution Service.

Family Law: Chambers offers expertise in matrimonial finance and in child law.

Personal Injuries: Chambers offers expertise in all areas of personal injury work especially industrial disease and accidents at work. Medical and pharmaceutical negligence is also covered. In larger cases or multiple party actions with voluminous papers chambers is able to put together a team charging hourly rates for specific tasks.

Commercial Law: Chambers has insolvency specialists and members advise on company, banking, insurance, partnership and business law generally including business leases.

Judicial Review: Several individuals in chambers are experienced in Crown Office work in the areas of housing, immigration and licensing in particular.
Individuals in chambers are able to advise on immigration, housing, employment, construction, licensing, ecclesiastical law, planning, local government and civil actions against the police.

LANGUAGES: French, German, Hindi, Punjabi, Spanish and Urdu.

RECRUITMENT AND TRAINING: Tenancy applications to Head of Chambers. Pupillage applications to James Cartwright.

137 MITRE HOUSE CHAMBERS (Francis P. Gilbert) Mitre

Set No.

House, 44 Fleet St, London, EC4Y 1BN **Tel:** (0171) 583 8233 **Fax:** (0171) 583 2692 **DX:** 0005 **Practice Manager:** Sarah Harrison **Tenants:** 22 Undertake a wide range of work including crime, family, licensing, landlord and tenant, social security, industrial tribunals, mental health work and immigration, personal injury.

138
et No.

NEW COURT (John Fitzgerald)

NEW COURT, TEMPLE, LONDON, EC4Y 9BE
DX: 420

TEL: (0171) 797 8999
FAX: (0171) 583 5885

HEAD OF CHAMBERS:
John Fitzgerald

SEN. CLERK:
Simon Coomber

TENANTS: 9

THE CHAMBERS: Each tenant specialises in intellectual property law.

MEMBERS:
J.V. Fitzgerald (1971), Nicolas Bragge (1972), Alison Firth (1980),
Richard A. Hodgson (1980), Alistair Kelman (1977), John Lambert (1977) MA,
Matthew Kime (1988), Richard Cole (1988), Ashley Roughton (1992).

WORK UNDERTAKEN: All areas of intellectual property law, including copyright and design right, passing off, confidential information, trademarks and service marks, registered designs, patents (UK and European), computer and telecommunications law and practice, entertainment and media law, plant breeders' rights, and semiconductor chip protection. As a result of their work in the field of intellectual property, several tenants also have experience with commercial contracts and licensing, music and character merchandising, malicious/injurious falsehood and trade libel, engineering and technical litigation, and UK and EC law governing restraint of trade and competition.

ADDITIONAL EXPERIENCE: Members of chambers have a broad range of scientific qualifications, both academic and vocational. John Fitzgerald has wide experience of highly technical commercial contract matters. Nicolas Bragge is a deputy High Court Master (Chancery Division). Several members' practices have an international dimension, Richard Hodgson is fluent in French and Alistair Kelman advises the European Commission on computer law. Alison Firth is joint author of the *Introduction to Intellectual Property Law* (3nd ed. 1995), and is the author of the recently published *Trade Marks the New Law*. Members of chambers also carry out prosecution/ defence work in relation to intellectual property matters.

RECRUITMENT & TRAINING: Applications for pupillages and tenancies should be sent either to Mr. John Fitzgerald or to Mr. Nicholas Bragge. Discretionary awards are available to pupils. Most successful applicants have a science degree, or some equivalent practical experience.

139
et No.

NEW COURT CHAMBERS (George Carman QC)

NEW COURT, TEMPLE, LONDON, EC4Y 9BE
DX: 363

TEL: (0171) 583 6166
FAX: (0171) 583 2827

HEAD OF CHAMBERS:
George Carman QC

SEN. CLERK:
Bill Conner

TENANTS: 26

MEMBERS:
George Carman QC (1953)(QC-1971), Frederic Reynold QC (1960)(QC-1982),
Peter Latham (1965), Charles Welchman (1966), Peter Susman (1966),
Malcolm Knott (1968), Anthony Clover (1971), Duncan Pratt (1971),
Michael Brompton (1973), Charles Howard (1975), Paul Stewart (1975),
Richard Clayton (1977), Gail Carrodus (1978), John Wardell (1979),
Michael McParland (1983), Hugh Tomlinson (1983), Terence Bergin (1985),
Jonathan Seitler (1985), David Walbank (1987), Andrew Davies (1988),
Georgina Middleton (1989), Daniel Gatty (1990), Tejina Mangat (1990),
Joel Donovan (1991), Suzanne McKie (1991), Tom Grant (1993).

THE CHAMBERS: New Court Chambers is a commercial and professional negligence set best known for commercial litigation, medical negligence and property litigation.

TECHNOLOGY: Chambers is equipped with the latest direct information exchange systems, so that re-typing is not necessary, and quality of documents, flexibility in drafting, and a fast response to instructions is ensured.

ADDITIONAL EXPERTISE: A number of members are admitted to practise or have litigation experience in other jurisdictions in the Far East, the United States of America and the Caribbean.

LANGUAGES: Some members are fluent in French and German.

RECRUITMENT: Chambers offers two pupillages of 12 months' duration with an award of £12,000 each.

140 1 NEW SQUARE (Eben Hamilton QC)
Set No.

1 NEW SQUARE, LINCOLN'S INN, LONDON, WC2A 3SA
DX: 295

TEL: (0171) 405 0884
FAX: (0171) 831 6109

THE CHAMBERS: A general chancery and commercial set, in spacious chambers with modern facilities.

MEMBERS:
Eben W. Hamilton QC (1962)(QC-1981), Rodney Stewart Smith (1964), Michael K.I. Kennedy (1967), John B.W. McDonnell QC (1968)(QC-1984), James Munby QC (1971)(QC-1988), Richard Granville Fawls (1973), Edward Alexander Bannister QC (1973)(QC-1991), Christopher Semken (1977), Michael Roberts (1978), Robin Hollington (1979), Clive Hugh Jones (1981), Philip Hoser (1982), Kathryn Lampard (1984), David G P Turner (1984), Jonathan Russen (1986), Sandra Corbett (1988), Colette Wilkins (1989), John Samuel Eidinow (1992).

Allan Heyman QC who is a member of the Institute of Arbitrators is attached to chambers and is available for arbitrations. Robin Hollington is the author of *Minority Shareholders*.

HEAD OF CHAMBERS:
Eben Hamilton QC

SEN. CLERK:
Warren Lee

TENANTS: 19

WORK UNDERTAKEN:

Main Areas of Work: General chancery and commercial litigation, including companies, insolvency, banking, corporate finance and financial services, property, trusts, landlord and tenant, charities and professional negligence.

Additional Areas of Work: Most other areas are handled, including arbitration, securities, partnership, family law, intellectual property, entertainment, fraud, housing, judicial review, pensions, private international law, sale of goods, sports law and wills.

CLIENTELE: Individuals, public and private companies. Most members accept Direct Professional Access; apply to the clerk for further details.

FOREIGN CONNECTIONS: Some members appear before the courts in Hong Kong, Singapore, Malaysia, Bermuda, the Cayman Islands and Gibraltar.

LANGUAGES SPOKEN: French, German.

RECRUITMENT & TRAINING: Pupillage applications to Kathryn Lampard. Awards are available.

141 3 NEW SQUARE (Sir William Goodhart QC)
Set No.

3 NEW SQUARE, LINCOLN'S INN, LONDON, WC2A 3RS
DX: 384 (Ch.Ln.)

TEL: (0171) 405 5577 (5 lines)
FAX: (0171) 404 5032

THE CHAMBERS: 3 New Square specialises in chancery, commercial and corporate litigation and advocacy. Advisory and drafting work are also regularly undertaken.

MEMBERS:
Sir William Goodhart QC (1957)(QC-1979), Peter Cowell (1964), Hedley Marten (1966), David Rowell (1972), David Parry (1972), Bernard Weatherill (1974), Andrew Walker (1975), Josephine Hayes (1980), Roger Mullis (1987), Adam Deacock (1991), Justin Holmes (1993).

HEAD OF CHAMBERS:
Sir William Goodhart QC

SEN. CLERK:
Richard Bayliss

TENANTS: 11

WORK UNDERTAKEN:

Chancery: Chambers have expertise in the whole range of chancery work, with a particularly strong reputation in real property, trusts and estates, pension schemes, tax planning, equitable remedies and contested probate.

Commercial: Chambers specialise particularly in: banking securities; commercial real property and conveyancing; commercial contracts; credit transactions; fraud, forgery and misrepresentation; insolvency; intellectual property; landlord and tenant; partnerships; sale, liens and title retention.

Company: Members litigate in the Companies Court, and advise on company law in all its aspects.

Professional negligence work (other than medical negligence) is regularly undertaken.

Members are especially pleased to accept work in new and developing areas of law related to their existing areas of practice. Direct Professional Access is welcomed.

Sir William Goodhart QC is the British member of the International Commission of Jurists. He is co-author (with Professor Gareth Jones QC) of *Specific Performance*, and of sections on *Corporations* and *Specific Performance* in *Halsbury's Laws*. A number of members contribute to legal periodicals.

ADDITIONAL SPECIALISATIONS: Court of Protection work; financial services; judicial review; Lands Tribunal work; revenue law.

Documents can be supplied on disk in WordPerfect 5.1, or by LIX. A brochure is available on request.

42
et No.

THREE NEW SQUARE (David E.M. Young QC)

3 NEW SQUARE, LINCOLN'S INN, LONDON, WC2A 3RS   TEL: (0171) 405 1111
DX: 454 (FORMERLY 6 PUMP COURT)   FAX: (0171) 405 7800

THE CHAMBERS: A specialist intellectual property set. The Chambers' clientele are mostly companies – Direct Professional Access is accepted.

Office Equipment: The chambers use IBM compatible equipment, and discs will be provided on request using Wordstar, WordPerfect and Word for Windows.

HEAD OF CHAMBERS:
David E.M. Young QC

SEN. CLERK:
Ian Bowie

TENANTS: 10

MEMBERS:
David Young QC (1966)(QC-1980), Antony Watson QC (1968)(QC-1986), Simon Thorley QC (1972)(QC-1989), Richard Miller QC (1976)(QC-1995), Guy Burkill (1981), Andrew Waugh (1982), Denise McFarland (1987), Colin Birss (1990), Justin Turner (1992), Douglas Campbell (1993).
Members belong to the Patent and Chancery Bars Associations. David Young is the author of *Passing Off*, Chairman of the Plant Seeds Varieties Tribunal, a recorder on the South Eastern Circuit and Deputy Judge of the Patent County Court. Both he and Antony Watson are Deputy High Court Judges in the Chancery Division. In addition, for many years, members have edited *Terrell on the Law of Patents*. Simon Thorley is Chairman of Patent Bar Association.

WORK UNDERTAKEN:
Main Areas of Law: *Intellectual Property:* Covering a wide range of subject areas, particularly science, technology, biotechnology, entertainment and media, including patents (UK and European), copyright, designs (registered and unregistered), service marks, plantbreeders rights, trade marks (registered and unregistered), passing off, trade libel and malicious falsehood, confidential information, franchising and licensing (including licences of right and product licensing) and information technology. Members also handle related aspects of EC law and general litigation with a significant technical content.

Additional Areas of Work: Arbitration and professional negligence.

CLIENTELE: Mainly companies.

FOREIGN CONNECTIONS: Chambers' QCs appear in Singapore and Hong Kong.

FORMER MEMBERS: Sir Douglas Falconer, Lord Justice Aldous.

LANGUAGES SPOKEN: French, German and Japanese.

THREE NEW SQUARE
INTELLECTUAL PROPERTY

RECRUITMENT & TRAINING: Tenancy and pupillage applications should be sent to Andrew Waugh before the closing date of 31st October. Awards of £7,500 per six months are available (currently under review). Mini-pupillages are offered throughout the year. A science degree is required.

---

143 4 NEW SQUARE (Nicholas Stewart QC)
Set No.

4 NEW SQUARE, LINCOLN'S INN, LONDON, WC2A 3RJ
DX: 209

TEL: (0171) 404 3800
FAX: (0171) 404 3900

THE CHAMBERS: Mr Stewart practises on his own in a well-equipped and staffed set of chambers above Wildy's Arch, with an extensive library and a separate large conference room. An information folder is available on request.

Mr Stewart and his practice managers are very willing to discuss any matter and to help with recommendations of other barristers (QCs or juniors). He is happy to act with or without a junior, according to the case, or to be instructed with a qualified solicitor advocate as his junior.

QUALIFICATIONS: Called 1971; QC 1987; Deputy High Court Judge, Chancery Division, since 1991; B.A. (Oxon); Certified Diploma in Accounting and Finance.

AREAS OF WORK UNDERTAKEN:

(1) **Civil Litigation** – Most types of civil litigation, with a particular emphasis on Chancery and commercial matters. Mr Stewart's work includes: contractual disputes; nuisance and negligence; company and partnership litigation; disputes involving sporting bodies; trust, pension and investors' litigation; professional negligence (especially lawyers, accountants and surveyors); conflict of laws; judicial review; constructive trusts and tracing; specific performance, injunctions and rescission; costs; housing and landlord and tenant; insurance; restraint of trade; wrongful dismissal and restrictive covenants; environmental litigation; disciplinary tribunals.

Outside those areas specifically mentioned, he is able to act in most areas of civil litigation except personal injuries, family law and specialised planning or tax cases.

(2) **Criminal cases** – In those areas related to his civil practice, particularly financial frauds, other white-collar crimes and environmental cases.

(3) **Arbitration, mediation and ADR** – There are ample facilities for Mr Stewart to provide these services at his chambers. Please enquire for more details.

FEES: Mr Stewart's guideline charging rate for a whole day in court or working in chambers is £1500. The aim is to provide the most suitable method of charging for each specific case and clients are invited to discuss fees either with Mr Stewart directly or with his practice managers.

HEAD OF CHAMBERS:
Nicholas Stewart QC

JOINT PRACTICE MANAGERS:
Jillian Adye (mornings);
Sandy Kellow (afternoons)

THE CHAMBERS OF NICHOLAS STEWART QC

---

144 5 NEW SQUARE (James Sunnucks)
Set No.

5 NEW SQUARE, LINCOLN'S INN, LONDON, WC2A 3RJ
DX: 272 London

TEL: (0171) 404 0404
FAX: (0171) 831 6016

THE CHAMBERS: A general chancery chambers but with a particular specialisation in intellectual property and entertainment law. Work is also undertaken in the Queen's Bench Division and the County Courts, as well as before other Tribunals.

MEMBERS:
James Sunnucks (1950), Ernest Scamell (1949), Sir Patrick Sinclair (1961),
John Ross-Martyn (1969)*, Jonathan Rayner James QC (1971)(QC-1988),
Kevin Garnett QC (1975)(QC-1991), Alexander Stewart (1975),
Edward Bragiel (1977), Paul Dickens (1978), Simon Barker (1979),
Mark Cunningham (1980), Amanda Michaels (1981), Julia Clark (1984),
Nicholas Caddick (1986), Gregory Banner (1989), Gwilym Harbottle (1987),
Simon Sugar (1990), Theresa Villiers (1992).
* *Recorder*

WORK UNDERTAKEN: Work in the traditional chancery fields covers both litigation and advice. A large volume of corporate and personal insolvency work is undertaken.

HEAD OF CHAMBERS:
James Sunnucks

SEN. CLERK:
Ian Duggan

TENANTS: 18

In the intellectual property and entertainment law field, chambers have particular experience in music industry, film and broadcasting work. Apart from High Court litigation, clients are represented before the Copyright Tribunal.

45
No.
7 NEW SQUARE (Nicholas Storey) 7 New Square, Lincoln's Inn, London, WC2A 3QS **Tel:** (0171) 430 1660 **Fax:** (0171) 430 1531 **DX:** 106 (Ch.Ln.) **Sen. Clerk:** Alistair Adams **Tenants:** 9 A set handling chancery, pensions, trusts family and employment matters.

46
No.
8 NEW SQUARE (Michael Fysh QC SC)

8 NEW SQUARE, LINCOLN'S INN, LONDON, WC2A 3QP

TEL: (0171) 405 4321
FAX: (0171) 405 9955

THE CHAMBERS: The chambers specialise in intellectual property law of all kinds, and are the largest set in the country specialising in this area. Many members of chambers are authors of, or contributors to, the leading books and encyclopaedias on intellectual property law. All are members of the Patent and Chancery Bar Associations.

MEMBERS:
Michael Fysh QC SC (1965)(QC-1989), Alun Kynric Lewis QC (1954)(QC-1978), Peter Prescott QC (1970)(QC-1990), John Baldwin QC (1977)(QC-1991), Mark Platts-Mills QC (1974)(QC-1995), George Hamer (1974), Mary Vitoria (1975), David Kitchin QC (1977)(QC-1994), Martin Howe (1978), Alexander Drysdale Wilson (1981), Fiona Clark (1982), James Mellor (1986), Daniel Alexander (1988), Robert Onslow (1991), Michael Tappin (1991), Richard Meade (1991), Nicholas Shea (1993) BA (Oxon), Adrian Speck (1993) BA (Cantab).

FORMER MEMBERS: Mr Justice Jacob, Mr Justice Laddie

WORK UNDERTAKEN: Intellectual property, including patents, copyright, passing off, trade and service marks, designs and registered designs, counterfeiting, data protection, franchising, hallmarks, plant breeders' rights, publishing, telecommunications, trade libel, trade descriptions, trade secrets and confidential information. Members also specialise in European law, competition and restrictive trade practices, entertainment and media law, advertising law, computer law, licensing and administrative law, (principally where these are ancillary to intellectual property cases). Commercial, environmental and other work with a significant scientific or technical content is also handled.

CLIENTELE: Companies and corporations, from hi-tech to fashion houses, and some individuals.

FOREIGN CONNECTIONS: Several members of chambers conduct cases in the Far East, Australia, India and Ireland.

LANGUAGES SPOKEN: French, German, Spanish and Welsh.

RECRUITMENT & TRAINING: Up to three pupillages are offered each year, usually for six months, extendable to twelve. Pupils with scientific or technical backgrounds are strongly encouraged, although others will be considered in exceptional circumstances. An award of £7,500 is offered for the first six months, with an income guarantee of the same amount for the second six. Applications for pupillage for 1995/ 1996 and requests for further information should be sent to Mr. David Kitchin. Applications should include a CV, the names and addresses of two referees, and an outline of why the prospective pupil is interested in practising intellectual property law. A pupillage guide is available on request. Students are welcome to apply for mini-pupillages and should send their applications to Mr. John F. Call, Senior Clerk.

HEAD OF CHAMBERS:
Michael Fysh QC SC
SEN. CLERK:
John F. Call
DEPUTY SENIOR CLERK: Tony Liddon
ASSISTANT CLERK: Susan Harding
TENANTS: 18

147

11 NEW SQUARE (Peter Crampin QC & Miles Shillingford)

11 NEW SQUARE, LINCOLN'S INN, LONDON, WC2A 3QB
DX: 319

TEL: (0171) 831 0081
FAX: (0171) 405 0798/2560

MEMBERS:
Peter Crampin QC (1976)(QC-1993), Miles Shillingford (1964), Jock Craven (1961), Roger Horne (1967), Dirik Jackson (1969), Peter Castle (1970), Stephen Whitaker (1970), Stephen Lloyd (1971), Sonia Proudman QC (1972)(QC-1994), Jill Gibson (1972), Michael Jefferis (1976), Mark Studer (1976), Robert Pearce (1977), Andrew Francis (1977), Thomas Dumont (1979), Michael Furness (1982), Alistair Craig (1983), Gilead Cooper (1983), Ulick Staunton (1984), Piers Feltham (1985), Howard Smith (1986), Charles Holbech (1988), Mark Hubbard (1991), Marie-Claire Bleasdale (1993).

HEAD OF CHAMBERS:
Peter Crampin QC, Miles Shillingford

SEN. CLERK:
Michael Gibbs

ASST. SEN. CLERK: Gary Ventura

TENANTS: 24

WORK UNDERTAKEN: Chambers have a long established expertise in all aspects of chancery practice. In addition, members have considerable experience in commercial law and professional negligence. Both advisory work and contentious litigation is covered, some members having exclusively litigious practices. Individual members' specialisations include administration of estates, banking, breach of confidence, charities, company law, corporate and personal insolvency, Court of Protection, family provision, land law and conveyancing, landlord and tenant, mortgages, partnership, passing off, pensions, planning, private international law, restraint of trade, taxation, trusts and wills and probate.

DIRECT PROFESSIONAL ACCESS: Chambers accept instructions from members of the professional bodies recognised by the Bar Council: for inquiries, contact Michael Gibbs.

LANGUAGES SPOKEN: French, German, Dutch, Italian, Spanish.

RECRUITMENT & TRAINING: There are 2-4 pupils in Chambers at any one time. Pupillages are granted (initially) for 6 months. A pupillage fund is available out of which awards can be made at the discretion of Chambers. Applications should be addressed to Thomas Dumont.

148

11 NEW SQUARE (John Gardiner QC) 11 New Square, Lincoln's Inn, London, WC2A 3QB **Tel:** (0171) 242 4017 **Fax:** (0171) 831 2391 **DX:** 315 **Sen. Clerk:** Mr. J. Moore **Tenants:** 6 Specialise in revenue law. Specialise in the areas of taxation and commercial litigation, including arbitration.

149

12 NEW SQUARE (John Mowbray QC) 12 New Square, Lincoln's Inn, London, WC2A 3SW **Tel:** (0171) 405 3808 **Fax:** (0171) 831 7376 **DX:** 366 **Sen. Clerk:** Clive Petchey **Tenants:** 21 Chambers undertake a wide variety of chancery work, including litigation, landlord and tenant, and commercial work.

150

17 OLD BUILDINGS (Geoffrey Jaques)

17 OLD BUILDINGS, LINCOLN'S INN, LONDON, WC2A 3UP
DX: 300 LDE

TEL: (0171) 405 9653
FAX: (0171) 404 8089

MEMBERS:
Geoffrey Jaques (1963), John Child (1966), Robert Wakefield (1969), Gregory Hill (1972), Oliver Albery (1972), Andrew Lloyd-Davies (1973), Owen Rhys (1976), William Henderson (1978), Alexandra Mason (1981), Michael Michell (1984), Joanne Wicks (1990), Marian Conroy (1991), Samuel Laughton (1993).

HEAD OF CHAMBERS:
Geoffrey Jaques

SEN. CLERK:
John Lister

TENANTS: 13

WORK UNDERTAKEN:

General Description: Chambers provide a comprehensive service in all aspects of modern chancery work, with an emphasis on real property and trusts. Direct professional access work is accepted.

MAIN AREAS OF WORK:

Real Property: including restrictive covenants, mortgages, easements, contracts, conveyances and commons.

Landlord and Tenant: including business, residential and agricultural tenancies.

Trusts & Probate: including administration of estates, contentious probate, family provision and wills.

Tax Planning: including inheritance tax and capital gains tax.

Company Law: including companies, partnerships, joint ventures, insolvency, securities and receivership.

Other: Court of Protection matters, ecclesiastical law, professional negligence, private international law.

RECRUITMENT & TRAINING: Pupillage or tenancy applications to Joanne Wicks on application forms only. Up to four six-month pupillages are available each year, one bearing an award of £8,000.

19 OLD BUILDINGS (Alastair Wilson QC)

19 OLD BUILDINGS, LINCOLN'S INN, LONDON, WC2A 3UP
DX: 397 (Ch.Ln.)

TEL: (0171) 405 2001
FAX: (0171) 405 0001

THE CHAMBERS: Recently relocated from 3 Pump Court, this set – founded by Sir Duncan Kerly – has specialised for over a century in intellectual property law. Chambers also offer expertise in cases relating to computers and other technical subject matter, competition and media and entertainment. Publications written or contributed to by members of chambers include: *European Patent Office Reports, The Future of Legal Protection for Industrial Design, The CIPA Black Book, Halsbury's Laws of England* and *Vaughan's Law of the EC* (on EC Competition Law), *Melville's Forms and Agreements on Intellectual Property and International Licensing.* Direct Professional Access work is undertaken. A chambers brochure is available on request.

HEAD OF CHAMBERS:
Alastair Wilson QC

SEN. CLERK:
Mrs. Barbara Harris

TENANTS: 9

MEMBERS:

Alastair Wilson QC (1968)(QC-1987) MA (Cantab), Brian Reid (1971) MA (Cantab), LLM (Lond), Cedric Puckrin (1990) BA, LLB (Cape Town), Graham Shipley (1973) MA (Cantab), Dip Comp Sci (Cantab), Michael Hicks (1976) BA (Cantab), Christine Fellner (1981) MA (Oxon), BCL, Jonathan D.C. Turner (1982) MA (Cantab), Lic Sp Dr Eur (Brussels), Peter McLean Colley (1989) BSc (Lond), PhD (Lond), LLB (Lond), Rory Sullivan (1992) MA (Oxon).

WORK UNDERTAKEN:

Intellectual Property: Patents, copyright, designs, trade and service marks, passing off, plant varieties, confidential information (including ex-employee cases).

Computers and other technical subject-matter: Advocacy requiring technical or scientific ability.

Competition Law: UK and EC monopolies and restrictive practices law, in particular relating to r and d, licensing, distribution and franchising.

Media and Entertainment: Public performance, film, recording and performers' rights; merchandising; broadcasting, cable and satellite distribution.

Additional areas: Pharmaceutical registration, pollution, rights of common, lotteries and gaming.

LANGUAGES: French, German, Spanish, Italian, Dutch.

152
Set No

22 OLD BUILDINGS (John Samuels QC)

22 OLD BUILDINGS, LINCOLN'S INN, LONDON, WC2A 3UJ
DX: 201

TEL: (0171) 831 0222
FAX: (0171) 831 2239

THE CHAMBERS: A broadly-based common law set within which more senior members tend to concentrate on specific, complementary, areas. Chambers are computerised and draft documents can be provided in a variety of media.

MEMBERS:

John Samuels QC (1964)(QC-1981), Patrick Hamlin (1970),
Ian Peddie QC (1971)(QC-1992), Mark Batchelor (1971), Bruce Coleman (1972),
Margaret Bickford-Smith (1973), Roger McCarthy (1975), John Stevenson (1975),
Peter Horrocks (1977), Caroline Budden (1977), Anne Ralphs (1977),
Judith Rowe (1979), Stephen Cobb (1985), Jonathan Bennett (1985),
Caroline Streets (1986), John Stocker (1985), Benedict Patten (1986),
Juliet Bernard (1987), Tina Cook (1988), Frank Feehan (1988),
Andrew Bagchi (1989), Michael Liebrecht (1989), Joanna Bond (1988),
Lee Arnot (1990), Mary Lazarus (1991), Emma Romer (1992), John Horan (1993),
Daniel Oudkerk (1992), John Cooper (1993), Philip Rogers (1994),
M. Bickford-Smith (1973).

WORK UNDERTAKEN:

General Description: General common law and commercial chambers. Chambers operate an informal 'department' system within particular areas of practice, to promote a progressive exchange of professional views and information. Whilst most of chambers' work is in London and the South East, members of chambers also practice regularly elsewhere, particularly in the Midlands, West Country and the North East.

Main Areas of Work: Professional negligence, personal injury, insurance, commercial and general chancery, matrimonial finance, child care, administrative law, local government, planning, landlord and tenant, employment, immigration and crime.

CLIENTELE: Private clients (personal and corporate), professional indemnity and other insurers, fire authorities, local authorities, and trade unions and staff federations.

LANGUAGES SPOKEN: French, German and Italian.

RECRUITMENT: Pupillage applications to John Samuels QC. Each year at least two awards are made; each is to be worth £12,000 for 1995/96. Mini-pupillages are welcomed.

HEAD OF CHAMBERS:
John Samuels QC

SEN. CLERK:
Alan Brewer

TENANTS: 30

22 Old Buildings
Lincoln's Inn

153
Set No

24 OLD BUILDINGS (C.A. Brodie QC)

24 OLD BUILDINGS, LINCOLN'S INN, LONDON, WC2A 3UJ
DX: 307 (Ch.Ln.)

TEL: (0171) 404 0946
FAX: (0171) 405 1360

THE CHAMBERS: A specialist chancery, company and commercial law set with an emphasis on litigation. Chambers comprises 5 silks and 17 juniors, including Standing Counsel to the DTI (insolvency) and Junior Counsel to the Crown (Chancery).

Members appear in all civil courts and tribunals both in the UK and overseas, including the Cayman Islands, the British Virgin Islands, Bermuda, Hong Kong, Singapore, and the Turks & Caicos. Chambers has connections in New York, Geneva, Rome & Milan. All members undertake Direct Professional Access instructions from members of recognised professional institutions, particularly accountants and surveyors.

MEMBERS:

Colin Brodie QC (1954)(QC-1980), Martin Mann QC (1968)(QC-1983),
Alan Steinfeld QC (1968)(QC-1987), Roger Kaye QC (1970)(QC-1989),
Lawrence Cohen QC (1974)(QC-1993), Thomas Baxendale (1962),
Michael King (1971), Paul Teverson (1976), John Davies (1977),
Richard Ritchie (1978), Francis Tregear (1980), Daniel Gerrans (1981),
Michael Gadd (1981), Elizabeth Weaver (1982), Stephen Moverley Smith (1985),
Helen Galley (1987), Adrian Francis (1988), Amanda Harington (1989),

HEAD OF CHAMBERS:
C.A. Brodie QC

SEN. CLERK:
Nicholas Luckman

DEPUTY: Jeremy Hopkins
LISTING: Simon Weatherley
FEES ADMINISTRATION: Tony Steeden

TENANTS: 22

Elspeth Talbot Rice (1990), Nicholas Cherryman (1991), Christopher Young (1988), Clare Stanley (1994).

WORK UNDERTAKEN: Principal areas of specialisation: –

Company law including mergers and acquisitions, reductions of capital, shareholders' rights, directors' duties and liability, directors' disqualification.

Commercial Law including commercial contracts, banking, mortgages, guarantees, securities and bills of exchange.

Insolvency personal and corporate, including liquidations, administration and receivership.

Land law including commercial property, conveyancing, easements, restrictive covenants and vendor and purchaser.

Landlord and tenant including business, residential and agricultural tenancies.

Partnership Law professional and trading partnerships.

Pension Law occupational pension schemes & trusts.

Professional Negligence including solicitors, accountants and surveyors.

Other specialities include: Civil fraud. Financial services law. Inheritance and familiy provision. Trust and settlements. Private international law. Consumer credit law and sale of goods. Passing off, restraint of trade and intellectual property. Clubs & friendly societies. Ecclesiastical Law.

ADMINISTRATION: Chambers has invested heavily in information technology to aid the efficient administration of its practice. The clerks and members of chambers are connected to a Novell PC network to ensure efficient communication and data storage within chambers. Chambers uses Wordperfect 5.1/6.0 word proccessing software and documents are regularly transferred to and from firms of solicitors using communications software such as LIX and Link.

RECRUITMENT & TRAINING: Much importance is placed on attracting high calibre pupils from whom tenants can be selected. Four funded pupillages are offered annually, each presently attracting awards of £8,500. Applications (by letter with CV) for the 1996/7 year should be made to Amanda Harington before 22 September 1995.

54
No.

24 OLD BUILDINGS (M.E.P. Jump) 24 Old Buildings (First Floor), Lincoln's Inn, London, WC2A 3UJ **Tel:** (0171) 242 2744 **Fax:** (0171) 831 8095 **DX:** 386 **Sen. Clerk:** Anthony Hall **Tenants:** 11 A specialist revenue law set, dealing with the whole range of tax matters with an emphasis on revenue litigation.

55
No.

9 OLD SQUARE (Robert Reid QC)

---

9 OLD SQUARE, LINCOLN'S INN, LONDON, WC2A 3SR
DX: 305

TEL: (0171) 405 4682
FAX: (0171) 831 7107

THE CHAMBERS: A well-established chancery set. The practice of chambers extends to all aspects of landlord and tenant and real property, company, partnership, insolvency, mortgages and professional negligence with a strong emphasis on litigation.

HEAD OF CHAMBERS:
Robert Reid QC

SEN. CLERK:
Martin Poulter

TENANTS: 18

MEMBERS:
Robert Reid QC (1965)(QC-1980), Michael Driscoll QC (1970)(QC-1992), Nicholas Patten QC (1974)(QC-1988), Judith Jackson QC (1975)(QC-1994), Simon Berry QC (1977)(QC-1990), David Hodge (1979), Daniel Hochberg (1982), John Dagnall (1983), John McGhee (1984), Timothy Harry (1983), Edwin Johnson (1987), Thomas Leech (1988), Katharine Holland (1989), Christopher Stoner (1991), Andrew P.D. Walker (1991), Simon Burrell (1988), Michael Pryor (1992), Alan Johns (1994).

WORK UNDERTAKEN:

Real Property: Including vendor and purchaser, mortgages, restrictive covenants, easements, conveyancing, possessory title, licences and estoppel interests, nuisance and other property related torts.

Professional Negligence: Including solicitors, surveyors, accountants and other finance and property related professional negligence, professional disciplinary proceedings and wasted costs orders.

Landlord and Tenant: Including rent reviews, dilapidations claims and other Official Referees Business, leasehold enfranchisement, business, residential and agricultural tenancies.

Commercial: Loans, guarantees, mortgages, partnerships, personal property, including retention of title, sale of goods and consumer credit, confidential information, passing off, covenants restricting trade or employment, fraud, misrepresentation, conspiracy and other economic torts, Mareva and Anton Piller Orders.

Insolvency: Personal and corporate insolvency, receivers and administrators.

Company: Including minority shareholder protection, shares sale disputes, directors' duties and directors' disqualification.

Trusts and Related Areas: Constructive trusts, tracing claims, settlements and wills, probate, administration of estates and family provision, charities, unincorporated associations and clubs.

INDIVIDUAL SPECIALISATIONS: Individual members have additional fields of specialisation which include building societies, computer law, judicial review, local government, the law of markets and fairs and shops, oil and mining law, parliamentary work, planning law, environmental law, sports law and trading standards.

CLIENT BASE: Chambers act for a broad range of commercial and private clients; legal aid work is undertaken. Most members accept Direct Professional Access work (contact clerks for details). Members are instructed by lawyers in the Far East, the Bahamas, Bermuda, the Cayman Islands, Jersey, and other jurisdictions.

LANGUAGES: French, German, Spanish.

INFORMATION TECHNOLOGY: Most IBM compatible word-processing software can be accommodated. Electronic transfer of documents is available (LIX). Dedicated electronic data links can be established with individual firms, on request. Contact clerks for details.

156 10 OLD SQUARE (Leolin Price QC)
Set No.

10 OLD SQUARE, LINCOLN'S INN, LONDON, WC2A 3SU
DX: 306

TEL: (0171) 405 0758
FAX: (0171) 831 8237

MEMBERS:
Leolin Price QC (1949)(QC-1968)*, Hubert Picarda QC (1962)(QC-1992),
Philip Rossdale (1948)°, David Ritchie (1970), Shân Warnock-Smith (1971),
James Arbuthnot (1975), David Schmitz (1976), Andrew De La Rosa (1981),
Araba Taylor (1985), Paul Stafford (1987), Eason Rajah (1989),
Jeremy Callman (1991), Jonathan Gavaghan (1992),.
At 18 St. John Street, Manchester.
James Bonney QC (1975)(QC-1995),Malcolm McEwan (1976),
David Partington (1987).
° Author of *Rossdale – Probate and the Adminstration of Estates: A Practical Guide.*
* Author of *Picarda – Law and Practice Relating to Charities* (2nd ed. 1995) and
Picarda – Law Relating to Receivers Managers and Adminstrators (2nd ed. 1990).

Door Tenants:
Ms Frances Burton (Senior Lecturer in Law, London Guildhall University)
Mr Jeffrey Price (Senior Lecturer in Taxation, Kings College, London)
Professor Jill Martin (Professor of English Law, Kings College, London)

WORK UNDERTAKEN:
General Description: Primarily chancery chambers dealing with a wide range of property, trust, tax and commercial work. In addition to litigation, the practices of members include a considerable amount of advisory and drafting work. Direct Professional Access work is welcomed.

HEAD OF CHAMBERS:
Leolin Price QC

SEN. CLERK:
Mr Keith Plowman

TENANTS: 16

10 OLD SQUARE

Emphasis: Trusts, charities, probate and administration of estates, receivers and insolvency, taxation, landlord and tenant, company law, property, building law and commercial litigation.

Additional Specialisations: Commercial and financial regulation; litigation in foreign courts, Privy Council Appeals and employment law.

LANGUAGES: French, Spanish, Malay, Italian.

57
◄ No.

11 OLD SQUARE (Timothy Lloyd QC)

---

11 OLD SQUARE, LINCOLN'S INN, LONDON, WC2A 3TS
DX: 1031 LIX: LON 042

TEL: (0171) 430 0341
FAX: (0171) 831 2469

MEMBERS:
Timothy Lloyd QC (1970)(QC-1986) A-G to the Duchy of Lancaster,
Carol Ellis CBE QC (1951)(QC-1980), Patrick Powell (1973), Gordon Nurse (1973),
Grant Crawford (1974), Jonathan Simpkiss (1975), Reziya Harrison (1975),
Malcolm Waters (1977), Stephen Acton (1977), Elizabeth Ovey (1978),
Keith Rowley (1979), Siân Thomas (1981), Richard Walford (1984),
Glenn Campbell (1985), Mark West (1987), Katherine McQuail (1989),
Nigel Burroughs (1991), Kathryn Purkis (1991), Peter Dodge (1992),
Benjamin Davey (1994).

HEAD OF CHAMBERS:
Timothy Lloyd QC

SEN. CLERK:
Keith Nagle

TENANTS: 20

WORK UNDERTAKEN:

General Description: The work undertaken by members of chambers is primarily in the chancery and commercial fields, and extends to a wide range of litigation, advisory and drafting work.

Property: Conveyancing, land law, landlord and tenant, (business, residential, leasehold enfranchisement and agricultural), mortgages and securities, rent reviews, nuisance and property-related torts.

Commercial: Commercial agreements, sale of goods, economic torts, guarantees, joint ventures, partnerships, restraint of trade and consumer credit.

Company: Minority shareholder protection and other intra-company disputes, directors' fiduciary duties, take-overs, mergers and acquisitions.

Insolvency: Corporate and individual insolvency, receiverships, liquidations, administrations and voluntary arrangements.

Professional Negligence: Claims involving solicitors, barristers, accountants, surveyors and others.

Chancery: Trusts, breach of trust, charities, clubs and friendly societies, Court of Protection, wills, probate, administration of estates and family provision.

Building Societies: Constitution and powers, relations with members and third parties, mergers, take-overs and conversion, standard documentation.

Finance: Banking (including security documentation) and financial services.

Additional areas: Confidential information, copyright and passing off, conflict of laws, judicial review, pensions.

CLIENTELE: Chambers operate the Direct Professional Access scheme. Instructions are also accepted from lawyers abroad, in particular the Far East, but also from jurisdictions in Europe and elsewhere.

LANGUAGES: French, German, Italian and Afrikaans.

WORD PROCESSING SYSTEM: Microsoft Word, IBM compatible, 3.5" disks. Please speak to the clerks if you wish to deliver or receive text on disk or by electronic communication.

---

11 OLD SQUARE (James Thrower)

158
Set No.

11 OLD SQUARE, LINCOLN'S INN, LONDON, WC2A 3TS
DX: 164

TEL: (0171) 242 5022
FAX: (0171) 404 0445

THE CHAMBERS: An established set of Chambers which has recently been refurbished in traditional style, with a broad practice covering Chancery, common law and criminal matters.

MEMBERS:
J. Simeon Thrower (1973), Christopher H. Cutting (1973), Francesca Quint (1970), K. Mydeen (1973), Gordon Apsion (1977), Malcolm D. Sinclair (1978), Nicholas Macleod-James (1986), Marc C. Maitland (1988), David W. Giles (1988), Jennifer Gray (1992), Gabriel Buttimore (1993), Sima Kothari (1993), Patrice Wellesley-Cole (1975).

WORK UNDERTAKEN: Banking, chancery, charities, company and commercial, construction, criminal, family, fraud – both civil and criminal, immigration, insolvency, landlord and tenant, licensing, personal injury, probate, product liability, professional negligence, property, sale of goods, trusts and wills.

CLIENTELE: Members of Chambers act for individuals, public and private companies, banks and financial institutions. Chambers operate the Direct Professional Access scheme and also Century Briefs.

FOREIGN LANGUAGES: German, French and Urdu.

RECRUITMENT & TRAINING: Applications for pupillage or tenancy should be addressed to Mr. David Giles.

HEAD OF CHAMBERS:
James Thrower

SEN. CLERK:
Christopher Watts

TENANTS: 13

159
Set No.

12 OLD SQUARE (Charlotte Boaitey) 12 Old Square, Lincoln's Inn, London, WC2A 3TX **Tel:** (0171) 404 0875 **Fax:** (0171) 404 8377 **Sen. Clerk:** Angela Greaves **Tenants:** 21   A common law set undertaking a range of work including Landlord & Tenant, Employment, Immigration, Family, Personal Injury and Crime (Prosecution & Defence).

---

13 OLD SQUARE (Mr. E.W.H. Christie)

160
Set No.

13 OLD SQUARE, LINCOLN'S INN, LONDON, WC2A 3UA
DX: 326

TEL: (0171) 404 4800
FAX: (0171) 405 4267

THE CHAMBERS: A long-established set and one of the larger chancery chambers, which aims to provide clients with specialist advice and representation across the wide range of matters encompassed by the description "chancery", in its modern sense.

Members of chambers specialise in various areas of practice, and this specialisation is strengthened by a comprehensive approach which recognises that legal problems are rarely confined to one particular area. Much of chambers' work involves litigation and arbitration, but members frequently appear in court cases or give advice in other parts of the United Kingdom and abroad. Members also appear before the new tribunals which regulate the provision of financial and insolvency services.

MEMBERS:
William Christie (1952), Terence Cullen QC (1961)(QC-1978), Michael Lyndon-Stanford QC (1962)(QC-1979), Christopher McCall QC (1966)(QC-1987), William Charles (1971), David Oliver QC (1972)(QC-1986), Hazel Williamson QC (1972)(QC-1988), Richard McCombe QC (1975)(QC-1989), Robert Powell-Jones (1978), Christopher Pymont (1979), Catherine Newman QC (1979)(QC-1995), Timothy Evans (1979), Anthony Trace (1981), Paul Girolami (1983), Matthew Collings (1985), John Nicholls (1986), Carolyn Walton (1980), Fernanda Pirie (1988),

HEAD OF CHAMBERS:
Mr. E.W.H. Christie

SEN. CLERK:
Mr. J.C. Moore

TENANTS: 23

Richard Morgan (1988), Nicholas Peacock (1989), Amanda Tipples (1991), Jacqueline Crawford (1993), Michael Gibbon (1993).

Academic Members: Chambers has five "door tenant" barristers, who concentrate on academic law or aspects of international law: Sir Robert Jennings QC (1943)(QC– 1969) (formerly the President of the International Court of Justice), Reginald Dias (1945), Kurt Lipstein (1950), John Hopkins (1963), Vijay Shankardass (1972).

Former Members: Previous members of chambers include Lord Oliver of Aylmerton, Sir Brian Dillon, Lord Nicholls of Birkenhead, Mr Justice Blackburne, and Mr Justice Rimer.

WORK UNDERTAKEN:

General Description: The chambers' chancery practice has evolved to include the business litigation previously considered the province of general commercial chambers. The fields of practice can be divided into four main areas, although these are not distinct categories.

Company Law: *Work includes:* shareholders' rights, breach of fiduciary duty, corporate insolvency, financial regulation, monopolies and mergers.

Property: *Work includes:* landlord and tenant, vendor and purchaser, conveyancing, mortgages and securities on land, easements and covenants, boundaries, trespass and nuisance.

Commercial Law: *Work includes:* commercial contracts, banking, guarantees and securities, insurance, consumer credit, restraint of trade, partnership, personal insolvency/ bankruptcy, professional negligence and pre-trial remedies. The chambers regularly deal with urgent cases and can offer both experience and immediate action.

Trusts and Related Areas: *Work includes:* wills and probate, administration of estates, family provision, charities, building and friendly societies, trusts, unincorporated associations and capital taxes.

Additional Areas of Work: In addition to the four main areas above, practitioners have experience in diverse specialist fields, including EC and international law, competition law, highways, markets and commons, fishing, inland navigation and the water industry, intellectual property, copyright, passing off, Roman Dutch law and the petroleum industry.

CLIENTELE: Many of chambers' clients come from the corporate business community, but individual clients are as welcome as the large organisations and legal aid matters are regularly undertaken.

FOREIGN CONNECTIONS: Members of chambers are members of the Isle of Man Bar, the Northern Ireland bar, the Falkland Islands Bar, and the Singapore, Malaysia, Hong Kong and Bermuda Bars. One member has a Licence Spéciale en Droit Européen (Brussels). The Queen's Counsel in particular often appear in courts in the Far East and provide advice for many overseas clients.

LANGUAGES: Working knowledge of French, German and Russian.

61
et No.

13 OLD SQUARE (Charles Sparrow QC) 13 Old Square, Lincoln's Inn, London, WC2A 3UA **Tel:** (0171) 242 6105 **Fax:** (0171) 405 4004 **DX:** 1025 **Sen. Clerk:** Terry Buck **Tenants:** 19 A general chancery set with an emphasis on business and commercial work.

162
Set No.
OLD SQUARE CHAMBERS(Hon. John Melville Williams QC)

1 VERULAM BUILDINGS, GRAY'S INN, LONDON, WC1R 5LQ
DX: 1046

TEL: (0171) 831 0801
FAX: (0171) 405 1387

Old Square Chambers, Hanover House 47 Corn Street, Bristol BS1 1HT
DX: 78229 Bristol

Tel: (0117) 9277111
Fax: (0117) 9273478

MEMBERS:
The Hon. John Melville Williams QC (1955)(QC-1977), John Hendy QC (1972)(QC-1987), John Hand QC (1972)(QC-1988), Lord Lord Wedderburn QC (1953)(QC-1990), Jeremy McMullen QC (1971)(QC-1994), Charles Lewis (1963), Professor Bob Hepple (1966), Stephen Zollner (1969), Christopher Carling (1969), William Birtles (1970), Diana Brahams (1972), Christopher Makey (1975), Nigel Cooksley (1975), Charles Pugh (1975), Matthias Kelly (1979), Toby Kempster (1980), Paul Rose (1981), Barry Cotter (1985), Jennifer Lemkey (1987), Louise Chudleigh (1987), Timothy Portwood (1988), Ijeoma Omambala (1988), Jennifer Eady (1989), Philip Meade (1989), Thomas Linden (1989), Tess Gill (1990), Sarah Moor (1991), Ian Scott (1991), Oliver Segal (1992), Helen Gower (1992), Professor Roy Lewis (1992).

WORK UNDERTAKEN: Employment law, environmental law, personal injury and medical negligence, business and mercantile law.

LANGUAGES SPOKEN: French, German, Spanish, Italian, Dutch, Afrikaans, Serbo-Croat, Ibo.

FOREIGN CONNECTIONS: There are door tenants practising at the Hong Kong, Bermuda and Jersey Bars.

HEAD OF CHAMBERS:
Hon. John Melville Williams QC

SEN. CLERK:
John Taylor

TENANTS: 31

OLD SQUARE CHAMBERS

163
Set No.
1 PAPER BUILDINGS (Robert Nelson QC)

1 PAPER BUILDINGS, TEMPLE, LONDON, EC4Y 7EP
DX: 80

TEL: (0171) 583 7355
FAX: (0171) 353 2144

THE CHAMBERS: A leading common and commercial law set, undertaking a wide range of general and specialist work and committed to providing the same high quality of service, whether to a major international corporation or a private individual on legal aid. In addition to legal analysis, advice and specialist knowledge, chambers believe advocacy skills to be of paramount importance; members appear regularly before courts and tribunals at every level. A brochure is available on request.

HEAD OF CHAMBERS:
Robert Nelson QC

SEN. CLERK:
Julian Campbell

TENANTS: 28

MEMBERS:
Robert Nelson QC (1965)(QC-1985), Anthony Machin QC (1951)(QC-1973), John Slater QC (1969)(QC-1987), Michael Spencer QC (1970)(QC-1989), Andrew Bartlett QC (1974)(QC-1993), Simon Brown QC (1976)(QC-1995), Dr Michael Powers QC (1979)(QC-1995), Martyn Berkin (1966), William Stevenson (1968), Richard Hone (1970), Colin Nixon (1973), John Powles (1975), Nicholas Davies (1975), Jonathan Waite (1978), Gordon Catford (1980), Julian Field (1980), Jane Davies (1981), Steven Coles (1983), James Medd (1985), Shaun Ferris (1985), David Platt (1987), William Vandyck (1988), Marion Egan (1988), Erica Power (1990), Benedict Newman (1991), Toby Gee (1992), Alexander Antelme (1993), Dr Margaret Branthwaite (1993).

All members belong to the London Common Law and Commercial Bar Association and a majority are members of the Official Referees Bar Association; Andrew Bartlett is a fellow of the Chartered Institute of Arbitrators. Several members of chambers act as arbitrators and appear before Professional Conduct Tribunals.

WORK UNDERTAKEN:
Main Areas of Work: *Common Law:* Professional negligence (all forms); misconduct and disciplinary tribunals; product liability, including pharmaceuticals; property damage disputes, including fire and flooding claims; personal injury, including industrial disease.

Construction: Building, civil engineering and computer contract cases and arbitrations.
Insurance: Insurance and reinsurance.
Commercial: Company/ commercial work; general commercial disputes; contract claims; agency; sale and carriage of goods; consumer law; private international law.
Public Law: Public inquiries; local government; judicial review.

Additional Areas of Work: Education, employment law, civil rights, entertainment, rating, family property, fraud, landlord and tenant, licensing, livestock and mental health.

CLIENTELE: Insurance companies, corporations, private individuals, manufacturers, landowners, local authorities and their insurers, and a variety of professionals, including accountants, architects, civil engineers, doctors, insurance brokers, solicitors, valuers and surveyors. Some members of chambers accept Direct Professional Access.

FOREIGN CONNECTIONS: Martyn Berkin has experience of American law, and of working with American firms. He is a member of the Dallas Bar Association.

LANGUAGES SPOKEN: French, German and Italian.

RECRUITMENT & TRAINING: Pupillage applications should be sent to Erica Power by 16th September 1994. Chambers take on three pupils per year, offering £7,500 each for their first six months, and a guaranteed income of £7,500 for their second six. A minimum 2:1 degree is required, though not necessarily in law. Mini-pupillages are available.

164
Set No.

1 PAPER BUILDINGS (Roger Titheridge QC)

1 PAPER BUILDINGS (1ST FLOOR), TEMPLE, LONDON, EC4Y 7EP
DX: 332

TEL: (0171) 353 3728
FAX: (0171) 353 2911

THE CHAMBERS: A long-established chambers with 26 practitioners in the fields of general common law and crime.

MEMBERS:

Roger N. Titheridge QC (1954)(QC-1975), David Elfer QC (1964)(QC-1981), Michael J. Hubbard QC (1967)(QC-1989),
Christopher H. de V. Leigh QC (1967)(QC-1989), James E. Bullen (1966),
Roger D. Harrison (1970), Bernard C. Buckley (1970), John M.H. Farmer (1970),
Alastair R. Malcolm (1971), Anthony M. Davies (1971), J. Charles Kellett (1971),
Simon K. Privett (1976), Timothy Swan (1983), Stephen N. Spence (1983),
Karim S. Khalil (1984), Maria J. Lamb (1984), Christopher Morgan (1987),
Mark A. Norman (1989), Rupert D.C.J. Burke-Gaffney (1988),
Matthew Jewell (1989), Charles A.M. Thomas (1990), Anne Johnston (1990),
Stephen M. Ferguson (1991), Nicole D. Curtis (1992), Penelope Small (1992),
Peter Glenser (1992), Christopher Morgan (1987).

HEAD OF CHAMBERS:
Roger Titheridge QC

SEN. CLERK:
Nigel Witchell

TENANTS: 26

WORK UNDERTAKEN:

Crime: All classes of criminal work and courts martial including specialist advocacy and advice in commercial fraud. Chambers act in both private and legally-aided cases and for prosecution and defence; members regularly carry out prosecutions for the Inland Revenue, Customs and Excise and the Department of Social Security.

Contract: Including commercial; sale of goods and consumer law; carriage of goods; and building work.

Tort: Personal injuries including industrial, sporting and fatal accidents and disaster litigation; medical, solicitors', accountants' and other professional negligence and disciplinary tribunals; inquests and inquiries; pharmaceutical litigation; passing off; and actions against the police.

Family: Matrimonial finance; inheritance disputes; domestic violence; and child law (including wardship).

Additional Specialisations: Administrative law; aviation; defamation; employment and industrial relations; landlord and tenant; licensing; and planning.

LANGUAGES: French, Italian and Spanish.

RECRUITMENT AND TRAINING: Pupillage applications to the Chairman of the Pupillage Committee. Chambers offer up to two funded pupillages per year. Further details on application.

---

2 PAPER BUILDINGS (Robin Griffiths)

2 PAPER BUILDINGS, TEMPLE, LONDON, EC4Y 7ET
DX: 210 (Ch.Ln.)

TEL: (0171) 936 2613
FAX: (0171) 353 9439

THE CHAMBERS: General common law work including civil, family and criminal. The criminal and family areas are extensive and well-established.

MEMBERS:
Robin Griffiths (1970), Richard Hayden (1964), Michael Carroll (1973),
Gerard Boyd (1967), Mrs Peta Gee (1973), Mark Wyeth (1983), Andrew Hill (1982),
Eric Ogden (1983), Wendy Fisher-Gordon (1983), Quentin Purdy (1983),
Susan Castle (1986), Najma Khatoon (1986), James Dennison (1986),
Sandra Briggs Watson (1985), Mark Stern (1988), Paul Orton (1988),
Jamal Sapsard (1987), Joseph Stone (1989), Brendan Farren (1988),
Kevin Dent (1991), S. Tolkien (1994).
One member of chambers is a recorder and another is a deputy stipendiary magistrate. One is an Associate of the Chartered Institute of Arbitrators.

WORK UNDERTAKEN: *Work includes:* arbitration; company/ commercial law, particularly sale of goods, tort and contract work; consumer law; criminal law; employment; family and matrimonial, including care proceedings; fraud; inquests; insurance; judicial review; landlord and tenant; licensing; local government; mental health; personal injury; police disciplinary cases; probate; professional negligence; and sports law.

CLIENTELE: Chambers act for a wide range of clients.

FOREIGN LANGUAGES: Urdu, Hindi.

RECRUITMENT & TRAINING: Chambers will always consider applications from experienced and well qualified barristers who wish to develop and specialise their practices. Tenancy applications should be sent to Robin Griffiths. Three pupils will be taken on in 1995 – applications should be sent to Najma Khatoon by October 1994. Mini-pupillages are offered. Financial assistance is available for pupils.

HEAD OF CHAMBERS:
Robin Griffiths

CLERKS:
Michael Sweeney and Marc Newson

TENANTS: 21

2 PAPER BUILDINGS (Steven Hadley)

2 PAPER BUILDINGS, TEMPLE, LONDON, EC4Y 7ET
DX: 286 LDE

TEL: (0171) 353 0933
FAX: (0171) 353 0937

THE CHAMBERS: Established Common Law set. Largely Criminal (both Prosecution and Defence). Family, Employment Law, Actions against the Police and other areas of Civil Law undertaken.

MEMBERS:
Steven Hadley (1987), George Adonis (1973), Feliks Kwiatkowski (1977),
Irshad Sheikh (1983), Christopher Baylis (1986), Linda Adams (1987),
Catryn McCann (1988), Gillian Etherton (1988), Sarah Lindop (1989),
Sarah Le Foe (1989), Tarik Hayatally (1990), Karen Rhodes (1990),
Christopher Morrison (1990), Virginia Cornwall (1990), Andrew Thompson (1991),
Amanda Tedore (1992), Matthew McNiff (1992), Timothy Clark (1993),
Dominic D'Souza (1993).

DOOR TENANT: Simon Sharples (1986).

HEAD OF CHAMBERS:
Steven Hadley

SEN. CLERK:
Ms Lynn Pilkington
SECOND CLERK: Gemma Snow

TENANTS: 20

2 PAPER BUILDINGS (Desmond de Silva QC)

FIRST AND SECOND FLOORS, 2 PAPER BUILDINGS, LONDON, EC4Y 7ET
DX: LDE 494   Out of Hours Tel: 0860 416061

TEL: (0171) 936 2611 10 lines
FAX: (0171) 583 3423   2 lines

MEMBERS:
Desmond de Silva QC (1964)(QC-1984), Lord Richard QC (1955)(QC-1971),
Harendra de Silva QC (1970)(QC-1995), Barry Payton (1951),
Vasant Kothari (1960), Gerald Bowden (1963), Panos C. Zorbas (1964),
Peter J. Martin (1969), Raymond Lewis (1971), Robin Pearse Wheatley (1971),
Lady Ponsonby (1971), Peter A. Corrigan (1972), John H. Bates (1973),
Christopher Strachan (1975), Notu Hoon (1975), Roderick Johnson (1975),
Paul G. O'Donovan (1975), Christopher Sutton-Mattocks (1975),
Jeremy Hayes (1977), Patrick Cahill (1979), Colin Campbell (1979),
John Causer (1979), Kim Hollis (1979), Michel G.A. Massih (1979),
Francis Jones (1980), Julia D. Postill (1982), Janina Pasiuk (1983),
David J. Brock (1984), Simon K. Ward (1984), Aruna Chandran (1985),
Lee Karu (1985), John Femi-Ola (1985), Steven Berrick (1986), Adrian Jack (1986),
Gerard McCoy (1986), Sharon Baxter (1987), Brian P. O'Neill (1987),
Sandra Folkes (1989), Marios P. Lambis (1989), Nicholina Ezechie (1990),
Delyth A. James (1990), Charles Benson (1990), Zöe Martin (1990),
Morag Duff (1991), Catherine M. Hill (1991), Fiona Henderson (1993),
Paul Mylvaganam (1993).

HEAD OF CHAMBERS:
Desmond de Silva QC

SEN. CLERK:
Robin Driscoll

1ST JUNIOR: Stephen Ball
2ND JUNIOR: John Gillespie

TENANTS: 47

WORK UNDERTAKEN: Chambers is primarily a criminal set, providing specialist defence counsel in commercial fraud cases, major drugs cases - including D.T.O.A. sexual offence cases and throughout the entire ambit of criminal law.

The majority of our members practice exclusively in crime and we are able to provide individual barristers to meet your every need.

Our out of hours number enables chambers to offer a service which covers 'over night' Magistrate Court hearings including Saturdays and Bank Holidays.

In addition we undertake general common law, family work and have a number of specialists in planning, environmental and immigration law. A brochure is available on request.

3 PAPER BUILDINGS (Isaac Jacob)

3 PAPER BUILDINGS, TEMPLE, LONDON, EC4Y 7EU
DX: 0071 (LDE)

TEL: (0171) 797 7000
FAX: (0171) 797 7100

THE CHAMBERS: A modern, well-equipped and expanding set with specialists in a broad range of business and commercial activities.

MEMBERS:
Isaac E. Jacob (1963), John Tackaberry QC (1967)(QC-1982),
Gerald Owen QC (1949)(QC-1969), Fenton Bresler (1951), Susan Solomon (1967),
Christopher Aylwin (1970), Robert Kirk (1972), Richard Jones (1972),
Dennis Sharpe (1976), Ajmalul Hossain (1976), Jonathan Tecks (1978),
Peter McMaster (1981), Edward Denehan (1981), David Marshall (1981),
Matthew Duckworth (1982), Martin Young (1984), Sheila Foley (1988),
Julie Browne (1989), Geoffrey Killen (1990), Angus Piper (1991),
Anthony Bingham (1992), Andrew Bruce (1992).

HEAD OF CHAMBERS:
Isaac E. Jacob

SEN. CLERK:
Stephen Evers

TENANTS: 22

WORK UNDERTAKEN: Administrative law, banking and bills of exchange, contracts of carriage, company and corporate law, computer law and data protection, construction and engineering contracts, employment, financial services, guarantee and indemnity, injunctions and pre-emptive remedies, insolvency, intellectual property, landlord and tenant, matrimonial finance and property and children, partnership, personal injury, planning and local government, professional negligence, real property, sale of goods.

CLIENTELE: In addition to English solicitors (in private practice and employed), clients include law firms in the USA and Europe, and professionals entitled to direct access.

RECRUITMENT & TRAINING: There are normally 4 pupillage vacancies (each of 6 months) per year. Further information is contained in the Statement of Pupillage Policy, which is available on request.

---

169 3 PAPER BUILDINGS (Michael Parroy QC)
Set No.

3 PAPER BUILDINGS, TEMPLE, LONDON, EC4Y 7EU
DX: 1024

TEL: (0171) 583 8055
FAX: (0171) 353 6271

THE CHAMBERS: A long established set providing a specialist advocacy and advisory service in London, Bournemouth, Oxford, Winchester and on the Western Circuit. Chambers are equipped with spacious conference rooms and computing and word processing facilities and provide a thorough, comprehensive and friendly service.

MEMBERS:

Michael Parroy QC (1969)(QC-1991), David M. Harris QC (1969)(QC-1989), R.A. Fordham QC (1967)(QC-1993), Peter Hughes QC (1971)(QC-1993), Stewart Jones QC (1972)(QC-1994), Harold Hebron (1960), Susan Trevethan (1967), John Haynes (1968), David Swinstead (1970), Derwin Hope (1970), Michael Norman (1971), Anthony Ward (1971), Leo Curran (1972), Peter Jennings (1972), Ben Stephenson (1973), Linda Litchfield (1974), David Bartlett (1975), Garth Richardson (1975), Richard Tyson (1975), Peter Henry (1977), Nigel Mitchell (1978), Nigel Seed (1978), Peter Kent (1978), Ian Partridge (1979), Robert Grey (1979), Nicholas Leviseur (1979), Timothy Coombes (1980), Paul Cairnes (1980), Ian Edge (1981), Martin Strutt (1981), Nigel Lickley (1983), Mark Lomas (1983), Irvine Maccabe (1983), Kate Branigan (1984), Sarah O'Hara (1984), David Sanderson (1985), Russell Bailey (1985), Christopher Parker (1986), Elisabeth Hudson (1987), Paul Letman (1987), Helen James (1988) (Door Tenant), Nicholas Rowland (1988), Patricia Kelly (1988), Paul Hester (1989), Sally Ball (1989), Guy Opperman (1989), Timothy Bradbury (1989), Jean Henderson (1990), Amanda Buckley-Clarke (1991), Iain Ross (1991), David Steenson (1991), Christian Sweeney (1992), Marie Kelly (1992), Caspar Glyn (1992), Krystyna Kirkpatrick (1992), Robert Weir (1992).

WORK UNDERTAKEN: General common law work and in particular:

Contract/ Commercial: including construction, employment, insurance and sale of goods.

Personal Injury: acting for individuals as well as trade union and insurance company clients.

Professional Negligence: covering all areas of chambers' specialisations.

Crime: including commercial fraud and all manner of crime on the Western Circuit.

Property: including landlord and tenant, housing and other real property and boundary disputes.

Chancery: including company and insolvency.

Family: including financial provision, wardship and Inheritance Act work.

EC: in particular competition and public procurement law.

In addition individual members of chambers specialise in planning, financial services and ecclesiastical work.

ANNEXE CHAMBERS: Chambers have annexes in Bournemouth, Winchester and Oxford.

RECRUITMENT & TRAINING: Four fully-funded 12 month pupillages each year. Applications to David Sanderson enclosing CV and SAE.

HEAD OF CHAMBERS:
Michael Parroy QC

CHIEF CLERK:
J. Charles Charlick

SENIOR CLERK: Stephen Clark
JUNIOR CLERKS: Alan Odiam, Russell Porter

FEES/ADMIN: Paul Queenan

TENANTS: 56

THE CHAMBERS OF MICHAEL PARROY Q.C.

---

170 3 PAPER BUILDINGS (Samuel Parrish)
Set No.

3 Paper Buildings, Temple, London, EC4Y 7EU **Tel:** (0171) 353 6208 **Fax:** (0171) 353 5435 **DX:** 337 **Sen. Clerk:** Angela May **Tenants:** 21 An established general common law set containing niche practitioners in a broad spectrum of areas. DPA available.

4 PAPER BUILDINGS (Harvey McGregor QC)

4 PAPER BUILDINGS (GROUND FLOOR), TEMPLE, LONDON, EC4Y 7EX
DX: 1036

TEL: (0171) 353 3366
FAX: (0171) 353 5778

THE CHAMBERS: This is an established set with members specialising in a number of different areas of commercial and common law. Further details are set out in the chambers brochure. Most members have their own computers; chambers are considered to be in the forefront of information technology and written work can be provided on disk in most word-processing formats or by direct electronic link.

HEAD OF CHAMBERS:
Harvey McGregor QC

SEN. CLERK:
Stephen Smith

TENANTS: 29

MEMBERS:
Harvey McGregor QC (1955)(QC-1978), James Wadsworth QC (1963)(QC-1981),
Harold Burnett QC (1962)(QC-1982), R.G. Marshall-Andrews QC (1967)(QC-1987),
Douglas Hogg QC (1968)(QC-1990), Jean Ritchie QC (1970)(QC-1992),
Nicholas Davidson QC (1974)(QC-1993), Christina Gorna (1960),
Michael Keane (1963), Roderick Doggett (1969), Anthony De Freitas (1971),
L.J. West-Knights (1977), Michael Pooles (1978), Jane Mishcon (1979),
Martin Spencer (1979), Eleanor Sharpston (1980), Derek Holwill (1982),
Patrick Lawrence (1985), Richard Ough (1985), Matthew Jackson (1986),
Julian Picton (1988), Clare Shine (1988), Francis Bacon (1988),
William Flenley (1988), Clare Price (1988), Alison Gulliver (1989),
Mark Simpson (1992), Graham Reid (1993), Simon Wilton (1993).

WORK UNDERTAKEN:
Main Areas of Work: All aspects of commercial law, contracts, personal injury litigation (for plaintiffs and insurers), professional negligence, medical negligence, family law, matrimonial finance, commercial fraud and business crime. Members have wide experience of work involving very urgent interlocutory relief.
Additional Areas: Agricultural law, landlord and tenant, EC law, Official Referees' business and employment law.
LANGUAGES: French, German, Danish, Italian, Russian, Spanish, Portuguese and Dutch.
RECRUITMENT & TRAINING: Chambers offer two pupillages supported by substantial awards dependant upon merit. Applications should be made through the COMPAS scheme.

4 PAPER BUILDINGS (Lionel Swift QC)

4 PAPER BUILDINGS, TEMPLE, LONDON, EC4Y 7EX
DX: 1035

TEL: (0171) 583 0816
FAX: (0171) 353 4979

MEMBERS:
Lionel Swift QC (1959)(QC-1975), Gordon Murdoch QC (1970)(QC-1995),
Anna Pauffley QC (1979)(QC-1995), Harry Turcan (1965), Roger Smith (1968),
Donald Cryan (1970), Amanda Barrington-Smyth (1972), Jonathan Cohen (1974),
Ian Ridd (1975), Robin Barda (1975), Michael Sternberg (1975),
Peter Jackson (1978), Christopher Coney (1979), Marcus Scott-Manderson (1980),
Charles Joseph (1980), Michael Stern (1983), David Reade (1983),
Elizabeth Coleman (1985), Catherine Wood (1985), Sam Neaman (1988),
Barbara Mills (1990), Christopher Cope (1990), Gavin Mansfield (1992),
Justin Ageros (1993).

HEAD OF CHAMBERS:
Lionel Swift QC

SENIOR CLERKS:
Dennis Davies, Michael Reeves

TENANTS: 24

WORK UNDERTAKEN: An established set with members specialising in family law (children and matrimonial finance), commercial law, personal injury, professional negligence, landlord and tenant, construction, employment and crime.

173
Set No.

5 PAPER BUILDINGS [Inc. European Law Chambers]   (Antonio Bueno QC)

5 PAPER BUILDINGS (GROUND FLOOR), TEMPLE, LONDON, EC4Y 7HB
DX: 415 LIX: LON 135

TEL: (0171) 583 9275/4555
FAX: (0171) 583 1926/583 2031

THE CHAMBERS: A largely common law set, but of sufficient size to offer specialists in a number of fields. Members of chambers produce *European Brief*, a quarterly bulletin analysing recent developments in European law and practice. Past and present members have edited the last five editions of *Byles on Bills of Exchange* and other works in the field of banking.

HEAD OF CHAMBERS:
Antonio Bueno QC

SEN. CLERK:
Alan Stammers

TENANTS: 21

MEMBERS:
Antonio Bueno QC (1964)(QC-1989), Rt. Hon. Sir Ian Percival QC (1948)(QC-1963), Anthony McClellan (1958) CBE, Angus Nicol (1963), Steven Walsh (1965), Robert Denman (1970), Graham Platford (1970), Nicholas Wood (1970), Donald Broatch (1971), Robert Percival (1971), Richard King (1978), Adrian Iles (1980), Paul Infield (1980), Richard Hedley (1983), Ann Brownlow (1984), Simon Devonshire (1988), Jonathan Rich (1989), Satinder Gill (1991), Paul Stallebrass (1991), Richard Evans (1993), Nicola Rushton (1993).

WORK DESCRIPTION:

Commercial Law: Including banking, negotiable instruments, securities, financial services, consumer credit, international trade, sale of goods, restraint of trade, companies and partnerships.

General Common Law: Including product liability, personal injury, professional negligence, employment, adminstrative law, family, immigration and criminal law (in particular criminal fraud).

European Law: Including advocacy before the European Commissions and Courts.

International Law: Including jurisdiction and conflicts of laws, foreign constitutional law and treaties, shipping and marine pollution.

General Chancery Law: Including real property law and town and country planning.

RECRUITMENT: Pupillage and tenancy applications to Richard Hedley on Chambers' application form. Awards are available: details on application.

174
Set No.

5 PAPER BUILDINGS (Brian Higgs QC) 5 Paper Buildings, Temple, London, EC4Y 7HB **Tel:** (0171) 353 5638 **Fax:** (0171) 353 6166 **DX:** 367 **Sen. Clerk:** Russell Ayles **Tenants:** 25 Primarily a common law set which deals mainly with criminal, matrimonial and personal injury matters.

175
Set No.

5 PAPER BUILDINGS (John Mathew QC)

5 PAPER BUILDINGS, TEMPLE, LONDON, EC4Y 7HB
DX: 365

TEL: (0171) 583 6117
FAX: (0171) 353 0075

MEMBERS:
John Mathew QC (1949)(QC-1977), Michael Corkery QC (1949)(QC-1981), Timothy Cassel QC (1965)(QC-1988), David Stokes QC (1968)(QC-1989), Godfrey Carey QC (1969)(QC-1991), Stanley Hughes (1971), Oliver Sells QC (1972)(QC-1995), Graham Parkins QC (1972)(QC-1990), Jonathan Caplan QC (1973)(QC-1991), Kuldip Singh QC (1975)(QC-1993), Edward Jenkins (1977), Graham Trembath (1979), Simon Mehigan (1980), Charles Judge (1981), Maurice Aston (1982), Miranda Moore (1983), Amanda Pinto (1983), Simon Spence (1985), Miles Bennett (1986), David Groome (1987), Robert O'Sullivan (1988), Julian Christopher (1988), Martin Evans (1989), Anuja Dhir (1989), Lynn Griffin (1991), Justin Cole (1991), Nicholas Griffin (1992).

HEAD OF CHAMBERS:
John Mathew QC

SEN. CLERK:
Stuart Bryant

TENANTS: 27

DOOR TENANTS:
Charles Barton QC (1969)(QC-1989), James Tabor (1974), Jonathan Haworth (1971) and Gareth Hawkesworth (1972).

PUBLICATIONS: Mehigan and Griffiths: *Restraint of Trade and Business Secrets: Law and Practice* (Longman: Third Edition 1995), *Patents and Licensing Acts* (Simon Mehigan).

WORK UNDERTAKEN: This chambers, consisting of 9 silks and 18 juniors, primarily specialises in criminal work with a strong bias towards commercial fraud. Members of chambers appeared in the Guinness, Blue Arrow and Nissan tax trials. Additionally, a significant number of members of chambers specialise in the following areas of civil law: restraint of trade, breach of confidence, defamation, media law, passing off, copyright, EC and UK competition law, adminstrative law, licensing and civil fraud claims. Members appear in courts and tribunals throughout the UK and at the European Court of Justice. Silks also advise and appear as advocates on matters throughout the rest of the world and in particular in Hong Kong. A chambers' brochure is available on request.

FOREIGN CONNECTIONS: Associated chambers in Brussels and Hong Kong.

LANGUAGES SPOKEN: French, German and Spanish.

RECRUITMENT & TRAINING: There are six pupillages available annually, each of six months, commencing in April and October each year. Substantial fee income is available. A good degree is essential, and preference is given to those who have completed or arranged an initial six month pupillage in commercial or general civil chambers. Applications to be made to 'Pupillage Selection Committee' with full, typed CV and two references. Tenants are selected from successful pupils.

No. 76 **PEPY'S CHAMBERS (Terence de Lury)** 17 Fleet Street, London, EC4Y 1AA **Tel:** (0181) 294 1158 **Fax:** (0171) 294 1084 **DX:** 463 Ch.Ln. **Administrator:** Wanda Bogucka **Tenants:** 20 A group of barristers who each work from home sharing the use of conference and administration facilities at 17 Fleet Street.

No. 77 **PERIVALE CHAMBERS (Saleem Ahmed)** 15 Culwyn Avenue, Perivale, Ealing, London, UB6 8JX **Tel:** 0181 998 1935 **Fax:** 0181 991 1823 **Sen. Clerk:** Laila Ahmed **Tenants:** 2 Civil, criminal, common law, immigration and Islamic law.

No. 78 # 1 PLOWDEN BUILDINGS(Bruce McIntyre and William Lowe)

1 PLOWDEN BUILDINGS, TEMPLE, LONDON, EC4Y 9BU	TEL: (0171) 583 0808
DX: 0020 (Ch.Ln.)	FAX: (0171) 583 5106

THE CHAMBERS: A general common law set practising in London and on the North East Circuit. Half the members of chambers are resident on the North East Circuit. The chambers were established in 1980.

HEAD OF CHAMBERS:
Bruce McIntyre, William Lowe

SEN. CLERK:
Paul Hurst

TENANTS: 26

MEMBERS:
Bruce McIntyre (1969), Stephen Duffield (1969), Charlotte Buckhaven (1969), William Lowe (1972), Elizabeth Hindmarsh (1974), Michael Heywood (1975), David Trotter (1975), Richard Craven (1976), Ian West (1985), Jonathan Holmes (1985), Catherine Foster (1986), Jane Probyn (1988), Simon Dyer (1987), David de Jehan (1988), Camilla Quigley (1988), David Brook (1988), Peter Morton (1988) LLB, LLM, Joy Brereton (1990), Alexander Foster (1990), Graeme Gaston (1991), Cyrus Larizadeh (1992), Peter Freeman (1992), Claire Lindsay (1991), Marcia Hyde (1992), S arah Barlow (1993), Susuan Gore (1993).

WORK UNDERTAKEN: General common law work, dealing with civil and criminal cases, including building and engineering disputes, chancery and commercial work, defamation, employment law, family law, insurance, landlord and tenant, partnership, personal injury litigation, professional negligence and sale of goods.

NATURE OF CLIENTELE: Lay clients include trade unions, insurance companies, landlords and tenants, employers and employees, and husbands and wives. On the criminal side, they include the Customs and Excise and Crown Prosecution Service and defendants.

LANGUAGES SPOKEN: French, German and Italian.

RECRUITMENT & TRAINING: Financial assistance is available for those in pupillage, with needs and merit being the main criteria for awards. Reasonable earnings can be expected during the second six months of pupillage.

179
Set No.

6 PUMP COURT (David E.M. Young QC) 6 Pump Court, Temple, London, EC4Y 7AR **Tel:** 0171 405 1111 **Fax:** 0171 405 7800 **DX:** 454 **Sen. Clerk:** Ian Bowie **Tenants:** 10 See under Three New Square.

180
Set No.

PUMP COURT CHAMBERS (Guy Boney QC)

3 PUMP COURT, TEMPLE, LONDON, EC4Y 7AJ
DX: 362

TEL: (0171) 353 0711
FAX: (0171) 353 3319

31 Southgate Street, Winchester SO23 9EE
DX: 2514

Tel: (01962) 868161
Fax: (01962) 867645

THE CHAMBERS: An established set undertaking a wide variety of work, with individual members having particular specialisations. Direct professional access work is accepted.

MEMBERS:

Guy Boney QC (1968)(QC-1990), John Spokes QC (1955)(QC-1973), Nigel Pascoe QC (1966)(QC-1988), Christopher Clark QC (1969)(QC-1989), Henry Blacksell QC (1972)(QC-1994), John Aspinall QC (1971)(QC-1995), John Ungley (1965), Geoffrey Still (1966), Stewart Patterson (1967), Adam Pearson (1969), Frank Moat (1970), Giles Harrap (1971), Keith Cutler (1972), Frank Abbott (1972), Michael Montgomery (1972), Paul Garlick (1974), John Ker-Reid (1974), Philip Gillibrand (1975), Andrew Barnett (1977), Jane Miller (1979), Miranda Allardice (1982), Damien Lochrane (1983), Mark Johnstone (1984), Susan Hunter (1985), Oba Nsugbe (1985), Matthew Scott (1985), Desmond Bloom-Davies (1986), Mark Hill (1987), Anne Waddington (1988), Hugh Travers (1988), Edward Boydell (1989), Leslie Samuels (1989), Anthony Akiwumi (1989), Justin Gau (1989), Richard Price (1990), Sean Brunton (1990), Penelope Howe (1991), Geoffrey Kelly (1992), Patricia Poyer-Sleeman (1992).

Twelve members of chambers are recorders and two are assistant recorders. In addition, John Spokes QC is Chairman of the Data Protection Tribunal. Paul Garlick is Standing Counsel to HM Customs and Excise (Western Circuit). Michael Montgomery is Standing Counsel to the D.T.I. (SE Circuit).

WORK UNDERTAKEN:

Main Areas of Work: Family and Matrimonial; Employment; Inheritance and Property Law; Personal Injury. All aspects of Criminal Law including Customs & Excise; Serious Fraud; Drugs; Sexual Offences; extradition proceedings and Criminal Appeals.

Specialisations include: Professional and Medical Negligence; Contract; Consumer Law; Ecclesiastical Law, Inheritance Act.

Additional Areas of Work: Agricultural; Aviation; Boundaries, Rights of way; I.T.; Courts Martial; Coroner's Court; Defamation; EC and Environment Law; Judicial Review; Landlord and Tenant; Motor racing litigation; Police and general Disciplinary Tribunals; Road Traffic; Yachting.

INTERNATIONAL CONNECTIONS: Oba Nsugbe is a barrister and solicitor of the Supreme Court of Nigeria and advises on all aspects of Nigerian law. He has direct access to established chambers in Lagos. Dr. Gerhard Dannemann is a member of the German Bar and is a door-tenant of chambers.

LANGUAGES: French, German.

HEAD OF CHAMBERS:
Guy Boney QC

SEN. CLERK:
David Barber

TENANTS: 45

ASSOCIATED CHAMBERS: Chambers are also at Pump Court Chambers, 31 Southgate Street, in Winchester.

RECRUITMENT & TRAINING: Tenancy and pupillage applications should be sent to Damien Lochrane. Chambers have six to eight pupils at any one time and offer generous awards and travel allowance; second six month pupils are generally busy. Applications should be marked "Pupillage" and enclose SAE.

81
t No.

1 PUMP COURT (Robert Latham) 1 Pump Court, Temple, London, EC4Y 7AB **Tel:** (0171) 583 2012 **Fax:** (0171) 353 4944 **DX:** 109 **Sen. Clerk:** Ian Burrow **Tenants:** 37 A general common law set specialising in criminal, family and housing law. Also handle administrative law and civil liberties work.

82
t No.

2 PUMP COURT (Philip Singer QC) 2 Pump Court, Temple, London, EC4Y 7AH **Tel:** (0171) 353 5597 **Fax:** (0171) 583 2122 **DX:** 290 (Ch.Ln.) **Sen. Clerk:** John Arter **Tenants:** 32 A long-established common law set, offering advocates and draftsmen of great experience in a wide variety of fields.

83
t No.

4 PUMP COURT (Bruce Mauleverer QC)

---

4 PUMP COURT, TEMPLE, LONDON, EC4Y 7AN
DX: 303

TEL: (0171) 353 2656
FAX: (0171) 583 2036

MEMBERS:
P. Bruce Mauleverer QC (1969)(QC-1985), John Beveridge QC (1963)(QC-1979), Anthony Temple QC (1968)(QC-1986), David Friedman QC (1968)(QC-1990), David Blunt QC (1967)(QC-1992), Christopher Moger QC (1972)(QC-1992), Jeremy Storey QC (1974)(QC-1994), Jonathan Marks QC (1975)(QC-1995), Michael Douglas (1974), Laurence Marsh (1975), Allen Dyer (1976), Jeremy Nicholson (1977), Jonathan Acton Davis (1977), John Rowland (1979), Oliver Ticciati (1979), Nigel Tozzi (1980), Andrew Fletcher (1980), Lindsay Boswell (1982), Peter Hamilton (1968), Alexander Charlton (1983), David Sears (1984), Adrian Hughes (1984), James Cross (1985), Duncan McCall (1988), Aidan Christie (1988), Andrew Neish (1988), Kirsten Houghton (1989), Dominic McCahill (1991), Phyllida Cheyne (1992), Simon Henderson (1993), Michael Davie (1993).

HEAD OF CHAMBERS:
Bruce Mauleverer QC

SEN. CLERK:
Carolyn McCombe

TENANTS: 31

WORK UNDERTAKEN:
Main Areas of Work: Members specialise in all aspects of commercial law including: banking, financial services and Stock Exchange work; commercial arbitration, including international arbitration; consumer credit; insurance and reinsurance; international trade and transport, including carriage and sale of goods. Chambers also handle a variety of common law matters, including: construction; EC; employment law; gaming and licensing; personal injury; professional negligence and disciplinary tribunals; property, including landlord and tenant, tribunals and inquiries.
Additional Areas: Agency; matrimonial finance; conflict of laws; entertainment; and shipping.

RECRUITMENT & TRAINING: Chambers offer up to four pupillages a year, including a twelve-month scholarship for suitable applicants. Awards are available for all pupils, and student visits are encouraged. Further details can be obtained from chambers' pupillage guide.

84
t No.

5 PUMP COURT (Rex Bryan) 5 Pump Court, Temple, London, EC4Y 7AP **Tel:** (0171) 353 2532 **Fax:** (0171) 353 5321 **DX:** 497 **Sen. Clerk:** Robin Butchard **Tenants:** 29 Civil, family and criminal work, including building, professional negligence, landlord and tenant, personal injury and employment.

185
Set No.

6 PUMP COURT (Kieran Coonan QC)

6 PUMP COURT, GROUND AND LOWER GROUND, LONDON, EC4Y 7AR
DX: 409

TEL: (0171) 583 6013
FAX: (0171) 353 0464

THE CHAMBERS: 6 Pump Court provides a broad common law service for London and provincial solicitors. Specialist teams cover the areas of work undertaken.

MEMBERS:
Kieran Coonan QC (1971)(QC-1990), Michael Curwen (1966), Jon Williams (1970),
David Morris (1976), Richard Craven (1976), Jeremy Morgan (1989),
Siobhan Goodrich (1980), Richard Power (1983), Alan Jenkins (1984),
Dr Simon Taylor (1984), Andrew Hockton (1984), Susan Burden (1985),
Lucy Dennis (1988), Christina Lambert (1988), Andrew Post (1988),
John Gordon (1989), Andrew Kennedy (1989), Rosamund Oddie (1990),
Róisín Lacey (1991), Annalissa Garrett (1991), Alexander Hutton (1992),
Nicholas Peacock (1992), Katharine Gollop (1993), John Davies (1955).

HEAD OF CHAMBERS:
Kieran Coonan QC

SEN. CLERK:
Adrian Barrow

TENANTS: 24

WORK UNDERTAKEN: Medical and Health Service (medical negligence, group actions, coroners' inquests, inquiries – e.g. Jasmine Beckford, Tyra Henry, Cleveland, Ashworth Special Hospital – disciplinary and professional tribunals, health authorities and trusts, mental health), professional negligence, personal injury, commercial and consumer, family, landlord and tenant, employment, crime and the law of costs.

RECRUITMENT & TRAINING: Tenancy applications to the Head of Chambers. Pupillage applications to Alan Jenkins. Details of scholarship awards on application.

186
Set No.

6 PUMP COURT (Michael Gale QC)

6 PUMP COURT, TEMPLE, LONDON, EC4Y 7AR
DX: 293

TEL: (0171) 797 8400
FAX: (0171) 797 8401

Additional premises at 6 & 8 Mill Street, Maidstone, Kent ME15 6XH.

MEMBERS:
Michael Gale QC (1957)(QC-1979), Stephen Hockman QC (1970)(QC-1990),
Heather Hallett QC (1972)(QC-1989), Elisabeth Brann (1970),
Andrew Goymer (1970), Martin Joy (1971), Adèle Williams (1972),
Michael Harington (1974), Christopher Kinch (1976), Louis French (1979),
Richard Barraclough (1980), Simon Russell Flint (1980), Usha Teji (1981),
Carol O'Leary (1982), Nicholas Baldock (1983), Mark Bailey (1984),
Caroline Topping (1984), David Walden-Smith (1985), Peter Gower (1985),
Peter Harrison (1987), Peter Forbes (1990), Oliver Saxby (1992),
Patrick Chamberlayne (1992), Judith Butler (1993), Paul Mee (1992).
Consultant: Anthony Kinch

HEAD OF CHAMBERS:
Michael Gale QC

CLERKS:
John Rugg, Richard Constable

TENANTS: 25

WORK UNDERTAKEN: The work of chambers includes a wide range of common law work in London and on the South Eastern Circuit. The set has specialists in planning, local government and administrative law, criminal law and family law. Other areas include judicial review, landlord and tenant, licensing, personal injury, professional negligence and sale of goods. Chambers accept direct access from the approved professions.

LANGUAGES SPOKEN: French, German, Italian and Russian.

RECRUITMENT & TRAINING: Chambers offers up to four pupillages each year, including funded pupillages in excess of Bar Council guidelines. Applications should be forwarded to Mr Peter Forbes, with detailed CV and references.

187
Set No.

PUMP COURT TAX CHAMBERS (Andrew Thornhill QC)
16 Bedford Row, London, WC1R 4EB **Tel:** (0171) 414 8080 **Fax:** (0171) 414 8099
DX: 312 **Sen. Clerk:** Graham Kettle **Tenants:** 17 Specialist tax/revenue law chambers, dealing with all contentious and non-contentious domestic and foreign fiscal matters.

188
Set No.

QUEEN ELIZABETH BUILDING (Ian Karsten QC)

QUEEN ELIZABETH BUILDING, TEMPLE, LONDON, EC4Y 9BS
DX: London 339

TEL: (0171) 797 7837
FAX: (0171) 353 5422

MEMBERS:
Ian Karsten QC (1967)(QC-1990), David Bodey QC (1970)(QC-1991),
Paul Coleridge QC (1970)(QC-1993), Florence Baron QC (1976)(QC-1995),
Lord Phillimore (1972), Lord Lord Meston (1973), Peter Wright (1974),
Michael Hosford-Tanner (1974), Andrew Tidbury (1976), Thomas Brudenell (1977),
Andrew Moylan (1978), Roderick Blyth (1981), Oliver Wise (1981),
Rowena Corbett (1984), David Bradly (1987), Timothy Amos (1987),
Jennifer Roberts (1988), Sarah Edwards (1990), Matthew Firth (1991),
Elizabeth Clarke (1991), Camilla Henderson (1992), Stewart Leech (1992),
Edward Vaizey (1993), Richard Pates (1993).

HEAD OF CHAMBERS:
Ian Karsten QC

SEN. CLERK:
Ivor Treherne

TENANTS: 24

WORK UNDERTAKEN: A set covering a range of specialist fields of the common law, with some members specialising in family law, and others concentrating on a range of work including commercial law, criminal law, disciplinary tribunals, employment law, equine and animal law, EC law, insolvency, judicial review, landlord and tenant, medical negligence, partnership law, personal injuries, private international and foreign law, probate, professional negligence and sports law.

LANGUAGES SPOKEN: French, German and Italian.

189
Set No.

QUEEN ELIZABETH BUILDING (Geoffrey Brice QC)

QUEEN ELIZABETH BUILDINGS (1ST FLOOR), TEMPLE, LONDON, EC4Y 9BS
DX: 483

TEL: (0171) 353 9153
FAX: (0171) 583 0126

MEMBERS:
Geoffrey Brice QC (1960)(QC-1979), Andrew Rankin QC (1950)(QC-1968),
Richard Stone QC (1951)(QC-1968), John Reeder QC (1971)(QC-1989),
Allan Myers (1988), Sarah Miller (1971), Jervis Kay (1972), Lloyd Lloyd (1973),
Alison Green (1974), James Thom (1974), William Whitehouse-Vaux (1977),
Elizabeth Blackburn (1978), Robert Bourne (1978), Daphne Romney (1979),
Lionel Persey (1981), Nigel Meeson (1982), Mark Sutton (1982),
Yvonne Green (1982), Vasanti Selvaratnam (1983), Miranda Whiteley (1985),
David Goldstone (1986), Nicholas Saunders (1989), Christopher Smith (1989),
Michael Davey (1990), Stephen Wilson (1990), Arshad Ghaffar (1991),
Timothy Hill (1990).

HEAD OF CHAMBERS:
Geoffrey Brice QC

SEN. CLERK:
Christopher James

CLERKS: Paul Coveney, Vemtia Jeffcock, Jonathan Gardner

TENANTS: 27

MAIN AREAS OF WORK: Members of chambers provide a comprehensive service in all aspects of commercial work, and in particular the following: admiralty practice, aviation, banking and finance, commercial arbitration, carriage of goods by sea, road, rail and air, charterparties, collisions at sea, company law, conveyancing and real property, education, employment law, European Community law, general and marine construction, general public and marine inquiries, international sale of goods, insolvency, landlord and tenant, marine and non-marine insurance and reinsurance, mergers and takeovers, partnership law, pollution, professional negligence, public law, restrictive trade practices, salvage and taxation.

FOREIGN CONNECTIONS: Chambers tenants are members of the Bars of Gibraltar, New South Wales, California

LANGUAGES: French, German, and Italian.

QUEEN ELIZABETH BUILDING(David Jeffreys QC & Peter Whiteman QC)

190
Set No.

HOLLIS WHITEMAN CHAMBERS, QUEEN ELIZABETH BUILDING, TEMPLE,
LONDON, EC4Y 9BS   DX: 482

TEL: (0171) 583 5766
FAX: (0171) 353 0339

THE CHAMBERS: A large established set specialising in criminal law.

WORK UNDERTAKEN: The chambers cover the whole range of criminal work from the most serious cases – murder, rape, robbery, drugs and burglary, to motoring offences, with particular emphasis towards fraud, commercial crime and VAT related cases. Members undertake disciplinary tribunal work for the General Medical and Dental Councils and other bodies, together with some industrial tribunal work. There are also several specialists in licensing.

MEMBERS:

David A. Jeffreys QC (1958)(QC-1981), Peter Whiteman QC (1967)(QC-1977), Lord Carlisle QC (1954)(QC-1971), Robin D. Grey QC (1957)(QC-1979), Julian Bevan QC (1962)(QC-1991), Alan B. Suckling QC (1963)(QC-1983), John Hilton QC (1964)(QC-1990), Anthony T. Glass QC (1965)(QC-1986), Timothy Langdale QC (1966)(QC-1992), Graham Boal QC (1966)(QC-1993), Vivian Robinson QC (1967)(QC-1986), Brian J. Barker QC (1969)(QC-1990), David H. Evans QC (1972)(QC-1991), David C. Paget QC (1967)(QC-1994), David Bate QC (1969)(QC-1994), Rebecca M. Poulet (1975), Anthony Wilcken (1966), Anthony G. Longden (1967), Christopher R. Mitchell (1968), David Calvert-Smith (1969), Peter E. Kyte (1970), Warwick N. McKinnon (1970), Stephen P. Waller (1972), Peter W. Clarke (1973), Neill A. Stewart (1973), Linda D. Strudwick (1973), Ian F. Paton (1975), William H. Boyce (1976), Richard E. Horwell (1976), Jeremy Donne (1978), Peter Anthony Finnigan (1978), J. Kelsey-Fry (1978), Mark Ellison (1979), G.N.M. Wood (1980) MA (Oxon) LLM (Indiana, USA), Thomas V.W. Kark (1982), Edward F.T. Brown (1983), Anna Christofides (1983), Ian M. Stern (1983), Jane Sullivan (1984), Phillip Bennetts (1986), Sean Larkin (1987), Jocelyn Sparks (1987), Edward Henry (1988), Sarah Plaschkes (1988), Ian Winter (1988), Zoe Johnson (1990), Emma Lowry (1991), Lydia Barnfather (1992), Victoria Coward (1992), William Wastie (1993), Peter Warne (1993).

Lord Carlisle QC is Chairman of the Criminal Injuries Compensation Board.

HEAD OF CHAMBERS:
David Jeffreys QC, Peter Whiteman QC

SEN. CLERK:
Michael Greenaway

TENANTS: 51

QUEEN ELIZABETH BUILDING   (Ernst Horridge)

191
Set No.

QUEEN ELIZABETH BUILDING, TEMPLE, LONDON, EC4Y 9BS
DX: 340 (Ch.Ln.)

TEL: (0171) 353 7181 (12 lines)
FAX: (0171) 353 3929 (2 lines)

MEMBERS:

· Ernst Horridge (1970), Richard Guy (1970), Shelagh Farror (1970), Peter Stage (1971), Lindsay Burn (1972), Jonathan Lowen (1972), Peter Prideaux-Brune (1972), Richard McGregor-Johnson (1973), Mary Jane Mowat (1973), James Pavry (1974), Keith Salvesen (1974), Duncan Munro Kerr (1975), Simon Wild (1977), David Jeremy (1977), Laura Harris (1977), Peter Walsh (1978), Walton Hornsby (1980), Nicola Simpson (1982), Charles Digby (1982), Anthony Haycroft (1982), Fiona Gibb (1983), Carol Atkinson (1985), Philip St. John-Stevens (1985), Divya Bhatia (1986), Fiona Munro (1986), Karen Holt (1987), Barbara Philcox (1988), Paul Ozin (1987), Garrett Byrne (1986), Jennifer Driscoll (1989), John Talbot-Bagnall (1988), Rebecca Westerland (1992), Colm Nugent (1992), Sharon Sawyerr (1992), Niki Langridge (1993).

WORK UNDERTAKEN:

General Description: General criminal practice, undertaking both prosecution and defence, with 24 barristers specialising in this area, primarily in London and the South Eastern Circuit.

HEAD OF CHAMBERS:
Ernst Horridge

SEN. CLERK:
Michael Price

TENANTS: 35

Other Areas of Work: *Work includes:* common law, contract law, courts martial, employment, family law (12 barristers), fraud, landlord and tenant, matrimonial, personal injury litigation, sale of goods, licensing and tribunals.

3 RAYMOND BUILDINGS (Clive Nicholls QC)

3 RAYMOND BUILDINGS, GRAY'S INN, LONDON, WC1R 5BH
DX: 237

TEL: (0171) 831 3833
FAX: (0171) 242 4221

THE CHAMBERS: Established in the early 1920s, chambers now have thirty-two members (including 11 QCs) who practise in a broad area of criminal, licensing and administrative law, ranging from appearances in Magistrates' Courts and Crown Courts to the special demands of disciplinary, regulatory and appellate tribunals and international courts. Chambers' practice has developed extensively in recent years, and members now advise and appear in cases throughout the world.

3 Raymond Buildings have been completely refurbished. They provide large conference rooms and are equipped with the latest computer and communications facilities.

MEMBERS:

Clive Nicholls QC (1957)(QC-1982), Colin Nicholls QC (1957)(QC-1981),
Gilbert Gray QC (1953)(QC-1971), Richard Beckett QC (1965)(QC-1987),
John Nutting QC (1968)(QC-1995), Stephen Batten QC (1968)(QC-1989),
Alun Jones QC (1972)(QC-1989), David Whitehouse QC (1969)(QC-1990),
Nicholas Price QC (1968)(QC-1992), Montague Sherborne QC (1960)(QC-1993),
Francis Evans QC (1977)(QC-1994), Colin Pitt (1968), John Blair-Gould (1970),
Andrew Muir (1975), Kevin De Haan (1976), Michael Bromley-Martin (1979),
Mark Harris (1980) BA (Oxon), Clare Montgomery (1980), James Hines (1982),
James Rankin (1983), Jane Humphryes (1983), Neil Saunders (1983),
Crispin Aylett (1985), Alexander Cameron (1986), Helen Malcolm (1986),
James Lewis (1987), Hugo Keith (1989), Hugh Davies (1990),
Campaspe Lloyd-Jacob (1990), Tania Bromley-Martin (1983),
Richard Wormald (1993).

WORK UNDERTAKEN:

Criminal Law: Cases are handled at all levels of gravity, both for the prosecution and the defence. Chambers specialise in complex commercial crime including cases in the Far East. Several members are on the panel of DTI Inspectors.

Extradition: Extradition proceedings are handled for foreign governments and defendants, both in the United Kingdom and elsewhere.

Licensing: Some members practise exclusively in licensing law, with particular specialisations in betting, gaming and lotteries and in liquor and public entertainment.

Tribunals and Administrative Law: Tribunal work includes coroners' inquests, regulatory and disciplinary tribunals. Associated with this, and with other areas of practice, is an expanding volume of work in Administrative law and Judicial Review.

Human Rights Law: Members handle cases before the European Commission and the Court of Human Rights.

Privy Council Cases: Members present constitutional, criminal and common law appeals from Commonwealth countries to the Privy Council.

Environmental Law and Consumer Law: Pollution control and statutory nuisances, consumer protection and trading law, regulation under the Health and Safety at Work Act 1974 and associated legislation.

Other Areas: Individual members specialise in all aspects of common law and matrimonial law.

HEAD OF CHAMBERS:
Clive Nicholls QC

SEN. CLERK:
Ronald Butler

TENANTS: 30

193 FOUR RAYMOND BUILDINGS (Jeremy Lever QC)
Set No.

4 RAYMOND BUILDINGS, GRAY'S INN, LONDON, WC1R 5BP
DX: 257

TEL: (0171) 405 7211
FAX: (0171) 405 2084

MEMBERS:
Jeremy Lever QC (1957)(QC-1972), David Kemp QC (1948)(QC-1973),
Anthony Guest QC (1956)(QC-1987) CBE, Richard Fowler QC (1969)(QC-1989),
Derrick Turriff (1964), Richard Seymour QC (1972)(QC-1991),
Stephen Richards (1975), Kenneth Parker QC (1975)(QC-1992),
Peter M. Roth (1976), Paul Lasok QC (1977)(QC-1994), Nicholas Paines (1978),
Christopher Vajda (1979), Mark Pelling (1979), Rupert Anderson (1981),
Michael Patchett-Joyce (1981), Stephen Bate (1981), Melanie Hall (1982),
Barbara Hewson (1985), Andrew Macnab (1986), Jonathan Turner (1988),
Peter Mantle (1989), Rhodri Thompson (1989), Jennifer Skilbeck (1991),
Raymond Hill (1992), Jessica Simor (1992), Alistair Lindsay (1993).

HEAD OF CHAMBERS:
Jeremy Lever QC

SEN. CLERK:
Graham Lister

TENANTS: 26

WORK UNDERTAKEN: European Community law, competition law and trade regulation, administrative law, commercial law, public law, media and entertainment law. For further information please ask for a copy of the chambers brochure or contact the senior clerk.

RECRUITMENT: Pupillage awards are made annually. For further information please contact Yvonne Cocklin.

194 5 RAYMOND BUILDINGS (Patrick Milmo QC) 5 Raymond
Set No. Buildings, Gray's Inn, London, WC1R 5BP **Tel:** (0171) 242 2902 **Fax:** (0171) 831 2686 **DX:** 1054 **Sen. Clerk:** Kim Janes **Tenants:** 17 Specialists in the field of law concerning the media and entertainment industry, especially defamation. Also handle substantial commercial work.

195 No. 1 SERJEANTS' INN (Crawford Lindsay QC)
Set No.

NO. 1 SERJEANTS' INN, LONDON, EC4Y 1LL
DX: 364

TEL: (0171) 353 9901
FAX: (0171) 583 2033

THE CHAMBERS: No. 1 Serjeants' Inn is an established common law set of chambers. Members provide a complete range of advocacy, advisory and arbitration services throughout England and Wales, the European Community and other jurisdictions.

MEMBERS:
Crawford Lindsay QC (1961)(QC-1987), Martin Wilson QC (1963)(QC-1982),
Adrian Redgrave QC (1968)(QC-1992), Brian Leech (1967),
Nicholas Browne QC (1971)(QC-1995), John Ross (1971), William Hunter (1972),
Edward Faulks (1973), Anthony Baldry (1975) M.P., Veronica Hammerton (1977),
David Pittaway (1977), Nicholas Yell (1979), Simon Readhead (1979),
John Norman (1979), Karen Rea (1980), John Price (1982),
Alastair Hammerton (1983), Edward Bishop (1985), Sarah Paneth (1985),
Marc Rivalland (1987), Julian Waters (1986), Justin Althaus (1988),
Mary Pinder (1989), Selena Marris (1991), Gerard Boyle (1992),
Wendy Herring (1993), Andrew Warnock (1993).

HEAD OF CHAMBERS:
Crawford Lindsay QC

SEN. CLERK:
Clark Chessis

TENANTS: 27

ASSOCIATE MEMBERS:
W.P. Andreae-Jones QC (1965) (QC-1984) *,
Jonathon Foster QC (1970) (QC-1989) *.
* *Recorder*

WORK UNDERTAKEN: The principal areas of practice are general commercial law (including sale and carriage of goods, restraint of trade, confidentiality, product liability and employment law), commercial fraud, insurance and reinsurance, all areas of professional negligence, disaster litigation, personal injuries (including employers' liability and occupational diseases), construction and property law, and European

Community Law. This list is not exhaustive and individual members of chambers offer expertise in administrative law and judicial review, criminal law, landlord and tenant, defamation, family law and professional disciplinary tribunals.

RECRUITMENT AND TRAINING: Pupillages and mini-pupillages by arrangement. Apply to secretary of Pupillage Committee.

CLIENTS: Chambers act for a wide range of clients, including UK and multinational corporations, major insurance companies, national and local government, and private clients.

FOREIGN LANGUAGES: French, German, Italian and Spanish.

CHARGES: The Senior Clerk will provide details on request.

OFFICE EQUIPMENT: Members of chambers are familiar with leading forms of computer software, including WordPerfect 5.1/ 6 and Wordstar 2000. Data transfer facilities are available.

196
Set No.

1 SERJEANTS' INN (Lionel Read QC)

1 SERJEANTS' INN, LONDON, EC4 1NH
DX: 440

TEL: (0171) 583 1355
FAX: (0171) 583 1672

THE CHAMBERS: A specialist planning and local government set, in modern and spacious accommodation. Members undertake both advocacy and advisory work and accept Direct Professional Access from the approved professions. There is an emphasis on public inquiry work.

MEMBERS:
Lionel Read QC (1954)(QC-1973) MA (Cantab)*,
David Woolley QC (1962)QC-1980) MA(Cantab),
Anthony Rumbelow QC (1967)(QC-1990) BA(Cantab)*,
Patrick Clarkson QC (1972)(QC-1991) +,
Christopher Whybrow QC (1965)(QC-1992) LLB(London),
William Hicks QC (1975)(QC-1995) MA (Cantab),
David Altaras (1969) BA MA(TCD), DipCrim(Cantab)*,
Martin Wood (1972) LLB(London), Arthur Ward (1973) BA,
Rhodri Price Lewis (1975) MA(Oxon)DipCrim(Cantab)+,
John Pugh-Smith (1977) MA(Oxon), Simon Pickles (1978) MA (Cantab),
John Dagg (1980), Neil Cameron (1982) BA(Dunelm),
Stephen Morgan (1983) LLB(Warw), MA(Nott), Richard Langham (1986) BA (Oxon), Russell Harris (1986) MA(Cantab), Megan Thomas (1987) BA(Sheff),
Roy Martin (1990) LLB(Glasgow), William Upton (1990) MA, LLM(Cantab),
Sasha White (1991) MA(Cantab), Robert Douglas White (1993) LLB(LSE),
Richard Harwood (1993) MA,LLM(Cantab).
  * *Recorder*
  + *Assistant recorder.*

HEAD OF CHAMBERS:
Lionel Read QC

SEN. CLERK:
William King

TENANTS: 23

WORK UNDERTAKEN: Town and country planning; environmental protection; integrated pollution control; waste disposal; hazardous substances; compulsory purchase and compensation; highways; public health; local government; statutory undertakers; administrative law and judicial review; parliamentary work; landlord and tenant.

FOREIGN CONNECTIONS: Members of chambers have been involved in arbitrations abroad and practise in Scotland.

RECRUITMENT & TRAINING: Pupillage applications should be sent to Rhodri Price Lewis. Chambers offer up to two first six months' and up to two second six months' pupillages each year. Chambers may offer a twelve months' pupillage. Awards and mini-pupillages are available.

---

3 SERJEANTS' INN (Adrian Whitfield QC)

3 SERJEANTS' INN, LONDON, EC4Y 1BQ
DX: 421

TEL: (0171)353 5537 Mbl(0385)736844
FAX: (0171) 353 0425

HEAD OF CHAMBERS:
Adrian Whitfield QC

SEN. CLERK:
Nick Salt Tel: (0181) 368 6554

FIRST JUNIOR CLERK: Lee Johnson

ADMINISTRATOR Anne Hughes

TENANTS: 24

MEMBERS:
Adrian Whitfield QC (1964)(QC-1983), Philip Naughton QC (1970)(QC-1988), Robert Francis QC (1973)(QC-1992), Nicola Davies QC (1976)(QC-1992), John Grace QC (1973)(QC-1994), Philip Gaisford (1969), Malcolm Fortune (1972), Geoffrey D. Conlin (1973), Huw Lloyd (1975), T. Deva Pillay (1976), Anthony Cottle (1978), James Watson (1979), Andrew Grubb (1980), Fiona Neale (1981), Mary O'Rourke (1981), George Hugh-Jones (1983), Adrian Hopkins (1984), Angus Moon (1986), Ian Wright (1989), John Beggs (1989), Jonathan Holl-Allen (1990), Christopher Johnston (1990), Michael Horne (1992), Fionnuala McCredie (1992).

TYPES OF WORK UNDERTAKEN:

Professional Negligence: In the medical, dental, and pharmaceutical fields tenants act for plaintiffs and defendants, including health authorities throughout the country and all the medical defence organisations. Tenants have appeared in many of the major cases in this field including **Sidaway, Hotson, Roberts v Johnstone, Rance,** the pertussis vaccine litigation and claims pioneering structured settlements in medical cases.

Tenants also deal with a wide range of other forms of professional liability, including that of architects, surveyors, engineers and lawyers and matters governed by the Health & Safety at Work Act.

Professional discipline and ethics: Tenants appear before disciplinary tribunals, including the General Medical and Dental Councils, FHSA appeals, the Pharmaceutical Society and at internal hospital inquiries and public inquiries e.g. the Cleveland inquiry. Cases in which tenants have also appeared include **Bland, re F (sterilisation), re J (medical treatment), Roy, Egdell** and the GMC case concerning the sale of kidneys.

Construction and Engineering: The principal areas of work undertaken concern standard form and other contracts for building and civil, mechanical, electrical, chemical and process engineering projects; defects in design and workmanship; performance obligations; loss and expense claims; and warranties. Associated areas of work include the professional negligence of architects, engineers, surveyors and valuers; nuisance; matters governed by the Health & Safety at Work regulations; and environmental matters.

Employment: Work undertaken includes advising and acting in wrongful dismissal claims, industrial tribunal cases, the drafting of employment contracts, race and sex discrimination claims and European law.

Crime: Both defence and prosecutions are undertaken. Tenants who specialise in crime have particular experience in proceedings relating to professional practice, fraud, Health and Safety at Work and medical and ethical issues.

Personal Injuries/ Commercial Contract: In addition, a wide range of common law work is undertaken.

LANGUAGES: French.

RECRUITMENT AND TRAINING: Chambers offer two to three 12 month pupillages starting each October.

AWARDS: Chambers offer each of the candidates an award of £7,500 and guarantee minimum earnings of £7,500 during the second 6 months.

APPLICATIONS: 3 Serjeants' Inn is a member of the Common Law Chambers Pupillage Application Scheme ("COMPAS") which will receive and process all applications for pupillage here.

Full details of how the scheme works and an application form can be obtained from the secretary of the scheme, Martin Spencer, COMPAS Secretary, 4 Paper Buildings, Temple, LONDON EC4Y 7EX.

THREE
SERJEANTS'
INN

198
Set No.

SOMERSETT CHAMBERS (Lanre Oke) 52 Bedford Row, London, WC1R 4LR **Tel:** (0171) 404 6701 **Fax:** (0171) 404 6702 **DX:** 44 (Ch.Ln.) **Sen. Clerk:** Ms Rosemarie Phillips **Tenants:** 12 General common law set with particular emphasis on crime, personal injury, employment, matrimonial and childcare, landlord and tenant and housing.

199
Set No.

3-4 SOUTH SQUARE (Michael Crystal QC)

3-4 SOUTH SQUARE, GRAY'S INN, LONDON, WC1R 5HP
DX: 338 (Ch.Ln.)

TEL: (0171) 696 9900
FAX: (0171) 696 9911

THE CHAMBERS: Members of these chambers practice primarily in business,financial and commercial law and have particular experience in insolvency law. Other areas of specialisation are detailed below.

Members of chambers practice regularly in the Companies Court, Commercial Court, Queen's Bench and Chancery Divisions of the High Court, the Court of Appeal, the House of Lords and the Privy Council and the provincial Courts in England and Wales.

Members of chambers have experience of advocacy in foreign Courts and tribunals, of acting as arbitrators or examiners in connection with English and overseas litigation and disputes, and of acting as expert witnesses on English law in cases proceeding in other jurisdictions.

They are able to accept instructions direct from overseas lawyers and from members of professional bodies authorised by the General Council of the Bar to instruct counsel without the intervention of a solicitor.

HEAD OF CHAMBERS:
Michael Crystal QC

CHIEF EXECUTIVE:
David Hatchard

SEN. CLERKS: Neil Atkin, Jason Pithers
ADMINISTRATOR: Lynne Isaacs

TENANTS: 32

MEMBERS:

Michael Crystal QC (1970)(QC-1984) LLB (Lond), BCL (Oxon),
Muir Hunter QC (1938)(QC-1965) MA (Oxon),
Christopher Brougham QC (1969)(QC-1988) BA (Oxon),
Gabriel Moss QC (1974)(QC-1989) MA, BCL (Oxon),
Simon Mortimore QC (1972)(QC-1991) LLB (Exon), John Higham QC (1976)(QC-1992) MA, LLM (Cantab), Marion Simmons QC (1970)(QC-1994) LLB, LLM (Lond), Richard Adkins QC (1982)(QC-1995) MA (Oxon), Clive Cohen (1989) (SC 1975) BA, LLB (Witwatersrand), John Briggs (1973) LLB, (Lond) Ex, Du D d'U (Nancy), David Marks (1974) MA, BCL (Oxon), Richard Hacker (1977) MA (Cantab) Lic sp Dr Eur (Bruxelles), Martin Pascoe (1977) BA, BCL (Oxon), Richard Sheldon (1979) MA (Cantab), Robin Knowles (1982) MA (Cantab), William Trower (1983) MA (Oxon), Susan Prevezer (1983) MA (Cantab) MA (Brandeis), Mark Phillips (1984) LLB, LLM (Bristol), Robin Dicker (1986) BA, BCL (Oxon), David Alexander (1987) MA (Cantab), Antony Zacaroli (1987) BA, BCL (Oxon), Mark Arnold (1988) BA (Cantab), Lexa Hilliard (1987) LLB, (Lond), Stephen Atherton (1989) LLB,(Lancaster) LLM (Cantab), Sandra Bristoll (1989) BA (Cantab), Adam Goodison (1990) BA(Dunelm), Hilary Stonefrost (1991) MSC (Lond), Lloyd Tamlyn (1991) BA(Cantab), Glen Davis (1992) MA(Oxon), Andreas Gledhill (1992) MA(Cantab), Fidelis Oditah (1992) MA BCL D Phil (Oxon), Roxanne Ismail (1993) LLB (Lond).

WORK UNDERTAKEN INCLUDES: Corporate and International Insolvency: Receivership; Administration; Liquidation; Arrangements with creditors; Insolvent Partnerships.

Company Law: Mergers and Acquisitions; Shareholders and Directors disputes; Partnership Disputes.

Banking: Credit and Security; Factoring; Mortgages; Finance Leasing; Guarantees; Bills of Exchange; Bonds relating to Construction Contracts and International Trade.

Personal Insolvency.Financial Services: City, Market and Banking Regulation; Stock Exchange, Commodity and Currency Transactions, Derivatives.

Commercial and Business Law: Civil aspects of Commercial Fraud; Breach of Contract; Sale of Goods; Retention of Title; International Trade; Insurance and Reinsurance; Tax-related litigation; Tracing Remedies; Pre-trial Remedies and Enforcement of Foreign and Domestic Judgements; Obtaining Evidence for Foreign Proceedings.

Professional Negligence and disciplinary proceedings, particularly concerning Accountants; Financial Advisers and Solicitors.

LANGUAGES SPOKEN: French, German, Italian, Spanish, Chinese (Mandarin) and Afrikaans.

---

200 11 SOUTH SQUARE (Christopher Floyd QC)
Set No.

11 SOUTH SQUARE (2ND FLOOR), GRAY'S INN, LONDON, WC1R 5EU
DX: 433

TEL: (0171) 405 1222
FAX: (0171) 242 4282

MEMBERS:
Christopher Floyd QC (1975)(QC-1992)[+], C.D. (Henry) Whittle (1975), Nicholas Pumfrey QC (1975)(QC-1990)[+], Michael Silverleaf (1980)[*], Henry Carr (1982), Richard Hacon (1979), Iain Purvis (1986), Richard Arnold (1985), Dr Heather Lawrence (1990), Mark Vanhegan (1990), Jacqueline Reid (1992), Piers Acland (1993).
[*] *Junior Counsel to the Treasury in respect of patent and trademark matters.*
[+] *Assistant Recorder at the Patents County Court.*

WORK UNDERTAKEN: The chambers specialise principally in patent and other intellectual property matters and related EC and domestic competition law. The majority of members of chambers have academic or practical technical and scientific backgrounds to the equivalent of at least degree level. They also act in matters with a high technical content outside the field of intellectual property and are happy to accept instructions in commercial and other disputes in this category, such as computer, pharmaceutical, engineering and similar matters.

HEAD OF CHAMBERS:
Christopher Floyd QC

CLERKS:
Frances Smith, Martyn Nicholls

TENANTS: 12

---

201 STAPLE INN CHAMBERS (Veronica Ramsden)
Set No.

9 Staple Inn, London, WC1V 7QH **Tel:** (0171) 242 5240 **Fax:** (0171) 405 9495 **DX:** 132 **Sen. Clerk:** Brian Monument, Stuart Davis **Tenants:** 17 *Work includes:* crime, family, wardship, housing, employment, immigration, personal injury, professional negligence, landlord and tenant, trusts and wills, gas and fuel rights, licensing, arbitration.

---

202 2 STONE BUILDINGS (Jamal Nasir)
Set No.

1st Floor, 2 Stone Buildings, Lincoln's Inn, London, WC2A 3XB **Tel:** (0171) 405 3818 **Fax:** (0171) 831 1971 **Sen. Clerk:** Adrienne Bianchet **Tenants:** 1 Specialises in foreign laws, private and public international law and Islamic law. Membership of the Jordan, other Arab, and Nigerian Bars.

---

203 3 STONE BUILDINGS (D.R. Stanford)
Set No.

3 STONE BUILDINGS, LINCOLN'S INN, LONDON, WC2A 3XL
DX: 317

TEL: (0171) 242 4937
FAX: (0171) 405 3896

THE CHAMBERS: 3 Stone Buildings is an established and expanding set of general chancery chambers with a considerable breadth of expertise. Individual attention is combined with professional efficiency. The chambers have experienced practitioners in most areas of financial litigation and advisory work.

MEMBERS:
David R. Stanford (1951) LLB, MA (Cantab), Geoffrey J. Topham (1964) MA (Cantab), Andrew J. Cosedge (1972) LLB (Exon), Alan M. Tunkel (1976) BA (Oxon), Geoffrey C. Vos QC (1977)(QC-1993) MA (Cantab),

HEAD OF CHAMBERS:
D. R. Stanford

SEN. CLERK:
Andrew Palmer

TENANTS: 14

David Da Silva (1978) MA (Oxon), Robert A. Hantusch (1982) MA (Cantab),
Sarah J. Asplin (1984) MA (Cantab), BCL (Oxon), Sarah E. Girling (1986) MA
(Cantab), David W. Lord (1987) LLB (Bristol),
Carlos A.L.de S. Pimentel (1990) LLB, LLM(Exon), Asaf Kayani (1991) LLB
(Leeds), BCL (Oxon), Sarah H. Lacey (1991) BA (Cantab),
Andrew M. Twigger (1994) BA (Oxon).

WORK UNDERTAKEN: Particular specialisations include company and commercial
litigation, revenue law, trusts and property, insolvency, and partnership formation and
disputes. Tax planning and pension matters, and the drafting of settlement, conveyancing and commercial documentation are extensively undertaken.

NATURE OF CLIENTELE: Companies, banks, trustees and private clients. Direct access
instructions are accepted from accountants and other professionals, and from overseas
lawyers. Chambers have founder membership of C.E.D.R. (alternative dispute resolution).

FOREIGN LANGUAGES SPOKEN: French, Portuguese and Spanish.

RECRUITMENT & TRAINING: The chambers offer 4 x 6 month pupillages each year.
Awards are available in appropriate cases. Contact David Lord. Applications close
on 31st October each year, for pupillages in the year commencing in the following
October.

:04
t No.

4 STONE BUILDINGS (Peter Curry QC)

4 STONE BUILDINGS, LINCOLN'S INN, LONDON, WC2A 3XT
DX: 385

TEL: (0171) 242 5524
FAX: (0171) 831 7907

THE CHAMBERS: An elegantly-furnished and spacious set, combining an established
and broadly-based company/ commercial practice with general chancery work. Most
members specialise in litigation and handle a variety of interlocutory applications.

MEMBERS:
Peter Curry QC (1953)(QC-1973) MA (Oxon),
Edward Davidson QC (1966)(QC-1994) MA LLB (Cantab), Stephen Hunt (1968) BA
(Oxon), Philip Heslop QC (1970)(QC-1985) BA LLB (Cantab),
John Bertin (1972) MA (Cantab), Anthony George Bompas QC (1975)(QC-1994) BA
(Oxon), Robert Hildyard QC (1977)(QC-1994) BA (Oxon),
Peter Griffiths (1977) MA (Cantab), John Brisby (1978) MA (Oxon),
Jonathan Crow (1981) BA (Oxon), Malcolm Davis-White (1984) BA (Oxon),
Robert Miles (1987) BA (Oxon), Rosalind Nicholson (1987) BA (Oxon),
Sarah Harman (1987) BA (Oxon), Christopher Harrison (1988),
Jonathan Brettler (1988), Paul Greenwood (1991), Andrew Clutterbuck (1992),
Nicholas Cox (1992), Richard Hill (1993).
One member of chambers is the Chairman of IMRO disciplinary hearings. Two mem-
bers are Treasury Counsel (company matters).

HEAD OF CHAMBERS:
Peter Curry QC

SEN. CLERK:
David Goddard

TENANTS: 20

WORK UNDERTAKEN:
Main Areas of Work:
Company/ Commercial: Litigation includes all aspects of fraud; shareholder and
boardroom disputes; takeovers; investor protection and disputes with creditors;
insolvency and liquidations; directors' disqualification; Capital Reductions and
transfer of Insurance buisnesses; financial services disputes and disciplinary proceedings brought by the SROs; general commercial disputes.
    Non-litigious work includes reductions of capital, insurance transfer schemes,
advice on and drafting of company Memoranda and Articles of Association,
resolutions, prospectuses, press releases and documentation for mergers and demergers, as well as advice on and drafting of commercial contracts generally,
standard terms of trading and banking securities.
General Chancery: *Work includes:* professional negligence, partnership, personal
insolvency, trusts, the administration of estates, property matters, mining and
subsidence.

CLIENTELE: Mainly corporate and regulatory bodies, government departments and overseas clients.

FOREIGN CONNECTIONS: Members undertake work abroad, particularly in Hong Kong, Bermuda, the Bahamas, the British Virgin Islands and the Cayman Islands.

LANGUAGES: French and Spanish.

RECRUITMENT AND TRAINING: Applications for pupillage will be considered only for those with at least an upper second degree, though not necessarily in law. Awards of up to £10,000 are offered per six months. Application forms pupillage can be obtained by writing to "David Goddard, The Senior Clerk. supported by a typed CV and the names of two referees.

205
Set No.

5 STONE BUILDINGS (Henry Harrod)

5 STONE BUILDINGS, LINCOLN'S INN, LONDON, WC2A 3XT
DX: 304 (Ch.Ln.) LIX: LON 175

TEL: (0171) 242 6201
FAX: (0171) 831 8102

THE CHAMBERS: These chambers cover the full range of commercial, property-related, and private client work (contentious and advisory) undertaken by a modern general chancery set. With particular expertise and strengths in the law of trusts (including pension schemes), charities, estate planning and succession, fiduciary duties (with particular reference to partners and company directors), revenue law, insolvency, professional negligence (legal and financial services), mental health, probate, wills and land law (including landlord and tenant). Members litigate in all Divisions of the High Court, the County Court, and all appellate courts, as well as undertaking arbitration and tribunal work. The clerks are always ready to be consulted on individual specialities and aptitudes. Chambers accept Direct Professional Access from approved professions.

Alastair Norris is a Fellow of the Chartered Institute of Arbitrators.

HEAD OF CHAMBERS:
Henry Harrod

SEN. CLERK:
David Butler

TENANTS: 18

MEMBERS:
Henry Harrod (1963)*, John Jopling (1960), Michael Hart QC (1970)(QC-1987),
John Boggis QC (1972)(QC-1993)*, Alastair Norris (1973),
The Hon. Michael Templeman (1973), Mark Herbert QC (1974)(QC-1995),
Mark Blackett-Ord (1974), The Hon. Launcelot Henderson QC (1977)(QC-1995),
Andrew Simmonds (1980), Elaine Webb (1982), Christopher Tidmarsh (1985),
Michael O'Sullivan (1986), Sally Barber (1988), Barbara Rich (1990),
Tracey Angus (1991), The Hon. Henry Legge (1993), David Rees (1994).
*Recorder
Michael Hart QC sits as a Deputy High Court Judge in the Chancery Division of the High Court. Christopher Tidmarsh is Standing Junior Counsel to the Inland Revenue (Chancery).

- 5 -
STONE
BUILDINGS

206
Set No.

7 STONE BUILDINGS (Charles Aldous QC)

7 STONE BUILDINGS, LINCOLN'S INN, LONDON, WC2A 3SZ
DX: 335

TEL: (0171) 405 3886
FAX: (0171) 242 8502

THE CHAMBERS: A specialist chancery set, founded in the 1870s, handling all aspects of chancery and commercial practice other than shipping. Much of the work is contentious. All members accept direct professional access.

HEAD OF CHAMBERS:
Charles Aldous QC

SEN. CLERK:
Tony Marsh

ADMINISTRATOR: Shona Kelly B.A.

TENANTS: 14

MEMBERS:
Charles Aldous QC (1967)(QC-1985), Michael Nield (1969),
David Unwin QC (1971)(QC-1995), Fergus Ungoed-Thomas (1973),
Nigel Davis QC (1975)(QC-1992), Alastair Walton (1977),
John Randall QC (1978)(QC-1995) (Cantab), Guy Newey (1982),
Christopher Parker (1984), James Clifford (1984), Lindsey Stewart (1983),

Michael A. Green (1987), Edmund Cullen (1991), Patricia Carswell (1993), Tom Bannister (1993).

WORK UNDERTAKEN:

Main Areas of Work: Company and commercial law; corporate finance; credit and security and banking; entertainment law; equitable remedies; mistake and misrepresentation; fiduciary duties; constructive trusts; tracing; financial services; fraud; freezing and recovery of assets; insolvency; insurance; intellectual property; judicial review; pre-trial remedies; Anton Piller and Mareva Orders; landlord and tenant; pensions; professional negligence and regulation; property; tax; trusts and charities; wills, probate and administration of estates.

Additional Areas of Work: Specialist areas such as European Community law, administrative law and private international law are undertaken in the context of the above. Chambers' brochure has further details.

ASSOCIATED CHAMBERS: John Randall practises principally at 7 Fountain Court, Birmingham.

CLIENTELE: Mainly businesses and professions, particularly accountants in various capacities.

OFFICE EQUIPMENT: Chambers use the word processing system Word Perfect 5.1.

RECRUITMENT & TRAINING: Chambers offer awards during pupillage. Mini-pupillages are encouraged.

7 STONE BUILDINGS

207
Set No.

7 STONE BUILDINGS (John Bishop)

7 STONE BUILDINGS, LINCOLN'S INN, LONDON, WC2A 3SZ
DX: 1007

TEL: (0171) 242 0961
FAX: (0171) 405 7028

MEMBERS:

John Bishop (1970), Godfrey Ashmore (1961), Gay Martin (1970), Robert Conway (1974), Julian Lynch (1976), Patricia Farrall (1976), Simon Birks (1981), Cheryl Williams (1982), John Cooper (1983), Susan Pyle (1985), Oliver Heggs (1987), Matthew Owens (1988), Patricia Cave (1989), Adam Swirsky (1989), Shabbir Lakha (1989), Linda Goldman (1990), Sarah Winfield (1990), Johnathon Tod (1990), Peter Bruton-Phillips (1994).

Mr. G. Ashmore sits on the Rent Assessment Tribunal.

HEAD OF CHAMBERS:
John Bishop

SEN. CLERK:
Miss T. Grant

TENANTS: 19

WORK UNDERTAKEN: General common law, including crime, family, commercial, landlord and tenant, personal injuries, town and country planning, local government and environment, tribunals and licensing work, professional negligence and sale of goods, education.

LANGUAGES SPOKEN: French, German, Swahili, Gujrati, Punjabi, Maltese.

RECRUITMENT & TRAINING: There are, on average, 2 pupils in chambers at any one time. Pupillage applications with CV and the names of 2 referees should be sent to Mr. Shabbir Lakha. Tenancy applications to Mr. John Bishop.

---

8 STONE BUILDINGS (Michael Mark & Francis Barlow)

8 STONE BUILDINGS, LINCOLN'S INN, LONDON, WC2A 3TA
DX: 313 Ch.Ln.

TEL: (0171) 242 5002
FAX: (0171) 831 9188

HEAD OF CHAMBERS:
Michael Mark, Francis Barlow

SEN. CLERK:
Marc Schofield

TENANTS: 11

THE CHAMBERS: A long established set of chancery chambers with a practice covering civil litigation in the appellate courts, all divisions of the High Court and the County Courts, and advisory and drafting work in a range of specialised fields. Chambers accept instructions from professions registered by the Bar Council for Direct Professional Access.

MEMBERS:
Michael Mark (1964), Francis Barlow (1965), Michael Miller QC (1958)(QC-1974),
David Ainger (1961), Richard Wallington (1972), Geraint Thomas (1976),
Simon Taube (1980), Nigel Gerald (1985), Colin Wright (1987),
Susannah Meadway (1988), Kevin Farrelly (1993).

APPOINTMENT: David Ainger is one of the Conveyancing Counsel of the Supreme Court.

PUBLICATIONS: Michael Mark is the editor of *Chalmers' Sale of Goods* and he is joint editor of the Sale of Goods section in the current edition of *Halsbury's Laws of England.* Francis Barlow is a joint editor of *Williams on Wills* and a correspondent of and contributor to *Private Client Business.* Richard Wallington is a joint editor of *Williams on Wills* and is general editor of *Foster's Inheritance Tax.* Geraint Thomas is a contributor to *International Trust Laws* and is preparing a new edition of *Farwell on Powers.* Colin Wright has contributed to the journal *Professional Negligence.* Susannah Meadway is a contributor to *Foster's Inheritance Tax.*

MAIN AREAS OF WORK:

Trust and Taxation Work: Including the drafting and construction of wills, settlements and other trust documents, the management and administration of trusts and estates, associated inheritance tax, capital gains tax and income tax problems and estate planning generally; litigation relating to the rectification, enforcement and variation of trusts and wills, breach of trust, and the administration of estates, probate, family provision, court of protection, the formation and administration of charitable trusts, companies and associations; pension funds and trusts in commercial contexts.

Commercial and Property Work: Including advice, drafting and the conduct of litigation and arbitrations in relation to conveyancing and property matters; landlord and tenant (business, agricultural and residential tenancies), mortgages, guarantees and other financial arrangements, banking law, companies, partnerships, joint ventures and other business arrangements, Friendly Societies and Industrial and Provident Societies, business agreements and breach of contract, bankruptcy, insolvency and receivership, confidential information and passing off, sale of goods and consumer credit, carriage of goods, charterparties, insurance and water law including fisheries, water supply and waterways.

ADDITIONAL AREAS OF WORK: Chambers has considerable experience in professional negligence work, particularly in relation to solicitors, accountants, surveyors and trustees. The set also deals with private international law problems and questions of European law arising in fields of practice.

FOREIGN CONNECTIONS: Chambers undertakes both contentious and advisory work in overseas common law jurisdictions. Colin Wright is a member of the Bars of New South Wales and Victoria. There are members with considerable experience of conducting litigation in Singapore, Hong Kong, Bermuda and the British Caribbean, the Isle of Man and the Channel Islands.

ASSOCIATED CHAMBERS: Francis Barlow also accepts work at Albion Chambers, Broad Street, Bristol BS1 1DR. *Tel:* (0117) 9272144; *Fax:* (0117) 9262569; *DX:* 7822 Bristol.

RECRUITMENT AND TRAINING: Applications to Susannah Meadway with CV and stamped addressed envelope. Mini-pupillages are available.

11 STONE BUILDINGS (Michael Beckman QC)

11 STONE BUILDINGS, LINCOLN'S INN, LONDON, WC2A 3TG
DX: 1022 Chancery Lane   LINK: Christopher Berry. LIX Point: LAW011

TEL: (+44) 0171 831 6381
FAX: (+44) 0171 831 2575

HEAD OF CHAMBERS:
Michael Beckman QC

SENIOR CLERK:
Christopher Berry

TENANTS: 30

THE CHAMBERS: 11 Stone Buildings is a Commercial and Chancery set of Chambers specialising in commercial, company, insolvency and property law. Chambers is also known for its expertise in intellectual property, entertainment and media law, and cases involving civil and criminal fraud both in the UK and abroad. Services are provided for London, provincial and international law firms.

MEMBERS:
Michael Beckman QC (1954)(QC-1976), Peter Sheridan QC (1956)(QC-1977),
Murray Rosen QC (1976)(QC-1993), Edward Cousins (1971), Edward Cohen (1972),
Alan Bishop (1973), Adrian Salter (1973), Donald McCue (1974),
Nigel Meares (1975), Victor Joffe (1975), Robert Deacon (1976),
Susan Cooper (1976), Jonathan Arkush (1977), Jane Giret (1981),
Sidney Ross (1983), Roland Higgs (1984), Marc Dight (1984), Alan Gourgey (1984),
Tina Kyriakides (1984), Raquel Agnello (1986), Marcia Shekerdemian (1987),
Tim Penny (1988), Marilyn Kennedy-McGregor (1989),
Jonathan Middleburgh (1990), Jill Johnston (1990), Birgitta Meyer (1992),
Sheila Macdonald (1993), Max Mallin (1993), James Barnard (1993),
Nick Parfitt (1993).
Edward Cousins is the author of *Cousins on Mortgages* and *Pease & Chitty's Law of Markets and Fairs*.
Sidney Ross is the author of *Inheritance Act Claims, Law and Practice*.

WORK UNDERTAKEN:
Commercial: All areas, including banking and securities, building, competition, computer, conflict of laws, consumer credit, contract, disputes involving shareholders and directors, employment, financial services, fraud and tracing, guarantees, insurance, intellectual property (including scientific and technical issues in patent infringement cases), partnership, restraint of trade, retention of title, and sale of goods.

Company/ Insolvency: Administrations, bankruptcy, corporate ventures, takeovers and mergers, corporate voluntary arrangements, directors' personal liability, directors' powers and duties, disqualification of directors, individual voluntary arrangements, liquidations, receiverships, schemes of arrangements and capital reductions, shareholders' disputes and wrongful trading.

Entertainment and Media: Confidential information, copyright, film and music contracts, passing off, press freedom, trade marks and defamation.

Property: Landlord and tenant, mortgages, markets and fairs, conveyancing, easements and restrictive covenants, planning, housing, property implications of insolvency and boundary disputes.

Succession and Trusts: Capital taxes, charities, Inheritance Act claims, probate, settlements and wills.

Criminal: Commercial fraud, mortgage fraud, professional misconduct, serious crime and VAT fraud.

Common Law: Including licensing, matrimonial finance, medical negligence, personal injury, product liability and professional negligence.

Public Law and Tribunals: Civil liberties, disciplinary proceedings, education, human rights (including international freedom of movement), immigration, industrial tribunals, judicial review, rating and VAT.

FOREIGN CONNECTIONS: Roland Higgs has been admitted to the Bars of California and Eire. Marc Dight has been called to the Bar of New South Wales. Tim Penny and Jonathan Middleburgh have had experience with the legal systems of the US and New Zealand.

LANGUAGES SPOKEN: French, German, Italian, Portuguese, Spanish and Swedish.

Michael Beckman QC

11 STONE BUILDINGS
Ground Floor Chambers

210
Set No.

11 STONE BUILDINGS (D.J.M. Campion) First Floor Chambers,
11 Stone Buildings, Lincoln's Inn, London, WC2A 3TG **Tel:** (0171) 404 5055
Fax: (0171) 405 1551 **DX:** 314 **Sen. Clerk:** Alan Austin **Tenants:** 14 A general chancery
set undertaking litigation, advisory work and drafting over a full range of subjects.

211
Set No.

199 STRAND (R.M. Stewart QC)

199 STRAND, LONDON, WC2R 1DR
DX: 322 Ch.Ln.

TEL: (0171) 379 9779
FAX: (0171) 379 9481

THE CHAMBERS: A long established set of chambers undertaking a wide range of civil work, now located in modern premises close to the Temple. Chambers accept instructions from the approved professions under the Direct Professional Access scheme.

HEAD OF CHAMBERS:
R.M. Stewart QC

SEN. CLERK:
Martin Griffiths

TENANTS: 32

MEMBERS:
Robin Stewart QC (1963)(QC-1979)*, Simon Hawkesworth QC (1967)(QC-1982)*,
Peter Andrews QC (1970)(QC-1991), Robin De Wilde QC (1971)(QC-1993),
Kieran May (1971), Alan Green (1973), Keith Walmsley (1973),
Steven Whitaker (1973), David C. Wilby (1974), David Phillips (1976),
Simon Levene (1977), Quintin Tudor-Evans (1977), Andrew Goodman (1978),
Philip Lehain (1978), Francis Treasure (1980), Christopher Hough (1981),
Martin Kurrein (1981), Jacqueline Beech (1981), Pamela Fine (1983),
Patrick Sadd (1984), Philomena Harrison (1985), Martin Hutchings (1986),
Michael Harrison (1986), Henry Charles (1987), James Aldridge (1987),
Richard Serlin (1987), Henry Witcomb (1989), Sophie Garner (1990),
Timothy Nesbitt (1991), Rachael Vickers (1992), Portia Spears (1992),
Eliot Woolf (1993), Mark Wonnacott (1989).
* Recorder

ASSOCIATE TENANTS:
Dr Stephen Guest (1980), Clive Coleman (1986), Keith Northrop (1989).

MAIN AREAS OF WORK: The principal areas of work undertaken by chambers are:

Personal injuries: Accidents, occupational diseases, medical accidents, health and safety, product liability.

Professional Negligence: Including that of doctors, dentists, lawyers, architects, engineers, surveyors, valuers, accountants, financial intermediaries and insurance brokers.

Property: Conveyancing, boundary disputes, commercial developments of land, mortgages.

Landlord and Tenant: Housing, residential and commercial leases, rent reviews, dilapidation, agricultural tenancies.

Building and Engineering Disputes.

Commercial: Contract, sale of goods, carriage of goods, insolvency, partnership, insurance, consumer credit, company law, competition law, passing off, financial services, fraud, franchising.

Employment: Wrongful and unfair dismissal, protection of confidential information, restrictive covenants, sex and race discrimination, transfer of undertakings.

Transport: With particular reference to operators licensing and construction and use in road haulage and coach industries.

LANGUAGES: French.

RECRUITMENT AND TRAINING: Two funded 12-month pupillages are available; six-month pupillages are also offered; and applications from students for mini-pupillages are welcomed throughout the year. All enquiries and applications should be addressed to Henry Charles.

212
Set No.

169 TEMPLE CHAMBERS (Evan Ashfield) 2nd Floor, 169 Temple Chambers, Temple Avenue, London, EC4Y 0DA **Tel:** (0171) 583 7644
Fax: (0171) 353 8554 **DX:** 348 **Sen. Clerk:** Arthur Dorsett **Tenants:** 11 General common law and commercial set.

13
No.

1 TEMPLE GARDENS (Hugh Carlisle QC) 1 Temple Gardens, Temple, London, EC4Y 9BB **Tel:** (0171) 583 1315 **Fax:** (0171) 353 3969 **DX:** 382 London **Sen. Clerk:** Alan Luff **Tenants:** 29 Professional negligence; personal injury; health and safety; administrative law and judicial review; planning; immigration; employment; landlord and tenant; ecclesiastical; tax and medical negligence.

14
No.

2 TEMPLE GARDENS (Patrick Phillips QC)

2 TEMPLE GARDENS, LONDON, EC4Y 9AY
DX: 134 (Ch.Ln.)

TEL: (0171) 583 6041
FAX: (0171) 583 2094

HEAD OF CHAMBERS:
Patrick Phillips QC

SEN. CLERK:
Christopher Willans

DEPUTY SEN. CLERK: Tom Grove
ADMINISTRATOR: Louise Jennings

TENANTS: 41

THE CHAMBERS: This set occupies some of the finest rooms in the Temple offering outstanding facilities for conferences, comfortably accommodating up to 20. Chambers main areas of work cover a wide range of common law and commercial practice. Members carry out advocacy and advisory work in the UK (both in London and on circuit) and internationally.

MEMBERS:
Patrick Phillips QC (1964)(QC-1980), William Crowther QC (1963)(QC-1980), Timothy Preston QC (1964)(QC-1982), Dermod O'Brien QC (1962)(QC-1983), Patrick Twigg QC (1967)(QC-1985), Michael de Navarro QC (1968)(QC-1990), Andrew Collender QC (1969)(QC-1991), Robert Moxon-Browne QC (1969)(QC-1990), Henry de Lotbiniere (1968), Rosalind Foster (1969), Roger Hetherington (1973), Daniel Pearce-Higgins (1973), Timothy Lamb QC (1974)(QC-1995), Alexander Layton QC (1976)(QC-1995), Benjamin Browne (1976), Howard Palmer (1977), Jeremy Stuart-Smith (1978), Stephen Archer (1979), Monya Anyadike-Danes (1980), Susan Rodway (1981), John McDonald (1981), David Thomas (1982), Christopher Russell (1982), Sarah Vaughan-Jones (1983), Graham Eklund (1984), Martin Porter (1986), Catherine Rabey (1987), Andrew Miller (1989), Neil Moody (1989), Jennifer Smith (1988), Bradley Martin (1990), Timothy Otty (1990), Daniel Crowley (1990), John Snell (1991), Paul Downes (1991), Tim Lord (1992), Marie Louise Kinsler (1993), Rupert Reece (1993), David Turner (1993), Doré Green (1994), Clare Brown (1993).

WORK UNDERTAKEN: The major areas of practice are general commercial law (including sale and carriage of goods, restraint of trade, confidentiality, product liability, mergers and acquisitions, company and employment law, and arbitrations), commercial and civil fraud, insurance and reinsurance, all areas of professional negligence, disaster litigation, environmental law (including cases concerning fire, flood, electricity, gas, water, highways and health and safety at work), personal injuries (including employers' liability and occupational diseases), and building construction and engineering cases. Disputes involving conflicts of law and jurisdiction and EC problems are regularly handled. This list is not exhaustive and individual members of chambers offer expertise in administrative law and judicial review, criminal law, landlord and tenant and professional disciplinary tribunals.

RECRUITMENT & TRAINING: Pupillages and mini-pupillages by arrangement. Apply to the Secretary of the Pupillage Committee.

NATURE OF CLIENTELE: Insurance companies; UK and international construction companies; UK and international businesses of all sizes and across a wide field of activity; private clients.

FOREIGN LANGUAGES: French, German, Italian, Spanish.

CHARGES: The senior clerk will be happy to provide details on request.

OFFICE EQUIPMENT: Chambers makes full use of modern technology. Chambers and members of chambers use WordPerfect 5.1 on IBM compatible computers for word processing. Documents can be converted to other word processing formats, can be sent and received electronically on LIX (Legal Information Exchange), and will be sent on disc when required.

3 TEMPLE GARDENS (David Braham QC)

3 TEMPLE GARDENS, TEMPLE, LONDON, EC4Y 9AU

TEL: (0171) 353 7884
FAX: (0171) 583 2044

THE CHAMBERS: A specialist revenue law set, handling all aspects of tax law and company law generally. The Chambers accept Direct Professional Access from the approved professions.

MEMBERS:
David Braham QC (1957)(QC-1979), Richard Bramwell QC (1967)(QC-1989), John Dick (1974), Stephen Silman (1974), Michael Sherry (1978), Alun James (1986).
One member of chambers belongs to the Institute of Taxation and Chartered Accountants in England and Wales, and all are members of the Revenue Bar Association.

Publications: Members have written, edited or contributed to the following: *The Taxation of Companies and Company Reconstructions; Inheritance Tax on Lifetime Gifts; The Offshore Tax Planning Review; Weinberg and Blank on Takeovers and Mergers; Practical Tax Planning and Precedents; Copinger and Skone James on Copyright,* (taxation editor); *Whiteman on Income Tax.*

WORK UNDERTAKEN: All areas of tax law: corporate and business tax, including company reconstructions and demergers; personal tax, including Capital Gains Tax, trusts and inheritance tax planning; employee remuneration, pension schemes and share option schemes; back duty investigations; tax litigation and VAT; associated drafting.

ASSOCIATED CHAMBERS: Michael Sherry also practises in Manchester, in the Chambers of Michael Shorrock QC at Peel Court Chambers, 45 Hardman Street. Alun James also practises in Liverpool, in the Chambers of John Kay QC at Exchange Chambers, Pearl Assurance House, Derby Square.

RECRUITMENT & TRAINING: Mini pupillages are available.

HEAD OF CHAMBERS:
David Braham QC

SEN. CLERK:
Frank Skelton

TENANTS: 6

---

3 TEMPLE GARDENS (John Coffey) 3 Temple Gardens, Temple, London, EC4Y 9AU **Tel:** (0171) 353 3102 **Fax:** (0171) 353 0960 **DX:** 485 **Sen. Clerk:** Kevin Aldridge **Tenants:** 31 A well-established set of chambers specialising in all areas of criminal law, family law and several other areas of common law.

3 TEMPLE GARDENS (Jonathan Goldberg QC) 3 Temple Gardens, Temple, London, EC4Y 9AU **Tel:** (0171) 583 1155 **Fax:** (0171) 353 5446 **DX:** 0064 **Sen. Clerk:** Adrian Duncan **Tenants:** 22 Specialist criminal set, handling prosecution and defence work. Road Traffic Act and licensing cases also undertaken.

3 TEMPLE GARDENS (D.C. Gordon) 3 Temple Gardens, Temple, London, EC4Y 9AU **Tel:** (0171) 353 0832 **Fax:** (0171) 353 4929 **DX:** 427 **Sen. Clerk:** James Edmiston MA (Oxon) **Tenants:** 23 An expanding set, the members of which specialise in all areas of criminal and commercial law. Tenants also have experience with a broad range of common law matters.

3 TEMPLE GARDENS (Dermot Wright) 3 Temple Gardens, Temple, London, EC4Y 9AU **Tel:** (0171) 583 0010 **Fax:** (0171) 353 3361 **DX:** 0073 **Sen. Clerk:** Richard Deller **Tenants:** 20 Broad-based common law chambers with particular experience in criminal, family, landlord and tenant and personal injury work.

220 **THOMAS MORE CHAMBERS** More House, 51-52 Carey Street, Lincoln's Inn, London, WC2A 2JB **Tel:** (0171) 404 7000 **Fax:** (0171) 831 4606
Set No. **DX:** 90 (Ch.Ln.) **Sen. Clerk:** Christopher Hallett **Tenants:** 15 A set of common law chambers with particular expertise in fraud and customs cases.

221
Set No.
14 TOOKS COURT (Michael Mansfield QC)

14 TOOKS COURT, CURSITOR ST, LONDON, EC4A 1JY   TEL: (0171) 405 8828
DX: 68 (Ch.Ln.)   FAX: (0171) 405 6680

THE CHAMBERS: Founded in 1984 by a group of barristers determined to combine high standards of advice and dedication to clients with a strong commitment to civil liberties and equal opportunity policy for recruitment of pupils and tenants. Members accept work all over the country. Chambers are fully computerised.

MEMBERS:

Michael Mansfield QC (1967)(QC-1989), Alper Ali Riza QC (1973)(QC-1991),
Adrian Fulford QC (1978)(QC-1994), John Reilly (1972), Vera Baird (1975),
Dora Belford (1977), Patrick Roche (1977), Yaa Yeboah (1977),
Stephen Kamlish (1979), Janet Plange (1981), Sandra Graham (1982),
Christiana Hyde (1982), Emily Thornberry (1983), Tanoo Mylvaganam (1983),
Joel Bennathan (1985), Anne Shamash (1986), Michael Topolski (1986),
Jo Delahunty (1986), Julia Dick (1988), Martin Huseyin (1988),
Peter Wilcock (1988), Margo Boye-Anawoma (1989), Karon Monaghan (1989),
Sarah Maguire (1990), Martin Soorjoo (1990), Carol Hawley (1990),
Stephen Bowen (1990), Leon Daniel (1992), Allison Munroe (1992),
Tim Moloney (1993), Sandhya Drew (1993).
* Michael Topolski – Solicitor 1974.

HEAD OF CHAMBERS:
Michael Mansfield QC

SEN. CLERK:
Carol Thomas

CLERKS: Martin Parker, Michelle Hughton, Lee Wakeling, Karen Jackson, Marsha Jackson, iSandra Watson

TENANTS: 31

WORK UNDERTAKEN:
Criminal: All areas of the criminal law. Members have extensive experience in appellants work and related areas such as inquiries, inquests and judicial review.
Civil: Members' work covers every area of common law. Their specialisations include discrimination, employment, actions against the police, personal injury litigation, landlord and tenant and mental health work.
Public and Administration Law: Members have wide experience of applications for judicial review and immigration law. Cases have involved advising local authorities and participation in inquiries.
Family and Matrimonial: All areas covered.

RECRUITMENT: Pupillage applications to Pupillage & Tenancy Committee. Equal opportunities recruitment policy. First and second 6 months pupils receive £3,000.

222
et No.
TOWER HAMLETS CHAMBERS 72 Brick Lane, London, E1 6RL **Tel:** (0171) 247 9825 **Fax:** (0171) 377 0315 **Practice Manager:** Ali Reza Khan **Tenants:** 10 General Common Law set.

223
et No.
VERULAM CHAMBERS **(Michael Edwards QC)** Peer House, 8-14 Verulam Street, London, WC1X 8LX **Tel:** (0171) 242 7646 **Fax:** (0171) 405 3870 **DX:** 436 **Sen. Clerk:** Fredric Greene **Tenants:** 23 Commercial, chancery, private international law, interlocutory applications, arbitration, general common law (including crime and family/ matrimonial), planning and French law.

224 WARWICK HOUSE CHAMBERS (Christopher & Cheryl Drew)
Set No.

WARWICK HOUSE CHAMBERS, 8 WARWICK COURT, GRAY'S INN, LONDON,
WC1R 5DJ   DX: 1001

TEL: (0171) 430 2323
FAX: (0171) 430 9171

THE CHAMBERS: Warwick House Chambers offers an efficient and progressive service to professional and lay clients. Members appear in a variety of courts and tribunals, ranging from the Magistrates' Court to the European Court of Justice.

MEMBERS:
Christopher Drew (1969), Cheryl Drew (1972), Upali Wickremeratne (1962), Joanna Toch (1988), Andrew Mackintosh (1990), Jaya Patel (1990), Deborah Rowe (1990), Kerim Fuad (1992), Stavros Haidemenos (1992), Arthur J. Moore (1992), Jennifer Moore (1992), Philip Moser (1992), Lisa Peacock (1992), Daniel Barnett (1993), Heather Erwood (1993).

WORK UNDERTAKEN:

General Civil Law: Professional negligence (including medical), personal injury, employment law and industrial disputes, judicial review, property law (including landlord and tenant), insolvency.

Commercial Law: Contractual disputes, with clients ranging from small businesses to insurance companies and international corporations. Special expertise in European law, shipping and freight forwarding, banking, insurance, conflict of laws, computer disputes.

Family Law: Emergency applications, children law (both public and private) for parents and local authorities, matrimonial and cohabitation financial/ property disputes.

Crime: Defence and prosecution (including a Standing Counsel to the DTI), social security and other fraud, courts martial.

PUBLICATIONS: Books on conveyancing, divorce and wills; contributions to Atkin's Court Forms; articles in the legal periodicals (including the Law Society Gazette, the Solicitors' Journal and the New Law Journal).

LANGUAGES: French, German, Greek and Gujerati.

A brochure is available on request.

HEAD OF CHAMBERS:
Christopher Drew, Cheryl Drew

SEN. CLERK:
Christopher Dear

TENANTS: 15

---

225 WILBERFORCE CHAMBERS (Edward Nugee QC)
Set No.

8 NEW SQUARE, LINCOLN'S INN, LONDON, WC2A 3QP
DX: 311 London Chancery Lane WC2

TEL: (0171) 306 0102
FAX: (0171) 306 0095

MEMBERS:
Edward Nugee QC (1955)(QC-1977), Jules Sher QC (1968)(QC-1981), David Lowe QC (1965)(QC-1984), Terence Etherton QC (1974)(QC-1990), John Martin QC (1972)(QC-1991), Nicholas Warren QC (1972)(QC-1993), Robert Ham QC (1973)(QC-1994), Anthony Taussig (1966), Charles Turnbull (1975), Thomas Seymour (1975), Gabriel Hughes (1978), Brian Green (1980), Christopher Nugee (1983), Michael Tennet (1985), James Ayliffe (1987), Judith Bryant (1987), Paul Newman (1991), Gabriel Fadipe (1991), Caroline Furze (1992), Jonathan Evans (1994).

TYPES OF WORK UNDERTAKEN: Wilberforce Chambers has a committed and direct approach to practice, combining imagination and intellectual rigour to provide expert legal analysis, practical advice, and effective litigation across an exceptionally broad spread of commercial and chancery work.

Areas of particular strength include property and all matters relating to freehold and leasehold land, commercial and other contracts, occupational and personal pension schemes, trusts, settlements, wills, estate planning and associated tax advice, banking, insurance, financial services, and equitable remedies. Specialist work is also undertaken in company law, insolvency, professional negligence, and charities.

Edward Nugee QC, Jules Sher QC, and John Martin QC sit as Deputy High Court Judges in the Chancery Division of the High Court, and Terence Etherton QC is a Fellow of the Chartered Institute of Arbitrators. Members of Chambers also belong to the Chancery Bar Association, the Commercial Bar Association, the Association of Pension Lawyers, and the Revenue Bar Association.

HEAD OF CHAMBERS:
Edward Nugee QC

SEN. CLERK::
Roy Beazley

TENANTS: 20

A–Z DIRECTORY OF BARRISTERS – PROVINCIAL

Sets of chambers are listed under the following towns:

Birmingham	Ipswich	Portsmouth
Bournemouth	Leeds	Preston
Bradford	Leicester	Reading
Brighton	Lewes	Redhill
Bristol	Liverpool	Sheffield
Cambridge	Luton	Solihull
Canterbury	Maidstone	Southampton
Cardiff	Manchester	Southsea
Chelmsford	Middlesbrough	St. Albans
Chester	Newcastle upon Tyne	Stoke on Trent
Chichester	Newport	Swansea
Colchester	Northampton	Taunton
Coventry	Norwich	Truro
Eastbourne	Nottingham	Watford
Enfield	Oxford	Winchester
Exeter	Peterborough	Wolverhampton
Guildford	Pinner	York
Harrow-on-the-Hill	Plymouth	
Hull	Poole	

Birmingham

26
t No.

COLERIDGE CHAMBERS (Simon D. Brand) Coleridge Chambers, 190 Corporation Street, Birmingham, W. Midlands, B4 6QD **Tel:** (0121) 233 3303 **Fax:** (0121) 236 6966 **DX:** 23503 **Sen. Clerk:** W.B. Maynard **Tenants:** 15
General common law practice with bias towards crime. Have expertise in personal injury and matrimonial law.

27
t No.

1 FOUNTAIN COURT (Anthony Hughes QC)

1 FOUNTAIN COURT, STEELHOUSE LANE, BIRMINGHAM, W. MIDLANDS, B4 6DR
DX: 16077

TEL: (0121) 236 5721
FAX: (0121) 236 3639

THE CHAMBERS: Broadly based chambers covering crime, personal injuries, medical negligence, commercial law and other contracts, sale of goods and consumer credit, chancery, landlord and tenant, family law and wardship, employment, defamation, licensing, planning, copyright, EC competition law, intellectual property. The set also has experience in internal, domestic, disciplinary and professional tribunals.

MEMBERS:
Anthony Hughes QC (1970)(QC-1990), David Crigman QC (1969)(QC-1989),
Malcolm Morse (1967), Robert Hodgkinson (1968), Michael Dudley (1972),
John Wait (1972), Richard Griffith-Jones (1974), Thomas Busby (1975),
Christopher Millington (1976), Giles Harrison-Hall (1977), Robin Rowland (1977),

HEAD OF CHAMBERS:
Anthony Hughes QC

SEN. CLERK:
Mr. C.T. Hayfield

TENANTS: 31

Rosalind Bush (1978), Benjamin Nicholls (1978), Michael Conry (1979), Melbourne Inman (1979), Stephen Eyre (1981), Thomas Dillon (1983), John Evans (1983), Neal Williams (1984), Simon Ward (1986), Jonathan Salmon (1987), Caroline Baker (1988), Sarah Buxton (1988), Paul Farrer (1988), Richard Atkins (1989), James Puzey (1990), Gary Thornett (1991), Anthony Johnston (1993), Nicholas Smith (1994), Joanne Duffy (1994), Neal Williams (1984).

NUMBER
ONE
FOUNTAIN
COURT

228 3 FOUNTAIN COURT (Colman Treacy QC)
Set No.

3 FOUNTAIN COURT, STEELHOUSE LANE, BIRMINGHAM, W. MIDLANDS, B4 6DR
DX: 16079

TEL: (0121) 236 5854
FAX: (0121) 236 7008

THE CHAMBERS: A long-established set, handling a broad range of civil matters and able to provide counsel at all levels of seniority for criminal cases. A chambers brochure is available on request.

MEMBERS:
Colman Treacy, QC (1971)(QC-1990), Anthony Palmer QC (1962)(QC-1979), Peter Andrews QC (1970)(QC-1991), Conrad Seagroat QC (1970)(QC-1983), David Jones (1967), Donald McConville (1963), Jayne Calderwood (1964), Trevor Faber (1970), Marten Coates (1972), Peter Arnold (1972), Robert Juckes (1974), Sybil Thomas (1976), Philip Parker (1976), Ann Chavasse (1971), Patrick Darby (1978), Michael Burrows (1979), Bernard Linnemann (1980), David Travers (1981), Mark Anderson (1983), Christopher Bright (1985), Andrew Jackson (1986), Francis Laird (1986), David Mason (1986), William Wall (1985), Michael Duck (1988), Andrew Wallace (1988), Adrian Keeling (1990), Carolyn Hilder (1991), Justine Lattimer (1991), Steven Bailey (1992), Matthew Barnes (1992), Tom Storey (1992), Heidi Kubik (1993).

WORK UNDERTAKEN:

Crime: Prosecution and defence work at all levels (including the Court of Appeal). There is a large team of specialists which can deal with the most complex cases. The work covers armed robbery, rape, child abuse, complicated commercial fraud, consumer protection and trade description, police disciplinary tribunals and road traffic.

Civil: Building contracts, chancery, commercial litigation, company law, consumer credit, criminal injuries compensation, defamation, divorce, employment and industrial relations, family provision, insolvency, intellectual property, judicial review, landlord and tenant, licensing, local government, matrimonial finance and property, family and child welfare, mental health tribunals, personal injury compensation, planning, probate and wills, professional and medical negligence, professional disciplinary tribunals, real property and trusts.

RECRUITMENT & TRAINING: There is a policy of active recruitment administered through a pupillage committee. Mini-pupillages are encouraged and expenses reimbursed. Chambers provide generous scholarship awards which give financial assistance through Bar School and pupillage. One carries a guaranteed minimum income for a first-year tenant. Pupillage and tenancy applications should be addressed to Michael Burrows.

HEAD OF CHAMBERS:
Colman Treacy QC

SEN. CLERK:
Jonathon Maskew

TENANTS: 32

4 FOUNTAIN COURT (Richard Wakerley QC)

4 FOUNTAIN COURT, STEELHOUSE LANE, BIRMINGHAM, W. MIDLANDS, B4 6DR
DX: 16074

TEL: (0121) 236 3476
FAX: (0121) 200 1214

THE CHAMBERS: A well-balanced set with 3 Queen's Counsel (all of whom practise from Birmingham) and 28 Juniors, it is chambers' intention to continue to expand along the specialist lines below. The expansion will be gradual and controlled with the emphasis on quality. Chambers see no advantage in being large for the sake of it.

MEMBERS:

R.M. Wakerley QC (1965)(QC-1982) Leader of the Midland and Oxford Circuit,
J. Mitting QC (1970)(QC-1987), J. Saunders QC (1972)(QC-1991),
D.T. Hallchurch (1953), J.F.M. Maxwell (1965), Sir J.A. Watson (1966),
N. Webb (1972), P.A. Thomas (1973), S. Redmond (1975), S. Tonking (1975),
J.V. Cousins (1977), N. Cadbury (1979), S.R.J. Clegg (1980), J. Gosling (1980),
P.A.M. Glenn (1983), M. Parkes (1984), R. Moat (1985), M. Wall (1985),
Mrs C. Wall (1986), Mrs A. Rowley (1987), A.H.K. Smail (1987),
A.S. Muller (1990), A.M. Farrer (1992), J. de Waal (1992), Miss E. Branch (1992),
Miss R. Campbell (1993), P.S. Tiwana (1993), Miss A. Garland (1994).

HEAD OF CHAMBERS:
Richard Wakerley QC

SEN. CLERK:
Mr Rodney Neeld

TENANTS: 28

WORK UNDERTAKEN:

Main Areas of Work: The five principal areas of work undertaken by these chambers are commercial, crime, personal injury, family and licensing. Teams of members of chambers work within each area.

Commercial: *Work includes:* banking and finance house matters (including professional negligence relating to such institutions), building contracts, and sale of goods.

Criminal: Work embraces all areas including fraud, homicide and sexual abuse cases.

Personal Injury: *Work includes:* both plaintiffs' and defendants' work (the latter including work for a number of insurance companies).

Family: *Work includes:* divorce, matrimonial finance and children (including wardship).

Licensing: Work ranges from a simple off-licence to national gaming.

ADDITIONAL AREAS: Substantial groups of members of chambers also specialise in property, landlord and tenant and employment.
Individuals specialise in intellectual property, planning and local government.
Door tenants specialise in revenue law, and immigration.

RECRUITMENT: Applicants with at least a good upper second degree are preferred. Generous pupillage awards are available and negotiable.

5 FOUNTAIN COURT (Anthony Barker QC)

5 FOUNTAIN COURT, STEELHOUSE LANE, BIRMINGHAM, W. MIDLANDS, B4 6DR
DX: 16075 Fountain Ct. Birmingham

TEL: (0121) 606 0500
FAX: (0121) 606 1501

THE CHAMBERS: The chambers are divided into sections, each with its own areas of specialisation. The younger tenants usually gain experience from several disciplines until their particular field of expertise is ascertained, at which point they will join one of the established specialist sections.

These specialist sections currently include Planning, Personal Injury (including medical negligence), Employment, Construction, Intellectual Property, Crime and Licensing, Family, Commercial and Company, Chancery, Property & Insolvency including Landlord & Tenant, Revenue Law.

HEAD OF CHAMBERS:
Anthony Barker QC

SEN. CLERK:
Tony McDaid
SEN. CLERK Tony McDaid

TENANTS: 64

MEMBERS:

Harry Wolton QC (1969)(QC-1982), Anthony Barker QC (1966)(QC-1985),
Douglas Draycott QC (1950)(QC-1965), David Stembridge QC (1955)(QC-1990),
Estella Hindley QC (1971)(QC-1992), Martin Kingston QC (1972)(QC-1992),
Nicholas Worsley QC (1966)(QC-1993), Stephen Linehan QC (1970)(QC-1993),
Gareth Evans QC (1973)(QC-1994), Robert Solman (1958),

Nicholas Budgen (1962) MP, John West (1965), William Wood (1970),
Stephen Oliver-Jones (1970), Michael Elsom (1972), Mark Eades (1974),
Jeremy Cahill (1975), Roger Giles (1976), Anne Smallwood (1977),
Christopher James (1977), David Iles (1977), Kevin O'Donovan (1978),
Paul Bleasdale (1978), Ralph Lewis (1978), Robert Holdsworth (1979),
Jean Draycott (1980), Timothy Newman (1981), Neil Thompson (1982),
Stephanie Brown (1982), Michael Stephens (1983), Andrew McGrath (1983),
Satinder Hunjan (1984), David Stockill (1985), Richard Lee (1985),
Ian Dove (1986), Lorna Meyer (1986), Bernard Thorogood (1986),
Mark Heywood (1986), Simon Drew (1987), Aubrey Craig (1987),
Adam Oyebanji (1987), Eugene Hickey (1988), Malcolm Duthie (1989),
Michael Fay (1989), Martin Liddiard (1989), Stephen Howd (1989),
Sara Williams (1989), Michael Anning (1990), Melanie MacDonald (1990),
Ashley Wynne (1990), Alan Dooley (1991), Mark Radburn (1991),
Michele Friel (1991), Jennifer Jones (1991), Susan Todd (1991),
Hugh O'Brien-Quinn (1992), David Park (1992), Peter Goatley (1992),
Nicholas Xydias (1992), Marc Wilkinson (1992), Nicola Preston (1992),
Hugh Richards (1992), Isabel Hitching (1992), Jonathan Down (1993).

RECRUITMENT & TRAINING: Grants are awarded to successful applicants for pupillages of either 6 or 12 months, although the 2nd 6-month pupillage is generally self-financing from the income earned from existing work available within chambers. Applications should be made in writing to the Head of Chambers, Harry Wolton QC, enclosing a full CV. Applications from experienced and established barristers are treated in the strictest confidence.

231
Set No.

NO.6 FOUNTAIN COURT (Roger Smith QC) 6 Fountain Court, Steelhouse Lane, Birmingham, W. Midlands, B4 6DR **Tel:** (0121) 233 3282 **Fax:** (0121) 236 3600 **DX:** 16076 **Sen. Clerk:** Mike Harris **Tenants:** 27 Expertise in crime, all civil litigation, planning, wills and trusts, insolvency, taxation and matrimonial law.

232
Set No.

7 FOUNTAIN COURT (Rex Tedd QC)

7 FOUNTAIN COURT, STEELHOUSE LANE, BIRMINGHAM, W. MIDLANDS, B4 6DR
DX: 16073

TEL: (0121) 236 8531
FAX: (0121) 236 4408

THE CHAMBERS: A modern, expanding set handling all areas of common law and criminal work. Several members concentrate on complex chancery and commercial litigation. Chambers are associated with 9 Bedford Row, London, WC1R 4AZ, (Stephen Coward QC).

HEAD OF CHAMBERS:
Rex Tedd QC

PRACTICE MANAGER:
Clive Witcomb

CLERKS: Matthew Fleming, Richard Fowler, Duncan Eley

TENANTS: 34

MEMBERS:
Rex Tedd QC (1970)(QC-1993) MA, BCL (Oxon), Henry Graham (1969) MA, BCL (Oxon), Christopher Hotten QC (1972)(QC-1994) LLB, John Randall QC (1978)(QC-1995) (Cantab), Michael Challinor (1974) LLB (Hons), William Davis (1975) LLB (Hons), James Corbett (1975) LLB, LLM, Timothy Jones (1975),
Guy Spollon (1976) BA (Hons), Richard Perks (1977), James Gibbs (1978),
Anthony Warner (1979) BA, James Burbidge (1979) LLB (Hons),
David Worster (1980) MA (Cantab), Kevin Hegarty (1982) LLB,
Petar Starcevic (1983) LLB, Peter Haynes (1983) LLB, J. Edwards (1983),
Roger Dyer (1980) BA, Dip Arch, ARIBA, FCIArb, FASI, Peter McCartney (1983),
David Lock (1985), Anna-Rose Landes (1986) BA (Oxon), Dip Law,
Elizabeth McGrath (1987) LLB, Lawrence Watts (1988) LLB,
Amarjit Singh Rai (1989) LLB, Philip Capon (1990), Conrad Rumney (1989),
Timothy Hanson (1989), Ms Sarah George (1991), Hugh Williams (1992),
Samantha Powis (1985), Julie Moseley (1992), Jane Owens (1994),
Devan Ramersad (1994), P. McCartney (1988).

DOOR TENANTS:
David Farrer QC – 9 Bedford Row, Temple; Timothy Barnes QC – 9 Bedford Row;
John Goldring QC – 9 Bedford Row; Nigel Baker QC – 9 Bedford Row;

Michael Stokes QC (QC-1994) – 1 Kings Bench Walk, Temple; David Lee – 1 Kings Bench Walk, Temple; Howard Morrison OBE – 1 Kings Bench Walk, Temple; Michael Greaves – 22 Albion Place, Northampton; Philip Shears – 9 Bedford Row; Simeon Maskrey QC (QC-1995) – 9 Bedford Row; Nigel Godsmark – 9 Bedford Row.

WORK UNDERTAKEN: Criminal law, including fraud. A broad range of civil matters, including arbitration, aviation law, construction law, consumer credit, defamation, employment, family law (including matrimonial work, wardship and childcare), immigration, judicial review, landlord and tenant, personal injury, planning, professional negligence (especially medical negligence), and trading standards. Chancery and commercial law, including wills and trusts, company law, and insolvency. A general chambers brochure, and also (i) specialist commercial and chancery and (ii) local goverment, planning and enviromental brochures are available upon request.

7 FOUNTAIN COURT

233
et No.

8 FOUNTAIN COURT (John D. Royer) 8 Fountain Court, Steelhouse Lane, Birmingham, W. Midlands, B4 6DR **Tel:** (0121) 236 5514 **Fax:** (0121) 236 8225 **DX:** 16078 **Sen. Clerk:** Christina Maloney **Tenants:** 21 Common law chambers with emphasis on crime, divorce, building disputes and other civil litigation. Also expertise in employment, planning and company/ commercial law.

234
et No.

NEW COURT CHAMBERS (Christopher Morris) Suite 200, Gazette Buildings, 168 Corporation Street, Birmingham, W. Midlands, B4 6TZ **Tel:** (0121) 693 6656 **Fax:** (0121) 693 6657 **DX:** 23533 **Sen. Clerk:** Andrew Butcher **Tenants:** 11 General common law, criminal law, environment, family, housing, immigration, inheritance, landlord and tenant, matrimonial, professional negligence, wardship and childcare.

235
et No.

PRIORY CHAMBERS (Patricia Deeley)

2 FOUNTAIN COURT, STEELHOUSE LANE, BIRMINGHAM, W. MIDLANDS, B4 6DR
DX: 16071

TEL: (0121) 236 3882
FAX: (0121) 233 3205

THE CHAMBERS: Priory Chambers (formerly called 2 Fountain Court), is a well established set that provides a comprehensive and specialist service in virtually all main areas of law.

HEAD OF CHAMBERS:
Patricia Deeley

SEN. CLERK:
Patrick Hawkins

TENANTS: 27

MEMBERS:
Patricia Deeley (1970), Michael Pratt QC (1954)(QC-1976),
David McEvoy QC (1964)(QC-1983), Ronald Newbold (1965),
Michael Garrett (1967), Brian Healy (1967), John Price (1969),
Douglas Readings (1972), Graham Cliff (1973), Patrick McCahill (1975),
William Pusey (1977), Makhan Shoker (1981), David Hershman (1981),
Stephen Campbell (1982), Thomas Rochford (1984), Christopher Adams (1986),
Lance Ashworth (1987), Lorna Findlay (1988), Alison Cook (1989),
Edward Pepperall (1989), Ailsa Cox (1989), Edmund Beever (1990),
Morris Cooper (1979), Andrew Lockhart (1991), Robin Lewis (1991),
Philip Le Cornu (1992), Claire Starkie (1991), Belinda Honess (1993),
Anthony Verduyn (1993).

DOOR TENANTS:
Piers Ashworth QC (1956) (QC-1973), Martin Wilson QC (1963) (QC-1982)

WORK UNDERTAKEN: Commercial law, family law (both matrimonial finance and child care), criminal law and personal injury with specialisations including professional negligence, medical negligence, insolvency, landlord and tenant, administrative law, building and construction work, licensing, inheritance, real property, town and country planning, chancery, company, trade descriptions, food and drugs, weights and measures, local authority work, immigration, mental health, housing, social security, employment and tribunal work.

236
Set No.

ROWCHESTER CHAMBERS (Wilbert A. Harris) Rowchester Chambers, 4 Rowchester Court, Whitall St, Birmingham, W. Midlands, B4 6DH **Tel:** (0121) 233 2327 **Fax:** (0121) 236 7645 **DX:** 16080 **Sen. Clerk:** Andrew M. Trotter **Tenants:** 15 Common law and criminal practice. Main areas are civil litigation, employment, matrimonial, crime and personal injury. One tenant specialises in Health and Safety at Work matters.

237
Set No.

ST. IVE'S CHAMBERS (Edward Coke)

ST. IVE'S CHAMBERS, 9 FOUNTAIN COURT, STEELHOUSE LANE, BIRMINGHAM, W. MIDLANDS, B4 6DR   DX: 16072

TEL: (0121) 236 0863/0929
FAX: (0121) 236 6961

THE CHAMBERS: A forward-looking set, handling a wide variety of work. While continuing to deal with matters across the range of the legal spectrum, chambers' members also specialise in four distinct fields: commercial law, criminal law, family and childcare and personal injury.

MEMBERS:
Edward Coke (1976), Charles Cunningham (1970), Margaret Hodgson (1975), Peter Carr (1976), Roderick Henderson (1978), Julia Macur (1979), Kenneth Bladon (1980), Peter Anthony (1981), Barry Berlin (1981), Michael Keehan (1982), Paul Lopez (1982), Edward Dismorr (1983), Rehna Azim (1984), Peter Grice (1984), David Jackson (1986), Stuart Clarkson (1987), Michael Singleton (1987), Catherine Preen (1988), Jayne Mullen (1989), Andrew Maguire (1988), Janet Newman (1990), Matthew Haynes (1991), Gregory Rogers (1992), Richard Dewsbery (1992), Barbara Schenkenberg (1993), Nicholas Cole (1993), Ian Thomas (1993).

Work Undertaken: Includes consumer law, landlord and tenant work, licensing law, environmental and pollution law, property, road traffic law, sale of goods, trading and environmental health.

LANGUAGES: German, Punjabi and Urdu are all spoken by members of chambers.

HEAD OF CHAMBERS:
Mr. Edward Coke

CLERKS:
Jean Moore, Linda Butler, Craig Travers

TENANTS: 27

238
Set No.

VICTORIA CHAMBERS (Rowland R. Hopkins) Victoria Chambers, 177 Corporation St, Birmingham, W. Midlands, B4 6RG **Tel:** (0121) 236 9900 **Fax:** (0121) 233 0675 **DX:** 23520 **Sen. Clerk:** Sara Richmond **Tenants:** 15 Common law chambers with expertise in crime, family law, and all civil litigation. Also specialise in public and administrative law together with immigration. Developing EC section.

Bournemouth

239
Set No.

LORNE PARK CHAMBERS (Michael Parroy QC)

LORNE PARK CHAMBERS, 20 LORNE PARK ROAD, BOURNEMOUTH, DORSET, BH1 1JN   DX: 7612

TEL: (01202) 292102
FAX: (01202) 298498

THE CHAMBERS: A long established set providing a specialist advocacy and advisory service in London, Bournemouth, Oxford and Winchester on the Western Circuit. Chambers are equipped with spacious conference rooms and computing and word processing facilities and provide a thorough, comprehensive and friendly service. Annexe of 3 Paper Buildings in London.

MEMBERS:
Michael Parroy QC (1969)(QC-1991), David M. Harris QC (1969)(QC-1989), R.A. Fordham QC (1967)(QC-1993), Peter Hughes QC (1971)(QC-1993), Stewart Jones QC (1972)(QC-1994), Harold Hebron (1960), Susan Trevethan (1967), John Haynes (1968), David Swinstead (1970), Derwin Hope (1970),

HEAD OF CHAMBERS:
Michael Parroy QC

SEN. CLERK:
Kevin Turner

TENANTS: 56

Michael Norman (1971), Anthony Ward (1971), Leo Curran (1972),
Peter Jennings (1972), Ben Stephenson (1973), Linda Litchfield (1974),
David Bartlett (1975), Garth Richardson (1975), Richard Tyson (1975),
Peter Henry (1977), Nigel Mitchell (1978), Nigel Seed (1978), Peter Kent (1978),
Ian Partridge (1979), Robert Grey (1979), Nicholas Leviseur (1979),
Timothy Coombes (1980), Paul Cairnes (1980), Ian Edge (1981),
Martin Strutt (1981), Nigel Lickley (1983), Mark Lomas (1983),
Irvine Maccabe (1983), Kate Branigan (1984), Sarah O'Hara (1984),
David Sanderson (1985), Russell Bailey (1985), Christopher Parker (1986),
Elisabeth Hudson (1987), Paul Letman (1987), Helen James (1988) (Door Tenant),
Nicholas Rowland (1988), Patricia Kelly (1988), Paul Hester (1989),
Sally Ball (1989), Guy Opperman (1989), Timothy Bradbury (1989),
Jean Henderson (1990), Amanda Buckley-Clarke (1991), Iain Ross (1991),
David Steenson (1991), Christian Sweeney (1992), Marie Kelly (1992),
Caspar Glyn (1992), Krystyna Kirkpatrick (1992), Robert Weir (1992).

WORK UNDERTAKEN: General common law work and in particular:

Contract/ Commercial: including construction, employment, insurance and sale of goods.

Personal Injury: acting for individuals as well as trade union and insurance company clients.

Professional Negligence: covering all areas of chambers' specialisations.

Crime: including commercial fraud and all manner of crime on the Western Circuit.

Property: including landlord and tenant, housing and other real property and boundary disputes.

Chancery: including company and insolvency.

Family: including financial provision, wardship and Inheritance Act work.

EC: in particular competition and public procurement law.
In addition individual members of chambers specialise in planning, financial services and ecclesiastical work.

ANNEXE CHAMBERS: Chambers have annexes in Bournemouth, Oxford and Winchester.

RECRUITMENT & TRAINING: Four fully-funded 12 month pupillages each year. Applications to Peter Jennings enclosing CV and SAE.

THE CHAMBERS OF MICHAEL PARROY Q.C.

Bradford

40
t No.

BROADWAY HOUSE (Sydney Levine) Broadway House, Bank St, Bradford, W. Yorks, BD1 1TW **Tel:** (01274) 722560 **Fax:** (01274) 370708 **DX:** 11746 **Sen. Clerk:** Neil Appleyard **Tenants:** 28 A general common law set which also has specialists in civil, commercial and chancery.

Brighton

41
t No.

CROWN OFFICE ROW CHAMBERS (Mr Robert Seabrook QC)

BLENHEIM HOUSE, 120 CHURCH STREET, BRIGHTON, E. SUSSEX, BN1 1WH
DX: 36670 Brighton 2

TEL: (01273) 625625
FAX: (01273) 698888

THE CHAMBERS: Chambers have been in Brighton for some 20 years as an Annexe of 1 Crown Office Row, a long-established common law set in the Temple which has maintained strong Sussex connections for nearly half a century. Brighton-based members practise from centrally located modern premises on one floor with the benefit of a lift. The Brighton County and Magistrates' Courts are a few minutes' walk away. Chambers are equipped with modern computer technology and direct telephone and computer links to 1 Crown Office Row. Conference facilities are excellent.

WORK UNDERTAKEN: Chambers undertake all types of general common law work – civil, criminal and family. Particular expertise can be offered in the areas of profes-

HEAD OF CHAMBERS:
Mr Robert Seabrook QC

SEN. CLERK:
Alan G. Smith

CLERK (BRIGHTON): Jenny Lewis

TENANTS: 11

sional negligence, personal injury, landlord and tenant, building, employment, matrimonial property, child care and licensing.

BRIGHTON MEMBERS:

Christopher Smyth (1972), Anthony Niblett (1976), James King-Smith (1980), Janet Waddicor (1985), Paul Rogers (1989), Keeley Bishop (1990), Martin Downs (1990), Jeremy Cave (1992), Judith Clarke (1993), Gabrielle Forrest (1993), Giles Colin (1994).

All Brighton-based members live locally as do the staff who are available between 8.30 am and 6 pm. For a list of London members please see entry for 1 Crown Office Row or contact the Senior Clerk, Alan Smith, on (0171) 797 7500.

RECRUITMENT & TRAINING: Please apply to James King-Smith for pupillages in Brighton.

242
Set No.

SUSSEX CHAMBERS (Paul Ashwell) Sussex Chambers, 9 Old Steine, Brighton, E. Sussex, BN1 1FJ **Tel:** (01273) 607953 **Fax:** (01273) 571839 **DX:** 2724 **Sen. Clerk:** Stewart Dewar **Tenants:** 12 General common law chambers with expertise in criminal law, general civil litigation, matrimonial, commercial, property, and planning law.

Bristol

243
Set No.

ALBION CHAMBERS (J.C.T. Barton QC)

ALBION CHAMBERS, BROAD ST, BRISTOL, BS1 1DR
DX: 7822

TEL: (0117) 9272144
FAX: (0117) 9262569

THE CHAMBERS: A large and still expanding set, the members of which handle a wide variety of specialist legal areas. Chambers accommodation now includes two boardroom-style rooms for major conferences.

HEAD OF CHAMBERS:
J.C.T. Barton QC

SEN. CLERK:
D.H. Milsom

JUNIOR CLERKS: Bonnie Colbeck (criminal), Michael iHarding (civil/family)

TENANTS: 38

BRISTOL MEMBERS:

Charles Barton QC (1969)(QC-1989), Elizabeth Hailstone (1962), Christopher Jervis (1966), Timothy Hills (1968), Nicholas O'Brien (1968), Sally Porter (1970), David Fletcher (1971), Hon David Spens (1972), Paul Barclay (1972), James Tabor QC (1974)(QC-1995), Michael Roach (1975), Neil Ford (1976), Martin Steen (1976), Gavin Chalmers (1979), John Geraint-Norris (1980), Stephen Wildblood (1981), William Hart (1979), Michael Mather-Lees (1981), Martin Picton (1981), Tacey Cronin (1982), Julian Lambert (1983), Caroline Wright (1983), David Gilchrist (1987), Stephen Mooney (1987), Charles Hyde (1988), Claire Wills-Goldingham (1988), Patrick Burrowes (1988), John Livesey (1990), Alexander Ralton (1990), Nkumbe Ekaney (1990), Claire Rowsell (1991), Michael Cullum (1991), Michael Fitton (1991), Simon Burns (1992), Nicholas Sproull (1992), Paul Cook (1992), Allan Fuller (1993), Rebecca Curtis (1993).

Revenue Law: A. Thornhill QC (1969)(QC-1985).

WORK UNDERTAKEN:

Bristol: Individual members practise across a broad range of legal areas, including agriculture, arbitration, banking and securities, general chancery work, commercial and company law, crime (including Courts Martial), employment law, family law, housing, inheritance, insolvency, judicial review, landlord and tenant, local government, Official Referee's business (business contracts, etc), personal injury, planning, professional negligence, property, tribunal work (including employment, disciplinary and mental health tribunals), and trusts, wills and probate law. Members work predominantly on the Western Circuit. A chambers' information booklet is available on request.

RECRUITMENT AND TRAINING: Applications for pupillage to N.M. Ford, with CV. There are usually three or four pupils in chambers, and six- and twelve-month pupillages are available. Interviews are held in November and December, or subsequently by special appointment.

ALL SAINTS CHAMBERS (Simon Quadrat)

ALL SAINTS CHAMBERS, 9-11 BROAD STREET, BRISTOL, BS1 2HP
DX: 7870 Bristol

TEL: (0117) 921 1966
FAX: (0117) 927 6493

THE CHAMBERS: An established set handling a broad range of criminal, civil and family work.

MEMBERS:

Simon Quadrat (1969), David Lane QC (1968)(QC-1991), Brendan Shiner (1955), Roger Carne (1969), R.W. George Threlfall (1972), Steven Whitaker (1973), Ann Darian (1974), Nicholas Fridd (1975) MA (Oxon), Charles Auld (1980), Christopher Taylor (1982), Paul Cadney (1984), Don Tait (1987), Peter Heywood (1988), Ray Tully (1987), Fiona Elder (1988), Jonathan Clarke (1990), Anita Meech (1991), Edward Lucas (1991), Robin Shellard (1992), Sarah MacKean (1992), Roger Harper (1994), Mark Hollier (1994), Rebecca Dennis (1994).

Door Tenants:

Thomas Field-Fisher QC, Patrick Back QC, Rosina Hare QC, Nigel Pascoe QC, David Lane QC, Anthony Donne QC, Philip Gillibrand QC, Michael Dineen.

MAIN AREAS OF WORK: Individual members specialise in a broad range of areas, including criminal law (covering serious crimes and fraud), family, matrimonial and childcare law, town and country planning, landlord and tenant work, general chancery (especially boundary disputes), ecclesiastical law, consumer credit, trading standards (especially cases involving the Food Act), drink-driving, copyright, employment law. There are also members who are experienced in bankruptcy cases, licensing, judicial review, partnership law, personal injury, professional negligence, copyright, and defamation cases.

Some members of chambers accept instructions under the Direct Professional Access scheme. Enquiries should be addressed to the Senior Clerk.

HEAD OF CHAMBERS:
Mr. Simon Quadrat

SEN. CLERK:
Paul Miller

TENANTS: 22

ASSIZE COURT CHAMBERS (Graeme Wood) Assize Court Chambers, 14 Small St, Bristol, BS1 1DE **Tel:** (0117) 9264587 **Fax:** (0117) 9226835 **DX:** 78134 **Sen. Clerk:** Peter Nixon **Tenants:** 23 A general common law set which handles chancery, crime, common law, landlord and tenant, family, commercial law, construction law, mental health law and employment law.

FREDERICK PLACE CHAMBERS (Robert Spicer) 9 Frederick Place, Clifton, Bristol, BS8 1AS **Tel:** (0117) 973 8667 **Fax:** (0117) 973 8667 **Sen. Clerk:** Charlotte Burroughs **Tenants:** 4 Prompt advice and opinions in general civil law; particularly employment law, health and safety at work and succession.

GUILDHALL CHAMBERS (John Royce QC) Guildhall Chambers, Broad Street, Bristol, BS1 2HG **Tel:** (0117) 9273366 **Fax:** (0117) 9298941 **DX:** 7823 **Sen. Clerk:** Mrs Dorothy Hewitt **Tenants:** 36 A broadly based set of chambers with specialists in most fields.

OLD SQUARE CHAMBERS (Hon. John Melville Williams QC)

248
Set No.

HANOVER HOUSE, 47 CORN STREET, BRISTOL, BS1 1HT
DX: 78229 Bristol

TEL: (0117) 9277111
FAX: (0117) 9273478

Old Square Chambers, 1 Verulam Buildings, Gray's Inn, London WC1R 5LQ
DX: 1046

Tel: (0171) 831 0801
Fax: (0171) 405 1387

MEMBERS:
The Hon. John Melville Williams QC (1955)(QC-1977), John Hendy QC (1972)(QC-1987), John Hand QC (1972)(QC-1988), Lord Lord Wedderburn QC (1953)(QC-1990), Jeremy McMullen QC (1971)(QC-1994), Charles Lewis (1963), Professor Bob Hepple (1966), Stephen Zollner (1969), Christopher Carling (1969), William Birtles (1970), Diana Brahams (1972), Christopher Makey (1975), Nigel Cooksley (1975), Charles Pugh (1975), Matthias Kelly (1979), Toby Kempster (1980), Paul Rose (1981), Barry Cotter (1985), Jennifer Lemkey (1987), Louise Chudleigh (1987), Timothy Portwood (1988), Ijeoma Omambala (1988), Jennifer Eady (1989), Philip Meade (1989), Thomas Linden (1989), Damian Brown (1989), Tess Gill (1990), Christopher Walker (1990), Sarah Moor (1991), Ian Scott (1991), Professor Roy Lewis (1992), Helen Gower (1992), Oliver Segal (1992).

HEAD OF CHAMBERS:
Hon. John Melville Williams QC

SEN. CLERK:
John Taylor

TENANTS: 31

WORK UNDERTAKEN: Employment law, personal injury, medical negligence, environmental law, business and mercantile law.

LANGUAGES SPOKEN: French, German, Spanish, Italian, Dutch, Afrikaans, Serbo-Croat, Ibo.

FOREIGN CONNECTIONS: There are door tenants practising at the Hong Kong, Bermuda and Jersey Bars.

OLD SQUARE CHAMBERS

ST. JOHN'S CHAMBERS (Roderick Denyer QC)

249
Set No.

ST. JOHN'S CHAMBERS, SMALL ST, BRISTOL, BS1 1DW
DX: 78138

TEL: (0117) 9213456
FAX: (0117) 9294821

MEMBERS:
Roderick Denyer QC (1970)(QC-1990), Nigel Hamilton QC (1965)(QC-1981), Roger Kaye QC (1970)(QC-1989), Stanley Cartledge (1957), Mark Evans QC (1971)(QC-1995), T. Alun Jenkins (1972), Paul Darlow (1973), Paul Grumbar (1974), Christopher Sharp (1975), Ian Bullock (1975), Nicholas Marston (1975), Timothy Grice (1975), Mark Horton (1976), John Blackmore (1983), Michael Longman (1978), Richard Stead (1979), Robert Duval (1979), Ralph Dixon (1980), Susan Jacklin (1980), Peter Wadsley (1984), Ian Dixey (1984), Richard Bromilow (1977), Leslie Blohm (1982), Glyn Edwards (1987), Simon Morgan (1988), Louise O'Neill (1989), Jean Corston (1991), Julian Ironside (1985), Neil Levy (1986), Guy Adams (1989), Susan Evans (1989), Andrea Hopkins (1992), John Sharples (1992), Richard Williams (1992), Dianne Martin (1992), Christine Bateman (1992), Edward Burgess (1993), Kathryn Skellorn (1993).

HEAD OF CHAMBERS:
Roderick Denyer QC

SEN. CLERK:
Richard Hyde

TENANTS: 37

ASSOCIATE MEMBERS: Professor Nigel Lowe (1972), Professor Roy Light (1992).

WORK UNDERTAKEN: Banking, building disputes and construction law, civil liberties, company and commercial work, corporate and consumer contractual disputes, consumer credit and leasing, crime (including fraud and economic crime), employment law, environmental law, judicial review, landlord and tenant disputes, licensing and planning appeals, matrimonial/ family law, mental health, personal injury, product liability, professional negligence, trading standards and consumer protection, and all chancery matters.

Cambridge

FENNERS CHAMBERS (Jonathan Haworth)

FENNERS CHAMBERS, 3 MADINGLEY ROAD, CAMBRIDGE, CAMBS, CB3 0EE
DX: 5809

TEL: (01223 368761
FAX: (01223) 313007

THE CHAMBERS: Undertake all common law and most chancery work. In the main areas of work, chambers are organised on the basis of groups, consisting of those tenants who practise extensively in that particular field. Identified specialists undertake work in the additional areas of practice. Chambers occupy extensive premises with ample on-site parking and easy access for the disabled. Also at 8-12 Priestgate, Peterborough.

MEMBERS:

Kenneth Wheeler (1956), David Stokes QC (1968)(QC-1989),
Jonathan Haworth (1971), Michael Yelton (1972), Gareth Hawkesworth (1972),
Geraint Jones (1972), Oliver Sells QC (1972)(QC-1995), Andrew Gore (1973),
Lindsay Davies (1975), Susan Espley (1976), Caroline Pointon (1976),
Simon Tattersall (1977), Paul Leigh-Morgan (1978), Tim Brown (1980),
Paul Hollow (1981), Jane Bridge (1981), Stuart Bridge (1981), Martin Collier (1982),
Liza Gordon-Saker (1982), Meryl Hughes (1987), Rebecca Litherland (1987),
George Foxwell (1987), Alasdair Wilson (1988), Andrew Howarth (1988),
Clive Pithers (1989), Timothy Meakin (1989), Hazel Clark (1990),
James Wilson (1991), Phillipa Eade (1992), Nicola Stubbings (1993).

WORK UNDERTAKEN:

Main Areas of Work: Contract and commercial, personal injury, property, crime, matrimonial and family, employment, and planning, local government and environmental law.

Additional Areas: Company and partnership, building contracts, agricultural work, licensing, professional negligence, conveyancing, contentious and non-contentious probate.

NATURE OF CLIENTELE: Includes local government, public utilities, Inland Revenue and Customs and Excise.

RECRUITMENT & TRAINING: Tenancy and pupillage applications to Susan Espley: awards of £10,000 for 12 months pupillage. Contact Alasdair Wilson for student visits/mini-pupillage.

HEAD OF CHAMBERS:
Jonathan Haworth

SEN. CLERK:
Mr. Peter Wright

TENANTS: 28

REGENCY CHAMBERS (Raymond Croxon QC)

2 SALISBURY VILLAS, STATION ROAD, CAMBRIDGE, CAMBS, CB2 2LA
DX: 5834

TEL: (01223) 301517
FAX: (01223) 359267

THE CHAMBERS: A recently established set, whose members and Door Tenants handle a broad range of criminal and civil matters. Also at 18 Cowgate, Peterborough.

MEMBERS:

Raymond Croxon QC (1960)(QC-1983), Catherine Crean (1982),
Marion Lonsdale (1984), Kevin Leigh (1986),
Andrew Martin Tettenborn (1988) LLB MA (Cantab) (L Nov 1988),
Margot Elliott (1989), Ian Martignetti (1990), Jonathan Buckle (1990),
Christopher Ellis (1991), Kerry Cox (1990), Simon Stanyer (1992),
Samuel Roberts (1973), Pauline Bennet (1991).

DOOR TENANTS: Catherine Crean (1982), Marion Lonsdale (1984), Kevin Leigh (1986).

WORK UNDERTAKEN: ·Members practise in all areas of criminal law and civil common law, as well as in the fields of family and child care, employment law, licensing, personal injury, chancery, and landlord and tenant cases. The Door Tenants specialise in construction law, Irish law and EC law, trusts and wills, taxation, planning, commercial law and personal injury. Andrew Tettenborn is a Fellow of Pembroke College, Cambridge.

HEAD OF CHAMBERS:
Raymond Croxon QC

SEN. CLERK:
Anthony Halls

TENANTS: 12

RC
REGENCY CHAMBERS

Canterbury

252
Set No.

BECKET CHAMBERS

17 NEW DOVER ROAD, CANTERBURY, KENT, CT1 3AS	TEL: (01227) 786331
DX: 5330 Canterbury	FAX: (01227) 786329

THE CHAMBERS: Becket Chambers are located only a few minutes walk from the local courts and the city centre. There is a dedicated conference facility, and a large private car park.

The Senior Clerk will be happy to provide further details on any aspect upon request.

MEMBERS:
David Garside (1982), Philip Newton (1984), Ronald Edginton (1984), Kevin Jackson (1984), Christopher Wall (1987), Corey Mills (1987), Jeremy Hall (1988), Gregory Dowell (1990), Clive Styles (1990), Paul Tapsell (1991).

WORK UNDERTAKEN: Chambers undertake all aspects of general common law and criminal work. Members specialise in the following areas: children and family proceedings, matrimonial finance and family provision, medical and professional negligence, personal injury, bankruptcy and insolvency, employment, sale of goods, consumer credit, housing, landlord and tenant, road traffic, licensing, inquests.

SEN. CLERK:
Julie Lewis-Mackay

TENANTS: 10

253
Set No.

STOUR CHAMBERS (Roy Warne) Stour Chambers, Barton Mill House, Barton Mill Road, Canterbury, Kent, CT1 1BP **Tel:** (01227) 764899 **Fax:** (01227) 764941 **DX:** 5342 Canterbury **Sen. Clerk:** Neil Terry **Tenants:** 7 Mainly matrimonial practice also specialising in criminal, personal injury, chancery, medical and professional negligence, landlord and tenant and child law.

Cardiff

254
Set No.

9 PARK PLACE (Philip Rees)

9 PARK PLACE, CARDIFF, S. GLAM, CF1 3TN	TEL: (01222) 382731
DX: 50751 Cardiff 2	FAX: (01222) 222542

THE CHAMBERS: A long established set of chambers, offering varied legal services. Members undertake a broad range of work, although each has particular areas of specialisation. Former members of chambers include a Lord Justice of Appeal, and several circuit judges. Current members include three Queen's Counsel, five recorders and four assistant recorders. Specialisations include: Criminal, personal injury, professional negligence, chancery, planning, commerical, family and employment.

MEMBERS AND WORK UNDERTAKEN:
Philip Rees (1965), Roger Thomas QC (1969)(QC-1994), Ian Murphy QC (1972)(QC-1992), Martyn Kelly (1972), Peter Jacobs (1973), Gregg Taylor (1974), Richard Francis (1974), David Essex Williams (1975), Leighton Davies QC (1975)(QC-1994), Geraint Jones (1976), Richard Twomlow (1976), Ian Pritchard-Witts (1976), Keith Thomas (1977), Gareth George (1977), Nicholas Cooke (1977), Marian Lewis (1977), Philip Davies (1978), Isabel Parry (1979), Ieuan Morris (1979), Milwyn Jarman (1980), Karl Williams (1982), Janet McDonald (1984), Owen Prys Lewis (1985), Susan Ferrier (1985), Andrew Keyser (1986), Peter Brooks (1986), Sarah Jones (1989), Brian Jones (1992), Steven Donoghue (1992), Amanda Johnson (1992), John McGlyne (1993), Hugh Wallace (1993), David Elias (1994).
Several members of chambers are fluent in Welsh.

ASSOCIATED CHAMBERS: Several members of chambers also practise from Farrar's Building, Temple.

HEAD OF CHAMBERS:
Philip Rees

SEN. CLERK:
James Williams

CLERK: Nigel East

CONSULTANT: Charles Crookes

TENANTS: 35

255
et No.

30 PARK PLACE (Philip Richards) 30 Park Place, Cardiff, S. Glam, CF1 3BA **Tel:** (01222) 398421 **Fax:** (01222) 398725 **DX:** 50756 Cardiff 2 **Sen. Clerk:** Huw Davies **Tenants:** 29 General common law set practising in a wide range of civil work, family law and crime.

256
et No.

32 PARK PLACE (Christopher Williams) 32 Park Place, Cardiff, S. Glam, CF1 3BA **Tel:** (01222) 397364 **Fax:** (01222) 238423 **DX:** 50769 **Sen. Clerk:** Mr. David Brinning **Tenants:** 23 Common law chambers with emphasis on crime and family law. Some commercial and landlord and tenant work.

257
et No.

33 PARK PLACE (Wyn Williams QC) 33 Park Place, Cardiff, S. Glam, CF1 3BA **Tel:** (01222) 233313 **Fax:** (01222) 228294 **DX:** 50755 **Sen. Clerk:** Graham Barrett **Tenants:** 27 Senior long established common law and criminal chambers. Specialists in planning, personal injury, local government, employment, licensing and criminal law.

Chelmsford

258
et No.

TINDAL CHAMBERS (A.T.C. Nicholson)

TINDAL CHAMBERS, CHANCELLOR PLACE, BROOMFIELD ROAD, CHELMSFORD, ESSEX, CM1 1SW   DX: 3358

TEL: (01245) 267742
FAX: (01245) 359766

THE CHAMBERS: Established in 1976, the chambers have grown rapidly by placing the qualities of accessibility and understanding alongside analytical and advocacy skills. This means Tindal Chamber's legal resources currently rival many London sets and its highly professional levels of administrative and support services are second to none.

Now, with the addition of London premises, Tindal Chambers can offer the advantages of conference facilities in the Temple and Chelmsford with cost efficient centralised administration.

HEAD OF CHAMBERS:
A.T.C. Nicholson

SEN. CLERK:
Paul A. Green

TENANTS: 23

MEMBERS:
A.T.C. Nicholson (1962), David Moore (1983), Charles Llewellyn (1978), Jonathan Chrispin (1979), John Dagg (1980), Bruce Silvester (1983), John Davis (1983), John Butcher (1984), Tina Harrington (1985), Lesley Carter (1986), Robin Howard (1986), Caroline Beasley-Murray (1988), Joseph Quinn (1988), Andrew Taylor (1989), Craig Rush (1989), Philip Aliker (1990), Anna Williams (1990), Nicholas Bacon (1992), Christopher Paxton (1991), Adam Budworth (1992), Andrew Bailey (1992), Josephine Spratt-Dawson (1993), Jeremy Simison (1993).

Chester

259
t No.

40 KING ST (David Hale) 40 King St, Chester, CH1 2AH **Tel:** (01244) 323886 **Fax:** (01244) 347732 **DX:** 22154 **Sen. Clerk:** Robert King **Tenants:** 25 Chambers' work includes crime, common law, landlord and tenant, family work, employment and chancery.

260
t No.

SEDAN HOUSE (Derek Halbert) Sedan House, Stanley Place, Chester, CH1 2LU **Tel:** (01244) 348282 **Fax:** (01244) 342336 **DX:** 19984 **Sen. Clerk:** Royce V. Parsons **Tenants:** 15 Common law and criminal chambers with some members specialising in planning, chancery, landlord and tenant, agricultural holdings, trade descriptions, local government, licensing, matrimonial and employment.

261 WHITE FRIARS CHAMBERS (K.E.Barnett) 21 White Friars,
Set No. Chester, CH1 1NZ **Tel:** (01244) 323070 **Fax:** (01244) 342930 **DX:** 19979 **Sen.**
Clerk: Robin Whinnett **Tenants:** 18 General common law work including civil,
family and criminal. The civil side has been expanding recently; the criminal and
family areas are extensive and well-established.

Chichester

262 CHICHESTER CHAMBERS (Michael Beckman QC) 3 East
Set No. Pallant, Chichester, W. Sussex, PO19 1TR **Tel:** (01243) 784538 **Fax:** (01243)
780861 **DX:** 30303 **Sen. Clerk:** Jonathan Kay **Tenants:** 12 This is primarily a civil
litigation set with expertise in matrimonial, child care and crime. There are also
commercial (contract, company and fraud) specialists.

Colchester

EAST ANGLIAN CHAMBERS (John Holt)
263
Set No.

53 NORTH HILL, COLCHESTER, ESSEX, CO1 1PY   TEL: (01206) 572756
DX: 3611   FAX: (01206) 562447

THE CHAMBERS: A broadly-based common law set, with chambers also in Ipswich
and Norwich, which aims to provide a comprehensive specialist service across the
legal spectrum. Instructions are accepted from the approved professions under the
Direct Professional Access scheme.

HEAD OF CHAMBERS:
John Holt

SEN. CLERK:
Fraser McLaren

TENANTS: 42

MEMBERS:
John Holt (1970), André de Moller (1965), John Akast (1968),
Caroline Ludlow (1970), John Wardlow (1971), Peter Wain (1972),
Marcus Pearce (1972), Andrew Marsden (1975), Edward Irving (1976),
Stephen Ridley (1977), Timothy McLoughlin (1978), Celia Miller (1978),
David Pugh (1978), Martyn Levett (1978), Peter Fenn (1979),
Graham Sinclair (1979), John Hamey (1979), Anthony Kefford (1980),
John Brooke-Smith (1981), Roderick Newton (1982), Graham Parnell (1982),
Simon Redmayne (1982), Michael Lane (1983), Hugh Vass (1983),
Jane Davies (1983), Lindsay Cox (1984), Janet Bettle (1985), Steven Dyble (1986),
Anthony Bate (1987), Nicholas Elcombe (1987), Jonathan Seely (1987),
Rebecca Degel (1987), Ann Greaves (1989), Andrew Jackson (1990),
John Greenwood (1990), Ray Smith (1991), Sean Hammond (1991),
David Holborn (1991), Marika Bell (1991), Carole Parry-Jones (1991),
Dominic Barratt (1992), Katharine Bundell (1991).

WORK UNDERTAKEN: Agriculture, bankruptcy and insolvency, boundaries and easements, building and construction, general chancery work, commercial and company
law, criminal law, employment law, family law (including childcare and matrimonial
finance), footpaths, fraud, insurance, landlord and tenant, licensing, local authority
work, medical negligence, partnership law, personal injury, town and country planning, property, public and administrative law, and shipping.

ADDITIONAL EXPERTISE: There are five members of the Local Government, Planning
and Environmental Bar Association. Janet Bettle and John Hamey are co-authors of
Personal Injury Claims in the County Court, (Tolley). Anthony Bates MRCVS
specialises also in the law relating to veterinary medicine. Celia Miller has particular
knowledge of horses and the law.

LANGUAGES SPOKEN: French, German, Italian, Spanish and Russian.

EAST
ANGLIAN
CHAMBERS
NORWICH · IPSWICH · COLCHESTER

Coventry

264
Set No.
3 CASTLE YARD (Roy Ashton) Hay Lane, Coventry, Warks, CV1 5RF **Tel:** (01203) 553354 **Fax:** (01203) 559848 **Sen. Clerk:** Andrew Hutchins **Tenants:** 20 An annexe of 22 Albion Place, Northampton.

Eastbourne

265
Set No.
EASTBOURNE CHAMBERS (William Khan) Calverley Walk, 41 South Street, Eastbourne, E. Sussex, BN21 4UP **Tel:** (01323) 416466 **Fax:** (01323) 642102 **DX:** 6925 Eastbourne **Sen. Clerk:** Paul Buckland **Tenants:** 4 A common law set, specialising in criminal, family, immigration, landlord and tenant, sale of goods and personal injury law.

266
Set No.
KING'S CHAMBERS (Stephen Hall-Jones) 27 Gildredge Road, Eastbourne, E. Sussex, BN21 4RU **Tel:** (01323) 416053 **Fax:** (01323) 416110 **DX:** 6931 Eastbourne 1 **Sen. Clerk:** Kevin Barry **Tenants:** 6 Established in December 1992, this set's main areas of practice are company/ commercial, chancery, crime, general common law and family.

Enfield

267
Set No.
ENFIELD CHAMBERS (Peter C.C. Gibbs) First Floor, 36-38 London Road, Enfield, Middx, EN2 6ED **Tel:** (0181) 364 5627 **Fax:** (0181) 364 5973 **DX:** 90638 Enfield 1 **Sen. Clerk:** Kevin Tarrant **Tenants:** 11 A common law chambers with expertise in chancery, immigration, employment, landlord and tenant, crime and family.

Exeter

268
Set No.
BARNFIELD CHAMBERS (Martin Meeke)

BARNFIELD CHAMBERS, 15 BARNFIELD RD, EXETER, DEVON, EX1 1RR
DX: 8330 Exeter

TEL: (01392) 74898
FAX: (01392) 412368

MEMBERS:
Martin Meeke (1973), Richard Merrett (1959), Stephen Lowry (1960), Michael Brabin (1976), David Puttick (1971), David Steele (1975), Richard Crabb (1975), Julie MacKenzie (1978), Mark V. Horton (1981), Mark Whitehall (1983), Terence Holder (1984), Peter M. Ashman (1985), Jonathan Farquharson (1988), Melissa Barlow (1991).

DOOR TENANTS:
Paul Chadd QC (1952)(QC-1973), Richard Rains (1963).

ANNEXE AT: Powlett House, 34 High Street, Taunton, Somerset, TA1 3PY. *Tel:* 01823 324252, *Fax:* 01823 327489, *DX:* 96100 Taunton 1.

HEAD OF CHAMBERS:
Martin Meeke

SEN. CLERK:
Philip Alden

TENANTS: 14

CASTLE CHAMBERS (Christina Gorna)

3 QUEENS TERRACE, EXETER, DEVON, EX4 4HR
DX: 115580 Exeter (St. Davids)

TEL: (01392) 420345
FAX: (01392) 427708

MEMBERS AND WORK UNDERTAKEN: Members of Chambers specialise in the following areas of law:

Christina Gorna (1960): Family, crime, licensing, media and libel law, PI, professional negligence and discrimination. Is the author of several articles on children's matters, with a book in preparation. Also at 4 Paper Buildings, Temple. Broadcasts frequently on legal matters.

Alastair Gunning (1961): Commercial, insurance, insolvency and employment, professional negligence, general common law and family law. London Court of International Arbitration. Also at 4 Paper Buildings, Temple.

Francesca Quint (1970): Chancery, especially: charities and kindred institutions, trusts, wills, land law and conveyancing and ecclesiastical law. Publications on chancery matters.

Marisa Smith (1982): General common law, including family and crime, European Community law, personal injury and Courts Martial.

Graham Howard (1987): General common law including personal injury, medical negligence, and family.

John Lloyd (1988): Planning, public law, judicial review, employment and personal injury. Publications on planning and public law matters.

Michael Berkley (1989): Commercial and contract, landlord and tenant, consumer credit, partnership, professional negligence, general common law, intellectual property and defamation.

Michael Furminger (1991): Family law, especially children and prison law.

Stefan Kolodynski (1993): Landlord and tenant, personal injury, general contract, professional negligence, torts and crime.

Gavin Collett (1993): Planning and environmental law, building, landlord and tenant, crime, (inclu.courts martial) and general common law. Publications on planning.

Lance Ware (1994).

LANGUAGES SPOKEN: French, Italian, German, Dutch.

HEAD OF CHAMBERS:
Christina Gorna
SEN. CLERK:
Mrs Jan Wood
MEMBERS: 11

33 SOUTHERNHAY EAST (David Tyzack)

33 SOUTHERNHAY EAST, EXETER, DEVON, EX1 1NX
DX: 8353

TEL: (01392) 55777
FAX: (01392) 412021

MEMBERS:
David Tyzack (1970), George Meredith (1969), Hugh Lewis (1970), Robert Alford (1970), Alastair Norris (1973), The Hon. Michael Templeman (1973), Christopher Naish (1980), Graham Thrussell (1983), James Hayward (1985), Rebecca Ogle (1989), Jacqueline Ahmed (1988), Aelred Hookway (1990), Emma Crawforth (1992).

WORK UNDERTAKEN: Mainly civil, with strong emphasis on family, and also including personal injury, torts, contract, employment, landlord and tenant, planning and administrative law. To provide a full service, connections have been established with 5 Stone Buildings, Lincoln's Inn (main chambers of Alastair Norris and Michael Templeman, specialising in chancery, professional negligence, trusts and wills); with 2 Essex Court, Temple (commercial, company and insurance matters), and with Pump Court Tax Chambers, 16 Bedford Row (revenue law – personal or commercial). Brochure on request.

HEAD OF CHAMBERS:
David Tyzack
SEN. CLERK:
Joy Daniell
TENANTS: 13

271
Set No.

WALNUT HOUSE (Francis Gilbert QC)

WALNUT HOUSE, 63 ST. DAVID'S HILL, EXETER, DEVON, EX4 4DW
DX: 115582 Exeter St. Davids

TEL: (01392) 79751
FAX: (01392) 412080

THE CHAMBERS: Established in 1972 the chambers now have 16 members including four who sit as recorders and two who sit as assistant recorders. Formerly an annexe of 4 Pump Court, the chambers are now independent although close links remain.

MEMBERS:
Francis Gilbert QC (1970)(QC-1992), Paul Dunkels QC (1972)(QC-1993),
Francis Burkett (1969), Jonathan Barnes (1970), John Neligan (1975),
Geoffrey Mercer (1975), Andrew Chubb (1975), Iain Leadbetter (1975),
Corinne Searle (1982), Sarah Munro (1984), Martin Edmunds (1983),
Michael Melville-Shreeve (1986), Mark Treneer (1987), Andrew Eaton Hart (1989),
Robert MacRae (1990), Shane Lyon (1976).

WORK UNDERTAKEN:
General Description: The work of chambers covers the full range of civil and criminal matters in the South West. Each member of chambers has areas of the law in which he or she takes a particular interest. These the Senior Clerk is always happy to discuss. Each member undertakes legal aid work.
Main Areas of Work: Work undertaken includes construction, courts martial, criminal law, discrimination, employment, family, children, general common law, general chancery, housing, judicial review, landlord and tenant, licensing, matrimonial, mental health, personal injury, planning, police cases, probate, professional negligence, sale of goods, trusts and wills.

HEAD OF CHAMBERS:
Francis Gilbert QC
SEN. CLERK:
David Parker
TENANTS: 16

Guildford

272
Set No.

GUILDFORD CHAMBERS (Jeffrey Widdup)

STOKE HOUSE, LEAPALE LANE, GUILDFORD, SURREY, GU1 4LY
DX: 97863 Guildford 5

TEL: (01483) 39131
FAX: (01483) 300542

THE CHAMBERS: In recent years these chambers have expanded rapidly and they now offer a comprehensive and friendly service across a broad range of family, criminal and civil matters. Members attend conferences at any venue convenient to the client, and appear in courts and tribunals across the country. Several members have lectured at the University of Surrey, and one of the Door Tenants is the Professor of Competition Law at University College, London.

MEMBERS:
Jeffrey Widdup (1973), Suzan Matthews QC (1974)(QC-1993),
Selwyn Shapiro (1979), Jonathan Davies (1981), Simon Oliver (1981),
laire Shrimpton (1983), Matthew Pascall (1984), Paula Clements (1985),
Jacqueline Ross (1985), Janet Haywood (1985), Laura Smallwood (1987),
Jerome Wilcox (1988), Mark Kessler (1988), Janise Narayan (1989),
Jennifer Shaw (1990), George Coates (1990), Ghislaine Watson-Hopkinson (1991),
Richard Button (1993).

WORK UNDERTAKEN:
Common Law and Civil Work: Including landlord and tenant, contract, tort (including professional negligence), personal injuries, building disputes and official referee work, sale of goods, licensing, employment and industrial tribunals, mental health tribunals, inquests and arbitrations.
Family: Including divorce, financial claims, Inheritance Act claims, wardship custody and children cases, adoption, cohabitees and injunctions, the Children Act, and international child disputes.

HEAD OF CHAMBERS:
Jeffrey Widdup
SEN. CLERK:
Richard Moore
TENANTS: 18

Chancery: Including property disputes, rights of way, covenants and boundary disputes, company and partnerships, and insolvency.

Local Government and Public Law: Including planning appeals, enforcement of planning control, pollution, highways, public authority prosecution and defence work, housing law and judicial review.

Crime: All areas including fraud. Chambers has developed a specialisation in cases involving illegal radio stations.

Harrow-on-the-hill

273 **HARROW ON THE HILL CHAMBERS (Marc Beaumont)**
Set No. 60 High Street, Harrow on the Hill, Middx, HA1 3LL **Tel:** (0181) 423 7444 **Fax:** (0181) 423 7368 **DX:** 37601 South Harrow **Chambers Manager:** Michele Acton **Tenants:** 14 A new set of chambers established in 1991. Mainly common law work; also property-oriented chancery work.

Hull

274 **WILBERFORCE CHAMBERS (Lorna Cole)** Wilberforce Chambers,
Set No. bers, 171 High St, Hull, Humbs, HU1 1NE **Tel:** (01482) 23264 **Fax:** (01482) 25533 **DX:** 11940 **Sen. Clerk:** John Kennedy **Tenants:** 19 Although a general common law set, these chambers specialise in family law and civil litigation. Other areas covered include criminal, personal injury, and medical negligence.

Ipswich

275 **EAST ANGLIAN CHAMBERS (John Holt)** 5 Museum St, Ips-
Set No. wich, Suffolk, IP1 1HW **Tel:** (01473) 214481 **Fax:** (01473) 231388 **DX:** 3227 **Sen. Clerk:** Peter Hall **Tenants:** 42 General common law set specialising equally in matrimonial law, civil litigation, and crime. Some planning work also undertaken.

Leeds

276 # ENTERPRISE CHAMBERS (Benjamin Levy)
Set No.

38 PARK SQUARE, LEEDS, W. YORKS, LS1 2PA
DX: 26448 (Leeds Park Square)

TEL: (0113) 2460391
FAX: (0113) 2424802

This is the Leeds branch of Enterprise Chambers, a commercial chancery set at 9 Old Square, Lincoln's Inn, London and provides an ideal venue for regular seminars. All members accept direct professional access work.

MEMBERS: Charles Morgan (1978), Michael James (1976), Hugo Groves (1980), Hugh Jory (1992) are all based in Leeds (for full list of members see Enterprise Chambers, London.

MAIN AREAS OF WORK UNDERTAKEN:
  Banking securities and insolvency
  Building and engineering
  Company, contract and partnership
  Equitable remedies (including Anton Piller and Mareva orders)
  Intellectual property
  Insurance
  Judicial review
  Landlord and tenant and housing

HEAD OF CHAMBERS:
Benjamin Levy

CLERKS:
Carol Shaw (Barry Clayton, Justine Hickman)

TENANTS: 23

Professional negligence (except medical negligence)
Property, building and construction
Trusts, pensions and probate
ADDITIONAL SPECIALISATIONS: include financial services, pension schemes, copyright, water law, shipping disputes, cross border litigation, employment, public utilities and transport law.
LANGUAGES: French, Italian, Portuguese, Spanish.
For further information and details of charging rates, please see the chambers brochure.

277 *Set No.* **GOODBARD HOUSE (F.J. Muller QC)** 3rd Floor Consultation Rooms, Goodbard House, Infirmary St, Leeds, W. Yorks, LS1 2JS **Tel:** (0113) 2451156 **Fax:** (0113) 2445564 **DX:** 26433 **Sen. Clerk:** A. T. Blaney **Tenants:** 18 Consultation rooms for 11 King's Bench Walk, London. Covers general common law matters with various specialisations.

278 *Set No.* **PARK COURT CHAMBERS (Gilbert Gray QC & Brian Walsh QC)** Park Court Chambers, 40 Park Cross St, Leeds, W. Yorks, LS1 2QH **Tel:** (0113) 2433277 **Fax:** (0113) 2421285 **DX:** 26401 **Sen. Clerk:** Roy Kemp **Tenants:** 37 General common law set covering most civil and criminal work including personal injury, landlord and tenant, matrimonial, defamation, employment and licensing.

279 *Set No.*
6 PARK SQUARE (Shaun M. Spencer QC)

6 PARK SQUARE EAST, LEEDS, W. YORKS, LS1 2LW
DX: 26402

TEL: (0113) 2459763
FAX: (0113) 2424395

MEMBERS:
Stephen Williamson QC (1964)(QC-1981), Mr Edward Lyons QC (1952)(QC-1974), S.M. Spencer QC (1968)(QC-1988), S.W. Lawler QC (1971)(QC-1993), J.D. Hitchen (1961), J.F. Winteler (1969), A.R. Clarkson (1971), R. Bartfield (1971), G. Lakin (1972), J. Brennan (1973), Miss Jane Shipley (1974), T. Clayson (1974), Mrs J.C. Kershaw (1974), J.R.W. Goss (1975), R.M.M. Jameson (1976), D.L. Rose (1977), T.H. Stead (1979), Miss Eleanor W. Hamilton (1979), M. Smith (1980), J. Hill-Baker (1983), S. Morris (1983), M. Gargan (1983), R. Frieze (1985), Miss Jill M. Bradshaw (1986), T. Capstick (1986), R. Clews (1986), N.A. Clark (1987), Mrs Madeleine L. Reeds (1988), Mrs S. Smales (1990), Andrew Mitchell (1991), Richard Mansell (1991), Richard Gioserano (1992), Nicholas Hill (1993).

HEAD OF CHAMBERS:
Shaun M. Spencer QC
SEN. CLERK:
Geoffrey Elliott
TENANTS: 33

WORK UNDERTAKEN: General common law work including civil, criminal and family; also chancery work, licensing, planning, employment, insolvency, and environmental.
RECRUITMENT & TRAINING: Pupillage and tenancy applications to Mr. T. Capstick. Pupillage awards available at the discretion of chambers.

280 *Set No.* **10 PARK SQUARE (A.N. Campbell QC)** 10 Park Square, Leeds, W. Yorks, LS1 2LH **Tel:** (0113) 2455438 **Fax:** (0113) 2423515 **DX:** 26412 **Sen. Clerk:** Stephen Collis **Tenants:** 23 Broadly based set covering many areas of the law including company and commercial work, insolvency, crime, family law, personal injuries, landlord and tenant, building and licensing.

25 PARK SQUARE (J.H. Muir)

25 PARK SQUARE, LEEDS, W. YORKS, LS1 2PW
DX: 26408

TEL: (0113) 2451 841
FAX: (0113) 2420 194

THE CHAMBERS: A long-established set which retains the traditional breadth of practice of a provincial circuit chambers, while individual groups of members have developed considerable expertise in a number of specialised areas of law.

HEAD OF CHAMBERS:
John Muir

SEN. CLERK:
Paul Slater

1ST JUNIOR CLERK: Chris Dixon

TENANTS: 24

MEMBERS:
John H. Muir (1968), Lionel H. Scott (1955), Stephen J. Gullick (1971), D. Peter Hunt (1974), Geoffrey C. Marson (1975), Richard L. Newbury (1976), Patrick J.S. Palmer (1978), Charles W. Ekins (1980), Mushtaq A. Khokhar (1982), Steven D. Garth (1983), David M. Gordon (1984), Marilyn A. Fricker (1969), Lynn Driscoll (1981), Gerard M. Heap (1985), Andrew W. Lewis (1985), Mark D. McKone (1988), Stephen Bedeau (1980), Denise L. Gresty (1990), Andrew P. Haslam (1991), Roger A. Birch (1979), David S. Dixon (1992), Nicholas Lumley (1992), Charity E. Rigby (1993), Andrew B. Semple (1993).

DOOR TENANTS:
John Mowbray QC (1953), John MacDonald QC (1955), Eleanor Platt QC (Miss) (1960), Charles Purle QC (1970), George S. Laurence (1972), William D.C. Poulton (1965), Lynton A. Tucker (1971), Colin Braham (1971),Christopher G. Russell (1971), Nicholas Le Poidevin (1975), Stuart Barber (1979), Sara Hill (Mrs) (1979), Robin Andrews (1971), Jane A. Bridge (Mrs) (1981), Margaret McCabe (Miss) (1981), Stephen J. Smith (1983), Leigh Sagar (1983), Claire Staddon (Miss) (1985), Ross Crail (Miss) (1986), Ian Peacock (1990).

WORK UNDERTAKEN: Building disputes, commercial and civil litigation, company law, criminal law, employment law, environmental/pollution law, family law (including childcare and matrimonial finance), housing, immigration, inheritance disputes, insolvency, insurance, judicial review, landlord and tenant, licensing, local authority work, partnership law, personal injury, medical negligence, planning, property law, professional negligence, public law, race relations cases and intellectual property law.

LANGUAGES: French, German, Greek, Hindi, Italian, Punjabi, Urdu, Czech.

32 PARK SQUARE (J.W. Mellor)

32 PARK SQUARE, LEEDS, W. YORKS, LS1 2PF
DX: 26411

TEL: (0113) 243 6388
FAX: (0113) 242 3510

THE CHAMBERS: Specialists in criminal and family law. Also undertake work (including non-contentious and advisory) in a wide range of common law subjects. Advocates with experience in all courts, tribunals and inquiries.

HEAD OF CHAMBERS:
J.W. Mellor

PRACTICE MANAGER:
L.J. McGregor

CLERKS: J.M. Burnley, J. Thompson

TENANTS: 21

MEMBERS:
J.W. Mellor (1953), P. Collier QC (1970)(QC-1992), J.M. Black QC (1976)(QC-1994), A. Kershaw (1975), D.A. McGonigal (1982), M. Haigh (1970) (formerly a solicitor), S.N. Haring (1982), M.S. Rodger (1983), R.M.L. Hallam (1984), K. Buckingham (1986), C.L. Hill (1988), S.K. Fricker (1988), C. Burn (1985), M. Pearson (1984), A. Granville-Fall (1990), J. Hargan (1990), R. Cole (1991), N. Frith (1992), M. Teeman (1993) formerly a solicitor, T. White (1993), I. Shields (1992).

WORK UNDERTAKEN: All aspects of family law: divorce, child care, injunctions; criminal defence and prosecution: common law expertise in personal injury, contract, property disputes, professional negligence, licensing and insolvency.

283
Set No.

37 PARK SQUARE (John Sleightholme)

37 PARK SQUARE, LEEDS, W. YORKS, LS1 2NY
DX: 26405 Leeds

TEL: (0113) 2439422
FAX: (0113) 2424229

MEMBERS:
John Sleightholme (1982), Anthony Richardson (1951), John Hampton (1952),
John Graham (1955), Barbara Wootliff (1956), Rodney Ferm (1972),
John Dunning (1973), Stephen Glover (1978), Paul Kirtley (1982),
Paul Fleming (1983), Freddy Apfel (1986), Jeremy Lindsay (1986),
Amanda Ginsburg (1985), Dawn Tighe (1989), Linda Caines (1990),
Tony Kelbrick (1992), Steven Crossley (1992), Piers Hill (1987),
Caroline Ford (1993), Mark Gore (1994).

WORK UNDERTAKEN: General common law including criminal law, licensing, family
law, personal injury, contract, employment law, company and commercial, landlord
and tenant, real property disputes, planning and local government law.

HEAD OF CHAMBERS:
John Sleightholme

SEN. CLERK:
Mrs. Ann Fothergill

TENANTS: 20

284
Set No.

39 PARK SQUARE (T.M.A. Bubb) 39 Park Square, Leeds, W. Yorks,
LS1 2NU **Tel:** (0113) 2456633 **Fax:** (0113) 2421567 **DX:** 26407 **Sen. Clerk:** Colin
Hedley **Tenants:** 21 Handles common law and chancery, including company com-
mercial, family, personal injury, planning, and landlord and tenant. Also at 7 Lisbon
Square, Leeds LS1 1NY.

285
Set No.

PEARL CHAMBERS (Martin Bethel QC)

PEARL CHAMBERS, 22 EAST PARADE, LEEDS, W. YORKS, LS1 5BU
DX: 26404

TEL: (0113) 2452702
FAX: (0113) 2420683

THE CHAMBERS: The set aims to provide a service to clients across the North Eastern
Circuit. Members practise in all areas of the general common law and the criminal
law, but as chambers continue to expand, the range of individual specialisations is
increasing.

HEAD OF CHAMBERS:
Martin Bethel QC

SEN. CLERK:
John Payne

TENANTS: 20

MEMBERS:
Martin Bethel QC (1965)(QC-1983) MA, LLM (Cantab),
Stuart Brown QC (1974)(QC-1991) BA, BCL (Oxon),
Christopher Storey QC (1979)(QC-1995), Alaric Dalziel (1967),
Howard Elgot (1974) BA, BCL (Oxon), Angela Finnerty (1976) LLB,
Elizabeth O'Hare (1980) LLB (Hons), George Sigsworth (1977) MA (Cantab),
Lindy Armitage (1985) LLB, David Zucker (1986) LLB (Hons),
Christopher Saul (1987) BA (Oxon), Richard L. Barlow (1970) LLB (Lond),
William Hanbury (1985) LLB, Simon Thorp (1988) BA, Joanne Fielding (1989) LLB
Hons, Richard Copnall (1990) BSc, Kaiser Nazir (1991) LLB,
Andrew Axon (1992) BA, Adam Korn (1992) MA, James Murphy (1993) BA Hons.

MAIN AREAS OF WORK: Personal injury (including industrial disease claims), professional negligence (including claims against architects, surveyors, accountants and
solicitors), medical negligence and drug-related injury claims, crime, family law
(including all aspects of ancillary financial relief and custody disputes), contractual
disputes, sale of goods claims, carriage of goods and misrepresentation claims,
employment (both at common law and before tribunals), real property (including
landlord and tenant), general chancery and company law, injunctions and all other
aspects of interlocutory relief, planning, licensing, and taxation (particularly concerning VAT).

ADDITIONAL AREAS: Insurance, business and commercial litigation, housing, local
government, building and engineering disputes, fraud, partnership disputes, defamation, aviation claims and arbitration.

286
Set No.

ST. PAUL'S CHAMBERS (Nigel Sangster)

5TH FLOOR, ST. PAUL'S HOUSE, 23 PARK SQUARE SOUTH, LEEDS,
W. YORKS, LS1 2ND   DX: 26410 Leeds (Park Square)

TEL: (0113) 2455866
FAX: (0113) 2455807

THE CHAMBERS: Founded in 1982, St. Paul's Chambers have expanded to 23 practitioners. Members have complementary areas of expertise with the specific intention of providing a service in most areas of legal work.

MEMBERS:
Nigel Sangster (1976), Timothy R. Newcombe (1972), David C. Wilby (1974),
Peter C. Benson (1975), Colin T. Harvey (1975), Jeremy V. Barnett (1980),
Philip A. Standfast (1980), Jonathan L. Rose (1981), Guy A. Kearl (1982),
Andrew J. Lees (1984), Alison J. Hunt (1986), Howard K. Crowson (1987),
Andrew J. Stubbs (1988), Simon Bickler (1988), Christopher M. Batty (1989),
Jonathan S. Godfrey (1990), Alex Foster (1990), Jonathan Sandiford (1992),
Nicola Saxton (1992), Michael S. Burdon (1993), Sukhbir S. Bassra (1993),
Michael J. Harrison (1994), Alex Bates (1994), John Harrison (1994).
Neil Berragan and Peter F. Feinberg are both door tenants who practise from London chambers. Peter Benson sits as a recorder. Members of chambers belong to the Family Law Bar Association and the Common Law Bar Association.

HEAD OF CHAMBERS:
Nigel Sangster

SEN. CLERK:
Catherine J. Grimshaw

TENANTS: 23

WORK UNDERTAKEN:
Criminal: *Work includes:* the traditional areas of crime with members acting for both prosecution and defence. In addition there are specialists in fraud, serious crime (including violence and sexual offences), breathalyser cases, licensing, Courts Martial, and Firearms Act offences.
Civil: Chambers have particular expertise in personal injury claims, employment, landlord and tenant, Trading Standards cases, family and child care work, matrimonial, professional negligence and police disciplinary cases.

287
Set No.

9 WOODHOUSE SQUARE (John Morris Collins)

9 WOODHOUSE SQUARE, LEEDS, W. YORKS, LS3 1AD
DX: 26406

TEL: (0113) 2451986
FAX: (0113) 2448623

THE CHAMBERS: General common law set with expertise in matrimonial, civil litigation, employment, personal injury, personal tax, wills, trusts, probate and crime; also undertake chancery and company/ commercial work.

MEMBERS:
John M. Collins (1956), Benjamin Nolan QC (1971)(QC-1992),
Sarwar Saleem (1960), Charles R. Sinclair-Morris (1966), Gerald Lumley (1972),
Paul Isaacs (1974), Simon Jack (1974), Rebecca Thornton (1976),
Jeffrey Lewis (1978), Bryan Cox (1979), Raphael Cohen (1981), David Hall (1980),
Helen Hendry (1983), Christopher Dodd (1984), Sarah Greenan (1987),
Austin Newman (1987), Roger Bickerdike (1986), John Stiles (1986),
Jane Hodgson (1989), John Holroyd (1989), Mavis Pilkington (1990),
Steven Lunt (1991), William Tate (1992), Joanna Cross (1992),
Eimear McAllister (1992), Justin Crossley (1993).

HEAD OF CHAMBERS:
John Morris Collins

SEN. CLERK:
Carole Dexter

TENANTS: 26

Leicester

288
Set No.

65-67 KING ST (Graham Buchanan) 65-67 King St, Leicester, Leics, LE1 6RP **Tel:** (0116) 2547710 **Fax:** (0116) 2470145 **DX:** 10873 **Sen. Clerk:** Jeanette Petty **Tenants:** 17 General common law set covering broad range of law, including all civil litigation, planning, personal injury, medical negligence, matrimonial, crime, and employment.

289
et No.

2 NEW ST (Paul Spencer) 2 New St, Leicester, Leics, LE1 5NA
Tel: (0116) 2625906 **Fax:** (0116) 2512023 **DX:** 17404 Leicester 3 **Sen. Clerk:** Neil
Calver **Tenants:** 21 General common law set with specialists in most fields including
crime, civil, commercial, matrimonial, chancery and immigration.

290
et No.

NEW WALK CHAMBERS (Philip C. Bown) 27 New Walk,
Leicester, Leics, LE1 6TE **Tel:** (0116) 255 9144 **Fax:** (0116) 255 9084 **DX:** 10872
Leicester 1 **Sen. Clerk:** Mr. Michael J. Ryan **Tenants:** 23 Handle several areas of
law, including crime, general civil litigation, company and commercial, immigration,
personal injury, professional negligence, matrimonial, building disputes and arbitration.

291
et No.

21 PORTLAND RD (John Whitmore) 21 Portland Road, Leicester,
Leics, LE2 3AB **Tel:** (0116) 2706235 **Fax:** (0116) 2705532 **Sen. Clerk: Tenants:** 2
Expertise in civil liberties and equal opportunities on both a litigation and advisory basis.

Lewes

292
et No.

WESTGATE CHAMBERS (John Collins) Westgate Chambers,
144 High St, Lewes, E. Sussex, BN7 1XT **Tel:** (01273) 480510 **Fax:** (01273)
483179 **DX:** 50250 **Sen. Clerk:** Peter Farrow **Tenants:** 15 Expertise in crime,
general common law, family, personal injury, planning, police cases, employment
and landlord and tenant law.

Liverpool

293
et No.

14 CASTLE ST (Adrian Smith) 14 Castle St, Liverpool, Merseyside,
L2 0NE **Tel:** (0151) 236 4421 **Fax:** (0151) 236 1559 **DX:** 14176 **Practice Manager:** Susan Henshaw **Tenants:** 22 General common law practice with expertise in
most areas of the law.

294
et No.

25-27 CASTLE STREET (Stephen Riordan QC)

25-27 CASTLE STREET, 1ST FLOOR, LIVERPOOL, MERSEYSIDE, L2 4TA
DX: 14224

TEL: (0151) 236 5072
FAX: (0151) 236 4054

THE CHAMBERS: A general common law set.
MEMBERS:
Stephen Riordan QC (1972)(QC-1992), Gerard Wright QC (1954)(QC-1973),
Gerald Baxter (1971), Brian Lewis (1973), Pamela Badley (1974),
Michael Henshell (1975), Anthony Barraclough (1978), Anthony Goff (1978),
Brendan Carville (1980), David Owen (1981), Wendy-Jane Lloyd (1983),
Desmond J. Lennon (1986), Nicholas Johnson (1987), Timothy Kenward (1987),
Edmund Haygarth (1988), Lesley Carter (1990), Ian Harris (1990),
Anya Horwood (1991), Simon Driver (1991), Nigel Power (1992),
Charles Lander (1993), Teresa Loftus (1994).

WORK UNDERTAKEN: Criminal law, family law and civil law including personal injury
litigation and professional negligence for both plaintiff and defendant, contract,
employment, landlord and tenant and licensing.

RECRUITMENT & TRAINING: Please contact Miss Pamela Badley.

HEAD OF CHAMBERS:
Stephen Riordan QC

SEN. CLERK:
Joanne Stapley

TENANTS: 22

295 CHAVASSE COURT CHAMBERS (Andrew Mattison) 2nd
Set No. Floor, Chavasse Court, Lord Street, Liverpool, Merseyside, L2 1TA Tel: (0151) 707
1191 Fax: (0151) 707 1189 DX: 14223 Sen. Clerk: Colin Cubley Tenants: 23
Long-established general set with particular emphasis on criminal work. Also handle
civil litigation, family law, commercial law, and employment.

---

296 # DERBY SQUARE CHAMBERS (John Phipps)
Set No.

REFUGE ASSURANCE HOUSE, DERBY SQUARE, LIVERPOOL,
MERSEYSIDE, L2 1TS   DX: 14213 Liverpool 1

TEL: (0151) 709 4222
FAX: (0151) 708 6311

HEAD OF CHAMBERS:
John Phipps

SEN. CLERK:
Allan Weston

TENANTS: 19

THE CHAMBERS: An established expanding set with members specialising in a number
of different areas of work, particularly industrial accidents and personal injuries,
medical and professional negligence, contract, employment, matrimonial and crime.
   Members offer a wide range of advocacy and advisory skills.
   Members belong to the Family Bar Law Association, Professional Bar Negligence
Association, the Association of Personal Injury Lawyers, the Ecclesiastical Law
Society and the Criminal Bar Association.

MEMBERS AND KEY WORK AREAS: All members handle general common law with the
following special interests:
   John Phipps (1970)Personal injury, professional negligence and local authority work.
   Simon Newton (1970)Occupational Health and Safety, industrial deafness,
WRULD, VWF, major trauma/ injury of utmost severity.
   Graham Morrow (1974)Personal injury, medical negligence, employment, torts
involving police.
   Scott Donovan (1975)Major trauma/ injury of utmost severity, medical negligence,
pharmaceutical product liability, employment, torts involving the police and crime.
   David Brunnen (1976)Personal injury, medical and other professional negligence,
employment law, general contract and torts.
   Tom Ryan (1979)Employment, licensing, planning, administrative law, profes-
sional negligence, personal injury.
   Graham Wells (1981)Personal injury, medical negligence and other professional
negligence, torts involving the police, nuisance, contract.
   James Byrne (1983)Personal injury, negligence, professional negligence, employ-
ment law, crime.
   Bernadette Goodman (1983)Crime, family, employment, mental health, judicial
review and trusts.
   Darren O'Keeffe (1984)General common law excluding family.
   James Prowse (1986)Personal injury, sale of goods, employment, crime.
   Catherine Ellis (1987)Personal injury, contract, landlord and tenant, crime.
   Ann Louise Beattie (1989)Family, personal injury, torts involving the police.
   Ian Garden (1989)Personal injury, general commercial contract, professional and
other negligence, ecclesiastical law.
   Simon Dawes (1990)General common law.
   Frank Ledwidge (1990)Personal injury, torts involving the police, crime.
   Celestine Greenwood (1991)Family, environmental law, crime.
   Timothy Holloway (1991)Personal injury, child law, landlord and tenant (residen-
tial), crime.
   Philippa Jones (1992)General common law.
RECRUITMENT AND TRAINING: One or two pupillages offered most years. Applications
to Scott Donovan with CV.

---

297 EXCHANGE CHAMBERS (William Waldron QC) Pearl As-
Set No. surance House, Derby Square, Liverpool, Merseyside, L2 9XX Tel: (0151) 236 7747
Fax: (0151) 236 3433 DX: 14207 Practice Manager: Tom Handley Tenants: 31 All
aspects of general common law work, with an approximately equal split between civil
and criminal.

98
No.
FIRST NATIONAL BUILDING (John Leach) 2nd Floor, 24 Fenwick Street, Liverpool, Merseyside, L2 7NE **Tel:** (0151) 236 2098 **Fax:** (0151) 255 0484 **DX:** 14167 Liverpool 1 **Sen. Clerk:** Mark Bloor **Tenants:** 10 A small set (founded 1982) which practises mainly criminal law; also family, local authority and civil liberties work undertaken.

99
No.
MARTIN'S BUILDING (R.A. Fordham QC)

2ND FLOOR, MARTIN'S BUILDING, 4 WATER ST, LIVERPOOL,
MERSEYSIDE, L2 3SP   DX: 14232

TEL: (0151) 236 4919
FAX: (0151) 236 2800

THE CHAMBERS: A long-established set of chambers handling the full range of general common law work, with a rapidly developing commercial law practice. Situated in Martin's Building since 1971, chambers have excellent conference facilities and make full use of computer technology. Current members include four Recorders and one Assistant Recorder. Members belong to The Family Law Bar Association, The Bar European Group, The Commercial Bar Association, The Northern Bar Association, The Association of Personal Injuries Lawyers and the Irish Bar.

HEAD OF CHAMBERS:
R.A. Fordham QC

SEN. CLERK:
J. Kilgallon

TENANTS: 24

MEMBERS AND WORK UNDERTAKEN: All members have a general common law practice with the following specialities:

Robert Fordham QC (1968)	Family law, Planning, Licensing, Personal Injury, Crime
David Boulton (1970)	Crime, Fraud, Police Discipline
David Geey (1970)	Personal Injury, Professional Negligence, Employment, Crime, Commercial, Licensing
Andrew McDonald (1971)	Crime, Personal Injury, Professional Negligence, Employment law
David Kerr (1971)	Crime, Sale of Goods, Personal Injury, Negligence
Jack Cowan (1971)	Crime
Rodney Halligan (1972)	Crime
Mary Compton-Rickett (1972)	Crime, Family law, Landlord and Tenant, Mental Health Tribunal work, Personal Injury, Financial Ancillary Relief, Child Law
Antonis Georges (1972)	Crime including Fraud, Personal Injury, Sale of Goods, Administrative Law, Professional Negligence
Stuart Baker (1974)	Personal Injury and Fatal Accidents, Commercial and Consumer, Insurance, Crime, Mental Health, Adminstrative law, Professional Negligence
Graham Morris (1975)	Sale of Goods, Commercial Leasing, Retention of Title clauses, Protection of confidential information, Employment, Personal Injury, Construction law, Professional Negligence
Michael Davis (1979)	Crime, Judicial Review
Andrew Menary (1982)	Personal injury, Crime, Commercial, Building, Landlord & Tenant, Medical Negligence, Police Discipline
Kevin Reade (1983)	Personal Injury, Employment, Family, Child law, Wardship, Matrimonial Finance and Property
Mark Chatterton (1983)	Crime, Family, Insurance, Personal Injury claims involving motor vehicles, Medical Negligence
Deidre McGuire (1983)	Child law, Matrimonial Finance and Property, Personal Injury, Crime
Stephen Knapp (1986)	Crime, Licensing, Personal Injury
Peter Kidd (1987)	Family and child law, Personal Injury, Industrial Accident Litigation, Employment, Landlord & Tenant, General Contract, Consumer credit
Nigel Lawrence (1988)	Crime, Personal Injury, General commercial and contractual, Family and Child care law, Landlord & Tenant, Licensing

Edward Morgan (1989)	Personal Injury, Contractual disputes, Professional Negligence, Landlord & Tenant, General commercial litigation
Andrew Downie (1990)	Crime
Kate Symms (1990)	Crime, Fraud, Family
Timothy Grover (1991)	Personal Injury, Employment, Crime
Nicola Shaw (1992)	Family and Child Law, Crime, Personal Injury, Employment, Matrimonial Finance and Property
Charan Romain (1991)	Family and Child Law, Crime

RECRUITMENT & TRAINING: Applicants for pupillage should have a good degree and should apply to Miss Compton-Rickett.

300
Set No.

20 NORTH JOHN ST (William George)

20 NORTH JOHN ST, LIVERPOOL, MERSEYSIDE, L2 9RL
DX: 14220

TEL: (0151) 236 6757
FAX: (0151) 227 3098

THE CHAMBERS: A well-established set of chancery chambers.

MEMBERS:
William George (1968), Nicholas Orr (1970), David Dennis (1979), Ian Johnson (1982), Neil Cadwallader (1984), Celia Lund (1988), Stephen Pritchett (1989), Graham Sellers (1990), Richard Hall (1991).

WORK UNDERTAKEN: Chancery work (all aspects), landlord and tenant, insolvency, company/ commercial, capital taxation, planning and professional negligence.

ASSOCIATED CHAMBERS: 5 Stone Buildings, Lincoln's Inn, London WC2A 3XT.

HEAD OF CHAMBERS:
Alastair Wilson QC

SEN. CLERK:
Mrs. Barbara Harris

TENANTS: 9

301
Set No.

ORIEL CHAMBERS (Andrew T. Sander)

ORIEL CHAMBERS, 5 COVENT GARDEN, LIVERPOOL, MERSEYSIDE, L2 8UD
DX: 14106 Liverpool LIX: LIV001

TEL: (0151) 236 7191
FAX: (0151) 227 5909

THE CHAMBERS: A broadly based set, the members of which have experience in a number of specialised areas of the law.

MEMBERS:
A.T. Sander * (1970), B.S. Joynes (1957), A. Edwards ^ (1972), W. Rankin (1972), A. Murray ^ (1974), N.A. Wright ^ (1974), R. Bradley (1978), P. Cowan (1980), P. Fogarty (1982), G. Bundred (1982), S. Evans (1985), G. Thomas (1977), A. Fox (1986), P. Goodbody (1986), J. Nicholls (1989), J. Baldwin (1990), A. Sellers + (1991), J. Gruffydd + (1992), H. Belbin (1992), P. Brant (1993), H. Brandon (1993).

* Recorder
^ Assistant Recorder
+ Former solicitor

HEAD OF CHAMBERS:
Andrew T. Sander

SEN. CLERK:
J. Laking

TENANTS: 21

WORK UNDERTAKEN: Arbitration, banking, building, childcare, commercial and company law, general common law, consumer credit, consumer law, criminal law, defamation, disaster litigation, employment law, environmental law, family law, housing, insurance, international trade, landlord and tenant, leasing and factoring agreements, licensing, local government, matrimonial ancillary relief, medical law, partnerships and business arrangements, personal injury, planning, professional negligence, tribunals and inquiries.

302
et No.

PEEL HOUSE (Nigel Gilmour QC)

GROUND FLOOR, PEEL HOUSE, 5-7 HARRINGTON ST, LIVERPOOL,
MERSEYSIDE, L2 9QA   DX: 14225

TEL: (0151) 236 4321
FAX: (0151) 236 3332

THE CHAMBERS: A general common law chambers dealing with all aspects of the laws of tort, contract, crime and family.

MEMBERS:
Nigel Gilmour QC (1970)(QC-1990), Arthur Noble (1965), Martyn Bennett (1969), Christopher Alldis (1970), Philip J. Hall (1973), Neville L. Biddle (1974), Charles Feeny (1977), Heather Lloyd (1979), Thomas Somerville (1979), Titus Gibson (1981), Peter Gregory (1982), James McKeon (1982), Gwynn Price Rowlands (1985), Mark Breheny (1986), Margaret Hickland (1988), Jason Smith (1989), Deborah Gould (1990), Joanne Lewthwaite (1990), Yaqub Rahman (1991), Steven G. Swift (1991), Fiona McNeill (1992), Rory Mates (1993), Roma Gilpin (1993).
Two members of chambers are Recorders of the Crown Court.

WORK UNDERTAKEN: Includes building and construction law, child care law, consumer credit, contract law, work in the Coroner's Court, criminal law (including fraud), divorce and ancillary relief, employment and industrial relations, family and childcare law (including divorce, custody and matrimonial finance), health and safety at work, injunctive and other equitable remedies, judicial review, landlord and tenant, licensing, medical negligence and other professional negligence, personal injury, planning, road traffic, and sale of goods.

HEAD OF CHAMBERS:
Nigel Gilmour QC

SEN. CLERK:
Michael R. Gray

TENANTS: 23

03
t No.

PEEL HOUSE (David Harris QC)

3RD FLOOR, PEEL HOUSE, 5-7 HARRINGTON STREET, LIVERPOOL, MERSEYSIDE, L2 9XN   DX: 14227

TEL: (0151) 236 0718
FAX: (0151) 255 1085

THE CHAMBERS: There are currently 29 members, comprising 1 Queen's Counsel and 28 Juniors.

MEMBERS:
David M. Harris QC (1969)(QC-1989), John Briggs (1953), Michael E. Wolf (1964), Robert K. Atherton (1970), Michael D. Byrne (1971), Raymond C. Herman (1972), Richard P. Brittain (1971), Stephen J. Bedford (1974), Geoffrey J. Lowe (1975), Maureen B. Roddy (1977), Ross Duggan (1978), Graham N. Wood (1979), Gail A. Owen (1980), Simon J. Killeen (1984), Michael J. Kennedy (1985), Jean France-Hayhurst (1987), Charles Davey (1989), Damian Sanders (1988), Simon M. Holder (1989), Rachel Andrews (1989), Louis Browne (1988), Zia Chaudhry (1991), Jonathan Taylor (1991), Patricia Pratt (1991), Jonathan Butler (1992), John Gibson (1993), Benjamin W. Jones (1993), David Flood (1993), Leona Harrison (1993).

WORK UNDERTAKEN:

Main Areas of Work: Chambers practise in the following fields (i) crime, both prosecution and defence, including fraud work; (ii) all aspects of family work, including disputes about children and ancillary relief claims; (iii) personal injury litigation; (iv) commercial disputes; (v) professional negligence claims; (vi) employment law; and (vii) general common law.

Additional Areas: Certain members of chambers have experience in (i) building disputes, (ii) administrative law, (iii) insurance disputes, (iv) landlord and tenant, (v) licensing, (vi) financial services, (vii) company law, partnership disputes, and (viii) contract law.

RECRUITMENT & TRAINING: Normally one pupillage each year. Financial support on merit and subject to negotiation. All pupils stand a good chance of tenancy.

HEAD OF CHAMBERS:
David M. Harris QC

PRACTICE MANAGER/ SEN. CLERK:
J. Robert Moss

CLERK: Helen Berkley

JUNIOR CLERKS: Alastair Webster, Gail Curran, Neil McHugh

TENANTS: 29

304 7 QUEEN AVENUE (Nicholas Riddle)
Set No.

2ND FLOOR, 7 QUEEN AVENUE, LIVERPOOL, MERSEYSIDE, L2 4TZ
DX: 14229

TEL: (0151) 236 8240
FAX: (0151) 227 3005

THE CHAMBERS: A set devoted exclusively to chancery and related commercial work.
MEMBERS:
Nicholas F. Riddle (1970) MA (Cantab), C.R. Green (1982) BA, Dip Law,
S.M. Booth (1985) LLB, John J. McCarroll (1988) LLB (Dublin),
Julie Case (1990) LLB, N.D.K. Jackson (1992) LLB, D.C. Green (1993) LLB.

HEAD OF CHAMBERS:
Nicholas Riddle
SEN. CLERK:
Gary Quinn
TENANTS: 7

305 THE CORN EXCHANGE (David Steer QC & I. Goldrein)
Set No.

THE CORN EXCHANGE CHAMBERS, THE CORN EXCHANGE (5TH FLOOR),
FENWICK ST, LIVERPOOL, MERSEYSIDE, L2 7QS   DX: 14221

TEL: (0151) 227 1081/5009
FAX: (0151) 236 1120

THE CHAMBERS: General common and commercial law set.
MEMBERS:
David Steer QC (1974)(QC-1993), Iain S. Goldrein (1975), W. Gordon Bellis (1972),
Michael J. Pickavance (1974), David Aubrey (1974), Nicholas Gilchrist (1975),
Mark Brown (1975), Michael Abelson (1976), Margaret R. de Haas (1977),
Kevin Grice (1977), Richard Pratt (1980), Neil Flewitt (1981), Henry Riding (1981),
Grant Lazarus (1981), Andrew Loveridge (1983), Philip J. O'Neill (1983),
Donal McGuire (1983), B. Jamil Khan (1986), Peter Davies (1986),
Janet Reaney (1987), Steven Parker (1987), John Lever (1978), Keith Sutton (1988),
Christine Bispham (1991), Trevor Parry-Jones (1992), Fiona Jordan (1991),
Robert Altham (1993), Rachael Hamilton-Hague (1993), Elaine Jones (1984).
David Bulmer (1952), Jonathan Arkush (1977) and Ann Laycock (1980) are door
tenants.
WORK UNDERTAKEN: General commercial and common law including crime; personal injury litigation including product liability and disaster litigation; professional negligence (in particular medical, legal and surveyors') pre-emptive injunctions; employment; family including property distribution on divorce and general child care; landlord and tenant; licensing and local government work.

HEAD OF CHAMBERS:
David Steer QC, I. Goldrein
SEN. CLERK:
Ms Alex Keith
TENANTS: 29

306 VICTORIA CHAMBERS (Vincent Deane)
Set No.
25 Victoria Street, Liverpool, Merseyside, L1 6BD **Tel:** (0151) 236 9402 **Fax:** (0151) 231 1296 **DX:** 14193 **Clerk:** Jenny Connor **Tenants:** 6 General common law chambers with emphasis on crime, family law and civil litigation. Some chancery work.

Maidstone

308 MAIDSTONE CHAMBERS
Set No.
33 Earl St, Maidstone, Kent, ME14 1PF **Tel:** (01622) 688592 **Fax:** (01622) 683305 **DX:** 51982 Maidstone 2 **Sen. Clerk:** Mary Gunner **Tenants:** 10 Maidstone Chambers is a general common law set.

Manchester

309
t No.

BRIDGE ST CHAMBERS (Peter Keenan)

BRIDGE ST CHAMBERS, 72 BRIDGE ST, MANCHESTER, M3 2RJ | TEL: (0161) 834 8468
DX: 14307 | FAX: (0161) 835 2432

THE CHAMBERS: A small set, specialising in chancery and commercial matters.

MEMBERS:
Peter Bernard Keenan (1962) LLB, B.Litt., Peter William Watkins (1952) BCL, MA,
Charles Kim Machin (1973) MA (Oxon), Michael E. Heywood (1975) BSc (Lond),
Richard D. Oughton (1978) MA (Cantab) LLM (Penn),
Sarah L. Harrison (1989) LLB, (Hons)(Leics), Sean Kelly (1990),
Jonathan M. Smith (1991), Sarah Richardson (1993) (Notts),
James Hilsdon (1993) (Cantab), John Leslie Ogilvie Holden (1981) LLB, (Cantab),
Dilys Margaret Gibbons Turner (1961), Matthew Kime (1988).
James Morris (U.S. Resident Attorney).
Michael Heywood also practises from 1 Plowden Buildings, Temple, and Matthew
Kime is also a member of chambers at New Court, Temple.

WORK UNDERTAKEN: Chancery and commercial litigation, advice and drafting with
members specialising in:- Conveyancing, trusts, settlements, wills, probate and family
inheritance, landlord and tenant, companies, partnerships, insolvency, computers and
telecommunications, patents, copyrights, trademarks and designs, planning and compensation, restraint of trade, financial services, pensions, professional negligence,
ecclesiastical law and building contracts.

HEAD OF CHAMBERS:
Peter Keenan

SEN. CLERK:
Miss Nichola Cross (Sen. Clerk)

TENANTS: 14

10
t No.

BYROM CHAMBERS (B.A. Hytner QC) 25 Byrom St, Manches-
ter, M3 4PF **Tel:** (0161) 834 5238 **Fax:** (0161) 834 0394 **DX:** 718156 **Sen. Clerk:**
Peter Collison **Tenants:** 10 General common law set handling a wide range of matters
including contracts, sale of goods, commercial intellectual property, employment law,
crime, family, landlord and tenant and judicial review. Also in London.

11
t No.

DEANS COURT CHAMBERS (H.K. Goddard QC)

DEANS COURT CHAMBERS, CUMBERLAND HOUSE, CROWN SQUARE, | TEL: (0161) 834 4097
MANCHESTER, M3 3HA   DX: 718155 Manchester 3 | FAX: (0161) 834 4805

THE CHAMBERS: A well-established set, numbering among its tenants five silks and
28 juniors. Members appear before courts and tribunals across England and Wales,
including London. Some accept direct access from the approved professions. Enquiries should be addressed to the Clerk of chambers.

MEMBERS:
Harold Keith Goddard QC (1959)(QC-1979), Richard Henriques QC (1967)(QC-1986),
Mark Stephen Eastburn Grime QC (1970)(QC-1987),
Raymond Donatus Machell QC (1973)(QC-1988),
David Andrew Stockdale QC (1975)(QC-1995), Cecil Quixano Henriques (1936),
Richard Kevin Kent Talbot (1970), John Duncan (1971),
John Bromley-Davenport (1972), John Raymond Gregory (1972),
David Thomas Fish (1973), Peter Atherton (1975), Alan James Booth (1978),
Lady Ruth Trippier (1978), Philip Andrew Butler (1979),
Mark George Turner (1981), Craig Gardner Sephton (1981),
Patrick John Field (1981), Stuart Henry McDonald Denney (1982),
Timothy Oliver Trotman (1983), Warwick Timothy Cresswell Smith (1982),
Russell Davies (1983), Anna Louise Bancroft (1985),
Paul Benedict Humphries (1986), Karen Rachel Brody (1986),
Christopher John Hudson (1987), Jonathan Robert Grace (1989),
Nicholas Edward Grimshaw (1989), Andrew Timothy Grantham (1991),

HEAD OF CHAMBERS:
H. K. Goddard QC

SEN. CLERK:
Terry Creathorn

TENANTS: 33

Seamus Ronald Andrew (1991), Janet Ironfield (1992), Mark Savill (1993), Sebastian Clegg (1994).

WORK UNDERTAKEN:

Civil work, including all personal injury matters, commercial disputes (including international litigation), product liability, arbitration (domestic and overseas), professional negligence (particularly solicitors, accountants, doctors, architects, surveyors, civil engineers and insurance brokers), construction and building disputes, insurance law, environmental law and pollution, and consumer credit.

Criminal work, including homicide and sexual offences, commercial fraud, conspiracy, drug importation and supply, and excise and revenue offences.

Family law, covering all areas of the law in this field including the financial consequences of divorce and separation, preservation of assets and injunctive relief, emergency protection for spouses and children, inter-jurisdictional disputes, disputes concerning children and all aspects of the Children Act 1989.

ADDITIONAL AREAS: Individual members' practices also cover general chancery work, agricultural matters, landlord and tenant disputes, judicial review, false imprisonment and wrongful arrest, employment law and industrial relations, markets and fairs.

LANGUAGES SPOKEN: French and German.

ASSOCIATED CHAMBERS: Chambers has an annexe in Preston, and some members are also tenants of sets in London.

312
Set No.
211 DEANSGATE (M.J. Holt) 2nd Floor Central Buildings, 211 Deansgate, Manchester, M3 3NW **Tel:** (0161) 833 1900 **Fax:** (0161) 832 5027 **Sen. Clerk:** Miss Louise Cuttle **Tenants:** 9 Criminal, common law, personal injury, landlord and tenant and matrimonial work undertaken.

313
Set No.
334 DEANSGATE CHAMBERS (Ian Walker McIvor) 334 Deansgate, Manchester, M3 4LY **Tel:** (0161) 834 3767 **Fax:** (0161) 839 6868 **Sen. Clerk:** Helen Sutton **Tenants:** 1 A general common law set of chambers.

314
Set No.

HOLLINS CHAMBERS (Howard Baisden)

HOLLINS CHAMBERS, 64A BRIDGE ST, MANCHESTER, M3 3BA
DX: 14327

TEL: (0161) 835 3451
FAX: (0161) 835 2955

THE CHAMBERS: A set offering a wide range of services encompassing several specialisations as well as the traditional mainstay of general common law and crime.

MEMBERS:

H. Baisden (1972), J. Broadley (1973), N. Fieldhouse (1976), S. Neale (1976), H. Narayan (1970), M. Goldwater (1977), D. Berkley (1979), P. Fallows (1981), D. Uff (1981), Stephen Cogley (1984), L. Blackwell (1985), I. Metcalfe (1985), R. Hartley (1985), M. Monaghan (1987), D. Hymanson (1988), J. Woodward (1989), T. Willitts (1989), L. Webster (1984), M. Willems (1990), J. Cheetham (1990), J. Gregg (1990), R. Dalal (1991), R. Kitching (1989), A. Woodward (1992), S. Nichol (1994), D. Riddell (1993), R. Gee (1993), D. Feetham (1994).

HEAD OF CHAMBERS:
Howard Baisden

SEN. CLERK:
Robert Davis

TENANTS: 28

WORK UNDERTAKEN:

Criminal Law: Including fraud, violent crime and sex offences, and Customs and Excise work.

Commercial Law: Including partnership, insolvency, finance (corporate, consumer and banking), commercial landlord and tenant, employment, general chancery, contentious company law, and pre-emptive remedies.

General Common Law: Including personal injury, building contracts, professional negligence, general crime, and landlord and tenant. `

Family: All areas of the Children Act and matrimonial finance.

Defamation: Including media law.

5 JOHN DALTON ST   (M.J.H. Lamberty)

5 JOHN DALTON ST, MANCHESTER, M2 6ET
DX: 18182

TEL: (0161) 834 6875
FAX: (0161) 834 8557

Very broad-based chambers specialising in all the major areas of legal work.

HEAD OF CHAMBERS:
M.J.H. Lamberty

SEN. CLERK:
T. Mylchreest

TENANTS: 27

MEMBERS:
Sir J.C. Wood (1950), J.C.W Bailey (1966), M. Stalker (1967), K.S. Thomas (1969),
J.C. Wood (1950), M.J.H. Lamberty (1970), R.J.B. Green (1972), M. Stalker (1967),
P.E. Buckley (1972), T.E. Shannon (1974), K.S. Thomas (1969), T.R. Ryder (1977),
N.A. Fewtrell (1977), M.J.H Lamberty (1970), H.S Bradshaw (1977),
P.C. Holmes (1979), R.J.B Green (1972), D.P. Mercer (1980), J.S. Lasker (1976),
P.E. Buckley (1972), 'R. Osman (1974), P.G. Hennell (1982), T.E. Shannon (1974),
J.S.R.C. Barker (1983), H.M. Davies (1982), T.R. Ryder (1977), A.R. Bower (1986),
S. Grocott (1986), N.A. Fewtrell (1977), H.F. Hobson (1987), H.S. Bradshaw (1977),
P.M. Thompson (1990), P.C. Holmes (1979), P.U. Laing (1991), C. Godfrey (1993),
D.P. Mercer (1980), Michael P. Hayton (1994), Laura A. Paonessa (1994),
J.S. Lasker (1976), R. Osman (1974), P.G. Hennell (1982), J.S.R.C. Barker (1983),
H.M. Davies (1982), A.R. Bower (1986), S. Grocott (1986), H.F. Hobson (1987),
P.M. Thompson (1990), P.U. Laing (1991), C. Godfrey (1993),
Michael P. Hayton (1994), Laura A. Paonessa (1994), Andrew Brown (1982).

ANNEXE: Chambers have an annexe in Preston at 4 Camden Place (See under Preston).

KENWORTHY'S CHAMBERS (Frank Burns) Kenworthy's
Chambers, 83 Bridge St, Manchester, M3 2RF **Tel:** (0161) 832 4036 **Fax:** (0161)
832 0370 **Sen. Clerk:** Stuart Johnson **Tenants:** 19 General common law chambers,
with expertise in civil litigation, criminal and C.I.C.B. work, family law and Children's Act, employment, defamation, landlord and tenant, housing, licensing and
personal injury.

8 KING ST (Brendan Hegarty QC)

8 KING ST, MANCHESTER, M2 6AQ
DX: 14354 ISDN 0161 835 1402 X2

TEL: (0161) 834 9560
FAX: (0161) 834 2733

THE CHAMBERS: Chambers have had a long and distinguished history and from an
original bias towards common law a wide range of services has been developed. These
cover the entire field of civil, matrimonial, criminal, chancery and commercial
litigation.

HEAD OF CHAMBERS:
Brendan Hegarty QC

SEN. CLERK:
Peter Whitman

TENANTS: 27

MEMBERS:
Brendan Hegarty QC (1970)(QC-1992) MA, LLB (Cantab),
J.J. Rowe QC (1960)(QC-1982) (Oxon), Keith Armitage QC (1970)(QC-1994) LLB
(Hons), T.J. Mort (1972) BA (Cantab), Elizabeth Rylands (1973) LLB (Hons),
David Eccles (1976) BA (Cantab), Jeffrey Terry (1976) LLB, MA,
Gerard McDermott (1978) LLB, Digby C. Jess (1978) BSc (Hons), LLM, ACIArb,
Ernest Ryder (1981) MA (Cantab), Philip Holmes (1980) MA (Cantab),
Peter Main (1981) LLB, DipPetLaw, Kim Frances Foudy (1982) LLB,
Farooq Tahir Ahmed (1983) LLB, Stephen Davies (1985),
Shirley Worrall (1987) LLB, Michael Joseph Smith (1989) MA (Oxon), BCL,
Ian Wood (1990), Jonathan Thompson (1990) (Cantab) LLM,
Mark Forte (1989) LLB, Christopher Scorah (1991) (Oxon),
Timothy Hodgson (1991) BA D.Phil (Oxon), Joanne Connolly (1992) LLB,
Timothy Edge (1992) (Oxon), Kevin Naylor (1992) CHB LLB LLM,
Kirsten Barry (1993) LLB, John Parr (1989) LLB.

WORK UNDERTAKEN: General common law, commercial and chancery, criminal law, personal injury, medical and professional negligence, employment (including race and sex discrimination), commercial fraud, matrimonial and child care law, landlord and tenant, contract (including building), administrative law, Anglo-American disputes, insurance law, arbitration, environmental law, company law, licensing, construction, sale of goods and consumer credit. Video conferencing is available within chambers.

318
Set No.

40 KING ST (John Hoggett QC)

40 KING ST, MANCHESTER, M2 6BA
DX: 718188

TEL: (0161) 832 9082
FAX: (0161) 835 2139

THE CHAMBERS: A large and well-established set, the members of which appear before the full range of courts and statutory tribunals. Counsel are available at all ranks of seniority, including seven silks, and the breadth of individual specialities and aptitudes available in chambers means that it offers a wide range of specialist advisory and advocacy services.

MEMBERS:

John Hoggett QC (1969)(QC-1986), Andrew Gilbart QC (1972)(QC-1991), Peter Smith QC (1975)(QC-1992), Roger Farley QC (1974)(QC-1993), Stephen Sauvain QC (1977)(QC-1995), Eric Owen (1969), John Jackson (1970), Harold Halliday (1972), Frances Patterson (1977), Alan Evans (1978), Shokat Khan (1979), Vincent Fraser (1981), David Manley (1981), Michael Booth (1981), John Barrett (1982), Sonia Gal (1983), Nicholas Braslavsky (1983), Paul Chaisty (1982), Mark Halliwell (1985), Anthony Crean (1987), Simon Hilton (1987), Katherine Dunn (1987), Ruth Stockley (1988), Fiona Ashworth (1988), Paul Tucker (1990), Geoffrey Pass (1975), Andrew Singer (1990), Lesley Anderson (1989), Matthew Smith (1991), Sally Harrison (1992), Martin Carter (1992), Wilson Horne (1992), Lucy Powis (1992), Mark Harper (1993), Stephen Baker (1994), Sarah Pritchard (1993).

Members have written, edited or contributed to a large number of legal journals, most notably in the fields of planning, local government, and highway law.

ASSOCIATE MEMBERS: John Tackaberry QC (1967) (QC-1982), John Campbell (1981), Julian Ghosh (1993)

MAIN AREAS OF WORK: Town and country planning, local government law and finance, administrative law, parliamentary law, compulsory purchase and compensation, highways law, environmental protection, public health, commercial chancery litigation, landlord and tenant law, law of trusts, partnerships, intellectual property, insolvency (corporate and individual), banking, wills and intestacy, civil liability, personal injury, professional liability, employment and industrial law, building disputes, consumer credit, sale of goods, family and matrimonial law, hire purchase, licensing, and criminal law.

ADDITIONAL AREAS: Markets and fairs, trading standards, EC law, housing, data protection, company law, immigration and defamation.

Members accept Direct Professional Access from the approved professions.

LANGUAGES: French, German, Hungarian, Norwegian, Punjabi, Romanian, Urdu.

HEAD OF CHAMBERS:
John Hoggett QC

SEN. CLERK:
William Brown

ADMINISTRATOR: Mary Daintree

TENANTS: 40

319
Set No.

58 KING ST (Beverly Lunt) 58 King St, First Floor Kingsgate House, 51-53 South King St, Manchester, M2 6DE **Tel:** (0161) 831 7477 **Fax:** (0161) 832 5645 **Sen. Clerk:** Mrs C. Thomas **Tenants:** 16 General common law chambers.

320
et No.

LINCOLN HOUSE CHAMBERS (Mukhtar Hussain QC)
5th Floor Lincoln House, 1 Brazennose Street, Manchester, M2 5EL **Tel:** (0161) 832 5701 **Fax:** (0161) 832 0839 **Sen. Clerk:** Terence Hevicon **Tenants:** 24 A common law set with an extensive practice both prosecuting and defending all areas of criminal work. Particular expertise in immigration law.

321
et No.

LLOYDS HOUSE CHAMBERS (Paul Marshall) 3rd Floor,
Lloyds House Chambers, 18 Lloyd Street, Manchester, M2 5WA **Tel:** (0161) 839 3371 **Fax:** (0161) 832 3371 **DX:** 14388 Manchester 1 **Sen. Clerk:** Barbara Boulton **Tenants:** 6 Mainly criminal law set, specialising in defence work. Also handles some civil work.

322
et No.

MANCHESTER HOUSE CHAMBERS (J.D.S. Wishart)
Manchester House Chambers, 18-22 Bridge St, Manchester, M3 3BZ **Tel:** (0161) 834 7007 **Fax:** (0161) 834 3462 **DX:** 718153 Manchester 3 **Sen. Clerk:** W. Sheldon **Tenants:** 19 General common law set. Practice includes personal injury, matrimonial law, crime and civil litigation.

323
et No.

OLD COLONY HOUSE (Susan Klonin) South King Street (Paul
McDonald), Manchester, M2 6DQ **Tel:** (0161) 834 4364 **Fax:** (0161) 832 9149 **DX:** 18160 Manchester 3 **Sen. Clerk:** L.F. Dooley **Tenants:** 15 A common law set undertaking a broad range of work, with a particular expertise in criminal work.

324
t No.

PEEL COURT CHAMBERS (Michael Shorrock QC)

PEEL COURT CHAMBERS, 45 HARDMAN STREET, MANCHESTER, M3 3HA
DX: 14320

TEL: (0161) 832 3791
FAX: (0161) 835 3054

HEAD OF CHAMBERS:
Michael Shorrock QC

SEN. CLERK:
Donald Waller

TENANTS: 30

THE CHAMBERS: A large general common law set.
MEMBERS:
J.M. Shorrock QC (1966)(QC-1988), J. Hugill QC (1954)(QC-1976), Antony Morris QC (1970)(QC-1991), C.P.L. Openshaw QC (1970)(QC-1991), N.H. Simmonds (1969), H.L. Bentham (1970), P.B. Richardson (1972), S.C. Meadowcroft (1973), A.P. Russell (1974), R.L. Marks (1975), B.L. Lever (1975), A.J.M. O'Byrne (1978), A.R. Wallace (1979), A.P. Long (1981), Mrs. F. Brereton (1979), C. Melton (1982), D.M.W. Pickup (1984), R.W. Pearce (1985), J.R. Taylor (1986), J.G. Grout-Smith (1986), N. Fryman (1989), M. Walsh (1990), Miss R.C. Smith (1990), G.R. Knowles (1990), W. Baker (1991), M. Ainsworth (1992), H. Blackshaw (1993), R. Orme (1993), C. Evans (1994), R. Lloyd-Smith (1994).

WORK UNDERTAKEN: A wide range of common law work is covered, with particular emphasis on crime, medical negligence, licensing (gaming and liquor), family law, including childcare and matrimonial finance, employment law, personal injury and professional negligence. Chambers also handle consumer credit and commercial law, sale of goods, and health and safety law. Members specialise in licensing law – including the four QCs in chambers – European and revenue law.
LANGUAGES SPOKEN: French, German and Mandarin.

325 ST. JAMES'S CHAMBERS (R.A. Sterling)
Set No.

ST. JAMES'S CHAMBERS, 68 QUAY ST, MANCHESTER, M3 3EJ
DX: 14350 M1

TEL: (0161) 834 7000
FAX: (0161) 834 2341

HEAD OF CHAMBERS:
R.A. Sterling

SEN. CLERK:
Stephen J. Diggles

TENANTS: 24

THE CHAMBERS: A chancery and general common law set of chambers.

MEMBERS:
Robert Sterling (1970), Percy Wood (1960), Robert Mundy (1966),
Arthur Stuttard (1967), Maura Logan (1971), Barrie Searle (1975),
Anthony Elleray QC (1977)(QC-1993), David Porter (1980), Timothy Lyons (1980),
Mark Cawson (1982), Edmund Farrell (1981), Michael Mulholland (1976),
David Binns (1983), Richard Quenby (1985), Ian Foster (1988), David Dixon (1983),
Lucy Wilson-Barnes (1989), Jonathan Cannan (1989), Sarah Wheeldon (1990),
Elisabeth Alton (1990), Ruth Tankel (1990), Christopher Cook (1990),
Giles Maynard-Connor (1992), Jonathan Rule (1993).

DOOR TENANT:
Anthony Rubin (1971), Joseph Jaconelli (1972).

WORK UNDERTAKEN:

Chancery: All aspects of property law, including land law, mortgages, nuisance and trespass, rights of way, landlord and tenant, joint property, agricultural holdings work, trusts, settlements and wills; pension schemes; charities; personal property and intellectual property. Business and commercial law, including business agreements and breach of contract; injunctions and other equitable remedies; fraud; professional negligence and indemnity insurance; loans and securities; companies and partnerships; associations; receivers; bankruptcy and insolvency; confidential information; taxation; and tribunals.

Common Law: Including building and construction law; sale of goods; contract law; consumer and consumer credit law; crime; employment law; employer's liability and health and safety at work; environmental law; family (divorce, children, matrimonial finance and property); licensing; personal injuries; professional and medical negligence; police disciplinary hearings; road traffic cases; and tribunals.

OTHER EXPERTISE: Timothy Lyons has written works on inheritance tax and insolvency, and sits on the editorial board of the *Law and Tax Review*.

LANGUAGES: French, German, Hebrew, Russian, and Spanish.

326 9 ST. JOHN STREET (John Hand QC)
Set No.

9 ST. JOHN STREET, MANCHESTER, M3 4DN
DX: 14326

TEL: (0161) 955 9000
FAX: (0161) 955 9001

HEAD OF CHAMBERS:
John Hand QC

CLERKS:
Graham Rogers, Graham Livesey

TENANTS: 35

MEMBERS:
John Hand QC (1972)(QC-1988), Ian Leeming QC (1970)(QC-1988),
Roderick Carus QC (1971)(QC-1990), Charles Garside QC (1971)(QC-1993),
Leslie Portnoy (1961), Christopher St. John Knight (1966), Terence Rigby (1971),
Michael Johnson (1972), Leslie Hull (1972), Christine Riley (1974),
Jonathan Harding (1975), John Dowse (1973), Peter Cadwallader (1973),
Simon Temple (1977), Jonathan Parkin (1978), Michael Murray (1979),
Nicholas Hinchliffe (1980), Timothy Horlock (1981), Nicholas Clarke (1981),
Neil Berragan (1982), Nigel Grundy (1983), Michael P.G. Leeming (1983),
Gillian Irving (1984), Steven Johnson (1984), Paul Gilroy (1985),
Jane Walker (1987), Carlo Breen (1987), Ian Little (1989), Simon James (1988),
Christopher L.P. Kennedy (1989), Nigel Bird (1991), Anthony Howard (1992),
Rachel Wedderspoon (1993), Jaime Hamilton (1993), Tariq Sadiq (1993).

327
et No.

18 ST. JOHN STREET (Rodney C. Klevan QC) 18 St. John Street, Manchester, M3 4EA **Tel:** (0161) 834 9843 **Fax:** (0161) 835 2051 **DX:** 728854 Manchester 4 **Administrator:** Alison Marshall **Tenants:** 30 Common law and chancery set with a substantial criminal practice (prosecuting and defending).

328
et No.

28 ST. JOHN ST (Charles Bloom QC) 28 St. John St, Manchester, M3 4DJ **Tel:** (0161) 834 8418 **Fax:** (0161) 835 3929 **DX:** 728861 Manchester 4 **Senior Clerks:** Jack Pickles/ Christopher Ronan **Tenants:** 40 All-round common law chambers with particular emphasis on personal injury/ crime, commercial, family matters and planning. Some members undertake chancery, landlord and tenant, licensing, and industrial tribunal work.

329
et No.

24A ST. JOHN STREET (Paul Chambers)

24A ST. JOHN STREET, MANCHESTER, M3 4DF

TEL: (0161) 833 9628
FAX: (0161) 834 0243

THE CHAMBERS: An established common law set with wide experience, recently relocated.

MEMBERS:
Paul Chambers (1973), John McNeill (1974), J.P. McClure (1975),
Yvonne R. Coppel (1976), Graham J. Campbell (1982), Keith Harrison (1983),
Peter Harrison (1983), Aftab Khawar (1983), John Chaplin (1986),
Richard Gray (1986), Simon J.G. Crabtree (1988), Paula A. Davitt (1988),
Peter R. Smith (1988), John Barker Wilson (1988), Lisa S. Partington (1989),
Mark Rhind (1989), Alexandra Simpson (1989), Michael Lavery (1990),
Abigail Holt (1993), Finola Barr (1994), Christopher Tehrani (1990).

WORK UNDERTAKEN:

Civil Litigation: Including drafting and advisory work, commercial business, personal injury, professional and medical negligence, landlord and tenant and employment on behalf of Plaintiffs and Defendants.

Child Care and Family Law: Embracing all aspects of divorce, ancillary and financial relief, public and private law, children's proceedings for parents, relatives, Local Authorities and Guardians.

Criminal Law: Wide experience in all areas including company, commercial, revenue and VAT.

HEAD OF CHAMBERS:
Paul Chambers

SEN. CLERK:
Lynn Wallwork

TENANTS: 20

330
t No.

YOUNG STREET CHAMBERS (Christopher Limb) 38 Young Street, Manchester, M3 3FT **Tel:** (0161) 833 0489 **Fax:** (0161) 835 3938 **DX:** 25583 M5 **Sen. Clerk:** Valerie Willeringhouse **Tenants:** 21 Wide ranging common law chambers, with particular emphasis on crime, family law, personal injury, professional negligence, commercial law, and contract.

Middlesbrough

31
t No.

CLEVELAND CHAMBERS (George B. Stewart) 63-65 Borough Rd, Middlesbrough, Clev, TS1 3AA **Tel:** (01642) 226036 **Fax:** (01642) 245987 **DX:** 60549 **Sen. Clerk:** Sean Flaherty **Tenants:** 22 General common law set strong in both criminal and civil litigation. Several members specialise in family and employment law.

332 COUNSELS' CHAMBERS (Stuart Lightwing)
Set No.

YORK HOUSE, BOROUGH ROAD, MIDDLESBROUGH, CLEV, TS1 2HJ
DX: 60524 (Middlesbrough)

TEL: (01642) 213000
FAX: (01642) 213003

THE CHAMBERS: Counsels' Chambers were formed in 1993, and are specifically intended to serve the civil, corporate and family client. Direct professional access is also offered.

MEMBERS:
Stuart Lightwing (1972) (Also Barrister in NSW Aust). Also at 22 Old Buildings, Lincoln's Inn (0171 831 0222). Harmsworth Law Scholar. Chairman of Medical Appeal Tribunals. (LL.B. FCIS. MBIM. FRSA. FCI Arb.).
Luke Swinhoe (1987) B.A., LL.M.
Derek Hall (1994) (Former Solicitor - Admitted 1977) LL.B.

WORK UNDERTAKEN: Administrative law/ judicial review, arbitration, building and construction law, commercial law/ company matters, contract/ sale of goods, employment and unfair dismissal, environmental law, family including children and financial relief, landlord and tenant/ housing/ agricultural holdings, licensing, local government, medical and other professional negligence, personal injury matters, real property and general chancery matters, town and country planning and wills and succession.

HEAD OF CHAMBERS: Stuart Lightwing
CLERK: Mrs Pam Haw
TENANTS: 3

333 FOUNTAIN CHAMBERS (Peter J.B. Armstrong) Cleveland
Set No. Business Centre, 1 Watson Street, Middlesbrough, Clev, TS1 2RQ **Tel:** (01642) 217037 **Fax:** (01642) 232275 **DX:** 60527 **Sen. Clerk:** Robert F. Minns **Tenants:** 19 Broadly-based general chambers specialising in all areas of the law.

Newcastle upon Tyne

334 BROAD CHARE CHAMBERS (Christopher Walton)
Set No.

BROAD CHARE CHAMBERS, 33 BROAD CHARE, NEWCASTLE UPON TYNE, TYNE & WEAR, NE1 3DQ   DX: 61001

TEL: (0191) 232 0541
FAX: (0191) 261 0043

THE CHAMBERS: A large and long-established set, with an increasing range of specialists.
MEMBERS:
Christopher Walton (1973), James Harper (1957), Frederick Such (1960), Euan Duff (1973), Christine Harmer (1973), Timothy Hewitt (1973), J. Ronald Mitchell (1973), Eric Elliott (1974), Paul Batty QC (1975)(QC-1995), Beatrice Bolton (1975), Anthony Hawks (1975), Robin Horner (1975), Patrick Cosgrove QC (1976)(QC-1994), Sally Bradley (1978), Judith Moir (1978), Christopher Dorman O'Gowan (1979), Roderick Hunt (1981), Kester Armstrong (1982), Ian Kennerley (1983), Lesley McKenzie (1983), Pauline Moulder (1983), Anne Richardson (1986), David Rowlands (1988), Carl Gumsley (1989), James Brown (1990), Michelle Temple (1991), S. Anderson (1993), Mark Styles (1988), John O'Sullivan (1984), J. O'Sullivan (1984).
Five members of chambers are Recorders, four are Assistant Recorders and one is a Deputy Chancery Master.

WORK UNDERTAKEN:
Criminal work: all aspects.
Family law: including all aspects of child law, financial disputes, divorce, Inheritance Act cases and emergency protection.
Civil work: including personal injury, professional negligence, general contract, building disputes, employment law, licensing, planning and some commercial.
Chancery work: most aspects.

HEAD OF CHAMBERS: Christopher Walton
SEN. CLERK: Brian Bell
TENANTS: 29

NEW COURT CHAMBERS (David Robson QC)

335
Set No.

NEW COURT CHAMBERS, 3 BROAD CHARE, NEWCASTLE UPON TYNE,
TYNE & WEAR, NE1 3DQ   DX: 61012

TEL: (0191) 232 1980
FAX: (0191) 232 3730

THE CHAMBERS: A large, well-equipped and modern chambers. The breadth of individual members' specialities means that chambers are able to provide a comprehensive advocacy and advisory service for clients throughout the North of England.

MEMBERS:
David Robson QC (1965)(QC-1980) MA, Roger Thorn QC (1970)(QC-1990) LLB,
Roger Moore (1969) LLB, LLM, Timothy Parkin (1971) LLB,
Glenn Gatland (1972) LLB, John Evans (1973) BA, Michael Hodson (1977) Dip Ed,
Jamie Adams (1978) LLB, Ian Graham (1978) MA, David Callan (1979) MA,
Paul Cross (1981) BA, Christopher Prince (1981) BA, Jeremy Freedman (1982) BA,
Philip Kramer (1982) LLB, Peter Schofield (1982) BA, Robin Patton (1983) BA,
Robert Woodcock (1978) LLB, Peter Walsh (1982) BA,
Penelope Moreland (1986) LLB, Paul Richardson (1986) LLB,
Alec Burns (1988) LLB, Sarah Mallett (1988) BA, Hari Menon (1989),
Susan Taylor (1987), Nicholas Cartmell (1990), John Russell Aitken (1984) BA,
Paul Cape (1990), William Brodrick (1991), Julian Smith (1991),
Jonathan Carr (1990), Rachel Smith (1992), Jaime Valles (1992),
James Adkin (1992).

WORK UNDERTAKEN: Includes company and commercial law, courts martial, criminal law, employment law, family law (including all areas of matrimonial and childcare law), insolvency, partnership law, personal injuries, professional negligence claims in all fields, landlord and tenant (including rent review and Part II tenancies generally), arbitration, aviation, official referees' business, taxation and revenue law, wills and probate and ecclesiastical law.

HEAD OF CHAMBERS:
David Robson QC

SEN. CLERK:
Frank Hughes

TENANTS: 33

TRINITY CHAMBERS (J.T. Milford QC)

336
et No.

TRINITY CHAMBERS, 9-12 TRINITY CHARE, QUAYSIDE,
NEWCASTLE UPON TYNE, TYNE & WEAR, NE1 3DF   DX: 61185

TEL: (0191) 232 1927
FAX: (0191) 232 7975

THE CHAMBERS: A long-established chambers, located opposite the new Law Courts on the Quayside. Trinity Chambers provides a broadly-based common law, criminal law and family law service together with a specialist chancery, construction and commercial service for most leading local solicitors and local authorities. Several members will accept instructions under the Direct Professional Access scheme, particularly from accountants, arbitrators, chartered surveyors and architects. Enquiries to Clerk.

MEMBERS:
J.T. Milford QC (1969)(QC-1989), C.L. Kelly (1965), J.H. Fryer-Spedding (1970),
J.J.L. Hargrove (1970), C.J. Knox (1974), A.T. Hedworth (1975), J. Lowe (1976),
C.J.F. Vane (1976), B.C. Forster (1977), M.J. Wilkinson (1979), P.K. Sloan (1981),
J.A. Smart (1981), S.E. Wood (1981), J.D. Richardson (1982), T.H. Spain (1983),
R.S.M. Hudson (1985), P.T.G. Walling (1986), I.D. Atherton (1988),
C.T. Goodwin (1988), R.B. Cooper (1989), S.A. Jarron (1990),
Timothy Gittins (1990), F. McCrae (1987), S.J. McKinnell (1991),
C.A. Oliver (1990), R.G.S Adams (1993), A.M. Ditchfield (1993).
Four members of chambers are Recorders. One is Chairman of the VAT Tribunal.
One is part time Chairman of the Industrial Tribunal. One sits as an arbitrator.
David Allen (1989) who practises at 7 King's Bench Walk is a door tenant.

WORK UNDERTAKEN:
Main Areas of Work: Administrative law; chancery, including land law, administration of estates, trusts, charities and Court of Protection; commercial law, including banking, insurance, sale of goods, carriage of goods, shipping, commercial credit, company and insolvency law; company law; competition law and restraint of trade;

HEAD OF CHAMBERS:
J.T. Milford QC

SEN. CLERK:
Colin Hands

TENANTS: 25

construction and engineering law and related professional negligence matters; consumer credit law; contractual disputes; criminal law; employment disputes, particularly Industrial Tribunal work; environmental and public utilities law; family law; insolvency law; landlord and tenant law; licensing law; local government law; matrimonial law; medical negligence; partnership law; personal injury; professional negligence; rating; and tax and EC law relating to all the preceding fields.

Additional Areas of Work: There are groups of practitioners specialising solely in chancery law, construction and commercial law, family law and criminal law, who are thus able to offer a specialist service not ordinarily found on circuit.

337 67 WESTGATE RD (Ian Dawson)
Set No.

67 WESTGATE RD, NEWCASTLE UPON TYNE, TYNE & WEAR, NE1 1SG
DX: 61044

TEL: (0191) 261 4407
FAX: (0191) 222 1845

THE CHAMBERS: A broadly based general common law and chancery set, offering a comprehensive service for local solicitors and local authorities.

HEAD OF CHAMBERS:
Ian Dawson

SEN. CLERK:
Philip Alexanders

TENANTS: 15

MEMBERS:
Ian Dawson (1971), Antony Braithwaite (1971), Geoffrey Hunter (1979), Thomas Finch (1981), Brian Mark (1981), David Mason (1984), Richard Selwyn Sharpe (1985), Anthony Davis (1986), Shaun Routledge (1988), Joseph O'Brien (1989), Susan Boothroyd (1990), Claire Middleton (1991), Michael James (1989), Sarah Woolrich (1994).

WORK UNDERTAKEN:

Chancery: Including charities, land law, landlord and tenant, mortgages, probate, settlements and wills, trusts, and related fields of taxation law.

Commercial: Including admiralty, business agreements and breach of contract, carriage of goods by road and sea, company law, competition, construction law, consumer credit, injunctions and other equitable remedies, insolvency, insurance, partnerships, professional negligence, restraint of trade, and related areas of EC and tax law.

General Common Law: Including contract disputes, conversion, hire purchase, medical negligence, nuisance, personal injury, sale of goods and trespass.

Family: Including all aspects of financial disputes, divorce and private and public family law.

Criminal Law

Public Administrative Law: Including judicial review, local government, and town and country planning.

Employment Law: Mr David Mason is a part-time Regional Chairman of the Industrial Tribunals.

Newport

338 NEWPORT CHAMBERS (Hilary Roberts) 12 Clytha Park Rd,
Set No.
Newport, Gwent, NP9 4SL **Tel:** (01633) 255855 **Fax:** (01633) 253441 **DX:** 33208
Newport **Sen. Clerk:** Antony Naylon **Tenants:** 11 General common law set with particular emphasis on crime, personal injury, employment and family work.

Northampton

339 22 ALBION PLACE (Roy Ashton) 22 Albion Place, Northampton,
Set No.
Northants, NN1 1UD **Tel:** (01604) 36271 **Fax:** (01604) 232931 **DX:** 12464 **Sen. Clerk:** Andrew Hutchins **Tenants:** 18 Busy and expanding set undertaking a variety of work, especially family, and criminal and civil litigation, now with an annexe in Coventry.

340
et No.

1 KING'S BENCH WALK (James Hunt QC) 24 Albion Place, Northampton, Northants, NN1 1VD **Tel:** (01604) 602333 **Fax:** (01604) 601600 **DX:** 18544 Northampton 2 **Sen. Clerk:** Graeme Logan **Tenants:** 35 Annexe of 1 King's Bench Walk. London.

Norwich

341
et No.

EAST ANGLIAN CHAMBERS (John Holt) East Anglian Chambers, 57 London Street, Norwich, Norfolk, NR2 1HL **Tel:** (01603) 617351 **Fax:** (01603) 633589 **DX:** 5213 **Sen. Clerk:** Gill Wilkins **Tenants:** 38 Established in three centres in East Anglia (also in Colchester and Ipswich) chambers have a general common law practice with a 60/ 40 civil litigation/ crime ratio.

342
et No.

OCTAGON HOUSE CHAMBERS (Paul H. Downes) Octagon House Chambers, 19 Colegate, Norwich, Norfolk, NR3 1AT **Tel:** (01603) 623186 **Fax:** (01603) 760519 **DX:** 5249 **Sen. Clerk:** Corinne Ashton **Tenants:** 15 A mixed common law set with extensive criminal prosecution and defence work. The civil side includes matrimonial, company and commercial work.

Nottingham

343
et No.

NO.1 HIGH PAVEMENT (John B. Milmo QC)

NO.1 HIGH PAVEMENT, NOTTINGHAM, NOTTS, NG1 1HF
DX: 10168 Nottingham

TEL: (0115) 9418218
FAX: (0115) 9418240

THE CHAMBERS: This specialist criminal set of chambers was established on the 1st of January 1990 to provide a comprehensive service to both prosecution and defence in all aspects of criminal work including serious fraud. For details of areas of expertise of individual barristers please contact the Senior Clerk.

HEAD OF CHAMBERS:
John B. Milmo QC

SEN. CLERK:
David Duric

TENANTS: 35

MEMBERS:
John B. Milmo QC (1966)(QC-1984), Peter Joyce QC (1968)(QC-1991), John Warren QC (1968)(QC-1994), John Deave (1952), William Joss (1957), Peter Walmsley (1964), John Machin (1965), Jonathan Teare (1970), Andrew Congdon (1973), Michael Pearce (1975), Stuart Rafferty (1975), John Burgess (1978), Guy Napthine (1979), Paul Mann (1980), Gregory Dickinson (1981), Shaun Smith (1981), Balraj Bhatia (1982), Timothy Palmer (1982), Maureen Baker (1984), Godfrey Napthine (1983), Errol Ballentyne (1983), Audrey Campbell-Moffat (1987), Clive Stockwell (1988), Michael Evans (1988), Christopher Geeson (1989), Richard Thatcher (1989), James McNamara (1990), Michael Auty (1990), Andrew Easteal (1990), Avik Mukherjee (1990), Kate Hargreaves (1991), Dawn Pritchard (1992), Paul King (1992), Sarah Munro (1990), Robert Manning (1992), Steven Coupland (1993).

344
t No.

KING CHARLES HOUSE (Richard Inglis)

KING CHARLES HOUSE, STANDARD HILL, NOTTINGHAM, NOTTS, NG1 6FX
DX: 10042

TEL: (0115) 9418851
FAX: (0115) 9414169

THE CHAMBERS: Chambers have for many years provided specialist barrister services to solicitors throughout the Shires of Nottingham, Derby, Lincoln, Leicester, Stafford, South Yorkshire and Humberside. Almost all areas of law are covered individually amongst the 34 specialist tenant members of King Charles House Chambers, whose chambers' clerks will gladly advise of choice of specialist practitioners, to take up the clients particular case whether it be litigious or advisory in nature.

HEAD OF CHAMBERS:
Richard Inglis

SEN. CLERK:
Geoff Rotherham

TENANTS: 34

MEMBERS:

Richard Inglis (1971), Michael O'Connell (1966), Eric Dumbill (1971),
William Everard (1973), John Stobart (1974), Keith Jackson (1975),
James Howlett (1980), Vivien Buchanan (1981), Martin Elwick (1981),
Sara Richards (1981), Stephen Lowne (1981), Richard Toombs (1983),
Amanda Cranny (1984), Pami Dhadli (1984), Kevin Salmon (1984),
Patrick Gallagher (1984), Caroline Bradley (1985), Mohammed Zaman (1985),
Rowena Bridge (1975), Michael Cranmer-Brown (1986),
Mark Van der Zwart (1988), Katherine Skinner (1988), Ian Way (1988),
Jonathan Dee (1989), Mark Knowles (1989), Sharron McNeilis (1990),
Margo Ford (1991), Adrian Jackson (1990), Jane Morris (1991),
Alastair Munt (1989), Jonathan Straw (1992), Richard Jones (1991),
Libby Grimshaw (1993), Jeremy Janes (1992).

WORK UNDERTAKEN: Virtually all main areas of law are covered including: building, chancery, commercial, company, crime, employment, family, intellectual property, landlord and tenant, licensing, negligence, personal injury and town and country planning. Chambers have developed teams of specialists to provide a wide variation of expertise and experience across the whole price range.

TRAINING AND RECRUITMENT: Chambers will always consider tenancy applications from experienced and well qualified existing barristers who wish to develop and specialise their practices. Pupillages are awarded to suitable applicants for either 6 or 12 months and excellent financial assistance is available. All applications together with CV should be addressed to Richard Inglis, the Head of Chambers.

345 ROPEWALK CHAMBERS (Richard Maxwell QC)
Set No.

24 THE ROPEWALK, NOTTINGHAM, NOTTS, NG1 5EF
DX: 10060

TEL: (0115) 9472581/2/3/4
FAX: (0115) 9476532

HEAD OF CHAMBERS:
Richard Maxwell QC

SEN. CLERK:
David Austin

TENANTS: 29

THE CHAMBERS: Ropewalk Chambers provide a comprehensive and specialised, largely civil advocacy service, together with all the necessary advice and paperwork for proceedings in most courts, inquiries and tribunals throughout the country. The administration and clerking provide an efficient infrastructure. Chambers are open from 8.00am to 6.00pm and provide conference rooms (up to 20 people) (with full facilities for the disabled) and client car parking.

MEMBERS:

R. Maxwell QC (1968)(QC-1988), W.C. Woodward QC (1964)(QC-1985),
A. Goldstaub QC (1972)(QC-1992), I. McLaren QC (1962)(QC-1993),
H. Swindells QC (1974)(QC-1995), Richard Anthony Payne (1964),
G.M. Jarand (1965), G.E. Machin (1965), R. Swain (1969), R.H. Burns (1967),
A. Berrisford (1972), S. Beresford (1976), R.F. Owen (1977), S. Gash (1977),
A.W. Hampton (1977), S. Beard (1980), J. Adams (1982), R. Coe (1983),
D. Nolan (1985), B.J. Clark (1985), A. Prestwich (1986), P. Limb (1987),
S.P.I. Din (1984), A. Nightingale (1987), P. Turton (1989), T. Stewart (1989),
C. Fisher (1990), Jonathan Mitchell (1992), Professor Michael Bridge (1994).

WORK UNDERTAKEN:

Personal Injury - including industrial and insidious disease, (asbestos induced, asthma, cancer, dermatitis, poisoning, radiation, stress, RSI and VWF), road traffic and industrial disaster, medical accidents, product liability, health and safety at work, medical negligence.

Business and Property - including commercial, (banking, corporate finance, sale of goods, consumer credit and protection, competition) company, professional negligence, (legal, financial and negligence within the building, engineering and surveying professions) building, construction, engineering, landlord and tenant, (commercial, residential, agricultural and housing) chancery, (boundaries, conveyancing, easements, inheritance, probate, wills and trusts) intellectual property.

Employment - (Wrongful and unfair dismissal, restrictive covenants, trade secrets discrimination).

Planning and Environment - including administrative, compulsory purchase heritage, judicial review, local government, lands tribunal, pollution, nature conservation, rating.

Family Law - Matrimonial, finance and property, wardship and children.

Also Full Arbitration - including alternative dispute resolution facilities.

CLIENTELE: All clients, without discrimination, insurance company, trade union, corporate, local government, privately funded or otherwise. Direct Professional Access is available.

CHARGES AND FURTHER INFORMATION: Please contact David Austin, Chambers Clerk on 0115 947 2581

346
et No.

ST. MARY'S CHAMBERS **(Christopher Butler)** 50 High Pavement, Nottingham, Notts, NG1 1HW **Tel:** (0115) 9503503 **Fax:** (0115) 9583060 **DX:** 10036 **Sen. Clerk:** David Wilson **Tenants:** 31 General wide-ranging common law, crime and matrimonial chambers.

Oxford

347
et No.

1 ALFRED STREET   (Michael Parroy QC)

1 ALFRED STREET, HIGH STREET, OXFORD, OXON, OX1 4EH
DX: 4302

TEL: (01865) 793736
FAX: (01865) 791631

THE CHAMBERS: A long established set providing a specialist advocacy and advisory service in London, Bournemouth, Oxford, Winchester and on the Western Circuit. Chambers are equipped with spacious conference rooms and computing and word processing facilities and provide a thorough, comprehensive and friendly service. Annexe of 3 Paper Buildings in London.

For conference facilities contact London chambers.

HEAD OF CHAMBERS:
Michael Parroy QC

TENANTS: 56

MEMBERS:

Michael Parroy QC (1969)(QC-1991), David M. Harris QC (1969)(QC-1989),
R.A. Fordham QC (1967)(QC-1993), Peter Hughes QC (1971)(QC-1993),
Stewart Jones QC (1972)(QC-1994), Harold Hebron (1960), Susan Trevethan (1967),
John Haynes (1968), David Swinstead (1970), Derwin Hope (1970),
Michael Norman (1971), Anthony Ward (1971), Leo Curran (1972),
Peter Jennings (1972), Ben Stephenson (1973), Linda Litchfield (1974),
David Bartlett (1975), Garth Richardson (1975), Richard Tyson (1975),
Peter Henry (1977), Nigel Mitchell (1978), Nigel Seed (1978), Peter Kent (1978),
Ian Partridge (1979), Robert Grey (1979), Nicholas Leviseur (1979),
Timothy Coombes (1980), Paul Cairnes (1980), Ian Edge (1981),
Martin Strutt (1981), Nigel Lickley (1983), Mark Lomas (1983),
Irvine Maccabe (1983), Kate Branigan (1984), Sarah O'Hara (1984),
David Sanderson (1985), Russell Bailey (1985), Christopher Parker (1986),
Elisabeth Hudson (1987), Paul Letman (1987), Helen James (1988) (Door Tenant),
Nicholas Rowland (1988), Patricia Kelly (1988), Paul Hester (1989),
Sally Ball (1989), Guy Opperman (1989), Timothy Bradbury (1989),
Jean Henderson (1990), Amanda Buckley-Clarke (1991), Iain Ross (1991),
David Steenson (1991), Christian Sweeney (1992), Marie Kelly (1992),
Caspar Glyn (1992), Krystyna Kirkpatrick (1992), Robert Weir (1992).

THE CHAMBERS OF MICHAEL PARROY Q.C.

WORK UNDERTAKEN: General common law work and in particular:

Contract/ Commercial: including construction, employment, insurance and sale of goods.

Personal Injury: acting for individuals as well as trade union and insurance company clients.

Professional Negligence: covering all areas of chambers' specialisations.

Crime: including commercial fraud and all manner of crime on the Western Circuit.

Property: including landlord and tenant, housing and other real property and boundary disputes.

Chancery: including company and insolvency.
Family: including financial provision, wardship and Inheritance Act work.
EC: in particular competition and public procurement law.
   In addition individual members of chambers specialise in planning, financial services and ecclesiastical work.
ANNEXE CHAMBERS: Chambers have annexes in Bournemouth, Winchester and Oxford.
RECRUITMENT & TRAINING: Four fully-funded 12 month pupillages each year. Applications to David Sanderson enclosing CV and SAE.

---

348 **HARCOURT CHAMBERS (Patrick Eccles QC)** Harcourt
Set No. Chambers, Churchill House, 38 St. Aldates, Oxford, Oxon, OX1 1BA **Tel:** (01865) 791559 **Fax:** (01865) 791585 **DX:** 4371 **Sen. Clerk:** Brian Wheeler **Tenants:** 21 Annexe of 2 Harcourt Buildings (Patrick Eccles QC), London.

349 **KING'S BENCH CHAMBERS (Graeme Williams QC)**
Set No. King's Bench Chambers, Wheatsheaf Yard, High St, Oxford, Oxon, OX1 4EE **Tel:** (01865) 791654 **Fax:** (01865) 791659 **DX:** 4318 **Sen. Clerk:** Stephen Buckingham **Tenants:** 35 Connected to 13 King's Bench Walk, London. Contract, commercial, personal injury, landlord and tenant, building, licensing, employment, professional negligence, planning, family and criminal law.

Peterborough

350 # FENNERS CHAMBERS (Jonathan Haworth)
Set No.

FENNERS CHAMBERS, 8-12 PRIESTGATE, PETERBOROUGH, CAMBS, PE1 1JA	**TEL:** (01733) 62030
DX: 12314 Peterborough 1	**FAX:** (01733) 343660

MEMBERS:
   Kenneth Wheeler (1956), Jonathan Haworth (1971), Michael Yelton (1972), Gareth Hawkesworth (1972), Geraint Jones (1972), Andrew Gore (1973), Lindsay Davies (1975), Susan Espley (1976), Caroline Pointon (1976), Simon Tattersall (1977), Paul Leigh-Morgan (1978), Tim Brown (1980), Paul Hollow (1981), Jane Bridge (1981), Stuart Bridge (1981), Martin Collier (1982), Liza Gordon-Saker (1982), Meryl Hughes (1987), George Foxwell (1987), Rebecca Litherland (1987), Alasdair Wilson (1988), Andrew Howarth (1988), Clive Pithers (1989), Timothy Meakin (1989), Hazel Clark (1990), James Wilson (1991), Phillipa Eade (1992), Nicola Stubbings (1993).
Also at 3 Madingley Road, Cambridge. Please see the Cambridge entry.

HEAD OF CHAMBERS:
Jonathan Haworth

SEN. CLERK:
Mr Peter Wright

TENANTS: 28

---

351 **REGENCY CHAMBERS (Raymond Croxon QC)** 18 Cowgate,
Set No. Peterborough, Cambs, PE1 1NA **Tel:** (01733) 315215 **Fax:** (01733) 315851 **DX:** 12349 Peterborough 1 **Sen. Clerk:** Roy Bromwich **Tenants:** 13 General common law, family and crime. Individual specialists in commercial, construction, planning and tax. Branch in Cambridge.

Pinner

352 **WESTGATE CHAMBERS (John Collins)** Paramount House, 23-
Set No. 25 Bridge Street, Pinner, Middx, HA5 3HR **Tel:** (0181) 429 4833 **Fax: DX:** 35605 Pinner **Sen. Clerk:** Maureen Flanagan **Tenants:** 25 An annexe of Westgate Chambers, Lewes, with a general common law practice.

Plymouth

53
No. **DEVON CHAMBERS (Richard Hough)** 3 St. Andrew Street, Plymouth, Devon, PL1 2AH **Tel:** (01752) 661659 **Fax:** (01752) 601346 **DX:** 8290 Plymouth 2 **Sen. Clerk:** Mrs Roberta Kaye **Tenants:** 10 Small common law set undertaking general civil law, matrimonial and criminal cases (defence and prosecution).

54
No. **KING'S BENCH CHAMBERS (Anthony Donne QC)** King's Bench Chambers, 115 North Hill, Plymouth, Devon, PL4 8JY **Tel:** (01752) 21551 **Fax:** (01752) 664379 **DX:** 8254 **Sen. Clerk:** Mr. R. L. D. Plager **Tenants:** 50 Annexe of 2 King's Bench Walk, London.

Poole

55
No. **EATON HOUSE (Rupert Massey)** First Floor, 4 Eaton Road, Branksome Park, Poole, Dorset, BH13 6DG **Tel:** (01202) 766301 **Fax:** (01202) 766301 **Sen. Clerk:** Jean Alexander-Brown **Tenants:** 2 Handles general common law matters.

Portsmouth

56
No. **COLLEGE CHAMBERS (Robin Belben)** 3 Hampshire Terrace, Portsmouth, Hants, PO1 2QF **Tel:** (01705) 833220 **Fax:** (01705) 828419 **DX:** 2212 **Sen. Clerk:** Wayne Effeny **Tenants:** 12 General common law chambers, family and crime, with specialists in planning, betting and gaming and other licensing, and child care work.

57
No. **GUILDHALL CHAMBERS PORTSMOUTH (Edo de Vries)** Prudential Buildings, 16 Guildhall Walk, Portsmouth, Hants, PO1 2DE **Tel:** (01705) 752400 **Fax:** (01705) 753100 **DX:** 2225 Portsmouth 1 **Sen. Clerk:** Tristan Thwaites **Tenants:** 7 A recently established common law set of chambers handling a wide range of law including landlord and tenant, tax, personal injury, professional negligence, family and crime.

58
No.
PORTSMOUTH BARRISTERS' CHAMBERS (Andrew Parsons)

THE PORTSMOUTH CHAMBERS, 'VICTORY HOUSE' 7 BELLEVUE TERRACE, SOUTHSEA, PORTSMOUTH, HANTS, PO5 3AT   DX: 2239

TEL: (01705) 831292
FAX: (01705) 291262

MEMBERS:
  Andrew J. Parsons (1985), Martin Green (1989), John Barker (1992), Lincoln Brookes (1992), Timothy Concannon (1993), Matthew Gilpin (1993).

DOOR TENANTS: Guy J. Russell (1985).

WORK UNDERTAKEN:

General Description: Chambers undertake the whole spectrum of common law and chancery work and have specialists in financial services and commercial law.

Main Areas of Work: Commercial, company, construction, environment, family, financial services, insolvency, landlord and tenant, licensing, matrimonial, personal injury, professional negligence, property, sale of goods.

HEAD OF CHAMBERS:
Mr. Andrew Parsons

SEN. CLERK:
Jackie Morrison

TENANTS: 6

Preston

359
Set No.
4 CAMDEN PLACE (Mark Lamberty) 4 Camden Place, Preston, Lancs, PR1 3JL **Tel:** (01772) 828300 **Fax:** (01772) 825380 **DX:** 17156 Preston 1 **Sen. Clerk:** Terence Mylchreest **Tenants:** 27 Annex of 5 John Dalton Street, Manchester M2 6ET.

360
Set No.
DEANS COURT CHAMBERS (Harold Goddard QC) 41-43 Market Place, Preston, Lancs, PR1 1AH **Tel:** (01772) 555163 **Fax:** (01772) 555941 **Sen. Clerk:** Trevor Doyle **Tenants:** 32 Annexe of Deans Court Chambers, Manchester.

361
Set No.
NEW BAILEY CHAMBERS (Pat Bailey) 10 Lawson Street, Preston, Lancs, PR1 2QT **Tel:** (01772) 258087 **Fax:** (01772) 880100 **DX:** 25266 Preston 2 **Sen. Clerk:** Alastair G.R. Campbell **Tenants:** 12 A common law set with expertise in chancery, personal injury, family, commercial and crime.

362
Set No.
15 WINCKLEY SQUARE (R.S. Dodds)

15 WINCKLEY SQUARE, PRESTON, LANCS, PR1 3JJ
DX: 17110 Preston

TEL: (01772) 252828
FAX: (01772) 258520

THE CHAMBERS: A medium sized set, seeking to provide a comprehensive service to solicitor clients both in private and institutional practice throughout the town, the county and beyond into Cumbria, Manchester and Merseyside.

MEMBERS:
R.S. Dodds (1976), R.M. Baldwin (1969), Barbara J. Watson (1973),
Simon Newell (1973), Robert Crawford (1976), P. Nicholas D. Kennedy (1977),
Timothy G. White (1978), Richard A. Haworth (1978), David J. Kenny (1982),
Jane E. Cross (1982), Anthony Cross (1982), Paul Hart (1982), Roger Lowe (1984),
John Woodward (1984), Richard M. Hunt (1985), D. Mark Stuart (1985),
Richard J. Bennett (1986), P. Bruce Henry (1988), P.J. Anderson (1988),
Kathryn Johnson (1989), Samantha Bowcock (1990), Simon Burrows (1990),
Paul Creaner (1990), Michael Whyatt (1992), Louise Harvey (1991),
Marie Mitchell (1991), Julie Taylor (1992), Emma Cornah (1992),
Frazer Livesey (1992), Paul Hague (1983).

MEMBERSHIP: Several tenants are members of the Family Law Bar Association.

WORK UNDERTAKEN: All common law work with particular emphasis and experience in all areas of family work, crime, contract, personal and industrial injury, licensing, planning, landlord and tenant and employment law. Work on a Direct Access basis is accepted.

HEAD OF CHAMBERS:
R.S. Dodds

SEN. CLERK:
Michael Jones

TENANTS: 29

WINCKLEY
15
SQUARE

Reading

363
Set No.
CHAMBERS OF NEVILLE DIGBY

172 FRIAR STREET, READING, BERKS, RG1 1HE
DX: 54723 Reading 2

TEL: (01734) 575888
FAX: (01734) 583111

THE CHAMBERS: Established in October 1992 in premises close to Reading County Court, this civil set is conveniently situated for all courts in Berkshire and the Thames Valley.

MEMBERS:
Neville Digby (1977), Clifford Joseph (1975) MA (Oxon)*, LMRTPI,
Manjeet Mendhir (1980), Miss Anne Bulloch (1988), Dr Roger Smithers (1990),
Miss Susan Glanville (1991), Miss Robina Omar (1991),
Mrs Felicity Mitchell (1992), Pramod Joshi (1992).
* Solicitor (1957) # Member of the Malaysian Bar

HEAD OF CHAMBERS:
Neville Digby

TENANTS: 9

WORK UNDERTAKEN: Chambers contain members with expertise in most areas of civil practice including banking, chancery, company and commercial, consumer credit, crime, employment, family (Children Act, domestic violence and ancillary relief), intellectual property (patents, copyright and design, passing off, trade and service marks), landlord and tenant, personal injury and personal insolvency, planning and local government and judicial review.

Members belong to specialist Associations including the Insolvency Lawyers Association, the Patent Bar Association, and the Royal Town Planning Institute.
LANGUAGES SPOKEN: French, German, Hindi, Malay, Punjabi and Urdu.

Redhill

364
et No.

REDHILL CHAMBERS (Richard Mandel) Seloduct House, 30 Station Road, Redhill, Surrey, RH1 1NF **Tel:** (01737) 780781 **Fax:** (01737) 761760 **DX:** 100203 Redhill 1 **Sen. Clerk:** Jan Rogers **Tenants:** 22 General common law set, with several members also practising criminal and family law. Also at 11 Bolt Court, London.

Sheffield

365
et No.

BANK HOUSE CHAMBERS (Mr J. Durham'Hall QC)

OLD BANK HOUSE, HARTSHEAD, SHEFFIELD, S. YORKS, S1 2EL
DX: 10522

TEL: (0114) 2751223
FAX: (0114) 2768439

THE CHAMBERS: A medium sized set, handling a wide range of general common law and criminal matters, with individual practitioners specialising in a particular field.
Membership: Several tenants are members of the Family Bar Association.
WORK UNDERTAKEN: All aspects of criminal, and most aspects of civil litigation (especially personal injury work) are covered, including tribunal and arbitration work. Members specialise in civil, criminal or family law.

HEAD OF CHAMBERS:
Mr J. Durham'Hall QC

CLERKS:
Miss D. Peat, Mrs D. Chilton

TENANTS: 19

366
et No.

FIGTREE LANE CHAMBERS (D. Gothorp) 19 Figtree Lane, Sheffield, S. Yorks, S1 2DJ **Tel:** (0114) 2759708 **Fax:** (0114) 2724915 **DX:** 10629 Sheffield 1 **Sen. Clerk:** Lesley D. Inman **Tenants:** 10 General common law with expertise in crime, personal injury, planning, labour law, landlord and tenant, licensing, matrimonial, professional negligence and chancery.

367
et No.

12 PARADISE SQUARE (Roger Keen QC) 12 Paradise Square, Sheffield, S. Yorks, S1 2DE **Tel:** (0114) 2738951 **Fax:** (0114) 2760848 **DX:** 10565 **Sen. Clerk:** Tim Booth **Tenants:** 22 Cover every aspect of general common law including crime, matrimonial, etc.

Solihull

368
et No.

BERKELEY CHAMBERS (Anthony Smith QC) 321 Stratford Road, Shirley, Solihull, W. Midlands, B90 3BL **Tel:** (0121) 733 6925 **Fax:** (0121) 733 6926 **DX:** 13865 Shirley 2 **Sen. Clerk:** Elizabeth Butler **Tenants:** 3 A small set specialising in planning and building work.

Southampton

369
Set No.

17 CARLTON CRESCENT (Mr Jeremy Gibbons QC)

17 CARLTON CRESCENT, SOUTHAMPTON, HANTS, SO15 2XR
DX: 96875 Southampton Carlton Crescent

TEL: (01703) 320320
FAX: (01703) 320321

MEMBERS:
Jeremy S. Gibbons QC (1973)(QC-1995), Jonathan M. Fulthorpe (1970),
Anthony J.S. Coleman (1973), Peter J.H. Towler (1974), Michael P. Kolanko (1975),
William H. Webster (1975), Nicholas Somerset Haggan (1977), Hugh Merry (1979),
Margaret Anne Pine-Coffin (1981), Malcolm T.P. Gibney (1981),
Timothy D. Howard (1981), Philip A. Glen (1983), Michael W. Forster (1984),
Gary A. Grant (1985), Dylan R. Morgan (1986), Timothy K. Moores (1987),
Simon Edwards (1987), Peter Doughty (1988), Roberta Holland (1989),
Adam Hiddleston (1990), Trevor Ward (1991), Catherine Burrett (1992),
Sara Ferrari (1993).

HEAD OF CHAMBERS:
Mr Jeremy Gibbons QC

SEN. CLERK:
Gregory P. Townsend

ADMINISTRATOR: Kay May

TENANTS: 23

370
Set No.

EIGHTEEN CARLTON CRESCENT

EIGHTEEN CARLTON CRESCENT, SOUTHAMPTON, HANTS, SO15 2XR
DX: 96877 Southampton Carlton Crescent

TEL: (01703) 639001
FAX: (01703) 339625

MEMBERS:
Andrew Massey (1969), Alastair Haig-Haddow (1972), Ashley Ailes (1975),
Gary Fawcett (1975), Keith Wylie (1976), Michael Dineen (1977),
Charles Cochand (1978), Robert Hill (1980), Richard Egleton (1981),
Martin Blount (1982), Christopher Wing (1985), Elizabeth Manuel (1987),
Andrew Houston (1989), Omar Malik (1990), Christine Munks (1991),
Imogen Robins (1991), Helen Fields (1993), Roderick Moore (1993).

DOOR TENANTS: Guy Boney QC, Geoffrey Still, Michael Ollerenshaw and Jonathan
Speck.

WORK UNDERTAKEN: *Work includes:* general common law including personal injury;
criminal law; family and matrimonial law including child care law, wardship and
matrimonial property; landlord and tenant; planning; employment; commercial law;
licensing; professional negligence and chancery.

RECRUITMENT & TRAINING: Chambers policy is to attract intelligent and lively applicants with good university degrees. Chambers consist of united and companionable
members and seek to continue this atmosphere. Awards are available at chambers'
discretion. Mini pupillages are offered.

HEAD OF CHAMBERS:
Andrew Massey

SEN. CLERK:
Mrs. Lynda Knight, Mr. Paul Cooke

TENANTS: 17

371
Set No.

COLLEGE CHAMBERS (Robin Belben) College Chambers, 2-3
College Place, London Rd, Southampton, Hants, SO1 2FB **Tel:** (01703) 230338
Fax: (01703) 230376 **DX:** 38533 (Southampton 3) **Sen. Clerk:** Wayne Effeny
Tenants: 12 General common law chambers, family and crime, with specialists in
planning, betting and gaming and other licensing, and child care work.

Southsea

372
Set No.

SOUTHSEA CHAMBERS (G.H. Garner) PO Box 148, Southsea,
Hants, PO5 2TV **Tel:** (01705) 291261 **Fax:** (01705) 826685 **DX:** 2266 **Sen. Clerk:**
Mrs Babette Lodge **Tenants:** 2 Handles general common law, personal injury,
professional negligence, matrimonial and family and landlord and tenant.

St. Albans

373
Set No.
TRAFALGAR CHAMBERS (Rebecca Littlewood) 21 Victoria
Street, St Albans, Herts, AL1 3JJ **Tel:** (01727) 866655 **Fax:** (01727) 860605
DX: 6103 **Sen. Clerk:** Nigel Coyne **Tenants:** 34 A common law set with a varied
practice including civil, criminal and chancery law.

Stoke on Trent

374
Set No.
REGENT CHAMBERS (Peter Crichton-Gold) 29 Regent Street,
Stoke on Trent, Staffs, ST1 3BT **Tel:** (01782) 286666 **Fax:** (01782) 201866
DX: 20720 (Hanley) **Sen. Clerk:** Patricia Lancaster **Tenants:** 6 General civil law
including matrimonial, landlord and tenant, equity and trusts, land law, housing,
personal injury, and arbitration, planning and construction law.

Swansea

375
Set No.
ANGEL CHAMBERS (T. Glanville Jones) Angel Chambers, 94
Walter Rd, Swansea, W. Glam, SA1 5QA **Tel:** (01792) 464623 **Fax:** (01792)
648501 **DX:** 39566 **Sen. Clerk:** Derek Squire **Tenants:** 21 Chambers handle all
areas of general common law.

376
Set No.
GOWER CHAMBERS (Bryan Thomas) 53 Mansel Street, Swan-
sea, W. Glam, SA1 5TD **Tel:** (01792) 644466 **Fax:** (01792) 644321 **DX:** 52956
Sen. Clerk: Jeremy Thorne **Tenants:** 12 Chambers undertake a wide variety of work
including criminal, matrimonial, general common law, construction, planning and
chancery matters.

377
Set No.
ISCOED CHAMBERS (Wyn Richards)

ISCOED CHAMBERS, 86 ST. HELEN'S RD, SWANSEA, W. GLAM, SA1 4BQ
DX: 39554 Swansea

TEL: (01792) 652988/9
FAX: (01792) 458089

MEMBERS:
Wyn Richards (1968), Lawrence Griffiths (1957), Kenneth Lloyd Thomas (1966),
Trevor Lawton Tucker (1971), Trefor Davies (1972),
Peter Christopher Rouch (1972), Kevin Riordan (1972), Frank Phillips (1972) LLB,
Patrick Thomas John Griffiths (1973), David Vivian Manning-Davies (1973),
John James Jenkins (1974), Philip Derek Marshall (1975), Paul Huw Thomas (1979),
Robert Michael Craven (1979), Stephen Robert Tristram Rees (1979),
Elwen Mair Evans (1980), Stewart Karl Anthony Sandbrook-Hughes (1980),
Owen Huw Rees (1983), Ruth Henke (1987), John Hipkin (1989),
David Andrew Harris (1990), Robert James Buckland (1991),
Catherine Louise Heyworth (1991), William Peters (1992), Kate Hughes (1992),
Ian Wright (1994), Iwan Davies (1995).

HEAD OF CHAMBERS:
Wyn Richards

SEN. CLERK:
Wally Rainbird

1ST JUNIOR: Jeff Evans
2ND JUNIOR: Kris Thorne

TENANTS: 27

WORK UNDERTAKEN: This well established set of chambers offers an all round service
to solicitors and others with the right of direct professional access. The principal fields
of work are civil, criminal and family law but with specialised expertise in a variety
of areas including personal injury, planning, local government, environment, highways, fraud, trade descriptions, licensing, family, child law, chancery and housing.

Taunton

378
Set No.

BARNFIELD CHAMBERS (Martin Meeke)

POWLETT HOUSE, 34 HIGH ST, TAUNTON, SOMERSET, TA1 4PN
DX: 96100 Taunton 1

TEL: (01823) 324252
FAX: (01823) 327489

MEMBERS:
Martin Meeke (1973), Richard Merrett (1959), Stephen Lowry (1960),
Michael Brabin (1976), Anthony Puttick (1971), David Steele (1975),
Richard Crabb (1975), Julie Mackenzie (1978), Mark V. Horton (1981),
Mark Whitehall (1983), Terence Holder (1984), Peter M. Ashman (1985),
Jonathon Farquharson (1988), Melissa Barlow (1991).

DOOR TENANTS: Paul Chadd QC (1952) QC-(1973), Richard Rains (1963).

ALSO AT: 15 Barnfield Road, Exeter, Devon, EX1 1RR. *Tel:* 01392 74898, *Fax:*
01392 412368, *DX:* 8330 Exeter.

HEAD OF CHAMBERS:
Martin Meeke

SEN. CLERK:
Philip Alden

TENANTS: 14

379
Set No.

SOUTH WESTERN CHAMBERS (Brian Lett) 12 Middle Street,
Taunton, Somerset, TA1 1SH **Tel:** (01823) 331919 **Fax:** (01823) 330553
DX: 32146 (Taunton) **Sen. Clerk:** Stephen Ward **Tenants:** 9 General common law,
family, criminal, employment, personal injury, civil litigation, landlord and tenant,
licensing, planning, serious fraud.

Truro

380
Set No.

GODOLPHIN CHAMBERS (Barry Van Den Berg) 50 Castle
Street, Truro, Cornwall, TR1 3AF **Tel:** (01872) 76312 **Fax:** (01872) 71902
DX: 81220 **Sen. Clerk:** Julian Coia **Tenants:** 11 Common law set handling both
civil and criminal work.

Watford

381
Set No.

WATFORD CHAMBERS (Aisha Henthorn) 74 Mildred Avenue,
Watford, Herts, WD1 7DX **Tel:** (01923) 231325/220553 **Fax:** (01923) 222618 **Sen.
Clerk:** Valerie Bartels **Tenants:** 3 General common law set handling a wide range
of matters.

Winchester

382
Set No.

PUMP COURT CHAMBERS (Guy Boney QC) Pump Court
Chambers, 31 Southgate Street, Winchester, Hants, SO23 9EE **Tel:** (01962) 868161
Fax: (01962) 867645 **DX:** 2514 **Sen. Clerk:** David Barber **Tenants:** 45 Chambers
are also located at 3 Pump Court, London EC4Y 7AJ.

4 ST. PETER STREET (Michael Parroy QC)

4 ST. PETER STREET, WINCHESTER, HANTS, SO23 8BW
DX: 2507

TEL: (01962) 868884
FAX: (01962) 868644

THE CHAMBERS: A long established set providing a specialist advocacy and advisory service in London, Bournemouth, Oxford, Winchester and on the Western Circuit. Chambers are equipped with spacious conference rooms and computing and word processing facilities and provide a thorough, comprehensive and friendly service. Annexe of 3 Paper Buildings in London.

MEMBERS:
Michael Parroy QC (1969)(QC-1991), David M. Harris QC (1969)(QC-1989), R.A. Fordham QC (1967)(QC-1993), Peter Hughes QC (1971)(QC-1993), Stewart Jones QC (1972)(QC-1994), Harold Hebron (1960), Susan Trevethan (1967), John Haynes (1968), David Swinstead (1970), Derwin Hope (1970), Michael Norman (1971), Anthony Ward (1971), Leo Curran (1972), Peter Jennings (1972), Ben Stephenson (1973), Linda Litchfield (1974), David Bartlett (1975), Garth Richardson (1975), Richard Tyson (1975), Peter Henry (1977), Nigel Mitchell (1978), Nigel Seed (1978), Peter Kent (1978), Ian Partridge (1979), Robert Grey (1979), Nicholas Leviseur (1979), Timothy Coombes (1980), Paul Cairnes (1980), Ian Edge (1981), Martin Strutt (1981), Nigel Lickley (1983), Mark Lomas (1983), Irvine Maccabe (1983), Kate Branigan (1984), Sarah O'Hara (1984), David Sanderson (1985), Russell Bailey (1985), Christopher Parker (1986), Elisabeth Hudson (1987), Paul Letman (1987), Helen James (1988) (Door Tenant), Nicholas Rowland (1988), Patricia Kelly (1988), Paul Hester (1989), Sally Ball (1989), Guy Opperman (1989), Timothy Bradbury (1989), Jean Henderson (1990), Amanda Buckley-Clarke (1991), Iain Ross (1991), David Steenson (1991), Christian Sweeney (1992), Marie Kelly (1992), Caspar Glyn (1992), Krystyna Kirkpatrick (1992), Robert Weir (1992).

WORK UNDERTAKEN: General common law work and in particular:
Contract/ Commercial: including construction, employment, insurance and sale of goods.
Personal Injury: acting for individuals as well as trade union and insurance company clients.
Professional Negligence: covering all areas of chambers' specialisations.
Crime: including commercial fraud and all manner of crime on the Western Circuit.
Property: including landlord and tenant, housing and other real property and boundary disputes.
Chancery: including company and insolvency.
Family: including financial provision, wardship and Inheritance Act work.
EC: in particular competition and public procurement law.
   In addition individual members of chambers specialise in planning, financial services and ecclesiastical work.
ANNEXE CHAMBERS: Chambers have annexes in Bournemouth, Winchester and Oxford.
RECRUITMENT & TRAINING: Four fully-funded 12 month pupillages each year. Applications to David Sanderson enclosing CV and SAE.

THE CHAMBERS OF MICHAEL PARROY Q.C.

Wolverhampton

CLOCK CHAMBERS 78 Darlington Street, Wolverhampton, W. Midlands, WV1 4LY **Tel:** (01902) 313444 **Fax:** (01902) 21110 **DX:** 10423 Wolverhampton **Practice Manager:** Edward Soulsby **Tenants:** 12 Recently established set handling civil, commercial and criminal matters. Work includes family law, personal injury, professional negligence, landlord and tenant, employment, race and sex discrimination.

York

YORK CHAMBERS (Simon Hawkesworth QC) 14 Toft Green, York, N. Yorks, YO1 1JT **Tel:** (01904) 620048 **Fax:** (01904) 610056 **DX:** 65517 York 7 **Sen. Clerk:** Kevin Beaumont **Tenants:** 29 General common law including crime, medical negligence, building and commercial work, chancery, matrimonial, planning and education.

INDEX TO THE BAR (including PROFILES)

INDEX KEY: **Aldous,** Charles (1967 - *Call date*) (QC-85 - *Year took silk*)
Set 206 - *Set no. in A-Z section.* Profile p.1016,**997** - *Main profile entry in bold type, ie 997.*

BAR INDEX

INDEX KEY: **Aldous,** Charles (1967 - *Call date*) (QC-85 - *Year took silk*)
Set 206 - *Set no. in A-Z section.* Profile p.1016,**997** - *Main profile entry in bold type, ie 997.*

BAR INDEX

INDEX KEY: **Aldous,** Charles (1967 - *Call date*) (QC-85 - *Year took silk*)
Set 206 - *Set no. in A-Z section.* Profile p.1016,**997** - *Main profile entry in bold type, ie 997.*

BAR INDEX

INDEX KEY: **Aldous,** Charles (1967 - *Call date*) (QC-85 - *Year took silk*)
Set 206 - *Set no. in A-Z section.* Profile p.1016,**997** - *Main profile entry in bold type, ie 997.*

BAR INDEX

INDEX KEY: **Aldous,** Charles (1967 - *Call date*) (QC-85 - *Year took silk*)
Set 206 - *Set no. in A-Z section.* Profile p.1016,**997** - *Main profile entry in bold type, ie 997.*

BAR INDEX

INDEX KEY: **Aldous,** Charles (1967 - *Call date*) (QC-85 - *Year took silk*)
Set 206 - *Set no. in A-Z section.* Profile p.1016,**997** - *Main profile entry in bold type, ie 997.*

BAR INDEX

INDEX KEY: **Aldous,** Charles (1967 - *Call date*) (QC-85 - *Year took silk*)
Set 206 - *Set no. in A-Z section.* Profile p.1016,**997** - *Main profile entry in bold type, ie 997.*

BAR INDEX

INDEX KEY: **Aldous,** Charles (1967 - *Call date*) (QC-85 - *Year took silk*).
Set 206 - *Set no.* in A-Z section. Profile p.1016, **997** - *Main profile entry in bold type, ie 997.*

INDEX KEY: **Aldous,** Charles (1967 - *Call date*) (QC-85 - *Year took silk*)
Set 206 - *Set no.* in *A-Z section.* Profile p.1016,**997** - *Main profile entry in bold type, ie 997.*

INDEX KEY: **Aldous,** Charles (1967 - *Call date*) (QC-85 - *Year took silk*)
Set 206 - *Set no.* in A-Z section. Profile p.1016, **997** - *Main profile entry in bold type, ie 997.*